2019 DIR National Minority and Women-Owned Business Directory
Fiftieth Edition

HISTORY

Diversity Information Resources was founded in Minneapolis in 1968 by H. Peter Meyerhoff, a Honeywell aeronautics engineer, who sought to advance race relations by improving economic conditions for Blacks after the assassination of Dr. Martin Luther King, Jr. Meyerhoff and his wife were European Jews who managed to escape Hitler at the outset of World War II. Themselves victims of discrimination, they were motivated by Dr. King's death to launch the "Buy Black" directory - a 10 page directory of black-owned businesses.

In 2001 DIR partnered with an IT firm and developed an online Supplier Diversity Database Management Portal. The dynamic portal allows corporations online access to certified minority and women-owned businesses, veteran, service-disabled veteran, LGBT and HUBZone businesses, supplier registration, certification validation, diversity spend reporting and data cleansing, tier 2 reporting. (Please contact Diversity Information Resources at (612) 781-6819 or www.diversityinforesources.com for more information). A Board of Directors, representative of major U.S. corporations set policy and direction for Diversity Information Resources.

MISSION

To develop, maintain, and provide information resources that enhance supplier diversity initiatives and support the development and economic growth of diverse businesses.

INCLUSION CRITERIA AND LISTING PROCESS

In identifying minority-owned businesses, fifty-one percent of the business must be owned, operated and controlled by minority group members who are U.S. citizens, capable of national and/or regional sales and physically located in the United States or its trust territories. In identifying woman-owned businesses, at least fifty-one percent or more is owned by a woman (or women), who is a U.S. citizen, and who controls the firm by exercising the power to make policy decisions and operates the business by being actively involved in day-to-day management. It must be profit seeking and capable of national and/or regional sales.

CERTIFICATION

Information on certification(s) held is also validated and reported. Buyers are advised to contact firms directly if clarification on certification is needed. The following certifications are validated:

- State — State Agencies
- City — City Agencies
- WBENC — Women's Business Enterprise National Council
- NWBOC — National Women Business Owners Corporation
- NMSDC — National Minority Supplier Development Council
- CPUC — California Public Utilities Commission (M/WBE Clearinghouse)
- SDB — Small Business Administration's Small Disadvantaged Business
- 8(a) — SBA's 8(a) Business Development Program

OWNERSHIP CLASSIFICATION

The following code indicates ownership type:

- AA — African American
- Hisp — Hispanic American
- Nat Ame — Native American
- As-Pac — Asian Pacific American
- As-Ind — Asian Indian American

LIABILITY DISCLAIMER

Although the information listed herein has been compiled with the utmost care and is believed by the publisher to be reliable, its accuracy or completeness cannot be guaranteed. The publishers and sponsors assume no responsibility for transactions resulting from the use of information herein and do not guarantee the quality or reliability of products or services listed. The content of the advertising copy contained in this Directory is the sole responsibility of those firms, which submitted it. Diversity Information Resources assumes no responsibility for its accuracy.

Directory Format:

- The Table of Classifications on the next page gives the section numbers for each category and the range of numbers in that category. The Table of NAIC codes list the two-digit NAIC code for each category.
- Firms are listed by state, in alphabetical order, in each category.
- An alphabetical listing of companies (page ii-1) appears at the back of the directory.
- See codes to identify certification and ownership type on the back of the first printed page: "2019 DIR National Minority and Women-Owned Business Directory Fiftieth Edition."

An Example:

If you are looking for a supplier to print a company brochure, first you look up "brochure" in the Keyword Index. You will see that the Keyword Index refers you to the "Printing and Engraving" category.

Turning to the "Printing and Engraving" section, you will find suppliers listed alphabetically, according to the state in which they reside. A typical entry might appear as follows:

7600   ABC Printing Company
1234 XYZ Avenue NE   New York, NY 10001
(212) 555-1234   R. Smith, pres.
Fax: (212) 555 5678
Email: Rsmith@www.net
Web Site: www.print.com
4-5 color offset presses. In-house 4-color, bindery, die cutting,
mounting & finishing. (AA, est. 1965, empl 45, sales $4,000,000, cert: State, NMSDC, SDB)

OTHER PRODUCTS AND SERVICES PROVIDED BY DIVERSITY INFORMATION RESOURCES

"The Business of Supplier Diversity: A Handbook of Essential Contacts and Information for Navigating the Industry"
This fifth edition combines the best of DIR's previously published "Purchasing People in Major Corporations" and the "Supplier Diversity Information Resource Guide". This book provides a road map for diverse-owned suppliers and supplier diversity professionals by combining who-to-call with where-to-look. DIR, the leader in supplier diversity data management, combines a detailed contact list of over 1500 supplier diversity and procurement contacts from major corporations, government agencies, large nonprofit organizations, and educational institutions. It also details information on certification, legislation, regional and national networking opportunities, diverse business resources and much more.

Corporate Supplier Diversity Seminars
Now in their thirty-second year, these seminars teach methods to establish or enhance Supplier Diversity Programs. Diversity Information Resources offers "Building Strategic Phases of a Supplier Diversity Process" seminar and the "Best Practices in Supplier Diversity Strategies and Initiatives" seminar.

For further information on any of the above resources, please contact DIR at (612) 781-6819 or visit
www.diversityinforesources.com

TABLE OF CLASSIFICATIONS

TABLE OF NAICS

ACCOUNTING FIRMS
Certified public accounting firms, usually maintaining full time office staff in more than one city. NAICS Code 54

California

1000 The Gilson Group, LLC
2967 Michelson Dr Ste G102 Irvine, CA 92612
(949) 830-3499 Catherine Doll CEO
Fax:
Email: Catherine@TheGilsonGroup.com
Website: www.TheGilsonGroup.com
Accounting, mergers, financial analysis, due diligence, internal controls, general ledger, forecasting, cash flow, process improvement, Quickbooks, SOX, SEC, cost accounting, financial reporting, internal audit, risk management, GAAP. (Woman/White, estab 2006, empl 20, sales $502,000, cert: WBENC)

1001 The Zamzow Group, Inc.
264 S La Cienega Blvd, Ste 1120 Beverly Hills, CA 90211
(310) 551-3000 Brenda Zamzow President
Fax: (310) 551-2969
Email: wbe@thezamzowgroup.com
Website: www.thezamzowgroup.com
Accounting services. (Woman/White, estab 2003, empl 20, sales $1,600,000, cert: State, City)

Delaware

1002 Faw Casson
160 Greentree Dr, Ste 203 Dover, DE 19904
(302) 674-4305 Lisa Hastings Director of Ops
Fax: (302) 674-0910
Email: lsh@fawcasson.com
Website: www.fawcasson.com
Employee benefit plan audits, business valuations, fraud services, EBP audits, agreed-upon procedures, internal audit staffing & tax services. (Woman/White, estab 1944, empl 41, sales $5,946,271, cert: WBENC)

Georgia

1003 Infinite Financial Concepts, LLC
P.O. Box 953 Stone Mountain, GA 30086
(678) 933-5304 Amin Hassan President
Fax:
Email: amin@ifc326.com
Website: www.ifc326.com
Accounting & financial reporting. (AA, estab 2011, empl 1, sales $67,000, cert: City)

1004 Lewis Business Services, Inc.
43 Forsyth St Atlanta, GA 30303
(404) 521-3634 Alberteen Lewis President
Fax:
Email: lbstax@bellsouth.net
Website:
Accounting, budgeting, auditing, financial advisory, tax representation & tax return preparation, collections & group entertainment. (Woman/AA, estab 1998, empl 4, sales , cert: State)

1005 VAAS Professionals, LLC
325 Edgewood Ave Ste 600 Atlanta, GA 30312
(404) 223-1058 Steve Julal Owner
Fax:
Email: steve.julal@vaasprofessionals.com
Website: www.vaasprofessionals.com
Accounting & finance services, audits, payroll solutions, capital & treasury management, reviews, computer & technology assessments, financial reporting, due diligence & human capital management. (AA, estab 2005, empl 4, sales , cert: 8(a))

Illinois

1006 A3B, LLC
100 S Saunders Rd, Ste 150 Lake Forest, IL 60045
(847) 574-7227 Betsey Robinson President
Fax: (847) 574-5701
Email: betsey@a3bllc.com
Website: www.a3bllc.com
Accounting & Finance Consulting Services, business process improvements resulting in cost savings, financial accounting reporting & analysis, financial transformation of shared services centers, management of change. (Woman/AA, estab 2013, empl 3, sales $97,438, cert: NMSDC, WBENC)

1007 Adelfia LLC
400 E Randolph Str Ste 705 Chicago, IL 60601
(312) 240-9500 Stella Marie Santos
Fax: (312) 240-0295
Email: sbsantos@adelfiacpas.com
Website: www.adelfiacpas.com
Assurance & advisory services: financial audit, compliance examination, internal audit, agreed-upon procedures, tax services, tax preparation, payroll tax returns, tax notices/audit assistance, tax planning, accounting services. (Woman/As-Pac/Hisp, estab 2011, empl 30, sales $541,996, cert: State, City, NMSDC)

1008 Benford Brown & Associates LLC
8334 S Stony Island Ave Chicago, IL 60617
(773) 731-1300 Kim Ellen Partner
Fax: (773) 731-1301
Email: kellen@benfordbrown.com
Website: www.benfordbrown.com
Auditing, accounting, tax & small business consulting services. (Woman/AA, estab 1996, empl 7, sales $1,005,155, cert: State, NMSDC, WBENC)

Indiana

1009   Moore Accounting, LLC
       9465 Counselors Row, Ste 200   Indianapolis, IN
       46240
       (317) 504-0296 April Moore Owner
       Fax: (317) 805-4723
       Email: afreeman@mooreacctg.com
       Website: www.mooreacctg.com
Accounting, bookkeeping, Tax, Payroll, Tier 2 Audit
Services, Davis Bacon & Related Acts, Long-Term Care,
Mental Health, Transportation, A133, Echos, Housing
Authority, Section 8, Tax Credit Housing, Public Housing.
(Woman/AA, estab 2010, empl 3, sales $77,000, cert:
State, City, WBENC)

1010   Thomas & Reed, LLC
       148 E. Market St Ste 300   Indianapolis, IN 46204
       (317) 955-6933 Stephen A Reed
       Fax: (317) 955-6933
       Email: tclemons@trllc-cpa.com
       Website: www.trlllc-cpa.com
Certified public accounting: auditing, reviews, compilations, controllership, bookkeeping, financial software
system installation & training, payroll, staff outsourcing,
rate analysis, Davis Bacon Compliance, contract compliance. (Woman/AA, estab 2004, empl 3, sales $267,340,
cert: City)

Maryland

1011   Intelligent Fiscal Optimal Solutions
       10632 Little Patuxent Pkwy Ste 306 Columbia, MD
       21044
       (301) 837-9735 Brian Schwartz Corp. Business Dev
       Mgr
       Fax: (301) 837-9734
       Email: inquiry@ifoscorp.com
       Website: www.ifoscorp.com
Accounting, GAAP, GAGAS, Budget, Payroll, Cost Account-
ing, Grants Admin, Grants Onsite/Desk Reviews, Audit
Readiness & Remediation, Reconciliations, Year-End
Closing, e-Travel, Travel Program & Travel Card Admin,
Acquisition SME, Contract Audits. (Woman/AA, estab
2009, empl 30, sales , cert: 8(a))

1012   Premier Group Services Inc.
       4200 Forbes Blvd Ste 208 Lanham, MD 20706
       (301) 577-6444 Joye Smith
       Fax: (301) 576-5000
       Email: jsmith@pgservicesinc.com
       Website: www.pgservicesinc.com
CPA & management: audits, fraud, waste & abuse support,
government contracting consulting & audits, temporary
accounting staff, attestation services, business consulting,
budgeting, taxes & payroll, financial forecasting & projections. (Woman/AA, estab 2005, empl 5, sales $139,000,
cert: State, NMSDC, 8(a))

1013   SB & Company, LLC.
       200 International Cir, Ste 5500   Hunt Valley, MD
       21030
       (410) 584-9302 Stacy Wenzl Principal of Practice
       Dev
       Fax: (410) 584-0061
       Email: swenzl@sbandcompany.com
       Website: www.sbandcompany.com
Accounting services. (Woman/AA, estab 2005, empl 95,
sales $14,050,000, cert: State, NMSDC)

1014   The CTS Group, LLC
       13407 Tamarack Rd   Silver Spring, MD 20904
       (301) 801-1193 Calvin L. Scott, Jr. Managing
       Member
       Fax:
       Email: cscott@ctsgroupllc.com
       Website: www.ctsgroupllc.com
Comprehensive accounting & advisory business services,
account maintenance, financial management, budget
development & analysis, interim outsourcing, transaction analysis, transaction processing, data analysis &
summarization. (AA, estab 2007, empl 1, sales $175,000,
cert: State, 8(a))

1015   TSC Enterprise
       5211 Auth Rd Ste 100 Suitland, MD 20746
       (124) 045-5748 Salome Tinker Managing Partner
       Fax: (202) 478-2092
       Email: sjtinker@tsccpas.com
       Website: www.TSCcpas.com
Certified public accounting, FIAR, audit readiness, tax,
financial transition, compliance, assurance, management consulting, A133, yellow book, cost recovery,
performance reviews, financial system implementation,
financial support & staffing. (Woman/AA, estab 2001,
empl 6, sales $250,000, cert: WBENC)

Michigan

1016   EVO Accounting & Financial Services
       16200 W Seven Mile Rd   Detroit, MI 48235
       (313) 835-3900 Vencie Jackson President
       Fax: (313) 835-7982
       Email: vjackson@evoaccounting.com
       Website: www.evoaccounting.com
Accounting & financial services, tax & payroll. (AA, estab
1970, empl 15, sales $748,478, cert: State)

1017   Martin, Arrington, & Desai, & Meyers P.C., CPA
       30200 Telegraph Rd, Ste 444   Bingham Farms, MI
       48025
       (248) 645-5370 Bettye Arrington Managing Dir
       Fax: (248) 645-5020
       Email: bvam49@sbcglobal.net
       Website: www.madmcpa.com
Audit, accounting, agreed upon procedures, due
diligence, revenue recovery, tax consulting, information
technology, survey & evaluation research, professional
recruitment. (AA, estab 1975, empl 16, sales $1,300,000,
cert: State)

New York

1018 KBL, LLP Certified Public Accountants & Advisors
110 Wall St, 11th Fl New York, NY 10005
(212) 785-9700 Richard Levychin Partner
Fax: (212) 785-0700
Email: rlevychin@kbl.com
Website: www.kbl.com
Audit & assurance, agreed-upon procedures, compilation & review procedures, business process outsourcing, risk management & advisory services, cross border international practices, small business services, tax compliance. (AA, estab 1994, empl 50, sales $5,000,000, cert: NMSDC)

1019 Masterpiece Accounting Services LLC
2 Hamilton Ave Ste 206 New Rochelle, NY 10801
(914) 661-2798 Ibanessa Hogan Principal
Fax: (914) 363-9784
Email: i.hogan@masterpieceaccounting.com
Website: www.masterpieceaccounting.com
Accounting & bookkeeping services, tax preparation & QuickBooks consulting. (Woman/Hisp, estab 2010, empl 1, sales , cert: State, WBENC)

1020 Mitchell & Titus LLP
One Battery Park Plaza, 27 Fl New York, NY 10004
(312) 325-7422 Irene Davis CFO
Fax: (866) 220-4197
Email: IDavis@MitchellTitus.com
Website: www.mitchelltitus.com
Certified public accounting & mgmt consulting. (AA, estab 1974, empl 97, sales $17,000,000, cert: State, NMSDC)

1021 Torres Llompart, Sanchez Ruiz LLP
Bowling Green Station P.O. Box 850 New York, NY 10274
(646) 214-1064 Frank Sanchez-Ruiz Partner
Fax: (917) 591-8701
Email: fsanchez@tlsr.com
Website: www.tlsr.com
Certified public accountants & business consulting: accounting, auditing, tax & corporate advisory, operational studies, management advisory, risk management, marketing consulting, franchising services, international commerce. (Hisp, estab 1989, empl 35, sales $2,410,000, cert: City, NMSDC)

1022 VJN Associates. LLC
39-38 Bell Blvd, Ste 202 Bayside, NY 11361
(718)2791600 Victor Chin Ops Mgr
Fax:
Email: victorc@vjnassociates.com
Website: www.vjnassociates.com
Assurance, accounting, book keeping, audits both financial & compliance. (Woman/As-Pac, estab 2012, empl 10, sales $169,000, cert: City, NMSDC)

Ohio

1023 Kaiser Consulting, LLC
818 Riverbend Ave Powell, OH 43065
(614) 300-1088 Lori Kaiser CEO
Fax:
Email: lkaiser@kaiserconsulting.com
Website: www.kaiserconsulting.com
Financial & accounting consulting. (Woman, estab 1994, empl 63, sales $4,440,000, cert: WBENC)

1024 Parms & Company, LLC
585 S Front St Ste 220 Columbus, OH 43215
(614) 224-3078 John Parms
Fax: (614) 224-4616
Email: jparms@parms.com
Website: www.parms.com
Auditing, accounting, agreed-upon procedures, forensic accounting, consulting & tax-related services. (AA, estab 1983, empl 14, sales $1,335,851, cert: State, NMSDC)

1025 Richardson and Associates, LLC
427 Appaloosa Ct Cincinnati, OH 45231
(513) 772-8348 Sherri Richardson Owner
Fax:
Email: sherri@richardsonandassociates.com
Website: www.richardsonandassociates.com
Accounting services, audits, writing policies & procedures. (Woman/AA, estab 2007, empl 12, sales $205,000, cert: State, NMSDC, WBENC)

Pennsylvania

1026 Milligan & Company LLC
105 N 22nd St, 2nd Fl Philiadelphia, PA 19103
(215) 496-9100 Angela Giunta Director of Mktg
Fax: (215) 496-0980
Email: agiunta@milligancpa.com
Website: www.milligancpa.com
Consulting & certified public accounting. (AA, estab 1985, empl 45, sales $6,400,000, cert: State)

1027 Parrish Law Offices
788 Washington Rd Pittsburgh, PA 15228
(412) 561-6250 Debra Parrish Partner
Fax: (412) 561-6253
Email: Debbie@dparrishlaw.com
Website: www.dparrishlaw.com
Legal support for provider and beneficiary appeals of denied claims by payers, including Medicare through the administrative process up to and including Federal court litigation; appeals of post-payment overpayment determinations (Woman/White, estab 2000, empl 4, sales $833,635, cert: WBENC)

Texas

1028 DWG CPA PLLC
        5100 Westheimer, Ste 200   Houston, TX 77056
        (281) 201-8348 Elaine Goodman Managing Dir
        Fax: (713) 429-1812
        Email: info@dwgcpatx.com
        Website: www.dwgcpatx.com
Tax, accounting, auditing & financial management. (AA, estab 2005, empl 2, sales $99,108, cert: State, NMSDC)

1029 Harris & Dickey, LLC.
        4127 Wycliff Ave   Dallas, TX 75219
        (972) 672-7597 Kelly Harris Partner
        Fax: (214) 219-0455
        Email: Kelly.Harris@Harris-Dickey.com
        Website: www.harris-dickey.com
Accounting, finance, tax, internal audit, technology risk & special project assistance. (Woman/White, estab 2010, empl 12, sales $1,662,658, cert: State, City, WBENC)

1030 McConnell & Jones LLP
        4828 Loop Central Dr, Ste 1000   Houston, TX 77081
        (713) 968-1600 Lori Jamail Mktg Director
        Fax: (713) 968-1601
        Email: info@mjlm.com
        Website: www.mcconnelljones.com
Financial statement audits, benefit plan audits, tax returns, compilations, accounting & bookkeeping services, SEC compliance services & single audits. (AA, estab 1987, empl 85, sales $10,063,908, cert: NMSDC)

1031 State Tax Group, LLC
        5050 Quorum Dr, Ste 700   Dallas, TX 75254
        (972) 492-9841 Richard Fleming
        Fax: (469) 327-0835
        Email: rfleming@statetaxgroup.com
        Website: www.statetaxgroup.com
State audit representation, sales tax compliance review, tax refund reviews, litigation support, dispute resolution, sampling analysis & evaluation, voluntary disclosures. (AA, estab 2005, empl 4, sales $518,000, cert: NMSDC)

ADVERTISING
Advertising agencies which provide clients with full service from conception to completion. Other services listed in this category include graphic arts, direct mail & list maintenance, sign manufacturing and engraving. (See also PROFESSIONAL SERVICES: Public Relations/Marketing). NAICS Code 54

Arkansas

1032   The C3 Group
       P.O. Box 157   Greenland, AR 72737
       (479) 445-2657 Bobby Cook President
       Fax: (479) 267-5766
       Email: Bcook@thec3group.net
       Website: www.Thec3group.net
Advertising media buying, marketing consulting, promotional products, web development, interactive design, bilboards, banners. (Nat Ame, estab 2005, empl 5, sales $650,000, cert: State)

1033   Creative Merchandise Displays Inc.
       1839 W 1st Ave   Mesa, AZ 85202
       (480) 668-7225 Debra Mendoza COO
       Fax: (480) 615-1418
       Email: deb@cmdracks.com
       Website: www.cmdracks.com
Mfr point-of-purchase display racks, point-of-purchase display design, engineering, manufacturing, finishing, assembly & packaging. (Woman/White, estab 2008, empl 12, sales $1,041,286, cert: City, WBENC, SDB)

1034   Double T. Signs Inc.
       1835 S Alvernon Ste 214 Tucson, AZ 85711
       (520) 750-0189 David Torres President
       Fax: (520) 747-0078
       Email: dave@doubletsigns.com
       Website: www.doubletsigns.com
Mfr & install signs: billboards, displays, electrical, neon, signboards, display lettering services, sign lettering, window dressing, ad displays, identification plates & tags. (Hisp, estab 1993, empl 6, sales $601,161, cert: State, City)

1035   Language Concepts Consulting LLC
       8502 E Princess Dr, Ste 230   Scottsdale, AZ 85255
       (480) 626-2926 Katherine Paredes Managing Dir
       Fax:
       Email: kathy.paredes@languageconceptsllc.com
       Website: www.languageconceptsllc.com
Translation services: English, Spanish, Chinese, Portuguese, Korean, German & Vietnamese. Document Translation, Linguistic Validation, Linguist Testing and Bug Reporting (sites), Multilingual graphic design, Localization, Transcription. (Woman/Hisp, estab 2009, empl 1, sales $112,000, cert: NMSDC)

California

1036   1-Stop Translation
       3700 Wilshire Blvd, Ste 630   Los Angeles, CA 90010
       (213) 480-0011 Diana Chi Mktg Mgr
       Fax: (213) 232-3223
       Email: diana@1stoptr.com
       Website: www.1stoptr.com
Translation and interpretation services with a specialty in Asian languages, including typesetting, desktop publishing, web localization, software testing, budding & subtitling services. (As-Pac, estab 2001, empl 8, sales , cert: CPUC)

1037   3V Signs & Graphics, LLC
       434 Pacific Coast Hwy   Hermosa Beach, CA 90254
       (310) 372-0888 Pat Dacy Sec/Treas
       Fax: (310) 371-5888
       Email: Pat@3Vsigns.com
       Website: www.3Vsigns.com
Sign & graphic consultation & design, production, delivery & installation services: architectural signs, window, wall, ground or vehicle graphics, point-of-purchase posters or a building identification signs. (Woman/Hisp, estab 2010, empl 5, sales $186,000, cert: City)

1038   Aahs Entertainment, Inc.
       10707 Camarillo St, Ste 312   Toluca Lake, CA 91602
       (818) 279-2416 Gwenn Smith President
       Fax:
       Email: gwenn@aahsentertainment.com
       Website: www.aahsentertainment.com
Video Production Services, Media Production, Media Services, Advertising, Marketing, Content Creation, Branded Content, Brand Marketing, DVD Extras, DVD Special Features, Marketing, Advertising, EPKs. (Woman/AA, estab 2011, empl 1, sales , cert: WBENC)

1039   Artisan Creative Inc.
       1830 Stoner Ave Ste 6 Los Angeles, CA 90025
       (310) 312-2062 Katty Douraghy President
       Fax: (310) 312-0670
       Email: kattyd@artisancreative.com
       Website: www.artisancreative.com
Design & development solutions: marketing, advertising, communications & production teams in the digital, broadcast, mobile & print space. (Woman/White, estab 1996, empl 15, sales $3,000,000, cert: WBENC)

1040   Carmazzi of Florida, Inc.
       8926 Beckington Dr   Elk Grove, CA 95624
       (888) 452-6543 Angela Carmazzi President
       Fax: (866) 648-3431
       Email: sales@carmazzi.com
       Website: www.carmazzi.com/
Translations, interpretations & transcriptions. (Woman/Hisp, estab 1998, empl 8, sales $1,900,000, cert: CPUC)

1041 Coast Sign Inc.
1500 W Embassy St.   Anaheim, CA 92802
(714) 999-1900 Charlie Alemi President
Fax: (714) 520-5847
Email: charlie.alemi@coastsign.com
Website: www.coastsign.com
Mfr electrical signage, ATM surrounds & kiosks, project management, design, engineering, lighting, installation, service & maintenance. (Woman/White, estab 1964, empl 300, sales $36,500,000, cert: CPUC, WBENC)

1042 Competitive Edge Media Management
3261 S Higuera St Ste 110 San Luis Obispo, CA 93401
(805) 788-0966 Suzy da Silva President
Fax: (805) 788-0723
Email: suzy@cemm.com
Website: www.cemm.com
Media buying, brand promotion plans, product launch, direct-to-consumer sales strategy, hybrid campaigns. (Woman/White, estab 2007, empl 8, sales $6,874,176, cert: WBENC)

1043 CR&A Custom, Inc.
312 W Pico Blvd   Los Angeles, CA 90015
(213) 749-4440 Vince Norcia Acct Exec
Fax: (213) 749-4446
Email: vince@cracustom.com
Website: www.cracustom.com
Large format digital printing, embroidery, promotional products, custom designs, carwraps, banners, billboards, tents, POP displays. (Woman/Hisp, estab 1993, empl 31, sales $5,900,000, cert: NMSDC, CPUC, 8(a))

1044 Direct Results Radio, Inc.
815 Hamton Dr, Ste 2   Venice, CA 90291
(310) 441-9100 Sheri White Business Dev Dir
Fax:
Email: sheriwhite@directresults.com
Website: www.directresults.com
Advertising agency, audio & radio. (Woman, estab 2007, empl 20, sales , cert: NWBOC)

1045 Everfield Consulting, LLC
2075 W 235th Pl   Torrance, CA 90501
(310) 251-7165 Delbara Dorsey Partner/Mktg Dir
Fax:
Email: deldorsey@everfieldconsulting.com
Website: www.everfieldconsulting.com
Marketing Consulting Services, Administrative & Management, Display Advertising, Advertising, Public Relations, Media Buying, Direct Mail Advertising, Advertising Material Distribution Services. (Woman/AA/As-Pac, estab 2011, empl 2, sales , cert: State, City, CPUC, WBENC)

1046 Exponential Interactive, Inc.
5858 Horton St, Ste 300   Emeryville, CA 94608
(510) 250-5500 Catherine Avenido Sr Mgr, Intl Ops
Fax: (510) 250-5700
Email: MBE@exponential.com
Website: www.exponential.com/
Advertising intelligence & digital media solutions. (As-Ind, estab 2000, empl 690, sales $219,740,000, cert: NMSDC, CPUC)

1047 Fraser/White, Inc.
1631 Pontius Ave   Los Angeles, CA 90025
(310) 319-3737 Renee Fraser CEO
Fax: (310) 319-1537
Email: rfraser@frasercommunications.com
Website: www.frasercommunications.com
Advertising, marketing, market research, display advertising, media planning, media buying, qualitative research, quantitative research, strategic planning, outdoor advertising. (Woman/White, estab 1998, empl 25, sales $40,000,000, cert: WBENC)

1048 Frisson, Inc.
12 Geary St, Ste 607   San Francisco, CA 94108
(415) 922-1482 Deboran N Loeb President
Fax: (415) 922-1483
Email: purchasing@brainchildcreative.com
Website: www.brainchildcreative.com
Advertising agency; marketing-branding vonsulting services; commercial production services. (Woman/White, estab 2001, empl 7, sales $16,700,000, cert: CPUC, WBENC)

1049 Global Language Solutions
19800 MacArthur Blvd Ste 750 Irvine, CA 92612
(949) 798-1400 Inna Kassatkina President
Fax: (949) 798-1410
Email: info@globallanguages.com
Website: www.globallanguages.com
Translation svcs: document & web site translations, conference interpretation, multimedia production & graphic design services. (Woman/White, estab 1994, empl 50, sales $16,300,000,000, cert: WBENC)

1050 Hawthorne Direct, LLC
1201 W 5th St Ste T230 Los Angeles, CA 90017
(310) 844-0606 Karla Crawford Kerr VP Mktg
Fax: (641) 209-3134
Email: kcrawfordkerr@hawthornedirect.com
Website: www.hawthornedirect.com
Advertising, strategic planning, creative development, production, media planning, buying, analytics & campaign management. (Woman/White, estab 1986, empl 70, sales $14,100,000, cert: WBENC)

1051 I. Studio, Inc.
51 E Colorado Blvd   Pasadena, CA 91105
(626) 683-3101 Gabriel Avalos Principal
Fax: (626) 683-3202
Email: g.avalos@interiorstudioinc.com
Website: www.interiorstudioinc.com
I, Studio, Inc, is a full service Interior Planning & Design Firm. Our services included programming, schematic design, design development, contract documents, construction administration. (Hisp, estab 2006, empl 3, sales $80,000, cert: State, NMSDC)

1052   IW Group, Inc.
       6300 Wilshire Blvd. Ste 2150   Los Angeles, CA
       90048
       (310) 289-5500 Nita Song President
       Fax: (310) 289-5501
       Email: nita.song@iwgroupinc.com
       Website: www.iwgroupinc.com/
Advertising & PR, creative development, research, media
planning, media buying, production, events, cultural
training. (As-Pac, estab 1990, empl 50, sales $10,506,000,
cert: NMSDC, CPUC)

1053   Kramer Translation
       893 Massasso St   Merced, CA 95341
       (209) 385-0425 Keith Ensminger Principal
       Fax: (209) 385-3747
       Email: keith@kramertranslations.com
       Website: www.kramertranslations.com
Translation svcs: personal, business & government documents. (Woman/As-Pac, estab 1995, empl 3, sales
$701,672, cert: State, NMSDC, CPUC)

1054   Local Concept
       1510 Front St, Ste 200   San Diego, CA 92101
       (619) 295-2682 Michael Cardenas Localization
       Solutions Specialist
       Fax: (619) 295-2984
       Email: amarklein@localconcept.com
       Website: www.localconcept.com
Localization, translation, foreign language typesetting &
multimedia for all languages. (Hisp, estab 1985, empl 25,
sales $1,435,306, cert: NMSDC)

1055   Motivate, Inc.
       4141 Jutland Dr Ste 300 San Diego, CA 92117
       (866) 664-4432 Trevor Hansen SVP, Finance
       Fax: (858) 272-7275
       Email: account@motivateroi.com
       Website: www.MotivateROI.com
Media representation, consumer event marketing services.
(Woman/White, estab 1977, empl 25, sales $40,690,000,
cert: WBENC)

1056   Muse Communications, Inc.
       5358 Melrose Ave West Bldg, Ground Fl Hollywood,
       CA 90038
       (323) 960-4080 Norma Keffer
       Fax: (323) 960-4081
       Email: norma@museusa.com
       Website: www.musecordero.com
Advertising, marketing, promotions & public relations
programs. (AA, estab 1985, empl 35, sales $5,975,000,
cert: CPUC)

1057   Nonpareil Ventures LLC
       710 C St, Ste 206   San Rafael, CA 94901
       (415) 404-7409 Zeeshan Ahmed Mgr
       Fax: (415) 456-9735
       Email: seanahmed@gmail.com
       Website: www.signzsf.com
Advertising services, sign manufacturing, repair & mainte-
nance. (As-Ind, estab 2011, empl 5, sales $250,000, cert:
State)

1058   Paragon Language Services, Inc.
       5055 Wilshire Blvd Ste 835 Los Angeles, CA
       90036
       (323) 966-4655 Marina Mintz President
       Fax: (323) 651-1867
       Email: marina@paragonls.com
       Website: www.paragonls.com
Foreign language translation, adaptation, interpreting,
typesetting/desktop publishing, internationalization,
globalization, localization, cultural and linguistic consulting, dialog/dialect coaching, captioning, subtitling,
narrations. (Woman/White, estab 1991, empl 10, sales
$2,600,000, cert: City, CPUC, WBENC)

1059   Quigley-Simpson & Heppelwhite, Inc.
       11601 Wilshire Blvd 7th Fl Los Angeles, CA 90025
       (310) 996-5820 Gerald Bagg Co-Chairman
       Fax: (310) 943-1414
       Email: GeraldB@quigleysimpson.com
       Website: www.quigleysimpson.com
Direct response advertising agency. (Woman/White,
estab 2002, empl 180, sales , cert: WBENC)

1060   RBG MARKETING, INC. DBA CRESCENDO
       5000 Executive Parkway Ste 350 San Ramon, CA
       94583
       (925) 939-1800 A.K. Ahuja Managing Dir
       Fax: (925) 939-1829
       Email: aka@crescendoagency.com
       Website: www.crescendoagency.com
Marketing & advertising, creative, media planning &
media buying in-house. (As-Ind, estab 2003, empl 30,
sales $9,000,000, cert: State, NMSDC, CPUC)

1061   RP & Associates, Inc.
       2205 Pacific Coast Hwy   Hermosa Beach, CA
       90254
       (310) 372-9709 Lisa Pola CEO
       Fax: (310) 376-5819
       Email: lpola@mac.com
       Website: www.rpandassociates.com
Marketing solutions, branded products & programs,
custom packaging, premiums & promotional items.
(Woman/Hisp, estab 1988, empl 34, sales
$2,306,595,900, cert: NMSDC)

1062   Sensis Inc.
       818 South Broadway, Ste 110   Los Angeles, CA
       90014
       (213) 341-0171 Dreux Dougall
       Fax: (213) 861-7436
       Email: ddougall@sensisagency.com
       Website: www.sensisagency.com
Advertising, digital marketing & communications
services, online media & marketing, web design &
development, online creative strategy, analytics &
planning. (Hisp, estab 1998, empl 90, sales $11,100,000,
cert: CPUC)

1063　Simply Displays
　　　12200 Los Nietos Rd　Santa Fe Springs, CA 90670
　　　(888) 767-0676　Mila Thompson President
　　　Fax:
　　　Email: mthompson@simplydisplays.com
　　　Website: www.simplydisplays.com
Mfr Point of Purchase Displays & Store Fixtures, Sign
Holders, Hospitality & Retail Signage (Woman/White,
estab 2002, empl 16, sales $36,000,000, cert: WBENC)

1064　Think Ink
　　　927 Mariner St　Brea, CA 92821
　　　(714) 672-0017　Mary Sanchez Dir of Sales
　　　Fax: (714) 672-0021
　　　Email: info@thinkinkinfo.com
　　　Website: www.thinkinkinfo.com
Creative marketing, graphic design, print & promotions.
(As-Pac/Hisp, estab 2002, empl 5, sales $1,105,519, cert:
NMSDC, CPUC)

1065　Tylie Jones & Associates, Inc.
　　　58 E Santa Anita Ave　Burbank, CA 91502
　　　(818) 955-7600　Sheri Lawrence President
　　　Fax: (818) 955-8542
　　　Email: slawrence@tylie.com
　　　Website: www.tylie.com
Broadcast advertising services: SD & HD audio & video
spot duplication & digital distribution; post production,
closed captioning, tagging, versioninig, encoding; production element vaulting/storage. (Woman/White, estab
1971, empl 35, sales , cert: WBENC)

1066　Unique Image, Inc.
　　　19365 Business Center Dr. Bldg. 1　Northridge, CA
　　　91324
　　　(818) 727-7785　Wafa Kanan President
　　　Fax: (818) 727-7735
　　　Email: kelly@uniqueimageinc.com
　　　Website: www.uniqueimageinc.com
Printing & marketing svcs: strategic campaigns, print
media, design & direct mail. (Woman/White, estab 1992,
empl 10, sales $1,200,000, cert: CPUC)

1067　Weldon Works, Inc.
　　　1650 Mabury Rd　San Jose, CA 95133
　　　(408) 251-1161　Jennifer Easom CEO
　　　Fax: (408) 251-1162
　　　Email: jenn@weldonworks.com
　　　Website: www.weldonworks.com
Plastic Fabrication & Signage, Interior & Exterior Signs,
ADA Signage, Lobby Signs, Window Graphics & Lettering,
Menu Boards, Isle Signage, Banner, Stencils, Reflective
Road Work/ Parking Signs, Full Color Digital Printing.
(Woman/White, estab 1982, empl 3, sales $100,000, cert:
State)

1068　Zeesman Communications, Inc.
　　　6255 Sunset Blvd. Ste 1040　Los Angeles, CA
　　　90028
　　　(323) 658-8000　Bonnie Nijst President
　　　Fax:
　　　Email: bonnie@zeesman.com
　　　Website: www.zeesman.com
Marketing, advertising & design: branding programs,
logos, corporate identity, collateral, direct mail, print
advertising & web design. (Woman/As-Pac, estab 1990,
empl 10, sales $1,967,000, cert: NMSDC, CPUC, WBENC)

Colorado

1069　Altitude Technologies, Inc.
　　　54 Girard St STE A　Durango, CO 81303
　　　(800) 766-1365　Marcus Benally VP of Procure-
　　　ment & Contracts
　　　Fax: (970) 375-6343
　　　Email: marcus@chinookmed.com
　　　Website: www.chinookmed.com
Chinook offers the latest technology and competitive
prices in medical supplies; specializing in custom medical
solutions for the harshest environments on Earth!
(Woman/White, estab 1990, empl 13, sales $4,700,000,
cert: State)

Connecticut

1070　Andrew Associates, Inc.
　　　6 Pearson Way　Enfield, CT 06082
　　　(860) 918-5041　Tim Drugan Acct Exec
　　　Fax: (860) 253-0007
　　　Email: tdrugan@andrewdm.com
　　　Website: www.andrewdm.com
Data management, digital printing, bulk mailing services,
labeling, inserting, stamping, sorting & literature
fulfillment services. (Woman/White, estab 1985, empl
60, sales $7,600,000, cert: WBENC)

1071　Crew Design Inc.
　　　P.O. Box 400　Kent, CT 06757
　　　(860) 927-5001　Gil Aviles CEO
　　　Fax: (860) 927-3844
　　　Email: gil@crewdesign.com
　　　Website: www.crewdesign.com
Custom in store display & merchandising equipment:
signage, merchandising fixtures, point of purchase
displays. (Hisp, estab 1998, empl 13, sales $4,469,789,
cert: NMSDC)

1072　Desai Communication
　　　34 Oakwood Avenue Ste 102　Norwalk, CT 06850
　　　(203) 324-6000　Amanda Desai Acct Exec
　　　Fax: (203) 831-0879
　　　Email: amanda@desaicomm.com
　　　Website: www.desaicomm.com
Web design & hosting, promotions, premiums, fulfillment, graphic design, computer graphics, digital
retouching, power point pesentations, pint avertising &
promotional material, trade show displays, B/W & color
printing. (Woman/Hisp, estab 1979, empl 11, sales
$1,500,000, cert: State, NMSDC)

1073 Point View Displays, LLC
200 Morgan Ave   East Haven, CT 06512
(203) 468-0887 Cynthia Sedlmeyer Owner
Fax: (203) 468-0485
Email: cindy@pointviewdisplays.com
Website: www.pointviewdisplays.com
Press conference backdrops, displays, indoor/outdoor banner stands & graphics. (Woman/White, estab 2001, empl 4, sales $400,000, cert: WBENC)

1074 Tanen Directed Advertising
12 South Main St   South Norwalk, CT 06854
(203) 855-5855 Ilene Tanen President
Fax: (203) 855-5865
Email: ilene@tanendirected.com
Website: www.tanendirected.com
Advertising, direct marketing, integrated marketing, online marketing, direct mail, email, print ads, collateral, sales presentations, human resources communications, benefits communications materials, employee communications. (Woman/White, estab 1985, empl 10, sales $1,865,652, cert: WBENC)

District of Columbia

1075 APCO Worldwide Inc.
700 12th St NW, Ste 8   Washignton, DC 20005
(202) 778-1000 Lisa Carr President
Fax: (202) 466-6002
Email: supplierregistration@apcoworldwide.com
Website: www.apcoworldwide.com
Global communication consulting: advertising, antitrust & competition, branding, broadcast film, video & multimedia production, business diplomacy, coalition building, corporate restructuring communication. (Woman/White, estab 1984, empl 638, sales $240,000,000, cert: WBENC)

1076 SRB Communications, LLC
1020 16th St, NW Ste 400 Washington, DC 20036
(202) 775-7721 Sheila Brooks CEO
Fax: (202) 775-7421
Email: sbrooks@srbcommunications.com
Website: www.srbcommunications.com
Media & communications: video production, advertising, lay-out & design, copywriting services, media placement & webcasting. (Woman/AA, estab 1990, empl 7, sales , cert: State, City, NMSDC)

1077 The Language Doctors, Inc.
412 H St NE Ste 302   Washington, DC 20002
(202) 544-2942 Adam Bouc Director of Sales and Mktg
Fax: (202) 547-2311
Email: abou@tldinc.org
Website: www.tldinc.org
Translation & intepretation svcs: advertising, banking, communications, computer svcs, legal, insurance, law enforcement. (AA, estab 1994, empl 4, sales $350,000, cert: State)

Delaware

1078 Keen Branding
17601 Coastal Hwy., Ste. 11-416   Nassau, DE 19969
(302) 644-6885 Alicia Stack Principal
Fax: (302) 450-4008
Email: astack@keenbranding.com
Website: www.keenbranding.com
Identity creation & design: logos, packaging, look & feel programs, identity mgmt. (Woman/White, estab 2000, empl 14, sales , cert: WBENC)

1079 Meetings by Design, Inc.
312 Nonantum Dr   Newark, DE 19711
(302) 738-8318 Jan White President
Fax: (302) 738-8326
Email: jan.white@meetingsbydesign.net
Website: www.meetingsbydesign.net
Business meetings & special events production. (Woman/White, estab 1993, empl 2, sales $200,000, cert: State, WBENC)

Florida

1080 Adventures in Advertising dba Resource Marketing
2520 Illinois St   Orlando, FL 32803
(407) 228-0881 Christyl Seymour President
Fax: (407) 228-3873
Email: cseymour@advinadv.com
Website: www.resourcemarketinginc.net
Graphic design/art services, product research support, custom design, online store solution, fulfillment svcs, direct import, promotional svcs, website searchable database, promotion design & implementation. (Woman/White, estab 2002, empl 1, sales $3,175,125, cert: WBENC)

1081 Atlas Sign Industries
1077 W Blue Heron Blvd   West Palm Beach, FL 33404
(561) 863-6659 Dusty Smith Natl Business Dev
Fax: (561) 863-6659
Email: dusty.a@atlassignindustries.us
Website: www.atlassignindustries.us
Design, mfr & install signs. (Woman/White, estab 1991, empl 185, sales $723,593, cert: WBENC)

1082 Avanza Advertising
5465 NW 36 St Ste 100 Miami Springs, FL 33166
(786) 565-7601 Alejandro Perez-Eguren CEO
Fax: (305) 814-7601
Email: Alejandro@AvanzaAd.com
Website: www.avanzaad.com
Advertising, design, digital media & video. (Hisp, estab 2013, empl 6, sales $500,000, cert: NMSDC, CPUC, 8(a))

1083 Baron Sign Manufacturing
      900 W 13th St Riviera Beach, FL 33404
      (800) 531-9558 Sandra Foland CEO
      Fax: (561) 848-2270
      Email: sandie@baronsign.com
      Website: www.baronsign.com
Interior & exterior signage, awards, plaques. (Woman/
White, estab 1983, empl 43, sales , cert: State, City)

1084 Black Dog Inc. DBA Next Day Signs
      6744 Memorial Hwy Tampa, FL 33615
      (813) 249-6398 Dorothy Johnson President
      Fax: (813) 249-6399
      Email: djohnson@nextdaysignstampa.com
      Website: www.nextdaysignstampa.com
Vinyl signs, banners, digital printing, vehicle & boat
graphics & lettering, directional signs, promotional signs,
trade show & conventions, sandblasted, electrical,
coroplast, point of purchase, magnets, screen printing,
real estate, constrcution. (Woman/White, estab 2003,
empl 3, sales $429,460, cert: State)

1085 BroadBased Communications, Inc.
      1301 Riverplace Blvd, Ste 1830 Jacksonville, FL
      32207
      (904) 398-7279 Jan Hirabayashi CEO
      Fax: (904) 398-6696
      Email: jan@bbased.com
      Website: www.bbased.com
Marketing plans, branding, direct mail, publication design,
exhibit design, annual reports, web sites, fleet graphics,
copywriting, art direction. (Woman/White, estab 1996,
empl 7, sales $880,951, cert: State, WBENC)

1086 Catalyst Advertizing
      737 W Colonial Dr Orlando, FL 32804
      (407) 425-5646 Edward Rees Agent
      Fax: (407) 425-7156
      Email: edrees@catalystholdingsco.com
      Website: www.catalystadvertizing.com
Advertising & marketing services, creative writing, art,
graphics, market analysis, planning, buying, media
relations, full design, production & coordination services.
(Hisp, estab 1989, empl 8, sales $750,000, cert: 8(a))

1087 Celestar Corporation
      9501 East US Hwy 92 Tampa, FL 33610
      (813) 627-9069 Lori Larsen VP Business Dev
      Fax:
      Email: llarsen@celestarcorp.com
      Website: www.celestarcorp.com
Media communications: marketing, training, branding,
mobile/portable distribution, broadcast media, internet,
entertainment. (AA, estab 2001, empl 58, sales
$5,615,000, cert: State)

1088 Certified Translations LLC
      11663 Vicolo Loop Windermere, FL 34786
      (407) 205-9494 Mara Cawthorn Managing Dir
      Fax:
      Email: certifiedtranslationsllc@gmail.com
      Website: www.certifiedtranslationsllc.com
Language Translation & Interpreting Services: Legal,
Technical, Mechanical, Medical, & Business / Finance.
Spanish, Portuguese, Creole, Mandarin, Cantonese,
French, Italian, German, etc. (Woman/Hisp, estab 2013,
empl 2, sales , cert: NMSDC)

1089 Kreative Kontent Co.
      4044 NE 7th Ave Ste 100 Fort Lauderdale, FL
      33334
      (954) 312-3660 Deborah Margolis Horwitz
      President/Exec Producer
      Fax: (954) 312-3661
      Email: debbie@kreativekontent.com
      Website: www.kreativekontent.com
Production specializing in content creation, broadcast,
web based, theatrical & marketing fulfillment programs,
broadcast commercials, corporate video communications, product placement, branded content, promotional
products. (Woman/White, estab 2010, empl 4, sales
$2,000,000, cert: WBENC)

1090 KVJINC Consulting
      7016 San Ramon Pl Ste. 202 Tampa, FL 33617
      (813) 987-9083 Kimberly Jackson Owner
      Fax:
      Email: kvjinc@yahoo.com
      Website: www.kvjincpr.com
Public, media relations, strategic, crisis communications,
press conferences, kits, event planning, image consult-
ing, sponsorship procurement & market research.
(Woman/AA, estab 1999, empl 3, sales $100,000, cert:
State, City)

1091 LanguageSpeak, Inc.
      5975 Sunset Dr Ste 803 Miami, FL 33143
      (305) 668-9797 Annette Taddeo CEO
      Fax: (305) 668-0435
      Email: acct@languagespeak.com
      Website: www.languagespeak.com
Language svcs: document translation, language instruction, conference interpretation, software localization,
website translation, cross cultural training. (Woman/
Hisp, estab 1995, empl 5, sales , cert: NMSDC, WBENC)

1092 Lombardi Enterprises, Inc.
      1145 N Tropical Trail Merritt Island, FL 32953
      (321) 449-8857 Ann Lombardi President
      Fax:
      Email: Ann@mihomeoffice.com
      Website:
Signs, labels & decals, asset control & printing software,
hardware, name badges & plates, promotional items &
marking products. (Woman/White, estab 2002, empl 4,
sales $88,556, cert: City)

1093   MarkMaster, Inc.
       11111 N 46th St   Tampa, FL 33617
       (813) 988-6000   Deborah Jordan Sales Rep
       Fax: (813) 985-6860
       Email: sales@markmasterinc.com
       Website: www.markmasterinc.com
Mfr rubber stamps, engraved & screened signage &
badges; industrial marking equip. (Hisp, estab 1933, empl
65, sales $8,700,993, cert: NMSDC)

1094   Multi Image Group, Inc.
       1701 Clint Moore Rd   Boca Raton, FL 33487
       (917) 319-8127   David Gordon President
       Fax: (561) 241-1616
       Email: david.gordon@mig.cc
       Website: www.mig.cc
Meeting production & staging, video & audio production,
graphic design, signage printing, set construction, web &
teleconferencing services, trade show exhibits, lighting
rentals. (Woman, estab 1979, empl 106, sales
$28,400,000, cert: NWBOC)

1095   Sunlure, Inc.
       3700 NW 124 Ave Unit 140 Coral Springs, FL 33065
       (754) 484-7929 Craig Sage Mgr
       Fax: (214) 960-4232
       Email: craig.sage@sunlure.com
       Website: www.sunlure.com
Promotional Products
Apparel Products
Custom imprinted apparel
Writing Products
Candy, Food and Water
Customized Drinkware Products
Bags for Marketing Campaigns
Toys and Novelties
Office products
Outdoor and Leisure
Health and Personal Care
Aut (Woman, estab 2003, empl 7, sales $900,000, cert:
State, NMSDC)

1096   T Wynne Art & Design Inc.
       1401 Manatee Ave W, Ste 1005   Bradenton, FL
       34205
       (941) 906-7124 Tanya Wynne Williams President
       Fax: (941) 906-7078
       Email: tanya@twynne.com
       Website: www.twynne.com
Package graphic design & and point of sale (POS) design.
(Woman/White, estab 1991, empl 8, sales $2,430,822,
cert: WBENC)

1097   The Language Corner, LLC
       2103 Coral Way Ste 700 Miami, FL 33145
       (888) 422-9964 Soledad Judge Director of Ops
       Fax: (305) 437-7685
       Email: soledad@thelanguagecorner.com
       Website: www.thelanguagecorner.com
Translation services, document translation, website
localization, desktop publishing, editing & proofreading,
copywriting & technical writing, glossary development.
(Woman/Hisp, estab 2001, empl 2, sales $216,429, cert:
State)

1098   Thomas Sign and Awning Company, Inc.
       4590 118th Avenue N. 33762 Clearwater, FL
       33762
       (727) 573-7757 Patti Canady Mktg Director
       Fax: (727) 573-0328
       Email: patti.canady@thomassign.com
       Website: www.thomassign.com
Design, mfr, install & service illuminated electrical signs.
LED, neon, vinyl graphics, permit acquisition, variance
applications, turnkey project mgmt. (Woman/White,
estab 1969, empl 180, sales $21,000,000, cert: WBENC)

Georgia

1099   AEE Productions
       1073 Huff Rd NW, Ste A   Atlanta, GA 30318
       (404) 352-2201 Yergan Jones President
       Fax:
       Email: yerganjones@aeeproductions.com
       Website: www.aeeproductions.com
Audio visual services. (AA, estab 1990, empl 6, sales
$975,000, cert: NMSDC)

1100   American Systems, Inc. dba Simon Sign Systems
       2158 Sylvan Rd   Atlanta, GA 30344
       (404) 766-5208 Simon Robinson President &
       General Mgr
       Fax: (404) 766-5210
       Email: gen-info@simonsignsystems.com
       Website: www.simonsignsystems.com
Mfr signs: interior & exterior, banners, digital & screen
printing, posters, corporate apparel & promotional
items. (AA, estab 1989, empl 5, sales $300,670, cert:
NMSDC)

1101   Basiqa, LLC
       1555 Oakbrook Dr Ste 135   Norcross, GA 30093
       (678) 824-6460 Winston Dzose VP Digital Mktg
       Fax: (678) 824-6467
       Email: winston@basiqa.com
       Website: www.basiqa.com
Direct mail, advertising, material preparation services
for mailing or other direct distribution, digital printing.
(AA, estab 2009, empl 16, sales $3,000,000, cert:
NMSDC)

1102 CK&M Direct Mail Advertising, Inc.
      1250 Northmeadow Pkwy Ste 116 Roswell, GA
      30076
      (770) 442-2166 Gary Kern GM
      Fax: (678) 325-4795
      Email: gkern@ckmdirect.com
      Website: www.ckmdirectmail.com
Lettershop services, fulfillment, distribution, warehousing,
list broker. (Hisp, estab 1992, empl 7, sales $1,992,000,
cert: NMSDC)

1103 Dove Direct
      5601 Fulton Industrial Blvd SW   Atlanta, GA 30336
      (404) 629-0122 Travis L Benjamin Business Dev Exec
      Fax: (404) 346-2019
      Email: tbenjamin@dovedirect.com
      Website: www.dovedirect.com
First class barcoding, third class mail, lettershop svcs,
personalization, list, data mgmt, fulfillment svcs, design
analysis, etc. (Woman/AA, estab 1987, empl 59, sales
$24,000,000, cert: NMSDC)

1104 Exhibits South
      1000 Satellite Blvd Ste 120 Suwanee, GA 30024
      (678) 225-5200 Nichole Holliday VP
      Fax: (678) 377-0998
      Email: nholliday@exhibitssouth.com
      Website: www.exhibitssouth.com
Dist & rent portable, modular & custom displays, graphic
production & design department, tradeshow services,
logistics & exhibit storage. (Woman/White, estab 1983,
empl 35, sales $9,696,527, cert: WBENC)

1105 Mail Centers Plus, LLC
      17 Executive Park Dr Ste 230 Atlanta, GA 30329
      (404) 321-1010 John Smithson Business Devel
      Analyst
      Fax: (404) 321-1888
      Email: jsmithson@mailcentersplus.com
      Website: www.mailcentersplus.com
Document distribution & mail center solutions. (AA, estab
2000, empl 140, sales $5,500,000, cert: NMSDC)

1106 PM Publicidad
      1776 Peachtree St Atlanta, GA 30309
      (404) 844-5757 philip polk EVP, General Mgr
      Fax:
      Email: info@pm3.agency
      Website: www.pm3.agency
Multicultural advertising solutions in the Hispanic market
segment, account services, broadcast production, media
planning & buying, sports marketing, market research,
strategic account planning, experiential & event marketing. (Hisp, estab 2004, empl 35, sales $23,307,370, cert:
NMSDC)

1107 Profitmaster Displays Inc.
      6190 Powers Ferry Road Ste #510 Atlanta, GA
      30339
      (800) 633-5454 Carol Beerman
      Fax: (804) 798-9794
      Email: cbeerman@profitmasterdisplays.com
      Website: www.profitmasterdisplays.com
Point of purchase displays & racks: wire, sheet metal,
wood, plastic & corrugated paperboard. (Woman/White,
estab 1984, empl 18, sales $20,000,000, cert: WBENC)

1108 Shared Vision LLC
      225 Ottley Dr NE Ste 140 Atlanta, GA 30324
      (678) 694-1965 Doug Jackson Principal
      Fax:
      Email: djackson@shared-vision.net
      Website: www.shared-vision.net
Marketing & advertising, strategic & creative services.
(Woman/AA, estab 2006, empl 20, sales $2,500,000,
cert: NMSDC)

1109 Solomon Says, Inc.
      887 W Marietta St NW, Ste M-102   Atlanta, GA
      30318
      (404) 881-1808 Loren Solomon President
      Fax: (404) 881-1809
      Email: loren@solomonsaysinc.com
      Website: www.solomonsays.com
Branding, marketing & advertising: corporate communications, print advertising, collateral, video, multi-media
& web. (Woman/White, estab 1996, empl 5, sales
$1,500,000, cert: WBENC)

1110 TDEFERIAMEDIA, Inc.
      9795 Talisman Dr   Johns Creek, GA 30022
      (404) 630-0639 Antenor Tony President
      Fax: (770) 619-5982
      Email: contact@tdeferiamedia.com
      Website: www.tdeferiamedia.com
Marketing, branding consulting & creative production,
ethnic market study & plans, media buying, translation
& interpretation in Spanish, digital & social media
expertise. (Hisp, estab 2007, empl 1, sales $140,000,
cert: NMSDC)

1111 The Symmetry Group, LLC
      600 W Peachtree St Ste 510 Atlanta, GA 30308
      (404) 237-2378 Scott Robinson President
      Fax: (404) 237-2379
      Email: scott@tsgatl.com
      Website: www.tsgatl.com
Graphic design, radio/TV production, print/outdoor
advertising production, event development, management & production, promotion development & execution. (AA, estab 2001, empl 6, sales $1,200,000, cert:
NMSDC)

1112 Viswam Bala Enterprises
      440 Barrett Pkwy, Ste 33   Kennesaw, GA 30144
      (770) 421-8110 Giridhar Iyer President
      Fax: (770) 421-8413
      Email: giri.iyer@fastsigns.com
      Website: www.fastsigns.com/201
Marketing strategy creation, brand /product identity
creation, graphic design services, production/printing &
installation services, static signs, banners, posters, decals,
vehicle art/wraps, cutting-edge digital signs & visual
magnetic solutions. (As-Ind, estab 1994, empl 6, sales
$1,047,000, cert: City, NMSDC)

1113 Yellobee Studio
      750 Hammond Dr Ste 350 Bldg 15 Atlanta, GA
      30328
      (404) 249-6407 Alison Scheel Creative Director
      Fax:
      Email: ascheel@yellobee.com
      Website: www.yellobee.com
Bilingual design & marketing, promotional communications, brand identity & packaging, direct mail design,
brochures, newsletters, web design, banner & poster art,
tradeshow displays, court graphics, typography,
illustration,photography. (Woman/White, estab 1998,
empl 4, sales $850,000, cert: WBENC)

Illinois

1114 1st Metropolitan Translation Services, Inc.
      875 North Michigan Avenue Ste 3100 Chicago, IL
      60611
      (312) 621-1500 Shannon Ewasiuk President
      Fax: (312) 621-1500
      Email: firstmetro@sbcglobal.net
      Website: www.1stmetropolitan.info
Foreign language interpreters & translations. (Woman/
White, estab 2000, empl 1, sales $222,810, cert: State,
WBENC)

1115 Angel Flight Marketing Services, Inc.
      1006 S. Michigan Ave Ste 606 Chicago, IL 60605
      (312) 933-1878 Gabriel Mitchell President
      Fax: (312) 577-0738
      Email: gmitchell@angelfly.com
      Website: www.angelfly.com
Direct mail, graphic design, call center, market research.
(AA, estab 1992, empl 10, sales $1,220,000, cert: City,
NMSDC)

1116 commonground
      600 W Fluton Fl 4 Chicago, IL 60661
      (312) 384-1906 Sherman Wright Managing Partner
      Fax: (312) 633-1906
      Email: AlicePollard@discovercg.com
      Website: www.discovercg.com
Marketing, advertising, cultural consulting, brand strategy,
promotions. (AA, estab 2003, empl 75, sales $24,367,000,
cert: NMSDC)

1117 Cor Creative, Inc.
      1412 W Jarvis Chicago, IL 60626
      (773) 381-3811 Linda Tuke-Larkin President
      Fax:
      Email: linda@corcreate.com
      Website: www.corcreate.com
Design, advertising, production, web site design &
programming, strategy, branding, social media, marketing, creative, media placement. (Woman/White, estab
2006, empl 1, sales $100,000, cert: City)

1118 Jayne Agency, LLC
      1231 Eastwood Ave Highland Park, IL 60035
      (312) 464-8100 Brooke Foley CEO
      Fax:
      Email: brooke@jayneagency.com
      Website: www.jayneagency.com
Creative, Strategy, Media, Digital Strategy & Technology.
(Woman/White, estab 2009, empl 4, sales $2,300,000,
cert: WBENC)

1119 Linguanational Translations, Inc.
      401 N Michigan Ave Ste 1200 #12135 Chicago, IL
      60611
      (312) 833-1399 Janie Markos President
      Fax:
      Email: jmarkos@linguanational.com
      Website: www.linguanational.com
Translation services: interpretation, typesetting, transcription & desktop publishing. (Woman/White, estab
2009, empl 3, sales $50,000, cert: WBENC)

1120 Mail Everything, Inc.
      325 N Fourth St Libertyville, IL 60048
      (847) 573-9999 Mary Trifunovich President
      Fax: (847) 949-5188
      Email: Mary@maileverything.com
      Website: www.maileverything.com
Direct mail & fulfillment services: addressing, inserting,
tabbing, folding, mailing lists, printing, warehousing, dist
literature, product & promotional items, kitting &
assembly. (Woman/White, estab 2002, empl 16, sales
$1,300,000, cert: WBENC)

1121 Media Link, Inc.
      1902 17th St Rock Island, IL 61201
      (309) 786-5142 Adrian Wille Mktg Consultant
      Fax:
      Email: adrian@medialinkinc.com
      Website: www.medialinkinc.com
Media Buying, Advertising, Marketing, PR, Public
Relations, Media Campaign, Marketing Research.
(Woman/White, estab 2001, empl 4, sales $1,046,821,
cert: State, WBENC)

1122 Medius & Associates, Inc.
      13175 Cold Springs Dr Huntley, IL 60142
      (847) 609-8165 Karen Holmes President
      Fax: (847) 609-8165
      Email: kholmes@mediusinc.com
      Website: www.mediusinc.com
Graphic design, illustration, photography & printing:
brochures, catalogs, ads, point of purchase, tradeshow
graphics & web design. (Woman/White, estab 1993,
empl 2, sales , cert: WBENC)

1123 NorthStar Strategies, Inc.
      448 Greenwood Ave   Glencoe, IL 60022
      (847) 242-9107 Dinny Cosyns Sr partner
      Fax: (847) 242-9108
      Email: dinny@northstarstrategies.biz
      Website: www.northstarstrategies.biz
Marketing & advertising agency. (Woman/White, estab
2004, empl 3, sales $240,000, cert: State, WBENC)

1124 Suncraft Technologies, Inc.
      1301 Frontenac Rd   Naperville, IL 60563
      (630) 369-7900 Scott Hayes VP of New Business
      Devel
      Fax: (630) 369-7070
      Email: shayes@suncraft-tech.com
      Website: www.suncraft-tech.com
Inline and conventional direct mail with variable data.
digital storefront, signage, inventory management,
creative format design, graphic design, fulfillment, kitting
and mailing services. (Woman/White, estab 1993, empl
125, sales $40,000,000, cert: CPUC, WBENC)

Indiana

1125 L & D Mail Masters Inc.
      110 Security Pkwy   New Albany, IN 47150
      (812) 981-7161 Jill Peden Business Dev Mgr
      Fax: (812) 981-7169
      Email: jpeden@ldmailmasters.com
      Website: www.ldmailmasters.com
Direct mail processing. (Woman/White, estab 1986, empl
110, sales $25,000,000, cert: WBENC)

1126 RLR Associates, Inc.
      1302 N Illinois St   Indianapolis, IN 46202
      (317) 632-1300 Ryan Scott President
      Fax: (317) 632-1302
      Email: ryan@rlr.biz
      Website: www.rlr.biz
Professional design services: corporate identity & branding, signage, wayfinding programs, interiors & interpretive
spaces.
 (AA, estab 1994, empl 6, sales $710,000, cert: State, City)

Kentucky

1127 Life's Eyes Media, LLC
      1717 Dixie Hwy, Ste 150   Fort Wright, KY 41011
      (859) 363-3916 Kristan Getsy CEO
      Fax: (859) 363-3916
      Email: kgetsy@lifeseyesmedia.com
      Website: www.lifeseyesmedia.com
Corporate Video, Commercial Video Production, Motion
Graphics, After Effects, DSLR Production, DSLR, Creative,
Creative Agency, Agency, Non-Profit Video, Scriptwriting,
Scripting, Web Video, Social Media Video. (Woman/White,
estab 2005, empl 3, sales $263,704, cert: WBENC)

1128 New West LLC
      9630 Ormsby Station Rd   Louisville, KY 40223
      (888) 867-7811 Melvin Graham Managing Dir
      Fax: (502) 891-2514
      Email: mgraham@newwestagency.com
      Website: www.newwestagency.com
Advertising, Public Relations, Brand Strategy, Website &
Mobile App Development, Social Media, Multicultural
Marketing, SEO/SEM/PPC, Event Planning & Video
Production. (AA, estab 2002, empl 28, sales $5,500,000,
cert: NMSDC)

1129 Vest Marketing Design, LLC
      3007 Sprowl Rd   Louisville, KY 40299
      (502) 267-5335 Sabrina Hayes Healthcare Mktg
      Dir
      Fax:
      Email: sabrinah@vestadvertising.com
      Website: www.vestadvertising.com
Digital, video, print & comprehensive media strategy &
implementation. (Woman/White, estab 1991, empl 40,
sales $8,500,000, cert: WBENC)

Massachusetts

1130 Buyer Advertising & Talent Solutions
      189 Wells Ave Ste 201A Newton, MA 02459
      (617) 404-0860 Charles Buyer President
      Fax: (617) 969-0755
      Email: cbuyer@buyerads.com
      Website: www.buyerads.com
Website Design & Development, Search Engine Optimization (SEO), Search Engine Marketing, Mobile marketing, Social Networking, Facebook Advertising, Facebook
Applications, Employer Brand Development, market
Research & Analysis. (Woman/White, estab 1966, empl
32, sales $15,877,337, cert: State)

1131 Carroll Communications Group
      P.O. Box 401   Milton, MA 02186
      (781) 248-2125 Marc Carroll Principal
      Fax: (617) 698-1377
      Email: mcarroll@carrollcommunications.net
      Website: www.carrollcommunications.net
Advertising agency: web design, graphic design,
branding strategies, social media strategies, on-line
marketing, media planning & media buying. (AA, estab
2008, empl 3, sales $100,000, cert: State)

1132 Color Media Group, LLC
      4 Copley Pl, Ste 120   Boston, MA 02116
      (617) 266-6961 Josefina Bonilla President
      Fax: (617) 663-6961
      Email: josefina@colorboston.com
      Website: www.colormagazineusa.com
Web advertising, signature events, event management,
strategic marketing initiatives, new markets, media
buying services, public relations. (Woman/Hisp, estab
2007, empl 3, sales $289,000, cert: State)

1133 Rapport International, LLC
      93 Moore Rd   Sudbury, MA 01776
      (978) 443-2540 Wendy Pease Owner, Exec Director
      Fax: (206) 339-7160
      Email: wmpease@rapportintl.com
      Website: www.rapporttranslations.com
Translation & interpretation services in over 100 languages. (Woman/White, estab 1987, empl 5, sales $1,200,000, cert: WBENC)

1134 Sky Rise, LLC
      26 Howland St   Plymouth, MA 02360
      (508) 732-0455 Sylvester Ryan Managing Dir
      Fax: (508) 732-0488
      Email: sryan@skyrisellc.com
      Website: www.skyrisellc.com
Marketing communications & advertising consulting, corporate events, tradeshows, design exhibits, displays, create logos, brochures, business cards, website design, graphic design, & packaging. (AA, estab 2005, empl 3, sales $30,000, cert: State)

1135 Spectrum Broadcasting Corporation
      114 Wrentham St   Boston, MA 02124
      (617) 287-8770 Tessil Collins CEO
      Fax:
      Email: ceo@spectrumbroadcastingcorp.com
      Website: www.spectrumbroadcastingcorp.com
Media streaming & production, advertising creative services, training & management, internet, television, radio, graphic & web design, product & artist management, training, facilitation & consultation services. (AA, estab 1998, empl 5, sales $11,000, cert: State, City)

1136 TSM Design, Inc.
      293 Bridge St   Springfield, MA 01103
      (413) 731-7600 Nancy Urbschat Principal
      Fax: (413) 730-6689
      Email: nancy@tsmdesign.com
      Website: www.tsmdesign.com
Integrated branding, multi-channel marketing & standout graphic design services. (Woman/White, estab 2005, empl 7, sales $900,000, cert: State)

Maryland

1137 21st Century Expo Group, Inc.
      3321 75th Ave, Ste P   Landover, MD 20785
      (301) 386-9771 Leslie McFarland President
      Fax: (301) 386-9780
      Email: lmcfarland@21stceg.com
      Website: www.21stceg.com
Exhibit mgmt, marketing, dist displays & decorating svcs. (AA, estab 1991, empl 9, sales , cert: NMSDC, WBENC)

1138 A. Bright Idea
      210 Archer St   Bel Air, MD 21014
      (410) 836-7180 Anita Brightman CEO
      Fax: (410) 836-0186
      Email: info@abrightideaonline.com
      Website: www.abrightideaonline.com
Advertising, public relations & graphic design support. (Woman/White, estab 1996, empl 35, sales $2,100,000, cert: WBENC)

1139 American International Mailing, Inc.
      3916 Vero Rd Ste K Baltimore, MD 21227
      (410) 247-4900 Tom Parry VP
      Fax: (410) 247-4928
      Email: tomp@aimmailing.com
      Website: www.aimmailing.com
International mailing & distribution svcs: letter mail, direct mail, catalogs, publications, parcels & freight. (Woman/White, estab 2004, empl 25, sales $10,600,000, cert: WBENC)

1140 ArachnidWorks, Inc.
      5104 Pegasus Court Ste B Frederick, MD 21704
      (240) 285-9844 Monica Kolbay CEO
      Fax: (240) 235-4305
      Email: monica@arachnidworks.com
      Website: www.arachnidworks.com
Advertising, internet marketing, logo design, print media, ad creation & copywriting, web design & development. (Woman, estab 2008, empl 3, sales $158,335, cert: State)

1141 Barb Clapp Advertising and Marketing, LLC
      6115 Falls Rd Penthouse Baltimore, MD 21209
      (410) 561-8886 Barb Clapp President
      Fax: (410) 561-9064
      Email: lisa@barbclapp.com
      Website: www.clappcommunications.com
Advertising, marketing & public relations. (Woman/White, estab 2000, empl 6, sales $354,737, cert: State)

1142 Catalpha Advertising & Design
      6801 Loch Raven Blvd   Towson, MD 21286
      (410) 337-0066 Don Keller VP
      Fax: (410) 296-2297
      Email: dkeller@catalpha.com
      Website: www.catalpha.com
Design & produce product & event promotional signs & materials: banners, fact tags, headers, danglers, hang tags, counter cards. (Woman/White, estab 1986, empl 6, sales $720,000, cert: State)

1143 Harvey & Daughters, Inc.
      952 Ridgebrook Rd, Ste 1000   Sparks, MD 21152
      (410) 771-5566 Jade Reider Office Mgr
      Fax: (410) 771-5559
      Email: jreider@harveyagency.com
      Website: www.harveyagency.com
Brand activation, purchasing strategy, package design, logo development & graphic design. (Woman/White, estab 1986, empl 35, sales $6,000,000, cert: WBENC)

1144   Herrmann Advertising|Branding|Technology
        30 West St   Annapolis, MD 21401
        (410) 267-6522 Jane Farrell Sr Acct. Exec.
        Fax: (410) 295-0266
        Email: jane@herrmann.com
        Website: www.herrmann.com
Advertising agency: market research, creative design,
media management, print management, photography,
copy writing & technology. (Woman/White, estab 1979,
empl 14, sales $3,663,968, cert: State, City, WBENC)

1145   Media Works, Ltd.
        1425 Clarkview Rd Ste 500 Baltimore, MD 21209
        (443) 470-4400 Michele Selby President
        Fax: (443) 470-4425
        Email: mselby@medialtd.com
        Website: www.medialtd.com
Advertising agency, research, plan & place media.
(Woman/White, estab 1989, empl 34, sales $887,604,
cert: City)

1146   Pure Advertising, LLC
        137 National Plaza Ste 300 Oxon Hill, MD 20745
        (301) 646-4392 Sidney Shelton Managing Partner
        Fax:
        Email: sidney@pureadsww.com
        Website: www.pureadsww.com
Outdoor advertising & graphic design, taxi advertising,
transit, airport advertising & billboards. (AA, estab 2010,
empl 2, sales $200,000, cert: State, NMSDC)

Michigan

1147   Graphicolor Systems, Inc.
        12788 Currie Court   Livonia, MI 48150
        (248) 347-0271 Anita Mitzel President
        Fax: (248) 347-0737
        Email: anita@graphicolor.com
        Website: www.graphicolor.com
Design trade show displays & corporate signage. (Woman/
White, estab 1984, empl 8, sales $1,002,000, cert:
WBENC)

1148   Immersion Graphics Inc.
        1020 Metro Dr   Commerce, MI 48390
        (248) 624-6520 Pat Hernandez President
        Fax: (248) 624-6518
        Email: pat@immersion-graphics.com
        Website: www.immersion-graphics.com
Engineering & audio visual systems solutions. (Hisp, estab
1998, empl 10, sales $3,439,000, cert: NMSDC)

1149   J & L Business Solutions
        1809 Haggerty Rd   Commerce Township, MI 48390
        (248) 960-7525 Natasha Vassallo Owner
        Fax: (248) 668-0172
        Email: nata@signaramastore.com
        Website: www.signaramact.com
Design & install signs: interior & exterior architectural
signs, wayfinding signage, vehicle lettering, illuminated
signs, ADA, architectural signage, engraved tags & plates.
(Woman/AA, estab 2004, empl 3, sales $207,000, cert:
State)

1150   LA Exhibits, Inc.
        1091 Centre Rd, Ste 130 Auburn Hills, MI 48326
        (248) 340-1144 Della Dotson President
        Fax:
        Email: della@laexhibits.com
        Website: www.laexhibits.com
Design, build & support tradeshow displays & events,
portable, modular & custom displays, design & production, warehousing. (Woman/White, estab 1991, empl 6,
sales $470,000, cert: WBENC)

1151   Languages International Inc.
        4665 - 44th St SE Ste A1101 Grand Rapids, MI
        49512
        (616) 285-0005 Beverly Wall Owner
        Fax: (616) 285-0004
        Email: beverly@lang-int.com
        Website: www.lang-int.com
Foreign language translation & interpreting services.
(Woman/White, estab 1988, empl 7, sales $400,000,
cert: WBENC)

1152   PALS International
        900 Wilshire Dr Ste 105 Troy, MI 48084
        (248) 362-2060 David Schroeder VP Business Dev
        Fax:
        Email: dschroeder@palsintl.com
        Website: www.palsintl.com
Translations & interpretations; language instruction;
cross-cultural programs; accent reduction; global
relocation; videovoice-overs. (Woman/Hisp, estab 1983,
empl 80, sales $1,509,900, cert: NMSDC, WBENC)

1153   Pro-Motion Technology Group
        29755 Beck Rd   Wixom, MI 48393
        (248) 560-0521 Brian Flewelling Acct Mgr
        Fax: (248) 694-0911
        Email: hello@promotion.tech
        Website: www.promotion.tech
Audiovisual technology solutions. (Woman/White, estab
2002, empl 45, sales $25,000,000, cert: WBENC)

1154   Stage 3 Productions
        27500 Donald Court   Warren, MI 48092
        (586) 576-0625 Andre LaRoche President
        Fax: (586) 576-0626
        Email: success@stage3.com
        Website: www.stage3.com
Commercial, advertising photography, digital imaging,
illustration, graphic design, stage rental. (AA, estab
1984, empl 8, sales , cert: NMSDC)

1155   STS Marketing Services, LLC
        22840 Woodward Ave   Ferndale, MI 48220
        (248) 548-1011 Theresa Bland Business Mgr
        Fax: (248) 548-1282
        Email: tbland@stsmktg.com
        Website: www.stsmktg.com
Editorial boutique editing, internal/external corporate
communications packages, production services. (AA,
estab 1994, empl 1, sales $812,000, cert: NMSDC)

1156   Tiger Studio Co.
       418 E 8th St   Holland, MI 49423
       (616) 748-7532 Luciano Hernandez Owner
       Fax: (616) 931-3231
       Email: luciano@tigerstudiodesign.com
       Website: www.tigerstudiodesign.com
Product, Interaction, Brand, and Strategy. (Hisp, estab 2000, empl 4, sales , cert: NMSDC)

1157   Trent Design LLC
       114 E Second St   Rcohester, MI 48307
       (248) 652-8307 Marilyn Trent Principal
       Fax: (248) 651-0031
       Email: marilyn@trentcreative.com
       Website: www.trentcreative.com
Graphic design, digital media, web design & development, advertising, social media marketing. (Woman/White, estab 1991, empl 5, sales $600,000, cert: WBENC)

1158   Wensco of Michigan Corporation
       5760 Safety Dr NE   Belmont, MI 49306
       (800) 253-1569 Jim Redmer Director of Mktg
       Fax: (800) 449-0448
       Email: jredmer@wensco.com
       Website: www.wensco.com
Dist signs: digital inkjet media & laminates, cut vinyls, banners, neon, l.e.d.'s, ballasts, plywood, metal & plastic substrates, aluminum, polycarbonate, acrylic, plexiglass, aluminum composite panels. (Woman/White, estab 1937, empl 50, sales $22,000,000, cert: WBENC)

Minneapolis

1159   Adobe DeSigns LLC.com
       3745 Bloomington Av So   Minneapolis, MN 55407
       (612) 822-2385 Vivian Guerra CEO
       Fax: (509) 357-2474
       Email: vguerra@adobedesignsllc.com
       Website: www.adobedesignsllc.com
Interior/Exterior Signage: ADA, Parking, Wayfinding, Building, Mounments, Murals, Banners, Vinyl, Architectural Fusions (Di Noc, Belbien, Realtec, LG). (Woman/AA/Hisp, estab 2014, empl 6, sales , cert: NMSDC)

1160   Bella Creative
       16860 Judicial Rd   Lakeville, MN 55044
       (952) 232-6411 Stacy A Parizek Owner
       Fax: (612) 435-8207
       Email: stacy@bella-creative.net
       Website: www.bellaexhibts.com
Mfr trade show exhibits, off-the-shelf displays to custom booths. (Woman/White, estab 2008, empl 1, sales $200,000, cert: WBENC)

1161   Betmar Languages, Inc.
       6260 Hwy 65 NE, Ste 308   Minneapolis, MN 55432
       (763) 572-9711 Beth Loo President
       Fax: (763) 571-3467
       Email: bloo@betmar.com
       Website: www.betmar.com
Translation svcs: on site interpreters; voice-over services for audio, video & interactive projects; typesetting; document translation; cultural diversity training. (Woman/White, estab 1985, empl 4, sales $949,266, cert: WBENC)

1162   cmnd+m LLC
       867 Pierce Butler Route   St. Paul, MN 55104
       (612) 867-6273 Krista O'Malley
       Fax: (678) 807-2981
       Email: accounting@cmndm.com
       Website: www.cmndm.com
Design, production, engineering, retail, advertising, project management, construction, and training. (Woman/As-Pac, estab 2011, empl 11, sales $700,000, cert: NMSDC, WBENC)

1163   Deep Well, Inc.
       123 N 3rd St Ste 700 Minneapolis, MN 55401
       (612) 338-7947 Phil Nelson
       Fax:
       Email: phil@crash-sues.com
       Website: www.crash-sues.com
Advertising, marketing, production, video editing, animation, 3D, traditional animation, stop motion, graphics, effects, color, media, web apps, strategy, creative, branding, brand development, ideation, web development, post-production. (Woman/White, estab 2008, empl 12, sales $1,600,000, cert: WBENC)

1164   Designer Sign Systems
       9975 Flanders Ct NE   Blaine, MN 55449
       (763) 784-5858 Karen Fisher CEO
       Fax: (763) 784-2300
       Email: customerservice@designersign.com
       Website: www.designersign.com
Mfr & design architectural interior & exterior signage. (Woman/White, estab 1984, empl 30, sales $5,246,000, cert: WBENC)

1165   Dudak Production, Inc.
       582 Bavaria Lane   Chaska, MN 55318
       (952) 443-0097 Shirley Dudak President
       Fax: (952) 443-3723
       Email: shirley.dudak@dudakproductioninc.com
       Website: www.dudakproductioninc.com
Advertising, Graphic Design Services, Marketing Consulting Services, Commercial Gravure Printing, Commercial Screen Printing, Packing & Crating, Print Advertising, Direct Marketing Fulfillment, Marketing & Distribution, Printing, Brand Marketing. (Woman/White, estab 1996, empl 3, sales $1,675,000, cert: WBENC)

1166 IN Food Mktg & Design, Inc.
      600 N Washington Ave Ste C101 Minneapolis, MN
      55401
      (612) 353-3410 Anita M Nelson President
      Fax:
      Email: anita@infoodmktg.com
      Website: www.infoodmktg.com
Marketing & communications: brand building & product
promotions. (Woman/White, estab 1995, empl 12, sales
$1,215,000, cert: WBENC)

1167 Intercross Design, Inc.
      2238 Edgewood Ave S   Minneapolis, MN 55426
      (952) 935-2994 Karen Chenvert Accountant
      Fax: (952) 935-0168
      Email: Diana.maples@intercross.com
      Website: www.intercross.com
Advertising agency: branding, videos, websites, collateral
& advertising. (Woman, estab 1997, empl 13, sales
$2,400,000, cert: WBENC)

1168 JPG & Associates, Inc.
      8991 33rd St N   Lake Elmo, MN 55042
      (651) 779-1072 Jerry Grohovsky President
      Fax: (651) 779-8599
      Email: jerry@jpgassoc.com
      Website: www.jpgassoc.com
Technical publications, temporary staffing & off-site
production, technical writing, instructional design,
marketing writing, graphic design, desktop publishing,
web site development, web-based help development.
(Woman/White, estab 1993, empl 30, sales $2,000,000,
cert: WBENC)

1169 KJ International Resources, LTD
      800 Washington Ave North Ste 905 Minneapolis,
      MN 55401
      (612) 288-9494 Annie Sligh President
      Fax: (612) 288-9496
      Email: asligh@kjinternational.com
      Website: www.kjinternational.com
Language translation & validation, desktop publishing,
web translation & localization, voice-overs, etc. (Woman,
estab 1994, empl 75, sales $6,400,000, cert: WBENC)

1170 KNOCK, inc.
      1307 Glenwood Ave   Minneapolis, MN 55405
      (612) 333-6511 Tom Newton VP Business Dev
      Fax: (612) 455-6866
      Email: tom.newton@knockinc.com
      Website: www.KNOCKinc.com
Graphic design, branding, marketing, advertising, packaging, illustration, photo art direction. (Woman/Hisp, estab
2001, empl 74, sales $27,030,000, cert: NMSDC, WBENC)

1171 Latitude Prime LLC
      80 S 8th St Ste 900 Minneapolis, MN 55402
      (888) 341-9080 Nat LeBrun
      Fax: (888) 341-9120
      Email: email@latitudeprime.com
      Website: www.latitudeprime.com
Multilingual translation services, media & document
translation, interpretation, localization, transcription,
proofreading/editing & DTP services. (Woman/As-Ind,
estab 2009, empl 100, sales $1,009,350, cert: City,
NMSDC, WBENC, 8(a))

1172 Northcott Banners, Inc.
      2645 - 26th Ave S, Ste 400   Minneapolis, MN
      55406
      (612) 722-1733 Millie Northcott Owner
      Fax:
      Email: millie@northcottbanner.com
      Website: www.northcottbanner.com
Mfr banners: fabric, vinyl, interior & exterior applications. (Woman/White, estab 1984, empl 9, sales
$712,698, cert: WBENC)

1173 Oceandrum LLC dba Zydeco Design
      231 2nd St   Excelsior, MN 55331
      (612) 202-7421 Nathalie Wilson President
      Fax: (651) 925-0106
      Email: nathaliew@zydecodesign.com
      Website: www.zydecodesign.com
Brand & design, branding strategy, brand experience
strategy, brand architecture, naming, identity, image
system, packaging, annual reports, corporate social
responsibility & sustainable development. (Woman/
White, estab 2009, empl 2, sales $300,000, cert: State,
WBENC)

1174 Peggy Lauritsen Design Group, Inc.
      125 Main St. SE Ste 125   Minneapolis, MN 55414
      (612) 623-4200 Linda Gosslin Chief Exec artist
      Fax: (612) 623-9802
      Email: lgosslin@pldg.com
      Website: www.pldg.com
Corporate & brand identity, graphic & communications
sesign, marketing communications, website design,
event communications, print or electronic media.
(Woman/White, estab 1979, empl 9, sales , cert:
WBENC)

1175 Portage Marketing
      2401 Sheridan Ave So   Minneapolis, MN 55405
      (612) 381-0621 Laureen Carlson President
      Fax:
      Email: lcarlson@portagemarketing.com
      Website: www.portagemarketing.com
Advertising agency & media placement. (Woman/White,
estab 2000, empl 1, sales $5,000,000, cert: WBENC)

1176 Tembua Inc (fka Precision Language Services)
17595 Kenwood Trail Ste 120 Lakeville, MN 55044
(952) 435-8178 Paula Town Exec Admin Asst
Fax: (952) 435-3626
Email: office@tembua.com
Website: www.tembua.com
Document translation: bilingual, bicultural translations.
(Woman/AA, estab 1993, empl 36, sales $700,000, cert:
WBENC)

1177 Visual Commnications
475 Cleveland Ave N Ste 223 St. Paul, MN 55104
(651) 644-4494 Richard Lang Principal
Fax: (651) 644-4289
Email: lang@visualcomm.com
Website: www.visualcommunications.com
Experiential design, signage system design, graphic
design, wayfinding, programming, ADA signage survey,
Life Safety analysis, history walls, donor recognition &
master plan development. (Woman, estab 1991, empl 6,
sales $600,000, cert: State, City, WBENC)

1178 Wrap City Graphics
62 6th Ave S Hopkins, MN 55343
(952) 920-4664 Kimberly Korb President
Fax:
Email: kimberly@wrapcitygraphics.com
Website: www.WrapCityGraphics.com
Commercial signage & digitally printed wide-format
adhesive backed vinyl graphics for vehicle graphics/
wraps, window/wall graphics, dimensional letters/logos
& architectural products. (Woman, estab 2005, empl 7,
sales $745,000, cert: WBENC)

Missouri

1179 Brighton Agency, Inc.
7711 Bonhomme Ave Ste 100 Saint Louis, MO
63105
(314) 726-0700 Tina VonderHaar CEO
Fax: (314) 721-8517
Email: accounting@brightonagency.com
Website: www.brightonagency.com
Strategic planning, brand development, digital marketing
& production, marketing consulting, public relations,
advertising, promotions, media planning, audio & video
production, event marketing, online, mobile & app
development. (Woman/White, estab 1989, empl 71,
sales $9,030,143, cert: State, WBENC)

1180 Harris Graphic Design
7309 Natural Bridge Rd   St. Louis, MO 63121
(314) 389-2636 Lee Harris Designer
Fax: (314) 389-2636
Email: harrisgd@anet-stl.com
Website:
Advertising svcs: annual reports, maps, posters, graphic
design, A-V presentations, brochures, displays & exhibits,
letterhead, newsletter, etc. (AA, estab 1978, empl 2,
sales , cert: State, CPUC)

1181 Language Solutions Inc.
230 South Bemiston Ave. Ste 610 St. Louis, MO
63105
(314) 725-3711 Melissa Wurst President
Fax: (314) 725-3713
Email: melissa@langsolinc.com
Website: www.langsolinc.com
Written translation & multilingual typesetting: over 40
languages. (Woman/White, estab 1998, empl 3, sales
$385,000, cert: WBENC)

1182 Schisla Design, LLC dba Enrich
12 N Sarah St St. Louis, MO 63108
(314) 553-9500 Suzanne Duvald'Adrian Mktg &
Social Media
Fax: (314) 553-9501
Email: suzanne@enrichcreative.com
Website: www.enrichcreative.com
Branding programs: audits & research, Strategy and
Development, Naming, Logo Design, Strategic Messag-
ing, Positioning, Brand Guides & Product, Service and
Event Branding. (Woman/White, estab 2002, empl 4,
sales $438,502, cert: WBENC)

North Carolina

1183 Crutchfield & Associates Inc.
515 College Rd, Ste 14 Greensboro, NC 27410
(336) 297-1222 Bernadette Trinidad President
Fax: (336) 297-1333
Email: bernadette@ca-ideas.com
Website: www.ca-ideas.com
Advertising agency, integrated, strategic & innovative
marketing & communications solutions. (Woman/Hisp,
estab 1985, empl 3, sales $121,707, cert: NMSDC)

1184 Fly My Photo, LLC
560 Davidson Gateway Dr Ste 101 Davidson, NC
28036
(855) 347-4922 Susan Boaz President
Fax: (800) 641-7954
Email: susan@flagology.com
Website: www.flagology.com
Mfr decorative flags, printed & appliqued, photo flags,
monogram flags, signage, flag poles & brackets, door
mats, monograms & personalized flags. (Woman/White,
estab 2013, empl 1, sales $77,000, cert: WBENC)

1185 Jervay Agency, LLC
338 S Sharon Amity, Ste 302 Charlotte, NC 28211
(704) 780-7004 Adria Jervay Media Acct Rep
Fax:
Email: adria@thejervayagency.com
Website: www.TheJervayAgency.com
Advertising & marketing materials. (Woman/AA, estab
2012, empl 3, sales $24,000, cert: City)

1186 Language Resource Center Inc.
      P.O. Box 18066   Charlotte, NC 28218
      (704) 464-0016 Abdullahi Sheikh CEO
      Fax: (704) 208-4018
      Email: abdullah.sheikh@languagerc.com
      Website: www.languagerc.com
Interpretation & translation service providers. (AA, estab 2009, empl 15, sales $1,428,268, cert: State, City)

1187 Main Street Mobile Billboards
      2610 Tuckaseegee Rd   Charlotte, NC 28208
      (888) 788-7492 Brendon Henderson CEO
      Fax:
      Email: brendon@mainstreetmobilebillboards.com
      Website: www.mainstreetmobilebillboards.com
Mobile truck billboard & walking billboards advertising. (AA, estab 2013, empl 2, sales , cert: State, City, NMSDC)

New Hampshire

1188 Kelley Solution, Inc.
      210 West Rd Unit 3 Portsmouth, NH 03801
      (603) 431-3881 Lisa Finneral President
      Fax: (603) 430-6855
      Email: lfinneral@kelleysolutions.com
      Website: www.kelleysolutions.com
E-business solutions & svcs: online fulfillment, graphic design, strategic sourcing, warehousing, distribution, integrated marketing campaigns & direct mail management. (Woman/White, estab 1972, empl 6, sales $2,200,000, cert: WBENC)

1189 Polaris Direct
      300 Technology Dr   Hooksett, NH 03106
      (603) 626-5800 Judith Maloy CEO
      Fax: (603) 626-5031
      Email: diversity@polarisdirect.net
      Website: www.polarisdirect.net
Direct mail, data processing, ink jet & laser personalization, mailing services, bindery & print management. (Woman/White, estab 2003, empl 83, sales $36,508,458, cert: WBENC)

New Jersy

1190 CQ fluency
      238 Main St   Hackensack, NJ 07601
      (201) 487-8007 Elisabete Miranda VP - Healthcare
      Fax: (201) 487-8052
      Email: info@cqfluency.com
      Website: www.cqfluency.com
Translation services: 180 languages, web localization, cultural consulting, desktop publishing, phone interpretation, multimedia production, tape transcription. (Woman/Hisp, estab 2000, empl 10, sales $3,844,722, cert: State, NMSDC, WBENC)

1191 Digital Outdoor Advertising
      788 Shrewsbury Ave   Tinton Falls, NJ 07724
      (732) 491-8726 Christine Lanziano President
      Fax: (732) 491-8726
      Email: christine@digitaloutdooradvertising.com
      Website: www.digitaloutdooradvertising.com
Digital & static outdoor billboards, mall kiosks & bus advertising. (Woman/White, estab 2012, empl 7, sales $6,000,000, cert: WBENC)

1192 Eclipse Marketing Services Inc.
      490 Headquarters Plaza North Tower, 10th Fl
      Morristown, NJ 07960
      (800) 837-4648 Margaret Boller President
      Fax: (973) 695-0209
      Email: mboller@eclipse2.com
      Website: www.eclipsemarketingservices.com
Advertising Services: campaigns; Hispanic Marketing Consulting; Graphic Design; Website design; Marketing programs; Promotional printing; Magazine advertising and publishing; Coop Marketing & promotion; Digital & social media. (Woman/White, estab 1992, empl 39, sales $10,980,994, cert: WBENC)

1193 Encore Events, ltd. dba ENCORE DESIGN
      31 Industrial Ave., Ste 7   Mahwah, NJ 07430
      (973) 890-0088 Kathleen Orbe Principal & Creative Director
      Fax: (973) 890-0080
      Email: encoredesign@mac.com
      Website: www.encoredesign.com
Design services: strategic identity & branding. (Woman/White, estab 1994, empl 7, sales $750,000, cert: WBENC)

1194 Expect Advertising, Inc.
      1033 Route 46   Clifton, NJ 07013
      (973) 777-8886 Ravi Sachdev President
      Fax:
      Email: ravi.sachdev@expectad.com
      Website: www.expectad.com
Medical marketing & communications: advertising, promotion, branding, web design, web marketing, sales incentive programs, premiums, trade shows, public relations, media planning, market research. (As-Ind, estab 1996, empl 16, sales $2,000,000, cert: NMSDC)

1195 Graphic Matter, Inc.
      601 Route 206, Ste 26-405   Hillsborough, NJ 08844
      (908) 359-8760 Beverly Thomas President
      Fax: (908) 359-1414
      Email: wbe@graphicmatter.com
      Website: www.graphicmatter.com
Creative services: print & web. (Woman/White, estab 2002, empl 6, sales $297,570, cert: State, WBENC)

1196   Jouard Wozniak LLC dba JWDesign
       165 Passaic Ave Ste 410 Fairfield, NJ 07004
       (973) 244-9191 Faith Wozniak President
       Fax: (973) 244-9193
       Email: faith@jwadv.com
       Website: www.jwadv.com
Advertising & design, creative, design & marketing
services, web & print, trade show graphics, promotional
events, video & audio production, photography & retouching. (Woman/White, estab 1989, empl 4, sales $178,000,
cert: WBENC)

1197   Newtype, Inc.
       447 Route 10 East Ste 14 Randolph, NJ 07054
       (973) 361-6000 Jo Ann Porto CEO
       Fax: (973) 361-6005
       Email: jporto@newtypeinc.com
       Website: www.newtypeinc.com
Translations & desktop publishing svcs in over 130 languages. (Woman/White, estab 1966, empl 12, sales
$1,700,000, cert: WBENC)

1198   Para-Plus Translations, Inc.
       2 Coleman Ave   Cherry Hill, NJ 08034
       (856) 547-3695 Carlos Santiago VP
       Fax: (856) 547-3345
       Email: csantiago@para-plus.com
       Website: www.para-plus.com
Translation & interpretation svcs: technical reports,
medical reports, legal documents, oral & written depositions, audio tapes, video tapes, patents, manuscripts,
manuals, product literature, web sites. (Woman/Hisp,
estab 1980, empl 15, sales $3,028,000, cert: State)

1199   Personal Mail International, Inc.
       5 Cold Hill Rd S, Ste 28   Mendham, NJ 07945
       (973) 543-6001 Debra Seyler President
       Fax: (973) 543-7911
       Email: dseyler@pmipmi.com
       Website: www.pmipmi.com
International & domestic mail & package forwarding
services. (Woman/White, estab 1987, empl 11, sales
$950,000, cert: WBENC)

1200   Seliger-Braun Inc. dba Keylingo Translations
       Princeton Forrestal Village 116 Village Blvd, Ste 200
       Princeton, NJ 08540
       (609) 423-1077 Sherry Braun Managing Dir
       Fax:
       Email: sherry.braun@keylingo.com
       Website: www.keylingo.com/
Translations services: localization, transcreation, interpretation & tele-interpretation. (Woman/White, estab 2011,
empl 2, sales $106,775, cert: State, WBENC)

1201   Sign Up Inc.
       255 Route 3 E   Secaucus, NJ 07094
       (201) 902-8640 Elizabeth Selbach President
       Fax:
       Email: liz.selbach@fastsigns.com
       Website: www.fastsigns.com/153
Signs: vinyl, wood, windows, walls or vehicles, channel
letters, window graphics, trade show booths, exhibits and
displays, flags and banners, cut-outs, dimensional letters,
banner stands, vehicle graphics, vinyl lettering, posters,
murals. (Woman/White, estab 1992, empl 8, sales
$87,542,162, cert: State)

1202   Sunset Printing and Engraving Corp
       10 Kice Ave   Wharton, NJ 07885
       (732) 335-2165 Deron Wainer
       Fax:
       Email: dwainer@sunsetcorpid.com
       Website: www.sunsetcorpid.com
Corporate identity campaigns: printing, engraving,
embossing & foil stamping. (Hisp, estab 1945, empl 45,
sales $8,912,453, cert: NMSDC)

1203   The S3 Agency
       716 Main St   Boonton, NJ 07005
       (973) 257-5533 Denise Blasevick CEO
       Fax: (973) 257-5543
       Email: dblasevick@theS3agency.com
       Website: www.theS3agency.com
Advertising & marketing: print, tv, radio, outdoor, online,
public relations, collateral, direct mail & direct marketing, e-marketing, websites, product launches, POP,
business-to-business & consumer marketing, internal
communications. (Woman/White, estab 2001, empl 25,
sales $3,100,000, cert: WBENC)

1204   TriStar Fulfillment Services, Inc.
       520 Pedricktown Rd   Bridgeport, NJ 08014
       (972) 355-6256 Susan Harker Owner
       Fax: (856) 467-3853
       Email: sharker@tristarfulfillment.com
       Website: www.tristarfulfillment.com
Rebates, gift cards, merchandise, sweepstake offers, online order entry, reporting, tracking, billing, data entry,
data processing, telemarketing, ondemand printing,
sampling, direct mail, warehousing & distribution.
(Woman/White, estab 1976, empl 135, sales
$30,000,000, cert: WBENC)

New Mexico

1205   Greetings etc! inc.
       2505 Commercial NE   Albuquerque, NM 87102
       (505) 242-7232 Martin Candelaria CEO
       Fax: (505) 247-9327
       Email: greetingsetc2@qwestoffice.net
       Website: www.greetingsetcprintandmail.com
Printing, direct mail, graphic design, fullfillment, bindery.
(Woman/Hisp, estab 1999, empl 7, sales $794,950, cert:
State)

Nevada

1206   AirGo USA LLC
       10161 Park Run Ste 150 Las Vegas, NV 89145
       (702) 835-6851 Norvel McDonald VP Mktg &
       Sales
       Fax: (702) 431-9042
       Email: norvelm@airgousa.com
       Website: www.airgousa.com
Facilities maintenance and management, HVAC, electrical, mechanical, grounds maintenance, custodial,
security, equipment installation and maintenance, fire &
smoke alarm installation & maintenance, security alarm
installation (AA, estab 2002, empl 100, sales $7,000,000,
cert: State)

1207   El Mundo, Ltd.
760 N Eastern Ave, Ste 110   Las Vegas, NV 89101
(702) 649-8553   Hilda Escobedo CEO
Fax: (702) 649-7429
Email: hescobedo@elmundo.net
Website: www.elmundo.net
Advertising, display advertising, graphic design, Spanish publication, Spanish readers, advertising in Spanish, display ads in Spanish, Spanish, newspaper, (Woman/Hisp, estab 1980, empl 9, sales $1,347,788, cert: State)

New York

1208   Adventium Marketing & Design
320 E 35th St, Ste 5B   New York, NY 10016
(212) 481-9576   Penny Chuang President
Fax:
Email: penny@adventium.net
Website: www.adventium.net
Marketing collateral, graphic design, brochures, advertising, direct mail, corporate communications, newsletters, catalogs, videos, invitations, logo design, media kits, posters, signage, trade show exhibits, web design & architecture, web banners. (Woman/As-Pac, estab 1992, empl 3, sales $370,000, cert: State, City)

1209   Baseline Design
220 E. 23rd St, Ste 405   New York, NY 10010
(212) 925-1656   Darcy Flanders Principal
Fax: (212) 925-1105
Email: darcy@baselinedesign.com
Website: www.baselinedesign.com
Design solutions, printing, logo design & corporate identity programs, fund rollouts, conference support materials, brochures, catalogs, newsletters, direct mail pieces, advertising
& annual reports. (Woman/White, estab 1997, empl 8, sales , cert: State, WBENC)

1210   Brand Cool Marketing, Inc.
2300 East Ave   Rochester, NY 14610
(585) 381-3350   Sue Kochan CEO
Fax: (585) 381-3425
Email: doorsopen@brandcoolmarketing.com
Website: www.brandcool.com
Advertising services. (Woman/White, estab 1997, empl 20, sales $4,360,000, cert: WBENC)

1211   Create Group NYC LLC
180 Varick St Ste 212   New York, NY 10014
(646) 682-7791   Natalie McDonald President
Fax:
Email: natalie@createnyc.com
Website: www.createnyc.com
Pharmaceutical advertising services. (Woman/White, estab 2009, empl 21, sales $14,908,530, cert: WBENC)

1212   Crown Sign Systems
7 Odell Plaza   Yonkers, NY 10701
(914) 375-2118   Michelle Strum President
Fax: (914) 375-1891
Email: mstrum@crownsigns.com
Website: www.crownsigns.com
Mfr interior & exterior architectural signage. (Woman, estab 1994, empl 14, sales $22,000,000, cert: State)

1213   Darby/Darby Creative
2376 Adam Clayton Powell Jr Blvd   New York, NY 10030
(646) 489-1256   Keith Darby President
Fax: (212) 283-3850
Email: keithdarby01@netscape.net
Website:
Advertising, marketing, advertising design services. (Woman/AA, estab 2003, empl 2, sales , cert: State)

1214   DePirro/GarroneLLC
25 W 13th St Ste 6NN   New York, NY 10011
(212) 206-6967   Lisa Garrone CEO
Fax: (212) 206-6987
Email: lgarrone@depirrogarrone.com
Website: www.depirrogarrone.com
Creative advertising, size or media channel, traditional or digital, online or offline. Flexible & scalable. (Woman/White, estab 2008, empl 8, sales $1,000,000, cert: City, WBENC)

1215   Eriksen Translations Inc.
50 Court St, Ste 700   Brooklyn, NY 11201
(718) 802-9010   Vigdis Eriksen President
Fax: (718) 802-0041
Email: vigdis.eriksen@eriksen.com
Website: www.eriksen.com
Multilingual services, translation, interpreting, typesetting, project management, web localization & cultural consulting in over 75 languages. (Woman/White, estab 1986, empl 20, sales $4,017,469, cert: State, City, WBENC)

1216   Fusia Communications, Inc.
45 Main St, Ste 212   Brooklyn, NY 11201
(718) 643-0311   Elizabeth Kay President
Fax: (866) 897-4574
Email: ekay@fusia.net
Website: www.fusia.net
Marketing, strategic consulting, media planning & buying, media tracking, design/production, copywriting, translations. (Woman/As-Pac, estab 2002, empl 4, sales $514,627, cert: City)

1217   Harquin Graphics, Inc.
170 Hamilton Ave Ste 100   White Plains, NY 10601
(914) 738-9620   Sherry Bruck President
Fax:
Email: sbruck@harquin.com
Website: www.harquin.com
Graphic design, printing & web design. (Woman/White, estab 1992, empl 9, sales , cert: State, City)

1218   Keeper of the Brand
894 Otsego Rd   West Hempstead, NY 11552
(917) 697-1699   Donyshia Boston-Hill CEO
Fax: (347) 454-9432
Email: db@keeperofthebrand.com
Website: www.keeperofthebrand.com/
Marketing Plans & Strategies, Media Buying, TV, Radio, Print & Digital Solutions, Broadcast Media Distribution, Brand Development, Consumer Insight, Copyright, Transactional Engagement, Programming & Campaign Mgmt, Graphic Design, Creative Services. (Woman/AA, estab 2013, empl 6, sales $125,000, cert: State, NMSDC, WBENC)

1219 MAD Studio LLC
1123 Broadway, Ste 707   New York, NY 10010
(212) 982-4613 Sara Matiz Principal
Fax:
Email: smatiz@mad-nyc.com
Website:
Brand marketing & design: positioning, logo development, stationery, brochures, email campaigns, websites, exhibits, packaging, promotional items, advertising. (Woman/White, estab 2011, empl 3, sales , cert: City, WBENC)

1220 Mix On Digital, LLC
1867 Amsterdam Ave Ste 3F New York, NY 10034
(917) 383-8121 Christina Mixon Managing Dir
Fax:
Email: christina@mixondigital.com
Website: www.mixondigital.com
Digital media design & consulting, social, mobile & digital platforms. (Woman/AA/As-Pac, estab 2012, empl 2, sales $385,000, cert: City)

1221 Retail Solution Center
75 Hanse Ave   Freeport, NY 11520
(516) 771-7000 Deborah Leo CEO
Fax: (516) 771-7001
Email: debleo@rsc-ny.com
Website: www.rsc-ny.com
Point of purchase displays, merchandising systems, mfr & design. (Woman/White, estab 2003, empl 49, sales $15,428,108, cert: WBENC)

1222 Signs & Decal Corp.
410 Morgan Ave   Brooklyn, NY 11211
(718) 486-6400 Hasnain Khalfan VP of Sales and Mktg
Fax: (718) 388-3166
Email: salesadmin@signsanddecal.com
Website: www.signsanddecal.com
Mfr & install signage, signs. (As-Ind/As-Pac, estab 1972, empl 30, sales $7,204,781, cert: City)

1223 SpikeDDB, LLC
437 Madison Ave 20 FL New York, NY 11201
(718) 596-5400 Sterling Green
Fax: (718) 596-7256
Email: Joel@spikeddb.com
Website: www.spikeddb.com
Advertising agency. (AA, estab 1997, empl 30, sales $6,000,000, cert: NMSDC)

1224 Squeaky Wheel Media Inc.
640 W 28th St 6th Fl New York, NY 10001
(212) 994-5270 Luis Garay Mktg Strategist
Fax: (212) 994-5271
Email: lou@squeaky.com
Website: www.squeaky.com
Design interface, web design, flash animation, e-commerce, database. (AA/Hisp, estab 2001, empl 30, sales , cert: State, NMSDC)

1225 The Language Shop
114-26 146th St   Jamaica, NY 11436
(646) 245-4129 Deborah Lockhart Dir of Ops
Fax: (718) 641-7667
Email: deborah.lockhart@thelanguageshop.org
Website: www.thelanguageshop.org
Translation & interpreting legal, medical, financial, corporate, commercial, marketing, online games, website translation & localization. (Woman/Nat Ame, estab 2007, empl 1, sales $122,000, cert: City)

1226 TITANIUM Worldwide LLC
350 7th Ave Ste 1403 New York, NY 10001
(646) 952-8440 Erin Geoghegan Director of Client Relations
Fax: (212) 695-6664
Email: sd@titaniumww.com
Website: www.titaniumww.com
Media, marketing, communications & consulting: Branding/Creative/Strategy, Content/Messaging, Digital/Social/Mobile, Film/Video Production, Event Marketing, Business Intelligence, Data Warehousing, Development/Deployment. (Woman/White, estab 2014, empl 4, sales , cert: WBENC)

1227 Visual Citi Inc.
110-30 Dunkirk St   St. Albans, NY 11412
(718) 479-5500 Mirza Kermani Acct Exec
Fax: (718) 479-5688
Email: mirza@visualciti.com
Website: www.visualciti.com
Digitally Printed Signs & Graphics, Banners, POP Displays, Window Signs & Graphics, Cutout logos & letters, Silk Screen printing, ADA Signs, Etched Signs & Custom Fabrication. (As-Ind, estab 2004, empl 25, sales $200,000, cert: City, NMSDC)

1228 Womenkind LLC
1441 Broadway, Ste 3101   New York, NY 10018
(212) 660-0400 Sandy Sabean President
Fax: (212) 221-7047
Email: sandy@womenkind.net
Website: www.womenkind.net
Advertising & marketing communications. (Woman/White, estab 2007, empl 2, sales $1,800,000, cert: WBENC)

Ohio

1229 Baker Creative Ltd.
386 Main St   Groveport, OH 43125
(614) 836-3845 Michele Cuthbert Principal
Fax: (614) 836-1801
Email: mbaker@baker-creative.com
Website: www.baker-creative.com
Graphic Design, Marketing Consulting, Advertising, Public Relations, Display Advertising. (Woman/Hisp, estab 2003, empl 10, sales $150,000, cert: State, WBENC, SDB)

1230 Bernard R. Doyle, Inc.
2102 St. Claire Ave NE   Cleveland, OH 44114
(216) 523-2288 Kay Doyle President
Fax:
Email: 333@fastsigns.com
Website:
Create effective, high impact sign designs. (Woman, estab 1999, empl 10, sales $1,100,000, cert: City, WBENC)

1231 Brigadier Construction Services LLC
3100 E 45th St Ste 526 Cleveland, OH 44127
(216) 857-4777 Jason Schenk
Fax: (216) 426-8922
Email: jschenk@brigadierconst.com
Website: www.brigadierconstruction.com
Since 2004, Brigadier has completed numerous hospital projects varying in size, scope, and complexity, and various institutional and commercial projects, for the Department of Veteran Affairs and USACE. (Woman/AA, estab 2004, empl 17, sales $13,362,998, cert: State)

1232 Bright Future Partners, Inc. dba RED212
5509 Fair Lane   Cincinnati, OH 45227
(513) 772-1020 Donna Zaring Director Business Dev
Fax: (513) 772-6849
Email: donnazaring@red212.com
Website: www.red212.com
Marketing communications, production & post production services. (Woman/White, estab 2001, empl 18, sales $3,971,726, cert: WBENC)

1233 Commercial Cutting & Graphics, LLC
208 Central Ave 208 Central Ave Mansfield, OH 44905
(714) 493-4714 Irene Hoffman Natl Sales Exec
Fax: (419) 526-5328
Email: ihoffman@commercialcutting.com
Website: www.commercialcutting.com
Design & mfr temporary point of purchase displays. (Woman/White, estab 1986, empl 42, sales $6,800,001, cert: WBENC)

1234 Dayton Mailing Services, Inc.
888 Dayton St Yellow Springs, OH 45387
(937) 222-5056 Barbara Deer Sales Exec
Fax: (937) 222-2696
Email: barbara.deer@dmsink.us
Website: www.daytonmailing.com
Digital printing, variable printing, direct mail, inserting, inkjetting, product fulfillment, collation, labeling, tipping, folding/glue. (Woman/As-Pac, estab 1900, empl 1, sales $8,625,000, cert: State, WBENC)

1235 INNERSOURCE Inc.
755 Wick Ave   Youngstown, OH 44505
(330) 799-7619 Gloria Byce Principal
Fax: (330) 799-5222
Email: gbyce@innersourceinc.com
Website: www.innersourceinc.com
Interior Signage, Exterior Signage, ADA Signage, Room Identification Signage, Way Finding, Directories, Temporary Signage, Modular Systems, Custom Signage, Donor Plaques, Dimensional Letters, Corporate Identity, Digital Printing, Banners. (Woman/White, estab 1996, empl 7, sales , cert: WBENC)

1236 MRA Advertising/Production Support Services, Inc.
3979 Erie Ave Cincinnati, OH 45208
(513) 561-5610 Stacey St. John Director, Business Dev
Fax: (513) 561-9185
Email: diversity@mraservices.com
Website: www.mraservices.com
Advertising production management & cost control. (Woman/As-Pac, estab 1980, empl 25, sales $8,400,000, cert: WBENC)

1237 Skyline Exhibits of Central Ohio, LLC
2801 Charter St Columbus, OH 43228
(614) 684-2050 Mark Armbrust President
Fax: (614) 684-2055
Email: mark@skylineohio.com
Website: www.skylineohio.com
Exhibits, displays, kiosks, graphics, accessories & services for trade shows & events, pop ups, banner stands, portable displays, custom modular exhibits, hanging signs & structures. (Woman/White, estab 2001, empl 12, sales $3,108,655, cert: WBENC)

1238 Swath Design, LLC
30 Garfield Place Ste 1020 Cincinnati, OH 45202
(513) 421-1773 Sandra Lange CEO
Fax: (513) 421-1774
Email: sandie@swathdesign.com
Website: www.swathdesign.com
Environmental graphic design, wayfinding, signage, interior design, architectural design, branding, marketing & print communications & interactive media. (Woman/White, estab 1991, empl 6, sales $475,000, cert: State, WBENC, SDB)

1239 Vocalink, Inc.
405 W First St Dayton, OH 45402
(877) 492-7754 Jill A. Mead Compliance Counsel
Fax: (866) 264-1163
Email: rfp@vocalinkglobal.com
Website: www.vocalinkglobal.com/
Translation & web localization services: documentation & online content, multimedia
Linguistic asset mgmt, terminology mgmt, web content & e-commerce sites, server side scripting. (Woman/Hisp, estab 1995, empl 450, sales $4,985,940, cert: State, NMSDC, WBENC)

1240 Xela Group, LLC dba Grupo Xela
1775 Mentor Ave, Ste 404   Cincinnati, OH 45212
(513) 351-2200 Jose D. Cuesta Managing Partner
Fax: (815) 301-9209
Email: info@grupoxela.com
Website: www.grupoxela.com
Hispanic marketing research: questionnaire dev, focus groups, bilingual moderators, surveys, data collection & tabulation, interpreting, corporate identity, collateral design, media buying, web dev, translation svcs. (Hisp, estab 2002, empl 10, sales , cert: State)

Oregon

1241   Hanlon Brown Design
2130 NW 29th Ave   Portland, OR 97210
(503) 944-1005 Gail Snow Sr Acct Exec
Fax: (503) 944-1030
Email: gail@hbdesign.com
Website: www.hbdesign.com
Design services: print, web, interactive & catalog, graphic design, programming, software engineering, quality assurance & project management. (Woman/White, estab 1978, empl 25, sales $5,500,000, cert: State)

Pennsylvania

1242   Anderson Advertising dba The Anderson Group
879 Fritztown Rd   Sinking Spring, PA 19608
(610) 678-1506 Julie LaSalle
Fax: (610) 678-5891
Email: jlasalle@theandersongrp.com
Website: www.theandersongrp.com
Brand development & continuity programs: strategic planning, corporate identity, advertising & creative services, interactive services, media placement & public relations. (Woman/White, estab 1987, empl 18, sales $2,961,323, cert: State, WBENC)

1243   Domus Inc.
123 Avenue of the Arts Ste 1980 Philadelphia, PA 19109
(215) 772-2179 Lynda Steinbeck Finance & Ops Dir
Fax: (215) 772-2191
Email: lsteinbeck@domusinc.com
Website: www.domusinc.com
Traditional advertising, public relations, soical media, online advertising, internal/corporate communications. (Woman/White, estab 1993, empl 18, sales $6,659,848, cert: WBENC)

1244   Harmelin Media
525 Righters Ferry Rd   Bala Cynwyd, PA 19004
(610) 668-7900 Mary Meder President
Fax: (267) 948-2276
Email: mmeder@harmelin.com
Website: www.harmelin.com
Media planning & buying company. (Woman/White, estab 1982, empl 204, sales $25,000,000, cert: WBENC)

1245   Ideamart Inc.
232 Conestoga Rd   Wayne, PA 19087
(610) 971-2000 Tom King Owner
Fax: (610) 971-1620
Email: tom@23k.com
Website: www.23k.com
Advertising, direct marketing, interactive, social media, branding/identity, packaging & retail POS. (As-Pac, estab 1991, empl 15, sales $2,185,947, cert: NMSDC)

1246   Language Services Associates
455 Business Center Dr Ste 100 Horsham, PA 19044
(215) 259-7000 Jerry Lotierzo Natl sales Mgr
Fax: (215) 259-7302
Email: lsavendor@lsaweb.com
Website: www.lsaweb.com
Foreign language translation & interpretation: 175 languages, sign language. (Woman/Hisp, estab 1991, empl 157, sales , cert: NMSDC, WBENC)

1247   Media Advantage, Inc.
78 Second St Pike   Southampton, PA 18966
(800) 985-5596 Adraiane Thomson President
Fax: (888) 501-3329
Email: athomson@mediaadvantage.com
Website: www.mediaadvantage.com
Sign and graphic design. (Woman/White, estab 2009, empl 8, sales $675,000, cert: State)

1248   Mendoza Group Inc.
9 W Front St   Media, PA 19063
(610) 627-1000 Mia Mendoza CEO
Fax: (610) 627-0480
Email: mmendoza@mendozagroup.com
Website: www.mendozagroup.com
Translation, marketing & advertising agency. (Woman/ Hisp, estab 1995, empl 7, sales $1,984,611, cert: State, NMSDC, WBENC)

1249   MTM LINGUASOFT
705 S. 50th St 2nd Fl Philadelphia, PA 19143
(215) 729-6765 Myriam Siftar President
Fax: (267) 636-4167
Email: siftar@mtmlinguasoft.com
Website: www.mtmlinguasoft.com
Translation & localization services: websites, software & online applications, e-learning modules, document translation & multilingual desktop publishing services. (Woman/White, estab 2003, empl 5, sales $496,685, cert: WBENC)

1250   Munroe Creative Partners
121 S. Broad St. Ste 1900 Philadelphia, PA 19107
(215) 563-8080 Brianna Schmidt
Fax: (215) 563-1270
Email: bschmidt@munroe.com
Website: www.munroe.com
Corporate identity launches, brochures, print and online advertising, direct mail campaigns, and web site creation. (Woman/White, estab 1989, empl 20, sales $2,019,757, cert: State, WBENC)

1251   NetPlus Marketing, Inc.
625 Ridge Pike, Blg E, Ste 300   Conshohocken, PA 19428
(610) 897-2380 Robin Neifield CEO
Fax: (610) 897-2381
Email: rn@netplusmarketing.com
Website: www.netplusmarketing.com
Online advertising: branding & direct response objectives, sponsorships, email marketing & search engine marketing. (Woman/White, estab 1996, empl 18, sales , cert: WBENC)

1252 SSKJ Enterprises Inc. dba Vital Signs
      2812 Idlewood Rd   Carnegie, PA 15106
      (412) 494-3308 Sandy Burkett President
      Fax: (412) 494-3325
      Email: sandy@vitalsignspgh.com
      Website: www.vitalsignspgh.com
Mfr interior & exterior signage, large digital format
printing, promotional items, ADA signage, architectural,
banners, bar code labels, business graphics, buttons,
channel letters, commercial awnings, corporate identification, custom displays. (Woman/Nat Ame, estab 2005, empl
4, sales $342,350, cert: NMSDC)

Puerto Rico

1253 Arteaga & Arteaga Advertising
      P.O. Box 70336   San Juan, PR
      (787) 620-1600 Juan Arteaga VP - Strategy & New
      Business
      Fax: (787) 759-6939
      Email: jat@arteaga.com
      Website: www.arteaga.com
Advertising, marketing, public relations, media, creative,
interactive, packaging design, event planning, strategic
planning, youth marketing. (Hisp, estab 1984, empl 40,
sales $21,000,000, cert: NMSDC)

South Carolina

1254 Harland Enterprises Inc.
      7364 Two Notch Rd   Columbia, SC 29229
      (803) 462-0433 Lekita Hargrave Owner
      Fax:
      Email: lhargrave@signsbytomorrow.com
      Website: www.signsbytomorrow.com/columbiane/
ADA & and digital graphics, Advertising specialties, Digital
Signage. (AA, estab 2012, empl 5, sales $504,000, cert:
State)

Tennessee

1255 FlagCenter.com, LLC
      4550 Summer Ave   Memphis, TN 38122
      (901) 762-0044 Maureen Criscuolo Owner
      Fax: (901) 762-8565
      Email: maureen@flagcenter.com
      Website: www.flagcenter.com
Mfr custom nylon & vinyl signs, street banners, banners,
flags, table covers & banners. (Woman/White, estab 2006,
empl 6, sales $550,000, cert: State)

1256 Signet, Inc.
      1801 N Shelby Oaks Dr, Ste 12   Memphis, TN 38134
      (901) 387-5555 Elizabeth Tate CEO
      Fax: (901) 387-5544
      Email: etate@gosignet.com
      Website: www.gosignet.com
Advertising agency. (Woman/White, estab , empl 1, sales
$11,000,000, cert: WBENC)

1257 Three Point Graphics, Inc.
      750 Eaton St   Memphis, TN 38120
      (901) 537-0537 Sabrina Whisenant Owner
      Fax: (901) 537-0536
      Email: sabrina@threepointgraphics.com
      Website: www.3ptgraphics.com
Mission critical & complex graphic & signage products.
(Woman/White, estab 2004, empl 1, sales $100,000,000,
cert: State, City)

Texas

1258 Asher Media, Inc.
      15303 Dallas Pkwy Ste 1300 Addison, TX 75001
      (972) 732-6464 Kalyn Asher President
      Fax:
      Email: kalyn@ashermedia.com
      Website: www.ashermedia.com
Strategic planning & buying solutions. (Woman/White,
estab 1999, empl 27, sales , cert: State, WBENC)

1259 B2B Enterprises Inc. dba Prism Sign Group
      3645 Dallas Pkwy, Ste 535   Plano, TX 75093
      (972) 403-7770 Bill Brooks CEO
      Fax: (972) 403-7010
      Email: bbrooks@prismsigngroup.com
      Website: www.prismsigngroup.com
Mfr signs: banners, vehicle wraps, advertising specialties, business cards, awards/recognition. (AA, estab
2007, empl 4, sales $40,100, cert: State, NMSDC)

1260 Blue Sun LLC
      4650 Lockheed Lane, Unit 104   Denton, TX 76207
      (800) 238-6064 Gulnara Balic Owner
      Fax: (877) 206-3608
      Email: gulnara@dallasdigitalsigns.com
      Website: www.dallasdigitalsigns.com
Mfr, install & repair Interior & exterior electrical signs,
graphic design. (Woman/As-Pac, estab 2012, empl 6,
sales $360,000, cert: State)

1261 Brown Graphics Inc.
      11404 Chairman Dr   Dallas, TX 75243
      (214) 553-9988 Melanie Brown President
      Fax: (214) 553-9989
      Email: melanie@browngraphics.com
      Website: www.browngraphics.com
Designs & mfr architectural signs: monuments,
wayfinding, suite signs, cubicle, reception area, garage,
directories, crown & building signage. (Woman/White,
estab 1989, empl 8, sales $765,816, cert: State)

1262 Cartel Creativo, Inc.
      5835 Callaghan Rd Ste 600 San Antonio, TX 78228
      (210) 602-8880 Sean Salas CEO
      Fax: (210) 696-4299
      Email: ssalas@thecartel.com
      Website: www.thecartel.com
Advertising agency: research & planning, creative
development, production & in-house audio. (Hisp, estab
1994, empl 10, sales $4,400,000, cert: NMSDC)

1263   Castle Business Solutions, LLC
       2777 North Stemmons Frwy Ste 1242 Dallas, TX
       75207
       (214) 599-2880 Sharon King CEO
       Fax:
       Email: sharon@castlebusinesssolutions.net
       Website: www.castlebusinesssolutions.com/
Directory & mailing list publishing, direct mail advertising,
packaging & labeling services, warehousing & storage,
custom computer programming services, data processing,
hosting & related services. (Woman/AA, estab 2010, empl
3, sales $615,880, cert: State, NMSDC, NWBOC)

1264   Desert Star Enterprises, Inc
       8409 Sterling St Ste B Irving, TX 75063
       (972) 915-6970 Myra Brown President
       Fax: (972) 915-2867
       Email: myra@highvaluesigns.com
       Website: www.highvaluesigns.com
Create & install signs: wayfinding signs, banners, car wraps
& monument signs. (Woman/White, estab 2014, empl 3,
sales $300,000, cert: State, WBENC)

1265   Digital Thrive, LLC
       1910 Anita Dr   Austin, TX 78704
       (512) 900-7699 Jennifer Mansfield Co-Founder,
       CMO
       Fax: (512) 900-7698
       Email: jen@digthrive.com
       Website: www.digthrive.com
Graphic design & media: website design, mobile application design & development, animation & video production, print collateral & promotional materials. (Woman/
White, estab 2010, empl 10, sales , cert: State, WBENC)

1266   DMN3
       2190 North Loop W, Ste 200   Houston, TX 77018
       (713) 868-3000 Pamela Lockard President
       Fax: (713) 868-1388
       Email: accounting@dmn3.com
       Website: www.dmn3.com
Direct mail & print advertising, e-marketing, multicultural
marketing, event promotions, internal communication,
radio & TV placement, data processing & mgt, interactive
& promotional mktg, outdoor media, sponsorships, print
colateral. (Woman/White, estab 1985, empl 9, sales
$4,267,600, cert: State, City, WBENC)

1267   Enigma, LLC
       100 Crescent Ct. Ste 700 Dallas, TX 75201
       (214) 459-8208 Sherilyn K Smith-Rudolph President
       Fax: (214) 988-5128
       Email: sherilyn@enigmallc.com
       Website: www.enigmallc.com
Advertising & marketing agency. (Woman/AA, estab 2003,
empl 4, sales , cert: NMSDC, 8(a))

1268   Excalibur Exhibits
       7120 Brittmoore Rd, Ste 430   Houston, TX 77041
       (713) 856-8853 Peggy Swords President
       Fax: (713) 856-8854
       Email: pswords@excaliburexhibits.com
       Website: www.excaliburexhibits.com
Design & build custom, portable, modular & system
solutions. (Woman/White, estab 1997, empl 26, sales
$5,628,500, cert: WBENC)

1269   Gilbreath Communications, Inc.
       15995 N Barkers Landing, Ste 100 Ste 100
       Houston, TX 77079
       (281) 649-9595 Debra Johnson VP
       Fax: (281) 752-6899
       Email: debra@gilbcomm.com
       Website: www.gilbcomm.com
Advertising: ad campaigns, promotional materials,
media relations, public relations, press relations,
community relations, employee communications, press
conferences, press releases, press kits, speeches &
scripts, graphic design, etc. (Woman/AA, estab 1990,
empl 11, sales , cert: State, City)

1270   Latin Works Marketing LLC
       2500 Bee Cave Rd Bldg 2 Austin, TX 78746
       (512) 479-4580 Alejandro Ruelas CMO
       Fax:
       Email: a.ruelas@latinworks.com
       Website: www.latinworks.com
Cultural Branding, Account Management, Strategic
Planning & Research, Integrated Creative Development
& Production, Digital & Social Media, Media Buying &
Planning, Grassroots & Event Activations. (Hisp, estab
1998, empl 85, sales , cert: NMSDC)

1271   Latinworks
       410 Baylor St Austin, TX 78703
       (512) 479-6200 Marly Ramstad CEO
       Fax:
       Email: m.ramstad@latinworks.com
       Website: www.latinworks.com
Advertising agency. (Hisp, estab 1998, empl 174, sales ,
cert: State, NMSDC)

1272   Limb Design LLC
       1702 Houston Ave   Houston, TX 77007
       (713) 529-1117 Biddie Webb Partner
       Fax:
       Email: biddie@limbdesign.com
       Website: www.limbdesign.com
Marketing, graphic design & web site design.
 (Woman/White, estab 1983, empl 13, sales $1,200,000,
cert: WBENC)

1273   Lopez Marketing Group, Inc.
       11169 La Quinta Pl   El Paso, TX 79936
       (915) 772-8018 Jose Luis Lopez President
       Fax: (915) 772-9333
       Email: jllopez1@lopezgroup.com
       Website: www.lopezgroup.com
Advertising, Hispanic marketing, public relations. (Hisp,
estab 1989, empl 16, sales $4,500,000, cert: State,
NMSDC)

1274 MasterWord Services, Inc.
      303 Stafford St Houston, TX 77079
      (281) 589-0810 Ludmila Golovine President
      Fax: (281) 589-1104
      Email: hr@masterword.com
      Website: www.masterword.com
Translation, interpretation, language training & assessments, cultural intelligence training & language compliance consulting. (Woman/White, estab 1993, empl 96, sales $14,620,522, cert: WBENC)

1275 Mentler & Company
      4819 Broadway St Addison, TX 75001
      (972) 233-1414 Lisa CeBallos Controller
      Fax: (972) 239-7361
      Email: accounting@mentler.net
      Website: www.mentlerandcompany.com
Advertising & marketing, branding, design. (Woman/White, estab 1982, empl 21, sales $1,722,013, cert: State, WBENC)

1276 One Pytchblack, LLC DBA PytchBlack
      1612 Summit Ave Ste 415 Fort Worth, TX 76102
      (817) 570-0915 Andre Yanez Owner / Managing Partner
      Fax:
      Email: aryanez@pytchblack.com
      Website: www.pytchblack.com
Advertising agency, website design, trademark and identity design, product design, media buying & graphic design. (Hisp, estab 2013, empl 2, sales $115,000, cert: State, NMSDC)

1277 Preferred Translations, Inc.
      P.O. Box 42065 Houston, TX 77242
      (281) 882-3080 Gina Guerrero Managing Dir
      Fax:
      Email: Projects@preferredTranslationsInc.com
      Website: www.preferredTranslationsInc.com
Language Translation, Interpretation, Multilingual Desktop Publishing, Transcription, Voiceover, and subtitling. (Woman/Hisp, estab 2012, empl 1, sales $20,000, cert: State)

1278 Reach Media Inc.
      13760 Noel Rd Ste 750 Dallas, TX 75240
      (972) 789-1058 Reggie Denson VP sales
      Fax:
      Email: reggie.denson@reachmediainc.com
      Website: www.reachmediainc.com
African-American advertising for the Tom Joyner Morning Show. (AA, estab 2001, empl 92, sales $53,000,000, cert: State, NMSDC)

1279 St. Julien Communications Group, LLC
      P.O. Box 3724 Houston, TX 77253
      (713) 965-7084 Jaa St. Julien CEO
      Fax:
      Email: jaa@stjuliencg.com
      Website: www.stjuliencg.com
Advertising, public relations, marketing, media placement, strategy development, graphic & web design, web development, mobile app development, photography, videography consulting, community outreach. (AA/Nat Ame/Hisp, estab 2007, empl 1, sales $196,000, cert: State, NMSDC)

1280 SuperLatina Inc.
      4200 South Frwy Ste 2370 Fort Worth, TX 76115
      (214) 431-5783 Andres Suarez CEO
      Fax: (214) 960-4232
      Email: andres@aganarmedia.com
      Website: www.aganarmedia.com
Multicultural marketing services, video & interactive campaigns for television & digital (Woman/Hisp, estab 2007, empl 8, sales $787,000, cert: State)

1281 Techstyle Group LLC
      P.O. Box 692347 Houston, TX 77269
      (281) 251-2436 Laurel Prokop CEO
      Fax: (281) 251-2437
      Email: lp.info@techstyle.com
      Website: www.techstylegroup.com
Document, presentation & written-content production. (Woman/White, estab 1986, empl 5, sales , cert: City)

1282 Universe Technical Translation, Inc.
      9225 Katy Frwy Ste 400 Houston, TX 77024
      (713) 827-8800 Andreas Nordquist BD Mgr
      Fax: (713) 464-5511
      Email: marion@universe.us
      Website: www.universetranslation.com
Technical & legal written translation. (Woman/White, estab 1981, empl 40, sales $9,618,844, cert: State, WBENC)

1283 Web-Hed Technologies, Inc. dba Webhead
      1710 N Main Ave San Antonio, TX 78212
      (210) 354-1661 Angela Gonzales Director, Business Ops
      Fax: (877) 702-1007
      Email: Contracts@webheadtech.com
      Website: www.webheadtech.com
Hispanic interactive marketing svcs: media & animated graphics, online & interactive games & sweepstakes. (Woman/Hisp, estab 1995, empl 15, sales , cert: State)

1284 What's the Big Idea?
      5603 Kingston Court Richardson, TX 75082
      (972) 509-0081 Tracy Cink President
      Fax: (972) 509-9788
      Email: Tracy_cink@wtbi.com
      Website: www.wtbi.com
Advertising & graphic design. (Woman, estab , empl 1, sales , cert: WBENC)

Utah

1285 Infinite Scale Design Group
      16 Exchange Place Salt Lake City, UT 84111
      (801) 363-1881 Molly Mazzolini Managing Member
      Fax:
      Email: molly@infinitescale.com
      Website: www.infinitescale.com
Brand strategy, logo design, creative briefs, identity systems, collateral, website design, environmental graphics, master plan, interpretive design, wayfinding signage, recognition & donor, signage, uniform systems, vehicle graphics. (Woman/White, estab 2010, empl 1, sales , cert: State)

1286   U.S. Translation Company
        320 W 200 S   Salt Lake City, UT 84101
        (801) 393-5300 Kathy Sprouse Director of Ops
        Fax: (801) 393-5500
        Email: kathy@ustranslation.com
        Website: www.ustranslation.com
Language services, document formatting, interpreting
services. (Hisp, estab 1995, empl 15, sales $2,987,864,
cert: NMSDC)

Virginia

1287   AB Design, Inc.
        10005 Stonemill Rd   Richmond, VA 23233
        (804) 346-4771 Gladys Brenner President
        Fax: (804) 346-3048
        Email: gbrenner@abdesignonline.com
        Website: www.abdesignonline.com
Environmental graphic design: interior & exterior signage,
dev wayfinding systems & architectural graphics, site
analysis/evaluation, master planning & comprehensive
wayfinding systems. (Woman/Hisp, estab 1991, empl 3,
sales $182,000, cert: State)

1288   Advanta Pacific International
        9336 Braymore Circle   Fairfax Station, VA 22039
        (703) 226-9605 Adam Tran Managing Dir
        Fax: (703) 552-2949
        Email: contact@vernacularlanguage.com
        Website: www.vernacularlanguage.com
Translation & interpretation services in over 200 languages
and dialects, including sign language. (Woman/As-Pac,
estab 2009, empl 4, sales $150,000, cert: State)

1289   Capital Exhibits
        8245-B Backlick Rd   Lorton, VA 22079
        (540) 219-9372 Jennifer Warren Sales
        Fax: (703) 370-9579
        Email: Jennifer@capitalexhibits.com
        Website: www.capitalexhibits.com
Indoor & outdoor signage, tradeshow displays, banners &
banner stands, channel lettering, wayfinding & directional
signage, temporary signage, hard or thick signage, custom
flirting titles, fabric & vinyl signs. (As-Ind, estab 1994, empl
6, sales , cert: State)

1290   Eighth Day Design
        7653 Leesburg Pike   Falls Church, VA 22043
        (703) 562-3636 Carol Muszynski President
        Fax: (703) 562-3637
        Email: carol@eighthday.com
        Website: www.eighthday.com
Productivity & image solutions, architecture & design,
programming, space planning, design dev, sustainable
design, exhibit design, construction documents, construction administration, move coordination & facilities maintenance support. (Woman/White, estab 1989, empl 21, sales
$3,800,000, cert: WBENC)

1291   Hybrid Studios LLC
        1940 Duke St Ste 200 Alexandria, VA 22314
        (703) 671-6975 Susan Yates Mgr
        Fax:
        Email: susan@hybrid-studios.com
        Website: www.hybriddc.com
Communications solutions: print, interactive development, advertising, corporate identity, direct marketing
& social media marketing services. (Woman/White,
estab 2002, empl 2, sales $532,000, cert: State)

1292   Mail Call Direct LLC
        5616 Eastport Blvd   Henrico, VA 23231
        (804) 222-0608 Lisa Jacoby Co-Owner
        Fax:
        Email: lisa@mailcalldirect.com
        Website: www.MailCallDirect.com
Direct mail services, digital lasering, inkjet & insert, data
processing, mailing lists, barcode printing, variable data,
stamping, metering, permits, hand fulfillment, parcel
fulfillment, folding bindery services, glue dotting, poly
bagging. (Woman/White, estab 2014, empl 8, sales ,
cert: State)

1293   Nvision Media Group, LLC
        114 W Hicks St   Lawrenceville, VA 23868
        (866) 848-8822 David Fant Owner
        Fax: (434) 848-3464
        Email: david.fant@nvisn.net
        Website: www.nvisn.net
Indoor advertising. (Woman/AA, estab 2006, empl 6,
sales $100,000, cert: State)

1294   Tandem By Design LLC
        306 N 26th St, Ste 227   Richmond, VA 23223
        (804) 239-2539 Bev Gray President
        Fax:
        Email: bev@tandembydesign.com
        Website: www.tandembydesign.com
Marketing & advertising solutions,one-to-one marketing, B2B sales collateral, B2C POP/POS, packaging
design, corporate communications, corporate & brand
videos, grassroots campaigns, social media. (Woman/
White, estab 2012, empl 1, sales , cert: State)

1295   West Cary Group
        5 W Cary St   Richmond, VA 23220
        (804) 343-2029 Moses Foster CEO
        Fax: (804) 343-2028
        Email: mfoster@westcarygroup.com
        Website: www.westcarygroup.com
Marketing communications & advertising. (AA, estab
2007, empl 20, sales $2,586,876, cert: State, NMSDC)

Washington

1296   Dynamic Language
       15215 52nd Ave S, Ste 100   Seattle, WA 98188
       (206) 244-6709 Rick Antezana Partner
       Fax: (206) 243-3795
       Email: rick@dynamiclanguage.com
       Website: www.dynamiclanguage.com
Foreign language translation, desktop publishing services, narration, language & ASL interpreting services. (Woman/Hisp, estab 1985, empl 47, sales $10,500,000, cert: State, NMSDC, WBENC)

1297   TDW+Co
       600 Stewart St, Ste 800   Seattle, WA 98101
       (206) 623-6888 Tim Wang Principal
       Fax: (206) 623-6889
       Email: biz@tdwandco.com
       Website: www.tdwandco.com
Marketing communications & advertising agency. (As-Pac, estab 2004, empl 25, sales $10,015,295, cert: State, NMSDC, CPUC)

1298   Thinking Cap Communications & Design
       9 S Washington Ste 201 Spokane, WA 99201
       (509) 747-4930 Marvin Reguindin President
       Fax: (509) 458-2349
       Email: marvo@tcapdesign.com
       Website: www.tcapdesign.com
Advertising & graphic design, creative & account services, websites, radio & TV/video spots. (As-Pac, estab 1995, empl 3, sales $124,753, cert: State, NMSDC)

1299   Translation Solutions Corp.
       1201 Pacific Avenue Corp Ste 600 Tacoma, WA 98402
       (808) 404-1270 Rosa Capdevielle Project Management
       Fax: (503) 248-9948
       Email: rosa@translationsolutions.org
       Website: www.translationsolutions.org
Translations & interpretation services. (Woman/Hisp, estab 1994, empl 5, sales , cert: State, NMSDC)

1300   Trio Northwest Business Solutions, Inc.
       239 SW 41st St   Renton, WA 98057
       (206) 728-8181 Jeffrey Quint EVP Sales & Mktg
       Fax: (206) 728-1334
       Email: info@triogroupnw.com
       Website: www.triogroupnw.com/
Brand management, advertising, marketing, strategy, campaign development, project management, marcom strategy, web development, mobile app development, media buying, social media strategy & deployment. (Nat Ame, estab 2000, empl 6, sales $1,300,000, cert: NMSDC)

1301   Triple Threat Editorial
       18574 NE 57th St   Redmond, WA 98052
       (425) 867-3224 Jody Allard Owner
       Fax:
       Email: allardjr@yahoo.com
       Website:
Writing & editing, marketing copy, web content, technical writing, proofreading, basic web design & operate internal web sites. (Woman/White, estab 2004, empl 1, sales , cert: State)

Wisconsin

1302   Everbrite, LLC
       4949 S 110th St   Greenfield, WI 53228
       (414) 529-3500 Nicki LaFrance Sales Admin
       Fax: (414) 529-3500
       Email: supplierdiversity@everbrite.com
       Website: www.everbrite.com
Outdoor illuminated identification signage. (Woman/White, estab 1927, empl 850, sales , cert: WBENC)

1303   Revelation, LLC
       222 N Midvale Blvd Ste 18   Madison, WI 53705
       (608) 622-7767 Brian Lee President
       Fax:
       Email: brian@experiencerevelation.com
       Website: www.experiencerevelation.com
Public relations, media buying, ad buying, advertising, social media consulting, internet marketing, web marketing & speaking engagements. (As-Pac, estab 2010, empl 3, sales $170,000, cert: NMSDC)

1304   The Geo Group Corporation
       6 Odana Court   Madison, WI 53719
       (608) 230-1000 Georgia Roeming President
       Fax: (608) 230-1010
       Email: georgia.roeming@thegeogroup.com
       Website: www.thegeogroup.com
Translation of radio, TV, website & print advertising. (Woman/White, estab 1991, empl 30, sales $6,003,156, cert: State, WBENC)

ADVERTISING SPECIALTIES
Supply advertising specialties, premium and promotional products, or travel incentives. Includes frims which do silkscreening and embroidery on various products. NAICS Code 42

Alabama

1305 Concepts & Associates
105 19th St S   Birmingham, AL 35210
(205) 870-1111 Tim Hennessy President
Fax: (205) 870-1131
Email: tim@conceptsusa.com
Website: www.conceptsusa.com
Corporate gifts & promotional products, embroidery & fulfillment center. (Woman/White, estab 1983, empl 15, sales , cert: State)

1306 LogoBranders Inc.
1161 Lagoon Business Loop   Montgomery, AL 36117
(334) 277-1144 Dean Flynn Branding Specialist
Fax: (334) 277-2999
Email: dean@logobranders.com
Website: www.logobranders.biz/
Promotional items, executive gifts, embroidery, screen print, hardline, health and safety, computer and electronic products, wearables, bags, writing instruments, drinkwear, desk/office business accessories, calenders, person products, etc. (Woman/White, estab 1993, empl 34, sales $6,000,000, cert: WBENC)

Arizona

1307 Sunset Trading Company, LLC
15619 N 50th St   Scottsdale, AZ 85254
(602) 494-6419 Linda Williams Owner
Fax: (602) 926-2278
Email: linda@sunsettradingco.com
Website: www.sunsettradingco.com
Customer & employee reward, recognition & incentive programs, premiums & promotional advertising products. (Woman/White, estab 1999, empl 1, sales $935,000, cert: WBENC)

1308 Triumphant Staffing LLC
3255 S Dorsey Ln Ste 1081 Tempe, AZ 85282
(480) 306-9653 John Galloway CEO
Fax: (612) 724-4365
Email: John.Galloway@triumphantstaffing.com
Website: www.triumphantstaffingllc.com
Provide Temp to Perm Services, Permanent Hire, Temp Hire. (AA, estab 2016, empl 5, sales $150,000, cert: State)

California

1309 Apropos Promotions
1401 N Broadway Ste 280 Walnut Creek, CA 94596
(925) 274-5700 Ann Auelmann President
Fax: (925) 274-5704
Email: ann@apropospromotions.com
Website: www.apropospromotions.com
Promotional merchandise: tradeshow giveaways, staff appreciation, gifts, special events, etc. (Woman/White, estab 2002, empl 4, sales , cert: WBENC)

1310 Avid Promotions
499 Nibus St Unit C Brea, CA 92821
(949) 387-9890 Dena Gibbs CEO
Fax: (866) 205-0891
Email: Dena@AvidPromotions.com
Website: www.AvidPromotions.com
Promotional products, marketing materials, and apparel/corporate uniforms. (Hisp, estab 2009, empl 4, sales $540,000, cert: NMSDC, CPUC)

1311 Beyond Zebra Inc.
1443 E Washington Blvd, Ste 641   Pasadena, CA 91104
(818) 435-8202 Stacy Burleson CFO
Fax: (818) 671-5555
Email: sales@beyondzebra.net
Website: www.beyondzebra.net
Promotional products: bags, desk accessories, apparel, hats, memo pads, housewares, sales incentive & corporate gift programs. (Woman/As-Pac, estab 2000, empl 4, sales $1,043,151, cert: WBENC)

1312 Caden Concepts
13412 Ventura Blvd Ste 300 Sherman Oaks, CA 91423
(323) 651-1190 Paul David VP of Sales
Fax: (323) 651-0343
Email: paul@cadenconcepts.com
Website: www.cadenconcepts.com
Dist advertising specialties: logoed corporate wearables, giveaways, incentives, employee awards & tradeshow projects, embroidery silk screen & pad printing. (Woman/White, estab 1998, empl 12, sales , cert: CPUC)

1313 Elementi Designs
1655 22nd Ave   San Francisco, CA 94122
(415) 887-3889 Ken Lou President
Fax: (415) 874-3001
Email: elementidesigns@gmail.com
Website: www.elementidesigns.com
Corporate promotional items, apparel & printing, fashion jewelry & accessories, wedding party supplies, gift items, home decor products & car assortments. (Woman/As-Pac, estab 2004, empl 5, sales $194,902, cert: CPUC)

1314   Ellen's Silkscreening, Inc.
1500 Mission St   South Pasadena, CA 91030
(626) 441-4415   Ellen Daigle Owner
Fax: (626) 441-2788
Email: ellenteez@aol.com
Website: www.ellenssilkscreening.com
Screen printed & embroidered goods & promotional products. (Woman/White, estab 1978, empl 15, sales $2,087,125, cert: WBENC)

1315   Forum Info-Tech, Inc.
1307 W Sixth St, Ste 215   Corona, CA 92882
(951) 256-4070   Biren Shukla President
Fax: (951) 278-0673
Email: bids@foruminfotech.net
Website: www.foruminfotech.net
Network Cabling Services, Managed Services Providers, Website, SEO, Virtualization, Cloud Computing, VoIP, Wireless Solutions (Woman/As-Ind, estab 2005, empl 9, sales $256,000, cert: State)

1316   Gorilla Marketing
4100 Flat Rock Dr, Ste A   Riverside, CA 92505
(951) 353-8133   Karlyne Eygendaal VP Ops
Fax: (951) 353-1647
Email: karlyne@gorillamarketing.net
Website: www.gorillamarketing.net
Imprinted promotional products, advertising specialties. (Hisp, estab 1985, empl 10, sales $1,700,000, cert: NMSDC)

1317   Infocus Specialties, Inc.
1655 Hauser Circle   Thousand Oaks, CA 91362
(805) 379-9192   Steve Leo Co-Owner
Fax: (805) 379-9193
Email: steve@infocusspecialties.com
Website: www.infocusspecialties.com
Promotional and advertising impressions. (Woman/White, estab 2013, empl 2, sales $720,000, cert: WBENC)

1318   Intention Advertising
2995 Bonnie Lane   Pleasant Hill, CA 94523
(925) 274-1774   Mara Villa Owner
Fax:
Email: mara@intentionadvertising.com
Website: www.intentionadvertising.com
Promotional products, t-shirts to pens, etc. (Woman/White, estab 2011, empl 1, sales $400,000, cert: State)

1319   Janco & Winnex Inc
3018 Durfee Ave, Ste E   El Monte, CA 91732
(626) 454-4882   Jennifer Renshaw President
Fax: (626) 454-1480
Email: jenniferjan@yahoo.com
Website: www.jancoline.com
Dist folding chairs, promotional stationery & bags. (Woman/As-Pac, estab 1996, empl 9, sales , cert: State, 8(a))

1320   JLT Promotions Inc.
24238 Hawthorne Blvd   Torrance, CA 90505
(310) 791-7006   John Tulchin CFO
Fax:
Email: jtulchin@thepromotionsdept.com
Website: www.instadiumpromotions.com
Sports & team promotional items & stadium giveaways. (Woman/White, estab 1990, empl 10, sales $5,700,000, cert: State, CPUC)

1321   Keystone Gifts
3182 Campus Dr, Ste 424   San Mateo, CA 94403
(650) 401-6066   Elizabeth Tsuji President
Fax: (650) 401-7606
Email: liz@keystonegifts.com
Website: www.keystonegifts.com
Promotional branded merchandise: pins, pennants, rally towels, seat cushions, water bottles, cups, mugs, cooler bags, lunch bags, duffel bags, fanny packs, backpacks, caps, tee shirts, sweatshirts, jackets, jewelry, etc. (Woman/As-Pac, estab 1992, empl 2, sales $443,744, cert: State, NMSDC, CPUC)

1322   KV & Associates, LLC
5694 Mission Center Rd, Ste 357   San Diego, CA 92108
(858) 277-7036   Kathy Valadez President
Fax: (858) 368-8583
Email: info@kvapromotions.com
Website: www.KVAPromotions.com
Promotional & merchandise, graphic design, corporate apparel, women, men, infant, jackets, polo's, long sleeve, short sleeve, caps, visors, T-shirts, embroidery, silk screen, writing pens, pencils, markers, cups. (Woman/Hisp, estab 2000, empl 1, sales $490,000, cert: NMSDC, WBENC, SDB)

1323   Laughing Willow, Inc.
1110 Quintana Rd   Morro Bay, CA 93442
(805) 772-4770   Elizabeth Espy CEO
Fax: (805) 772-4877
Email: liz@doghousepromotions.com
Website: www.doghousepromotions.com
Advertising specialty, apparel, awards, bags, banners, brand names, conventions, corporate gifts, custom merchandise, drink ware, eco-friendly, embroidery, gift baskets, headwear, hospitality, incentive programs. (Woman, estab 1998, empl 4, sales $2,029,491, cert: WBENC)

1324   Macro Industries, Inc
5595 Daniels St Ste F   Chino, CA 91710
(909) 364-8100   Cynthia Phillips Mktg Mgr
Fax: (909) 364-8055
Email: sales106@goldensundirect.com
Website: www.3cfactory.com
Dist safety vests, safety t-shirts, safety jackets, ANSI/ISEA 107-2004 Class 2, Class 3, gloves, caps, hats, uniforms, bags, backpacks, tote bags, custom-made orders, imprint, embroidery. (As-Pac, estab 2001, empl 7, sales $1,020,000, cert: CPUC)

1325 Matel Manufacturing Inc.
13205 Estrella Ave Unit A Gardena, CA 90248
(310) 217-9111 Nagendra Bolla President
Fax: (310) 538-8949
Email: bobbolla@matelinc.com
Website: www.matelinc.com
Leather & Metal desk accessories, letter trays, form holders, business cards, desk pads, pen sets, bill holders, book ends, memo boxes, coasters & conference pads. (As-Ind, estab 1985, empl 7, sales $720,000, cert: CPUC)

1326 Modernmart, Inc.
6120 Wilderness Ave.   Riverside, CA 92504
(909) 573-0050 Alison Hsu President
Fax: (909) 393-7553
Email: alison@modernmart.com
Website: www.modernmart.com
Promotional products, pens, coffee mugs, caps, T-shirts with logos imprint & embroidery. (Woman/As-Pac, estab 2001, empl 12, sales $709,000, cert: State)

1327 O2 Marketing & Design, Inc.
401 ROLAND WAY   OAKLAND, CA 94621
(510) 553-0202 Sabina Rica Treasurer
Fax: (510) 553-0201
Email: sabina@o2marketing.com
Website: www.O2MARKETING.COM
promotional products: tradeshow giveaways, corporate branding, employee incentive programs, awards. (Woman/As-Ind, estab 2000, empl 7, sales $200,000, cert: CPUC, WBENC)

1328 PMP Products Inc.
1210 W Jon St, Ste B Torrance, CA 90502
(310) 547-8064 Peter Newhouse President
Fax: (310) 513-6668
Email: petern@american-casuals.com
Website: www.american-casuals.com
Promotional products, apparel (soft goods) headwear, hard goods. (Woman/As-Pac, estab 2003, empl 10, sales , cert: NMSDC)

1329 PromoShop Inc.
PromoShop Headquarters 5420 McConnell Ave. Los Angeles, CA 90066
(310) 821-1780 sabrina kahan Supplier Diversity Relations Mgr
Fax: (310) 301-7484
Email: sabrina@promoshopla.com
Website: www.promoshopinc.com
Dist advertising specialty items & promotional products; e-commerce solutions, in-house warehousing & fulfillment svcs. (Hisp, estab 1998, empl 79, sales $45,000,000, cert: NMSDC)

1330 Resources Unlimited, Inc.
317 Bay Shore Ave, Ste A   Long Beach, CA 90803
(310) 717-0261 Tina Valdez Acct Mgr
Fax:
Email: tina@resourcesunlimitedinc.com
Website: www.resourcesunlimitedinc.com
Custom promotional materials, decorated apparel, screen printed tees & embroidered hats & polos, logoed gifts. (Woman/White, estab 1994, empl 3, sales $1,000,000, cert: CPUC)

1331 Seba International
1210 W Jon St Torrance, CA 90502
(310) 549-5122 Mariah M. Qian CEO
Fax: (310) 549-4787
Email: seba@globalxlr.com
Website: www.sebaintl.com
Promotional items: sports Jerseys, shirts, jackets, sweatshirts, caps & hats. (Woman/As-Pac, estab 2013, empl 8, sales $5,171,671, cert: NMSDC)

1332 Sun Coast Merchandise Corporation
6315 Bandini Blvd Los Angeles, CA 90040
(800) 432-4274 Dilip Bhavnani President
Fax: (323) 720-1988
Email: dilip@sunscopeusa.com
Website: www.sunscopeusa.com
Promotional products. (As-Pac, estab 1943, empl 48, sales $108,000,000, cert: NMSDC)

1333 The Corporate Gift Service, Inc.
4120 W Burbank Blvd Burbank, CA 91505
(818) 845-9500 Savannah Cotter Accting Dept
Fax: (818) 845-6110
Email: accounting@corpgiftservice.com
Website: www.thecorporategiftservice.com
Handmade Custom Gift Baskets, Embroidered Corporate Apparel, High End Corporate Gifts, Branded Promotional Products & Advertising Specialties. (Woman/White, estab 1990, empl 7, sales $1,600,000, cert: WBENC)

1334 Together We Plan
5104 Odin Ct Rocklin, CA 95765
(916) 435-4304 Carol Ann Whiteman Owner
Fax: (916) 624-4563
Email: carolann@togetherweplan.com
Website: www.togetherweplan.com
Advertising specialties, awards, custom labels, stationery & business cards. (Woman/Hisp, estab 2002, empl 7, sales , cert: State)

1335 TSG Direct LLC
20992 Avenida Amapola Lake Forest, CA 92630
(650) 224-9146 Gregg Moschides Director of Sales
Fax:
Email: gmoschides@tsgdirectllc.com
Website: www.tsgdirectllc.com
Print, direct mail & fulfillment services, promotional products, branded apparel, uniforms & office supplies. (Woman/White, estab 2014, empl 5, sales , cert: State, CPUC)

1336 Wearable Imaging, Inc.
      26741 Portola Pkwy Ste 1E, 608 Foothill Ranch, CA 92610
      (949) 888-7837 Robin Richter President
      Fax: (949) 888-7831
      Email: robin@wearableimaging.com
      Website: www.wearableimaging.com
Screenprinting & embroidered apparel: t-shirts, polo's, hats & caps, pens, travel mugs, etc. (Woman/Nat Ame, estab 1992, empl 5, sales $782,693, cert: CPUC, WBENC)

Colorado

1337 AC Flag & Banner, Inc.
      10184 W Belleview Ave   Littleton, CO 80127
      (303) 948-9774 Wendy Willson President
      Fax: (303) 948-9776
      Email: wendy@acflag.com
      Website: www.acflagandbanner.com
Custom logo flags & banners. (Woman/White, estab 2004, empl 4, sales $225,000, cert: WBENC)

1338 Artistic Promotions
      2168 S Birch St   Denver, CO 80222
      (303) 759-5559 Radhika Hess Sales Assoc
      Fax: (303) 759-8330
      Email: sharon@artisticpromo.com
      Website: www.artisticpromo.com
Advertising specialties: marketing programs, special events, promotional products, logo apparel, incentive & safety programs, events items, trade shows, convention gifts, corporate awards, etc. (Woman/White, estab 1991, empl 4, sales , cert: WBENC)

Connecticut

1339 Church Hill Classics
      594 Pepper St   Monroe, CT 06468
      (800) 477-9005 Lucie Voves Sales and Mktg Rep
      Fax: (203) 268-2468
      Email: lucie@diplomaframe.com
      Website: www.diplomaframe.com
Corporate frames & gifts: custom designed insignias awards, recognition certificates & events. (Woman/White, estab 1991, empl 73, sales , cert: WBENC)

1340 GBG The Corporate Gift Source, Inc.
      204 Spring Hill Rd   Trumbull, CT 06611
      (203) 459-4424 Charlotte O'Banion President
      Fax: (203) 459-9400
      Email: charlotte@gbginc.com
      Website: www.gbginc.com
Promotional products, logoed apparel, warehousing & catalog programs, fulfillment services, employee award redemption programs, premiums & sales incentives. (Woman/As-Pac, estab 1987, empl 5, sales $2,350,000, cert: NMSDC)

1341 John Michael Associates, Inc.
      94 Holmes Rd   Newington, CT 06111
      (860) 666-1414 Paul Sposito Exec VP
      Fax: (860) 666-1515
      Email: paul@jmalogos.com
      Website: www.jmalogos.com
Logo apparel & merchandise, corporate online stores, awards, recognition & loyalty programs, fulfillment, event, incentive & sales marketing, importing, trade shows & fundraisers, kitting, collating & custom packaging, creative services. (Woman/White, estab 1980, empl 27, sales $12,000,000, cert: State, WBENC)

1342 Preferred Promotions, LLC
      1801 Berlin Turnpike P.O. Box 307 Berlin, CT 06037
      (860) 829-1317 Dottie Nelson Owner
      Fax: (860) 828-7855
      Email: dnelson@preferredpromo.com
      Website: www.preferredpromos.com
Promotional products: imprinted wearables, engraved awards.. (Woman/Nat Ame, estab 2003, empl 5, sales $725,000, cert: State)

District of Columbia

1343 The Hamilton Group
      4406 Gault Place NE   Washington, DC 20019
      (202) 689-4304 Kaari Hamilton President
      Fax: (202) 204-6083
      Email: kayhhpbp@verizon.net
      Website: www.thehamiltongroupllc.net
Dist office supplies, advertisement & promotional products, office equipment & clothing wearables. (Woman/AA, estab 2007, empl 1, sales $731,000, cert: City, NMSDC)

Delaware

1344 Promo Victory, Inc.
      4142 Ogletown-Stanton Rd, Ste 238   Newark, DE 19713
      (800) 385-7573 Vicki Lam President
      Fax: (877) 573-1146
      Email: vlam@promovictory.com
      Website: www.promovictory.com
Promotional products. (Woman/As-Pac, estab 2008, empl 1, sales , cert: State, WBENC)

Florida

1345 Ad Specs of FL, LLC dba Proforma Global Sourcing
      2415 N. Albany Ave   Tampa, FL 33607
      (813) 397-1655 Michele Adams President
      Fax: (813) 873-8090
      Email: michele.adams@proforma.com
      Website: www.proformaglobalsourcing.com
Print & promotional products. (Woman/White, estab 2005, empl 5, sales $1,230,000, cert: WBENC)

1346   American Traders Enterprises, Inc.
         2900 Glades Circle, Ste 1250   Weston, FL 33327
         (954) 888-9206 Josie Musch President
         Fax: (954) 888-9735
         Email: josie@americantraders.com
         Website: www.americantraders.com
Promotional products. (Woman/Hisp, estab 1996, empl 6,
sales , cert: NMSDC)

1347   American Trading International Co, LLC
         13866 SW 256 Terr   Homestead, FL 33032
         (813) 810-1610 Juan Penso Owner
         Fax:
         Email: sales@atipromotions.com
         Website: www.atipromotions.com
Promotional products, gifts, awards, souvenirs, business
cards, advertising specialties. (Hisp, estab 2007, empl 1,
sales $65,000, cert: State, NMSDC)

1348   Bilmor with Advertising Specialties Inc.
         16155 SW 117th Ave, Unit B-19   Miami, FL 33177
         (305) 232-3323 Andrew Headley Director
         Fax: (305) 232-8338
         Email: support@bilmoradv.com
         Website: www.bilmoradv.com
Dist promotional items: custom embroidery, heat transfers, pad printing, hot stamping, awards & recognition
gifts. (AA, estab 1985, empl 4, sales $614,000, cert: State)

1349   Design & Promotions Corp.
         12333 SW 132nd Ct   Miami, FL 33186
         (305) 232-8119 Vicente Buraglia President
         Fax: (305) 256-2892
         Email: service@design-promotions.com
         Website: www.design-promotions.com
Custom promotional products, custom packaging, custom
displays, P.O.P. material, graphic design. (Hisp, estab 1990,
empl 4, sales , cert: NMSDC)

1350   Entertainment Retail Enterprises, LLC
         2437 E LandSt Rd Orlando, FL 32824
         (407) 649-6552 Melinda Wenderlein Dir of Finance
         Fax: (407) 649-4290
         Email: melinda@ere-sri.com
         Website: www.ere-sri.com
CAT workwear, menswear, thermos, lunch bags, mugs
(Woman/White, estab 2008, empl 102, sales $45,000,000,
cert: WBENC)

1351   I Love Promos, Inc.
         6627 NW 25th Way Ste 100 Boca Raton, FL 33496
         (866) 546-7001 Mary Turel SVP
         Fax: (866) 354-0054
         Email: mary@ilovepromos.com
         Website: www.ilovepromos.com
Promotional products, apparel, writing instruments, eco-
friendly items. (Woman/Hisp, estab 2013, empl 2, sales
$3,200,000, cert: WBENC)

1352   JT Promotions
         4378 LB Mcleod Rd   orlando, FL 32811
         (407) 730-7990 James Stillwell Owner
         Fax:
         Email: info@aclipsemarketing.net
         Website: www.aclipsemarketing.net
Embroidery, silk screening, promotional & novelty items,
event planning & execution. (AA, estab 2003, empl 4,
sales $250,000, cert: NMSDC)

1353   LEGitimate Productions, Inc. dba Legwerks
         6822 22nd Ave N Ste 430 Saint Petersburg, FL
         33710
         (727) 344-3082 Lisa René LeClair CEO
         Fax: (404) 759-2802
         Email: lisa@legwerks.com
         Website: www.legwerks.com
Branding solutions, promotional products & gifts,
employee recognition & customer acquision programs.
(Woman/White, estab 2001, empl 1, sales $368,233,
cert: State)

1354   Levy Marketing and Awards
         2415 N Albany Ave, Unit 1   Tampa, FL 33607
         (813) 252-2328 Vanessa Leon VP of Business Dev
         Fax: (813) 873-8090
         Email: info@levymarketingawards.com
         Website: www.levymarketingawards.com
Mfr medals, medallions & emblematic jewelry, custom
design awards, promotional products, branded apparell
& business gifts. (Woman/White, estab 1960, empl 38,
sales , cert: WBENC)

1355   Merchandise Partners
         11111 N 46th St Tampa, FL 33617
         (404) 460-7190 Wendy Knapp
         Fax: (813) 985-6860
         Email: wendy@merchandisepartners.com
         Website: www.merchandisepartners.com
Corporate promotions, merchandising solutions, retail
programs, sponsorship promotions, sales promotions,
dealer networks, web stores. (Hisp, estab 2006, empl 6,
sales $35,000,000, cert: NMSDC)

1356   MH Specialties LLC
         9896 White Sands Place Bonita Springs, FL 34135
         (313) 268-5907 Tondalaya (Mike) Herbert CEO
         Fax: (877) 846-2563
         Email: mike@mhspecialties.com
         Website: www.mhspecialties.com
Rewards & Recognition, wall/desk custom designed
plaques, recognition jewelry, awards rings & promotional jewelry, premium incentives gifts for Safety
Programs & Training, employees recognition awards,
corporate awards/gifts. (Woman/White, estab 2002,
empl 1, sales $300,000, cert: WBENC)

1357   SpringboardPC
        4517 W. Dale Ave   Tampa, FL 33609
        (813) 918-0371 Wendy Pepe President
        Fax:
        Email: Wendy@springboardpc.com
        Website: www.springboardpc.com
Advertising specialty, promotional products. (Woman/
White, estab 1992, empl 5, sales $2,400,000, cert: State,
City, WBENC)

1358   Tampa T-Shirts
        5112 N 22nd St   Tampa, FL 33610
        (813) 879-3298 Juan Davis Mgr
        Fax:
        Email: juan@fastlaneclothing.com
        Website: www.fastlaneclothing.com
Apparel, logo shirts, lab coats, promotional items.
(Woman/Hisp, estab 1985, empl 19, sales $1,480,000,
cert: State, City)

1359   Think Tank Studio
        626 Lakeview Rd, Ste A   Clearwater, FL 33756
        (727) 441-4488 Marlies Schoenau President
        Fax: (727) 447-9261
        Email: mus@thinktankstudio.com
        Website: www.thinktankstudio.com
Promotional marketing services, logo apparel, hats, drink
ware, office items, pens, bags, awards, signage, tradeshow hand-outs. (Woman/White, estab 1998, empl 7,
sales $1,487,596, cert: WBENC)

1360   Underground Graphics Inc.
        13355 Belcher Rd S Unit H Largo, FL 33773
        (727) 535-9582 Grace Newcomer President
        Fax: (727) 536-5777
        Email: grace@undergroundgraphics.us
        Website: www.undergroundgraphics.us
Promotional products: pens, mugs, keychains etc.
(Woman/White, estab 1993, empl 4, sales $165,000, cert:
State)

1361   Wendt Productions Inc.
        17301 Solie Rd   Odessa, FL 33556
        (813) 920-5000 Susan Wendt President
        Fax: (813) 920-8611
        Email: swendt@wendtpro.com
        Website: www.wendtpro.com
Advertising, marketing & promotional products. (Woman/
White, estab 1986, empl 9, sales $1,450,000, cert: State)

1362   Y-not Design &Mfg Inc
        3485 nw 65 St   miami, FL 33147
        (855) 843-1422 Angelina Garcia CEO
        Fax: (786) 597-7389
        Email: contactus@y-not.com
        Website: www.Y-not.com
Promotional & gifts products. (Woman/Hisp, estab 2005,
empl 31, sales , cert: NMSDC, WBENC)

1363   Zoya, Inc.
        641 SW 3rd Ave   Fort Lauderdale, FL 33315
        (954) 523-6531 Zoya Hajianpour President
        Fax: (954) 779-1900
        Email: zoya@zoyainc.com
        Website: www.zoyainc.com
Promotional items. (Woman/White, estab 2001, empl 1,
sales , cert: WBENC)

Georgia

1364   Atlanta Brand Central LLC
        880 Glenwood Ave se unit 1317   Atlanta, GA
        30316
        (404) 312-8777 Darryl Armstrong Owner
        Fax:
        Email: darryl@abcatl.com
        Website: www.abcatl.com
Promotional products & sourcing. (AA, estab 2008, empl
4, sales $170,000, cert: NMSDC)

1365   Atlanta Promotional Products
        911 High Green Court   Marietta, GA 30068
        (770) 310-9860 Glynis Holihan Managing Partner
        Fax:
        Email: glynis@atlpromo.com
        Website: www.atlpromo.com
Advertising specialty, logoed merchandise, corporate
gifts & apparel. (Woman/White, estab 2004, empl 3,
sales $1,196,294, cert: CPUC)

1366   Barazzo, LLC
        2221 Peachtree Rd NE Ste D357 Atlanta, GA
        30309
        (888) 716-5785 Quiana Lloyd Member
        Fax:
        Email: quiana@barazzo.com
        Website: www.barazzo.com
Custom gift & accessory solutions, corporate brand
identity & marketing solutions. (Woman/AA, estab 2009,
empl , sales , cert: State, NMSDC, SDB)

1367   Blue Rose Promotions, LLC
        2660 Holcomb Bridge Road Ste 200 Alpharetta,
        GA 30022
        (770) 695-7673 Jennifer Pines VP Sales
        Fax:
        Email: jennifer@bluerosepromotions.com
        Website: www.bluerosepromotions.com
Promotional marketing with access to over 700,000
products. (Woman/White, estab 2013, empl 4, sales
$4,165,561, cert: WBENC)

1368 Brand Spirit Inc.
      245 N Highland Ave NE Ste 230-272 Atlanta, GA
      30307
      (877) 804-7906 Jenna Banks President
      Fax: (877) 804-7906
      Email: jenna@gobrandspirit.com
      Website: www.gobrandspirit.com
Branded gifts, promotional items, printed materials,
business forms, logo apparel, badges & credentials,
awards, uniforms, lanyards, brochures & business cards.
(Woman/White, estab 2012, empl 1, sales $430,400, cert:
NWBOC)

1369 Capital Ideas, Inc.
      990 Hammond Dr Ste 620 Atlanta, GA 30328
      (678) 320-1630 Gina Sealey Acct Mgr/ VP
      Fax: (678) 320-0899
      Email: gsealey@capitalideas.net
      Website: www.capitalideas.net
Promotional products. (Woman/White, estab 1987, empl
8, sales $4,162,000, cert: WBENC)

1370 Choice Premiums
      560 Arlington Pl Macon, GA 31201
      (478) 741-8888 Lynn Lavery President
      Fax: (478) 742-2587
      Email: lynn@choicepremiums.com
      Website: www.choicepremiums.com
Promotional products & marketing. (Woman/White, estab
1996, empl 4, sales $402,067, cert: WBENC)

1371 Creative Corporate Ideas Inc
      1010 Huntcliff Ste.1350 Atlanta, GA 30350
      (404) 252-2588 Creative Corporate Ideas Inc Owner
      Fax: (404) 252-2588
      Email: cwalina@bellsouth.net
      Website: www.creativecorporateideas.com
Promotional items, logo merchandise & wearables.
(Woman/White, estab 1993, empl 2, sales $500,000, cert:
WBENC)

1372 Creative Innovators, Inc.
      1797 Spring Rd, Ste 6 Smyrna, GA 30080
      (770) 435-7552 Omar Horton Mgr
      Fax: (770) 435-7553
      Email: sales@creativeinnovators.net
      Website: www.creativeinnovators.net
Embroidery, screen printing, signs, banners, advertising
specialty & promotional items. (AA, estab 1999, empl 3,
sales $150,000, cert: State, City)

1373 FireSign Inc. Promotional Products & Print
      4480-H S Cobb Dr, Ste 540 Smyrna, GA 30080
      (678) 574-2461 Jen Lyles Lead Ignitor
      Fax: (678) 574-2460
      Email: jlyles@firesigninc.com
      Website: www.firesigninc.com
Promotional product & print services, (Woman/AA, estab
2003, empl 5, sales $1,295,000, cert: NMSDC)

1374 Henry-Aaron Inc.
      754 Woodson St Atlanta, GA 30315
      (404) 622-4308 Aaron Turpeau President
      Fax: (404) 622-7638
      Email: info@aarongroup.us
      Website: www.henry-aaroninc.logomall.com/
Premium & promotional items. (AA, estab 1991, empl
3, sales $2,189,931, cert: State, NMSDC)

1375 Jansen Advertising
      1845 Remington Rd Atlanta, GA 30341
      (770) 452-0252 Paige Jansen-Nichols VP Sales
      Fax: (770) 452-0253
      Email: paige@jansenadvertising.com
      Website: www.jansenadvertising.com
Custom promotional, incentive & recognition merchandise. (Woman/White, estab 1993, empl 8, sales ,
cert: WBENC)

1376 NorthStar Print, LLC
      6050 Peachtree Pkwy Ste 240359 Norcross, GA
      30092
      (770) 490-6251 Jacki Suckow President
      Fax: (770) 225-0155
      Email: jacki@northstarprint.net
      Website: www.northstarprint.net
Print & promotional products, marketing materials,
traditional business forms, POP items, promotional
items & just-in-time digital printing, distribution &
kitting services. (Woman/White, estab 1991, empl 8,
sales $3,000,000, cert: NWBOC)

1377 Successful Images
      114 Oakview Club Dr Macon, GA 31216
      (478) 923-9231 Anthony Steedley President
      Fax:
      Email: ssteedleya@aol.com
      Website: www.successfulimages.biz
Screen printing, embroidery, advertising specialties &
promotional products. (AA, estab 1993, empl 5, sales
$300,000, cert: State)

1378 Universal Graphics, Inc.
      2931 Lewis St, Ste 301 Kennesaw, GA 30144
      (678) 581-1221 Celia Reed Sales
      Fax: (678) 581-1124
      Email: ccmem@aol.com
      Website: www.ugiinc.biz
Silk screening, embroidery, promotional items,
corporate apparel, printing. (AA, estab 2000, empl 10,
sales , cert: NMSDC)

Iowa

1379   World of Colors - Break The Cycle LLC
       1624 7th Ave SE, Ste 7000   Cedar Rapids, IA 52403
       (319) 447-7282 Rick Rodriguez Owner
       Fax:
       Email: rrodri7855@aol.com
       Website: www.worldofcolors.us
Design, print & dist screen printed bags, shirts, hats &
specialty items. (Hisp, estab 2012, empl 5, sales $24,000,
cert: NMSDC)

Illinois

1380   Action Health
       1001 Entry Dr   Bensenville, IL 60106
       (630) 496-6253 Erin Moeller Director of Sales
       Fax: (630) 496-6253
       Email: emoeller@actionhealth.com
       Website: www.actionhealth.com
Printed bags, bags, retail packaging products, printed
promotional products, promotional items, packaging
supplies, labels, tissue paper, gift cards, specialty packaging, custom bags, custom printed items, rush orders, in-
stock products. (Woman/White, estab 1980, empl 35, sales
, cert: City, WBENC)

1381   B. Gunther & Company, Inc.
       4742 Main St   Lisle, IL 60532
       (630) 969-5595 Jeanne Brommer President
       Fax: (630) 969-5768
       Email: jeanne@bgunther.com
       Website: www.bgunther.com
Promotional products, business gifts, imprinted pens to
the leather portfolio or high end wearables. (Woman/
White, estab 1985, empl 9, sales $1,220,000, cert: WBENC)

1382   Bienali Promotions, LLC
       1811 St. Johns Ave, Ste 201   Highland Park, IL
       60035
       (847) 926-7253 Lauri Zessar President
       Fax: (847) 926-7250
       Email: lzessar@bienali.com
       Website: www.bienali.com
Promotional merchandise, logo apparel, premiums,
incentives, gifts, custom merchandise, bags, recyclable
bags, laminate bags, totes. (Woman/Hisp, estab 2012,
empl 7, sales , cert: NMSDC, WBENC)

1383   Corporate Identity, Inc.
       223 W Main St   Barrington, IL 60010
       (847) 304-8550 Debbie Story Sales Mgr
       Fax: (847) 304-8558
       Email: dstory@corpid.com
       Website: www.corpid.com
Promotional products, awards, logo apparel, trade show
giveaways, corporate gifts, notepads, golf balls, banners,
table throws, business forms, labels, folders, nameplates,
tags. (Woman/White, estab 1976, empl 9, sales
$4,800,000, cert: WBENC)

1384   eLead Resources, Inc.
       125 S Clark St 17th Fl Chicago, IL 60603
       (888) 420-1788 Michael Wheeler VP
       Fax: (224) 220-9664
       Email: mike@eleadresources.com
       Website: www.eleadresources.com
Promotional marketing products & brand consulting.
(AA, estab 2006, empl 8, sales $4,328,835, cert:
NMSDC)

1385   Excel Screen Printing & Embroidery, Inc.
       10507 Delta Pkwy   Schiller Park, IL 60176
       (847) 801-5200 Leon Johnson President
       Fax: (847) 801-5205
       Email: leon@excelscreenprinting.com
       Website: www.excelscreenprinting.com
Screen printed & embroidered apparel, imprinted
glassware, premiums, etc. (AA, estab 2005, empl 63,
sales $4,500,000, cert: NMSDC)

1386   Global Sourcing Connection, Ltd.
       2610 Lake Cook Road Ste 190 Riverwoods, IL
       60015
       (847) 317-9000 Jennifer Arenson CEO
       Fax: (847) 236-0427
       Email: jarenson@gloso.com
       Website: www.gloso.com
Mfr & import headwear, apparel & promotional items.
(Woman/White, estab 2001, empl 24, sales
$9,200,000, cert: WBENC)

1387   Konik & Company, Inc.
       7535 N Lincoln Ave   Skokie, IL 60076
       (847) 933-1817 Sandy Simon Sales
       Fax: (847) 933-1818
       Email: sandy@konik.com
       Website: www.simonstore.net
Premium & promotional products: apparel, drinkware,
dental sampling bags, bag, plush toys, technology
items, brand name products, desk accessories,
conference items, awards/recognition gifts, etc.
(Woman/White, estab 1991, empl 18, sales
$11,000,000, cert: WBENC)

1388   L and N Promotions, Inc.
       99 Oak Leaf Lane #203   Vernon Hills, IL 60061
       (847) 612-9215 Kristi Marquardt President
       Fax: (847) 949-9966
       Email: lnpromotionsinc@aol.com
       Website: www.companycasuals.com/
       lnpromotions
Promotional, incentive & specialty premium items.
(Woman/White, estab 1996, empl 2, sales $585,000,
cert: WBENC)

1389   LinJen Promotions, Inc.
       15519 Harbor Town Dr   Orland Park, IL 60462
       (708) 478-8222 Linda Heyse-Highland President
       Fax: (708) 478-6222
       Email: sales@linjen.com
       Website: www.linjen.com
Promotional solutions ideas & products. (Woman/
White, estab 2000, empl 6, sales $1,250,000, cert:
WBENC)

1390   M.R. Nyren Company
       600 Academy Dr Ste 110 Northbrook, IL 60062
       (800) 323-8066 Kim Nyren Acct Exec
       Fax: (847) 272-5824
       Email: kim@nyren-tms.com
       Website: www.companycasuals.com/nyrencompany
Textile & promotional products: apparel, bags, hats,
towels, blanets, golf accessories, etc. (Woman/White,
estab 1963, empl 7, sales $4,880,454, cert: WBENC)

1391   Overture, LLC
       595 N. Lakeview Parkway   Vernon Hills, IL 60061
       (847) 573-6080 Jo Ann Gilley CEO
       Fax: (847) 680-0114
       Email: jog@overturepromo.com
       Website: www.overturepromotions.com
Promotional products, awards, incentive & recognition
programs, giveaways, logo merchandise, ad specialties,
apparel, t-shirts, fulfillment. (Woman/AA/As-Ind, estab
2001, empl 135, sales $47,091,020, cert: WBENC)

1392   Positive Impact Advertising, Inc.
       1001 North Ave   Waukegan, IL 60085
       (847) 625-8629 Jody O'Rourke Owner
       Fax: (847) 625-8631
       Email: jorourke@positiveimpactadv.com
       Website: www.positiveimpactadv.com
Advertising specialties: custom imprinted awards, trade
show items, in house graphics, fulfillment & storage
facilities. (Woman, estab 1995, empl 5, sales $900,000,
cert: NWBOC)

1393   Premium Surge Promotions
       640 North LaSalle St Ste 540 Chicago, IL 60654
       (312) 951-2303 Pam Crain EVP Mktg/Client Service
       Fax: (312) 951-2371
       Email: pcrain@surge-innovations.com
       Website: www.surge-innovations.com/
Marketing, creative & promotional product design and
manufacturing. (Nat Ame/Hisp, estab 2001, empl 67, sales
$98,000,000, cert: NMSDC)

1394   Pro Biz Products LLc.
       16W211 S Frontage Rd   Burr Ridge, IL 60527
       (312) 945-6703 richard smith President
       Fax: (773) 277-0973
       Email: r.smith@probizproducts.com
       Website: www.probizproducts.com
Screen printing or embroidery, office supplies, furniture,
janitorial products & promotional items. (AA, estab 2014,
empl 6, sales $15,000,000, cert: NMSDC)

1395   Pro-Am Team Sports
       8940 W 192nd St Ste J Mokena, IL 60648
       (708) 995-1511 Mary Dolan Owner
       Fax:
       Email: mary@pro-amteamsports.com
       Website: www.pro-amteamsports.com
Branded, customized name-brand apparel & equipment.
(Woman/White, estab 2014, empl 60, sales $4,200,000,
cert: WBENC)

1396   TBK Promotions, Inc.
       3055 W 111th St 2 South Chicago, IL 60655
       (773) 239-2222 Kevin Flynn Dir of Sales
       Fax: (773) 239-2223
       Email: k@tbkpromotions.com
       Website: www.tbkpromotions.com
Promotional products, advertising specialties & branded
wearable items. (Woman/White, estab 1990, empl 5,
sales $502,500, cert: State)

1397   The Certif-a-gift Company Inc.
       1625 E Alqonqion Rd   Arlington Heights, IL 60005
       (847) 718-0300 Trish Duh President
       Fax: (847) 718-1011
       Email: tduh@certif-a-gift.com
       Website: www.certif-a-gift.com
Incentive programs. (Woman/White, estab 1954, empl
50, sales $15,600,000, cert: WBENC)

1398   Windy City Silkscreening, Inc.
       2715 S Archer   Chicago, IL 60608
       (312) 842-0030 Jessica Trojanowski Cstmr Svc
       Mgr
       Fax: (312) 842-8574
       Email: jessicat@wcsTshirts.com
       Website: www.wcsshirts.com
Custom screen printed apparel: t-shirts, sweats, hats,
jackets, towels, hot-market printing, rally towels,
promotional products. (Woman/White, estab 1978,
empl 36, sales $1,380,000, cert: WBENC)

1399   World Of Promotions
       1310 Louis Ave   Elk Grove Village, IL 60007
       (847) 439-7930 Layla Rosenfeld President
       Fax: (847) 439-4302
       Email: rosenfeldlayla@yahoo.com
       Website: www.aworldofpromotions.com
Promotional products: pens, mugs, hats, clothing, bags.
(Woman/White, estab 2003, empl 8, sales $1,120,000,
cert: State)

Indiana

1400   Awards Unlimited, Inc.
       3031 Union St   Lafayette, IN 47904
       (765) 447-9413 Stacey Shirar President
       Fax: (765) 447-2005
       Email: sjs@awardsunlimitedinc.net
       Website: www.awardsunlimitedinc.net
Advertising specialties. (Woman/White, estab 1978,
empl 12, sales $500,000, cert: WBENC)

1401   Bardach Awards, Inc.
       4222 W 86th St   Indianapolis, IN 46268
       (317) 872-7444 Diane Bardach Beck CEO
       Fax: (317) 872-7481
       Email: dbardach@bardachawards.com
       Website: www.bardachawards.com
Custom corporate awards: plaques, trophies, crystal,
acrylic, plates, marble, glass, leather items such as
portfolios, name badges, medals, ribbons, bronze
castings, donor recognition, signage, jewelry, executive
gifts. (Woman/White, estab 1969, empl 36, sales
$2,960,000, cert: State)

1402 Communications Products, Inc.
      7301 E. 90th St Ste 111 Indianapolis, IN 46256
      (317) 576-0332 Nancy Doucette
      Fax: (317) 842-0278
      Email: ndoucett@commprod.com
      Website: www.commprod.com
Nortel voice maintenance programs, voice & data cabling,
overhead paging systems, fiber terminations, patch panels,
data switches, VPN's, IP network security, T1 routers,
wireless LANS, WIFI telephones. (Hisp, estab 1982, empl
60, sales $11,000,000, cert: State)

1403 Karm Corporation
      2017 N Bedford Ave   Evansville, IN 47711
      (812) 426-1323 Kena Campbell President
      Fax: (812) 426-0125
      Email: kcampbell@promarkin.com
      Website: www.promarkin.com
Screen printing, embroidery, labels, stickers, decals,
promotional products, t-shirts, uniforms. (Woman/White,
estab 1976, empl 24, sales $2,900,000, cert: State,
WBENC)

1404 Linz and Company
      8231 Hohman Ave Ste 200 Munster, IN 46321
      (708) 757-7800 Heather Koetteritz Sales/Import
      Mgr
      Fax:
      Email: heather@linzco.com
      Website: www.linzco.com
Promotional products: apparel, housewares, novelties,
personal care items, etc. (Woman/White, estab 2000, empl
4, sales $3,007,000, cert: WBENC)

1405 M. Nelson and Associates
      4011 Vincennes Rd   Indianapolis, IN 46268
      (317) 228-1422 Carolina Pimental-Nelson President
      Fax: (317) 228-1401
      Email: carolina@mnelson.com
      Website: www.mnelson.com
Promotional products, printing services, graphic design &
screen-print/embroidery of apparel. (Woman/Hisp, estab
1991, empl 4, sales , cert: State, 8(a))

1406 Media Hub, LLc dba Office Hub
      60 E Washington St   Shelbyville, IN 46176
      (317) 398-3070 Shannon Huber CEO
      Fax: (317) 398-6418
      Email: shannonhuber@iwantmysupplies.com
      Website: www.officehubonline.com
Office supplies, printing and promotional products.
(Woman, estab 2006, empl 7, sales $941,136, cert: State)

1407 OmniSource Marketing Group, Inc.
      8945 N Meridian St Ste 150 Indianapolis, IN 46260
      (317) 575-3318 Janet Calderon Goldberg President
      Fax: (317) 575-3333
      Email: jgoldberg@omnisourcemarketing.com
      Website: www.omnisourcemarketing.com
Custom promotional products & packaging, embroidery,
fulfillment, graphic services & design, screen printing.
(Woman/White, estab 1989, empl 30, sales $10,400,000,
cert: WBENC)

1408 PlaqueMakerPlus, Inc.
      5713 Park Plaza Ct   Indianapolis, IN 46220
      (317) 594-5556 Edson Pereira President
      Fax: (317) 913-0530
      Email: edson@plaquemakerplus.com
      Website: www.plaquemakerplus.com
Mfr awards, plaques, name badges, name plates &
signs. (Woman/White, estab 1995, empl 6, sales
$640,000, cert: State)

1409 Table Thyme Designs
      217 W 10th St Ste 125 Indianapolis, IN 46202
      (317) 634-0281 Laurie Rice Owner
      Fax: (317) 634-0746
      Email: coloredthreads@sbcglobal.net
      Website: www.colored-threads.com
Promotional products & embroidered apparel &
accessories, screen printing. (Woman, estab 2002, empl
2, sales , cert: State, City)

1410 Thomas E. Slade, Inc.
      6220 Vogel Road   Evansville, IN 47715
      (812) 437-5233 Lisa Slade President
      Fax: (812) 491-3850
      Email: tom@sladeprint.com
      Website: www.sladeprint.com
Printing, graphic design, website design, wide format
posters & banners, mailing, promotional products,
letterhead, envelopes, business cards, labels, tags,
inserts, marketing services, augmented reality, QR codes
for tracking, signs. (Woman/White, estab 1993, empl 17,
sales $2,500,000, cert: State)

1411 Wolf Run Marketing
      6020 N Emerson Ave   Indianapolis, IN 46220
      (317) 445-5180 Susan Fryer Owner
      Fax: (317) 252-5751
      Email: susan@wolfrunmarketing.com
      Website: www.wolfrunmarketing.com
Promotional products, logoed apparel, service & safety
awards, employee & customer recognition awards,
tradeshow handouts, conference materials, incentives,
safety apparel, graphic design, logo devel. (Woman/
White, estab 2009, empl 2, sales $200,000, cert: City)

Kansas

1412 Grapevine Designs, LLC
      8406 Melrose Dr   Lenexa, KS 66214
      (913) 307-0225 Bob Offord VP Business Devel
      Fax: (913) 307-0096
      Email: bob.offord@abrandcompany.com
      Website: www.grapevinedesigns.com/
Promotional marketing, promotional products, creative
design, corporate giveaways, tradeshow giveaways,
corporate branding, branded merchandise. (Woman/
White, estab 2000, empl 72, sales $8,000,000, cert:
WBENC)

1413 Promo Depot Inc.
2266 N Ridge Rd   Wichita, KS 67205
(316) 722-2500 Rick McKay President
Fax: (316) 722-0404
Email: rick@4mypromo.com
Website: www.4mypromo.com
Promotional products: logo wearables & printed ad specialty products, embroidery & screeen printing, wards & recognition products. (Hisp, estab 1997, empl 15, sales $2,600,000, cert: NMSDC, NWBOC)

Kentucky

1414 Ad-Venture Promotions
2625 Regency Rd   Lexington, KY 40503
(859) 263-4299 Cathy Stafford Owner
Fax: (859) 263-7023
Email: cathy@ad-venturepromotions.com
Website: www.ad-venturepromotions.com
Advertising specialties & promotional products. (Woman/White, estab 2004, empl 6, sales , cert: WBENC)

1415 Presence Inc.
2311 Mohican Hill Ct   Louisville, KY 40207
(502) 365-4616 Gail Iwaniak President
Fax: (502) 365-4617
Email: gail@stuffology.com
Website: www.stuffology.com
Promotional marketing & products. (Woman/White, estab 1989, empl 2, sales $350,000, cert: City)

1416 The Logo Warehouse
1963 Meadowcreek Dr   Louisville, KY 40218
(502) 451-5421 Leah Scott Owner
Fax: (502) 451-5422
Email: lscott@thelogowarehouse.com
Website: www.thelogowarehouse.com
Promotional products & apparel. (Woman/AA, estab 2008, empl 1, sales , cert: City)

1417 Walker Flags, Inc.
8134 New LaGrange Rd, Ste 200   Louisville, KY 40222
(502) 394-1474 Donna Walker Mancini Owner
Fax: (502) 394-1476
Email: customercare@walkerflags.com
Website: www.walkerflags.com
Flags, Banners, Flagpoles, Flag & Flagpole Accessories. (Woman/White, estab 1960, empl 3, sales , cert: State)

Louisiana

1418 Augie Leopold Advertising Specialties, Inc.
3214 Roman St   Metairie, LA 70001
(504) 836-0525 Leeanne Leopold CEO
Fax: (504) 836-2396
Email: leeanne@augieleopold.com
Website: www.augieleopold.com
Advertising specialties, promotional items, premium gifts, casino monthly giveaways, safety programs. (Woman, estab , empl 1, sales , cert: WBENC)

1419 Executive Promotions, LLC
P.O. Box 81916   Lafayette, LA 70598
(337) 261-9025 Rebecca Bell Owner
Fax: (337) 261-9026
Email: epart@bellsouth.net
Website: www.executivepromotionsla.com
Promotional products, t-shirts, caps, drink ware, safety awards, uniforms, etc. (Woman/White, estab 2004, empl 3, sales $230,591, cert: State)

1420 Impress Marketing Studios, LLC
P.O. Box 38845   Shreveport, LA 71133
(888) 773-0183 Janelle Marks Owner
Fax: (888) 773-6617
Email: JMarks@ImpressMarketingStudios.com
Website: www.ImpressMarketingStudios.com
Marketing & promotional, premiums, advertising specialties, apparel & signage. (Woman/AA, estab 2014, empl 2, sales $127,000, cert: NMSDC)

1421 The Creative Touch, Inc.
7725 Jefferson Hwy   Baton Rouge, LA 70809
(225) 925-0022 Maureen Kahl President
Fax: (225) 925-0311
Email: maureen@creativetouchembroidery.com
Website: www.creativetouchembroidery.com
Embroidery, silk screening, promotional products, (Woman, estab 1982, empl 7, sales $489,000, cert: WBENC)

1422 Wilkin Enterprises, Inc.
2323 Bainbridge St, Bldg B, Ste 13   Kenner, LA 70062
(504) 464-2520 Kathleen Wilkin President
Fax: (504) 464-2525
Email: kwilkin@gosafeguard.com
Website: www.safeguardprints.com
Full color printing, promotional items & embroidered apparel. (Woman/White, estab 1993, empl 7, sales $1,458,066, cert: WBENC)

Massachusetts

1423 Ellco Promotions, Inc.
113 Smoke Hill Ridge Road   Marshfield, MA 02050
(508) 641-6274 Max Cohen VP
Fax: (585) 486-1033
Email: max@ellcopromotions.com
Website: www.ellcopromotions.com
Promotional/premium product & apparel agency. (Woman, estab 2010, empl 2, sales $150,000, cert: WBENC)

1424 GAP Promotions LLC
1 Washington St   Gloucester, MA 01930
(978) 281-0083 Gayle Piraino CEO
Fax: (978) 281-1103
Email: Gayle.piraino@gappromo.com
Website: www.gappromo.com/
Promotional programs and products. (Woman/White, estab 2006, empl 15, sales , cert: WBENC)

1425 Infinart, Inc.
      44 Mechanic St Newton, MA 02464
      (617) 964-3279 Felicity Green President
      Fax: (617) 244-6451
      Email: felicityinfinart@gmail.com
      Website: www.infinart.com
Custom branding, logo embroidery, silk screening,
imprinted promotional products, awards, corporate gifts
incentives, signage, banners. (Woman/White, estab 1980,
empl 5, sales $105,000, cert: State)

1426 Jazzy Sportswear Promotional Co.
      90 Munroe P.O. Box 349 Lynn, MA 01903
      (781) 593-7197 Vincent Williams President
      Fax: (781) 581-6478
      Email: jazzypc@jazzysportswear.com
      Website: www.jazzysportswear.com
Screen printing, embroidery, and a wide array of promotional items, banners, awards. (AA, estab 1997, empl 1,
sales $189,000, cert: State, NMSDC)

Maryland

1427 APISource, Inc.
      4471 Nicole Dr Lanham, MD 20706
      (301) 731-6100 Cindy Brown President
      Fax: (301) 731-6101
      Email: cindy.brown@apisource.com
      Website: www.apisource.com
Promotional products: t-shirts, collared shirts, polo shirts,
hats, jackets, bags, computer accessories, pens, note pads,
mugs, novelties, giveaways, awards, premiums, incentives,
fulfillment services. (Woman/As-Pac, estab 1900, empl 1,
sales $37,000,000, cert: WBENC)

1428 Debbie Lynn, Inc.
      952 Ridgebrook Rd Ste 1100 Sparks, MD 21152
      (443) 595-8178 Stephanie Bloom Ops Mgr
      Fax: (856) 494-1196
      Email: stephanie@debbielynn.net
      Website: www.debbielynn.net
Writing instruments, office accessories, Back to School &
novelty products. (Woman, estab 1998, empl 5, sales
$10,200,000, cert: WBENC)

1429 Products 2 Brand, LLC
      8217 Cloverleaf Dr Millersville, MD 21108
      (301) 787-0077 Macgill Antor President
      Fax:
      Email: macgill@products2brand.com
      Website: www.products2brand.com
Promotional product brand merchandise, tradeshow
registration bags, totes, briefcases, luggage, lanyards,
name badges. (Woman/White, estab 2007, empl 22, sales ,
cert: City)

1430 projectWorks, LLC
      6900 English Muffin Way, Ste E Frederick, MD
      21703
      (301) 682-4800 Michelle Stephens CEO
      Fax: (541) 962-0588
      Email: michelle@projectworks.com
      Website: www.projectworks.com
Fulfillment & marketing support svcs: warehouse &
distribution, assembly & order fulfillment, printing &
direct mail, eCommerce & inventory mgmt, advertising
specialties & premiums. (Hisp, estab 1998, empl 7, sales
$808,117, cert: State)

1431 Williams Solutions Group, LLC
      20140 Scholar Dr, Ste 315 Hagerstown, MD
      21742
      (301) 739-7532 Peter E. Perini, Sr. VP
      Fax:
      Email: peter.perini@WilliamsSolutionsGroup.com
      Website: www.WilliamsSolutionsGroup.com
Promotional items, marketing items, tchotchkies, give-
away items, logo branded items. (AA, estab 2009, empl
2, sales $100,000, cert: State)

Michigan

1432 Alfie Logo Gear
      2425 Switch Dr Traverse City, MI 49684
      (231) 935-1488 Bonnie Alfonso President
      Fax: (231) 935-1740
      Email: Bonnie@GoAlfie.com
      Website: www.GoAlfie.com
Logowear, embroidery, screen printing & promotional
products, uniforms, rewards & incentives, trade show
giveaways. (Woman/White, estab 1990, empl 18, sales
$2,863,520, cert: WBENC)

1433 All American Essentials
      31600 Plymouth Rd Livonia, MI 48150
      (734) 421-9292 Sandeep Narang President
      Fax: (734) 421-0505
      Email: sandeepnarang2@aol.com
      Website: www.aae4ever.com/
Apparel, uniforms, & promotional products. (As-Pac,
estab 1998, empl 25, sales $67,500, cert: 8(a))

1434 Antina Promotions, LLC
      84 Leslie Lane Waterford, MI 48328
      (248) 254-3845 Christina Concord Managing
      Partner
      Fax:
      Email: christina@antinapromo.com
      Website: www.antinapromo.com
Promotional Products, Exhibit Displays, Corporate Gifts,
Awards, Signage, Branded Apparel, Company Stores,
Custom Packaging, Marketing Materials. (Woman, estab
2010, empl 2, sales $39,219, cert: WBENC, SDB)

1435 CE Competitive Edge LLC
5924 Red Arrow Hwy   Stevensville, MI 49127
(269) 429-0404 Mary Tomasini CEO
Fax: (269) 429-0158
Email: mjtomasini@competitive-edge.net
Website: www.competitive-edge.net
Incentive & promotional products, ideas & services.
(Woman/White, estab 1993, empl 15, sales , cert: WBENC)

1436 Graphix 2 Go
7200 Tower Rd   Battle Creek, MI 49014
(269) 969-7321 Amy Howard Sales Mgr
Fax: (269) 969-7455
Email: amy@graphix2goinc.com
Website: www.graphix2goinc.com
Promotional products. (Woman/White, estab 1997, empl
8, sales $3,500,000, cert: WBENC)

1437 Krystal Marketing, Inc.
1120 E Long Lake Rd, Ste 200   Troy, MI 48085
(248) 619-9000 Carolyn Boccia Mktg Mgr
Fax: (248) 619-9004
Email: carolyn@krystalmarketing.com
Website: www.krystalmarketing.com
Promotional products, awards & incentives. (Woman/
White, estab 1987, empl 10, sales , cert: WBENC)

1438 Mercury P&F
35610 Mound Rd   Sterling Heights, MI 48310
(1586) 825-9300 Betsy Canova Business Dev Mgr
Fax: (586) 825-9399
Email: canovab@mercuryfs.com
Website: www.mercuryfs.com
Branded merchandise & premiums. (Woman/AA, estab
1996, empl 70, sales $25,000,000, cert: NMSDC, WBENC)

1439 Mixed Promotions, LLC
3759 S Baldwin Rd, Ste 222   Lake Orion, MI 48359
(248) 783-4099 Lona Carson CEO
Fax: (248) 783-4099
Email: Lcarson@mixedpromotions.com
Website: www.mixedpromotions.com
Promotional products. (Woman/As-Pac, estab 2000, empl
1, sales $462,000, cert: NMSDC)

1440 Premier Sales & Marketing, Inc.
2328 Livernois Ste 1050 Troy, MI 48083
(248) 526-9792 Janine Brown President
Fax: (248) 526-9794
Email: qualimotive2@wwnet.net
Website:
Promotional products. (Woman/White, estab 1992, empl
3, sales $177,000, cert: WBENC)

1441 Promotion Concepts Inc.
414 S Burdick St   Kalamazoo, MI 49007
(269) 488-2987 Lauren A. Powers President
Fax: (269) 372-9991
Email: laurene.powers@promotionconcepts.com
Website: www.promotionconcepts.com
Incentive marketing svcs, sales promotion, promotional
products, premium incentives programs, awards, recognition, brand-building. (Woman/White, estab 1982, empl 18,
sales , cert: WBENC)

1442 Promotional Solutions LLC
48530 Van Dyke Ave   Shelby Township, MI 48317
(586) 739-1132 Kathy Ferguson Member
Fax: (586) 739-1132
Email: promotionalsolutions@onemain.com
Website: www.promotionalsolutionsonline.com
Advertising specialty goods & services. Logowear
embroidered or screen print,
wwards & trophys, special event gifts, employee
appreciation items. (Woman/White, estab 2001, empl 8,
sales $622,000, cert: WBENC)

1443 The Bradley Company, Inc.
26777 Central Park Blvd Ste 180 Southfield, MI
48076
(248) 538-1909 Marci Taran CEO
Fax: (248) 538-1472
Email: marcit@thebradco.com
Website: www.thebradco.com
Advertising specialties, Assembly, Awards, Branded
merchandise, Branding, Commemorative items, Corpo-
rate apparel, Corporate gifts, Corporate identity,
Corporate webstores, Custom packaging, etc. (Woman/
White, estab 2004, empl 11, sales $5,000,000, cert:
WBENC)

1444 Tier One Marketing
3160 Belle Terr   Commerce Township, MI 48382
(313) 274-1179 Jeanne Snyder President
Fax: (313) 274-4702
Email: jeannesnyder@sbcglobal.net
Website: www.tierone.biz
Ad specialties: coffee cups, pens, portfolios, golf items,
technology driven give-a-ways, coolers, tote bags,
flashlights, key chains, awards, custom pieces,
collectables. (Woman/White, estab 2003, empl 2, sales
$250,000, cert: WBENC)

1445 Unique Expressions, LLC
22050 Woodward Ave   Ferndale, MI 48220
(248) 547-9300 Beverly Bantom CEO
Fax: (248) 547-9482
Email: info@uniquex.net
Website: www.UniqueX.net
Dist promotional products. (AA, estab 1999, empl 6,
sales $1,000,000, cert: NMSDC)

Minnesota

1446 2020 Brand Solutions
135 Grand Ave East   South St. Paul, MN 55075
(651) 451-3850 Dan Livengood VP Sales and Mktg
Fax: (651) 453-1303
Email: dan.livengood@2020brands.com
Website: www.2020collection.com
Corporate Apparel & Uniform Programs, Branded
Merchandise, Incentives & Recognition, Print Manage-
ment & Specialty Fulfillment. (Nat Ame, estab 2014,
empl 62, sales $20,000,000, cert: NMSDC)

1447   Corporate Advertising & Incentives
       6289 Niagara Lane N   Maple Grove, MN 55311
       (763) 559-8388 Loni Spence Promotional Consult-
       ant
       Fax: (763) 559-8488
       Email: lspence@corpadvertising.net
       Website: www.corpadvertising.net
Promorional products. (Woman/White, estab 2003, empl
3, sales $150,000, cert: WBENC)

1448   Creative Resources Agency
       1208 5th St South   Minneapolis, MN 55343
       (952) 988-9407 Caren Schweitzer CEO
       Fax: (952) 988-9408
       Email: caren@acreativeresource.com
       Website: www.acreativeresource.com
Promotional products, direct mail, trade show give-aways,
corporate holiday gifts, lead generators & client thank-you
gifts. (Woman/White, estab 1995, empl 24, sales
$5,700,000, cert: WBENC)

1449   Ithaca Promotions
       P.O. Box 220   Wahkon, MN 56386
       (612) 669-7833 Katrina Chang President
       Fax: (320) 495-3792
       Email: katrina@ithacapromotions.com
       Website: www.ithacapromotions.com
Promotional, incentive, corporate gifts, gift certificates,
gift checks, American Express Gift Cheques, banners, etc.
(Woman/As-Pac, estab 1991, empl 1, sales $631,227, cert:
State, NMSDC, WBENC)

1450   J Michael Industries
       1086 W 7th St   St Paul, MN 55102
       (651) 698-3333 Jamie Flynn Owner
       Fax: (651) 698-3039
       Email: jamiemm@extendedexposure.com
       Website: www.extendedexposure.com
Design, create & source give-away mementos, memorable
keepsakes & corporate gifts. (Woman/White, estab 1999,
empl 7, sales $1,200,000, cert: WBENC)

1451   M Plus Embroidery & Promotions.
       5 Viking Dr W   Little Canada, MN 55117
       (651) 777-3624 Beth Mulcahy Owner
       Fax: (651) 777-9752
       Email: beth@mplus-embroidery.com
       Website: www.mplus-embroidery.com
Embroidery, silk screening, direct to garment, polo's, t-
shirts, sweatshirts/pants, caps, hats, bags, etc. (Woman/
White, estab 1984, empl 7, sales $324,800, cert: WBENC)

1452   Rutabaga Rags, Inc.
       8700 West 36th St Ste 3E   St. Louis Park, MN 55426
       (952) 938-4841 Julie Miller Owner
       Fax: (952) 303-5412
       Email: julie@rutabagarags.com
       Website: www.rutabagaragsshop.com
Promotional products & stadium giveaways: baseball caps,
jerseys, bats, gloves, toys, banks, bracelets, lip balm,
magnets, pens, schedules, memo pads, padfolios, portfolios, duffles, bags, backpacks, cinch sacks, mugs, coffee
tumblers, stuffed animals. (Woman/White, estab 1993,
empl 3, sales $600,000, cert: WBENC)

1453   Spartan Promotional Group, Inc.
       711 Hale Ave N   Oakdale, MN 55128
       (309) 827-2215 Dan Perdue Sales Assoc
       Fax: (651) 735-1333
       Email: phyllisohenwald@spartanpromo.com
       Website: www.spartanpromo.com/index.html
Advertising specialties: keychains, magnets, pens,
distribution services, promotional marketing programs.
(Woman/White, estab 1966, empl 80, sales , cert:
WBENC)

1454   St. Croix Promotions & Retail, Inc.
       2500 W Cty Rd 42, Ste 110   Burnsville, MN 55337
       (952) 854-9202 Tony Pesante President
       Fax: (952) 854-9209
       Email: tonyp@scpromo.com
       Website: www.scpromo.com
Promotional products, logo merchandise, custom
apparel, gift store merchandise, give-away items,
premiums, awards. (Woman/White, estab 2004, empl
21, sales $5,500,000, cert: NMSDC, WBENC)

1455   Vickerman Construction LLC
       2526 24th Ave S   Minneapolis, MN 55406
       (612) 867-4277 Nina Nieman
       Fax: (612) 724-4365
       Email: nina_nieman@yahoo.com
       Website:
unknown (Woman/White, estab 2003, empl 2, sales
$500,000, cert: City)

Missouri

1456   Accent Group Solutions
       1154 Reco Ave   St. Louis, MO 63110
       (314) 965-5388 Erica Hughes CEO
       Fax: (651) 450-9386
       Email: erica.hughes@accentgroupsolutions.com
       Website: www.accentgroupsolutions.com
Warehousing, Distribution Services, Pick Pack & Ship,
Custom Fulfillment, Publisher Services, Logo Apparel &
Promotional Products, Printing, Converting Printed
Materials, Literature Fulfillment, Container Manage-
ment. (Woman/White, estab 2003, empl 26, sales
$5,000,000, cert: WBENC)

1457   Blue Sky Apparel & Promotions, LLC
       12732 Pennridge Dr   Bridgeton, MO 63044
       (314) 739-4531 Kathy Gralike Owner
       Fax: (314) 344-4391
       Email: kgralike@aol.com
       Website: www.blueskypromotion.com/
Promotional products: pens, coffee mugs, apparel &
caps. (Woman/White, estab 2002, empl 5, sales
$1,369,654, cert: State)

Mississippi

1458   Zebra Marketing Corporation
       289 Commerce Park Dr, Ste E   Ridgeland, MS 39157
       (251) 438-2422 sharon Thompson Sales Exec
       Fax:
       Email: sharon.thompson@zebrapromos.com
       Website: www.zebrapromos.com
Advertising specialties, service awards, clothing-jackets, t-
shirts, sport shirts, trade show give aways. (Woman/White,
estab 2000, empl 14, sales $7,000,000, cert: WBENC)

North Carolina

1459   Adsource Media, Inc.
       8313-101 Six Forks Rd   Raleigh, NC 27615
       (919) 871-9990 Sara Tomlinson Brand Acct Exec
       Fax: (919) 871-6972
       Email: sara@am3adsource.com
       Website: www.am3adsource.com
Branded merchandise, decorated apparel, medical educational material, dimensional packaging, imported product,
trade show supplies, direct mailing, signage, training board
games. (Woman/White, estab 1999, empl 4, sales
$675,000, cert: WBENC)

1460   Austin Business Forms Inc.
       P.O. Box 1905   Matthews, NC 28016
       (704) 821-6165 Nick Sangermano Acct Exec
       Fax: (704) 821-4295
       Email: nick@printwithaustin.com
       Website: www.printwithaustin.com
Printing, graphic design, screen printing & embroidery,
promotional products. (Woman/White, estab 1991, empl
6, sales $1,514,990, cert: WBENC)

1461   Bob Williams Specialty Co.
       5539 Monroe Rd   Charlotte, NC 28212
       (704) 568-3411 Pamela McManus VP sales
       Fax: (704) 535-6662
       Email: bws@carolina.rr.com
       Website: www.bobwilliamsspecialty.com
Imprinted promotional products. (Woman, estab 1961,
empl 5, sales $800,000, cert: City)

1462   BrandRPM, LLC
       4910 Starcrest Dr   Monroe, NC 28110
       (704) 225-1800 Keith Brent VP strategic sales
       Fax: (704) 225-1900
       Email: keithb@brandrpm.com
       Website: www.brandrpm.com
Corporate apparel & branded merchandise. (Woman/As-
Pac, estab 2008, empl 40, sales $5,000,000, cert: State,
NMSDC)

1463   Crown Trophy Winston-Salem
       2869 Reynolda Rd   Winston-Salem, NC 27106
       (336) 723-7400 Michael Robinson
       Fax: (336) 723-7470
       Email: crowntrophy79@cs.com
       Website: www.crowntrophy.com
Awards & recogniton: badges, signage, corporate
awards, plaques, trophies, ribbons, medallians, promotional items, cast bronze, etc. (Woman/AA, estab 1978,
empl 5, sales , cert: State, City, NMSDC)

1464   Daybreak Marketing Services, LLC
       14460 Falls of Neuse Rd Ste 149-326 Raleigh, NC
       27614
       (919) 926-1452 Dawn Nakash COO
       Fax: (732) 901-7837
       Email: Dawn@DaybreakMarketing.com
       Website: www.DaybreakMarketing.com
Promotional Products, Advertising Specialties, Silk
Screening, Embroidery, Debossing, Embossing
Imprinted, Pens, mugs, t-shirts, magnets, pins, buttons,
uniforms, awards, bags, desk and auto accessories, flash
drives, power banks. (Woman/White, estab 1998, empl
1, sales $150,000, cert: State)

1465   G. ALAN Inc.
       5317 Highgate Dr Ste 212 Durham, NC 27713
       (919) 544-0055 Gregory Harris
       Fax: (919) 572-0950
       Email: gregory@imwithg.com
       Website: www.imwithg.com
Embroidery, screenprinting & promotional products.
(AA, estab 1994, empl 2, sales $422,500, cert: State,
NMSDC)

1466   PIA International LLC
       P.O. Box 481232   Charlotte, NC 28269
       (704) 593-1256 Donna Daniels Owner
       Fax: (704) 593-1257
       Email: donna@piapromo.com
       Website: www.piapromo.com
Promotional products, ad specialties, t-shirts, sports
uniforms & equipment, safety wear, etc. (Woman/AA,
estab 2003, empl 1, sales $98,900, cert: State, NMSDC)

1467   PROMOQUEST Inc.
       1308 Ballyclare Ct Raleigh, NC 27614
       (919) 845-3448 Pam Williams President
       Fax: (919) 845-5448
       Email: pam@promoquest.com
       Website: www.promoquest.com
Imprinted promotional products: screenprinting,
embroidery, lithography, digital printing, emboss,
deboss, laser, t-shirts, jackets, fleece, athletic apparel,
pants, bumper stickers, signs, buttons, pens note pads.
(Woman/AA, estab 1994, empl 1, sales , cert: State)

New Jersey

1468   3D Promoplastic, Inc.
       31 Summer Rd   Flemington, NJ 08822
       (469) 955-6282 Sibel Toy Owner
       Fax: (201) 983-4202
       Email: mail@3dpromoplastic.com
       Website: www.3d-promo.com
Promotional products, plastic promotional products,
custom mold clip pens, promotional give aways, ballpoint
pens, pen holders & eco friendly products. (Woman/
White, estab 2002, empl 50, sales $500,000, cert: State)

1469   Aberson Narotzky & White
       945 Lincoln Ave E   Cranford, NJ 07016
       (908) 789-2700 Shelly Aberson President
       Fax: (908) 789-9641
       Email: shelly@anwinc.com
       Website: www.anwinc.com
Advertising specialties, promotional products. (Woman/
White, estab 1989, empl 7, sales $3,100,000, cert: WBENC)

1470   Action Calendar & Specialty Co., Inc.
       5 Underwood Ct   Delran, NJ 08075
       (856) 764-4000 Lora Dunnigan President
       Fax: (856) 764-4360
       Email: lora.dunnigan@renpromo.com
       Website: www.wellnesseducationkits.com
Dist promotional products, on-site distribution center,
graphic arts, web dev, customer care call center, on-line
company stores. (Woman/White, estab 1975, empl 10,
sales $6,121,000, cert: WBENC)

1471   Balady Promotions, Inc.
       1719 Route 10 Ste 103 Parsippany, NJ 07054
       (973) 682-8440 Joanne Balady President
       Fax: (973) 682-8439
       Email: jbalady@balady.com
       Website: www.balady.com
Promotional product & decorated apparel programs, trade
show exhibits, signage & giveaways, business gifts/
premiums & award programs for employee achievement,
sales rewards & years of service. (Woman/White, estab
1989, empl 7, sales $2,951,425, cert: WBENC)

1472   Blank2Branded powered by Axis
       160 Main Rd   Montville, NJ 07045
       (973) 917-3100 Marcia Tarnoff President
       Fax: (973) 794-6320
       Email: marcia@blank2branded.com
       Website: www.blank2branded.com
Promotional solutions. (Woman/White, estab 2013, empl
5, sales $1,900,000, cert: WBENC)

1473   Compas, Inc.
       4300 Haddonfield Rd Ste 200 Pennsauken, NJ
       08109
       (856) 667-8577 Robert Kadar SVP
       Fax: (856) 667-3010
       Email: rkadar@cmicompas.com
       Website: www.compasonline.com
Media & promotional svcs. (AA, estab 1900, empl 1, sales
$250,000,000, cert: NMSDC)

1474   Daystar Promotions, Inc.
       83 Bergerville Rd   Freehold, NJ 07728
       (732) 409-0531 Loreley De George President
       Fax: (732) 409-1139
       Email: loreley@daystarpromotions.com
       Website: www.daystarpromotions.com
Promotional products & branded merchandise.
(Woman/White, estab 1989, empl 3, sales , cert:
WBENC)

1475   Distinctive Promotions inc
       268 Route 206 Ste 404 Flanders, NJ 07836
       (973) 584-6800 Michelle Slapa President
       Fax: (973) 927-8485
       Email: michelleslapa@distinctivepromotions.com
       Website: www.distinctivepromotions.com
Online web programs; wearables, awards, electronics,
etc. (Woman/White, estab 1983, empl 6, sales
$2,841,261, cert: WBENC)

1476   East West Connection
       389 Pittstown Rd   Pittstown, NJ 08867
       (908) 713-9655 Ralph Weaver President
       Fax: (908) 713-9797
       Email: rweaver_ewc@blast.net
       Website: www.eastwestconnection.com
Premium & promotional merchandise, custom design,
graphic & web design services, promotional writing, gift
wrapping, custom design projects, warehouse & fulfillment services. (AA, estab 1990, empl 20, sales
$8,289,878, cert: NMSDC)

1477   Focus Merchandising
       127 East Ridgewood Ave   Ridgewood, NJ 07450
       (201) 445-5858 Allison Rao President
       Fax: (201) 445-5877
       Email: allisonr@focusmc.com
       Website: www.focusmerchandising.com
Promotional marketing & premium items. (Woman/
White, estab 2003, empl 8, sales $8,000,000, cert:
WBENC)

1478   Glazer Design, LLC
       330 Franklin Turnpike   Mahwah, NJ 07430
       (201) 684-1132 Trish Glazer Office Mgr
       Fax: (201) 684-1156
       Email: trish@glazerpromos.com
       Website: www.glazerpromos.com
Promotional products. (Woman, estab 2002, empl 7,
sales $669,828, cert: City)

1479   Graphics Solutions
       473 Chapel Heights Rd   Sewell, NJ 08080
       (877) 931-1636 Steven Riggs Owner
       Fax: (856) 579-8096
       Email: support@graphics-solution.com
       Website: www.graphics-solution.com
Marketing communications products, print products,
promotional products, customized apparel, signage,
graphic design, web design, marketing consulting,
audio/video production. (AA, estab 2008, empl 5, sales
$423,000, cert: NMSDC)

1480 Ideas to Impress, LLC
      35 Longman St   Toms River, NJ 08753
      (201) 750-0222 Debbie Dennerlein President
      Fax: (201) 768-8310
      Email: debbie@ideastoimpress.com
      Website: www.ideastoimpress.com
Dist promotional products, company brand / logo, customized printed, embroidered & laser etched products: t-shirts, polo shirts, sweatshirts & uniforms, pens, desk accessories, to signs, and table covers, executive gift & give-aways. (Woman/White, estab 2006, empl 1, sales $103,211, cert: WBENC)

1481 Imprint Source LLC
      15 Charles St   Westwood, NJ 07675
      (201) 358-1010 Karen Adler Acct Exec
      Fax:
      Email: Karen@theimprintsource.com
      Website: www.TheImprintSource.com
Imprinted promotional products. (Woman, estab 1994, empl 6, sales $2,733,386, cert: WBENC)

1482 Inkwell Global Marketing
      600 Madison Ave.   Manalapan, NJ 07726
      (732) 617-3500 Stacey Panassidi Global Mktg
      Fax: (732) 972-2547
      Email: Staceyp@inkwellusa.com
      Website: www.inkwellusa.com
Dist promotional products. (Woman, estab 1986, empl 45, sales $12,500,000, cert: WBENC, NWBOC)

1483 Marissa L. Promotions
      1020 Campus Dr W   Morganville, NJ 07751
      (732) 689-2299 Jennifer Sangastiano Mktg Mgr
      Fax: (732) 389-5588
      Email: jennifer.sangastiano@creativesolutions.net
      Website: www.creativesolutions.net
Promotional & advertising specialties: trade show give-aways, corporate gifts, screen printing, graphic design. (Woman/White, estab 1990, empl 20, sales $8,500,000, cert: WBENC)

1484 Progressive Promotions Inc.
      145 Cedar Lane   Englewood, NJ 07631
      (201) 945-0500 Julie Levi President
      Fax: (201) 945-2228
      Email: julie@progressivepromotions.com
      Website: www.progressivepromotions.com
Promotional products: corporate apparel, gifts, awards, uniforms, web stores, fulfillment, packaging & assembly. (Woman/White, estab 1987, empl 30, sales $20,000,000, cert: WBENC)

1485 Sabella Gabino Inc. dba Bella Marketing Inc.
      5 Deer Path PO Box 366 Holmdel, NJ 07733
      (917) 951-3025 Isabella Petruzzelli CEO
      Fax: (732) 946-4624
      Email: isabella@bellamarketinginc.com
      Website: www.bellamarketinginc.com
Custom designed, promotional branded products specializing in the medical & pharmaceutical industry. (Woman/Hisp, estab 2001, empl 1, sales $94,395, cert: NMSDC, WBENC)

1486 Stackable Sensations
      2200 Route 10 W Ste 206 Parsippany, NJ 07054
      (973) 442-2831 Shari Verrone President
      Fax: (973) 442-0558
      Email: shariv@stackablesensations.com
      Website: www.stackablesensations.com/
Promotional products, logoed apparel, advertising specialties. (Woman/White, estab 2003, empl 10, sales $1,750,000, cert: WBENC)

1487 The Artcraft Group, Inc. dba Artcraft Health
      39 Highway 12   Flemington, NJ 08822
      (908) 782-4921 Lisa Dec Business Devel Dir
      Fax: (908) 782-7158
      Email: LDec@artcrafthealth.com
      Website: www.artcrafthealth.com
Advertising specialties. (Woman/White, estab 1946, empl 150, sales $52,000,000, cert: WBENC)

1488 Thomas Direct Sales, Inc.
      30 Plymouth St   Fairfield, NJ 07004
      (973) 614-2307 Guy DAndrea COO
      Fax: (973) 574-2115
      Email: mmarinzulich@thomasdirect.com
      Website: www.thomasdirect.com
Promotional products, premium & incentive programs, importing, on-site design & illustration, graphic arts, technology & website development. (Woman/White, estab 1986, empl 12, sales $1,000,000, cert: WBENC)

Nevada

1489 Eagle Promotions
      4575 W Post Rd Ste 100 Las Vegas, NV 89118
      (702) 388-7100 Mario Stadtlander President
      Fax: (702) 853-5173
      Email: Mario@eaglepromotions.com
      Website: www.eaglepromotions.com
Advertising specialties: apparel, awards, catalog, company store fulfillment programs. (As-Pac, estab 2001, empl 203, sales $32,000,000, cert: NMSDC)

New York

1490 AIA New Dimensions in Marketing, Inc.
      124 S Central Ave   Elmsford, NY 10523
      (914) 348-4872 Maria Perez President
      Fax: (914) 347-4870
      Email: perez@effectivepromos.com
      Website: www.effectivepromos.com
Promotional & specialty advertising items. (Woman/Hisp, estab 1999, empl 3, sales $355,000, cert: State, WBENC)

1491   Crown Awards
       9 Skyline Dr   Hawthorne, NY 10532
       (914) 347-7700 Joseph SanGeorge Acct Mgr
       Fax:
       Email: Jsangeorge@crownawards.com
       Website: www.crownawards.com
Mfr awards. (Woman/White, estab 1980, empl 500, sales
$75,000,000, cert: WBENC)

1492   Dakota Print and Premiums LLC
       150 Barton Road   White Plains, NY 10605
       (914) 831-9101 Stuart Standard President
       Fax: (914) 831-0668
       Email: stuart@fuseprinting.com
       Website: www.fuseprinting.com
Promotional products, commercial printing, wide format &
transit advertising, vehicle wraps, directories, transit &
marketing tools provider, screen printing, banners,
posters, postcards, journals, award items, etc. (Woman/
AA, estab 2004, empl 3, sales $606,000, cert: State, City,
NMSDC)

1493   DRSolutions, Inc.
       41 Ridgefield Dr   Shoreham, NY 11786
       (631) 209-1086 Trisha Stolfi CEO
       Fax: (631) 209-1094
       Email: trisha.stolfi@proforma.com
       Website: www.proforma.com/drsolutions
Dist printed material: forms, labels, posters & displays,
promotional items, work aprons, etc. (Woman/White,
estab 2002, empl 2, sales , cert: State)

1494   Freestyle Marketing, LLC
       362 Fifth Avenue Ste 1003 New Y ork, NY 10001
       (212) 599-5995 Caryn Stoll President
       Fax:
       Email: info@freestylemktg.com
       Website: www.freestylemktg.com
Promotional marketing materials & premiums. (Woman/
White, estab 2001, empl 40, sales $7,000,000, cert:
WBENC)

1495   Fulcrum Group
       135 W 41st St   New York, NY 10036
       (203) 909-6362 GIA VACCA Partner
       Fax: (203) 909-6364
       Email: gia@fulcrumpromos.com
       Website: www.fulcrumgrp.com
Incentive Programs, Apparel, Promotional Merchandise,
Printing & Creative Services, Large Format & Signage,
Event Production, E-commerce& Fulfillment, Print Media.
(Woman/White, estab 2010, empl 7, sales $1,200,000,
cert: WBENC)

1496   Innovative Premiums Inc.
       3571 Hargale Rd   Oceanside, NY 11572
       (516) 766-3800 Judah Isaacs VP
       Fax: (516) 766-3860
       Email: Judah@innovativepremiums.com
       Website: www.innovativepremiums.com
Custom & standard promotional merchandise. (Woman/
White, estab 1980, empl 14, sales $9,000,000, cert:
WBENC)

1497   inQueue Designs LLC
       25 Central Park W   New York, NY 10023
       (917) 699-8259 Alison Schneiderman Co Owner
       Fax:
       Email: Alison@inQueuedesigns.com
       Website: www.inQueuedesigns.com
Custom branded, designed products, stationery goods,
seasonal promotions, corporate gifts, journal books, log
books, die-cut folders & boxes, ipad book case, (Woman/
White, estab 2010, empl 2, sales $65,279, cert: WBENC)

1498   KarSun Enterprises, Inc.
       1133 Broadway, Ste 1311   New York, NY 10010
       (212) 420-6688 Sung Park President
       Fax: (866) 644-8514
       Email: sung@customdirectpromo.com
       Website: www.karsunenterprises.com
Promotional & merchandise bags, backpacks & duffels.
(Woman/As-Pac, estab 1996, empl 10, sales $3,500,000,
cert: NMSDC)

1499   Multi Media Promotions
       33 Southwick Court S   Plainview, NY 11803
       (516) 935-0553 Beth Levine Managing Partner
       Fax: (516) 345-1614
       Email: beth@mmpromos.com
       Website: www.mmpromos.com
Promotional advertising & premium incentives, logos,
graphic design, printing, imprinting, embroidery,
embossing & engraving. (Woman, estab 2004, empl 3,
sales $600,000, cert: State, WBENC)

1500   National Gifts Ltd.
       6 Poole St   Oceanside, NY 11572
       (516) 763-9000 Elaine Goodman CEO
       Fax: (888) 900-8502
       Email: elaine@nationalgifts.com
       Website: www.nationalgifts.com
Advertising specialities, premiums, gifts, awards,
trophies, wearables, promotional items, etc. (Woman/
White, estab 1983, empl 6, sales $10,250,025, cert:
WBENC)

1501   Print & Mail Partners, Inc.
       2152 Ralph Ave Ste 317 Brooklyn, NY 11234
       (646) 771-4245 Rose Mazzone President
       Fax:
       Email: rose.mazzone@theperfectpromo.com
       Website: www.theperfectpromo.com
Custom imprinted T-shirts, advertising specialties,
promotional items, buttons, badges, premiums, corporate merchandise & giveaways. (Woman/White, estab
1997, empl 3, sales , cert: State, City)

1502   Sauerbach Associates
       1745 Merrick Ave Ste 27 Merrick, NY 11566
       (516) 868-9650 Janet Silver President
       Fax: (516) 868-3284
       Email: customerservice@sauerbach.com
       Website: www.sauerbach.com
Sales incentive programs, promotional products programs, company stores, trade show marketing, new
product launches, road shows, sales training meetings.
(Woman/White, estab 1954, empl 6, sales $1,600,000,
cert: WBENC)

1503   Sentec Promotions, Inc
         4367 Harlem Rd   Amherst, NY 14226
         (716) 839-2294 Susan Cataudella President
         Fax: (716) 839-3720
         Email: susiespec@aol.com
         Website: www.susiespecialties.com
Promotional products.
 (Woman/White, estab 1994, empl 3, sales $1,090,404,
cert: WBENC)

1504   Von Pok & Chang
         60 E 42 St, Ste 666   New York, NY 10165
         (212) 599-0556 Peter Sebastian Sales
         Fax: (212) 599-1196
         Email: peter.sebastian@vonpok.com
         Website: www.vonpok.com
Contract mfr & import promotional products. (As-Pac,
estab 1981, empl 8, sales , cert: NMSDC)

Ohio

1505   889 Global Solutions
         1156 Dublin Rd, Ste 105   Columbus, OH 43215
         (614) 235-8889 Brandon Meyer Govt Sales
         Project Mgr
         Fax: (720) 294-6551
         Email: info@889globalsolutions.com
         Website: www.889globalsolutions.com
Import/export products to and from China. (Woman/As-
Pac, estab 2000, empl 20, sales , cert: State, NMSDC)

1506   Airmate Company
         16280 County Rd D   Bryan, OH 43506
         (419) 636-3184 Carol Czech President
         Fax: (419) 636-4210
         Email: carol@airmatecompany.com
         Website: www.airmatecompany.com
Safety signs, promotional products, custom fabrication,
custom printing. (Woman/White, estab 1946, empl 35,
sales $4,200,000, cert: WBENC)

1507   Arrasmith Promotions LLC
         6115 Wiehe Rd   Cincinnati, OH 45237
         (513) 681-9400 Jerry Arrasmith Jr. President
         Fax: (513) 681-0444
         Email: sales@arrasmithpromotions.com
         Website: www.arrasmithpromotions.com
Advertising specialties & promotional items. (Woman/
White, estab 2003, empl 6, sales $2,100,000, cert:
WBENC)

1508   Bouzounis LLC dba Artina Promotional Products
         50 S Liberty St Ste 250 Powell, OH 43065
         (614) 635-8865 Lesley Jennings Sr Acct Exec
         Fax: (614) 635-8866
         Email: ljennings@artina.com
         Website: www.artina.com
Promotional products. (Woman, estab 1967, empl 22,
sales $4,353,500, cert: WBENC)

1509   City Apparel, Inc.
         120 Bentley Court   Findlay, OH 45840
         (419) 434-1157 Hilary Orians Acct Solutions
         Fax:
         Email: hilary@cityapparel.net
         Website: www.cityapparel.net
Uniform programs, corporate casual apparel, promotional products, employee incentive programs &
integrated e-commerce solutions. (Woman/White, estab
2001, empl 9, sales $2,300,000, cert: WBENC)

1510   Eat It Read It Placemats
         45 W Main St   McConnelsville, OH 43756
         (740) 962-6899 Heather Hill CEO
         Fax: (740) 962-3852
         Email: hbhill@ergraphics.com
         Website: www.ergraphics.com
Advertising specialties, apparel, uniforms, signs, website
design, printing. (Woman/AA, estab 2001, empl 3, sales
$175,000, cert: State)

1511   EB ART EB ADS LLC
         9045 Spooky Ridge Ln   Cincinnati, OH 45242
         (513) 984-5144 Eileen Bloustein CEO
         Fax: (513) 984-5184
         Email: sales@ebartebads.com
         Website: www.ebartebads.com
Dist promotional products: corporate awards, portraits,
limited editions giclee, digital art & sculpture. (Woman/
White, estab 1999, empl 1, sales , cert: WBENC)

1512   Global Promotions & Incentives, LLC
         3375 Gilchrist Rd   Mogadore, OH 44260
         (330) 798-5175 Jonathan Thornton Regional Dir,
         Key Accts Exec
         Fax: (330) 733-5196
         Email: JDThornton@aswglobal.com
         Website: www.shopglobalpai.com/
Promotional & incentive products, programs & event
planning. (AA, estab 2002, empl 31, sales $5,500,000,
cert: NMSDC)

1513   Hotcards
         2400 Superior Ave   Cleveland, OH 44114
         (216) 241-4040 Greg Schwartz Enterprise Sales
         Dir
         Fax:
         Email: gschwartz@hotcards.com
         Website: www.hotcards.com
Design, print, promotional, apparel & direct mail. (Hisp,
estab 1998, empl 20, sales , cert: State)

1514   Ketterer Company
         12110 Ellington Ct   Cincinnati, OH 45249
         (513) 247-0100 Kimberly W. Ketterer CEO
         Fax: (513) 247-0012
         Email: kim_ketterer@kettererco.com
         Website: www.getLOGOstuff.com
Promotional advertising: logo design, graphic art,
warehousing, distribution & fulfillment services, company stores & online rewards programs. (Woman/White,
estab 1955, empl 6, sales $3,609,077, cert: WBENC)

1515   Leader Promotions, Inc.
     790 E Johnstown Rd   Columbus, OH 43230
     (614) 416-6565   Lenny Friedland Director of
     Business Developement
     Fax: (614) 416-6566
     Email: lfriedland@leaderpromos.com
     Website: www.leaderpromos.com
Fulfillment programs, corporate apparel, promotional products & uniforms. (Woman/White, estab 1995, empl 70, sales $28,000,000, cert: WBENC)

1516   LIZard Apparel & Promotions
     775 Congress Park Dr   Dayton, OH 45459
     (937) 848-7100   Kelly Davis VP of Sales
     Fax: (866) 539-4041
     Email: kelly@lizardap.com
     Website: www.lizardap.com
Promotional, recognition & rewards programs, uniform fittings, Shoe programs, Uniform accessories, name badges, stethoscopes, scissors, arm sleeves. (Woman/White, estab 2013, empl 10, sales $1,231,824, cert: WBENC)

1517   Outreach Promotional Solutions
     111 Liberty St Ste 101   Columbus, OH 43215
     (216) 452-5319   Nevin Bansal President
     Fax: (614) 484-1537
     Email: bansal@outreachpromos.com
     Website: www.outreachpromos.com
Provides creative promotional product solutions. (As-Ind, estab 2012, empl 12, sales $1,000,000, cert: State)

1518   Palmer Promotions
     6203 Marcus Ct   Cincinnati, OH 45069
     (800) 697-0053   Steven Palmer Owner
     Fax: (866) 660-2183
     Email: steve@palmerpromotions.com
     Website: www.palmerpromotions.com
Promotional products, awards, business gifts & decorated apparel. (As-Pac, estab 1983, empl 2, sales $578,066, cert: NMSDC)

1519   Park Place Services, dba Proforma
     8800 E Pleasant Valley Rd   Cleveland, OH 44131
     (216) 520-8400   William Byrne President
     Fax: (216) 524-1289
     Email: bbyrne@proforma.com
     Website: www.proforma.com
Printing, Promotional products, Corporate Apparel, Marketing literature, Packaging, Trade Show Supplies & giveaways, Business Forms, labels, envelopes. (Woman/White, estab 1996, empl 700, sales $500,000,000, cert: NWBOC)

1520   Proforma Albrecht & Co.
     1040 Technecenter Dr   Milford, OH 45150
     (202) 237-2828   Suzette Albrecht
     Fax: (202) 652-1196
     Email: suzette@albrechtco.com
     Website: www.OnSalePromos.com
Promotional products, tees & clothing, custom logos & designs, decorated corporate gifts. (Woman/White, estab 1999, empl 150, sales $2,200,000, cert: WBENC)

1521   Proforma Joe Thomas Group
     13500 Pearl Rd, Ste 139-107   Cleveland, OH 44136
     (440) 268-0881   Joe Thomas President
     Fax:
     Email: joe@proformajoethomasgroup.com
     Website: www.proformajoethomasgroup.com
Advertising specialties. (As-Ind, estab 1999, empl 2, sales $1,123,000, cert: NMSDC)

1522   PromoHits! Ltd.
     141B N Main St   Bluffton, OH 45817
     (419) 358-0700   Melinda Bowden Owner
     Fax: (419) 358-0704
     Email: mbowden@wcoil.com
     Website: www.promohitsltd.com
Promotional items: gift & specialty baskets, jackets, shirts, sweatshirts, pants, hats, windshirts, mousepads, pencil holders, pens, paperclips, USB drives, flash drives/ memory drives. (Woman/White, estab 2000, empl 4, sales $382,780, cert: WBENC)

1523   Promotions Etc., LLC
     5000 Acme Dr. Unit A   Fairfield, OH 45014
     (513) 795-7021   Julie Holderbach CEO
     Fax: (513) 672-9866
     Email: julie@mypromotionsetc.com
     Website: www.mypromotionsetc.com
Promotional products: apparel & uniforms, corporate gifts, give-a-ways, awards, engraved items, decals, labels, trade show give-a-ways, booth display & signage. (Woman/White, estab 2012, empl 2, sales $125,000, cert: State)

1524   Race Ahead
     7100 Euclid Avenue Ste 175   Cleveland, OH 44103
     (440) 554-7018   Beth Eaton President
     Fax:
     Email: beth@raceaheadcle.com
     Website: www.raceaheadcle.com
Customized apparel & branded accessories. (Woman, estab 2016, empl 1, sales $89,000, cert: City)

1525   Schaffer Partners, Inc.
     6545 Carnegie Ave   Cleveland, OH 44103
     (863) 299-6392   Susan Mayrant VP Business Dev
     Fax: (216) 881-7413
     Email: susan.mayrant@spihq.com
     Website: www.pfi-awards.com
Incentive merchandise fulfillment & program administration resources, design & manage online & paper based solutions, brand name merchandise awards, travel rewards & event tickets. (Woman/White, estab 1968, empl 40, sales $10,017,858, cert: WBENC)

1526   Ten 10 Design LLC
     115 Wilson Mills Rd, Ste 6   Chardon, OH 44024
     (440) 286-4367   Joe Zulandt Sales Mgr
     Fax: (440) 286-5168
     Email: joe@ten10designllc.com
     Website: www.ten10designllc.com
Printing (offset and digital), promotional items, ad specialties, mailing services, labels & decals, graphic design, web design. (Woman/AA, estab 2008, empl 3, sales $250,000, cert: State, NMSDC, WBENC)

1527 The AG Group, Inc. dba AG PrintPromo Solutions
      960 Graham Rd, Ste 1 Cuyahoga Falls, OH 44221
      (330) 315-9600 Anup Gupta President
      Fax: (330) 315-9603
      Email: agupta@theaggroup.com
      Website: www.theaggroup.com
Dist promotional products, gifts, corporate apparel,
embroidered & screen printed. (Woman/As-Ind, estab
1996, empl 5, sales $3,400,000, cert: State)

1528 The Callard Company
      5780 Zarley St Ste B New Albany, OH 43054
      (614) 933-0303 Jennifer Duvuvuei Senior Natl Acct
      Exec
      Fax: (614) 933-0404
      Email: jenniferd@callard.com
      Website: www.callard.com
Promotional products & creative marketing: awards, trade
show giveaways, team rewards, client gifts, recruitment
incentives & golf outing supplies. (Woman/White, estab
1987, empl 24, sales $6,500,000, cert: WBENC)

1529 The John K. Howe Company, Inc.
      340 Gest St Cincinnati, OH 45203
      (513) 651-1888 Nancy Howe-Jones CEO
      Fax: (513) 651-1911
      Email: howejones.nk@ehowe.com
      Website: www.ehowe.com
Branded apparel, promotional products & business
recognition. (Woman/White, estab 1972, empl 10, sales
$3,923,395, cert: WBENC)

1530 Vorce & Associates
      1335 Dublin Rd Ste 216C Columbus, OH 43215
      (614) 488-5450 Donna Vorce Owner
      Fax: (614) 488-0117
      Email: donna@firstimpressionsohio.com
      Website: www.firstimpressionsohio.com
Promotional & imprinted apparel. (Woman/White, estab
1983, empl 2, sales $810,000, cert: State)

Oregon

1531 Enthusias Media Group
      1631 NE Broadway, Ste 614 Portland, OR 97232
      (503) 376-6839 Marcy Hall Reg Acct Mgr
      Fax: (503) 253-2234
      Email: info@enthusiastmediagroup.com
      Website: www.enthusiastmediagroup.com
Promotional & print items. (Woman/White, estab 2005,
empl 7, sales $2,000,000, cert: State)

Pennsylvania

1532 As You Wish Promotions
      3801 Germantown Pike Ste 202 Collegeville, PA
      19426
      (484) 973-6565 Alyssa Heininger Client Relation-
      ship Coord
      Fax: (484) 973-6936
      Email: aheininger@wishpromo.com
      Website: www.wishpromo.com
Promotional products, graphic arts capabilities, marketing, service, client support & customer relations, trade
show give-aways, corporate gifts, promotional apparel
& employee awards. (Woman/White, estab 1992, empl
5, sales $1,913,640, cert: WBENC)

1533 BDJ Ventures, LLC
      3024 Bainbridge Dr Lansdale, PA 19446
      (215) 266-2062 Bernard Wright Principal & Sr Dir
      Fax: (215) 256-9265
      Email: bwright@bdjventuresllc.com
      Website: www.bdjventuresllc.com
Premiums & promotional products. (AA, estab 2009,
empl 3, sales $31,096, cert: State, NMSDC)

1534 Bry-Lex Promotional LLC
      19 Nelson Dr Southampton, PA 18966
      (800) 251-9101 Bev Kaytes CEO
      Fax: (215) 355-8411
      Email: bev@brylex.com
      Website: www.bry-lex.com
Promotional items, imprinted logos, blank logos,
embroidery/silkscreen. (Woman/White, estab 1996,
empl 11, sales $550,000, cert: State, WBENC)

1535 CPI Creative
      336 1st St Pittsburgh, PA 15215
      (412) 782-2675 Carol Philp President
      Fax: (412) 782-1732
      Email: info@cpicreative.com
      Website: www.cpicreative.com
Design & fulfil custom programs: service awards, safety,
sales incentives, fundraising, trade shows, education,
product introduction, ad specialties & innovative
products. (Woman/White, estab 1994, empl 5, sales
$3,370,160, cert: WBENC)

1536 Signature Promotions
      715 Twining Road Ste 107 Dresher, PA 19025
      (215) 641-1168 Maureen Coffey Owner
      Fax: (215) 641-9364
      Email: sigpro@comcast.net
      Website: www.sigpromo.com
Promotional advertising products, grahic design,
product development & fulfillment capabilities.
(Woman/White, estab 1992, empl 1, sales , cert:
WBENC)

Rhode Island

1537 Ahlers Designs, Inc.
      999 Main St, Unit 707   Pawtucket, RI 02860
      (401) 365-1010 Gail Ahlers CEO
      Fax: (401) 365-1333
      Email: operations@ahlersdesigns.com
      Website: www.ahlersdesigns.com
Designs & mfr custom corporate gifts & awards, engraving,
custom cards or packaging. (Woman/White, estab 1989,
empl 3, sales $132,751, cert: State, WBENC)

South Carolina

1538 2 Oceans Promotions
      6175 Caravelle Court   Awendaw, SC 29429
      (843) 971-8499 Michele Johnson Owner
      Fax: (843) 971-8440
      Email: michele@2oceanspromotions.com
      Website: www.2oceanspromotions.com
Promotional marketing & products. (Woman/White, estab
2001, empl 6, sales $2,100,000, cert: WBENC)

1539 Promotions Unlimited, LLC
      327 Miller Rd, Ste E   Mauldin, SC 29662
      (864) 527-1193 Laura Campbell Dir of Sales
      Fax: (864) 527-1194
      Email: laura@promoultd.com
      Website: www.promoultd.com
Promotional Items, Uniform Programs (Woman/White,
estab 2005, empl 9, sales $2,254,086, cert: State, WBENC)

1540 Red Iron Brand Solutions, LLC
      104 Saluda Run Dr   Piedmont, SC 29673
      (800) 325-3824 Lucy Hoffman Owner
      Fax: (864) 299-1420
      Email: Lucy@redironbrand.com
      Website: www.redironbrand.com
Mfr & import event display items: Tablecovers & runners
in stretch fabric, polyester, polyvalue, plastic (cut table
covers and imprinted banquet rolls), and 400 denier.
(Woman/White, estab 2016, empl 10, sales $250,000, cert:
State)

Tennessee

1541 Imagination Specialties, Inc.
      230 Great Circle Rd, Ste 248 Ste 248 Nashville, TN
      37228
      (615) 255-5688 Dan Sargent Business Dev
      Fax: (615) 255-3513
      Email: becky@imaginationbranding.com
      Website: www.imaginationspecialties.com
Ad specialty & promotional products, corporate gifts,
baskets, event planning, event room drops, custom
printing, invitations, mail outs, online company stores,
warehousing, distribution & fulfillment services. (Woman/
White, estab 1989, empl 39, sales $11,275,000, cert:
WBENC)

1542 The Barr Group, Inc.
      230 Great Circle Road, Ste 234   Nashville, TN
      37228
      (615) 612-0444 Jim Barr Director of Sales
      Fax: (615) 865-4341
      Email: jim@barrgroupinc.com
      Website: www.barrgroupinc.com
Promotional products, printing, indoor & outdoor
signage, corrugated packagin, MRO items, transportation brokerage & hauling. (Woman/Hisp, estab 1999,
empl 6, sales $2,505,000, cert: WBENC)

Texas

1543 Ad-Image Creative Promotions Co.
      851 Lakeview Dr   Coppell, TX 75019
      (972) 462-0919 Terri Finazzo President
      Fax: (972) 462-0490
      Email: adimagedallas@aol.com
      Website: www.adimagedallas.com
Advertising specialties & promotional products.
(Woman/White, estab 1999, empl 2, sales $33,557,
cert: State, WBENC)

1544 Austin Ad Group
      5960 W Parker Rd, Ste 278 PMB 272 Plano, TX
      75093
      (972) 307-7100 Rhonda Aicklen President
      Fax:
      Email: Orders@AustinAdGroup.com
      Website: www.AustinAdGroup.com
Promotional logo/branded items: apparel, pens, bags,
hats, cups, trinkets, coolers, armbands, badges, balloons, bandana, buttons, flashlights, floor mats, jewelry,
tattoos, stuffed animals, awards, grills, etc. (Woman/
White, estab 1993, empl 7, sales , cert: State)

1545 Aztec Promotional Group, LP
      2815 Manor Rd   Austin, TX 78722
      (512) 744-0195 Patti Winstanley President
      Fax: (512) 744-0196
      Email: patti@aztecworld.com
      Website: www.aztecworld.com
Sscreen printed & embroidered textiles, advertising
specialty items & design. (Woman/AA, estab 1995, empl
25, sales $1,350,000, cert: State, WBENC)

1546 Beehive Specialty Co.
      8701 Wall St, Ste 900   Austin, TX 78754
      (512) 912-7940 Kelli Dillon Mgr/new Business
      dept
      Fax: (512) 997-7944
      Email: kelli@specialbee.com
      Website: www.beehivespecialty.com
Promotional products, custom product fabrication, online programs, high impact mail, packaging, fulfillment
& integrated project management. (Woman/White,
estab 1998, empl 12, sales $8,000,000, cert: WBENC)

1547   Cadena Specialty Advertising
       P.O. Box 150655   Arlington, TX 76015
       (817) 459-4474 Olga Quiroz Owner
       Fax: (817) 459-3323
       Email: olga_cadenaspecialty@yahoo.com
       Website: www.cadenausa.com
Dist promotional marketing products: pens, cups, key tags,
calendards, silkscreened & embroidered caps & apparel,
employee recognition & safety awards & gifts. (Woman/
Hisp, estab 1993, empl 1, sales $155,000, cert: State, City)

1548   CFJ Manufacturing
       5001 North Frwy   Fort Worth, TX 76106
       (817) 625-9559 Sharon Evans CEO
       Fax: (817) 625-2050
       Email: marketing@cfjmfg.com
       Website: www.cfjmfg.com
Promotional marketing & employee recognition solutions.
(Woman/White, estab 1983, empl 257, sales $61,892,315,
cert: State, WBENC)

1549   Creative Menus & Folders, LLC dba Texas Covers
       409 Old Hwy 80   Olden, TX 76466
       (254) 653-2775 Renee Forguson Asst Production
       Mgr
       Fax: (254) 653-2776
       Email: reneeforguson@texascovers.com
       Website: www.texascovers.com
Presentation/Executive Binders, folders, business cards,
printing (screen, digital, offset, foil stamp, deboss, specialty color cast printing, plastic ID badge holders, ID
badges, name tags, souvenir printing, banners, signage,
laminating, caps. (As-Pac, estab 2015, empl 19, sales
$135,353, cert: NMSDC)

1550   Davis & Stanton, Inc.
       4002 W Miller Rd, Ste 140   Garland, TX 75041
       (214) 340-1321 Charlee Castillo Owner
       Fax: (214) 340-1388
       Email: charlee@davstan.com
       Website: www.davstan.com
Advertising specialties, promotional products, plaques &
awards & police commendation bars. (Woman/Hisp, estab
1949, empl 26, sales $5,000,000, cert: State, WBENC)

1551   DBS Marketing & Promotions LLC
       24466 Pipestem Dr   Magnolia, TX 77355
       (281) 356-2386 Sue Becknell President
       Fax: (281) 356-2731
       Email: sue@dbspromo.com
       Website: www.dbspromo.com
Logo branded promotional products, corporate apparel,
awards, pens, notepads, shirts, caps, jackets, screen
printing, laser engraving, embroidery, pad folios, backpacks, duffel bags, tote bags, tee shirts, golf items, flyers,
etc. (Woman/White, estab 2005, empl 3, sales $1,230,000,
cert: WBENC)

1552   Distinctive Marketing Ideas
       3415 Custer Rd, Ste 133   Plano, TX 75023
       (972) 612-0050 Bonnie Shackelford Owner
       Fax: (972) 596-1018
       Email: bonnie.shack@dmipromotions.com
       Website: www.dmipromotions.com
Promotional products/premiums, warehouse & fulfillment. (Woman/White, estab 1992, empl 4, sales
$1,750,000, cert: State, WBENC)

1553   Fuel7 Inc.
       11910 Greenville Ave, Ste 275   Dallas, TX 75243
       (888) 669-4009 Steven Pratt
       Fax: (877) 669-4009
       Email: steven@fuel7.com
       Website: www.fuel7.com
Fuel7 provides embedded development services, both
hardware and software, specializing in new embedded
Linux projects. From design and architecture through
development and board bringup (Hisp, estab 2004, empl
12, sales $2,200,000, cert: NMSDC)

1554   Henya Direct LLC
       5555 W University Blvd   Dallas, TX 75209
       (214) 701-0671 Terence Johnson Natl Accts Mgr
       Fax: (866) 827-3830
       Email: tjohnson@henyadirect.com
       Website: www.henyadirect.com
Promotional merchandise: uniforms, hats, cups, stress
balls, pens, bags, watches, etc. (Woman/White, estab
2007, empl 3, sales $1,500,000, cert: WBENC)

1555   Holden Custom Products
       7920 Beltline Rd Ste 960 Dallas, TX 75254
       (214) 543-1133 MARNIE HOLDEN Dir major Accts
       Fax: (972) 231-0742
       Email: HOLDENLL@FLASH.NET
       Website: www.holdenbrand.com
Corporate packaging, promotional products, imports &
wearables. (Woman/White, estab 1978, empl 16, sales
$9,500,000, cert: State)

1556   I Chispa, LLC
       129 Thunderbird   El Paso, TX 79912
       (915) 239-7430 Horacio Arras VP Sales & Mktg.
       Fax: (915) 584-5464
       Email: Horacio@ichispa.us
       Website: www.ichispa.us
Promotional & sports items. (Woman/Hisp, estab 2010,
empl 5, sales , cert: State, NMSDC)

1557   IncentiveAmerica, Inc.
       18208 Preston Rd Ste D924 Dallas, TX 75252
       (972) 380-9990 Elizabeth Montgomery President
       Fax: (972) 380-9999
       Email: elizabethm@incentiveamerica.com
       Website: www.incentiveamerica.com
Pre-paid MasterCard gift cards & dining gift cards,
personalized, premium note card & gold-embossed
greeting card. (Woman/AA, estab 2003, empl 5, sales
$968,290, cert: State, NMSDC, 8(a))

1558　Insignia Marketing
32731 Egypt Lane Ste 301　Magnolia, TX 77354
(281) 465-0040　Christine McAtee President
Fax: (281) 465-0940
Email: Orders@VisiCare.com
Website: www.VisiCare.com
Promotional advertising: corporate brand identity, creativity, pens, coffee mugs, t-shirts & awards. (Woman/White, estab 2002, empl 3, sales $2,000,000, cert: State, WBENC)

1559　Malkoff Promotions
4904 Stony Ford Dr　Dallas, TX 75287
(972) 248-4354　Lynne Malkoff President
Fax:
Email: lynne@lmpspecialties.com
Website: www.lmpspecialties.com
Marketing & promotional solutions. (Woman/White, estab 1989, empl 5, sales , cert: State, WBENC)

1560　Network Embroidery Inc.
10600 Shadow Wood Dr Ste 201　Houston, TX 77043
(713) 865-8032　Lily Clark President
Fax:
Email: micael.shea@networkinterstateco.com
Website: www.networkinterstateco.com
Mfr & dist promotional products, catalog programs, awards, trophies, graphics, warehousing & fulfillment. (Woman, estab , empl 1, sales , cert: WBENC)

1561　Potenza Promotions, LLC
810 Genoa　Argyle, TX 76226
(940) 595-9555　Laura Hulke President
Fax: (480) 275-3708
Email: lhulke@potenzapromotions.com
Website: www.potenzapromotions.com
Promotional products: mugs, pens, stress balls, awards, office items, USB pens, etc. (Woman/White, estab 2006, empl 6, sales $147,000, cert: State)

1562　Power Of Two Productions, LLC
9901 Brodie Ln, Ste 160-279　Austin, TX 78748
(512) 872-5000　LeeAnn Wick CEO
Fax: (866) 764-7635
Email: leeann@ptwopromo.com
Website: www.PTwoPromo.com
Promotional products, business gifts, trade show give-aways, wellness programs, incentives, awards, safety, screen printing, embroidery, apparel, employee retention, sustainable, eco friendly, tote bags, promotions. (Woman/Hisp, estab 2007, empl 3, sales $419,000, cert: State, NMSDC, WBENC)

1563　RedMan I Am Promotions
1516 Wimberly Ct　Bedford, TX 76021
(817) 229-6271　Robert Whistler Owner
Fax:
Email: Redmaniam@msn.com
Website:
Custom imprinted logo merchandise: awards, aprons, badges, balls, balloons, banners, bottle openers,calculators, calendars, candy, caps, clocks, cups, desk sets, food gifts, first aid kits, flashlights, etc. (Nat Ame, estab 2011, empl 1, sales , cert: State)

1564　RG Apparel Co.
2912 N MacArthur, Ste 103　Irving, TX 75062
(972) 793-0583　Joe Temple COO
Fax: (972) 793-0588
Email: jt@rgapparel.com
Website: www.rgapparel.com
Mfr textiles: uniforms, work shirts, polos, tees, woven button up shirts & headwear, promotional marketing items & gifts. (AA, estab 2006, empl 6, sales $3,200,000, cert: State, NMSDC)

1565　The Donna Bender Company
6860 North Dallas Parkway Ste 200　Plano, TX 75024
(214) 520-8577　Donna Bender President
Fax: (214) 242-4747
Email: donna@donnaco.com
Website: www.donnaco.com
Promotional products; specialty advertising; business gifts; service, achievement & recognition awards; incentive & awareness programs. (Woman/White, estab 2007, empl 3, sales , cert: State, WBENC)

1566　TLC Adcentives LLC
21101 Kingsland Blvd. Ste. 1113　Katy, TX 77450
(281) 828-2270　Terri Hornsby President
Fax: (281) 828-0029
Email: terri@tlcadcentives.com
Website: www.tlcadcentives.com
Advertising promotional incentives, awards & trophies, cups & mugs, apparel & headgear, desk accessories, writing instruments, portfolios, briefcases. (Woman/AA, estab 1995, empl 4, sales , cert: State)

1567　Trademarks Promotional Products
11333 Todd St　Houston, TX 77055
(713) 680-3000　Kelli Cochran Acct Mgr
Fax: (713) 681-2900
Email: tpp@tmarks.com
Website: www.trademarkspromos.com
Promotional products, screenprinting, embroidery, direct digital garment printing, graphic design, award engraving, ad specialty items. (Woman/White, estab 1979, empl 60, sales $7,100,001, cert: State, WBENC)

1568　W. M. Martin Advertising
PO Box 795818　Dallas, TX 75379
(972) 732-8040　Wendy Fahle Owner
Fax:
Email: cs@wmmadv.com
Website: www.wmmadv.com
Advertising specialties: pens, shirts, caps, calendars, golf items. (Woman/White, estab 1983, empl 4, sales $850,000, cert: State, WBENC)

Virginia

1569 Fishnet, LLC
P.O. Box 7311 Charlottesville, VA 22906
(434) 409-6177 David Goloversic Sr Acct Exec
Fax: (866) 462-4010
Email: contactus@fishnetllc.com
Website: www.fishnetllc.com
Printing & promotional products: writing instruments, office accessories, food and drink ware, doormats, banners, flags, tents, table covers, displays, retractors, bags, health and safety items, coloring books, business cards. (Woman/Hisp, estab 2006, empl 2, sales $52,000, cert: State)

1570 Global Partner's of Virginia, LLC
3005 E Boundary Terr, Ste G Midlothian, VA 23112
(804) 744-8112 Norm Falkner VP
Fax: (804) 744-8114
Email: logos@globalpromosonline.com
Website: www.globalpromosonline.com
Logo wear, embroidery, silk screen, screen printing, direct to garment ink jet printing, heat transfer. Corporate apparel, mens, ladies, kids, uniforms. Promotional Products, pens, magnets, calendars, Bags, towels, luggage, sportwear, team uniforms. (Woman/White, estab 2001, empl 4, sales $350,000, cert: State)

1571 It's A Breeze Specialties, LLC
8221 Little Florida Rd Mechanicsville, VA 23111
(804) 779-0183 Shirley Husz President
Fax: (800) 801-0789
Email: shirley@itsabreez.com
Website: www.itsabreez.com
Promotional products, corporate apparel, screen printed & embroidered, awards, incentives & award programs. (Woman/White, estab 2002, empl 2, sales $140,000, cert: State)

1572 Rivanna Natural Designs, Inc.
3009 Lincoln Avenue Richmond, VA 23228
(434) 244-3447 Crystal Mario President
Fax: (703) 783-0095
Email: cmario@rivannadesigns.com
Website: www.rivannadesigns.com
Environmentally responsible gifts, plaques & awards. (Woman/White, estab , empl 1, sales $22,000, cert: State)

1573 The Advertising Specialist, L.C.
P.O. Box 5325 Midlothian, VA 23112
(804) 744-0044 Jeanette Mayo President
Fax: (804) 744-4446
Email: advertisingspecialist@verizon.net
Website: www.advertisingspecialist.com
Promotional products, banners, sport uniforms, T-Shirts, Website Design, Screen Printing & Embroidery. (Woman/AA, estab 1997, empl 3, sales $80,000, cert: State)

Washington

1574 Bravo! Promotional Products
569 Occidental Ave S Seattle, WA 98104
(206) 682-3953 Peggie Dickens President
Fax: (206) 682-0918
Email: peggie@bravobranding.com
Website: www.bravobranding.com
Offshore sourcing, fulfillment services, creative art services, event fulfillment. (Woman/White, estab 1995, empl 12, sales $5,969,545, cert: WBENC)

1575 Red Promotions Inc.
11522 114th Ct NE Kirkland, WA 98033
(206) 686-2001 Shelley Stewart President
Fax: (206) 686-2001
Email: shelley@redpromo.net
Website: www.redpromo.net
Marketing & promotional merchandise. (Woman/White, estab 2008, empl 1, sales $35,000, cert: State)

1576 Unique Experience Custom Embroidery & Screen-Print
234 First St Bremerton, WA 98337
(360) 373-2076 Ronald Flemister Mgr
Fax: (360) 495-1279
Email: un234@silverlink.net
Website: www.companycasuals.com/uniqueexperience
Custom embroidery, screen printing & promotional products. (Woman/AA, estab 1990, empl 3, sales $250,000, cert: State)

1577 ZippyDogs
6523 California Ave SW, Ste 329 Seattle, WA 98136
(206) 938-8828 Elise Lindborg
Fax: (206) 937-4186
Email: zippydogs@zippydogs.com
Website: www.zippydogs.com
Promotional products. (Woman/White, estab 2000, empl 3, sales $1,100,000, cert: State, CPUC, WBENC)

Wisconsin

1578 A Branovan Company, LLC.
6505 W Calumet Rd Milwaukee, WI 53223
(414) 352-5000 Marie Branovan CEO
Fax: (414) 352-5760
Email: marie@abcgifts.com
Website: www.abcgifts.com
Advertising specilties: custom embroidery & screen printing apparel. (Woman/White, estab 1996, empl 12, sales $3,712,200, cert: WBENC)

1579   Actualink Designs LLC
       N65W12525 Sycamore Ln   Menomonee Falls, WI
       53051
       (414) 349-4367 Anthony Martin Owner
       Fax:
       Email: info@actualinkdesigns.com
       Website: www.actualinkdesigns.com
Embroidery, screen printing & digital printing, polo shirts,
caps, graphic design studio. (AA, estab 2012, empl 3, sales
$19,000, cert: NMSDC)

1580   on3 Promotional Partners, LLC
       1543 Sheridan Rd   Kenosha, WI 53140
       (262) 551-8715 Lora Lehmann Owner
       Fax: (262) 551-8725
       Email: llehmann@on3promopartners.com
       Website: www.on3promopartners.com
Promotional products, incentive & loyalty programs,
fulfillment, packaging & collateral print needs. (Woman/
White, estab 2005, empl 6, sales $1,850,000, cert: State,
WBENC)

1581   Quali T Inc.
       513 Center St   Luxemburg, WI 54217
       (920) 845-1010 Susan Heim President
       Fax:
       Email: sales@qualitinc.com
       Website: www.QualiTInc.com
Embroidery, screen printing, promotional products,
custom apparel, advertising specialties, uniforms, safety
apparel, USA made apparel, work wear, Jackets, headwear,
outerwear, dress shirts, polos, sport shirts, etc. (Woman/
White, estab 1990, empl 25, sales $1,500,000, cert: State)

1582   Royal Recognition, Inc.
       S83 W19105 Saturn Dr   Muskego, WI 53150
       (262) 679-6050 Joseph Cull VP
       Fax: (262) 679-6052
       Email: jcull@royalrec.com
       Website: www.royalrec.com
Employee service awads, corporate apparel, recognition/
sales awards & promotional items. (Woman/White, estab
1983, empl 52, sales , cert: State)

DIR

DIVERSITY INFORMATION RESOURCES

2019 Supplier Diversity Seminar

Sponsored by DIR: Driving Supplier Diversity Success since 1968

"Building Strategic Phases of a Supplier Diversity Process"

February 20-21, 2019 • Residence Inn and SpringHill Suites Tampa Clearwater Beach, FL

AGENDA

Wednesday, February 20, 2019
:00 a.m. - 5:00 p.m. Seminar
:00 p.m. - 7:00 p.m. Reception

Thursday, February 21, 2019
:00 a.m. - 5:00 p.m. Seminar

Lunch and continental breakfast
served both days.

> ...cellent seminar conducted by a supplier
> ...versity expert. Covered a wide range
> ...information useful in educating peers
> ...d formalizing a supplier diversity
> ...gram.
>
> — 2018 Attendee

WHO ATTENDS?

- Supplier Diversity Professionals
- Purchasing Managers & Buyers
- VP's of Materials and Purchasing
- Procurement Managers
- Small Business Liaison Officers (SBLOs)

ACCOMMODATIONS

...tel reservation information is sent
...th your seminar registration
...nfirmation. A limited number of
...oms will be available for seminar
...tendees under DIR's special rate.

...U (Continuing Education Units)
...e Institute for Supply Management
...M) awards 14.5 CEUs for this DIR
...ining.

REGISTRATION FEE: $995

...gister early and SAVE! Sign up by
...ovember 1, 2018 and receive the EARLY BIRD
...te: $945
...ere is no on-site registration.

REGISTER ONLINE

...sit www.DiversityInfoResources.com
...contact us: 612-781-6819,
...fo@DiversityInfoResources.com

KNOWLEDGE, NETWORKING, IMPLEMENTATION

This seminar is specifically designed to enable the creation of and/or improvement to an effective supplier diversity process. The proven tactics, information and ideas presented will enable you to return to work with actions that can be immediately implemented.

This seminar will provide participants with the knowledge and assistance in developing their skills in: building and maintaining an effective supplier diversity program, engaging leadership, customers and process owners of various supply chain operations necessary for an effective program, understanding the various aspects of supplier diversity including multiple tier engagement and accountability, technical tactical and strategic aspects of program reporting and effective processes in supplier engagement and development

> A great, well developed training for supplier diversity professionals; classroom interaction is fantastic."

RELEVANT TOPICS

- Supplier Diversity Program Overview
- Company Overview and Supply Chain Strategy
- Roles and Responsibilities of Supplier Diversity Professionals
- Program Governance (policies and regulations)
- Program Administration and Execution
- Creating a Supplier Diversity Strategic Plan and Small Business Subcontracting Plan
- How to Engage all of the Players that Impact Supplier Diversity Performance
- Awards and Recognition
- Data Management Solutions: An Overview of Tracking and Reporting Spend

FACILITATOR: BENITA FORTNER

Ms. Fortner retired from Raytheon Company in March 2017 where she served as the Director of Supplier Diversity for over twenty seven years. Participants will benefit from her personal, industry and advocacy group experience in developing, administering and advancing supplier diversity within the supply chain. In addition, her knowledge and skills continue to be developed through involvement with WBENC, Go For the Greens and the American institute of Diversity and Commerce.
Ms Fortner is the immediate past chair of WBENC and continues to serve on the board of directors, chairs the government committee and Serves on the Encore Group of Distinguished Leaders. Her work with Go for the Greens and the AIDC helps advance Women business development, women involvement in golf as a business tool and ecognizes performance of Diversity and inclusion. Ms Fortner holds a Juris Doctors Degree from Golden West University.

ALARM SYSTEMS

Manufacturers or wholesalers of fire, security, intercom, CCTV, or other alarm components or systems. NAICS Code 33

Alabama

1583   Firelake Construction Inc.
       85 Trico Dr   Guntersville, AL 35976
       (256) 302-2355 William D. Slavin CEO
       Fax: (256) 429-9410
       Email: bslavin@firelakeconstruction.com
       Website: www.firelakeconstruction.com
Security alarm solutions: integrated systems design & installation, access control systems, closed circuit television (CCTV) systems, perimeter protection & integrated biometric technologies. (Nat Ame, estab 2010, empl 8, sales $1,900,000, cert: State)

Arizona

1584   American Fire Equipment
       3107 W Virginia Ave   Phoenix, AZ 85009
       (602) 433-2484 Rose Koppy Admin
       Fax: (602) 433-9626
       Email: info@americanfire.com
       Website: www.americanfire.com
Sells, designs, installs, services & repairs all types of fire protection systems, special hazards fire protection, building fire alarm, mass notification, fire sprinkler, kitchen fire suppression. (Woman/White, estab 1992, empl 125, sales $12,331,853, cert: WBENC)

1585   Mountain Power Electrical Contractor, Inc.
       4301 S Country Club   Tucson, AZ 85714
       (520) 294-1131 Josette Washington Business Dev spec
       Fax: (520) 294-0355
       Email: josette@mtnpower.com
       Website: www.mtnpower.com
Commercial lighting & power, industrial wiring, hospitals, fire alarms, sound systems, communications, substations, power line installation, traffic signals & underground power. (Woman/Hisp, estab 1985, empl 80, sales $6,229,000, cert: State)

California

1586   Aponi Products and Services
       3805 Florin Rd Ste 1228 Sacramento, CA 95823
       (916) 392-6571 Lisa M Davis lacy Owner
       Fax: (916) 392-6577
       Email: lisad@aponitelecommunication.com
       Website: www.aponitelecom.com
Telecommunication Equipment, Installation, Voice, Data, Cabling, Maintenance, Repair, Security System, DVR, Security Cameras. (Woman/Nat Ame, estab 2007, empl 7, sales $360,000, cert: State, 8(a))

1587   EARL Security, Inc.
       745 E Valley Blvd, Ste 518   San Gabriel, CA 91776
       (626) 285-9178 Lynn Chen CEO
       Fax: (626) 285-3223
       Email: Lynn.Chen@earl-security.com
       Website: www.earl-security.com
Install & maintain burglar/intrusion alarms, fire alarms, intercoms, access control closed circuit TV surveillance, metal detectors, electrical. (Woman/As-Pac, estab 1988, empl 6, sales $596,987, cert: CPUC)

Colorado

1588   FAS Systems Group, LLC
       4800 W 60th Ave   Arvada, CO 80003
       (303) 298-7900 Zach Carlson Business Devel
       Fax: (303) 650-2667
       Email: zach@systemsgroup.net
       Website: www.fassystemsgroup.net
Fire alarm detection & security system solutions for new construction & end-users. (Woman/White, estab 2005, empl 37, sales $5,800,000, cert: WBENC)

District of Columbia

1589   MJS Communications LLC
       1343 First St NW   Washington, DC 20001
       (888) 829-1658 Marlon Boykin President
       Fax: (888) 829-1658
       Email: mboykin@mjscommunications.biz
       Website: www.mjscommunications.biz
Information technology, telecommunications services, structure cabling system, voice/data cabling, CCTV cabling, POS & wireless, CCTV, digital video recorders, Interior/exterior cameras, monitors, perimeter security. (AA, estab 2009, empl 2, sales $110,000, cert: State, City)

Florida

1590   Aegis Fire and Integrated Services, LLC
       156 Industrial Loop S   Orange Park, FL 32073
       (904) 215-9669 Shelli Schmid Reg sales
       Fax: (904) 215-7779
       Email: sschmid@afps.com
       Website: www.aegisfis.com
Fire sprinkler, extinguishers & alarm systems. (As-Pac, estab 2004, empl 42, sales , cert: State, NMSDC)

1591   Audio Video Systems, Inc.
       1860 Old Okeechobee Rd, Ste 104   West Palm Beach, FL 33409
       (561) 686-4473 Angela Barnard President
       Fax: (561) 689-5520
       Email: angela@cctvrepair.com
       Website: www.cctvrepair.com
Commercial audio, video & electronic security projects, sales, service, installation & integration: burglar alarm, access control, CCTV/video surveillance, commercial audio, commercial video, business class projectors & displays. (Woman/White, estab 1981, empl 6, sales $800,000, cert: State, City)

1592   AVI Integrators Inc. dba Security 101
       1520 N Powerline Rd   Pompano Beach, FL 33069
       (954) 984-4282 Stacy Bjork Controller
       Fax: (954) 484-4284
       Email: sbjork@security101.com
       Website: www.Security101.com
Card access / Badging / CCTV / Intercom / Alarms / IP
video / Wireless mesh systems (Hisp, estab 2005, empl 37,
sales $7,296,000, cert: State)

1593   Curtoom Companies, Inc.
       1228 E 7th Ave P.O. Box 76192 Tampa, FL 33675
       (813) 405-8082 Paul Curtis CEO
       Fax: (888) 431-0028
       Email: support@curtoom.com
       Website: www.curtoom.com
Provide construction cost consulting in both the Southeast
United States and throughout the Atlantic seaboard areas.
We have built a business and reputation supplying
accurate and timely budgets, cost estimates, value
engineering (AA, estab 1989, empl 30, sales $3,600,000,
cert: State)

1594   HDJ Security, Inc.
       4105 LaFayette St   Marianna, FL 32446
       (850) 482-8660 Harvey Daniels, Jr. President
       Fax: (850) 482-8678
       Email: harvey@hdjsecurity.com
       Website: www.hdjsecurity.com
Dist & install electronic security, CCTV, access control,
intrusion detection, fire alarms, mass notification. (AA,
estab 2003, empl 9, sales $890,000, cert: 8(a))

1595   High Risk Security Services
       5012 Strada Dr   Winter Haven, FL 33880
       (863) 398-8881 Juan Garcia Owner
       Fax: (863) 294-7561
       Email: highrisk@att.net
       Website: www.atrisksecurity.com
Executive Security training, personal security training.
(Hisp, estab 2005, empl 1, sales , cert: State)

1596   Integrated Security Consultants Inc.
       6907 N. Nebraska Avenue   Tampa, FL 33604
       (813) 254-0033 Kenneth Stewart President
       Fax: (888) 502-3060
       Email: kstewart@iscsecurity.net
       Website: www.iscsecurity.net/
Electronic security integration, security system design,
sales, installation & service. (AA, estab 2008, empl 9, sales
$540,000, cert: State, City)

1597   Mainstream IP Solutions, Inc.
       6905 El Dorado Dr   Tampa, FL 33615
       (813) 549-7768 Arnie Solomon Acct Mgr
       Fax: (727) 726-9189
       Email: asolomon@mcsoftampa.com
       Website: www.mainstreamipsolutions.com
Electrical, structured cabling, audio-visual, security & fire
alarm systems. (AA, estab 2010, empl 5, sales $250,000,
cert: State, NMSDC, 8(a), SDB)

Georgia

1598   AAA Fire Protection Resources, Inc.
       P.O. Box 1122 Lawrenceville, GA 30046
       (770) 963-0887 Amy E. Cruce President
       Fax: (770) 995-6592
       Email: amyaaafirepro@outlook.com
       Website: www.aaafirepro.com
Fire Extinguisher Sales & Service, Recharging & Inspections, Emergency Exit Lighting. (Woman/White, estab
1982, empl 4, sales $977,756, cert: WBENC)

1599   Alliance Fire Protection Services, Inc.
       P.O. Box 1798 Loganville, GA 30052
       (770) 554-5004 Angie Jordan Office Mgr
       Fax: (770) 554-5095
       Email: acjordan@alliancefire.com
       Website: www.alliancefire.com
Life Safety Inspections & Service, Fire Alarm, Fire
Sprinkler, Extinguishers, Hydrants, Backflows & Fire
Pumps. (Woman/White, estab 1999, empl 75, sales
$7,768,000, cert: City, WBENC)

1600   Carter Brothers Security Services LLC
       3015 RN Martin St   Atlanta, GA 30344
       (404) 254-4200 John F. Carter CEO
       Fax: (404) 254-4240
       Email: cbregistrations@carterbrothers.com
       Website: www.carterbrothers.com
Project & program management, fire safety & security
systems. (AA, estab 2012, empl 145, sales $21,051,716,
cert: State, City, NMSDC)

1601   DH Security Solutions
       303 Perimeter Center N Ste 300 Atlanta, GA
       30346
       (678) 341-9451 Tina Dungy President
       Fax: (770) 888-8195
       Email: tdungy@dhsecuritysolutions.com
       Website: www.dhsecuritysolutions.com
Locksmith, access control, card readers, door hardware,
door closers, electronic gates, safes, vaults, CCTV, door
repair, high security solutions. (Woman/AA, estab 2011,
empl 12, sales $510,000, cert: NWBOC)

1602   Strickland Security & Safety Solutions
       541 Tenth St NW, Ste 135   Atlanta, GA 30318
       (800) 422-9075 Robert Strickland Owner
       Fax: (800) 750-9726
       Email: Rob@stricklandSecurity.com
       Website: www.stricklandsecurity.com
Service & equipment replacement: CCTV & alarm
systems components. (AA, estab 2007, empl 12, sales
$2,150,000, cert: NMSDC)

1603   UMC Inc. dba Unity ITS
       3420 Oakcliff Rd Ste 105 Doraville, GA 30340
       (770) 234-0221 David Park CEO
       Fax: (770) 234-0394
       Email: dpark@unityits.com
       Website: www.unityits.com
PC based camera security & surveillance system.
(Woman/As-Pac, estab 2001, empl 3, sales $221,681,
cert: State)

Illinois

1604 Applied Controls & Contracting Services, Inc.
537 W Taft Dr South Holland, IL 60473
(708) 596-7400 George Kinnison President
Fax: (708) 596-1020
Email: gkinnison@accshome.com
Website: www.accshome.com
Engineering design, project management & estimations, technical analysis, emergency dispatch services installation, design security ad alarm systems, fire detection systems, closed circuit tv system & card access. (AA, estab 1990, empl 11, sales $1,090,522, cert: State, NMSDC)

Indiana

1605 Geyer Fire Protection, LLC
700 N High School Rd Indianapolis, IN 46214
(317) 490-9357 Rosemily Geyer
Fax: (317) 253-4173
Email: rosemily@geyerfire.com
Website: www.geyerfire.com
Design, install, serve & maintain fire sprinkler systems, fire extinguishers & alarms. (Woman/Hisp, estab 2011, empl 12, sales $686,733, cert: State, City, NMSDC)

Louisiana

1606 Fire Boss of Louisiana, Inc.
7905 Hwy 90 W New Iberia, LA 70560
(337) 365-6729 Debra Denais Romero President
Fax: (337) 367-6655
Email: debbie@fireboss.com
Website: www.fireboss.com
Fire & safety protection services, DBI/SALA authorized distributor/repair center, fire & gas detection/suppression system design, engineering & installation, commercial inspection of portable fire extinguishing systems, foam & water systems. (Woman, estab 1975, empl 1, sales , cert: WBENC)

Maryland

1607 Digital Video Solutions, Inc.
7526 Connelley Dr Ste A Hanover, MD 21076
(240) 547-0143 John Webster President
Fax:
Email: jwebster@remoteeyes.com
Website: www.digitalvideosolutions.biz
Designs & integrate physical security systems: CCTV, access control, alarm, public address & intercom systems. (AA, estab 2008, empl 3, sales $302,000, cert: State, NMSDC)

1608 G TECH Contracting, LLC
8008 Dorado Terr Brandywine, MD 20613
(240) 793-8908 Agustin Nunez CEO
Fax: (301) 627-6037
Email: anunez@gtechcontracting.com
Website: www.gtechcontracting.com
Integrated security, voice/data communications, residential & small commercial A/V systems. (Hisp, estab 2013, empl 5, sales $1,200,000, cert: 8(a))

1609 Truth Technology Inc.
10901 Rhode Island Ave Unit 371 Beltsville, MD 20704
(240) 472-9833 April T. Brown CEO
Fax: (888) 501-0838
Email: atb@trutechi.com
Website: www.trutechi.com
CCTV, Key Card Access System, and Biometric devices, network & computer equipment, software. (Woman/AA, estab 2006, empl 1, sales $475,000, cert: 8(a))

Michigan

1610 Edgewood Electrical, LLC
3633 Michigan Ave Ste 100 Detroit, MI 48216
(313) 263-0440 Robert Bell Sr Project Mgr
Fax: (313) 263-0440
Email: robertb@edgewoodelectric.com
Website: www.edgewoodelectric.com
Electrical Installations, Design/Build, Design/Assist, Fire Alarm & Low Voltage Systems. (AA, estab 2008, empl 45, sales $12,000,000, cert: NMSDC)

Minnesota

1611 Castle Cop Inc.
17003 E Lake Netta Dr Ham Lake, MN 55304
(763) 438-2761 Barb Underdahl CEO
Fax:
Email: castlecopinc@earthlink.net
Website: www.castlecop.com
Dist stainless steel doorjamb reinforcing device. (Woman/White, estab 2003, empl 1, sales , cert: State)

1612 Lloyd Security Incorporated
5051 Highway 7 Ste 270 Minneapolis, MN 55416
(612) 874-9295 Me'Lea Connelly GM
Fax:
Email: info@lloydsecurity.com
Website: www.lloydsecurity.com
Installation, repair, service & monitoring of security systems, access control, surveillance and video, perimeter detection, safe rooms, CCTV & ballistic solutions. (Woman, estab 2001, empl 14, sales , cert: State, City)

Missouri

1613 AIE Inspection Services, Inc.
1314 Hwy DD Defiance, MO 63341
(636) 398-5288 Stephanie Lange VP Business Develop
Fax: (636) 828-5090
Email: stephanie.lange@aiefirestl.com
Website: www.aiefirestl.com
Inspection, maintenance, compliance & emergency service fire protection systems, sprinkler systems, kitchen hood systems, fire pumps, fire alarms, fire extinguishers & backflow preventers. (Woman/White, estab 1983, empl 22, sales $20,165,000, cert: WBENC)

Mississippi

1614   HC Services Fire Protection
       P.O. Box 243 1455 West Dr Laurel, MS 39440
       (601) 399-4800 Sue Bridges President
       Fax: (601) 399-4888
       Email: sue@hcservicesinc.com
       Website: www.hcservicesinc.com
Dist, service & install fire protection products: extinguishers, fire systems, detection, fire alarms, access control, sprinklers, Fm-200, inergen, halon & speciality hazards. (Woman/White, estab 1991, empl 13, sales $13,000,000, cert: State, City)

Montana

1615   Sterling Bank Services, Inc.
       P.O. Box 5108   Missoula, MT 59806
       (406) 360-6127 Amity Parks Exec VP
       Fax: (406) 251-8620
       Email: amity.parks@sterlingbankservices.com
       Website: www.sterlingbankservices.com
Fire alarm inspections, alarm & CCTV inspections. (Woman/Nat Ame, estab 1986, empl 200, sales $20,500,000, cert: NMSDC)

North Carolina

1616   SAF Technologies, Inc.
       2032 Independence Commerce Dr Ste B Matthews, NC 28105
       (704) 844-0955 Alan Weeks President
       Fax: (704) 844-0866
       Email: alan.weeks@saftechnologies.com
       Website: www.saftechnologies.com
Install, program & maintain security Systems, fire alarm, CCTV, surveillance & access control. (Woman/White, estab 2004, empl 40, sales , cert: WBENC)

1617   Video & Security Specialists
       2313 Wedgewood Dr   Matthews, NC 28104
       (704) 821-9396 Erika Gordon Partner
       Fax: (704) 821-9396
       Email: egordon@carolina.rr.com
       Website: www.videoandsecurityspecialists.com
Dist electrical & security products: alarm/security systems, fire alarm systems, structured wiring, access control, security cameras, networking, phone system, intercom & gates. (Woman/White, estab 1975, empl 7, sales $220,866, cert: State)

New York

1618   ASM Security Inc.
       8003 Myrtle Ave   Glendale, NY 11385
       (718) 839-6000 Simon Ruderman President
       Fax: (866) 611-6595
       Email: sruderman@asmintegrators.com
       Website: www.asmintegrators.com
Design, engineering, filing & expediting fire alarm & security systems. (Woman/Hisp, estab 2006, empl 28, sales $2,000,000, cert: State, City)

Ohio

1619   Alarm Core, LLC
       4555 Renaissance Pkwy, Ste 103   Warrensvile Heights, OH 44128
       (216) 831-2871 Kenneth Liddell President
       Fax: (216) 831-2917
       Email: alarmcoreohio@aol.com
       Website:
Install commercial & residential fire & burgular alarms, CCTV, remote surveillence systems, satellite systems. (AA, estab 1999, empl 8, sales , cert: State)

1620   Gene Ptacek & Son Fire Equipment Co, Inc.
       7310 Associate Ave   Brooklyn, OH 44144
       (216) 651-8300 Gene Ptacek VP
       Fax: (216) 651-3435
       Email: gene@gpsfire.com
       Website: www.gpsfire.com
Fire extinguishers, fire suppression systems, Fire alarm & fire sprinkler systems, Inspections, fire extinguisher training, dist fire hose, brass adapters & nozzles. (Woman/White, estab 1975, empl 52, sales , cert: City)

1621   Rika Group Corporation
       13701 Enterprise Avenue   Cleveland, OH 44135
       (216) 325-1006 Ryan Temple Director of Ops
       Fax: (216) 325-1010
       Email: ryan@pcsurveillance.net
       Website: www.pcsurveillance.net
Design, dist & install surveillance equipment & systems. (Woman/White, estab 2001, empl 20, sales $1,600,000, cert: City)

1622   TaiParker Consulting LLC
       4020 Sara Dr   Uniontown, OH 44685
       (330) 472-2115 Tai Parker Owner
       Fax:
       Email: tai@taiparkerconsulting.com
       Website: www.taiparkerconsulting.com
Video Systems Installation / Monitoring / Service, Real Time Remote Video Monitoring, Remote Video Storage, Cellular Only Video Camera Solutions, WiFi / IP Video Camera Solutions, Alarm Systems Installation / Monitoring / Service. (AA, estab 2010, empl 1, sales , cert: State, NMSDC)

1623 Veterans Electrical Group LLC
      3700 Northfield Rd, Ste 353   Highland Hills, OH
      44122
      (216) 600-5808 London Burnett President
      Fax: (216) 600-5808
      Email: london@vetelectrical.com
      Website:
High & low voltage electric services & computer cabling &
security alarms, CCTV Cabling. (AA, estab 2014, empl 12,
sales , cert: City)

Pennsylvania

1624 Arora Systems Group, LLC
      61 Wilmington-West Chester Pike Ste 100 Chadds
      Ford, PA 19317
      (610) 500-0714 Adam Oliver GM
      Fax:
      Email: aoliver@arorasystemsgroup.com
      Website: www.arorasystemsgroup.com
Facility Maintenance, testing, management, and code
consulting, Fire Alarm testing, maintenance & repair, Fire
Suppression, sprinkler system testing maintenance &
repair, Hydrant, Standpipe & Fire extinguisher testing. (As-
Ind, estab 2004, empl 17, sales $2,885,827, cert: City,
NMSDC)

1625 Fire Fighter Sales & Service Company
      791 Commonwealth Dr   Warrendale, PA 15086
      (724) 720-6000 Richard Malady VP
      Fax:
      Email: rmalady@all-lines-tech.com
      Website: www.firefighter-pgh.com
Alarms, sprinkler systems & fire protection. (Woman/
White, estab 1946, empl 125, sales $12,500,000, cert:
WBENC)

1626 Gabba LLC
      630 W Germantown Pike Ste 120 Plymouth
      Meeting, PA 19462
      (877) 933-2288 Lisa Burkhardt Finance & Office Ops
      Fax: (610) 456-2737
      Email: LISA@ISGPROTECT.COM
      Website: www.invisionsecuritygroup.com
Security system installation. (Woman/White, estab 2010,
empl 15, sales $3,500,000, cert: State, WBENC)

Puerto Rico

1627 EAS Systems, Inc.
      P.O. Box 482   Mercedita, PR 00715
      (787) 284-4007 Pedro Bonnin President
      Fax: (787) 284-2251
      Email: pbonnin@eas-pr.com
      Website: www.eas-pr.com
Install & Service Security: CCTV, Security Analog Cameras,
Security IP cameras, Access Control Systems, Intrusion
Detection Systems, Intercom Systems, Perimeter protec-
tion Systems, Barriers, Turnstiles, Wireless. (Hisp, estab
1995, empl 14, sales $1,280,879, cert: 8(a))

1628 Guardmax Corporation
      N 20, Ste B, Fagot Ave   Ponce, PR 00716
      (787) 806-5525 Manuel Santana CEO
      Fax: (787) 812-2882
      Email: manuelsantana@guardmaxpr.com
      Website: www.guardmaxpr.com
Security services, security technology integration,
service & maintenance, access control, asset conserva-
tion, automatic door repair & service, burglar alarms,
CCTV, analog & Matrix Systems, IP Systems, Wireless IP.
(Hisp, estab 2014, empl 16, sales $20,000, cert: NMSDC)

1629 One Corps, Inc
      P.O. Box 79767   Carolina, PR 00984
      (787) 776-0062 Sonia Fuentes
      Fax: (787) 768-2726
      Email: sfuentes@one-corps.com
      Website: www.one-corps.com
Armed & Unarmed Security Guards, IP Monitoring
Station with Patrol Response Service, Sales, Installation
& Maintenance of Cameras, Access Control, Fire Watch.
(Hisp, estab 2007, empl 134, sales $2,641,716, cert:
NMSDC)

1630 The Security Group Corp.
      Urb. Villa Blanca 42 Aquamarina Caguas, PR
      00725
      (787) 743-3299 Luis Benet President
      Fax: (787) 744-9699
      Email: info@securitygroupcorp.com
      Website: www.securitygroupcorp.com
Electronic security & automation: design, sale, installation, programming, service & maintenance of electronic
security & automation systems. (Hisp, estab 1988, empl
18, sales $901,822, cert: NMSDC)

South Carolina

1631 Quintech Security Consultants, Inc.
      102 Sangaree Park Court Ste 4 Summerville, SC
      29483
      (843) 695-0170 Harold Gillens President
      Fax: (843) 695-0222
      Email: hgillens@quintechengineering.com
      Website: www.quintechengineering.com
Security risk assessments, emergency response planning, security site surveys, surveillance system design,
alarm system design, access control systems, AV/
intercom systems. (AA, estab 1997, empl 11, sales
$5,227,488, cert: NMSDC)

Texas

1632 Action Fire Alarm and Action Automatic Sprinkler
      200 Sharron Dr Woodway, TX 76712
      (254) 235-8300 Patricia Green Sales Coord
      Fax: (254) 235-8311
      Email: pbreen@actionfirepros.com
      Website: www.actionfirepros.com
Inspect, service & install fire extinguishers, fire alarms,
fire sprinkler & backflows. (Woman/White, estab 1993,
empl 72, sales $9,005,218, cert: State, WBENC)

1633   Asez Inc.
       1716 S San Marcos, Ste 120   San Antonio, TX 78207
       (210) 736-6200 Robert Lozano CEO
       Fax: (210) 231-0301
       Email: corporate@asezinc.com
       Website: www.asezinc.com
Armed & unarmed security officers, security systems
services, security alarm systems, fire alarm systems, access
control, closed circuit television, alarm monitoring,
intergraded system. (Hisp, estab 2000, empl 75, sales
$2,575,000, cert: State, 8(a))

1634   Champion Life Safety Solutions
       2701 W. Plano Parkway Ste 500 Plano, TX 75075
       (972) 663-5000 Chuck Henderson President
       Fax:
       Email:
       Charles.henderson@championfiresecurity.com
       Website: www.championfiresecurity.com
Design, install, inspect & monitor fire sprinkler & other
suppression systems, fire alarm systems & security systems
for new construction, retrofit to existing facilities. (AA,
estab 2001, empl 112, sales $14,200,000, cert: State,
NMSDC)

1635   Laredo Technical Services, Inc.
       22011 Roan Bluff   San Antonio, TX 78259
       (210) 705-2904 Joseph Lukowski President
       Fax: (210) 247-9534
       Email: joseph@laredotechnical.com
       Website: www.laredotechnical.com/
Dist SpiderTech Security perimeter detection systems.
(Hisp, estab 2007, empl 23, sales $6,210,000, cert: State,
NMSDC, 8(a))

1636   Nationwide Investigations & Security, Inc.
       2425 West Loop South, Ste 200   Houston, TX 77027
       (713) 297-8830 Allen G Hollimon CEO
       Fax: (832) 553-7414
       Email: AHollimon@ntwinvestigations.com
       Website: www.ntwinvestigations.com
Security guard services, investigations, dignitary protection, communications cabling, CCTV/CATV, alarms, automated controls, networking, home theaters. (AA, estab
1999, empl 123, sales $398,000, cert: State, NMSDC)

1637   TotalCom Management Inc
       P.O. Box 460230   San Antonio, TX 78246
       (210) 366-1116 Moe Oroian President
       Fax: (210) 366-3104
       Email: moe@totalcom-inc.com
       Website: www.totalcom-inc.com
Dist, install & service voice & data cabling, fire systems,
security systems, access control systems, CCTV/CATV,
cameras & DVR recording systems, alarm monitoring,
telephone systems, blown fiber. (As-Ind, estab 1994, empl
19, sales $1,755,237, cert: State)

Virginia

1638   Quality CCTV Systems, Inc.
       3513 Gregory Pond Rd   Richmond, VA 23236
       (804) 276-7300 Dianne Rust President
       Fax: (804) 276-6714
       Email: dianne@qualitycctv.net
       Website: www.qualitycctv.net
Install & maintain security systems to include: video
surveillance, CCTV, access control systems, burglar & fire
systems, etc. (Woman/White, estab 1989, empl 14, sales
$1,240,000, cert: State)

APPAREL
Manufacturers or wholesalers of men's and women's clothing. Many firms listed are contract sewing houses. (See also APPAREL ACCESSORIES & NOTIONS). NAICS Code 54

California

1639   Abell Marketing Group, Inc.
       15057 Avenida De Las Flores   Chino Hills, CA 91709
       (909) 456-8905   James Lohan Project Mgr
       Fax: (888) 304-1065
       Email: james@abellmarketinggroup.com
       Website: www.abellmarketinggroup.com
Protective clothing & medical/industrial nitrile, vinyl & latex gloves. (Woman/White, estab 1998, empl 2, sales $375,000, cert: WBENC)

1640   Clipper Corporation
       21124 Figueroa St   Carson, CA 90745
       (310) 533-8585   Deena Conner VP Business Units
       Fax: (310) 533-8686
       Email: deena.conner@clippercorp.com
       Website: www.clippercorp.com
Mfr & dist uniforms & smallwares. (Woman/As-Pac/Hisp, estab 1900, empl 1, sales $30,000,000, cert: State, WBENC)

Connecticut

1641   PrintabiliTees, LLC
       180 Turn Of River Rd Ste 13D   Stamford, CT 06905
       (203) 322-3390   Jere Eaton President
       Fax: (203) 461-8744
       Email: jere@printabilitees.com
       Website: www.printabilitees.com
Custom apparel: screen printing, embroidery, document printing & promotional products. (Woman/AA, estab 2004, empl 1, sales $180,000, cert: State, NMSDC)

Florida

1642   Supreme Discount Uniforms, LLC
       7410 SW 15th St   Plantation, FL 33317
       (877) 535-2540   Victor Albo Dir Sales/Mktg
       Fax: (877) 535-2541
       Email: victor@supremediscountuniforms.com
       Website: www.discountuniformsonline.com
Uniforms, embroidered lab coats, maintenance uniforms, housekeeping uniforms & embroidered polo t-shirts. (Hisp, estab 2009, empl 2, sales $168,000, cert: State)

1643   Tampa T-Shirts
       5112 N 22nd St   Tampa, FL 33610
       (813) 879-3298   Juan Davis Mgr
       Fax:
       Email: juan@fastlaneclothing.com
       Website: www.fastlaneclothing.com
Apparel, logo shirts, lab coats, promotional items. (Woman/Hisp, estab 1985, empl 19, sales $1,480,000, cert: State, City)

1644   Tavarez Sporting Goods
       1840 22nd St   Miami, FL 33145
       (347) 441-9690   Manuel Tavarez Managing Partner
       Fax:
       Email: tavarezsports@gmail.com
       Website: www.tavarezsports.com
Sporting goods & fitness apparel, baseballs, softballs, baseball bats, gloves, batting gloves, catcher's equipment, helmets, volleyballs, soccer balls, basketballs, boxing equipment, martial arts equipment, sports bags to sports apparel. (Hisp, estab 2014, empl 5, sales , cert: NMSDC)

1645   The Beach Collection, Inc.
       4855 Pembroke Rd   Hollywood, FL 33021
       (954) 393-4029   Oscar Guzman President
       Fax: (954) 985-9430
       Email: animalprints@bellsouth.net
       Website:
Embroidery scrubs, uniforms, t-shirts, sweatshirts, beach towels. (Hisp, estab 1981, empl 3, sales $500,000, cert: NMSDC)

Georgia

1646   ERB Industries, Inc.
       1 Safety Way   Woodstock, GA 30188
       (770) 926-7944   Jackie Barker EVP
       Fax: (770) 924-3068
       Email: jbarker@e-erb.com
       Website: www.e-erb.com
Mfr & dist personal protective equipment & uniform apparel: head, eye, face, body & hand protection, hard hats, safety glasses, high visibility apparel, aprons, smocks, lab coats. (Woman/White, estab 1956, empl 100, sales $28,662,000, cert: WBENC)

1647   J.W. Outfitters
       3012 Oakcliff Industrial St   Atlanta, GA 30340
       (800) 554-7662   Michael Brautigan Controller
       Fax: (800) 304-0644
       Email: michael.brautigan@jwoutfitters.com
       Website: www.jwoutfitters.com
Uniform programs, logo apparel & corporate apparel. (Woman/White, estab 1975, empl 48, sales $7,500,000, cert: WBENC)

1648 O.G.I.H. Enterprises, Inc.
      201 17th St NW, Ste 30303   Atlanta, GA 30363
      (404) 478-7852 Benny Nesbitt, Jr. CEO
      Fax:
      Email: b.nesbitt@ogih-enterprises.com
      Website: www.invisibleigloves.com
Dist work safety gloves, protective clothing. (AA, estab
2012, empl 4, sales , cert: State)

1649 Staffwear 2
      155 Westridge Pkwy, Ste 307   McDonough, GA
      30253
      (800) 727-9289 Towanda Scott President
      Fax: (678) 272-2336
      Email: t.scott@staffwear2.com
      Website: www.staffwear2.com
Corporate branded apparel & national uniform programs.
(Woman/AA, estab 2008, empl 10, sales $502,438, cert:
NMSDC)

1650 Vanguard Distributors, Inc.
      107 NE Lathrop Ave P.O. Box 608 Savannah, GA
      31402
      (912) 236-1766 Howard Genser, Jr. President
      Fax: (912) 238-3072
      Email: howardg@vangdist.com
      Website: www.vangdist.com
Dist safety products & protective clothing, lab supplies.
(AA, estab 1984, empl 33, sales $40,000,000, cert: NMSDC)

Illinois

1651 JERO Medical Equipment & Supplies, Inc.
      4108 W Division St   Chicago, IL 60651
      (312) 829-5376 Julia Bowens President
      Fax: (312) 829-5671
      Email: juliabowens@jeromedical.com
      Website: www.jeromedical.com
Mfr disposbable wearing apparels, kit assembler, 1st aid,
disaster, admission. (AA, estab 1987, empl 24, sales
$4,000,000, cert: City)

Indiana

1652 RiverCity Workwear LLC
      4020 Earnings Way   New Albany, IN 47150
      (812) 948-9020 Tina Dotson
      Fax: (812) 949-8299
      Email: tina@rivercityworkwear.com
      Website: www.rivercityworkwear.com
Dist safety glasses, hard hats, safety vest, shirts, rainwear,
steel & non steel toe boots, tshirts, polos, jackets.
(Woman/White, estab 2004, empl 3, sales $78,000, cert:
State)

Louisiana

1653 Abform, Inc.
      167 Industrial Pkwy   Lafayette, LA 70508
      (337) 837-9675 Kim Leblanc Comptroller
      Fax: (337) 837-9337
      Email: kim@abform.com
      Website: www.abform.com
Dist uniforms & work wear. (Woman/White, estab 1981,
empl 20, sales , cert: WBENC)

1654 Denison Consulting Group LLC
      6221 S Claiborne Ave Ste 450 New Orleans, LA
      70125
      (504) 982-6110 Dianne Denison CEO
      Fax:
      Email: sales@denisonconsultinggroup.com
      Website: www.denisonconsultinggroup.com/
Dist corporate work wear, uniforms, apparel, protective
work wear, industrial clothing, flame retardant (FR)
clothing, FR shirts, FR pants, FR coveralls, FR coats, FR
jackets, FR jeans, rainwear, raingear. (Woman/White,
estab 2015, empl 6, sales , cert: WBENC)

Maryland

1655 Unitec Distribution Systems
      289 E Green St   Westminster, MD 21157
      (410) 876-6227 Elise Elfman CEO
      Fax:
      Email: EElfman@unitec-corp.com
      Website: www.unitec-corp.com
Provide uniforms & Total Uniform Management Solution
(TUMS). (Woman/White, estab 1927, empl 20, sales
$3,500,000, cert: State, WBENC)

Michigan

1656 All American Essentials
      31600 Plymouth Rd   Livonia, MI 48150
      (734) 421-9292 Sandeep Narang President
      Fax: (734) 421-0505
      Email: sandeepnarang2@aol.com
      Website: www.aae4ever.com/
Apparel, uniforms, & promotional products. (As-Pac,
estab 1998, empl 25, sales $67,500, cert: 8(a))

1657 StarSource Management Services, Inc.
      39080 Webb Dr   Westland, MI 48185
      (734) 721-8540 Melvin Brown CEO
      Fax: (734) 721-2860
      Email: sales@starsourceinc.com
      Website: www.starsourceinc.com
Dist uniforms, protective clothing, cutting tools, fasteners, janitorial chemical supplies, cleaning equipment,
paper towels, plastic liners, welding supplies, automotive cleaning supplies, cooling tower chemicals, laundry
services. (AA, estab 1997, empl 5, sales $6,000,000, cert:
NMSDC)

Missouri

1658   Cherry
     1712 Main St, Ste 232   Kansas City, MO 64108
     (816) 377-1832   Thalia Cherry President
     Fax:
     Email: info@cherrysportsgear.com
     Website: www.cherrysportsgear.com
Sporting goods, corporate apparel, tee shirts, athletic equipment & uniforms. (AA, estab 2011, empl 3, sales $87,000, cert: NMSDC)

North Carolina

1659   Gems Manufacturing Systems division of Indogem Inc.
     706 Statesville Road   North Wilkesboro, NC 28659
     (610) 481-0132   Arup Bhattacharjee President
     Fax:
     Email: Sales@gemsmfg.com
     Website: www.gemsmfg.com
Mfr special purpose gloves for the military. (As-Ind, estab 1993, empl 20, sales $1,600,000, cert: State, City)

New Jersey

1660   Design Alternatives NY LLC
     169 Boyd Ave   Jersey City, NJ 07304
     (973) 583-9553   Cenia Peredes President
     Fax:
     Email: cenia@ceniany.com
     Website: www.goo.gl/3f8E3Q
Women's Apparel (Woman, estab 1905, empl 2, sales , cert: NMSDC)

1661   Shani International Corporation
     8 Conifer Dr   Warren, NJ 07059
     (908) 484-7070   Arti Mohin VP
     Fax: (908) 484-7069
     Email: arti@shaniintl.com
     Website: www.shaniintl.com
Mfr & import uniforms (knit & woven tops & bottoms), lab & chef coats, aprons, non-woven bags & basic fashion items. (Woman/As-Ind, estab 2005, empl 4, sales , cert: NMSDC)

1662   Tronex International, Inc.
     300 International Dr   Mount Olive, NJ 07828
     (973) 355-2888   Edmund Tai VP Healthcare Division
     Fax: (973) 335-2900
     Email: etai@tronexcompany.com
     Website: www.tronexcompany.com
Dist disposable gloves & apparel products. (As-Pac, estab 1989, empl 65, sales $19,999,999,998, cert: NMSDC)

Nevada

1663   Dellrone Services LLC
     8550 W Charleston Blvd, Ste 228   Las Vegas, NV 89117
     (702) 457-7855   Willie Endsley President
     Fax: (702) 457-7855
     Email: admin@dellroneservices.com
     Website: www.dellroneservices.com
Dist safety clothing & equipment: fire safety jacket & pants, helmets, construction safety clothing: helmets, jackets, parkas, rain coats, safety vest, goggles & shoes. (Woman/AA, estab 2010, empl 4, sales $20,000, cert: NMSDC)

New York

1664   Hamburger Woolen Company
     23 Denton Ave   New Hyde Park, NY 11040
     (516) 352-7400   Ilene Rosen President
     Fax: (516) 352-7704
     Email: irosen@hwcny.com
     Website: www.hwcny.com
Dist uniform fabrics, law enforcement & public safety equipment: duty belts, flashlights, raincoats, reflective vests, protective eyewear & earwear. (Woman/White, estab 1940, empl 12, sales $6,105,831, cert: State, City)

1665   PKP Industries, Inc.
     1407 Broadway Ste 3412   New York, NY 10018
     (646) 586-3044   Puneet Pasricha
     Fax: (412) 561-6253
     Email: puneet@pkpindustries.com
     Website: www.pkpindustries.com
Wholesale apparel, clothing, women's tops, bottoms, skirts, dresses, pants. (Woman/As-Ind, estab 2014, empl 1, sales , cert: NMSDC)

1666   S & H Uniform Corp.
     1 Aqueduct Rd   White Plains, NY 10606
     (914) 937-6800   ROSA GRECO VP
     Fax: (914) 937-0741
     Email: INFO@SANDHUNIFORMS.COM
     Website: www.sandhuniforms.com
Workwear & footwear, outerwear/jackets, coveralls, hats, shirts, polos, t-shirts, pants, shorts, vests, flame resistant wear, Hi visibility, boots & shoes, medical uniforms, aprons, chef's apparel. (Woman/White, estab 1969, empl 40, sales $8,500,000, cert: City)

1667 Salsa-The Designer Solution LLC.
1441 Broadway 3 Fl, Ste 3021 New York, NY 10018
(212) 575-6565 Gigi De Jesus-Frerichs President
Fax: (585) 324-7881
Email: gigi@gicleeapparel.com
Website: www.SalsaProfessionalApparel.com
Mfr uniforms, sports apparel, collegiate apparel, varsity-wear, tees, tanks, polo shirts, sweatshirts, shorts, pants, lounge-wear & pajamas. (Woman/Hisp, estab 2000, empl 6, sales $10,000,000, cert: State, City, NMSDC, WBENC)

Ohio

1668 Alma Mater Designs LLC
117 W Church St Oxford, OH 45056
(513) 368-9839 Karen Lindner Owner
Fax:
Email: Karen.AlmaMaterDesigns@gmail.com
Website: www.AlmaMaterDesigns.com
Custom woven, logo-branded fabric elements. (Woman/White, estab 2011, empl 2, sales $69,996, cert: NWBOC)

1669 Liniform Service
1050 Northview Ave Barberton, OH 44203
(330) 825-6911 Jennifer Peroli VP
Fax: (330) 825-0920
Email: jenniferperoli@liniform.com
Website: www.liniform.com
Uniforms: lab coats, scrubs, jackets, warm-up jackets, maintenance uniforms, chef coats & cook apparel. Linens: patient gowns, mammo capes, sheets, pillowcases, blankets, towels & washcloths, tablecloths, skirting, napkins. (Woman/White, estab 1924, empl 60, sales $4,700,000, cert: WBENC)

1670 MASCOT Workwear
320 Springfield Dr, Ste 150 Fairlawn, OH 44333
(330) 618-3997 Michael Allio Sales
Fax:
Email: michael@maworkwear.com
Website: www.mascotworkwear.com
Dist MASCOT Workwear in North America. (Woman/White, estab 2013, empl 7, sales $1,000,000, cert: WBENC)

1671 Slate Rock Safety, LLC
755 W Smith Rd Unit C Medina, OH 44256
(866) 783-7977 Kim Wilson President
Fax:
Email: kwilson@slaterocksafety.com
Website: www.slaterocksafety.com
Flame resistant clothing & arc flash apparel & accessories. (Woman/White, estab 2007, empl 16, sales , cert: State)

1672 VDP Safety & Uniforms Ltd.
11811 Shaker Blvd Ste 416 Cleveland, OH 44120
(216) 352-1026 Phoebe Lee President
Fax: (440) 735-1934
Email: info@vdpsafety.com
Website: www.vdpsafety.com
Uniform apparel & safety supplies/equipment: high visibility shirts, safety vests, hard hats, traffic cones, jackets, hospital uniforms. (Woman/AA, estab 2013, empl 1, sales , cert: State)

Pennsylvania

1673 Watts Window Cleaning & Janitorial Company
5025 Wayne Ave Philadelphia, PA 19144
(215) 842-4900 Yvette Watts Owner
Fax: (408) 995-0236
Email: ybw@wattswindowcleaning.com
Website:
Janitorial, windo cleaning, ground care. (Woman/AA, estab 1960, empl 5, sales , cert: NMSDC)

South Carolina

1674 MVP Textiles and Apparel, Inc.
1031 Le Grand Blvd Charleston, SC 29492
(843) 216-8380 Mary Propes CEO
Fax: (843) 216-8386
Email: marypropes@mvpgroupint.com
Website: www.mvptextiles.com
Mfr textiles. (Woman/White, estab 2005, empl 15, sales $16,800,000, cert: WBENC)

Texas

1675 Career Uniforms
3800 Juniper Houston, TX 77087
(713) 645-3600 Rupendra Radia President
Fax: (713) 645-3618
Email: rradia@aol.com
Website: www.careeruniforms.com
Mfr uniforms: medical, governmental & restaurant. (As-Ind, estab 1980, empl 25, sales , cert: NMSDC)

1676 RG Apparel Co.
2912 N MacArthur, Ste 103 Irving, TX 75062
(972) 793-0583 Joe Temple COO
Fax: (972) 793-0588
Email: jt@rgapparel.com
Website: www.rgapparel.com
Mfr textiles: uniforms, work shirts, polos, tees, woven button up shirts & headwear, promotional marketing items & gifts. (AA, estab 2006, empl 6, sales $3,200,000, cert: State, NMSDC)

1677 Santex
      4211 W Illinois, Ste 100   Dallas, TX 75211
      (214) 256-2169 Jose Lopez Owner
      Fax:
      Email: karla.leal@santexallsports.com
      Website: www.santexallsports.com
Manufacturing business uniforms. (Hisp, estab 2013, empl
4, sales $160,000, cert: State)

1678 Wholesale T-shirts Depot, Inc.
      11311 Harry Hines Blvd, Ste 201   Dallas, TX 75229
      (972) 243-4785 Joe Turner Exec VP
      Fax:
      Email: info@wtdapparel.com
      Website: www.wtdapparel.com
Licensed military branded apparel & accessories. (As-Pac,
estab 2006, empl 18, sales $2,500,000, cert: NMSDC)

Virginia

1679 First Due Gear
      2111 Apperson Dr   Salem, VA 24153
      (540) 725-8850 Sarah Fuhrman Owner
      Fax: (540) 725-1333
      Email: firstduegear@yahoo.com
      Website: www.firstduegear.com
Dist Fire, EMS, swiftwater & technical rescue gear, apparel
& equipment. (Woman/White, estab 2006, empl 1, sales ,
cert: State)

1680 Global Partner's of Virginia, LLC
      3005 E Boundary Terr, Ste G   Midlothian, VA 23112
      (804) 744-8112 Norm Falkner VP
      Fax: (804) 744-8114
      Email: logos@globalpromosonline.com
      Website: www.globalpromosonline.com
Logo wear, embroidery, silk screen, screen printing, direct
to garment ink jet printing, heat transfer. Corporate
apparel, mens, ladies, kids, uniforms. Promotional Products, pens, magnets, calendars, Bags, towels, luggage,
sportwear, team uniforms. (Woman/White, estab 2001,
empl 4, sales $350,000, cert: State)

1681 The Uniform Store, LLC
      10 Weems Lane   Winchester, VA 22601
      (540) 678-8711 Lisa Beggs President
      Fax: (540) 678-8712
      Email: lisa@uniformstoreonline.com
      Website: www.uniformstoreonline.com
Dist ChefWorks, Edwards Garments & Uncommon Threads
for men & women in chef coats (executive chef & basic),
kitchen shirts, pants, aprons, headwear, neckwear, front of
the house (shirts, blouses, pants, vests, ties). (Woman/
White, estab 2009, empl 5, sales $455,781, cert: State,
WBENC)

APPAREL ACCESSORIES & NOTIONS
Manufacturers or distributors of work gloves, shoes, handbags, hats, sandals, slippers, hosiery, neckwear, etc. (See also APPAREL and LEATHER GOODS categories). NAICS Code31

California

1682   Blubandoo Inc.
       27128-B Paseo Espada Ste 602 San Juan Capistrano, CA 92675
       (949) 240-2617 Cindy Benedict President
       Fax: (949) 240-2618
       Email: cindy@blubandoo.com
       Website: www.blubandoo.com
Cooling headwear: caps/hats, fashionable visors, neckbands, cool ties, headbands & doorags. (Woman/White, estab 1993, empl 2, sales $5,500,000, cert: CPUC)

1683   College Express West, LLC
       1392 E Palomar St Ste 403 Chula Vista, CA 91913
       (866) 448-7865 Carlton Booker Mgr
       Fax: (619) 656-6467
       Email: lockitupcew@yahoo.com
       Website: www.expressluggageworldwide.com
Dist luggage, briefcases, notebook/computer cases & accessories. (AA, estab 2005, empl 3, sales $20,000, cert: State)

1684   ECO Trend Cases, LLC
       14242 Ventura Blvd Ste 203 Sherman Oaks, CA 91423
       (310) 770-6422 Sandy Rouse CEO
       Fax: (310) 943-1416
       Email: srouse@ecostylecases.com
       Website: www.ecostylecases.com
Mfr laptop, netbook & iPad cases: topload shoulder case, backpack, messenger case, rolling case & sleeves. (Woman/White, estab 2009, empl 4, sales $150,000, cert: WBENC)

1685   Kool Breeze Solar Hats, Inc.
       827 E Princeton Fresno, CA 93704
       (559) 456-8510 Tommie Nellon Owner
       Fax: (559) 456-2395
       Email: tnellon@koolbreezesolarhat.com
       Website: www.koolbreezesolarhat.com
Mfr solar cooling hats, Kool Breeze Solar Hats. (Woman/AA, estab 2012, empl 11, sales $205,000, cert: City)

1686   The Green Garmento, LLC
       20109 Nordhoff St Chatsworth, CA 91311
       (323) 512-2600 Jennie Nigrosh CEO
       Fax:
       Email: Jennie@thegreengarmento.com
       Website: www.thegreengarmeno.com
A reusable dry-cleaning bag, eco-friendly all-in-one laundry, reusable hanging garment bag, carrying & duffel bag, hanger hamper, "green" drycleaning bag. (Woman/White, estab 2008, empl 6, sales , cert: WBENC)

Illinois

1687   McKlein Company, LLC
       4447 W. Cortland St Chicago, IL 60639
       (773) 235-0600 Parinda Saetia CEO
       Fax: (773) 235-0615
       Email: psaetia@mckleincompany.com
       Website: www.mckleinsua.com
Mfr briefcases, computer cases, luggage, travel bags. (Woman/As-Pac, estab 1997, empl 12, sales $7,507,695, cert: WBENC)

Louisiana

1688   Cayenne Marketing
       2224 Shumark Trail Bossier City, LA 71111
       (318) 828-4684 Jennifer LaPierre Owner
       Fax:
       Email: jennifer@cayennemarketing.com
       Website: www.cayennemarketing.com
Advertising specialties, promotional items, custom apparel to gifts. (Woman/White, estab 2004, empl 2, sales $600,000, cert: WBENC)

Maryland

1689   janlitlfeather
       3813 Terka Circle Randallstown, MD 21133
       (410) 830-9244 Stephanie Gladden CEO
       Fax: (410) 521-1056
       Email: janlitlfeather@aol.com
       Website: www.janlitlfeather.com
Signature feathered ponytail holder, key chains, car mirror hangs, bow ties, earrings, neck ties, hat clips & hair accessories. (Woman/AA, estab 2010, empl 1, sales , cert: NMSDC)

Michigan

1690 BluCase
  250 Monroe NW, Ste 400 Grand Rapids, MI 49503
  (616) 717-5766 Bill McCurdy CEO
  Fax:
  Email: bmccurdy@blucase.com
  Website: www.blucase.com
Mfr innovative cellphone accessory products. (AA, estab 2014, empl 5, sales $12,000,000, cert: NMSDC)

North Carolina

1691 Century Hosiery, Inc.
  P.O. Box 1410 Denton, NC 27239
  (336) 859-3806 Malcolm Martin President
  Fax: (336) 859-2980
  Email: mmartin@centuryhosiery.com
  Website: www.centuryhosiery.com
Mfr hosiery products. (Woman, estab 1989, empl 140, sales $6,000,000, cert: State)

Texas

1692 Fresh Comfort, Inc.
  3200 Rifle Gap Rd, Ste 1470 Frisco, TX 75034
  (214) 705-0408 Maria E. Valencia President
  Fax: (214) 705-0408
  Email: maria.valencia@freshcomfortinc.com
  Website: www.freshcomfortinc.com
Adaptive intimate apparel (bras, panties, boxers), front Velcro & zipper closure bras for easy dressing & undressing, seamless bra & underwear. (Woman/Hisp, estab 2012, empl 1, sales $30,000, cert: State)

Virginia

1693 Sayre Enterprises Inc.
  45 Natural Bridge School Rd Natural Bridge Station, VA 24579
  (800) 552-6064 Danielle Ayres Commericial Rep
  Fax: (540) 291-2018
  Email: dayres@sayreinc.com
  Website: www.sayreinc.com
Reflective products: vests, belts, headbands, wrist & arm bands. (Woman/White, estab 1987, empl 104, sales $9,092,000, cert: State)

1694 The Todd Venture Group
  11625 Busy St Richmond, VA 23236
  (804) 379-4269 Andy Todd VP sales
  Fax: (804) 379-5765
  Email: andy@hitechribbongroup.com
  Website: www.snapsupplies.com
Dist disposable gloves. (Woman/White, estab 1983, empl 6, sales $1,600,000, cert: State)

Washington

1695 Bootie Shoe Cover Inc
  5616 NE 55 Circle Vancouver, WA 98661
  (360) 903-0992 Marla Gillette President
  Fax:
  Email: info@bootieshoecover.com
  Website: www.www,bootieshoecover.com
Dist reusable shoe covers. (Woman/White, estab 2009, empl 3, sales , cert: WBENC)

ARCHITECTS
Most firms have agreements with other state architects permitting them to work anywhere in the nation. Nearly all are members of the American Institute of Architects (AIA). (See ENGINEERING & SURVEYING SERVICES for civil, structural, electrical and mechanical engineers).   NAICS Code 54

Arizona

1696   Fore Dimensions LLC
4417 N 40th St Ste 300 Phoenix, AZ 85018
(602) 748-4664 Lisa Foreman Principal
Fax:
Email: lisa@foredimensions.com
Website: www.foredimensions.com
Architectural consulting, remodel, tenant improvements & new construction for transportation facilities, wet & dry labs, clean rooms, testing buildings, office & training centers. (Woman, estab 2001, empl 2, sales $500,000, cert: State, City, WBENC)

California

1697   Aetypic, Inc.
7 Freelon St San Francisco, CA 94107
(415) 762-8388 Dennis Wong
Fax: (415) 762-8390
Email: dennis.wong@aetypic.com
Website: www.aetypic.com
Architecture & engineering services: structural engineering, civil engineering, construction engineering & inspection, technology integration, & sustainable design. (As-Pac, estab 2011, empl 25, sales , cert: State, NMSDC)

1698   API Consultants
3151 Airway Ave Ste C-2 Costa Mesa, CA 92626
(714) 708-8090 Mitra Farokhpay Principal
Fax: (714) 708-8091
Email: mitra@apiconsultants.com
Website: www.apiconsultants.com
Planning, design & architectural services. (Woman, estab 1992, empl 7, sales $608,574, cert: City)

1699   Blackbird Associates, Inc.
2320 J St Sacramento, CA 95816
(916)4466227 Franc Blackbird President
Fax: (916) 446-7877
Email: franc@blackbirdassoc.com
Website: www.blackbirdassoc.com
Architecture and Project Management. (Nat Ame, estab 1994, empl 7, sales $1,311,000, cert: NMSDC, WBENC)

1700   H. Hendy Associates
4770 Campus Dr Ste 100 Newport Beach, CA 92660
(949) 851-3080 Heidi Hendy Principal
Fax: (949) 851-0807
Email: hhendy@hhendy.com
Website: www.hhendy.com
Interior architecture firm. (Woman/White, estab 1979, empl 30, sales $4,800,000, cert: CPUC, WBENC)

1701   Line2Line Architectural Design Group, LLP
2413 Webb Ave Ste D Alameda, CA 94501
(510) 995-8278 Angelus Cheng Principal
Fax:
Email: info@line2lineadg.com
Website: www.line2lineadg.com
Architectural & design, Feasibility Studies, ADA Consultation, Sustainability, Programming, Urban/Site Planning, Entitlement, Due Diligence, Project Mgmt, Site & Building Evaluations, Interior Design, Design presentations. (Woman/As-Pac, estab 2012, empl 4, sales $354,156, cert: NMSDC)

1702   M+M Design Construction Project Management (MPJI)
1503 Bainum Dr   Topanga, CA 90290
(310) 455-0064 Mohan Joshi President
Fax:
Email: mjoshi@mpji.net
Website: www.mpji.net
Architecture, interior design, planning & advisory services. (As-Ind, estab 2002, empl 1, sales $83,000, cert: NMSDC, 8(a))

1703   Source West
1631 Aspen Grove Lane   Diamond Bar, CA 91765
(909) 872-0010 Roberto Manzini Dir Business Dev
Fax: (909) 872-0014
Email: r.manzini@greencubicles.com
Website: www.greencubicles.com
Commercial architecture & interior design. (Woman/White, estab 1988, empl 25, sales $2,500,000, cert: State)

1704   TSAO Design Group
160 Pine St, Ste 650   San Francisco, CA 94111
(415) 398-5500 Jonathan Tsao Principal
Fax: (415) 398-5510
Email: jtsao@tsaodesign.com
Website: www.tsaodesign.com
Architectural & interior design. (As-Pac, estab 1981, empl 12, sales $1,750,000, cert: CPUC)

Colorado

1705   Coover-Clark & Associates, Inc.
1936 Market St   Denver, CO 80202
(303) 783-0040 Carol Coover-Clark President
Fax: (303) 783-0060
Email: marketing@cooverclark.com
Website: www.cooverclark.com
Architectural planning & design services, commercial & military aviation facilities. (Woman/White, estab 1987, empl 22, sales $2,800,000, cert: WBENC)

Connecticut

1706   Bavier Design, LLC
       277 Rowayton Avenue   Rowayton, CT 06853
       (203) 388-1818 Anne Bavier Principal
       Fax: (203) 388-1819
       Email: abavier@bavierdesign.com
       Website: www.bavierdesign.com
Architectural & interior design. (Woman/White, estab
2004, empl 8, sales $1,255,000, cert: WBENC)

District of Columbia

1707   Systems Design, Inc.
       1420 9th St NW   Washington, DC 20001
       (202) 232-5631 Darlene Mathis CEO
       Fax: (202) 232-5634
       Email: meka_mathis@msn.com
       Website: www.systemsdesignbuild.com
Interior design, space planning, architectural design svcs,
also dist lamps, tables, tile, window treatments & systems
furniture. (Woman/AA, estab 2002, empl 6, sales
$700,000, cert: 8(a))

Florida

1708   Architechnical, Inc.
       2908 Clubhouse Dr   Plant City, FL 33566
       (813) 312-2455 Erick Gulke President
       Fax:
       Email: egulke@architechnical.biz
       Website: www.architechnical.biz
Architectural design solutions & environments. (Hisp,
estab 2008, empl 3, sales , cert: City)

1709   Architectural Design Collaborative
       235 Alcazar Ave   Coral Gables, FL 33134
       (305) 442-1188 Raymundo Feito President
       Fax: (305) 445-1509
       Email: rfeito@adcinternational.net
       Website: www.adcinternational.net
Architectural, planning & interior design. (Hisp, estab
1984, empl 25, sales $7,600,000, cert: NMSDC)

1710   MGE Architects, Inc.
       3081 Salzedo St, 3rd Fl Coral Gables, FL 33134
       (305) 444-0413 Jose Estevez President
       Fax:
       Email: jestevez@mgearchitects.com
       Website: www.mgearchitects.com
Architectural services: private health systems, major
government hospitals, teaching facilities & small community hospitals. (Hisp, estab 1982, empl 23, sales
$7,937,182, cert: State)

1711   Rhodes+Brito Architects
       605 E Robinson St, Ste 750 Orlando, FL 32801
       (407) 648-7288 Linda Almeida Office Mgr
       Fax:
       Email: linda@rbarchitects.com
       Website: www.rbarchitects.com
Architectural Services. (AA, estab 1996, empl 19, sales
$3,024,653, cert: State, City, 8(a))

Georgia

1712   GSB Architects & Interiors, Inc.
       3091 E Shadowlawn Ave NE   Atlanta, GA 30305
       (770)6335952 Jennifer Mercier Interior Designer
       Fax: (214) 473-8041
       Email: jennifer@gsbarchitects.com
       Website: www.gsbarchitects.com
Architectural and interior design. (Woman/Hisp, estab
1998, empl 9, sales $2,900,000, cert: NMSDC)

1713   GSB Architects, Inc.
       3091 E Shadowlawn Ave   Atlanta, GA 30305
       (404) 233-6450 Maria Guerra-Stoll President
       Fax: (404) 233-6451
       Email: dany@gsbarchitects.com
       Website: www.gsbarchitects.com
Architectural services, interior design, construction
mgmt, project mgmt, space planning, move mgmt.
(Woman/Hisp, estab 1998, empl 8, sales $1,019,357,
cert: NMSDC, WBENC)

Illinois

1714   Bailey Edward Design, Inc.
       35 E Wacker Dr Ste 2800 Chicago, IL 60601
       (312) 440-2300 Ellen B. Dickson President
       Fax: (312) 440-2303
       Email: edickson@baileyedward.com
       Website: www.baileyedward.com
Architectural services, Interior design services, Drafting
services, Building inspection services
Engineering Services, Historical Preservation, Cost
Estimating (Woman/White, estab 1991, empl 36, sales
$5,247,963, cert: State, City, WBENC, NWBOC)

1715   Bauer Latoza Studio, Ltd.
       2241 S Wabash   Chicago, IL 60616
       (312) 567-1000 Edward Torrez President
       Fax:
       Email: etorrez@bauerlatozastudio.com
       Website: www.bauerlatozastudio.com
Architectural design, evaluation & renovation services.
(Hisp, estab 1990, empl 12, sales $2,195,986, cert: State)

1716 Brook Architecture
      2325 S Michigan Ave Ste 300 Chicago, IL 60616
      (312) 528-0890 Jeanne Franks Director of Mktg
      Fax: (312) 356-1041
      Email: jfranks@brookarchitecture.com
      Website: www.brookarchitecture.com
Design, urban planning, consulting, project management &
services, new construction & renovation of institutional,
residential, office & retail spaces. (Woman/AA, estab 1995,
empl 6, sales $1,495,915, cert: State, City, NMSDC, 8(a))

1717 EC Purdy & Associates
      53 W Jackson Blvd Ste 1631 Chicago, IL 60604
      (312) 408-1631 Elizabeth Purdy Architect
      Fax: (312) 408-1632
      Email: ecpurdy@ecpurdy.com
      Website: www.ecpurdy.com
Architectural, interior design planning services. (Woman/
As-Pac, estab 1994, empl 1, sales $563,878, cert: State)

1718 Muller & Muller Ltd.
      700 N Sangamon   Chicago, IL 60642
      (312) 432-4180 Mark Stromberg Principal
      Fax: (312) 432-4184
      Email: mstromberg@muller2.com
      Website: www.muller2.com
Architectural services: Feasibility Studies; Building Analysis; Schematic Design; Design Development; Construction
Documents; LEED; ADA Review; Presentations; Renderings;
3D Animations; Specifications; Cost Estimating. (Woman,
estab 1984, empl 20, sales $2,000,000, cert: State, City)

1719 Studio AH LLC dba HPZS
      213 West Institute Place Ste 502 Chicago, IL 60610
      (312) 944-9600 April Hughes Owner
      Fax:
      Email: ahughes@hpzs.com
      Website: www.hpzs.com
Architectural design, Interior Design, Historic Preservation,
Facade Maintenance & Sustainable Design, green renovation & design services. (Woman/White, estab 2015, empl
4, sales $133,310, cert: State, WBENC)

1720 Sumac Inc.
      3701 N Ravenswood Ave Ste 202 Chicago, IL 60613
      (773) 857-7906 Liliana Gonzalez VP
      Fax: (773) 857-7905
      Email: lgonzalez@sumacinc.com
      Website: www.sumacinc.com
Architecture & construction management: architectural
design, sustainable design, project scheduling, cost
estimating, construction procurement, construction
management services & general contracting. (Hisp, estab
2008, empl 10, sales $2,000,000, cert: NMSDC)

1721 Tigerman McCurry Architects
      444 N Wells St Ste 206 Chicago, IL 60654
      (312) 644-5880 Margaret McCurry President
      Fax: (312) 644-3750
      Email: tma@tigerman-mccurry.com
      Website: www.Tigerman-McCurry.com
Architectural & interior design services. (Woman/White,
estab 1967, empl 10, sales $1,200,000, cert: City)

Indiana

1722 Brenner Design Incorporated
      620 N Delaware St   Indianapolis, IN 46204
      (317) 262-1220 Diana Brenner President
      Fax: (317) 262-1260
      Email: dbrenner@brennerdesign.com
      Website: www.brennerdesign.com
Architecture; Interior Architecture; Historic Preservation;
Interior Design; Furniture Management Services;
Owner's Representative Services; Space Planning;
Project Management. (Woman/White, estab 1992, empl
10, sales $506,343, cert: State, City, WBENC)

1723 Jung Design, Inc.
      8910 Purdue Rd Ste 680 Indianapolis, IN 46268
      (317) 471-1221 Connie Jung President
      Fax: (317) 471-1224
      Email: cjung@jungdes.com
      Website: www.jungdes.com
Architectural & interior design services, master planning,
signage, programming, space planning. (Woman/White,
estab 2004, empl 3, sales $200,000, cert: State)

1724 Rowland Design, Inc.
      702 N Capitol Ave   Indianapolis, IN 46204
      (317) 636-3980 Sarah Schwartzkopf CEO
      Fax: (317) 263-2073
      Email: smschwartzkopf@rowlanddesign.com
      Website: www.rowlanddesign.com
Architecture, interior design & graphic design. (Woman/
White, estab 1968, empl 32, sales $4,050,000, cert:
State)

1725 Studio 3 Design, Inc.
      8604 Allisonville Rd Ste 330 Indianapolis, IN
      46250
      (317) 595-1000 Heather Leslie President
      Fax: (317) 572-1236
      Email: hleslie@studio3design.net
      Website: www.studio3design.net
Architectural & interior design services. (Woman/White,
estab 2002, empl 7, sales , cert: State, City)

1726 WDi Architecture, Inc.
      15 W 28th St Indianapolis, IN 46208
      (317) 251-6172 Daryl Williams-Dotson CEO
      Fax: (317) 921-0197
      Email: daryl_wd@wdiarchitecture.com
      Website: www.wdiarchitecture.com
Architectural design, space planning & programming,
feasibility studies, facilities evaluation, project
managment & existing conditions documentation.
(Woman/AA, estab 1995, empl 5, sales $400,000, cert:
State, City, WBENC)

Kentucky

1727   First World Architects Studio, PSC
15 E 9th St   Covington, KY 41011
(859) 431-1999   B. Charles Alexander President
Fax: (859) 431-2021
Email: alexcama@fuse.net
Website: www.1stworldarchitectsstudio.com
Architectural & engineering services: master planning &
project mgmt, construction mgmt, design/build, facility
assessments. (AA, estab 1982, empl 6, sales $415,000,
cert: State, 8(a))

Louisiana

1728   Marrero Couvillon & Associates, LLC
4354 S Sherwood Forest Blvd, Ste D200   Baton
Rouge, LA 70816
(225) 408-8249   Stacey Vincent Production Mgr
Fax:
Email: svincent@mca-llc.com
Website: www.mca-llc.com
Mechanical, Electrical, Plumbing, Fire Protection Engineer-
ing Services, Architectural Services and Construction
Management (Hisp, estab 1968, empl 17, sales
$2,800,000, cert: State, NMSDC, 8(a), SDB)

Maryland

1729   K. Dixon Architecture, PLLC
137 National Plaza, Ste 300   National Harbor, MD
20745
(301) 364-5053   Kathy Dixon Principal
Fax: (301) 686-8587
Email: kdixon@kdixonarchitecture.com
Website: www.kdixonarchitecture.com
Architectural design & planning services: commercial,
education, government, residential, and institutional.
(Woman/AA, estab 2003, empl 1, sales $100,000, cert:
State, City, WBENC)

1730   Mimar Architects & Engineers, Inc.
7004 Security Blvd Ste 210   Baltimore, MD 21244
(410) 944-4900   Maria Khalid Mktg Coord
Fax:
Email: mkhalid@mimarch.net
Website: www.mimarch.net
Architectural-engineering, architectural/planning, interior/
graphic design, engineering & construction management
services. (As-Ind, estab 1995, empl 25, sales $3,991,379,
cert: State)

1731   NFD, Inc.
124 Lakefront Dr   Hunt Valley, MD 21030
(410) 785-7795   Laura Schlicht Business Dev Dir
Fax: (410) 785-3680
Email: lschlicht@nfd.com
Website: www.nfd.com
Commercial interior design & planning: programming &
budgeting; schematic design; furniture/equipment
inventorying; space planning; 3D modeling; furniture &
finish specs; project coordination. (Woman/White, estab
1978, empl 9, sales $973,000, cert: State, City)

1732   Sugar Associates, LLC
2909 Old Court Rd   Baltimore, MD 21208
(410) 602-2909   Karen Sugar President
Fax: (410) 486-3696
Email:
Website: www.sugarassociates.com
Interior design & planning, space programming, 24-
hour-turn-around space planning & facility planning
services. (Woman/White, estab 1900, empl 1, sales
$212,000, cert: State, City)

Minnesota

1733   Studio Hive Inc.
901 N Third St, Ste 228   Minneapolis, MN 55401
(612) 279-0430   Shari Bjork Principal
Fax: (612) 279-0439
Email: sbjork@studiohive.com
Website: www.studiohive.com
Architectural & interior design. (Woman/White, estab
2003, empl 8, sales $1,098,036, cert: State)

1734   Welsh Architecture LLC
4350 Baker Rd Ste 400   Minnetonka, MN 55343
(952) 897-7854   Linda Solberg Director Corporate
Services
Fax: (952) 842-7654
Email: lsolberg@welshco.com
Website: www.welshco.com
Providing comprehensive architectural, design & project
management services. (Woman/White, estab 1995,
empl 11, sales $2,300,000, cert: WBENC)

Missouri

1735   Arcturis, Inc.
720 Olive St Ste 200   Saint Louis, MO 63101
(314) 206-7100   Julie Keil Principal
Fax: (314) 231-9801
Email: jkeil@arcturis.com
Website: www.arcturis.com
Architecture, interior design, landscape architecture,
urban planning, graphic design, workplace optimization,
master planning, site planning & building evaluation
services. (Woman/White, estab 1977, empl 50, sales
$8,500,000, cert: WBENC)

1736   Bozoian Group Architects, LLC
2201 S Brentwood Blvd Ste 105   St. Louis, MO
63144
(314) 962-4100   Katherine Bozoian President
Fax: (314) 962-4107
Email: information@bozoiangroup.com
Website: www.bozoiangroup.com
Architectural svcs: master planning, facility & needs
assessment, new building design, renovation, interior
design, adaptive re-use, re-purpose, sustainable design,
owners representation, construction administration.
(Woman/White, estab 1996, empl 6, sales $958,000,
cert: State, WBENC)

1737 CORE10 Architecture
4501 Lindell Blvd Ste 1a St. Louis, MO 63108
(314) 726-4858 Michael Byrd
Fax:
Email: mbyrd@core10architecture.com
Website: www.core10architecture.com
Architecture, Interior Design, Master Planning, Sustainable Design, LEED, Residential, Mixed Use, Multi-Family, Commercial, Office, Industrial. (AA/As-Pac/Hisp, estab 2007, empl 6, sales $881,934, cert: State, City)

1738 Gray Design Group, Inc.
Nine Sunnen Dr, Ste 110 Saint Louis, MO 63143
(314) 646-0400 Lorrie Kramer
Fax: (314) 646-0100
Email: lkramer@graydesigngroup.com
Website: www.graydesigngroup.com
Commercial architecture & interior design. (Woman/White, estab 1900, empl 1, sales $2,397,779, cert: State, City, WBENC)

1739 Oculus Inc.
1 S Memorial Dr, Ste 1500 St. Louis, MO 63102
(314) 367-6100 Shevaun McNaughton Mktg Director
Fax: (314) 367-1489
Email: ShevaunM@oculusinc.com
Website: www.oculusinc.com
Architecture, strategic planning, interior design & move management. (Woman/White, estab 1994, empl 32, sales $7,716,704, cert: State, WBENC)

North Carolina

1740 Arcons Design Studio Professional Corporation
10550 Independence Point Pkwy Ste 300
Matthews, NC 28105
(704) 542-5252 Rajeev Bhave President
Fax: (704) 542-2330
Email: rbhave@arconsds.com
Website: www.arconsds.com
Architectural services, retail, commercial, institutional and mixed use projects. (As-Ind/Hisp, estab 2004, empl 7, sales $1,400,000, cert: State)

1741 CSBO Architecture P.C.
1589 Skeet Club Rd Ste 102-172 High Point, NC 27265
(336) 617-3079 Carlos Sanchez President
Fax:
Email: carlos.sanchez@csboinc.com
Website: www.csboinc.com
Architectural design services. (Hisp, estab 2002, empl 2, sales $57,000, cert: State)

1742 Espinosa Architecture + Consulting, PC
937 Bryansplace Rd Winston Salem, NC 27104
(336) 407-8419 Carlos Espinosa President
Fax:
Email: Carlos@espinosaarchitecture.com
Website: www.espinosaarchitecture.com
Architecture services, architectural design, space planning, needs evaluation & programming, evaluation of existing structures, cost analysis, interior design. (Hisp, estab 2014, empl 3, sales , cert: State)

1743 Neighboring Concepts, PLLC
1230 W Morehead St Ste 204 Charlotte, NC 28208
(704) 374-0916 Eshe Glover Dir of Mktg/Business Dev
Fax: (704) 342-3808
Email: eshe@neighboringconcepts.com
Website: www.neighboringconcepts.com
Architectural design: concept, construction, post-construction services, urban planning, development & revitalization. (AA/As-Pac/Hisp, estab 1996, empl 17, sales $1,903,763, cert: State)

New Jersey

1744 Gramieri Design Services
353 Georges Rd, Ste C Dayton, NJ 08810
(732) 274-9540 Frank Gramieri President
Fax: (732) 274-1372
Email: fgramieri@gdsinc.net
Website: www.gdsinc.net
Interior architectural & engineering services: site analysis, design development, project budgeting & programming, space planning, schematics design, 3D rendering & modeling, architectural & engineering contract documents. (As-Ind/Hisp, estab 1992, empl 7, sales $638,903, cert: State, City, NMSDC)

1745 Kamlesh Shah Designs Inc.
18 Lovell Dr Plainsboro, NJ 08536
(609) 655-9908 Kamlesh Shah Principal
Fax: (609) 716-8265
Email: kshah@ksdarchitects.com
Website: www.ksdarchitects.com
Architectural, Interior Space Planning, Programing, Lab Design, Process Manufacuring Design, Mechanical, Electrical, Plumbing, Engineering Services. (As-Pac, estab 1998, empl 6, sales $2,115,234, cert: State)

1746 O&S Associates, Inc.
145 Main St Hackensack, NJ 07601
(201) 488-7144 Kelly O'Leary Director of Business Devel
Fax: (201) 488-7135
Email: kaoleary@oandsassociates.com
Website: www.oandsassociates.com
Planning, Design and Restoration of full building envelope, inclusive of roof, windows, facade. Specializing in parking planning, design & restoration. Engineers and Architects. (As-Pac/Hisp, estab 1996, empl 40, sales $6,500,000, cert: NMSDC)

Nevada

1747   KME Architects LLC
       231 W Charleston Blvd   Las Vegas, NV 89102
       (702)8882088 Melvin Green Principal
       Fax:
       Email: melvin@kmearchitects.com
       Website: www.kmearchitects.com/
Architectural services, interior design, landscape design,
sustainable design, Historic preservation, tenant improvements, fire code violations, master planning, laser scanning. (AA/Hisp, estab 2009, empl 9, sales , cert: NMSDC)

New York

1748   Avinash K. Malhotra Architects (AKM)
       148 W 24th St   New York, NY 10706
       (212) 808-0000 Richard Saunderson Associate
       Fax:
       Email: rsaunderson@akmarch.com
       Website: www.akmarch.com
Architectural solutions: high-rise buildings, large scale
conversions, historical preservation & landmarks re-use,
renovations & architectural interiors. (As-Ind, estab 1982,
empl 10, sales $1,900,000, cert: State, City, NMSDC)

1749   AWA Lighting Designers Inc.
       61 Greenpoint Ave   Brooklyn, NY 11222
       (212) 473-9797 Abhay Wadhwa CEO
       Fax:
       Email: abhay@awalightingdesigners.com
       Website: www.awalightingdesigners.com
Architectural lighting design, design & implement lighting
solutions for commercial, civic, cultural & residential
projects. (As-Ind, estab 2011, empl 27, sales $259,715,
cert: State)

1750   Foit-Albert Associates, Architecture, Engineering
       and Surveying, P.C.
       215 W 94th St, Ste 517   New York, NY 10025
       (716) 856-3933 Gregory Carballada President
       Fax: (716) 856-3933
       Email: cstoebe@foit-albert.com
       Website: www.foit-albert.com
Architecture, Engineering, Environmental & Land Surveying Consulting. (Hisp, estab 1977, empl 48, sales
$4,839,242, cert: State, City)

1751   JJ Falk Design LLC
       315 Fifth Ave, 11 Fl   New York, NY 10016
       (212) 685-1913 JJ Falk Managing Principal
       Fax: (212) 685-6471
       Email: jj@jjfalk.com
       Website: www.jjfalk.com
Architecture services: interior design. (Woman/AA/As-Pac,
estab 1998, empl 16, sales $1,700,000, cert: State,
WBENC)

1752   Kahn Architecture & Design, PC
       2 West 45th St Ste 501 New York, NY 10036
       (646) 253-9864 Heidi Kahn President
       Fax: (212) 736-6709
       Email: hwiley@kahnarchitecture.com
       Website: www.kahnarchitecture.com
Architecture, interior design & planning solution services
to commercial and retail clients. (Woman/White, estab
2005, empl 17, sales $2,200,000, cert: State, City,
WBENC)

1753   Kenne Shepherd Interior Design Architecture PLLC
       54 W 21st St, Ste 1208   New York, NY 10010
       (212) 206-6336 Kenne Shepherd Principal
       Fax: (212) 206-7337
       Email: kshepherd@kenneshepherd.com
       Website: www.kenneshepherd.com
Multi-disciplinary interior architectural, workspace, retail
store or residence, strategic planning, site evaluation,
code/zoning analysis, lease/workletter review, architectural design, sustainable design, construction documents, construction observation (Woman/White, estab
1993, empl 3, sales $73,000, cert: WBENC)

1754   Lewandowska Architect PLLC
       14 Wall St, 20th Floor   New York, NY 10005
       (212) 787-4558 Barbara Lewandowska Principal
       Fax:
       Email: barbara@lewandowskaarchitect.com
       Website: www.LewandowskaArchitect.com
Architectural, interior design & space planning services.
(Woman/White, estab 2002, empl 3, sales $200,000,
cert: State, City)

1755   SWITZER Architecture, P.C.
       255 W 36th St Ste 1101 New York, NY 10018
       (212) 391-1519 Gregory T Switzer Principal
       Fax: (212) 391-1519
       Email: gswitzer@switzerarchitecture.com
       Website: www.switzerpc.com
Architectural design & holistic management. (AA, estab
2003, empl 6, sales $750,000, cert: NMSDC)

1756   ZELJKA ONE Management LLC dba: Green Way
       Pavement
       P.O. Box 2927 Binghamton, NY 13902
       (607) 724-2438 Robert V Gerard Co-Owner
       Fax: (716) 604-1937
       Email: robertgerard@me.com
       Website: www.greenwaypavements.com
LEED architects & construction services. (Woman/White,
estab 2011, empl 2, sales $11,000,000, cert: State)

Ohio

1757 Brockman Designs LLC
27600 Chagrin Blvd Ste 260 Cleveland, OH 44122
(216) 504-4040 Sharon Brockman Principal
Fax:
Email: sbrockman@brockmandesigns.com
Website: www.brockmandesigns.com
Interior design, healthcare spaces & facilities, higher education & corporate offices, interior space planning, interior finish selections & specifications, furniture planning & specifications, project coordination. (Woman/White, estab 2001, empl 2, sales , cert: State, City)

1758 Calvin Singleton & Associates
13426 Cedar Rd Cleveland Heights, OH 44118
(216) 321-9953 Calvin M Singleton Jr. President
Fax: (216) 321-9953
Email: csa101@att.net
Website:
Architecture & planning services: commercial office, retail, educational, medical, transportation, institutional, restaurant, recreational, residential, new & renovated design work & interior design & planning services. (AA, estab 1984, empl 1, sales $35,890, cert: State)

1759 DNK Architects, Inc.
2616 Central Pkwy Cincinnati, OH 45214
(513) 948-4146 Guinette Kirk VP
Fax: (513) 679-4712
Email: gkirk@dnkarchitects.com
Website: www.dnkarchitects.com
Interior design & space planning services, Cadd drafting. (AA, estab 1986, empl 20, sales $2,000,000, cert: State, NMSDC)

1760 MD Interior Environments dba Design Details
700 W Pete Rose Way Cincinnati, OH 45203
(513) 793-0404 Molly Dietz President
Fax: (513) 793-0388
Email: mdietz@designdtls.com
Website: www.designstls.com
Interior design services. (Woman/White, estab 1994, empl 1, sales , cert: WBENC)

1761 Moody Nolan, Inc.
300 Spruce St Ste 300 Columbus, OH 43215
(614) 461-4664 Todd Dove Principal, Director Retail Studio
Fax: (614) 280-8881
Email: tdove@moodynolan.com
Website: www.moodynolan.com
Architecture, engineering & interior design. (AA, estab 1987, empl 200, sales $55,215,857, cert: NMSDC)

1762 Quinn Engineering & Employment Network LLC
125 W Market St, Ste 221 Warren, OH 44481
(330) 423-1923 Candys Mayo Owner
Fax:
Email: info@queen-ohio.com
Website: www.queen-ohio.com
Computer Aided Drafting and Engineering/Architecture support, Naval Architecture and Aerospace. (AA, estab 2015, empl 2, sales $20,000, cert: State)

1763 Robert P. Madison International, Inc.
2930 Euclid Ave Cleveland, OH 44115
(216) 861-8195 Sandra Madison, AIA CEO
Fax: (216) 861-1001
Email: rklann@rpmadison.com
Website: www.rpmadison.com
Architectural svcs; civil, structural, electrical & mechanical engineering. (Woman/AA, estab 1954, empl 12, sales $1,357,000, cert: State)

1764 SFA Architects, Inc.
555 Carr St. Cincinnati, OH 45203
(513) 721-0600 Sue Momberg President
Fax: (513) 721-0611
Email: smomberg@sfa-architects.com
Website: www.sfa-architects.com
Architectural, MEP Engineering, Interior Design & Project Management Services. (Hisp, estab 1967, empl 32, sales $5,222,194, cert: State, NMSDC)

1765 Ubiquitous Design, Ltd.
3443 Lee Rd Shaker Heights, OH 44120
(216) 752-4444 W. Daniel Bickerstaff, II Founder and Principal Architect
Fax: (216) 752-5011
Email: arcatek@udltd.com
Website: www.udltd.com
Architectural design services, conceptual design/feasibility analysis, construction administration. (AA, estab 2001, empl 2, sales $200,000, cert: City)

1766 WA, Inc. (dba WA Architects, Inc.)
807 Broadway St 2nd Fl Cincinnati, OH 45202
(513) 641-0111 Wade Price Principal
Fax: (513) 641-2401
Email: wprice@wa-inc.biz
Website: www.wa-architectsinc.com
Healthcare Design & Planning. (AA, estab 1971, empl 16, sales $1,600,000, cert: State, NMSDC)

1767 Wanix Architects, LLC
4208 Prospect Ave Cleveland, OH 44103
(440) 570-9829 Xin Wan Owner
Fax: (216) 302-3761
Email: xinwan@wanixarchitects.com
Website: www.wanixarchitects.com
Architectural design, site planning, interior space planning & 3D. (Woman/As-Pac, estab 2008, empl 2, sales , cert: City)

Pennsylvania

1768 Alexander Perry Inc.
100 S Broad St, Ste 1220 Philadelphia, PA 19110
(215) 636-4420 Patricia Sanford President
Fax: (215) 636-0504
Email: ap.designs@verizon.net
Website: www.alexanderperryinc.com
Interior design, project management, construction management, flooring & window treatments, furniture, signage. (Woman/AA, estab 1992, empl 13, sales , cert: City)

1769　DJDC Inc.
12300 Perry Hwy, Ste 204　Wexford, PA 15090
(412) 996-6771　Marcia Guth Principal
Fax: (724) 933-3151
Email: mguth@djdc.com
Website: www.djdc.com
Interior architecture design, space planning & facilities planning svcs. (Woman/White, estab 1972, empl 6, sales $243,000, cert: WBENC)

1770　Genesis Architects Inc.
1850 N Gravers Rd　Plymouth Meeting, PA 19462
(610) 592-0280　Meryl Towarnicki President
Fax: (610) 592-0286
Email: mtowarnicki@geiarc.com
Website: www.geiarc.com
Architecture, Engineering, Commissioning & Construction Management. (Woman/White, estab 2017, empl 30, sales , cert: WBENC)

1771　MKSD. LLC
1209 Hausman Rd, Ste A　Allentown, PA 18104
(610) 366-2081　Silvia Hoffman President
Fax: (610) 366-8399
Email: silvia@mksdarchitects.com
Website: www.mksdarchitects.com
Architecture, planning, design & construction for new buildings, additions & renovations. (Woman, estab 2005, empl 16, sales $3,103,884, cert: State, WBENC)

1772　SMC Consulting, LLC d/b/a/ Studio SMC
379 Insurance St　Beaver, PA 15009
(724) 728-8625　Sam McWilliams Managing Partner
Fax: (724) 703-1670
Email: sam@studio-smc.com
Website: www.studio-smc.com
Interior Design, Space Planning, Furniture Planning, Furniture Specification, Move Management, Project Management, Construction Administration. (Woman/White, estab 1999, empl 5, sales $213,544, cert: State)

1773　Styer & Associates, Inc.
412 Dekalb St　Norristown, PA 19401
(610) 275-6000　Amy Styer Tahtabrounian Principal
Fax: (610) 275-9650
Email: amy@styergroup.com
Website: www.styergroup.com
Architecture, engineering, interior design, construction, project management, purchase management. (Woman/White, estab 1985, empl 9, sales $550,000, cert: WBENC)

Puerto Rico

1774　Arco Caribe Architects, PSC
Cond. San Alberto, Ste 607 605 Condado St　San Juan, PR 00907
(787) 504-7104　Alberto Arroyo President
Fax: (787) 725-4433
Email: aarroyo@arcocaribe.com
Website: www.arcocaribe.com
Architectural & engineering design services. (Hisp, estab 1999, empl 2, sales $385,000, cert: 8(a))

1775　CMA Architects & Engineers LLC
1509 Ave FD Roosevelt　Guaynabo, PR 00968
(787) 792-1509　Jorge A. Tirado, PE Managing Member
Fax: (787) 783-6021
Email: jtirado@cmapr.com
Website: www.cmapr.com
Architectural design services, preparation of construction documents, field & construction management, environmental & permitting, electrical, mechanical, structural, transportation & infrastructure engineering. (Hisp, estab 1959, empl 90, sales $8,300,000, cert: NMSDC, SDB)

1776　UNIPRO Architects Engineers LLP
P.O. Box 10914　San Juan, PR 00922
(787) 793-3950　Jose R. Gonzalez Dir planning/ projects
Fax: (787) 793-8593
Email: jgonzalez@uniproaep.net
Website: www.uniproaep.com
Architecture, civil engineering, structural engineering, mechanical engineering, electrical engineering, environmental engineering, construction management. (Hisp, estab 1980, empl 30, sales $3,200,000, cert: NMSDC)

South Carolina

1777　Waldon Studio Architects PC
1100 Queensborough Blvd Ste 202　Mt Pleasant, SC 29464
(843) 518-3900　Michael Janaskie, AIA, NCARB Managing Principal
Fax:
Email: mjanaskie@waldonstudio.com
Website: www.waldonstudio.com
Architecture & interior design, building, project administration, additions, modernizations & interiors experience. (As-Pac, estab 2003, empl 26, sales $6,897,425, cert: State)

Texas

1778　Architect for Life - A Professional Corporation
2450 Louisiana St, Ste 400-233　Houston, TX 77006
(888) 986-7771　Lolalisa King
Fax: (888) 986-7772
Email: lking@architectforlife.com
Website: www.architectforlife.com
Green consulting professional services, develop & manage energy efficient strategies, programs, & projects, retrofit strategies, benchmarking building energy performance, long-term energy management & water saving goals assessment. (Woman/AA, estab 1995, empl 12, sales $108,000, cert: State, City, NMSDC, 8(a))

1779 Interprise/Southwest Interior & Space Planning, In
5080 Spectrum Dr Ste 115E Addison, TX 75001
(972) 385-3991 Lesley Leahy VP of Business Dev
Fax: (972) 960-2945
Email: lleahy@interprisedesign.com
Website: www.interprisedesign.com
Commerical interior design & space planning. (Woman/ White, estab 1981, empl 36, sales $5,000,000, cert: WBENC)

1780 R & T Architects, Inc.
3300 S Gessner, Ste 119 Houston, TX 77063
(713) 974-2008 Spencer Tsui Principal
Fax: (713) 974-2262
Email: rtarch@swbell.net
Website: www.rtarch.net
Architectural services: design & built. (As-Pac, estab 1982, empl 4, sales $110,000, cert: State, City)

1781 STOA International Architects, Inc.
6001 Savoy Dr, Ste 100 Houston, TX 77036
(713) 995-8784 Alice Hu President
Fax: (713) 995-8765
Email: stoaintl@globalxlr.com
Website: www.stoaintl.com
Architectural design, interior design, planning, construction management, architectural rendering. (As-Pac, estab 1995, empl 10, sales $750,000, cert: State, City, NMSDC)

1782 The idGroup, LLC
2641 Irving Blvd Dallas, TX 75207
(214) 638-6800 Theresa Johnson Principal
Fax: (214) 689-0301
Email: tjohnson@idgroupdallas.com
Website: www.idgroupdallas.com
Interior space planning, retail design & rollout, architectural services. (Woman/White, estab 2001, empl 28, sales $4,845,619, cert: WBENC)

1783 VAI Architects Inc.
16000 N Dallas Pkwy, Ste 200 Dallas, TX 75248
(972) 934-8888 William Vidaud Principal
Fax: (972) 458-2323
Email: wvidaud@vaiarchitects.com
Website: www.vaiarchitects.com
Architecture, master planning, feasibility analysis, interior planning & design, building condition assessments, CADD, renovation, alteration & expansion, demolition specifications, roofing assessments/corrective design. (Hisp, estab 1985, empl 28, sales $4,945,000, cert: State)

Virginia

1784 nbj Architecture
11537-B Nuckols Rd Glen Allen, VA 23059
(804) 273-9811 Neil Bhatt President
Fax: (804) 273-9843
Email: nbhatt@nbjarch.com
Website: www.nbjarch.com
Architectural, space planning, interior design, construction administration, feasibility studies & value engineering. (As-Ind, estab 2000, empl 12, sales $2,000,000, cert: State)

1785 SandHurst-AEC
1069 W Broad St, Ste 777 Falls church, VA 22046
(703) 533-1413 Kwafo Djan Principal
Fax: (703) 533-1413
Email: kdjan@sandhurstaec.com
Website: www.sandhurstaec.com
Architecture & Urban Planning, Program Management, Site Analysis, Feasibility Studies, Architectural Design, Construction, Documentation, Interior Design Services, Space Planning, Project Management. (AA, estab 2013, empl 3, sales , cert: State)

Washington

1786 Ato Apiafi Architects PLLC
10940 NE 33rd Place Ste 208 Bellevue, WA 98004
(425) 202-7760 Jeff Thompson
Fax: (425) 202-7763
Email: jeff.t@atoapiafi.com
Website: www.atoapiafi.com
Full service architectural firm. (AA, estab 2004, empl 2, sales $32,000, cert: State, NMSDC)

Wisconsin

1787 Continuum Architects + Planners, S.C.
228 S First Milwaukee, WI 53204
(414) 220-9649 Ursula Twombly Principal
Fax: (414) 220-9595
Email: ursula.twombly@continuumarchitects.com
Website: www.continuumarchitects.com
Master planning site selection site planning, pre-design studies. (Woman/White, estab 1996, empl 13, sales $1,700,000, cert: City)

AUTOMOBILES
New and used car dealerships. Distributors of single cars, trucks and fleet sales. Provide rental and leasing services. NAICS Code 44

California

1788 Premiere Solutions, LLC
11501 Dublin Blvd Ste 200   Dublin, CA 94568
(925) 467-1000 Holly Michael
Fax: (925) 467-1006
Email: holly@premieresolutionsllc.com
Website: www.premieresolutionsllc.com
Fleet management services: vehicle acquisition (lease, purchase or rental), vehicle disposal, fuel card, preventative maintenance, accident management, roadside assistance, transportation, licensing & registration. (AA, estab 2005, empl 6, sales $15,807,000, cert: NMSDC, CPUC)

1789 Rotolo Chevrolet, Inc.
16666 S Highland Ave   Fontana, CA 92336
(909) 822-1111 Jamie Harshman Dir fleet sales
Fax: (909) 428-9814
Email: jamie@rotolo.com
Website: www.rotolochevy.com
Sell & service Chevrolet light duty cars & trucks. (Woman/White, estab 1971, empl 104, sales $81,651,283, cert: CPUC)

Colorado

1790 Burt Fleet Services, Inc.
5210 S Broadway   Englewood, CO 80113
(303) 789-6701 Lloyd Chavez CEO
Fax: (303) 789-6706
Email: lgchavezjr@burt.com
Website: www.burt.com
National fleet vehicle sales & leasing. (Woman/Hisp, estab 2009, empl 6, sales $600,001, cert: NMSDC)

Florida

1791 NM1, LLC
16725 NW 57th Ave   Miami Gardens, FL 33055
(888) 423-7756 Rogelio (Roger) Tovar President
Fax: (305) 625-1835
Email: rogeliotovar@gmail.com
Website: www.palmetto57nissan.com
Sell new & used cars, parts & service. (Hisp, estab 2012, empl 110, sales $74,101,851, cert: NMSDC)

1792 Sun State International Trucks, LLC
6020 Adamo Dr   Tampa, FL 33619
(813) 769-2541 Dave Metcalf VP Director of Sales
Fax: (813) 628-0527
Email: Dave.Metcalf@sunstateintl.com
Website: www.sunstateintl.com
Medium & heavy duty commercial truck dealership. (AA, estab 1982, empl 163, sales $115,000,000, cert: NMSDC)

Illinois

1793 Advantage Chevrolet
9510 W. Joliet Rd   Hodgkins, IL 60525
(847) 561-5281 Rick Zureick GM
Fax: (708) 215-5020
Email: rzureick@advantagechev.com
Website: www.advantagechev.com
Automotive & commercial truck sales. (AA, estab 2000, empl 122, sales $91,265,959, cert: NMSDC)

1794 Sutton Ford, Inc.
21315 Central   Matteson, IL 60443
(708) 720-8034 Michael Miller Fleet Mgr
Fax: (708) 720-4299
Email: mmiller@suttonford.com
Website: www.suttonford.com
Ford cars, trucks, sales, service & parts. (AA, estab 1989, empl 80, sales , cert: State, NMSDC, CPUC)

Indiana

1795 Truck City of Gary, Inc
PO Box 64800   Gary, IN 46401
(219) 949-8595 Gerri Davis-Parker President
Fax: (219) 949-4578
Email: wbe@mytruckcity.com
Website: www.mytruckcity.com
Heavy Duty Trucks: Agricultural, Landscaping, Bucket, Vacuum, Fuel, Aerial, Welding, Digger Derrick, Pole, Straight, Box, Flat-bed, Bucket, Service, Platform, Dump, Runway Snow Plow, Railway, Refuse, Logging, Mounted Cranes, etc. (Woman/White, estab 1946, empl 58, sales $45,799,499, cert: State, WBENC)

Maryland

1796   K. Neal International Trucks, Inc.
       5000 Tuxedo Rd   Hyattsville, MD 20781
       (301) 772-5100 Sharon Calomese CEO
       Fax: (301) 322-3163
       Email: scalomese@knealinternational.com
       Website: www.knealinternational.com
Commercial truck dealership: International, Hino,
Mitsubishi Fuso trucks & IC Bus. Sales, service, parts &
body shop services, leasing & rental services. (AA, estab
1982, empl 90, sales $110,000,000, cert: State, City,
NMSDC)

Michigan

1797   Hall Whitener Investments, Inc.
       13475 Portage Rd   Vicksburg, MI 49097
       (269) 649-2000 Laura Awe Cstmr Relations Dir
       Fax: (269) 649-3824
       Email: laura.awe@vicksburgchrysler.com
       Website: www.vicksburgchryslerdodgejeepram.com
Sale & service Chrysler, Dodge, Jeep , Ram vehicles. (AA,
estab 2013, empl 32, sales , cert: NMSDC)

1798   Vicksburg Chrysler Dodge Jeep
       13475 Portage Rd P.O. Box 200 Vicksburg, MI 49097
       (269) 649-2000 Monti Long President
       Fax: (269) 649-0060
       Email: mlong007@comcast.net
       Website: www.VicksburgChryslerDodge.com
New & used cars, Chrysler, Dodge, Jeep retail, lease & fleet
services. (AA, estab 1989, empl 46, sales $22,521,322,
cert: NMSDC)

Minnesota

1799   Holt Motors, Inc
       245 Cokato St W P.O. Box 910 Cokato, MN 55321
       (320) 286-2176 Kate Keith President
       Fax:
       Email: katekeith@holtmotors.com
       Website: www.holtmotors.com
Ford Vehicles, Commercial Ford Fleet Program. (Woman,
estab 1951, empl 48, sales , cert: WBENC)

Ohio

1800   Auld Technologies, LLC
       2030 Dividend Dr   Columbus, OH 43228
       (614) 755-2853 Kelsie Bader Project Coord
       Fax:
       Email: kbader@auldtech.com
       Website: www.auldtech.com
Dist decorative emblems, trim, labels, overlays & coating
solutions. (Woman/White, estab 2009, empl 26, sales
$3,500,000, cert: WBENC)

1801   Bob Ross Auto Group
       85 Loop Rd   Centerville, OH 45459
       (937) 433-0990 Vauni Blaut Fleet FSP Mgr
       Fax: (513) 732-2968
       Email: fleet@bobrossauto.com
       Website: www.bobrossauto.com
New Vehicle Dealer, automobiles & light/medium duty
trucks: Buick, GMC Light Duty Trucks, Vans and SUVs;
Fiat Automobiles; Alfa Romeo Automobiles & Specialized
Equipped Fleet & Commercial Vehicles. (Woman/AA,
estab 1974, empl 92, sales $152,029,928, cert: State,
WBENC)

Pennsylvania

1802   Buick GMC of Moosic Inc.
       4230 Birney Ave   Moosic, PA 18507
       (570) 414-1000 Lori Guitson President
       Fax: (570) 414-0524
       Email: lori@sunbpg.com
       Website: www.sunbuickgmc.com
New Buick GMC's, economical cars to vehicles for
executives. (Woman/White, estab 2004, empl 18, sales
$14,000,000, cert: WBENC)

Texas

1803   Ancira
       10807 W IH 10   San Antonio, TX 78230
       (210) 558-1500 Betty Ferguson Mgr
       Fax:
       Email: ljust@ancira.com
       Website: www.ancira.com
Automobile dealership. (Hisp, estab 1985, empl 25, sales
, cert: State)

1804   Kahlig Enterprises, Inc
351 IH 35 South   New Braunfels, TX 78130
(210) 426-3295   Larry Brown Exec Director Fleet Sales
Fax: (866) 871-3908
Email: lbrown@kahligauto.com
Website: www.npbbfleet.com
New Ford, Lincoln & Jeep automobiles, light trucks & SUVs. (Hisp, estab 1984, empl 212, sales $343,000,000, cert: NMSDC)

1805   North Park Lincoln Mercury
P.O. Box 790467   San Antonio, TX 78279
(210) 426-3295   Larry Brown ED Fleet Sales
Fax: (866) 871-3908
Email: lbrown@kahligauto.com
Website: www.npbbfleet.com
Automotive service, mechanical & body shop services. (Hisp, estab 1982, empl 254, sales $266,000,000, cert: State, NMSDC)

1806   Rio Motor
4350 E Hwy 83   Rio Grande City, TX 78582
(956) 487-2596   O.C. Canales President
Fax: (956) 487-5700
Email: riomotorco@aol.com
Website: www.riomotors.com
Sell Chevrolet cars, trucks, van parts & servicing. (Hisp, estab 1953, empl 29, sales , cert: State)

California

1807   Concours Direct, Inc.
       3212 El Camino Real   Atascadero, CA 93422
       (805) 466-4040 William M Vega
       Fax: (805) 466-4090
       Email: wvega@concoursdirect.com
       Website: www.concoursdirect.com

Dist Automotive & Truck Performance Parts, Ford Performance Racing Parts, Edelbrock, MSD, Airaid, Readylift, MBRP, Moroso, Diablosport, Bullydog, Performance Automatic, Centerforce, Tremec, Powermaster, Holly, etc. (Hisp, estab 2005, empl 2, sales $2,412,993, cert: NMSDC, CPUC)

1808   VIAIR Corporation
       15 Edelman   Irvine, CA 92618
       (949) 585-0011 Alan Basham Director of Ops
       Fax: (949) 585-0188
       Email: alanb@viaircorp.com
       Website: www.viaircorp.com

Dist Air Compressor, Air Tank, LED Light, Air accessories for automotive industry. (As-Pac, estab 1998, empl 32, sales , cert: NMSDC)

Florida

1809   Astra/CFX Holdings, LLC
       11971 NW37th St   Coral Springs, FL 33065
       (954) 494-3948 Sharon McTurk President
       Fax: (954) 583-5778
       Email: smcturk@astraservices.com
       Website: www.astraservices.com

3PL Tire and Wheel Assembly, heavy Sub Assembly for all major vehicle modules. (Woman/Hisp, estab 1989, empl 217, sales $30,500,000, cert: NMSDC, WBENC)

1810   Indus Solutions LLC
       4260 NW 1st Ave   Boca Raton, FL 33433
       (248) 875-8010 Sandeep Vijay
       Fax: (904) 638-5522
       Email: sv@indus-sol.com
       Website: www.indus-sol.com

Mfr automotive parts & components, sub assemblies & assemblies of door, hood & tailgate systems, exhaust, steering & suspension, gaskets, rubber mounts, engine, electrical & electronics parts, wire harness & integrated products & prototyping. (As-Ind, estab 2015, empl 15, sales , cert: NMSDC)

1811   NM1, LLC
       16725 NW 57th Ave   Miami Gardens, FL 33055
       (888) 423-7756 Rogelio (Roger) Tovar President
       Fax: (305) 625-1835
       Email: rogeliotovar@gmail.com
       Website: www.palmetto57nissan.com

Sell new & used cars, parts & service. (Hisp, estab 2012, empl 110, sales $74,101,851, cert: NMSDC)

1812   Vehicle Maintenance Program, Inc.
       3595 N Dixie Hwy, Bay 7   Boca Raton, FL 33431
       (561) 362-6080 Penny Brooks President
       Fax: (561) 362-7994
       Email: sales@vmpparts.com
       Website: www.vmpparts.com

Dist vehicle repair parts: filters, wiper blades, lenses, lamps, bulbs, mirrors, batteries, seals, bearings, brake drums. (Woman/White, estab 1988, empl 15, sales $20,140,327, cert: State, WBENC)

Illinois

1813   Bearings & Industrial Supply
       431 Imen Ave   Addison, IL 60101
       (630) 628-1966 Sejal Khandwala Acct Exec
       Fax: (630) 628-0116
       Email: sejal@bearingsnow.com
       Website: www.bearingsnow.com

Dist bearings & power transmission products; pump & pump repair parts, HVAC & electrical parts. (As-Pac, estab 1982, empl 10, sales , cert: NMSDC)

1814   Chicago Parts & Sound, LLC
       1150 Lively Blvd   Elk Grove Village, IL 60007
       (630) 350-1500 Dennis Hoffberg Sales Mgr
       Fax:
       Email: sales@clickoncps.com
       Website: www.clickoncps.com/

Dist automotive parts, commodity lines such as Anco wiper blades. (Woman/Hisp, estab 1978, empl 80, sales , cert: City)

1815   Reliance Distributing
       3609 Pebble Beach Rd   Northbrook, IL 60062
       (847) 372-6125 Anne Chessick CEO
       Fax:
       Email: annieparts@aol.com
       Website: www.reliancedistributing.com

Automotive & truck lighting, flashers, wiper blades, fuses, hose clamps, halogen headlight sockets, permatex products (Woman/White, estab 2012, empl 1, sales $72,000, cert: WBENC)

Kentucky

1816   HJI Supply Chain Solutions
       13200 Complete Court   Louisville, KY 40223
       (502) 638-8064 Lynn Moore VP Finance & Administration
       Fax:
       Email: lmoore@hjisolutions.com
       Website: www.hjisolutions.com
Automotive parts: door panel/trim, switch bezels, running boards, driveshafts, shocks, corner pillars, floor mats & hub caps. (Woman/White, estab , empl 1, sales , cert: NMSDC, WBENC)

1817   LB Manufacturing
       360 Industry Dr   Springfield, KY 40069
       (859) 336-0090 Keith Hamilton CEO
       Fax: (859) 336-0093
       Email: hamiltonk@leanbmfg.com
       Website: www.LEANBMFG.COM
Automotive stamping, welding & mfg assemblies, mig & resistance, robotic, window glass & exhaust system assemblies. (AA, estab 1998, empl 40, sales $17,000,000, cert: NMSDC)

Michigan

1818   Advanced Assembly Products, Inc.
       1300 East Nine Mile Road   Hazel Park, MI 48030
       (248) 543-2427 Ron Waring IT Admin
       Fax: (248) 543-8435
       Email: rwaring@aapincorp.com
       Website: www.aapincorp.com
Body hardware, door hinges, door checks, strikers, hood hinges, deck lid hinges, stampings, welded assemblies, mechanical assemblies. (As-Ind, estab 1993, empl 90, sales $18,000,000, cert: NMSDC)

1819   CAMACO, LLC
       40000 Grand River Ste 110 Novi, MI 48375
       (248) 442-6800 Pamela Cooper Admin Coord
       Fax: (248) 442-6812
       Email: pcooper@camacollc.com
       Website: www.camacollc.com
Mfr auto components & assemblies. (As-Ind, estab 1987, empl 68, sales , cert: NMSDC)

1820   Capsonic Automotive & Aersopace
       3121 University Dr, Ste 120   Auburn Hills, MI 48326
       (248) 754-1100 George E. Albrecht CQA
       Fax:
       Email: georgea@capsonic.com
       Website: www.capsonic.com
Automotive assemblies. (AA, estab 1996, empl 449, sales $37,000,000, cert: NMSDC)

1821   Concept Industries, Inc.
       4950 Kraft Ave SE   Grand Rapids, MI 49512
       (616) 554-9000 David Foote, Troy Caswell CFO
       Fax: (616) 554-9099
       Email: dfoote@conceptind.com,
       troyc@conceptind.com
       Website: www.conceptind.com
Thermoforming, interior acoustical applications, engine side noise absorbers, dash insulators, package trays, load floors, undercarpet absorbers, headliners, trunk liners, needle punch, laminating, plastic vacuum forming, die cut. (Woman/As-Ind, estab 1984, empl 150, sales $20,000,000, cert: NMSDC)

1822   Dawson Mfg Co. - Benton Harbor Division
       1042 N Crystal Ave   Benton Harbor, MI 49022
       (269) 925-0100 Neil Trivedi VP
       Fax: (269) 925-0997
       Email: neil.trivedi@vibracoustic.com.com
       Website: www.dawsonmfg.com
Mfr body mounts, engine mounts, strut mounts, link assemblies & bushings, dist anti-vibration components, rubber injection molding. (As-Pac, estab 1988, empl 90, sales $36,000,000, cert: NMSDC)

1823   Detroit Chassis LLC
       6501 Lynch Rd   Detroit, MI 48234
       (313) 571-2100 Darin Burns VP Business Devel
       Fax: (313) 925-1676
       Email: dburns@detroitchassis.com
       Website: www.detroitchassis.com
Niche vehicle, motor home chassis & commercial truck assembly; complex sub-assemblies & sub-assemblies. (AA, estab 1998, empl 150, sales $7,615,052, cert: NMSDC)

1824   Diversitech, Inc.
       16620 Industrial St   Roseville, MI 48066
       (586) 445-7600 Roger Olle President
       Fax: (586) 445-7622
       Email: rho@div-techusa.com
       Website: www.div-techusa.com
Design & build automation assembly machines, leak test, special machines for powertrain & body & assembly, parts feeding & handling systems. (As-Ind, estab 2009, empl 4, sales $1,500,000, cert: NMSDC)

1825   Global Enterprises
       26909 Woodward Ave   Huntington Woods, MI 48070
       (248) 542-2000 Pat Vizcarra Business Dev
       Fax: (248) 542-4945
       Email: pvizcarra@globalent.org
       Website: www.globalent.org
Extrusion, die-cutting, compression molding, laminating & glueing interior trim components & assemblies. (Woman, estab 1998, empl 280, sales , cert: WBENC)

1826   H.R. Technologies, Inc.
       6570 Nineteen Mile Rd   Sterling Heights, MI 48314
       (586) 739-9455 Tushar Patel President
       Fax: (586) 739-9488
       Email: tpatel@hrtechinc.com
       Website: www.hrtechinc.com
Laminate fabrics & vinyl, carpet, die cutting, headliner
glass fiber reinforcements, headliner glass polypropylene
substrate materials. (As-Ind, estab 1996, empl 48, sales
$11,000,000, cert: NMSDC)

1827   Integrated Manufacturing and Assembly, LLC
       5200 Auto Club Dr   Dearborn, MI 48126
       (313) 593-9246 Leslie Thumm Financial Anyalyst
       Fax:
       Email: lthumm@lear.com
       Website: www.comerholdings.com/about.htm
Interior Systems; seat assemblies, foam & trim assemblies
& injection molded & painted interior components -
Exterior Systems; Exterior mirror assemblies, inection
molded & painted interiors. (AA, estab 1996, empl 700,
sales , cert: NMSDC)

1828   Intex Technologies LLC
       3133 Highland Blvd   Hudsonville, MI 49426
       (616) 662-0276 Kevin Ryan Sales Dir
       Fax: (616) 662-0276
       Email: kevin.ryan@intextech.net
       Website: www.intextech.net
Mfr integral skin flexible foam automotive interior parts:
arm rests, center console, console door, sun visor, steering
wheel, soft-touch points on door handles, cup holders,
seals, jounce bumpers & insulation components. (Hisp,
estab 2008, empl 36, sales $14,800,000, cert: NMSDC)

1829   La Solucion Corp.
       19930 Conner   Detroit, MI 48234
       (313) 893-9760 Patricia Leon CEO
       Fax: (313) 893-9761
       Email: patleon@la-solucion.com
       Website: www.la-solucion.com
Mfr & dist liquid & air filtration systems. (Woman/Hisp,
estab 1999, empl 4, sales , cert: NMSDC)

1830   Marimba Auto, LLC
       41133 Van Born Rd Ste 200 Belleville, MI 48111
       (734) 398-9000 Venkat Chigulla VP Admin
       Fax: (734) 398-9702
       Email: VChigulla@marimbaauto.com
       Website: www.marimbaauto.com
Import tubing, tube processing, global supply mgmt, in-
house engineering, warehousing. (As-Pac, estab 2003,
empl 35, sales $17,000,000, cert: NMSDC)

1831   Need a Part Now, LLC
       1157 Manufacturers Dr   Westland, MI 48186
       (888) 201-9061 Erin Brazill VP
       Fax: (734) 641-3335
       Email: erina@needapartnow.com
       Website: www.needapartnow.com
Mfr parts from AutoCad, blueprints, drawings, sketches,
or reverse engineer. (Woman/White, estab 2006, empl
20, sales $363,281, cert: WBENC)

1832   Piston Automotive
       12723 Telegraph Rd   Redford, MI 48239
       (313) 541-8674 James Edwards Sales Mgr
       Fax: (313) 541-8598
       Email: jedwards@pistongroup.com
       Website: www.pistongroup.com
Manufacturing, module assembly & sequencing, &
logistics management. (AA/As-Pac/Hisp, estab 1995,
empl 750, sales , cert: NMSDC)

1833   Sino Brite (USA), Inc.
       30600 Telegraph Rd, Ste 1131   Bingham Farms,
       MI 48025
       (659) 819-7871 Julinda Kong President
       Fax:
       Email: sales@sinobrite-sg.com
       Website: www.sinobrite-sg.com
Motor Vehicle Supplies & New Parts Merchant Wholesalers. (As-Pac, estab 2003, empl 5, sales , cert: NMSDC)

1834   Ventura Manufacturing
       471 E Roosevelt   Zeeland, MI 49464
       (616) 772-7405 Ana Figueroa Finance
       Fax: (616) 748-5166
       Email: ana.figueroa@venturamfg.com
       Website: www.venturamfg.com
Mfr automotive dimming rearview mirror components,
wire processing components, overhead grabhandles.
(Woman/Hisp, estab 1997, empl 140, sales $26,000,000,
cert: NMSDC)

Minnesota

1835   DV Roland Enterprises, Inc.
       15171 Freeland Ave N   Hugo, MN 55038
       (651) 429-9012 Kenny Scamp GM
       Fax: (651) 407-7069
       Email: Ken@jtservicesinc.com
       Website: www.jtservicesinc.com
Dist & service industrial diesel engines & diesel engine
parts. Supporting diesel engines for aerial lifts, air
compressors, backhoes, dozers, excavators, forklifts,
generators, light towers, rollers, skid steer loaders,
tractors, welders. (AA, estab 2004, empl 6, sales
$1,433,333, cert: City, NMSDC)

Missouri

1836 JCM Machine, Inc.
     5655 Old Hwy 21 House Springs, MO 63051
     (636) 942-4567 Laura Borrini Owner
     Fax:
     Email: lborrini@jcmmachineandcoatings.com
     Website: www.jcmmachineandcoatings.com
Automotive machine shop, cylinder head & engine
rebuilding, certified ceramic coatings applicators & dry film
lubricants. (Woman/White, estab 1976, empl 4, sales
$223,000, cert: State)

New Jersey

1837 Wexco Industries
     3 Barnet Rd Pine Brook, NJ 07058
     (973) 244-5777 Paula Lombard President
     Fax: (973) 244-9179
     Email: plombard@wexcoind.com
     Website: www.wexcoind.com
Dist complete windshield wiper systems. (Woman/White,
estab 1991, empl 30, sales $18,367,600, cert: WBENC)

Pennsylvania

1838 American Cable Company
     1200 E Erie Ave Philadelphia, PA 19124
     (215) 456-0700 Brian Thomas Direct of Ops -
     Contract Div.
     Fax: (215) 456-1330
     Email: bthomas@americancableco.com
     Website: www.americancableco.com
Mfr motor vehicular equipment components, battery
cables, wiring harness, grounding straps, panel assemblies
& related components. (Hisp, estab 2009, empl 5, sales ,
cert: NMSDC, SDB)

Tennessee

1839 Wingard Quality Supply, LLC
     5901 Shallowford Rd Ste 20 Chattanooga, TN 37421
     (423) 521-4600 James Wingard President
     Fax: (423) 521-4604
     Email: james@wingard.biz
     Website: www.wingardll.com
Automotive assembly: tire & wheel. (AA, estab 2002, empl
25, sales $60,000,000, cert: NMSDC)

BOXES & BAGS
Manufacture corrugated cardboard boxes or bags of various materials such as paper, plastic, etc. (See also PACKAGING & PACKING SERVICES & SUPPLIES; WOOD PRODUCTS for wood boxes/crates and PLASTIC PRODUCTS for plastic cases). NAICS Code 32

Alabama

1840   Prystup Packaging Products, Inc.
       101 Prystup Dr P.O. Box 1039 Livingston, AL 35470
       (205) 652-9583 Erin McGahey Natl Acct Rep
       Fax: (205) 652-2696
       Email: emcgahey@prystup.com
       Website: www.prystup.com
Mfr folding paper cartons: food, consumer goods & electronics. (Woman/Nat Ame, estab 1980, empl 160, sales $30,418,102, cert: NMSDC, WBENC)

California

1841   ACME Bag Inc Dba The Bulk Bag Company
       14730 Northam St, La Mirada, CA 90638
       (866) 517-4699 John Willoughby Natl Sales Director
       Fax: (714) 362-0261
       Email: john@thebulkbagcompany.com
       Website: www.thebulkbagcompany.com
Soilsaver Rolls, SOD Staples, Construction Fabrics, Landscaping Fabrics & Tarps, Agriculture Packaging, FIBC Bags & Woven Polypropyline Bags, Sand Bags- Burlap & WPP, Treated Burlap Sqares, Silt Fences, Truncated Wire Baskets. (As-Pac, estab 1975, empl 24, sales $20,000,000, cert: NMSDC)

1842   American Supply
       P.O. Box 2322 Chino, CA 91710
       (949) 216-0468 Vonn Castillo Business Dev Mgr
       Fax: (877) 678-4603
       Email: vcastillo@myamericansupply.com
       Website: www.myamericansupply.com
Mfr & customize bags & covers, janitorial, housekeeping, promotional & OEM products. Mfr replacement cart bags, laundry bags, caddy bags, laundry truck liners, hair dryer bags, etc. (Woman/As-Pac, estab 2013, empl 5, sales $300,000, cert: CPUC)

1843   IPS Industries, Inc.
       12641 166th St. Cerritos, CA 90703
       (562) 623-2555 Betty Yang VP
       Fax: (562) 623-2558
       Email: betty.green@ipspi.com
       Website: www.ipspi.com
Plastic bags. (As-Pac, estab 1985, empl 60, sales , cert: NMSDC)

Connecticut

1844   Eastern Bag & Paper Company, Inc.
       200 Research Dr   Milford, CT 06460
       (203) 878-1814 Meredith Reuben CEO
       Fax: (203) 783-9824
       Email: mreuben@ebpsupply.com
       Website: www.ebpsupply.com
Dist paper, packaging & allied products. (Woman, estab 1918, empl 270, sales $196,987,948, cert: WBENC)

1845   Flexo Converters USA, Inc.
       1200 Northrop Rd   Meridan, CT 06450
       (203) 639-7070 Emily Gerrard Mktg/Sales Mgr
       Fax: (203) 639-7079
       Email: egerrard@flexobags.com
       Website: www.flexobags.com
Mfr twisted handle paper shopping & merchandise bags. (As-Ind/As-Pac, estab 1994, empl 51, sales $15,000,000, cert: NMSDC)

Georgia

1846   Containers Unlimited, Inc.
       400 Claridge Trace   Atlanta, GA 30331
       (714) 734-8608 C. Eric Jones President
       Fax: (775) 269-9139
       Email: chuck@containersunlimited.net
       Website: www.containersunlimited.net
Diat stock & custom boxes & packaging materials. (AA, estab 1999, empl 4, sales , cert: State)

1847   E. Smith Box, Inc.
       1875 Rockdale Industrial Blvd   Conyers, GA 30012
       (770) 388-7787 Jaquacer Middlebrooks President
       Fax: (770) 388-7889
       Email: sales@esmithbox.com
       Website: www.esmithbox.com
Mfr corrugated boxes. (AA, estab 1987, empl 35, sales $20,384,000, cert: NMSDC)

Illinois

1848   Action Health
       1001 Entry Dr   Bensenville, IL 60106
       (630) 496-6253 Erin Moeller Director of Sales
       Fax: (630) 496-6253
       Email: emoeller@actionhealth.com
       Website: www.actionhealth.com
Printed bags, bags, retail packaging products, printed promotional products, promotional items, packaging supplies, labels, tissue paper, gift cards, specialty packaging, custom bags, custom printed items, rush orders, in-stock products. (Woman/White, estab 1980, empl 35, sales , cert: City, WBENC)

1849   Skyline Container Corporation
       9755 W 143rd St   Orland Park, IL 60462
       (708) 460-7965 Dawn Souliotis President
       Fax: (708) 460-8175
       Email: dawn@skyline99.com
       Website: www.skyline99.com
Dist corrugated boxes. (Woman/White, estab 1990, empl
5, sales $1,697,049, cert: City, WBENC)

Kansas

1850   Pitt Plastics, Inc. dba IBS Solutions
       P.O. Box 356   Pittsburg, KS 66762
       (800) 835-0366 Randy Orscheln VP of Sales,
       Strategic Accts
       Fax: (800) 314-8449
       Email: randyo@pittplastics.com
       Website: www.pittplastics.com
Dist bags: can liners & poly bags, rolls or flat pack. (Nat
Ame, estab 1971, empl 450, sales , cert: NMSDC)

Michigan

1851   Sibley Laboratories LLC
       8816 Charbane St   White Lake, MI 48386
       (248) 363-3972 Kathleen Sibley Managing Partner
       Fax: (248) 363-4169
       Email: ksibley@sibleylabs.com
       Website: www.sibleylabs.com
Dist ergonomically safe trash collection receptacles & trash
bags. (Woman/White, estab 2001, empl 3, sales , cert:
WBENC)

Minnesota

1852   Polybest, Inc.
       2962 Cleveland Ave N   Roseville, MN 55113
       (651)6331688 Zongzhao Li President
       Fax: (651) 633-9190
       Email: johnli@polybestinc.com
       Website: www.polybestinc.com
Mfr packaging materials such as all kinds of plastic and
compostable bags, hazard trash bags, disposal bags, trash
canliners, wrapping film, etc. (As-Pac, estab 2006, empl 4,
sales $1,234,157, cert: NMSDC)

Mississippi

1853   Innpack LLC
       10511 High Point Rd   Olive Branch, MS 38654
       (901) 949-4977 Jin Ahn CFO
       Fax: (901) 774-6201
       Email: jahn@innpack.com
       Website: www.innpack.com
Mfr & dist packaging solutions: burlap, cotton, PP
woven, laminated & FBIC bags. (As-Pac, estab 1997,
empl 20, sales $9,000,000, cert: NMSDC)

New Jersey

1854   Glopak Corporation
       132 Case Dr   South Plainfield, NJ 07080
       (908) 753-8735 Elyne Williams Sales Dir
       Fax: (908) 753-8739
       Email: Glopakinc@aol.com
       Website: www.glopakcorp.com
Dist plastic bags & liners. (Woman/AA, estab 1966, empl
33, sales , cert: NMSDC)

1855   RKS Plastics Inc.
       100 Jersey Ave   New Brunswick, NJ 08903
       (800) 635-9959 Sudhir Shah President
       Fax: (732) 828-7703
       Email: srshah@rksplastics.com
       Website: www.rksplastics.com
Dist polyethylene & polyproylene bags, drum/box liners,
sheeting & tubing, zipper lock bags, anti-static bags,
printed bags, wicket/staple pack, stretch wrap & tapes.
In addition, we also offer design services. (As-Pac, estab
1993, empl 7, sales $4,223,000, cert: NMSDC)

New York

1856   Aluf Plastics div. of API Industries, Inc.
       2 Glenshaw St   Orangeburg, NY 10962
       (845) 365-2200 Tom Cross VP of Retail Sales
       Fax: (845) 365-2294
       Email: Tom.c@alufplastics.com
       Website: www.alufplastics.com
Mfr plastic bags. (Woman/White, estab 1977, empl 314,
sales , cert: WBENC)

1857   Global Packaging Solutions LLC
       70 E Sunrise Hwy Ste 611 Valley Stream, NY
       11581
       (516) 256-7416 Mitchell Sloane Managing Dir
       Fax:
       Email: msloane@glopackllc.com
       Website: www.glopackllc.com
Bags, plastic bags, reusable bags, trash liners, shopping
bags. (AA, estab 2011, empl 5, sales $3,500,000, cert:
State)

1858   Star Poly Bag Inc.
       200 Liberty Ave.   Brooklyn, NY 11207
       (718) 384-3130 Rachel Posen President
       Fax: (718) 384-2342
       Email: rachel@starpoly.com
       Website: www.starpoly.com
Mfr poly bags. (Woman/White, estab 1961, empl 15, sales
$3,550,000, cert: State, City, WBENC)

Oregon

1859   Standard Bag Manufacturing Company
       1800 SW Merlo Dr N/A Beaverton, OR 97003
       (503) 616-7307 Rita Fung Controller
       Fax: (503) 848-6203
       Email: rfung@standardbag.com
       Website: www.standardbag.com
Mfr bags: sewn open mouth, pinch bottom open mouth &
pinch block bottom bags. (As-Pac, estab 1985, empl 140,
sales , cert: NMSDC)

South Carolina

1860   Milagro Packaging LLC
       60 Fairview Church Road   Spartanburg, SC 29306
       (864) 578-0085 Jill McCurry
       Fax: (864) 582-1178
       Email: jillm@concept-pkg.com
       Website: www.milagro-pkg.com
Mfr corrugated & solid fiber boxes, polystyrene foam
products & urethane foam products. (Hisp, estab 2001,
empl 425, sales $94,873,435, cert: NMSDC)

Tennessee

1861   OTB Container, LLC
       1380 Poplar Ave   Memphis, TN 38104
       (901) 270-5407 Daniel Coates President
       Fax: (901) 725-4753
       Email: daniel@otbcontainer.com
       Website: www.otbcontainer.com
Supplies corrugated shipping boxes. (AA, estab 2015, empl
5, sales $589,000, cert: State, NMSDC)

1862   RD Plastics
       P.O. Box 111300 Nashville, TN 37222
       (615) 781-0007 Jeffrey D. Loveless VP Natl Accts
       Fax: (615) 781-2828
       Email: JeffL@rdplastics.com
       Website: www.rdplastics.com
Bags: biohazard ziplock, clear ziplock, adhesive closure,
specimen transport, open end, security seals, pill crushers,
personal belonging. (Woman/White, estab 1975, empl 22,
sales $16,502,500, cert: WBENC)

Texas

1863   B.A.G. Corp.
       1155 Kas Dr. Ste 170 Richardson, TX 75081
       (214) 340-7060 Sherlene A Wegner Mktg Asst
       Fax:
       Email: sherlene@bagcorp.com
       Website: www.bagcorp.com
Bulk handling & supply chain solutions. (Woman/White,
estab 1969, empl 100, sales $70,000,000, cert: WBENC)

1864   Formers International, Inc.
       3533 Preston Ave   Pasadena, TX 77505
       (281) 998-9570 Corina Carmona Business Dev
       Mgr
       Fax: (281) 998-9692
       Email: corina@formers.com
       Website: www.formers.com
Mfr bag forming assemblies: vertical form, fill & seal
packaging machines. (Hisp, estab 1975, empl 39, sales ,
cert: City)

1865   Superbag USA Corp.
       9291 Baythorne Dr   Houston, TX 77041
       (713) 462-1173 Woody Hunt VP of Sales
       Fax: (713) 462-8145
       Email: whunt@superbag.com
       Website: www.superbag.com
Dist high density polyethylene grocery, retail bags &
woven polypropylene bags. (Hisp, estab 1999, empl 250,
sales $149,000,000, cert: State, NMSDC)

1866   TCP Universal
       3536 Hwy 6 South, Ste 118   Sugarland, TX 77478
       (281) 966-8208 Pep Ly President
       Fax:
       Email: Pep.ly@tcpuniversal.com
       Website: www.tcpuniversal.com
Can Liners, Biohazard Bags, Composite Bags, Ice Bags,
Poly Bags, Produce Bags. (Woman/As-Pac, estab 2015,
empl 3, sales , cert: State, City)

DIR

DIVERSITY INFORMATION RESOURCES

24th Annual
Supplier Diversity Seminar

"Best Practices in Supplier Diversity Strategies and Initiatives"

August 2019 • Boston, MA

AGENDA
Tuesday
8:00 am - 12:00 pm
Giving Back: Volunteering in the Local Communities

1:30 - 4:00 pm
Government Contracting and Reporting

Wednesday
8:00 am - 4:00 pm
Seminar General Session

5:30 - 7:00 pm
Networking Reception

Thursday
8:00 am - 4:00 pm
Seminar General Session

SEMINAR LOCATION
Location TBD, Boston, MA

ACCOMMODATIONS
Reservation information will be sent with registration confirmation.

FEE
$1,025*/person
Fee includes all sessions. seminar materials, continental breakfast, lunch and networking reception

SEMINAR REGISTRATION
www.diversityinforesources.com
or contact DIR directly at: 612-781-6819
info@diversityinforesources.com
NOTE: There is NO on-site registration

SPONSORED BY
Diversity Information Resources
2300 Kennedy Street NE, Suite 230
Minneapolis, MN 55413
www.diversityinforesources.com

Join experienced Supplier Diversity Professionals and subject matter experts for a series of presentations and networking events

"One of the best all-around events that I have attended ... this is an event that I definitely want to have in my yearly budget!"

"Great! I'm glad I attended."

TUESDAY: A special morning session: Giving Back - volunteering in the local communities. Afternoon session features experts on Government Reporting, Compliance, Contracting, Rules and Regulations. These are optional sessions, but highly recommended and are included in the registration fee.

WEDNESDAY & THURSDAY: Seminar agenda features noted supplier diversity professionals Past topics included:

- Disaster Recovery: Are you Prepared? Supporting Suppliers after a Natural Disaster
- Supplier Diversity Program Management
  - Documentation/Processes
  - Marketing, Public Relations Strategy, Metrics
  - Future Process of Corporate Procurement Process
- Professional Development: Unlocking personal agility to recognize, deal with and exploit opportunities in a changing environment
- Economic Impact
  - How to measure the economic impact of Supplier Diversity that can be presented to internal stakeholders
  - Disparity Studies
- Aligning Supplier Diversity with Diversity & Inclusion (D&I), Sustainability and Social Responsibility
- Supplier Performance
  - How to support a diverse supplier after engagement; record keeping and documentation; audit and quality assurance.
  - Processes to track specific information on bid processes.
  - Supplier Scorecards

WHO ATTENDS?
- Supplier Diversity Professionals
- Purchasing Managers/Buyers
- VP's of Materials and Purchasing Procurement Managers
- Small Business Liaison Officers (SBLO's)
- Lead staff with responsibility for implementing supplier diversity programs
- Graduates of DIR's "Building Strategic Phases of a Supplier Diversity Process" Seminar

Since 1968, DIR has been a leader in providing information resources that

CHEMICALS
Manufacturers and distributors of organic and inorganic chemicals, fertilizers, blasting materials, radioactive, cosmetic & industrial chemicals, photographic processing solutions, drilling mud, oil derivatives, pharmaceutical preservatives, blowing agents, coatings, lubricants and solvents. Also chemical and custom packaging. NAICS Code 42

Alabama

1867   Stutton Corporation
       1256 McCaig Rd   Lincoln, AL 35096
       (205) 763-2000 Lorraine Studin President
       Fax: (205) 763-2022
       Email: info@stuttoncorp.com
       Website: www.stuttoncorp.com
Mfr & dist chemicals: lubricants, greases, degreasers, cleaners, sealers, epoxy strippers, paint strippers, citrus solvents, deodorizers, corrosion barriers, rust penetrants, spray insulation, sealers, adhesives. (Woman/White, estab 1977, empl 12, sales $1,900,000, cert: State)

Arkansas

1868   Chemical Distribution Solutions, LLC
       1125 Oak St Ste 303 Conway, AR 72032
       (501) 978-1111 Anthony Wilmington President
       Fax:
       Email: twilmington@chemicalds.com
       Website: www.chemicalds.com
Custom Blending, Valued Products, Chemical Distribution (AA, estab 2011, empl 4, sales $9,500,000, cert: NMSDC)

California

1869   Anahau Energy, LLC
       2041 Rosecrans Ave, Ste 322   El Segundo, CA 90245
       (310) 414-2300 Suyen Pell CEO
       Fax: (310) 414-2301
       Email: proposals@anahauenergy.com
       Website: www.anahauenergy.com
Electric power, natural gas, and renewable products. (As-Pac, estab 2005, empl 10, sales , cert: NMSDC)

1870   Apac Chemical Corp.
       150 N. Santa Anita Ave, Ste 850   Arcadia, CA 91006
       (626) 203-0066 Tom Kusaka
       Fax:
       Email: sales@apacchemical.com
       Website: www.apacchemical.com
Mfr Sorbic acid & Potassium sorbate. (As-Pac, estab 1999, empl 7, sales $19,000,000, cert: NMSDC)

1871   Ensunet Consulting Corporation
       10679 WESTVIEW PARKWAY, 2ND FL   San Diego, CA 92126
       (858) 348-4690 Paul Robinson President
       Fax: (619) 568-3809
       Email: paul.robinson@ensucorp.com
       Website: www.ensunet.com
Dist lubricants, fuel additives & safety fluids. (AA, estab 2008, empl 8, sales $165,000, cert: NMSDC)

1872   Ferco Color
       2315 Baker Ave   Ontario, CA 91761
       (909) 930-0773 Jennifer Thaw President
       Fax: (909) 930-0775
       Email: info@fercocolor.com
       Website: www.fercocolor.com/
Mfr color & additives for plastics, bottles, closures. (Woman/White, estab 1994, empl 48, sales $16,000,000, cert: WBENC)

1873   LMC Enterprises, dba Chemco Products Company
       6401 Alondra Blvd   Paramount, CA 90723
       (866) 243-6261 Erica Utz Wochna VP of Human Resources
       Fax: (562) 602-2811
       Email: Erica@chemcoprod.com
       Website: www.chemcoprod.com
Chemical commodities: sodium hydroxide, potassium hydroxide, sulfuric acid, phosphoric acid, citric acid, sodium hypochlorite. (Woman/White, estab 1976, empl 125, sales $43,324,790, cert: WBENC)

1874   Pinnacle Petroleum, Inc.
       16651 Gemini Lane   Huntington Beach, CA 92647
       (714) 841-8877 Liz McKinley President
       Fax: (714) 841-8855
       Email: lmckinley@pinnaclepetroleum.com
       Website: www.pinnaclepetroleum.com
Dist petroleum & lubricants, fuel management services. (Woman/White, estab 1995, empl 25, sales $176,000,000, cert: WBENC)

1875   Pynergy, LLC
       4495 S Santa Fe Dr   Englewood, CA 80110
       (303) 292-5005 Darrell Jackson President
       Fax: (303) 292-5006
       Email: djackson@pynergy.com
       Website: www.pynergy.com
Dist Diesel, On-Site Refueling, Gasoline, Wet Hose Refueling, High Octane Fuels, Diesel Generator Fuel Delivery, Ethanol, Diesel Fuel Treatment Program, Biodiesel Kerosene, Lubricant/Fuel Management, Aviation Fuel & Lubricants. (Woman/AA, estab 1999, empl 44, sales $31,103,590, cert: City)

1876   Ramos Oil Company, Inc.
     1515 S River Rd   West Sacramento, CA 95691
     (916) 371-2570 Sarah Russell
     Fax: (916) 371-0635
     Email: sarahr@ramosoil.com
     Website: www.ramosoil.com
Dist fuel & oils. (Hisp, estab 1951, empl 185, sales , cert: CPUC)

1877   Sungro Products
     810 E 18th St Los Angeles, CA 90021
     (213) 747-4125 Teke Negus President
     Fax: (213) 747-0942
     Email: tnegus@sungroproducts.com
     Website: www.sungroproducts.com
Dist chemicals, water treatment, Institutional insecticides, herbicides, rodenticides, detergents, hand soaps, air fresheners, metal polishes, degreasers, deodorants, glass cleaners. (AA, estab 1967, empl 10, sales $1,500,000, cert: 8(a))

1878   Western States Distributing
     1790 S 10 St San Jose, CA 95112
     (482) 292-1041 Louis Burford Admin
     Fax: (408) 293-2093
     Email: slopes@lubeoil.com
     Website: www.lubeoil.com
Dist petroleum. (Hisp, estab 1956, empl 44, sales , cert: CPUC)

Colorado

1879   Birko Corporation
     9152 Yosemite St Henderson, CO 80640
     (303) 289-1090 Kelly Green President
     Fax: (303) 289-1190
     Email: kgreen@birkocorp.com
     Website: www.birkocorp.com
Mfr & dist chemicals, industrial hygiene, hand soaps & sanitizers, surface sanitizers & cleaners, specialty white-oil based lubricants, chemical dispensing equipment, chemical allocation tracking equipment, steam/water temperature control valves. (Woman/White, estab 1952, empl 59, sales , cert: WBENC)

Connecticut

1880   Prochimie International, Inc.
     2 Waterside Crossing Windsor, CT 06095
     (860)6838500 Anna Malz VP
     Fax: (860) 683-8551
     Email: amalz@prochimieinternational.com
     Website: www.prochimieinternational.com
Chemical products: Automotive/Tire, Agrochemical, Oil field, Water Treatment, Pharmaceutical, Photographic and Specialty chemicals. (Woman/White, estab 1975, empl 10, sales $6,000,000, cert: WBENC)

1881   U.S. Chemicals, LLC
     16 Thorndal Circle Darien, CT 06820
     (203) 202-2808 Carol Piccaro President
     Fax:
     Email: cpiccaro@uschemicals-wob.com
     Website: www.uschemicals-wob.com
Dist chemicals. (Woman/White, estab , empl 15, sales $90,000,000, cert: WBENC)

Florida

1882   Algon Corporation
     12000 SW 132 Court Miami, FL 33186
     (305) 253-6901 Eduardo Suarez-Troconis Director
     Fax: (305) 253-6952
     Email: edal@algon.com
     Website: www.algon.com
Chemical raw materials, laboratory supplies & machine parts. (Woman/Hisp, estab 1989, empl 24, sales $20,570,883, cert: NMSDC)

1883   Bell Performance
     1340 Bennett Dr Longwood, FL 32750
     (407) 831-5021 Deb Moon Director of Sales
     Fax: (407) 331-1125
     Email: dmoon@bellperformance.net
     Website: www.bellperformance.com
Mfr commercial grade treatments for diesel, ethanol, gasoline, fuel oil & power plant fuels. (Woman/White, estab 1909, empl 16, sales $1,543,035, cert: WBENC)

1884   Burck Oil Co., Inc.
     1401 53rd St West Palm Beach, FL 33407
     (561) 842-3600 Jefffrey Burck President
     Fax: (561) 842-3699
     Email: jeffburck@burckoil.com
     Website: www.burckoil.com
Dist oil, grease & lubricants; food grade lubricants. (Woman/White, estab 1996, empl 4, sales $3,600,000, cert: State)

1885   Chemical Systems
     P.O. Box 810 Zellwood, FL 32798
     (407) 886-2329 Corky Thein President
     Fax: (407) 886-4842
     Email: corky.thein@chemicalsystems.com
     Website: www.chemicalsystems.com
Mfr sanitation & specialty chemicals. (Hisp, estab 1979, empl 23, sales $10,000,000, cert: NMSDC)

1886   Graham Trading Company, LLC
     3001 N. Rocky Point Dr. East, Ste 200 Tampa, FL 33607
     (855) 256-8237 Darrell Graham CEO
     Fax: (813) 315-6342
     Email: info@gratraco.com
     Website: www.gratraco.com
Dist diesel, gasoline, jet fuel & lubricants. (AA, estab 2014, empl 2, sales $250,000, cert: State, NMSDC)

Georgia

1887 DES Wholesale, LLC
601 West Crossville Road   Roswell, GA 30075
(404) 474-4450 Allison de Aguero CEO
Fax:
Email: custreg@deswholesale.com
Website: www.diversifiedenergysupply.com
Dist natural gas, electric power & fleet fuel. (Woman/White, estab 2011, empl 9, sales $61,999,800, cert: WBENC)

1888 DJG Chemical, Inc.
4761 Hugh Howell Rd D   Tucker, GA 30084
(404) 244-4606 Carla Doleman CEO
Fax: (404) 244-4606
Email: cdoleman@djgchem.com
Website: www.djgchemical.com
Mfr & dist chemical products: adhesives, janitorial, lubricants, raw materials, water treatment chemicals, foam soaps, herbicides, cosmetic chemicals, etc. (AA, estab 2003, empl 8, sales $60,000, cert: NMSDC)

1889 PS Energy Group, Inc.
4480 N Shallowford Rd Ste 100 Dunwoody, GA 30338
(800) 334-7548 Karen Booker Proposal Writer
Fax: (770) 391-1928
Email: karen.booker@PSENERGY.COM
Website: www.psenergy.com
Dist natural gas, vehicle fleet fuel mgmt, diesel fuel, gasoline, jet fuel, propane, etc. (Woman/Hisp, estab 1985, empl 25, sales $165,000,000, cert: NMSDC, WBENC)

1890 Simcol Group, LLC
3455 Peachtree Rd NE, 5th Fl   Atlanta, GA 30326
(404) 995-7037 Simon Guobadia CEO
Fax: (404) 921-9602
Email: simon@simcolgroup.com
Website: www.simcolgroup.com
Fuel, gasoline, jet fuel, aviation fuel, diesel fuel, lubricants, wax. (AA, estab 2009, empl 10, sales $70,000, cert: NMSDC)

1891 Supreme Resources, Inc.
285 E Smoketree Terr   Alpharetta, GA 30005
(770) 475-4638 Victor Tan Business Dir
Fax: (770) 475-4618
Email: victortan@supremeresources.com
Website: www.supremeresources.com
Dist chemicals, resins, adhesives & raw materials. (As-Pac, estab 1988, empl 10, sales , cert: NMSDC)

1892 TDMC Enterprises Inc.
370 Great Southwest Pkwy P.O. Box 43545
Atlanta, GA 30336
(404) 699-5404 Chuck Smith President
Fax: (404) 699-5406
Email: cesmith@chemstationatlanta.com
Website: www.chemstation.com
Mfr industrial chemicals: cleaners, degreasers, vehicle & airplane cleaners, food processing, odor control, parts washing, scrubber soaps, asphalt release products, strippers, etc. (AA, estab 1991, empl 14, sales $870,000, cert: NMSDC)

Iowa

1893 Searle Petroleum Co.
P.O. Box A   Council Bluffs, IA 51502
(712) 323-2441 David Bills VP
Fax: (712) 323-1493
Email: davidb@redgiantoil.com
Website:
Dist engine oils, hydraulic, compressor, journal, grease. (Woman/White, estab 1910, empl 88, sales $53,500,000, cert: WBENC)

Illinois

1894 Blackdog Corporation
2305 Enterprise Dr   Westchester, IL 60154
(877) 617-4104 Marc Whitaker Chief Mktg Officer
Fax: (773) 697-3279
Email: marc@blackdogcorp.com
Website: www.blackdogcorp.com
Dist fuel, oil & lubricants. (As-Pac, estab 2006, empl 46, sales $23,500,000, cert: City, NMSDC)

1895 Cedar Concepts Corporation
4342 S Wolcott Ave   Chicago, IL 60609
(773) 890-5790 Roxanne Hubbard Mktg Mgr
Fax: (773) 890-1606
Email: roxanne@cedarconcepts.net
Website: www.cedarconcepts.net
Mfr surfactants & chemical intermediates. (Woman/AA, estab 1991, empl 41, sales $15,000,000, cert: WBENC)

1896 Essential Water Technologies LLC
1761 S. Naperville Road   Wheaton, IL 60189
(630) 344-6770 Diane Craig Supplier Diversity
Fax: (630) 344-3470
Email: diane@essentialwatertech.com
Website: www.essentialwatertech.com
Water treatment chemicals & services. (Woman/White, estab 2011, empl 8, sales $750,000, cert: WBENC)

1897   Natural Enrichment Industries
         1002 S Park St   Sesser, IL 62884
         (618) 625-2112 Richard Degler Inside Sales
         Fax: (618) 625-3112
         Email: irichardd@neitcp.com
         Website: www.neitcp.com
Mfr tricalcium phosphate. (Woman/White, estab 2000,
empl 26, sales $7,000,000, cert: State)

1898   Quimex, Inc.
         14702 S Hamlin   Midlothian, IL 60445
         (708) 597-6201 Felipe Estrada Acct Mgr
         Fax: (708) 597-8655
         Email: quimex@quimexinc.com
         Website: www.quimexinc.com
Dist industrial chemicals, oils, lubricants, solvents &
coatings. (Hisp, estab 1975, empl 14, sales $6,309,695,
cert: City)

1899   West Fuels Inc.
         82 S La Grange Road Ste 201 La Grange, IL 60525
         (708) 588-1900 Deborah Stange President
         Fax: (708) 588-8289
         Email: dstange@westfuels.com
         Website: www.westfuels.com
Dist petroleum products. (Woman/White, estab 1991,
empl 9, sales $10,600,000, cert: State, City, WBENC)

Indiana

1900   Advance Energy LLC
         3580 N Hobart Rd, Ste C   Hobart, IN 46342
         (219) 794-1277 Vance Kenney Managing Partner
         Fax: (312) 275-8411
         Email: vance.kenney@advanceegy.com
         Website: www.advanceegy.com
Petroleum related products & services: gas, diesel & oil
related products. (AA, estab 2012, empl 10, sales , cert:
NMSDC)

1901   Harris & Ford, LLC
         9307 E 56th St   Indianapolis, IN 46216
         (317) 591-0000 Jimmy Colon President
         Fax: (317) 541-4700
         Email: sales@harrisandford.com
         Website: www.harrisandford.com
Dist food, pharmaceutical, industrial chemicals & related
services. (AA, estab 1994, empl 50, sales $160,000,000,
cert: NMSDC)

1902   Harris and Ford, LLC
         9307 E 56th St   Indianapolis, IN 46216
         (317) 591-0000 Tim Harris II Business Devel
         Fax: (317) 541-4700
         Email: TTH@harrisandford.com
         Website: www.harrisandford.com
Dist chemicals & ingredients. (AA, estab 1994, empl 50,
sales $220,000,000, cert: NMSDC)

1903   J2 Systems and Supply, LLC
         803 E 38th St   Indianapolis, IN 46205
         (317) 602-3940 James Leonard Owner
         Fax: (866) 391-2772
         Email: jleonard@j2ssllc.com
         Website: www.j2systemsandsupply.com
Dist chemicals: water treatment, waste-water treatment,
metal surface cleaning & coating, food ingredients &
additives, industrial floor & general purpose cleaners.
(AA, estab 2007, empl 5, sales $245,949, cert: State,
NMSDC)

1904   Lemak, LLC dba Lemak Lubricants
         P.O. Box 1381   Noblesville, IN 46061
         (260) 906-6433 Elizabeth Reynolds President
         Fax: (260) 563-4692
         Email: beth@lemakllc.com
         Website: www.lemakllc.com/
Dist petroleum & chemicals: Industrial & Automotive
Lubricants, Propane, Fuels, Coolants and Cutting Fluids,
Antifreeze, Specialty & Commodity Chemicals. (Woman/
White, estab 2008, empl 2, sales $3,289,096, cert: State,
WBENC)

1905   Mays Chemical Company
         5611 E 71st St   Indianapolis, IN 46220
         (317) 558-2045 Julie Brown Inventory Planning
         Admin
         Fax: (317) 558-2267
         Email: julieb@mayschem.com
         Website: www.mayschem.com
Dist process chemicals: bags, drums & totes, technical,
reagent & USP/FCC grades. Electronic grade chemicals,
antifreeze, caustic soda, etc. (Woman/AA, estab 1980,
empl 70, sales $189,000,000, cert: NMSDC)

1906   Supreme Oil Company
         1319 Vincennes St   New Albany, IN 47150
         (812) 945-5266 Matt Sexton VP
         Fax: (812) 944-0429
         Email: msexton@heritageoil.com
         Website: www.supremelubricants.com
Mobil & Chevron oils, lubricants & greases, hydraulic oil,
motor oil, gear oil, synthetic oil, biodegradeable oil,
antifreeze, coolants & cleaners. (Woman/White, estab
1937, empl 7, sales $15,359,000, cert: NWBOC)

1907   VTI Contracting, Inc.
         831 Elston Dr   Shelbyville, IN 46176
         (317) 398-7911 Judy Montgomery President
         Fax: (317) 398-8788
         Email: jm@vtitotalsolutions.com
         Website: www.vtitotalsolutions.com
Concrete coatings, sealants, epoxy and resinous coatings, polishing, repair, staining, traffic coatings, striping,
caulking, expansion joints, joint filler, fire proof caulking,
air barriers, waterproofing. (Woman/White, estab 1985,
empl 30, sales $3,000,010,000, cert: State, City)

1908 WLS Enterprises, Inc.
      8108 Woodland Dr   Indianapolis, IN 46278
      (317) 337-1020 Andre Warren VP
      Fax: (317) 337-0478
      Email: andre@wls-enterprises.com
      Website: www.wls-enterprises.com
Dist chemicals, custom packaging, lab analysis.
(Woman/AA, estab 2000, empl 12, sales $7,600,000, cert:
NMSDC)

Kentucky

1909 Big Meadow Oil Company
      4564 Big Meadow Rd   Knob Lick, KY 42154
      (270) 432-7081 Betty Gentry President
      Fax: (270) 432-4647
      Email: bigmoil@scrtc.com
      Website:
Dist fuel: gasoline, kerosene, diesel, lubricants, etc.
(Woman/White, estab 1981, empl 10, sales $3,000,000,
cert: WBENC)

1910 Hexagon Technologies, Inc.
      P.O. Box 23163   Louisville, KY 40223
      (502) 429-8990 Mr. Kiran Shah President
      Fax: (502) 429-8911
      Email: hexafloc@bellsouth.net
      Website: www.hexagontech.net
Water & wastewater treatment chemicals & services. (As-
Ind, estab 1982, empl 6, sales , cert: NMSDC)

1911 Mid American Chemical Supply Co, Inc.
      115 MacArthur Ct   Nicholasville, KY 40356
      (859) 885-6400 Leon Higgins Acct Exec
      Fax: (859) 887-0822
      Email: leonhiggins@hotmail.com
      Website: www.midamericanchemical.com
Dist industrial & personal supplies, chemicals, non-durable
goods, industrial machinery & equipment. (AA, estab
1978, empl 54, sales , cert: State)

Louisiana

1912 Golden Leaf Energy, Inc.
      P.O. Box 3605   Harvey, LA 70059
      (504) 252-4838 Troy Clark CEO
      Fax: (504) 368-6352
      Email: troyclark@goldenleafenergy.com
      Website: www.goldenleafenergy.com
Mfr biodiesel for use as a solvent as well as bio-based
lubricants & other products. (AA, estab 2011, empl 9, sales
$55,361, cert: State)

Massachusetts

1913 Grimes Oil Co., Inc.
      P.O. Box 276   West Tisbury, MA 02575
      (617) 825-1200 Calvin Grimes, Jr. President
      Fax: (508) 693-0994
      Email: sales@grimesoil.com
      Website: www.grimesoil.com
Dist distillate & risidual heating oils, diesel fuels &
gasoline. (AA, estab 1940, empl 4, sales $3,925,000,
cert: State, City, NMSDC)

Maryalnd

1914 HIC Energy, LLC
      5937 Belair Rd   Baltimore, MD 21206
      (410) 914-7161 Troy Holland Mgr
      Fax: (253) 390-3031
      Email: th@hicenergy.com
      Website: www.hicenergy.com
Dist natural gas. (AA, estab 2015, empl 5, sales , cert:
NMSDC)

Michigan

1915 2V Industries, Inc.
      48553 West Rd   Wixom, MI 48393
      (248) 624-7943 Sharron Craig
      Fax: (248) 624-1824
      Email: scraig@2vindustries.com
      Website: www.2vindustries.com
Dist metalworking compounds, coolants, RPS, cleaners,
etc. (As-Ind, estab 1968, empl 20, sales , cert: NMSDC)

1916 Adhesive Systems, Inc.
      14410 Woodrow Wilson   Detroit, MI 48238
      (313) 530-6654 Randall Jaymes Tech. Sales Acct
      Mgr
      Fax: (313) 957-6340
      Email: randallj@dchem.com
      Website: www.dchem.com
Mfr hot melt, water base & pressure sensitive adhesives.
(AA, estab 1985, empl 28, sales $60,000,000, cert:
NMSDC)

1917 Adhezion, Inc.
      7730 Childsdale Ave   Rockford, MI 49341
      (616) 726-1775 Chris Telman Regional Acct Mgr
      Fax:
      Email: ctelman@adhezioninc.com
      Website:
Adhesives & coatings. (Woman, estab 2010, empl 7,
sales , cert: WBENC)

1918   C.J. Chemicals, LLC
       47635 Old US 23   Brighton, MI 48114
       (269) 788-2317 Eric Earl Regional Mgr
       Fax:
       Email: Eric@CJchemicals.net
       Website: www.cjchemicals.net
Dist Chemicals, Solvents & Oils used for water & wastewater treatment, cleaning, painting, metal finishing & other industrial & commercial applications. (Woman/White, estab 2011, empl 10, sales , cert: WBENC)

1919   ChemicoMays, LLC
       25200 Telegraph Rd   Southfield, MI 48034
       (248) 723-3263 Dave Macleod VP Business Dev
       Fax: (248) 646-1664
       Email: dmacleod@chemicomays.com
       Website: www.chemicomays.com
Chemical management, purchasing, distribution & logistics. (AA, estab 2005, empl 250, sales $86,000,000, cert: NMSDC)

1920   Chrysan Industries, Inc.
       14707 Keel St   Plymouth, MI 48170
       (734) 451-5411 Suk-Kyu Koh CEO
       Fax: (734) 862-4053
       Email: Skoh@chrysanindustries.com
       Website: www.chrysanindustries.com
Mfr industrial lubricants, cleaners, rust-preventatives, cutting fluids, stamping compounds, specialty chemicals, chemical mgmt. (As-Pac, estab 1977, empl 21, sales $10,300,000, cert: NMSDC)

1921   Diversified Chemical Technologies, Inc.
       15477 Woodrow Wilson   Detroit, MI 48238
       (313) 530-6630 Michael Joseff Director of Sales
       Fax: (313) 867-3831
       Email: mjoseff@dchem.com
       Website: www.dchem.com
Dist chemicals. (AA/Hisp, estab 1971, empl 185, sales $80,000,000, cert: NMSDC)

1922   Infiniti Energy & Environmental, Inc.
       24755 W. Five Mile Rd. Ste 100 Redford, MI 48239
       (313) 538-0172 Sherman Larkins
       Fax:
       Email: sl@infinitigroup.us
       Website: www.infinitigroup.us
Dist natural gas, oil, lubricant & petroleum products, waste recycling, consulting & industrial cleaning, waste hauling. (AA, estab 1997, empl 5, sales $2,300,000, cert: NMSDC)

1923   IPAX Atlantic LLC
       8301 Lyndon Ave   Detroit, MI 48238
       (313) 933-4211 Olti Tile Business Dev Mgr
       Fax: (313) 393-3445
       Email: akatz@ipax.com
       Website: www.ipax.com
Mfr cleaning compounds. (Woman, estab , empl 1, sales , cert: WBENC)

1924   MCEM LLC
       31153 Plymouth Rd   Livonia, MI 48150
       (517) 881-1226 BK Masti President
       Fax:
       Email: bkm@mcem.co
       Website: www.mcem.co
Lubricants, valves, conduit fittings. (As-Pac, estab 2011, empl 5, sales , cert: NMSDC)

1925   Parson Adhesives Inc.
       3345 Auburn Rd, Ste 107   Rochester Hills, MI 48309
       (248) 299-5585 Hammie Dogan NA Acct Mgr
       Fax: (248) 299-3846
       Email: hammie@parsonadhesives.com
       Website: www.parsonadhesives.com
Industrial adhesives in small and large packing sizes, (As-Pac, estab 2002, empl 45, sales , cert: NMSDC)

1926   RKA Petroleum Company, Inc.
       28340 Wick Rd   Romulus, MI 48174
       (734) 946-2202 Timothy Dluzynski Natl Acct Exec
       Fax: (734) 946-1920
       Email: tdluzynski@rkapetroleum.com
       Website: www.rkapetroleum.com
Dist refined & renewable fuel products and fuel management solutions. (Woman/White, estab 1969, empl 49, sales $675,365,826, cert: WBENC)

1927   Roy Smith Company *
       14650 Dequindre   Detroit, MI 48212
       (313) 883-6969 Peter Wong CPA Chairman
       Fax: (313) 883-0976
       Email: angela.summers@rscmain.com
       Website: www.rscmain.com
Industrial gases & welding, dist industrial bulk gas systems, packaged & cylinder specialty gases, welding equipment & consumables. (As-Pac, estab 1924, empl 20, sales $24,000,000, cert: NMSDC)

1928   Vik-Jay Industries, Inc.
       P.O. Box 3347   Farmington, MI 48333
       (248) 661-6228 Vik Bedi GM
       Fax: (248) 661-0230
       Email: vbedi@vikjay.com
       Website: www.vikjay.com
Dist metalworking lubricants, fluids & cleaners. (As-Ind, estab 1983, empl 36, sales $1,200,000, cert: NMSDC)

Minnesota

1929   LKT Laboratories, Inc.
       545 Phalen Blvd   Saint Paul, MN 55130
       (651) 644-8424 Luke Lam President
       Fax:
       Email: llam@lktlabs.com
       Website: www.lktlabs.com/
Mfr biochemicals for life science research, inhibitors,
activators, modulators, and many other high purity small
molecules, phytochemical isolation and analysis. (As-Pac,
estab 1990, empl 11, sales $1,300,000, cert: NMSDC)

Missouri

1930   Celta Chemical, Inc.
       639 Shadowridge Dr   Wildwood, MO 63011
       (314) 440-6194 Nancy Riordan President
       Fax: (314) 431-3030
       Email: nancy@celtachem.com
       Website: www.celtachem.com
Chemical & food ingredient toll manufacturer and supplier. (Woman/White, estab 2014, empl 4, sales
$6,600,000, cert: WBENC)

1931   Mind Safety Management, LLC/M-Cubed Info
       1509 Washington Ave, Ste 650   St. Louis, MO 63103
       (314) 436-3233 Ralph Thompson COO
       Fax: (314) 436-3646
       Email: ralphthompson@mcubedinfo.com
       Website: www.mindsafety.com
Dist adhesive products. (AA, estab 2001, empl 5, sales ,
cert: State)

1932   Petro Logistics, LLC
       910 S Kirkwood, Ste 120   Kirkwood, MO 63122
       (314) 835-9499 Lianne Reizer Managing Member
       Fax: (314) 835-9577
       Email: lianne@petrologisticsllc.com
       Website: www.petrologisticsllc.com
Dist petroleum, liquid asphalt products. (Woman/White,
estab 2012, empl 11, sales $6,200,000, cert: State, City,
WBENC)

1933   The Kiesel Company
       4801 Fyler Ave   St. Louis, MO 63166
       (314) 351-5500 Larry Gooden VP
       Fax: (314) 351-0894
       Email: Larry.Gooden@kieselco.com
       Website: www.thekieselcompany.com
Dist fuels & lubricants, emergency response services to
chemical & petroleum product releases, railroad tank car
cleaning, barge cleaning, non-hazardous & hazardous
waste disposal, demolition & petroleum-contaminated
waste water treatment & disposal. (Woman/White, estab
1900, empl 48, sales $75,010,000, cert: City)

1934   TransChemical, Inc.
       419 East Desoto Ave   Saint Louis, MO 63147
       (314) 231-6905 Marilyn Stovall FitzGerald
       President
       Fax:
       Email: marilyn.stovall@transchemical.com
       Website: www.transchemical.com
Dist chemicals. (Woman/White, estab 1973, empl 28,
sales $24,000,000, cert: WBENC)

1935   Wallis Lubricant LLC
       106 E Washington St   Cuba, MO 65453
       (573) 885-2277 Dave Anthes Dir of commercial
       sales
       Fax:
       Email: danthes@mail.wallisco.com
       Website:
Dist lubricant products, packaged & bulked industrial,
commercial & private vehicle oils. (Woman/White, estab
1998, empl 51, sales $49,270,518, cert: State, WBENC)

1936   Wallis Oil Company
       106 E Washington St   Cuba, MO 65453
       (573) 885-2277 Dave Anthes Managing Dir
       Fax:
       Email: dave.anthes@wallisco.com
       Website: www.wallisco.com
Dist petroleum. (Woman/White, estab 1968, empl 550,
sales $266,169,874, cert: State)

North Carolina

1937   Continental Chemicals, LLC
       4525 Park Rd Ste B-202 Charlotte, NC 28209
       (704) 535-1215 Brandon Lowery Natl Acct Exec
       Fax: (704) 535-5310
       Email: blowery@continentalchemicals.com
       Website: www.continentalchemicals.com
Dist chemicals & raw materials. (Nat Ame, estab 1975,
empl 5, sales $30,100,000, cert: NMSDC)

1938   NDR Energy Group, LLC
       4822 Albemarle Rd Ste 209 Charlotte, NC 28205
       (888) 756-0555 Solomon RC Ali CEO
       Fax: (980) 202-4636
       Email: Solomon.ali@ndrenergy.us
       Website: www.ndrenergy.us
Dist natural gas, propane, refined products, fuels &
energy efficient lighting, asset management services.
(AA, estab 2005, empl 7, sales $65,000,000, cert:
NMSDC)

1939 Newbold Corporation
      8015 W Kenton Cir Ste 115 Huntersville, NC 28078
      (704) 659-7800 Amoura Carter Acct Rep
      Fax: (704) 659-7804
      Email: amoura.carter@newboldonline.com
      Website: www.newboldonline.com
Dist MRO & chemical products & services, strategic
sourcing & reporting, outsourced procurement services.
(AA, estab 2000, empl 10, sales $14,000,000, cert: NMSDC)

1940 PHT International Inc.
      8133 Ardrey Kell Rd Ste 204 Charlotte, NC 28277
      (704) 246-3480 Ansley Proctor Cockerham Acct Rep
      Fax: (704) 849-7297
      Email: ACockerham@phtchemical.com
      Website: www.phtchemical.com
Mfr & source fine chemicals, organic intermediates &
API's. (Woman/As-Pac, estab 1993, empl 112, sales
$88,900,000, cert: NMSDC, WBENC)

1941 PolySi Technologies, Inc.
      5108 Rex McLeod Dr Sanford, NC 27330
      (919) 775-4989 Lynn Richardson Ops Mgr
      Fax: (919) 775-2460
      Email: Lynn@polysi.com
      Website: www.polysi.com
Mfr silicone, synthetic greases & silicone fluids, industrial
packaging, retail packaging, contract filling & custom
packaging. (Woman/White, estab 1995, empl 25, sales
$7,000,000, cert: WBENC)

New Jersey

1942 Ash Ingredients, Inc.
      65 Harristown Rd, Ste 307 Glen Rock, NJ 07452
      (201)61322 Phetmany Falconi Acct Mgr
      Fax:
      Email: phet@ashingredients.com
      Website: www.ashingredients.com
Mfr over 81 complex Intermediates for customers with
CDA's in place. (Woman/As-Pac, estab 1999, empl 4, sales ,
cert: City, NWBOC)

1943 Assaycell Technologies LLC
      36 Chestnut St Avenel, NJ 07001
      (732) 429-0199 Raja Sivalenka Director
      Fax:
      Email: rsivalenka@assaycell.com
      Website: www.assaycell.com
Dist biochemical reagents, bacterial & mammalian cell
culture media, reagents, assaykits, molecular biology
reagents, plastic ware glassware, laboratory supplies,
technical consultation. (Woman/As-Ind, estab 2017, empl
2, sales $120,000, cert: State, SDB)

1944 Bel-Ray Co.
      P.O. Box 526 Wall, NJ 07719
      (270) 585-9005 Bob Shrewsbury Acct Mgr
      Fax: (732) 938-4232
      Email: rshrewsbury@belray.com
      Website: www.belray.com
Mfr & dist high performance lubricants made for the
Mining, Industrial & Powersports markets world wide.
(Woman/White, estab 1946, empl 150, sales , cert:
State)

1945 BKM Resources, Inc. Global Chemicals
      P.O. Box 327 Eatontown, NJ 07724
      (732) 264-2300 Nancy Engkilterra President
      Fax: (732) 264-5527
      Email: nengkilterra@bkmresources.com
      Website: www.bkmresources.com
Dist commodity & specialty chemicals. (Woman/AA,
estab 1986, empl 10, sales $7,000,000, cert: NMSDC)

1946 Elan Chemical Co., Inc.
      268 Doremus Ave Newark, NJ 07105
      (973) 344-8014 Isabel Couto VP
      Fax: (973) 344-1948
      Email: icouto@elan-chemical.com
      Website: www.elan-chemical.com
Natural benzaldehyde, flavors, natural ingredients,
synthetic ingredients, vanilla, extracts, acetaldehyde,
ethyl benzoate, iso amyl alcohol, aldehydes, natural
esters, ethyl caproate, acetic acid, natural aromatic
chemicals, ethyl-2-methyl. (Woman/White, estab 1985,
empl 50, sales , cert: State, WBENC)

1947 Foodtopia, Inc.
      11 Harrisotwn Rd, Ste 101 Glen Rock, NJ 07452
      (201) 444-8810 Tae Kim GM
      Fax: (201) 444-8813
      Email: tkim@foodtopiausa.com
      Website: www.foodtopiausa.com
Food Additives, Nutritional Raw Materials, Amino Acids,
Sweeteners, Food Chemicals (As-Pac, estab 1997, empl
7, sales $4,000,000, cert: State)

1948 GJ Chemical
      40 Veronica Ave Somerset, NJ 08873
      (732) 740-9660 Fiore Masci Sr Acct Mgr
      Fax: (732) 249-0082
      Email: customerservice@gjchemical.com
      Website: www.gjchemical.com
Mfr & dist raw chemical. (Woman/White, estab 1974,
empl 60, sales $30,000,000, cert: WBENC)

1949   Global Essence
       8 Marlen Dr   Hamilton, NJ 08691
       (732) 677-1100 Jeanna Johnson VP of Sales
       Fax: (732) 677-1107
       Email: jjohnson@globalessence.com
       Website: www.globalessence.com
Dist flavor & fragrance raw materials: essential oils,
organic essential oils, oleoresins, concretes, absolutes an&
d synthetic aroma chemicals. (Woman/White, estab 1993,
empl 34, sales $47,300,000, cert: State, WBENC)

1950   INDOFINE Chemical Company
       121 Stryker Ln Bldg 30, Ste 1 Hillsborough, NJ
       08844
       (908) 359-6778 Sujata Moton VP
       Fax: (908) 359-1179
       Email: indofine@indofinechemical.com
       Website: www.indofinechemical.com
Provide custom synthesis, contract research & process
development. (Woman/As-Ind, estab 1981, empl 8, sales
$1,000,000, cert: NMSDC, WBENC)

1951   Kingchem
       5 Pearl Ct   Allendale, NJ 07401
       (201) 825-9988 Daniel Kukovski Diversity Supplier
       Mgr
       Fax:
       Email: d.kukovski@kingchem.com
       Website: www.kingchem.com
Mfr fluoro-organic compounds. (As-Pac, estab 1994, empl
13, sales $69,780,000, cert: NMSDC)

1952   Su International Group, Inc.
       1430 Rte 206, Ste 210 Bedminster, NJ 07921
       (908) 901-0102 Dan Downs Project Mgr
       Fax: (908) 901-9950
       Email: ddowns@suintl.com
       Website: www.suintl.com
Mfr chemicals: synthetic vitamins, food chemical, &
artificial sweeteners. (Woman/As-Ind, estab 1996, empl 6,
sales $18,946,253, cert: NMSDC, NWBOC)

New York

1953   Ampak Co., Inc.
       1890 Palmer Ave, Ste 301 Larchmont, NY 10538
       (914) 833-7070 Cindy Sturm Business Dev
       Fax: (914) 833-7878
       Email: csturm@ampakcompany.com
       Website: www.ampakcompany.com
Dist amino acids, antioxidants, preservatives, cellulosics,
hight intensity sweetners, humectants, hydrocolloids,
phosphates, colors, vitamins & minerals. (As-Ind, estab
1978, empl 19, sales $75,690,236, cert: NMSDC)

1954   Crescent Chemical Co., Inc.
       2 Oval Dr   Islandia, NY 11749
       (631) 348-0333 Ilene Cohen President
       Fax: (631) 348-0913
       Email: creschem@aol.com
       Website: www.crescentchemical.com
Dist pesticides & herbicides. (Woman/White, estab 1947,
empl 8, sales $3,000,000, cert: City, WBENC)

1955   Infinite Energy Corp d/b/a Definite Energy Group
       410 Park Ave, 15th Fl New York, NY 10022
       (212) 759-7426 Deborah Pinto President
       Fax: (212) 656-1621
       Email: dpinto@definiteenergy.com
       Website: www.definiteenergy.com
Dist petroleum products. (Woman/White, estab 1994,
empl 2, sales $16,814,844, cert: State, City, WBENC)

1956   Miles Petroleum Corp., Inc.
       66 Marine St Farmingdale, NY 11735
       (631) 694-4488 Angela Stern President
       Fax: (631) 337-9015
       Email: astern@milesoil.com
       Website: www.milesoil.com
Dist lubricating oils & greases. (Woman/White, estab
1937, empl 14, sales $4,300,000, cert: State)

1957   Tra-Lin Corp.
       248 Buell Road Rochester, NY 14624
       (585) 254-6010 Linda Fedele President
       Fax: (585) 254-6813
       Email: lindafedele@rochester.rr.com
       Website: www.samsonfuel.com/
Dist fuel & additives. (Woman/White, estab 1984, empl
10, sales $663,110, cert: State)

Ohio

1958   Accurate Lubricants & Metalworking Fluids Inc.
       P.O. Box 3807 Dayton, OH 45401
       (937) 461-9906 Marilyn Kinne President
       Fax: (937) 461-9917
       Email: mgkinne@acculube.com
       Website: www.acculube.com
Sales & technical support of industrial lubricants,
metalworking fluids, water treatment chemicals &
ancillary sales & services. (Woman, estab , empl 1, sales ,
cert: WBENC)

1959   Calvary Industries, Inc.
       9233 Seward Rd Fairfield, OH 45014
       (513) 874-1113 Austin Morelock New Business
       Dev Mgr
       Fax:
       Email: acmorelock@calvaryindustries.com
       Website: www.calvaryindustries.com
Mfr industrial & inorganic chemicals. (Nat Ame, estab
1983, empl 120, sales $78,000,000, cert: NMSDC)

1960   Coolant Control, Inc.
     5353 Spring Grove Ave   Cincinnati, OH 45217
     (513) 471-8770   Jorge Costa Owner
     Fax: (513) 471-2721
     Email: jcosta@coolantcontrol.com
     Website: www.coolantcontrol.com
Site chemical management services, mfr emulsifiers, corrosion inhibitors, cleaners, washers, coolants, coolant additives & odor control. (Hisp, estab 1975, empl 29, sales $100,000, cert: NMSDC)

1961   Global Environmental Products
     4624 Interstate Dr   Cincinnati, OH 45406
     (513) 984-5444   Mike Mamaligas President
     Fax: (513) 984-6461
     Email: mmamaligas@gepltd.com
     Website: www.gepltd.com
Dist absorbents, oil & chemical spill cleanup products. (AA, estab 2002, empl 5, sales $1,200,000, cert: NMSDC)

1962   Hightowers Petroleum Company
     3577 Commerce Dr   Middletown, OH 45005
     (513) 423-4272   Damon Kleasa Senior Director
     Fax: (513) 423-5750
     Email: dklesa@hightowerspetroleum.com
     Website: www.hightowerspetroleum.com
Dist & transport fuel & petroleum products: gasoline, diesel fuel, lubricants, oils, greases, speciality chemicals. (AA, estab 1985, empl 37, sales , cert: NMSDC)

1963   Lianda Corporation
     8285 Darrow Rd Ste 200   Twinsburg, OH 44087
     (330) 653-8341   Lifang Mao President
     Fax: (330) 653-3189
     Email: lmao@liandacorp.com
     Website: www.liandacorp.com
Import & dist synthetic rubber & related chemicals. (Woman/As-Pac, estab 1995, empl 11, sales , cert: NMSDC)

1964   Next Generation Fuel, LLC
     3589 Commerce Dr   Middletown, OH 45005
     (513) 435-4337   Dawn Lindsey CEO
     Fax: (513) 423-5750
     Email: dawn@nxtgenfuel.com
     Website: www.nxtgenfuel.com
Dist unleaded gasoline, high & low sulfur diesel fuels, bio-diesel, ethanol & fuel additives. (Woman/AA, estab 2014, empl 2, sales $10,519,712, cert: NMSDC)

1965   Orchem Corporation
     4927 Beech St   Cincinnati, OH 45212
     (513) 874-9700   Denise Ramey COO
     Fax: (513) 874-3624
     Email: denise.ramey@orchemcorp.com
     Website: www.orchemcorp.com
Mfr cleaning & sanitation chemicals. (Woman/AA, estab 1996, empl 28, sales $4,200,000, cert: State, NMSDC)

1966   Stevenson Oil & Chemical Corp.
     30130 Lakeland Blvd   Wickliffe, OH 44092
     (440) 943-3337   Suzanne Harkey
     Fax: (440) 943-1275
     Email: info@stevensonoil.com
     Website: www.stevensonoil.com
Dist industrial lubricants: engine oil, hydraulic oil, gear oil, cutting oil, metalworking fluid, turbine oil, general purpose lubricants, transmission oil, quenching oil, bio-friendly lubricants, grease & solvents. (Woman/White, estab 1969, empl 3, sales $1,904,092, cert: WBENC)

1967   The Blackfoot Company
     6061 Telegraph Rd, Ste P   Toledo, OH 43612
     (419) 478-8650   Leroy Pepion CEO
     Fax: (419) 478-0890
     Email: tblkftco@aol.com
     Website: www.theblackfootcompany.com
Dist industrial chemicals, winter maintenance products, facility & janitorial supplies, water treatment, parking lot maintenance. (Nat Ame, estab 1994, empl 5, sales $650,000, cert: State)

Oklahoma

1968   Advance Research Chemicals
     1110 W Keystone Ave   Tulsa, OK 74015
     (918) 266-6789   Mat Cleveland Sales Mgr
     Fax: (918) 266-6796
     Email: mathercleveland@fluoridearc.com
     Website: www.fluoridearc.com
Inorganic fluorides (As-Ind, estab 1987, empl 125, sales $50,000,000, cert: NMSDC)

1969   Sage Energy Trading, LLC
     8023 E 63rd Pl, Ste 350   Tulsa, OK 74133
     (918) 362-2310   Cindy Hughes President
     Fax: (918) 362-2333
     Email: chughes@sageenergytrading.com
     Website:
Dist natural gas. (Woman, estab 2004, empl 2, sales $9,359,750, cert: WBENC)

1970   Tiger Natural Gas, Inc.
     1422 E 71st St, Ste J   Tulsa, OK 74136
     (918) 491-6998   Johnathan Burris VP Mktg
     Fax: (918) 491-6659
     Email: diversity@tigernaturalgas.com
     Website: www.tigernaturalgas.com
Dist natural gas. (Woman/Nat Ame, estab 1991, empl 46, sales , cert: NMSDC, WBENC)

Pennsylvania

1971 Biopeptek Inc.
40 Lloyd Ave Ste 309 Malvern, PA 19355
(610) 643-4881 John Zhang CEO
Fax: (610) 910-3487
Email: johnzhang@biopeptek.com
Website: www.biopeptek.com
Mfr custom peptides services. (As-Pac, estab 2010, empl 55, sales $5,000,000, cert: NMSDC)

1972 Crystal Inc. PMC
601 W Eighth St   Lansdale, PA 19446
(215) 368-1661 Karen Roorda Exec Asst
Fax: (215) 368-3205
Email: kroorda@pmc-group.com
Website: www.crystalinc-pmc.com
Specialty & performance chemicals, sodium & potassium stearates, wax emulsions, specialty antifoams, rubber & plastics additives, process chemicals & cable filling jellies. (As-Pac, estab 1929, empl 80, sales , cert: NMSDC)

1973 Crystal, Inc.
601 W 8th St Lansdale, PA 19446
(215) 368-1661 Lynne Currie Exec/Mktg asst
Fax: (215) 368-3205
Email: epalincrystal@pmc-group.com
Website: www.pmc-group.com
Dist specialty & performance chemicals, sodium & potassium stearates, wax emulsions, specialty antifoams, rubber & plastics additives, process chemicals & cable filling jellies. (Other, estab 1929, empl 80, sales , cert: NMSDC)

1974 EMSCO Scientific Enterprises, Inc.
5070 Parkside Ave P.O. Box 28032 Philadelphia, PA 19131
(215) 477-5601 Roderick Clifford Asst VP
Fax: (215) 477-2526
Email: rpclifford2@emscoscientific.com
Website: www.emscoscientific.com
Dist production & laboratory chemicals. (AA, estab 1980, empl 9, sales $19,800,000, cert: City, NMSDC)

1975 GRP Services
P.O. Box 41 Pittsburgh, PA 15221
(412) 271-5231 Ernest Groover President
Fax: (206) 666-5133
Email: egroover@grpservices.net
Website: www.grpservices.net
Natural gas brokerage, utility cost recovery, telecommunications svcs. (AA, estab 2002, empl 3, sales $100,000, cert: NMSDC)

1976 Muscle Products Corp.
752 Kilgore Rd Jackson Center, PA 16133
(814) 786-0166 Sharon Murphy-Dittrich President
Fax: (814) 786-7321
Email: sharon@mpclubricants.com
Website: www.mpclubricants.com
Manufacture Lubricants & Greases, for General Industry & Automotive Use. (Woman, estab 1986, empl 1, sales , cert: WBENC)

1977 Naughton Energy Corp.
Rte 940 P.O. Box 709 Pocono Pines, PA 18350
(570) 646-0422 Sean Naughton VP
Fax: (570) 646-8766
Email: sean@naughtonenergy.com
Website: www.naughtonenergy.com
Energy products, energy services & lubricants: gasoline, heating oil, diesel, marine, kerosene, jet, residual & re-refined oil, Anthracite, Bituminous & Synfuel, natural gas. (Woman/As-Pac, estab 1976, empl 8, sales $14,000,000, cert: State, City, NMSDC)

1978 Randall Industries LLC
1401 Forbes Ave   Pittsburgh, PA 15219
(412) 281-6903 Gregory Spencer CEO
Fax: (412) 281-6905
Email: g.spencer11@verizon.net
Website: www.randall-industries.net
Mfr chemicals. (AA, estab 2006, empl 10, sales $800,000, cert: State)

Puerto Rico

1979 Lanco Manufacturing Corp.
Urb. Aponte 5   San Lorenzo, PR 00954
(787) 736-4221 Nelson Soto Category Mgr
Fax: (787) 736-5313
Email: nsoto@lancopaints.com
Website: www.lancopaints.com
Paints (Water and Oil Based), Enamels, Caulking, Spackling, Wood Stains, Wood Fillers, Adhesive, Roof Sealers, Concrete Bonding Agents and Solvents(Paint removers, Lacquer Thinners, Mineral Spirits). (Hisp, estab 1978, empl 250, sales $69,320,794, cert: NMSDC)

1980 Mays Ochoa
NO 515 Calle 2 Catano, PR 00962
(787) 788-8000 Rafael Marti VP/GM
Fax:
Email: Gloria.Rosado@maysochoa.com
Website: www.mayschem.com
Chemicals. (Hisp, estab 1984, empl 50, sales , cert: NMSDC)

1981   Sachs Chemical Inc.
P.O. Box 191670 KM 0 02 LOT, 18 RR 175 San Juan, PR 00725
(787) 745-2520 Laura Conde Accountant
Fax: (787) 745-2990
Email: laura@sachschem.com
Website: www.sachschem.com
Dist chemicals. (Hisp, estab 1986, empl 33, sales $32,000,000, cert: NMSDC)

Rhode Island

1982   Blue Sky Natural Gas & Petroleum, Inc.
99 Charlotte Dr   East Greenwich, RI 02818
(401) 465-1111 Leslie Mathews President
Fax: (401) 884-8758
Email: Blueskynaturalgas@gmail.com
Website:
Dist petroleum products, natural gas & electricity, low sulfur heating oil, low sulfur diesel fuel, bio-diesel, propane, #4 & #6 residual fuels, gasoline, kerosene etc. (Woman, estab 1992, empl 10, sales , cert: State)

South Carolina

1983   AmberTech Technologies LLC
2037 Summerton Hwy   Summerton, SC 29148
(803) 696-1152 Tom Massey Director
Fax: (803) 478-8807
Email: tmassey001@sc.rr.com
Website: www.ambertech-global.com
A USDA certified 99% bio-based metal conditioner used in all lubrication applications to reduce friction and heat. (Woman/White, estab 2011, empl 7, sales $1,600,000, cert: NWBOC)

Tennessee

1984   K-Chemicals, Inc
301 Industrial Dr   Bean Station, TN 37708
(865) 767-2342 Jeffery Kyle President
Fax: (865) 767-2325
Email: jeffkyle@k-chemicals.com
Website: www.k-chemical.com
Mfr specialty chemicals: car wash, janitorial & industrial chemicals, package & distribute production chemicals, solvents, caustics, acids, powdered products. (AA/Nat Ame/As-Pac, estab 1989, empl 10, sales $3,000,000, cert: NMSDC)

1985   Quality Adhesives, LLC
3835 Viscount, Ste 7   Memphis, TN 38118
(901) 375-3991 Curtis Hunt President
Fax: (901) 375-3993
Email: curtish@qualityadhesivesinc.com
Website: www.qualityadhesivesinc.com
Mfr & dist hot melt & liquid adhesives. (AA, estab 1999, empl 8, sales $8,000,000, cert: NMSDC)

Alabama

1986   American Chemie, Inc.
13706 Research Blvd Summit Executive Ctr, Ste 302 Austin, TX 78750
(512) 219-7400 Mike Kamdar
Fax: (512) 219-7700
Email: mike@americanchemie.com
Website: www.americanchemie.com
Dist Emulsifiers, Emollients, Esters, Fatty alcohols, Eco-Cert Natural Refined Shea Butter and other body Butters, Preservatives & Surfactants. (Woman/As-Ind, estab 1991, empl 9, sales $10,086,762, cert: State, NMSDC)

1987   AmPac Chemical Company Inc.
P.O. Box 272848 Houston, TX 77277
(713) 660-9383 Sonia Fujimoto President
Fax: (866) 317-0414
Email: sonia@ampacchemical.com
Website: www.ampacchemical.com
Dist chemicals. (Woman/As-Pac, estab 1996, empl 1, sales $2,217,678, cert: State, City, NMSDC)

1988   Atlantic Petroleum & Mineral Resources Inc.
723 Main St, Ste 207   Houston, TX 77002
(713) 223-2767 Donald Sheffield
Fax: (712) 223-5797
Email: drsheffield@atlantic-petro.com
Website: www.atlantic-petro.com
Dist branded & unbranded petroleum products. (AA, estab 2005, empl 8, sales $476,200, cert: State, City, NMSDC)

1989   Avalon Chemicals, Inc.
10101 Southwest Frwy Ste 400 Houston, TX 77074
(713) 219-1457 Vinay Deshmane President
Fax: (713) 219-1458
Email: info@avalonchemicals.com
Website: www.avalonchemicals.com
Phenolic antioxidants (BHT, TBHQ, BHA), antioxidants (DODPA). (As-Ind, estab 2002, empl 2, sales $1,260,000, cert: State, NMSDC)

1990 Champion Fuel Solutions
      P.O. Box 210191 Bedford, TX 76095
      (877) 909-9191 Patti Russell President
      Fax: (817) 834-1602
      Email: prussell@championfs.com
      Website: www.championfs.com
Dist gasoline & diesel fuel, biodiesel, kerosene, oils &
lubricants. (Woman/White, estab 2010, empl 2, sales ,
cert: State, WBENC)

1991 Cole Chemical & Distributing, Inc.
      1500 S Dairy Ashford Ste 450 Houston, TX 77077
      (713) 465-2653 Donna F. Cole President
      Fax: (713) 465-5738
      Email: colechem@colechem.com
      Website: www.colechem.com
Mfr & dist thermoformed products. (Woman/As-Pac,
estab 1980, empl 17, sales $47,000,000, cert: City,
NMSDC, WBENC)

1992 Dien, Inc.
      3510 Pipestone Rd Dallas, TX 75212
      (214) 905-1528 Dien Stout President
      Fax:
      Email: dien@dieninc.com
      Website: www.dieninc.com
Dist chemicals: industrial, food, solvents, greases &
lubricants, pharmaceutical & personal care. (Woman/
Nat Ame, estab 1996, empl 17, sales $46,627,700, cert:
State, NMSDC)

1993 Diversified Chemical and Supply, Inc.
      P.O. Box 1297 Humble, TX 77347
      (713) 461-9610 Donna Rosenstein President
      Fax: (713) 461-9634
      Email: dcsupply@sbcglobal.net
      Website: www.diversifiedchem.com
Dist janitorial & industrial chemicals & supplies.
(Woman/White, estab 1990, empl 3, sales $2,508,119,
cert: State, WBENC)

1994 Elevation Energy Group LLC
      P.O. Box 6036 Austin, TX 78762
      (317) 333-7281 Gwen Kyle President
      Fax:
      Email: tri@elevationeg.com
      Website: www.elevationeg.com
Natural gas supply and associated services. (As-Pac,
estab 2014, empl 15, sales , cert: NMSDC)

1995 Energy Utility Group, LL
      1301 N AW Grimes Blvd, Ste 1534 Round Rock,
      TX 78665
      (512) 805-8321 Melinda Zito O'Brien Managing
      Partner
      Fax: (713) 893-0210
      Email: melinda@energyutilitygroup.com
      Website: www.energyutilitygroup.com
Energy consulting & electricity & natural gas brokering
company. (Woman/White, estab 2013, empl 2, sales ,
cert: State, City, CPUC, WBENC)

1996 FSTI Inc.
      6300 Bridge Point Pkwy, Ste 1-200 Austin, TX
      78730
      (512) 278-8800 Coulter Gibson Director of
      Packaged Products
      Fax:
      Email: cgibson@fstichem.com
      Website: www.fstichem.com
Dist chemicals. (Woman/White, estab 1998, empl 50,
sales $19,100,000, cert: State, WBENC)

1997 Gasochem International LLC
      9509 Pemberton Crescent Dr Houston, TX 77025
      (713) 837-6116 Charu Jain President
      Fax:
      Email: charu@gasochem.com
      Website: www.gasochem.com
Dist chemicals: oilfield, water treatment, industrial,
agricultural & pharmaceutical. (Woman/As-Pac, estab
2012, empl 2, sales $200,000, cert: State, WBENC)

1998 Genoa International
      2245 Texas Dr, Ste 300 Sugar Land, TX 77479
      (281) 313-0120 Pamela Kahn Principal
      Fax: (281) 313-0122
      Email: pkahn@genoaint.com
      Website: www.genoaint.com
Specialty chemicals, surfactants, drilling fluids, solvents,
lubricants & commodities. (Woman, estab , empl 1, sales
, cert: State, WBENC)

1999 Global Amchem Inc.
      407 E Methvin, Ste 200 P.O. Box 2221 Longview,
      TX 75606
      (903) 236-0138 Debbie Scott Office Admin
      Fax: (903) 236-0139
      Email: debbie@amcheminc.com
      Website: www.amcheminc.com
Dist solvents & chemicals. (Hisp, estab 1993, empl 6,
sales $430,505, cert: State, NMSDC)

2000   GND Consulting & Supply LLC
1836 Snake River Rd, Ste A   Katy, TX 77449
(832) 415-4100   Jose Camacho Sales Mgr
Fax: (832) 565-8607
Email: camachojo@gndsc.com
Website: www.gndsc.com
Dist non-toxic, environmentally-safe cleaners, degreasers, solvents, lubricants & specialty chemical products. (Woman/Hisp, estab 2011, empl 8, sales $603,242, cert: State, NMSDC, WBENC)

2001   Gold Star Petroleum, Inc.
P.O. Box 11151   Spring, TX 77391
(281) 379-5928   JJ Rodriguez President
Fax: (281) 379-5928
Email: goldstarpetro@comcast.net
Website:
Dist gasolines & diesel fuels. (Hisp, estab 1981, empl 6, sales $34,100,000, cert: State, NMSDC)

2002   KAP TechnoChem USA, Inc.
4934 Cotter Lake Dr   Missouri City, TX 77459
(281) 403-0242   PRAVIN kapadia
Fax: (281) 261-0965
Email: HPKAPS@KAPTECHNO.COM
Website: www.kaptechno.com
Dist organic solvents, hydrocarbons, alcohol, ketones, fatty acids, glycols, inorganic chemicals, oil & lubs carnauba wax, castor wax activated carbons etc. (As-Ind, estab 2005, empl 2, sales , cert: 8(a))

2003   Lynx And Associate, LLC. DBA Lynx Chemicals
2309 Castle Creek Dr   Little Elm, TX 75068
(877) 405-9910   Jeffrey Bundo VP
Fax: (877) 617-8003
Email: jeffrey.bundo@lynx-Chemical.com
Website: www.lynx-chemical.com
Dist ingredients & chemicals, raw materials and services. (Woman/AA, estab 2006, empl 4, sales , cert: State)

2004   New K-Stone Management, Inc.
10718 Sentinel St   San Antonio, TX 78217
(210) 494-0507   Dana Stone President
Fax: (210) 494-1714
Email: dstone@kstoneinc.com
Website: www.kstonesupply.com
Industrial chemicals for automotive, animal shelters, food processing plants, physical plant supplies & chemicals for lab animal research. (Woman/White, estab 1997, empl 15, sales $1,147,125, cert: State)

2005   One Nation Energy Solutions, LLC
4404 Blossom St   Houston, TX 77007
(713) 861-0600   Terry Pierce President
Fax: (713) 861-0608
Email: tpierce@onenationenergy.com
Website: www.onenationenergy.com
Dist & market gas & power. (Woman/White, estab 2003, empl 3, sales $40,000,000, cert: State, City, CPUC, WBENC)

2006   Oxyde Chemicals, Inc.
225 Pennbright Dr Ste 101   Houston, TX 77090
(281) 874-9100   Elva Rojas sales agent
Fax: (281) 874-9172
Email: rojase@oxydeusa.com
Website: www.oxydeusa.com
Dist petrochemicals & plastics. (Hisp, estab 1950, empl 60, sales $650,000,000, cert: State, NMSDC)

2007   Premier Polymers LLC
16800 Imperial Valley, Ste 200   Houston, TX 77060
(281) 902-0909   Melwani Kwan Supply Chain Mgr
Fax: (832) 212-8882
Email: mkwan@premierpolymers.com
Website: www.premierpolymers.com
Dist Plastic Resin. (As-Pac, estab 2009, empl 22, sales , cert: State, NMSDC)

2008   Ricochet Fuel Distributors, Inc.
1201 Royal Pkwy   Euless, TX 76040
(800) 284-2540   Cass Roberts Mktg Coord
Fax: (817) 282-7497
Email: sales@ricochetfuel.com
Website: www.ricochetfuel.com
Dist diesel, gasoline, oil, antifreeze & kerosene, fuel mgmt & monitoring programs. (Woman/White, estab 1988, empl 27, sales $51,609,809, cert: State, WBENC)

2009   SolvChem, Inc.
1904 Mykawa   Pearland, TX 77546
(832) 300-4067   Stacey Barrett Acct Mgr
Fax: (281) 485-8162
Email: stacey_barrett@solvchem.com
Website: www.solvchem.com
Dist aircraft chemicals, chemicals blends, calibrating fluids, purging fluids. (Hisp, estab 1980, empl 40, sales $38,563,251, cert: State, NMSDC)

2010   Sun Coast Resources, Inc.
6405 Cavalcade, Building 1   Houston, TX 77026
(713) 844-9600   Kathy Lehne President
Fax: (713) 844-9699
Email: klehne@suncoastresources.com
Website: www.suncoastresources.com
Dist petroleum products (gasoline, diesel, etc.). (Woman/White, estab 1985, empl 1270, sales $860,000,000, cert: WBENC)

2011   Tri-Chem Specialty Chemicals, LLC
P.O. Box 2056   Cresson, TX 76035
(972) 745-6875   Leslie Hollis CEO
Fax: (972) 745-6870
Email: leslie@tri-chem.net
Website: www.tri-chem.net
Custom liquid & dry chemical blending, chemical & additive distribution. (Woman/Hisp, estab 1989, empl 14, sales $4,777,000, cert: WBENC)

2012   XD Ventures, LLC
       2555 South Shore Blvd. Ste C League City, TX
       77573
       (832) 557-6622 Xan Difede President
       Fax:
       Email: xan@fidelityfuels.com
       Website: www.fidelityfuels.com
Dist aliphatic solvents, mineral spirits & mineral seal oils.
(Woman/White, estab 2014, empl 1, sales , cert: State,
WBENC)

Utah

2013   CP Industries, LLC
       560 North 500 West   Salt Lake City, UT 84116
       (801) 521-0313 Erica Sellers
       Fax: (801) 433-1038
       Email: accounting311@cpindustries.net
       Website: www.cpindustries.net
Mfr ice melting compounds, customer chemical blending, liquid & powder detergents. (Woman/White, estab
1949, empl 19, sales $5,510,415, cert: WBENC)

2014   FYVE STAR, Inc.
       1972 E Dan Dr   Layton, UT 84040
       (801) 552-9100 Celeste Gleave CEO
       Fax: (801) 552-9103
       Email: celeste@fyvestar.com
       Website: www.fyvestar.com
Mfr & dist deicers. Calcium Chloride, Blends, Solar Salt,
Water Conditioning Salts, primary supplier to the US
Military on Liquid Runway & Aircraft Deicers. (Woman/
White, estab 1993, empl 2, sales $400,000, cert: State)

2015   The Horrocks Company LLC dba Volu-Sol
       5095 West 2100 South   Salt Lake City, UT 84120
       (801) 974-9474 Celeste Horrocks Owner
       Fax: (801) 974-9553
       Email: celeste.horrocks@volusol.com
       Website: www.volusol.com
Mfr chemicals, alcohols, reagents, diagnostic stains &
counterstains. (Woman, estab 2013, empl 10, sales
$470,000, cert: WBENC)

Virginia

2016   Coyanosa Gas Services Corporation
       1765 Greensboro Station Place Ste 900 McLean,
       VA 22102
       (703) 938-7984 Jerry Curry President
       Fax: (703) 790-9511
       Email: jerry@coyanosagasservices.com
       Website: www.coyanosagasservices.com
Dist natural gas & energy utilization consulting. (AA,
estab 1995, empl 3, sales $20,000,000, cert: NMSDC,
CPUC, SDB)

2017   Enspire Energy, LLC
       134 N Battlefield Blvd   Chesapeake, VA 23320
       (757) 963-9123 julie hashagen Director of Ops
       Fax: (757) 963-9133
       Email: jhashagen@enspireenergy.com
       Website: www.enspireenergy.com
Natural gas marketing & transportation. (Woman, estab
2005, empl 3, sales $979,376, cert: WBENC)

2018   James River Solutions
       10487 Lakeridge Parkway 23005 Ashland, VA
       23005
       (804) 358-9000 Elizabeth Austin Commercial
       Project Mgr
       Fax:
       Email: eaustin@jrpetro.com
       Website: www.JamesRiverPetroleum.com
Bulk Deliveries, Gasoline, Diesel, Dyed Diesel, Heating
Oil, DEF, Mobile Fueling, Fleet Fueling Cards. (Woman/
White, estab 2005, empl 61, sales $251,000,000, cert:
State)

Wisconsin

2019   ChemCeed LLC
       1720 Prosperity Court   Chippewa Falls, WI 54729
       (715) 726-2300 Myra Detienne Sales Rep
       Fax: (715) 726-2314
       Email: customerservice@chemceed.com
       Website: www.chemceed.com
Dist chemicals in bulk tankwagons, drums, totes, or
custom packaging, ethanols, alcohols, reagents, & other
solvents. (Woman/As-Pac, estab 2009, empl 10, sales ,
cert: State, NMSDC, WBENC)

> ### CLEANING PRODUCTS & SUPPLIES
> Manufacturers and distributors of maintenance supplies: all purpose cleaners, deodorizers, floor waxes, wax removers, oven cleaners, dishwashing & laundry detergents, soaps, hand cleaners, furniture & metal polishes, rug & upholstery shampoos, ammonia, janitorial services, etc. Most firms manu-

Arizona

2020   The Riley Kraus Group, LLC
2325 W. Cypress St.   Phoenix, AZ 85009
(602) 252-9402   Al Kraus CFO
Fax: (602) 252-9086
Email: info@maintenancemart.com
Website: www.maintenancemart.com
Dist commercial janitorial supplies, tools, motorized equipment, paper, trash liners, walk-off mats, indoor & outdoor receptacles & ash urns. (Woman/Hisp, estab 2001, empl 18, sales $4,510,000, cert: City)

California

2021   Able Building Maintenance
868 Folsom St   San Francisco, CA 94107
(800) 461-9033   Cassie King Business Devel
Fax:
Email: cassie.king@ableserve.com
Website: www.ableserve.com
Janitorial, engineering, metal & window cleaning services. (Woman/White, estab 1926, empl 14000, sales $500,000,000, cert: CPUC)

2022   Ahtna Government Services Corporation
3100 Beacon Blvd.   West Sacramento, CA 95691
(916) 372-2000   Craig O'Rourke President
Fax: (916) 372-9401
Email: info@ahtnagov.com
Website: www.ahtnagov.com
Ahtna provides high quality services worldwide and is CPUC-certified. Ahtna is one of the fastest growing small business firms in the United States. (Nat Ame, estab 1999, empl 120, sales $60,100,000, cert: CPUC)

2023   Avery Group Inc.
400 W Redondo Beach Blvd, Unit C   Gardena, CA 90248
(310) 217-1070   Leatora Morse President
Fax: (310) 217-1954
Email: leatora@averygroup-inc.com
Website: www.averygroup-inc.com
Mfr restroom hygiene products. (Woman/AA, estab 2003, empl 167, sales $7,348,953, cert: State)

2024   Ayota, LLC
122 15th St, Ste 681   San Diego, CA 92014
(914) 548-6193   Toya McWilliams Acct Mgr
Fax:
Email: tm@ayotainternational.com
Website: www.ayotainternational.com
Dist janitorial supplies. (Woman/AA, estab 2012, empl 3, sales $35,000, cert: State)

2025   BriteWorks, Inc.
620 Commerical Ave.   Covina, CA 91723
(626) 337-0099   Anita Ron President
Fax: (626) 337-3399
Email: anitaron@briteworks.com
Website: www.briteworks.com
Commercial & industrial janitorial services. General cleaning, construction cleaning, floor care & carpet care, window cleaning. (Woman/Hisp, estab 1997, empl 85, sales $5,600,000, cert: State, NMSDC, CPUC)

2026   Continental Building Maintenance
13316 Mapledale St   Norwalk, CA 90650
(562) 926-7474   Sanggwon Kim President
Fax: (562) 926-8484
Email: sgkim@continentalbm.com
Website: www.continentalbm.com
Janitorial Services & Supplies. (As-Pac, estab 2003, empl 120, sales $2,950,000, cert: CPUC)

2027   Corporate Image Maintenance
2700 S Main St, Ste D   Santa Ana, CA 92707
(714) 966-5325   Gil Gamboa President
Fax: (714) 966-5329
Email: corpimage@sbcglobal.net
Website: www.cimservices.com
Janitorial services: office, industrial & warehouse, carpet cleaning, pressure washing & window cleaning. (Hisp, estab 1995, empl 70, sales $1,176,190, cert: State)

2028   Eurow & O'Reilly Corp.
51 Moreland Rd   Simi Valley, CA 93065
(805) 421-4310   Martin Mair Director Inside Sales
Fax: (805) 579-7976
Email: mmair@eurow.com
Website: www.eurow.com
Dist janitorial cleaning products. (Woman/White, estab 1983, empl 26, sales $36,700,000, cert: WBENC)

2029   Kim Gardner, Inc.
1727 E 28th St   Signal Hill, CA 90755
(562) 988-7901   Dori Bailey Dir Business Dev
Fax: (323) 843-9268
Email: dori@mjmservices.com
Website: www.mjmservices.com
Facility Support Services, Custodial, Waste Management, Pest Control/Grounds, Maintenance Landscaping, Air Duct Cleaning, - General Office Cleaning, Construction Clean Up, Pressure Washing, Carpet & Upholstery. (AA, estab 1986, empl 35, sales $605,000, cert: 8(a))

2030   Los Angeles Chemical Co., Inc.
845 Sandhill Ave   Carson, CA 90746
(310) 323-7111   Jaza Shaikh Office Mgr
Fax: (310) 323-8111
Email: jaza@lacco.com
Website: www.lacco.com
Dist industrial chemicals, raw materials, janitorial cleaning supplies & equipment, food service supplies, personal care, safety supplies & institutional packaging. (Woman/As-Ind, estab 2015, empl 6, sales , cert: WBENC)

2031 Mar-Len Supply Inc.
      23159 Kidder St   Hayward, CA 94545
      (510) 782-3555 Shirley Winter Owner
      Fax: (510) 782-2032
      Email: marlensupply@aol.com
      Website: www.marlensupply.com
Dist & service industrial cleaning equipment & cleaning
agents. (Woman/White, estab 1956, empl 4, sales
$1,000,000, cert: CPUC)

2032 NMS Management Inc.
      155 W 35th St Ste A National City, CA 91950
      (619) 425-0440 David Guaderrama Director of
      Business Dev
      Fax: (619) 425-2432
      Email: nmsmanagement@msn.com
      Website: www.nms-management.com
Custodial services for military establishments, healthcare
facilities, institutions of higher education, public housing
agencies, public transportation authorities & federal, state
& municipal agencies. (Hisp, estab 1985, empl 168, sales
$3,822,801, cert: CPUC)

2033 Right Tek Enterprises
      1775 N Lee St   Simi Valley, CA 93065
      (877) 208-3717 Sandy Cohen Owner
      Fax: (805) 579-9077
      Email: righttek@pacbell.net
      Website: www.righttekenterprises
Dist preventative maintenance cleaning products:
magentic card readers, bill validators, thermal printers,
point of sale (pos) machines and key lock systems.
(Woman/White, estab 2001, empl 1, sales $272,000, cert:
WBENC)

2034 SBM Management Services, LP
      5241 Arnold Ave   McClellan, CA 95652
      (916) 922-7600 Stu Dalziel Natl Acct Dir
      Fax: (614) 386-2051
      Email: sdalziel@sbmcorp.com
      Website: www.sbmmanagement.com
Facilities support, janitorial, clean-room & laboratory
sanitizing, general building maintenance, recycling &
environmental awareness programs, move-add-change
support services, vendor management. (As-Pac/Hisp, estab
1982, empl 6500, sales $2,580,250,000, cert: NMSDC)

2035 SDI Systems Division, Inc.
      21 Morgan   Irvine, CA 92618
      (949) 583-1001 Jon Korbonski President
      Fax: (949) 583-7007
      Email: sdi@sdinetwork.com
      Website: www.sdinetwork.com
Manufacture and distribute cleaning equipment &
supplies. (Hisp, estab 2008, empl 20, sales $3,700,000,
cert: NMSDC)

2036 SeaYu Enterprises Inc.
      236 West Portal PBM 399 San Francisco, CA
      94127
      (415) 566-9677 Quincy Yu CEO
      Fax: (415) 566-9667
      Email: qyu@sea-yu.com
      Website: www.becleanandgreen.com
Natural cleaners, stain removers and odor eliminators
that are effective, easy to use, biodegradable and safe
for people, pets and the planet. (Woman/As-Pac, estab
2001, empl 2, sales , cert: NMSDC)

2037 U.S. Metro Group, Inc.
      3171 W. Olympic Blvd. #553 3171 W. Olympic
      Blvd., #553 Los Angeles, CA 90006
      (213) 382-6435 Philip W. Gregg Contracts
      Compliance
      Fax: (213) 382-9404
      Email: phil.g@usmetrogroup.com
      Website: www.usmetrogroup.com/
Janitorial maintenance services. (As-Pac, estab 1975,
empl 3500, sales $42,000,000, cert: NMSDC)

2038 Ultimate Maintenance Services, Inc.
      4237 Redondo Beach Blvd   Lawndale, CA 90260
      (310) 542-1474 Sherly Cstmr Service
      Fax: (310) 542-0073
      Email: sherly@umscorporation.com
      Website: www.umscorporation.com
Janitorial services & construction clean up services.
(Woman/Hisp, estab 1990, empl 50, sales $350,000,
cert: State)

2039 UNISERVE Facilities Services
      2363 S Atlantic Blvd   Commerce, CA 90040
      (213) 533-1000 Eugene Hwang Director of Mktg
      Fax: (213) 533-1001
      Email: ehwang@uniservecorp.com
      Website: www.uniservecorp.com
Janitorial services. (As-Pac, estab 1966, empl 250, sales
$21,000,000, cert: NMSDC)

2040 V.S. Supply Company
      910 81st Ave, Unit 11   Oakland, CA 94621
      (510) 834-9560 Vincent Stephenson CEO
      Fax: (510) 834-9563
      Email: vstephenson@vssupply.com
      Website: www.vssupply.com
Professional cleaning, dist cleaning supplies. (AA, estab
1990, empl 10, sales $375,901, cert: State)

Colorado

2041 American Facility Maintenance Group
      1075 S Yukon St Ste 300 Lakewood, CO 80226
      (303) 984-7400 Carmen Flores Business Dev
      Fax: (303) 922-8922
      Email: c.flores@afsg-us.com
      Website: www.aflmaingroup.com
Facility maintenance, management & real estate
services. (Woman/Hisp, estab 1900, empl 1, sales
$18,000,000, cert: NMSDC)

2042 Hill Enterprises Inc.
      6301 Ralston Rd   Westminster, CO 80002
      (303) 424-6262 Kay Kerlin CFO
      Fax: (303) 327-5783
      Email: cslocum@hillpet.com
      Website: www.hillpet.com
Biodiesel, Gasoline, Diesel, American lubricants, Ethanol,
24 hour delivery service (Woman/White, estab 1982, empl
58, sales $181,053,886, cert: State)

2043 SDV Supplies & Services LLP
      P.O. Box 13403   Denver, CO 80201
      (303) 256-4736 George Autobee CEO
      Fax: (303) 205-0599
      Email: gautobee@sdv1.com
      Website: www.sdv1.com
Office Supplies and Office Suites, Janitorial Supplies.
Also include IT and computer/wirless systems (Hisp, estab
2006, empl 3, sales $20,000, cert: State)

Connecticut

2044 C & C Janitorial Supplies, Inc.
      665 New Britain Ave   Newington, CT 06111
      (860) 594-4200 Grace Cafe President
      Fax: (860) 594-4250
      Email: gracec@ccsupplies.com
      Website: www.ccsupplies.com
Dist janitorial products, paper products & equip. (Woman/
White, estab 1988, empl 28, sales , cert: NMSDC)

2045 Horizon Services Company
      250 Governor St   East Hartford, CT 06108
      (860) 291-9111 Thomas Baerlein Senior Acct Rep
      Fax: (860) 291-9410
      Email: tbaerlein@horizonsvcs.com
      Website: www.horizonsvcs.com
Custodial services, supply & management, window
cleaning, clean room environmental svcs, hazardous
material site labor, exterior cleaning & landscaping, post
construction cleaning. (As-Pac, estab 1991, empl 412, sales
$7,400,000, cert: State, NMSDC)

2046 KEECLEAN Management Inc.
      2 Corporate Dr, Ste 242   Shelton, CT 06484
      (203) 397-2532 Keith Jang President
      Fax: (203) 632-1004
      Email: keithjang@keeclean.com
      Website: www.keeclean.com
Commercial cleaning, custodial & janitorial services: floor
care service, carpet cleaning, window washing services.
(As-Pac, estab 2007, empl 200, sales $3,444,178, cert:
State, City, NMSDC)

Delaware

2047 Star Building Services, Inc.
      106 Quigley Blvd   New Castle, DE 19720
      (302) 983-0275 Ernie Martin VP Sales & Mktg
      Fax: (302) 324-1638
      Email: emartin@sbsclean.com
      Website: www.sbsclean.com
Janitorial Services, Medical Device Cleaning Services.
(Woman, estab 1953, empl 300, sales , cert: WBENC)

Florida

2048 ABCO Products, Inc.
      6800 NW 36th Ave   Miami, FL 33147
      (786) 223-0944 Luis Janania Sales Mgr
      Fax: (222) 222-2222
      Email: luisj@abcoproducts.com
      Website: www.abcoproducts.com
Dist cleaning supplies. (Hisp, estab 1979, empl 54, sales ,
cert: State, NMSDC)

2049 All Pro Janitorial Service Inc.
      3843 N Tanner Rd   Orlando, FL 32826
      (407) 649-8878 Glenda Lee President
      Fax: (407) 479-3219
      Email: glenda@allprojan.com
      Website: www.procarpetcleanerorlando.com
Commercial janitorial cleaning, carpet cleaning, rug
cleaning, upholstery cleaning, ceramic tile & grout
cleaning, floor stripping, waxing, buffing & water
restoration. (Woman/AA, estab 2000, empl 15, sales
$166,000, cert: State, City, NMSDC)

2050 CRJ Management Services, Inc.
      12 Miracle Strip Pkwy, Ste 203B   Fort Walton
      Beach, FL 32548
      (850) 936-5060 Lee Jones President
      Fax: (850) 515-0036
      Email: crjmanagementservices@mchsi.com
      Website:
Janitorial services: general office cleaning, floor care,
stripping /waxing. (AA, estab 2003, empl 8, sales
$99,000, cert: State)

2051 D&A Building Services, Inc.
      321 Georgia Ave   Longwood, FL 32750
      (407) 831-5388 Albert Sarabasa CEO
      Fax: (407) 831-1377
      Email: al@dabuildingservices.com
      Website: www.dabuildingservices.com
Janitorial, window washing, pressure cleaning, caulking,
carpet, cleaning, construction cleaning, seal buildings,
light painting. (Hisp, estab 1985, empl 550, sales
$8,200,000, cert: State, City, NMSDC)

2052 GEM Janitorial LLC
9031 Pembroke Rd   Pembroke Pines, FL 33025
(954) 682-3594 Richard Addison President
Fax: (954) 284-6729
Email: homeownersservicesfla@gmail.com
Website: www.gemjanitorialcorp.com
Cleaning, Commercial Remodeling and Repair, Painting, Pressure Cleaning, Carpentry, Doors & Windows Installation, Drywall Repairs and Installation, Flooring Installation. (Woman/AA, estab 2006, empl 6, sales $320,000, cert: NMSDC)

2053 Grosvenor Building Services Iinc.
3398 Parkway Center Ct   Orlando, FL 32808
(407) 292-3383 Lee McDaniel Business Dev Mgr
Fax: (407) 291-4511
Email: lmcdaniel@grosvenorservices.com
Website: www.grosvenorservicescom
Janitorial Services. (Woman/White, estab 1984, empl 400, sales $6,000,000, cert: WBENC)

2054 Jimco Maintenance Inc.
710 Commerce Dr, Ste 107   Venice, FL 34292
(800) 392-8678 Lynn Moseley President
Fax: (877) 392-8678
Email: lynn@jimcos.com
Website: www.jimcos.com
Janitorial services. (Woman/White, estab 1983, empl 90, sales $12,900,000, cert: WBENC)

2055 Merton Partners LLC
692 Solana Court   Marco Island, FL 34145
(609) 773-0145 Nanette Rivera President
Fax: (609) 773-0126
Email: wordehoff@mertonpartners.com
Website: www.mertonpartners.com
Operations Management Consultants: SPC; facilities; maintenance; engineering; construction; validation; manufacturing; yield; optimization (Woman/Hisp, estab 2007, empl 50, sales $1,200,000, cert: NMSDC)

2056 RagsWarehouse & Cleaning Supplies
7221 NW 35th Ave   Miami, FL 33147
(202) 531-9225 Luther Pierre Sales Mgr
Fax:
Email: Luther.Pierre@ragswarehouse.com
Website:
Dist wiping materials ideal for painters or cleaners. (Woman/AA, estab 2015, empl 2, sales $30,000, cert: State)

2057 Siboney Contracting Co.
1000 Southern Blvd, Ste 300   West Palm Beach, FL 33405
(561) 832-3110 Dante Sevi VP
Fax: (561) 650-7330
Email: dsevi@siboneycc.com
Website: www.siboneycc.com
Hauling fill and aggregates, hauling hurricane debris (Hisp, estab 1972, empl 8, sales $23,789,190, cert: City)

2058 The American Cleaning Services Inc
8270 Woodland Center Blvd.   Tampa, FL 33614
(813) 961-6970 Marty Hales GM
Fax: (813) 961-5222
Email: callus1st@americancleaningservice.com
Website: www.americancleaningservice.com
Complete janitorial services, commercial & construction. (Woman/Hisp, estab 1989, empl 1, sales $367,000, cert: State)

2059 The Green Glider Company LLC
830 Harbor Cir   Palm Harbor, FL 34683
(727) 504-9441 Tanya Lewis President
Fax: (727) 785-1327
Email: tanya@gogreenglider.com
Website: www.gogreenglider.com
Green Glider Mop Pad, Reusable, Washable, Durable & Adjustable mop pad that fits onto virtually all of the Swiffer style/type mopping systems. (Woman/White, estab 2010, empl 1, sales $198,000, cert: WBENC)

Georgia

2060 5 Star Enterprise, Inc.
4705-G Bakers Ferry Rd SW   Atlanta, GA 30336
(404) 924-4290 Tracey Felder President
Fax: (404) 699-5406
Email: tfelder@5starchemicals.com
Website: www.5starchemicals.com
Mfr Green cleaning, soaps & detergent products, green certified chemicals. (Woman/AA, estab 2006, empl 10, sales $2,450,000, cert: State, City, NMSDC, WBENC)

2061 Frederick Hart Co. Inc.
2617 Talley St   Decatur, GA 30030
(404) 373-4030 Michael Hart
Fax: (404) 373-4855
Email: hartm1@compacind.com
Website: www.compacind.com
Mfr cleaning products: garbage disposal cleaner & deodorizer, scented sink strainer, bathroom, kitchen, auto, cleaners, closet & air fresheners, kitchen gadgets. (AA, estab 1979, empl 15, sales $3,500,000, cert: NMSDC)

2062 General Building Maintenance, Inc.
3835 Presidential Pkwy Ste 200 Atlanta, GA 30340
(770) 457-5678 Joe Woodson
Fax: (770) 452-7227
Email: marketing@gbmweb.com
Website: www.gbmweb.com
Janitorial svcs: carpet shampooing, stripping & waxing floors, marble & stone care, clean room cleaning & recycling. (As-Pac, estab 1983, empl 271, sales , cert: NMSDC)

2063　GMI Group, Inc.
470 Satellite Blvd NE, Ste R　Suwanee, GA 30024
(678) 482-5288　Kayla Dang CEO
Fax: (678) 482-7106
Email: kayla.dang@gmigroupinc.com
Website: www.thegmigroup.com
Commercial janitorial cleaning, marble maintenance & restoration, ReKRETE waterless concrete cleaning, pressure washing, graffiti removal, construction clean up. (Woman/As-Pac, estab 2005, empl 70, sales $4,058,445, cert: NMSDC, WBENC)

2064　ShockTheory Interactive, Inc.
12705 Century Dr Ste C　Alpharetta, GA 30004
(877) 747-4625　Sonja Williams VP
Fax: (866) 542-2071
Email: sonja.williams@shocktheory.com
Website: www.shocktheory.com
Web design and development, Interactive marketing, User Interface design, and social networking, collaboration and integration, ROI measurement and SEO strategies. (Woman/AA, estab 2003, empl 9, sales $120,000, cert: NMSDC)

2065　The Burks Companies, Inc.
191 Peachtree St NE Ste 800　Atlanta, GA 30303
(678) 686-3203　Frederick Burks Chairman
Fax: (404) 589-4601
Email: jweis@theburkscompanies.com
Website: www.theburkscompanies.com
Janitorial services. (AA, estab 1991, empl 625, sales $15,200,000, cert: NMSDC)

2066　Unique Cleaning Service, Inc.
3330 Cumberland Blvd. Ste 175　Atlanta, GA 30339
(770) 420-7660　Willie Sellers President
Fax: (866) 835-2626
Email: toney@uniqueclean.com
Website: www.uniqueclean.com
Commercial janitorial services, grounds maintenance services. (AA, estab 1996, empl 80, sales , cert: State)

Hawaii

2067　Building Maintenance Services, LLC
1541 S Beretania St, Ste 204　Honolulu, HI 96826
(808) 983-1269　Barbara Beckmeier Owner
Fax: (808) 983-1445
Email: barbara@bmsnationwide.com
Website: www.bmsnationwide.com
Janitorial services. (Woman/White, estab 2000, empl 45, sales , cert: WBENC)

Illinois

2068　A&R Janitorial Service, Inc.
10127 w. Roosevelt Rd.　Westchester, IL 60154
(708) 656-8300　Deborah Pintor Sr Exec VP
Fax: (708) 656-8555
Email: dpintor@arjanitorial.com
Website: www.arjanitorial.com
Janitorial services, commercial cleaning, carpet care, floor care, power washing, snow removal, after construction cleanup & emergency response cleaning. (Woman/Hisp, estab 1967, empl 383, sales $19,752,715, cert: State, City, NMSDC, WBENC)

2069　B & B Maintenance, Inc.
537 Capital Dr　Lake Zurich, IL 60047
(847) 550-6060　Pamela Seiser VP Sales
Fax: (847) 550-1551
Email: pseiser@bandbmaint.com
Website: www.bandbmaint.com
Building maintenance: janitorial, window cleaning, & painting, carpet care, power washing, hard surfaced floor care, tile restoration, fire safety programs, porter service & support personnel. (Hisp, estab 1979, empl 550, sales $1,800,000, cert: City, NMSDC, WBENC)

2070　Clean Impressions Corp.
127 N Northwest Hwy　Palatine, IL 60067
(847) 776-0706　Teresa Garvin President
Fax: (847) 221-2797
Email: cic@cleanimpressionscorp.com
Website: www.cleanimpressionscorp.com
Janitorial service, building maintenance, floor care, stripping & refinishing floor tile, carpet cleaning, stone care, crystalizing & acoustical tile cleaning. (Woman/White, estab 1998, empl 40, sales $665,000, cert: WBENC)

2071　ELB Enterprises, Inc.
4709 Bond Avenue　Alorton, IL 62207
(618) 394-1912　Rhonda Jones
Fax: (618) 482-2706
Email: rjones@elb1inc.com
Website: www.elbenterprisesinc.com
Dist janitorial supplies. (AA, estab 1993, empl 12, sales , cert: State, City, NMSDC)

2072　Emeric Facility Services
918 S Green Bay Rd　Waukegan, IL 60085
(847) 623-6912　Michael Ramirez Acct Exec
Fax:
Email: mramirez@emericservices.com
Website: www.emericservices.com
Janitorial services & carpet cleaning services. (Woman/Hisp, estab 2011, empl 46, sales $932,000, cert: City, WBENC)

2073　IDSC, Inc.
P.O. Box 1055　Woodstock, IL 60098
(815) 337-8066　Milissa Dooley President
Fax: (815) 337-8067
Email: milissa_ids@att.net
Website: www.idscinc.com
Dist sanitation supplies & equipment, PPE, paper goods, maintenance supplies & equipment, hoses. (Woman/White, estab 1990, empl 7, sales $480,000, cert: WBENC)

2074   LACOSTA Facility Support Services, Inc.
       440 W Bonner Rd   Wauconda, IL 60084
       (847) 487-3103 Jeff Johnson Natl Director
       Fax: (847) 526-7147
       Email: sales@cms4.com
       Website: www.lacostaservices.com
Janitorial services, painting services, facility maintanance services. (Woman/Hisp, estab 1988, empl 2400, sales $96,801,398, cert: NMSDC)

2075   United Building Maintenance, Inc.
       165 Easy St   Carol Stream, IL 60188
       (630) 653-4848 Amy Cabrera-Goddard Director of Sales & Mktg
       Fax: (630) 653-0660
       Email: agoddard@ubm-usa.com
       Website: www.ubm-usa.com
Janitorial, painting, pressure washing, snow removal, parking lot maintenance & landscape design. (Hisp, estab 1979, empl 1500, sales $63,800,000, cert: NMSDC)

2076   White Glove Janitorial Services & Supply, Inc.
       356 E Irving Park Rd   Wood Dale, IL 60191
       (630) 766-7466 Joyce Dickens Owner
       Fax: (630) 766-7466
       Email: whtglove@msn.com
       Website: www.whiteglovejanitorialservices.com
Janitorial services: carpet cleaning, landscaping, power washing, food plant sanitation, floor scrubbing & supplies. (Woman, estab 1975, empl 105, sales $2,476,000, cert: City)

Indiana

2077   Suzy Q Cleaning Services
       2401 N Tibbs Ave   Indianapolis, IN 46222
       (317) 755-7664 Suzett Moffitt Owner
       Fax: (317) 955-7567
       Email: suzettsuzett@gmail.com
       Website: www.suzyqcleaning.net
Janitorial, Ground and Building Maintenance, Commercial, Home-Maker Services, Renovation, Construction, Bridge, Road, Side Walk Repair. (Woman/AA, estab 2009, empl 10, sales $80,000, cert: State, City)

Kentucky

2078   Facility Maintenance & Services Group
       147 E Loudon Ave   Lexington, KY 40505
       (859) 554-6584 Frank HAll CEO
       Fax:
       Email: info@facilitymsg.com
       Website: www.facilitymsg.com
Janitorial, Facility Maintenance, Painting, Lawn Care, Pressure washing, High Dusting. (AA, estab 2015, empl 42, sales $1,000,019, cert: NMSDC)

2079   Superior Maintenance Co.
       618 D Westport Rd   Elizabethtown, KY 42701
       (270) 769-2553 Sid Shurn VP
       Fax: (270) 769-3257
       Email: sid@smc.cc
       Website: www.smc.cc
Janitorial & grounds maintenance, window cleaning, pest control, facility maintenance, HVAC, plumbing, chemicals, janitorial supplies & equip. (AA, estab 1988, empl 1200, sales $40,000,000, cert: NMSDC)

Louisiana

2080   Economical Janitorial & Paper Supplies
       1420F Sams Ave, Ste F   Harahan, LA 70123
       (504) 464-7166 Suzie Migliore President
       Fax: (504) 465-9563
       Email: suzie@economicaljanitorial.com
       Website: www.econoomicaljanitorial.com
Dist janitorial supplies, paper supplies, janitorial equipment, food service supplies. (Woman, estab 1983, empl 85, sales $31,015,000, cert: WBENC)

Massachusetts

2081   Dependable Facility Cleaning Services, LLC
       1074 Hyde Park Ave, Ste 4   Hyde Park, MA 02136
       (857) 261-4582 Chuck Ojoko Managing Dir
       Fax:
       Email: charles@dependablefacilitycleaning.com
       Website: www.dependablefacilitycleaning.com
Commercial cleaning & janitorial services. (AA, estab 2015, empl 6, sales , cert: NMSDC)

2082   Milhench Supply Company
       121 Duchaine Blvd   New Bedford, MA 02745
       (508) 995-8331 Angie Prevost Inside Sales
       Fax: (508) 995-4187
       Email: angie@milhench.com
       Website: www.milhench.com
Dist janitorial, paper, packaging & facility maintenance supplies. (Woman/White, estab 1932, empl 32, sales $16,315,760, cert: State)

2083   Moura's Cleaning Service, Inc.
       349 Lunenburg St   Fitchburg, MA 01420
       (978) 562-1839 Andre Thibodeau Sales Mgr
       Fax: (978) 567-0802
       Email: andre@mourascleaningservice.com
       Website: www.mourascleaningservice.com
Janitorial services: office cleaning, floor strip & wax, restroom service, odor control service, concrete cleaning, maintenance & sealing, carpet steam cleaning, upholstery steam cleaning, window cleaning, power washing of buildings. (Hisp, estab 1988, empl 150, sales $2,100,000, cert: State)

2084 Savin Products Co., Inc.
      214 High St P.O. Box 323 Randolph, MA 02368
      (781) 961-2743 Dona D'Ambrosia President
      Fax: (781) 986-6204
      Email: donamarie@savinproducts.com
      Website: www.savinproducts.com
Mfr cleaning products. (Woman/White, estab 1968, empl
10, sales , cert: State)

2085 Unic Pro Inc.
      415 Boston Tpk Ste 211B 1545 Shrewsbury, MA
      01545
      (877) 881-8642 Lilian Radke President
      Fax: (508) 845-4516
      Email: patty@unicpro.com
      Website: www.unicpro.com
Commercial Business Cleaning Services, Commercial
Carpet Cleaning, Floor Washing & Waxing, Green Cleaning
Commercial Services, Industrial Cleaning Services, Nightly
Office Cleaning, Post-Construction Cleaning. (Woman/
Hisp, estab 2007, empl 54, sales $2,450,000, cert: State,
WBENC)

Maryland

2086 Associated Building Maintenance Co., Inc.
      2140 Priest Bridge Court Ste 3 Crofton, MD 21114
      (410) 721-1818 Kurt Bender VP of Sales
      Fax: (410) 721-8616
      Email: kbender@abmcoinc.com
      Website: www.abmcoinc.com/
Commercial general contract cleaning, window cleaning,
carpet cleaning, snow removal, floor stripping & other
building related services. (Woman/White, estab 1987,
empl 1000, sales $25,599,000, cert: State)

2087 C.J. Maintenance, Inc.
      9254 Bendix Rd Columbia, MD 21045
      (410) 720-5157 Tyler Yoon Acct Exec
      Fax: (443) 283-4039
      Email: cjmaintenance@hotmail.com
      Website: www.cjmaint.com
Janitorial, custodial & housekeeping svcs: carpet cleaning,
hard wood floors, marble floor restoration. (As-Pac, estab
1985, empl 700, sales $14,499,999, cert: State, NMSDC)

2088 Red Coats, Inc.
      4520 East-West Highway Bethesda, MD 20814
      (301) 280-4414 Page Pollock Director of Regional
      Sales and Mktg
      Fax: (301) 654-6012
      Email: ppollock@redcoats.com
      Website: www.redcoats.com
LEED compliant cleaning services. (Woman/White, estab
1960, empl 7000, sales $203,366,500, cert: WBENC)

2089 Viking Chemicals, Inc.
      2325 Banger St Baltimore, MD 21230
      (410) 525-2100 Shannon Hodges VP
      Fax: (410) 525-0707
      Email: shodges@vikingchem.com
      Website: www.vikingjanitorsupplies.com
Dist janatorial supplies: paper, floor care equipement,
sweepers, vacuums, matting, brooms, brushes, trash
cans & trash can liners. (Woman/White, estab 1974,
empl 6, sales $2,206,148, cert: State, City)

Michigan

2090 Caravan Facilities Management, LLC
      1400 Weiss St Saginaw, MI 48602
      (989) 798-0977 Victor Gomez Diversity Coord
      Fax: (989) 399-0003
      Email: vg10@caravanfm.com
      Website: www.caravanfm.com
Facilities mgmt: janintorial, landscaping, snow removal,
HVAC, fleet mgmt & building services. (Hisp, estab 1997,
empl 2344, sales $139,000,000, cert: NMSDC)

2091 Caravan Technologies, Inc.
      3033 Bourke Detroit, MI 48238
      (313) 341-2551 Robert Charleston CEO
      Fax: (313) 341-1505
      Email: cti3033@aol.com
      Website: www.caravantech.com
Mfr industrial & commercial cleaning solutions, disinfecting agents & parts washer detergents. (AA, estab
1979, empl 10, sales $495,961, cert: NMSDC)

2092 Choctaw-Kaul Distribution Company
      3540 Vinewood Detroit, MI 48208
      (313) 895-3165 Caitlin Johnson Cstmr Dev Mgr
      Fax: (313) 894-7977
      Email: cjohnson@choctawkaul.com
      Website: www.choctawkaul.com
Mfr gloves & safety products, mgmt svcs, janitorial svcs,
industrial specialty cleaning, paint booth cleaning,
chemical mgmt, recycling, filter maintenance, truck
repair, construction mgmt, parking lot maintenance,
temp manpower, etc. (Nat Ame/As-Ind/As-Pac/Canadian
Aboriginal, estab 1998, empl 350, sales $107,000,000,
cert: NMSDC)

2093 CMS Sourcing Solutions
      29700 Harper Ave, Ste 2 St. Clair Shores, MI
      48082
      (586) 879-0669 CHERYL A KING Exec VP SALES &
      Admin
      Fax: (586) 879-0676
      Email: cheryl.king@cmsgroup.us
      Website: www.cmsgroup.us
Janitorial services, management, labor, supplies,
equipment & systems. (Woman/White, estab 2009,
empl 150, sales $5,500,110, cert: NMSDC)

2094   DFM Solutions (Devon Facility Management LLC)
       777 Woodward Avenue Ste 500A Detroit, MI 48226
       (313) 221-1510 Richard Shipton V.P. Business Dev
       Fax: (313) 221-1550
       Email: rchipton@dfmc3.com
       Website: www.dfm.solutions
Facility management, janitorial & building maintenance &
industrial cleaning services. (Woman/White, estab 2007,
empl 350, sales $45,000,000, cert: WBENC)

2095   Ipax Cleanogel, Inc.
       8301 Lyndon   Detroit, MI 48238
       (313) 933-4211 Veronika Maltsev CEO
       Fax: (313) 933-4454
       Email: vmaltsev@ipax.com
       Website: www.ipax.com
Mfr & dist quality cleaning & maintenance products.
(Woman/White, estab 1988, empl 12, sales $1,680,000,
cert: WBENC)

2096   Macomb Wholesale Supply Corp.
       17730 E 14 Mile Rd   Fraser, MI 48026
       (586)47400 Catherine David President
       Fax: (586) 415-7404
       Email: online@macombwholesale.com
       Website: www.macombwholesale.com
Dist Packaging, Safety, Janitorial & Facility Maintenance
Supplies, corrugated, poly bags, tape, paper, chemical,
packaging, gloves, safety & facility cleaning supplies.
(Woman/White, estab 1988, empl 10, sales $2,500,000,
cert: WBENC)

2097   Midwest Maintenance Services, Inc.
       3704 Trade Center Dr   Ann Arbor, MI 48108
       (734) 222-5902 Linda Johnson President
       Fax: (734) 222-5904
       Email: linda@midwestms.com
       Website: www.midwestms.com
Janitorial services & building maintenance. (Woman/
White, estab 1989, empl 35, sales $603,672, cert: WBENC)

2098   Perfection Commercial Services, Inc.
       905 N Church St P.O. Box 305 Tekonsha, MI 49092
       (888) 933-3103 Lori Smith Controller
       Fax: (517) 767-5208
       Email: lori@pcsmichigan.com
       Website:
       www.perfectioncommercialservicesinc.com
Perfection Commercial Services provides janitorial services
and supplies, which includes window and floor care.
(Woman/White, estab 1991, empl 212, sales $5,785,000,
cert: WBENC, NWBOC)

2099   Polstar Commercial Cleaning Services
       5124 Pontiac Trail   Ann Arbor, MI 48105
       (800) 557-9120 Kamil Krainski Sales Mgr
       Fax: (800) 557-9120
       Email: kamil@polstar.us
       Website: www.polstar.us
Contract janitorial & commercial cleaning services, floor
stripping & waxing, disinfection service, antimicrobial
coatings, carpet cleaning. (Woman/White, estab 2000,
empl 25, sales $903,146, cert: WBENC)

2100   PrimeSource Group, LLC
       4407 Center St   Saginaw, MI 48604
       (989) 752-6443 Brandon Bordeaux
       Fax: (989) 752-6443
       Email: brandon@bandwmgmt.com
       Website:
Dist janitorial supplies & equipment, equipment leasing
& facilities management. (Hisp, estab 2003, empl 20,
sales , cert: NMSDC)

2101   Sparkle Janitorial Service
       4100 Woodward Ave, Ste 9   Detroit, MI 48201
       (313) 831-1535 Loretta Watson President
       Fax: (313) 831-1555
       Email: watsonlorettam@sparklejani.com
       Website: www.saniglaze535.com
Complete janitorial service, window cleaning, carpet
cleaning, construction clean-up, tile & grout restoration.
(AA, estab 1989, empl 25, sales $330,604, cert: NMSDC)

2102   StarSource Management Services, Inc.
       39080 Webb Dr   Westland, MI 48185
       (734) 721-8540 Melvin Brown CEO
       Fax: (734) 721-2860
       Email: sales@starsourceinc.com
       Website: www.starsourceinc.com
Dist uniforms, protective clothing, cutting tools, fasteners, janitorial chemical supplies, cleaning equipment,
paper towels, plastic liners, welding supplies, automotive cleaning supplies, cooling tower chemicals, laundry
services. (AA, estab 1997, empl 5, sales $6,000,000, cert:
NMSDC)

2103   Tri County Cleaning Supply, Inc.
       7109 Dan McGuire Dr   Brigton, MI 48116
       (810) 229-6500 Geri Gee President
       Fax: (810) 229-5005
       Email: g.gee@tcclean.com
       Website: www.tcclean.com
Dist cleaning supplies. (Woman, estab , empl 1, sales ,
cert: WBENC)

Minnesota

2104   Allied National Services
       6066 Shingle Creek Pkwy#1105   Minneapolis, MN
       55430
       (763) 503-0707 Natalie Pope President
       Fax: (763) 503-6978
       Email: npope@alliedns.com
       Website: www.alliedns.com
Contract cleaning services. Floor care Restroom sanita-
tion. (AA, estab 2002, empl 541, sales $17,610,000, cert:
City, NMSDC, 8(a))

2105   Diverse Maintenance Solutions Inc.
       1523 94th Lane NE   Blaine, MN 55449
       (763) 230-7488 Rita Dumra President
       Fax: (763) 230-7493
       Email: rita.dumra@dmsimn.com
       Website: www.dmsimn.com
Dist maintenance supplies, janitorial supplies, rubbermaid
products, paper products, equipment, office supplies &
tools. (Woman/As-Ind, estab 1988, empl 7, sales $966,055,
cert: NMSDC, WBENC)

2106   Innovative Chemical Corporation
       7769 95th St South   Cottage Grove, MN 55016
       (651) 649-1762 Shelly Meyers Sales Mktg Director
       Fax: (651) 649-1787
       Email: smeyers@iccmn.com
       Website: www.iccmn.com
Mfr eco friendly cleaning & maintenance products, green
cleaning products. (As-Ind, estab 1994, empl 13, sales
$2,000,000, cert: NMSDC)

Missouri

2107   Centaur Building Services, Inc.
       4401 Ridgewood Ave   St. Louis, MO 63116
       (314) 201-6805 Jerry Ward Business Dev
       Fax: (314) 752-1747
       Email: jward@centaurservices.com
       Website: www.centaurservices.com
Janitorial services. (Woman/AA/Nat Ame/As-Pac/Hisp,
estab 1985, empl 1300, sales $32,625,937, cert: WBENC)

2108   Eagle Environmental Products, Inc.
       417 N High St   Jackson, MO 63755
       (573) 243-8111 Kenneth Waldron President
       Fax: (573) 243-8112
       Email: kwaldron@eaglesystem.biz
       Website: www.eaglesystem.biz
Dist hot steam vapor cleaners; automatic floor scrubbers;
yellow grease handling & grease trap equipment; janitorial
supplies; chemicals; solvents; gloves & safety products.
(Nat Ame, estab 1991, empl 4, sales $147,000, cert: State)

2109   HI-Gene
       1836 Linn St   North Kansas City, MO 64116
       (816) 472-4118 Barrie Evans Acct Mgr
       Fax: (816) 472-4118
       Email: barrie@higenesjanitorial.com
       Website: www.higenesjanitorial.com
Janitorial services. (Woman/White, estab 1969, empl 275,
sales $6,151,289, cert: NWBOC)

2110   J&B Franchise Venture, Inc.
       11684 Lilburn Park Rd   St Louis, MO 63146
       (314) 989-9997 Janet Mann President
       Fax: (314) 754-9879
       Email: janet.mann@jan-prousa.com
       Website: www.stlouis.jan-pro.com
Janitorial services, commercial cleaning, carpet cleaning,
floor cleaning services. (Woman/White, estab 2004, empl
8, sales $2,000,000, cert: State)

2111   Peistrup Paper Products, Inc.
       1185 Research Blvd   St. Louis, MO 63132
       (314) 993-0970 Dennis Burjoski Acct Exec
       Fax: (314) 993-9174
       Email: dburjoski@peistruppaper.com
       Website: www.peistrup.com
Dist janitorial, paper & safety supplies. (Woman/White,
estab 1960, empl 9, sales $200,000, cert: State, WBENC)

2112   Rockwell Labs Ltd.
       1257 Bedford Rd   North Kansas City, MO 64116
       (816) 283-3167 Cisse Spragins CEO
       Fax: (816) 283-3173
       Email: cspragins@rockwelllabs.com
       Website: www.rockwelllabs.com
Mfr & dist pest management & biological cleaning
products: baits for roaches, ants bed bugs & other
crawling insects. (Woman/White, estab 1998, empl 11,
sales , cert: NWBOC)

2113   Tier One Property Services
       8601 E 63rd St   Kansas City, MO 64133
       (816) 285-7439 Joel Sanders Business Dev
       Fax: (816) 358-7121
       Email: jsanders@tier1usa.com
       Website: www.tier1usa.com
Janitorial services. (AA, estab 2011, empl 750, sales
$4,200,000, cert: NMSDC)

2114   Wexford Labs, Inc.
       325 Leffingwell Ave   Kirkwood, MO 63122
       (800) 506-1146 Mary Anne Auer CEO
       Fax: (314) 966-4135
       Email: maryanne.auer@wexfordlabs.com
       Website: www.wexfordlabs.com
Mfr hard surface, EPA registered disinfectants, floor care
products, general purpose cleaners, hand soaps, alcohol
hand sanitizers. (Woman/White, estab 1974, empl 17,
sales $2,966,970, cert: State)

Mississippi

2115   Jefferson Cleaning Services, LLC
       06 Ray C. Nicks Rd   Jayess, MS 39641
       (601) 803-1601 Janice Jefferson President
       Fax:
       Email: jefferson.jan@gmail.com
       Website:
       www.jeffersoncleaningservices.weebly.com
Commercial janitorial services, corporate buildings, post
construction clean up, office space, hospitals, schools,
daycares, retail centers, etc. (AA, estab 2014, empl 1,
sales , cert: City, WBENC)

North Carolina

2116 Century Products LLC
404 Edwardia Dr Greensboro, NC 27409
(336) 292-8090 Evette Darden AVP of sales/gov Accts
Fax: (336) 292-5750
Email: edb@centuryproductsllc.com
Website: www.centuryproductsllc.com
Dist janitorial cleaning tools: mops, brooms, brushes for institutions & food industry. (AA, estab 1987, empl 21, sales , cert: NMSDC)

2117 Green's Commercial Cleaning
4421 Stuart Andrew Blvd Ste 604 Charlotte, NC 28217
(704) 201-6209 Kimberly Grace Dir of Sales
Fax: (704) 525-5860
Email: kimberly@greenscommercialcleaning.com
Website: www.greenscommercialcleaning.com
Janitorial services, medical curtain cleaning, floor & carpet care, pressure washing & building maintenance. (AA, estab 2003, empl 165, sales $2,300,000, cert: City, 8(a))

2118 JAC Janitorial Services
1101 Tyvola Rd, Ste 205 Charlotte, NC 28217
(980) 201-9099 Jose Jaramillo Sales Mgr
Fax: (980) 201-9543
Email: jjaramillo@jacjanitorialservice.com
Website: www.jacjanitorialservice.com
Cleaning services, hospitals, schools, business parks, government buildings, and more. (Hisp, estab 2006, empl 15, sales , cert: State, City)

New Jersey

2119 BRAVO! Building Services, Inc.
29 King George Road Green Brook, NJ 08812
(732) 465-0707 Frank S. Wardzinski COO
Fax: (732) 271-2763
Email: fwardzinski@bravobuildingservices.com
Website: www.bravogroupservices.com
Janitorial svcs, day porters & matrons, HVAC, mail room services. (Woman/Hisp, estab 1997, empl 3700, sales $95,000,000, cert: NMSDC)

2120 Capstone Facilities Group LLC
609 Park Ave Brielle, NJ 08730
(877) 765-2242 Jrhosaboy President
Fax: (973) 695-1473
Email: jrhosaboyj@gmail.com
Website: www.capstonefacilities.com
Dist foodservice, healthcare & janitorial disposables & equipment: paper towels, toilet paper, handsoap, cleaning chemicals, flatware, napkins. (AA, estab 2012, empl 3, sales $10,500, cert: NMSDC)

2121 CSS Building Services Inc
846 Livingston Ave North Brunswick, NJ 08902
(609) 655-5000 Liz Coury VP of Internal Ops
Fax: (609) 655-4309
Email: lcoury@cssbuildingservices.com
Website: www.cssbuildingservices.com
Janitorial, builiding maintenance, professional services. (Woman/White, estab 1976, empl 450, sales $40,000,000, cert: WBENC)

2122 HARVARD Services Group, Inc.
33 Wood Ave S, Ste 600 Iselin, NJ 08830
(973) 515-9302 Nathalie Doobin CEO
Fax: (212) 398-6599
Email: ndoobin@harvardsg.com
Website: www.harvardsg.com
Janitorial services & maintenance services. (Woman/White, estab 1986, empl 476, sales $11,898,931, cert: State, WBENC)

2123 Janel Inc.
7 Mountain Ave Bound Brook, NJ 08805
(732) 271-4700 Colleen McAteer President
Fax: (732) 271-4814
Email: colleenm@janelinc.com
Website: www.janelonline.com
Dist cleaning products, assemble, test & repair electronic equipment. (Woman/White, estab 1960, empl 8, sales $2,897,219, cert: State, WBENC)

2124 Shore Manufacturing LLC
1709 Highway 34 Unit 5 Wall, NJ 07727
(732) 894-9810 William Vogel President
Fax: (732) 894-9812
Email: williamjvogel@aol.com
Website: www.shoremfgllc.com
Mfr non woven disposable food service wipers. (Woman/White, estab 2013, empl 8, sales , cert: State, WBENC)

2125 TUCS Cleaning Service, Inc.
166 Central Ave Orange, NJ 07050
(973) 673-0700 Ingrid Schaefer VP of Accts
Fax: (973) 673-1911
Email: ischaefer@tucscleaning.com
Website: www.tucscleaning.com
Janitorial svcs: window cleaning, general office & warehouse cleaning, strip & wax hard floors,carpet shampoo, upholstery shampoo, cleaning above/below raised computer floors, power washing & construction. (Hisp, estab 1983, empl 600, sales , cert: City, NMSDC)

New Mexico

2126 Specialized Services, LLC
3150 Carlisle NE Ste, 6 Albuquerque, NM 87110
(505) 881-5237 Faith St. Clair
Fax: (505) 333-4143
Email: faith.specializedservices@gmail.com
Website: www.specializedservicesnm.com
Commercial maintenance, floor maintenance, strip & waxing, cleaning & disinfecting tile & grout. (Hisp, estab 2009, empl 26, sales $125,165,468, cert: NMSDC)

Nevada

2127 Smalls Senibaldi Services LLC
      4127 Falcons Flight Ave   North Las Vegas, NV 89084
      (702) 636-1316 Iris Senibaldi CEO
      Fax: (702) 477-7771
      Email: iris@smaseni.com
      Website: www.smaseni.com
Commercial & residential cleaning, janitorial services.
(Woman/AA, estab 2013, empl 20, sales $24,000, cert:
NMSDC)

2128 Smart Cleaning Solutions LLC
      57 Spectrum Blvd   Las Vegas, NV 89101
      (702) 685-7055 Salvador Canales Mgr
      Fax: (888) 645-4390
      Email: scanales@mysmartcleaningsolutions.com
      Website: www.smartcleaningsolutionsllc.vom
Escalator Step Cleaning, Escalator Step Refurbishment,
Powder Coating, Demarcations Lines, Commercial Clean-
ing, Industrial Cleaning, Final Cleaning, Power Wash,
Custodial Services, Janitorial Services. (Woman/Hisp, estab
2011, empl 38, sales $950,000, cert: State)

New York

2129 A&A Maintenance Enterprise Inc.
      965 Midland Ave   Yonkers, NY 10704
      (914) 969-0009 Armando Rodriguez Jr. President
      Fax: (914) 969-0070
      Email: arodriguez@aamaintenance.com
      Website: www.aamaintenance.com
Janitorial services. (Hisp, estab 1983, empl 2600, sales
$23,000,000, cert: City, NMSDC)

2130 Alliance Supply, Inc.
      1743-48 St   Brooklyn, NY 11204
      (347) 564-0022 Sylvia Spielman President
      Fax: (888) 259-4547
      Email: sylvia@alliancesupply.net
      Website: www.alliancesupply.net
Dist janitorial supplies & food service disposables.
(Woman/White, estab 2005, empl 4, sales $850,000, cert:
City)

2131 American Maintenance Janitorial Services &
      Supplies Co. Corp.
      1074 Home St   Bronx, NY 10459
      (718) 409-0021 Jessica Ortiz-Gonzalez Acct Mgr
      Fax: (718) 892-5490
      Email: americanmaintenance3jss@gmail.com
      Website: www.americanmaint1807.com
Commercial janitorial services; custodial services
floor & carpet care; construction cleanup; window
cleaning; building maintenance. (Hisp, estab 2004, empl
25, sales $800,000, cert: State, City, NMSDC)

2132 Anthony's Janitorial/Maintenance Service Ltd.
      24-20 Jackson Ave   Long Island City, NY 11101
      (718) 737-5806 Anthony Fisher President
      Fax:
      Email: anthonyjanitorialmaintenance@gmail.com
      Website:
      www.anthonysjanitorialmaintenance.com
Janitorial Supplies & Services. (AA, estab 2010, empl
100, sales $450,000, cert: City)

2133 Gilbert International Inc.
      1001 Avenue of the Americas 12th Fl New York,
      NY 10018
      (212) 628-5305 Kevin Gilbert President
      Fax: (212) 628-5306
      Email: kevin@gilbertinternational.com
      Website: www.gilbertinternational.com
Integrated facilities services, janitorial & facilities
support. (Woman/Hisp, estab 1992, empl 266, sales
$22,760,946, cert: State, City, NMSDC, WBENC)

2134 Global Traders, Inc.
      496 Powell St   Brooklyn, NY 11212
      (347) 240-9900 Charles Ossa President
      Fax: (718) 504-6099
      Email: cossa@globaltradersusa.us
      Website: www.globaltradersusa.us
Cavicide surface disinfectant & decontaminant cleaner.
(Woman/AA, estab 1999, empl 4, sales $400,000, cert:
State, City)

2135 H. Weiss LLC
      12 Labriola Court   Armonk, NY 10504
      (914) 273-4400 Elizabeth Weiss Managing
      Member
      Fax: (914) 273-4400
      Email: eweiss@hweiss.net
      Website: www.hweiss.net
Dist disposables, janitorial, small wares & supply items
for the kitchen. (Woman/Nat Ame, estab 2003, empl 46,
sales $958,779,300, cert: WBENC)

2136 Jelmar LLC
      620 State Stree 3rd Floor   Schenectady, NY 12305
      (800) 323-5497 Glenn Poticha VP of Sales
      Fax: (847) 675-8780
      Email: Glenn@jelmar.com
      Website: www.jelmar.com
Dist cleaning products. (Woman/White, estab 1949,
empl 14, sales $36,745,934, cert: WBENC)

2137 Premier Supplies
      460 W 34th St New York, NY 10001
      (732) 240-6900 Brad Singer Dir Jan/San Div
      Fax: (732) 240-3599
      Email: bsinger@premiersupplies.com
      Website: www.premiersupplies.com
Dist cleaning products & equipment. (Woman/White,
estab 1962, empl 7, sales $1,250,000, cert: State)

2138 Quality Building Services
801 Second Ave 8th Fl New York, NY 10017
(212) 883-0009 ANDREA BARRAGAN Research and Dev
Fax: (212) 883-6770
Email: ANDREA.B@QBS.CO
Website: www.qualitybuildingservices.com
Janitorial services: offices, conference rooms, kitchens, bathrooms, lobbies and other common spaces. (Woman/White, estab 2000, empl 600, sales $50,050,000, cert: City, WBENC)

2139 Snappy Solutions
106 Sycamore Dr East Hampton, NY 11937
(212) 748-9030 Maureen Fairlie President
Fax: (212) 535-1971
Email: sales@snappysolutions.com
Website: www.snappysolutions.com
Dist janitorial, material maintenance products & safety products. (Woman/White, estab 2003, empl 2, sales $430,000, cert: WBENC)

Ohio

2140 Janitorial Services Inc.
5795 Canal Rd Valley View, OH 44125
(216) 341-8601 Ronald Martinez Jr. VP
Fax: (216) 341-8554
Email: rmartinez@jsijanitorial.com
Website: www.jsijanitorial.com
Commercial Cleaning Services, Construction Cleaning, Window Washing, Wall Washing, Carpet Cleaning, Hard Surface Floor Care. (Hisp, estab 1972, empl 400, sales , cert: NMSDC)

2141 Poly Services Inc.
16606 S Waterloo Rd Cleveland, OH 44110
(216) 531-5681 Rhonda Bolden Office Mgr
Fax: (216) 481-1140
Email: polyservices@sbcglobal.net
Website:
Dist janitorial & packaging products, gloves, paper products, maintenance items. (AA, estab 1989, empl 5, sales $952,323, cert: State, NMSDC)

2142 Ramos Cleaning LLC
3660 Washington Park Blvd Newburgh Hts, OH 44105
(216) 262-7655 Marylin Ramos Owner
Fax:
Email: ramoscleaningllc@sbcglobal.net
Website:
Commercial Cleaning, Carpet Cleaning, Office Cleaning, Post Construction Cleaning. (Woman/Hisp, estab 2008, empl 1, sales $33,633, cert: City)

Pennsylvanie

2143 Homeland Industrial Supp
3045 McCann Farm Dr, Unit 102 Garnet Valley, PA 19060
(844) 350-1550 Patrick King COO
Fax:
Email: patrickking@homelandindustrialsupply.com
Website: www.homelandindustrialsupply.com
Dist specialty maintenance products & janitorial supplies. (Woman/White, estab 2014, empl 11, sales $1,500,000, cert: State, City)

2144 T. Frank McCall's, Inc.
601 Madison St Chester, PA 19013
(610) 876-9245 Lisa Witomski President
Fax: (610) 876-9189
Email: lisa@tfrankmccalls.com
Website: www.tfrankmccalls.com
Janitorial, maintenance & dist paper. (Woman/White, estab 1900, empl 23, sales , cert: WBENC)

Rhode Island

2145 Universal Cleaning Concept LLC
77 Burgess Ave East Providence, RI 02914
(401) 952-2844 Evanisio Oliveira Owner
Fax:
Email: universalcc14@gmail.com
Website: www.universalcleaning.org
Commercial office cleaning services. (AA, estab 2007, empl 14, sales $145,000, cert: State, 8(a), SDB)

South Carolina

2146 Clean Advantage, Inc.
5 N Watson Rd Taylors, SC 29687
(800) 322-6641 Linda Black President
Fax: (800) 322-6966
Email: linda@cleanadvantage.com
Website: www.cleanadvantage.com
Mfr & package specialty cleaning products, private label packaging. (Woman/White, estab 1993, empl 25, sales , cert: WBENC)

2147 Quality Touch Janitorial Service, Inc.
7252 Investment Dr North Charleston, SC 29418
(843) 552-7303 John Brown President
Fax: (843) 552-0456
Email: jbrown@qualitytouchjanitorial.com
Website: www.wwwqualitytouchjanitorial.com
Janitorial services, general cleaning, construction cleanup & floor maintenance. (Woman/AA, estab 1900, empl 1, sales $1,650,000, cert: State, City, SDB)

Tennessee

2148 Action Chemical, Inc.
275 Cumberland St   Memphis, TN 38112
(901) 522-8783 Charles E. Barnes President
Fax: (901) 452-1366
Email: charles@actionjps.com
Website: www.actionchemical.com
Dist janitorial supplies & equipment, maintenance supplies & equipment, industrial supplies, paper products, safety products, cleaning chemicals, odor control products, skin care, personal hygiene products, mops, brooms, brushes. (AA, estab 1994, empl 16, sales $5,481,460, cert: State, City, NMSDC)

2149 Ezie's Cleaning Supply
2524 Hospitality Dr   Columbia, TN 38401
(931) 487-9933 Errol Murphy Owner
Fax: (931) 487-9934
Email: eziesclean@cpws.net
Website:
Dist janitorial & paper products supplies. (AA, estab 2004, empl 2, sales , cert: State, NMSDC)

2150 Fayette Janitorial Service LLC
P.O. Box 866   Sommerville, TN 38068
(901) 465-1529 Michael Kellon general sales Mgr
Fax: (901) 465-1813
Email: mburns@fayettejanitorialservice.com
Website: www.fayettejanitorialservice.com
Janitorial services. (Woman/White, estab 1995, empl 15, sales $5,374,273, cert: WBENC)

2151 Ladd Safety, LLC
3901 Lighthouse Lane   Lakeland, TN 38002
(901) 268-2098 Jessica Ladd Owner
Fax:
Email: jessica@laddsafety.com
Website: www.laddsafety.com
Dist Safety PPE & Janitorial supplies. (Woman/White, estab 2016, empl 3, sales , cert: WBENC)

2152 Mason's Professional Cleaning Service, LLC
1422 Menager Rd   Memphis, TN 38106
(901) 775-7778 Dorothy Mason President
Fax: (901) 367-2434
Email: dotm20032003@yahoo.com
Website: www.masonprofessionalcleaningservicellc.com
Commercial janitorial cleaning services, carpet cleaning, hard surface flooring cleaning, pressure washing, groundskeeping/landscaping service. (Woman/AA, estab 2000, empl 21, sales $550,000, cert: State, City, NMSDC)

2153 Premiere Building Maintenance Corporation
1416 McCalla Ave   Knoxville, TN 37915
(865) 773-9524 Tom Poovey Dir of Business Devel
Fax: (865) 546-6708
Email: tpoovey@premierebuilding.com
Website: www.premierebuilding.com
Full Janitorial Service, Maintenance & Facility Management (AA, estab 1996, empl 500, sales $13,900,000, cert: State, NMSDC)

2154 Strategic Cleaning Services
7320 Patsy Circle N   Memphis, TN 38125
(901) 755-4484 Vincent Dandridge CEO
Fax: (901) 755-4478
Email: vincentdanbridge@bellsouth.net
Website: www.strategiccleaningtn.com
Commercial cleaning services, carpet cleaning, stripping & waxing floors, window cleaning & pressure washing. (AA, estab 2007, empl 25, sales $300,000, cert: State)

2155 Universal Sanitizers and Supplies, Inc.
P.O.Box 50305   Knoxville, TN 37853
(865) 573-7296 Emilia Rico-Munoz CEO
Fax: (865) 573-7298
Email: emirico@msn.com
Website: www.universalsanitizers.com
Sanitation cleaners & sanitizers, conveyor lubricants, janitorial products, sanitation consulting, training & audits, contract cleaning, fogging, sanitation equipment, water treatment, environmental testing. (Woman/Hisp, estab 1994, empl 15, sales $3,000,000, cert: WBENC)

Texas

2156 AHI Facility Services, Inc.
625 Yuma Ct   Dallas, TX 75208
(800) 472-5749 Bethany Lorentzen Mktg Coord
Fax: (214) 741-9935
Email: bethanylorentzen@ahifs.com
Website: www.ahifs.com
Janitorial svcs, carpet & floor care, minor & general maintenance, landscaping, groundskeeping, parking lot sweeping & striping, garage maintenance, window washing, power washing, document shredding, recycle programs. (Woman/White, estab 1968, empl 1500, sales $39,000,000, cert: WBENC)

2157 Aztec Facility Management, LP
11000 S Wilcrest, Ste 125   Houston, TX 77099
(281) 668-9000 Andrea Bradshaw Proposal & Mktg Mgr
Fax: (281) 669-9003
Email: andrea@aztec1.com
Website: www.aztecfacility.com
Facility management & support services: janitorial, grounds & preventive maintenance, pest control, parking lot maintenance, construction clean-up, property warehousing, environmental services. (Woman/AA, estab 1981, empl 900, sales $23,500,000, cert: State, NMSDC)

2158 CalGar Enterprises, LLC
3712 Arapaho Rd   Addison, TX 75001
(972) 437-6555 Rick Calabrese
Fax: (972) 636-8497
Email: rbraucht@calgar-ent.com
Website: www.calgar-ent.com
Maintenance & Detailed Cleaning of Cleanrooms, Data Center, Sub-Flooring Cleaning, Terminal Cleaning, Construction Clean Services, Site Preparation Contractors, Janitorial, Custodial, Green Cleaning, LEED. (Hisp, estab 2005, empl 30, sales $1,200,000, cert: State)

2159 Competitive Choice, Inc.
      P.O. Box 35743 Houston, TX 77235
      (832) 724-5300 Aundrea Williams President
      Fax: (713) 838-1188
      Email: aundrea@competitivechoice.net
      Website: www.competitivechoice.net
Dist industrial maintenance & cleaning chemicals: lubricants, solvents, degreasers, hand cleaners & wipes,
disinfectants, deodorizers, greases & oils, coil cleaners &
pan tabs, drain & sewer maintainers, insecticdes & safety
supplies. (Woman/AA, estab 2003, empl 6, sales $700,000,
cert: State)

2160 Contractors Corner, LLC
      9515 Maverick Point San Antonio, TX 78240
      (210) 462-3110 Eduardo Garcia Owner
      Fax: (210) 775-5940
      Email: agarcia@concorusa.com
      Website: www.concorusa.com
Commercial janitorial services, floor care, strip & wax,
buffing, polishing concrete floors & building maintenance
services. (Hisp, estab 2009, empl 72, sales $1,000,000,
cert: State)

2161 Evelyn's Professional Janitorial Services, Inc.
      1617 N Central Exprwy Dallas, TX 75075
      (972) 516-9550 Tammy Pearce Business Devel Dir
      Fax: (972) 516-9868
      Email: CustomerService@ALLjanitorial.net
      Website: www.alljanitorial.net
Janitorial service; window cleaning; power washing; floor
maintenance; janitorial supplies; window cleaning equipment; window cleaning supplies; floor scrubbers; floor
buffers; cleaning chemicals; floor sweepers; carpet
vacuum. (Woman/Hisp, estab 1992, empl 110, sales
$1,258,040, cert: State, NMSDC, WBENC)

2162 Industrial Solution Company
      2514 Oak Hill Dr Arlington, TX 76006
      (214) 200-6535 Barbara Oldums Owner
      Fax:
      Email: industrialsolutions513@yahoo.com
      Website: www.indsolbo.com
Mfr Disposable Towel TUF Towels, Dist Cloth Towels,
Gloves, Safety Supplies, Packaging Supplies & Janitorial
Supplies. (Woman/AA, estab 2011, empl 2, sales $32,000,
cert: State, City)

2163 La Med Facility Maintenance
      10815 Gulfdale San Antonio, TX 78216
      (210) 464-0107 Eduardo Tijerina CEO
      Fax: (210) 310-3226
      Email: edwardtij@hotmail.com
      Website: www.lamedfm.com
Facility maintenance, commercial cleaning, transportation.
(Woman/Hisp, estab 2011, empl 32, sales $1,250,987, cert:
State)

2164 M.A.N.S. Distributors, Inc.
      6719 Levelland Dr Ste 200 Dallas, TX 75252
      (972) 380-2062 Arvin Kara Project Mgr
      Fax: (972) 248-6267
      Email: sales@mans.us
      Website: www.mans.us
Dist industrial janitorial & maintenance supplies.
(Woman/As-Pac, estab 1980, empl 5, sales $3,500,000,
cert: State)

2165 MarFran Cleaning, LLC
      15502 Old Galveston Rd, Ste 718 Webster, TX
      77598
      (832) 885-6692 Naomi Scales Managing Member
      Fax: (281) 984-7651
      Email: naomi@marfrancleaning.com
      Website: www.marfrancleaning.com
Custodial/Janitorial Services, Landscaping Services,
Carpet & Upholstery Cleaning, Facilities Maintenance
Support, Painting & Flooring, Minor Construction,
Remodeling & Renovations. (Woman/AA, estab 2006,
empl 15, sales $543,650, cert: State, City, 8(a))

2166 Prestige Maintenance USA Ltd.
      1808 10th St, Ste 300 Plano, TX 75074
      (972) 578-9801 Rachel Sanchez CEO
      Fax: (972) 578-9592
      Email: rsanchez@prestigeusa.net
      Website: www.prestigeusa.net
Contract cleaning: retail, office, industrial & warehouse
facilities. (Woman/White, estab 1976, empl 2900, sales
$74,851,169, cert: WBENC)

2167 Redlee/SCS, Inc.
      10425 Olympic Dr, Ste A Dallas, TX 75220
      (214) 357-4753 Chuck Redfearn CEO
      Fax: (214) 357-9435
      Email: credfearn@redleescs.com
      Website: www.redleescs.com
Commerical janitorial services, carpet cleaning, & hard
surface flooring maintenance & restoration. (Nat Ame,
estab 1982, empl 225, sales $30,353,905, cert: State,
NMSDC)

2168 SOYAC Industrial
      12514 Willow Breeze Dr Tomball, TX 77377
      (877) 243-0445 Roberto Schnakofsky President
      Fax: (954) 495-8382
      Email: roberto@soyacindustrial.com
      Website: www.soyacindustrial.com
Environmentally & Regulatory Friendly Solvents,
Degreasers, Cleaners, Penetrating Lubricants. (Hisp,
estab 2004, empl 3, sales $273,532, cert: State, City)

2169 Supply Sanitation Systems
      1450 Preston Forest Sq, Ste 209 Dallas, TX 75230
      (972) 458-2555 Sally Seegers Sales
      Fax: (972) 458-2566
      Email: sallys@supplysystemsusa.com
      Website: www.supplysystemsusa.com
Mfr & dist cleaning chemicals. (Woman/White, estab
1992, empl 6, sales , cert: State)

2170   Texas Microfiber
        2515 Tarpley Rd, Ste 118   Carrollton, TX 75006
        (800) 742-2913 Alisa Kraemer-O'Banion CEO
        Fax: (972) 267-3421
        Email: alisa@texasmicrofiber.com
        Website: www.texasmicrofiber.com
Mfr microfiber mop pads, microfiber mops, microfiber
cloths, microfiber towels, telescopic microfiber high
dusters & duster socks, aluminum mop handles & heads,
cotton hand towels, cotton bar towels, logo cotton towels,
logo microfiber towels. (Woman/White, estab 2010, empl
3, sales $223,399, cert: State, WBENC)

2171   TFOM Corpoation
        1106 Clayton Ln, Ste 208E   Austin, TX 78723
        (512) 374-9167 Terry Christopher President
        Fax: (512) 374-9157
        Email: TerryLC@JDDAinc.com
        Website: www.jddainc.com
Facility maintenance & janitorial services. (AA, estab 2005,
empl 13, sales $352,000, cert: 8(a))

2172   The Entermedia Group, LLC
        900 RR620 S Ste C101-153 Austin, TX 78734
        (512) 553-8341 Lorraine Jordan CEO
        Fax: (210) 775-5940
        Email: lorraine.jordan@tegteam.com
        Website: www.tegteam.com
We provide support . (Woman/AA, estab 2010, empl 10,
sales , cert: State, NMSDC, WBENC)

2173   XD Ventures, LLC
        2555 South Shore Blvd. Ste C League City, TX 77573
        (832) 557-6622 Xan Difede President
        Fax:
        Email: xan@fidelityfuels.com
        Website: www.fidelityfuels.com
Dist aliphatic solvents, mineral spirits & mineral seal oils.
(Woman/White, estab 2014, empl 1, sales , cert: State,
WBENC)

Virginia

2174   A&L Service Industries, Inc
        10366A Democracy Lane   Fairfax, VA 22030
        (703) 359-0555 Andrea Sax President
        Fax: (703) 359-6091
        Email: diversity@alsi.us.com
        Website: www.alsi.us.com
Janitorial services, commercial & residential buildings, new
construction cleanup, parking lot/garage cleaning, day
porter service, carpet cleaning, window cleaning, floor
restoration. (Woman/White, estab 1978, empl 62, sales
$3,244,673, cert: State)

2175   Environmental Facility Services (EFS)
        1359 Beverly Rd, Ste 115 P.O. Box 458 McLean,
        VA 22101
        (703) 338-7888 Art Evans Business Dev
        Fax: (703) 641-8491
        Email: info@efsgreen.com
        Website: www.efsgreen.com
Commercial janitorial services. (Woman/As-Pac, estab
2006, empl 10, sales $500,000, cert: State)

2176   Hutchins & Hutchins, Inc.
        39 Hutchwood Ln   Waynessboro, VA 22980
        (540) 949-6663 Kristyn Henke Mktg Coord
        Fax: (540) 943-9803
        Email: kristyn@yourcleanroomsupplier.com
        Website: www.yourcleanroomsupplier.com
Dist clean room supplies & safety apparel. (Woman/
White, estab 1984, empl 17, sales $4,503,300, cert:
State)

Washington

2177   AMEX Investments, LLC
        730 West A St   Pasco, WA 99301
        (509) 545-3903 Deborah Bermudez Owner
        Fax:
        Email: deb@acompletejanitorial.com
        Website: www.acompletejanitorial.com
Cleaning supplies, chemicals, equipment & parts.
(Woman/As-Pac, estab 2012, empl 6, sales $500,000,
cert: State)

2178   Nexo Services LLC
        12819 SE 38th St   Bellevue, WA 98006
        (206) 518-3235 Fatima Sotelo Principal
        Fax: (781) 631-0841
        Email: patty@nexoservices.net
        Website: www.nexoservices.net
Janitorial, Maintenance, Office, Industrial, Foodservice
Supplies. (Woman/Hisp, estab 2014, empl 1, sales , cert:
State)

Wisconsin

2179   Lavelle Industries, Inc.
        665 McHenry St   Burlington, WI 53105
        (262) 757-2213 Megan Schmidt Natl Acct Mgr
        Fax: (262) 763-5607
        Email: mschmidt@lavelle.com
        Website: www.lavelle.com
Mfr Korky brand toilet repair products: toilet flappers,
toilet fill valves & flush valves. (Woman/White, estab
1912, empl 450, sales , cert: WBENC)

2180   Performance Clean LLC
        One Brewers Way   Milwaukee, WI 53214
        (414) 902-4439 Steven O'Connell GM
        Fax: (414) 902-4055
        Email: info@performanceclean.com
        Website: www.performanceclean.com
Janitorial & building maintenance. (AA, estab 2001,
empl 350, sales $4,381,330, cert: NMSDC)

CONSTRUCTION: General Contractors
Companies listed are bonded general contractors who perform or will perform on a regional or national basis. NAICS Code 23

Alabama

2181 Dine Modular Construction, LLC
P.O. Box 1327 2515 11th Avenue Haleyville, AL 35565
(205) 485-1267 Pam Morton Senior Project Mgr
Fax: (205) 486-2166
Email: pparrish@dineconstruction.com
Website: www.dineconstruction.com
General construction: design/build construction, pre-engineered steel & modular buildings. (Woman/Nat Ame, estab 2003, empl 6, sales $1,000,002, cert: WBENC)

Arizona

2182 DAP Construction Management, LLC
516 W Vermont Ave Phoenix, AZ 85013
(602) 541-0229 Alicia Hernandez President
Fax: (602) 454-1777
Email: ahernandez@dapconstructionmgt.com
Website: www.dapconstructionmgt.com
General construction: self performing, rough framing, landscaping, roofing, painting, flooring & material supplies. (Woman/Hisp, estab 2009, empl 2, sales $102,000, cert: State, City)

2183 Eagle EGC dba Miura Contracting
4001 S Contractors Way, Ste 121 Tucson, AZ 85716
(520) 292-3939 Liz Joye Office Mgr
Fax: (520) 292-4670
Email: ljoye@miuracontracting.com
Website: www.miuracontracting.com/
General Contracting, horizontal construction projects (highway, road, utilities, and site development) & vertical construction projects (commercial building and building improvements). (Hisp, estab 2008, empl 13, sales $1,400,000, cert: City, 8(a), SDB)

2184 JOATMON Construction LLC
1308 N Stockton Hill Rd, Ste A305 Kingman, AZ 86401
(928) 718-2000 J R Avila Managing Member
Fax: (928) 718-2012
Email: jr@joatmonllc.com
Website: www.jclaz.com
General Contractor, Structural Steel Fabrication & Erection, Commercial & Industrial Construction & Maintenance, Communication Towers & Maintenance , Cell Tower Erection, Modification & Fabrication, Network Upgrades, Concrete Structures. (Hisp, estab 2000, empl 10, sales $1,000,000, cert: 8(a))

2185 Pacificspan LLC
6908 W Southgate Ave Phoenix, AZ 85043
(480) 882-8015 John Lee President
Fax: (480) 899-3566
Email: john@pacificspan.com
Website: www.pacificspan.com
Project feasibility planning, design development, & construction, remodeling of restaurants and bars, medical and research facilities, computer and chemical laboratories, salons and spas, apartment complexes, churches and offices, etc. (As-Pac, estab 2005, empl 8, sales $988,180, cert: 8(a))

2186 Sentinel Fence and Contracting LLC
6908 East Alta Hacienda Dr Scottsdale, AZ 85251
(602) 828-4866 Sharon Hamilton President
Fax: (480) 961-7723
Email: sharonh@sentinelfence.com
Website: www.sentinelfence.com
General contracting, commercial renovations, high security fencing, gates, bollards, barriers & barricades. (Woman/Hisp, estab 2002, empl 8, sales , cert: City, 8(a))

2187 Troon Inc.
16441 N 90th St Scottsdale, AZ 85260
(480) 626-4300 Ray Garcia President
Fax: (480) 718-7817
Email: ray@trooninc.com
Website: www.trooninc.com
General contracting. (Hisp, estab 2002, empl 11, sales $11,000,000, cert: State)

California

2188 Anacapa Technologies, Inc.
301 E Arrow Hwy, Ste 106 San Dimas, CA 91773
(909) 394-7795 Dorothy Delaney
Fax: (909) 394-9895
Email: dorothy@anacapa-tech.net
Website: www.anacapa-tech.net
Anacapa Technologies is the developer and manufacturer of Branded and Patented products that fall into the category of topical anti-infective agents used in dialysis, infection control, skin and wound care applications. (Woman/White, estab 2001, empl 5, sales $415,000, cert: State)

2189 Anderson Burton Construction
121 Nevada St Arroyo Grande, CA 93420
(805) 481-5096 Joni Anderson President
Fax:
Email: joni@andersonburton.com
Website: www.andersonburton.com/
General Engineering, Procurement, General Contracting, Energy (Woman/Hisp, estab 1999, empl 155, sales $30,198,963, cert: CPUC)

2190   Aqual Corp.
        7951 North Ave   Lemon Grove, CA 91945
        (619) 741-9028 Lanette McAfee Business Ops
        Fax: (619) 741-9731
        Email: lanette@aqualcorp.com
        Website: www.aqualcorp.com
Construction Management Cost Plus, GMP Design Build &
Lump Sum, Multi Family Commercial & Industrial Tenant
Improvements, Concrete, horizontal/vertical, drywall &
taping, painting, framing, carpentry, tile, doors, plumbing.
(AA/As-Pac, estab 2008, empl 4, sales $1,049,692, cert:
NMSDC)

2191   Bjork Construction Co. Inc.
        4420 Enterprise Place   Fremont, CA 94538
        (510) 656-4688 Jean Bjork President
        Fax: (510) 656-0806
        Email: jbjork@bjorkconstruction.com
        Website: www.bjorkconstruction.com
General contracting: self preforms, construction management, carpentry rough & finish, metal stud framing,
sheetrock systems & painting. (Woman/White, estab 1988,
empl 35, sales $2,580,000, cert: City, CPUC, WBENC)

2192   Cabral Roofing & Waterproofing Corp.
        675 W. Terrace Dr   San Dimas, CA 91773
        (323) 832-9100 Desi Cabral PR/sales
        Fax: (323) 832-9300
        Email: desi@cabralroofing.com
        Website: www.cabralroofing.com
General contracting: roofing & waterproofing (Hisp, estab
1997, empl 70, sales , cert: CPUC)

2193   Casco Contractors, Inc.
        9850 Irvine Center Dr.   Irvine, CA 92618
        (949) 679-6880 Cheryl Osborn President
        Fax: (949) 679-6890
        Email: cheryl@cascocontractors.com
        Website: www.cascocontractors.com
General contracting, TI construction, construction management. (Woman/White, estab 2001, empl 44, sales
$32,000,000, cert: CPUC, WBENC)

2194   Commercial Site Improvements, Inc.
        192 Poker Flat Rd   Copperopolis, CA 95228
        (209) 785-1920 Kim Batch Owner
        Fax: (209) 785-1921
        Email: mainoffice@comimprovementsinc.com
        Website: www.comsiteimprovementsinc.com
Construction maintenance & remodeling. (Woman, estab
2012, empl 50, sales $130,000,000, cert: CPUC)

2195   Cornejo Construction Co.
        P.O. Box 22302   Santa Barbara, CA 93121
        (805) 448-2201 Jesse Cornejo Owner
        Fax:
        Email: jcornejo@cornejoco.com
        Website: www.cornejoco.com
Remodeling assembly lines, replacing air ducts, replacing
equipment, moving walls, crane placement, building
hangars, epoxy flooring, etc. (Hisp, estab 1989, empl 7,
sales $250,000, cert: 8(a))

2196   Fasone Construction inc
        9124 Norwalk Blvd   Santa Fe Springs, CA 90670
        (562) 322-0828 Andrea N Garrido President
        Fax: (562) 948-4509
        Email: andrea@fasonegbc.com
        Website: www.fasonegbc.com
Design & general construction contracting. (Woman/
Hisp, estab 1995, empl 21, sales $3,800,500, cert: City,
CPUC, WBENC, 8(a))

2197   FS3, Inc.
        1201 Puerta del Sol, #314   San Clemente, CA
        92673
        (949) 445-3734 Garrett Terlaak Principal
        Fax:
        Email: garrett@fs3h.com
        Website: www.fs3h.com
Project Management, Construction Management, CPM
Scheduling, Cost Estimating, Inspection, Constructibility
Analysis, Risk Management (Hisp, estab 2011, empl 10,
sales $1,200,000, cert: State)

2198   Gaff Group, Inc.
        2698 Junipero Ave, Ste 110   Signal Hill, CA 90755
        (562) 989-3820 Angela Foster Proj Admin
        Fax: (562) 492-6533
        Email: angelafoster@gaffgroup.com
        Website: www.gaffgroup.com
Demolition, concrete, steel stud framing & drywall,
acoustic ceilings/walls, pinting cabinetry, rough & finish
carpentry, plumbing, ceramic tile. (AA, estab 1972, empl
24, sales $5,500,000, cert: State)

2199   Health Education Services
        1000 Varian St, Ste A San Carlos, CA 94070
        (650) 321-6500 Jenny Fernando
        Fax: (561) 752-4181
        Email: jfernando@healtheducationservices.net
        Website: www.healtheducationservices.net
Health Education Services provides turnkey AED program implementation and management - sales, compliance, maintenance, database tracking, training.
(Woman/White, estab 1979, empl 18, sales $900,000,
cert: CPUC, WBENC)

2200 Herca Telecomm Services Inc
      18610 Beck St   Perris, CA 92570
      (951) 940-5941 Hector Castellon CEO
      Fax: (951) 940-5458
      Email: hector.castellon@hercatelecomm.com
      Website: www.hercatelecomm.com
Tower erection, lines & antennas, microwave, general
construction, excavation, trenching, electrical, concrete,
demolition. (Hisp, estab 2005, empl 29, sales $4,035,556,
cert: State)

2201 Hollister Construction Company
      4065 E La Palma Avenue Ste C Anaheim, CA 92807
      (714) 632-1800 Holli Evelyn Carpenter President
      Fax: (714) 000-0000
      Email: holli@hollico.net
      Website: www.hollico.net
General contracting, turn-key design & constuction
services. (Woman/White, estab 1992, empl 12, sales
$2,150,000, cert: CPUC, WBENC)

2202 Interior Plus, Inc.
      8620 Sorenson Ave, Ste 2   Santa Fe Springs, CA
      90670
      (562) 464-6950 Stephen Munoz President
      Fax:
      Email: smunoz@interior-plus-inc.com
      Website: www.interiorplusinc.us
General contracting, commercial & industrial interior
construction & improvements, tenant improvements.
(Hisp, estab 1992, empl 11, sales $2,261,918, cert: CPUC,
8(a))

2203 KW Construction
      841 F St   West Sacramento, CA 95605
      (916) 372-8600 Kevin Wong President
      Fax: (916) 372-8688
      Email: kwong@mgci.com
      Website:
General contracting: electric, plumbing, HVAC, painting,
grading & paving, finish & rough carpentry. (As-Pac, estab
1989, empl 15, sales $4,072,182, cert: State)

2204 Larco Development Inc.
      540 S. Andreasen Dr. Ste E   Escondido, CA 92029
      (951) 201-5126 Paul Larez President
      Fax: (760) 317-1456
      Email: paul@larco-inc.com
      Website: www.larco-inc.com
General contracting, in-house trades: Electrical, HVAC,
Plumbing, Flooring, Concrete/Asphalt, Carpentry/Framing,
Painting, Drywall, Interior Finishes, Underground Utilities,
Communications
Landscape, Irrigation, Demolition. (Hisp, estab 1993, empl
46, sales $7,269,480, cert: 8(a))

2205 Menco Pacific, Inc.
      15110 Keswick St.   Van Nuys, CA 91405
      (760) 747-4405 Jenna Lockstedt Procurement
      Mgr
      Fax: (760) 747-4482
      Email: jlockstedt@menco-pacific.com
      Website: www.menco-pacific.com
Construction services. (Hisp, estab 2007, empl 100, sales
$20,500,000, cert: State, CPUC, 8(a))

2206 MSH Construction Co., Inc.
      15301 Connector Lane   Huntington Beach, CA
      92649
      (714) 899-9509 Lisa Moss President
      Fax: (714) 899-9510
      Email: lmoss@mshconstruction.com
      Website: www.mshconstruction.com
General contractoring: tenant improvement & civil
construction, concrete, demolition, grading & general
maintanence labor. (Woman/White, estab 2003, empl
12, sales $6,679,909, cert: CPUC, WBENC)

2207 MZN Construction, Inc.
      701 N Harbor Blvd   La Habra, CA 90631
      (562) 694-5441 Michael A. Munoz President
      Fax: (562) 694-5622
      Email: mmunoz@mznconstruction.com
      Website: www.mznconstruction.com
General Contracting, Facilities Management & Engineering Construction Management. (Hisp, estab 1984, empl
20, sales $5,400,000, cert: State)

2208 OST Trucks and Cranes, Inc.
      2951 N Ventura Ave P.O. Box 237 Ventura, CA
      93002
      (805) 643-9963 L. Dennis Zermeno President
      Fax: (805) 643-7618
      Email: ostcranes@aol.com
      Website: www.ostcranes.com
General & hazardous substance removal & remedial
action, hydraulic cranes 5 to 140. (Hisp, estab 1947,
empl 69, sales , cert: State, NMSDC, CPUC)

2209 ProWest Engineering, Inc.
      1442 E Lincoln St Ste 360 Orange, CA 92865
      (866) 278-0572 Sherri Barrera Sales/Mktg
      Director
      Fax: (714) 242-0387
      Email: sherri@prowest-engineering.com
      Website: www.prowest-engineering.com
General contracting, asphalt paving removal or
maintainance, concrete repairs, seal/slurry coat,
stenciling & re-striping & ADA compliant (Woman/Hisp,
estab 2005, empl 8, sales $1,500,000, cert: CPUC)

2210   Pub Construction, Inc.
    23441 Golden Springs Dr, Ste 104   Diamond Bar, CA 91765
    (909) 455-0187   Chris Yi President
    Fax: (909) 455-0188
    Email: pubconstruction@yahoo.com
    Website: www.pubconstruction.com
General contracting services, building, carpet, flooring, tile, painting. (As-Pac, estab 2000, empl 13, sales $15,000,000, cert: NMSDC)

2211   Shames Construction
    5826 Brisa St, Ste E   Livermore, CA 94550
    (925) 606-3000   Carolyn Shames President
    Fax: (925) 606-3003
    Email: cshames@shames.com
    Website: www.shames.com
Commercial construction. (Woman/White, estab 1987, empl 50, sales $94,000,000, cert: CPUC)

2212   South City Construction Inc.
    1111 Rancho Conejo Blvd Ste 205   Newbury Park, CA 91320
    (805) 376-2000   Andrew Solimine President
    Fax: (805) 852-7019
    Email: a.solimine@southcityconstruction.com
    Website: www.southcityconstruction.com
General contracting, construction management, program management, value engineering, scheduling, cost estimating. (Woman/White, estab 2011, empl 8, sales $100,000, cert: CPUC)

2213   TGC/The G Crew
    225 E Broadway Ste 202   Glendale, CA 91205
    (818) 240-4157   Ella Daya VP
    Fax:
    Email: info@thegcrew.com
    Website: www.thegcrew.com
Inspection, Construction Management, & Project Support services (Woman/As-Pac, estab 2001, empl 20, sales , cert: CPUC)

2214   True Champions
    5234 Cushman Pl, Ste 200   San Deigo, CA 92110
    (619) 276-6999   Kristi Vega Admin Mgr
    Fax: (619) 276-8783
    Email: kristi@truechampions.net
    Website: www.truechampions.net
General contracting, design build, concrete restoration/ protective coatings, waterproofing & commercial flooring. (Hisp, estab 1995, empl 23, sales , cert: CPUC)

2215   Vanir Construction Management, Inc.
    4540 Duckhorn Dr, Ste 300   Sacramento, CA 95834
    (916) 575-8888   Dorene Dominguez Bus Dev Dir
    Fax: (916) 575-8887
    Email: melinda.guzman@vanir.com
    Website: www.vanir.com
Construction management services. (Woman/Hisp, estab 1980, empl 334, sales $129,308,942, cert: NMSDC, CPUC)

2216   WMB Financial Solutions
    1999 Harrison St Ste 1800   Oakland, CA 94612
    (510) 210-8052   Franck Waota President
    Fax: (415)52588
    Email: fwaota@wmbgc.com
    Website: www.wwww.wmbgc.com
General construction, tenant improvement & remodeling, design build, operation & maintenance of real estate properties (Residential & commercial). (Woman/ AA, estab 2004, empl 25, sales $3,700,000, cert: State, 8(a))

Colorado

2217   Alvarado Construction, Inc.
    924 W Colfax Ave Ste 301   Denver, CO 80204
    (303) 629-0783   Jennifer Coons VP
    Fax: (303) 595-4354
    Email: jcoons@alvaradoconstruction.com
    Website: www.alvaradoconstruction.com
Commercial General Contracting, Construction Manager, Development, Design/Build & Property Management. (Woman/Hisp, estab 1976, empl 50, sales , cert: NMSDC, WBENC)

2218   B&M Construction, Inc.
    3134 Beacon St   Colorado Springs, CO 80907
    (719) 577-4550   Barbara Myrick
    Fax: (719) 577-4560
    Email: bmyrick@bmc-i.com
    Website: www.bmc-i.com
Project Management, Design-Build Services, Furniture Acquisition & Procurement, Electrical Design & Installation, Construction/Infrastructure, Tenant Finish/ Renovation Services, Satellite Communications Repair & Overhaul. (Woman/AA, estab 2005, empl 33, sales $13,000,000, cert: State, NMSDC)

2219   Rhinotrax Construction, Inc.
         1035 Coffman St   Longmont, CO 80501
         (303) 682-9906 Michele Noel President
         Fax: (303) 532-0106
         Email: michelenoel@rhinotrax.com
         Website: www.rhinotraxconstruction.com
General contracting: demolition, rough concrete, masonry,
drywall & framing, doors & hardware, etc. (Woman/White,
estab 2004, empl 12, sales $4,500,000, cert: City)

2220   Tah Yas JV 1
         12655 W 54th Dr   Arvada, CO 80002
         (719) 352-6409 Douglas Wells Dir Business Dev
         Fax:
         Email: dougwells@tahyas.com
         Website: www.tahyas.com
Pre-construction & construction management services.
(Nat Ame, estab 2002, empl 125, sales , cert: 8(a))

2221   Torix General Contractors a Tepa Company
         5045 List Dr   Colorado Springs, CO 80919
         (719) 596-8114 Marvin Maples GM
         Fax: (719) 596-5969
         Email: marvin.maples@tepa.com
         Website: www.tepa.com
New construction & rennovations: design-build, general
contracting & construction management. (Nat Ame, estab
1988, empl 180, sales $105,000,000, cert: NMSDC)

Connecticut

2222   Diggs Construction, LLC
         1010 Wethersfield Ave Ste 201 Hartford, CT 06114
         (860) 296-1664 Derrick Diggs VP
         Fax: (860) 296-1554
         Email: ddiggs@diggsconstruction.com
         Website: www.diggsconstruction.com
Program Management, Construction Management,
Contract Administration & General Contracting solutions.
(AA, estab 1999, empl 35, sales $11,000,000, cert: State,
NMSDC)

2223   TRI-CON Construction Managers, LLC
         59 Amity Rd, Ste 11   New Haven, CT 06515
         (203) 772-4229 Larry Stewart Exec Project Mgr
         Fax: (203) 773-3818
         Email: lmstewart@tri-con.org
         Website: www.tri-con.org
Construction management, general contracting, project
management, value engineering, contract administration,
estimating,owners representation services. (AA, estab
2002, empl 11, sales $58,500, cert: State, NMSDC)

2224   West Reach Construction Company, Inc.
         P.O. Box 1328   Manchester, CT 06045
         (860)6497607 Kerry Hainsey President
         Fax:
         Email: westreachcon@comcast.net
         Website: www.westreachconstruction.com
General contracting, commercial, industrial construction. (Woman/White, estab 1987, empl 18, sales
$10,000,000, cert: WBENC)

District of Columbia

2225   Columbia Enterprises
         1018 7th St SE   Washington, DC 20003
         (202) 547-7979 Bruce Mitchell President
         Fax: (202) 547-4959
         Email: bmitchell@columbiadb.com
         Website: www.columbiadb.com
Construction management & general contracting
services. (AA, estab 1993, empl 15, sales $3,600,000,
cert: State)

2226   Drake Incorporated
         4315 Sheriff Rd NE   Washington, DC 20019
         (202) 291-3174 Stephanie Y Drake CEO
         Fax:
         Email: sdrake@drake-inc.com
         Website: www.drake-inc.com
Construction, design / build & project management.
(Woman/AA, estab 2002, empl 24, sales $7,088,479,
cert: State)

2227   The ELOCEN Group
         1341 H St, NE Ste 301 Washington, DC 20002
         (202) 644-8500 Taryn Lewis Director of Ops
         Fax:
         Email: tarynl@elocengroup.com
         Website: www.elocengroup.com
Program & Project Management, Construction Management, Interior Design, Information Technology, Facilities/
Logistics, and Healthcare Facilities/Logistics/Manage-
ment. (Woman/AA, estab 2007, empl 62, sales
$20,089,894, cert: State, City, WBENC, 8(a))

Florida

2228   Albu & Associates, Inc.
         2711 W Fairbanks Ave   Winter Park, FL 32789
         (407) 788-1450 Jason Albu
         Fax: (407) 788-1463
         Email: jasonalbu@albu.biz
         Website: www.albu.biz
General contracting, design build, construction
management & consulting. (Hisp, estab 1994, empl 20,
sales $20,000,000, cert: City, NMSDC)

2229　Arkren Inc.
6278 N Federal Hwy Ste 430　Fort Lauderdale, FL 33308
(954) 210-8886　Mark Barati Sr VP
Fax: (954) 252-2236
Email: mark@arkren.com
Website: www.arkren.com
Telecommunications, general construction(commercial and residential), design, Procurement, logistics, warehousing, transportation, temporary housing/life support, professional/craft labor, O&G/LNG. (Woman/White, estab 2013, empl 15, sales $960,000, cert: WBENC)

2230　Cortes Construction Services, LLC
720 Anclote Rd　Tarpon Road, FL 34689
(727) 937-4700　Michael Corral VP
Fax: (727) 937-4701
Email: mcorral@cortesconstruction.com
Website: www.cortesconstruction.com
Commercial construction company specializing in hotel renovations. (Hisp, estab 2004, empl 30, sales $5,178,771, cert: State)

2231　Dominion Builders, LLC
4942 S LeJeune Rd Ste 203　Coral Gables, FL 33146
(305) 661-2700　Mark Gemignani President
Fax: (305) 397-1188
Email: mgemignani@dominionbuild.com
Website: www.dominionbuild.com
General contracting services. (Nat Ame, estab 2008, empl 7, sales $5,000,000, cert: State, 8(a))

2232　Fine Line Construction contractors, Inc.
6500 Georgia Ave　Florida, FL 33405
(561) 582-7880　Bob Waskiwicz VP
Fax: (561) 582-7892
Email: bobw@finelinecontractors.com
Website: www.finelinecontractors.com
General contracting, commercial construction, commecial buildout, commercial renovations, interior remodel, building expansion, full buildout, interior improvements, warehouse expansion, warehouse renovations. (Woman/White, estab 2010, empl 15, sales $5,867,874, cert: WBENC)

2233　Hatcher Construction & Development, Inc.
3300 S Congress Ave Ste 15　Boynton Beach, FL 33426
(561) 752-4100　William Hatcher
Fax: (561) 752-4181
Email: hatchergc@bellsouth.net
Website: www.hatcher-construction.com
Commercial Institutional Bldg, General Contractor, Asphalt roofing, Asphalt Coating & Sealing, Concrete, Painting, spraying, or coating, Facilities Support Mgmt, Electrical, Residential Construction, multifamily, Landscaping. (AA, estab 1999, empl 7, sales $1,350,000, cert: State, 8(a))

2234　Nakitare Builders LLC
11806 Foxglove Dr　Clermont, FL 34711
(352) 857-0000　Robert Mack GM
Fax: (407) 391-3777
Email: Buld2006@aol.com
Website: www.sustainable-roofs.com
Construction services, inspections. (AA, estab 2006, empl 5, sales $390,000, cert: NMSDC)

2235　R L Burns Inc.
1203 W Gore St　Orlando, FL 32805
(407) 839-1131　Jessica Burns
Fax: (407) 839-1185
Email: jburns@rlburnsinc.com
Website: www.rlburnsinc.com
Construction management svcs: project management, consulting, cost estimating, pre-construction planning & design, schedule / CPM management, general construction, design/build, new construction, renovation. (AA, estab 1994, empl 9, sales $3,000,000, cert: State)

2236　Stoner Construction, Inc.
100 SW 101st Terr　Plantation, FL 33324
(954) 474-8460　Lynn Stoner President
Fax: (954) 252-2152
Email: lynnstoner@aol.com
Website:
General contracting: residential renovations, additions & commercial tenant improvements. (Woman/White, estab 2004, empl 9, sales , cert: City)

2237　T&G Corporation
8623 Commodity Circle　Orlando, FL 32819
(407) 352-4443　Mark Knott Director of Business Dev & Mktg
Fax: (407) 352-0778
Email: officedepot@t-and-g.com
Website: www.t-and-g.com
General contracting: facility operation/maintenance support services, commercial building, construction management & design-build services. (Hisp, estab 1987, empl 85, sales $23,214,524, cert: State, NMSDC)

2238　Thomco Enterprises Inc.
745 Hollywood Blvd NW　Fort Walton Beach, FL 32548
(850) 244-0811　Darryl Embrey President
Fax: (850) 244-4924
Email: darryle@thomcoent.com
Website: www.thomcoent.com
Construction, construction management, facility maintenance, renovations, upgrades, vertical construction, bank facility construction, commercial & government construction, development, project management. (AA, estab 1993, empl 35, sales $11,245,342, cert: State)

2239 Thornton Construction Company, Inc.
      4300 Biscayne Blvd, Ste 207   Miami, FL 33137
      (305) 649-1995 Nataly Guevara Business Devel Mgr
      Fax: (714) 821-0009
      Email: businessdevelopment@thornton-inc.com
      Website: www.thornton-inc.com
Contracting and construction management firm. (Hisp, estab 1998, empl 55, sales $36,613,094, cert: State)

2240 Validus Construction Services LLC
      7130 S Orange Blossom Trail Ste 111 Orlando, FL 32809
      (407) 413-5022 Nicole Wickens Owner
      Fax: (407) 674-8985
      Email: validuscs@gmail.com
      Website: www.validuscs.net
New construction, remodel, remediation, design-build, renovation, office renovations, warehouse renovations, landscaping, parking lot, sidewalks, windows, doors, flooring, interiors, exteriors, HVAC, plumbing, electrical. (Woman/White, estab 2012, empl 9, sales $183,430, cert: WBENC)

Georgia

2241 Colliers Facility Solutions, LLC
      1230 Peachtree St Ste 800 Atlanta, GA 30309
      (404) 574-1014 Holly Hughes CEO
      Fax: (404) 574-1114
      Email: holly.hughes@colliers.com
      Website: www.colliers.com/en-us/atlanta/services
Facility management, project management, construction management, interior, exterior & maintenance, energy efficiency, systems optimization, risk mitigation & cost savings. (Woman/White, estab 2014, empl 115, sales $1,566,887, cert: WBENC)

2242 Hawk Construction Company LLC
      158 Fairview Rd Ste E Ellenwood, GA 30294
      (678) 565-5120 Miles Traylor CEO
      Fax: (678) 565-7950
      Email: mhawkconstruction@yahoo.com
      Website: www.mhawkconstruction.com
General contracting, commercial new construction, facility maintenance, landscaping & tenant improvement. (AA, estab 2003, empl 3, sales $217,000, cert: NMSDC)

2243 Pinnacle Services Group, Inc.
      10270 Oxford Mill Circle   Alpharetta, GA 30022
      (770) 355-7156 Jerry Peljovich President
      Fax: (770) 754-0058
      Email: Jerryp@PSGinc-ga.com
      Website: www.PSGinc-ga.com
General contracting. (Hisp, estab 2004, empl 5, sales $3,207,000, cert: State, City, NMSDC)

2244 Pioneer Construction, Inc.
      31 Park of Commerce Way Ste 100 Savannah, GA 31405
      (912) 650-1850 Whitney Butler Dir Mktg/brand
      Fax: (912) 650-1851
      Email: wbutler@pioneersavannah.com
      Website: www.pioneersavannah.com
General Contractors specializing in commercial construction. (Woman/As-Pac, estab 1994, empl 20, sales $10,000,000, cert: State)

2245 Synergy Development Partners, LLC
      83 Walton St, NW Ste 400 Atlanta, GA 30303
      (404) 254-4755 Ralph Phillips Ops Mgr
      Fax: (404) 254-4742
      Email: rphillips@synergydp.com
      Website: www.synergydp.com
General contracting, construction management, drywall, framing, renovation, restoration, roof repair, carpentry, flooring, paint, trim, tentant build-out & new construction. (Woman/AA, estab 2003, empl 8, sales , cert: State, City, 8(a))

2246 The Chester Group, Inc.
      231 Peters St SW   Atlanta, GA 30313
      (786) 586-3941 Wallace Chester President
      Fax: (404) 549-4384
      Email: wchester@thechestergroup.com
      Website: www.thechestergroup.com
General contracting & construction mgmt: renovation; design/build; maintenance; roofing; concrete placement; debris removal; fencing; asphalt resurfacing; masonry; interior build-out; windows; doors; painting; flooring; electrical. (AA, estab 2002, empl 1, sales $100,000, cert: State)

2247 Time Out Systems, Inc.
      308 Indian Creek Circle   Adel, GA 31620
      (229) 896-6190 Tim LeBlanc CFO
      Fax: (866) 210-3044
      Email: admin@timeoutsystems.com
      Website: www.timeoutsystems.com
General Construction, Remolding, Roofing, Painting, Security, Surround Sound, Televisions, Home Automation, Yard Maintenance, Door and Window Replacement, Blind Installation, Deck Construction, Bathroom Remolding. (Woman/White, estab 1991, empl 120, sales $6,000,000, cert: WBENC)

Iowa

2248 Gethmann Construction Company, Inc.
P.O. Box 160   Marshalltown, IA 50158
(641) 753-3555 Jill Craft President
Fax: (866) 561-7550
Email: jill@gethmann.com
Website: www.gethmannconstruction.com
Concrete work, excavation, backfill, foundations, slabs, pads, elevated slabs, concrete demo, structural steel fab, crane rental & operators. (Woman/White, estab 1937, empl 67, sales $22,000,000, cert: WBENC)

2249 Knight Eagle Contracting Group, Inc.
P.O. Box 5305   Coralville, IA 52241
(319) 338-7360 Steve Marshall Business Dev Mgr
Fax: (319) 338-7361
Email: smarshall@knighteagle.net
Website: www.knighteagle.net
Construction Services, General Contractor, Construction Management, Commercial Roofing,
Professional Services, Staff Augmentation, Administration, Engineering, Safety. (Woman/Nat Ame/Hisp, estab 2010, empl 3, sales , cert: 8(a))

Illinois

2250 CREA Construction
161 N Clark, Ste 4700   Chicago, IL 60601
(312) 371-3827 Rea Johnson President
Fax: (877) 711-2732
Email: rea1_23@yahoo.com
Website: www.creagc.com
Construction management, general contracting, estimating & engineering services. (Woman/AA, estab 2007, empl 10, sales $1,000,000, cert: State, NMSDC, 8(a))

2251 GACC Video Electronics Inc.
700 Nicholas Blvd Ste 103 Elk Grove Village, IL 60007
(312) 733-5774 Jennifer Chang Sec/Treas
Fax: (312) 733-5320
Email: jennifer@gaccvideo.com
Website: www.gaccvideo.com
Audio and Video Service and repair. Audio and Video Sales of microphones, cameras, decks, monitors in such brands as Sony, Lectrosonics, Sound Devices, Josephson, Sanken, Panasonic, JVC, Canon, Fujinon. Audio Video Rental in (Woman/As-Pac, estab 2000, empl 3, sales $450,000, cert: City)

2252 Integrated Construction Technology Corp.
126 S Villa Ave   Villa Park, IL 60181
(630) 993-1800 Les Shy President
Fax: (630) 993-1809
Email: lshy@integratedusa.com
Website:
Design & build construction, general contracting, property managment, supplies & services. (AA/As-Pac, estab 1994, empl 30, sales $18,000,000, cert: City)

2253 Otis Construction Company
111 W Jackson Blvd Ste 1105 Chicago, IL 60604
(312) 786-9877 Glenn Otis, Jr. President
Fax: (312) 786-9878
Email: gotis@otiscc.com
Website: www.otiscc.com
Construction svcs: interior building alterations, commercial & industrial facilities, green construction & maintenance, specialty projects, facilities maintenance, emergency repairs. (AA, estab 1999, empl 4, sales $1,500,000, cert: NMSDC, 8(a))

2254 Sumac Inc.
3701 N Ravenswood Ave Ste 202 Chicago, IL 60613
(773) 857-7906 Liliana Gonzalez VP
Fax: (773) 857-7905
Email: lgonzalez@sumacinc.com
Website: www.sumacinc.com
Architecture & construction management: architectural design, sustainable design, project scheduling, cost estimating, construction procurement, construction management services & general contracting. (Hisp, estab 2008, empl 10, sales $2,000,000, cert: NMSDC)

2255 The Landmark Group Companies LLC
6735 Vistagreen Way Ste 100 Rockford, IL 61107
(815) 639-0034 Bob Sanches CEO
Fax: (815) 639-0029
Email: bsanches@lmcos.com
Website: www.lmcos.com
Construction management of new & existing facilities. (Hisp, estab 2006, empl 8, sales $30,500,000, cert: NMSDC)

2256 Total Response Technology, LLC
1921 Richfield Ave   Highland Park, IL 60035
(312) 513-0478 Sandra Bast President
Fax: (225) 356-1709
Email: sandra@trt-llc.com
Website: www.totalresponsetechnology.com
Total Response Technology (TRT) increases your profitability by leveraging temporary specialized professionals to implement or maintain your IT investments. By using TRT for your business processing needs, goals are met (Woman/Hisp, estab 2009, empl 20, sales $1,400,000, cert: City)

2257 Trinidad Construction, LLC
      18505 West Creek Dr Ste 1B Tinley Park, IL 60477
      (773) 429-4600 Brian Ortiz President
      Fax: (773) 429-4601
      Email: bortiz@trinidadllc.com
      Website: www.trinidadllc.com
General contracting, construction management. (Hisp, estab 2010, empl 75, sales $25,000,000, cert: NMSDC)

2258 Vistara Construction Services, Inc.
      728 W Jackson Blvd, Ste 402 Chicago, IL 60661
      (312) 986-8660 Bina Nair President
      Fax: (312) 986-9530
      Email: info@vistara.com
      Website: www.vistara.com
General construction. (Woman/As-Ind, estab 1994, empl 10, sales , cert: City)

Indiana

2259 Custom Mechanical Systems, Corp.
      691 Industrial Blvd Bargersville, IN 46106
      (617) 803-0714 William Beach VP of Business Devel
      Fax: (317) 422-4470
      Email: wbeach@cms-corporation.com
      Website: www.cms-corporation.com
New construction, renovations, energy & sustainability, building operations maintenance & repairs. (Hisp, estab 1996, empl 110, sales $42,753,323, cert: State, NMSDC)

2260 Finch Constructors, Inc.
      5528 W 84th St P.O. Box 681275 Indianapolis, IN 46268
      (317) 916-6770 Tammy Brooks Ops Mgr
      Fax: (317) 916-6774
      Email: tbrooks@finchconstructors.com
      Website: www.finchconstructors.com
Industrial, commercial & municipal construction & management services: mechanical piping, equipment erection, HVAC & electrical services. (AA, estab 2004, empl 42, sales $20,000,000, cert: NMSDC)

2261 Harmon Construction, Inc.
      621 S State St P.O. Box 386 North Vernon, IN 47265
      (812) 346-2048 Ardell Mitchell Sr Project Mgr/Estimator
      Fax: (812) 346-2054
      Email: ardell.mitchell@harmonconstruction.com
      Website: www.harmonconstruction.com
Contracting, design-build capabilities. (AA, estab 1955, empl 81, sales $8,478,000, cert: State, NMSDC)

2262 K&S Construction Group, Inc.
      9148 Louisiana St, Unit F Merrillville, IN 46410
      (219) 794-9550 Vance R. Kenney CEO
      Fax: (219) 794-9551
      Email: vkenney@k-sconstruction.com
      Website: www.k-sconstruction.com
Heavy construction, construction mgmt, demolition, design build, excavation, reinforced concrete, concrete forming, sidewalk, curb, crushed granite, levees, revetments, carpentry, railroad construction, fencing, environmental. (AA, estab 1992, empl 25, sales $3,200,000, cert: State, NMSDC)

2263 Powers & Sons Construction Co, Inc.
      2636 W 15th Ave Gary, IN 46404
      (219) 949-3100 Kelly Powers Baria Dir Business Dev
      Fax: (219) 949-5906
      Email: kbaria@powersandsons.com
      Website: www.powersandsons.com
Construction svcs. (AA, estab 1967, empl 50, sales $30,390,330, cert: State, NMSDC)

2264 Pyro Industrial Services
      6610 Shepherd Ave Portage, IN 46368
      (219)75700 Terry McNew President
      Fax: (219) 787-0700
      Email: tmcnew@pyroindustrial.com
      Website: www.pyroindustrial.com
General contracting & refractory, refractory, brick, gunite, shotcrete & fiber installation, induction change outs, storage & rebuilds, steel conditioners, fluxes & additives, slag conditioners, alloys, desulfurizers & lime products. (Woman/White, estab 1975, empl 500, sales $22,000,000, cert: State, WBENC)

2265 Shawnee Construction and Engineering
      7701 Opportunity Dr Fort Wayne, IN 46825
      (260) 489-1234 Matt Schenkel President
      Fax: (260) 489-3402
      Email: Matt@ShawneeConstruction.com
      Website: www.ShawneeConstruction.com
General contracting, new construction & remodeling, commercial & industrial. (Hisp, estab 1968, empl 42, sales $17,300,000, cert: State, City)

2266 Taylor Bros. Construction Co, Inc.
      4555 Middle Rd Columbus, IN 47203
      (812) 379-9547 Jeffrey Chandler VP
      Fax: (812) 372-4759
      Email: jchandler@tbcci.com
      Website: www.tbcci.com
General contracting & construction mgmt svcs. (AA, estab 1933, empl 100, sales $24,000,000, cert: NMSDC)

Kansas

2267   NCRI-National Catastrophe Restoration, Inc.
8447 E 35th St N   Wichita, KS 67226
(800) 598-6274   Reuben Kerbs VP of Natl Accts
Fax: (316) 636-5712
Email: r.kerbs@ncricat.com
Website: www.ncricat.com
Emergency restoration svcs: fire, water, smoke, wind, mold, emergency dry out, structure repair, document & record restoration, mold remediation, dry ice blasting, airduct cleaning, drying equipment rental. (Woman/White, estab 1971, empl 90, sales $12,500,000, cert: WBENC)

Louisiana

2268   Lafayette Steel Erector
313 Westgate Rd   Lafayette, LA 70506
(337)2349435   John Prudhomme President
Fax:
Email: janice@l-s-e.com
Website: www.LSEcrane.com
Crane, steel erection, precast erectors, equipment installation. (Nat Ame, estab 1957, empl 115, sales , cert: NMSDC)

2269   Tillage Construction LLC
1824 N Acadian Thruway W   Baton Rouge, LA 70802
(225) 356-1700   Etonya Senigaur
Fax: (225) 356-1709
Email: esenigaur@tillageconstruction.com
Website: www.tillageconstruction.com
Commercial building construction, commercial renovations, project manaagement, cabinets & millwork. (AA, estab 2001, empl 8, sales , cert: State)

2270   Triple L Management Corp.
1181 Hawn Ave   Shreveport, LA 71107
(318) 424-8037   O. J. Romero Dir Mktg
Fax: (318) 424-0018
Email: ojr@lllconstruction.com
Website: www.lllconstruction.com
Construction services: concrete, dirt, pipe laying, building construction & renovation, industrial plant renovations & shutdown project, etc. (AA, estab 1979, empl 72, sales $7,200,000, cert: State)

Massachusetts

2271   Essex Newbury North Contracting Corporation
65 Parker St, Unit 5   Newburyport, MA 01950
(978) 463-5414   Delano Brooks President
Fax: (978) 463-5415
Email: delano_br@yahoo.com
Website: www.essexnewburynorth.com
General Contracting, construction management, commercial & industrial construction, lead abatement & asbestos remediation, finish carpentry, commercial & institutional bldg construction, painting & wall coverings, site preparation. (AA, estab 1997, empl 400, sales $31,000,000, cert: State, City, NMSDC)

2272   J&J Contractors, Inc.
101 Billerica Ave Bldg 5 Ste 2   North Billerica, MA 01862
(978) 452-9898   Kamlesh Patel CEO
Fax: (978) 452-3796
Email: KamP@jjcontractor.com
Website: www.jjcontractor.com
Construction management, general contracting & design/build. (As-Ind, estab 1997, empl 23, sales , cert: State)

Maryland

2273   Buch Construction Inc.
11292 Buch Way   Laurel, MD 20723
(301) 369-3500   Denise Buch Controller
Fax: (301) 369-3501
Email: dbuch@buch.us.com
Website: www.buchconstruction.com
General contracting, interior construction, carpentry, drywall, electric, painting, new construction, doors & hardware, structural steel. (Woman/White, estab 1984, empl 65, sales $6,210,000, cert: WBENC)

2274   Estime Enterprises, Inc.
4640 Forbes Blvd Ste 100   Lanham, MD 20706
(301) 731-8316   Lunique Estime President
Fax: (301) 731-9779
Email: lestime@estimeinc.com
Website: www.estimeinc.com
Construction management, renovation, environmental consulting services, green sustainable solutions (wind power generation, solar harvesting, triban antimicrobial systems, and photovoltaic roofing solutions). (AA, estab 1996, empl 35, sales $4,296,512, cert: State, NMSDC)

Michigan

2275 Blaze Contracting, Inc.
5640 St. Jean   Detroit, MI 48213
(313) 361-1000 Gayl Turk Dir Business Dev
Fax: (313) 361-6850
Email: gturk@blazecontracting.net
Website: www.blazecontracting.com
Site Preparation Contractor; Excavation, Grading, Storm
Sewer, Sanitary Sewer, Watermain, Water Detention
Systems; (AA, estab 2000, empl 120, sales $19,000,000,
cert: NMSDC)

2276 Commercial Construction Inc.
7428 Kensington Rd   Brighton, MI 48116
(248) 685-3263 ROBERT L. GARCIA President
Fax: (248) 685-9892
Email: pgarcia@cci-rigging.com
Website: www.cci-rigging.com
Millwright & migging contractor, install machinery, convey-
ors, robots, automation for automotive industry, industrial
process. (Hisp, estab 1991, empl 40, sales $3,100,000, cert:
NMSDC)

2277 Construction Logistic LLC
1360 Oakman Blvd   Detroit, MI 48238
(313) 494-5527 Eric Means
Fax: (888) 758-7908
Email: emeans@meansgroup.com
Website:
Construction management, General Contracting, Design/
Build, Program Management, Owner Representation,
Development & Property Management. (AA, estab 2009,
empl 3, sales $3,476,219, cert: NMSDC)

2278 Hale Contracting, Inc.
18407 Weaver St   Detroit, MI 48228
(313) 272-9400 Lawrence Hale President
Fax: (313) 272-5264
Email: lawrence.hale@halecontracting.com
Website: www.Halecontracting.com
General contracting. (AA, estab , empl 1, sales , cert:
NMSDC)

2279 Hamilton Contracting
30375 Northwestern Hwy Ste 102   Farmington Hills,
MI 48334
(734) 895-3547 Melissa Grundy Business Dev Exec
Fax: (248) 630-7011
Email: mgrundy@hamilton-contracting.com
Website: www.hamilton-contracting.com
General contracting: demolition, machinery installation &
relocation, conveyor installation, structural installation,
platform installation, automation installation, preventative
maintenance & machine precision alignments. (Woman/
White, estab 2011, empl 45, sales $5,400,000, cert:
WBENC)

2280 Ideal Contracting, LLC
2525 Clark St   Detroit, MI 48209
(313) 843-8000 Kevin Foucher VP
Fax: (313) 843-2532
Email: kfoucher@idealcontracting.com
Website: www.idealcontracting.com
General contracting, construction management &
design/build services. (Hisp, estab 1998, empl 325, sales
$191,613,602, cert: NMSDC)

2281 Jenkins Construction, Inc.
985 E Jefferson, Ste 300   Detroit, MI 48207
(313) 625-7200 Darwyn Parks Project Exec
Fax: (313) 625-7209
Email: dparks@jenkinsconstruction.com
Website: www.jenkinsconstruction.com
Design/build, construction management, general
contractor & excavation. (AA, estab 1989, empl 50, sales
$65,000,000, cert: NMSDC)

2282 McKissack & McKissack Midwest, Inc.
1300 Broadway St 5th Fl Detroit, MI 48225
(313) 962-6900 Hansel Whiteurst VP
Fax: (312) 751-1667
Email: solicitationsmw@mckinc.com
Website: www.mckinc.com
Architectural, engineering, and construction services.
(Woman/AA, estab 2002, empl 35, sales $5,602,457,
cert: NMSDC, WBENC)

2283 Optimum Contracting Solutions
2211 Devonshire Rd   Bloomfield Hills, MI 48302
(248) 346-3069 Anamaria Tet Owner
Fax: (248) 732-7171
Email: anamaria.optimum@att.net
Website: www.optimum1.net
General Contracting, Project Management, Residential
Building & Remodeling Services , Commercial Remodeling Services, Roofing, Siding, Additions, Drywall, Rough
and Finish Carpentry ,Painting, Electrical, HVAC, Doors &
window installation. (Woman/White, estab 2010, empl
10, sales $400,000, cert: WBENC)

2284 PAT USA, Inc.
2927 Waterview Dr   Rochester Hills, MI 48309
(248) 299-2410 Fenar Mayes Sr Project Mgr
Fax: (248) 299-2413
Email: fenar@pat-engineering.com
Website: www.pat-engineering.com
General contracting services, engineering & construction services. (Woman/White, estab 2011, empl 10,
sales , cert: WBENC)

2285   Payne Landscaping, Inc.
       5385 Rohns   Detroit, MI 48213
       (313) 995-2767 James Parker Sr VP of Ops
       Fax: (313) 924-0301
       Email: communicate2000@earthlink.net
       Website:
Landscape construction, grounds maintenance, janitorial, facilities management, tree services, lawn care, snow removal. (AA, estab 1989, empl 25, sales $500,000, cert: NMSDC)

2286   R.B. Construction Company
       6489 Metro Pkwy   Sterling Heights, MI 48312
       (586) 264-9478 Russell Beaver President
       Fax: (586) 446-4685
       Email: rbeaver@rb-construction.com
       Website: www.rb-construction.com
Construction, renovation, building, pre-engineered building, remodel. (Nat Ame, estab 1984, empl 7, sales $3,318,000, cert: NMSDC, 8(a))

2287   Rickman Enterprise Group, LLC
       15533 Woodrow Wilson   Detroit, MI 48238
       (313) 454-4000 Lawrence Bost CEO
       Fax: (313) 454-4011
       Email: lawrence@rickmanenterprise.com
       Website: www.RickmanEnterprise.com
Industrial Painting/Environmental, Flooring, Demo. (AA, estab 2007, empl 131, sales $5,800,000, cert: NMSDC)

2288   Sieler Construction
       11119 E US 223   Blissfield, MI 49228
       (517) 486-3050 Jeff Sieler VP
       Fax:
       Email: lue@sielerconstruction.com
       Website: www.sielerconstruction.com
General Contracting, excavation, concrete, steel trades, steel fabrication, holding tanks, shut-down / machinery relocation, water & fire main repairs, water lines. (Woman, estab 2000, empl 12, sales , cert: WBENC)

2289   Stenco Construction Company, LLC
       12741 Farmington Rd   Livonia, MI 48150
       (734) 427-8843 Rick Kolozsi President
       Fax: (734) 427-8871
       Email: rkolozsi@stencoconstruction.com
       Website: www.stencoconstruction.com
General contruction: interior finish, earthwork, concrete, steel & rigging projects. (As-Pac, estab 1998, empl 20, sales $33,650,000, cert: NMSDC)

2290   The FOG Group, Inc.
       217 Fisher Building 3011 W Grand Blvd. Detroit, MI 48202
       (313) 309-2020 Sherwood Merrill Chairman
       Fax: (313) 309-2007
       Email: smerrill@powerlinkonline.com
       Website: www.powerlinkonline.com
Facilities management, maintenance services, & construction. (AA, estab 2002, empl 350, sales $15,900,000, cert: NMSDC)

2291   The Ideal Group
       2525 Clark St   Detroit, MI 48209
       (313) 842-7290 Linzie Venegas Sales
       Fax: (313) 842-7860
       Email: linzie@idealshield.com
       Website: www.weareideal.com
Architectural & engineering svcs; general contracting & construction mgmt, rigging. Mfr, dist, fabricate & erect structural & misc steel. Patent for "Ideal Shield" Protective Guard Rail System. (Hisp, estab 1979, empl 120, sales , cert: NMSDC)

2292   Tooles Contracting Group LLC
       500 Griswold St, Ste 1620   Detroit, MI 48226
       (313) 221-8500 Laura Ottman Mgr Business Dev
       Fax: (313) 221-8501
       Email: laura.ottman@toolesgroup.com
       Website: www.toolesgroup.com
Commercial & industrial construction, general contracting, construction & pogram management, equipment installation, self perform services & design build. (AA, estab 2002, empl 38, sales $119,996,211, cert: NMSDC)

2293   W-3 Construction Company
       7601 Second Ave   Detroit, MI 48202
       (313) 875-8000 Walter E. Watson, Jr. President
       Fax: (313) 875-4711
       Email: w3@w3group.net
       Website:
General contracting, project managers, self perform concrete, drywall & accoustical. (AA, estab 1987, empl 49, sales $19,901,023, cert: NMSDC)

2294   Zebing Solutions LLC
       15617 Marksman Rd   Lanse, MI 49946
       (877) 585-8171 Arlan Friisvall President
       Fax: (810) 519-4997
       Email: info@zebingsolutions.com
       Website: www.zebingsolutions.com
Construction, electrical, mechanical & engineering services. (Nat Ame, estab 2011, empl 20, sales $500,000, cert: NMSDC)

Minnesota

2295 Loeffler Construction and Consulting, LLC
20520 Keokuk Ave, Ste 100   Lakeville, MN 55044
(952) 955-9119 Doug Loeffler President
Fax: (952) 236-9960
Email: dloeffler@loefflerconstruction.com
Website: www.loefflerconstruction.com
Construction and consulting services, new construction & remodeling projects. (Woman/Nat Ame, estab 2010, empl 6, sales $21,922,187, cert: NMSDC)

2296 Moltron Builders Inc.
2900 North 2nd St   Minneapolis, MN 55411
(612) 354-2730 Patrick Buckner President
Fax: (763) 432-7988
Email: patrick.buckner@moltronbuilders.com
Website: www.moltronbuilders.com
General Construction, Construction Management & Design Build. (AA, estab 2007, empl 5, sales , cert: State, City)

2297 Shaw-Lundquist Associates, Inc.
2757 W Service Rd   St. Paul, MN 55121
(651) 454-0670 Joni Bonnell Business Dev Dir
Fax: (651) 454-7982
Email: info@shawlundquist.com
Website: www.shawlundquist.com
General construction & mgmt: commercial, industrial & institutional, multi-unit residential, tenant improvements, contract service work, etc. (As-Pac, estab 1974, empl 60, sales $121,348,000, cert: NMSDC)

2298 Tarraf Construction, Inc.
7454 Washington Ave S   Eden Prairie, MN 55344
(612) 623-4800 Salah Tarraf President
Fax: (612) 623-0995
Email: salah-tarraf@tarrafconstruction.com
Website: www.tarrafconstruction.com
General construction, site development earthwork, site utilities, demolition, carpentry, environment, specialty maintenance, disposal system, supplies. (Hisp, estab 2001, empl 15, sales , cert: State, City, NMSDC)

2299 THOR Construction Inc.
5400 NE Main St, Ste 203   Minneapolis, MN 55421
(763) 571-2580 Lisa M. Crawford Exec Asst
Fax: (763) 571-2631
Email: thormail@thorcon.net
Website: www.thorcon.net
General contracting, construction mgmt, design/build, rough carpentry & concrete. (AA, estab 1980, empl 150, sales $67,600,000, cert: NMSDC)

2300 Welsh Construction, LLC
4350 Baker Rd Ste 400 Minnetonka, MN 55343
(952) 897-7854 Linda Solberg Corporate Services Director
Fax: (952) 842-7654
Email: lsolberg@welshco.com
Website: www.welshconstruct.com
General contracting, commercial new construction, office & industrial, expansions & renovations of existing office & industrial space. (Woman/White, estab 1977, empl 43, sales $73,308,502, cert: WBENC)

Missouri

2301 Amodu Engineering Solutions, LLC
1201 Garden Village Dr   Florissant, MO 63031
(314) 249-8623 Anthony Osuma President
Fax: (512) 219-7700
Email: aosuma@amodu-engineering.com
Website: www.amodu-engineering.com
Mechanical design & consulting services, electrical plumbing & fire protection systems, construction admin services. (AA, estab 2007, empl 5, sales $100,000, cert: State, City, NMSDC)

2302 Legacy Building Group
3242 S. Kingshighway   Saint Louis, MO 63139
(314) 361-3535 Todd Weaver President
Fax: (314) 361-3838
Email: weavert@legacybg.com
Website: www.legacybg.com
Doors & frames installation & concrete footings & foundations. (AA, estab 2003, empl 20, sales $7,123,000, cert: State, City, NMSDC)

2303 Tarlton Corporation
5500 W Park Ave   St. Louis, MO 63110
(314) 633-3354 Ted Guhr Director of Business Dev
Fax: (314) 647-1940
Email: TAGuhr@tarltoncorp.com
Website: www.tarltoncorp.com
General contracting & construction management. (Woman/White, estab 1945, empl 350, sales $207,000,000, cert: State, WBENC)

2304 Tehama, LLC
1600 Genessee Ste 318 Kansas City, MO 64102
(816) 678-7510 David Brewer GM
Fax:
Email: david.brewer@tehamallc.com
Website: www.tehamallc.com
Engineering/Architectural design, Environmental Consulting Services & Construction Support Services. (Nat Ame, estab 2009, empl 2, sales $52,275, cert: 8(a))

North Carolina

2305 Crescent Construction Services, LLC
303 S Main GQ St   Salisbury, NC 28146
(704) 633-9697 Traci Williams President
Fax: (704) 633-2795
Email: traci@crescentconstructionservices.com
Website: www.crescentconstructionservices.com
Commissioning & engineering surveys, project management. (Woman/White, estab 2004, empl 15, sales $1,310,000, cert: WBENC)

2306 Golden Sands General Contractors
10924 Granite St, Ste 700   Charlotte, NC 28273
(704) 727-6000 Jody Pinkston Project Coord
Fax: (704) 817-9811
Email: jody.pinkston@goldensandsgc.com
Website: www.goldensandsgc.com
Design/Build, New Construction, Tenant Improvements, Major & Minor Renovations, Dedicated Facilities Maintenance Department, Dedicated Disaster Recovery Department. (Woman/White, estab 1988, empl 167, sales $62,000,000, cert: WBENC)

2307 Holt Brothers Construction LLC
421 Fayetteville St Stes 1300 Raleigh, NC 27601
(919) 787-1981 Patrice Gilmore VP Diversity & Inclusion
Fax: (919) 787-8666
Email: pgilmore@holtbrothersinc.com
Website: www.holtbrothersconstruction.com
Construction management, design-build & general contracting services. (AA, estab 2007, empl 28, sales $2,021,973, cert: State)

2308 Marand Builders, Inc.
4534 Old Pineville Rd Ste A   Charlotte, NC 28217
(704) 525-1824 Francisco Alvarado CEO
Fax: (704) 544-8819
Email: falvarado@marandbuilders.com
Website: www.marandbuilders.com
Commercial & industrial general contracting: demolition, new construction & renovations. (Hisp, estab 1999, empl 15, sales $2,500,011, cert: NMSDC)

2309 Metcon Inc.
763 Comtech Dr   Pembroke, NC 28372
(910) 521-8013 Aaron Thomas CEO
Fax: (910) 521-8014
Email: athomas@metconus.com
Website: www.metconus.com
General contracting, panelized metal studs & truss. (Nat Ame, estab 1999, empl 75, sales $24,180,330, cert: NMSDC)

2310 Miles McClellan Construction Co., Inc.
2201-E Crownpoint Executive Dr   Charlotte, NC 28227
(704) 900-1170 Melia Mauldin Sales & Mktg Coord
Fax:
Email: melia.mauldin@mmbuildings.com
Website: www.mmbuildings.com
Design & build, construction mgmt, general contracting, masonry. (AA, estab 1978, empl 75, sales $50,889,458, cert: State, NMSDC)

2311 Modern Construction Services, LLC
20464 Chartwell Center Dr, Ste E P.O. Box 92 Cornelius, NC 28031
(704) 765-9937 Tracy Snowdy President
Fax: (980) 231-5564
Email: tsnowdy@modernconstructionsvc.com
Website: www.modernconstructionsvc.com
General Contractor & Facility Repairs, Interior demolition & up-fits, exterior refreshes, parking lot repairs/resurfacing, doors, windows, drywall, painting, rough & finish carpentry, ADA upgrades. (Woman/White, estab 2015, empl 10, sales $978,644, cert: State, City, WBENC)

2312 R.J. Leeper Construction, LLC
601 Morris St   Charlotte, NC 28202
(704) 334-3223 Ron Leeper V.P. Business Dev
Fax: (704) 348-1898
Email: ronl@leeperconstruction.com
Website: www.leeperconstruction.com
Construction management & general contracting. (AA, estab 1993, empl 20, sales $12,541,795, cert: State)

2313 Red Rooster Contractors, LLC
5101 Summer Gate Dr   Charlotte, NC 28226
(704) 634-4622 Milagritos Aguilar CEO
Fax:
Email: mily.aguilar19@gmail.com
Website:
Commercial & residential: roofing, windows, doors, painting, gutters, flooring, carpentry interior & exterior renovations. (Woman/Hisp, estab 2009, empl 1, sales $250,000, cert: City)

2314 Sutton Industrial Maintenance & Piping, Inc.
P.O. Box146 Castalia, NC 27816
(919) 853-6901 Kim Sutton President
Fax: (919) 853-9901
Email: suttonkim@embarqmail.com
Website:
General contract services, sheet metal fabrication, boiler room, welding, pipefitting, general labor, mechanical work. (Woman/White, estab 2001, empl 12, sales $1,047,068, cert: WBENC)

New Jersey

2315 Argent Associates, Inc.
140 Fieldcrest Ave   Edison, NJ 08837
(732) 512-9009 William Donadio VP Supply Chain
Fax: (732) 512-9549
Email: bdonadio@argentassociates.com
Website: www.argentassociates.com
Inventory mgmt, warehousing, dist, logistics, packaging, installation & commercial construction. (Woman/Hisp, estab 1998, empl 30, sales $181,676,013, cert: NMSDC, WBENC)

2316 BTII Institute
414 Eagle Rock Ave, Ste 100 D   West Orange, NJ 07052
(973) 325-9001 Sharon Bussey CEO
Fax: (813) 855-5665
Email: sharon.bussey@btiitraining.com
Website: www.btiitraining.com/
BTII Institute is a consulting and training company specializing in Project Management, Professional Development and Microsoft. BTII's Portfolio/Program/Project Management services better enable organizations to achieve strategic objectives and a sustaina (Woman/AA, estab 2009, empl 1, sales $158,000, cert: NMSDC)

2317 Ferreira Construction Co Inc.
31 Tannery Rd   Branchburg, NJ 08876
(908) 534-8655 Megan Carton Dir of Mktg
Fax: (908) 534-7763
Email: MCARTON@ferreiraconstruction.com
Website: www.ferreiraconstruction.com
Utility Construction: Gas, Transmission and Distribution, Foundations, Water, Sewer, Fiber Optic. Heavy Civil Construction: Bridges, Highways, Airports, Excavation, Sitework
Marine Construction: Dredging, Seawalls, Docks/Piers (Hisp, estab 1988, empl 1000, sales $350,000,000, cert: State, City, NMSDC, CPUC)

2318 HC Constructors, Inc.
P.O. Box 855 Whitehouse Station, NJ 08889
(908) 534-3833 Lisa Chowansky President
Fax: (908) 534-3851
Email: lchowansky@hcconstructors.com
Website: www.hcconstructors.com
General contracting: Underground Excavation for Electrical & Telecommunication, Masonry, Bridgework, Sound Walls, Concrete - Wall, foundations & floors. (Woman/White, estab 1989, empl 15, sales $15,000,000, cert: WBENC)

2319 Hydro-Marine Construction Company, Inc.
1345 Route 38 West Tynddol Bldg Hainesport, NJ 08036
(609) 261-6353 Janet Castle President
Fax: (609) 261-3422
Email: hmc@wjcastlegroup.com
Website: www.wjcastlegroup.com
Marine structures construction services: repair, replacement & maintenance of bulkhead & pier construction & rehabilitation, cable inspection & location, bridge undermining repairs, pile repair, underwater concreting, steel sheeting cofferdams. (Woman/White, estab 1997, empl 13, sales $2,000,000, cert: WBENC)

2320 Maysonet LLC
4 Orchard Terrace   Clark, NJ 07066
(732) 396-0873 Mark Maysonet Managing Member
Fax: (732) 396-0009
Email: info@maysonetllc.com
Website: www.maysonetllc.com
Commercial & residential construction: carpentry, drywall, framing, general contracting. (Hisp, estab 2005, empl 18, sales $751,588, cert: State)

2321 N.C. & Sons
201 Chambersbrook Rd   Branchburg, NJ 08876
(908) 575-0055 Brandon Nicholson VP
Fax:
Email: accounting@nicholsoncorp.com
Website: www.nicholsoncorp.com
General contracting &construction management. (Woman/Hisp, estab 1997, empl 95, sales $34,654,000, cert: State, NMSDC, WBENC)

2322 Wu & Associates, Inc.
100 Gaither Dr, Ste C   Mount Laurel, NJ 08054
(856) 857-1639 Kirby Wu President
Fax: (856) 857-1729
Email: info@wuassociates.com
Website: www.wuassociates.com
General contracting: govt, commercial, institutional & industrial, renovations, new construction, environ cleanups. (As-Pac, estab 1990, empl 22, sales $15,878,337, cert: State, NMSDC)

New Mexico

2323 Zohnnie Construction Industries, Inc.
P.O. Box 745 Farmington, NM 87499
505-860077 Harrietta Zohnnie President
Fax: 505-329177
Email: zohninc@aol.com
Website: www.zohnnieconstruction.com
Construction administration & project management, residential construction, commercial & industrial Construction. (Woman/Nat Ame, estab 2004, empl 5, sales $600,000, cert: 8(a))

Nevada

2324 Advanced Pro Remediation, a LLC
5961 McLeod Dr   Las Vegas, NV 89120
(702) 252-0880 Sachi Okata Office Mgr
Fax: (702) 543-5238
Email: info@calladvancedpro.com
Website: www.advancedprorestoration.com/
Construction/rebuild, water extraction, flood recovery,
structural drying, remediation, mold removal & abatement, drywall, texture, mud, paint, cabinetry & finished
carpentry. (Woman/As-Pac, estab 2003, empl 25, sales ,
cert: State)

2325 KMG Solutions, Inc.
7800 Via Costada St   Las Vegas, NV 89123
(503) 754-7592 Gina Webb CFO
Fax:
Email: Gina@KMGSolutionsInc.com
Website: www.KMGSolutionsInc.com
General Contracting & Construction Management,
Carpentry, Painting & Flooring. (Woman/White, estab
2002, empl 5, sales , cert: WBENC)

New York

2326 ACC Construction Corporation
6 E 32nd St   New York, NY 10016
(646) 509-2600 Michelle Medaglia Mktg Coord
Fax: (212) 686-9332
Email: mmedaglia@acc-construction.com
Website: www.acc-construction.com
General contracting & construction mgmt, phased,
interior renovations. (Woman/White, estab 1984, empl
55, sales $28,748,041, cert: City, WBENC)

2327 Al-Pros Construction Inc.
109-20 121 St   South Ozone Park, NY 11420
(718) 848-3666 Imran Ali Office Mgr
Fax: (718) 848-3732
Email: iali@alprosconstruction.com
Website: www.alprosconstruction.com
General contracting & maintenance services. (As-Pac,
estab 1995, empl 30, sales $500,000, cert: City)

2328 BLM Construction Company, Inc.
P.O. Box 316   Kendall, NY 14476
(585) 659-2784 Linda Convery President
Fax:
Email: linda@blmconstruction.com
Website: www.blmconstruction.com
General contracting: commercial & multi-family projects.
(Woman/White, estab 2001, empl 14, sales , cert:
WBENC)

2329 C.W. Brown Inc.
1 Labriola Court   Armonk, NY 10504
(914) 219-8323 Erin Griffin Business Dev Mgr
Fax: (914) 741-1274
Email: info@cwbrown.com
Website: www.cwbrown.com
General contracting/construction management.
(Woman/White, estab 1984, empl 72, sales $48,000,000,
cert: City, WBENC)

2330 Con Rac Construction Group LLC
1895 Walt Whitman Rd Ste 2 Melville, NY 11747
(631) 756-0101 John Coleman EVO
Fax: (631) 454-1212
Email: jcoleman@conracgroup.com
Website: www.conracgroup.com
General contracting & construction management.
(Woman/White, estab 2010, empl 4, sales $13,009,136,
cert: State, City)

2331 Construction and Service Solutions Corp.
216 Main Rd   Akron, NY 14001
(716) 570-1352 Suzanne Witnauer President
Fax: (585) 542-1605
Email: suzanne@csscbuilds.com
Website: www.csscbuilds.com
General contractor: drywall, doors & hardware, acoustic
ceilings, siding, windows, cabinetry, countertops,
framing, trim & finish carpentry installations. (Woman/
White, estab 2002, empl 15, sales $340,860, cert: State,
City, WBENC)

2332 Genesus One Enterprise, Inc.
43-24 54th Rd Ste 203 Maspeth, NY 11378
(718) 361-7516 David Turner CEO
Fax: (718) 361-7519
Email: office@genesusconstruction.com
Website: www.genesusconstruction.com
General contracting, construction management, interiors construction, site work, pavement, concrete,
masonry, metal work & other trades. (AA, estab 1999,
empl 16, sales $3,500,000, cert: State)

2333 Henegan Construction Co., Inc.
250 W 30th St   New York, NY 10001
(212) 947-6441 Maureen Henegan CEO
Fax: (212) 643-1053
Email: mahenegan@henegan.com
Website: www.henegan.com
Construction management & general contracting:
interior building alterations, renovations & infrastructure upgrades. (Woman, estab 1959, empl 150, sales
$238,724,000, cert: City, WBENC)

2334 K-Pak Consulting, Inc.
29 Elves Ln   Levittown, NY 11756
(718) 813-7755 Khurram Bajwa President
Fax: (718) 749-0136
Email: bajwa@kpakconsulting.com
Website: www.kpakconsulting.com
General contracting: remodeling, renovations, carpentry, drywall, cement, flooring, masonry, demolition, painting, doors & windows. (As-Ind, estab 2012, empl 4, sales $169,960, cert: State)

2335 Mamais Contracting Corp.
256 West 124th St   New York, NY 10027
(212) 865-1666 Stavroula Mamais-Lorino President
Fax: (212) 316-3921
Email: voula@mamais.com
Website: www.mamais.com
General contracting, high-end alterations & renovations, rapid repair services. (Woman/White, estab 1968, empl 142, sales $17,367,537, cert: City, WBENC)

2336 Theodore Williams Construction Company, LLC
641 Lexington Avenue   New York, NY 10022
(212) 593-9700 Shelby Johnson President
Fax: (212) 754-0168
Email: Sjohnson@twcc-llc.com
Website: www.twcc-llc.com
General contracting & construction management: interior buildouts, alterations, restorations & base building construction. (Woman/White, estab 1972, empl 24, sales $25,988,000, cert: WBENC)

Ohio

2337 Bambeck & Vest Associates, Inc.
49 E Fourth St, Ste 1020 Dixie Terminal Bldg Cincinnati, OH 45202
(513) 621-5654 Ed Roark President
Fax: (513) 621-5663
Email: ed@bambeckandvest.com
Website: www.bambeckandvest.com
General contracting, office renovations, new buildings, general repair work. (Woman/White, estab 1964, empl 35, sales $10,000,000, cert: WBENC)

2338 Better Built Construction Services, Inc.
1240 Central Ave   Middletown, OH 45044
(513) 727-8637 Karen Halsey President
Fax: (513) 217-4696
Email: ksh@betterbuiltcs.com
Website: www.betterbuiltcs.com
Pre-engineered steel building, steel erection. (Woman/Nat Ame, estab 1995, empl 5, sales $1,245,340, cert: State)

2339 C&B Construction Company Ltd.
3713 Lee Rd   Cleveland, OH 44120
(216) 905-2617 Barbara Coker President
Fax: (216) 751-6002
Email: candbcont@sbcglobal.net
Website: www.candbconstoh.com
General construction, rehab, new construction, residential & commercial properties. (Woman/AA, estab 2007, empl 4, sales $990,000, cert: State)

2340 Construction Support Solutions, LLC
P.O. Box 48   Avon Lake, OH 44012
(440) 541-6642 Anna Klee President
Fax: (440) 653-9482
Email: anna.klee@constructionsupportsolutions.com
Website: www.constructionsupportsolutions.com
Construction management: scheduling, estimating, constructability review, contract administration, project controls, on site inspections & close out services. (Woman/White, estab 2008, empl 3, sales $250,000, cert: State)

2341 Cook Paving & Construction Co., Inc.
11360 Brookpark Rd, Ste 212   Brooklyn, OH 44130
(216) 267-7705 Georgia Gallagher President
Fax: (216) 267-7595
Email: Georgia.gallagher@cookpaving.com
Website:
Construction management, underground utilities installation & maintenance telecommunication & electrical ductbank systems, directional boring, site development, commercial & heavy hwy hotmix asphalt & concrete paving, excavation & trenching. (AA, estab 1950, empl 100, sales , cert: State, City, NMSDC)

2342 D.A.G. Construction Company, Inc.
4924 Winton Rd   Cincinnati, OH 45232
(513) 542-8597 Lindsay Wilhelm Mktg Dir
Fax: (513) 542-9286
Email: lwilhelm@dag-cons.com
Website: www.dag-cons.com
General construction, construction management, design/build & renovations. (AA/As-Pac, estab 1990, empl 35, sales $21,000,000, cert: NMSDC)

2343 Dawn Incorporated
106 E Market St Ste 505 Warren, OH 44481
(330) 652-7711 Dawn Ochman President
Fax: (330) 652-7714
Email: dawn@dawnincorporated.com
Website: www.dawnincorporated.com
General contracting, pre-construction planning, quality control & customer service. (Woman/White, estab 1993, empl 15, sales $1,014,000, cert: State)

2344 Dynamix Engineering Ltd.
      855 Grandview Ave, 3rd Fl   Columbus, OH 43215
      (614) 443-1178 Eugene Griffin President
      Fax: (614) 443-1594
      Email: ggriffin@dynamix-ltd.com
      Website: www.dynamix-ltd.com
Electrical, mechanical, plumbing, technology systems
design; assessments & standard operating & maintenance procedures. (AA, estab 1997, empl 40, sales
$11,700,000, cert: State, NMSDC)

2345 G. Stephens, Inc
      133 N Summit St   Akron, OH 44304
      (330) 762-1386 Glen Stephens President
      Fax: (330) 762-0044
      Email: compliance@gstephensinc.com
      Website: www.gstephensinc.com
Project & construction management, engineering services,
real estate procurement, general contracting, managing
consulting, contract compliance, specializing government,
public, private sectors. (AA, estab 1992, empl 62, sales
$6,094,632, cert: State, City)

2346 Hammond Corporation
      1285 E 49 St   Cleveland, OH 44114
      (216) 431-7861 Jacqueline Hammond President
      Fax: (216) 431-7864
      Email: hammondco@aol.com
      Website:
General construction, mechanical, HVAC, process piping,
etc. (Woman/AA, estab 1985, empl 3, sales $4,055,392,
cert: City)

2347 JWT&A LLC
      3615 Superior Ave, Bldg 31-1J   Cleveland, OH 44114
      (216) 426-1580 John Todd President
      Fax: (216) 426-1717
      Email: jwtassoc@sbcglobal.net
      Website: www.jwta-construction.com
Construction management, general contractor, acoustical
ceilings, drywall, drywall insulation, framing, gypsum
board, metal studs & taping. (AA, estab 2005, empl 7, sales
$969,473, cert: City)

2348 Kerricook Construction, Inc.
      20355 Vermont St   Litchfield, OH 44253
      (440) 647-4200 Ann Smith Owner
      Fax: (440) 647-4244
      Email: ann@kerricook.com
      Website: www.kerricook.com
Ground-up construction, design build construction, tenant
build-out construction, open store remodels, facilities
maintenance. (Woman/White, estab 2003, empl 20, sales
$5,393,450, cert: WBENC)

2349 MBJ Consultants, Inc.
      30 W 3rd St, Ste 4M   Cincinnati, OH 45202
      (513) 631-9600 Monroe Barnes President
      Fax: (513) 631-9613
      Email: mbarnes@mbjconsultants.com
      Website: www.mbjconsultnats.com
General contracting & construction management. (AA,
estab 1992, empl 30, sales $1,300,000, cert: NMSDC)

2350 Mel Lanzer Co.
      2266 N Scott St   Napoleon, OH 43545
      (419) 592-2801 Charlotte Zgela President
      Fax: (419) 599-2861
      Email: czgela@MelLanzer.com
      Website: www.www,mellanzer.com
General contracting: renovations, additions, or new
construction. (Woman/White, estab 1950, empl 31,
sales $17,000,000, cert: WBENC)

2351 Ozanne Construction Co., Inc.
      1625 E 25th St   Cleveland, OH 44114
      (216) 696-2876 Dominic L. Ozanne CEO
      Fax: (216) 696-8613
      Email: dozanne1@ozanne.com
      Website: www.ozanne.com
Multi-Diciplenary Construction Management; Construc-
tion Management Agency, Construction Management at
Risk, Design-Build, Design-Bid-Build/General Contract-
ing, Owner's Representative, Program Management,
Task Order Contracting. (AA, estab 1956, empl 37, sales
$50,000,000, cert: State, City, NMSDC)

2352 PPW Builders Inc.
      11875 Bellaire Rd   Cleveland, OH 44135
      (216) 862-1677 Sandy Speck President
      Fax: (216) 862-1676
      Email: sandy@ppwbuilders.com
      Website: www.ppwbuilders.com
General contracting, high performance coatings,
architectural finishes & carpentry, project management
services, engineering, & design/build capable. (Woman/
White, estab 2000, empl 5, sales $750,000, cert: 8(a))

2353 Precision Engineering & Contracting, Inc.
      31340 Solon Rd, Stes 25 & 26   Solon, OH 44139
      (440) 349-1204 Sekhar Narendrula President
      Fax: (440) 349-1205
      Email: kmoomaw@precisioneng.us
      Website: www.precisioneng.us
Site work, demolition & construction. (As-Ind, estab
2001, empl 37, sales , cert: State)

2354   ProjDel Corporation
One North Commerce Park Dr, Level G   Cincinnati,
OH 45215
(513) 931-0900 Eric Browne Principal
Fax: (513) 931-2857
Email: brownee@projdel.com
Website: www.projdel.com
Construction management, project management &
construction technologies. (AA, estab 1995, empl 13, sales
$1,500,000, cert: NMSDC)

2355   R L Hill Management, Inc.
31875 Aurora Road   Solon, OH 44139
(440) 439-0490 Ralphael Hill President
Fax:
Email: pam@rlhillmgmt.com
Website: www.rlhillmgmt.com
General contracting, construction management, architec-
tural millwork, drywall, etc. (AA, estab 1998, empl 12, sales
$1,744,631, cert: State, City)

2356   R.J. Runge Company, Inc.
3539 NE Catawba Rd   Port Clinton, OH 43452
(419) 740-5781 Amy Runge President
Fax: (419) 797-9379
Email: arunge@rjrunge.com
Website: www.rjrunge.com
Construction Management, CM at Risk, General Contract-
ing, Scheduling, Cost Management, Pre Construction
Services, Electrical Contractor, Carpentry, Concrete, Site
Work, Rough Carpentry, Interior Finishes. (Woman/White,
estab 2004, empl 30, sales $5,571,511, cert: State, City)

2357   The Coniglio Co.
4400 Commerce Ave.   Cleveland, OH 44103
(216) 391-1800 Gwenay Reaze-Coniglio President
Fax: (216) 391-1801
Email: coniglioco@aol.com
Website: www.theconigliocompany.com
General contracting services, general trades, carpentry,
custom cabinetry, pre-fabricated office structures.
(Woman/AA, estab 1994, empl 20, sales $1,091,271, cert:
City, NMSDC)

2358   The Mark Madison Company Inc.
7861 Hamilton Ave   Cincinnati, OH 45231
(513) 522-7676 Mark Madison President
Fax: (513) 522-7686
Email: mmadisoncompany@aol.com
Website:
Commercial contractin: demo & construction, metal
framing, drywall, acoustical ceiling, insulation, sound
attenuation, painting, doors, locks & hardware. (AA, estab
1990, empl 20, sales , cert: NMSDC)

2359   Welling Inc.
7781 Cooper Rd   Cincinnati, OH 45242
(513) 793-6900 Amy Smith Acctg Mgr
Fax:
Email: amy@wellinginc.com
Website: www.wellinginc.com
Commercial Construction; install trash & linen chutes,
security screens, interior window shading systems.
(Woman/White, estab 1987, empl 6, sales $900,000,
cert: WBENC)

2360   Wise Construction Management, Inc.
1705 Guenther Rd   Dayton, OH 45427
(937) 854-0281 David Abney President
Fax: (937) 837-4890
Email: dfa@wiseconstructionco.com
Website: www.wiseconstructionco.com
Construction management, design/build. (AA, estab
2001, empl 7, sales $804,000, cert: NMSDC)

Oklahoma

2361   DBG Construction, LLC
P.O. Box 674   Oklahoma City, OK 73101
(405) 601-2700 Deemah Ramadan Managing
Partner
Fax: (405) 601-2706
Email: info@dbgconstruction.com
Website: www.dbgconstruction.com
Commercial Construction, Pre-Construction, Design/
Build, General Contracting & Construction Manage-
ment. (Woman/White, estab 2007, empl 15, sales
$5,000,000, cert: WBENC)

2362   The Ross Group Construction Corporation
510 E 2nd St   Tulsa, OK 74120
(918) 234-7675 Brittanie White Ops Specialist
Fax: (918) 234-3811
Email: certifications@trgcc.com
Website: www.trgcc.com
General contracting, construction management &
facilities maintenance services. (Nat Ame, estab 1979,
empl 150, sales $88,398,046, cert: NMSDC)

Oregon

2363   Art Cortez Construction, Inc.
15783 NW Dairy Creek Rd   North Plains, OR
97133
(503) 841-5732 Art Cortez President
Fax: (503) 719-6956
Email: art@artcortezconstruction.com
Website: www.artcortezconstruction.com
Commercial construction, general contracting, steel
frame construction & interior systems, MEP services.
(Hisp, estab 2007, empl 25, sales $3,185,945, cert:
State)

2364 Cooper Zietz Engineers, Inc.
      421 SW Sixth Ave, Ste 1210   Portland, OR 97204
      (503) 253-5429 Fred Cooper President
      Fax: (503) 253-5412
      Email: fredc@coopercm.com
      Website: www.coopercm.com
Construction management services. (Nat Ame, estab 1990,
empl 35, sales $4,600,000, cert: State)

Pennsylvania

2365 AHJ Construction, LLC
      1208 Main St   Darby, PA 19023
      (215) 900-3508 Henry Robinson President
      Fax: (866) 745-3450
      Email: hrobinson@ahjconstructionco.com
      Website: www.ahjconstructionco.com
Commercial & industrial construction projects. (AA, estab
2010, empl 8, sales $360,235, cert: State)

2366 CD & Associates, Inc.
      725 Skippack Pike Ste 140 Blue Bell, PA 19422
      (215) 793-9069 Lisa Casiello President
      Fax: (215) 793-9067
      Email: lcasiello@CDandAssociatesInc.com
      Website: www.CDandAssociatesInc.com
Design & construction. (Woman/White, estab 1989, empl
24, sales $51,131,458, cert: WBENC)

2367 Chatham Properties, LLC
      101 Lindenwood Dr Ste 225 Malvern, PA 19335
      (484) 875-3073 Jeff Berlin Mgr
      Fax:
      Email: jeff.berlin@chathamprops.com
      Website: www.chathamprops.com
Construction & property management, commercial &
residential construction service, excavation, site preparation, refurbishments, repairs, refits or complete new build
outs. (Nat Ame, estab 1999, empl 6, sales $706,880, cert:
8(a))

2368 Crawford Consulting Services, Inc.
      239 Highland Ave   East Pittsburgh, PA 15112
      (412) 823-0400 Beth Cheberenchick
      Fax: (412) 823-2004
      Email: info@crawfordconsultingservices.com
      Website: www.crawfordconsultingservices.com
Construction consulting services: cost estimating, value
engineering, inspections, project (CPM) scheduling,
project mgmt, construction mgmt, owner's representation
& general construction. (Woman/White, estab 1993, empl
23, sales $1,050,000, cert: State, WBENC)

2369 DK Cleaning Contractors, LLC
      6418 Woodland Ave Ste 1FF Philadelphia, PA
      19142
      (610) 883-3133 Chidozie Dike President
      Fax: (610) 833-8091
      Email: cdike@dkconstructionservicesllc.com
      Website: www.dkconstructionservicesllc.com
Project & Construction Management, Repair & Renovation, Drywall & Insulation, Painting & Wall Covering,
Framing, Masonry, & Siding Contractors, Plumbing,
HVAC, Electrical, Mechanical, Carpentry, Demolition, Site
work. (AA, estab 2010, empl 5, sales $300,000, cert: City,
8(a))

2370 ecoservices, LLC
      407 W Lincoln Hwy, Ste 500   Exton, PA 19341
      (484) 872-8884 Linda DeNenno President
      Fax: (484) 872-8898
      Email: LDeNenno@eco-pa.com
      Website: www.eco-pa.com
Construction management / project management,
industrial site rehabilitation, demolition, asbestos
abatement, roof removal, lead & mold abatement &
remediation. (Woman/White, estab 2009, empl 30, sales
$5,293,485, cert: State, City)

2371 Northeast Construction Contractors, Inc.
      4827 Wingate St   Philadelphia, PA 19136
      (215) 624-3667 April Slobodrian President
      Fax: (215) 624-4634
      Email: info@northeastconstructioninc.com
      Website: www.northeastconstructioninc.com
General construction management, construction related
property maintenance, snow removal & general carpentry work, walls, wall coverings, FRP, ACT, ceilings, doors,
windows, hardware, accessories, drywall, painting,
electrical, interior. (Woman/White, estab 2004, empl 12,
sales $1,520,000, cert: State)

2372 Perryman Building and Construction Services, Inc.
      4548 Market St   Philadelphia, PA 19139
      (215) 243-4109 Angelo Perryman President
      Fax: (215) 243-4102
      Email: admin@perrymanbc.com
      Website: www.perrymanbc.com
Genenral construction: commercial interiors, building &
project management services. (AA, estab 1998, empl 26,
sales , cert: NMSDC, 8(a))

2373 Robert Ganter Contractors, Inc.
      595 E Pumping Station Rd   Quakertown, PA
      18951
      (215) 538-3540 Donna Ganter President
      Fax: (215) 538-3542
      Email: dganter@gantercontractors.com
      Website: www.gantercontractors.com
Architectural roofing & sheet metal servicing, commercial, industrial builders & architects. (Woman/White,
estab 2000, empl 25, sales $37,735,416, cert: WBENC)

2374 Tracy Becker Construction, Inc.
5012 Medical Center Circle Ste 3 Allentown, PA 18106
(610) 366-1119 Tracy Becker President
Fax: (610) 366-0880
Email: tb@tbcinstalls.com
Website: www.tbcinstalls.com
General contracting & construction. (Woman/White, estab 1997, empl 19, sales , cert: WBENC)

2375 U.S Construction Group Inc.
6100 Henry Ave Ste 2N Philadelphia, PA 19128
(215) 756-1364 Yaw Danso President
Fax:
Email: ydanso@usconstructgroup.com
Website: www.usconstructgroup.com
General Construction, Sitework, Utilities, Demolition, waste disposal, Hazardous waste disposal, Paving. (AA, estab 2008, empl 5, sales $517,000, cert: State, City, NMSDC)

2376 U.S. Facilities, Inc. PRWT Services Company
30 N 41st St Ste 400 Philadelphia, PA 19104
(215) 564-1448 David Groomes Sr VP
Fax: (215) 564-1529
Email: david.groomes@usfacilities.com
Website: www.usfacilities.com
Facilities support svcs, building operations & maintenance, subcontract mgmt svcs, project mgmt. (AA, estab 2000, empl 462, sales , cert: City, NMSDC)

Puerto Rico

2377 BNS Engineering Inc.
Rafael Cordero, Ste 140 HC 02 Box 14212 Gurabo, PR 00778
(787) 745-4848 Bienvenido Negron
Fax: (787) 286-3492
Email: b.negron@bns-eng.com
Website: www.bns-eng.com
Construction design/build, project management, equipment, maintenance, turnarounds, program/project management, procurement & safety. (Hisp, estab 2001, empl 25, sales $1,599,871, cert: NMSDC)

2378 CPM PR, LLC
Corporate Office Park, CPM Plaza 44 Road 20 Ste 201 Guaynabo, PR 00966
(787) 999-4000 Francisco Martínez Bus Dev Mgr
Fax: (787) 999-4010
Email: fmartinez@cpmintl.com
Website: www.cpmintl.com
Program, project & construction management & consulting services. (Hisp, estab 1991, empl 125, sales $9,849,191, cert: NMSDC)

2379 CSCG Inc.
P.O. Box 991 Aguada, PR 00602
1 787-4030 Victor Jose Garcia Ruiz VP
Fax: 1 787-5737
Email: vgarciaruiz@cscginc.com
Website: www.cscginc.com
Pre construction: Conceptual Estimating, Budget Development, Project Phasing, General Contractor, Cost Monitoring & Control, Subcontractor Management, Safety Assurance, Quality Control, Civil and Structural Works. (Hisp, estab 2000, empl 60, sales $13,107,533, cert: NMSDC)

2380 Damiani Contractors, Inc.
HC 05 Box 23646 Lajas, PR 00667
(787) 899-5763 Jabes Damiani Ramos President
Fax: (787) 899-4709
Email: damianicontractors@gmail.com
Website:
General construction in industrial installations & facilities for the pharmaceutical areas: interiors, electrical systems, plumbing, HVAC, sprinklers systems, steel structures & site utilities. (Hisp, estab 2009, empl 10, sales , cert: NMSDC)

2381 JCD Engineering, Inc.
P.O. Box 192372 San Juan, PR 00919
(787) 787-7211 Juan C. del Pino President
Fax: (787) 787-9338
Email: jcdelpino@jcdengineering.com
Website: www.jcdengineering.com
Civil, electrical & mechanical engineering: concrete & steel small buildings, interiors work, hung ceilings, floors, gypsum board, electrical power & controls, fiber optics, local area networks (LAN), process and AHU control systems. (Hisp, estab 1996, empl 11, sales $1,327,000, cert: NMSDC)

South Carolina

2382 ALS Services, Inc.
2395 Peach Orchard Rd Sumter, SC 29154
(803) 499-5045 Alfonza McCutchen President
Fax:
Email: amccutchen@alsservices.net
Website: www.alsservices.net
Contracting svcs, new construction, renovation, landscaping, rehabilitation, repairs & additions, lead & asbestos, structures, roads, drainage systems, mechanical, electrical, communications & utility system requirements. (AA, estab 1998, empl 10, sales , cert: 8(a))

2383   Built Right Construction, LLC
       1524 Ashley River Rd   Charleston, SC 29407
       (843) 882-7632 Chris Pelletier Owner
       Fax: (843) 300-3015
       Email: chris@brcsc.com
       Website: www.brcsc.com
Construction management, equipment rental, development, HVAC & plumbing & facility operations & maintenance. (Nat Ame, estab 2007, empl 10, sales $1,000,000, cert: State, City)

2384   CCCS International, LLC
       2414 Clements Ferry Rd   Charleston, SC 29492
       (843) 856-4874 Calvin Whitfield CEO
       Fax: (843) 856-4891
       Email: cwhitfield@cccsinternational.com
       Website: www.cccsinternational.com
On-site construction management, project operations, site security, site clearing, site utilities, deep foundations, waterproofing & sealants, pre-treatment for mold & termites, concrete slab on grade, miscellaneous concrete, masonry. (Woman/AA, estab 1900, empl 1, sales $2,500,000, cert: State, City, NMSDC, SDB)

2385   Greenwood, Inc.
       160 Milestone Way   Greenville, SC 29615
       (540) 298-2628 Sherry Harris Dir Sales/Mktg
       Fax: (864) 244-9669
       Email: sharris@gwood.com
       Website: www.GreenWoodInc.com
Construction, maintenance & workforce solutions. (Woman/White, estab 1990, empl 680, sales $60,000,000, cert: WBENC)

2386   Lipscomb Plant Services, Inc.
       160 Milestone Way Ste B Greenville, SC 29376
       (864) 244-9669 Eric Burnette Business Dev
       Fax: (864) 244-4718
       Email: eburnette@gwood.com
       Website: www.LIPSCOMBINC.COM
Industrial maintenance, construction, construction management & workforce solutions. (Woman/White, estab 2009, empl 4, sales $2,635,406, cert: WBENC)

Tennessee

2387   SRS, Inc.
       131 Saundersville Rd, Ste 210   Hendersonville, TN 37075
       (615) 230-2966 Dewayne Scott CEO
       Fax: (615) 206-0201
       Email: dscott@srsincorp.com
       Website: www.srsincorp.com
Construction Management and Disaster Recovery Services (AA, estab 2001, empl 55, sales $16,974,636, cert: NMSDC)

Texas

2388   3i Construction, LLC
       400 N Saint Paul St Ste 700 Dallas, TX 75201
       (214) 231-0675 Micheal Williams VP Business Devel
       Fax: (214) 231-0672
       Email: mwilliams@3iconstruction.com
       Website: www.3iconstruction.com
General commercial construction. (AA, estab 2001, empl 27, sales $22,146,587, cert: State, NMSDC)

2389   Adams Remodeling and Repair, LLC
       5821 Madison Dr   The Colony, TX 75056
       (214) 783-7948 Georgiann Crawford Owner
       Fax: (469) 579-5033
       Email: remodelwithadams@gmail.com
       Website: www.adamsremodeling and repair.com
General contracting: drywall repair & installation with texture matching, wallpaper, painting, wood staining & finishing, dry-rot & water damage repairs, mold abatement , plumbing repairs & installations. (Woman/White, estab 2009, empl 3, sales $646,000, cert: State, WBENC)

2390   American Renewable Energy
       3890 North Frwy, Unit F Houston, TX 77022
       (713) 690-1116 JC Avila Mgr
       Fax: (866) 364-0624
       Email: jca@arebuildingco.com
       Website: www.arebuildingco.com
General contracting & design construction. (Woman/Hisp, estab 2010, empl 20, sales $5,000,000, cert: 8(a))

2391   Beach Construction, Inc.
       1271 Record Crossing   Dallas, TX 75235
       (214) 920-9100 Denice VanBuren
       Fax: (214) 920-9103
       Email: denice@beachconstructiontx.com
       Website: www.beachconstructiontx.com
Commerical general contracting. (Woman/Hisp, estab 2002, empl 10, sales $2,740,000, cert: State)

2392   Callier & Garza, L.L.P.
       4900 Woodway, Ste 700   Houston, TX 77056
       (713) 439-0248 Bernardo Garza Partner
       Fax: (713) 748-6320
       Email: garza@callierandgarza.com
       Website: www.callierandgarza.com
The firm specializes in representing large entities, private and government, insured and self insured, in State and Federal co urtsin the following areas: (1) Employment Litigation (including age, gender, race, ADA and FLA (AA/Hisp, estab 1985, empl 8, sales $1,650,000, cert: State, NMSDC)

2393 Davitz Group
6220 Pine Ridge Blvd   McKinney, TX 75070
(972) 746-6045 Earl Davis President
Fax:
Email: tarad@davitzgroup.com
Website: www.davitzgroup.com
Construction, design / build, LEED project design & construction, building information modeling (BIM), large projects & small task orders, procurement services. (AA, estab 2006, empl 3, sales $2,000,000, cert: State, 8(a))

2394 Diversity Resources Group
101 E Park Blvd Ste 600 Plano, TX 75074
(214) 352-2284 Wayne Lawrence President
Fax: (214) 279-0788
Email: wlawrence@diversityroofing.com
Website: www.diversityroofing.com/
Construction management, commercial roofing services. (AA/Hisp, estab 2015, empl 80, sales , cert: State, NMSDC)

2395 DMG Commercial Construction Services, Inc.
3939 Beltline Rd Ste 540 Addison, TX 75001
(972) 630-6900 Stephanie Hilburn President
Fax: (972) 630-6904
Email: stephanie@dmginc.net
Website: www.dmginc.net
General contracting: renovations, finish out, additions & new build construction. (Woman/White, estab 2006, empl 17, sales $3,600,000, cert: State, WBENC)

2396 Falkenberg Construction Company, Inc.
4850 Samuell Blvd   Mesquite, TX 75149
(214) 324-4779 Trish Gomez Sales
Fax: (214) 324-4667
Email: pag@falkenbergconstruction.com
Website: www.falkenbergconstruction.com
Commercial general contracting. (Hisp, estab 1983, empl 14, sales $6,000,000, cert: State)

2397 High Plains Contactors and Management Group, Inc.
414 S. Dumas Ave.   Dumas, TX 79029
(806) 935-5858 Michael Ramirez President
Fax: (806) 935-0388
Email:
michael.ramirez@highplainsmanagement.com
Website: www.highplainsmanagement.com
General construction, project management, plumbing, dry ice blasting & powder coating services. (Hisp, estab 2009, empl 12, sales $8,500,000, cert: State, 8(a))

2398 HJD Capital Electric, Inc.
5424 W Hwy 90 San Antonio, TX 78227
(210) 681-0954 Heather Washburn Proposal Admin
Fax: (210) 684-0009
Email: marketing@hjdcapital.com
Website: www.hjdcapital.com
Design Build, General construction, electrical, Plumbing, Sitework, SWPPP, Erosion control, Underground electrical, Overhead electrical, Datacomm, Telecommunications, Pole lighting bases, Electrical meters, Gas meters, Outside plant copper fiber. (Hisp, estab 1994, empl 150, sales $17,354,379, cert: State, City)

2399 Icon Construction, Inc.
9893 W University Dr Ste 119 McKinney, TX 75071
(214) 504-9098 Joe Green Dir of Mktg
Fax: (214) 504-9198
Email: jgreen@icon-construction.com
Website: www.icon-construction.com
General contracting, design/build permanent & relocatable modular buildings. (Nat Ame, estab 1998, empl 52, sales $3,540,844, cert: State)

2400 Largin Construction Services LLC
1959 Saratoga Blvd, Bldg. 10   Corpus Christi, TX 78417
(361) 723-1573 Billy Largin VP
Fax: (361) 723-1579
Email: billy@larginconstruction.com
Website: www.larginconstruction.com
General contracting: construction, new buildings, remodel & maintenance, new custom housing, remodel & repair, site work, concrete, masonry, metals, carpentry, environmental, doors & windows, finishes, specialties, equipment. (Woman/White, estab 2006, empl 25, sales $3,500,000, cert: State)

2401 Marvin Groves Electric Company, Inc.
P.O. Box 2305 Wichita Falls, TX 76307
(940) 767-2711 Marvin Groves President
Fax: (940) 767-4688
Email: m.groves@marvingroveselectric.com
Website: www.marvingroveselectric.com
Install electrical wiring for new and exist bldg. (Nat Ame, estab 1972, empl 13, sales , cert: State)

2402 Midwest Steel Company, Inc.
9825 Moers Rd Houston, TX 77075
(713) 991-7843 Christopher Given VP
Fax: (713) 991-4745
Email: chrisgiven@midwest-steel.com
Website: www.midwest-steel.com
Dismantling & demolition contracting. (Woman/White, estab 1968, empl 89, sales $10,755,892, cert: State, WBENC)

2403   Minority Print Media, LLC
        2646 South Loop West Ste 600 Houston, TX 77054
        (713) 748-6300 Barry Simmons Advertising Dir
        Fax: (713) 748-6320
        Email: advertising@stylemagazine.com
        Website: www.stylemagazine.com
educated Urban view inside the worlds of
celebrity, business, fashion, beauty, health, travel, transportation, culinary, real estate,
arts, cultural and entertainment. (AA, estab 1989, empl 15,
sales $539,868, cert: State, City, NMSDC)

2404   North American Commercial Construction, LP
        11577 Goodnight Lane   Dallas, TX 75229
        (972) 620-9975 Lynn Dunlap Managing Partner
        Fax: (972) 620-9979
        Email: lynn@naccolp.com
        Website: www.naccolp.com
General Contractor. (Woman, estab 2004, empl 10, sales
$12,000,000, cert: State, WBENC)

2405   Office Design Concepts, LLC
        6750 Brittmoore Rd   Houston, TX 77041
        (713) 849-3611 Joseph Sylvan President
        Fax: (832) 383-1430
        Email: admin@odc-llc.com
        Website: www.odc-llc.com
Office furniture, carpet & flooring, moving services,
furniture installation, and painting (AA, estab 1999, empl
5, sales , cert: State, NMSDC)

2406   Pecos Construction
        8111 LBJ Freeway Ste 625 Dallas, TX 75251
        (214) 299-4900 Mitzi Green Business Dev Mgr
        Fax: (214) 299-4448
        Email: mdgreen@pecosconstruction.com
        Website: www.pecosconstruction.com
Pre-construction, construction management, general
contracting, design-build, small projects, large projects &
self-perform services. (AA, estab 2003, empl 20, sales
$16,616,224, cert: State)

2407   Prim Construction LLC
        252 Roberts Cut Off Rd   Fort Worth, TX 76114
        (817) 885-7851 Trent Prim COO
        Fax: (817) 885-7852
        Email: TPrim@primconstruction.com
        Website: www.primconstruction.com
Commercial general contracting, end user/tenant improve-
ment/retail, mission critical, corporate campuses, health
care & institutional service providers. (Woman/White,
estab 2007, empl 10, sales $10,000,000, cert: State,
WBENC)

2408   Samaripa Oilfield Services, LLC
        2855 N Mechanic St   El Campo, TX 77437
        (979) 257-9385 Amy Samaripa President
        Fax: (979) 543-0072
        Email: amy@samaripaofs.com
        Website: www.samaripaofs.com
Pressure washing services, oil & chemical spill clean up,
disaster cleanup & disposal, construction site clean up &
reclamation, general construction, general labor hands &
transport of equipment and supplies. (Woman/Nat Ame/
Hisp, estab 2011, empl 15, sales $850,000, cert: NMSDC,
WBENC)

2409   Sun Builders Co.
        15012 FM 529 Rd   Houston, TX 77095
        (281) 815-1020 Mary Miller Sec/Treas
        Fax: (281) 815-1021
        Email: mmiller@sunbuildersco.com
        Website: www.sunbuildersco.com
General Contractor. (Woman/White, estab 1979, empl 25,
sales $16,919,787, cert: WBENC)

2410   Synergy Project Consultants, Inc.
        1801 Wyoming, Ste 204   El Paso, TX 79902
        (915) 613-1442 Mark Young COO
        Fax: (915) 875-1929
        Email: mcyoung@spc-pm.com
        Website: www.spc-pm.com
General contracting, construction renovation & repairs,
design-build construction, architectural, engineering
design management, construction project management,
commissioning. (Hisp, estab 2007, empl 29, sales
$2,100,000, cert: State)

2411   Tejas Premier Building Contractor, Inc.
        9200 Broadway, Ste 120   San Antonio, TX 78217
        (210) 821-5858 Julissa Carielo President
        Fax: (210) 821-5862
        Email: julissa@tejaspremierbc.com
        Website: www.tejaspremierbc.com
Commercial general contracting. (Woman/Hisp, estab
2006, empl 15, sales $2,280,000, cert: State)

2412   The Trevino Group, Inc.
        11410 Brittmoore Park   Houston, TX 77041
        (713) 863-8333 Erin Trevino Sec/Treas
        Fax: (713) 863-8522
        Email: etrevino@trevinogroup.com
        Website: www.trevinogroup.com
General contracting, construction management, design/
build. (Hisp, estab 1976, empl 65, sales $19,500,000, cert:
State, City)

2413   UCS Group LLC
        5910 N. Central Expy Ste 900 Dallas, TX 75206
        (214) 349-1600 Henry Rodriguez Director of Mktg
        Business Dev
        Fax: (214) 349-1616
        Email: henryr@universaltx.com
        Website: www.universaltx.com
General contracting, tenant improvements, renovations,
design & build, construction management, ground up,
office space remodeling, restaurant build out. (Hisp, estab
2000, empl 20, sales $5,000,000, cert: State, NMSDC)

Virginia

2414   Alkat Electrical Contractors, Inc.
        P.O. Box 6903 Richmond, VA 23230
        (804) 354-0944 KATHERINE MICKENS
        Fax: (804) 342-0053
        Email: katherinemickens@alkatelectric.com
        Website:
Integrated business systems, conduits, raceways, fittings &
related items, wire, cable, lugs, terminations, busways.
(AA, estab 1983, empl 45, sales $4,780,000, cert: State,
NMSDC)

2415   BFE Construction, Inc.
        7620 Whitepine Rd Richmond, VA 23237
        (804) 714-2540 Travis Bowers President
        Fax: (804) 714-2483
        Email: tbowers@bfe-llc.com
        Website: www.bfe-llc.com
General contracting: bonded, commercial. (AA, estab
1998, empl 19, sales $3,392,519, cert: State, NMSDC)

2416   Diamonds Management Group, Inc.
        10117 Residency Rd Manassas, VA 20110
        (703) 257-0017 Glenn Bertrand President
        Fax: (703) 257-0114
        Email: dmgincservices@outlook.com
        Website: www.diamondsmanagement.com/
General contracting. (AA, estab 1994, empl 4, sales
$300,000, cert: State)

2417   J. L. Bennett Construction Inc.
        P.O. Box 340 Hopewell, VA 23860
        (804) 452-4209 Joseph Bennett President
        Fax: (804) 452-2450
        Email: jlbennettconst@aol.com
        Website:
Commercial & industrial construction svcs: masonry,
concrete, interior & exterior carpentry, floor covering,
drywall, painting & renovations. (AA, estab 1994, empl 6,
sales $250,000, cert: State)

2418   J. R. Caskey, Inc.
        P.O. Box 305 Oilville, VA 23129
        (804) 784-8001 Ginger Caskey President
        Fax: (804) 784-8003
        Email: gec@jrcaskey.com
        Website: www.jrcaskey.com
Engineering, Layout & Surveying, Clearing & Demoli-
tion, Earthwork, Grading & Excavation, Erosion &
Sediment Control, Traditional Stormwater Management
Systems, Low-Impact Development Systems, Under-
ground Water & Sanitary Sewer Utilities. (Woman/
White, estab 1985, empl 42, sales $6,630,000, cert:
State)

2419   Prestige Construction Group, Inc.
        219 Turner Rd Richmond, VA 23225
        (804) 745-0000 John Scott President
        Fax: (804) 745-1557
        Email: johns@prestigeconstruction.com
        Website: www.prestigeconstruction.com
General contracting, construction management. (AA,
estab 1991, empl 25, sales $10,919,532, cert: State)

2420   ProTech Restoration, LLC
        3730 Glenmore Rd Scottsville, VA 24590
        (434) 960-4456 Frank Trimble President
        Fax:
        Email: protechrestorationva@gmail.com
        Website: www.protechva.com
Disaster restoration & construction services. (Woman/
White, estab 2015, empl 1, sales $50,000, cert: State)

2421   RMT Construction & Development Group, Inc.
        571 Southlake Blvd Richmond, VA 23236
        (804) 464-2673 Warren Thomas VP of Construc-
        tion
        Fax: (804) 464-2691
        Email: wthomas@rmt-construction.com
        Website: www.rmt-construction.com
Commercial & industrial construction. (Woman/AA,
estab 2007, empl 10, sales $2,000,000, cert: State)

2422   Robra Construction, Inc.
        708 Rosemont Rd, Ste 102 Virginia Beach, VA
        23452
        (757) 340-4140 Aubrey Wilson President
        Fax: (757) 201-6996
        Email: wilson@robraconstruction.com
        Website: www.robraconstruction.com
General construction. (AA, estab 1997, empl 9, sales
$4,100,000, cert: State)

2423　T. K. Davis Construction, Inc.
711 Dawn St　Richmond, VA 23222
(804) 321-7822　Thomas Davis
Fax: (804) 321-7823
Email: smosby@tkdavis.com
Website: www.tkdavis.com
General contracting: commercial, light industrial, retail, medical, office, storage facilities, athletic facilities, multi-family, design build, construction mgmt. (AA, estab 2001, empl 9, sales $21,819,325, cert: State, NMSDC)

2424　United Unlimited Construction, Inc.
213 East Clay St, Ste A　Richmond, VA 23219
(804) 343-7266　Merlin Hargrove President
Fax: (804) 225-8301
Email: Mharuuc@cavtel.net
Website: www.uucirichmond.com
General contracting: painting, concrete, demolition, renovations & retrofit, masonry, carpentry, miscellaneous & structural steel. (AA, estab 1983, empl 32, sales $1,946,879, cert: State)

2425　Wunna Contracting Corporation
43695 John Mosby Hwy　Chantilly, VA 20152
(703) 957-4266　Darnell Ingram Business Devel Dir
Fax: (703) 957-4722
Email: dingram@wunnacontracting.com
Website: www.wunnacontracting.com
Concrete installation, rehabilitation & repair, building entrances; foundations, driveways; walkways; stairs; colums, walls, patios; landscape; retaining walls. (As-Ind, estab 2007, empl 30, sales $3,000,000, cert: State)

Washington

2426　A&D Quality Construction Company, LLC
220 SW Sunset Blvd Ste E202　Renton, WA 98057
(425) 271-7751　Annette Demps Owner
Fax: (425) 226-0111
Email: annette@adqualityco.com
Website: www.In-Work
General contractoring: commercial & residential construction, demolition, excavation, site clearing, grading, dirt removal, utilities, footing, foundation & concrete. (Woman/AA, estab 1991, empl 2, sales $270,000, cert: State)

2427　Jimale Technical Services, LLC
1825 S Jackson St, Ste 102　Seattle, WA 98144
(206) 861-8000　Matthew Lee
Fax: (206) 861-1115
Email: operations@jts-seattle.com
Website: www.jtsmanageservices.com
Project controls & development: construction mgmt, project cost control, CPM scheduling, document control planning, reporting, construction inspection, construction admin. (Woman/AA, estab 1993, empl 5, sales , cert: State)

2428　JTS Manage Services
526 Yale Avenue North, Ste A　Seattle, WA 98109
(206) 861-8000　Douglas Hamilton Mktg Coord
Fax: (206) 861-1115
Email: douglas@jtsmanageservices.com
Website: www.jts-seattle.com/
Construction management & project controls. (Woman/AA, estab 1993, empl 10, sales $650,000, cert: State)

2429　MACNAK Construction LLC
2624 112th St S, Ste A1　Lakewood, WA 98499
(253) 212-2378　Santiago Mateo Project Mgr
Fax: (253) 267-5586
Email: smateo@macnak.com
Website: www.macnak.com
General Construction Design-Build & Design-Bid-Build projects, site work, concrete, rough carpentry, finish carpentry, plumbing, mechanical, electrical, painting & roofing, fire alarm system & access control systems. (Nat Ame/As-Pac, estab 2007, empl 35, sales $84,000,000, cert: State)

2430　RHD Enterprises, Inc.
817 78th Avenue SW　Tumwater, WA 98501
(360) 705-9459　Rozanne Garman President
Fax: (360) 705-9456
Email: rozanne@rhdenterprises.com
Website: www.rhdenterprises.com
General contracting: marine/subsea construction, remodels, design/build services, new construcion, pre-engineered metal buildings, modular facilities, laboratory modernizations. (Woman/As-Pac, estab 2005, empl 25, sales $13,199,569, cert: NMSDC, WBENC, 8(a))

2431　Sybis LLC
9925 NE 134th Ct Ste 100　Kirkland, WA 98034
(206) 686-8463　Jonathan Djajadi Partner
Fax: (206) 686-8463
Email: jon@sybissolution.com
Website: www.sybissolution.com
CyberLock is an innovative electronic lock system that easily converts existing mechanical locks into an access control system, helping organization increase key control and accountability. With electronic lock cylinders, programmable keys (As-Pac, estab 2012, empl 3, sales $198,621, cert: State, NMSDC)

Wisconsin

2432   Arteaga Construction, Inc.
       4000 S Pine Ave   Milwaukee, WI 53207
       (414) 744-7944 Anthony Arteaga President
       Fax: (414) 744-2774
       Email: anthony@arteagaconstruction.com
       Website:
General contracting: masonry, carpentry, concrete,
demolition & HVAC. (Hisp, estab 1986, empl 75, sales
$25,000,000, cert: State, NMSDC)

2433   Sirrah Construction & Co, LLC
       3430 N 53rd St   Milwaukee, WI 53216
       (414) 442-7477 James Harris Managing Member
       Fax: (414) 442-8256
       Email: james@sirrahconstruction.net
       Website:
General contracting: flatwork concrete & asphalt paving,
demolition services. (AA, estab 2005, empl 6, sales
$1,250,000, cert: State, City)

> **COSMETICS**
> Formulate, manufacture & distribute face and eye products, hair care products, perfumes, hand and body lotions, wig cleaners and sprays, and cosmetics for men. NAICS Code 32

California

2434 Garcoa, Inc.
      26135 Mureau Rd Ste 100 Calabasas, CA 91302
      (818) 225-0375 Deborah Reidy CEO
      Fax: (818) 225-9251
      Email: debbie@garcoa.com
      Website: www.Garcoa.com
Mfr branded, private label, control label & branded external liquid fill health & beauty products. (Woman/White, estab 1983, empl 48, sales $126,000,000, cert: WBENC)

2435 Plantlife Natural Body Care
      961 Calle Negocio   San Clemente, CA 92673
      (888) 708-7873 Nancy Baldini Sales Mgr
      Fax: (888) 708-7871
      Email: nbaldini@plantlife.net
      Website: www.plantlife.net
Mfr All Natural Organic Aromatherapy products: Soaps, Lotions, Essential Oils, Body/Massage Oils, Bath Salts, Natural Homeopathic Pain Relief, Natural Pest repellent. (Woman/White, estab 1994, empl 20, sales $3,000,000, cert: WBENC)

Colorado

2436 Crossing Cultures LLC
      1821 Lefthand Cir, Ste D   Longmont, CO 80501
      (303) 651-3678 Dennis O'Toole Natl sales Mgr
      Fax: (888) 370-2878
      Email: dennis@goddessgarden.com
      Website: www.goddessgarden.com
Organic skincare products. (Woman/White, estab 2009, empl 12, sales $1,429,113, cert: WBENC)

District of Columbia

2437 Shea Yeleen Health and Beauty, LLC
      417 H St NE Ste 2 Washington, DC 20002
      (202) 285-3435 Rahama Wright CEO
      Fax:
      Email: rwright@sheayeleen.com
      Website: www.sheayeleen.com
Premium natural & organic shea butter bodycare products. (Woman/AA, estab 2012, empl 1, sales , cert: NMSDC)

Florida

2438 High End Beauty Inc.
      1120 Holland Dr, Ste 2   Boca Raton, FL 33487
      (561) 665-1968 Tricia Morris CEO
      Fax: (888) 794-0359
      Email: Tricia@Highendbeauty.com
      Website: www.highendbeauty.com
Dist hair, skin, cosmetics & nail products. (Woman/White, estab 2011, empl 6, sales , cert: WBENC)

2439 NAIWBE Natural As I Wanna Be
      2 Independent Dr Ste 108 Jacksonville, FL 32202
      (904) 634-7607 Sylvia Walker President
      Fax:
      Email: sylvia@naiwbellc.net
      Website: www.naiwbellc.net
Organic Skin Care Products. (Woman/AA, estab 2011, empl 3, sales $100,000, cert: State)

Indiana

2440 Elwood Staffing Services, Inc.
      4111 Central Avenue   Columbus, IN 47202
      (812) 372-6200 Kimberly Randall Director, Business Dev
      Fax: (812) 348-6201
      Email: info@elwoodstaffing.com
      Website: www.elwoodstaffing.com
Organic skincare products. (AA, estab 1980, empl 260, sales $95,010,000, cert: NMSDC)

New Jersey

2441 Custom Essence
      53 Veronica Ave   Somerset, NJ 08873
      (732) 249-6405 Colin O'Such President
      Fax: (732) 249-6405
      Email: cosuch@customessence.com
      Website: www.CustomEssence.com
Manufacture Fragrance & Cosmetic Products. (As-Ind, estab 1985, empl 43, sales , cert: NMSDC)

2442 Health and Natural Beauty Corp LLC (SprinJene is a trade name)
      140 Ethel Rd, Ste W   Piscataway, NJ 08854
      (732) 640-1832 Alexandra DePierro Sales and Mktg Mgr
      Fax: (732) 601-2367
      Email: a.depierro@sprinjene.com
      Website: www.sprinjene.com
Mfr oral care products. SprinJene is our line of superior toothpastes combining the power of black seed oil, zinc, and xylitol. (AA, estab 2012, empl 11, sales $250,000, cert: State)

2443   US Organic Group Corp.
       90 Dayton Ave. STE 132 Bldg 18, Unit 1P Passaic, NJ
       07055
       (201) 252-4269 Leonard Moon President
       Fax: (201) 399-4325
       Email: mij3461@us-organic.com
       Website: www.us-organic.com
Mfr USDA certified organic topical & personal care
products. (As-Pac, estab 2011, empl 7, sales $590,303,
cert: NMSDC)

2444   Xenna Corporation
       33 Witherspoon St Ste 200 Princeton, NJ 08542
       (609) 921-1101 Carol Buck CEO
       Fax: (609) 921-2517
       Email: cbuck@xenna.com
       Website: www.xenna.com
Dist personal care products for foot care & hair care.
(Woman/White, estab 1996, empl 5, sales $3,355,705,
cert: WBENC)

Ohio

2445   Shema Global, LLC
       825 N Houk Rd Delaware, OH 43015
       (740) 953-0292 mark butler Managing Dir
       Fax: (740) 363-5725
       Email: contact@shemaglobal.com
       Website: www.shemaglobal.com
Mfr & dist all natural hair & body care products. (Woman/
AA, estab 2009, empl 2, sales , cert: State)

Tennessee

2446   Keystone Laboratories, Inc.
       1103 Kansas St Memphis, TN 38106
       (901) 774-8860 Melinda Menke Owner
       Fax: (901) 774-0675
       Email: mmburns@earthlink.net
       Website: www.keystone-labs.com
Personal care products, ethnic hair care, skin care, toilet-
ries. (Woman/White, estab 1934, empl 21, sales
$3,793,002, cert: WBENC)

Texas

2447   Clavél
       4150 E Overland Trail Abilene, TX 79601
       (325) 676-9655 Dason Williams EVP Sales & Mktg
       Fax: (325) 676-9656
       Email: dason@clavel.com
       Website: www.clavel.com
Private label, over the counter skin creams, pain creams,
and scar creams. (Woman, estab 1988, empl 12, sales
$2,423,653, cert: WBENC)

2448   Synergy Bodycare LLC.
       5653 Winding Woods Trail Dallas, TX 75227
       (214) 460-1500 Rosie Hill CEO
       Fax: (972) 330-5678
       Email: Rosielh@synergibody.com
       Website: www.synergibody.com
Performance Skin & Hair Care for women & men of all
skin types, tones & hair. (Woman/AA, estab 2009, empl
1, sales , cert: State, NMSDC)

Virginia

2449   Tree Naturals Inc.
       4204 Riding Place Rd Richmond, VA 23223
       (804) 514-4423 LaTresha Sayles CEO
       Fax:
       Email: customerservice@treenaturals.com
       Website: www.treenaturals.com
Natural hair and body line created to add moisturize to
dry hair & skin. (Woman/AA, estab 2011, empl 1, sales ,
cert: State)

DETECTIVE & SECURITY AGENCIES
Provide civil, criminal and private investigations; security consulting services and security guard services. NAICS Code 54

Alaska

2450 NMS Security Services, LLC
      800 E Domind Blvd, Ste 3-450   Anchorage, AK 99515
      (907) 273-2400 Mari Gallion Proposal Mgr
      Fax: (907) 273-2424
      Email: registration@nmsusa.com
      Website: www.nmsusa.com
Security and investigative services. (Nat Ame, estab 2007, empl 72, sales $4,910,108, cert: NMSDC)

Alabama

2451 Discreet Claim Assessment Investigations (DCA&I)
      P.O. Box 94672   Birmingham, AL 35220
      (205) 305-1782 Rafael Portis Owner
      Fax: (801) 348-3282
      Email: admin@dcainvestigations.com
      Website: www.dcainvestigations.com
Video & photo surveillance, activity checks, background records investigations, recorded statements, elderly/disability interviews, hospital/pharmacy canvass & depo/trail testimony.
Workers Compensation Claims Investigations/Surveillance (AA, estab 2004, empl 1, sales $62,911, cert: State)

2452 Dothan Security Inc. dba DSI Security Services
      600 W Adams St   Dothan, AL 36303
      (334) 793-5720 Boyd Clark Dir Sales/Mktg
      Fax: (334) 793-9111
      Email: bclark@dsisecurity.com
      Website: www.dsisecurity.com
Uniformed security officers. (Woman/White, estab 1969, empl 4000, sales $52,000,000, cert: WBENC)

2453 Employment Screening Services
      2500 Southlake Park   Birmingham, AL 35244
      (314) 282-0154 Jared Balint Enterprise Sales Mgr
      Fax:
      Email: jbalint@es2.com
      Website: www.es2.com
Criminal checks, credit checks, drug testing, motor vehicle checks, electronic fingerprinting, education, employment & reference verifications. (Woman/White, estab 1994, empl 85, sales $12,500,000, cert: WBENC)

2454 Workable Solutions Investigative & Protective Services, LLC
      5925 Carmichael Rd Ste D Montgomery, AL 36117
      (334) 262-0432 Tyron Works CEO
      Fax: (334) 262-0499
      Email: tyron.works@wsips.net
      Website: www.workable-solutions.org/
Security Guards & Patrol Services, Investigation Services, Special Events Security, Background Investigations, CCTV Monitoring, Loss Prevention, Home Watch, Protection/Bodyguard Services, Security Training. (AA, estab 2009, empl 25, sales , cert: State)

Arizona

2455 Hope Capital LLC
      P.O. Box 74554   Phoenix, AZ 85087
      (602) 899-1606 Sarah Hope CEO
      Fax: (602) 899-1698
      Email: sarah@verticalidentity.com
      Website: www.verticalidentity.com
Develop, implement & provide screening programs, background investigations, Employment Verification, Criminal Background Checks, Motor Vehicle Record Check, Government Watch Lists, Fingerprinting. (Woman/Hisp, estab 2014, empl 6, sales $55,000, cert: WBENC)

2456 Law Enforcement Specialists, Inc.
      P.O. Box 11656   Glendale, AZ 85318
      (623) 825-6700 Bonnie Lucas CEO
      Fax: (623) 825-6718
      Email: bonnie@lesaz.com
      Website: www.offdutypoliceofficers.com
Law Enforcement Officers off-duty armed, uniformed & plain clothes. (Woman/White, estab 1994, empl 8, sales $5,610,458, cert: WBENC)

California

2457 Accurate Background
      7515 Irvine Center Dr   Irvine, CA 92618
      (949) 609-2277 Matthew Schneider Enterprise Acct Exec
      Fax: (949) 380-2377
      Email: mschneider@accuratebackground.com
      Website: www.accuratebackground.com
Background screening: criminal background checks, drug screening, fingerprinting, verifications, & compliance services. (Hisp, estab 1997, empl 700, sales $236,000,000, cert: NMSDC, CPUC)

2458   AccuSource, Inc.
        1240 E Ontario Ave Ste 102-140 Corona, CA 92881
        (888) 649-6272 Cynthia Woods VP Sales & Mktg
        Fax: (888) 649-6244
        Email: diversity@accusource-online.com
        Website: www.accusource-online.com
Screening services: criminal backgrounds checks, social
security traces, DMV records, drug testing, international
criminal & reference, employment verfications, domestic
employment verification, license verification, I-9 compliance. (Woman/White, estab 1900, empl 1, sales
$4,160,000, cert: WBENC)

2459   A-Check Global
        1501 Research Park Dr   Riverside, CA 92507
        (951) 750-1501 Mike Primbsch Director of Mktg
        Fax: (951) 750-1301
        Email: diversity@acheckglobal.com
        Website: www.acheckglobal.com
Screening services: background & drug-screening.
(Woman/AA, estab 1998, empl 209, sales $24,200,000,
cert: NMSDC, CPUC, WBENC)

2460   American Custom Private Security, Inc.
        1110 W Kettleman Lane   Lodi, CA 95240
        (209) 369-1200 Rajesh Patti President
        Fax: (209) 333-6200
        Email: rpatti@customofficers.com
        Website: www.customofficers.com
Security solutions, unarmed/armed guards to local, state,
federal governments & commercial customers. (As-Ind,
estab 2008, empl 25, sales $419,000, cert: 8(a))

2461   American Eagle Protective Services Inc.
        425 West Kelso St   Inglewood, CA 90301
        (213) 427-0715 Maria Moreno Business Devel dept
        Fax: (213) 427-0732
        Email: officeadmi@aeprotectiveservices.com
        Website: www.aeprotectiveservices.com
\Security guard services & patrol services. (Woman/AA,
estab 2012, empl 102, sales , cert: NMSDC, CPUC)

2462   Apex Investigative Services Inc.
        11171 Sun Center Dr Ste 120 Rancho Cordova, CA
        95670
        (916) 858-2999 JR Robles CEO
        Fax: (916) 853-2227
        Email: jr@apexpi.com
        Website: www.apexpi.com
Investigation svcs: surveillance, workers compensation
fraud, liability, disability mgmt, sexual harassment, due
diligence, SIU fraud, employee terminations, background
investigation, discrimination, witness interviews, etc. (Hisp,
estab 1997, empl 55, sales $1,555,730, cert: NMSDC)

2463   Covenant Security & Patrol
        P.O. Box 292   Etiwanda, CA 91739
        (866) 869-5653 Charles Christian Owner
        Fax: (866) 869-5653
        Email: covenantsecurity@charter.net
        Website:
Security guard services. (AA, estab 2006, empl 5, sales
$35,000, cert: CPUC)

2464   Global Unit 1
        15603 Firmona Ave   Lawndale, CA 90260
        (310) 760-1957 Ferdinand Ndedi COO
        Fax:
        Email: ferdinandd@globalunit1.com
        Website: www.globalunit1.com
Security guards, patrol services, access control, perimeter patrol, vehicle & bike patrol, special events &
parties, control room surveillance, gate house & reception services. (Woman/AA, estab 2010, empl 500, sales
$600,000, cert: State, City)

2465   Immediate Guard Services Inc.
        P.O. Box 2008 Norwalk, CA 90651
        (866) 415-0933 Ernesto Arellano President
        Fax:
        Email: earellano@immediateguardservices.com
        Website: www.immediateguardservices.com/
        campaign0415
Retail security guards, construction site security,
commercial security guards, mobile security patrols, fire
watch services, school security guards, event security.
(Hisp, estab 2012, empl 90, sales $80,000, cert: State,
CPUC)

2466   Infortal Associates, Inc. dba Infortal Worldwide
        1590 The Alameda Ste 100 San Jose, CA 95126
        (408) 298-9700 Candice Tal CEO
        Fax: (408) 298-9701
        Email: ctal@infortal.com
        Website: www.infortal.com
Global security & risk mitigation, risk management &
investigation services, business due diligence, reputation
due diligence, M&A, board advisory, international
executive travel, competitive intelligence, FCPA due
diligence. (Woman/White, estab 1985, empl 12, sales
$1,159,505, cert: WBENC)

2467   Inter-Con Security Systems, Inc.
        210 S De Lacey Ave   Pasadena, CA 91105
        (626) 535-2234 Neil Martau CAO
        Fax: (626) 685-9120
        Email: marketing@icsecurity.com
        Website: www.icsecurity.com
Physical security services. (Hisp, estab 1973, empl
25000, sales , cert: NMSDC, CPUC)

2468   JLR Invesitgations
        9375 Archibald Ave, Ste 103   Rancho Cucamonga,
        CA 91730
        (909) 888-8880 Ruth Riddle CEO
        Fax: (909) 494-7915
        Email: ruth@jlrinvestigations.com
        Website: www.jlrinvestigations.com
Investigative services, Surveillance & Sub Rosa, Background Investigations, AOE/COE Statements & Field
Interviews, Activity Checks, Database Searches, Mortgage fraud Investigations. (Woman/AA, estab 2004, empl
34, sales $186,000, cert: NMSDC)

2469 Locked on Referrals Protection Inc.
4202 Atlantic Ave, Ste 212 Long Beach, CA 90807
(562) 552-7972 Kris Potter CEO
Fax: (866) 865-2827
Email:
Website: www.lorprotection.com
Security guard services. (Woman/AA, estab 2013, empl 30, sales $247,000, cert: NMSDC, CPUC)

2470 National Eagle Security, Inc.
3200 Wilshire Blvd, Ste 1208 Los Angeles, CA 90010
(213) 637-0200 Maria Castillo Business Devel
Fax: (213) 637-0202
Email: nesbestone@yahoo.com
Website: www.nationaleaglesecurity.com
Security Officers, Public Relations Officers, Vehicle Patrol. (AA, estab 2014, empl 45, sales $768,194, cert: NMSDC, CPUC)

2471 Pacific Protection Services, Inc.
22144 Clarendon St, Ste 110 Woodland Hills, CA 91367
(818) 313-9369 Bob Pina CEO
Fax: (818) 313-9155
Email: bob.pina@pacific-protection.com
Website: www.pacific-protection.com
Uniform unarmed, armed security guard services & Law Enforcement Experience Agents (ODO). (AA, estab 1984, empl 400, sales $5,123,267, cert: NMSDC, CPUC)

2472 Private Eyes, Inc
2700 Ygnacio Valley Rd Ste 100 Via Monte WALNUT CREEK, CA 94598
(925) 927-3333 Sandra James CEO
Fax: (925) 927-3330
Email: sandra@pebackgroundchecks.com
Website: www.privateeyesbackgroundchecks.com
Pre-employment screening, employment background investigations. (Woman/White, estab 1999, empl 45, sales $6,500,000, cert: WBENC)

2473 RCI Associates
5030 Business Center Dr Ste 280 Fairfield, CA 94534
(866) 668-4732 Mitchell Brooks
Fax: (866) 479-8235
Email: mbrooks@rciassociatesinc.com
Website: www.rciassociatesinc.com
Corporate & Insurance Investigations, Security Consulting, Global Threat Management, Special Events & Specialized Unarmed & Armed Uniform Services. (Nat Ame, estab 2012, empl 5, sales $1,495,000, cert: NMSDC, 8(a))

2474 Rene Garza and Associates, Inc.
2660 W. Shaw Lane, Ste 110 Fresno, CA 93711
(559) 399-3113 Audra da Rosa President
Fax:
Email: audra@rga-pi.com
Website: www.rga-pi.com
Investigative Services: Workers Compensation, Criminal Defense, Pre-Employment Background & Reference Checks. (Hisp, estab 2009, empl 5, sales $284,000, cert: NMSDC)

2475 RMI International
8125 Somerset Blvd Paramount, CA 90723
(562) 806-9098 Roxanne Rodriguez President
Fax: (562) 806-7017
Email: roxanner@rmiintl.com
Website: www.rodbat.com
Security svcs: armed & unarmed security, off-duty law enforcement protection, background screening, investigations, security system design & engineering, training, worldwide executive protection & consulting services. (Woman/Hisp, estab 1996, empl 60, sales , cert: NMSDC)

2476 Spearhead Protection Inc.
P.O. Box 605 Antioch, CA 94509
(925) 308-7778 Cherokee Martin Admin Asst
Fax: (925) 308-7770
Email: cherokee.spearheadpro@hotmail.com
Website: www.spearheadpros.com
Security services. (AA, estab 2006, empl 22, sales $400,000, cert: State)

Colorado

2477 IBC
P.O. Box 1052 Arvada, CO 80001
(303) 403-0807 Bob Linderman Dir Business Dev
Fax: (303) 403-0809
Email: blinderman@industrialbuyers.com
Website: www.intelligentbackground.com
Employment background screening, workers comp credit identity, investigations. (Hisp, estab 1991, empl 35, sales , cert: NMSDC)

Florida

2478 Darwin Securities, LLC
16350 Bruce B Downs, Ste 47178 Tampa, FL 33646
(813) 468-3504 Michael Dastolfo Owner
Fax: (813) 388-6583
Email: michael@darwinsecurities.com
Website: www.darwinsecurities.com
Private Investigation, Executive Protection & Process Service Agency. (As-Pac, estab 2005, empl 2, sales $10,000, cert: State)

2479 Drakonx, Inc.
127 Grand Ave Coral Gables, FL 33133
(866) 224-1245 Fernando Alvarez President
Fax:
Email: info@drakonx.com
Website: www.drakonx.com
Private Investigations, Surveillance, Background Checks, Due Diligence, Skip Tracing, Executive Protection, Risk Assessments, Insurance Fraud, Employee Misconduct Investigations. (Hisp, estab 2003, empl 2, sales , cert: NMSDC)

2480   First Choice Background Screening
       6365 Taft St Ste 2000 Hollywood, FL 33024
       (888) 222-9688 Jacqueline Loriga
       Fax: (954) 602-9269
       Email: sales@firstchoicebackground.com
       Website: www.firstchoicebackground.com
Pre-employment background screening & drug testing,
criminal history, motor vehicle records, social security
verification, credit report. (Woman/Hisp, estab 1996, empl
48, sales $4,600,000, cert: NMSDC, WBENC)

2481   P. Eagle Protection, LLC (Miami Branch)
       777 Brickell Ave Ste 500, Rm 81 Miami, FL 33131
       (305) 721-2819 Daniel Peterson CEO
       Fax: (305) 721-2701
       Email: DPeterson@MiamiPEP.com
       Website: www.MiamiPEP.com
Security services, camera installation, property patrols,
crowd control, personal protection (body guards), personal
escorts (private drivers), etc. (AA, estab 2016, empl 22,
sales $18,000, cert: State)

2482   Westmoreland Protection Agency, Inc.
       10194 NW 47th St Sunrise, FL 33351
       (954) 318-0532 Paul Spence President
       Fax: (954) 318-0544
       Email: pspence@wpafla.com
       Website: www.wpafla.com
Security svcs: armed & unarmed security officers. (AA/As-
Ind, estab 2002, empl 101, sales $2,901,382, cert: NMSDC)

Georgia

2483   ALL(n)1 Security Services, Inc.
       3915 Cascade Rd, Ste 340 Atlanta, GA 30331
       (404) 691-4915 Robert Botts Director of Mktg and
       New Business Dev
       Fax: (404) 691-3279
       Email: rmangum@alln1security.com
       Website: www.allnsecurity.com
Security officers, off-duty police, background checks,
motor vehicle reports, drug screening, security surveys,
risk assessment analysis, consulting, seminars & workshops & security system designs, CCTV monitors. (Woman/
AA, estab 2001, empl 200, sales $7,000,000, cert: State,
NMSDC, WBENC, 8(a))

2484   Global Bureau of Security & Investigations
       240 Auburn Ave Atlanta, GA 30303
       (404) 876-7273 Robert Conley President
       Fax: (404) 348-4400
       Email: chez@gbsillc.com
       Website: www.gbsillc.com
Full service private investigation & security firm. (AA, estab
2012, empl 8, sales $32,301, cert: NMSDC)

2485   Global Investigations Inc.
       P.O. Box 473 Fayetteville, GA 30214
       (770) 477-9879 Tracey Brown
       Fax: (770) 477-2264
       Email: tbrown@globalpi.us
       Website: www.globalpi.us
Surveillance, background checks & liability cliams.
(Woman/AA, estab 2003, empl 10, sales $327,000, cert:
NMSDC)

2486   InfoMart
       1582 Terrell Mill Rd Marietta, GA 30067
       (770) 984-2727 Michelle Summers Supplier
       Diversity Admin
       Fax: (770) 984-8997
       Email: InfoMartWBE@BackgroundScreening.com
       Website: www.backgroundscreening.com
Background checks, criminal history searches, reference
checks, education verification, professional license
certification, drug screening, business reports, credit/
driving history. (Woman/White, estab 1989, empl 125,
sales $25,400,000, cert: WBENC, NWBOC)

2487   IPROVEIT.COM
       6340 Sugarloaf Parkway Ste 200 Duluth, GA
       30097
       (770) 239-1707 Vaughn Harvey President
       Fax: (810) 454-8296
       Email: vharvey@iproveit.com
       Website: www.iproveit.com
Background screening, investigations, fingerprint
services, fingerprint equipment. (AA, estab 2005, empl
3, sales $315,000, cert: NMSDC)

2488   Nu Image Protection Agency LLC
       201 17th St NW, Ste 300 Atlanta, GA 30363
       (678) 860-4634 Stepfan Williams CEO
       Fax:
       Email: stepfan@nuimage.agency
       Website:
Armed & Unarmed Security Guard Svcs, Access Control;
Executive Protection; Event Security; Escort Service;
Rover Patrol, Law Enforcement Training Pre-employment
background screening & Criminal record searches. (AA,
estab 2012, empl 27, sales $844,000, cert: State, 8(a))

2489   Safeguard Security Solutions LLC
       1781 Hwy 42 N McDonough, GA 30253
       (404) 545-3023 Rahul Anand CEO
       Fax: (503) 284-7977
       Email: mrandall@safeguardsecurityllc.com
       Website: www.safeguardsecurityllc.com
Security guards, staffing & janitorial services. (AA, estab
2010, empl 5, sales $348,000, cert: NMSDC, 8(a))

2490   The Cedalius Group LLC
       2900 Delk Rd, Ste 700 Marietta, GA 30067
       (404) 963-9772 Melissa Foiles CEO
       Fax:
       Email: mfoiles@thecedaliusgroup.com
       Website: www.thecedaliusgroup.com
Background screening, criminal, credit reports an& d
drug screening, talent selection research support,
vendor/franchisee vetting & international searches.
(Hisp, estab 2012, empl 5, sales $50,000, cert: NMSDC)

2491 The Guardian Protective Services, LLC
2839 Church St   Atlanta, GA 30344
(404) 766-2611 Jennifer Rocke VP Accting/Business
Dev
Fax: (404) 766-5936
Email: JenniferR@theguardiansecurity.com
Website: www.theguardiansecurity.com
Security guard service, armed & unarmed, security
consultation & analysis, loss prevention, security concierge
services, patrol services. (Woman/AA, estab 1998, empl
200, sales $1,900,000, cert: State)

Iowa

2492 3rd Degree Screening Inc.
100 E. Broadway Ste 201 Council Bluffs, IA 51503
(712) 256-1701 Jeanie Waters President
Fax: (866) 551-4908
Email: jeanie.waters@3rddegreescreening.com
Website: www.3rddegreescreening.com
International comprehensive background screening,
verifications services & drug testing services. (Woman/
White, estab 2012, empl 8, sales $646,000, cert: WBENC)

Illinois

2493 AGB Investigative Services, Inc.
2033 W 95th St   Chicago, IL 60643
(773) 445-4300 John Griffin Jr. President
Fax: (773) 445-4316
Email: john,griffin@agbinvestigative.com
Website: www.AGBinvestigativeservices.com
Asset protection, risk mitigation, computer forensics &
network security, fraud management, assurance services,
private security services. (AA, estab 1999, empl 100, sales
$2,600,000, cert: State, City, 8(a))

2494 Allpoints Security & Detective, Inc.
2112 E 71st St   Chicago, IL 60649
(773) 955-6700 Dolores Thibodeaux CEO
Fax: (773) 667-9266
Email: mail@allpointssecurityinc.com
Website: www.allpointssecurityinc.com
Armed/unarmed security guard & mobile patrol services.
(Woman/AA, estab 2000, empl 210, sales $4,940,000, cert:
State, City)

2495 Fact Finders Group, Inc.
4747 Lincoln Mall Dr, Ste 300   Matteson, IL 60443
(708) 283-4200 Kenneth Webb Sr. CEO
Fax: (708) 283-8106
Email: kenwebb@factfindersgroup.com
Website: www.factfindersgroup.com
Investigative & security consulting agency. (AA/As-Ind,
estab 1996, empl 16, sales $1,000,000, cert: State, City,
NMSDC, 8(a))

2496 HLSA Inc. Security & Investigations
7561 W Myrtle   Chicago, IL 60631
(773) 315-1848 Dawn Pet Security Consultant
Fax:
Email: dawnpet.hls@gmail.com
Website: www.HLSAINC.com
Uniformed Security Officers, Armed & Unarmed Security
Guards, Executive protection, Armed Escort, High Value
Freight, Private Investigators, Pre-Employment Screen-
ings, Shopping Services, Integrity Checks, Mobile Patrol
Vehicles. (Woman/White, estab 2012, empl 25, sales
$125,000, cert: City)

2497 Page Security Inc.
9453 S Ashland Ave   Chicago, IL 60620
(773) 239-5256 Henry Page COO
Fax:
Email: pagesecurity@msn.com
Website: www.pagesecurityagency.net
Armed & unarmed security guards, live scan fingerprint-
ing & background. (AA, estab 2001, empl 100, sales
$1,500,000, cert: State, 8(a))

2498 Securatex Ltd.
651 W Washington Blvd Ste 105 Chicago, IL
60661
(708) 536-3771 Patricia J. DuCanto
Fax: (312) 207-1632
Email: pducanto@securatex.com
Website: www.securatex.com
Armed & unarmed physical security/guards, patrol
services, background investigations, pre-employment
screenings. (Woman/White, estab 1986, empl 838, sales
$12,518,000, cert: State, City)

2499 Security Professionals of Illinois, Inc.
7120 Windsor Lake Pkwy Ste 102 Loves Park, IL
61111
(815) 637-6950 Angela Larson Director of Dev
Fax: (815) 637-6955
Email: alarson@getspi.com
Website: www.getspi.com
Security risk management services & solutions. (Hisp,
estab 2003, empl 50, sales $542,000, cert: State, City,
8(a))

Louisiana

2500 Crescent Guardian
4640 S Carrollton Ave   New Orleans, LA 70119
(504) 483-7811 Marian Pierre CEO
Fax: (504) 483-9005
Email: guard504@aol.com
Website: www.crescentguardianinc.com
Professional armed & unarmed guard services. (Woman/
AA, estab 1993, empl 300, sales , cert: State)

2501   L&R Security Services, Inc.
3930 Old Gentilly Rd   New Orleans, LA 70126
(504) 943-3191 Edward Robinson President
Fax: (504) 944-1142
Email: ejrobinson@lrsecurity.com
Website: www.lrsecurity.com
Security guard & special events services. (AA, estab 1979, empl 250, sales $6,000,000, cert: NMSDC)

2502   Southern Guard Service, Inc.
P.O. Box 1030   Larose, LA 70373
(985) 693-4316 Peggy Terrebonne VP
Fax: (985) 693-4369
Email: southernguard@mobiletel.com
Website: www.southernguard.com
Armed & unarmed security guards. (Woman/White, estab 1972, empl 120, sales $2,400,000, cert: WBENC)

2503   Tracepoint, LLC
P.O. Box 24059   New Orleans, LA 70184
(504) 284-2285 Kristi Barranco Owner
Fax: (888) 958-5504
Email: kristi@tracepointllc.com
Website: www.tracepointllc.com
Background & drug screening. (Woman/White, estab 2012, empl 3, sales $64,432, cert: WBENC)

Maryland

2504   Bradley Technologies Inc.
8701 Georgia Ave Ste 804 Silver Spring, MD 20910
(301) 562-9201 Angela Bradley President
Fax: (301) 562-9202
Email: angelabradley@btisecurity.com
Website: www.btisecurity.com
Unarmed & armed guard security guard services, access control & monitoring services. (Woman/AA, estab 2000, empl 157, sales $9,116,610, cert: State, NMSDC, WBENC, 8(a))

2505   PChange LLC
4400 Stamp Rd Ste 302 Temple Hills, MD 20748
(240) 619-3507 Rosa Griffin
Fax: (412) 561-6253
Email: r.griffin@pchangellc.com
Website: www.pchangellc.com
Guard services & patrol. (Woman/AA/Hisp, estab 2003, empl 165, sales $5,388,000, cert: State, City)

2506   Security 1 Solutions LLC
845 Quince Orchard Blvd Ste Q Gaithersburg, MD 20878
(301) 926-4957 Bruce Alexander President
Fax: (301) 926-7819
Email: balexander@security1solutions.com
Website: www.security1solutions.com
Manned-guarding & related security solutions, Security staffing, Emergency response services, Special event security, Safety auditing & awareness, Security training, Conceptual security systems design. (AA, estab 2012, empl 80, sales $2,400,000, cert: State)

2507   Strategic Protective Services, Inc.
4300 Forbes Blvd Ste 220 Lanham, MD 20706
(301) 322-9585 Brian Lassiter VP/COO
Fax: (301) 322-9587
Email: blassiter@spsinc-usa.com
Website: www.spsinc-usa.com
Uniformed security guard & patrol services (AA, estab 2008, empl 65, sales $375,000, cert: 8(a))

Michigan

2508   Del Ray Security
34215 Jefferson   Harrison Township, MI 48045
(586) 415-4518 Rudy Garcia President
Fax: (586) 415-4519
Email: Delraypd@aol.com
Website: www.delraysecurity.com
Armed/unarmed security guard services. (Hisp, estab 1998, empl 25, sales $400,000, cert: NMSDC)

2509   Lagarda Security
2123 S Center Rd   Burton, MI 48519
(877) 944-8400 Elena Rathburn Aacounting specialist
Fax:
Email: elenarathburn@lagardasecurity.com
Website: www.lagardasecurity.com
Security officers. (Woman/White, estab 2010, empl 1, sales , cert: WBENC)

2510   Pyratech Security Systems, Inc.
20150 Livernois   Detroit, MI 48221
(313) 345-2000 Larry Teamer
Fax: (313) 345-2200
Email: larry@pyratechsecurity.com
Website: www.pyratechsecurity.com
Security service: homeland security, alarm system design, uniformed security guards, private investigations, security & fire detection systems. (AA, estab 1993, empl 45, sales , cert: NMSDC)

2511   Tricon Security Group, LLC
3011 W Grand Blvd, Ste 407   Detroit, MI 48202
(877) 641-2600 Michael Whittaker CEO
Fax: (313) 873-9431
Email: mwhittaker@rsigsecurity.com
Website: www.triconsecurity.com
Uniformed security officers, loss prevention education, personal protection training, executive protective, event security. (AA/As-Pac, estab 2004, empl 1100, sales $10,000,000, cert: NMSDC)

2512   Armor Security, Inc.
2601 Stevens Ave   Minneapolis, MN 55408
(612) 870-4142 Inge Black Security Consultant
Fax: (612) 870-4289
Email: inge@armorsecurity.com
Website: www.armorsecurity.com
Security systems, sprinkler monitoring, video surveillance systems (CCTV), card access control systems, professional locksmiths & safe service. (Woman/Hisp, estab 1972, empl 26, sales $2,575,000, cert: State)

Minnesota

2513　Twin City Security, Inc.
　　　519 Coon Rapids Blvd　Coon Rapids, MN 55433
　　　(763) 784-4160　Jeff Flattum Reg Accts/ Sales Mgr
　　　Fax: (786) 784-7800
　　　Email: j.flattum@twincitysecurity.com
　　　Website: www.twincitysecurity.com
Armed & unarmed security guard services. (Woman/
White, estab 1974, empl 650, sales , cert: State)

Missouri

2514　Discreet Check, LLC
　　　655 NE Swann Circle　Lees Summit, MO 64086
　　　(816) 600-6200　Joyce Oxford Owner
　　　Fax:
　　　Email: joyce@discreetcheck.com
　　　Website: www.discreetcheck.com
Global Criminal Background Checks, National Criminal
Background Checks, National Background Screenings,
National Drug Testing. (Woman/White, estab 2012, empl
1, sales , cert: CPUC, WBENC)

Mississippi

2515　Sanjo Security Services, Inc.
　　　1615 S Gallatin St　Jackson, MS 39201
　　　(601) 969-7205　Kolean Sanders President
　　　Fax: (601) 969-7208
　　　Email: koleanwsanders@aol.com
　　　Website: www.sanjosecurity.com
Electronic surveillance & physical security: management,
supervision, manpower, training, equipment, armed &
unarmed security guard services. (Woman/AA, estab 2000,
empl 54, sales $2,525,000, cert: State)

North Carolina

2516　J.P. Investigative Group, Inc.
　　　9716-B Rea Rd, Ste 211　Charlotte, NC 28277
　　　(704) 243-1137　Joe Paonessa Co-Owner
　　　Fax: (704) 243-1224
　　　Email: info@jpinvestigations.com
　　　Website: www.jpinvestigations.com
Video surveillance & special investigations for potentially
fraudulent workers' compensation, property/casualty &
general liability claims. (Woman/White, estab 2000, empl
15, sales $665,091, cert: State)

2517　Professional Police Services Inc.
　　　4428 Taggart Creek Rd Ste 105　Charlotte, NC 28208
　　　(704) 442-9499　Lee Ratliff CEO
　　　Fax: (704) 442-9899
　　　Email: lratliff@pssprotection.com
　　　Website: www.pssprotection.com
Security guard and patrol services, law enforcements
services, alarm response, crowd control, surveillance,
escorts, personal protection. (Woman/AA, estab 2000,
empl 95, sales $2,000,000, cert: State)

2518　Safe & Secure Worldwide Protection Group
　　　4925 W Market St Ste 1142　Greensboro, NC
　　　27409
　　　(888) 476-6388　Lance Jones President
　　　Fax: (803) 218-9588
　　　Email: chiefjones@safesecureworldwide.com
　　　Website: www.safesecureworldwide.com
Security guards, armed guards, loss prevention agents,
executive protection agents. (Woman/AA, estab 2009,
empl 157, sales , cert: NMSDC)

2519　TriMetro Security Services LLC
　　　224 E Holding Ave　Wake Forest, NC 27588
　　　(919) 623-4354　Terry Walser CEO
　　　Fax: (919) 761-8547
　　　Email: TerryWalser@TriMetroSecurity.com
　　　Website: www.TriMetroSecurity.com
Guard staffing & patrol services. (AA, estab 2009, empl
9, sales $200,000, cert: State)

New Hampshire

2520　STANDA, Inc.
　　　41 Micah Terr P.O. Box 1008　Milton, NH 03851
　　　(603) 652-7225　David G Duchesneau GM
　　　Fax: (603) 652-7354
　　　Email: info@standa.com
　　　Website: www.standa.com
Security & Investigations consultant. (Woman/White,
estab 1991, empl 8, sales $150,000, cert: State)

New Jersey

2521　Data Access Inc.
　　　999 McBride Ave Ste C205　Woodland Park, NJ
　　　07424
　　　(973) 774-0030　Karen Jacobsen President
　　　Fax: (973) 256-2072
　　　Email: karen@datascreening.com
　　　Website: www.datascreening.com
Background screening for pre-employment & tenant
screening. (Woman/White, estab 1996, empl 5, sales
$300,000, cert: State, City, WBENC)

2522　M.E.R.I.T. Investigative Services, Inc.
　　　1 Bloomfield Ave　Newark, NJ 07104
　　　(973) 483-9699　Jose Rodriguez President
　　　Fax: (973) 481-3985
　　　Email: meritsecurity@verizon.net
　　　Website: www.merit-security.com
CCTV system design & installation, security assessments,
risk analysis, security guard services, investigations,
training. (Hisp, estab 2000, empl 6, sales $100,000, cert:
State)

2523 We See You limited liability
      116 N 2nd St Ste 208   Camden, NJ 08102
      (609) 914-5775 Raymond Jones President
      Fax: (856) 642-1309
      Email: weseeyoullc@gmail.com
      Website: www.we-see-you.net
Unarmed security & safety, uniformed & plain clothes, foot
& vehicle patrols. (AA, estab 2010, empl 75, sales
$761,000, cert: NMSDC, 8(a), SDB)

New York

2524 A.C. Roman & Associates, Inc.
      300 Merrick Rd4th Floor   Lynbrook, NY 11563
      (516) 596-3300 Kimberly Roman-Podlinski Asst VP
      Fax: (516) 596-4380
      Email: kroman@romansearch.com
      Website: www.romansearch.com
Insurance, corporate, fraud, surveillance & criminal
investigation services. (Hisp, estab 1998, empl 65, sales
$4,000,000, cert: City)

2525 AWICS Security & Investigations, Inc.
      962 East 31 St   Brooklyn, NY 11210
      (718) 338-0882 Barrington Pinto President
      Fax: (718) 374-6616
      Email: awicslisa@gmail.com
      Website: www.iawics.com
Security, training, investigative & emergency management
operations, armed & unarmed Peace Enforcement Officers, private investigators. (AA, estab 2000, empl 12, sales
$50,000, cert: State, 8(a))

2526 Bay Ridge Security Service, Inc.
      110 Bay Ridge Ave   Brooklyn, NY 11220
      (718) 238-2974 Anthony La Bella
      Fax: (718) 238-2974
      Email: alabella@bayridgesecurity.com
      Website: www.bayridgesecurity.com
Uniformed & plainclothes security guard services, armed
& unarmed, executive protection, vehicle patrol & armed
transportation. (Woman/White, estab 1973, empl 175,
sales $3,159,632, cert: State, City)

2527 Commercial Investigations LLC
      270 River St Ste 3R Troy, NY 12180
      (800) 284-0906 Michelle Pyan President
      Fax: (212) 937-3858
      Email:
      michellepyan@commercialinvestigationsllc.com
      Website: www.commercialinvestigationsllc.com
Employment background investigations, volunteer screening solutions, drug testing, pre-employment physicals,
tenant background investigations, cyber investigations,
executive due diligence reports. (Woman/White, estab
2004, empl 8, sales $1,175,000, cert: State)

2528 ISS Action, Inc.
      158-12 Rockaway Blvd   Queens, NY 11434
      (718) 978-3000 Pamela Newman CEO
      Fax: (718) 978-3001
      Email: pnewman@issaction.com
      Website: www.issaction.com
Armed & unarmed uniformed security guard services.
Aviation security, ramp security, mobile security.
Security planning FCL Clearance Federal security
contractor. (Woman/White, estab 1991, empl 200, sales
$11,340,577, cert: State, City, 8(a))

2529 Johnson Security Bureau, Inc.
      609 Walton Ave   Bronx, NY 10451
      (718) 402-3600 Jessica A. Johnson President
      Fax: (718) 402-3934
      Email: info@johnsonsecuritybureau.com
      Website: www.johnsonsecuritybureau.com
Watch, guard & patrol agency: armed & unarmed guard
services. (Woman/AA, estab 1962, empl 115, sales
$5,054,344, cert: City, NMSDC, WBENC)

2530 Lemire LLC
      44 Wall St, Fl 12   New York, NY 10005
      (212) 461-2158 Christine O'Sullivan Analyst
      Fax:
      Email: cosullivan@lemirellc.com
      Website: www.lemirellc.com
Investigative due diligence, complex investigations,
monitorships, background screening, sexual misconduct
investigations, construction integrity monitoring & cyber
forensics. (Woman, estab 2013, empl 10, sales , cert:
State, City, WBENC)

2531 Miracle Security Inc.
      193-49 Williamson Ave, Ste B Springfield
      Gardens Queens, NY 11413
      (718) 525-8030 James Obayagbona President
      Fax: (718) 949-2176
      Email: jambona193@aol.com
      Website: www.miracle4security.com
Security guard services. (AA, estab 2005, empl 150, sales
$200,000,000, cert: State)

2532 Outsource Consultants, Inc.
      237 W 35th St, Fl 12A   New York, NY 10001
      (212) 732-6933 Diego Caballero President
      Fax: (212) 732-6933
      Email: dcaballero@outsourceconsultants.com
      Website: www.outsourceconsultants.com
building code and zoning consultation, offering a broad
scope of services that includes approvals, permit
expediting, and sign offs. (As-Ind/Hisp, estab 1993, empl
50, sales $5,500,000, cert: NMSDC)

Ohio

2533   Amerisearch Background Alliance
       2529 S Ridge Rd E   Ashtabula, OH 44004
       (800) 569-6133 Kelley Groff Sales & Mktg
       Fax: (440) 992-8491
       Email: kelleygroff@hotmail.com
       Website: www.amerisearchbga.com
Background screening, electronic I-9s solutions, drug
screening, behavioral assessments & information services.
(Woman/White, estab 2006, empl 11, sales $750,000, cert:
WBENC)

2534   National Alliance Security Agency, Inc.
       7918 N Main St   Dayton, OH 45415
       (937) 387-6517 Deborah Young President
       Fax: (937) 387-6519
       Email: administrative@nationalalliancesecurity.com
       Website: www.nationalalliancesecurity.com
Uniformed armed & unarmed security guard services.
(Woman, estab 2005, empl 92, sales $1,091,995, cert:
State, WBENC)

2535   Safe Choice LLC
       11811 Shaker Blvd, Ste 415   Cleveland, OH 44120
       (216) 231-7233 Anthony Spencer VP
       Fax:
       Email: Safechoice1@att.net
       Website: www.Safechoicellc.com
Armed & Unarmed Security Guards & Police Officers,
Security for Public & Private Events, Traffic Control,
Employee Investigations, Theft, Drug & Alcohol Testing,
Professional & Secure, employee Removal Assistance, Body
Guard Services. (Woman/AA, estab 2010, empl 382, sales
$3,115,948, cert: State, SDB)

Oklahoma

2536   Superior Security
       4419 N. Bryan Ave.   Shawnee, OK 74804
       (405) 275-9072 Louis Maltos CEO
       Fax: (405) 273-3667
       Email: lmaltos@superiorsecurityusa.com
       Website: www.superiorsecurityusa.com
Security svcs: physical security, executive & personal
protection, access control, CCTV cameras, life safety, on
call emergency response, pre-employment screening,
terrorism watch list searches, security guard analysis, crisis
mgmt. (Hisp, estab 1994, empl 140, sales $8,000,000, cert:
NMSDC)

Pennsylvania

2537   Century Security Services, Inc.
       6 Rose Lane   Wilkes Barre, PA 18702
       (800) 927-0524 Mary Ruane President
       Fax: (570) 829-6448
       Email: CenturyHR@ptd.net
       Website: www.centurysecurityservices.com
Armed & unarmed security officers, ambulance standby, medical transports. risk assessment, general security
consultation, private investigation, alarm & surveillance
equipment. (Woman/White, estab 1984, empl 70, sales ,
cert: State)

2538   Gentile and Associates, Inc.
       3645 Brodhead Rd   Monaca, PA 15061
       (724) 775-3511 Christine Selden Principal
       Fax: (724) 775-3599
       Email: cselden@gentilesecurity.com
       Website: www.gentilesecurity.com
Pre-employment background screening, risk management, workplace investigations, vulnerability analysis,
executive protection, surveillance, security guards.
(Woman/White, estab 2009, empl 314, sales
$15,000,000, cert: WBENC)

2539   Peak Security Inc.
       103 Yost Blvd, Ste 100   Pittsburgh, PA 15221
       (412) 349-0850 Jay Krznaric Sales Consultant
       Fax: (412) 349-0855
       Email: jkrznaric@peaksecurityinc.com
       Website: www.peaksecurityinc.com
Armed & unarmed guard services, emergency operations planning & design, ID badging, security system
services. (Woman/White, estab 1997, empl 150, sales
$678,000, cert: State)

2540   Tactical Response Security Consulting Inc.
       3565 Sepviva St   Philadelphia, PA 19134
       (888) 755-9111 Luis Torres President
       Fax: (888) 755-9111
       Email: tacresp@msn.com
       Website: www.tacticalresponsesecurity.com
Security & detective services, armed & unarmed security
& investigative services. (Hisp, estab 2008, empl 50,
sales $1,800,000, cert: NMSDC)

Puerto Rico

2541   One Corps, Inc
       P.O. Box 79767   Carolina, PR 00984
       (787) 776-0062 Sonia Fuentes
       Fax: (787) 768-2726
       Email: sfuentes@one-corps.com
       Website: www.one-corps.com
Armed & Unarmed Security Guards, IP Monitoring
Station with Patrol Response Service, Sales, Installation
& Maintenance of Cameras, Access Control, Fire Watch.
(Hisp, estab 2007, empl 134, sales $2,641,716, cert:
NMSDC)

2542 Vigilantes, Inc.
623 Ponce De Leon Ave, Ste 204   Hato Rey, PR 00917
(787) 763-2080 Edgar Pedrosa President
Fax: (787) 763-2720
Email: epvigilantes@gmail.com
Website:
Security & safety officers, special investigations & consulting, electronic security systems. (Hisp, estab 1972, empl 1, sales , cert: NMSDC)

South Carolina

2543 G&I Security Company, LLC.
9444 Two Notch Rd Ste B-1 Columbia, SC 29223
(803) 661-9221 Melvin Dewitt CEO
Fax:
Email: info@gisecuritycompany.com
Website: www.gisecuritycompany.com
Security services. (AA, estab 2011, empl 30, sales $270,000, cert: State)

Tennessee

2544 Metropolitan Security Inc. dba Walden Security
100 E Tenth St Ste 400 Chattanooga, TN 37402
(423) 702-8200 Lauren Tudor EVP of Mktg and Sales
Fax: (423) 702-8202
Email: marketinginfo@waldensecurity.com
Website: www.waldensecurity.com
Security services. (Woman/White, estab 1990, empl 5200, sales $149,618,801, cert: WBENC)

2545 Phelps Security Inc.
4932 Park Ave Memphis, TN 38117
(901) 365-9728 Andrew Phelps Business Mgr
Fax: (901) 365-7753
Email: andy@phelpssecurity.com
Website: www.phelpssecurity.com
Armed/unarmed security officers, commercial/residential patrols, commercial alarm/emergency response, investigations. (Woman/White, estab 1953, empl 300, sales $8,000,000, cert: WBENC)

2546 Security Walls LLC
130 N Martinwood Rd   Knoxville, TN 37923
(865) 546-2597 Juanita Walls Chief Mgr
Fax: (865) 546-2474
Email: jwalls@securitywalls.net
Website: www.securitywalls.net
Security & Protective Services: security guard services, armed & unarmed, visitor/access control, SCIF security, international visitor escort/control, post & roving patrols, electronic security monitoring, CCTV systems, emergency plans & procedures. (Woman/AA, estab 2003, empl 376, sales $15,000,000, cert: State)

Texas

2547 Ameritex Guard Services
100 N Central Expwy, Ste 350 Richardson, TX 75080
(972) 231-6395 Christopher ONeal Sr Acct Exec
Fax: (972) 231-6396
Email: isf972@earthlink.net
Website: www.ameritexguardsaervices.com
Uniformed security guards. (Woman/Hisp, estab 1994, empl 256, sales $7,400,000, cert: State, NMSDC)

2548 Asez Inc.
1716 S San Marcos, Ste 120 San Antonio, TX 78207
(210) 736-6200 Robert Lozano CEO
Fax: (210) 231-0301
Email: corporate@asezinc.com
Website: www.asezinc.com
Armed & unarmed security officers, security systems services, security alarm systems, fire alarm systems, access control, closed circuit television, alarm monitoring, intergraded system. (Hisp, estab 2000, empl 75, sales $2,575,000, cert: State, 8(a))

2549 Boutchantharaj Corporation
5705 Airport Freeway Fort Worth, TX 76117
(817) 831-2000 Kit Boutchantharaj President
Fax: (817) 831-2112
Email: kit@dfwsecurityprotectiveforce.com
Website: www.dfwsecurityprotectiveforce.com
Provide unarmed & armed on-site security guard services. (As-Pac, estab 2000, empl 250, sales $7,000,000, cert: State, 8(a))

2550 Nationwide Investigations & Security, Inc.
2425 West Loop South, Ste 200 Houston, TX 77027
(713) 297-8830 Allen G Hollimon CEO
Fax: (832) 553-7414
Email: AHollimon@ntwinvestigations.com
Website: www.ntwinvestigations.com
Security guard services, investigations, dignitary protection, communications cabling, CCTV/CATV, alarms, automated controls, networking, home theaters. (AA, estab 1999, empl 123, sales $398,000, cert: State, NMSDC)

2551 Night Eyes Protective Services Inc.
2407 E Yandell, Ste C El Paso, TX 79903
(915) 549-0501 Barbara Rodriguez VP
Fax: (915) 351-0831
Email: nebarb01@night-eyes.com
Website: www.night-eyes.com
Security officers/guards, patrol officers & armored courier services. (Hisp, estab 1999, empl 200, sales $3,400,000, cert: State, NMSDC)

2552 Ruiz Protective Service, Inc.
      2646 Andjon Dr   Dallas, TX 75220
      (214) 357-0820 Devin Peck Sales Mgr
      Fax: (214) 357-0838
      Email: sales@ruizservices.com
      Website: www.ruizservices.com/
Security guard & patrol services: armed & unarmed guard
services. (Hisp, estab 1998, empl 550, sales $6,000,000,
cert: State)

2553 Z-MAS International
      2626 South Loop West, Ste 250   Houston, TX 77054
      (832) 489-0960 Janie Pinkney Managing Dir
      Fax:
      Email: Securitieszmas@outlook.com
      Website: www.zmassecurity.wixsite.com/
      zmassecurity
Certified, licensed, insured & bonded security officers,
armed guards, unarmed guards, investigations. (AA, estab
2017, empl 5, sales , cert: State)

Utah

2554 Toyakoi Ventures, LLC
      95 Bridger Cir   Woodland Hills, UT 84653
      (801) 634-4194 Elliot Collins President
      Fax:
      Email: ecollins@Toyakoi.com
      Website: www.toyakoi.com
SAP consulting & full-service background checks. (Nat
Ame, estab 2010, empl 12, sales $664,000, cert: 8(a))

Virginia

2555 Top Guard, Inc.
      P.O. Box 55030   Norfolk, VA 23505
      (757) 722-3961 Chris Stuart VP
      Fax: (757) 722-9902
      Email: cstuart@topguardinc.com
      Website: www.topguardinc.com
Guard services, uniformed private security officers.
(Woman/White, estab 1996, empl 575, sales $15,250,000,
cert: State)

Washigton

2556 Goldbelt Specialty Services LLC
      200 West Thomas STE 420 Seattle, WA 98119
      (206) 234-8759 Gino DCafango Business Dev Mgr
      Fax:
      Email: g.dcafango@gbss.us
      Website: www.gbss.us
Security services: aromored transpot, vehicle, foot patrol
& stationary security officers. (Nat Ame, estab 2005, empl
18, sales $996,994, cert: NMSDC)

Wisconsin

2557 Nexus Pest Solutions, Inc.
      3900 W Brown Deer Rd PMB 281 Brown Deer, WI
      53223
      (414) 355-3732 Will White President
      Fax: (414) 434-3797
      Email: wwhite@nexuspestsolutions.com
      Website: www.nexuspestsolutions.com
We Provide pest control services for
commercial,industrial,institutional,manufacturing, and
hospitality facilities. (AA, estab 2007, empl 4, sales
$126,000, cert: State, City, NMSDC)

EDUCATIONAL MATERIALS
Manufacturers and wholesale distributors of text books, films, tapes, posters, magazines and teaching guides. NAICS Code 42

California

2558 El Mundo Communications
      7444 E Chapman Ave Ste B Orange, CA 92869
      (714) 366-3225 Martha Montoya Publisher
      Fax: (714) 242-6612
      Email: martha@elmundous.com
      Website: www.elmundous.com
Spanish language newspaper. (Hisp, estab 1988, empl 7, sales $700,000, cert: NMSDC)

Indiana

2559 Briljent, LLC
      7999 Knue Road, Ste. 200 Indianapolis, IN 46250
      (317) 220-1563 Jennifer Duszynski Mgr, Client Services
      Fax:
      Email: jduszynski@briljent.com
      Website: www.briljent.com
Develop customized technical writing, education manuals, systems documentation, training & adult learner educational programs. (Woman/White, estab 1998, empl 120, sales $35,250,000, cert: State)

2560 Hilton Publishing Company
      1630 45th Ave Ste B101 Munster, IN 46321
      (219) 922-4868 Bruce Petty CEO
      Fax: (219) 924-6811
      Email: bpetty@hiltonpub.com
      Website: www.hiltonpub.com
Trade publishing: books, pamphlets, brochures, booklets, journals, newsletters, to comic books, e-zines, interactive DVD's, e-learning & web-based content. (AA, estab 1996, empl 8, sales , cert: NMSDC)

2561 MPM Marketing, Inc
      8918 Squire Ct Indianapolis, IN 46250
      (317) 440-9376 Mary Pat McKee President
      Fax: (317) 841-8950
      Email: marypat@mpmmarketinginc.com
      Website: www.indyboomer.com
Publish an annual visitor guides for several hospitals in Indiana, sell advertising & work with large marketing departments. (Woman/White, estab 2005, empl 1, sales , cert: State)

Massachusetts

2562 Victory Productions, Inc.
      55 Linden St Worcester, MA 01609
      (508) 798-6218 Victoria Porras President
      Fax: (508) 755-0025
      Email: anthony.medico@victoryprd.com
      Website: www.victoryprd.com
Develop educational products: print & electronic products in English and Spanish, concept development, design, editorial, translation, technology, & production. (Woman/Hisp, estab 1996, empl 35, sales $5,500,000, cert: NMSDC, WBENC)

Missouri

2563 Unique Books, Inc.
      5010 Kemper Ave St Louis, MO 63139
      (800) 533-5446 Damian Conley Bid Mgr
      Fax: (800) 916-2455
      Email: damian@uniquebooksinc.com
      Website: www.uniquebooksinc.com
Publications, audios & prerecorded videos. (Woman/White, estab 1997, empl 10, sales , cert: State)

New Jersey

2564 American Overseas Book Company, Inc.
      550 Walnut St Norwood, NJ 07648
      (201) 767-7600 Peter Lieb Dir of Ops
      Fax: (201) 784-0263
      Email: plieb@aobc.com
      Website: www.aobc.com
Dist books, CDs, DVDs & journal subscriptions. (Woman/White, estab 1969, empl 7, sales $4,500,000, cert: State)

Texas

2565 Complete Book & Media Supply, LLC
      1200 Toro Grande Dr, Ste 200 Cedar Park, TX 78613
      (800) 986-1775 Cameron Bird Sales Dir
      Fax: (512) 616-0410
      Email: cam@completebook.com
      Website: www.completebook.com
Dist books. (As-Ind, estab 1996, empl 24, sales $19,259,500, cert: NMSDC, 8(a))

2566   Minority Business News
     13111 N Central Expressway, Ste 400   Dallas, TX
     75044
     (214) 369-3200   Mia Smith Project Mgr
     Fax: (214) 369-3317
     Email: mbnusa@globalxlr.com
     Website: www.mbnusa.biz
Magazine/internet supplier diversity publishing. (AA, estab
1988, empl 10, sales $1,300,000, cert: NMSDC)

2567   Minority Opportunity News, Inc.
     P.O. Box 763866   Dallas, TX 75376
     (972) 516-4191   Thurman Jones Publisher
     Fax: (972) 509-9058
     Email: businessoffice@northdallasgazette.com
     Website: www.northdallasgazette.com
Newspaper: advertising & media, paper & internet. (AA,
estab 1991, empl 5, sales $50,000, cert: State)

2568   Southern Chinese Daily News LLC
     11122 Bellaire Blvd   Houston, TX 77072
     (281) 498-4310   Mia Smith Project Mgr
     Fax: (281) 498-2728
     Email: scdn@globalxlr.com
     Website: www.scdaily.com/
Publishing, advertising. (As-Pac, estab 1978, empl 19, sales
$2,327,224, cert: City, NMSDC)

Wisconsin

2569   Best Ed, LLC
     10936 N Port Washington Rd, Ste 269 Ste 269
     Mequon, WI 53092
     (414) 313-9762   June Perry Co-Owner
     Fax: (262) 242-6158
     Email: contact@bestedbusiness.com
     Website: www.bestedbusiness.com
Dist school supplies, games, materials. (Woman/AA, estab
2004, empl 2, sales $525,000, cert: State, City, NMSDC)

ELECTRONIC ASSEMBLY

Electro-mechanical job shops. Manufacturers of electro-mechanical devices: PC boards, wire harnesses, cables, circuit components, housing, power supplies, etc. (See also ELECTRONIC & ELECTRICAL DIST. and ELECTRONIC & ELECTRICAL MFG.) NAICS Code 33

Alabama

2570 Mtronics.com, Inc.
325 Electronics Blvd SW Ste C Huntsville, AL 35824
(256) 461-8883 Mary Fields Mgr, Quality Admin
Fax: (256) 461-8538
Email: mary@mtronics.com
Website: www.mtronics.com
Mfr automotive electronic assemblies. (As-Ind, estab 1987, empl 61, sales $53,431,545, cert: NMSDC)

Arizona

2571 EDS Manufacturing Inc.
765 N Target Range Rd Nogales, AZ 85621
(520) 287-9711 Tony Milo VP of Sales & Mktg
Fax: (949) 831-3714
Email: tmilo@EDSManufacturing.com
Website: www.edsmanufacturing.com
Molding, wire harness assembly, automatic cut, strip & crimp. (Hisp, estab 1990, empl 1800, sales $45,687,820, cert: NMSDC)

2572 Tooh Dineh Industries, Inc.
HC 61, Box E Winslow, AZ 86047
(928) 686-6477 Casey Dooley GM
Fax: (928) 686-6516
Email: cdooley@toohdineh.com
Website: www.toohdineh.com
Electronic mfg services: surface mount technology, thru-hole technology, cables, harnesses. (Nat Ame, estab 1982, empl 63, sales $11,000,000, cert: State)

California

2573 Aeroflite Enterprises
261 GEMINI BREA, CA 92821
(714) 773-4251 Pamela DePape Sales Mgr
Fax: (714) 773-4973
Email: pdepape@aeroflite.com
Website: www.aeroflite.com
Dist aerospace electronics, custom cable assemblies & electrical connectors assemblies. (Woman/White, estab 1977, empl 65, sales $20,000,000, cert: NWBOC)

2574 Black Diamond Manufacturing Company
755 Bliss Ave Pittsburg, CA 94565
(925) 439-9160 Barbara Williams Supplier Diversity Admin
Fax: (925) 439-1339
Email: bwilliams@bwc.com
Website: www.blackdiamondmfg.com
Mechanical sub-assemblies, manufacture specialty parts, in-house manufacturing experiences & capabilities, single source solution for custom sub-assemblies. (Woman/White, estab 2008, empl 3, sales $99,000, cert: WBENC)

2575 Cal-Am Switch & Relay Co., Inc.
8837 Lankershim Blvd Sun Valley, CA 91352
(818) 252-0507 Max Beno COO
Fax: (818) 252-1169
Email: lg@welcoelectronics.com
Website: www.welcoelectronics.com
Avionic components, batteries, bearings, bushings, cables assemblies, cable ties, capacitors, connectors, expando sleeve, fuses, circuit breakers, lacing cords, relays, resistors, semiconductors, switches, wire, cable, tubing. (Woman/Hisp, estab 1971, empl 7, sales $1,250,000, cert: NMSDC)

2576 Calpak USA, Inc.
13750 Prairie Ave Hawthorne, CA 90250
(310) 937-7335 Danish Qureshi VP
Fax: (310) 937-7219
Email: danish@calpak-usa.com
Website: www.calpak-usa.com
Electronic Design, Electronics Engineering, Contract Manufacturing Services (CMS), Electronic Manufacturing Services (EMS), PCB Layout, PCB Design, PCB Assembly. (As-Pac, estab 1978, empl 15, sales $2,400,000, cert: State, NMSDC, SDB)

2577 LeeMAH Electronics Inc.
1088 Sansome St San Francisco, CA 94111
(972) 570-7170 Brent Liebel Business Dev
Fax: (972) 783-4336
Email: bliebel@leemah.com
Website: www.leemah.com
Cable harness, printed circuit board stuffing; SMT assembly. Machine-programmed auto. printed circuit board testing, coil winding, transformer production, radio frequency cables. Mfr for special communications systems. Custom injection molding. (As-Ind, estab 1971, empl 650, sales $46,000,000, cert: NMSDC)

2578   Micro Analog Inc.
       1861 Puddingstone Dr   La Verne, CA 91750
       (909) 392-8277 Kim Bickmeier Dir of Sales
       Fax: (909) 392-3487
       Email: kimbickmeier@micro-analog.com
       Website: www.micro-analog.com
Mfr electronics: printed circuit board assembly PCBA,
custom cable & wire harness assembly, box/system build.
(Woman/As-Pac, estab 1991, empl 155, sales $15,698,000,
cert: NMSDC)

2579   Sierra Proto Express, Inc.
       1108 W Evelyn Ave   Sunnyvale, CA 94086
       (408) 735-7137 Greg Lawson Acct Rep
       Fax: (408) 735-1408
       Email: gregl@protoexpress.com
       Website: www.protoexpress.com
Mfr & assemble Printed Circuit Boards manufacturer, quick
turn PCBs & medium production. (Woman/As-Ind, estab
1986, empl 353, sales , cert: NMSDC)

2580   Transline Technology, Inc.
       1106 S Technology Circle   Anaheim, CA 92805
       (714) 533-8300 Judy Warner President
       Fax: (714) 533-8791
       Email: judy@translinetech.com
       Website: www.translinetech.com
Mfr printed circuit boards, PCB, PWB, hybrid, exotic, RF &
microwave, FR4 PCB. (As-Ind, estab 1996, empl 24, sales
$1,600,000, cert: 8(a))

Colorado

2581   Premier Manufactuirng and Supply Chain Services
       7755 Miller Dr   Frederick, CO 80504
       (303) 776-4145 Edmond Johnson President
       Fax: (303) 776-2957
       Email: ejohnson@pmscs.com
       Website: www.pmscs.com
Contract mfr of printed circuit board assemblies for
prototypes, production, sub assemblies, cable harness &
test. (AA, estab 2000, empl 55, sales $12,000,000, cert:
NMSDC)

Connecticut

2582   Accutron Inc.
       149 Addison Rd   Windsor, CT 06095
       (860) 683-8300 Jim Foss Outside Sales Mgr
       Fax:
       Email: jfoss@accutroninc.com
       Website:
Printed circuit board assembly, surface mount assembly,
thru-hole assembly, box build assembly, ICT, functioanl
testing, flying probe testing. (As-Pac, estab 1989, empl
130, sales $25,000,000, cert: NMSDC)

2583   I C D I INC
       407 Brookside Rd   Waterbury, CT 06708
       (203) 753-8551 Steve Villodas President
       Fax: (203) 757-5882
       Email: svillodas@icdi-inc.com
       Website: www.icdi-inc.com
Contract mfr electronic high tech equip & systems,
turnkey program mgmt, eng design, microprocessor
systems, PC layout, PC board & automated surface-
mount assembly, wave soldering, vapor degreasing,
custom cables, ATE testing. (Hisp, estab 1975, empl 22,
sales $3,019,307, cert: NMSDC)

Florida

2584   Aero Electronics Systems, Inc.
       411 S Park Ave   Titusville, FL 32796
       (321) 269-0478 Bill Campopiano Sales Mgr
       Fax: (321) 269-9687
       Email: bcampo@aeroelectronics.net
       Website: www.aeroelectronics.net
Mfr custom cable assemblies, RF cables, Molded Cables,
Molded Ribbon Assemblies, Wiring Harnesses, Box
Build. (Woman, estab 2003, empl 80, sales $10,000,000,
cert: State)

2585   Mashack & Associates, Inc.
       503 Tuscanny St   Brandon, FL 33511
       (813) 662-7353 Brenda Rhym President
       Fax: (813) 662-7353
       Email: bdrhym@verizon.net
       Website:
CNC machining & printed circuit board assembly.
(Woman/AA, estab 1998, empl 2, sales $105,000, cert:
8(a))

Georgia

2586   i-Tech e-Services, LLC
       4020 Steve Reynolds Blvd   Norcross, GA 30093
       (770) 455-8449 Racheal Hotran President
       Fax: (404) 393-9218
       Email: rhotran@itecheservices.com
       Website: www.itecheservices.com
PCB assembly, POS repair & refurbishment, deployment,
wiring sub systems & custom cable harnesses. (Woman/
As-Pac, estab 2004, empl 95, sales $5,000,000, cert:
NMSDC, WBENC, SDB)

2587   Lows Enterprise Inc.
       3966 Shirley Dr.   Atlanta, GA 30336
       (404) 699-0582 Barbara Whitlow President
       Fax: (404) 699-0276
       Email: low1dl96@aol.com
       Website: www.lowsenterprise.com
Electronic mfg: printed wiring boards assemblies, cable
assemblies, wiring harnesses, power supplies. (Woman/
AA, estab 1984, empl 9, sales , cert: State)

2588   Nijsha Enterprise Inc
       9048 Jimmy Lee Circle   Jonesboro, GA 30238
       (770) 210-1302 Jerrell Johnson President
       Fax: (770) 210-1303
       Email: nijsha@att.net
       Website: www.nijshaenterprise.com
Custom cables & harness assemblies, coaxial cables, RF
cables & semi rigid, electronic components, electro
mechanical assemblies, PCB assemblies, surface mount &
through hole
assembly, box builds. (AA, estab 2006, empl 2, sales
$300,000, cert: NMSDC)

2589   Roytec Industries LLC
       306 Bell Park Dr   Woodstock, GA 30188
       (770)95470 Amanda Chapman CEO
       Fax: (770)95247
       Email: mchapman@roytecind.com
       Website: www.roytecind.com
Mfr electrical wire harnesses & electrical wire assemblies.
(Woman/White, estab 1984, empl 500, sales $36,734,238,
cert: WBENC)

Illinois

2590   Alpha Circuit Corporation
       730 N Oaklawn Ave   Elmhurst, IL 60126
       (630) 617-5555 Steven Ryan Business Dev
       Fax: (630) 617-5598
       Email: stever@alphacircuit.com
       Website: www.alphacircuit.com
Mfr single sided, double sided & multilayer printed circuit
boards. (As-Ind, estab 1981, empl 42, sales $3,200,000,
cert: NMSDC)

2591   American Standard Circuits
       475 Industrial Dr   West Chicago, IL 60185
       (630) 639-5444 Anaya Vardya CEO
       Fax: (630) 293-1240
       Email: anaya@asc-i.com
       Website: www.asc-i.com
Mfr quality rigid, metal-backed, flex & rigid-flex printed
circuit boards, RF/microwave printed circuit boards. (As-
Ind, estab 1988, empl 120, sales $20,823,000, cert:
NMSDC)

2592   CAMtek, Inc.
       2402 E Empire St   Bloomington, IL 61704
       (309) 661-0348 Christine Davis President
       Fax: (309) 661-1809
       Email: cdavis@camtek-mfg.com
       Website: www.camtek-mfg.com
Printed circuit board assembly, surface mount &
through-hole placement, fine pitch & ball grid array
placements, stencil, reflow, automated optical inspection, wave, wash, wire stripping, cable assembly,
potting, conformal coating. (Woman/White, estab 1999,
empl 86, sales $3,000,000, cert: WBENC)

2593   Casco Manufacturing, Inc
       600 Territorial Dr Unit C Bolingbrook, IL 60440
       (630) 771-9555 David Cohen Sales Rep
       Fax:
       Email: dc@cascomanufacturing.com
       Website: www.cascomanufacturing.com
Mfr custom cable assemblies, wiring harnesses, fiber-
optic cables, patch cords, capabilities to solder, tin, and/
or crimp our terminals. (Woman/White, estab 1997,
empl 25, sales $3,100,000, cert: State)

2594   Circuitronics LLC
       201 N Gables Blvd   Wheaton, IL 60510
       (630) 668-5407 Shelley Lara VP Sales
       Fax: (630) 462-7590
       Email: shelleylara@yahoo.com
       Website: www.circuitronicsllc.com
Mfr high tech printed circuit boards, exotic materials
and alternate finishes (As-Ind, estab 1993, empl 55, sales
$18,000,000, cert: NMSDC)

2595   General Circuit Corporation
       1370 Lively Blvd   Elk Grove Village, IL 60007
       (847) 758-8000 Janice Rosario Sales/Mktg
       Fax: (847) 758-8010
       Email: janice@deltapcb.COM
       Website: www.Deltapcb.com
Mfr printed circuit boards: single, double & multi-layers
in small, medium & high volumes. (As-Ind, estab 1996,
empl 25, sales $4,600,000, cert: NMSDC)

2596   KLI Inc.
       304 Roma Jean Pkwy   Streamwood, IL 60107
       (630) 213-1283 Lisa Carso President
       Fax: (630) 213-1297
       Email: Support@kli-inc.com
       Website: www.kli-inc.com
Mfr electronic components; electronic assembly; main
harness & cable to mil specs. (Woman/As-Pac, estab
1987, empl 15, sales , cert: State, NMSDC)

2597 Midwest Molding, Inc.
      1560 Hecht Dr   Bartlett, IL 60103
      (224) 208-1110 Sanjay Patel Dir of purchasing
      Fax: (224) 208-1111
      Email: sanjay.patel@mwmolding.com
      Website: www.mwmolding.com
Injection molding, insert molding, two shot molding, IMD molding, wire harness assembly & multi-component assembly. (As-Pac, estab 1996, empl 70, sales , cert: NMSDC)

Indiana

2598 Precision Wire Assemblies, Inc.
      551 E Main St   Hagerstown, IN 47346
      (765) 489-6302 Penny Wickes President
      Fax: (765) 489-4240
      Email: penny@pwawire.com
      Website: www.pwawire.com
Mfr wire harnesses & assemblies, cable assemblies. (Woman/White, estab 1987, empl 75, sales $6,130,594, cert: State)

Kansas

2599 S and Y Industries, Inc.
      606 Industrial Rd   Winfield, KS 67156
      (620) 221-4001 Ron Chiles Dir Sales/Mktg
      Fax: (620) 221-4002
      Email: ron.chiles@sandyindustries.com
      Website: www.sandyindustries.com
Printed circuit boards, wire harnesses, cable assemblies, connectors, surface mount. (Woman/White, estab 1984, empl 80, sales $7,660,639, cert: WBENC)

Massachusetts

2600 Cable Harness Resources, Inc.
      One Robert Bonazzoli Ave   Hudson, MA 01749
      (978) 562-4352 Kim Nguyen
      Fax: (978) 568-9814
      Email: knguyen@cableharnessresources.com
      Website: www.cableharnessresources.com
Electrical wire harness& cable asembly, Mil-Spec source, cut, strip, tin, twist, splice, crimp, solder, coil, end-prep, connector/component installation. (Woman/As-Pac, estab 2008, empl 10, sales $800,000, cert: NMSDC)

Michigan

2601 Advanced-Cable, LLC
      1179 Chicago Rd   Troy, MI 48083
      (248) 268-3167 Deanna Zwiesele Owner
      Fax: (248) 629-7387
      Email: deanna@advanced-cable.com
      Website: www.advanced-cable.com
Mfr custom cable assemblies (molded and non molded) & wire harnesses, dist bulk wire, cable & various electronic components. (Woman/White, estab 2012, empl 15, sales $2,000,000, cert: WBENC)

2602 American Hydrostatics Distribution Co.
      6626 Sims Dr   Sterling Heights, MI 48313
      (248) 649-2587 Drew Parikh Business Devel
      Fax: (248) 649-8783
      Email: dp@americanhydrostatics.com
      Website: www.americanhydrostatics.com
Build small automation & assembly equipment, rebuild machines & general assembly services. (As-Pac, estab 1982, empl 25, sales $3,000,000, cert: NMSDC)

2603 GM&T Engineering, Inc.
      775 Davis St Ste 4 Plymouth, MI 48170
      (734) 679-8340 Carlos Gutierrez President
      Fax:
      Email: Cgutierrez@GMT-engineering.com
      Website: www.gmt-engineering.com
Testing of Electrical Distribution Systems (Wire Harnesses, batteries), Engineering of EDS, Process and Product quality audits, Staffing and recruiting, Small Wire Harnesses and prototypes
Testing tooling and equipment. (Hisp, estab 2005, empl 16, sales , cert: NMSDC)

2604 Newtech 3, Inc.
      28373 Beck Rd Ste H7 Wixom, MI 48393
      (248) 912-1062 Gail Gyenese Director of Sales
      Fax: (248) 912-0809
      Email: ggyenese@newtech3inc.com
      Website: www.newtech3.com
Mfr lower to mid volume wire harness & circuit board assemblies. (AA, estab 2009, empl 32, sales $3,965,000, cert: NMSDC)

2605 Orri Corporation
      5385 Perry Dr   waterford, MI 48329
      (248) 618-1104 Randy Kosek Sales
      Fax: (248) 618-1142
      Email: r.kosek@orricorp.com
      Website: www.orricorp.com
Wire harnesses, cable assemblies, electrical test fixtures, robotic vision guidance software. (Woman/White, estab 2001, empl 12, sales , cert: WBENC)

2606 Saturn Electronics Corporation
28450 Northline Road   Romulus, MI 48174
(734) 941-8100 Parthiv Trivedi Director Business Dev
Fax: (734) 941-3707
Email: parthiv@saturnelectronics.com
Website: www.saturnelectronics.com
Printed circuit boards: prototype & production; 1 to 20 layers. (As-Ind, estab 1985, empl 190, sales $40,025,000, cert: NMSDC)

2607 Wolverine Assemblies, LLC
30260 Oak Creek Dr   Wixom, MI 48393
(248) 822-8056 Adam Claytor Senior Lead Analyst
Fax:
Email: aclaytor@taghold.com
Website: www.wolverine-llc.com/
Modular assembly, warehousing, sequencing, import & export, fabrication, machining, kitting, supply chain management, pre delivery inspection, repack and test, containment & sorting. (AA, estab 2010, empl 6, sales $12,000,000, cert: NMSDC)

Minnesota

2608 Aero Assemblies, Inc.
12012 - 12th Ave S   Burnsville, MN 55337
(952) 894-5552 Anthony Winick President
Fax: (952) 894-5798
Email: tonyw@aeroassemblies.com
Website: www.aeroassemblies.com
Contract manufacturing, wire rope assembly, electronic cable assembly, print finishing, bindery, eyeletting (As-Pac, estab 1972, empl 16, sales $3,000,000, cert: NMSDC)

2609 Quantronic Corporation
8300 89th Ave N   Brooklyn Park, MN 55445
(763) 425-2602 Gabriela Faouen Acct Mgr
Fax: (763) 425-2248
Email: gfaouen@quantronic.net
Website: www.quantronic.net
Surface Mount & Thru Hole Assemblies, Incircuit & Functional testing, Prototype & Product development, Circuit Board Rework & modifications, Complete Product & and sub assemblies, Packaging Solutions, Conformal Coating. (As-Pac/Hisp, estab 1995, empl 65, sales $15,000,000, cert: NMSDC)

New Hampshire

2610 Custom Manufacturing Services
235 Main Durnstable Rd   Nashua, NH 03062
(603) 883-1355 Ray Durand VP sales
Fax: (603) 883-1707
Email: ray.durand@cms-nh.com
Website: www.cms-nh.com
Contract assembly services, printed circuit board assembly, prototypes & production runs, ECO changes & PWB repairs, wave soldering, mechanical assembly, electro-mechanical assembly, chassis assembly & testing, cable & harness assembly. (Woman, estab 1976, empl 20, sales , cert: SDB)

New Jersey

2611 Delaire USA, Inc.
1913 Atlantic Ave   Manasquan, NJ 08736
(732) 528-4520 Lorraine Hallock President
Fax: (732) 528-4521
Email: lori@delaireusa.com
Website: www.delaireusa.com
Mfr custom RF & fiber optic cables & assemblies, box level assemblies, precision soldering & testing. (Woman/White, estab 1994, empl 19, sales , cert: State, WBENC)

2612 Precision Graphics, Inc.
21 County Line Rd   Somerville, NJ 08876
(908) 707-8880 Alec Weissman VP
Fax: (908) 707-8884
Email: aweissman@precisiongraphics.us
Website: www.precisiongraphics.us
Mfr printed circuit board assemblies, surface mount, through hole, or RoHs processing. (Woman/White, estab 1971, empl 55, sales $13,000,000, cert: NWBOC)

Nevada

2613 Power Assemblies LLC
7061 W Arby Rd Ste 120 Las Vegas, NV 89113
(541) 610-6494 Patricia Knowles Owner
Fax:
Email: gknowles@powerassemblies.com
Website: www.powerassemblies.com
Assemble portable power & industrial products, flexible power cable assemblies, connectors, generator docking stations, enclosed variable speed drives & cam lock panels, custom portable power products ranging from 20A to 4000A. (Woman/White, estab 2006, empl 9, sales $350,000, cert: State)

New York

2614   Eltrex Industries, Inc.
     65 Sullivan St   Rochester, NY 14605
     (585) 454-6100   Avis Williams Business Dev Mgr
     Fax: (585) 263-7766
     Email: avis.williams@eltrex.com
     Website: www.eltrex.com
Mechanical & electromechanical assemblies, remanufacturing, kitting & logistics services: material purchasing & consignment, packaging & distribution, warehousing. (AA, estab 1968, empl 200, sales $18,000,000, cert: State)

2615   Hazlow Electronics
     49 St. Bridgets Dr   Rochester, NY 14605
     (585) 263-7852   Alma Publow CEO
     Fax: (585) 325-4308
     Email: alma@hazlow.com
     Website: www.hazlow.com
Wire harnesses, printed circuit boards, cable assemblies, sub assembly. (Woman/Nat Ame/Hisp, estab 1971, empl 40, sales $3,500,000, cert: State)

2616   Tony Baird Electronics, Inc.
     461 East Brighton Avenue   Syracuse, NY 13210
     (315) 422-4430   Matt Tessier VP Sales
     Fax: (315) 422-4435
     Email: matt@tonybairdelectronics.com
     Website: www.tonybairdelectronics.com
Mfr electronic components, printed circuit assembly, electronic assembly, fiber optic cable. (AA, estab 2005, empl 10, sales $1,900,000, cert: SDB)

Pennsylvania

2617   Contine Corporation
     1820 Nagle Rd   Erie, PA 16510
     (814) 899-0006   Constance Ellrich President
     Fax: (814) 899-2796
     Email: cellrich@continedbe.com
     Website: www.continedbe.com
Assembly & test mechanical & electro-mechanical devices, machining, sheet metal fabrication & plastic injection molding, switches, latches, rack assemblies, display units, control panels, wire harnesses etc. (Woman/White, estab 1981, empl 43, sales $9,175,996, cert: CPUC, WBENC)

2618   John A. Romeo & Asscoiates, Inc.
     890 Pittsburgh Rd, Ste 7   Butler, PA 16002
     (724) 586-6961   Pamela Romeo CEO
     Fax: (724) 586-2234
     Email: pdromeo@jara-mfg.com
     Website: www.jara-mfg.com
Mfr Custom Cables, Wiring Harnesses & Electromechanical Assemblies. (Woman/White, estab 1990, empl 15, sales $1,506,698, cert: WBENC)

South Carolina

2619   North American Assemblies, LLC
     2222 Cale Yarborough Hwy   Timmonsville, SC 29161
     (248) 342-6500   William Rucker
     Fax: (586) 461-1175
     Email: warucker@naa-llc.com
     Website: www.naa-llc.com
Mfg & assembly services. (AA, estab 2004, empl 17, sales $3,000,000, cert: NMSDC)

Texas

2620   Accurate Connections Inc.
     13801 Hutton Dr, Ste 100   Farmers Branch, TX 75234
     (972) 484-8500   Peggy Kovling President
     Fax: (972) 484-8502
     Email: pkovling@accurateconnections.com
     Website: www.accurateconnections.com
Cable assemblies, fiber optic & copper. (Woman/White, estab 2003, empl 26, sales $3,246,807, cert: State, WBENC)

2621   Arise Solutions Inc.
     5862 Cromo Ste 149   El Paso, TX 79912
     (915) 345-9134   Daniel Laing President
     Fax:
     Email: sales@arisesolutions.biz
     Website: www.arisesolutions.biz
Custom designed wire harness, cable assembly, bulk wire, signal cable, specialty bolts, screws, Nut Rivets, Inserts, Fasteners, Spacers, Connectors & Fittings for automotive industry. (As-Pac, estab 2012, empl 5, sales $1,000,000, cert: State, NMSDC)

2622   Electro Plate Circuitry, Inc.
     1430 Century Dr   Carrollton, TX 75006
     (972) 466-0818   Nicolas Garcia President
     Fax: (972) 446-8632
     Email: nickg@eplate.com
     Website: www.eplate.com
Mfr printed circuit boards: GF,GI, RF, insulators, heatsinks, blind buried vias, controlled impedance. (Hisp, estab 1981, empl 80, sales $9,000,000, cert: NMSDC)

2623   Electronic Assembly Services, Inc.
4501 S Pinemont, Ste 108   Houston, TX 77041
(713) 686-4390   Evelyn Fletcher CEO
Fax: (713) 686-4399
Email: efletcher@easinchou.com
Website: www.eashouston.com/
Custom electric & electronic assemblies & sub-assemblies: control panels, cable wire harnesses, electro-mechanical assemblies, printed circuit board assemblies, rack-mount assemblies. (Woman/Hisp, estab 1987, empl 13, sales $1,500,000, cert: State, NMSDC)

2624   Galaxy Electronics Company
201 E Arapaho Rd   Richardson, TX 75081
(972) 234-0065   Will Moore Sales Mgr
Fax: (972) 234-0066
Email: wmoore@galaxyee.com
Website: www.galaxyee.com
Fiber optic & copper cable assembly. (As-Pac, estab 1988, empl 31, sales , cert: State, NMSDC)

2625   JG Haney & Associates LLC
9711 Haven Crossing Court   Houston, TX 77065
(281) 653-2441   Joyce Haney CEO
Fax: (281) 653-2134
Email: haney@jghaneyassociates.com
Website: www.jghaneyassociates.com
Telecommunications Services, IT products & services, data acquisition systems, telemetry products, circuit card assemblies, shipping containers, test set cases, special nonmetallic, preformed packing material & acquisition program management. (Woman/AA, estab 2011, empl 2, sales $300,000, cert: 8(a))

2626   JVB Electronics dba Multilayer Technology
3835 Conflans Rd   Irving, TX 75061
(972) 790-0062   Johnnie Feathers Dir of Sales
Fax: (972) 790-0293
Email: johnnie@multilayer.com
Website: www.multilayer.com
Mfr printed circuit boards. (As-Ind, estab 1986, empl 45, sales $720,000, cert: State, NMSDC)

2627   Optical Interconnect
2621 Summit Ave Ste 100   Plano, TX 75074
(214) 239-3988   Steve Wade Acct Exec
Fax: (972) 331-3410
Email: swade@opticalinterconnect.com
Website: www.opticalinterconnect.com
Dist fiber optic cable assemblies, copper cable assemblies, rack/wall mount metal enclosures. (Woman/White, estab 2004, empl 15, sales $100,000, cert: State, WBENC)

2628   Precision Technology, Inc.
3601 E Plano Pkwy, Ste 200   Plano, TX 75074
(214) 343-0131   Johnnie Feathers Sales Dir
Fax: (214) 343-8216
Email: johnnie@ptiassembly.com
Website: www.ptiassembly.com
Printed circuit board assemblies, Electronic enclosure assemblies, Electromechanical assemblies, Wire harness assemblies, Electrical cable assemblies. (As-Ind, estab 1980, empl 140, sales $22,500,000, cert: State)

2629   THT Electronics Company, Inc.
17000 Dallas Pkwy Ste 200   Dallas, TX 75248
(972) 979-3204   Scott Sewell CEO
Fax: (314) 432-3955
Email: scott.sewell@thtelec.com
Website: www.thtelec.com
Electronic components, cable assemblies. (Nat Ame, estab 1996, empl 6, sales $126,000, cert: State, NMSDC)

2630   Trendsetter Electronics
425 Round Rock W Dr, Ste 110   Round Rock, TX 78681
(512) 310-8858   Carol Williams President
Fax: (512) 310-8892
Email: carolw@trendsetter.com
Website: www.trendsetter.com
Stocking programs & stocking replinishment, kitting, cable & harness assemblies, lead forming & modifying, part sleeving & custom transformers. (Woman/White, estab 1995, empl 20, sales $2,610,000, cert: WBENC)

2631   Trilogy Circuits, Inc.
1717 Firman Dr Ste 200   Richardson, TX 75081
(972) 907-2727   Mark T McCrocklin
Fax: (972) 907-2730
Email: mark@trilogycircuits.com
Website: www.trilogycircuits.com
Printed circuit board design/layout. (As-Pac, estab 2001, empl 27, sales $5,000,000, cert: State, NMSDC)

Wisconsin

2632   A1 Cable Solutions, Inc.
665 Commercial Ave   Waterloo, WI 53594
(608) 444-3072   Laurie Hoffmann President
Fax:
Email: ljhoffmann@usa1cable.com
Website: www.usa1cable.com
Battery Cables, Ground Straps, Wire Harnesses, Electro-mechanical Assemblies, Panel Assembly & Wiring, Prototypes, Testing & Reporting. (Woman/White, estab 2001, empl 2, sales , cert: WBENC)

ELECTRONICS & ELECTRICAL DIST.
Distribute a wide range of electrical or electronic products: battery chargers, communications equipment, video equipment, radios, measuring instruments, etc. (See also ELECTRONIC ASSEMBLY and ELECTRONICS & ELECTRICAL MFG.) NAICS Code 42

Alabama

2633　Mayer Electric Supply Company
3405 4th Ave S　Birmingham, AL 35222
(205) 583-3337　Andrew Long Supplier Diversity Mgr
Fax: (205) 252-0315
Email: along@mayerelectric.com
Website: www.mayerelectric.com
Dist electrical & lighting supplies. (Woman/White, estab 1930, empl 1035, sales $750,000,000, cert: State)

2634　Scott Lighting Supply Co., Inc.
2301 Washington Cir NW　Huntsville, AL 35811
(256) 536-6776　Joan Trew VP
Fax: (256) 536-7093
Email: jtrew@scottlighting.com
Website: www.scottlighting.com
Dist lighting supplies, lamps, batteries, ballasts, emergency lighting, lighting fixtures & lamp parts. (Woman/White, estab 1992, empl 9, sales $1,863,518, cert: WBENC)

Arizona

2635　Aegis Electronic Group, Inc.
1465 North Fiesta Blvd Ste 101　Gilbert, AZ 85233
(480) 635-8400　Sonja Walker
Fax: (480) 635-9272
Email: aegis-g2@aegiselect.com
Website: www.aegis-elec.com/
Dist industrial imaging equipment: cameras, lenses, monitors, cables, connectors, power supplies, frame grabbers, software, etc. (Woman/White, estab 1989, empl 17, sales $9,000,000, cert: WBENC)

2636　Infinite Supply LLC
15230 N 75th St, Ste 1001　Scottsdale, AZ 85260
(623) 242-1595　Lucas White Regional VP
Fax: (866) 648-0634
Email: lucas@infinite-supply.com
Website: www.infinite-supply.com
Mfg miitary hardware, electrical components, connects, back-shells & aircraft parts. (Woman, estab 2004, empl 10, sales $350,000, cert: State)

2637　Spirit Distribution and Logistics, Inc.
23910 N 19th Ave Ste 26　Phoenix, AZ 85085
(480) 998-1533　Vickie Wessel President
Fax: (480) 998-1427
Email: v.wessel@spiritelectronics.com
Website: www.spiritelectronics.com
Dist passive components, memory products, obsolete & hard-to-find semiconductors & electromechanical devices. (Woman/Nat Ame, estab 1979, empl 15, sales $29,307,000, cert: NMSDC, WBENC)

2638　Tooh Dineh Industries, Inc.
HC 61, Box E　Winslow, AZ 86047
(928) 686-6477　Casey Dooley GM
Fax: (928) 686-6516
Email: cdooley@toohdineh.com
Website: www.toohdineh.com
Electronic mfg services: surface mount technology, thru-hole technology, cables, harnesses. (Nat Ame, estab 1982, empl 63, sales $11,000,000, cert: State)

California

2639　AAA Electrical Supply, Inc.
1014 S Montebello Blvd　Montebello, CA 90640
(323) 721-2700　Alfred Alvarez President
Fax: (323) 721-5437
Email: zirma@aaaelectricalsupply.com
Website: www.aaaelectricalsupply.com
Dist electrical supplies: conduit fittings, wire, cable, steelboxes, weatherproof boxes, lighting, ballasts, hand tools, circuit breakers, panelboards, switchgear, transformers, wiring devices, lamps, incandescent, fluorescent, HID & LED lighting. (Hisp, estab 1988, empl 7, sales $3,426,300, cert: State, City, CPUC)

2640　Aeroflite Enterprises
261 Gemini　Brea, CA 92821
(714) 773-4251　Pamela DePape Sales Mgr
Fax: (714) 773-4973
Email: pdepape@aeroflite.com
Website: www.aeroflite.com
Dist aerospace electronics, custom cable assemblies & electrical connectors assemblies. (Woman/White, estab 1977, empl 65, sales $20,000,000, cert: NWBOC)

2641　American Industrial Control, Inc.
170 N Maple St Ste 104　Corona, CA 92880
(951) 520-0613　Monica Pratt President
Fax: (951) 520-9390
Email: Monica@aicesupply.com
Website: www.aicesupply.com
Dist electrical supplies, mfr industrial control panels. (Woman/Hisp, estab 2000, empl 4, sales $1,010,254, cert: NMSDC, CPUC, WBENC)

2642   AREA51-ESG
     51 Post   Irvine, CA 92618
     (949) 333-5348   Khanh Hoang   OEM Sales
     Fax: (949) 748-0051
     Email: khanh.hoang@area51esg.com
     Website: www.area51esg.com
Dist electronic components, cables, hardware, mil spec hardware, rotables, expandables, etc. (As-Pac, estab 2000, empl 53, sales $24,900,000, cert: NMSDC)

2643   AutoCell Electronics
     7311 Greenhaven Dr   Sacramento, CA 95831
     (888) 393-6668   Mark Hardwick Acct Mgr
     Fax: (916) 393-6871
     Email: mark@autocell.net
     Website: www.autocell.net
CFLs (compact fluorescent lights), linear fluorescent lights, LED (Light Emitting Diode) lights, indoor & outdoor hardwired light fixtures (luminaires), LED Desk Lamps. (As-Pac, estab 2000, empl 5, sales $2,000,000, cert: CPUC)

2644   B&K Electric Wholesale
     P.O. Box 54507   Los Angeles, CA 90054
     (626) 435-2101   Todd Brown CEO
     Fax: (626) 964-1293
     Email: marketing@bk-electric.com
     Website: www.bk-electric.com
Dist electrical products. (Woman/White, estab 1958, empl 80, sales $34,200,000, cert: CPUC, WBENC)

2645   Bright Light LED Inc.
     7751 Alabama Ave, Warehouse 7-8   Canoga Park, CA 91304
     (310) 987-6670   Rami Vardi CEO
     Fax: (800) 770-9788
     Email: rvardi@brightlightled.net
     Website: www.brightlightled.net
Residential & commercial LED bulbs & fixtures. (Woman/White, estab 2008, empl 200, sales $2,050,000, cert: NMSDC)

2646   C Plus Electronics, Inc.
     17842 Irvine Blvd B144   Tustin, CA 92780
     (714) 783-7141   Edgar Castillo Ops Mgr
     Fax: (714) 783-7766
     Email: edgar@cpluselectronics.com
     Website: www.cpluselectronics.com
Dist electronic components: ICs, passives; interconnect products, memory modules & other computer related products. (Woman/Hisp, estab 2004, empl 15, sales $2,150,000, cert: NMSDC, SDB)

2647   Callor Sales, Inc
     3850 Cedar Ave   Long Beach, CA 90807
     (562) 426-6209   Lori Nelson Owner
     Fax: (562) 426-6090
     Email: lori.nelson@callorsales.com
     Website: www.callorsales.com
Dist electrical, electronic & telecommunications materials & equipment. (Woman/White, estab 2005, empl 1, sales , cert: State)

2648   CE Supply
     1111 W Victoria   Compton, CA 90220
     (310) 735-2006   Jonathan Joseph Senior Director
     Fax: (310) 735-2006
     Email: jjoseph@cesupply.com
     Website: www.cesupply.com
Dist wireless & electronics accessories. (Woman/As-Pac, estab 2008, empl 5, sales $2,879,544, cert: CPUC, WBENC)

2649   DWY Inc.
     911 S Primrose Ave, Ste I   Monrovia, CA 91016
     (626) 357-0500   Daniel Yohannes
     Fax: (626) 357-0079
     Email: honeylyn@ecads-na.com
     Website: www.ecads-na.com
Dist LED & solar products, energy saving LED bulbs & solar panels. (AA, estab 2001, empl 4, sales $1,100,000, cert: NMSDC)

2650   Electronic Distribution Services
     5445 Peck Rd   Arcadia, CA 91006
     (626) 258-0400   Dr. G. Martin CEO
     Fax: (626) 258-0401
     Email: drg.martin@eds-sales.com
     Website: www.eds-sales.com
Dist electronics. (AA, estab 1995, empl 10, sales , cert: State)

2651   Forza Electronics
     1110 S El Camino Real Ste C   San Clemente, CA 92672
     (949) 276-8686   James Cassano President
     Fax: (949) 276-8688
     Email: james@forzaelectronics.com
     Website: www.forzaelectronics.com
Dist electronics components, semiconductors, capacitors, resistors, switches, relays, connectors, diodes, computer peripherals, computer hardware & electromechanical devices. (Woman/White, estab 2006, empl 5, sales $794,000, cert: WBENC)

2652   FTS Lighting Services, Inc.
160 S. Cypress St,, Ste 200   Orange, CA 92866
(800) 994-0440   Dorri Daly Project Mgr
Fax: (714) 289-0672
Email: dorri@ftslighting.com
Website: www.ftslighting.com
Energy Saving Lights & Analysis, LEDs, Induction, tubes, ballast, fixtures, aircraft, xenon, HID, Metal halide. (Woman/Hisp, estab 2010, empl 5, sales $350,000, cert: State, CPUC, WBENC)

2653   Integra Electronics, Inc.
1363 Lewis St   Anaheim, CA 92805
(714) 282-4990   Victor Montez President
Fax: (714) 282-4991
Email: vicm@integrasmp.com
Website: www.integrasmp.com
Dist electronic components: Lampholders, Panel Mount indicator lights, incandescent & neon indicator lights, LED Panel lenses & Cable assemblies, Electro-Mechanial products. (Hisp, estab 1997, empl 11, sales $3,960,000, cert: State, NMSDC)

2654   MCV Technologies Inc.
6640 Lusk Blvd, Ste A102   San Diego, CA 92121
(858) 450-0468   Edward Liang VP
Fax: (858) 869-8404
Email: eliang@mcv-microwave.com
Website: www.mcv-microwave.com
MCV Microwave designs, manufactures and markets RF/ Microwave Filter, Antenna, Dielectric Resonator and Microelectronic Circuit. Bandpass Filter, Notch Filter, Lowpass Filter, Highpass Filter, Duplexer, Triplexer, Multiplexer. (Woman/As-Pac, estab 1995, empl 25, sales $2,000,000, cert: CPUC)

2655   Meritke Electronics Corp.
5160 Rivergrade Rd.   Baldwin Park, CA 91706
(626) 373-1728   Oliver Su President
Fax: (626) 214-4075
Email: sales@meritekusa.com
Website: www.meritekusa.com
Dist electronics. (As-Pac, estab 1983, empl 36, sales $20,000,000, cert: NMSDC)

2656   One Source Distributors
3951 Oceanic Dr   Oceanside, CA 92056
(760) 966-4500   Carol Ulak Minority Business Coord
Fax: (760) 966-4599
Email: culak@1sourcedist.com
Website: www.1sourcedist.com
Dist electrical components. (Hisp, estab 1983, empl 295, sales , cert: NMSDC)

2657   Onesource Distributors, Inc.
3951 Oceanic Dr   Oceanside, CA 92056
(760) 966-4500   Jeremy Schmidt Dir diversity & Natl
Fax: (760) 966-4599
Email: jschmidt@1sourcesupplysolutions.com
Website: www.1sourcedist.com
Dist electrical related materials. (Hisp, estab 1983, empl 310, sales $250,000,000, cert: NMSDC)

2658   Perfect Parts Corporation
7545 Irvine Center Dr, Ste 200   Irvine, CA 92618
(949) 209-1655   Lulu Jaff Owner
Fax: (312) 421-4659
Email: lulu@perfectelectronicparts.com
Website: www.perfectelectronicparts.com
Dist electronic components. (Woman, estab 2013, empl 5, sales $50,000, cert: WBENC)

2659   RAK Technologies LLC
23122 Mountain Pine   Mission Viejo, CA 92692
(949) 633-9845   Mark Meeks President
Fax: (949) 340-6460
Email: mark@rak-techca.com
Website: www.raktechca.com
Dist electronic components: semiconductors, connectors, power, sensors, relays etc. (Nat Ame, estab 2007, empl 4, sales , cert: NMSDC)

2660   SilenX Corporation
10606 Shoemaker Ave Ste A   Santa Fe Springs, CA 90670
(562) 941-4200   PK Karunphan Sales Mgr
Fax: (562) 946-3570
Email: pkarun@silenx.com
Website: www.silenx.com
Replace & install energy-efficient LED light tubes. (As-Pac, estab 2004, empl 6, sales $2,077,409, cert: NMSDC)

2661   Steven Engineering, Inc.
230 Ryan Way   South San Francisco, CA 94080
(800) 258-9200   Bonnie A, Walter VP Mktg
Fax: (888) 258-9200
Email: bonnie_walter@steveneng.com
Website: www.stevenengineering.com
Dist electronic pneumatic products, electronic components, electrical parts, industrial automation & controls. (Woman/White, estab 1975, empl 123, sales $46,500,000, cert: CPUC, WBENC)

2662 telCade.Com
2914-24th Avenue San Francisco, CA 94132
(408) 955-9268 Jerry Chan VP of Sales
Fax: (415) 665-0608
Email: jerry@telCade.com
Website: www.catalog.telcade.com/
Custom cable & wire harness, coaxial connector & cables, xDSL/ VDSL filter/splitter, connectors, optical cables & connectors, power cord, power supply adapter/chargers. (Woman/As-Ind, estab 1993, empl 168, sales $6,100,000, cert: CPUC)

2663 THISAI LLC
1834 Blazewood St Simi Valley, CA 93063
(747) 206-3886 Ramalingam Subramaniam Owner
Fax:
Email: ram@thisaillc.com
Website: www.thisaillc.com
Electrical products, cables, switches, wire, lighting fixtures, metal products, aluminum, sheet metal, laser cut, bent & fabricated. (As-Ind/As-Pac, estab 2015, empl 2, sales , cert: State)

2664 Unical Aviation Inc.
4775 Irwindale Ave Irwindale, CA 91706
(626) 813-1901 Ray Daljeet Mgr
Fax: (909) 337-2108
Email: rdaljeet@unical.com
Website: www.unical.com
Kitts, connector, wire, hardware, flight component, Avionic, engine component, MROs. (As-Pac, estab 1990, empl 160, sales $2,000,000, cert: NMSDC)

2665 Waisun Corporation
13321 Alondra Blvd, Ste D Santa Fe Springs, CA 90670
(562) 394-6922 Albert Hui President
Fax: (562) 356-9917
Email: optolight@msn.com
Website: www.optolight.com
Dist LED products, LED light bulbs, recess downlight, etc. (As-Pac, estab 1988, empl 8, sales , cert: CPUC)

2666 Western Switches and Controls, Inc.
2400 Pullman St Santa Ana, CA 92705
(800) 454-8144 Robert Crow Mgr
Fax: (949) 252-9199
Email: bob.crow@westernswitches.com
Website: www.westernswitches.com
Dist electronics: motor control, contactors, timers, relays, safety switches, disconnect switches, switchboards, panelboards, breakers, programmable logic control, AC/DC drives, enclosures, terminal blocks wiring supplies. (As-Pac/Hisp, estab 1976, empl 64, sales , cert: NMSDC)

Colorado

2667 Innov8 Solutions USA,LLC
1500 W 47th Ave Denver, CO 80211
(303) 328-8888 Dan Montoya Dir of sales Ops
Fax: (303) 433-9888
Email: dmontoya@innov8supplies.com
Website: www.innov8solutions.com
Dist electrical & telecommunications supplies, warehouse services of cable stubbing, custom cutting, order fulfillment & kitting operations. (Hisp, estab 2001, empl 20, sales , cert: NMSDC)

District of Columbia

2668 Ideal Electrical Supply Corporation
3515 V St NE Washington, DC 20018
(202) 526-7500 Cora Williams President
Fax: (202) 526-7508
Email: cwilliams@idealelectric.com
Website: www.idealelectric.com
Dist electrical, industrial, data & telecommunications, networking products, lighting tools & safety equipment. (Woman/AA, estab 1991, empl 21, sales $50,000,000, cert: NMSDC, WBENC)

Florida

2669 Aero Supply USA
21941 US Hwy 19 N Clearwater, FL 33765
(727) 754-4915 Robert Ramirez Business Dev Mgr
Fax: (727) 754-4920
Email: rramirez@aerosupplyusa.com
Website: www.aerosupplyusa.com
Dist aerospace parts & electronic components. (Woman/Hisp, estab 2012, empl 12, sales , cert: NMSDC, SDB)

2670 Chase Components LLC
647 Arnau Dr New Smyrna Beach, FL 32168
(386) 426-1367 Cristal Dongilli CEO
Fax:
Email: cristal@chasecomponents.com
Website: www.chasecomponents.com
Dist board level electronic components. (Woman/White, estab 2003, empl 10, sales $2,907,439, cert: WBENC)

2671 Efficient Lighting Technologies
12555 Orange Dr Ste 4002 Fort Lauderdale, FL 33330
(954) 623-7102 Jose Trevino Director of Ops
Fax:
Email: jtrevino@elt-us.com
Website: www.elt-us.com
Dist LED light bulbs & linear fluorescent lamps. (Hisp, estab 2005, empl 22, sales $10,123,250, cert: NMSDC)

2672   LedZed International Inc.
2240 Palm Beach Lakes Blvd   West Palm Beach, FL 33409
(954) 629-0768   Helena Lahtinen CEO
Fax:
Email: helena@ledzed.com
Website: www.ledzed.com
Mfr & dist energy efficiency led lights. (Woman/White, estab 2011, empl 1, sales , cert: City)

2673   The Bernd Group Inc.
1251 Pinehurst Rd   Dunedin, FL 34698
(727) 733-0122   Pilar Bernd President
Fax:
Email: businessdevelopment@berndgroup.com
Website: www.berndgroup.com
Material handling equip, safety products, hand & power tools, pumps & compressors, motors, generators, electrical hardware, batteries, lighting fixtures, lockers, bins, shelving, lab equip. (Woman/Hisp, estab 1992, empl 66, sales , cert: NMSDC)

Georgia

2674   AC & DC Power Technologies
125 Cavalier Ct   Fayetteville, GA 30215
(404) 361-3788   Charles McCartha Office Mgr
Fax: (404) 361-3791
Email: charles@acdcpowertechnologies.com
Website: www.acdcpowertechnologies.com
Integrate, dist & engineer electrical systems: transformers, switchgear, batteries, generators, capacitor banks, resistors, ground fault protection, etc. (Woman/Hisp, estab 1997, empl 14, sales $3,800,000, cert: State, NMSDC, WBENC)

2675   GC Electrical Solutions, LLC
120 Cecil Court   Fayetteville, GA 30214
(770) 716-5400   George Lottier President
Fax: (770) 825-8612
Email: glottier@gcelectrical.com
Website: www.gc-es.com
Dist electrical components: lamps, wire, conduit, panel boards, transformers, fixtures, wiring devices. (AA, estab 2003, empl 5, sales , cert: NMSDC)

2676   NAECO, LLC
100 NAECO Way   Peachtree City, GA 30269
(770) 487-6006   Steven Jones Director, Sales & Mktg
Fax: (770) 487-8525
Email: stevej@naeco.net
Website: www.naeco.net
Dist Electrical Contacts, Contact Assemblies, Tungsten based Heavy Metal Products & Machined Parts. (AA/As-Pac/Hisp, estab 1999, empl 25, sales $11,111,301, cert: NMSDC)

2677   Quality Standby Services, LLC
1649 Sands Place SE Ste C   Marietta, GA 30067
(770) 916-1747   Paul Whitaker GM
Fax: (770) 916-1749
Email: paul@qualitystandbyservices.com
Website: www.qualitystandbyservices.com
Dist, install, maintain & test standby power systems: batteries, battery racks, chargers & spill containment. (Woman/White, estab 2006, empl 20, sales $11,025,722, cert: State)

Illinois

2678   Bearings & Industrial Supply
431 Imen Ave   Addison, IL 60101
(630) 628-1966   Sejal Khandwala Acct Exec
Fax: (630) 628-0116
Email: sejal@bearingsnow.com
Website: www.bearingsnow.com
Dist bearings & power transmission products; pump & pump repair parts, HVAC & electrical parts. (As-Pac, estab 1982, empl 10, sales , cert: NMSDC)

2679   Electric Motor Corporation
3865 N Milwaukee Ave   Chicago, IL 60641
(773) 725-1050   Isabell Siegel President
Fax: (773) 725-1169
Email: Isabell@electricmotorcorp.us
Website: www.electricmotorcorp.us
Electric motor repair. (Woman/White, estab 1960, empl 25, sales $2,488,000, cert: WBENC)

2680   Electro-Kinetics Inc.
859 N Sivert Dr   Wood Dale, IL 60191
(630) 595-6700   Aileen Sonderman President
Fax: (630) 595-7622
Email: aileens@e-kinetics.com
Website: www.e-kinetics.com
Dist electric & electronic components: sensors, relays, contactors, controls, fuses, fuse blocks, circuit breakers, solenoids, timers, transducers, boots/seals, cable cordsets, cable ties, connectors, cord grips, current operated switches. (Woman/As-Pac, estab 1957, empl 8, sales $2,400,000, cert: NMSDC, WBENC)

2681   Electro-Wire Inc.
933 E Remington   Schaumburg, IL 60173
(847) 944-1500   Mike Schmidt VP
Fax: (847) 944-1512
Email: mschmidt@electrowire.com
Website: www.electrowire.com
Dist wire & cable, cable assemblies, mechanical cable, harness assemblies & electromechanical sub-assemblies. (As-Pac, estab 1978, empl 100, sales $80,000,000, cert: NMSDC)

2682 Evergreen Supply Company
312 N. May St Ste B Chicago, IL 60607
(773) 908-1021 Colleen Kramer Owner
Fax: (773) 375-4765
Email: info@evergreensupply.com
Website: www.evergreensupply.com
Dist electronic supplies & materials. (Woman, estab , empl
1, sales , cert: State, WBENC)

2683 Go Green LED-Alternatives, LLC
P.O. Box 277 Yorkville, IL 60560
(630) 802-4213 Sandra Goeken CEO
Fax: (630) 554-8518
Email: s.miles@gogreenled.com
Website: www.gogreenled.com
LED, light, lighting, security, value added reseller, control
systems, street lighti (Woman/White, estab 2008, empl 2,
sales $2,937,513, cert: CPUC, WBENC)

2684 Gordon Electric Supply Co.
1290 N Hobbie Kankakee, IL 60901
(800) 892-1866 Randy Molthan CFO
Fax: (815) 932-7484
Email: rmolthan@gordonelec.com
Website: www.gordonelectricsupply.com
Dist elelctrical supplies. (Woman/White, estab , empl 20,
sales $8,500,000, cert: State, WBENC)

2685 Halogen Lighting Products Corp.
P.O. Box 229 Kaneville, IL 60144
(800) 621-0001 Gloria Stewart President
Fax: (800) 700-6166
Email: info@halogen-lighting.com
Website: www.halogen-lighting.com
LED & fluorescent industrial machine lights with with a
wide range of wattages, lumens capable of operating in
environments of 90 - 260 volts & some are compatible
with 24VDC. (Woman/White, estab 1993, empl 5, sales
$16,602, cert: City, NWBOC)

2686 Hinsdale Lighting
777 N York Rd Ste 19 Hinsdale, IL 60521
(630) 734-0662 David Laughter Warehouse Mgr
Fax: (630) 734-0664
Email: hlighting@hinsdalelighting.com
Website: www.hinsdalelighting.com
Lighting design, light fixture & light bulb distributor.
(Woman/White, estab 2008, empl 6, sales $1,100,000,
cert: WBENC)

2687 JP Simons & Co.
1426 Brook Dr Downers Grove, IL 60641
(630)6930300 Jean Bradfield President
Fax:
Email: roger@jpsimons.net
Website: www.jpsimons.com
Dist wiring devices & switches, electrical tapes, fittings,
wire, cable & cords, transformers, electrical boxes, tools
& testers, terminals & lugs, circuit breakers, fuses &
terminal strips, cables ties, etc. (Woman, estab 1919,
empl 7, sales $10,000,000, cert: State)

2688 Midco Electric Supply
7237 W 90th Pl Bridgeview, IL 60455
(888) 446-4326 Tony Niedospial Sales
Fax: (708) 599-4178
Email: tony@midcoelectric.com
Website: www.midcoelectric.com
Dist motor controls, fuses, wire & wiring devices, circuit
breakers, switches, transformers, tie wraps, conduit &
accessories, liquid tight & fittings, signal towers, PLC's,
HMI's, relays, enclosures, timers, light fixtures, ballasts,
batteries, tape, etc (Woman/White, estab 1979, empl
11, sales $13,500,000, cert: State, WBENC)

2689 Ottsie, LLC
1412 Sioux Dr Ottawa, IL 61350
(815) 378-7841 Sally Rutledge Ott President
Fax: (815) 378-7841
Email: ottsiesupply@gmail.com
Website: www.ottsiesupply.com
Dist electrical & plumbing supplies, generators.
(Woman/White, estab 2014, empl 1, sales $437,000,
cert: State)

Indiana

2690 Diesel Electrical Equipment, Inc.
139 N Griffith Blvd Griffith, IN 46319
(219) 922-1848 Susan Pappas President
Fax: (219) 922-1849
Email: Susan@dieselelectricalequipment.com
Website: www.dieselelectricalequipment.com
Dist & service diesel electric locomotive components.
(Woman, estab , empl 1, sales , cert: WBENC)

2691 UV Solutions, LLC
9118 Pinecreek Court Indianapolis, IN 46256
(317) 345-9899 Calvin Stewart CEO
Fax:
Email: calvin@uvsolutions-indy.com
Website: www.uvsolutions-indy.com
UV germicidal equipment & LED lighting. (AA, estab
2007, empl 3, sales $350,000, cert: State)

Kansas

2692   AJ Smith Enterprise Inc
     9320 Johnson Dr   Merriam, KS 66203
     (913) 677-3008   Leon Delmez
     Fax: (913) 677-3358
     Email: leon.delmez@wattsuplighting.com
     Website: www.wattsuplighting.com
Dist lighting supplies: light bulbs, ballasts, sockets, fixtures, capacitors, starters, lenses, emergency batteries & emergency ballasts, lighting fixtures, LED bulbs & LED tape. (Hisp, estab 1985, empl 7, sales $3,000,000, cert: NMSDC)

Kentucky

2693   Asia-Link, Inc.
     12540 Westport Rd   Louisville, KY 40245
     (502) 394-3900   Andrew Lorenz Admin Mgr
     Fax: (502) 394-3928
     Email: andrew.lorenz@asialnk.com
     Website: www.asialnk.com
Data & communication, coaxial cables & connectors, communication connectors & kits, data/LAN cables, telephone cords, voice & data connectors, wire terminals, insulation displacement connectors, shrink tubing. (Woman/White, estab 1986, empl 18, sales $16,000,000, cert: WBENC)

Massachusetts

2694   C & D Electronics
     28 Appleton St   Holyoke, MA 01040
     (413) 493-1217   Shelly Kubereit Acct Mgr
     Fax: (413) 493-1212
     Email: skubereit@cdindustries.com
     Website: www.cdindustries.com
Dist electronic parts & equipment. (Woman/AA, estab 1982, empl 18, sales $11,000,000, cert: NMSDC)

2695   Eastern States Components, LLC dba ES Components
     108 Pratts Junction Rd   Sterling, MA 01564
     (978) 422-7641   Michelle Aubrey President
     Fax: (978) 422-0011
     Email: maubrey@escomponents.com
     Website: www.escomponents.com
Dist electronic components. (Woman/White, estab 1981, empl 19, sales , cert: WBENC)

2696   Integrated Control Solutions Inc.
     28 Bridge Ave   Scituate, MA 02066
     (781) 545-5100   Tara Miller President
     Fax: (781) 545-1949
     Email: icstara@comcast.net
     Website: www.icsonline.net
Japanese, Korean, and Chinese MRO parts.
Omron, Fuji Electric, Mitsubishi, Idec Relays, motors, gear reducer, sensors, solenoids, breakers, switches, timers,counters (Woman/White, estab 1990, empl 3, sales $1,400,000, cert: WBENC)

Maryland

2697   GreenerVolts
     801 N East St Ste 9A   Frederick, MD 21701
     (888) 495-3629   Erin Ickes Business Devel
     Fax:
     Email: erin@greenervolts.com
     Website: www.greenervolts.com
LED lighting, lighting controls, warehousing & fulfillment. (Hisp, estab 2010, empl 5, sales $1,800,000, cert: NMSDC)

2698   IVS Solutions, LLC
     1040 West St   Laurel, MD 20707
     (240) 487-0295   Brian Smith President
     Fax: (301) 362-4360
     Email: brian.smith@ivssolutions.net
     Website: www.ivssolutions.net
IVS Solutions is a supplier diversity data management company that provides customized information technology solutions to manage and enrich supplier diversity data for corporations. Formed in 2011 to address industry needs of (AA, estab 2011, empl 2, sales , cert: NMSDC)

2699   MX4 Electronics, Inc.
     2203 Greenspring Dr   Timonium, MD 21093
     (410) 252-1192   Susan Grill Owner
     Fax: (410) 561-2458
     Email: susan@mx4elect.com
     Website: www.mx4elect.com
Dist electronic components & accessories. (Woman/White, estab 1976, empl 3, sales $2,821,076, cert: State, City)

Michigan

2700 Arrow Motor & Pump Inc.
692 Central Ave   Wyandotte, MI 48192
(734) 285-5700 Gloria Marquess Inside Sales
Fax: (734) 285-7758
Email: sales@arrowmotor.net
Website: www.arrowmotor.net
Sales & repair electric motors, pumps & power transmission products, reducers, gearmotors, etc. (Woman/White, estab 1988, empl 14, sales $2,128,352, cert: WBENC)

2701 Bluecolt Lighting LLC
4403 Concourse Dr STE B   Ann Arbor, MI 48108
(734) 864-5533 Jaspreet Sawhney
Fax: (800) 646-1880
Email: service@falconinnovations.com
Website: www.bluecoltlighting.com
L.E.D. (Light Emitting Diode) lighting. (As-Ind, estab 2003, empl 9, sales $3,000,000, cert: NMSDC)

2702 Ebinger Manufacturing Company
7869 Kensington Ct   Brighton, MI 48116
(248) 486-8880 Janny Lu President
Fax: (248) 486-8080
Email: emc@ebinger-mfg.com
Website: www.ebinger-mfg.com
Dist electrical, plumbing, work gloves, HVAC & safety products. (Woman/As-Pac, estab 1974, empl 1, sales , cert: NMSDC)

2703 Empire Electric
3575 Vinewood   Detroit, MI 48208
(313) 895-1920 Bob Pauline VP
Fax: (313) 895-1921
Email: bob@empireec.com
Website: www.empirewc.com
Dist electrical, industrial & networking products & supplies. Also mfr wire harnesses & cable assemblies. (AA, estab 2003, empl 10, sales $1,005,000,000, cert: NMSDC)

2704 Industrial Control Service, Inc.
9267 Riley St   Zeeland, MI 49464
(800) 087-8672 Dale Venema VP
Fax: (616) 748-8800
Email: dale@industrialcontrol.com
Website: www.industrialcontrol.com
Dist controls: Cognex, DVT, Banner, Turck, Sunx, X-Rite, Spectrum Illumination,Nerlite, RFID, Microscan, Eaton Cutler-Hammer, Parker, Danaher, IAI, Panasonic, Hyde Park, Giddings & Lewis, Nachi, Encoder Products, GE Industrial. (Nat Ame, estab 1975, empl 10, sales $5,157,803, cert: NMSDC)

2705 Manufacturing & Automation Cost Solutions, LLC
28795 Goddard Rd, Bldg 6, Ste 201   Romulus, MI 48174
(248) 321-2433 Kenneth M President
Fax:
Email: kgutierrez@macostsolutions.com
Website: www.macostsolutions.com
Dist non-production maintenance spare parts in the Electrical and Mechanical sector to support machines, robots, automation and clean rooms. (Hisp, estab 2016, empl 2, sales $500,000, cert: NMSDC)

2706 Opus Auto Systems, Inc.,
4790 Mariners Point P.O. Box 431 Harbor Springs, MI 49740
(248) 613-3344 Shige Baker President
Fax:
Email: opusb@earthlink.net
Website:
Dist electrical cables & wire harnesses, Dc motors, step motors & plastic resins. (Woman/As-Pac, estab 1999, empl 3, sales $510,000, cert: NMSDC)

2707 Sawyer Services Inc.
46405 Continental Dr   Chesterfield, MI 48047
(586) 646-5181 Kim Sawyer Office Mgr
Fax: (586) 816-0323
Email: Kim@sawyerservices.net
Website: www.sawyer-services.com
Design, installation, management & maintenance of facility lighting, electrical & sign systems to achieve significant energy cost savings and more efficient facility operations. (Woman/Hisp, estab 2009, empl 20, sales $3,000,000, cert: NMSDC, WBENC)

2708 Strike Group LLC
18800 Fairway Dr, Ste 10   Detroit, MI 48221
(313) 586-0003 Lane coleman President
Fax: (313) 586-0003
Email: Lanec@strikegroup.org
Website: www.strikegroup.org
Dist electrical products. (AA, estab 1998, empl 3, sales $3,200,000, cert: NMSDC)

2709 York Electric Motors, Inc.
611 Andre St   Bay City, MI 48706
(989) 684-7460 Thomas Hunter Acct Mgr
Fax: (989) 684-7465
Email: tomh@yorkelectric.com
Website: www.yorkelectric.com
Dist & svc electric motors, generators, transformers, inverters, pumps, etc. (Nat Ame, estab 1971, empl 37, sales , cert: NMSDC)

Minnesota

2710 Carlo Lachmansingh Sales, Inc.
      4801 4th Ave S   Minneapolis, MN 55419
      (612) 827-2211 Carl Lachmansingh VP
      Fax: (612) 821-0161
      Email: carlo@carloelectrical.com
      Website: www.carloelectrical.com
Dist electrical supplies. (As-Ind, estab 1990, empl 2, sales
$2,800,000, cert: State, 8(a))

2711 JCB Enterprises, Inc. dba Reluminate
      1408 Northland Dr, Ste 105   Mendota Heights, MN
      55120
      (612) 378-1677 Brigid Brady CEO
      Fax: (612) 378-7870
      Email: brigid@reluminate.com
      Website: www.reluminate.com
Commercial lighting service, interior & exterior lighting.
(Woman/White, estab 2014, empl 10, sales $1,450,000,
cert: WBENC)

2712 Recycle Technologies, Inc.
      4000 Winnetka Ave N, Ste 210   Minneapolis, MN
      55427
      (763) 559-5130 Lynn Petros CEO
      Fax: (763) 559-0840
      Email: Lynn@recycletechnologies.com
      Website: www.recycletechnologies.com
Recycle fluorescent bulbs, ballasts, batteries, electronics,
computers, mercury containing devices, & special industrial waste. (Woman/White, estab 1993, empl 18, sales
$2,010,000, cert: WBENC)

Missouri

2713 Communications & Electrical Supplies, Inc.
      13288 Newt Dr   Neosho, MO 64850
      (417) 451-1789 Amanda Murphy Accts Mgr
      Fax: (417) 451-3111
      Email: amanda@ceslive.com
      Website: www.ceslive.com
Dist tools & electrical equipment. (Woman/White, estab
1990, empl 8, sales $3,000,000, cert: WBENC)

2714 Cooling Components Inc.
      2320 Marconi Ave   St. Louis, MO 63110
      (314) 772-8311 Julia Taylor President
      Fax: (314) 772-1313
      Email: julia@coolingcomponents.com
      Website: www.coolingcomponents.com
Dist, service, repair & erect cooling towers & related
equipment. (Woman/White, estab 2000, empl 10, sales ,
cert: State, WBENC)

2715 Electronic Supply Co, Inc.
      4100 Main St   Kansas City, MO 64111
      (816) 931-0250 Bob Niekamp Mgr
      Fax: (816) 753-2595
      Email: bobn@eskc.com
      Website: www.eskc.com
Dist electronic parts, wire/cable, tools, test equipment,
security cameras & systems, access control systems,
computer networking equipment. (Woman/White, estab
1952, empl 33, sales $17,300,000, cert: City)

2716 US Electronics Inc.
      1590 Page Industrial Blvd   Saint Louis, MO 63132
      (314) 423-7550 Anil Arekapudi President
      Fax: (314) 423-0585
      Email: anil@us-electronics.com
      Website: www.us-electronics.com
Dist electrical & electronic components. Mfr electrical
bulbs, Halogen, energy saving & LED bulbs. (As-Ind,
estab 1995, empl 15, sales $2,200,000, cert: NMSDC)

North Carolina

2717 Tiger Controls Inc.
      7615 Business Park Dr   Greensboro, NC 27409
      (336) 889-6265 Neeta Singh President
      Fax: (336) 889-5436
      Email: neeta@tigercontrols.com
      Website: www.tigercontrols.com
Dist electronic, electrical & industrial supplies. (Woman/
As-Pac, estab 1999, empl 23, sales $9,005,000, cert:
NMSDC)

2718 Video & Security Specialists
      2313 Wedgewood Dr   Matthews, NC 28104
      (704) 821-9396 Erika Gordon Partner
      Fax: (704) 821-9396
      Email: egordon@carolina.rr.com
      Website: www.videoandsecurityspecialists.com
Dist electrical & security products: alarm/security
systems, fire alarm systems, structured wiring, access
control, security cameras, networking, phone system,
intercom & gates. (Woman/White, estab 1975, empl 7,
sales $220,866, cert: State)

New Jersey

2719   Samson Electrical Supply Co Inc
1764 New Durham Road   South Plainfield, NJ 07080
(732) 393-7070   Joan Cohen President
Fax: (732) 777-0743
Email: yourdiversesupplier@samsonelectrical.com
Website: www.samsonelectrical.com
Dist electrical supplies. (Woman/White, estab 1949, empl 51, sales $36,225,000, cert: City, WBENC)

2720   Weissco Power Limited Liability Company
516 Route 513   Califon, NJ 07830
(908) 832-2173   Stacy Weiss President
Fax: (908) 832-2121
Email: sweiss@weisscopower.com
Website: www.weisscopower.com
DIst uninterruptible power supply products & services, preventative maintenance, emergency services, load testing, battery installation & removal, equipment removal & battery maintenance. (Woman/White, estab 1999, empl 10, sales $2,700,000, cert: State)

Nevada

2721   Codale Energy Services & Supply, LLC
3920 W Sunset Rd, Ste A   Las Vegas, NV 89118
(702) 384-8500   Oscar Aliaga President
Fax:
Email: oscara@codaleess.com
Website: www.codaleess.com
Dist electrical supplies: commercial construction, hospitality MRO, solar, comm data, Outside plant, & Utility. (Hisp, estab 2010, empl 21, sales $21,500,000, cert: NMSDC)

New York

2722   Aurora Electric Inc.
141 Federal Circle   Jamaica, NY 11430
(718) 371-0385   Veronica Rose President
Fax: (718) 371-0390
Email: vrose@auroraelectric.org
Website: www.auroraelectric.org
Data communication & electrical installation & maintenance. (Woman/White, estab 1993, empl 17, sales $795,628, cert: State, City)

2723   Deep Roof Lighting
27 Hall St   Brooklyn, NY 11205
(718) 243-9388   Jay Chen Exec
Fax: (718) 243-9403
Email: deeproof@aol.com
Website: www.deeprooflighting.com
Software controlled patent daylight harvest dimming control system. Dimmanble LED, Dimmable and Non-dim Fluorescent, HID, Halogen Recess housings, Track lighting, Pendant lights, Flush mount ceiling. (As-Pac, estab 1997, empl 7, sales $2,000,000, cert: City)

2724   East Coast Metallic Tubing & Hardware Supply Corp
1951 Ocean Ave, Unit 4   Ronkonkoma, NY 11779
(631) 676-5570   Deborah Ehmann CEO
Fax: (631) 981-1063
Email: eastcoastmthsc@aol.com
Website: www.eastcoastmetallic.com
Dist metallic & conduit hardware. (Woman/White, estab 2001, empl 2, sales $80,053, cert: State)

2725   Edge Electronics Inc.
75 Orville Dr   Bohemia, NY 11716
(631) 471-3343   Mitchel Auerbach VP Ops
Fax: (631) 471-3405
Email: mauerbach@edgeelectronics.com
Website: www.edgeelectronics.com
Dist electronics. (Woman/White, estab 1990, empl 34, sales $33,009,000, cert: City, WBENC)

2726   Linrose Electronics Inc.
29 Cain Dr   Plainview, NY 11803
(516) 293-2520   Debra Freedman President
Fax: (516) 292-2464
Email: debra@linrose.com
Website: www.linrose.com
Dist CML - Led indicators. (Woman/White, estab 1964, empl 5, sales $510,000, cert: WBENC)

2727   North Shore Components Inc.
9 Sawgrass Dr   Bellport, NY 11713
(631) 504-6038   David Hochhauser Acct Mgr
Fax: (631) 924-5243
Email: davidh@nscomponents.com
Website: www.nscomponents.com
Dist IC's, semiconductors, capacitors, connectors, resistors, diodes, etc. (Woman/White, estab 2001, empl 22, sales , cert: WBENC)

2728 Serendipity Electronics, Inc.
      152 E Main St   Huntington, NY 11743
      (631) 424-2244 Yovanna Camargo Acct Mgr
      Fax: (631) 424-2208
      Email: yovannac@serendipityelectronics.com
      Website: www.serendipityelectronics.com
Dist electronic components; capacitors, resistors, diodes,
computer peripherals, active & passive components.
(Woman/White, estab 1992, empl 9, sales $19,000,000,
cert: WBENC)

2729 Southtown Electronics Inc.
      75 Lake St   Hamburg, NY 14075
      (716) 648-6565 Heather Sidorowicz Owner
      Fax:
      Email: heather@southtownav.com
      Website: www.southtownav.com
Dist & install commercial Audio Video Technology Solutions: Audio Video Systems, Digital Signage, Electronics
Sales (TVs, Speakers, Racking Equipment), Music Systems,
interactive Rooms & Conference rooms. (Woman/White,
estab 1984, empl 6, sales , cert: State)

2730 Venus Power-Com Supply, LLC
      54-07 46th St   Maspeth, NY 11378
      (646) 248-7050 Sheena King President
      Fax: (646) 248-7052
      Email: sheena@venussupply.com
      Website: www.venussupply.com
Dist electrical, data & power products. (Woman, estab
2014, empl 5, sales , cert: City, WBENC)

Ohio

2731 CEC Electronics Corporation
      1739 Akron Peninsula Rd   Akron, OH 44313
      (330) 916-8100 Valerie George Acct Rep
      Fax:
      Email: vgeorge@cecelectronics.com
      Website: www.cecelectronics.com
Dist electronic components. (Hisp, estab 1981, empl 9,
sales , cert: State)

2732 Daycoa, Incorporated
      50 Walnut Rd P.O. Box 8 Medway, OH 45341
      (937) 849-1315 Tamela Chenault Sales Consultant
      Fax: (937) 849-1165
      Email: tami@daycoa.com
      Website: www.daycoa.com
Dist lighting products. (Woman/White, estab 1957, empl
14, sales $33,866,096, cert: WBENC)

2733 E-Z Electric Motor Service, Inc.
      8510 Bessemer Avenue   Cleveland, OH 44127
      (216) 581-8820 Demetrius Ledgyard VP sales
      Fax: (216) 581-8618
      Email: demetrius@ezelectricmotor.com
      Website: www.ezelectricmotor.com
Dist & repair electric motors: complete rewinds, rebuild, machine shop services, repair pumps, & gearboxs,
dynamic balancing. (AA, estab 1965, empl 16, sales
$196,687, cert: State, NMSDC)

2734 Mirg Corporation
      6270 Este Ave   Cincinnati, OH 45232
      (513) 679-2020 Michael Griffie President
      Fax: (513) 679-2032
      Email: mgriffie@mirgcorp.com
      Website: www.mirgcorp.com
Dist electrical supplies, electrical contracting. (AA, estab
1989, empl 9, sales , cert: State, NMSDC)

2735 Peak Electric, Inc.
      320 N Byrne Rd   Toledo, OH 43607
      (419) 726-4848 Milton McIntyre President
      Fax: (419) 726-6206
      Email: mmcintyre@peakelectrictoledo.com
      Website: www.peakelectrictoledo.com
Dist lighting, LED indoor & outdoor, fixtures, lamps,
ballast & components, switchgear, transformers,
panelboards & disconnects, fuses, wire, conduits, fittings
& boxes, telecommunication equip, high voltage equip.
(Woman/AA, estab 2000, empl 3, sales $7,000,000, cert:
State, City, NMSDC)

2736 US Communications and Electric
      4933 Neo Pkwy   Garfield Heights, OH 44128
      (216) 478-0810 Jim Connole COO
      Fax: (216) 478-0829
      Email: jconnole@uscande.com
      Website: www.uscande.com
Technology-based communications cabling systems,
design & install outdoor copper systems, horizontal
copper cabling solutions. (Woman/White, estab 1996,
empl 78, sales $17,000,000, cert: State, City, WBENC)

2737 Wheatley Electric Service Co.
      2046 Ross Ave Cincinnati, OH 45212
      (513) 531-4951 Dorothy Elsbrock President
      Fax: (513) 531-5035
      Email: motor@fuse.net
      Website: www.wheatleyelectric.com
Dist & repair electric motors & pumps, recondition,
rebuild & re-design motors. (Woman/White, estab 1934,
empl 9, sales , cert: WBENC)

Oregon

2738   Super Stores Service
       11170 SW 5th St   Beaverton, OR 97005
       (800) 462-2370 Mary Kroger Acct Mgr
       Fax: (503) 366-5939
       Email: MaryK@superstoresservice.com
       Website: www.superstoresservice.com
Dist replacement parts for manual & electric pallet jacks used to handle palletized goods. (Woman/White, estab 1986, empl 20, sales $4,200,000, cert: WBENC)

Pennsylvania

2739   Decision Distribution America, Inc.
       4548 Market St, Ste 215   Philadelphia, PA 19139
       (215) 493-4400 Bernie Hopewell President
       Fax: (215) 324-3292
       Email: bernie@ddistribution.com
       Website: www.ddistribution.com
Dist electrical, hvac, mechanical, plumbing, supplies & equipment. (AA/As-Pac, estab 2004, empl 7, sales $14,000,000, cert: State, NMSDC)

2740   DEW Electric, Inc.
       189 Enterprise Ln   Connellsville, PA 15425
       (724) 628-9711 Wendy Wiltrout CEO
       Fax: (724) 628-9722
       Email: wendy@dewelectric.com
       Website: www.dewelectric.com
Dust & repair motors, electronic drives, gearboxes, generators, control panel fabrication. (Woman/White, estab 1993, empl 4, sales $935,000, cert: WBENC)

2741   Electrical Systems & Construction Supplies
       5131-37 N 2nd St, Bldg 12   Philadelphia, PA 19120
       (215) 324-3291 Bernard Hopewell CEO
       Fax: (215) 324-3292
       Email: bhopewell@escsinc.net
       Website: www.escsinc.net
Dist electrical equipment, construction supplies, wire & cable & lighting. (AA, estab 2003, empl 3, sales $1,440,000, cert: State, City)

2742   Lights for Less, LLC
       500 N Walnut Rd   Kennett Square, PA 19348
       (610) 925-5740 Melissa Nolan
       Fax: (610) 925-5741
       Email: mnolan@lightsforlessllc.com
       Website: www.l4less.com
Dist lamps, fixtures & ballasts. (Woman/White, estab 1998, empl 3, sales $1,330,000, cert: State, WBENC)

2743   R. Scheinert & Sons, Inc.
       10092 Sandmeyer Ln   Philadelphia, PA 19116
       (215) 673-9800 Sheree Miller President
       Fax: (215) 673-9360
       Email: sheree@scheinert.com
       Website: www.scheinert.com
Repair, rewind & dist AC & DC electric motors, pump repair & refurbish, new cooling tower technology, eliminating gearboxes, warranty center. (Woman/White, estab 1904, empl 24, sales $6,000,000, cert: City, WBENC)

2744   Unity Electric Discount, LLC
       5040 Overbrook Ave   Philadelphia, PA 19131
       (267) 701-5856 Clyde Mason CEO
       Fax:
       Email: cmason215@verizon.net
       Website:
Dist electric generation supplies. (AA, estab 2011, empl 4, sales $22,000, cert: City, NMSDC)

2745   Valenko Incorporated
       4124 Clendenning Rd   Gibsonia, PA 15044
       (888) 908-6322 Jim Perko VP
       Fax: (888) 908-6334
       Email: info@valenko.com
       Website: www.valenko.com
Dist electrical products: custom transformers, panels, wire, cable, power distribution equipment, hand tools, conduit, couplings, cable assemblies, cable management, UPS, data center. (Woman/White, estab 2007, empl 5, sales $4,013,000, cert: State)

Puerto Rico

2746   Wholesale Electric Caribe Inc.
       P.O. Box 2057   Barceloneta, PR 00617
       (787) 846-5755 Miguel Barrios President
       Fax: (787) 846-5777
       Email: sales@wecipr.com
       Website: www.wecipr.com
Dist electronic products: automation & control products. (Hisp, estab 1999, empl 43, sales $7,331,560, cert: NMSDC)

South Carolina

2747   Carolina Product Solutions, LLC
       P.O. Box 12901 Florence, SC 29504
       (843) 409-6922 Sean Tanner President
       Fax: (843) 669-3443
       Email: stanner@cpsled.com
       Website: www.cpsled.com
LED Lighting. (Nat Ame, estab 2008, empl 4, sales $2,800,000, cert: NMSDC)

2748   Electritex
     321 Alliance Parkway   Williamston, SC 29697
     (864) 226-4438   Tracie Craft President
     Fax: (864) 226-9338
     Email: andersonoffice@electritex.com
     Website: www.electritex.com
Dist & service electric motors. (Woman/White, estab 1980, empl 20, sales , cert: WBENC)

Tennessee

2749   Diversified Supply, Inc.
     210 N Highland Park Ave   Chattanooga, TN 37404
     (314) 502-0490   Janice Brown Acct Mgr
     Fax: (423) 698-1554
     Email: jbrown@diversifiedsupply.com
     Website: www.diversifiedsupply.com
DIst electrical & instrument materials. (AA, estab 1987, empl 51, sales $35,000,000, cert: NMSDC)

2750   Edwards Supply Company
     315 Oak Ridge Turnpike   Oak Ridge, TN 37830
     (865) 483-1766   Tracie Miller CEO
     Fax: (865) 483-3562
     Email: tracie@edwardssupply.com
     Website: www.edwardssupply.com
Dist electrical supplies: ballast, batteries, conduit, electric, electrical, janitorial, lamps, lighting, motors, tools, wire. (Woman/Nat Ame, estab 1993, empl 14, sales $3,800,000, cert: NMSDC, WBENC)

2751   Industrial Sales Company of Memphis Inc.
     7520 Bartlett Corporate Dr   Bartlett, TN 38133
     (901) 380-5460   Judy May Owner
     Fax: (901) 380-5570
     Email: judymay1@bellsouth.net
     Website:
Dist electrical components. (Woman/White, estab 1965, empl 10, sales $4,800,000, cert: City)

Texas

2752   Advanced Equipment Co. dba Prime Distributing Co.
     P.O. Box 946   Allen, TX 75013
     (972) 562-0170   Carole Booth Inside Sales
     Fax: (972) 542-5844
     Email: caroleb@primedistributing.com
     Website: www.primedistributing.com
Dist electronic components. (Woman/White, estab 1972, empl 8, sales $1,135,426, cert: WBENC)

2753   Crawford and Wilson Enterprises
     1251 Industrial Blvd, Ste A   Plano, TX 75074
     (972) 422-2280   Lena Wilson Owner
     Fax: (972) 422-5852
     Email: cwelectric@att.net
     Website:
Electrical materials, GE lighting, indoor fixtures, outdoor fixtures, hazardous location, control systems, signage, non-led lamps, refit solutions, led lamps and modules, transportation, ballast and drivers, refrigerated display, wire, lamps. (Woman/White, estab 1978, empl 5, sales , cert: State)

2754   Demand Lighting USA Inc
     1321 Rutherford Lane Ste 150,   Austin, TX 78753
     (512) 822-1100   Gary Morrissey COO
     Fax: (512) 312-7386
     Email: garymorrissey@demandlighting.com
     Website: www.demandlighting.com
Dist DLC, Energy Star LED lighting solutions. (Woman/White, estab 2013, empl 12, sales $2,600,000, cert: State, WBENC, SDB)

2755   Mavich LLC
     525 Commerce St.   Southlake, TX 76092
     (682) 503-4484   Vincent Manfredini Ops
     Fax: (682) 503-6576
     Email: Vincent.Manfredini@mavich.com
     Website: www.mavich.com
Dist MRO & industrial supplies: electronic components, connectors, passives, resistors, etc. (Woman/Hisp, estab 2010, empl 10, sales $3,000,000, cert: State)

2756   NOVA Electronic Materials LLC
     1189 Porter Rd   Flower Mound, TX 75022
     (972) 478-7002   Lauri Boudreaux President
     Fax: (972) 478-7110
     Email: lboudreaux@novawafers.com
     Website: www.novawafers.com
Dist silicon wafers & cleanroom consumables. (Woman/White, estab 1989, empl 5, sales $4,216,523, cert: State)

2757   Specialty Optical Systems, Inc.
     10210 Forest Ln   Dallas, TX 75243
     (214) 340-8574   Terry Nelson
     Fax: (214) 340-5723
     Email: Sales@SOSsupply.com
     Website: www.soslightbulbs.com
Dist lightbulbs: lamps & bulbs, ballasts & fixtures. (Woman/White, estab 1981, empl 14, sales $5,015,000, cert: WBENC)

2758   Supa Tech Inc.
     17304 Preston Rd Ste 800   Dallas, TX 75252
     (972) 238-8958   Sue Glover President
     Fax:
     Email: sglover@supatech.net
     Website: www.supatech.net
Information technology products & printed circuit boards. (Woman/Nat Ame, estab 1980, empl 3, sales $285,000, cert: State)

2759 Telecom Electric Supply Company
1304 Capital Ave   Plano, TX 75074
(972) 422-0012 Bill Hargraves Sales Exec
Fax: (972) 422-0467
Email: bill@tes.com
Website: www.tes85.com
Dist electric, utility, construction & telecommunication
supplies. (AA, estab 1985, empl 16, sales $22,900,000,
cert: State, NMSDC)

2760 Villarreal & Sons Enterprises, Inc.
P.O. Box 2258   Anthony, TX 79821
(915) 351-2444 Rick Villarreal President
Fax: (915) 351-7979
Email: Linda@Electric-1.com
Website: www.Electric-1.com
Electrical construction, voice, data & video network
cabling, power analysis, control systems repair & installa-
tion, custom lighting design. (Hisp, estab 1986, empl 10,
sales , cert: State)

2761 Wholesale Electric Supply of Houston
4040 Gulf Fwy   Houston, TX 77004
(713) 749-8461 Pam McKellop President
Fax: (713) 749-8418
Email: khighland@wholesaleelectric.com
Website: www.wholesaleelectric.com
Dist electrical & data communications material. (Woman/
White, estab 1949, empl 284, sales , cert: WBENC)

Virginia

2762 Bright Regards LLC
5837 Governors Hill Dr   Alexandria, VA 22310
(703) 349-1709 Yvonne Herrera President
Fax: (703) 960-6056
Email: yvonne@brightregards.com
Website: www.brightregards.com
Commercial LED, induction & solar lighting solutions.
(Woman/As-Pac, estab 2014, empl 1, sales $15,000, cert:
State)

2763 Delta Automation, Inc.
2704 Charles City Rd   Richmond, VA 23231
(804) 236-2800 Margarete Culley CEO
Fax: (804) 236-2900
Email: plc@deltaautomation.com
Website: www.deltaautomation.com
Industrial electronic control equipment, PLCs & drives.
(Woman/White, estab 1996, empl 19, sales , cert: State)

2764 JO KELL Inc.
1716 Lambert Ct   Chesapeake, VA 23320
(904) 260-8420 Patricia Galiney
Fax: (904) 260-8401
Email: customerservice@jokell.com
Website: www.jokell.com
Dist electrical apparatus & equipment, wiring supplies &
related equipment. (Woman/White, estab 1977, empl
50, sales $30,383,075, cert: WBENC)

2765 Reynolds Lighting Supply Co.
606 Research Rd   Richmond, VA 23236
(804) 897-2300 Valerie Reynolds President
Fax: (804) 379-7853
Email: Valarie@reynoldslighting.com
Website:
Dist replacement light bulbs, ballasts, fixtures, electrical
& electronic items. (Woman/White, estab 1987, empl 7,
sales $2,250,000, cert: State)

Vermont

2766 Granite City Electric Supply
14 Morse Rd   Bennington, VT 05201
(617) 472-6500 Phyllis Papani Godwin Chairman
of the Board
Fax: (617) 773-8941
Email: phyllisg@granitecityelectric.com
Website: www.granitecityelectric.com
Dist electrical products. (Woman/White, estab 1923,
empl 70, sales $90,000,000, cert: State)

Washington

2767 Mobile Electrical Distributors, Inc.
14050 Lake City Way NE   Seattle, WA 98125
(206) 363-2400 Tanya Hallett Sales
Fax: (206) 363-2781
Email: tanya.hallett@mobileelec.com
Website: www.mobileelec.com
Dist electrical supplies: ballasts, boxes, conduit &
fittings, lighting, service gear, tools, testers, wire, wiring
devices, motor controls, fuses, etc. (Woman/White,
estab 1956, empl 11, sales $925,000, cert: State)

Wisconsin

2768 First American Engineered Solutions, LLC
136 Jackson St, Ste C   Oshkosh, WI 54901
(920) 231-8501 Gerald Morris President
Fax: (920) 231-8506
Email: gmorris@firstamericanllc.com
Website: www.firstamericanllc.com
Dist electronics, electrical equipment, industrial equipment & supplies, office equipment & supplies & ordnance. (Nat Ame, estab 1997, empl 12, sales $4,500,000,
cert: NMSDC, 8(a))

ELECTRONICS & ELECTRICAL MFG.
Firms design, develop and make (turnkey) electro-mechanical devices on contract or market their own products such as power supplies, test equipment, guidance systems, robotics, radar, CMOS-IC, connectors, modems, military trainers, motors, etc. NAICS Code 33

Alabama

2769 Global Manufacturing, Inc.
248 N Main St Arab, AL 35016
(256) 789-0948 Kathy Bennefield Mgr
Fax: (256) 586-1544
Email: kathy@globalmanufacturing.us
Website: www.globalmanufacturing.us
Custom fabricated wire harnesses & cables, Data cables, MIL-SPEC, Coaxial, Power assemblies. (Hisp, estab 2014, empl 17, sales $1,824,260, cert: NMSDC)

California

2770 Abbott Technologies
8203 Vineland Ave Sun Valley, CA 91352
(818) 504-0644 Kerima Batte President
Fax: (818) 768-0395
Email: kmbatte@abbott-tech.com
Website: www.abbott-tech.com
Power Management Solutions, Military Transformers & Rectifiers, Custom Power Supplies & Magnetic Components, Wide Range of AC to DC Standard. (Woman/Hisp, estab 1961, empl 43, sales $5,110,790, cert: State)

2771 American Industrial Control, Inc.
170 N Maple St Ste 104 Corona, CA 92880
(951) 520-0613 Monica Pratt President
Fax: (951) 520-9390
Email: Monica@aicesupply.com
Website: www.aicesupply.com
Dist electrical supplies, mfr industrial control panels. (Woman/Hisp, estab 2000, empl 4, sales $1,010,254, cert: NMSDC, CPUC, WBENC)

2772 Berkeley Integration Group dba Fiber.com
2200 Powell St, Ste 1200 Emeryville, CA 94608
(510) 227-5583 Sophia Mendoza-Hirano Acct/Sales Mgr
Fax: (510) 217-4450
Email: sophia@fiber.com
Website: www.fiber.com
Fiber optic cables, connectors and accessories, fiber jumpers, patch cords, pigtails, multi-strand, armored, aerial, indoor/outdoor, plenum, LSZH. (As-Pac, estab 1989, empl 4, sales , cert: NMSDC)

2773 Bishop-Wisecarver Corporation
2104 Martin Way Pittsburg, CA 94565
(888) 580-8272 Barbara Williams Supplier Diversity Admin
Fax: (925) 439-5931
Email: bwilliams@bwc.com
Website: www.bwc.com
Mfr linear & rotary motion components, custom engineering services, bearings, vee guide wheels, linear guides, linear actuator, custom machine shop, XYZ systems, gantry, rotary tables, custom assembly, linear slides, linear bearing, dualvee. (Woman/White, estab 1950, empl 58, sales $21,000,000, cert: WBENC)

2774 Calpak USA, Inc.
13750 Prairie Ave Hawthorne, CA 90250
(310) 937-7335 Danish Qureshi VP
Fax: (310) 937-7219
Email: danish@calpak-usa.com
Website: www.calpak-usa.com
Electronic Design, Electronics Engineering, Contract Manufacturing Services (CMS), Electronic Manufacturing Services (EMS), PCB Layout, PCB Design, PCB Assembly. (As-Pac, estab 1978, empl 15, sales $2,400,000, cert: State, NMSDC, SDB)

2775 Century Wire & Cable
7400 E Slauson Ave Commerce, CA 90040
(800) 999-5566 Bob Arthur Acct Exec
Fax: (323) 888-9430
Email: arthur@centurywire.com
Website: www.centurywire.com
Mfr electrical wire & cable products. (Hisp, estab 1965, empl 110, sales $40,000,000, cert: City)

2776 Doc Stephens Scientific
5851 S Garth Ave Los Angeles, CA 90056
(310) 568-9082 David Stephens CEO
Fax: (310) 568-9082
Email: david.stephens@dsscientific.com
Website: www.dsscientific.com
Equipment & electronic manufacturing services related to infrared, visual cameras & imaging systems, RF & high speed fiber optic telecommunication circuits, sensor designs, silicon III-V semiconductor processing. (AA, estab 2014, empl 2, sales , cert: NMSDC)

2777 Interlog Corporation
1295 N Knollwood Circle Anaheim, CA 92801
(714) 529-7808 Justin Kwon President
Fax: (714) 527-6436
Email: jkwon@interlogcorp.com
Website: www.interlogcorp.com
Mfr lighting & signal products for commercial, construction & automotive market. (As-Pac, estab 1993, empl 26, sales $9,000,000, cert: State)

2778 KR Wolfe, Inc.
10015 Maine Ave   Lakeside, CA 92040
(619) 368-1544 Kasey Pitchford Director of Client Relations
Fax: (619) 749-7339
Email: Kasey.pitchford@krwolfe.com
Website: www.krwolfe.com
Low voltage systems installation & integration, design, layout & installation/integration of A/V & control systems. (Woman/White, estab 2007, empl 34, sales $5,500,000, cert: WBENC)

2779 Ledtronics, Inc.
23105 Kashiwa Court   Torrance, CA 90505
(630) 243-0412 Janelle Mika-Palmer Manufacturer Rep
Fax: (630) 243-0411
Email: janemika@mikasales.com
Website: www.ledtronics.com
Design & mfr light emitting diodes (LEDs). (As-Ind/As-Pac, estab 1983, empl 125, sales $12,470,700, cert: NMSDC, CPUC)

2780 Magnuson Products LLC
1990 Knoll Dr Bldg A   Ventura, CA 93003
(805) 765-5562 Nader Rayes Brand Mgr
Fax:
Email: nader.rayes@magnusonproducts.com
Website: www.magnusonsuperchargers.com
Design, fabrication & mfr superchargers. (Woman/White, estab 2010, empl 60, sales $14,649,000, cert: WBENC)

2781 Micro Analog Inc.
1861 Puddingstone Dr   La Verne, CA 91750
(909) 392-8277 Kim Bickmeier Dir of Sales
Fax: (909) 392-3487
Email: kimbickmeier@micro-analog.com
Website: www.micro-analog.com
Mfr electronics: printed circuit board assembly PCBA, custom cable & wire harness assembly, box/system build. (Woman/As-Pac, estab 1991, empl 155, sales $15,698,000, cert: NMSDC)

2782 Myers Power Products, Inc.
2950 E Philadelphia St   Ontario, CA 91761
(909) 923-1800 Diana Grootonk CEO
Fax: (951) 278-1648
Email: diana.grootonk@myerspower.com
Website: www.myerspower.com
Mfr low voltage & med voltage electrical distribution equipment, 5,15,27 & 38kv switchgear, LV switchgear, switchboards, panel boards, inverters, converters & electrical products & circuit breakers. (Woman/White, estab 2001, empl 500, sales $263,101,084, cert: CPUC, WBENC)

2783 NexEco Energy Conservation, Inc.
9370 Studio Court, Ste 168   Elk Grove, CA 95758
(855) 711-6868 Nick Potter Acct Mgr
Fax: (916) 393-8228
Email: nick@nexeco.net
Website: www.nexeco.net
Mfr energy efficient LED lighting products, LED Bulbs, LED Fixtures, LED Hardwired Interior Ceiling Fixture, LED Hardwired Exterior Porch lanterns, LED Hardwired Vanity Fixture. (Woman/As-Pac, estab 2016, empl 5, sales $800,000, cert: State)

2784 One-E-Way, Inc.
3016 E Colorado Blvd Ste 70848   Pasadena, CA 91107
(310) 743-4081 Cedric Woolfork CFO/VP
Fax:
Email: cedric@one-e-way.com
Website: www.wayvz.com/
Design & mgr electronic products. (AA, estab 2004, empl 5, sales $90,800, cert: NMSDC)

2785 PalPilot Corp.
3000 Kenneth St   Santa Clara, CA 95054
(408) 855-8866 Amy Huang Acct Mgr
Fax: (408) 855-8868
Email: amy.huang@palpilot.com
Website: www.palpilot.com
Printed circuit board design & offshore mfg, CM, plastics, sheet metal & connectors. (Woman/As-Ind, estab 1988, empl 100, sales , cert: State)

2786 Philatron Wire and Cable
15315 Cornet Ave   Santa Fe Springs, CA 90670
(562) 802-2570 Phillip Ramos III GM
Fax: (562) 921-5770
Email: p3@philatron.com
Website: www.philatron.com
Design & mfr electrical, electronic, instrumentation, control & communication wire & cable. (Hisp, estab 1974, empl 85, sales $24,000,000, cert: NMSDC)

2787 Precise Panel Engraving, Inc.
12881 Western Ave, Unit B   Garden Grove, CA 92841
(714) 898-6510 Joan VonKarvaly President
Fax:
Email: precisepanel@verizon.net
Website: www.government-vendor.us/
precisepanel
Industrial engraving: signs, labels, nameplates, control panels; sheet metal fab; metal & plastic panel machining; mylar & metal marking. (Woman/White, estab 1978, empl 7, sales $255,000, cert: CPUC)

2788　Pro-Lite
　　　3505 Cadillac Ave, Bldg D　Costa Mesa, CA 92626
　　　(714) 668-9988　Andy Kaoh President
　　　Fax: (714) 668-9898
　　　Email: ak@pro-lite.com
　　　Website: www.pro-lite.com
Mfr LED signs & LED displays. (As-Pac, estab 1981, empl
400, sales , cert: CPUC)

2789　Solartech Power, Inc.
　　　901 E Cedar St　Ontario, CA 91761
　　　(714) 630-8880　Sherry Fu Owner
　　　Fax: (714) 630-8887
　　　Email: sherry.fu@solartechpower.com
　　　Website: www.solartechpower.com
Mfr solar photovoltaic panels & equipment. (Woman/As-
Ind, estab 2001, empl 10, sales $3,000,000, cert: CPUC)

2790　Steren Electronics International, LLC
　　　6260 Sequence Dr Ste 110　San Diego, CA 92121
　　　(800) 266-3333　E'Lisa Jones Corp Dir of Business
　　　Devel
　　　Fax: (858) 546-5001
　　　Email: elisa@steren.com
　　　Website: www.sterenusa.com
Mfr voice, video & data connectivity solutions. (Hisp, estab
1978, empl 100, sales $56,000,000, cert: CPUC)

2791　Transline Technology, Inc.
　　　1106 S Technology Circle　Anaheim, CA 92805
　　　(714) 533-8300　Judy Warner President
　　　Fax: (714) 533-8791
　　　Email: judy@translinetech.com
　　　Website: www.translinetech.com
Mfr printed circuit boards, PCB, PWB, hybrid, exotic, RF &
microwave, FR4 PCB. (As-Ind, estab 1996, empl 24, sales
$1,600,000, cert: 8(a))

2792　Unicorp, Inc.
　　　5780 Smithway St　Commerce, CA 90040
　　　(323) 890-9246　Susan Larson VP Business Dev
　　　Fax: (323) 890-9249
　　　Email: susanl@uninex.com
　　　Website: www.uninex.com
LED lighting technology, Indoor & Outdoor Electric Lighting
Fixtures, Residential Electrical Lighting Fixture, Commer-
cial, Industrial, Institutional Electrical Lighting Fixture,
Other Lighting Equipment. (As-Pac, estab 1989, empl 14,
sales , cert: State, CPUC)

Colorado

2793　Premier Manufactuirng and Supply Chain Services
　　　7755 Miller Dr　Frederick, CO 80504
　　　(303) 776-4145　Edmond Johnson President
　　　Fax: (303) 776-2957
　　　Email: ejohnson@pmscs.com
　　　Website: www.pmscs.com
Contract mfr of printed circuit board assemblies for
prototypes, production, sub assemblies, cable harness &
test. (AA, estab 2000, empl 55, sales $12,000,000, cert:
NMSDC)

2794　Quality Concepts Manufacturing Inc.
　　　1635 S Murray Blvd　Colorado Springs, CO 80911
　　　(719) 574-1013　Robert Millemon Program Mgr
　　　Fax: (719) 574-5327
　　　Email: robert@qcmi.com
　　　Website: www.qcmi.com
Electronic Manufacturing Services, Quick-turn
prototyping, pre-production & full production support
services, mechanical assembly. (Woman/White, estab
1988, empl 30, sales , cert: City)

Connecticut

2795　I C D I INC
　　　407 Brookside Rd　Waterbury, CT 06708
　　　(203) 753-8551　Steve Villodas President
　　　Fax: (203) 757-5882
　　　Email: svillodas@icdi-inc.com
　　　Website: www.icdi-inc.com
Contract mfr electronic high tech equip & systems,
turnkey program mgmt, eng design, microprocessor
systems, PC layout, PC board & automated surface-
mount assembly, wave soldering, vapor degreasing,
custom cables, ATE testing. (Hisp, estab 1975, empl 22,
sales $3,019,307, cert: NMSDC)

Florida

2796　Avionics Support Group Inc.
　　　13155 SW 132nd Ave　Miami, FL 33186
　　　(305) 378-9786　Hugo L Fortes VP
　　　Fax: (305) 378-9726
　　　Email: hfortes@asginc.net
　　　Website: www.asginc.net
Avionics engineering, mfg & installations. (Hisp, estab
1996, empl 25, sales , cert: State)

2797   CableNetwork Associates Inc.
       4800 N Federal Hwy, Ste E300   Boca Raton, FL
       33431
       (954) 312-1200 Marcela Gutierrez
       Fax: (561) 672-8768
       Email: mgutierrez@cablenetwork.net
       Website: www.cablenetwork.net
Mfr coax cable, drop & trunk cable. (Hisp, estab 1997,
empl 300, sales $2,284,358,226, cert: NMSDC)

2798   Curtoom Companies, Inc.
       1228 E 7th Ave P.O. Box 76192 Tampa, FL 33675
       (813) 405-8082 Paul Curtis CEO
       Fax: (888) 431-0028
       Email: support@curtoom.com
       Website: www.curtoom.com
Provide construction cost consulting in both the Southeast
United States and throughout the Atlantic seaboard areas.
We have built a business and reputation supplying
accurate and timely budgets, cost estimates, value
engineering (AA, estab 1989, empl 30, sales $3,600,000,
cert: State)

2799   High Risk Security Services
       5012 Strada Dr   Winter Haven, FL 33880
       (863) 398-8881 Juan Garcia Owner
       Fax: (863) 294-7561
       Email: highrisk@att.net
       Website: www.atrisksecurity.com
HRSS CONDUCTS:
1) EXECUTIVE SECURITY TRAINING
2) TRAVEL SECURITY TRAINING
3) ANTI-TERRORISM TRAINING
4) PERSONAL SECURITY TRAINING (Hisp, estab 2005, empl
1, sales , cert: State)

2800   LedZed International Inc.
       2240 Palm Beach Lakes Blvd   West Palm Beach, FL
       33409
       (954) 629-0768 Helena Lahtinen CEO
       Fax:
       Email: helena@ledzed.com
       Website: www.ledzed.com
Mfr & dist energy efficiency led lights. (Woman/White,
estab 2011, empl 1, sales , cert: City)

2801   Mainstream IP Solutions, Inc.
       6905 El Dorado Dr   Tampa, FL 33615
       (813) 549-7768 Arnie Solomon Acct Mgr
       Fax: (727) 726-9189
       Email: asolomon@mcsoftampa.com
       Website: www.mainstreamipsolutions.com
Electrical, structured cabling, audio-visual, security & fire
alarm systems. (AA, estab 2010, empl 5, sales $250,000,
cert: State, NMSDC, 8(a), SDB)

2802   Paradym Engineering, LLC
       8338 Windsor Bluff Dr   Tampa, FL 33647
       (888) 667-5459 Tim Keeley CEO
       Fax: (888) 597-4478
       Email: tk@paradymengineering.com
       Website: www.paradymengineering.com
Electrical & mechanical equipment & engineering
services. (AA, estab 2001, empl 6, sales $800,000, cert:
State)

2803   PowerLogics, Inc.
       1115 Marbella Plaza Dr   Tampa, FL 33619
       (813) 645-2971 Barbara Smith Sales Assoc
       Fax: (813) 645-8233
       Email: barbarasmith@powerlogics.com
       Website: www.powerlogics.com
Transient voltage surge suppression, uninterruptible
power systems, power conditioning equip, battery
replacements, generators, automatic transfer switches,
AC & DC invertors. (Woman/White, estab 1981, empl 6,
sales $4,000,000, cert: State)

Georgia

2804   Georgia Green Energy Services
       335 Wilma Ct SW   Atlanta, GA 30331
       (404) 334-3323 Gavin Ireland CEO
       Fax: (404) 889-6058
       Email: GIreland@GaGreenEnergySVC.com
       Website: www.gagreenenergysvc.com
Light retrofitting, LED lighting, occupancy sensors, solar
power systems, alternative & renewable energy systems,
Energy audting, energy reduction reports, energy audits.
(AA, estab 2007, empl 1, sales $1,099,000, cert: NMSDC,
8(a))

2805   Roytec Industries LLC
       306 Bell Park Dr   Woodstock, GA 30188
       (770)95470 Amanda Chapman CEO
       Fax: (770)95247
       Email: mchapman@roytecind.com
       Website: www.roytecind.com
Mfr electrical wire harnesses & electrical wire assemblies. (Woman/White, estab 1984, empl 500, sales
$36,734,238, cert: WBENC)

2806   Southern States, LLC
       30 Georgia Ave   Hampton, GA 30228
       (770) 946-4562 Daniel Miller Sr reg Mgr
       Fax: (770) 897-0725
       Email: dmiller@keelermiller.COM
       Website: www.southernstatesllc.com
Mfr high voltage electrical airbreak switchgear, power
fuses, circuit switchers & capacitor bank switching
devices. (As-Ind, estab 1916, empl 300, sales , cert:
NMSDC)

Iowa

2807   Ensign Corporation
PO Box 383   Addison, IA 52031
(563) 872-3900   Ajay Sharma VP Sales and Mktg
Fax: (630) 628-9922
Email: susan.h@ensigncorp.com
Website: www.ensigncorp.com
Build & dist power transformers, off-the-shelf & custom.
(As-Pac, estab 1939, empl 39, sales $3,900,000, cert:
NMSDC)

Illinois

2808   AC Gentrol, Inc.
100 S Fourth St   Chillicothe, IL 61523
(309) 274-5486   Angelito Capati President
Fax: (309) 274-9001
Email: info@acgentrol.com
Website: www.acgentrol.com
Mfr specialized electrical controls systems. (Woman/As-
Pac, estab 1985, empl 12, sales $1,100,000, cert: State)

2809   Capsonic Group, LLC
460 S Second St Slot B-8 Elgin, IL 60123
(847) 888-7242   George Albrecht Regional Sales Mgr
Fax: (847) 888-7543
Email: georgea@capsonic.com
Website: www.capsonicgroup.com
Insert & composite molding: product design, prototype,
automation. (AA, estab 1968, empl 225, sales , cert:
NMSDC)

2810   CEC Industries Ltd.
599 Bond St   Lincolnshire, IL 60069
(847) 599-6132   Michelle Draper
Fax:
Email: michelle@cecindustries.com
Website: www.ceclighting.com
Mfr miniature halogen lamps, LED lamps, electronic turn
signal flashers. (As-Ind, estab 1979, empl 66, sales , cert:
NMSDC)

2811   KLI Inc.
304 Roma Jean Pkwy   Streamwood, IL 60107
(630) 213-1283   Lisa Carso President
Fax: (630) 213-1297
Email: Support@kli-inc.com
Website: www.kli-inc.com
Mfr electronic components; electronic assembly; main
harness & cable to mil specs. (Woman/As-Pac, estab 1987,
empl 15, sales , cert: State, NMSDC)

2812   PowerVolt Inc. (DBA Ensign Corporation)
300 W Factory Rd   Addison, IL 60101
(630) 628-9999   Ajay Sharma VP Sales/Mktg
Fax: (630) 628-9922
Email: ajays@powervolt.com
Website: www.ensigncorp.com
Mfr power transformers & DC power supplies. (As-Ind,
estab 1986, empl 39, sales $3,330,000, cert: NMSDC)

2813   S & M Group, Inc.
2503 Pan Am Blvd   Elk Grove Village, IL 60007
(630) 766-1000   JAY VORA
Fax: (630) 766-1006
Email: JAY@FLEXTRONASSEMBLY.COM
Website: www.flextronassembly.com
Electronics contract mfr: printed circuit boards &
assemblies, proto through production, consignment or
turnkey, leaded & lead-free, large boards, cable assemblies, wire harness, box & mechanical assemblies. (As-
Pac, estab 2002, empl 25, sales $2,825,000, cert: State)

2814   Tempco Electric Heater Corp.
607 N Central Ave   Wood Dale, IL 60191
(630) 350-2252   William Kilberry CFO
Fax: (630) 350-0232
Email: williamkilberry@tempco.com
Website: www.tempco.com
Mfr thermal component products: electric heating
elements, temperature controls, temperature sensors &
turnkey process heating systems. (Hisp, estab 1972,
empl 330, sales $28,500,000, cert: NMSDC)

2815   WarmlyYours.com Inc.
590 Telser Rd, Ste B   Lake Zurich, IL 60047
(800) 875-5285   Julia BIllen President
Fax: (888) 526-1231
Email: jbillen@warmlyyours.com
Website: www.WarmlyYours.com
Manufacturer Electric Radiant Floor Heating Systems.
(Woman/White, estab 1999, empl 28, sales $5,888,379,
cert: WBENC)

Indiana

2816   ATEC Electrical Contractors
419 Ransdell Rd   Lebanon, IN 46052
(765) 482-8926   C. Shane Conner President
Fax: (765) 482-8936
Email: s.conner@atec-electric.com
Website: www.atec-electric.com
Electrical and telecommunications sales, service and
support, engineering, project management and sustainable energy consulting and installation. (Hisp, estab
2005, empl 25, sales $5,547,137, cert: NMSDC)

2817   Carson Manufacturing Company, Inc.
       5451 N Rural St   Indianapolis, IN 46220
       (317) 257-3191 Barbara Ferguson President
       Fax: (317) 254-2667
       Email: receptionist@carson-mfg.com
       Website: www.carson-mfg.com
Contract mfg electromechanical assemblies & equipment,
mfr emergency vehicle sirens, rotary switches & voting
machines. Prototyping, testing, quick turns, stocking
programs & turn-key capabilities. (Woman, estab 1946,
empl 20, sales $2,500,000, cert: State, City)

2818   Continental Manufacturing, LLC
       1524 Jackson St   Anderson, IN 46016
       (765) 298-8030 Chris Petty Natl Sales Mgr
       Fax:
       Email: cpetty@solasray.com
       Website: www.solasray.com
Mfr, design, engineer & test LED technology lighting
solutions for commercial, industrial & educational applications. (Woman/White, estab 2007, empl 10, sales
$900,000, cert: State, WBENC)

2819   Electric Motors and Specialties, Inc.
       701 W King St   Garrett, IN 46738
       (847) 559-6132 Rick Moore President
       Fax:
       Email: rmoore@emsmotors.com
       Website: www.emsmotors.com
Design, mfg & application of shaded pole, PSC & electroni-
cally commutated unit bearing motors. (Woman/White,
estab 1946, empl 200, sales , cert: WBENC)

Kentucky

2820   Dollar Aisle, LLC
       165 Woods Dr   Brandenburg, KY 40108
       (502) 303-4518 rahul anand President
       Fax: (270) 422-2524
       Email: dollaraisle@gmail.com
       Website: www.wenlighting.com
Mfr led tube lights, wall packs, hig bays, led light bulbs etc.
(As-Pac, estab 2011, empl 3, sales $650,000, cert: NMSDC)

Massachusetts

2821   Adcotron EMS
       12 Channel St   Boston, MA 02210
       (617) 598-3000 Don MacNeil Business Dev Sales
       Rep
       Fax: (617) 598-3001
       Email: donimac@comcast.net
       Website: www.adcotron.com
Electronic mfg service, printed circuit board assembly,
system integration, system assembly. (Woman/As-Pac,
estab 1977, empl 100, sales $30,200,000, cert: State)

2822   International Coil, Inc.
       15 Jonathan Dr Unit 1 Brockton, MA 02301
       (508) 580-8515 George Machadinho President
       Fax: (508) 580-8511
       Email: gmachadinho@internationalcoil.com
       Website: www.internationalcoil.com
Mfr Transformers (wire wound products) & Power
Supplies. (AA, estab 1995, empl 12, sales $1,000,000,
cert: State)

Maryland

2823   Armacost Lighting LLC
       140 Baltic Ave   Baltimore, MD 21225
       (410) 354-6000 Terry Armacost President
       Fax: (410) 834-5503
       Email: tarmacost@armacostlighting.com
       Website: www.armacostlighting.com
Architectural quality LED lighting fixtures, LED tape
lighting is ultra-thin, flexible, fully dimmable, can be cut
to size or multiple strips. (Woman/White, estab 2011,
empl 8, sales $3,700,000, cert: WBENC)

2824   JEM Engineering, LLC
       8683 Cherry Ln   Laurel, MD 20707
       (301) 317-1070 Nancy Lilly CEO
       Fax: (301) 317-8683
       Email: nlilly@jemengineering.com
       Website: www.jemengineering.com
Design & prototype military & commercial antennas: HF
to millimeter-wave, microstrip patch antennas & arrays,
wire, aperture, broadband, active & low-observable
antennas. (Woman/Hisp, estab 2001, empl 30, sales
$1,754,917, cert: State)

Michigan

2825   AG Manufacturing Inc.
       319 Industrial Pkwy   Harbor Beach, MI 48441
       (989) 479-9590 Marlo Klaus Cstmr Service
       Fax: (989) 479-9579
       Email: mklaus@agmanufacturing.com
       Website: www.agmanufacturing.com
Mfr wire harnesses. (AA, estab 2004, empl 101, sales ,
cert: NMSDC)

2826   Amtech Electrocircuits, Inc.
       701 Minnesota Dr   Troy, MI 48083
       (248) 583-1801 Jay Patel President
       Fax: (248) 583-1802
       Email: jrp@amelectro.com
       Website: www.amelectro.com
Electronic manufacturing services, contract manufacturer, printed circuit boards, wire harnesses & electronic
assemblies. (As-Ind, estab 1997, empl 10, sales
$800,000, cert: NMSDC)

2827   Eisen Electric Corporation
     3340 Pinetree Rd   Lansing, MI 48911
     (517) 393-5850   Lokesh Kumar GM
     Fax: (517) 393-0590
     Email: LKumar@eisennet.com
     Website: www.eisennet.com
Mfr terminal screws, electrical fasteners & springs. (As-Ind, estab 1994, empl 72, sales $4,200,000, cert: NMSDC)

2828   Empire Electric
     3575 Vinewood   Detroit, MI 48208
     (313) 895-1920   Bob Pauline VP
     Fax: (313) 895-1921
     Email: bob@empireec.com
     Website: www.empirewc.com
Dist electrical, industrial & networking products & supplies. Also mfr wire harnesses & cable assemblies. (AA, estab 2003, empl 10, sales $1,005,000,000, cert: NMSDC)

2829   Excel Electrocircuit Inc.
     50 Northpointe Dr   Orion, MI 48359
     (248) 373-0700   Nipur Shah President
     Fax: (248) 373-5036
     Email: sales@excelcircuits.com
     Website: www.excelelectro.com
Mfr printed circuit boards. (As-Ind, estab 1970, empl 25, sales , cert: NMSDC)

2830   Hart Precision Products, Inc.
     12700 Marion   Redford, MI 48239
     (313) 537-0490   Darlene Hart President
     Fax: (313) 537-7222
     Email: d.hart@hart-precision.com
     Website: www.Hart-Precision.com
Mfr precision components & assemblies for the Transportation Industry. (Woman/White, estab 1953, empl 48, sales $5,100,000, cert: WBENC)

2831   Hybrid Design Services
     2479 Elliott Dr   Troy, MI 48083
     (248) 298-3400   James Pinon President
     Fax: (248) 298-3402
     Email: jpinon@hybriddesignservices.com
     Website: www.hybriddesignservices.com
Engineering, design, prototyping, testing services specializing in hybrid vehicles & systems, electric vehicles & systems, HEV systems, EV systems, hybrid and electric vehicle R&D, high voltage systems, energy storage. (Hisp, estab 2007, empl 20, sales $2,000,000, cert: NMSDC)

2832   Industrial Control Repair - ICR Services
     28601 Lorna Ave   Warren, MI 48092
     (58586) 582-1500   Marlies Davis Business Dev
     Fax: (58586) 582-1501
     Email: mdavis@icrservices.com
     Website: www.icrservices.com
Dist & repair industrial electronics: robots, PLCs drives, welders, encoders, temperature controls, displays, monitors, power sources, etc. (Hisp, estab 1992, empl 155, sales $80,000,000, cert: NMSDC)

2833   JA Quality Assurance Group, LLC
     537 Bradford   pontiac, MI 48341
     (248) 506-3316   Julio Rodriguez CEO
     Fax: (248) 335-3431
     Email: jrodriguez@jaqualityassurance.com
     Website: www.jaqualityassurance.com
Mfr prototype harnesses. (Hisp, estab 2000, empl 104, sales $3,935,000, cert: NMSDC)

2834   JMC Electrical Contractor, LLC dba JMC Technologies
     33651 Giftos   Clinton Township, MI 48035
     (586) 773-8026   Bob Locklear VP Technologies
     Fax: (586) 773-8090
     Email: blocklear@jmcelectricllc.com
     Website: www.jmcelectricllc.com
Electrical service, installation, Structured Cable, Fiber Optic Cable, Voice, Data, Security, CCTV, Intrusion Detection, Access Control, Audio/Visual, CATV, Wireless, Wi-Fi, DAS & Building Automation Systems installation. (Woman/White, estab 2010, empl 45, sales $6,000,000, cert: State)

2835   Johnico LLC
     400 Monroe St Ste 480   Detroit, MI 48226
     (248) 895-7820   john economy Managing Partner
     Fax:
     Email: johneconomy@yahoo.com
     Website: www.americasgreenline.com
Commercial & industrial LED manufacturer. (Woman/White, estab 2011, empl 10, sales $3,500,000, cert: WBENC)

2836   Lotus International Company
     6880 Commerce Blvd   Canton, MI 48187
     (734) 245-0140   Darren Ivey Director Sales & Mktg
     Fax: (734) 245-0170
     Email: divey@licus.com
     Website: www.licus.com
Electrical & electro-mechanical contract mfg, wire harness, navigation CRT & LCD displays, aluminum & zinc die cast, electronics repair. (As-Ind, estab 1991, empl 200, sales $50,000,000, cert: NMSDC)

2837   Myron Zucker, Inc.
       36825 Metro Ct   Sterling Heights, MI 48312
       (586) 979-9955 Mary Anderson Buyer
       Fax: (586) 979-9484
       Email: dzobel@myronzucker.com
       Website: www.myronzucker.com
Engineer & mfr low-voltage power products: power factor
correction capacitors, harmonic filters & surge suppres-
sors. (Woman/White, estab 1967, empl 10, sales
$1,050,000, cert: WBENC)

2838   Newtech 3, Inc.
       28373 Beck Rd Ste H7 Wixom, MI 48393
       (248) 912-1062 Gail Gyenese Director of Sales
       Fax: (248) 912-0809
       Email: ggyenese@newtech3inc.com
       Website: www.newtech3.com
Mfr lower to mid volume wire harness & circuit board
assemblies. (AA, estab 2009, empl 32, sales $3,965,000,
cert: NMSDC)

2839   Orri Corporation
       5385 Perry Dr   waterford, MI 48329
       (248) 618-1104 Randy Kosek Sales
       Fax: (248) 618-1142
       Email: r.kosek@orricorp.com
       Website: www.orricorp.com
Wire harnesses, cable assemblies, electrical test fixtures,
robotic vision guidance software. (Woman/White, estab
2001, empl 12, sales , cert: WBENC)

Minnesota

2840   Electro Mechanical Industries (EMI)
       13300 6th Ave N   Plymouth, MN 23606
       (763) 546-5998 Holly Hicks Sales/Mktg
       Fax: (763) 546-5214
       Email: hhicks@e-m-i.com
       Website: www.e-m-i.com
Low voltage switchgear, metal clad & metal enclosed
medium voltage switchgear, paralleling switchgear, control
panels, special wire ways, wall & floor ducts, pull boxes &
sound-attenuated generator enclosures. (Woman/White,
estab 1981, empl 36, sales $8,522,000, cert: WBENC)

2841   Telamco, Inc.
       636 Industrial Dr SE   Lonsdale, MN 55046
       (507) 744-5504 Tracy Humann President
       Fax: (507) 744-2304
       Email: tracy@telamcoinc.com
       Website: www.telamcoinc.com
Mfr custom heat sealed membrane switches & quality
assemblies. (Woman/White, estab 1968, empl 11, sales
$1,500,000, cert: NWBOC)

North Carolina

2842   Adams Electric Company
       P.O. Box 958   Reidsville, NC 27323
       (800) 349-6283 Joy Jones Business Dev
       Fax: (336) 349-5990
       Email: joyjones@adams-electric.com
       Website: www.adams-electric.com
Electrical design-build, clean rooms, critical power,
pharmaceuticals, health care, industrial & large commercial. (Woman/White, estab 1928, empl 300, sales
$35,000,000, cert: State)

2843   TEC Electric, LLC
       6612G East WT Harris Blvd   Charlotte, NC 28215
       (704) 394-5097 Donald James President
       Fax: (704) 567-0974
       Email: donald.james@harriselec.com
       Website: www.harriselec.com
Electical contracting, engineering, controls & conveyor
installation. (AA, estab 2006, empl 15, sales $1,900,000,
cert: NMSDC)

2844   Thermal Control Products
       6324 Performance Dr   Concord, NC 28027
       (704) 454-7605 Geoff Nilsen Commercial Sales
       Exec
       Fax:
       Email: gnilsen@thermalcontrolproducts.com
       Website: www.thermalcontrolproducts.com
Mfr thermal & protective components, Protective
shielding / robotics, Weld splatter shielding, Weld head
covers, Gun Bags, Computer monitor protectors, Weld
screens, Transport bags. (Woman/White, estab 1993,
empl 40, sales , cert: State)

Nevada

2845   VaOpto, LLC
       5178 W Patrick Lane   Las Vegas, NV 89118
       (702) 517-5789 Charles Li Acct Mgr
       Fax: (702) 979-3582
       Email: charles.li@vaopto.com
       Website: www.vaopto.com
Mfr LED lightings & LED fixtures. (As-Pac, estab 2010,
empl 5, sales $6,000,000, cert: NMSDC)

New York

2846   AmpliTech Inc.
     1373 Lincoln Ave   Holbrook, NY 11741
     (631) 521-7831   Walter Rojas President
     Fax: (631) 521-7871
     Email: sales@amplitechinc.com
     Website: www.amplitechinc.com
Design, develop & mfr custom & standard RF components, microwave amplifiers & components. (Hisp, estab 2002, empl 12, sales $2,000,000, cert: State)

2847   Integrated Control Corporation
     748 Park Ave   Huntington, NY 11743
     (631) 673-5100   Roberta Salerno CEO
     Fax: (631) 673-6756
     Email: roberta@goicc.com
     Website: www.goicc.com
Mfr electronic control & communication devices, system integrated design. (Woman/White, estab 1986, empl 21, sales $6,100,000, cert: WBENC, NWBOC)

2848   Tony Baird Electronics, Inc.
     461 East Brighton Avenue   Syracuse, NY 13210
     (315) 422-4430   Matt Tessier VP Sales
     Fax: (315) 422-4435
     Email: matt@tonybairdelectronics.com
     Website: www.tonybairdelectronics.com
Mfr electronic components, printed circuit assembly, electronic assembly, fiber optic cable. (AA, estab 2005, empl 10, sales $1,900,000, cert: SDB)

Ohio

2849   S & V Industries, Inc.
     3535 S Smith Rd   Fairlawn, OH 44333
     (330) 408-3078   Denise Uher Acct Exec
     Fax: (330) 666-4109
     Email: Denise.Uher@SVIndustries.com
     Website: www.svindustries.com
Mfr gears, spur, helical, double helical, worm straight bevel, spiral bevel, herringbone, gear boxes, worm gear boxes, helical gear boxes, bevel helical gear boxes, custom or special gear boxes, geared motors. (As-Pac, estab 1993, empl 30, sales $40,000,000, cert: NMSDC)

Oregon

2850   Powin Energy Corporation
     20550 SW 115th Ave   Tualatin, OR 97062
     (503) 598-6659   Victor Liu Sales
     Fax: (503) 598-3941
     Email: victorl@powinenergy.com
     Website: www.powinenergy.com
Design & develop advanced battery management technology & manufactures battery energy storage solutions. (As-Pac, estab 2011, empl 43, sales $183,187, cert: NMSDC)

Pennsylvania

2851   American Cable Co., Inc.
     231 E Luzerne St   Philadelphia, PA 19124
     (215) 456-0700   Rolando Sanchez Business Dev
     Fax: (215) 456-1603
     Email: rsanchez@americancableco.com
     Website: www.americancableco.com
Mfr battery cable assemblies, wire harnesses, and ground straps. (Hisp, estab 1976, empl 150, sales $15,000,000, cert: NMSDC)

2852   Butler Technologies, Inc.
     231 W Wayne St   Butler, PA 16001
     (724) 283-6656   Marilyn Suchy Sales Admin
     Fax: (724) 283-4447
     Email: msuchy@butlertechnologies.com
     Website: www.butlertechnologies.com
Mfr graphic overlays, membrane switches, labels, decals & printed electronics. (Woman/White, estab 1990, empl 61, sales $6,974,188, cert: WBENC)

2853   Contine Corporation
     1820 Nagle Rd   Erie, PA 16510
     (814) 899-0006   Constance Ellrich President
     Fax: (814) 899-2796
     Email: cellrich@continedbe.com
     Website: www.continedbe.com
Assembly & test mechanical & electro-mechanical devices, machining, sheet metal fabrication & plastic injection molding, switches, latches, rack assemblies, display units, control panels, wire harnesses etc. (Woman/White, estab 1981, empl 43, sales $9,175,996, cert: CPUC, WBENC)

2854   John A. Romeo & Asscoiates, Inc.
     890 Pittsburgh Rd, Ste 7   Butler, PA 16002
     (724) 586-6961   Pamela Romeo CEO
     Fax: (724) 586-2234
     Email: pdromeo@jara-mfg.com
     Website: www.jara-mfg.com
Mfr Custom Cables, Wiring Harnesses & Electromechanical Assemblies. (Woman/White, estab 1990, empl 15, sales $1,506,698, cert: WBENC)

2855   TJM Electronic Associates
     2924 New Rogers Rd   Bristol, PA 19007
     (215) 788-2278   Jim Wood Dir New Business Dev
     Fax: (215) 788-2342
     Email: tom@tjmelectronics.com
     Website: www.tjmeast.com
Electronic contract mfr, electronic design, packaging & manufacturing, circuit board assembly, engineering, design,systems integration & test & turnkey production. (Woman/White, estab 1990, empl 60, sales $10,000,000, cert: NWBOC)

Puerto Rico

2856 Advanced Control Services, Inc.
425 Rd. 693, PMB 205, Ste 1 425 rd. 693 PMB 205
Dorado, PR 00646
(787) 502-8752 Victor M. Taveras Ops Mgr
Fax:
Email: victor@advcontrolservices.com
Website: www.advcontrolservices.com
Engineering & validation services, systems integration
services, control panels, VFDs, electrical services, SCADA,
HMI, instrumentation services. (Hisp, estab 1999, empl 7,
sales $621,123, cert: NMSDC)

2857 AG Group Inc.
Centro Industrial Minellas, Carr. 174TH KM 3.0
Bayamon, PR 00959
(787) 707-0022 Elliott Gonzalez Sales Mgr
Fax: (787) 707-0065
Email: info@aggpr.com
Website: www.aggroupinc.com
Engineering, System Integration, Installations, Calibrations,
Validations. (Hisp, estab 1997, empl 105, sales $7,892,343,
cert: State, NMSDC)

2858 Hi-Tech Products, Inc.
P.O. Box 4956 Carolina, PR 00984
(787) 257-1707 Daisy Maldonado Admin Officer
Fax: (787) 276-1888
Email: daisy@hi-techproducts.com
Website: www.hi-techproducts.com
Mfr reps for industrial control products, electronics,
electrical & pneumatics. (Hisp, estab 1991, empl 40, sales ,
cert: NMSDC)

2859 Invision Engineering Corp.
P.O. Box 6567 Mayaguez, PR 00681
(787) 831-0070 Jose Vazquez President
Fax: (787) 831-0071
Email: jvazquez@invisioneng.com
Website: www.invisioneng.com
Automation, Control System Design, System Integrations,
Instrumentation, Calibrations and Installations, Electrical
Installations, Computer System Validations, Software
Validations, Software design. (Hisp, estab 2002, empl 35,
sales $3,137,957, cert: NMSDC)

South Carolina

2860 Amec, LLC
4601 E White Horse Rd Greenville, SC 29611
(864) 269-0222 Kevin Lindsey Project Mgr
Fax:
Email: kevin@amecllc.net
Website: www.amecsc.net
Industrial & commercial electrical applications, industrial electrical maintenance, thermal imaging, de-
energized maintenance, studies for lighting improvements, breaker testing, power analysis, installation of
service entrance equipment. (Woman/White, estab
2009, empl 11, sales $838,385, cert: State)

2861 Arva, LLC
3705 Centre Circle Fort Mill, SC 29715
(803) 336-2235 Shahil Amin Director
Fax: (803) 336-2231
Email: shahilamin@arva.us
Website: www.hyliteledlighting.com/
Mfr energy-efficient, indoor & outdoor LED & Induction
Lighting & Retrofit Kits. (Woman/As-Ind, estab 2010,
empl 7, sales $1,200,000, cert: NMSDC)

Texas

2862 Blackhawk Management
1322 Space Park Dr Ste A220 Houston, TX 77058
(832) 536-3703 Gabrielle Busby Admin
Fax: (832) 536-3704
Email: busbyg@blackhawkmgmt.com
Website: www.blackhawkmgmt.com
Electrical & mechanical engineering design services,
prototyping, short production runs, printed circuit
board design, 3D machining, digital, analog design,
power electronics. (Woman/Nat Ame, estab 1992, empl
24, sales $10,000,000, cert: WBENC, SDB)

2863 Electro Plate Circuitry -Dragon Circuits
1430 Century Dr Carrollton, TX 75006
(972) 466-0818 Gunny Babaria VP
Fax:
Email: gunnyb@eplate.com
Website: www.eplate.com
Mfr printed circuit boards: 40 layers, blind & buried vias,
impedance control, heatsink bonding, small hole drilling
& quick turn around. (Woman/As-Ind, estab 1985, empl
50, sales $8,000,000, cert: NMSDC)

2864   Electro Plate Circuitry, Inc.
     1430 Century Dr   Carrollton, TX 75006
     (972) 466-0818   Nicolas Garcia President
     Fax: (972) 446-8632
     Email: nickg@eplate.com
     Website: www.eplate.com
Mfr printed circuit boards: GF,GI, RF, insulators, heatsinks, blind buried vias, controlled impedance. (Hisp, estab 1981, empl 80, sales $9,000,000, cert: NMSDC)

2865   GCI Technologies
     1301 Precision Dr   Plano, TX 75074
     (972) 423-8411   Hinkki Chen CEO
     Fax: (972) 423-4550
     Email: mike.beauchamp@gcitechnologies.com
     Website: www.gcitechnologies.com
Mfr magnetics: engineering, telecom, audio, power transformers, external power supplies, chokes, ferrite beads, cores. (As-Ind/As-Pac/Hisp, estab 1982, empl 420, sales $25,000,000, cert: NMSDC)

2866   Krypton Solutions
     3060 Summit Ave 75074   Plano, TX 75074
     (214) 882-2363   Carol Primdahl Director of Sales
     Fax: (972) 424-3882
     Email: Carol@krypton-solutions.com
     Website: www.krypton-solutions.com
Electronic contract manufacturer. (As-Pac, estab 2005, empl 51, sales $5,100,000, cert: State)

2867   MHC Semiconductor Processing Inc.
     13581 Pond Springs Rd   Austin, TX 78729
     (512) 331-6632   Marc Yeates Sales Dir
     Fax: (512) 331-6631
     Email: myeates@mhcsemi.com
     Website: www.mhcsemi.com
Hybrid & chip die processing: wire application. (Woman/ White, estab 1996, empl 8, sales , cert: State)

2868   PanAmerica Supply, Inc.
     21414 Provincial Blvd   Katy, TX 77450
     (281) 646-8472   Shaun Choi President
     Fax: (281) 646-8474
     Email: sychoi@pasihouston.com
     Website: www.pasihouston.com
Mfr power cables (HV, Med XLPE), transformer (up to 230kV). (As-Pac, estab 2005, empl 3, sales $8,000,000, cert: City)

2869   Roman Industries, Inc.
     10945 Estate Ln, Ste E115   Dallas, TX 75238
     (214) 503-3100   Shawn Quiroga Owner
     Fax: (214) 503-3190
     Email: shawn@romanindustriesinc.com
     Website: www.romanindustriesinc.com
Mfr custom cable, dist power lugs & RF connectors. (Woman/White, estab 2008, empl 3, sales $75,000, cert: State)

2870   Telco Intercontinental Corporation
     9812 Whithorn Dr   Houston, TX 77095
     (281) 855-2218   Paolo Longo Director of Sales
     Fax: (281) 500-8827
     Email: plongo@telcointercon.com
     Website: www.telcointercon.com
Mfr electric motors, Permanent Magnet DC motor, PMDC, coreless, core-less DC, gearmotor, high speed, high torque, miniature, stepper, Brushless DC motor, BLDC, green energy efficient ECM motor, fan, blower. (As-Pac, estab 1985, empl 22, sales $19,000,000, cert: NMSDC)

2871   Texas Mgt Associates, Inc
     7001 Fairgrounds Parkway   San Antonio, TX 78238
     (210) 673-8422   Dora Mendoza Business Dev
     Fax: (210) 673-3622
     Email: dmendoza@t-m-a.com
     Website: www.t-m-a.com
Electrical engineering & mfg: cable harnesses, electrical components, test station fixtures, circuit boards, restraint test stations, electrical housings, both complex & simple. (Hisp, estab 1991, empl 20, sales $4,368,852, cert: State, NMSDC)

Virginia

2872   Atomized Products Group of Chesapeake, Inc.
     808 Curtis Saunders Ct   Chesapeake, VA 23321
     (757) 793-2922   Lee Puckett Exec VP/Chief Operating Officer
     Fax: (757) 687-1539
     Email: Lee.Puckett@atomizedproductsgroup.com
     Website: www.atomizedproductsgroup.com
Mfr & dist negative plate expander for lead-acid battery applications. (Woman/White, estab 2013, empl 13, sales, cert: WBENC)

Washington

2873   CETS LLC
     1441 N Northlake Way, Ste 211   Seattle, WA 98103
     (206) 588-1239   Tim Tracey Purchasing
     Fax: (206) 686-8463
     Email: info@cetsinc.com
     Website: www.cetsinc.com
Develop & build new electrical systems; constructing additions, alterations & repairs, UL508 LISTED Open & Closed Industrial Panel, marine electrical construction services, electrical power distribution design & repair. (AA, estab 2013, empl 12, sales $1,500,000, cert: City, NMSDC)

2874 Charter Controls, Inc.
      1705 NE 64th Ave Ste B Vancouver, WA 98661
      (360) 695-2161 Randy Ayala VP Industrial Sales
      Fax:
      Email: Randy@chartercontrols.us
      Website: www.chartercontrols.us
Design, engineer & mfr industrial control systems.
(Woman/White, estab 2004, empl 15, sales $3,000,000,
cert: State)

2875 Eworld Solutions, Inc.
      19550 7th Ave NE   Shoreline, WA 98155
      (206) 659-1988 Nasir Junejo CEO
      Fax: (206) 260-3966
      Email: nasir@eworldsolutions.com
      Website: www.eworldsolutions.com
Contractor placement for design and verification. Specializ-
ing in SystemVerilog, UVM and Mixed Signal verification.
Consulting Service to audit verification and design environ-
ments, Consulting Service to create re-usable template
(As-Ind, estab 2010, empl 3, sales , cert: NMSDC)

2876 Focal PLLC
      900 1st Ave S, Ste 201   Seattle, WA 98134
      (206) 718-4250 Venkat Balasubramani Owner/
      Partner
      Fax: (206) 260-3966
      Email: info@focallaw.com
      Website: www.focallaw.com
Focal is a boutique, minority-owned law firm specializing
in internet and technology-related issues. We handle
transactional and counseling issues (e.g., drafting terms of
service/privacy policy; data license agreements) as well as
(AA/As-Ind, estab 2009, empl 11, sales $666,153, cert:
NMSDC)

2877 Reliable Investments LLC
      801 2nd Ave Ste 800 Seattle, WA 98104
      (800) 918-4380 Anthony Obiako President
      Fax: (866) 811-1612
      Email: anthony@reliableinvestmentsllc.com
      Website: www.reliableinvestmentsllc.com
Procurement & supply chain management, field engineering, installation, repair, calibration and rental services. (AA,
estab 2010, empl 3, sales $2,000,000, cert: State)

Wisconsin

2878 Arnev Products, Inc.
      N1530 Spring Glen Rd   Keshena, WI 54135
      (715) 799-5944 Patricia Evensen President
      Fax: (715) 799-3117
      Email: arnev@frontiernet.net
      Website: www.arnev.com
Mfr decorative electrical hardware. (Woman, estab 1990,
empl 2, sales $550,000, cert: State)

2879 Convenience Electronics, Inc.
      4405 Triangle St   McFarland, WI 53558
      (608) 838-4300 J. Harry Lum President
      Fax: (608) 838-4355
      Email: hlum@convenienceelectronics.com
      Website: www.convenienceelectronics.com
Mfr custom computer cables & harnesses, fiber optic
cables, molded cables, etc. (As-Pac, estab 1989, empl 45,
sales $4,000,000, cert: NMSDC)

2880 Dairyland Electric Co, Inc.
      12770 W. Custer Ave   Butler, WI 53007
      (262) 783-1550 Chris Martinez President
      Fax: (262) 738-1551
      Email: cmartinez@dairylandelectric.com
      Website: www.dairylandenergy.com/
Electrical construction, data & communication, cabling,
testing & certifying, electrical, telecom, fiber, alarms &
video installation. (Hisp, estab 1998, empl 11, sales ,
cert: State, NMSDC)

2881 Electrical Testing Solutions
      2909 Green Hill Ct, Ste I   Oshkosh, WI 54904
      (920) 420-2986 Scott Banaski Business Dev Mgr
      Fax: (920) 230-6970
      Email: sbanaski@electricaltestingsolutions.com
      Website: www.electricaltestingsolutions.com
Power system components for low, medium voltage &
parallel switchgear troubleshooting,
commissioning, design, analysis, repair & testing. (Hisp,
estab 2005, empl 25, sales $4,300,000, cert: State,
NMSDC)

2882 Professional Power Engineering Company, LLC
      P.O. Box 0122 W266 N7220 Kettle Ridge Ct
      Sussex, WI 53089
      (262) 372-4220 Glenn Wilder President
      Fax: (262) 820-3655
      Email: gwilder@ppecompany.com
      Website: www.ppecompany.com
Uninterruptible power supply systems, generator sets,
automatic transfer switches, batteries, battery racks &
cabinets & preventive maintenance services. (AA, estab
2006, empl 3, sales $185,000, cert: NMSDC)

ENGINEERING & SURVEYING SERVICES
Most of these firms are engaged in civil, structural and sanitation engineering services. May also do land surveying, environmental impact studies, testing and sampling. (See also ENVIRONMENTAL SERVICES). NAICS Code 54

Alabama

2883   Building & Earth Sciences, Inc.
5545 Derby Dr   Birmingham, AL 35210
(205) 836-6300 Matt Adams Director of Corp Client Dev - Principal
Fax: (205) 836-9007
Email: madams@buildingandearth.com
Website: www.buildingandearth.com
Consulting Engineering, geotechnical, environmental & construction materials testing & special inspection services. (Woman/As-Ind, estab 1998, empl 185, sales $19,000,000, cert: City, WBENC)

2884   Mesa Associates Inc.
9238 Madison Blvd, Ste 116   Madison, AL 35758
(256) 772-7025 Ranjana Savant President
Fax: (256) 772-3579
Email: rsavant@mesainc.com
Website: www.mesainc.com
Civil, electrical, mechanical, structural engineering services: integration, surveying, transmission, substation, controls, panel build, telecommunication, fiber optic engineering, robotic vehicle payloads & devices. (Woman/As-Pac, estab 1988, empl 356, sales $36,000,000, cert: NMSDC, WBENC)

Arizona

2885   G.D. Barri & Associates, Inc.
6860 W Peoria Ave   Peoria, AZ 85345
(623) 773-0410 Georgia D. Barri CEO
Fax: (623) 773-2924
Email: leslie.manley@gdbarri.com
Website: www.gdbarri.com
Engineering, management & technical support: environmental assessment, analysis, design, systems, baseline engineering, training, procedure development, quality assurance & quality control. (Woman/White, estab 1989, empl 331, sales $54,435,707, cert: CPUC, WBENC)

California

2886   Aetypic, Inc.
7 Freelon St   San Francisco, CA 94107
(415) 762-8388 Dennis Wong
Fax: (415) 762-8390
Email: dennis.wong@aetypic.com
Website: www.aetypic.com
Architecture & engineering services: structural engineering, civil engineering, construction engineering & inspection, technology integration, & sustainable design. (As-Pac, estab 2011, empl 25, sales , cert: State, NMSDC)

2887   Blair, Church & Flynn
451 Clovis Ave, Ste 200   Clovis, CA 93612
(559) 326-1400 David Mowry Principal
Fax: (559) 326-1500
Email: dmowry@bcf-engr.com
Website: www.bcf-engr.com
Engineering, land surveying, planning, civil engineering, landscape architecture & construction management. (Nat Ame, estab 1958, empl 49, sales $5,200,000, cert: CPUC)

2888   Calvada Surveying, Inc.
411 Jenks Cir Ste 205 Corona, CA 92880
(951) 280-9960 Armando Dupont President
Fax: (951) 280-9746
Email: armando@calvada.com
Website: www.calvada.com
Environmental site surveying & mapping, design topographic surveying & mapping, boundary surveys, construction staking, encumbrance mapping. (Hisp, estab 1989, empl 35, sales $4,200,000, cert: NMSDC, CPUC)

2889   Eagle Engineering Construction Inc.
1175 Palomar Dr, Ste 100   Redwood City, CA 94062
(650) 367-8000 Curtis Brooks President
Fax: (650) 367-8282
Email: clbrooks@sbcglobal.net
Website:
General engineering & electrical contracting, civil, electrical, mechanical & construction management. (AA, estab 1993, empl 36, sales $3,000,000, cert: State, CPUC)

2890   Engineering/Remediation Resources Group, Inc.
4585 Pacheco Blvd Ste 200 Martinez, CA 94553
(925) 969-0750 Tyson Appel Senior Project Mgr
Fax: (925) 969-0751
Email: tyson.appel@errg.com
Website: www.errg.com
Engineering & remediation services, environmental, civil & geotechnical engineers, geologists, soil physicists, scientists, construction managers, construction superintendents, equipment operators, certified hazardous waste technicians. (Woman/As-Pac, estab 1997, empl 175, sales $81,494,792, cert: CPUC)

2891 Luster National, Inc.
1701 Westwind Dr, Ste 117   Bakersfield, CA 93301
(661) 869-0157 Stephanie Ochoa CEO
Fax: (661) 327-3606
Email: sochoa@luster.com
Website: www.luster.com
Construction & program mgmt svcs: transportation, building & water supply/wastewater treatment; planning, scheduling, estimating, cost control, quality assurance. (AA, estab 1990, empl 99, sales $9,000,000, cert: State)

2892 Mercado Associates
25583 Avenue Stanford   Valencia, CA 91355
(661) 753-9295 Lizandro Mercado Principal
Fax: (661) 753-9298
Email: monicaf@mercadoassociates.com
Website: www.mercadoassociates.com
Structural consulting engineering services. (Hisp, estab 1998, empl 5, sales $480,000, cert: State, NMSDC)

2893 National Relocation Services, Inc. dba NRS, Inc.
2671 Pomona Blvd   Pomona, CA 91768
(909) 869-5748 Irene Ito CEO
Fax: (909) 869-7548
Email: icito@nrsca.com
Website: www.nrsca.com
Asset mgmt, online inventory, project & move mgmt, space planning, warehousing, inventory & bar coding, furniture installation, workstation, cubicle reconfiguration, furniture planning, CAD & CAFM. (Woman/As-Pac, estab 1994, empl 48, sales $4,373,000, cert: State, CPUC)

2894 Pari & Gershon Inc.
2053 Lincoln Ave Ste A San Jose, CA 95125
(408) 966-7184 Romena Jonas President
Fax: (408) 267-7196
Email: rjonas@pgiinc.net
Website: www.pgicompany.com
Environmental Consulting, Engineering Design & Construction. (Woman/White, estab 2009, empl 5, sales $100,000, cert: State, WBENC)

2895 Pivox Corporation
3240 El Camino Real Ste 230 Irvine, CA 92602
(949) 727-1400 Sean Shahin VP
Fax: (949) 727-1455
Email: sean@pivox.com
Website:
Remediation of soil & groundwater, demolition, project & construction management, permitting, design, feasibility study, treatment system installation (civil, mechanical, electril, and instrumentation). (Woman/White, estab 2004, empl 20, sales $8,000,000, cert: CPUC)

2896 Quest Project Controls, Inc.
114 W Colorado Blvd   Monrovia, CA 91016
(626) 639-2613 Robyn Coates CEO
Fax: (626) 301-4425
Email: robyn@thecmsolution.com
Website: www.thecmsolution.com
Project controls services & staff augmentation, project scheduling & planning, cost engineering, estimating & management of change. (Woman/White, estab 2002, empl 23, sales $1,959,183, cert: State, City, CPUC, WBENC)

2897 R.J. Roberts, Inc.
145 John Glenn Dr   Concord, CA 94520
(925) 689-8080 Terri Van De Veire Acct Mgr
Fax: (925) 689-8728
Email: van_t@robertscompanies.net
Website: www.robertscompanies.net
Consulting engineering services: civil, structural, electrical & mechanical. (Woman, estab 1978, empl 80, sales $9,712,761, cert: WBENC)

2898 RFE Engineering, Inc.
8680 Greenback Ln, Ste 107   Orangevale, CA 95662
(916) 989-3285 Bob Eynck President
Fax: (916) 989-3597
Email: reynck@rfeengineering.com
Website: www.RFEengineering.com
Surveying, boundary & topographic surveys, aerial control, ALTA/ACSM, parcel/subdivision maps, construction staking planning, military facility master planning, development feasibility analysis, zoning & use permits, master planning. (Hisp, estab 2003, empl 8, sales $640,000, cert: State, CPUC, 8(a))

2899 TEC, Inc.
510 S. La Brea Ave.   Inglewood, CA 90301
(949) 450-8200 Steven Youschak Sales
Fax: (949) 450-8210
Email: syouschak@teccm.com
Website: www.teccm.com
Engineering & construction mgmt svcs: CPM scheduling, cost control, constructability review, claims analysis, design mgmt & contract administration. (AA, estab 1988, empl 32, sales , cert: NMSDC, CPUC)

2900 The CAD-Scan Connection
1111 Riverside Ave Ste 405 Paso Robles, CA 93446
(805) 237-9347 Linda Martini Posner CEO
Fax: (805) 237-7723
Email: lindap@cadscanconnection.com
Website: www.cadscanconnection.com
Engineering/architectural technical support services, Conversion to CAD architectural, engineering drawings to AutoCAD. Revit, Map 3D, ArcView,GIS, Large format Description scanning. (Woman/White, estab 1998, empl 3, sales $43,060, cert: CPUC)

2901   The R.E.M. Engineering Co., Inc.
       1575 N Lake Ave, Ste 200   Pasadena, CA 91104
       (626) 296-7200 Robert Milton, Jr. GM
       Fax: (626) 296-7201
       Email: remeng@remengr.com
       Website: www.remengr.com
Engineering services: civil, structural, electrical & mechanical, design & design-build, scheduling, project status reporting, construction management. (AA, estab 1979, empl 10, sales $509,540, cert: State, CPUC)

2902   TTG Engineers
       300 N Lake Ave 14th Fl Pasadena, CA 91101
       (626) 463-2800 Carmen Gonzalez Mktg Mgr
       Fax: (626) 463-2801
       Email: cgonzalez@ttgcorp.com
       Website: www.ttgcorp.com
Engineering services: mechanical, electrical, plumbing, fire protection, structural & civil systems, cogeneration, thermal energy storage, LEED project certification, solar energy & commissioning. (As-Pac, estab 1955, empl 400, sales $51,991,145, cert: NMSDC)

Colorado

2903   F&D International, LLC
       5723 Arapahoe Ave Ste 1B Boulder, CO 80303
       (303) 652-3200 Teri Ficken President
       Fax: (303) 652-8555
       Email: teri@fdi-one.com
       Website: www.fdi-one.com
F&Engineering, architecture & construction management, engineering consulting (civil & structural), facility condition assessments, site plans, construction consulting, architectural design & CAD drawings. (Woman/White, estab 2001, empl 10, sales $1,400,000, cert: WBENC)

2904   High Energy Inc.
       625 Hudson St   Denver, CO 80220
       (303) 399-1098 Dragana Acimovic
       Fax: (303) 399-7825
       Email: dragana.acimovic@highenergyinc.com
       Website: www.highenergyinc.com
Engineering, design, drafting, project & construction mgmt, EPC for transmission lines, substations, distribution systems, operation & maintenance programs, feasibility, system planning, grounding, insulation coord, protective relaying. (Woman/White, estab 1998, empl 10, sales $392,600, cert: WBENC)

Delaware

2905   Mountain Consulting, Inc.
       103 S Bradford St   Dover, DE 19904
       (302) 744-9875 Kim Adams President
       Fax: (866) 672-6428
       Email: kadams@mountainconsultinginc.com
       Website: www.mountainconsultinginc.net
Engineering, land survey & technical services: Military Housing Privatization, Resident Construction Management, Contract Program Management, Title II Services, and Project Oversight. (Woman/AA, estab 2003, empl 5, sales , cert: State, NWBOC, 8(a))

Florida

2906   Diversified Design & Drafting Services, Inc.
       2374 Capital Circle NE   Tallahassee, FL 32308
       (850) 385-1133 Pam Nobles President
       Fax: (850) 385-1236
       Email: pam@dddsinc.com
       Website: www.dddsinc.com
Land surveying, boundary surveys, topographic surveys, LiDAR surveys, aerial surveys. (Woman/White, estab 1991, empl 15, sales $987,000, cert: State, City)

2907   Diversified Technology Consultants
       650 Central Avenue Unit 3 Sarasota, FL 34236
       (203)2394200 Robert Hammersley Program Mgr
       Fax:
       Email: robert.hammersley@teamdtc.com
       Website: www.teamdtc.com
Civil, environmental, transportation, structures, water pollution control, solid/hazardous waste mgmt, survey, electrical, mechanical, construction inspection & admin, CADD svcs, landscape architecture. (As-Pac, estab 1979, empl 55, sales $6,724,276, cert: State)

2908   EAC Consulting, Inc.
       815 NW 57th Ave, Ste 402   Miami, FL 33126
       (305) 264-2557 Enrique Crooks President
       Fax: (305) 264-8363
       Email: eac@eacconsult.com
       Website: www.eacconsult.com
Civil structural, bridge & highway design, construction engineering & inspection svcs. (AA, estab 1994, empl 34, sales , cert: State)

2909 Frazier Engineering, Inc.
       2289 W Eau Gallie Blvd   Melbourne, FL 32935
       (321) 253-8131 Michelle Shoultz Principal
       Fax: (321) 255-2231
       Email: mshoultz@fraziereng.com
       Website: www.fraziereng.com
Civil, structural, environmental engineering & surveying:
design, permitting & construction administration of site
plans, utility improvements, water, sewer, reuse, drainage,
roadway improvements, bridges. (Woman/As-Pac, estab
1992, empl 10, sales $1,200,000, cert: State, NMSDC, 8(a))

2910 Holland Engineering Inspection Services dba HEIS
       3900 Hollywood Blvd Ste 303 Hollywood, FL 33021
       (954) 626-0550 Catherine MacAskill CEO
       Fax: (954) 633-5012
       Email: catherine@heisflorida.com
       Website: www.heisflorida.com/
Civil engineering inspections & certifications, 5-Year
Surface Water Management Renewals, Stormwater
Certifications, Stormwater Drainage Cleaning & Repairs,
SSES. (Woman/White, estab 2016, empl 2, sales $400,000,
cert: State)

Georgia

2911 R2T, Inc.
       580 W Crossville Rd Stes 101-102 Roswell, GA
       30075
       (770) 569-7038 Kimberly Ajy President
       Fax: (770) 594-7477
       Email: kim.ajy@r2tinc.com
       Website: www.r2tinc.com
Civil & environmental engineering & construction services:
watershed/stormwater mgmt, conceptual planning, water
& wastewater system design, design/build construction.
(Woman/AA, estab 2005, empl 17, sales $6,810,190, cert:
City, WBENC)

2912 The Black Book, Inc.
       3500 Lenox Ste 1500 Atlanta, GA 30326
       (888) 808-9542 Rochelle Brown Owner
       Fax: (970) 266-8876
       Email: rochelle@theblackbookvip.com
       Website: www.theblackbookvip.com
The BLACK BOOK is a premiere luxury concierge service
and lifestyle management agency. We serve a plethora of
individuals from athletes and sports organizations ,
entertainers and production companies to high-net-
individuals (Woman/AA, estab 2013, empl 5, sales
$120,000, cert: NMSDC)

Illinois

2913 Advanced Cad/Cam Service dba
       EngineeringPeople
       801 W Main St Peoria, IL 61606
       (309) 621-5792 Jim Montelongo CEO
       Fax: (309) 495-7996
       Email: jim@engineeringpeople.com
       Website: www.engineeringpeople.com
Engineering service support, mechanical, electrical,
hydraulic, structural, engineering staffing. (Hisp, estab
1991, empl 60, sales $5,700,000, cert: NMSDC)

2914 Nest Builders
       303 W Erie St Ste 510 Chicago, IL 60654
       (312) 915-0557 Victor Avila Principal
       Fax:
       Email: vavila@dbhms.com
       Website: www.dbhms.com
Engineering services: mechanical, electrical, plumbing &
fire protection design. (Hisp, estab 2002, empl 60, sales
$700,000, cert: City)

2915 Prairie Engineers
       107 N Main St, Ste 3C   Columbia, IL 62236
       (217) 605-0403 Michelle Chambliss Business Dev
       Fax:
       Email: mchambliss@prairieengineers.com
       Website: www.prairieengineers.com
Engineering services: planning, project management,
civil engineering, water resources engineering, land
surveying, land acquisition, environmental science &
natural resources management & construction management. (Woman/White, estab 2010, empl 20, sales
$2,000,000, cert: City, WBENC, 8(a))

2916 Primera Engineers
       100 S Wacker Dr Ste 700 Chicago, IL 60606
       (312) 606-0910 Al Perla President
       Fax: (312) 606-0415
       Email: aperla@primeraeng.com
       Website: www.primeraeng,com
Engineering design: mechanical, electrical, plumbing,
fire protection, architecture, commissioning, structural,
civil, telecommunications, utility distribution & substation engineering. (Hisp, estab 1987, empl 170, sales
$21,910,784, cert: State, City, NMSDC)

2917 Structure Designs, Inc.
       309 W Washington St Ste 325 Chicago, IL 60606
       (312) 551-9780 Olufemi Oladeinde President
       Fax: (312) 551-9784
       Email: oao@structuredesignsinc.com
       Website: www.sdiengr.com
Civil Engineering, Structural Engineering, Architectural
Engineering, Land Surveying, Construction management.
(AA, estab 1994, empl 30, sales $12,500,000, cert:
NMSDC, 8(a))

2918   Valdes Engineering Company
100 W 22nd St Ste 185   Lombard, IL 60148
(630) 792-1886   Melissa Rasper Mktg Coord
Fax: (630) 792-1986
Email: mrasper@valdeseng.com
Website: www.valdeseng.com
Engineering svcs to process facilities, chemical, food, pharmaceutical, power & steel mfg plants in piping design, mechanical, civil & structural engineering, architecture & process engineering. (Hisp, estab 1992, empl 200, sales $28,000,000, cert: NMSDC)

Indiana

2919   Americas Engineers, Inc.
1449 Kimber Ln, Ste 101   Evansville, IN 47715
(812) 473-1905   KC Jain President
Fax: (812) 402-1379
Email: kcjain@americasengineers.com
Website: www.americasengineers.com
Civil engineering: surveying, site plans, drainage systems, grading & approach roads, access roads & storm water management. (As-Ind, estab 2004, empl 7, sales $1,200,000, cert: NMSDC)

2920   Consulting Management Inspection Design, Inc.
1402 N Capitol Ave Ste 250   Indianapolis, IN 46202
(317) 917-4244   Stacey L. Harrell Exec Admin Asst
Fax: (317) 917-4254
Email: sharrell@cmidinc.com
Website: www.cmidinc.com
Architectural, structural, mechanical, electrical, environmental, civil, commissioning & construction management & inspection services. (AA, estab 1996, empl 24, sales $3,500,000, cert: State, City)

Kentucky

2921   Pioneer Logistics Group, Inc.
2208 Sieger Villa Ct   Louisville, KY 40218
(502) 479-3546   Phillip Shoulders President
Fax: (502) 479-9962
Email: pioneergroupse@msn.com
Website: www.pioneergroupse.com
Logistics, inventory control management, warehouse services, facilities management, (AA, estab 2010, empl 25, sales $2,000,000, cert: NMSDC)

Louisiana

2922   Gulf South Engineering & Testing, Inc.
2201 Aberdeen St Ste B   Kenner, LA 70062
(504) 305-4401   Chad Poche VP
Fax: (504) 305-4408
Email: cpoche@gulfsoutheng.com
Website: www.gulfsoutheng.com
Geotechnical engineering, foundation engineering, soil borings, facility permitting, laboratory testing, construction materials testing & inspection, concrete testing, pile testing & inspection. (AA, estab 2010, empl 8, sales $550,000, cert: City)

2923   Smith Research Group
4811 Hooper Rd   Baton Rouge, LA 70811
(225) 356-9344   James Smith, Jr. CEO
Fax: (225) 356-9761
Email: Jim@src1.net
Website: www.src1.net
Research, mgmt; facility planning, architectural design, engineering; mechanical, electrical, civil & structural; program mgmt, project mgmt, scheduling, construction mgmt, environ eng, technical support & computer processing. (AA, estab 1994, empl 10, sales , cert: State)

Massachusetts

2924   Corporate Environmental Advisors, Inc.
127 Hartwell St   West Boylston, MA 01583
(800) 358-7960   Scott Soucy Health, Safety & Compliance
Fax: (508) 835-8812
Email: contactus@cea-inc.com
Website: www.cea-inc.com/
Environmental engineering, consulting & contracting firm. (Woman/White, estab 1985, empl 20, sales $3,878,000, cert: State)

Maryland

2925   Site Resources, Inc.
14315 Jarrettsville Pike P.O. Box 240   Phoenix, MD 21131
(410) 683-3388   Sharon Elliott Mktg Mgr
Fax: (410) 683-3389
Email: selliott@siteresourcesinc.com
Website: www.siteresourcesinc.com
Civil engineering, landscape architecture & land planning services. (Woman/White, estab 1994, empl 28, sales $4,126,649, cert: State, City)

Michigan

2926 ABE Associates, Inc.
440 Burroughs St, Ste. 605   Detroit, MI 48221
(313) 961-5170 Andre Brooks President
Fax: (800) 451-2165
Email: andreb@abe-engineers.com
Website: www.abe-engineers.com
Architectural design, civil, environmental, fire protection, mechanical & structural engineering, project management, program management, drafting, surveying, construction inspection, land acquisition services. (AA, estab 1997, empl 3, sales $250,000, cert: State, NMSDC)

2927 Byce & Associates, Inc.
487 Portage St   Kalamazoo, MI 49007
(269) 381-6170 Brenda Longman VP
Fax: (269) 381-6176
Email: corporate@byce.com
Website: www.byce.com
Structural, mechanical & electrical engineering design services. (Hisp, estab 1959, empl 34, sales , cert: NMSDC)

2928 Crystal Engineering Solutions
645 Executive Dr   Troy, MI 48083
(248) 588-1390 Chris Kizy VP
Fax: (248) 588-9545
Email: ckizy@crystaleng.com
Website: www.crystaleng.com
Engineering Services, Controls Engineering (Hisp, estab 1999, empl 18, sales $10,000,000, cert: NMSDC)

2929 CTI and Associates, Inc.
28001 Cabot Dr Ste. 250 Novi, MI 48377
(248) 486-5100 Robyn James Director
Fax: (248) 486-5050
Email: rjames@cticompanies.com
Website: www.cticompanies.com
Engineering consulting & construction management. (As-Ind, estab 1976, empl 90, sales $23,000,000, cert: NMSDC)

2930 Doshi Associates, Inc.
5755 New King St Ste 210 Troy, MI 48098
(248) 247-3030 Shailesh Doshi CEO
Fax: (248) 247-3057
Email: shailesh.doshi@doshigroup.net
Website: www.doshigroup.net
Architecturel, civil, structural, mechanical & electrical engineering. (As-Pac, estab 1991, empl 30, sales $2,550,000, cert: NMSDC)

2931 Feamold, Inc.
1441 W Long Lake Rd, Ste 240   Troy, MI 48098
(248) 680-4628 Shrikant Oak President
Fax: (248) 686-3500
Email: oak@feamold.com
Website: www.feamold.com
Engineering Consulting. (As-Ind, estab 1994, empl 5, sales , cert: NMSDC)

2932 Gala & Associates Inc.
31455 Southfield Rd   Beverly Hills, MI 48025
(248) 642-8610 Chuni Gala President
Fax: (248) 642-1409
Email: cgala@galaandassociates.com
Website: www.galaandassociates.com
Electrical, mechanical, structural, civil & architectural engineering svcs, CAD services. (Nat Ame/As-Ind/Hisp, estab 1987, empl 50, sales $6,000,000, cert: NMSDC)

2933 I*LOGIC, Inc.
999 Tech Row   Madison Heights, MI 48071
(248) 616-4506 Sharon Weatherspoon President
Fax: (248) 616-4550
Email: sweatherspoon@goilogic.com
Website: www.goilogic.com
Program management, containerization management, industrial engineering, material flow engineering, procurement services, design services & IT services. (Woman/As-Pac, estab 1995, empl 32, sales , cert: NMSDC, WBENC)

2934 MPS Group, Inc.
38755 Hills Tech Dr   Farmington Hills, MI 48331
(313) 841-7588 Bryon Lawrence Director of Sales & Mktg
Fax: (248) 489-0656
Email: blawrence@mpsgrp.com
Website: www.mpsgrp.com
Environmental Consulting & Engineering. (AA, estab 1995, empl 495, sales $46,200,000, cert: NMSDC)

2935 Optimal Computer Aided Engineering, Inc.
47802 W Anchor Court   Plymouth, MI 48170
(734) 414-7933 Song Young CEO
Fax: (734) 414-7944
Email: ksrinivas@optimalinc.com
Website: www.optimalinc.com
CAD/CAM/CAE/PDM services, contract engineering services & metrology product sales & support. (As-Pac, estab 1986, empl 100, sales $10,000,000, cert: NMSDC)

2936 PAT USA, Inc.
2927 Waterview Dr   Rochester Hills, MI 48309
(248) 299-2410 Fenar Mayes Sr Project Mgr
Fax: (248) 299-2413
Email: fenar@pat-engineering.com
Website: www.pat-engineering.com
General contracting services, engineering & construction services. (Woman/White, estab 2011, empl 10, sales , cert: WBENC)

2937   Renaissance S & S Inc.
26637 Golfview   Dearborn Heights, MI 48127
(313) 561-3897   Smith Sylvester CEO
Fax: (313) 561-3664
Email: rssgroup@sbcglobal.net
Website: www.renaissancessgroup.com
Engineering consulting services. (AA, estab 1996, empl 4, sales , cert: NMSDC)

Minnesota

2938   EVS, Inc.
10025 Valley View Rd Ste 140   Eden Prairie, MN 55344
(952) 646-0236   Andy Kim President
Fax: (952) 646-0290
Email: akim@evs-eng.com
Website: www.evs-eng.com
Civil engineering, site development, surveying & environmental, permits, assessments & NEPA documentation. (As-Pac, estab 1979, empl 30, sales $3,545,458, cert: City, NMSDC)

2939   Hansen Thorp Pellinen Olson, Inc.
7510 Market Place Dr   Eden Prairie, MN 55344
(952) 829-0700   Tim Johnson Business Dev Dir
Fax: (952) 829-7806
Email: tjohnson@htpo.com
Website: www.htpo.com
Engineering svcs: land surveying, civil engineering, landscape architecture design & construction. (Woman/White, estab 1980, empl 23, sales $2,876,105, cert: City)

2940   Sambatek
14800 28th Ave N, Ste 140   Plymouth, MN 55447
(763) 476-6010   Erik Miller
Fax: (763) 476-8532
Email: Emiller@sambatek.com
Website: www.sambatek.com
Civil engineering, land planning & surveying, water & waste water treatment process engineering, enviornmental assesments. (As-Pac, estab 1966, empl 46, sales $5,269,743, cert: State)

Missouri

2941   Civil Design Inc.
5220 Oakland Ave   St. Louis, MO 63110
(314)85570   Lori Daiber Business Devel Mgr
Fax: (314) 863-5578
Email: ldaiber@civildesigninc.com
Website: www.civildesigninc.com
Civil & Site Engineering, Land Surveying, Transportation, Water Resources, Infrastructure & Analytics. (Woman/White, estab 1996, empl 52, sales $5,800,000, cert: State, WBENC, NWBOC)

2942   EFK Moen, LLC
13523 Barrett Parkway Dr Ste 250   St. Louis, MO 63021
(314) 729-4104   Darrell Eilers VP
Fax: (314) 729-4199
Email: dleilers@efkmoen.com
Website: www.EFKMoen.com
Civil engineering & land surveying, roadway/highway engineering, bridge/structural design, site/development engineering, water/wastewater, traffic/transportation engineering. (Woman/White, estab 1998, empl 35, sales $2,700,000, cert: State)

2943   Peoria Contract Services, LLC
6428 Lipizzaner Dr   Imperial, MO 63052
(314) 761-5470   Kyle Pogue CEO
Fax: (314) 657-9753
Email: kyle@peoriacontractservices.com
Website: www.peoriacontractservices.com
Engineering, Electrical, Mechanical, Chemical, Process, Civil, Structural, Patented Modular Extrusion Process; ASME/API Storage Vessels; Bulk Material Handling/Storage; Automation; Piping Design & Pipe Supply; Hydraulic & Pneumatic. (Nat Ame, estab 2012, empl 5, sales , cert: State, NMSDC)

2944   Webb Engineering Services, Inc.
4670 Lansdowne Ave, Ste 111   St. Louis, MO 63116
(314) 351-0440   Stanley Webb President
Fax: (314) 351-4619
Email: webbs@webb-engineering.com
Website: www.webb-engineering.com
Mechanical, electrical, fire protection, plumbing, & civil design services. (AA, estab 1999, empl 8, sales $1,000,000, cert: City, 8(a))

North Carolina

2945   Crescent Construction Services, LLC
303 S Main GQ St   Salisbury, NC 28146
(704) 633-9697   Traci Williams President
Fax: (704) 633-2795
Email: traci@crescentconstructionservices.com
Website: www.crescentconstructionservices.com
Commissioning & engineering surveys, project management. (Woman/White, estab 2004, empl 15, sales $1,310,000, cert: WBENC)

New Jersey

2946 Industrial Fiberglass Services
145 Millbrook Rd Washington, NJ 07882
(908) 689-3417 Rita (Joanie) George CEO
Fax: (908) 689-3417
Email: sales@industrialfiberglassservices.com
Website: www.industrialfiberglassservices.com
Civil, Mechanical, FRP Repair & Installation. (Woman/
White, estab 2000, empl 7, sales $3,000,000, cert: WBENC)

2947 KS Engineers, P.C.
494 Broad St, 4th Fl Newark, NJ 07102
(973) 623-2999 Kamal Shahid President
Fax: (972) 242-2955
Email: kshahid@kseng.com
Website: www.kseng.com
Engineering, surveying & construction management. (As-
Ind, estab 1991, empl 250, sales $25,000,000, cert: State,
City, NMSDC)

2948 Matrix New World Engineering, Inc.
26 Columbia   Florham Park, NJ 07932
(973) 240-1800 Mayoor Sheth President
Fax: (973) 240-1818
Email: msheth@matrixneworld.com
Website: www.matrixneworld.com
Environmental, geotechnical, civil engineering, survey &
building facility consulting & engineering firm. (Woman/
White, estab 1990, empl 70, sales $20,526,967, cert: City,
CPUC)

2949 MFS Engineers & Surveyors
2780 Hamilton Blvd   South Plainfield, NJ 07080
(908) 922-4622 Kayla Ziegler Project Admin
Fax: (866) 517-7413
Email: ks@mfsengineers.com
Website: www.MFSengineers.com
Site/civil, structural, geotechnical & foundation, environmental engineering, construction layout, sustainable
design & construction management services. (As-Pac/Hisp,
estab 2009, empl 32, sales $4,403,207, cert: State, City,
8(a))

2950 Sovereign
111 A North Gold Dr   Robbinsville, NJ 08691
(609) 259-8200 Michael Hanlon Mgr
Fax: (609) 259-8200
Email: mhanlon@sovcon.com
Website: www.sovcon.com
Environmental consulting & remediation services, environmental, civil & geotechnical engineering; remediation
system evaluation, optimization, design & construction/
installation; environmental, land use & natural resources
permitting. (As-Pac, estab 1999, empl 165, sales
$35,466,433, cert: NMSDC)

New York

2951 Dose Engineering, PLLC
817 Broadway, 5th Fl New York, NY 10003
(646) 715-2096 Anostere Jean Principal
Fax: (646) 715-2096
Email: ajean@dose-engineering.com
Website: www.dose-engineering.com
Engineering design, engineering design drawings, due
diligence reports Mechanical: HVAC Electrical: Lighting
and Power Plumbing Fire Alarm Fire Protection LEED:
Leadership in Energy and Environmental (AA, estab
2009, empl 5, sales $300,000, cert: City)

2952 Environmental Design & Research, DPC
217 Montgomery St Ste 1000 Syracuse, NY 13202
(315) 471-0688 Joanne Stewart Associate
Fax: (315) 471-1061
Email: jstewart@edrdpc.com
Website: www.edrdpc.com
Landscape architecture, civil engineering, community
planning, visualization, environmental regulatory,
ecological, geographic information systems mapping &
analysis, historic preservation, cultural resources,
archeology. (Woman/White, estab 1979, empl 38, sales
$4,500,000, cert: State)

2953 Foit-Albert Associates, Architecture, Engineering
and Surveying, P.C.
215 W 94th St, Ste 517 New York, NY 10025
(716) 856-3933 Gregory Carballada President
Fax: (716) 856-3933
Email: cstoebe@foit-albert.com
Website: www.foit-albert.com
Architecture, Engineering, Environmental & Land
Surveying Consulting. (Hisp, estab 1977, empl 48, sales
$4,839,242, cert: State, City)

2954 Sabir, Richardson & Weisberg Engineers PLLC
37 W 39th St, Ste 1005   NYC, NY 10018
(646) 863-6160 Yvette Richardson Principal
Fax: (856) 310-5501
Email: info@srw-eng.com
Website: www.srw-eng.com
Engineering svcs: architectural, mechanical, electrical,
fire protection & plumbing consulting. (Woman/AA/
Hisp, estab 2004, empl 1, sales $1,000,000, cert: City)

2955 W. Allen Engineering PLLC
2934 Hering Avenue Bronx, NY 10469
(917) 295-8275 Wayne Allen Principal
Fax: (718) 652-1031
Email: wla@wallenengineering.com
Website: www.wallenengineering.com
Civil & mechanical engineering, construction inspection/
management services, contract admin, owner representation, cost estimating, lead based paint abatement,
drafting, HVAC design. (AA/As-Ind, estab 1997, empl 6,
sales $1,200,000, cert: State, City)

2956   Watts Engineering & Architecture, P.C.
     95 Perry St Ste 300   Buffalo, NY 14203
     (716) 836-1540   Edward Watts President
     Fax: (716) 836-2402
     Email: ewatts@wattsengineers.com
     Website: www.wattsengineers.com
Civil, environmental, mechancial & electrical engineering &
architecture consulting. (AA, estab 1986, empl 73, sales
$6,800,000, cert: City, NMSDC)

Ohio

2957   CAD Concepts, Inc.
     1328 Dublin Rd, Ste 201   Columbus, OH 43215
     (614) 485-0670   Joyce K Johnson
     Fax: (614) 485-0677
     Email: certifications@ccitechs.com
     Website: www.ccitechs.com
Engineering support services: CAD, GIS, field work &
administrative services. (Woman/White, estab 1984, empl
8, sales , cert: State, WBENC)

2958   Crawford & Associates Services, LLC
     100 E Campus View Blvd Ste 250   Columbus, OH
     43235
     (614) 557-1498   Troy Crawford Principal
     Fax: (614) 438-2626
     Email: tcrawford@cas-associates.com
     Website: www.cas-associates.com
Commercial & Industrial Commissioning of Mechanical/
Electrical/Plumbing Systems, including Heating, Ventilating
and Air Conditioning Systems and Building Automatic
Temperature Control Systems. (AA, estab 2007, empl 5,
sales $293,055, cert: 8(a))

2959   CTL Engineering, Inc.
     2860 Fisher Rd P.O. Box 44548 Columbus, OH 43204
     (614) 276-8123   C.K. Satyapriya President
     Fax:
     Email: ctl@ctleng.com
     Website: www.ctleng.com
Geotechnical, construction inspection, environmental,
mining engineering, analytical chemistry, forensic science,
metallurgy, product testing, research & development, roof
engineering, existing structure evaluation, asbestos
inspection. (As-Ind, estab 1928, empl 187, sales , cert:
State)

2960   DHDC Engineering Consulting Services, Inc.
     2390 Advanced Business Center Dr   Columbus, OH
     43228
     (614) 527-7656   Savvas Sophocleous President
     Fax: (614) 527-7489
     Email: sophocleous@dhdcinc.com
     Website: www.dhdcinc.com
Laboratory testing services, geotechnical (engineering,
drilling, and laboratory) & subsurface utility engineering
(SUE). (As-Pac, estab 2012, empl 15, sales $500,000, cert:
State)

2961   DLZ Industrial, LLC
     6121 Huntley Rd   Columbus, OH 43229
     (614) 888-0040   Kurt Schmiegel CEO
     Fax: (614) 431-3854
     Email: mbe@dlz.com
     Website: www.dlz.com
Industrial surveying, close tolerance machinery surveying, setting & realignment, construction, topographical,
hydrographic & property surveying. (As-Ind/As-Pac,
estab 1989, empl 568, sales , cert: NMSDC)

2962   Moody Engineering, LLC
     300 Spruce St Ste 200   Columbus, OH 43215
     (614) 280-8999   David Moody CEO
     Fax:
     Email: dmoody@moody-eng.com
     Website: www.moody-eng.com
Stormwater management, Site design, Sediment and
erosion control, Roadway, Permits - NPDES, PTI, zoning,
Vehicular access, Grading, Pedestrian traffic, Drainage,
Parking lots, Wet and dry ponds, Utility design, Domestic
water, Underground infrastructure. (AA, estab 2015,
empl 10, sales $590,000, cert: State, City)

2963   On Line Design, Inc.
     12057 Sheraton Ln   Cincinnati, OH 45246
     (513) 346-4343   Jeannie Smith President
     Fax: (513) 346-4340
     Email: jeannie@o-l-design.com
     Website: www.o-l-design.com
Engineering & technical personnel: plant & capital
projects, design/build equipment. (Woman/White, estab
1989, empl 50, sales $2,200,000, cert: WBENC)

2964   R Engineering Team, LLC
     3100 E 45th St, Ste 306   Cleveland, OH 44127
     (216) 361-2500   Tom Roberts President
     Fax: (216) 361-2222
     Email: rengineeringteam@gmail.com
     Website: www.rengineeringteam.com
Consulting engineering in the disciplines of electrical
engineering, mechanical engineering, construction
administration, and computer CAD drafting. (AA, estab
2008, empl 7, sales $488,131, cert: NMSDC)

Oklahoma

2965   Aero Tech Service Associates, Inc.
     909 S Meridian Ave, Ste 200   Oklahoma City, OK
     73108
     (405) 946-2872   John Howard CEO
     Fax: (405) 946-2889
     Email: atsa@atsainc.com
     Website: www.atsainc.com
Aviation systems requirements, systems engineering &
operations, information technology, communications,
technical training, technical & administrative svcs &
support. (AA, estab 1991, empl 180, sales , cert: State)

2966 Excellence Engineering, LLC
      8670 S Peoria Ave   Tulsa, OK 74132
      (918) 298-5500 Deyona Hays CEO
      Fax: (918) 298-5501
      Email: dee.hays@eeinco.com
      Website: www.eeinco.com
Engineering, civil, structural, process, piping, mechanical, electrical, instrument, controls, startup & commissioning. (Woman/White, estab 2001, empl 40, sales , cert: WBENC)

Pennsylvania

2967 Advantus Engineers
      300 Bilmar Dr Ste 150   Pittsburgh, PA 15205
      (412) 489-9090 Alicia Avick President
      Fax:
      Email: aavick@advantusengineers.com
      Website: www.advantusengineers.com
Facilities design engineering, commissioning, project management & construction management services for the commercial, institutional & light industrial markets. (Woman/Hisp, estab 2004, empl 10, sales $550,000, cert: State, WBENC)

2968 Dawood Engineering, Inc.
      2020 Good Hope Rd   Enola, PA 17025
      (717) 732-8576 Kristal Martinez
      Fax: (717) 732-8596
      Email: kmartinez@dawood.cc
      Website: www.dawood.cc
Civil Site Design, Survey & Mapping, Environmental Consulting, Mechanical & Electrical Engineering, Geotechnical Engineering
Structural Engineering. (As-Ind, estab 1992, empl 161, sales $20,100,000, cert: NMSDC)

2969 First Capital Engineering
      48 S Richland Ave   York, PA 17404
      (717) 845-3227 Ann Luciani CEO
      Fax:
      Email: annl@fcap.com
      Website: www.fcap.com
Civil engineering, land surveying, landscape architecture, environmental & construction inspection services. (Woman/White, estab 1995, empl 17, sales $1,949,255, cert: State, WBENC)

2970 IES Engineers
      1720 Walton Rd   Blue Bell, PA 19422
      (610) 828-3078 Lisa Wallis Mgr, Accting & Admin Services
      Fax: (610) 828-7842
      Email: lwallis@iesengineers.com
      Website: www.iesengineers.com
Engineering & environmental, health & safety consulting, regulatory compliance. (As-Ind, estab 1991, empl 30, sales $8,223,000, cert: NMSDC)

2971 Keystone Aerial Surveys, Inc.
      P.O. Box 21059 NE Philadelphia Arprt Philadelphia, PA 19114
      (215) 677-3119 Mary Potter President
      Fax: (215) 464-2889
      Email: mpotter@keystoneaerialsurveys.com
      Website: www.keystoneaerialsurveys.com
Aerial imagery acquisition & remote sensing, aerial photographic & digital reproduction. (Woman/White, estab 1963, empl 44, sales $7,578,019, cert: City)

2972 Rodriguez Consulting LLC
      1301 N 2nd St Philadelphia, PA 19122
      (215) 839-8087 Yarelis Franco Mktg Coord
      Fax: (877) 839-6975
      Email: yfranco@rodriguezconsulting.biz
      Website: www.rodriguezconsulting.biz
Civil engineering, site design, environmental engineering, land surveying, traffic data collection and engineering, construction inspection & geographic information systems (GIS) services. (Hisp, estab 2007, empl 22, sales $909,000, cert: City, 8(a))

2973 TREC Group, Inc.
      900 Old Marple Rd.   Springfield, PA 19064
      (610) 328-6465 Bill Horan Director of Business Dev
      Fax: (610) 328-3716
      Email: bill@trecgroup.com
      Website: www.trecgroup.com
Mechanical, electrical & civil engineering, project management, construction management, drafting & AUTOCAD capabilities. (Woman/White, estab 2001, empl 11, sales , cert: State, WBENC)

Puerto Rico

2974 Intelligent Software Solutions Corporation
      P.O. Box 363601   San Juan, PR 00936
      (787) 625-1500 Edgar Guerrero
      Fax: (787) 782-2513
      Email: 787-625-5150
      Website: www.isspr.com
Construction mgmt, inspection, project mgmt, autocad & microstation drafting, tagging, P&ID, drawing update, scheduling, validation, qualification, regulatory compliance, quality, risk mgmt, commissioning. (Hisp, estab 1990, empl 33, sales $14,960,000, cert: NMSDC)

2975   JCD Engineering, Inc.
P.O. Box 192372   San Juan, PR 00919
(787) 787-7211   Juan C. del Pino President
Fax: (787) 787-9338
Email: jcdelpino@jcdengineering.com
Website: www.jcdengineering.com
Civil, electrical & mechanical engineering: concrete & steel small buildings, interiors work, hung ceilings, floors, gypsum board, electrical power & controls, fiber optics, local area networks (LAN), process and AHU control systems. (Hisp, estab 1996, empl 11, sales $1,327,000, cert: NMSDC)

2976   NOVO Consulting Group LLC
PMB 9 6400   Cayey, PR 00737
(787) 413-7379   Claritza Millan President
Fax:
Email: cmillan@novo-pr.com
Website: www.novo-pr.com
Design Qualification, Engineering Studies, Installation Qualification, Operational Qualification, Performance Qualification, Process Verification/Validation, Project Management, Process Improvement/Optimization, Quality Assurance, CAPA, NCRs. (Woman/Hisp, estab 2015, empl 2, sales , cert: NMSDC)

2977   UNIPRO Architects Engineers LLP
P.O. Box 10914   San Juan, PR 00922
(787) 793-3950   Jose R. Gonzalez Dir planning/ projects
Fax: (787) 793-8593
Email: jgonzalez@uniproaep.net
Website: www.uniproaep.com
Architecture, civil engineering, structural engineering, mechanical engineering, electrical engineering, environmental engineering, construction management. (Hisp, estab 1980, empl 30, sales $3,200,000, cert: NMSDC)

South Carolina

2978   Atlantic South Consulting Services
3030 Ashley Town Center Dr Ste 101A   Charleston, SC 29414
(843) 266-3998   Adrian Williams President
Fax: (843) 266-3999
Email: awilliams@atlanticsouthconsulting.com
Website: www.atlanticsouthconsulting.com
Engineering, surveying, and right-of-way acquisition services, transportation & utility designs, site development & land planning, construction inspection & management services, easement. (AA, estab 2004, empl 6, sales $668,000, cert: State)

Texas

2979   Aguirre Roden Inc.
10670 N Central Expressway 6th Fl   Dallas, TX 75231
(972) 789-2662   Peter Aguirre, CFM SVP program Devel
Fax: (972) 788-1583
Email: paaguirre@aguirre.com
Website: www.aguirreroden.com
Architecture, mechanical, electrical & structural engineering, general contracting. (Hisp, estab 1960, empl 65, sales , cert: State, NMSDC)

2980   Arias & Associates, Inc.
142 Chula Vista   San Antonio, TX 78232
(210) 308-5884   Jeremy Arias Business Devel
Fax: (210) 308-5886
Email: PurchaseOrders@ariasinc.com
Website: www.ariasinc.com
Geotechnical engineering svcs, construction materials testing & observation, environmental svcs. (Hisp, estab 1996, empl 79, sales , cert: State, SDB)

2981   Bastion Technologies, Inc.
17625 El Camino Real   Houston, TX 77058
(281) 283-9330   Jorge Hernandez President
Fax: (281) 283-9333
Email: jhernandez@bastiontechnologies.com
Website: www.bastiontechnologies.com
Engineering design, analysis, systems engineering, information technology applications, engineering research, mechanical engineering, structural engineering, safety & reliability engineering, systems safety, hazard analysis. (Hisp, estab 1998, empl 400, sales $42,711,000, cert: State, NMSDC)

2982   Charles Gojer & Associates, Inc.
11615 Forest Central Dr, Ste 303   Dallas, TX 75243
(214) 340-1199   Charles Gojer President
Fax: (214) 348-8053
Email: cgojer@cgojer.com
Website: www.cgojer.com
Civil & structural engineering. (Hisp, estab 1973, empl 10, sales , cert: State, NMSDC)

2983   Elements of Architecture, Inc.
1201 6th Ave Ste 100   Fort Worth, TX 76104
(817) 333-2880   Debbie Fulwiler President
Fax: (817) 333-2883
Email: dfulwiler@elementsofarc.com
Website: www.elementsofarc.com
Architectural & engineering svcs: environmental, structure & facility, electrical, mechanical, fire protection, alarming. (Woman/White, estab 1996, empl 7, sales , cert: State, WBENC)

2984 First Assured Quality Systems, LLC
P.O. Box 535812 GRAND PRAIRIE, TX 75053
(817) 538-9240 Brittany Stovall President
Fax: (210) 978-5465
Email: bstovall@assuredqualitysystems.com
Website: www.assuredqualitysystems.com
Quality Control Services- Containment, Sorting, Rework,
Inspection, Liaison Support, Engineering Support & Launch
Support. (Woman/AA/Hisp, estab 2013, empl 35, sales
$2,872,632, cert: NMSDC, WBENC)

2985 Galosi LLC
16800 Dallas Pkwy, Ste 210 Dallas, TX 75248
(972) 267-9907 J. Wayne Trimmer EVP
Fax: (214) 420-6638
Email: wayne.trimmer@galosi.com
Website: www.galosi.com
Cost of Money - Audit Discounts
Credit Memo Errors
Defective or Spoiled Goods Audit
Duplicate Payments
Errors Involving Returns (Hisp, estab 2001, empl 27, sales
$2,100,000, cert: State, NMSDC)

2986 GMR Protection Resources, Inc.
P.O. Box 645 Rockwall, TX 75087
(972) 771-6038 Ken Foley Sr VP
Fax: (972) 772-1339
Email: ken@gmr1.com
Website: www.gmr1.com
Facilties-related inspections & site lighting analysis &
design, property reviews & assessments, branding/signage
quality control verifications, equipment inventory programs and acquisition/disposition asset inventory programs. (Woman/White, estab 1991, empl 55, sales
$8,128,000, cert: WBENC)

2987 Johnson & Pace Inc.
1201 NW Loop 281, Ste 100 Longview, TX 75604
(903) 753-0663 Delcine Johnson President
Fax: (903) 753-8803
Email: delcinej@johnsonpace.com
Website: www.johnsonpace.com
Engineering services: civil, mechanical, electrical, struc-
tural, architectural services, land surveying. (Woman/
White, estab 1995, empl 75, sales $9,500,000, cert: State)

2988 JQ Infrastructure, LLC
100 Glass St Ste 201 Dallas, TX 75207
(972) 392-7340 Stephen Lucy Principal
Fax: (214) 550-2536
Email: slucy@jqeng.com
Website: www.jqieng.com/
Surveying services, building, structures & components
consulting, engineering consulting, civil engineering,
concrete engineering, drainage engineering, foundation
engineering, inspection, general/engineering. (As-Pac,
estab 2003, empl 105, sales $6,471,893, cert: State,
NMSDC)

2989 M.E.P. Consulting Engineers, Inc.
2928 Story Rd W Irving, TX 75038
(972) 870-9060 Camilla Beavers Admin Asst
Fax: (972) 870-9056
Email: mail@mepce.com
Website: www.mepce.com
Mechanical, electrical, plumbing, fire protection &
information technology design engineering & commissioning for aviation facilities, municipalities, educational
facilities, government, health care & commercial
facilities. (Woman, estab 1998, empl 14, sales
$4,000,000, cert: State, WBENC)

2990 MULTATECH
2821 W 7th St Ste 400 Fort Worth, TX 76107
(817) 877-5571 Hong P. Chen President
Fax: (817) 877-4245
Email: hchen@multatech.com
Website: www.multatech.com
mechanical, electrical, plumbing & civil consulting
engineering services, architectural design services. (Hisp,
estab 1986, empl 74, sales $11,048,061, cert: State,
NMSDC)

2991 SeaMax Corporation
3720 W Alabama St Ste 3108 Houston, TX 77027
(713) 584-3643 BRENDAN ISIDIENU Structural
Engineer
Fax:
Email: ibrendan@seamax.org
Website: www.seamax.org
Engineering consulting, structural engineering & and
design of offshore & onshore soil & gas structures. (AA,
estab 2015, empl 2, sales $15,000, cert: NMSDC)

2992 Sunland Group
10400 Westoffice Dr, Ste 116 Houston, TX 77042
(713) 467-8484 Sales/Marketing
Fax: (713) 467-3353
Email: info@sunlandgrp.com
Website: www.sunlandgrp.com
Design build: civil, structural, environmental engineering, architecture, design & construction surveying, value
engineering. (Hisp, estab 1985, empl 85, sales
$8,200,000, cert: State)

2993 Systems Integration, Inc.
7316 Business Pl Arlington, TX 76001
(817) 468-1494 Rhonda Smith Acct Mgr
Fax: (817) 468-7975
Email: rsmith@sitexas.com
Website: www.sitexas.com
Engineering & Design, Reverse Engineering, Fabrication,
Installation, Structural & Civil, Manufacturing, Machin-
ery, Mechanical, CNC Machining, Electrical & Controls,
Test Structures, Tooling. (Hisp, estab 1992, empl 20,
sales $4,000,000, cert: State)

Virginia

2994 Ashe Consultants, PLLC
      950 Herndon Pkwy Ste 320 Herndon, VA 20170
      (703) 230-2500 Sharon Gorick President
      Fax: (103) 871-6812
      Email: sgorick@asheconsultants.com
      Website: www.asheconsultants.com
Mechanical, electrical & plumbing engineering design
services for buildings. (Woman/White, estab 2008, empl 5,
sales $130,660, cert: State)

2995 MKAssociates, Inc.
      6593 Commerce Ct, Ste 100 Warrenton, VA 20187
      (540) 428-3550 Michelle R. Kilby President
      Fax: (540) 428-3560
      Email: mkilby@mkassociates.com
      Website: www.mkassociates.com
Land surveying coordination. (Woman/White, estab 1998,
empl 12, sales $350,000,000, cert: WBENC)

Washington

2996 CS3W Associates, Inc.
      2821 167th Ave NE   Bellevue, WA 98008
      (425) 922-5900 Christopher Sims President
      Fax: (425) 881-1648
      Email: csims@cs3w.com
      Website: www.cs3w.com
Engineering & management services, electrical & struc-
tural/seismic engineering services, project management &
analysis support. (AA, estab 1999, empl 8, sales $671,000,
cert: State)

2997 Garry Struthers Associates, Inc.
      3150 Richards Rd   Bellevue, WA 98005
      (425) 519-0300 Garry Struthers President
      Fax: (425) 519-0309
      Email: garrys@gsassoc-inc.com
      Website: www.gsassoc-inc.com
Engineering, construction, environmental science, facilities
maintenance. (AA, estab 1988, empl 106, sales
$21,000,000, cert: NMSDC)

2998 GeoTest Services, Inc.
      741 Marine View Dr   Bellingham, WA 98225
      (360) 733-7318 Jeremy Wolf VP
      Fax: (360) 733-7418
      Email: jeremyw@geotest-inc.com
      Website: www.geotest-inc.com
Geotechnical engineering, environmental services, special
inspection & materials testing, facilities, structures, roads,
bridges & all types of infrastructure. (Woman/White, estab
1993, empl 33, sales $6,000,000, cert: State)

2999 Land Development Consultants, Inc.
      14201 NE 200th St Ste 100 Woodinville, WA
      98072
      (425) 806-1869 Frank Lemos President
      Fax: (425) 482-2893
      Email: flemos@ldccorp.com
      Website: www.ldccorp.com
Civil Engineering, Land Survey, Land Use Planning/
Permitting, A/E Design, Commercial Site Design, Road-
way Design, Drainage Design and Reporting, GIS ESRI
Mapping, Water Systems. (Hisp, estab 2003, empl 40,
sales $5,354,378, cert: State, NMSDC)

3000 WHPacific, Inc.
      12100 NE 195th St Ste 300 Bothell, WA 98011
      (425) 951-4000 Carl Romig Dir ICS
      Fax: (425) 951-4808
      Email: cromig@whpacific.com
      Website: www.WHPacific.com
Accessibility/Universal Access, Aviation Planning &
Design, Bridge Design and Rehabilitation, Civil Engineer-
ing, Commissioning, Community & Urban Design,
Construction Inspection, Construction Management,
Construction Management. (Nat Ame, estab 1981, empl
351, sales $55,249,100, cert: NMSDC)

Wisconsin

3001 Fusion Integrated Solutions LLC
      416 Security Blvd   Green Bay, WI 54313
      (920) 593-4200 Seaphes Miller CEO
      Fax: (920) 592-4201
      Email: solutions@fusion-etc.com
      Website: www.fusion-etc.com
Mechanical, civil & structural, electrical & process
engineering & design svcs, project management,
materials procurement, construction field supervision,
electrical panel construction & custom machine design
& manufacture. (AA, estab 2004, empl 60, sales
$9,113,000, cert: State, NMSDC, 8(a))

3002 K. Singh & Associates, Inc.
      3636 N 124th St   Wauwatosa, WI 53222
      (262) 821-1171 Pratap Singh CEO
      Fax: (262) 821-1174
      Email: gmiller@ksaconsultants.com
      Website: www.ksaconsultants.com
Environmental engineering & management services,
transportation, structural, environmental & civil engi-
neering, land surveying & construction management.
(As-Ind, estab 1987, empl 33, sales $3,000,000, cert:
State)

ENGINEERING, SPECIAL SERVICES
Many of these firms are engaged in electromechanical design and testing. Others are in areas such as R&D, systems engineering, manufacturing, etc. Included are plant noise studies, digital design, radio active waste disposal, nuclear power, blueprinting services, etc. (See also INFORMATION TECHNOLOGY: Services). NAICS Code 54

Alaska

3003 Katmai Support Services, LLC
701 E Tudor Rd, Ste 215   Anchorage, AK 99503
(907) 333-7000 Katherine Tweidt Business Dev
Fax: (907) 333-7099
Email: eric@anc8a.com
Website:
Mfr, overhaul, repair & modification of advanced composites & bonded honeycomb structures for numerous space & airframe applications in new generations of aircraft and space vehicles. (Nat Ame, estab 2003, empl 1, sales $521,411, cert: State)

Alabama

3004 GASmith Enterprises, Inc.
464 Cahaba Park Cir   Birmingham, AL 35242
(205) 981-5391 George A. Smith President
Fax: (205) 981-8087
Email: info@signarama-bham.com
Website: www.signarama-bham.com
SIGN-A-RAMA is your full service sign center. We use the latest technology and highest quality products to produce custom signs for your business. We can make the perfect signs to advertise your products or to inform your (AA, estab 2010, empl 6, sales $3,000,000, cert: State, NMSDC)

Arizona

3005 Engineering Science Analysis, Corp.
6105 S Ash Ave Ste A-4   Tempw, AZ 85283
(602) 625-6259 Martin Martinez President
Fax: (480) 283-0064
Email: Martin.A.Martinez@esacorp.com
Website: www.esacorp.com
Product development, research & development, engineering design, advanced simulation analysis, manufacturing, test & advanced software tools for CAD/CAE applications. (Hisp, estab 1991, empl 8, sales $750,000, cert: State)

California

3006 Fakouri Electrical Engineering, Inc.
30001 Comcercio   Rancho Santa Margarita, CA 92688
(800) 669-8852 Ms. Findlay Corp facil
Fax: (949) 888-2414
Email: lfindlay@fee-ups.com
Website: www.fee-ups.com
Engineer, install & maintain UPS systems: batteries, power systems, etc. (Woman/White, estab 1979, empl 50, sales $14,000,000, cert: CPUC)

3007 GDSTA, LLC
2000 Wyatt Dr, Ste 10   Santa Clara, CA 95054
(408) 980-8399 Daphne Liu President
Fax: (972) 550-9490
Email: daphneliu@gdsta.net
Website: www.gdsta.net
Light emitting diode (LED) lighting & smart lighting devices, reduce carbon dioxide emission, energy usage, energy cost, lighting pollution, waste & return on investment (ROI). (Woman/As-Pac, estab 2009, empl 8, sales , cert: NMSDC)

3008 Quality Assurance and Risk Management Services,Inc
22 Highridge Dr   American Canyon, CA 94503
(707) 557-1942 Robert Navarro CEO
Fax: (435) 578-5864
Email: RNavarro@QAandRM.com
Website: www.QAandRM.com
Safety & mission assurance (SMA) support for NASA missions & payloads, safety, reliability & quality engineering/assurance & continuous risk management. (Hisp, estab 2005, empl 6, sales $667,971, cert: State)

3009 Solartech Power, Inc.
901 E Cedar St   Ontario, CA 91761
(714) 630-8880 Sherry Fu Owner
Fax: (714) 630-8887
Email: sherry.fu@solartechpower.com
Website: www.solartechpower.com
Mfr solar photovoltaic panels & equipment. (Woman/As-Ind, estab 2001, empl 10, sales $3,000,000, cert: CPUC)

3010 Vistam, Inc.
2375 Walnut Ave   Signal Hill, CA 90755
(562) 912-7779 Arley Tamayo Sales
Fax: (562) 912-4077
Email: art.tamayo@vistam.com
Website: www.vistam.com
Electrical engineering & testing services, substation maintenance & commissioning projects, scheduled maintenance programs. (As-Pac, estab 1992, empl 18, sales $1,752,000, cert: State)

3011 WRW Engineering
      2104 Martin Way   Pittsburg, CA 94565
      (925) 439-8272 Barbara Williams Supplier Diversity
      Admin
      Fax: (925) 439-5931
      Email: bwilliams@wrweng.com
      Website: www.wrweng.com
Mechanical, electrical & software engineering, automated
flexible testing stations, smart products & autonomous
machines. (Woman/White, estab 2012, empl 2, sales
$60,000, cert: WBENC)

3012 Zelos Consulting, LLC
      2400 Wyandotte St Ste A Mountain View, CA 94043
      (650) 462-1696 Sabrina Sirwet Business Dev Mgr
      Fax: (650) 968-4001
      Email: sabrina.sirwet@zelos.com
      Website: www.zelos.com
Turnkey & customized engineering: staffing services,
payroll services, engineering project design services.
(Woman/As-Pac, estab 1996, empl 40, sales $3,000,000,
cert: CPUC, WBENC)

Colorado

3013 Special Aerospace Services LLC
      3005 30th St Boulder, CO 80301
      (303) 625-1010 Heather Bulk CEO
      Fax:
      Email: hbulk@specialaerospaceservices.com
      Website: www.specialaerospaceservices.com
Tactical engineering services: safety, mission assurance,
integration, design & concept development. (Woman,
estab 2007, empl 40, sales $3,000,000, cert: 8(a))

Delaware

3014 Bethrant Industries LLC
      7 Midfield Rd   New Castle, DE 19720
      (302) 322-0521 Ashly Bethrant President
      Fax:
      Email: Ashly17@comcast.net
      Website: www.bethrantdesign.com
Design, engineering, CAD, graphics, illustration, rendering,
prototype models & fixture fabrication, point of purchase
displays, shelving design, exhibit booths. (Woman/AA/
Hisp, estab 2016, empl 4, sales , cert: NMSDC)

3015 Mechanical Design Solutions, Inc.
      5577 S DuPont Pkwy   Smyrna, DE 19977
      (302) 659-0233 Dianne Bingham President
      Fax: (302) 659-1928
      Email: dbingham@mds13.com
      Website: www.mds13.com
Mechanical, electrical & instrument system design, P&ID
walkdown, verification, fabrication orthography, isomet-
rics, bill of material & scopes of work, stress analysis, PSV
survey & modeling, Installation. (Woman/Nat Ame, estab
1998, empl 6, sales $875,000, cert: State)

Florida

3016 EDF Company
      8390 Currency Dr, Ste 4   Riviera Beach, FL 33404
      (561) 863-6770 Karla Watkins Director
      Fax: (561) 842-3929
      Email: karla@edfinc.com
      Website: www.edfinc.com
Complex design & engineering support services to the
Aerospace industry. Test Facilities & Test Equipment
Design/Build for multiple Engine Test Programs, F100/
F14, F119/F22, Joint Strike Fighter (JSF). (Woman/White,
estab 1978, empl 25, sales $3,355,920, cert: WBENC)

3017 Engineered Design Services LLC
      410 S Ware Blvd Ste 405 Tampa, FL 33619
      (813) 816-0301 Craig McKenzie President
      Fax:
      Email: craigmckenzie@edsengineers.com
      Website:
Mechanical & Electrical Engineering, Process Design,
Pumping Systems, 3D Modeling, Food Grade Piping
Design, Structural/Concrete
Vessel Design, Dry Material Handling, Material Convey-
ing & Dust Collection. (AA, estab 2013, empl 4, sales
$119,829, cert: State)

3018 ITG Global, LLC
      11235 St. Johns Industrial Pkwy N Ste 2A Jackson-
      ville, FL 32246
      (904) 425-4760 Joseph Lukowski CEO
      Fax:
      Email: almaferrante@itgtec.com
      Website: www.itgtec.com
Automation Design, PLC Programming, Software
Development, Technologies Consulting, Motion Design,
Robot programming, MES, OEE, Data Analytics, Condi-
tion Monitoring, Control System Design, UL 508A Panel
Shop, Control Panel. (Woman/Hisp, estab 2003, empl 27,
sales $3,000,000, cert: NMSDC)

3019 JIRACOR
      3275 Progress Dr Ste A Orlando, FL 32825
      (407) 910-1146 Richard Coronado President
      Fax: (407) 910-1136
      Email: r.coronado@jiracor.com
      Website: www.jiracor.com
Engineering services: aerospace, aviation, commercial &
defense. (Woman/Hisp, estab 2011, empl 12, sales
$1,000,000, cert: 8(a))

3020 RLJ Enterprises Inc. dba Genesis VII, Inc.
      1605 White Dr   Titusville, FL 32780
      (321) 383-4813 Robert Jordan CEO
      Fax: (321) 383-3247
      Email: robert.jordan@genesisvii.com
      Website: www.genesisvii.com
Engineering, Logistics & Constructions Services, Design
Engineering, 3D CAD, Reverse Engineering, Procurement, Facilities mgmy, Construction mgmt. (AA, estab
1989, empl 9, sales $3,900,000, cert: NMSDC, SDB)

3021   Southern Energy Solution Group, LLC
       2336 S East Ocean Blvd, Ste 204   Stuart, FL 34996
       (772) 919-2844 Oswald Hoffler Managing Member
       Fax: (772) 872-5240
       Email: ohoffler@soenergy-grp.com
       Website: www.soenergy-grp.com
Renewable Energy Generation and RECs (AA, estab 2010, empl 5, sales $250,000, cert: CPUC)

Georgia

3022   BREED Enterprises, Inc.
       4501 Circle 75 Pkwy Ste A-1160 Atlanta, GA 30339
       (678) 324-0105 Bobby Reed CEO
       Fax: (678) 550-9591
       Email: breed@breedenterprisesinc.com
       Website: www.breedenterprisesinc.com
LEED programs, LED lighting products. (AA, estab 2005, empl 45, sales $2,500,000, cert: State, NMSDC)

3023   Greenspeed Energy Solutions, LLC
       2148 Hills Ave NW Ste H Atlanta, GA 30318
       (404) 924-7400 Thomas McNeill Business Dev Mgr
       Fax:
       Email: tmcneill@greenspeedenergy.com
       Website: www.greenspeedenergy.com
Design/build energy services, audit & design, implementation (installation) of energy efficiency measures. (As-Pac, estab 2006, empl 20, sales $4,000,000, cert: State, NMSDC)

3024   Present Energi LLC
       411 S Greenwood St Ste B LaGrange, GA 30240
       (706) 883-7336 Renee Warrick Managing Partner
       Fax: (706) 884-2429
       Email: renee@presentenergi.com
       Website: www.presentenergi.com
Solar Photovoltaic & Solar Thermal systems for residential, commercial, industrial & utility scale customers; engineering, project management & construction for large scale systems. (Woman/White, estab 2009, empl 2, sales , cert: WBENC)

3025   Prime Power Services
       8225 Troon Circle   Austell, GA 30168
       (770) 739-2300 Addie Mathes President
       Fax: (770) 739-0723
       Email: gmaddox@primepower.com
       Website: www.primepower.com
Power generation svcs: maintenance & emergency response, testing, inspection, calibration & repair, rentals, installations, retrofit, commissioning, ngineering studies & analysis, support, investigation & consulting, training. (Woman/White, estab 1992, empl 50, sales $11,600,000, cert: WBENC)

Illinois

3026   CSMI-KAE Consultants, Inc.
       1750 E Golf Rd Ste 490 Schaumburg, IL 60173
       (847) 605-0080 Karen Eng President
       Fax: (847) 605-1055
       Email: keng@csmius.com
       Website: www.csmius.com
Engineering & design services: project management, electrical, mechanical, packaging, automation engineering & CAD services. (Woman/As-Pac, estab 1983, empl 24, sales $3,900,000, cert: State, WBENC)

3027   PMA Consultants of Illinois LLC
       333 W Wacker Dr, Ste 880   Chicago, IL 60606
       (312) 920-0404 Gui Ponce de Leon Managing Principal
       Fax: (312) 920-0405
       Email: kflood@pmaconsultants.com
       Website: www.pmaconsultants.com
Engineering consulting services: CPM scheduling, claims mitigation, change order management, contract document review, cost estimating, value engineering, training & expert analysis and testimony. (Hisp, estab 1971, empl 190, sales , cert: State, NMSDC)

3028   Solved Engineering
       55 E Monroe, Ste 3800   Chicago, IL 60603
       (800) 975-9723 Edward William Prin Engineer
       Fax: (180) 097-5972
       Email: ewilliam@solvedeng.com
       Website: www.solvedeng,com
Electrical Engineer & and Consulting, Engineering Design, Subject Matter Testimony & Engineering Calculation / Studies Service. (AA, estab 2015, empl 5, sales $30,000, cert: City, NMSDC, CPUC)

3029   Sterling Engineering, Inc.
       Two Westbrook Corporate Center Ste 300
       Westchester, IL 60154
       (630) 993-3433 Rama Kavaliauskas President
       Fax: (630) 516-1192
       Email: rama@sterling-engineering.com
       Website: www.sterling-engineering.com
Engineering & technical staff augmentation solutions. (Woman/White, estab 1969, empl 75, sales $2,691,294, cert: WBENC)

Indiana

3030   Durkin & Villalta Partners Engineering
       8440 Woodfield Crossing Blvd, Ste 175   Indianapolis, IN 46240
       (317) 472-3883 Alvaro Villalta CEO
       Fax: (317) 472-3884
       Email: avillalta@dvpe.net
       Website: www.dvpe.net
Mechanical, electrical, plumbing & fire protection design firm. (Hisp, estab 2007, empl 22, sales $3,000,000, cert: 8(a))

3031 K & S Engineers, Inc.
      9715 Kennedy Ave   Highland, IN 46322
      (219) 924-5231 Debbie Pilawski President
      Fax: (219) 924-5271
      Email: dpilawski@Kandsengineers.com
      Website: www.kandsengineers.com
Geotechnical engineering & consulting, drilling soil borings
& caissons, rock coring, lab & field testing of soil, concrete,
asphalt & steel, environmental consulting & forensic
investigation of construction materials. (As-Ind, estab
1984, empl 36, sales $4,515,115, cert: State, NMSDC)

Kansas

3032 Choson Resource LLC
      1999 N Amidon, Ste 100B   Wichita, KS 67203
      (316) 729-0312 Kim Silcott President
      Fax: (316) 729-0709
      Email: kim@chosonresource.com
      Website: www.Chosonresource.com
Aerospace engineering & staffing services for the air,
defense & space industries. (Woman/As-Pac, estab 2010,
empl 4, sales $4,254,100, cert: NMSDC)

Kentucky

3033 LECGI Inc.
      13113 Eastpoint Park Blvd Ste D Louisville, KY
      40223
      (502) 425-1647 Don Liu President
      Fax:
      Email: dliu@lecgi.us
      Website: www.lecgi.us
Engineering design & structural steel detailing, structural
steel connection design & structural analysis of steel
structures, handrails, and stairs for steel fabricators. (As-
Pac, estab 2004, empl 10, sales $633,000, cert: State, 8(a))

Louisiana

3034 Venoscope, LLC
      1018 Harding St Ste 104 Lafayette, LA 70503
      (337) 234-8993 Frank Creaghan
      Fax: (337) 268-4080
      Email: info@venoscope.com
      Website: www.venoscope.com
Manufacturer and distributor of the Venoscope model
VT03 and Neonatal Transilluminator model NT01 and
related accessories. (Woman/White, estab 1990, empl 2,
sales , cert: State)

Massachusetts

3035 RRMAE Engineering LLC
      46 Loring Ave   Boxborough, MA 01719
      (508) 517-4913 Anton Edmund Owner
      Fax:
      Email: anton.edmund@rrmaeengineering.com
      Website: www.rrmaeengineering.com
Process Design, Process Improvement, Risk assessment,
Process Validation, Validation, Commissioning & Qualification, Quality Engineering, Data analysis, Lean management, Process Automation. (As-Ind, estab 2013, empl 2,
sales $267,000, cert: State)

Maryland

3036 Robotic Research, LLC
      555 Quince Orchard Road, Ste 300   Gaithersburg,
      MD 20878
      (240) 631-0008 Alberto Lacaze President
      Fax: (240) 631-0092
      Email: lacaze@roboticresearch.com
      Website: www.roboticresearch.com
Robotics, intelligent control, sensor processing &
specialized computer programming. (Hisp, estab 2002,
empl 15, sales $3,000,000, cert: State)

3037 Strategic Technology Institute, Inc. (STi)
      6000 Executive Blvd Ste #205 Rockville, MD
      20852
      (301) 770-7077 Rakesh Chopra President
      Fax: (301) 881-8488
      Email: rchopra@sti-inc.com
      Website: www.sti-inc.com
System effectiveness, design assurance, SRM&QA,
maintainability, quality assurance, reliability, FMECA,
SCA, EMI/EMC, EMP, radiation effects, aging effects,
engineering svcs, FRACAS, hazard analysis, OSHA, system
safety. (As-Ind, estab 1986, empl 20, sales $1,500,000,
cert: State)

3038 The Perara Group Inc.
      1610 Professional Blvd Stes E & F Crofton, MD
      21114
      (410) 451-4141 Yancey Brown Telecomm Dir
      Fax: (410) 451-4410
      Email: ybrown@peraragroup.com
      Website: www.peraragroup.com
DNA research support, genetic models, bio-analytical
chemistry models, metabolism & pharmacokinetics,
oncology models, toxicology
lab diagnostics, vaccine & vector safety, bio-safety
testing. (Woman/AA, estab 2001, empl 7, sales
$1,700,000, cert: State)

3039 Titus LLC
23219 Stringtown Rd Ste 155 Clarksburg, MD 20871
(240) 252-1341 Otis Miller VP
Fax: (240) 252-2374
Email: olmiller@titusllc.com
Website: www.titusllc.com
Design, implement & maintain mechanical, electrical, life safety, security & communication systems. critical power solutions for data
centers, communications environments & data monitoring centers. (Woman/AA, estab 2002, empl 9, sales $2,800,000, cert: State)

Michigan

3040 4D Systems
4130 Market Place Flint Twp, MI 48507
(248) 535-0758 Jean-Pierre Rasaiah President
Fax: (888) 861-5730
Email: jp.rasaiah@4dsysco.com
Website: www.4dsysco.com
Robotic Systems Build (Specializing in glass handling), Robot Programming (All applications), Robotic Simulation, Siemens software reseller, NX Design, Robcad Simulation, Process Simulate Simulation, Controls Design, Panel build. (As-Pac, estab 2010, empl 65, sales $8,000,000, cert: NMSDC)

3041 AMBE Engineering, LLC
15424 Prestwick Circle Northville, MI 48168
(734) 667-3167 Rashmi Zaveri VP
Fax: (734) 336-4004
Email: rashmis@ambeeng.com
Website: www.ambeeng.com
Engineering: corrective actions implementations, design optimization, CAD/CAE design support, quality containment support. (Woman/As-Pac, estab 2001, empl 120, sales $25,000,000, cert: NMSDC, WBENC)

3042 Capitol Reproductions, Inc.
215 E 12 Mile Rd Madison Heights, MI 48071
(313) 564-4820 Laura Muresan GM
Fax: (248) 398-2425
Email: lauram@capitolgroup.net
Website: www.capitolgroup.net
Engineering, CAD design & technical Illustration services. (Woman, estab 1946, empl 48, sales $6,750,000, cert: WBENC)

3043 Detroit Engineered Products (DEP).
850 E Long Lake Rd Troy, MI 48085
(248) 219-9838 John Gelmisi Director Business Dev
Fax:
Email: john_gelmisi@depusa.com
Website: www.depusa.com
Reverse Engineering, Benchmarking, Scanning, Prototyping, Project Outsourcing, Offshore/Domestic Design support, and Technical Services. (As-Ind, estab 1998, empl 380, sales $18,000,000, cert: NMSDC)

3044 Engineering Design Solutions PLC
5220 Lovers Lane, Ste LL-120 Portage, MI 49002
(269) 903-2652 Irfan Ahmed, MSCE, PE President + Principal Structural Engineer
Fax:
Email: irfan.ahmed@enggdesigns.com
Website: www.enggdesigns.com
Manufacturing & industrial building design & CAD designing automobile facilities. (As-Ind, estab 2004, empl 8, sales $600,000, cert: NMSDC)

3045 ETCS Inc.
275 Executive Dr Troy, MI 48083
(248) 763-9467 Ravi Kapur Dir of Sales
Fax: (248) 281-0592
Email: ravi@etcsinc.com
Website: www.etcsinc.com
Engineering, reverse engineering, tool design, staffing, offshore component sourcing. (As-Ind/As-Pac, estab 2003, empl 52, sales $4,826,000, cert: NMSDC)

3046 Future Technologies, Inc.
2490 E Midland Rd Bay City, MI 48706
(989) 686-6200 Brent Waldie Applications Engineer
Fax: (989) 686-3070
Email: brentw@futuretechnologies.com
Website: www.futuretechnologies.com
Custom leak testing systems, function testing equipment, welding & assembly automation & calibrated standard leaks. (Hisp, estab 1989, empl 33, sales , cert: NMSDC)

3047 Generalety, LLC
5820 N Canton Center Rd Ste 140 Canton, MI 48187
(734) 522-1488 Sheng-Dong Liu CEO
Fax: (734) 468-6362
Email: sliu@generalety.com
Website: www.generalety.com
Computer aided design (CAD) & computer aided engineering (CAE) services in the automotive industry. (As-Pac, estab 2003, empl 60, sales $1,250,000, cert: NMSDC)

3048 Global Supply Innovative Engineering LLC
200 E Big Beaver Troy, MI 48083
(248)4574592 Dayle Farrimond VP
Fax:
Email: dfarrimond@gsiengineering.com
Website: www.gsiengineering.com
Injection Mold Building, Program Management, Engineering
Sample Facility, Production Manufacturing Facility. (Woman, estab 2005, empl 7, sales $2,800,000, cert: WBENC)

3049   Hybrid Design Services
2479 Elliott Dr   Troy, MI 48083
(248) 298-3400   James Pinon President
Fax: (248) 298-3402
Email: jpinon@hybriddesignservices.com
Website: www.hybriddesignservices.com
Engineering, design, prototyping, testing services specializing in hybrid vehicles & systems, electric vehicles & systems, HEV systems, EV systems, hybrid and electric vehicle R&D, high voltage systems, energy storage. (Hisp, estab 2007, empl 20, sales $2,000,000, cert: NMSDC)

3050   Magnys Innovative Solutions LLC
42500 W Eleven Mile Rd Ste B   Novi, MI 48375
(248) 449-2600   Mary Willy Office Mgr
Fax: (248) 449-4250
Email: mwilly@magnys.com
Website: www.magnys.com
Design, oversee process, project engineering services, manufacturing engineering, 3-D simulation & PLC emulation software modeling. (AA, estab 1999, empl 210, sales $25,000,000, cert: NMSDC)

3051   Sigma Associates, Inc.
1900 St. Antoine St   Detroit, MI 48226
(313) 963-9700   Kathy Cotton Admin Asst
Fax: (313) 963-1578
Email: kcotton@sigmaassociates.com
Website: www.sigmaassociates.com
Multi-disciplinary engineering, architectural, program management, construction contract admin, construction management, design-build capabilities & information technology services. (Woman/White, estab 1978, empl 51, sales , cert: State, WBENC, SDB)

3052   Special Projects, Inc.
45901 Helm   Plymouth, MI 48170
(734) 455-7130   Jill Cornell Admin Dir
Fax: (734) 455-8101
Email: jcornell@specproj.com
Website: www.specproj.com
Concept vehicle & component design & support services. (Hisp, estab 1983, empl 65, sales $1,606,583, cert: NMSDC)

3053   Universal Tool Equipment & Controls, Inc.
6525 Center Dr   Sterlng Heights, MI 48312
(586) 268-4380   Bill Bartolotta VP
Fax: (586) 803-8329
Email: bbartolotta@universaltecinc.com
Website: www.universaltecinc.com
Automation & welding systems, robotics, weld guns, vision systems, sealant systems, drawn arc welders, projection welders, material handling end effectors & welding fixtures. (Woman/AA, estab 2009, empl 29, sales $10,000,000, cert: WBENC)

3054   Willie Horton Inc. Technologies
7784 Ronda Dr   Canton, MI 48187
(248) 855-2215   Deryl Horton President
Fax: (734) 459-7863
Email: dhorton@horton-inc.com
Website: www.horton-inc.com
Heat-treating, hardening, surface engineering, tool steel, mechcanical & electrical engineering. (AA, estab 2003, empl 20, sales $300,000, cert: NMSDC)

Minnesota

3055   Fourth Factor Engineering, LLC
10636 Maryland Ave S   Bloomington, MN 55438
(612) 708-2562   Elizabeth Becker President
Fax:
Email: liz.becker@fourth-factor-engineering.com
Website: www.fourth-factor-engineering.com
Engineering analysis: system safety, software safety, human factors, reliability, maintainability, testability & logistics analysis. (Woman/White, estab 2010, empl 6, sales $1,049,233, cert: State, WBENC)

3056   Questions & Solutions Engineering
1079 Falls Curve   Chaska, MN 55318
(612) 309-0503   Rebecca Ellis
Fax: (952) 361-9343
Email: rebecca.ellis@qseng.com
Website: www.QSEng.com
Commissioning program development, training & project execution, existing building troubleshooting, retro-commissioning, re-commissioning, HVAC system planning & implementing capital projects. (Woman/White, estab 2005, empl 4, sales $181,000, cert: City, WBENC)

North Carolina

3057   ENPULSE Energy Conservation, Inc.
100 N Elm St, Ste 138   Greensboro, NC 27401
(336) 370-1088   Derrick Giles President
Fax: (336) 230-0554
Email: info@enpulse.com
Website: www.enpulse.com
Engineering services, energy management, utility bill audits, engineering studies, measurement & verification, building commissioning (AA, estab 2002, empl 3, sales $82,000, cert: State, City)

3058   ImmunoReagents Inc.
6003 Chapel HillRdSte. 153   Raleigh, NC 27607
(919) 831-2240   Ann Black CEO
Fax: (919) 831-2240
Email: sales@immunoreagents.com
Website: www.immunoreagents.com
Mfr highly purified polyclonal antibodies used in the life sciences & immunodiagnostic industries. (Woman/White, estab 2005, empl 14, sales $1,636,402, cert: WBENC)

3059 John Davenport Engineering, Inc.
305 W Fourth St Ste 2A Winston Salem, NC 27101
(336) 744-1636 Shari Mauk Chief Admin Officer
Fax: (336) 458-9377
Email: smauk@davenportworld.com
Website: www.davenportworld.com
Roadway design, traffic signal design, transportation engineering, civil engineering, transportation planning, construction engineering & inspection, traffic data collection, turning movement counts. (AA, estab 2002, empl 21, sales $1,629,947, cert: State, City, 8(a))

3060 Sud Associates PA
1813 Chapel Hill Rd   Durham, NC 27707
(919) 493-5277 Ish Sud President
Fax: (919) 493-5549
Email: sudmain@sudassociates.com
Website: www.sudassociates.com
Energy svcs & studies: recycling process produced heat, energy conserving HVAC, electrical, plumbing. (As-Ind/As-Pac, estab 1980, empl 23, sales $2,000,000, cert: State, City)

New Jersey

3061 3A Engineering & Validation LLC
122 Lexington Ave   Maplewood, NJ 07040
(973) 715-0541 Adebayo Boboye Principal Engineer
Fax: (973) 378-3453
Email: adebayo.boboye@3a-engineering.com
Website: www.3a-engineering.com
Engineering services, qualification, commissioning & validation of manufacturing processes & products. (AA, estab 2007, empl 1, sales $120,000, cert: NMSDC)

3062 inRange Solutions II, LLC
695 Route 46 W, Ste 103   Fairfield, NJ 07004
(845)5482934 Edwin Gomez President
Fax: (973) 860-2424
Email: ss@inrange-llc.com
Website: www.inrangesolutions.com
DAS, Wireless &Telecom Design &Engineering, Site Acquisition, Zoning &Permitting, Project Management, Architectural Engineering and Design, Electrical & Mechanical Engineering and Design. (As-Pac, estab 2011, empl 24, sales $6,000,000, cert: State, City, NMSDC)

New York

3063 Associated Renewable
1370 Broadway 5th Fl New York, NY 10018
(212) 444-8214 Manoj Patel CEO
Fax: (646) 330-5155
Email: mbe@associatedrenewable.com
Website: www.associatedrenewable.com/
Energy management, cut energy costs, reduce energy wastage, meet regulatory requirements, building energy audits, install new energy-efficient equipment, supply electricity, natural gas & renewable energy. (As-Pac, estab 2010, empl 8, sales $420,000, cert: NMSDC)

3064 SoundSense, LLC
46 Newtown Lane Ste 1 East Hampton, NY 11937
(631) 324-2266 Maryann Buquicchio Sr Admin Asst
Fax: (631) 324-6750
Email: maryann@soundsense.com
Website: www.soundsense.com
Acoustic consulting & design services, efficacy & compliance testing, site inspection services & innovative acoustical products. (Woman/White, estab 1981, empl 9, sales $2,623,444, cert: City)

3065 WM Group Services, LLC
Two Penn Plaza Ste 552 New York, NY 10121
(646) 827-6400 Hemant Mehta Controller
Fax:
Email: hmehta@wmgroupeng.com
Website: www.wmgroupeng.com
Study, Design, optimization of Central Utilities Systems: cooling, heating & power. (As-Pac, estab 2011, empl 11, sales $2,697,396, cert: NMSDC)

Ohio

3066 Airecon Manufacturing Corporation
5271 Brotherton Court   Cincinnati, OH 45227
(513) 561-5522 Josh Jacobs President
Fax: (513) 561-0166
Email: josh@airecon.com
Website: www.airecon.com
Design, fabricate & install industrial dust, mist & fume control equipment & systems, fume exhaust pneumatic conveying, supply & exhasut ventilation, clean air rooms & other industrial air handling systems. (Hisp, estab 1979, empl 40, sales $9,000,000, cert: NMSDC)

3067 Atmos360, Inc
64 Circle Freeway Dr   Cincinnati, OH 45246
(513) 330-6688 Icy Williams President
Fax: (513) 772-6950
Email: iwilliams@atmos360.com
Website: www.atmos360.com
Engineering & design of air system & custom/specialty fabricated products, Dust/Aerosol Control, Process Air, Central Vacuum Cleaning, HVAC and Heated air Make-up Systems. (Woman/AA, estab 1989, empl 40, sales $17,000,000, cert: State, NMSDC, WBENC)

3068 Balance Product Development, Inc.
3615 Superior Ave. Ste 4402B Cleveland, OH 44114
(440) 247-4711 Rene Polin President
Fax: (216) 938-5572
Email: rene@balanceinc.com
Website: www.balanceinc.com
Industrial Design, product design, CAD development, prototype development, concept ideation, packaging design, graphic design, innovation, engineering, product research, ergonomic research, user interface design. (Hisp, estab 2004, empl 10, sales , cert: NMSDC)

3069   THORS, LLC
     5054 Paramount Blvd.   Medina, OH 44256
     (330) 576-4448   Senthil Kumar Founder
     Fax:
     Email: sales@thors.com
     Website: www.thors.com
Mfg process training for procurement, design engineers & quality teams in commodities such as - castings, machining, gears, steel manufacturing, forgings, polymers with a tools center that includes a supplier manager, tooling manager & parts manager. (Woman/As-Pac, estab 2010, empl 11, sales $10,000, cert: NMSDC)

3070   Williams Engineering LLC
     1836 Dana Ave   Cincinnati, OH 45207
     (513) 731-6400   Kennard Williams President
     Fax: (513) 731-6848
     Email: keino.williams@williamsenginedesign.com
     Website: www.williamsenginedesign.com
Engineering & mfg services, 3D CAD modeling & product development of machine tools, aerospace, medical and automotive aftermarket parts. (AA, estab 2005, empl 1, sales $85,000, cert: State)

Oklahoma

3071   Cherokee CRC
     916 W 23rd St   Tulsa, OK 74107
     (918) 582-9110   John Sparkman Program Mgr
     Fax: (918) 583-7948
     Email: jsparkman@cherokee-crc.com
     Website: www.cherokee-crc.com
Research & development, administrative support services, construction management, environmental services & aviation consulting services. (Nat Ame, estab 2005, empl 40, sales $14,671,425, cert: State)

3072   Greenwood Aviation, Inc.
     2117 N Waverly   Ponca City, OK 74601
     (580) 762-2580   Chuck Greenwood President
     Fax: (580) 762-8070
     Email: airport@cableone.net
     Website: www.greenwoodaviation.com
Special mission aircraft: low level advanced atmospheric research, airborne surveillance & logistical operations at remote sites. (Nat Ame, estab 1982, empl 9, sales $650,000, cert: State)

Oregon

3073   Elcon Associates, Inc.
     12670 NW Barnes Rd   Portland, OR 97229
     (503) 644-2490   Donna Freeman Mktg Mgr
     Fax: (503) 644-2911
     Email: dfreeman@elcon.com
     Website: www.elcon.com
Electrical energy: high voltage, project management, studies, cost estimating, and construction management, utility power systems, power distribution, PLC based control systems, energy management/SCADA. (As-Ind, estab 1975, empl 47, sales $5,600,000, cert: NMSDC)

Pennsylvania

3074   Biopharm Project Solutions
     119 Jaffrey Rd   Malvern, PA 19355
     (484) 614-0869   Surjit Sengha President
     Fax:
     Email: surjs@biopharmprojects.com
     Website: www.biopharmprojects.com
Process engineering, equipment, utilities & equipment cleaning/sterilization systems, automation engineering, project management & engineering staffing, equipment design engineering, factory testing, start-up. (As-Ind, estab 1987, empl 15, sales $2,500,000, cert: NMSDC)

3075   Chester Engineers, Inc.
     1555 Coraopolis Heights Rd   Moon Township, PA 15108
     (412) 809-6576   Elaine Talak Exec Asst
     Fax: (412) 809-6006
     Email: etalak@chesterengineers.com
     Website: www.chesterengineers.com
Engineering consulting , construct. mgmt, water resource mgmt., scientific research & environmental mgmt. (AA, estab 1987, empl 200, sales $14,500,000, cert: NMSDC)

3076   Diversified Global Systems, LLC.
     721 Arbor Way Ste 100   Blue Bell, PA 19422
     (703) 963-4942   Dale Hobbie Managing Dir
     Fax:
     Email: dale.hobbie@diversifiedglobalsystems.com
     Website: www.diversifiedglobalsystems.com
Finance, Site Development, Design, Engineering, Procurement Management, Construction Management, Project Management, Program Management & Operations & Maintenance services. (Nat Ame, estab 2016, empl 5, sales $265,000, cert: NMSDC)

3077   GAI Construction Monitoring Services, Inc. dba CMT Services Group
     470 Drew Court   King of Prussia, PA 19406
     (610) 731-0430   Valerie Moody President
     Fax:
     Email: v.moody@cmtservicesgroup.com
     Website: www.cmtservicesgroup.com
Geotechnical engineering, environmental consulting, construction materials testing, special inspections, engineering materials forensic investigations. (Woman/White, estab 1986, empl 23, sales $2,200,000, cert: WBENC)

3078   TesTex, Inc.
     535 Old Frankstown Rd, Ste A   Pittsburgh, PA 15239
     (412) 798-8990   Sunil Ramchandran President
     Fax: (412) 798-8995
     Email: sunil@testex-ndt.com
     Website: www.testex-ndt.com
Electromagnetic NDT systems & services: inspect ferrous & non-ferrous components. (As-Ind/As-Pac, estab 1987, empl 50, sales $14,700,000, cert: NMSDC)

3079 Aquatech International Corporation
1 Four Coins Dr Canonsburg, PA 15317
(724) 746-5300 Francis D'sa Reg sales Mgr
Fax: (724) 746-5359
Email: aic@aquatech.com
Website: www.aquatech.com
Mfr water & waste water treatment equip & systems.
ASME tank & piping fabricators. (Woman/As-Ind, estab
1981, empl 450, sales $80,000,000, cert: NMSDC)

Puerto Rico

3080 LabChemS
P.O. Box 1022 Boqueron, PR 00622
(787) 920-4657 Efrain Rivera Torres CEO
Fax:
Email: efrain.rivera@labchemspr.com
Website: www.labchemscorp.com/
Engineering Consulting, Manufacturing & Packaging
Equipments, Facilities & Manufacturing Process Validation,
Quality Engineering & Six Sigma tools. (Hisp, estab 2009,
empl 10, sales $1,200,000, cert: NMSDC)

3081 SQS, Inc. (Successful Quality Systems)
Palmas Industrial Park Road 869 KM. 2.0 Street 4
Catano, PR 00962
(787) 275-2424 Wilda Aguirre President
Fax: (787) 275-2428
Email: wildaaguirre@sqswarehouse.com
Website: www.sqswarehouse.com
Specialized Storage and Inventory Management Services,
safe-guarding of documents (Woman/Hisp, estab 2003,
empl 8, sales $2,500,000, cert: NMSDC)

3082 Visional Technology LLC
400 Calle Calaf, Ste 49 San Juan, PR 00918
(787) 717-0881 Joyce Rotger President
Fax:
Email: joycemar@visionaltechnology.com
Website: www.visionaltechnology.com
Engineering services, dimensional metrology solutions,
vision systems, coordinate measurement machines (CMM),
laser measurements, 3D scanning, reverse engineering &
computer aided inspections. (Woman/Hisp, estab 2013,
empl 5, sales , cert: NMSDC)

South Carolina

3083 Amee Bay LLC
915 Commerce Cir Hanahan, SC 29410
(843) 725-6800 William Messing Sr program Mgr
Fax: (843) 725-6801
Email: Bmessing@ameebay.com
Website: www.ameebay.com
General/mechanical contracting, power & pressure
process piping installation, repair mechanical systems on
commercial and industrial pressure vessels, conveyors &
auxiliary systems. (Nat Ame, estab 2006, empl 184, sales
$26,000,000, cert: State)

3084 Diverse Industries, Inc.
260 Morley Court, Ste A Duncan, SC 29334
(864) 400-9741 Laura Charles Office Mgr
Fax: (864) 810-0920
Email: laurac@diverseii.com
Website: www.diverseii.com
We experience implementing solutions & fixes for many
customers in a variety of industries.
Contract Robot Programming, Panel View & Thin Client
HMI's, Training, Robot & PLC, Vision, Robot Guidance,
Inspection & Code Reading. (Woman, estab 2007, empl
40, sales $5,114,985, cert: State)

Tennessee

3085 GQSI
3777 Winchester Rd Ste 1 Memphis, TN 38118
(901) 365-9566 Williette Graham President
Fax:
Email: willgraham@gqsi.net
Website: www.gqsi.net
Engineering & technical services, medical devices,
process & special processes equipment & validation,
laser marking, CMM inspection services, product
inspection, engineering support, supplier support
services. (Woman/AA, estab 2005, empl 6, sales
$160,000, cert: State)

Texas

3086 Aerolution Inc.
10803 Gulfdale, Ste 208 San Antonio, TX 78216
(210) 524-9831 Kyle kim President
Fax: (210) 524-9833
Email: kkim@aerolutioninc.com
Website: www.aerolution.com
Structural/mechanical design & analysis, aircraft system
design & analysis, CAD capabilities, stress analysis &
finite element modeling, aircraft repair & modernization,
enhanced data management systems. (As-Pac, estab
2007, empl 12, sales $1,900,000, cert: 8(a))

3087 ALTECOR Engineering
3617 Flamingo Ave McAllen, TX 78504
(956) 687-7389 T. G. Altecor Sr staff engineer
Fax: (956) 687-7390
Email: info@altecoreng.com
Website: www.altecoreng.com
Structural dynamics & control systems engineering,
equipment-machinery installations, optimizations,
maintenance, reliability. (Woman/White, estab 2007,
empl 7, sales $100,000, cert: State)

3088   Basal Solutions LLC
1301 Texas Ave Ste 122 Houston, TX 77002
(713) 393-8767 Branden Morris
Fax: (407) 270-9241
Email: branden@basalsolutionsllc.com
Website: www.basalsolutionsllc.com
Engineering & business management consulting, project management, develop, test & integrate 0-D/1-D dynamic mathematical models, create FMEA & DFMEA for various vehicle platforms, test script design & implementation. (AA, estab 2014, empl 10, sales , cert: State, NMSDC)

3089   BEPC, Inc.
3240 Executive Dr   San Angelo, TX 76904
(325) 944-0169 Liza Dennis Director of New Business
Fax: (325) 944-0105
Email: Liza.Dennis@bepcinc.com
Website: www.bepcinc.com
Engineering services: validations of equipment, processes, audit & qualification of external suppliers, quality systems & validations, R&D product design & testing. (Hisp, estab 2005, empl 460, sales $20,038,327, cert: State, NMSDC)

3090   Gap Engineering
21703 Kingsland Blvd, Ste 103   Katy, TX 77450
(281) 578-0500 Mike Homma
Fax: (214) 420-6638
Email: mhomma@gap-eng.com
Website: www.gap-eng.com
Engineering, design & drafting services, develop instrument Specs, Detail Design, Distributive Control Systems (DCS), Fieldbus, Programmable Logic Controllers (PLC), Safety Instrumented Systems (SIS), Fiber Optic Comm Networks. (As-Pac, estab 2004, empl 25, sales $2,800,000, cert: NMSDC, 8(a))

3091   JAT Energy Services LLC
111 Soledad St, Ste 1900   San Antonio, TX 78205
(916) 429-9096 Keith Allen President
Fax:
Email: Keith@jatenergies.com
Website: www.JATEnergies.com
Energy solutions, engineering & management firm, custom engineered solutions to reduce energy consumption in commercial & industrial spaces. (AA, estab 2012, empl 8, sales $500,000, cert: State, NMSDC)

3092   Robert Heath Trucking, Inc.
P.O. Box 2501   Lubbock, TX 79408
(806) 747-1651 Terri Heath Shankle President
Fax:
Email: tshankle@robertheath.com
Website: www.robertheath.com
Long haul trucking of frozen meat and other food products, refrigerated fresh vegetables, refrigerated flowers and other refrigerated or frozen products (Woman/White, estab , empl 1, sales , cert: WBENC)

3093   Standard Industrial Products Company
12610 Galveston Rd   Webster, TX 77059
(281) 480-8711 Walter Gomez Dir Operation & Mktg
Fax: (281) 480-8656
Email: wgomez@sipco-mls.com
Website: www.sipco-mls.com
Engineering, Electro - Mechanical Design, Validation & System Integration, CNC Milling, CNC Turning, Sawing, Mechanical System assembly & integration, Gearing - Design, Sourcing, Assembly & System Integration. (Hisp, estab 1984, empl 15, sales $2,099,000, cert: NMSDC)

3094   STS Systems Integration, LLC
1077 Central Pkwy S Bldg A, Ste 150 San Antonio, TX 78232
(210) 888-2631 Dan Beard Sr program Mgr
Fax:
Email: daniel.beard@ssi-anc.com
Website: www.ssi-anc.com
System engineering, performance, mission readiness & sustainment for weapon systems, propulsion systems & information systems. (Nat Ame, estab 2011, empl 143, sales $13,000,000, cert: 8(a))

3095   United Geo Technologies LLC
7715 Mainland Dr, Ste 110   San Antonio, TX 78250
(210) 684-2147 Patricia Ingram President
Fax: (210) 764-5022
Email: pingram@unitedgeotech.com
Website: www.unitedgeotech.com
Softcopy photogrammetric mapping, digital orthophotography, GIS services, geospatial database architecture, raster/vector data layer production, CAD to GIS data integration, remotely updating of GIS layers & solution development. (Woman/White, estab 2011, empl 6, sales , cert: State)

Utah

3096   Avalon Business Engineering Services
908 W Gordon Ave, Ste 6   Layton, UT 84041
(801) 668-5823 Lorraine Peart CEO
Fax:
Email: lpeart@avalonbes.com
Website: www.avalonbes.com
Engineering Services, Aerospace Engineering (Weapons System Sustainment), Finite Element Analysis, Structural Analysis, CAD, Environmental Engineering, Technical/Functional Writing & Analysis. (Woman/AA/As-Ind, estab 2010, empl 21, sales , cert: 8(a))

Virginia

3097   Alpha Construction and Engineering Corporation
       21351 Ridgetop Cir Ste 200 Dulles, VA 20166
       (703) 450-0800 Philios Angelides Sr VP
       Fax: (703) 450-0043
       Email: pangelides@alphacorporation.com
       Website: www.alphacorporation.com
Project management, construction management &
professional engineering svcs: scheduling, cost estimating,
project controls, construction inspection, condition
inspections, constructibility reviews, value engineering,
claims avoidance. (Woman/White, estab 1979, empl 197,
sales $29,609,371, cert: State)

3098   INTERSPEC, LLC
       464 S Independence Blvd Ste C-104 Virginia Beach,
       VA 23452
       (757) 622-6299 Sean Murphy Business Devel Dir
       Fax:
       Email: murphys@interspecllc.net
       Website: www.interspecllc.net
Tank, piping & pressure vessel inspections, STI storage tank
inspections, Non-Destructive Examination/Testing steel
structures, Spill Prevention Control & Countermeasure
(SPCC) plans, Oil Discharge Control Plans (ODCP. (Nat Ame,
estab 2001, empl 22, sales $1,200,000, cert: State, 8(a))

3099   Lu Smith Engineers
       4604 Sadler Grove Way   Glen Allen, VA 23060
       (804) 519-9306 Dawen Lu President
       Fax: (804) 925-2600
       Email: dlu6838@gmail.com
       Website: www.lsengineers.net
Building system commissioning services, energy modeling/
audit services, geothermal system study & design, sustainable design/LEED consultation & administration, mechanical, electrical, plumbing & fire protection system design.
(As-Pac, estab 2012, empl 12, sales $1,400,000, cert: State)

3100   Raul V. Bravo + Associates, Inc.
       1889 Preston White Dr Ste 202 Reston, VA 20191
       (703) 326-9092 Claudio Bravo VP
       Fax: (703) 326-9096
       Email: procurement@rvba.com
       Website: www.RVBA.com
Rail Car Design, Mechanical, CADD, Electrical schematics,
Telecommunication Design, Security Design, Electrical
Diagrams Wiring, Smoke Detector Layout, CCTV & MATV
Design, Power Supplies. (As-Pac/Hisp, estab 1979, empl 63,
sales $60,000, cert: State)

3101   Unified Industries Inc.
       6551 Loisdale Ct Ste 400 Springfield, VA 22150
       (703) 922-9800 Tom Callahan
       Fax: (703) 971-5892
       Email: callahan@uii.com
       Website: www.uii.com
Metrology & calibration services, life cycle logistics
planning, supply chain support, ship outfitting, distance
support, obsolescence analysis. (AA, estab 1970, empl
200, sales $16,045,000, cert: State)

Washington

3102   Professional CAD Services, Inc. dba PCSI Design
       18916 N Creek Pkwy Ste 103 Bothell, WA 98011
       (425) 485-3420 Carlos Veliz CEO
       Fax: (425) 485-3425
       Email: carlos@pcsidesign.com
       Website: www.pcsidesign.com
Product design & engineering services focused on
assisting companies to translate conceptual design into
market-ready production products. Our product &
solution offerings extend to many industries. (Hisp,
estab 1997, empl 5, sales $1,116,889, cert: NMSDC)

Wisconsin

3103   Datasyst Engineering & Testing
       S14 W33511 Hwy 18   Delafield, WI 53018
        Rose Hoisington CFO
       Fax: (262) 968-3050
       Email: mhoisington@datasysttest.com
       Website: www.datasysttest.com
Mechanical & electrical equipment testing & engineering: medical, telecommunications, construction, mining
& process, industrial, automotive. (Woman/Hisp, estab
1990, empl 11, sales , cert: NMSDC)

3104   PSJ Engineering, Inc.
       7665 N Port Washington Rd   Milwaukee, WI
       53217
       (414) 352-2211 Parmjit Jaspal CEO
       Fax: (414) 351-8835
       Email: jesse@psjengineering.com
       Website: www.psjengineering.com
Consulting engineering svcs: heating, ventilation, air
conditioning, plumbing & fire protection. (As-Pac, estab
1986, empl 13, sales $1,186,006, cert: State, City)

ENVIRONMENTAL SERVICES
Firms are engaged in underground and above ground storage tank removal and installation, assessment and remediation, lead and asbestos abatement, hazardous waste management, pollution, etc. NAICS Code 54

Alabama

3105 One Stop Environmental, LLC
4800 Division Ave, Birmingham, AL 35222
(205) 595-8188 Elizabeth Hinson Mktg Director
Fax: (205) 595-8901
Email: ehinson@onestopenv.com
Website: www.onestopenv.com
Hazardous waste transport & disposal, confined space entry, industry cleaning, emergency response, remediation, oil/water separator, lead/asbestos abatement, environmental consulting. (Woman/White, estab 1999, empl 42, sales $4,000,000, cert: WBENC)

3106 Orrs Environmental, LLC
515 Sparkman Dr Huntsville, AL 35756
(256) 556-1220 Debra Sanders Mgr
Fax: (866) 739-0182
Email: orrsenvironmental@gmail.com
Website: www.orrsenvironmental.com
Rail, air, water, trucking multimodal service, general & climate control warehousing, waste management assessments, spill response supplies & PPE, safety training, haz mat disposal & recycling services. (Woman/AA, estab 2004, empl 12, sales $268,000, cert: State)

3107 Slade Land Use, Environmental & Transportation Planning LLC
1500 1st Ave N, Unit 54 Birmingham, AL 35203
(205) 413-4685 L'Tryce Slade Owner
Fax: (800) 618-8602
Email: Lslade@sladellc.com
Website: www.sladellc.com
General Contracting, Environmental Consulting, Geotechnical Services, Construction Material Testing, Urban Planning. (AA, estab 2006, empl 6, sales $586,962, cert: NMSDC, WBENC, 8(a))

3108 Vulcan Industrial Contractors Co., LLC
4625-A Valleydale Rd Birmingham, AL 35242
(205) 313-4766 Sandra Killion CEO
Fax: (205) 991-7745
Email: skillion@vindco.com
Website: www.vindco.com
Asbestos & lead removal. (Woman/White, estab 1949, empl 727, sales $68,000,000, cert: WBENC)

Arizona

3109 Archaeological Consulting Services, Ltd.
424 W Broadway Rd Tempe, AZ 85282
(480) 894-5477 Margerie Green President
Fax: (480) 894-5478
Email: mgreen@acstempe.com
Website: www.acstempe.com
Cultural resource services, class I to class III studies, testing, & data recovery, environmental services, biological assessments/evaluations, environmental project management, paleo environmental analysis, GIS mapping. (Woman/White, estab 1977, empl 34, sales $1,945,942, cert: State, City, CPUC)

3110 Beck Environmental and Remediation, Ltd.
772 S Holmes Rd Apache Junction, AZ 85119
(480) 671-1365 Julie Beck President
Fax: (480) 983-1558
Email: julie.beck@earthlink.net
Website: www.beckenvironmental.com
Environmental assessments, site characterizations, remediation, air monitoring, hazardous materials management, environmental impact statements, health & safety, environmental engineering, mitigation modeling. (Woman/White, estab 1998, empl 5, sales $292,915, cert: WBENC, 8(a))

3111 Darling Geomatics
9040 S Rita Rd, Ste 2350 Tucson, AZ 85747
(520) 298-2725 Mary Darling CEO
Fax: (520) 298-2767
Email: marydarling@darlingltd.com
Website: www.darlingltd.com
Environmental consulting. (Woman/White, estab 1997, empl 15, sales $1,600,000, cert: City, CPUC, WBENC)

3112 Gutierrez-Palmenberg, Inc.
2922 W Clarendon Ave Phoenix, AZ 85017
(602) 234-0696 Jason Weed engineer
Fax: (602) 234-0699
Email: jason.w@gpimail.com
Website: www.gpieng.com
Environmental consulting & engineering support services, site characterizations, design, identifying potential environmental impacts of planned operations, remediation, monitoring and protecting valued resources. (Hisp, estab 1980, empl 25, sales $2,250,273, cert: NMSDC)

3113 Harris Environmental Group, Inc.
      650 N 6th Ave   Tucson, AZ 85705
      (520) 628-7648 Lisa Harris President
      Fax: (520) 628-1458
      Email: lharris@heg-inc.com
      Website: www.heg-inc.com
Natural & cultural resources consulting: archaeologists,
cultural resource management specialists, wildlife biolo-
gists, environmental compliance specialists, environmental
scientists, plant ecologists, landscape & historic architects.
(Woman/White, estab 1992, empl 15, sales $800,000, cert:
8(a))

3114 The Green Way Environmental Group, LLC.
      P.O. Box 5705   Scottsdale, AZ 85261
      (480) 639-0389 Chris McNally Business Dev/Office
      Mgr
      Fax: (480) 588-7856
      Email: chris@gweg-az.com
      Website: www.greenway-environmental.com
Environmental, construction & restoration, sampling &
clearance sampling of asbestos, lead based paint &
microbial, environmental compliance, consulting, industrial hygiene & occupational safety. (Woman/White, estab
2010, empl 5, sales $616,000, cert: WBENC)

California

3115 B & B Environmental Safety, Inc.
      17416 Murphy Pkwy   Lathrop, CA 95330
      (209) 858-4447 Kenneth S. Baugh President
      Fax: (209) 858-4420
      Email: Ken@bbensafety.com
      Website: www.bbensafety.com
Health Physics consulting svcs: decommissioning surveys,
industrial radiography protection svcs, radiological lab
audits, radioactive & mixed waste remediation & disposal
svcs, dose assessments. (AA, estab 2005, empl 10, sales
$3,672,515, cert: State)

3116 BC Laboratories, Inc.
      4100 Atlas Court   Bakersfield, CA 93308
      (800) 878-4911 Mark Ellis Business Devel Dir
      Fax: (661) 327-1918
      Email: mark.ellis@bclabs.com
      Website: www.bclabs.com
Analytical Services for Groundwater, Drinking Water,
Wastewater, Soils & Air, Certified Testing Services, Sampling & Monitoring. (Woman/White, estab 1949, empl 97,
sales $1,000,000,000, cert: CPUC)

3117 CAL Inc.
      2040 Peabody Rd   Vacaville, CA 95687
      (707) 446-7996 David Esparza President
      Fax: (707) 446-7906
      Email: desparza@cal-inc.com
      Website: www.cal-inc.com
General contracting: Asbestos & Lead Abatement,
Demolition, Remediation Services & Environmental &
Safety Training. (Hisp, estab 1979, empl 40, sales
$4,786,000, cert: CPUC)

3118 California Hazardous Services, Inc.
      2205 S Yale St   Santa Ana, CA 92704
      (714) 434-9995 Belinda Bain. President
      Fax: (714) 434-9998
      Email: bbain@calhaz.com
      Website: www.calhaz.com
Fuel tank service, cleaning, waste disposal, water
intrusion pump-outs, environmental compliance tank
testing, tank removals, tank installations, tank upgrades.
(Woman/White, estab 1988, empl 38, sales $4,600,000,
cert: CPUC, WBENC)

3119 Del Mar Environmental & Construction Services,
      Inc
      629 Del Mar Ave   Chula Vista, CA 91910
      (619) 638-3679 Juan Diez de Bonilla President
      Fax:
      Email: jdiezdebonilla@dmecservices.com
      Website: www.dmecservices.com
Environmental Consulting & Remediation, Stormwater
Management/Erosion Control, Range Maintenance /
Lead Recovery, Habitat Restoration, Demolition, Facility
Maintenance & Tenant Improvements. (Hisp, estab
2005, empl 10, sales $500,000, cert: 8(a))

3120 Desert Environmental Services, Inc.
      12563 Caballero Ct   Victorville, CA 92392
      (760) 949-1110 Fernando Nieves Project Mgr
      Fax: (760) 956-1666
      Email: desertfr@verizon.net
      Website:
Transportation & disposal of hazardous waste, lab
packing, emergency response,
spill remediation, hazardous waste container supplies.
(Hisp, estab 1999, empl 5, sales $351,745, cert: State)

3121 Energy Conservation Options (ECO)
      14439 Catalina St Ste 150 San Leandro, CA 94621
      (510) 647-8450 Dahlia Moodie President
      Fax: (510) 404-5307
      Email: Dahlia@ecoptions.biz
      Website: www.ecoptions.biz
Facility energy audits, energy savings solution recom-
mendation & technology solution implementation.
(Woman/AA/Hisp, estab 2008, empl 8, sales $3,400,000,
cert: CPUC)

3122   Engineering/Remediation Resources Group, Inc.
4585 Pacheco Blvd Ste 200   Martinez, CA 94553
(925) 969-0750   Tyson Appel Senior Project Mgr
Fax: (925) 969-0751
Email: tyson.appel@errg.com
Website: www.errg.com
Engineering & remediation services, environmental, civil & geotechnical engineers, geologists, soil physicists, scientists, construction managers, construction superintendents, equipment operators, certified hazardous waste technicians. (Woman/As-Pac, estab 1997, empl 175, sales $81,494,792, cert: CPUC)

3123   G2RJ Inc. dba Trevet
9888 Carroll Centre Rd, Ste 228   San Diego, CA 92126
(858) 578-8859   Don Peters Project Mgr
Fax:
Email: dpeters@trevetinc.com
Website: www.trevetinc.com
Engineering services, environmental remediation & waste management services. (As-Ind, estab 2005, empl 26, sales $8,371,299, cert: State)

3124   GGG Demolition Inc.
1130 W Trenton Ave   Orange, CA 92867
(714) 699-9350   Celin Miller President
Fax: (714) 699-9283
Email: celin@gggdemo.com
Website: www.gggdemo.com
Structural Demolition, Asbestos/Lead Abatement, Mold Remediation, Soil Remediation.
Selective Demolition. (Woman/White, estab 2013, empl 150, sales $12,000,000, cert: CPUC, WBENC)

3125   Global Transloading, LLC
16209 Paramount Blvd Ste 203   Paramount, CA 90723
(949) 307-4148   Shannon Griego President
Fax: (949) 673-0846
Email: shannongriego@globaltransloading.com
Website:
Hazardous waste transportation & disposal, hazardous waste management, logistics. (Woman/Nat Ame/Hisp, estab 2004, empl 6, sales $1,424,695, cert: State)

3126   Greenway Solid Waste & Recycling, Inc.
P.O. Box 1453   Claremont, CA 91711
(909) 518-7943   Charles Elias VP
Fax: (909) 992-3075
Email: celias@greenwayrecyclinginc.com
Website: www.greenwayrecyclinginc.com
Electronic waste recycling, nonhazardous waste treatment & disposal. (Woman/Hisp, estab 2006, empl 3, sales $321,000, cert: State, 8(a))

3127   Integrated Science Solutions (ISSI)
1777 N California Blvd Ste 305   Walnut Creek, CA 94596
(925) 979-1535   Cecelia Mccloy President
Fax: (925) 979-1434
Email: info@issi-net.com
Website: www.issi-net.com
Earth & environmental science, engineering, regulatory compliance, occupational safety & health, homeland security, emergency response, & energy, water & natural resource development. (Woman/White, estab 1999, empl 40, sales $5,035,703, cert: CPUC, WBENC)

3128   New World Environmental, Inc.
448 Commerce Way   Livermore, CA 94551
(949) 833-7113   Mark Davis VP Business Dev
Fax: (925) 443-0119
Email: Commercialdept@newworld.org
Website: www.newworld.org
Nuclear & hazardous materials, site remediation, characterization surveys, facility decontamination & decommissioning, unrestricted release surveys. (Nat Ame, estab 1988, empl 53, sales $8,245,469, cert: State)

3129   Ninyo & Moore
5710 Ruffin Rd   San Diego, CA 92123
(858) 576-1000   Elizabeth Brooks Business Dev Mgr
Fax: (858) 576-9600
Email: ebrooks@ninyoandmoore.com
Website: www.ninyoandmoore.com
Geotechnical & environmental sciences consulting: geotechnical engineering, engineering geology, engineering geophysics, hydrogeology, soil & materials testing & environmental sciences. (Hisp, estab 1986, empl 400, sales $69,000,000, cert: City, NMSDC, CPUC)

3130   Northstar Environmental Remediation
26225 Enterprise Ct   Lake Forest, CA 92630
(949) 580-2800   Katherine Tweidt President
Fax: (949) 580-2802
Email: ktweidt@cox.net
Website: www.northstarremediation.com
Environmental consulting & remediation of soil & groundwater, equipment fabrication, installation, & operation, permitting, consulting, soil & groundwater characterization, well installation, reporting, compliance activities. (Woman/White, estab 2002, empl 6, sales $1,250,000, cert: CPUC)

3131 Orange Coast Analytical, Inc.
3002 Dow Ave, Ste 532   Tustin, CA 92780
(714) 832-0064 Cindy Noorani President
Fax: (714) 832-0067
Email: cindyn@ocalab.com
Website: www.ocalab.com
Environmental & analytical testing laboratory, organic &
inorganic testing-water, waste water, soil, air, industial,
chemical & food products. (Woman, estab 1990, empl 15,
sales $1,450,178, cert: State, CPUC)

3132 OST Trucks and Cranes, Inc.
2951 N Ventura Ave P.O. Box 237 Ventura, CA 93002
(805) 643-9963 L. Dennis Zermeno President
Fax: (805) 643-7618
Email: ostcranes@aol.com
Website: www.ostcranes.com
General & hazardous substance removal & remedial
action, hydraulic cranes 5 to 140. (Hisp, estab 1947, empl
69, sales , cert: State, NMSDC, CPUC)

3133 Pari & Gershon Inc.
2053 Lincoln Ave Ste A San Jose, CA 95125
(408) 966-7184 Romena Jonas President
Fax: (408) 267-7196
Email: rjonas@pgiinc.net
Website: www.pgicompany.com
Environmental Consulting, Engineering Design & Construction. (Woman/White, estab 2009, empl 5, sales $100,000,
cert: State, WBENC)

3134 Piper Environmental Group, Inc.
11600 California St   Castroville, CA 95012
(831) 632-2700 Jane Piper CEO
Fax: (831) 632-2701
Email: jpiper@peg-inc.com
Website: www.peg-inc.com
Design ozone solutions, turn-key ozone trailer systems,
ozone sparging systems. (Woman/White, estab 1992, empl
3, sales $1,483,616, cert: CPUC, WBENC)

3135 Pivox Corporation
3240 El Camino Real Ste 230 Irvine, CA 92602
(949) 727-1400 Sean Shahin VP
Fax: (949) 727-1455
Email: sean@pivox.com
Website:
Remediation of soil & groundwater, demolition, project &
construction management, permitting, design, feasibility
study, treatment system installation (civil, mechanical,
electril, and instrumentation). (Woman/White, estab 2004,
empl 20, sales $8,000,000, cert: CPUC)

3136 Raibon & Colbert Associates, Inc.
50 California St, Ste 1500   San Francisco, CA
94111
(415) 951-4709 Regina Colbert President
Fax: (415) 439-5221
Email: grcolbert@comcast.net
Website:
Environmental health & safety services, hazardous
materials management, construction safety, stormwater
management, consulting & transportation. (Woman/AA,
estab 1997, empl 1, sales $157,000, cert: State, CPUC)

3137 RORE, Inc.
5151 Shoreham Place   San Diego, CA 92122
(858) 404-7393 Gita Murthy
Fax: (858) 404-7395
Email: RORE, Inc.
Website: www.roreinc.com
General & hazardous waste contracting, environmental
investigation & remediation. (Woman/As-Ind, estab
2003, empl 70, sales $15,000,000, cert: State)

3138 Spring Rivers Ecological Sciences LLC
P.O. Box 153 Cassel, CA 96016
(530) 335-5446 Maria Ellis Aquatic Ecologist
Fax: (530) 335-4591
Email: maria@springrivers.com
Website: www.springrivers.com
Aquatic ecology & resources consulting. (Woman/White,
estab 1994, empl 15, sales , cert: CPUC)

3139 TERRA Solutions & Services, LLC
3478 Buskirk Ave Ste 100 Pleasant Hill, CA 94523
(925) 651-6388 Bruce Borup Owner
Fax: (925) 944-2859
Email: bborup@sircorporation.com
Website: www.terras2.com
Environmental engineering, Phase I & Phase II property
assessment & site investigation,
underground storage tank assessment, removal, & site
restoration services, environmental construction &
remediation system installation. (Nat Ame, estab 2011,
empl 11, sales $222,248, cert: CPUC)

3140 Thomas Land Clearing Company
2170 W Esther St Long Beach, CA 90813
(562) 436-6025 Bernice Antimo
Fax: (562) 436-0328
Email: tlc.demo@verizon.net
Website: www.jesdbes.com
Demolition, asbestos abatement, lead based paint
removal & general land clearing. (AA, estab 1985, empl
5, sales $1,700,000, cert: State, CPUC)

3141   Three Squares International Inc.
     1507 7th St, Ste 05   Santa Monica, CA 90401
     (310) 403-6225   Jaime Nack President
     Fax: (888) 285-7782
     Email: jnack@threesquaresinc.com
     Website: www.threesquaresinc.com
Environmental consulting, strategy, planning & implementation of sustainability initiatives. (Woman, estab 2008,
empl 4, sales $500,000, cert: State, City, CPUC)

3142   Tycho Services, Inc.
     3906 W. Burbank Blvd.   Burbank, CA 91505
     (818) 840-9404   Raj Chhina President
     Fax: (818) 433-7554
     Email: raj@tychoservices.com
     Website: www.tychoservices.com
Pre & post event clean-up & biohazard waste removal and
clean-up. (As-Ind, estab 2009, empl 81, sales $1,600,000,
cert: NMSDC, CPUC)

3143   Veridian Environmental, Inc.
     425 Merchant St, Ste 101   Vacaville, CA 95688
     (707) 449-4400   Charlotte R. Symms President
     Fax:
     Email: csymms@veridianenv.com
     Website: www.veridianenv.com
Quality assurance environmental chemistry consulting
services: human health & ecological risk assessment, lab
audits, lab data validation, environmental data mgmt,
technical liaison services, QA/QC programs & documents,
litigation. (Woman/White, estab 2001, empl 5, sales
$210,000, cert: State, CPUC)

3144   West Coast Environmental Solutions
     2650 Lime Ave   Signal Hill, CA 90755
     (562) 448-9510   Beatriz Esparza Business Devel Mgr
     Fax: (562) 448-9517
     Email: beaesparza@westcoastes.com
     Website: www.westcoastes.com
24-hour hazardous & non-hazardous emergency response
spill cleanup; pipeline, facility, marine, rail, highway,
container spills, river, stream, harbor, shoreline, drug lab,
containment & protective booming, product skimming/
recovery & storage. (Woman/White, estab 2010, empl 35,
sales $5,768,900, cert: CPUC)

3145   Wildscape Restoration, Inc.
     2500 Channel Dr Ste A-1   Ventura, CA 93003
     (805) 644-6852   Noreen Cabanting Principal
     Fax: (805) 642-3164
     Email: noreen@wildscaperestoration.com
     Website: www.wildscaperestoration.com
Environmental consulting & contracting: habitat restoration, non-native invasive species removal, biological
surveys & monitoring, permitting & environmental
planning. (Woman/As-Pac, estab 2006, empl 8, sales
$415,369, cert: State)

Colorado

3146   Colorado's Advanced Restoration Experts, LLC
     P.O. Box 1592   Lyons, CO 80540
     (303) 588-6796   Theodore Pangilinan President
     Fax: (303) 374-2997
     Email: theo@restorationwithcare.com
     Website: www.restorationwithcare.com
Water damage mitigation, mold remediation, carpet
cleaning, fire & smoke restoration, odor control &
upholstery cleaning. (As-Pac, estab 2015, empl 12, sales
$350,000, cert: State)

3147   Diamond T Services Inc.
     112 N Rubey Dr Ste 101   Golden, CO 80403
     (303)45499   Vanessa Ingalls CEO
     Fax:
     Email: vanessa.ingalls@dtservices.com
     Website: www.diamondtservices.com
Soil stabilization & welding solutions, access & environmental matting, primary & secondary containment,
surface rentals, certified welding services for pipeline &
well sites, fabrication, roustabout, heavy equipment,
trucking & environmental services. (Woman/White,
estab 2009, empl 30, sales $7,434,245, cert: WBENC)

3148   Impact Mitigation Consultants LLC.
     9851 Castleridge Cir   Highlands Ranch, CO 80129
     (720) 285-9918   James Balman Owner
     Fax:
     Email: james@imcnow.com
     Website: www.imcnow.com
Environmental testing. Air quality, asbestos, mold, lead.
Mitigation consulting Construction services not exceed-
ing 2MMPlastic mold injection & design, IT develop-
ment. (Nat Ame, estab 2016, empl 5, sales $45,000, cert:
State)

3149   Marketing Data Solutions
     36424 Forest Trail   Elizabeth, CO 80107
     (720) 474-7604   Steven Winger CEO
     Fax:
     Email: Steve@r8int.com
     Website:
Environmental Remediation, RCRA Hazardous waste
packaging, transportation & disposal, TSCA waste,
Soils Excavation, Environmental services,
Hazardous waste profiling, Hazardous waste collection,
transfer and transportation. (Nat Ame, estab 2012, empl
1, sales , cert: 8(a))

3150 Munchiando Excavating, Inc.
      5040 Tabor St   Wheat Ridge, CO 80033
      (303) 940-6642 Linda Munchiando President
      Fax: (303) 420-9078
      Email: munchexc@aol.com
      Website:
Environmental clean-up, excavation & transportation,
excavation & earthwork, UST removal, underground
utilities, vacuum tanker, roll-off trailers, end-dumps, van
trailers & flatbed trailers. (Woman/White, estab 1987,
empl 6, sales $958,000, cert: State, City)

3151 Property Doctors Inc.
      14700 W 66th Place Unit 7 Arvada, CO 80004
      (888) 456-0911 Nancy Rees President
      Fax:
      Email: information@property-drs.com
      Website: www.property-drs.com
Asbestos abatement & removal, asbestos testing, asbestos
consulting, carpet cleaning. (Woman/White, estab 2005,
empl 12, sales $17,000,000, cert: City, WBENC)

3152 RDS Environmental, Inc.
      11603 Teller St   Broomfield, CO 80020
      (303) 444-5253 Tammy Linton President
      Fax: (303) 444-1331
      Email: Tammy@rdsenvironmental.com
      Website: www.rdsenvironmental.com
Environmental consulting, asbestos testing, mold testing,
mold remediation/removal, radon testing, radon mitigation installation. (Woman/White, estab 1978, empl 6, sales
$1,032,000, cert: WBENC)

3153 RMC Consultants, Inc.
      12345 W Alameda Pkwy Ste 205 Lakewood, CO
      80228
      (303) 980-4101 Richard Valdez President
      Fax: (303) 980-4107
      Email: rvaldez@rmc-consultants.com
      Website: www.rmc-consultants.net
Environmental services consulting: science & engineering,
project mgmt, planning & documentation, compliance,
mine reclamation, heavy equipment operation, waste
mgmt, remediation services. (Hisp, estab 1990, empl 56,
sales $3,980,000, cert: State, City)

District of Columbia

3154 Windjammer Environmental
      1001 G St NW Ste 800 Washington, DC 20001
      (888) 270-8387 Damien Hammond President
      Fax: (888) 505-8267
      Email: hammond@wjenviro.com
      Website: www.wjenviro.com
Industrial Hygiene Services: Indoor air Quality Surveys,
Mold & Moisture Investigation, General Air & Waterborne
Contaminate Sampling, Asbestos Management Services &
Lead Management Services, Environmental Health &
Occupational Safety Services. (AA, estab 2012, empl 5,
sales $350,000, cert: State, City, 8(a))

Delaware

3155 BrightFields, Inc.
      801 Industrial St   Wilmington, DE 19801
      (302) 656-9600 Donald Short CFO
      Fax: (302) 656-9700
      Email: dshort@brightfieldsinc.com
      Website: www.brightfieldsinc.com
Environmental consulting svcs: phase I & II investigations, multi-media sampling, above & underground
storage tanks, soil & groundwater remediation,
brownfield redevelopment, asbestos & lead svcs.
(Woman/White, estab 2003, empl 35, sales $5,907,000,
cert: WBENC)

Florida

3156 Advantage Environmental Services, Inc.
      2325 5th Ave N   St. Petersburg, FL 33713
      (727) 323-1902 Teresa Nixon Project Dir
      Fax: (727) 323-0430
      Email: tnixon@aesenv.com
      Website: www.aesenv.com
Remediation, waste management & construction
services. (Woman/AA, estab 1994, empl 3, sales
$1,351,000, cert: State, City)

3157 Advisory Environmental Technologies, Inc.
      4240 William Dr   Gulf Breeze, FL 32563
      (850) 356-2365 Gary Butler Business Devel Mgr
      Fax: (787) 724-5788
      Email: gbutler@aet-environmental.com
      Website: www.aet-environmental.com
Environmental Remediation Services, Indoor Air Quality
Remediation, Asbestos Abatement, Lead Abatement,
Laboratory Services, Environmental & Safety Training
Services, Problem Solving. (Woman/Hisp, estab 2007,
empl 4, sales $2,169,158, cert: 8(a))

3158 AirQuest Environmental, Inc.
      6851 SW 45th St   Fort Lauderdale, FL 33314
      (954) 792-4549 Traci-Anne Boyle President
      Fax: (954) 792-2221
      Email: traci@airquestinc.com
      Website: www.airquestinc.com
Environmental consulting: due diligence investigations,
Phase I & II site assessments, mold & asbestos surveys,
abatement mgmt, indoor air quality surveys, soil &
groundwater assessment & remediation, etc. (Woman/
White, estab 2002, empl 28, sales $600,000, cert: State,
City, WBENC)

3159 Ambient Technologies, Inc.
4610 Central Ave   St. Petersburg, FL 33711
(727) 328-0268 Carlos Lemos President
Fax: (727) 328-2477
Email: ambtec@aol.com
Website: www.ambienttech.com
Environmental & geotechnical drilling, geophysics & utility designating services. (Hisp, estab 1992, empl 30, sales $3,000,000, cert: State, NMSDC)

3160 Clark Environmental, Inc.
755 Prairie Industrial Pkwy   Mulberry, FL 33860
(863) 425-4884 Beth Clark President
Fax: (863) 425-4642
Email: bclark@clarkenvironmental.com
Website: www.ThermalTreatment.com
Thermal treatment facility: dispose petroleum contaminated soil, waste processing, hazardous & non-hazardous waste disposal & transportation services. (Woman/White, estab 1991, empl 23, sales , cert: State)

3161 Environmental Health and Safety Solutions, LLC
3126 Egans Bluff Rd   Amelia Island, FL 32034
(904) 556-6422 Frank Damato Director of Safety/ Training
Fax: (904) 277-3687
Email: fdamato@ehssgroup.com
Website: www.EHSSGroup.com
Environmental services, industrial hygiene monitoring services, air & noise monitoring surveys. (Woman/White, estab 2011, empl 5, sales $760,000, cert: State)

3162 Meryman Environmental, Inc.
10408 Bloomingdale Ave   Riverview, FL 33578
(813) 626-9551 Charles CEO
Fax: (813) 623-6613
Email: meryman@merymanenvironmental.com
Website: www.merymanenvironmental.com
Environmental consulting services: scientists, geologists, ecologists, forestry experts, & laboratory scientists. (Nat Ame, estab 1974, empl 9, sales $928,261, cert: State)

3163 OHC Environmental Engineering, Inc.
5420 Bay Center Dr, Ste 100   Tampa, FL 33609
(813) 626-8156 James Rizk President
Fax: (813) 623-6702
Email: jrizk@ohcnet.com
Website: www.ohcnet.com
Environmental consulting: asbestos & lead surveys, indoor air quality investigations, phase I & II assessments, subsurface investigations, asbestos, lead & mold remediation & hazardous material management. (AA, estab 1983, empl 45, sales $2,000,000, cert: State)

3164 Progressive Engineering & Construction, Inc.
3912 W Humphrey St   Tampa, FL 33614
(813) 930-0669 Jill Doyle Office Admin
Fax: (813) 930-9809
Email: jdoyle@progressiveec.com
Website: www.progressiveec.com
Environmental engineering, construction management services, environmental feasibility/technology evaluations, remedial/closure strategy development, remedy construction & enhancement. (Woman, estab 1999, empl 10, sales $2,854,865, cert: State)

3165 Pure Air Control Services, Inc.
4911 Creekside Dr, Ste C   Clearwater, FL 33760
(800) 422-7873 Alan Wozniak President
Fax: (727) 572-5859
Email: Awozniak@pureaircontrols.com
Website: www.pureaircontrols.com
Indoor environmental svcs: IEQ training, building & home diagnostics, mold identification, industrial hygiene svcs, forensic IEQ testimony, environmental lab svcs, environmental project mgmt, IAQ-screen test kits, HVAC cleaning. (Hisp, estab 1982, empl 35, sales $2,500,000, cert: State, NMSDC)

3166 Spaulding Decon, LLC
9420 lazy lane, E-9   tampa, FL 33614
(813) 298-7122 Laura Spaulding Owner
Fax: (813) 464-7676
Email: spaulding911@yahoo.com
Website: www.spauldingdecon.com
Bio-hazard clean up svcs: blood, vomit, feces, urine removal, odor abatement, dead animal removal. (Woman/White, estab 2005, empl 3, sales $300,000, cert: City, WBENC)

3167 Stone Environmental Services
6151 Lake Osprey Dr   Sarasota, FL 33946
(941) 628-5693 Anna Milantoni Owner
Fax: (800) 310-9226
Email: amilantoni@stoneenvironmentalservices.com
Website: www.stoneenvironmentalservices.com
Dist metal/plastic cleaning chemistry, refrigerants, disposal of non-hazardous & hazardous waste disposal, cleaning equipment. (Woman/White, estab 2001, empl 1, sales $446,000, cert: WBENC)

Georgia

3168 Basha Services, LLC
2336 Wisteria Dr Ste 510 Snellville, GA 30078
(678) 344-1161 Neville Anderson President
Fax: (678) 344-1163
Email: nanderson@bashaservices.com
Website: www.bashaservices.com/
Environmental services: remediation, emergency & spill response, soil remediation, excavation & restoration, groundwater remediation, UST/AST closure, cleaning, inspection & installation. (AA, estab 2007, empl 11, sales , cert: State, NMSDC)

3169 Cape Environmental Management Inc.
500 Pinnacle Court, Ste 100 Norcross, GA 30071
(610) 470-1189 Michael Healy Bus Develop Mgr
Fax: (443) 276-2078
Email: mhealy@cape-inc.com
Website: www.cape-inc.com
Environ remediation & consulting: base closures, USTS, ASTS, assessments, lead based paint, radon, asbestos, environ communication programs, hazardous wastes, soil & groundwater. (Hisp, estab 1985, empl 455, sales $128,148,143, cert: NMSDC)

3170 Kemron Environmental Services, Inc.
1359-A Ellsworth Industrial Blvd Atlanta, GA 30318
(404) 636-0928 John Dwyer Exec VP
Fax: (404) 636-7162
Email: mbe@kemron.com
Website: www.kemron.com
Environ svcs: consulting, site remediation, environ assessment, investigation & engineering, analytical svcs, geotechnical testing, treatability studies & technology evaluation. (Hisp, estab 1975, empl 165, sales $47,127,478, cert: NMSDC)

Idaho

3171 Wynsor, LLC
3605 Sycamore Circle Idaho Falls, ID 83402
(208) 681-7969 Lea Ann Rodriquez President
Fax:
Email: leaann@wynsorenv.com
Website: www.wynsorenv.com
Environmental Remediation Services: decontamination, decommissioning & demolition, Site characterization & hazardous assessment, Site restoration & closure, Environmental engineering services. (Woman/White, estab 2007, empl 6, sales $541,458, cert: 8(a))

Illinois

3172 All Service Contracting Corp.
2024 E Damon Ave Decatur, IL 62526
(217) 233-3018 Becky Burcham CEO
Fax: (217) 233-3019
Email: becky@allservice.com
Website: www.allservice.com
Dist, remove & install filter media, water & waste water plants, industial & municipal. (Woman/White, estab 1996, empl 12, sales , cert: WBENC)

3173 Anderson & Egan, Co.
124 N Water St Ste 206 Rockford, IL 61107
(815) 962-9000 Jennifer Anderson President
Fax: (815) 962-7978
Email: Janderson@andersonenveng.com
Website: www.andersonenveng.com
Air monitoring, asbestos abatements, environmental consulting & engineering, permitting assistance, underground storage tank removals, environmental site assessments. (Woman/White, estab 2003, empl 5, sales $469,000, cert: State, City)

3174 Endure, Inc.
360 Beinoris Dr Wood Dale, IL 60191
(630) 616-9700 Angelia Hopson Environmental Safety/Training
Fax: (630) 616-9798
Email: ahopson@endure-inc.com
Website: www.endureinc.com
Safety, health & environmental consulting, training for regulatory compliance to OSHA, EPA & DOT requirements. (Woman/AA, estab 2010, empl 17, sales $1,845,500, cert: City, NMSDC)

3175 Environmental Monitoring and Technologies
8100 N Austin Ave Morton Grove, IL 60053
(847) 324-3306 Brian Walsh Sales Exec
Fax: (847) 967-6735
Email: bwalsh@emt.com
Website: www.EMT.com
Environmental analytical laboratory, test water, soil & solid waste, environmental sampling services. (Woman/White, estab 1984, empl 65, sales $6,000,000, cert: State)

3176 Hygieneering, Inc.
7575 Plaza Court, Ste B Willowbrook, IL 60527
(630) 654-2550 George Guidarelli VP Sales
Fax: (630) 789-3813
Email: gguidarelli@hygieneering.com
Website: www.hygieneering.com
Environmental consulting. (Woman/White, estab 1987, empl 42, sales $2,750,000, cert: WBENC)

3177   NES Incorporated
19015 Jodi Rd Unit B   Mokena, IL 60448
(708) 478-5497   Kyla Lawson Sec/Treas
Fax: (708) 478-5801
Email: KLawson@nesincorp.com
Website: www.nesincorp.com
Asbestos abatement, operations & maintenance, inspections & sampling, lead removal, mitigation, sampling & testing, mold remediation, inspections & sampling, hazardous materials clean-up & infrared investigations. (Hisp, estab 2000, empl 10, sales $1,800,000, cert: State, NMSDC)

Indiana

3178   Hoosier Equipment Service, Inc.
8149 Network Dr   Plainfield, IN 46168
(317) 838-8988   Anne DaVega VP of Business Develop
Fax: (317) 838-8829
Email: adavega@hoosierequipment.com
Website: www.hoosierequipment.com
Environmental services, underground & aboveground storage tank work (removals, installs, repairs), oil/water separator cleanouts, & environmental remediation work, excavate contaminated soil. (Woman/White, estab 1978, empl 13, sales $3,169,000, cert: WBENC)

3179   Keramida Environmental, Inc.
401 N College Ave   Indianapolis, IN 46202
(317) 414-9862   Tim Higgins VP
Fax: (317) 685-6610
Email: thiggins@keramida.com
Website: www.keramida.com
Environmental, health & safety engineering & consulting, remediation, site assessments, permitting. (Woman/White, estab 1988, empl 50, sales $9,000,000, cert: WBENC)

Kansas

3180   EMR, Inc.
2110 Delaware, Ste B   Lawrence, KS 66046
(785) 842-9013   Pam Maley VP Mktg & Businessines Devel
Fax: (785) 842-3863
Email: pmaley@emr-inc.com
Website: www.emr-inc.com
Environmental consulting: compliance, industrial hygiene, mold, asbestos, lead paint, UST/AST investigation, hazardous waste mgmt, recycling, soil & groundwater remediation. (Woman/Nat Ame, estab 1988, empl 250, sales $44,000,000, cert: WBENC)

Kentucky

3181   Evergreen Environmental
7416 Hwy 329   Crestwood, KY 40014
(502) 241-4171   Hollis Flora Project Mgr
Fax: (502) 241-4347
Email: hflora@evgusa.com
Website: www.evgusa.com
Compliance plan dev, environmental process & RCRA audits, property audits, UST mgmt, hazard risk analysis, OSHA training & consulting, soil & groundwater remediation, permitting & closure plans, industrial cleaning, hazardous & waste mgmt, etc. (Woman/White, estab 1986, empl 26, sales $4,300,000, cert: WBENC)

3182   Specific Waste Industries
3600 Chamberlain Lane, Ste 104   Louisville, KY 40241
(1502) 425-2770   Victor Anderson President
Fax:
Email: vanderson@a-solutionsinc.com
Website: www.specificwaste.com
Regulated Medical Waste Removal & Treatment, Pharmaceutical Waste (Haz and Non-Haz), Sharps Waste (Reusable Sharps Program). (AA, estab 1900, empl 1, sales $500,000, cert: NMSDC)

Louisiana

3183   Quaternary Resource Investigations, LLC
13588 Florida Blvd   Baton Rouge, LA 70819
(225) 292-1400   Amie Chatman Business Devel Mgr
Fax: (225) 292-1404
Email: acha@qri.com
Website: www.qri.com
Litigation & strategy support; environmental sampling & lab data mgmt; groundwater geophysical svcs; remediation implementation; regulatory compliance; coastal & wetlands svcs. (Woman/White, estab 1986, empl 18, sales $31,000,000, cert: WBENC)

Massachusetts

3184   Capaccio Environmental Engineering Inc.
293 Boston Post Rd W   Marlborough, MA 01752
(508) 970-0033   Lisa Wilk President
Fax: (508) 970-0028
Email: lwilk@capaccio.com
Website: www.capaccio.com
Environmental engineering & consulting services, environmental compliance & permitting, occupational safety & health consulting services, environmental, health & safety management systems. (Woman/White, estab 1992, empl 30, sales $3,139,945, cert: State, WBENC)

3185 Corporate Environmental Advisors, Inc.
127 Hartwell St   West Boylston, MA 01583
(800) 358-7960 Scott Soucy Health, Safety & Compliance
Fax: (508) 835-8812
Email: contactus@cea-inc.com
Website: www.cea-inc.com/
Environmental engineering, consulting & contracting firm. (Woman/White, estab 1985, empl 20, sales $3,878,000, cert: State)

3186 CR Environmental, Inc.
639 Boxberry Hill Rd   East Falmouth, MA 02536
(508) 563-7970 Charlotte Cogswell President
Fax: (508) 563-7970
Email: charlotte@crenvironmental.com
Website: www.crenvironmental.com
Ecological risk assessments & characterizations of terrestrial, wetland & aquatic habitats. (Woman/White, estab 1994, empl 7, sales $1,984,067, cert: State, City)

3187 Essex Newbury North Contracting Corporation
65 Parker St, Unit 5   Newburyport, MA 01950
(978) 463-5414 Delano Brooks President
Fax: (978) 463-5415
Email: delano_br@yahoo.com
Website: www.essexnewburynorth.com
General Contracting, construction management, commercial & industrial construction, lead abatement & asbestos remediation, finish carpentry, commercial & institutional bldg construction, painting & wall coverings, site preparation. (AA, estab 1997, empl 400, sales $31,000,000, cert: State, City, NMSDC)

Maryland

3188 C&R Environmental Associates, Inc.
1415 Bush St 2nd Fl Baltimore, MD 21230
(410) 727-8762 Rudy Scipio President
Fax: (410) 727-5272
Email: rscipio@crdemoinc.com
Website: www.crdemoinc.com
Hazardous materials remediation & demolition services, construction/renovation services & design/build services. (AA, estab 1997, empl 15, sales $5,000,000, cert: State)

3189 Turtle Wings Inc.
1771 Olive St   Capitol Heights, MD 20743
(301) 583-8399 Elizabeth Wilmot President
Fax: (443) 346-0208
Email: info@datakillers.com
Website: www.datakillers.com
Environmental services. (Woman/White, estab 2005, empl 13, sales $1,200,000, cert: State, WBENC)

Maine

3190 Credere Associates, LLC
776 Main St   Westbrook, ME 04092
(207) 828-1272 Rip Patten, PE VP
Fax: (207) 887-1051
Email: rpatten@crederellc.com
Website: www.crederellc.com
Environmental consulting & engineering, cleanup, construction, adaptive reuse & Brownfields Redevelopment projects. (Woman/White, estab 2007, empl 11, sales $2,000,000, cert: 8(a))

Michigan

3191 Advanced Environmental Management Group, LLC
44339 Plymouth Oaks Blvd.   Plymouth, MI 48170
(734) 354-9070 Lleonard President
Fax: (734) 354-9087
Email: lleonard@environmental-help.com
Website: www.environmental-help.com
Environmental permitting, compliance assessments, dispersion modeling, stack & ambient air testing, due diligence & remediation svcs, ISO 14001 EMS svcs, facility closure & decommissioning services, spill & contingency plans. (As-Ind, estab 1998, empl 11, sales , cert: NMSDC)

3192 Atier
24074 Gibson Dr   Warren, MI 48089
(586) 759-4240 Patricia Schrenk Acct Mgr
Fax: (586) 759-5235
Email: patti.schrenk@atierpro.com
Website: www.atierpro.com
Total Quality Management & Engineering Consulting, Quality & Industrial Engineering, Containment, Supplier Representation, ISO & TS Implementation Audits, Quality Inspection, Launch support, Scrap Reduction, Project Management. (AA, estab 2012, empl 100, sales $4,700,000, cert: NMSDC)

3193 Cadena, LLC.
1099 Highland Dr, Ste A   Ann Arbor, MI 48108
(734) 418-1977 Armando Ojeda CEO
Fax: (734) 661-0114
Email: aojeda@cadenaco.com
Website: www.cadenaco.com
Environmental services, lab data, Level II & Level IV validations, environmental laboratory audits, archiving environmental data. (Hisp, estab 2013, empl 2, sales $384,654, cert: NMSDC, CPUC)

3194　Cleaning Contractors Inc.
　　　25600 Brest RD　Taylor, MI 48180
　　　(734) 946-4270　Mary Longsdorf President
　　　Fax: (734) 946-4372
　　　Email: mary@ccienv.com
　　　Website: www.ccienv.com
Industrial & Environmental Cleaning, wet/dry vacuum, water blasting, media blasting, sewer cleaning & tevevising, hydro excavation,
lead & mold abatement, confined space rescue, deep cleaning, paint shop cleaning. (Woman/White, estab 2009, empl 60, sales $9,000,000, cert: WBENC)

3195　EKS Services Incorporated
　　　7451 Third St　Detroit, MI 48202
　　　(313) 963-1433　Clarence E. Carpenter III CEO
　　　Fax:
　　　Email: clarencecarpenter@eksservices.com
　　　Website: www.eksservices.com
Environmental consulting & construction mgmt. (AA, estab 2000, empl 20, sales $1,500,000, cert: NMSDC)

3196　Environmental Compliance Office Inc.
　　　3011 W Grand Blvd, Ste 420　Detroit, MI 48202
　　　(313) 285-8401　Vimala Anishetty, Ph.D. President
　　　Fax: (313) 285-8401
　　　Email: vanishet@ecomain.com
　　　Website: www.ecomain.com
Environmental engineering & consulting svcs: air, water, waste, auditing, reporting & training. (Woman/As-Pac, estab 2007, empl 4, sales $310,000, cert: WBENC)

3197　Environmental Services of North America, Inc.
　　　10455 Ford Rd　Dearborn, MI 48126
　　　(313) 945-7400　Joe Coelho Owner
　　　Fax: (313) 581-9190
　　　Email: jcoelho@esnainc.com
　　　Website: www.esnainc.com
Facility svcs: waste disposal & recycling, snow removal, parking lot sweeping, power washing, janitorial services & supplies, landscaping, onsite & offsite document shredding, asbestos, lead based paint & mold, waste containers. (AA, estab 2000, empl 3, sales , cert: NMSDC)

3198　Environmental Testing and Consulting Inc.
　　　38900 W Huron River Dr　Romulus, MI 48174
　　　(734)9556600　Patricia Stephen Contract Mgr
　　　Fax: (734) 955-6604
　　　Email: sales@2etc.com
　　　Website: www.2etc.com
Environmental consulting firm, asbestos, lead based paint, mold surveys, risk assessments, clearances, O&M plans, project management and training, indoor air quality assessments. (Woman/White, estab 1989, empl 75, sales $3,270,519, cert: WBENC)

3199　Hur-Q-Clean Services, Inc. dba Diversified Environ
　　　3911 Barton Rd　Lansing, MI 48917
　　　(517) 323-2940　Donald Suttles President
　　　Fax: (844) 415-2124
　　　Email: desejs@sprynet.com
　　　Website:
Environmental compliance consulting, auditing, training, project management, wastewater treatment & boiler chemical sales & service. (AA, estab 1984, empl 4, sales $200,001, cert: NMSDC)

3200　Integrated Recycling Industries
　　　P.O. Box 581　Wyandotte, MI 48192
　　　(734) 818-9835　Richard Pacheco President
　　　Fax:
　　　Email: rpacheco.iri@gmail.com
　　　Website: www.integratedrecyclingindustries.com
Recycle Ferrous and Non-Ferrous scrap metals, Cardboard and Plastics. (Hisp, estab 2015, empl 2, sales $100,000, cert: NMSDC)

3201　McDonald & Assoc. Quality Management & Environment
　　　17561 Westhampton　Southfield, MI 48075
　　　(248) 559-5197　Sherman McDonald President
　　　Fax: (248) 569-0250
　　　Email: mcdonaldquality@msn.com
　　　Website: www.qltyenvsys.com
Leadership development, problem solving, 6 Sigma & 8D problem solving, waste management, environmental site assessment & environmental remediation. (AA, estab 1999, empl 10, sales $63,000, cert: State)

3202　Merit Laboratories, Inc.
　　　2680 E Lansing Dr　East Lansing, MI 48823
　　　(517) 332-0167　Maya Murshak President
　　　Fax:
　　　Email: mayamurshak@meritlabs.com
　　　Website: www.meritlabs.com
Environmental testing laboratory, RCRA remediation analytical, testing for soil, water & waste. We work with large and small industries, engineering firms, municipalities (Woman, estab 1987, empl 1, sales , cert: WBENC)

3203　MPS Group, Inc.
　　　38755 Hills Tech Dr　Farmington Hills, MI 48331
　　　(313) 841-7588　Bryon Lawrence Director of Sales & Mktg
　　　Fax: (248) 489-0656
　　　Email: blawrence@mpsgrp.com
　　　Website: www.mpsgrp.com
Environmental Consulting & Engineering. (AA, estab 1995, empl 495, sales $46,200,000, cert: NMSDC)

3204 RTI Laboratories, Inc.
      33080 Industrial Rd   Livonia, MI 48150
      (734) 422-8000 Kae Trojanowski President
      Fax: (734) 422-5342
      Email: ktrojanowski@rtilab.com
      Website: www.rtilab.com
Analytical testing laboratory: environmental, chemical &
metallurgical testing, environmental compliance field
sampling services. (As-Ind, estab 1986, empl 40, sales
$5,000,000, cert: NMSDC, SDB)

3205 Unlimited Recycling, Inc.
      P.O. Box 363   Richmond, MI 48062
      (586) 784-4980 Maria Marin-McInturf President
      Fax: (586) 784-4981
      Email: maria@unlimitedrecyclinginc.com
      Website: www.unlimitedrecyclinginc.com
Recycling svcs: spent electric lamps, batteries, electronic
equipment, mercury containing devices. In addition,
hazardous & non-hazardous waste, oil, solvents, paint,
antinfreeze. (Hisp, estab 1999, empl 7, sales $47,815, cert:
NMSDC)

3206 VMX International, LLC
      3011 W Grand Blvd Ste 2401 Detroit, MI 48202
      (313) 875-9450 Vickie Lewis CEO
      Fax: (313) 875-9759
      Email: vlewis@vmxi.com
      Website: www.vmxi.com
International waste management & recycling services.
(Woman/AA, estab 2001, empl 54, sales $3,140,800, cert:
NMSDC, NWBOC)

Minnesota

3207 EnviroBate, Inc.
      3301 E 26th Sttreet   Minneapolis, MN 55406
      (612) 437-5797 Dana Krakowski VP of Sales and
      Mktg
      Fax: (612) 729-1021
      Email: dkrakowski@envirobate.com
      Website: www.envirobate.com
Environmental remediation, asbestos & lead abatement,
mold remediation & Indoor Air Quality (Duct Cleaning),
hazardous waste disposal to include mercury, lead &
PCB's. (Woman/White, estab 1991, empl 80, sales
$14,000,000, cert: City, WBENC)

Missouri

3208 Ahrens Contracting, Inc.
      140 Lafayette Ave   St. Louis, MO 63104
      (314) 631-7799 Patricia Ahrens President
      Fax:
      Email: pahrens@ahrenscontracting.com
      Website: www.ahrenscontracting.com
Hauling Dirt, Rubbish, Trash, Special Waste, Hazardous
Waste, Clean Fill, etc. (Woman/White, estab , empl 1,
sales , cert: WBENC)

3209 Cardinal Environmental Operations Corp.
      4518 Woodson Rd   Saint Louis, MO 63134
      (314) 890-2088 Paula Milligan President
      Fax: (314) 890-0042
      Email: pmilligan@callcardinal.com
      Website:
Asbestos abatement, lead abatement, environmental
remediation, mold remediation, soil/water remediation,
UST/AST removal & installation, duct cleaning services,
consulting services, site assessments, demolition.
(Woman, estab 1993, empl 25, sales $2,000,000, cert:
State, City)

3210 CCI Environmental, Inc.
      6913 Noble Dr Hazelwood, MO 63024
      (314) 974-3893 Mark Briguglio President
      Fax: (314) 522-6802
      Email: marksbriguglio@gmail.com
      Website: www.ccienv.info
Asbestos abatement, inspections, testing, project
management & estimating to air monitoring & project
consulting. (Nat Ame, estab 1994, empl 7, sales
$930,000, cert: State)

3211 Global Environmental, Inc.
      6439 Plymouth Ave Ste 119 Wellston, MO 63133
      (314) 875-9501 John Dingus Project Mgr
      Fax: (314) 875-9603
      Email: john@globalabatement.com
      Website: www.globalabatement.com
Environmental remediation & consulting. (Woman/Nat
Ame, estab 1991, empl 10, sales $10,500,000, cert:
State, 8(a))

3212 Haz-Waste, Inc.
      12951 Gravois Rd Ste 110 St. Louis, MO 63127
      (800) 429-9783 Kimberly Medlock VP
      Fax: (314) 842-7772
      Email: kmedlock@haz-waste.com
      Website: www.haz-waste.com
Air pollution permitting, asbestos, abatement,
byproduct mgmt, environmental audits, field service,
industrial compliance, OSHA compliance, Phase I & II
site work, plant closures, pollution prevention.
(Woman/White, estab 1993, empl 34, sales $6,200,000,
cert: WBENC)

3213   Tehama, LLC
       1600 Genessee Ste 318 Kansas City, MO 64102
       (816) 678-7510 David Brewer GM
       Fax:
       Email: david.brewer@tehamallc.com
       Website: www.tehamallc.com
Engineering/Architectural design, Environmental Consulting Services & Construction Support Services. (Nat Ame, estab 2009, empl 2, sales $52,275, cert: 8(a))

3214   The Kiesel Company
       4801 Fyler Ave   St. Louis, MO 63166
       (314) 351-5500 Larry Gooden VP
       Fax: (314) 351-0894
       Email: Larry.Gooden@kieselco.com
       Website: www.thekieselcompany.com
Dist fuels & lubricants, emergency response services to chemical & petroleum product releases, railroad tank car cleaning, barge cleaning, non-hazardous & hazardous waste disposal, demolition & petroleum-contaminated waste water treatment & disposal. (Woman/White, estab 1900, empl 48, sales $75,010,000, cert: City)

North Carolina

3215   Environmental Process Solutions, PLLC
       7000 Stinson Hartis Rd Ste F   Indian Trail, NC 28079
       (980) 202-2377 Kellie Hedrick CEO
       Fax:
       Email: finance@epscharlotte.com
       Website: www.EPSCharlotte.com
Environmental Consulting, Industrial wastewater treatment, engineering services. (Woman/White, estab 2010, empl 5, sales $103,000, cert: WBENC)

3216   Environmental Service Systems, LLC
       5550 77 Center Dr. Ste 160   Charlotte, NC 28217
       (704) 527-4099 Ciara Lilly Dir, Corporate Diversity Relations
       Fax:
       Email: clilly@environmentalss.com
       Website: www.environmentalss.com
Facility maintenance & janitorial services. (AA, estab 1998, empl 8900, sales $241,700,000, cert: NMSDC)

3217   FireWater CleanUp Crew Corp.
       P.O. Box 78145 Greensboro, NC 27427
       (336) 666-1913 Jamal Mention President
       Fax: (336) 373-1912
       Email: jamalmention@firewatercleanupcrew.com
       Website: www.firewatercleanupcrew.com
Remediation/restoration services for smoke, fire & water damage. Trauma scene cleanup. (AA, estab 2016, empl 3, sales $50,000, cert: State)

3218   Porter Scientific Inc.
       PO Box 1359   Pembroke, NC 28372
       (910) 521-0549 Freda Porter President
       Fax: (910) 521-3599
       Email: fporter@porterscientific.com
       Website: www.porterscientific.com
Environmental consulting services, assessments, remediation & cleanup, pollution prevention, regulatory compliance, water, sewer & solid waste project management. (Woman/Nat Ame, estab 1997, empl 18, sales $3,458,000, cert: NMSDC)

3219   Reliable Solutions Construction, LLC dba Reliable Restorations
       8201 Arrowridge Blvd Ste 147 Charlotte, NC 28273
       (704) 909-7616 Johanna Suarez Ops Mgr
       Fax:
       Email: johanna@reliablerestorations.net
       Website: www.reliablerestorations.net
Disaster emergency response services, board ups, water extraction, fire & water damage restoration, odor & mold remediation, contents clean up & pack-outs, Non-Destructive Mold Remediation, Smoke & odor deodorization, Removal. (Woman/Hisp, estab 2009, empl 15, sales $1,426,000, cert: State)

Nebraska

3220   Inspection Experts, Inc.
       808 P St Ste 318 Lincoln, NE 68508
       (410) 715-3939 Maureen Faulconer VP
       Fax: (614) 386-1999
       Email: mfaulconer@ieinc.net
       Website: www.ieinc.net
Environmental services, health & safety consulting, industrial hygiene, facilities & asset management & development. (Woman/As-Ind, estab 2004, empl 16, sales $3,365,268, cert: State)

New Hampshire

3221   Absolute Resource Associates, LLC
       124 Heritage Ave Unit 16 Portsmouth, NH 03801
       (603) 436-2001 Susan Sylvester President
       Fax: (603) 430-2100
       Email: sues@absoluteresourceassociates.com
       Website: www.absoluteresourceassociates.com
Environmental laboratory testing & indoor air quality assessments. (Woman, estab 1994, empl 25, sales $3,000,000, cert: WBENC)

New Jersey

3222 BGI Resources International Corporation
205 Barclay Pavilion W Cherry Hill, NJ 08034
(856) 888-2396 Bassey Akpan CEO
Fax: (856) 685-7395
Email: info@BGIResourcesIntl.com
Website: www.BGIResourcesIntl.com
Air, Water Soil Sampling, Phase I, II, III Projects, GIS Mapping, Preliminary Assessments. (AA, estab 2010, empl 3, sales , cert: State)

3223 Cornerstone EHS, LLC
P.O. Box 1102 Mullica Hill, NJ 08062
(856) 776-0455 Marianne Payne President
Fax: (888) 864-1385
Email: mpayne@cornerstoneehs.com
Website: www.cornerstoneehs.com
Environmental, health, safety consulting & services, EHS program development & management; comprehensive EHS compliance & management system auditing; EHS related training, management systems development & implementation. (Woman/White, estab 2011, empl 1, sales $332,065, cert: WBENC)

3224 Environmental Industrial Services Corp. of NJ
288 Oak Grove Rd Swedesboro, NJ 08085
(856) 467-5001 Robert Feller Business Devel
Fax: (856) 467-5002
Email: rfeller@eisco4service.com
Website: www.eisco4action.com
Environmental remediation services, soil remediation, capping, stabilization, UST & AST cleaning & closure, subsurface exploratory/test pits, groundwater remediation, install systems, pump & treat, vapor extraction, vacuum enhanced recovery. (Woman/White, estab 1990, empl 55, sales $3,211,964, cert: State)

3225 Matrix New World Engineering, Inc.
26 Columbia Florham Park, NJ 07932
(973) 240-1800 MAYOOR SHETH President
Fax: (973) 240-1818
Email: MSHETH@MATRIXNEWORLD.COM
Website: www.matrixneworld.com
Environmental, geotechnical, civil engineering, survey & building facility consulting & engineering firm. (Woman/White, estab 1990, empl 70, sales $20,526,967, cert: City, CPUC)

3226 Prestige Environmental, Inc.
220 Davidson Ave Ste 307 Somerset, NJ 08873
(908) 757-9700 Girish Mehta President
Fax: (908) 757-5050
Email: girish.mehta@prestige-environmental.com
Website: www.prestige-environmental.com
Environmental consulting & contracting svcs: site assessments & feasibility studies; removal & installation of petroleum tanks; soil & groundwater investigations; site remediation; design, installation & operation of remediation systems. (As-Ind, estab 1993, empl 6, sales $1,092,700, cert: State)

3227 Sovereign
111 A North Gold Dr Robbinsville, NJ 08691
(609) 259-8200 Michael Hanlon Mgr
Fax: (609) 259-8200
Email: mhanlon@sovcon.com
Website: www.sovcon.com
Environmental consulting & remediation services, environmental, civil & geotechnical engineering; remediation system evaluation, optimization, design & construction/installation; environmental, land use & natural resources permitting. (As-Pac, estab 1999, empl 165, sales $35,466,433, cert: NMSDC)

Nevada

3228 The Westmark Group
2430 N Decatur Blvd Ste 140 Las Vegas, NV 89108
(702) 839-2960 Leslie Mujica Dir of BD & gov affairs
Fax: (702) 839-2962
Email: marketing@westmarkgroup.net
Website: www.westmarkgroup.net
Consulting & project management, environmental consulting, occupational safety & health services & waste management services. (Hisp, estab 1999, empl 25, sales $5,000,000, cert: State)

New York

3229 Abtron Associates Corp.
60A Corbin Ave Bay Shore, NY 11706
(631) 392-1330 Robert Green President
Fax: (631) 392-1328
Email: rgreen@abtronassociatescorp.com
Website: www.abtronassociatescorp.com
Environmental hazards/non-hazards services. (AA, estab 1997, empl 30, sales $1,055,000, cert: NMSDC, 8(a))

3230 American Environmental Assessment & Solutions
679 Lafayette Ave, 3rd Fl   Brooklyn, NY 11216
(718) 209-0653 Antoinette Ollivierre Principal
Fax: (718) 906-4090
Email: aollivierre@aeasinc.com
Website: www.aeasinc.com
Environmental services: Phase I, II and III Environmental
Site Assessments (ESA), soil & groundwater investigation,
remediation of contaminated sites, NYC E-designation
investigation and compliance. (Woman/AA, estab 2006,
empl 9, sales , cert: State, City)

3231 Atlantic Testing Laboratories, Limited
P.O. Box 29   Canton, NY 13617
(315) 386-4578 Eric M. Van Alstyne Bus Dev Mgr
Fax: (315) 386-1012
Email: evanalstyne@atlantictesting.com
Website: www.ATlanticTesting.com
Subsurface investigations, water-based investigations,
geotechnical engineering, construction materials engineering & testing, special inspection services, pavement
engineering, nondestructive testing & environmental
services. (Woman/White, estab 1967, empl 230, sales
$16,190,692, cert: State, City)

3232 CSA Central, Inc.
55 Broadway, 14th Fl   New York, NY 10006
(305) 461-5484 Frederik Riefkohl Sr VP
Fax: (305) 461-5494
Email: friefkohl@csagroup.com
Website: www.csagroup.com
Program & project mgmt, environmental services, archi-
tecture & engineering, Construction Management,
Operation & Maintenance. (Hisp, estab 1995, empl 55,
sales $4,963,359, cert: City, NMSDC)

3233 Environmental Design & Research, DPC
217 Montgomery St Ste 1000 Syracuse, NY 13202
(315) 471-0688 Joanne Stewart Associate
Fax: (315) 471-1061
Email: jstewart@edrdpc.com
Website: www.edrdpc.com
Landscape architecture, civil engineering, community
planning, visualization, environmental regulatory, ecological, geographic information systems mapping & analysis,
historic preservation, cultural resources, archeology.
(Woman/White, estab 1979, empl 38, sales $4,500,000,
cert: State)

3234 Foit-Albert Associates, Architecture, Engineering
and Surveying, P.C.
215 W 94th St, Ste 517   New York, NY 10025
(716) 856-3933 Gregory Carballada President
Fax: (716) 856-3933
Email: cstoebe@foit-albert.com
Website: www.foit-albert.com
Architecture, Engineering, Environmental & Land Surveying Consulting. (Hisp, estab 1977, empl 48, sales
$4,839,242, cert: State, City)

3235 LEADCARE, Inc.
10-25 44th Ave   Long Island City, NY 11101
(718) 706-8383 Sarah Attias-Dunn President
Fax: (718) 706-8389
Email: dunn@leadcare.com
Website: www.leadcare.com
Environmental testing, consultating & remediation
project management, asbestos, lead, mold & indoor air
quality investigations. (Woman/White, estab 1992, empl
10, sales $1,100,000, cert: State, City)

3236 Mechanical Testing, Inc.
70 Lake Ave.   Saratoga Springs, NY 12866
(518) 450-7292 Eileen Venn CEO
Fax: (518) 450-7294
Email: Eileenv@mechtest.com
Website: www.mechtest.com
Testing, Adjusting & Balancing of HVAC Systems, Indoor
Air Quality Testing, Performance Tests for HVAC Equip-
ment, Sound Testing, In Room/Space Pressure Relation-
ship Testing, Duct Pressurization, SMACNA. (Woman/
White, estab 1967, empl 27, sales $3,800,000, cert:
State, WBENC)

3237 NPTS, Inc.
2060 Sheridan Dr   Buffalo, NY 14223
(716) 876-8066 Hormoz Mansouri President
Fax: (716) 876-8004
Email: rbroman@eiteam.com
Website: www.npts.net
Engineering consulting: nuclear, fossil, petrochem, risk
assessment, thermohydraulic, design, outage mgmt,
technical support svcs, etc. (As-Ind, estab 1983, empl 15,
sales $1,521,462, cert: NMSDC)

3238 Sienna Environmental Technologies, LLC
350 Elmwood Ave   Buffalo, NY 14222
(716) 332-3134 Susanne Kelley President
Fax: (716) 332-3136
Email: skelley@siennaet.com
Website: www.siennaet.com
Asbestos inspections & contamination assessments,
lead-based paint inspection & risk assessment, indoor
air quality, microbial & radon testing & investigative
services, air, soil, dust, water & solid waste sampling.
(Woman/Hisp, estab 2000, empl 17, sales $2,000,000,
cert: State, City)

3239 Universal Environmental Consulting, Inc.
900 Merchants Concourse Ste 214 Westbury, NY
11590
(800) 552-0309 Christina Sorrentino Ops
Fax: (516) 489-3736
Email: csorrentino@uecny.com
Website: www.uecny.com
Collection management of solid waste & recyclables.
(Woman/White, estab 1995, empl 20, sales $33,785,084,
cert: WBENC)

Ohio

3240 CTL Engineering, Inc.
2860 Fisher Rd P.O. Box 44548 Columbus, OH 43204
(614) 276-8123 C.K. Satyapriya President
Fax:
Email: ctl@ctleng.com
Website: www.ctleng.com
Geotechnical, construction inspection, environmental, mining engineering, analytical chemistry, forensic science, metallurgy, product testing, research & development, roof engineering, existing structure evaluation, asbestos inspection. (As-Ind, estab 1928, empl 187, sales , cert: State)

3241 Environmental and Safety Solutions, Inc.
544 Tohatchi Dr Cincinnati, OH 45215
(513) 383-7703 Cindy Tomaszewski President
Fax: (513) 825-4471
Email: ctomaszewski@theessinc.com
Website: www.essinc.info
Enviromental, health & safety services. (AA, estab 2002, empl 9, sales $3,034,000, cert: State, NMSDC)

3242 Iron Eagle Enterprises, LLC
4991 Belmont Ave Youngstown, OH 44505
(330) 759-2760 Dana Mattern Business Dev
Fax:
Email: DMattern@IronEagleEnt.com
Website: www.IronEagleEnt.com
Custom frac & storage tank rentals, Vacuum truck service—wet & dry materials, Professional cleaning—disposal wells, drains, holding tanks, frac tanks, Solid waste disposal & hauling—rentals of vac boxes & sealed top boxes. (Woman/White, estab 2010, empl 14, sales $4,500,000, cert: WBENC)

3243 MCFS Enterprises, Inc.
P.O. Box 30207 Middleburg Heights, OH 44130
(440) 888-0497 Carrie Scaravelli Owner
Fax:
Email: cscaravelli@cox.net
Website: www.rainbowintl.com/cleveland
Water & fire restoration, smoke & odor remediation, mold, lead & asbestos testing & abatement, hazardous waste specialist. (Woman/White, estab 2007, empl 5, sales $798,000, cert: State, City)

3244 Property & Environmental Management, Inc.
6161 Busch Blvd, Ste 255 Columbus, OH 43229
(614) 210-7202 Thomas Zwick VP
Fax:
Email: tzwick@paeminc.com
Website: www.paeminc.com
Environmental consulting Services, Remediation Services, Facility Support Services, Residential Property Managers. (As-Ind, estab 2010, empl 8, sales $2,000,000, cert: 8(a))

3245 Stone Environmental Engineering & Science, Inc.
748 Green Crest Dr Westerville, OH 43081
(614) 865-1874 Mary Sharrett President
Fax: (614) 865-1879
Email: marysharrett@stoneenvironmental.com
Website: www.StoneEnvironmental.com
Assessment, Permitting, Design & Compliance, air, water, soil, waste streams, hazardous materials, storm water, natural resources, site civil, utilities, and structures. (Woman/White, estab 1989, empl 13, sales $1,400,000, cert: State, City, WBENC)

3246 Superior Environmental Corp.
1132 Luschek Dr Cincinnati, OH 45241
(513) 923-9000 Michael Weinstein Sr project Mgr
Fax: (513) 923-4050
Email: m.weinstein@superiorenvironmental.com
Website: www.superiorenvironmental.com
Environmental consulting: remedial design & implementation, property transfers. (Woman/White, estab 1989, empl 83, sales $12,200,000, cert: WBENC)

Oregon

3247 Paul Carlson Associates, Inc.
5775 Jean Rd. Ste 101 Lake Oswego, OR 97035
(503) 652-6040 Joel McCarthy Industrial Hygienist
Fax:
Email: joelm@pcasafety.com
Website: www.pcasafety.com
HAZsolutions designed to manage hazardous materials and waste in retail. (Woman/White, estab 1988, empl 12, sales , cert: State)

Pennsylvania

3248 Environmental Data Validation, Inc.
1326 Orangewood Ave Pittsburgh, PA 15216
(412) 341-5281 Maxine Wright-Walters President
Fax: (412) 571-1932
Email: mwalters@edv-inc.com
Website: www.edv-inc.com
Chemical & radiochemical data validation, environmental health & safety training, occupational health & safety consulting, industrial hygienist services, building inspections, environmental site assessments, risk assessment, hazard assessment. (Woman/AA, estab 1990, empl 8, sales $350,000, cert: State)

3249 Keating Environmental Management, Inc.
835 Springdale Dr   Exton, PA 19341
(484) 876-2200 Keith Choper President
Fax: (610) 594-6100
Email: kchoper@KEMpartners.com
Website: www.kempartners.com
Engineering, environmental engineering and consulting, brownfields redevelopment, groundwater studies, subsurface evaluations, geology, remediation management, asbestos, site assessments and environmental auditing. (Woman/White, estab 1988, empl 13, sales $2,250,000, cert: State, City, WBENC)

3250 Niche Waste Reduction and Recycling Systems, Inc
P.O. Box 245246   Philadelphia, PA 19119
(267) 269-6912 Maurice Sampson II CEO
Fax: (215) 843-2085
Email: msampson@nicherecycling.com
Website: www.nicherecycling.com
Waste Management & recycling planning & consultation svcs: site survey/waste assessments, Waste Audits, Architectural Design Consultation for Waste Management, In-house container, brochure, poster training & orientation. (AA, estab 1995, empl 1, sales $64,421, cert: State)

3251 Novel Geo-Environmental, LLC
171 Montour Run Rd   Moon Township, PA 15108
(412) 722-1970 Grace Aiken Office Mgr
Fax: (412) 722-1969
Email: gaiken@ngeconsulting.com
Website: www.ngeconsulting.com
Environmental & geotechnical engineering consulting, Multi- Media Compliance Auditing, Permitting, Reporting & Plan Development, Environmental Management Systems Design & Implementation. (Woman/White, estab 2002, empl 34, sales $5,579,823, cert: State)

3252 Polaris Engineering, Inc.
5015 Preakness Pl   Bethlehem, PA 18020
(610) 698-7185 Fidel Gonzalez President
Fax: (610) 691-5945
Email: fidel@polarisengineeringinc.com
Website: www.polarisengineeringinc.com
Civil engineering: feasibility studies, roadways, storm water management facilities, water line design, sanitary sewer design, site layout & site grading. (Hisp, estab 2007, empl 2, sales , cert: State)

3253 W. K. Merriman, Inc.
7038 Front River Rd   Pittsburgh, PA 15225
(412) 262-7024 Mary Ann Merriman CEO
Fax: (412) 262-7025
Email: m.merriman@wkmerriman.com
Website: www.wkmerriman.com
Dist commodity chemicals & environmental technology, neutralize wastewater, reduce sluge & cost saving alternatives. (Woman/White, estab 1986, empl 6, sales $6,377,400, cert: WBENC)

Puerto Rico

3254 RAC Enterprises, Inc.
Road 1, KM 24.8   Caguas, PR 00726
(787) 789-9338 Vivian Carballo President
Fax: (787) 789-9339
Email: rac@racsteeldrums.com
Website: www.racsteeldrums.com
Mfr steel drums, dist plastic, steel & stainless containers, sorbent products, secondary containment: spill pallets, drain seals. Stormwater management products, PPE & material handling, monitors. (Hisp, estab 1995, empl 15, sales $2,300,000, cert: NMSDC)

Rhode Island

3255 Full Circle Recycling
23 Green Hill Rd   Johnston, RI 02919
(401) 464-5996 Maria Vinagro President
Fax: (401) 464-5966
Email: maria@fullcircleri.com
Website: www.fullcirclerecyclingri.com
Full service recycling facility for metal, plastic, paper, fiber, and electronic post-industrial and post-consumer scrap materials and components. (Woman/AA, estab 2007, empl 30, sales , cert: WBENC)

South Carolina

3256 Air Hub, LLC
P.O. Box 2535   Mount Pleasant, SC 29465
(843) 343-3618 Terri Sciarro Owner/Member
Fax: (888) 203-2156
Email: tls@airhubllc.com
Website: www.airhubllc.com
Air permitting, air modeling, noise modeling & studies, stormwater pollution prevention plans (SWPPP), spill prevention control & countermeasure (SPCC), environmental consulting. (Woman/White, estab 2011, empl 1, sales , cert: State)

Tennessee

3257 EGSE Holdings, LLC. dba Emergency Response Team
195 Omohundro Pl, Unit H   Nashville, TN 37210
(615) 525-9075 Kevin Seats Sales Assoc
Fax:
Email: kseats@ertnashville.com
Website: www.fireandfloodexperts.com
Water Restoration, Fire & Smoke Mitigation, Mold Remediation. (AA, estab 2004, empl 5, sales $470,000, cert: State, NMSDC)

3258   iSustain Inc.
        12249 Wildlife Place   Soddy Daisy, TN 37379
        (423) 668-0111 Dawn Huber President
        Fax: (423) 668-0113
        Email: dhuber@isustain.expert
        Website: www.isustain.expert
Recycling & Waste Management. (Woman/White, estab
2014, empl 4, sales $2,653,697, cert: WBENC)

3259   Microbial Insights, Inc.
        10515 Research Dr   Knoxville, TN 37932
        (865) 573-8188 Anita Biernacki VP of Ops
        Fax:
        Email: info@microbe.com
        Website: www.microbe.com
Environmental biotechnology, bioremediation of chlori-
nated hydrocarbons, biofilm formation in drinking water
systems. (Woman/White, estab 1992, empl 15, sales
$2,951,477, cert: WBENC)

3260   Tioga Environmental Consultants, Inc.
        357 North Main St   Memphis, TN 38112
        (901) 791-2432 Larkin Myers VP
        Fax: (901) 791-2442
        Email: lmyers@tiogaenv.com
        Website: www.tiogaenv.com
Lead based paint inspections, mold sampling, IAQ investi-
gations, asbestos inspections, environmental sampling, soil
& groundwater sampling, environmental compliance,
SWPPP, SPCC Plans, waste water studies, erosion control.
(Woman/White, estab 2009, empl 7, sales $730,000, cert:
State, City)

Texas

3261   A & B Environmental Services, Inc.
        10100 East Fwy, Ste 100   Houston, TX 77029
        (713) 453-6060 Ram Ramakrishnan President
        Fax: (713) 453-6091
        Email: ram@ablabs.com
        Website: www.ablabs.com
Environmental svcs: wastewater, airborne chemicals,
asbestos, etc. (As-Ind/As-Pac, estab 1988, empl 1, sales ,
cert: State, City)

3262   ALPHA Facilities Solutions, LLC
        11503 NW Military Hwy, Ste 300   San Antonio, TX
        78231
        (210) 262-2634 Cassandra Garcia Mktg Mgr
        Fax:
        Email: cassy.garcia@alpha-fs.com
        Website: www.alphafacilities.com/
Capital planning, facility condition assessments (FCA),
maintenance management, environmental assessments,
hazardous materials management planning, investment
strategy & space planning services. (Hisp, estab 2007, empl
68, sales $9,000,000, cert: 8(a))

3263   Architect for Life - A Professional Corporation
        2450 Louisiana St, Ste 400-233   Houston, TX
        77006
        (888) 986-7771 Lolalisa King
        Fax: (888) 986-7772
        Email: lking@architectforlife.com
        Website: www.architectforlife.com
Green consulting professional services, develop &
manage energy efficient strategies, programs, &
projects, retrofit strategies, benchmarking building
energy performance, long-term energy management &
water saving goals assessment. (Woman/AA, estab 1995,
empl 12, sales $108,000, cert: State, City, NMSDC, 8(a))

3264   Bocci Engineering, LLC
        12709 Pine Dr.   Cypress, TX 77429
        (713) 575-2400 Lianne Lami President
        Fax: (832) 575-2499
        Email:
        Marketing_Bid_Notice@BocciEngineering.com
        Website: www.BocciEngineering.com
Efficiency & Optimization, Renewable Resources,
Combined Heat & Power, Distributed Generation,
Central Plant Projects, Emissions Reduction, Waste
Recovery, & Sustainability. Expect Engineering Excel-
lence. (Woman/White, estab 2002, empl 10, sales
$408,566, cert: State, City, WBENC, SDB)

3265   Dougherty Sprague Environmental, Inc.
        3902 Industrial St Ste A Rowlett, TX 75088
        (972) 412-8666 John Dougherty VP of Mktg
        Fax: (972) 412-8660
        Email: jdougherty@dsei.com
        Website: www.dsei.com
Environmental consulting, phase I & II site assessments,
groundwater modeling, industrial compliance, UST
removal & site clean-up, litigation support & expert
witness testimony. (Woman/White, estab 1998, empl 25,
sales $2,000,000, cert: State, WBENC)

3266   Green Planet, Inc.
        6371 State Highway 276 W.   Royse City, TX 75189
        (972) 636-1515 Virginia Belmore President
        Fax: (972) 636-3948
        Email: vbelmore@greenplanetinc.com
        Website:
Environmental services: labpack, hazardous Waste &
non-hazardous waste handling, packaging, transportation & disposal. (Woman/White, estab 1997, empl 10,
sales , cert: State, City)

3267   Lynx Ltd
P.O. Box 591540   Houston, TX 77259
(281) 797-2546   Darlene Sanchez VP
Fax: (281) 286-0313
Email: darlene.sanchez@lynxltd.com
Website: www.lynxltd.com
Environmental compliance & mechanical svcs: hazardous waste mgmt, hazardous waste permit compliance, environmental training, NPDES compliance, air quality compliance, spill response, NEPA review & compliance, asbestos & lead. (Hisp, estab 1998, empl 2, sales $119,640, cert: State, City)

3268   Nation Waste Inc.
12006 Proctor St   Houston, TX 77038
(713) 649-7776   Brendan Goodnough Chief Mktg Officer
Fax: (281) 260-9877
Email: bgood@nationwaste.us
Website: www.nationwaste.us
Commercial waste disposal: Construction, Demolition, Commercial & Industrial Non-Hazardous Waste Removal, Portable Toilets & Recycling services. (Woman/Hisp, estab 1997, empl 24, sales $3,200,000, cert: State, City)

3269   RNDI Companies, Inc.
2255 Ridge Rd, Ste 216   Rockwall, TX 75087
(214) 771-3977   Diana Cross President
Fax:
Email: diana@rndicompanies.com
Website: www.rndicompanies.com
Environmental services: asbestos, lead, mold remediation & abatement, demolition. (Woman/Hisp, estab 2005, empl 20, sales $2,000,000, cert: State)

3270   Separation Systems Consultants, Inc.
17041 El Camino Real, Ste 200   Houston, TX 77058
(281) 486-1943   Helen Hodges President
Fax: (281) 486-7415
Email: ssci@sscienvironmental.com
Website: www.sscienvironmental.com
Risk-based corrective action, remediation & closure, engineering & consulting, waste mgmt, petroleum storage tank, environmental site assessments, health, safety & environmental compliance audits, plans, permits & training. (Woman/White, estab 1986, empl 23, sales $4,000,000, cert: State)

3271   SIA Solutions, LLC
17171 Park Row Ste 370   Houston, TX 77084
(866) 768-4625   Mark Knight Program Mgr
Fax: (866) 696-8663
Email: Mjknight@siasolutions.com
Website: www.siasolutions.com
Environmental Consulting & Engineering, Asset Mgmt & Energy Consulting, Environmental Remediation, Radiological Services • Hazardous, Toxic & Radioactive Waste (HTRW) Management. (As-Ind, estab 2012, empl 49, sales $2,100,000, cert: City, 8(a))

3272   TGE Resources, Inc.
8048 Northcourt Rd   Houston, TX 77040
(713) 744-5800   Robin Franks President
Fax: (713) 744-5888
Email: melanie.rivas@tgeresources.com
Website: www.tgeresources.com
Full Service Environmental and Consulting & Managment Services (Woman/White, estab 1994, empl 20, sales $2,360,000, cert: State, City, WBENC)

Virginia

3273   Aegis Environmental, Inc.
11511 Allecingie Pkwy   Richmond, VA 23235
(804) 378-6015   Lori Bonds President
Fax: (804) 379-2389
Email: lbonds@aegisenv.com
Website: www.aegisenv.com
Air permitting & compliance, air dispersion modeling analyses, pollution control technology analyses, emissions estimates, environmental training & compliance, contingency planning, environmental mgmt systems dev & auditing. (Woman/White, estab 1996, empl 20, sales $1,500,000, cert: State)

3274   CMMD Enterprises, Inc.
7001 Loisdale Rd Ste C   Springfield, VA 22150
(703) 646-2900   Carolyn Marina CEO
Fax: (703) 595-8213
Email: carolyn.m@cmmdinc.com
Website: www.cmmdinc.com
Critical maintenance management & distribution, rotating process plant systems, wastewater treatment systems, potable water systems, chemical processes. (Woman/AA, estab 2001, empl 5, sales $483,000, cert: State, NMSDC)

3275   Environmental Waste Specialists, Inc.
4451 Brookfield Corporate Dr Ste 206   Chantilly, VA 20151
(703) 502-0100   Dawn Walker recycling Mgr
Fax: (703) 502-1796
Email: dawn@ewsihazmat.com
Website: www.EWSIhazmat.com
Package, transport, dispose & recycle hazardous & non-hazardous materials. (Woman/White, estab 1994, empl 4, sales $1,700,000, cert: State)

3276 Froehling & Robertson, Inc.
      3015 Dumbarton Rd   Richmond, VA 23228
      (804) 264-2701 Jackie Clingenpeel Exec Asst to CEO
      Fax: (804) 264-1202
      Email: jclingenpeel@fandr.com
      Website: www.fandr.com
Environmental services: phase I & II ESAs, EIRs, EIS, wetland & stream delineations, hazardous materials assessments, industrial hygiene svcs, asbestos & lead testing, environmental planning, property condition assessments. (Woman/White, estab 1904, empl 430, sales , cert: State)

3277 INTERSPEC, LLC
      464 S Independence Blvd Ste C-104 Virginia Beach, VA 23452
      (757) 622-6299 Sean Murphy Bus Devel Dir
      Fax:
      Email: murphys@interspecllc.net
      Website: www.interspecllc.net
Tank, piping & pressure vessel inspections, STI storage tank inspections, Non-Destructive Examination/Testing steel structures, Spill Prevention Control & Countermeasure (SPCC) plans, Oil Discharge Control Plans (ODCP. (Nat Ame, estab 2001, empl 22, sales $1,200,000, cert: State, 8(a))

3278 J. R. Caskey, Inc.
      P.O. Box 305 Oilville, VA 23129
      (804) 784-8001 Ginger Caskey President
      Fax: (804) 784-8003
      Email: gec@jrcaskey.com
      Website: www.jrcaskey.com
Engineering, Layout & Surveying, Clearing & Demolition, Earthwork, Grading & Excavation, Erosion & Sediment Control, Traditional Stormwater Management Systems, Low-Impact Development Systems, Underground Water & Sanitary Sewer Utilities. (Woman/White, estab 1985, empl 42, sales $6,630,000, cert: State)

3279 LaRock Associates, Inc.
      1816 Upper James Court Virginia Beach, VA 23454
      (202) 438-1920 Joan LaRock President
      Fax: (757) 496-7465
      Email: joan.larock@verizon.net
      Website:
Environmental & energy consulting, green building certification, energy efficient light bulbs. (Woman/White, estab 1998, empl 1, sales $138,000, cert: State)

3280 Mac-Par Services, LLC
      20 B Research Dr Hampton, VA 23666
      (866) 622-7271 David Parham President
      Fax: (757) 539-7290
      Email: dparham@macparservices.com
      Website: www.macparservices.com
Interior demolition, material & debris hauling, lead paint & asbestos abatements, mold remediation & HVAC duct cleaning. (AA, estab 1999, empl 3, sales $370,000, cert: State)

3281 Sea Consulting Group
      325 Mason Ave Cape Charles, VA 23310
      (757) 331-1787 Ann Hayward Walker President
      Fax:
      Email: ahwalker@seaconsulting.com
      Website: www.seaconsulting.com
Environmental consulting. (Woman/Hisp, estab 1983, empl 10, sales , cert: WBENC)

3282 Service Disabled Contracting Group, Inc.
      1108 Tidwater Dr Norfolk, VA 23504
      (757) 965-8496 Terry Penn President
      Fax: (757) 965-8497
      Email: tpenn@sdcgroup.net
      Website: www.sdcgroup.net
Environmental Remediation/Consulting. (AA, estab 2005, empl 27, sales $16,000,000, cert: 8(a))

Washington

3283 Dunkin & Bush, Inc.
      P.O. Box 97080 Kirkland, WA 98083
      (425) 885-7064 Deidre Dunkin President
      Fax: (425) 885-3790
      Email: Ddunkin@dunkinandbush.com
      Website: www.dunkinandbush.com
Industrial painting, scaffolding, insulation, rigging, containment, lead abatement, shop coating aplication, concrete restoration, plural applied tank linings, abrasive blasting, specialty blasting, water jetting, high heat coating applications. (Woman/White, estab 2008, empl 300, sales , cert: WBENC)

3284 EHS-International, Inc.
      1011 SW Klickitat Way, Ste 104 Seattle, WA 98134
      (425) 455-2959 Nancy Yee Mktg
      Fax: (425) 646-7247
      Email: nancyy@ehsintl.com
      Website: www.ehsintl.com
Environmental engineering & industrial hygiene svcs: workplace & environmental health & safety, hazards identification & removal, assessments & remediation, employee training & abatement management. (Hisp, estab 1996, empl 21, sales $1,489,983, cert: State)

3285 Environmental Assessment Services, LLC
      350 Hills St Ste 112 Richland, WA 99354
      (509) 375-4212 Brett Tiller
      Fax: (509) 371-5153
      Email: brett.tiller@easbio.com
      Website: www.easbio.com
Environmental characterization, Spill Response & Natural Resource Damage Assessments, Hazardous Waste Site Remedial Investigations, Risk Assessments, & Environmental Surveillance, Ecological Characterization & Restoration. (Nat Ame, estab 2005, empl 44, sales $2,700,000, cert: NMSDC)

3286 GeoTest Services, Inc.
      741 Marine View Dr   Bellingham, WA 98225
      (360) 733-7318 Jeremy Wolf VP
      Fax: (360) 733-7418
      Email: jeremyw@geotest-inc.com
      Website: www.geotest-inc.com
Geotechnical engineering, environmental services, special
inspection & materials testing, facilities, structures, roads,
bridges & all types of infrastructure. (Woman/White, estab
1993, empl 33, sales $6,000,000, cert: State)

Wisconsin

3287 K. Singh & Associates, Inc.
      3636 N 124th St   Wauwatosa, WI 53222
      (262) 821-1171 Pratap Singh CEO
      Fax: (262) 821-1174
      Email: gmiller@ksaconsultants.com
      Website: www.ksaconsultants.com
Environmental engineering & management services,
transportation, structural, environmental & civil engineering, land surveying & construction management. (As-Ind,
estab 1987, empl 33, sales $3,000,000, cert: State)

3288 OGC Construction, LLC
      w171 n10330 Wildrose Ln   Germantown, WI 53022
      (414) 383-4205 Michael Owens President
      Fax: (414) 383-4206
      Email: mowens@ogcconstruction.com
      Website: www.ogcconstruction.com
Hazardous waste removal remediation, construction lead
asbestos abatement. (AA, estab 2005, empl 18, sales
$117,000, cert: NMSDC)

3289 White Glove Group, Inc.
      8326 N Stevens Rd   Milwaukee, WI 53223
      (414) 760-1733 Joseph Njuguna Sales Dir
      Fax:
      Email: joe@wgginc.net
      Website: www.wgenvironmental.com
Environmental services, facility maintenance, demolition,
construction & demolition waste recycling program mgmt,
green construction final cleaning, LEED consulting,
sustainable product procurement for new construction &
existing buildings. (AA, estab 2003, empl 25, sales
$700,000, cert: NMSDC)

EXECUTIVE SEARCH
Search for and place personnel nationally. Most specialize in minority professionals and executives. (See also PROFESSIONAL SERVICES: Staffing Services). NAICS Code 54

Arizona

3290 DuffyGroup, Inc.
      4727 E Union Hills Dr, Ste 200   Phoenix, AZ 85050
      (602) 942-7112 Kathleen Duffy Ybarra President
      Fax: (602) 861-5876
      Email: kduffy@duffygroupinc.com
      Website: www.duffygroupinc.com
Executive search, sourcing, HR contracting & direct hire, short-term, extended assignments. (Woman/White, estab 1991, empl 25, sales $2,600,000, cert: WBENC)

3291 JBN & Associates, LLC.
      4040 E Camelback Rd Ste 280 Phoenix, AZ 85018
      (480) 344-2822 Dainiz Alvarez Exec Search Mgr
      Fax:
      Email: info@jbnassociates.com
      Website: www.jbnassociates.com
Recruiting firm, direct/perm placements, executive search & C-level positions. (Woman, estab 1999, empl 12, sales , cert: WBENC)

3292 Southwest Recruiting Services, LLC
      7409 E Chaparral Rd Ste A110 - PMB106 Scottsdale, AZ 85250
      (480) 657-8638 Krisanne Elsner Managing Dir
      Fax: (480) 423-6975
      Email: ke@southwestrecruiting.com
      Website: www.southwestrecruiting.com
Recruiting, talent acquisition, executive search. (Woman/White, estab 2003, empl 1, sales $115,000, cert: WBENC)

California

3293 Berkhemer Clayton
      241 S Figueroa St Ste 300 Los Angeles, CA 90012
      (213) 621-2300 Elaina Schmitz Exec Admin
      Fax: (213) 621-2309
      Email: elaina@berkhemerclayton.com
      Website: www.berkhemerclayton.com
Executive search firm. (Woman/White, estab 1994, empl 8, sales $140,000, cert: CPUC, WBENC)

3294 Canon Recruiting Group LLC
      26531 Summit Circle   Santa Clarita, CA 91351
      (661) 252-7400 Ryan McAhren Recruiting Mgr
      Fax: (661) 252-7880
      Email: ryan@canonrecruiting.com
      Website: www.canonrecruiting.com/index.htm
Identification, evaluation & recruit Executives, Professionals, IT Technical, Accounting, Environmental & Industrial staffing. (Woman/White, estab 1980, empl 300, sales $15,000,000, cert: WBENC)

3295 Dawson & Dawson Staffing Inc.
      26522 La Alameda Ste 110 Mission Viejo, CA 92691
      (949) 421-3966 Kathy Dawson President
      Fax: (949) 421-5155
      Email: kathy.dawson@dawsondawsoninc.com
      Website: www.dawsondawsoninc.com
National search & staffing employment services. (Woman/White, estab 2008, empl 14, sales $3,544,239, cert: WBENC)

3296 Domar Companies, LLC
      14742 Beach Blvd, Ste 256 La MIrada, CA 90638
      (714) 674-0391 Don Martinez CEO
      Fax:
      Email: martinezd@domarcompanies.com
      Website: www.domarcompanies.com
Executive search recruiting Hispanic & Multicultural Diversity Executives & Professionals. (Woman/Hisp, estab 2011, empl 8, sales $27,500,000, cert: CPUC)

3297 Voigt & Associates, Inc.
      22981 Sonriente Trail   Coto de Caza, CA 92679
      (949) 766-1100 Barbara Voigt President
      Fax: (949) 766-4400
      Email: bvoigt@voigtinc.com
      Website: www.voigtinc.com
Executive search services. (Woman/White, estab 2005, empl 1, sales $1,200,000, cert: CPUC)

3298 Whitham Group Executive Search
      8130 Luisa Way   Windsor, CA 95492
      (888) 238-1273 Carina Whitham President
      Fax: (707) 655-4365
      Email: Carina@WhithamGroup.com
      Website: www.WhithamGroup.com
Executive search & recruiting specializing in Utilities, Renewable Energy & Environmental Services. (Woman/White, estab 2010, empl 2, sales $1,174,000, cert: CPUC, WBENC)

Connecticut

3299 The Good Search, LLC
4 Valley Rd   Westport, CT 06880
(203) 227-8615   Krista Bradford CEO
Fax: (203) 286-1233
Email: krista.bradford@thegoodsearchllc.com
Website: www.thegoodsearchllc.com
Retained search & recruitment research, strategic recruitment initiatives of internal search teams. (Woman/White, estab 1999, empl 1, sales $662,398, cert: State, WBENC, 8(a))

3300 Walt Medina & Associates, LLC
1224 Mill St Bldg D, Ste 200 East Berlin, CT 06023
(860) 357-5002 Walt Medina CEO
Fax: (860) 357-2339
Email: wm@waltmedina.com
Website: www.waltmedina.com
Healthcare recruiting, recruit military personnel (veterans). (Hisp, estab 2003, empl 2, sales $252,000, cert: NMSDC)

Florida

3301 Career Solutions International Inc.
400 Lexington Green Lane   Sanford, FL 32771
(866) 484-4752 Suzette DiMascio CEO
Fax: (407) 688-4330
Email: suzette@csigroup.net
Website: www.csigroup.net
Executive search & recruiting services. (Woman/White, estab 2002, empl 8, sales $3,400,000, cert: WBENC)

3302 The CALER Group, Inc.
23337 Lago Mar Cir   Boca Raton, FL 33433
(561) 394-8045 Colleen Perrone President
Fax: (561) 394-4645
Email: cperrone@calergroup.com
Website: www.calergroup.com
Executive recruiting. (Woman/White, estab 1995, empl 6, sales $1,200,000, cert: WBENC)

Georgia

3303 CorTech
10 Glenlake Pkwy Ste 800 Atlanta, GA 30328
(770) 628-0268 JP Rogers Sr VP Sales
Fax: (678) 990-9304
Email: jrogers@cor-tech.net
Website: www.cor-tech.net
Recruiting svcs: technical, professional services, vendor mgmt (VMS). (Hisp, estab 1999, empl 7500, sales $173,181,332, cert: NMSDC)

3304 FirstPro Inc.
P.O. Box 420559 Atlanta, GA 30342
(404) 250-7179 Michelle Kennedy Dir of Mktg
Fax: (404) 257-7343
Email: m.kennedy@firstproinc.com
Website: www.firstproinc.com
Executive search, professional placement & staffing: accounting, administrative, call center, clerical, collections, finance, healthcare, human resources, information technology, legal, light industrial, life sciences, management consulting. (Woman/White, estab 1986, empl 125, sales $31,900,000, cert: WBENC)

3305 Forar Tech, LLC.
2754 Bridegegate Trace NE   Marietta, GA 30068
(678) 298-8241 SK Raj VP Business Devel
Fax:
Email: sk.raj@forartech.com
Website: www.forartech.com
Executive Staffing services, technical % administration. (Woman/As-Ind, estab 2006, empl 1, sales , cert: 8(a))

3306 The Royster Group
934 Glenwood Ave Ste 280 Atlanta, GA 30316
(770) 507-3353 Traci Brown Director of Recruitment
Fax: (770) 507-4034
Email: tbrown@roystergroup.com
Website: www.roystergroup.com
Diversity search: healthcare, financial services, consumer products & industrial. (AA, estab 2001, empl 20, sales $10,100,000, cert: NMSDC)

Illinois

3307 Arrow Strategies
233 N. Michigan Ave Ste 1960 Chicago, IL 60601
(312) 561-9202 Mike Colles Division Director
Fax:
Email: mikec@arrowstrategies.com
Website: www.arrowstrategies.com
Recruiting: source, profile & present high-end talent. (Nat Ame, estab 2002, empl 300, sales $48,000,000, cert: NMSDC)

3308 Carrington & Carrington
230 W Monroe St Ste 2250 Chicago, IL 60606
(312) 606-0503 Marian H Carrington Principal
Fax: (312) 606-0042
Email:
mcarrington@carringtonandcarrington.com
Website: www.carringtonandcarrington.com
Executive search, recruitment & placement of diverse professionals for senior management & executive level positions. (Woman/AA, estab 1979, empl 6, sales , cert: City, WBENC)

3309 DC McIssac Corp. dba FPC Arlington, Inc.
1400 Renaissance Dr Ste 100 Park Ridge, IL 60068
(847) 228-7205 Cathy McIsaac President
Fax: (224) 938-9560
Email: cathy@fpcarlington.com
Website: www.fpcarlington.com
Executive search & recruiting services. (Woman/White, estab 1959, empl 7, sales $800,000, cert: WBENC, NWBOC)

3310 Furst Services
2580 Charles St P.O. Box 5863 Rockford, IL 61125
(815) 997-1426 Darlene Furst President
Fax: (815) 229-9405
Email: darlene.furst@furststaff.com
Website: www.furststaff.com
Recruiting services. (Woman/White, estab 1971, empl 55, sales $25,000,000, cert: WBENC)

3311 Ignition Network dba Fielday
400 W Erie Chicago, IL 60654
(708) 223-1191 Josh Miller Partner
Fax: (708) 223-1192
Email: diversesupplier@fieldaymarketing.com
Website: www.fieldaymarketing.com
Recruit human resources professionals. (Woman/White, estab 1900, empl 5, sales $753,000, cert: WBENC)

3312 LBF Recruitment Strategies, LLC
330 N Clinton St Ste 606 Chicago, IL 60661
(312) 725-8544 Lisa Frank CEO
Fax:
Email: Lisa@LBFStrategies.com
Website: www.LBFStrategies.com
Executive Search & Career Coaching. (Woman, estab 2012, empl 1, sales $112,000, cert: WBENC)

3313 My Future Consulting, Inc
15255 S. 94th Avenue Ste 500 Orland Park, IL 60462
(708) 428-6462 Anthony Fletcher CEO
Fax: (708) 949-8593
Email: anthony.fletcher@myfutureconsulting.com
Website: www.myfutureconsulting.com
Executive search & recruitment. (AA, estab 2012, empl 5, sales , cert: NMSDC)

Michigan

3314 Aegis Group Search Consultants, LLC
1358 Village Dr Detroit, MI 48207
(248) 344-1450 John Green President
Fax: (248) 347-2231
Email: jgreen@aegis-group.com
Website: www.aegis-group.com
Executive search services. (AA, estab 1991, empl 4, sales $700,000, cert: NMSDC)

3315 Arps International LLC
3003 Silver Spring Dr Ann Arbor, MI 48103
(734) 945-3000 Arun Nikore VP
Fax: (734) 913-0431
Email: sales@arpsint.com
Website: www.arpsint.com
Executive recruiting services: engineering, information technology, manufacturing & operations, supply chain. (Woman/As-Ind, estab 2002, empl 2, sales $106,127, cert: NMSDC)

Minnesota

3316 Finnesse Partners LLC
5000 W 36th St Ste 220 St. Louis Park, MN 55416
(952) 232-6170 Janie Finn President
Fax:
Email: janie@finnessepartners.com
Website: www.finnessepartners.com
Recruit for the medical device industry. (Woman/White, estab 2012, empl 5, sales $804,442, cert: WBENC)

3317 The Mazzitelli Placement Group
500 Lake St, Ste 212 Excelsior, MN 55331
(952) 476-5449 Teresa Mazzitelli President
Fax: (952) 475-4932
Email: tm@mazzsearch.com
Website: www.mazzsearch.com
Executive search, recruitment & placement services. (Woman/White, estab 1988, empl 1, sales $110,000, cert: WBENC)

North Carolina

3318 Ascendo Resources, LLC
4201 Congress St, Ste 460 Charlotte, NC 28209
(704) 626-7486 Rick Ferretti Partner
Fax: (888) 758-5936
Email: rferretti@ascendo.com
Website: www.ascendo.com
Executive recruiting & temporary staffing, temporary & project opportunities. (Hisp, estab 2008, empl 100, sales $27,000,000, cert: NMSDC)

3319 BPN Concepts
8305 University Executive Park Dr Ste 330 Charlotte, NC 28262
(980) 335-0656 Brenda Harris Owner
Fax: (866) 214-5299
Email: info@bpnconcepts.com
Website: www.bpnconcepts.com
Executive search & staffing services. (Woman/AA, estab 2011, empl 6, sales , cert: State, City)

3320 Citywide Courier Service
      1409 East Blvd Ste 1E Charlotte, NC 28203
      (704) 344-0092 William Locklear Owner
      Fax: (704) 344-0910
      Email: William@citywidecouriersvc.com
      Website: www.citywidecouriersvc.com
Whether you need one quick pick-up and delivery or daily
service, Citywide Courier Service is THE courier service to
fill your needs. Citywide Courier Service is available 24
hours a day. (Nat Ame, estab 1998, empl 15, sales
$216,889, cert: State)

3321 CrossComm, Inc.
      P.O. Box 673 Durham, NC 27702
      (919) 667-9432 Beverly Williams Business Ops Mgr
      Fax: (919) 688-7686
      Email: beverlywilliams@crosscomm.com
      Website: www.crosscomm.com
Business Summary
CrossComm is a mobile and web application development
studio that builds custom iOS, Android, Web and Augmented Reality/Virtual Reality apps. A minority owned
small business since its founding in 1998, CrossComm has
worked on over 250 (As-Pac, estab 2000, empl 8, sales
$975,000, cert: NMSDC)

3322 Elite Touch Cleaning Services, Inc.
      4105-A Stuart Andrew Blvd Charlotte, NC 28217
      (704) 266-0623 Mario Mendigana President
      Fax: (704) 733-9337
      Email: mario@elitetouchcleaning.com
      Website: www.elitetouchcleaning.com
Janitorial Services, Floor Maintenance, Carpet care,
Construction clean up (Hisp, estab 2007, empl 5, sales
$1,668,000, cert: NMSDC)

3323 Golden Tech Systems Inc.
      2704 Twinberry Ln WAXHAW, NC 28173
      (704) 236-2939 Pushpinder Garcha President
      Fax: (704) 843-1356
      Email: pushpinder@golden-tech-systems.com
      Website: www.golden-tech-systems.com
Enterprise Application Development, n-tier Web Develop-
ment, Systems Integration, SCRUM Development, Cyber
Security, Migration Strategies, Change Management,
Program/Project Management, Automation Testing,
Application. (As-Ind, estab 2007, empl 5, sales $753,550,
cert: State, City, NMSDC, 8(a))

3324 Gregory Art Services Inc
      14700 Eastfield Rd Huntersville, NC 28078
      (704) 947-5503 Eugene Gregory President
      Fax: (704) 973-7804
      Email: information@gregoryartservices.com
      Website: www.gregoryartservices.com
We provide artwork and custom picture framing,
security mount installations, repairs, refurbish pick-up
and delivery, art consulting, art placement, large art
installations on time service and all work is guaranteed
with competitive pricing. (AA, estab 2001, empl 4, sales
$35,963,600, cert: NMSDC)

3325 Omni Source Solutions
      13016 Eastfield Rd Huntersville, NC 28078
      (704) 412-3031 Charisma Smith Managing
      Member
      Fax: (704) 973-7804
      Email: charisma@omnisourcesolutions.net
      Website: www.omnisourcesolutions.net
Offer skilled quality self-performing contractors throughout the Southeast. We provide flexible, reliable and
safety-minded tradesmen for a wide range of commercial construction jobs. We understand the importance of
having the right (Woman/AA, estab 2012, empl 2, sales ,
cert: City, NMSDC)

3326 Talented Fish, Inc.
      111 W Lewis St Ste 120 Greensboro, NC 27406
      (336) 279-7665 Tracey Wallace COO
      Fax: (336) 232-9332
      Email: tracey@talentedfish.com
      Website: www.talentedfish.com
Executive Search & Placement. (AA, estab 2017, empl 3,
sales , cert: NMSDC)

New Jersey

3327 JBK Associates International, Inc.
      607 E Palisade Ave Englewood Cliffs, NJ 07632
      (201) 567-9070 Shari Caloz Exec Admin
      Fax: (201) 567-9078
      Email: scaloz@jbkassociates.net
      Website: www.jbkassociates.net
Executive recruitment. (Woman/White, estab 2003,
empl 17, sales $4,642,327, cert: WBENC)

3328 L & L Associates Global Search, Inc.
      770 E Main St Moorestown, NJ 08057
      (856) 778-7488 LaCarole Faulkner President
      Fax: (856) 439-0011
      Email: lllacarole@erols.com
      Website: www.llassociatessearch.com
Executive search services. (Woman/AA, estab 1993,
empl 5, sales , cert: State)

New York

3329 24 Seven Inc.
       120 Wooster St   New York, NY 10012
       (212) 966-4426 Meghan Dewey President
       Fax: (212) 966-2313
       Email: mdewey@24seveninc.com
       Website: www.24seveninc.com
Staffing svcs: freelance, freelance to fulltime, fulltime &
executive search services. (Woman/White, estab 2000,
empl 93, sales $125,326,911, cert: WBENC)

3330 SRI - Steam Recruiters International
       916 Bedford Avenue   Brooklyn, NY 11205
       (929) 333-4593 Stevenson Dunn, Jr. VP
       Fax: (888) 530-7971
       Email: Stevenson@STEAMRecruiters.com
       Website: www.STEAMrecruiters.com
Technology staffing, executive search & professional
recruiting services. (AA/Nat Ame/As-Ind/Hisp, estab 2007,
empl 65, sales $2,000,000, cert: State, SDB)

3331 The Burgess Group - Corporate Recruiters Intl
       10 Barclay St Ste 16-C New York, NY 10007
       (212) 406-2400 William H. Burgess, III CEO
       Fax: (212) 406-2402
       Email: billburgess@theburgessgroup.com
       Website: www.theburgessgroup.com
Mid to senior level executive search, diversity recruiting,
training & management development consulting. (AA,
estab 1997, empl 5, sales $27,367, cert: NMSDC)

3332 The May Consulting Group Inc.
       174 County Hwy 67   Amsterdam, NY 12010
       (518) 843-4611 Sheila Greco CEO
       Fax: (518) 843-5498
       Email: sgreco@sgatalent.com
       Website: www.sgatalent.com
Recruitment research & strategic recruiting solutions.
(Woman/White, estab 1989, empl 20, sales , cert: WBENC)

Ohio

3333 Howard & O
       29525 Chagrin Blvd Ste 100 Cleveland, OH 44122
       (216) 514-8980 Lee Ann Howard
       Fax: (216) 514-7129
       Email: lah@howardobrien.com
       Website: www.howardobrien.com
Executive search consulting services. (Woman/White,
estab 2001, empl 4, sales $1,900,000, cert: WBENC)

3334 Minority Executive Search
       3060 Monticello Blvd.   Cleveland, OH 44118
       (216) 932-2022 Eral Burks CEO
       Fax: (216) 932-7988
       Email: eral@minorityexecsearch.com
       Website: www.minorityexecsearch.com
Women & Minority job placements. (AA, estab 1985,
empl 10, sales , cert: NMSDC)

Pennsylvania

3335 StarsHR, Inc.
       1700 N Highland Rd Ste 200 Pittsburgh, PA 15241
       (412) 927-0369 Robert Castner Dir Placement
       Svcs
       Fax: (412) 927-0369
       Email: rcastner@starshr.com
       Website: www.StarsHR.com
Executive placement services. (As-Ind, estab 2007, empl
5, sales $2,700,000, cert: State)

Puerto Rico

3336 Careers Inc.
       208 Ave Ponce De Leon, Ste 1100 Banco Popular
       Ctr San Juan, PR 00918
       (787) 764-2298 Blankie Hernandez Curt VP
       Admin
       Fax: (787) 764-2530
       Email: blankieh@careersincpr.com
       Website: www.careersincpr.com
Executive Search & Management Recruiting. (Woman/
Hisp, estab 1970, empl 21, sales $2,179,173, cert:
NMSDC)

South Carolina

3337 Benchmark Contracting, Inc.
       215 E Bay St Charleston, SC 29401
       (843) 628-5999 Jennifer Courville Dir of Business
       Devel
       Fax: (702) 648-2001
       Email: courvillej@benchmarkcontracting.org
       Website: www.BenchmarkContractingSC.com
General Contracting Industrial, Commercial and Residential Construction Public and Private Sector Projects
Design – Build Ground Up Construction Tenant Improvements (TI) Comprehensive rehabilitations/renovations/
remodels Project Management LEED/Gr (AA, estab 1998,
empl 20, sales $10,267,000, cert: State, City)

3338   G&S Janitorial Services, Inc.
       1008 Fontaine Rd   Columbia, SC 29223
       (803) 786-9710 Leroy Green CEO
       Fax: (803) 786-9770
       Email: tgnsservicesinc@aol.com
       Website: www.gandscarpetservices.com
G&S Janitorial Services entails carpet and upholstery
cleaning services as well as building and dwellings. G&S
has over 22 years of janitorial experience. (AA, estab 1988,
empl 30, sales $1,600,000, cert: State)

Texas

3339   ICON Information Consultants, LP
       100 Waugh Dr Ste 300 Houston, TX 77007
       (713) 438-0919 Pamela O'Rourke CEO
       Fax: (713) 438-0930
       Email: porourke@iconconsultants.com
       Website: www.iconconsultants.com
Recruit information technology, accounting & finance
professionals. (Woman/White, estab 1998, empl 3250,
sales $261,000,000, cert: WBENC)

3340   MRI of Dallas Parkway, LLC
       2121 W. Spring Creek Pkwy, Ste 113   Plano, TX
       75023
       (469) 475-2297 Mohammed Al-Baki Managing
       Partner
       Fax: (214) 597-4092
       Email: malbaki@mridallasparkway.com
       Website: www.softelsolutions.com
Recruiting practices & continuous training. (Woman/As-
Ind, estab 2010, empl 10, sales $749,000, cert: State)

3341   Nelson Search Group
       3001 Lake Oak Dr   Arlington, TX 76017
       (817) 466-7117 D. Gayle Barton Principal
       Fax:
       Email: gayle@nelsonsearchgroup.com
       Website: www.nelsonsearchgroup.com
Ethical, consultative, confidential, quality-driven direct
recruiting & on-boarding (full life-cycle). (Woman/White,
estab 2009, empl 1, sales $150,000, cert: State, WBENC)

3342   Recruiting Source International
       21414 Julie Marie Ln, Ste 2301   Katy, TX 77449
       (281) 277-1411 Bianca Jackson COO
       Fax: (866) 351-3590
       Email: bjackson@recruiting-source.com
       Website: www.recruiting-source.com
Executive Search, Staffing & 1099 Management Services.
(Woman/AA, estab 1900, empl 1, sales $1,410,000, cert:
State, City, NMSDC, WBENC, SDB)

3343   Search Plus International
       5900 Balcones Dr Ste 242 Austin, TX 78731
       (512) 459-8200 Bruce Bagwell Managing Dir
       Fax: (512) 459-8209
       Email: bbagwell@searchplustexas.com
       Website: www.searchplustexas.com
Executive mid-management & highly-technical searches.
(Woman/White, estab 1988, empl 9, sales $500,000,
cert: WBENC)

Virginia

3344   Alcove Resources
       1900 Campus Commons Dr, Ste 100   Reston, VA
       20191
       (703) 652-4732 Quan Woodard CEO
       Fax: (703) 880-6726
       Email: info@alcoveresources.com
       Website: www.alcoveresources.com
Recruiting & executive search services, information
management consulting. (Woman/AA, estab 2005, empl
5, sales $100,000, cert: State)

Washington

3345   Archer & Associates I, Inc.
       16625 Redmond Way, Ste M8   Redmond, WA
       98052
       (425) 869-6350 Ann-Marie Archer CEO
       Fax:
       Email: aarcher@archer-associates.com
       Website: www.archer-associates.com
Executive search & consulting. (Woman/White, estab
2000, empl 2, sales $852,500, cert: State)

Wisconsin

3346   JAC Consulting LLC dba The Champagne Group
       2233 N Summit Ave Ste 315 Milwaukee, WI
       53202
       (414) 704-0602 Jacquie Champagne President
       Fax:
       Email: jacquie@champagnegrp.com
       Website: www.champagnegrp.com
Executive search, legal services. (Woman/White, estab
2015, empl 1, sales $30,000, cert: WBENC)

Annual Client Packages

BASIC

- Access to certified diverse suppliers: small, minority, women, veteran, service-disabled veteran, LGBT, HUBZone, Disability-Owned Business Enterprises. Certifications include: NMSDC, WBENC, NWBOC, CPUC, 8(a), NGLCC, USBLN, WEConnect, CAMSC, State and City, MSDUK, and more)
- Data scrub: 1,500 records or less
- Supplier Diversity Handbook (online or in print)

STANDARD

- Access to certified diverse suppliers: small, minority, women, veteran, service-disabled veteran, LGBT, HUBZone, Disability-Owned Business Enterprises. Certifications include: NMSDC, WBENC, NWBOC, CPUC, 8(a), NGLCC, USBLN, WEConnect, CAMSC, State and City, MSDUK, and more)
- Data scrub: 3,000 records or less
- Supplier Diversity Handbook (online or in print)
- One registration at a DIR seminar (Phases or Best Practices)

ADVANCED

- Access to certified diverse suppliers: small, minority, women, veteran, service-disabled veteran, LGBT, HUBZone, Disability-Owned Business Enterprises. Certifications include: NMSDC, WBENC, NWBOC, CPUC, 8(a), NGLCC, USBLN, WEConnect, CAMSC, State and City, MSDUK, and more)
- Data scrub: 6,000 records or less
- Supplier Diversity Handbook (online or in print)
- One registration at a DIR seminar (Phases or Best Practices)

PRO

- Access to certified diverse suppliers: small, minority, women, veteran, service-disabled veteran, LGBT, HUBZone, Disability-Owned Business Enterprises. Certifications include: NMSDC, WBENC, NWBOC, CPUC, 8(a), NGLCC, USBLN, WEConnect, CAMSC, State and City, MSDUK, and more)
- Data scrub: 12,000 records or less
- One registration at a DIR seminar (Phases or Best Practices)
- Supplier Diversity Handbook (online or in print)
- A full page ad in DIR's Supplier Diversity Handbook

OR........customize a package to fit your needs!

For more information and pricing contact DIR at (612) 781-6819 or info@diversityinforesources.com

---

FOOD: Beverages & Dairy Products
Products include coffees, teas, bottled water, water filtration units, private label, milk and milk products. Also fruit juices and soft drinks. NAICS Code 31

Arizona

3347　Sir Aubrey's Tea Company, Ltd
15941 N 77th St Ste 3 Scottsdale, AZ 85260
(480) 607-5300 Kathryn Petty President
Fax: (480) 607-5393
Email: kpetty@whiteliontea.com
Website: www.whiteliontea.com
White Lion Tea offers a collection of rare & beautiful teas from the world's finest gardens. (Woman, estab 1998, empl 8, sales $998,470, cert: WBENC)

California

3348　Bellrose, LLC
2340 Powell St, Ste 127 Emeryville, CA 94608
(925) 628-1738 Onezime Biagas Jr Mgr
Fax: (510) 547-6877
Email: bellrose.llc@gmail.com
Website:
Dist fresh roasted whole bean or ground coffee: bulk, pre-measured, pillow pack, k-cup. (AA, estab 2005, empl 6, sales $120,000, cert: NMSDC)

3349　Cacique, Inc.
14940 Proctor Ave City of Industry, CA 91746
(626) 961-3399 Bob Cashen Dir of Sales
Fax:
Email: rcashen@caciqueinc.com
Website: www.caciqueinc.com
Mfr & dist food (dairy) products. (Hisp, estab 1973, empl 350, sales , cert: NMSDC)

3350　Carlos Steffens, Inc.
3061 Independence Dr, Ste E Livermore, CA 94550
(925) 838-2336 Carlos Steffens President
Fax: (925) 838-5304
Email: carlos@steffenscorp.com
Website: www.steffenscorp.com
Industrial ingredient brokers, concentrated fruit juice products. (Hisp, estab 2000, empl 6, sales , cert: NMSDC)

3351　F. Gavina & Sons, Inc.
2700 Fruitland Ave Vernon, CA 90058
(323) 605-5386 Tiffany Rojas Exec Admin
Fax: (323) 826-6190
Email: tiffany.rojas@gavina.com
Website: www.gavina.com
Coffee roasting, new blend development or matching of your current blend, brand & marketing support, brewing & espresso service & training. (Hisp, estab 1967, empl 265, sales $127,485,828, cert: NMSDC)

3352　P.S. Let's Eat Inc.
3943 Irvine Blvd, Ste 610 Irvine, CA 92602
(855) 998-3554 Preya Patel Bhakta President
Fax: (855) 653-8881
Email: preya@elliquark.com
Website: www.elliquark.com
Produce German style Quark products. (Woman/As-Pac, estab 2011, empl 2, sales , cert: WBENC)

Colorado

3353　Mona's Granola and Cookies, Inc.
651 Eldorado Broomfield, CO 80021
(727) 420-0707 Mona Gale CEO
Fax:
Email: Mona@MonasInc.com
Website: www.monasinc.com
All natural no white sugar nutrient rich granola cereal & ice cream toppings. (Woman/White, estab 1981, empl 27, sales $600,000, cert: WBENC)

Connecticut

3354　Gelato Giuliana, LLC
240 Sargent Dr New Haven, CT 06511
(203) 772-0607 Deborah Cairo Mktg
Fax: (203) 772-0612
Email: dcbottega@sbcglobal.net
Website: www.gelatogiuliana.com
Mfr & dist gelato under our label Gelato Giuliana. (Woman/White, estab 2006, empl 10, sales $882,662, cert: State)

District of Columbia

3355　Village Tea Company Distribution Inc.
1342 Florida Ave., NW Ste 225-B Washington, DC 20009
(888) 406-1138 Janon Costley CEO
Fax:
Email: janon@villageteaco.com
Website: www.villageteaco.com
100% organic & natural tea in biodegradable packaging, foodservice & bulk tea, tea dispensers & machines, packaged tea, tea bags, loose leaf tea, organic/natural tea. (AA, estab 2008, empl 12, sales $125,000, cert: NMSDC)

Florida

3356　Brisk/RCR Coffee Company
507 N. 22nd St Tampa, FL 33605
(813) 248-6264 Richard Perez CEO
Fax: (813) 248-2947
Email: customer@briskcoffee.com
Website: www.briskcoffee.com
Coffee importing, roasting, grinding, packaging & shipping. (Hisp, estab 1968, empl 30, sales , cert: State)

3357 COEX Coffee International Inc.
      525 NW 27th Ave   Miami, FL 33125
      (305) 459-5180 Robert Menos Senior Trader
      Fax:
      Email: lmones@coexgroup.com
      Website: www.coexgroup.com
Coffee trading, importing green coffee from all major
global coffee producing countries. (Hisp, estab 1980, empl
45, sales $415,000,000, cert: NMSDC)

3358 GFIS
      2525 Ponce de Leon Blvd Ste 300 Coral Gables, FL
      33134
      (305) 521-9094 Andrea Cordova Mgr
      Fax:
      Email: acordova@foodingredientsolution.com
      Website: www.foodingredientsolution.com
Frozen, Aseptic, No pasteurized, Unpasteurized, IQF,
Fruitm Vegetables, Puree, Juice, Concentrate, NFC, Single
Straight, Organic, Conventional, Acai, Acerola, Apple,
Blackberry, Blueberry, Cherry, Grapefruit, Guava, Kiwi,
Lemon, Lime, Mango, and more. (Woman/Hisp, estab
2016, empl 1, sales , cert: State)

3359 The Best Direct Marketing Group LLC
      250 N Orange Ave Ste 990 Orlando, FL 32801
      (407) 730-6569 Latif Qadri
      Fax: (407) 270-9241
      Email: Latif@bestdirectgroup.com
      Website: www.bestdirectgroup.com
Direct mail & staffed event company that can fulfill all
print needs ad creative design. (As-Ind, estab 2012, empl
4, sales $112,000, cert: NMSDC)

Illinois

3360 CBC Sales, Inc.
      5117 S Normandy Ave   Chicago, IL 60638
      (773) 218-9563 Desiree Alonzo President
      Fax:
      Email: desiree@cbcsalesinc.com
      Website: www.cicerobloodymary.com
Gourmet beverages, Craft Sodas & Bloody Mary Mixes,
Salted Caramel Root beer, Bacon Bloody Mary Mix.
(Woman/White, estab 2008, empl 1, sales $400,000, cert:
WBENC)

3361 Chapin LLC
      1350 N Wells St Ste F109 Chicago, IL 60610
      (312) 493-6976 Jennifer Alexander Monzón
      Fax: (208) 978-9431
      Email: jennifer@chapincoffee.com
      Website: www.ChapinCoffee.com
Specialty coffee, whole bean, ground & single serve (k-
cup). (Hisp, estab 2013, empl 2, sales $17,000, cert:
NMSDC)

3362 DAMRON Corporation
      4433 W Ohio St Chicago, IL 60624
      (773) 826-6000 Kimberly Owen Dir Sales & Mktg
      Fax: (773) 826-6004
      Email: kowen@damroncorp.com
      Website: www.damroncorp.com
Healing Tea Leaves of the World brand of Specialty Tea -
25 ct. teabag cartons (25% more than National Brands),
quality fully equal to or better than National Brands.
(AA, estab 1985, empl 30, sales $4,000,000, cert:
NMSDC)

3363 The Edlong Corporation
      225 Scott St   Elk Grove Village, IL 60007
      (847) 631-6775 Gail Scott Exec Asst
      Fax:
      Email: diversity@edlong.com
      Website: www.edlong.com
Dairy: cheese, butter, milk & cream, cultured, sweet &
functional dairy. (Woman/White, estab 1914, empl 100,
sales , cert: WBENC)

Massachusetts

3364 Adonai Spring Water Inc.
      31 West St, Ste 4   Randolph, MA 02368
      (844) 273-7672 Gloria Olatunji President
      Fax:
      Email: gloolat@aol.com
      Website: www.adonaisprings.com
Bottled water 5 Gallons, Bottled Water Coolers, Point of
Use Coolers, Drinking Water Fountains
Biodegradable & Compostable hot and cold cups, lids,
straws, trays, napkins, plates, trays clamshells, Table top
& Dinnerware. (Woman/AA, estab 2014, empl 2, sales
$35,000, cert: State, WBENC)

3365 R Square Desserts LLC
      P.O. Box 990031 Boston, MA 02199
      (857) 263-8833 Susie Parish Co-Owner
      Fax:
      Email: susie@batchicecream.com
      Website: www.batchicecream.com
Ice cream made from real ingredients & without additives. (Woman, estab 2009, empl 5, sales , cert: WBENC)

Maryland

3366 Caribbean Blue Organic Foods, LLC
      6701 Democracy Blvd Ste 300 Bethesda, MD
      20817
      (301) 564-4322 Lenore Travers President
      Fax: (301) 564-4323
      Email: Sales@CaribbeanBlueWater.com
      Website: www.CaribbeanBlueWater.com
Caribbean Blue Natural Spring Water. (AA, estab 2011,
empl 1, sales $185,000, cert: State)

3367 Collaborative Food & Beverage, LLC (DBA Mayorga Coffee)
15151 Southlawn Ln   Rockville, MD 20850
(301) 315-8093 Martin Mayorga President
Fax: (301) 315-8094
Email: martin@mayorgacoffee.com
Website: www.mayorgacoffee.com
Roasted whole bean specialty coffees, ground "portion packed" specialty coffees, custom blends, private labeling. (Woman/Hisp, estab 1997, empl 87, sales $17,500,000, cert: State)

North Carolina

3368 Calvine's Coffee LLC
P.O. Box 3005   Matthews, NC 28106
(800) 545-8553 Calvine Frazier President
Fax:
Email: morning@calvinescoffee.com
Website: www.calvinescoffee.com
Gourmet specialty roast blend of coffee beans from many origins around the world, including small farms and farmers. Our beans are roasted in small batches in a San Franciscan Artisan Roaster. (Woman/AA, estab 2015, empl 1, sales , cert: State)

3369 High Country Springs LLC
P.O. Box 238   Pilot Mountain, NC 27041
(336) 374-7474 Linda Tucker Partner
Fax: (336) 374-7298
Email: ltucker@highcountrysprings.com
Website: www.highcountrysprings.com
Provide 5-gallon, 3-gallon & 1-gallon Spring, Distilled, RO (Reverse Osmosis), Deionized, and Fluoride Water, water dispensers & coffee service. (Woman/White, estab 1992, empl 10, sales $605,431, cert: State)

3370 MyThreeSons Gourmet, LLC
2309 Lafayette Ave   Greensboro, NC 27408
(336) 324-5638 Cheryl Barnett President
Fax:
Email: mtsgourmet@gmail.com
Website: www.mtsgourmet.com
Mfr natural gourmet pimento cheese spread. (Woman/White, estab 2010, empl 10, sales $645,000, cert: WBENC)

New Jersey

3371 Harris Freeman & Co LP
344 New Albany Rd   Moorestown, NJ 08057
(856) 793-0290 Steve Sernka Natl Sales Mgr
Fax: (856) 793-0283
Email: steve.sernka@harrisfreeman.com
Website: www.HarrisTea.com
Manufacturer tea. (As-Ind, estab 1997, empl 129, sales , cert: NMSDC)

3372 JVM Sales Corp.
3401a Tremley Point Rd   Linden, NJ 07036
(908) 862-4866 Justin Tomasino Owner
Fax: (908) 862-4867
Email: justintomasino@aol.com
Website: www.jvmsales.com
Provide Grated, Shredded & Shaved Cheeses, Hard Italian Cheese, Custom blended cheeses. (Woman/White, estab 1983, empl 200, sales $50,000,000, cert: WBENC)

New York

3373 Thunder Island Coffee Roasters, L.L.C.
P.O. Box 1275   Southampton, NY 11969
(631) 204-1110 Benjamin Haile CEO
Fax: (631) 204-1110
Email: info@thunderislandcoffee.com
Website: www.thunderislandcoffee.com
Coffee roasting and packaging. (Nat Ame, estab 2005, empl 4, sales $16,674, cert: State)

Oregon

3374 Hood River Juice Company
550 Riverside Dr   Hood River, OR 97031
(541) 386-3003 David Ryan President
Fax: (541) 386-6114
Email: davidr@hrjco.com
Website: www.ryansjuice.com
Natural & organic apple juice, single strength, not from concentrate. (Hisp, estab 1982, empl 113, sales $35,000,000, cert: NMSDC)

Pennsylvania

3375 Enchanted Acres Farm, Inc.
200 N 8th St Ste 500 Reading, PA 19601
(877) 707-3833 Kelley Huff President
Fax: (877) 766-3167
Email: quality@enchantedacresfarm.net
Website: www.enchantedacresfarm.net
Mfr beverages: tea, coffee, cocoa. (Woman/White, estab 2002, empl 15, sales $700,000, cert: State)

South Carolina

3376 Pino Gelato, LLC
1000 William Hilton Pkwy, Ste G-1   Hilton Head Island, SC 29928
(843) 842-2822 Jessica Scott CEO
Fax:
Email: marketing@pinogelato.com
Website: www.pinogelato.com
Premium gelato & sorbetto. (Woman, estab 2004, empl 6, sales $1,748,000, cert: WBENC)

Texas

3377   Artesia Springs LLC
       8130 Interchange Pkwy   San Antonio, TX 78218
       (210) 637-5554 Rudy Ramon President
       Fax: (210) 637-5554
       Email: rudy@artesiasprings.com
       Website: www.artesiasprings.com
Bottled water in all sizes from 16.9 liters, 3 and 4 gallon
disposable and 5 gallon recyclable, Private label options,
water coolers, water filtration options. (Woman/Hisp,
estab 2004, empl 19, sales $1,400,000, cert: State,
NMSDC)

3378   Cadeco Industries, Inc.
       5610 Clinton Dr   Houston, TX 77020
       (713) 670-0700 Carlos deAldecoa President
       Fax: (713) 670-0702
       Email: carlos@cadeco.cc
       Website: www.cadeco.cc
Bulk coffee processing, storage & distribution services.
(Hisp, estab 1995, empl 45, sales $40,000,000, cert: State,
NMSDC)

3379   Global Coffee Company
       6161 Savoy Dr, Ste 821   Houston, TX 77236
       (713) 222-2291 Shaheed Momin President
       Fax:
       Email: shaheed@globalcoffeecompany.com
       Website: www.javatogo.com
Coffee, cappuccino, slushy, iced tea, juices, soda, water,
paper goods, etc. (As-Ind, estab 2007, empl 4, sales
$1,596,400, cert: State, City, NMSDC)

3380   Sociologie Wines Vintage LLC
       3901 Arlington Highlands Blvd Ste 200 Arlington, TX
       76018
       (832) 871-7917 Mark Hansen Owner
       Fax: (972) 291-3141
       Email: Mark@sociologiewine.com
       Website: www.sociologiewine.com
Refreshing blends of delicious fruits & natural ingredients,
Red Berry & Blushing Rose wine. (Woman/AA, estab 2012,
empl 3, sales $68,000, cert: NMSDC)

Virginia

3381   A M King LLC
       13241 Otto Rd   Woodbridge, VA 22193
       (703) 855-9822 Adima Aniteye CEO
       Fax:
       Email: amkingllc@gmail.com
       Website: www.queenvictoriaspunch.com
Mfr & dist fruit punches: The Queen-Grapefruit, Pine-
apple, Apple, Orange, The Duchess— Lemon, Pineapple,
Apple, Orange, The Baroness—Pomegranate, Pineapple,
Lemon, Lime, Agave. (Woman/AA, estab 2012, empl 2,
sales $19,005, cert: State)

3382   Amelia Distributing Company
       3420 Pump Rd Box 159 Henrico, VA 23233
       (804) 840-0228 Eve Painter President
       Fax: (866) 596-4960
       Email: evepainter@msn.com
       Website:
Seltzer water in liters and cans, distilled water in gallons
(Woman/White, estab 1994, empl 3, sales , cert: State)

3383   Greenberry's Coffee Roasters
       1610 Quail Run   Charlottesville, VA 22911
       (434) 964-1655 Todd Hicks COO
       Fax: (434) 964-1254
       Email: todd@greenberrys.com
       Website: www.greenberrys.com
Hand-roasted premium artisan coffees: Single Origin,
Signature Blends, Fair Trade Organic & Flavored.
(Woman, estab 2001, empl 10, sales $1,845,350, cert:
State)

Wisconsin

3384   Jeneil Biotech, Inc.
       400 N Dekora Woods Blvd   Saukville, WI 53080
       (262) 268-6815 Stephen Beaver Sales
       Fax: (262) 268-6820
       Email: s.beaver@jeneilbiotech.com
       Website: www.jeneilbiotech.com
Mfr natural dairy flavors in pastes & powders, natural
flavor aroma chemicals, soymilk powder, soy-cream
cheese, fermentation, enzymolysis & distillation. (As-Ind,
estab 1998, empl 43, sales $17,000,000, cert: NMSDC)

3385   Nanland LLC
       5959 N Shore Acres Rd   New Franken, WI 54229
       (920) 562-9822 Nan Bush President
       Fax: (510) 487-5347
       Email: nan@nanlandllc.com
       Website: www.nanlandllc.com
Provides premium, single origin, organic coffee, 100%
Arabica coffees from Peru, Nicaragua, Sumatra and
Colombia packaged in 12 or 42 single serve cup boxes.
(Woman/White, estab 2016, empl 2, sales $25,000, cert:
WBENC)

FOOD: Brokers & Wholesalers
Products include imported food products, rice, cooking wines, cattle, olive oil, snack items, candy, spices, canned foods, produce. (See also six other FOOD categories). NAICS Code 31

Alabama

3386 The Widget Development & Trading Company, LLC
      10 S Perry St   Montgomery, AL 36104
      (404) 695-0141 David Martin President
      Fax: (678) 609-1543
      Email: davidmartin@widgetdtc.com
      Website: www.widgetdtc.com
Dist nuts, meats, sauces, baked goods. (Woman/AA, estab 2011, empl 2, sales $80,000, cert: NMSDC)

Arizona

3387 Strategic Nutrition Alliance Brokers LLC
      8175 E Evans Rd, PO Box 12655   Scottsdale, AZ 85267
      (480) 299-2399 Ronald Coleman Managing Partner
      Fax:
      Email: sales@snabrokers.com
      Website: www.snabrokers.com
Dairy Commodities, Nutritional Ingredients, sweeteners & flavors, Turn-key Private Label Contract Manufacturing services. (AA, estab 2010, empl 1, sales $250,788, cert: NMSDC)

California

3388 C-Shore International Inc.
      1010 N Central Ave   Glendale, CA 91202
      (818) 909-4684 Jacques Isaac CEO
      Fax: (818) 909-4703
      Email: Mirline@aol.com
      Website: www.beantrader.com
Peas, beans, lentils, pre cooked flour, bread flour, wheat flour, dried malt extract roasted barley. (AA, estab 1988, empl 3, sales , cert: NMSDC)

3389 Valley Lahvosh Baking Co.
      502 M St   Fresno, CA 93721
      (559) 485-2700 Lori Miller President
      Fax: (559) 485-0173
      Email: customerservice@valleylahvosh.com
      Website: www.valleylahvosh.com
Mfr valley lahvosh crackerbreads & pita breads. (Woman/White, estab 1900, empl 1, sales $8,578,874, cert: WBENC)

Florida

3390 Delina Inc.
      1068 Pine Branch Dr   Weston, FL 33326
      (954) 306-0628 Deborah Dijkhuizen President
      Fax: (954) 217-1086
      Email: delina@bellsouth.net
      Website: www.delinainc.com
Dist asparagus spears, green pickled asparagus spears, cornichons, roasted red peppers, artichoke hearts, hearts of palm & organic coffee. (Woman/Hisp, estab 1998, empl 2, sales $20,000, cert: City)

3391 Sweet Additions, Inc.
      4440 PGA Blvd, Ste 600   Palm Beach Gardens, FL 33410
      (561) 472-0178 Ken Valdivia President
      Fax: (561) 575-0875
      Email: kvaldivia@sweetadditions.com
      Website:
Mfr & dist cane & grain based sweeteners. (Hisp, estab 2004, empl 3, sales $5,000,000, cert: NMSDC)

Georgia

3392 Diaz Foods
      5501 Fulton Industrial Blvd SW   Atlanta, GA 30336
      (404) 344-5421 Jorge Antona EVP
      Fax:
      Email: jorge.antona@diazfoods.com
      Website: www.diazfoods.com
Hispanic grocery distributor, grocery, frozen, dairy, meats & produce. (Hisp, estab 1980, empl 323, sales $168,000,000, cert: NMSDC)

3393 Seeds of Nature, LLC
      1456 Lechemin Dr   Snellville, GA 30078
      (877) 277-9260 Patricia Nowell Managing Member
      Fax: (718) 636-5164
      Email: pnowell@prodigy.net
      Website: www.seedsofnature.com
Premium Cocoa Beans sourced from Ivory Coast, Nigeria & Ghana. (Woman/AA, estab 2009, empl 3, sales $300,000, cert: NMSDC)

Illinois

3394   Compact Industries
         3945 Ohio Ave   St Charles, IL 60174
         (630) 513-9600 Dan Matyus VP Business Dev
         Fax: (630) 513-9655
         Email: matyus@compactind.com
         Website: www.compactind.com
Contract manufacturer of dry food products. (Woman, estab 1963, empl 120, sales $98,000,000, cert: WBENC)

3395   Cristina Foods Inc.
         1056 W Lake St   Chicago, IL 60607
         (312) 829-0360 Cesar Dovalina President
         Fax: (312) 829-0408
         Email: info@cristinafoodsinc.com
         Website: www.cristinafoodsinc.com
Dist fresh produce, frozen foods, spices, grocery & canned goods, meats, dairy, poultry, seafood, disposable paper & plastics. (Hisp, estab 1989, empl 13, sales $4,900,000, cert: City)

3396   Stern Ingredients, Inc.
         1030 N State St #10BC   Chicago, IL 60610
         (773) 472-0301 Joni Stern President
         Fax: (773) 304-3588
         Email: joni@sterningredients.com
         Website: www.sterningredients.com
Dist ingredients: confectionery, bakery, nutritional & snack food products. (Woman/White, estab 1990, empl 2, sales $653,000, cert: WBENC)

3397   Subco Foods
         1150 Commerce Dr   West Chicago, IL 60185
         (630) 231-0003 Mas Khan President
         Fax: (630) 231-0678
         Email: mkhan@subcofoods.com
         Website: www.subcofoods.com
Dist dry food products: randed, private label & contract packaging, drink mixes, gelatin & puddings, coffee creamer, hot chocolate, cappuccino, cake mixes, gravy mixes, seasonings, pancake mixes, soup bases, rice products, nutraceuticals. (As-Ind, estab 1994, empl 150, sales , cert: NMSDC)

Massachusetts

3398   Boston Baking, Inc.
         101 Sprague St   Boston, MA 02136
         (617) 364-6900 Julee Robey-Boschetto President
         Fax: (617) 364-6922
         Email: julee@bostonbaking.com
         Website: www.bostonbaking.com
Wholesale manufacturer of baked goods. (Woman/White, estab 2004, empl 54, sales $4,900,000, cert: City)

3399   VSR Enterprise, LLC
         1675 Dorchester Ave   Boston, MA 02121
         (617) 514-4711 Vernon Barsatee CEO
         Fax:
         Email: vernon@vsrenterprise.com
         Website: www.vsrenterprise.com
Food Brokerage, Import & Export of consumer sized packaged (CPG), frozen foods, spices, dairy products, meats, health & beauty aids. (As-Pac, estab 2012, empl 2, sales , cert: NMSDC)

Maryland

3400   Better and Best Corporation
         1601 Knecht Avenue   Halethorpe, MD 21227
         (410) 902-5701 Patricia Lobel President
         Fax: (410) 902-0600
         Email: patricia.lobel@avenuegourmet.com
         Website: www.avenuegourmet.com
Dist natural/organic products: sauces, marinades, fruit butters & spreads, cookies, crackers, cooking oils, vinegars, snacks, condiments & beverages. (Woman/White, estab 2000, empl 20, sales , cert: State)

3401   Soft Stuff Distributors, Inc.
         8200 Preston Court Ste L Jessup, MD 20794
         (301) 604-3300 Lois Gamerman President
         Fax: (301) 604-4179
         Email: loisg@gosoftstuff.com
         Website: www.gosoftstuff.com
Dist breads, bagels, cakes, cheesecakes, muffin batters & baked muffins, frozen doughs, preproofed danish & croisants, cookies-frozen doughs & prebaked, pizzas, soups fresh & frozen, catering dessert items. (Woman/White, estab 1989, empl 35, sales $10,500,000, cert: State, WBENC)

North Carolina

3402   FDY, Inc.
         2459 Wilkinson Blvd Ste 300 Charlotte, NC 28208
         (704) 523-6605 Keith Haywood VP sales/Mktg
         Fax: (704) 523-6674
         Email: khaywood@fdyinc.com
         Website: www.fdyinc.com
Food service mgmt: cafeteria, dining services, vending, catering, design. (Woman/AA, estab 1983, empl 275, sales $10,870,702, cert: City)

FOOD: Candies, Cookies, Jellies, Pastries, Snacks
(See also six other FOOD categories). NAICS Code 31

California

3403 Laxmi's Delights
      98 Brevensville Dr   San Ramon, CA 94583
      (925) 833-0115 Laxmi Hiremath Owner
      Fax: (925) 833-0115
      Email: laxmihiremath@gmail.com
      Website: www.laxmisdelights.com
Organic flaxseed spreads. (Woman/As-Ind, estab 2000, empl 1, sales $100,000, cert: WBENC)

3404 Ly Brothers Corp.
      1963 Sabre St   Hayward, CA 94545
      (415) 850-0404 Mark Ly Sales Mgr
      Fax:
      Email: mark_ly@sugarbowlbakery.com
      Website: www.sugarbowlbakery.com
Bakery manufacturing, finished, deposited, puff pastry cookies. (As-Pac, estab 1984, empl 275, sales $42,000,000, cert: State)

3405 The French Patisserie
      1080 Palmetto Ave   Pacifica, CA 94044
      (650) 738-4990 Janette Dolan Sales Support
      Fax: (650) 738-4995
      Email: janette@frenchpatisserie.com
      Website: www.frenchpatisserie.com
Mfr gourmet frozen desserts: macarons, individual mousse cakes, tarts, petits fours, cakes and briques. (Woman/White, estab 1989, empl 130, sales $8,200,000, cert: WBENC)

Connecticut

3406 Aurora Product Inc.
      205 Edison Road   Orange, CT 06477
      (203) 375-9956 Stephanie Blackwell Business Dev
      Fax: (203) 375-9734
      Email: sblackwell@auroraproduct.com
      Website: www.auroranatural.com
Natural & organic snacks: almonds, cashews, mixed nuts & peanuts, salted, unsalted & raw, dried fruits. (Woman/White, estab 1998, empl 225, sales $60,000,000, cert: WBENC)

3407 The Bites Company
      P.O. Box 122   Westport, CT 06881
      (203) 296-2482 Dina Upton Owner
      Fax:
      Email: sales@thebitescompany.com
      Website: www.thebitescompany.com
All natural, round, bite size pieces of Biscotti in 5 flavors; almond, orange, lemon, cocoa & coffee. (Woman/White, estab 2011, empl 1, sales $95,000, cert: State)

Florida

3408 Base Culture LLC
      4509 George Rd   Tampa, FL 33634
      (727) 667-5086 Jordann Windschauer CEO
      Fax:
      Email: jordann@baseculture.com
      Website: www.baseculture.com
Natural, gluten free bakery that provides paleo baked goods and snacks to wholesale and distributor accounts nation wide. Our products are shipped, stored and sold frozen. (Woman/White, estab 2012, empl 7, sales , cert: WBENC)

Illinois

3409 Cornfields, Inc.
      3898 Sunset Ave   Waukegan, IL 60087
      (847) 263-7000 JB Weiler VP sales
      Fax: (847) 263-7090
      Email: info@cornfieldsinc.com
      Website: www.cornfieldsinc.com
Mfr natural & organic snacks. (Woman/White, estab 1991, empl 60, sales $12,000,000, cert: WBENC)

3410 Jakpan Enterprises, Inc.
      41 Northfiled Terrace   Wheeling, IL 60090
      (312) 925-5289 harold triche President
      Fax: (312) 276-8878
      Email: haroldtriche@yahoo.com
      Website:
Snack foods: package peanuts & dry fruit. (AA, estab 2001, empl 4, sales , cert: NMSDC)

3411 The French Confectionery LLC
      P.O. Box 70   Barrington, IL 60011
      (630) 301-2345 Anne Shaeffer Founder
      Fax: (312) 276-4146
      Email: anne@sulpicechocolat.com
      Website: www.sulpicechocolat.com
Milk chocolate with salt and almonds; dark chocolate with cinnamon and cayenne pepper; dark chocolate with ginger and lemon; 70% dark chocolate with sea salt; white chocolate with cake batter. (Woman/White, estab 2009, empl 2, sales $200,000, cert: WBENC)

Massachusetts

3412 600 lb Gorillas, Inc.
558 Washington St   Duxbury, MA 02332
(781) 452-7273 Paula White CEO
Fax: (781) 452-7275
Email: Paula@600lbgorillas.com
Website: www.600lbgorillas.com
Dist premium frozen cookie dough. (Woman/White, estab 2000, empl 2, sales $3,000,000, cert: WBENC)

3413 Signature Breads, Inc.
100 Justin Dr   Chelsea, MA 02150
(617) 819-3105 Heidi Keathley VP Sales and Mktg
Fax: (617) 884-4508
Email: heidi.keathley@signaturebreads.com
Website: www.signaturebreads.com
Mfr par-baked breads: dinner rolls, sandwich rolls, baguettes, ciabattas, breadsticks, pieggas & artisan breads, individual & bulk packaging, frozen or par-baked. (Hisp, estab 2006, empl 280, sales $48,000,000, cert: NMSDC)

3414 SJB Bagel Makers of Boston
77 Rowe St   Newton, MA 02466
(617) 213-8400 Jeff Malich Dir of Sales
Fax: (617) 213-8401
Email: jeff@finagleonline.com
Website: www.finagleabagel.com/
Artisan all natural bagel baker. We product 2 oz - 5 oz premium bagels. (Woman/White, estab 1992, empl 130, sales $12,000,000, cert: State, WBENC)

Maryland

3415 CharmedBar, LLC
120 Canfield Hill Dr   Gaithersburg, MD 20878
(202) 430-5637 Debbi Ascher President
Fax:
Email: debbi@charmedbar.com
Website: www.charmedbar.com
CharmedBars are kosher, baked fruit & nut bars (nutrition/energy bars) that are certified gluten free and free of grains, dairy, soy, egg, refined sugars, GMOs, preservatives & artificial ingredients. (Woman/White, estab 2013, empl 2, sales $188,000, cert: WBENC)

Michigan

3416 Dual Sales & Associates, Inc.
P.O. Box 725   Clarkston, MI 48347
(248) 922-0874 Donna Levering Owner
Fax: (248) 575-4110
Email: Donna@dualsales.com
Website: www.dualsales.com
Dist shelled walnuts & pecans, specialty dried fruits. (Woman/White, estab 1993, empl 1, sales $120,000, cert: WBENC)

Minnesota

3417 Aarthun Enterprises, LLC dba Taste of Scandinavia
111 E County Rd F   Vadnais Heights, MN 55127
(651) 483-9242 Debra Brei CFO
Fax: (651) 483-0622
Email: dbrei@knowlans.com
Website: www.tasteofscandinavia.com
Hand crafted Cakes & Tortes, Cupcakes & Cookies both traditional & custom request. (Woman, estab 2004, empl 118, sales $7,062,388, cert: WBENC)

North Carolina

3418 Tropical Nut & Fruit, Inc.
1100 Continental Blvd   Charlotte, NC 28273
(704) 588-0400 Angela Bauer Owner
Fax: (704) 588-3092
Email: abauer@tropicalfoods.com
Website: www.tropicalfoods.com
Mfr & dist nuts, seeds, dried fruit, snack mixes, candy & specialty foods. (Woman/White, estab 1977, empl 210, sales $170,000,000, cert: WBENC)

New Hampshire

3419 Homefree, LLC
P.O. Box 491   Windham, NH 03087
(603) 898-0172 Jill Robbins President
Fax: (602) 899-1698
Email: info@homefreetreats.com
Website: www.homefreetreats.com
Mfr all natural or organic, ready-to-eat whole grain baked goods free of gluten & common food allergens. (Woman/White, estab 2009, empl 18, sales $624,408, cert: WBENC)

New Jerswey

3420 JK Enterprise Solutions LLC
1000 Delsea Dr Building I Unit 1 Westville, NJ 08093
(856) 228-5934 Abdul Ahad Butt Owner
Fax: (856) 228-3920
Email: ahad@jkens.com
Website: www.jkens.com
Dist snack food products: Bud's Best Cookies, Uncle AL's Cremes, Lil Dutch maid wirecut cookies, Mayfair Candy Carnival, Select Sweets Candy, Daddy Rays fruit bars, Marco Polo Preserves, Caribbean Ice pops, Kisko Freezies. (As-Ind, estab 2014, empl 1, sales $187,000, cert: NMSDC)

New York

3421   Allie's GF Goodies, LLC
       1B W Village Green   Hicksville, NY 11801
       (516) 216-1719 Allison Luckman Owner
       Fax: (516) 216-1119
       Email: agfgoodies@optimum.net
       Website: www.AlliesGFG.com
Certified gluten free & certified kosher pareve bakery:
breads, bagels, cookies, brownies, blondies, muffins,
cupcakes, cakes, cheesecakes & pies. (Woman/White,
estab 2012, empl 8, sales $50,000, cert: WBENC)

3422   Chocolate Promises, Inc.
       P.O. Box 694   Merrick, NY 11566
       (516) 299-6400 Cindy Zakalik President
       Fax: (516) 688-3923
       Email: cindy@chocolatepromises.com
       Website: www.chocolatepromises.com
Personalized chocolate with edible images. We'll custom
print your full color logo, picture, design and/or special
message directly on delicious chocolate coins, lollipops,
Belgian truffles and more. (Woman/White, estab 2012,
empl 2, sales $26,273, cert: State, City, WBENC)

3423   Golden Glow Cookie Co. Inc.
       1844 Givan Ave   Bronx, NY 10469
       (718) 379-6223 Joan Florio Mgr
       Fax: (718) 379-4417
       Email: ggcookies@aol.com
       Website: www.thecookiefactory.com
Wholesale bakery, cookies & other related bakery items in
bulk , plastic clamshells & individually wrapped. (Woman/
White, estab 1954, empl 15, sales , cert: City)

3424   IMK Products, Inc.
       244 Fifth Ave Ste D146 New York, NY 10001
       (914) 500-8127 Ilona Kovacs President
       Fax:
       Email: imkproductsinc@gmail.com
       Website: www.truetastebar.com
Dist nutritional bars, organic/non gmo, no added sugar,
vegan, gluten free, soy free, dairy free. (Woman/White,
estab 2011, empl 2, sales , cert: WBENC)

Ohio

3425   ABC Cookie Co., Inc.
       3 Nationwide Plaza   Columbus, OH 43215
       (614) 221-4442 Dee Tolber CEO
       Fax: (478) 329-8897
       Email: dee@ablessedcookie.com
       Website: www.ablessedcookie.com
Fresh baked cookies, muffins, coffee cake, custom shaped,
logo design cookies & custom gift items. (Woman/AA,
estab 1990, empl 4, sales $185,000, cert: NMSDC)

3426   Safety Services & Supply, Inc.
       14373 Rd. 23-M   Cloverdale, OH 45827
       (419) 615-9923 Andrea Vorst President
       Fax: (419) 453-2166
       Email: andreavorst@hotmail.com
       Website:
Grow & manufacture popcorn. (Woman/White, estab
2013, empl 5, sales , cert: State, WBENC)

3427   Super Bakery
       1667 E 40th St, Ste 1D3   Cleveland, OH 44103
       (216) 426-8989 Karen Cahill Corporate Admin
       Fax: (216) 426-8169
       Email: karen.cahill@superbakery.com
       Website: www.superbakery.com
Baked goods. (AA, estab 1989, empl 27, sales , cert:
NMSDC)

3428   Whitehall, Inc.
       4760 Paddock Rd   Cincinnati, OH 45229
       (513) 242-1004 Trent Doak Exec VP
       Fax:
       Email: tdoak@klostermanbakery.com
       Website: www.klostermanbakery.com
Restaurant quality bread, buns & rolls in a unique, handy
and more compact retail package. (Woman, estab 1900,
empl 560, sales $295,400,000, cert: WBENC)

South Carolina

3429   Sweet Bottom Cookies
       P.O. Box 355   Mt. Pleasant, SC 29466
       (843) 693-7366 Michele Lewis President
       Fax:
       Email: MLewis@SweetBottomCookies.Com
       Website: www.SweetBottomCookies.Com
Privately brands & wholesales jumbo (3.5oz), soft,
individually wrapped, fudge covered bottom cookies.
(Woman/White, estab 2010, empl 4, sales , cert:
WBENC)

3430   The Muffin Mam, Inc.
       3129 N Industrial Dr   Simpsonville, SC 29681
       (800) 948-4268 Greg Marshall VP Sales/Mktg
       Fax: (864) 962-0597
       Email: gmarshall@muffinmam.com
       Website: www.muffinmam.com
Mfr custom baked CrÃ¨me Cakes, Pound Cakes, Coffee
Cakes, Gourmet Muffins, & Brownies. Use recycled &
recycle able packaging. (Woman/White, estab 1990,
empl 70, sales $24,500,000, cert: WBENC)

South Dakota

3431 Native American Natural Foods LLC
      287 Water Tower Rd   Kyle, SD 57752
      (605) 455-2187 Mark Tilsen President
      Fax: (605) 455-2019
      Email: mtilsen@tankabar.com
      Website: www.tankabar.com
Gluten free, nitrate free, MSG free & hormone free
Tanka Bar, Tanka Bites, and Tanka Sticks. (Woman/Nat
Ame, estab 2007, empl 12, sales $1,525,000, cert: NMSDC)

Texas

3432 Cookies by Design
      1865 Summit Ave Ste 607 Plano, TX 75074
      (800) 347-3110 Darylyn Phillips Natl Sales Coord
      Fax: (972) 398-0015
      Email: dphillips@cookiesbydesign.com
      Website: www.cookiesbydesign.com
Customized, hand-decorated cookie baskets, cookie
bouquets, cookie cakes, individual logo cookies, gourmet
cookies, cupcakes, gluten free & sugar free. (Woman/
White, estab 1983, empl 54, sales $28,000,000, cert:
State, WBENC)

3433 Ezbake Technologies
      P.O. Box 270527   Flowermound, TX 75027
      (888) 287-8447 Rita Tolvanen CEO
      Fax: (817) 430-1780
      Email: rita@ezbake.net
      Website: www.ezbaketechnologies.com
Dist baking ingredients, enzyme based dough conditioners, shelf life extenders & specialty conditioners for
cookies, cakes, donuts, English muffins & low moisture
products. (Woman/White, estab 1993, empl 4, sales
$1,000,000, cert: WBENC)

Washington

3434 Kylie B's Pastry Case LLC
      4114 B Place NW, Ste 100   Auburn, WA 98001
      (253) 217-6131 Sabrina Bacungan Chief Mktg
      Officer
      Fax:
      Email: sabrina@kyliebbakery.com
      Website: www.kyliebbakery.com
Hand-made traditional shortbread. (Woman/As-Pac, estab
2016, empl 4, sales $70,000, cert: WBENC)

3435 Lanier's Fine Candies
      5710 S Bangor St   Seattle, WA 98178
      (206) 723-6465 Herman Lanier CEO
      Fax:
      Email: herman@laniersfinecandies.com
      Website: www.laniersfinecandies.com
Brittle candies: almond, cashew, peanut, pecan &
macadamia, hand dipped in dark & milk chocolate. (AA,
estab 2013, empl 2, sales , cert: NMSDC)

FOOD: Dressings, Flavoring, Sauces, Spices, Syrups
(See also six other FOOD categories). NAICS Code 31

Arkansas

3436   My Brother's Salsa LLC
PO Box 922   Bentonville, AR 72712
(479) 271-9404   Helen Lampkin Founder
Fax: (479) 271-9401
Email: helen@mybrotherssalsa.com
Website: www.mybrotherssalsa.com
Produce 9 salsa varieties some available in multiple heat levels. Salsas range from smooth to textured consistencies with flavor profiles the span from earthy to smoky to sweet and savory. (Woman, estab 2003, empl 5, sales , cert: WBENC)

California

3437   AG Commodties, Inc.
12815 Stevens Dr   Tustin, CA 92782
(612) 839-3385   Theresa Bailey VP Business Devel
Fax: (320) 215-1303
Email: ach112350@gmail.com
Website: www.agcommoditiesinc.com
Natural sweeteners & natural maltodextrins, rice maltodextrin, tapioca maltodextrin, rice syrups: brown & clarified, medium invert sugar cane syrup, clear tapioca syrups, organic sugar cane, organic glycerin, organic acacia powder, etc. (As-Ind, estab 2006, empl 10, sales $3,500,000, cert: NMSDC)

3438   Kruger Foods Inc.
18362 E Hwy 4   Stockton, CA 95215
(209) 941-8518   Kara Kruger CEO
Fax: (209) 941-8518
Email: k.kruger@krugerfoods.com
Website: www.krugerfoods.com
Pickles, Sweet Pickle Relish, Dill Pickle Relish, Hot Pepper Relish, Jalapeno Peppers (sliced, diced, whole), Banana Wax Peppers, Peppers, Giardinera. (Woman/White, estab 1930, empl 158, sales $65,400,000, cert: WBENC)

Colorado

3439   All American Seasonings, Inc.
10600 E 54th Ave, Unit B & C   Denver, CO 80239
(303) 623-2320   Andy Rodriguez President
Fax:
Email: andyr@allamericanseasonings.com
Website: www.allamericanseasonings.com
Custom blenders of food ingredients. (Hisp, estab 1968, empl 40, sales $18,000,000, cert: NMSDC)

3440   Mona's Granola and Cookies, Inc.
651 Eldorado   Broomfield, CO 80021
(727) 420-0707   Mona Gale CEO
Fax:
Email: Mona@MonasInc.com
Website: www.monasinc.com
All natural no white sugar nutrient rich granola cereal & ice cream toppings. (Woman/White, estab 1981, empl 27, sales $600,000, cert: WBENC)

Florida

3441   Emerald Cove Gourmet Products,Inc.
P.O. Box 380   Shalimar, FL 32579
(850) 651-4216   Susan Williford CEO
Fax: (850) 651-7023
Email: srwilli@cox.net
Website: www.susansmarinade.com
Mfr & dist gourmet marinade sauces for meats, poultry, fish & seafood. (Woman, estab 1992, empl 1, sales $30,000, cert: WBENC)

3442   Henry Roberts BBQ Sauce
2001 Art Museum Dr   Jacksonville, FL 32207
(904) 591-8102   Anthony Ammons VP
Fax: (904) 396-0994
Email: anthony.ammons@gmail.com
Website: www.HenryRoberts.com
Bottle & distribute barbecue sauce & chow chow. (Woman/AA, estab 1985, empl 4, sales $160,000, cert: City)

3443   M&G Expresso, Inc
13311 SW 132 Ave, Unit 3   Miami, FL 33186
(786) 200-9802   Gabriel Cortina VP
Fax: (786) 701-3037
Email: mgexpressinc@gmail.com
Website: www.ladybeehoney.net
Dist Lady Bee Honey. (Woman/Hisp, estab 2009, empl 3, sales , cert: NMSDC)

Georgia

3444   82's, LLC
1475 Buford Dr Ste 403-227   Lawrenceville, GA 30043
(770) 402-2226   Reginald Kelly Owner
Fax: (678) 889-2054
Email: contact@kyvan82.com
Website: www.kyvan82.com
All Natural Honey Apple Salsa (Hot & Mild), Sesame Garlic BBQ Sauce, Sweet BBQ Sauce, Hot Sauce. (AA, estab 2008, empl 7, sales $100,000, cert: NMSDC)

3445   Fire & Flavor Grilling Co.
1160 S Milledge Ave, Ste 230   Athens, GA 30605
(706) 369-9466   Davis Knox CEO
Fax: (706) 369-9468
Email: davis@fireandflavor.com
Website: www.fireandflavor.com
Dist spices, seasonings, sauces, brines, grilling planks, wood chips, charcoal & fire starters. (Woman/White, estab 2003, empl 6, sales $5,000,000, cert: WBENC)

Iowa

3446 Young G's Barbecue Sauce, LLC
      8211 Brookview Dr.   Urbandale, IA 50322
      (515) 331-8001 Gerald Young President
      Fax: -
      Email: youngsbbq@gmail.com
      Website: www.ygsbbq.com
Young G's is a gluten free low sodium content with no high
fructose corn syrup. (AA, estab 2010, empl 1, sales , cert:
NMSDC)

Illinois

3447 Baldwin Richardson Foods Co.
      One Tower Lane Ste 2390 Oakbrook Terrace, IL
      60181
      (630) 607-1780 Cara Hughes Dir of Sales & Mktg
      Fax: (630) 607-1781
      Email: chughes@brfoods.com
      Website: www.brfoods.com
Mfr custom sauces, condiments, syrups, toppings &
fillings. (AA, estab 1997, empl 287, sales , cert: NMSDC)

3448 Bell Marketing, Inc.
      10135 S Roberts Rd   Palos Hills, IL 60465
      (708) 598-8873 Mary Ann Bell President
      Fax: (708) 598-8968
      Email: Maryann@bellmarketing.com
      Website: www.bellmarketing.com
Fruit concentrates, purees, puree concentrates IQF frozen
fruit, all natural colors from fruit & vegetable juice concentrates, extracts, ice cream inclusions. (Woman/White,
estab 1986, empl 5, sales $10,000,000, cert: WBENC)

3449 Mullins Food Products, Inc.
      2200 S 25th Ave   Broadview, IL 60155
      (708) 344-3224 Andy Camp Dir of Sales
      Fax: (708) 344-2709
      Email: acamp@mullinsfood.com
      Website: www.mullinsfood.com
Custom mfr & package liquid condiments: sauces, salad
dressings, ketchup, mayonnaise, picante sauce, salsa
sauce, pizza sauce, asian style sauces, flavored syrups,
icing. (Woman/White, estab 1934, empl 350, sales , cert:
WBENC)

3450 Navisource Holdings LLC dba Golden Hill Foods LLC
      851 W Grand Ave 2nd Fl Chicago, IL 60642
      (312) 226-5900 Demetrio Garcia VP Business Dev
      Fax: (312) 226-5959
      Email: dgarcia@goldenhillfoods.com
      Website: www.goldenhillfoods.com
Import & dist dehydrated vegetables & spices. (Hisp, estab
2005, empl 6, sales $2,500,000, cert: NMSDC)

3451 Swagger Foods Corporation
      900 Corporate Woods Pkwy   Vernon Hills, IL 60061
      (847) 913-1200 Maria Shin
      Fax: (847) 913-1263
      Email: mwhalen@swaggerfoods.com
      Website: www.swaggerfoods.com
Mfr & package seasonings, spices, custom blends, gravy/
sauce mixes, marinades/rubs, dressing/dip mixes, dry side
dish mixes, salt & butter substitutes, etc. (As-Pac, estab
1978, empl 17, sales $10,000,000, cert: State)

Indiana

3452 Williams, West & Witt's Product Co.
      3501 W Dunes Hwy   Michigan City, IN 46360
      (219) 879-8236 Joanne Tica Steiger Natl Dir
      Business Devel
      Fax: (219) 879-8237
      Email: jtsteiger@integrativeflavors.com
      Website: www.integrativeflavors.com
Mfr healthy soup bases & innovative food flavor additives for the institutional, food service, corporate and
government user channels. (Woman/White, estab 1938,
empl 16, sales $2,025,000, cert: State, WBENC)

Louisiana

3453 Bridge Foods, Inc.
      P.O. Box 58698 New Orleans, LA 70158
      (504) 254-9770 Henry Chigbu President
      Fax: (504) 254-8088
      Email: hchigbu@bridgefoods.com
      Website: www.ashantifoods.com
Condiments: hot sauce, wing sauce, steak sauce,
worcestershire sauce, etc. (AA, estab 1993, empl 5, sales
$15,000,000, cert: NMSDC)

Massachusetts

3454 HimalaSalt - Sustainable Sourcing, LLC
      1375 Boardman St   Sheffield, MA 01257
      (413) 446-8927 melissa kushi CEO
      Fax: (413) 528-5172
      Email: melissa@himalasalt.com
      Website: www.himalasalt.com
Dist pink Himalayan sea salt produced in our owned
facility that is certified organic, Non-GMO, Gluten-Free,
Kosher for Passover & powered by 156 solar panels.
(Woman/White, estab 2006, empl 12, sales $2,500,000,
cert: State)

Maryland

3455 SoFine Food
      4825 Cordell Ave, Ste 200   Bethesda, MD 20814
      (301) 979-9555 Sophia Maroon CEO
      Fax:
      Email: Sophia@SoFineFood.com
      Website: www.dressitupdressing.com
Produce all-natural, shelf-stable vinaigrettes, called
Dress It Up Dressing, gluten-free, sugar-free & vegan.
(Woman, estab 2012, empl 2, sales $25,000, cert:
WBENC)

Michigan

3456　Keystone Universal Corporation
　　　P.O. Box 3241　Melvindale, MI 48122
　　　(313) 388-0063　Patricia Szccepanik Principal
　　　Fax: (313) 388-6495
　　　Email: ebonex@flash.net
　　　Website: www.keystoneuniversal.com
Dist baking ammonium carbonate: lump, chip or powder.
(Woman/White, estab 1973, empl 12, sales , cert: WBENC)

Minnesota

3457　Healthy America
　　　9768 Troy Lane N　Maple Grove, MN 55331
　　　(612) 548-1099　Sunil Kumar President
　　　Fax:
　　　Email: sunil.kumar@theamazingchickpea.com
　　　Website: www.theamazingchickpea.com
Produce Chickpea Spread that tastes like peanut butter but
does not contain any Nuts, Gluten Free and Dairy Free.
"The Amazing Chickpea - Creamy", "The Amazing Chickpea
- Crunchy","The Amazing Chickpea - Traditional". (As-Pac,
estab 2016, empl 1, sales $200,000, cert: NMSDC)

3458　Sweet Harvest Foods Management Company
　　　15100 Business Parkway　Rosemount, MN 55068
　　　(507) 263-8599　Joel Rengel Sales Dir
　　　Fax: (507) 263-8861
　　　Email: jrengel@sweetharvestfoods.com
　　　Website: www.sweetharvestfoods.com
Mfr honey, ingredient honey, pancake syrup (table syrup),
corn syrup & branded peanut butter. (Woman/White,
estab 1923, empl 50, sales , cert: WBENC)

North Carolina

3459　MyThreeSons Gourmet, LLC
　　　2309 Lafayette Ave　Greensboro, NC 27408
　　　(336) 324-5638　Cheryl Barnett President
　　　Fax:
　　　Email: mtsgourmet@gmail.com
　　　Website: www.mtsgourmet.com
Mfr natural gourmet pimento cheese spread. (Woman/
White, estab 2010, empl 10, sales $645,000, cert: WBENC)

3460　The Busha Group LLC
　　　302 Lord Court　Cramerton, NC 28032
　　　(704) 879-4411　Julie Busha CEO
　　　Fax: (704) 879-4570
　　　Email: jbusha@slawsa.com
　　　Website: www.slawsa.com
Mfr Slawsa, slaw-salsa hybrid condiment, all natural, fat-
free, cholesterol-free, gluten-free, low in sodium & kosher.
(Woman/White, estab 2013, empl 1, sales $363,320, cert:
WBENC)

New Hampshire

3461　Healthy Solutions Spice Blends, LLC
　　　P.O. Box 1094　Hampton, NH 03843
　　　(603) 622-8744　Shelly Wolcott Mgr
　　　Fax: (603) 218-6846
　　　Email: shelly@spiceblends.com
　　　Website: www.spiceblends.com
Produce all natural, high quality, recipe ready spice
blends. (Woman/White, estab 2013, empl 1, sales
$62,000, cert: WBENC)

New Jersey

3462　Advanced Food Systems
　　　21 Roosevelt Ave　Somerset, NJ 08863
　　　(732) 873-6776　Al Rose Midwest Sales Mgr
　　　Fax: (732) 873-4177
　　　Email: ajrose@charter.net
　　　Website: www.afsnj.com
Food ingredients: gums, starches, proteins, spices,
flavors, lab services. (As-Pac, estab 1980, empl 40, sales
$50,000,000, cert: NMSDC)

New York

3463　Lugo Nutrition Inc.
　　　51 N Broadway, Ste 2B　Nyack, NY 10960
　　　(302) 573-2301　Nick Lugo VP
　　　Fax: (845) 480-5122
　　　Email: nlugo@lugonutrition.com
　　　Website: www.lugonutrition.com
Gelatin, beta carotene. Bitterness masking, sweetness
enhancing, natural preservative/flavoring. (Hisp, estab
2010, empl 5, sales $4,500,000, cert: NMSDC)

3464　SFR&R Inc.
　　　9 Soundview Lane　Sands Point, NY 11050
　　　(516) 767-7286　Giovannina Bellino Owner
　　　Fax: (516) 883-1683
　　　Email: goddess6x8@aol.com
　　　Website: www.flavorbombs.net
Mfr frozen cooking bases & foods. Low Sodium, Gluten
Free, All Natural products. (Woman/White, estab 2008,
empl 1, sales , cert: WBENC)

Pennsylvania

3465　Casalingo LLC
　　　6321 S Highlings Circle　Harrisburg, PA 17111
　　　(717) 805-5088　Monette Roberto Member
　　　Fax:
　　　Email: monetteroberto@yahoo.com
　　　Website: www.casalingofoods.com
Four Generation homemade local pasta sauce. (Woman/
White, estab 2013, empl 2, sales , cert: WBENC)

3466 Dutch Gold Honey, Inc.
2220 Dutch Gold Dr   Lancaster, PA 17601
(717) 393-1716 Jill Clark
Fax:
Email: jclark@dutchgoldhoney.com
Website: www.dutchgoldhoney.com
Honey & maple syrup processing & packaging. (Woman/White, estab 1946, empl 75, sales , cert: WBENC)

South Carolina

3467 Charleston Gourmet Burger Company
4206 Sawgrass Dr   North Charleston, SC 29420
(843) 847-8369 chevalo wilsondebriano Owner
Fax: (843) 494-9070
Email: chevalo@charlestongourmetburger.com
Website: www.charlestongourmetburger.com
Charleston Gourmet Burger Marinade -blend of nine herbs & spices. (Woman/AA/Hisp, estab 2012, empl 2, sales $1,000,000, cert: NMSDC)

3468 Chef Belinda LLC dba Chef Belinda Spices
6 Mooney Court   Trenton, SC 29847
(803) 552-6450 Belinda Smith-Sullivan President
Fax:
Email: belinda@chefbelinda.com
Website: www.chefbelindaspices.com
Produce all-natural artisan spice blends. (Woman/AA, estab 2009, empl 3, sales $75,000, cert: NMSDC)

Texas

3469 Behrnes Pepper Salts
5313 E Side Ave   Dallas, TX 75214
(214) 724-0581 Jan Olavarri Owner
Fax:
Email: jan@behrnes.com
Website: www.behrnes.com
Mfr pepper salts blends using Chipotle, Cayenne & Green Jalapeno. (Woman/White, estab 2012, empl 1, sales , cert: WBENC)

3470 Clint's Picante Inc.
12 Thornhurst   San Antonio, TX 78218
(210) 274-5916 Keri Poulter CFO
Fax:
Email: keripoulter@yahoo.com
Website: www.clintspicante.com
Mfr Salsa & BBQ sauce. (Woman, estab 1996, empl 2, sales $29,990,000, cert: State, City)

3471 Twang Partners, Ltd.
6255 WT Montgomery Rd   San Antonio, TX 78252
(210) 226-7008 Elysia Gonzales Trade Mktg Mgr
Fax: (210) 226-4040
Email: etrevino@twang.com
Website: www.twang.com
Mfr premium-flavored salts, sugars & seasonings. (Hisp, estab 1986, empl 56, sales $15,464,847, cert: State, NMSDC)

Virginia

3472 Grandmas Garden
7044 Sauvage Ln   Gainesville, VA 20155
(571) 244-1443 Amy Weaver President
Fax:
Email: amyweaver@grandmasgarden.us
Website: www.grandmasgarden.us
All natural "Sweet" & "Spicy Sweet" gourmet relish: cabbage, peppers, tomatoes, onions & spices. (Woman/White, estab 2011, empl 2, sales , cert: State)

3473 Savaspice LLC
6247 Glen Wood Loop   Manassas, VA 20112
(703) 895-4800 Lova Mitchell Owner
Fax:
Email: savaspice@gmail.com
Website: www.savaspice.com
Madagascar vanilla & spices. (Woman/As-Ind, estab 2015, empl 1, sales , cert: State)

Washington

3474 Asenzya, inc. (formerly Foran Spice Company, Inc.)
7616 S 6th St P.O. Box 109   Oak Creek, WI 53154
(414) 764-1220 Patty Goto President
Fax: (414) 764-8803
Email: patty.goto@asenzya.com
Website: www.asenzya.com
Custom dry seasoning product development, custom dry seasoning blending & custom bulk & batch-specific-weight packaging services. (Woman/White, estab 1953, empl 140, sales $48,000,000, cert: WBENC)

FOOD: Ethnic
Includes manufacturers, distributors, or importers of various ethnic foods. (See also six other FOOD categories). NAICS Code 31

California

3475　Asiana Cusine Enterprises (ACE Sushi)
22771 S. Western Ave   Torrance, CA 90501
(310) 327-2223 Gary Chin CFO
Fax: (310) 327-9193
Email: gary.chin@acesushi.com
Website: www.acesushi.com
Dist Sushi. (As-Pac, estab 1998, empl 35, sales , cert: City)

3476　NC Moving & Storage Solutions
3146 Corporate Pl   Hayward, CA 94545
(510) 385-4441 Johanna Lobation Business Dev Mgr
Fax: (510) 780-2650
Email: jlobaton@ncmss.com
Website: www.ncmss.com
NC Moving & Storage Solutions is a full service household goods provider for both domestic and international moving services. We are an agent for North American Van Lines. (Woman/As-Pac, estab 2006, empl 19, sales $1,165,000, cert: NMSDC, CPUC)

Connecticut

3477　Carla's Pasta, Inc.
50 Talbot Lane   South Windsor, CT 06074
(860) 436-4042 Sandro Squatrito VP Business Dev
Fax:
Email: abiel@carlaspasta.com
Website: www.carlaspasta.com
Produce pasta & pesto products, Cheeseburger Ravioli, Buffalo Chicken Ravioli & Stromboli Ravioli. (Woman/White, estab 1978, empl 182, sales , cert: NWBOC)

District of Columbia

3478　Tribes-A-Dozen, LLC
P.O. Box 42063   Washington, DC 20015
(202) 684-8256 Leah Hadad President
Fax: (202) 684-8256
Email: leah@tribesadozen.com
Website: www.tribesadozen.com
Mfr three all-natural & kosher (OU) Voil! Hallah Egg Bread Mixes: Traditional, Wholey Wheat & Simply Spelt. (Woman, estab 2012, empl 1, sales $88,136, cert: WBENC)

Illinois

3479　Reggios' Pizza, Inc.
340 W 83rd St   Chicago, IL 60620
(773) 488-1411 Darryl Humphrey Sales & Mktg Dir
Fax: (773) 783-7333
Email: dhumphrey@reggiospizzainc.com
Website: www.reggios.com
Chicago Style Famous Buttercrust Pizza. (AA, estab 1972, empl 42, sales , cert: City)

3480　Thomas Imports LLC
1327 W. Washington BLVD Ste 3D   Chicago, IL 60607
(312) 929-2699 Chris Cottrell Sales, MBE
Fax: (312) 929-3749
Email: ccottrell@isiahinternational.com
Website: www.isiahimports.com
Corn tortillas, flour tortillas, flavored tortilla flour wraps; jalapeno wrap, tomato basil wrap, chipotle wrap, roasted garlic wrap, cheese, wraps corn chips, spices, chile peppers, canned sauces, frozen foods. (AA, estab 2016, empl 8, sales , cert: NMSDC)

3481　V&V Supremo Foods Inc.
2141 S Throop St   Chicago, IL 60608
(312) 421-1020 John Brandley Natl sales Mgr
Fax: (313) 224-2896
Email: johnb@vvsupremo.com
Website: www.vvsupremo.com
Produce Hispanic cheese, creams & Chorizo. (Hisp, estab 1964, empl 184, sales $67,142,000, cert: NMSDC)

Massachusetts

3482　Harbar LLC
320 Turnpike St   Canton, MA 02021
(800) 881-7040 Keith Brennan Retail Sales Mgr
Fax: (781) 828-0849
Email: kbrennan@harbar.com
Website: www.harbar.com
Mfr corn & flour tortillas. (Woman/Hisp, estab 1986, empl 140, sales , cert: NMSDC)

3483　Jensay Co.
61 Maple St   Acton, MA 01720
(978) 929-9797 Stephen Chen President
Fax: (978) 266-2400
Email: stephenchen@joycechenfoods.com
Website: www.joycechenfoods.com
Asian, Chinese cooking sauces, oils, comdiments, spices & Asian frozen prepared food products. (As-Pac, estab 2006, empl 1, sales $950,000, cert: State)

3484 Monsoon Kitchens, Inc.
      159 Memorial Dr Unit G Shrewsbury, MA 01545
      (704) 778-8090 Rusty Michael Business Dev Mgr
      Fax: (617) 629-0160
      Email: rusty@monsoonkitchens.com
      Website: www.monsoonkitchens.com
Mfr Indian style frozen chicken entrees, vegetarian entress
& appetizers. (As-Ind, estab 2003, empl 6, sales , cert:
NMSDC)

Maryland

3485 Demeter's Pantry (dba): GreenFood Associates LLC
      419 Greenbrier Dr   Silver Spring, MD 20910
      (301) 587-0048 Maria Kardamaki Robertson
      Managing Partner
      Fax: (309) 502-5486
      Email: maria@demeterspantry.com
      Website: www.thegreektable.net
Dist ethnic foods, Mediterranean (Greek prepared foods,
entrées, side dishes & bean salad dishes. (Woman/White,
estab 2003, empl 2, sales $490,058, cert: State)

New Jersey

3486 Soul Sisters Foods, Inc.
      41 Prince St, Ste B11   Paterson, NJ 07505
      (973) 742-8255 Betty Dixon President
      Fax: (973) 333-3784
      Email: betty.dixon@unilever.com
      Website: www.soulroll.com
Retail frozen food, Soul Rolls: collard greens, marinated
meats, cheddar cheese, onions, green peppers, and
tomatoes, seasoned to perfection in a crispy flour tortilla.
(Woman/AA, estab 2006, empl 2, sales , cert: WBENC)

Nevada

3487 Tortillas Inc.
      2912 N Commerce St   North Las Vegas, NV 89030
      (702) 399-3300 Gustavo Gutierrez President
      Fax: (702) 399-2507
      Email: gus@tortillasinc.com
      Website: www.tortillasinc.com
Corn tortillas, flour tortillas, flavored tortilla flour wraps;
jalapeno wrap, tomato basil wrap, chipotle wrap, roasted
garlic wrap, cheese, wraps corn chips, spices, chile peppers, canned sauces, frozen foods. (Hisp, estab 1979, empl
76, sales $8,000,000, cert: NMSDC)

Oregon

3488 Lucky Foods, LLC
      7774 SW Nimbus Ave, Bldg 10   Beaverton, OR
      97008
      (503) 641-6602 Tammy Jo President
      Fax:
      Email: tammyjo@luckyfood.com
      Website: www.luckyfood.com
Asian foods. (Woman/As-Pac, estab 1985, empl 16, sales
$1,547,000, cert: State)

Pennsylvania

3489 Gourmail Inc.
      300 Elmwood Ave   Sharon Hill, PA 19079
      (610) 522-2650 Sunil Manchanda Business Mgr
      Fax: (610) 522-2652
      Email: sunil@jyotifoods.com
      Website: www.jyotifoods.com
Ready to serve vegetarian entrees, soups and sauces for
at-home cooking, packed in cans. Indian Dals (Legumes),
in pouches. (Woman/As-Pac, estab 1979, empl 25, sales
$30,000,000, cert: NMSDC)

FOOD: Fish, Seafood & Prepared Meats
(See also six other FOOD categories). NAICS Code 31

California

3490 Fusion Ranch, Inc. dba Fusion Jerky
      405 South Airport Blvd   South San Francisco, CA 94080
      (650) 589-8899 Kaiyen Mai CEO
      Fax: (650) 589-3157
      Email: kaiyen@fusionranch.com
      Website: www.fusionjerky.com
Jerky, Sausage, Ham, Shredded Pork. (Woman/As-Pac, estab 2014, empl 46, sales , cert: NMSDC, WBENC)

3491 Somax Inc.
      339 S Notre Dame Ave   Orange, CA 92869
      (714) 633-6614 Grace Knight Owner
      Fax: (714) 922-6271
      Email: graceknight@sanluissausage.com
      Website: www.sanluissausage.com
Healthy, preservative free pork & chicken gourmet sausages. (Woman/White, estab 1991, empl 2, sales $2,200,286, cert: WBENC, NWBOC)

Connecticut

3492 Heidi's Real Food LLC
      47 Hillside Rd   Greenwich, CT 06830
      (203) 219-4202 Heidi Matonis Owner
      Fax: (713) 780-8056
      Email: heidi@heidisrealfood.com
      Website: www.heidisrealfood.com
Heidi's Meatless "Meat"balls also available in bulk for food service and prepared foods. (Woman/White, estab 2013, empl 1, sales , cert: WBENC)

Florida

3493 Quirch Foods Co.
      2701 S. LeJeune Rd. 12th Fl Miami, FL 33134
      (305) 691-3535 Elijah Davis Natl Acct Sales Mgr
      Fax:
      Email: elijah.davis@quirchfoods.com
      Website: www.quirchfoods.com
Dist & export meat & seafood. (Hisp, estab 1967, empl 500, sales $747,373,931, cert: NMSDC)

Georgia

3494 H. Walker Enterprises, LLC
      22 E Montgomery Crossroads   Savannah, GA 31406
      (912) 961-0002 Herschel Walker CEO
      Fax: (912) 961-0017
      Email: hwrmi34@aol.com
      Website: www.34promotions.com
Mfr & dist poultry, beef & pork food products. (AA, estab 2002, empl 4, sales , cert: NMSDC)

Maryland

3495 MAS Foods International, LLC
      P.O. Box 2886   Montgomery Village, MD 20886
      (301) 591-9728 Michael Short Chief Managing Officer
      Fax: (301) 960-4536
      Email: mshort@masfi.com
      Website: www.masfi.com
Gourmet chicken sausage & personal chicken pizza made from halal products. (AA, estab 2004, empl 2, sales $76,910, cert: NMSDC)

New Jersey

3496 Groezinger Provisions, Inc.
      1200 Seventh Ave   Neptune, NJ 07753
      (800) 927-9473 Laurie Cummins President
      Fax: (732) 775-3223
      Email: laurie@alexianpate.com
      Website: www.alexianpate.com
Perishable prepared food mfg: meat, sausages, pates & prepared meats. (Woman/White, estab 1982, empl 20, sales , cert: WBENC)

South Carolina

3497 Spartanburg Meat Processing Co., Inc.
      3003 N Blackstock Rd   Spartanburg, SC 29301
      (800) 315-5159 Christiann Marchand Dir of Business Devel
      Fax: (864) 574-2208
      Email: cmarchand@eatbbqribs.com
      Website: www.eatbbqribs.com
Meat processing plant, pork, beef & chicken. Baby Back Ribs w/Sauce, Back Ribs, Pulled Pork w/Sauce, Pulled Chicken w/Sauce, Custom Proteins & Sauces. (Woman/White, estab 1999, empl 51, sales $25,533,338, cert: State, WBENC)

Wisconsin

3498   Fair Oaks Farms, LLC
        7600 95th St   Pleasant Prairie, WI 53158
        (262) 947-0320 Michael Thompson Natl Acct Sales
        Mgr
        Fax: (262) 947-0340
        Email: mthompson@osigroup.com
        Website: www.fairoaksfarms.com
Dist meats. (AA, estab 1985, empl 260, sales , cert:
NMSDC)

FOOD: Fruits & Vegetables
(See also six other FOOD categories). NAICS Code 31

California

3499   American Food Ingredients, Inc.
2521 Oceanside Blvd, Ste I   Oceanside, CA 92054
(760) 967-6287 Karen Koppenhaver President
Fax: (760) 967-1952
Email: amerfood@aol.com
Website:
Dist dehydrated & freeze dried vegetables. (Woman/As-Pac, estab 1993, empl 15, sales , cert: State)

3500   Frieda's Inc.
4465 Corporate Center Dr   Los Alamitos, CA 90720
(714) 826-6100 Karen Caplan CEO
Fax: (714) 816-0273
Email: karen.caplan@friedas.com
Website: www.friedas.com
Specialty Fruits (including Fresh Tropicals and Dried Fruits), Specialty Vegetables (including cooking vegetables and leafy greens), Hispanic Fruits & Vegetables (including fresh & dried chile peppers), Asian Fruits & Vegetables. (Woman/White, estab 1962, empl 75, sales $46,000,000, cert: WBENC)

3501   Got Broccoli, Inc.
6201 Progressive Ave Ste 400 San Diego, CA 92154
(619) 661-0909 Art Sanchez Director
Fax:
Email: Art@gotbroccoli.com
Website: www.frugo.com.mx
IQF Vegetables, Asparagus, Broccoli, Cauliflower, Celery, Cucumber, Jalapeno, Spinach, Kale. (Hisp, estab 2010, empl 2, sales $10,000,000, cert: NMSDC)

3502   Peas of Mind LLC
2339 3rd St Unit 53-3R San Francisco, CA 94107
(415) 504-2556 Jill Litwin CEO
Fax: (415) 759-8615
Email: jill@peasofmind.com
Website: www.peasofmind.com
Mfr healthy eating options. (Woman/White, estab 2005, empl 4, sales $2,800,000, cert: WBENC)

District of Columbia

3503   Hard Light Consulting Group
2119 First St NW   Washington, DC 20001
(202) 232-0355 Don Smith Exec VP
Fax: (202) 232-0356
Email: don@hlcg.biz
Website:
Dist imported sugars & fruits. (Woman/AA, estab 2002, empl 2, sales , cert: City)

Florida

3504   MH Food Group LLC
1800 Sunset Harbour Dr, Ste P   Miami Beach, FL 33139
(954) 501-6215 Calvin Harris President
Fax:
Email: charris@mhfoodgroup.com
Website: www.mhfoodgroup.com
Pack & dist frozen fruit & industrial food ingredients. (Woman/Hisp, estab 2014, empl 4, sales $1,000,000, cert: NMSDC)

Illinois

3505   Frey Produce
RR 1 Box 89   Keenes, IL 62851
(618) 835-2536 Renee Mattingly VP sales/Mktg
Fax:
Email: reneemattingly@freyproduce.com
Website: www.freyproduce.com
Grow, pack & dist fresh fruits & vegetables: watermelons, cantaloupe, green bell peppers, sweet corn, pumpkins, squash, soybeans, wheat. (Woman/White, estab 1996, empl 20, sales $50,000,000, cert: WBENC)

Massachusetts

3506   Cape Cod Select LLC
73 Tremont St   Carver, MA 02330
(508) 866-1149 Cindy Rhodes Owner
Fax: (508) 866-1152
Email: crhodes@capecodselect.com
Website: www.capecodselect.com
Harvest, pack & dist cranberries. (Woman/White, estab 2009, empl 3, sales , cert: WBENC)

Maine

3507 Blue Sky Produce
      243 Tory Hill Rd   Phillips, ME 04966
      (207) 684-2172 Lynn Thurston Owner
      Fax:
      Email: hope@tdstelme.net
      Website: www.blueskyproduce.com
Pesticide Free & Conventionally grown Frozen Wild
Blueberries packed in 14 oz containers. (Woman/White,
estab 1987, empl 6, sales , cert: WBENC)

Michigan

3508 Flamm Pickle & Packing Co., Inc.
      4502 Hipps Hollow Rd   Eau Claire, MI 49111
      (269) 461-6916 Dorothy Munao Dir of Ops
      Fax: (269) 461-6166
      Email: dorothymunao@flammpickle.com
      Website: www.flammpickle.com
Mfr dill pickles & sweet pickle relishes. (Woman/White,
estab 1917, empl 16, sales $1,885,000, cert: WBENC)

New Jersey

3509 Crispy Green Inc.
      10 Madison Rd   Fairfield, NJ 07004
      (973) 679-4515 Angela Liu President
      Fax:
      Email: angela@crispygreen.com
      Website:
Crispy Green Fruit product line is created using a sophisticated freeze-drying process where water is removed from
the fresh fruit in a cold (freezing) vacuum condition,
leaving behind the true essence of the fruit in a light and
crispy texture. (Woman/As-Pac, estab 2004, empl 10, sales
$19,000, cert: State)

Ohio

3510 Urban Food Concepts LLC
      852 E Highland Rd   Macedonia, OH 44056
      (330) 908-0493 Claude Booker President
      Fax: (330) 908-0671
      Email: claude@simplysouthernsides.com
      Website: www.simplysouthernsides.com
Fully cooked & seasoned vegetables & side dishes.
(Woman/AA, estab 2007, empl 3, sales $4,000,000, cert:
State, NMSDC, WBENC)

Pennsylvania

3511 A.S.K. Foods Inc.
      71 Hetrick Ave   Palmyra, PA 17078
      (717) 838-6356 Liz Burkholder Reg sales Mgr
      Fax:
      Email: ldurr@askfoods.com
      Website: www.askfoods.com
Mfr prepared deli salads, entrees, side dishes, soups
with no preservatives added. (Woman/White, estab
1947, empl 175, sales $42,200,000, cert: WBENC)

Washington

3512 Lynnae's Gourmet Pickles LLC
      3024 S Mullen #F   Tacoma, WA 98466
      (253) 226-2370 Lynnae Schneller President
      Fax:
      Email: lynnae@lynnaesgourmetpickles.com
      Website: www.lynnaesgourmetpickles.com
Mfr all natural, high quality pickles with unique flavor
combinations. (Woman/White, estab 2011, empl 3, sales
$285,000, cert: State)

FREIGHT FORWARDING SERVICES
Handle all transportation details including custom house clearance, export documentation, export packing and crating. Some have warehousing facilities. NAICS Code 48

Arizona

3513   BC Logistics LLC
4405 E Baseline Rd Ste 114 Phoenix, AZ 85042
(480) 966-5000 Vicki Boisjolie President
Fax: (480) 967-3009
Email: phx@bclogisticsllc.com
Website: www.bclogisticsllc.com
Air afreight, ground transportation, domestic & international, next flight out, same day, conventions, blank wrap, pad van, flat beds, double flat beds. (Woman/White, estab 2001, empl 15, sales $3,061,531, cert: WBENC)

3514   Mach 1 Global Services, Inc.
1530 W Broadway Rd   Tempe, AZ 85282
(480) 921-3900 Jamie Fletcher CEO
Fax: (480) 361-0671
Email: jfletcher@mach1global.com
Website: www.mach1global.com
Transportation & logistics, domestic heavy weight expedited freight forwarding, international freight forwarding, ocean & air import & export, distribution, warehousing & supply chain management. (Woman/As-Pac, estab 1988, empl 250, sales $105,000,000, cert: WBENC)

3515   QBP Logistics, Inc.
6006 N 83rd Ave Ste 201 Glendale, AZ 85303
(602) 314-5099 Marlin Banks Ops Mgr
Fax: (602) 296-0232
Email: marlin@landstarmail.com
Website: www.qbpfreight.com
Transportation. Truckload transportation, Rail Intermodal service, Heavy Haul Specialized transport, Ocean freight forwarding, Expedited ground transport & Air freight forwarding. (AA, estab 2007, empl 6, sales $560,000, cert: CPUC)

3516   Team Worldwide
3837 E Wier Ave Ste 8 Phoenix, AZ 85040
(602) 305-7488 Susanne Ingram Owner
Fax: (602) 305-7478
Email: susanne.ingram@teamww.com
Website: www.teamww.com
Logistics, air, land & sea. (Woman/White, estab 2001, empl 5, sales $1,624,039, cert: State, City, WBENC)

3517   The ILS Company

8350 E Old Vail Rd   Tucson, AZ 85747
(520) 618-4309 Roy Austin Business Dev Dir
Fax: (520) 618-4307
Email: roy.austin@ilscompany.com
Website: www.ilscompany.com
International Freight Forwarding & Logistics Services, Door to Door Transportation Management (Air, Ground, Ocean and Rail), Project Cargo Management, Vendor Managed Inventory, Hot Shot, Remote & White Glove. (Hisp, estab 2002, empl 54, sales $24,320,000, cert: NMSDC)

California

3518   Aeronet Logistics Inc.
42 Corporate Park   Irvine, CA 92606
(949) 474-9292 Andres Aceves President
Fax: (949) 474-9292
Email: diversity@Aeronet.com
Website: www.aeronet.com
Global integrated logistics svcs: freight & cargo transportation, distribution & supply chain mgmt, air freight, expedited ground freight & urgent shipments, ocean cargo, import & export. (Hisp, estab 1982, empl 125, sales $70,858,000, cert: NMSDC)

3519   Aeronet, Inc.
P.O. Box 17239 Irvine, CA 02397
(949) 474-3000 Benita Rosendal Business Dev Mgr
Fax: (949) 474-1477
Email: diversityl@aeronet.com
Website: www.aeronet.com
Integrated logistics solutions, global supply chain management, domestic & international shipping & handling. (Hisp, estab 1982, empl 140, sales $48,700,000, cert: NMSDC, CPUC)

3520   Casas International Brokerage, Inc.
9355 Airway Rd, Ste 4 Otay Mesa San Diego, CA 92154
(619) 710-4619 Syliva Casas President
Fax: (619) 661-0047
Email: s.casas@casasinternational.com
Website: www.casasinternational.com
US Customs broker & freight forwarder, warehouse & distribution. (Woman/Hisp, estab 1984, empl 85, sales $6,055,615, cert: NMSDC)

3521   FNS, Inc.
18301 S Broadwick St   Rancho Dominguez, CA 90220
(310) 747-8530 Josh Taxon Sales/Mktg Mgr
Fax:
Email: joshua.taxon@pantos.com
Website: www.fnsusa.com
Global third party logistics: ocean transport, air transport, trucking, warehousing & custom house brokerage. (As-Pac, estab 1995, empl 250, sales $12,881,358, cert: NMSDC)

3522 Freight Express Shipping Corp (FESCO)
      15330 Fairfield Ranch Rd., Unit G   Chino Hills, CA
      91709
      (909) 586-3000 Michael Yu GM
      Fax: (909) 586-3030
      Email: service@fescous.com
      Website: www.fescous.com
Import & export freight forwarding
services. (Woman/As-Pac, estab 2012, empl 6, sales
$900,000, cert: State)

3523 Golden Gate Air Freight Inc.
      1809 Sabre St   Hayward, CA 94545
      (510) 785-5720 John Cardenas President
      Fax: (510) 786-3277
      Email: jcardenas@ggaf.com
      Website:
Domestic & international freight forwarding. (Hisp, estab
1982, empl 22, sales $8,055,928, cert: NMSDC)

3524 KW International, Inc.
      18655 Bishop Ave   Carson, CA 90746
      (310) 354-6944 Steve Cho Senior Mgr
      Fax:
      Email: steve@kwinternational.com
      Website: www.kwinternational.com/default.aspx
Total logistics, transportation, freight forwarding, in-house
customs brokerage, warehousing & distribution, reverse
logistics, customer call center, field service, drayage,
information & technology. (As-Pac, estab 1996, empl 1000,
sales , cert: NMSDC)

3525 Roland International Freight Services, Inc.
      5710 W Manchester Ave Ste 104 Los Angeles, CA
      90045
      (310) 337-1775 Roland Furtado President
      Fax: (310) 337-0310
      Email: roland@rolandfreight.com
      Website: www.rolandfreight.com
International freight forwarder handling shipments by air
& ocean. (As-Ind, estab 1991, empl 4, sales $1,310,617,
cert: State, CPUC, 8(a))

3526 Say Cargo Express, Inc.
      700 E Debra Lane   Anaheim, CA 92805
      (714) 772-7735 Doug Childers President
      Fax: (714) 772-7732
      Email: dchilders@saycargo.com
      Website: www.saycargo.com
Freight; Shipping; Expedited; Cargo; Oversized;
Tradeshows; Logistics; LTL; Air Freight; Truckload, domestic
freight forwarder that specializes in expedited freight.
(Woman/Hisp, estab 2000, empl 13, sales $2,200,000,
cert: State, WBENC)

3527 Trans Global Shipping Alliance, LLC
      25255 Cabot Rd Ste 212   Laguna Hills, CA 92653
      (949) 699-1491 William Cordova President
      Fax: (949) 699-1495
      Email: bill@trustglobal.com
      Website: www.trustglobal.com
Global shipping, trucking, ocean, air & special air
couriers - standard & charter, full truckloads, flatbeds to
LTL. (Woman, estab 2000, empl 5, sales $338,896, cert:
State, CPUC)

3528 Transit Air Cargo Inc.
      2204 East 4th St   Santa Ana, CA 92705
      (714) 915-0657 Gulnawaz Khodayar President
      Fax: (714) 460-1835
      Email: gkhodayar@transitair.com
      Website: www.transitair.com
Global tradeshow logistics: air, ocean & ground. Product
freight services international & domestic. (Woman/As-
Ind, estab 1989, empl 55, sales $23,933,988, cert:
NMSDC, WBENC)

Colorado

3529 Logistics Innovators Inc. dba Adcom Worldwide
      16600 E 33rd Dr, Unit 26   Aurora, CO 80011
      (303) 329-0702 Toni Brock President
      Fax: (303) 344-2302
      Email: tbrock@adcomworldwide.com
      Website: www.adcomworldwide.com
Worldwide logistics, customs brokerage, ocean, air
ground, warehouse. (Woman/White, estab 1997, empl
10, sales $2,167,000, cert: WBENC)

Florida

3530 Air Marine Forwarding Co., Inc.
      12250 NW 25th St Ste 115 Miami, FL 33182
      (305) 477-3496 Roger Madan President
      Fax: (305) 477-4296
      Email: r.madan@airmarine.com
      Website: www.airmarine.com
Global logistics, intl air & ocean freight forwarding,
customs brokerage, NVOCC, warehousing & distribution,
bonded facilities & trucks, packing & crating. (Hisp, estab
1968, empl 28, sales $3,108,366, cert: NMSDC)

3531 Clover Systems Inc.
      1910 NW 97th Ave   Miami, FL 33172
      (305) 499-7056 Frank DeValdivielso Jr. Dir
      Business Dev
      Fax:
      Email: miami@clovergroup.com
      Website: www.clovergroup.com
Integrated logistics, air & ocean shipping, domestic &
intl distribution svcs, warehouse, export packing &
trucking. (Hisp, estab 1985, empl 70, sales $10,071,210,
cert: NMSDC)

3532   Edward Estevez CHB, Inc.
6910 Main St, Ste 150   Miami Lakes, FL 33014
(786) 247-1961   Edward Estevez President
Fax: (305) 821-2589
Email: admin@eechb.com
Website: www.eechb.com
U.S. Customs brokerage & logistics services. (Hisp, estab 2004, empl 1, sales , cert: State)

3533   Ocean Cargo Logistics Group, LLC
12161 SW 132 Ct   Miami, FL 33186
(305) 471-8442   Lorenzo Macias Sales
Fax: (305) 471-8403
Email: lorenzo@oceancargologistics.com
Website: www.oceancargologistics.com
Freight Forwarding, Air transportation, Domestic Trucking Transportation, Deep Ocean Transportation, Packing & Crating, LCL, FCL, LTL. (Hisp, estab 2008, empl 4, sales $1,200,000, cert: 8(a))

3534   Prime Air Cargo Inc.
1316 NW 78th Ave   Doral, FL 33126
(305) 592-2044   Omar Zambrano GM
Fax: (305) 592-2054
Email: ozambrano@primeaircargo.com
Website: www.primeaircargo.com
Air, land & ocean transport services. (Hisp, estab 2004, empl 15, sales , cert: NMSDC)

3535   Robertson Forwarding Company Inc.
1951 NW 7th Avenue Ste 600   Miami, FL 33136
(305) 477-5548   Stefan Ahrens GM
Fax: (305) 477-5435
Email: sahrens@rfclogistics.com
Website: www.rfclogistics.com
Logistics, warehousing, import & export documentation, air charter brokerage, in house customs broker, trucking, hazardous documentation, out of gage cargo, NVOCC, ocean shipments. (Woman/AA, estab 1968, empl 10, sales $2,500,000, cert: State)

3536   Time Definite Services Transportation, LLC
1935 CR525E   Sumterville, FL 33521
(800) 466-8040   Michael Suarez President
Fax: (847) 531-4501
Email: sales@timedefinite.com
Website: www.timedefinite.com
Freigth transportation: truckload LTL air freight, hot shots, warehousing, domestic & international. (Hisp, estab 1990, empl 60, sales $64,000,000, cert: NMSDC)

Georgia

3537   AFCLS Logistics Services LLC
975 Cobb Place Blvd Ste 101   Kennesaw, GA 30144
(770) 514-1456   Brenda Collins Brown VP
Fax: (678) 354-1183
Email: brenda.collinsbrown@afcls.com
Website: www.afcls.com
Global freight logistics svcs: motor freight forwarding, freight brokerage, ocean transportation intermediary & non-vessel operating common carrier services & indirect air carriage. (AA, estab 2008, empl 10, sales $1,300,000, cert: NMSDC)

3538   Bennett International Group LLC
1001 Industrial Pkwy   McDonough, GA 30253
(770) 957-1866   Lynette Alt VP of Diversity
Fax: (770) 957-8272
Email: lynette.alt@bennettig.com
Website: www.bennettig.com
Transportation: NVOCC, customs brokerage, freight forwarding air & ocean, project cargo, domestic trucking, oversized & over weight cargo, warehousing, third party logistics. (Woman/White, estab 1973, empl 650, sales , cert: WBENC)

3539   Expedited Transportation Services, Inc
505 Plantation Park Dr   Atlanta, GA 30052
(770) 413-1700   Charlene Taylor President
Fax: (770) 413-9186
Email: charlene@ets-atlanta.com
Website: www.ets-atlanta.com
Mail & cargo transport, air cargo, local area trucking, marine cargo, rail cargo, regional or natl trucking, vehicle carrier services, air charter transport. (Woman/White, estab 1982, empl 11, sales , cert: WBENC)

3540   Premier Expediters, Inc.
598 Red Oak Rd   Stockbridge, GA 30281
(859) 331-7447   Jeff George Business Devel Mgr
Fax: (859) 212-0867
Email: cvg@shippei.com
Website: www.shippei.com
Transportation, Carrier Authority, Freight Forwarding Authority & Brokerage, FTL, LTL, Expedited, Specialized, Air & Ocean Freight services. (Woman/White, estab 1992, empl 32, sales $13,000,000, cert: WBENC)

3541   S-2international LLC
5916 East Lake Pkwy Ste 311   McDonough, GA 30253
(678) 432-9502   Jennifer Mead CEO
Fax:
Email: jennifer.mead@s-2international.com
Website: www.s-2international.com
Transportation services, expedited/JIT movement, LTL, Airfreight, Charter & Ocean shipments. (Woman/White, estab 2005, empl 30, sales $15,000,000, cert: WBENC)

3542 Vector Global Logistics LLC
887 W Marietta St NW, Ste M201 23 Atlanta, GA 30318
(404) 554-1150 Enrique Alvarez Managing Dir
Fax: (404) 554-1155
Email: enrique.alvarez@vectorgl.com
Website: www.VectorGL.com
Sea freight, air freight, truck, rail & general logistics. (As-Pac/Hisp, estab 2012, empl 19, sales $9,100,000, cert: NMSDC)

Illionis

3543 Milano Railcar Services
P.O. Box 1357 Mount Vernon, IL 62864
(618) 242-4004 Mary Burgan President
Fax: (618) 242-0949
Email: mary@milanorail.com
Website: www.milanorail.com
Logistics, Storage, Pipe Laydown Yard, Trucking, Logistics, Inventory Control, Warehousing, Materials Handling, Transloading, Consulting. (Woman/White, estab 2009, empl 3, sales $264,085, cert: WBENC)

3544 Pactrans Air & Sea, Inc.
951-961 W Thorndale Ave Bensenville, IL 60106
(847) 766-9988 Kitty Pon President
Fax: (847) 766-9025
Email: kittyp@pactrans.com
Website: www.pactrans.com
International freight forwarding: air & sea freight consolidation logistics, world wide charter, warehousing, distribution, trucking & Customs brokerage services. (Woman/As-Pac, estab 1991, empl 50, sales $30,000,000, cert: City, NMSDC)

3545 Reilly International Ltd.
1555 N Michael Dr Wood Dale, IL 60191
(630) 238-4900 Vickie Reilly President
Fax: (630) 238-9040
Email: vickie@reillyinternational.com
Website: www.reillyinternational.com
International freight forwarding, consolidation & brokerage. (Woman/White, estab 1984, empl 20, sales $8,417,000, cert: WBENC)

Kentucky

3546 Liberty Transportation, Inc. dba Team Worldwide
1348 Jamike Dr Erlanger, KY 41018
(859) 282-0505 Bobbie Mattis President
Fax: (859) 282-8348
Email: bobbie.mattis@teamww.com
Website: www.teamww.com
Freight forwarding & logistics services. (Woman/White, estab 1989, empl 15, sales $6,000,000, cert: WBENC)

Massachusetts

3547 Advantage Global Logistics
41 Highland Ave Randolph, MA 02368
(781) 986-3832 Maureen Powers VP Sales
Fax: (781) 986-3834
Email: maureen.powers@landstarmail.com
Website: www.landstar.com
Domestic & international, white glove inside delivery, debris removal & scheduled appointment deliveries, exporting & importing, air or ocean, door to door or door to airport/port, clear customs. (Woman, estab 1960, empl 5000, sales $2,200,000,000,000, cert: State)

Maryland

3548 Patriot Air Freight, Inc.
806 Cromwell Park Dr Glen Burnie, MD 21061
(410) 766-2422 Heidi Gordon Acct Exec
Fax:
Email: hgordon@aitworldwide.com
Website: www.aitworldwide.com
Domestic Air Freight, Ground Transportation, International Air & Ocean, Custom House Brokerage, Transborder Services. (Woman/White, estab 1980, empl 16, sales $4,790,000, cert: WBENC)

3549 Samuel Shapiro & Company, Inc.
1215 E. Fort Ave. Ste 201 Baltimore, MD 21230
(410) 539-0540 Olga Lyakhovetskaya Mktg & Business Devel
Fax: (410) 547-6935
Email: web@shapiro.com
Website: www.shapiro.com
Transport management/freight forwarding, ocean, air, surface, documentation & letters of credit, Automated Export System (AES), classification & binding rulings, export compliance & consulting, public & private export seminars. (Woman/White, estab 1915, empl 120, sales $12,284,800, cert: WBENC)

Michigan

3550 Aero Expediting Inc.
37529 Huron Pointe Dr Harrison Township, MI 48045
(586) 792-4202 Colleen Taylor President
Fax: (586) 792-4246
Email: colleenliz@aeroexp.com
Website: www.aeroexp.com
Air freight forwarding services. (Woman/White, estab 1988, empl 3, sales $750,000, cert: WBENC)

3551 BLT Logistics LLC
34450 Goddard Rd Romulus, MI 48174
(586) 467-1437 Joe Goryl VP Supply Chain
Fax:
Email: JGoryl@BLTship.com
Website: www.bltship.com
Transportation & logistics services in the U.S., Canada, and Mexico, domestic intermodal, drayage, air & ocean forwarding services. (Woman, estab 2014, empl 22, sales $1,500,000, cert: WBENC)

3552 Chat of Michigan Inc.
      35790 Northline Rd P.O. Box 74498 Romulus, MI
      48174
      (734) 941-5004 Greg Katcher President
      Fax: (734) 941-4918
      Email: chatgk@aol.com
      Website: www.chatofmichigan.com
Transportation, crating, rigging, plant relocation, freight
forwarding. (AA, estab 1995, empl 40, sales $5,758,000,
cert: NMSDC)

3553 Global TEAM Associates, LLC
      11301 Metro Airport Center Dr Ste 170 Romulus,
      MI 48174
      (734) 992-3208 Petra Clark CEO
      Fax:
      Email: petra.clark@globalteamusa.com
      Website: www.globalteamusa.com
Freight Forwarding & Customs House Brokerage services.
(Woman, estab 2013, empl 21, sales , cert: WBENC)

3554 HNT Logistics LLC
      P.O. Box 603 New Boston, MI 48164
      (866) 984-8840 Mark Bowers VP of Ops
      Fax: (734) 331-2997
      Email: sales@hntlogistics.net
      Website: www.hntlogistics.com
3PL logistics, truck freight, bulk freight, ocean freight, air
freight, expedited freight & rail freight. (Woman/White,
estab 2005, empl 34, sales $23,000,000, cert: WBENC)

3555 MBA Logistics, LLC
      11455 Narin Dr Brighton, MI 48114
      (810) 225-0295 Martin Stapleton Ops
      Fax: (810) 225-9480
      Email: mbalogistics@comcast.net
      Website:
International ocean freight forwarding, freight management, U.S. Customs compliance & general logistics
services. (Woman/As-Pac, estab 2004, empl 1, sales
$30,000, cert: NMSDC)

3556 Prime Time Delivery
      9354 Harrison Rd Romulus, MI 48174
      (800) 336-3678 Paul Davis CEO
      Fax: (734) 947-1684
      Email: pdavis@ptlogistics.com
      Website: www.ptlogistics.com
Nationwide airfreight & ground transportation. (AA, estab
1997, empl 11, sales $3,000,000, cert: NMSDC)

3557 SEKO Worldwide
      6800 S Cypress Romulus, MI 48174
      (734) 641-2100 Tanya Bartelo Owner
      Fax: (734) 641-2199
      Email: tanya.bartelo@sekoworldwide.com
      Website: www.sekoworldwide.com
Transportation services: domestic expedited, international
air & ocean. (Woman/White, estab 1976, empl 1800, sales
, cert: WBENC)

3558 Trans Overseas Corp.
      P.O. Box 847 Taylor, MI 48180
      (734) 946-8750 James Gannon President
      Fax: (734) 946-8197
      Email: jgannon@trans-overseas.com
      Website: www.trans-overseas.com
US Customs Broker, International Air/Ocean Freight
Forwarder, Bonded Warehouse, Foreign Trade Zone,
Container Freight Station, Barcode Labeling, Inspections,
Repackaging & Distribution. (Woman/White, estab 1978,
empl 47, sales $5,600,000, cert: WBENC)

3559 Transphere Inc.
      5800 Commerce Dr Westland, MI 48185
      (734) 727-1307 SMITA KORADIA CEO
      Fax: (734) 727-1358
      Email: skoradia@transphereinc.net
      Website: www.transphereinc.com
International logistics/transportation, warehousing,
cargo by sea, air & land. (Woman/As-Ind, estab 1987,
empl 3, sales $980,000, cert: NMSDC)

North Carolina

3560 SOS Global Express, Inc.
      P.O. Box 12307 New Bern, NC 28561
      (252) 635-1400 Dan Cash Natl sales
      Fax: (252) 635-1920
      Email: dcash@sosglobal.com
      Website: www.sosglobal.com
Transportation: air, ocean & truck. (Hisp, estab 1994,
empl 169, sales , cert: NMSDC)

New Jersey

3561 Andrew Vazquez Inc.
      P.O. Box 1010 24 Tuttle Ave Bedminster, NJ 07921
      (908) 719-2444 Andrew Vazquez President
      Fax: (908) 719-2772
      Email: Avaquez@DLGroup.com
      Website: www.aviquality.com
Vehicle Logistics Services (Hisp, estab 1979, empl 30,
sales $4,500,000, cert: NMSDC)

3562 Blisset Transportation
      50 Triangle Blvd. Carlstadt, NJ 07072
      (201) 549-0672 Roseanne Magliato President
      Fax: (201) 933-5050
      Email: rmagliato@blissetllc.com
      Website: www.blissetllc.com
Transportation & logistics services, warehousing,
fulfillment & technology solutions. (Woman/Hisp, estab
1991, empl 35, sales $10,000,001, cert: NMSDC,
WBENC)

3563 Ltd Logistics, Inc.
        222 Outwater Lane Ste 3 Garfield, NJ 07026
        (973) 340-4428 Tracy Flood Transportation Sales
        Rep
        Fax: (973) 340-4423
        Email: tracy.flood@ltdnj.com
        Website: www.ltdnj.com
Ground & air freight transportation, full truckload & LTL/
partials via over the road, intermodal & air freight.
(Woman/White, estab 1995, empl 10, sales $4,922,477,
cert: State, City)

New York

3564 AWLI Group, Inc.
        147-60 175 St Jamaica, NY 11434
        (718) 244-8923 Keith Milliner VP
        Fax: (718) 244-8665
        Email: keith@amberworldwide.com
        Website: www.amberworldwide.com
International freight forwarding. (Woman/White, estab
1990, empl 20, sales $12,594,223, cert: State)

3565 MSL Express, Inc.
        160-19 Rockaway Blvd   Jamaica, NY 11434
        (718) 528-1833 Chester Tong President
        Fax: (718) 528-1507
        Email: chester.tong@mslexpress-us.com
        Website: www.mslexpress.com
International freight transportation: ocean & air, imports/
exports, air charters. (As-Pac, estab 1988, empl 9, sales
$7,000,000, cert: State)

3566 Walker International Transportation, LLC
        70 E Sunrise Hwy Ste 611 Valley Stream, NY 11581
        (516) 568-2080 Maria Hill Director of Sales
        Fax: (516) 568-2036
        Email: mhill@walkerscm.com
        Website: www.walkerscm.com
International transportation, logistics, sub- assembly,
sequencing, kitting, warehousing, distribution & customs
brokarage. (AA, estab 1999, empl 275, sales , cert: NMSDC,
SDB)

Ohio

3567 ASW Global, LLC
        3375 Gilchrist Rd   Mogadore, OH 44260
        (1330) 733-8176 Pam Harris Mgr, Mktg & Supplier
        Diversity
        Fax: (330) 733-5196
        Email: PHarris@aswglobal.com
        Website: www.aswglobal.com
Third-party logistics, warehousing, order fulfillment, pick
pack & ship, pkging/re-packaging, contract logistics retail
supply chain support, real estate devel proj mgmt, bulk
resin transloading, records retention, file storage, &
retrieval services. (AA, estab 1983, empl 120, sales
$30,822,703, cert: NMSDC)

3568 Grand Aire, Inc.
        11777 W. Airport Service Road Toledo Express
        Airport Swanton, OH 43558
        (419) 861-6700 Katrina Cheema Business Advisor
        Fax: (419) 861-6806
        Email: diversity@grandaire.com
        Website: www.grandaire.com
Air charter transportation: passengers & cargo. (As-Ind,
estab 1997, empl 20, sales $13,126,078, cert: NMSDC,
SDB)

3569 KLN Logistics dba AIT Worldwide Logistics
        6749 Eastland Rd, Ste C   Middleburg Heights, OH
        44130
        (440) 816-1505 Kimberly Martinez-Giering Owner
        Fax: (440) 816-1509
        Email: info@klnlogistics.com
        Website: www.klnlogistics.com
Air freight, expedited trucking, import, export, logistics.
(Woman/Hisp, estab 2005, empl 28, sales $427,000,000,
cert: State, NMSDC, WBENC)

3570 Marine Services International, Inc.
        14508 S Industrial Ave   Cleveland, OH 44137
        (216) 587-3500 Michelle Panik President
        Fax:
        Email: michelle@marineservicesintl.com
        Website: www.marineservicesintl.com
Air, Sea, Land International Freight Transportation
(freight forwarder), warehousing, labeling, repackaging,
packaging & re-palletizing capabilities. (Woman/As-Ind,
estab 2006, empl 18, sales $5,000,000, cert: State)

Puerto Rico

3571 Nestor Reyes, Inc.
        P.O. Box 9023474   San Juan, PR 00902
        (787) 289-6465 Edmundo Rodriguez President
        Fax: (787) 289-6457
        Email: e.rodriguez@nreyes.com
        Website: www.nreyes.com
Foreign freight forwarding. (Hisp, estab 1973, empl 35,
sales $7,753,580, cert: NMSDC)

South Carolina

3572 Alpha Logistics Solutions, Inc.
        1750 Hwy 160 West, Ste 101   Fort Mill, SC 29708
        (877) 356-6102 Arthur Cottingham VP of Business
        Devel
        Fax: (803) 626-0645
        Email: alphals2014@gmail.com
        Website: www.alphalogisticssolutions.com
Less Than Truckload (LTL), Truckload (TL), Domestic Air &
Ground Expedited Shipping, International, Intermodal.
(Woman/AA, estab 2014, empl 5, sales $350,000, cert:
NMSDC)

3573 Atlantic-Pacific Express, Inc.
      1350 Browning Rd, Ste B Columbia, SC 29210
      (877) 739-1116 Irene Brotherton President
      Fax: (803) 739-2611
      Email: irene@apexpedite.com
      Website: www.apexpedite.com
Asset based & non-asset based ground & air freight.
(Woman/White, estab 16, empl 13, sales $28,000,000,
cert: WBENC)

Tennessee

3574 Total Control Logistics
      1519 Union Ave, Ste 177   Memphis, TN 38104
      (901) 830-1864 Terica Lamb President
      Fax:
      Email: tlamb@tclogistix.com
      Website: www.tclogistix.com
Third party logistics provider (3PL), Warehousing &
Distribution. (Woman/AA, estab 2009, empl 1, sales , cert:
NMSDC)

Texas

3575 Epsilon Brokerage Corporation
      12110 Sara Rd   Laredo, TX 78045
      (956) 728-8713 Rick Laurel President
      Fax: (800) 871-9412
      Email: rick.laurel@epsilonbrokerage.com
      Website: www.epsilonbrokerage.com
Logistics, customs broker, freight forwarding, warehousing.
(Hisp, estab 2011, empl 50, sales $4,000,000, cert: State,
NMSDC)

3576 InstiCo Freight Management, Inc.
      3011 Gateway Dr. Ste 340 Irving, TX 75063
      (469) 293-9549 Cory Allen Business Dev Exec
      Fax:
      Email: callen@insticologistics.com
      Website: www.insticologistics.com
International Services- Ocean cargo, Air cargo, and Non-
Vessel Operating Common Carrier. (Hisp, estab 2011, empl
25, sales , cert: NMSDC)

3577 Intel-Logistics, Inc.
      5226 N Sam Houston Pkwy E   Houston, TX 77032
      (281) 449-5067 Van Clark President
      Fax: (281) 449-9285
      Email: van-clark@intel-logisticsinc.com
      Website: www.lognetworldwide.com
Cargo transportation & logistics svcs: air freight, trucking &
ocean freight for domestic and international shipping. (AA,
estab 1993, empl 8, sales $796,102, cert: State)

3578 Multi-Trans, Inc.
      606 Grand Central Blvd.   Laredo, TX 78045
      (210) 418-4889 Emilio Villarreal New Projects
      Fax: (210) 418-3209
      Email: evillarreal@multitransinc.com
      Website: www.multitransinc.com
Air, Sea & Land Transportation service, LTL, TL & Sea
Containers, Flat Beds, Lowboys, Drop Decks & Heavy
Equipment Hauling, Air Charters. (Woman/Nat Ame,
estab 2000, empl 8, sales $10,000,000, cert: State,
WBENC)

3579 Trans-Expedite, Inc.
      7 Founders Blvd   El Paso, TX 79906
      (915) 779-9100 Keeli Jernigan CEO
      Fax: (915) 775-0344
      Email: kjernigan@trans-expedite.com
      Website: www.trans-expedite.com
Transportation & logistics: air charters, warehousing,
customs brokerage. (Woman/White, estab 2001, empl 3,
sales $70,000,000, cert: CPUC, WBENC)

3580 Twenty-Two Global Transport, LP
      P.O. Box 62588   Houston, TX 77205
      (901) 362-3707 Kevin Smoot Reg Mgr
      Fax: (901) 362-3710
      Email: ksmoot@22global.com
      Website: www.xxiiglobal.com
International ocean freight forwarding, customs brokerage, hot shot/expedited services, logistics services,
global information services. (AA, estab 2007, empl 4,
sales $200,000, cert: NMSDC)

FREIGHT TRANSPORTATION
Transport office and household furniture and equipment. Many transport commercial freight and general commodities and have ICC rights for other states. Many firms also provide storage and packaging services. Includes charter bus and limousine service and air couriers. NAICS Code 48

Alabama

3581 ARD Logistics, LLC
      10098 Brose Dr   Vance, AL 35490
      (205) 393-5207 Courtney Waters Sales & Mktg Rep
      Fax:
      Email: cwaters@ardlogistics.com
      Website: www.ardlogistics.com
Distribution operations: sequencing, sub-assembly, warehousing, inventory mgmt, shipping & receiving materials handling maintenance, packaging & repackaging, transportation mgmt, transportation svcs. (AA, estab 1998, empl 900, sales $68,717,549, cert: NMSDC)

3582 ARI Logistics LLC
      204 20th St North Ste 200 Birmingham, AL 35203
      (205) 271-4434 Brennan Waters Sales
      Fax: (205) 271-4434
      Email: brennan.waters@actn.com
      Website: www.actn.com
Hazardous waste transport, in-plant, remediation, & logistics services. (AA, estab 2008, empl 55, sales $48,000,000, cert: NMSDC)

3583 Armstrong Relocation Company
      2775 Wall Triana Hwy Ste E Huntsville, AL 35824
      (256) 509-9002 Leslie Coleman Sr VP
      Fax: (256) 772-8399
      Email: lesliecoleman@goarmstrong.com
      Website: www.huntsville.armstrongrelocation.com/
Household Goods moving and storage. (Woman/White, estab 1998, empl 35, sales $2,834,851, cert: WBENC)

3584 B & F Trucking, Inc.
      3086 Laurel Lake Cove   Bessemer, AL 35022
      (205) 464-8644 Bill Brown Jr. President
      Fax: (205) 464-8645
      Email: Strolldaddy1@aol.com
      Website:
General freight transportation. (AA, estab 1998, empl 40, sales $1,400,000, cert: NMSDC)

3585 Universal Logistics Services, Inc.
      5330 Stadium Trace Pkwy, Ste 200   Birmingham, AL 35244
      (205) 682-8505 Alan Washburn Ops Mgr
      Fax: (205) 682-8508
      Email: AWashburn@ufsystems.com
      Website: www.universallogisticsservices.com
Transportation services. (AA, estab 1999, empl 100, sales $3,500,000, cert: NMSDC)

Arkansas

3586 Goddess Logistics
      6142 Getty Dr   North Little Rock, AR 72117
      (501) 541-2379 Quintin Fleming Director of Transportaion/Logistics
      Fax: (501) 372-4032
      Email: quintinf@gpitrans.com
      Website: www.gpilogistics.com
Logistics/transportation & office supplier. (Woman/AA, estab 2006, empl 15, sales , cert: WBENC)

3587 Heartland Supply Company
      1248 Pump Station Rd   Fayetteville, AR 72702
      (479) 444-0970 Sarah McCoy Business Dev and Sales Mgr
      Fax: (479) 521-5022
      Email: sarahm@heartlandsupply.com
      Website: www.heartlandsupply.com
Logistic, distribution, supply chain optimization & warehousing services. (Nat Ame, estab 1987, empl 13, sales $40,000,000, cert: NMSDC)

3588 WMJ Enterprises, LLC.
      P.O. Box 979   Lowell, AR 72745
      (888) 782-5828 Justin Winberry VP
      Fax: (888) 782-5306
      Email: jwinberry@leon-cannon.com
      Website: www.leon-cannon.com
Asset based transportation & logsitics. (Hisp, estab 1994, empl 38, sales $27,200,000, cert: State)

Arizona

3589 Aerocean Freight Solutions, Inc.
      9414 E. San Salvador Dr Ste 242 Scottsdale, AZ 85258
      (480) 515-1912 Yeon-Hee (Jennifer) Hwang President
      Fax: (480) 502-0784
      Email: jennifer@aeroceanfreight.com
      Website: www.aeroceanfreight.com
Third party logistical services, road transportation, rail, ocean freight transportation. (Woman/As-Pac, estab 2006, empl 4, sales $5,314,734, cert: WBENC)

3590 Mach 1 Global Services, Inc.
      1530 W Broadway Rd   Tempe, AZ 85282
      (480) 921-3900 Jamie Fletcher CEO
      Fax: (480) 361-0671
      Email: jfletcher@mach1global.com
      Website: www.mach1global.com
Transportation & logistics, domestic heavy weight expedited freight forwarding, international freight forwarding, ocean & air import & export, distribution, warehousing & supply chain management. (Woman/As-Pac, estab 1988, empl 250, sales $105,000,000, cert: WBENC)

3591 Patriot Movers, LLC
      3060 N Ridgecrest, Unit 128   Mesa, AZ 85207
      (877) 793-7775 Christopher Palos COO
      Fax: (480) 248-3129
      Email: patriotmovers57@yahoo.com
      Website: www.Patriotmover.us
Moving & Transportation, Local a& nd Long Distance
Moving, (intrastate and interstate), Packing, Unpacking,
Crating, Specialized Freight,   Residential, Commercial,
Office, Relocation services. (Woman/Hisp, estab 2012,
empl 5, sales $103,573, cert: City)

3592 Reflex Logistics, LLC
      7114 E Stetson Dr Ste 400 Scottsdale, AZ 85251
      (602) 859-5969 Cory Clapper VP of Sales
      Fax: (602) 297-6810
      Email: coryclapper@reflexlogistics.com
      Website: www.reflexlogistics.com
Domestic full truckload van, refrigerated & flatbed transportation services. (Woman/White, estab 2013, empl 8,
sales $750,000, cert: WBENC)

California

3593 1st Choice Logistics LLC
      312 Laurel Avenue   South San Francisco, CA 94080
      (415) 590-0211 Destiny Jimenez President
      Fax: (415) 869-3728
      Email: dj@1stchoicelogistics.us
      Website: www.1stchoicelogistics.us
Logistic solutions, Truckload, Refrigerated, Dry van,
Flatbed, Over-dimensional, Heavy haul, Expedited, Partials.
(Woman/Hisp, estab 2012, empl 1, sales $769,000, cert:
NMSDC, CPUC, WBENC)

3594 Bulk or Liquid Transport, LLC
      140 W Branch St   Arroyo Grande, CA 93420
      (800) 975-2658 Tracy Thomas CEO
      Fax: (805) 202-2204
      Email: tthomas@BOLT-Transport.com
      Website: www.BOLT-Transport.com
Interstate transportation: liquid food-grade products.
(Woman/White, estab 2006, empl 11, sales $3,167,483,
cert: WBENC)

3595 Contractors Cargo Companies
      500 S Alameda St   Compton, CA 90221
      (310) 609-1957 Steve Cummins Natl Sales Mgr
      Fax:
      Email: scummins@contractorscargo.com
      Website: www.contractorscargo.com
Heavy haul transportation company, oversized, overweight
or overdimensional cargo, rail logistics, heavy haul trans-
port & shipping, nationally & internationally. (Woman/
White, estab 1929, empl 85, sales $24,000,000, cert:
CPUC)

3596 Crown Xpress Transport Inc.
      9931 Via de la amistad   San Diego, CA 92154
      (619) 671-9611 Lorena Guillen Business Dev
      Fax: (619) 671-0162
      Email: assistant@crownxt.com
      Website: www.crownxt.com
FTL freight services. (Woman/Hisp, estab 2003, empl 39,
sales $12,434,665, cert: NMSDC, WBENC)

3597 CurDor Group Inc.
      2321 Del Amo Blvd   Rancho Dominguez, CA
      90220
      (310) 885-5200 Curlee Dorn President
      Fax: (310) 885-5201
      Email: curlee.dorn@360globaltransportation.com
      Website: www.360globaltransportation.com
Intermodal, Import / Export, Haz-mat, Over-Weight
Containers, Warehousing, Less Than truck Load,
Transloading, Dedicated Services, Flatbed, Reefer, Rail
Services, Cross-Drocking, Truckload (TL), Outsourcing,
Dryvan. (AA, estab 2012, empl 7, sales $400,000, cert:
NMSDC)

3598 D.W. Morgan Company, Inc.
      4185 Blackhawk Plaza Circle Ste 260 Danville, CA
      94506
      (925) 460-2700 Maria Guerrero VP Sales/Mktg
      Fax:
      Email: erica.aguilar@dwmorgan.com
      Website: www.dwmorgan.com
Supply chain consulting, transportation management,
and thrid-party logistics. (As-Pac, estab 1990, empl 250,
sales $50,000,000, cert: NMSDC, CPUC)

3599 EXCEL Moving Services
      30047 Ahern Ave   Union City, CA 94587
      (800) 392-3596 Bruce Owashi President
      Fax: (510) 324-9716
      Email: bruce@excelmoving.com
      Website: www.excelmoving.com
Moving & storage, employee relocations, storage &
distribution, air-ride inside PU/Del transportation, intl
shipping/receiving, household goods specialist. (AA/As-
Pac, estab 1994, empl 55, sales $4,000,000, cert: State,
NMSDC, CPUC)

3600 Global Freight Experts, Inc.
      1950 E Miner Ave   Stockton, CA 95205
      (209) 547-9210 Rajinder Singh President
      Fax: (209) 547-9211
      Email: raj@gfbontime.com
      Website: www.gfbontime.com
Asset based trucking. (As-Pac, estab 2010, empl 25, sales
$3,100,000, cert: NMSDC)

3601 Intrade Industries, Inc.
2559 S East Ave   Fresno, CA 93706
(559) 256-3291 Tracy Farrell logistics/Mktg Mgr
Fax: (559) 256-3295
Email: tracy.intradeindustries@gmail.com
Website: www.intradeindustries.com
Transportation services for refrigerated cargo & freight from coast to coast. (Woman/As-Ind, estab 1997, empl 14, sales $23,000,000, cert: NMSDC)

3602 KLS Air Express, Inc. dba Freight Solution Provide
2870 Gold Tailings Ct.   Rancho Cordova, CA 95670
(513) 532-1297 Chrissie Cruz Natl Exec Accts Mgr
Fax:
Email: chrissie_cruz@shipfsp.com
Website: www.shipfsp.com/about/index.html
Customized frieght transportation, logistics, warehousing & supply chain management solutions. (Woman/As-Pac, estab 1989, empl 110, sales $42,000,000, cert: NMSDC, WBENC)

3603 KW International, Inc.
18655 Bishop Ave   Carson, CA 90746
(310) 354-6944 Steve Cho Senior Mgr
Fax:
Email: steve@kwinternational.com
Website: www.kwinternational.com/default.aspx
Total logistics, transportation, freight forwarding, in-house customs brokerage, warehousing & distribution, reverse logistics, customer call center, field service, drayage, information & technology. (As-Pac, estab 1996, empl 1000, sales , cert: NMSDC)

3604 Mayor Logistics Inc.
17214 S Figueroa St   Gardena, CA 90248
(424) 221-5225 Henry Mayor
Fax: (559) 441-9001
Email: hruiz@mayorusa.com
Website: www.mayorusa.com
Domestic drayage, import/export, truckload, local & over the road, regional carrier. (Hisp, estab 2004, empl 10, sales $5,636,670, cert: NMSDC)

3605 Music Express Limousine Service
2601 Empire Ave   Burbank, CA 91504
(818) 260-6602 Joseph Murray VP Corp sales
Fax: (818) 955-9377
Email: jmurray@musicexpress.com
Website: www.musicexpress.com
National & international limousine svcs. (Woman/White, estab 1972, empl 500, sales , cert: WBENC)

3606 National Freight Logistics Inc.
3150 N Weber Ave   Fresno, CA 93722
(559) 474-6994 Cherly Lim-Harris
Fax: (559) 441-9001
Email: cherly.limharris@nflfreight.com
Website: www.NFLfreight.com
Freight transportation & logistics. (Woman/As-Ind, estab 2006, empl 4, sales $1,534,690, cert: NMSDC)

3607 Northwest Freightway Inc.
3421 Industrial Dr   Yuba City, CA 95991
(539) 788-2742 Nicholas Schlaff Dir of Sales
Fax:
Email: nick@nwfreightway.com
Website: www.nwfreightway.com
Freight transportation services. (AA, estab 2007, empl 26, sales $28,000,000, cert: NMSDC)

3608 Oakley Relocation LLC
13026 Stowe Dr   Poway, CA 92064
(858) 602-1010 Sara Oakley Dir of Business Dev
Fax: (858) 602-1001
Email: sara@oakleyrelocation.com
Website: www.oakleyrelocation.com
Full-service moving & storage company. (Woman/White, estab 2008, empl 15, sales $4,250,000, cert: WBENC)

3609 Public Special
3147 Progress Circle   Mira Loma, CA 91752
(951) 360-4466 Anna Aguiar President
Fax: (951) 360-2077
Email: aaguiar@publicspecial.net
Website: www.publicspecial.net
Transportation, US and Canada. (Woman/Hisp, estab 1980, empl 4, sales $22,048,000, cert: NMSDC)

3610 Red Rose Transportation, Inc
5705 N West Ave   Fresno, CA 93711
(559) 277-1060 Mark Rose Ops Mgr
Fax: (559) 277-1067
Email: Mark@redrosetrans.net
Website: www.redrosetransportation.com
Logistic services, dedicated truckloads, Heavy haul, 53' dry van & reefers, flatbeds & LTL. (Woman/As-Pac, estab 2007, empl 7, sales $8,300,000, cert: CPUC, WBENC)

3611 Tricor America, Inc.
P.O. Box 8100 - SFIA   San Francisco, CA 94128
(650) 877-3650 Scott Tanaka Major Acct Exec
Fax: (650) 583-3197
Email: scott.tanaka@mail.tricor.com
Website: www.tricor.com
National & intl courier services. (As-Pac, estab 1957, empl 500, sales , cert: NMSDC)

Colorado

3612 Craters and Freighters
331 Corporate Circle, Ste J   Golden, CO 80401
(720) 287-7805 Chad Brockmeyer Natl Sales Mgr
Fax:
Email: chad@cratersandfreighters.com
Website: www.cratersandfreighters.com
Custom wood crating, plastic hard cases and freight services. (Woman/White, estab 1990, empl 12, sales $55,000,000, cert: WBENC)

3613 FAK, Inc.
      10885 E 51st Ave   Denver, CO 80239
      (303) 289-5433 Ron Harms GM
      Fax: (303) 289-1674
      Email: rharms@fakinc.com
      Website: www.fakinc.com
Transportation: refrigerated, dry van, flatbed, specialized &
intermodal. US & Canada. (Woman/White, estab 1983,
empl 62, sales $69,359,561, cert: WBENC)

3614 Freight All Kinds, Inc.
      10885 E 51st Ave   Denver, CO 80239
      (303) 289-5433 Ron Harms GM
      Fax: (303) 289-1674
      Email: rharms@fakinc.com
      Website: www.fakinc.com
Transportation: refrigerated, dry van, flatbed, specialized &
intermodal, US & Canada. (Woman/White, estab 1983,
empl 45, sales $55,000,000, cert: WBENC)

3615 Innovative Solutions Development
      13404 Locust St   Thornton, CO 80602
      (303) 428-6034 Darryl Johnson Owner
      Fax: (303) 428-6040
      Email: darrylj@landstarmail.com
      Website:
Transportation, distribution, logistics, warehousing, &
information management domestically & globally. (AA,
estab 2000, empl 3, sales $1,500,000, cert: State)

Florida

3616 Faith Transport & Logistics, Inc.
      190 SE 3rd Ave   Deerfield Beach, FL 33441
      (954) 274-0357 Aldo Goncalves Jr. President
      Fax:
      Email: transportwithfaith@faithtlinc.com
      Website: www.transportwithfaith.com
Transportation & logistics, United States & Canada as an
Interstate Motor Carrier. (Hisp, estab 2012, empl 3, sales
$244,948, cert: NMSDC)

3617 Florida Freight Lines Inc.
      451 Harbor Dr N   Indian Rocks Beach, FL 33785
      (727) 800-9870 Marie Mazzara President
      Fax: (866) 985-5070
      Email: mmazzara@FloridaFreightLines.com
      Website: www.FloridaFreightLines.com
LTL (Less Than Truckload), Full Truckload, Dry, Fresh,
Frozen. (Woman/White, estab 2013, empl 2, sales
$245,570, cert: WBENC)

3618 Giovanni Transport, LLC
      3066 Shady Dr   Jacksonville, FL 32257
      (904) 612-5988 Shatise Johnson President
      Fax: (866) 301-6127
      Email: smjohnson@giovannitrans.com
      Website: www.giovannitrans.com
Transportation solutions, ship truckload freight, dedicated
dry van transportation. (Woman/AA, estab 2006, empl 4,
sales $230,000, cert: State)

3619 GlobalTransService Corp.
      10200 W StateRd84 Ste. 209 Davie, FL 33324
      (954) 414-0561 Tatiana Guydouk President
      Fax: (954) 842-7158
      Email: info@globaltransservice.net
      Website: www.globaltransservicecorp.com/
Dry Van, Reefer, Flat Bed, Tracking Shipment, Logistics.
(Woman/White, estab 2014, empl 5, sales $2,300,000,
cert: WBENC)

3620 Hermes Global Logistic Services, LLC
      5323 Millenia Lakes Blvd Ste 300 Orlando, FL
      32839
      (407) 734-4046 Dena Kirschbaum
      Fax: (407) 734-4001
      Email: dena.kirschbaum@hglservices.com
      Website: www.hglservices.com
3PL supply chain management solutions, integrating
operations, warehousing & transportation services.
(Woman/AA, estab 2015, empl 4, sales $500,000, cert:
NMSDC)

3621 Interstate Transport, Inc.
      324 1st Avenue North   St. Petersburg, FL 33701
      (727) 822-9999 Zach Aufmann COO
      Fax: (727) 895-1025
      Email: ZAufmann@InterstateTransport.com
      Website: www.InterstateTransport.com
TL (truckload) & LTL (less than truckload) freight in US &
Canada. Specialized freight capabilities (live goods,
plants, perishables, lumber) dry, flatbed & refrigerated
(reefer/refer) trailers, utilizing single or team drivers.
(Woman/White, estab 2002, empl 50, sales $25,900,000,
cert: WBENC)

3622 Newco Services, Inc.
      1831 16th St   Boynton Beach, FL 33435
      (561) 375-9930 Kimberly Presson Sales
      Fax: (561) 375-9510
      Email: kimberly@newcoservices.com
      Website: www.newcoservices.com
Transportation, warehousing, repair, refurbishment,
prevenative maintenance, data reporting & consolidated
billing svcs. (Woman/White, estab 1994, empl 20, sales
$4,200,000, cert: WBENC)

3623 North American Transport Services LLC
      160 Ali baba Ave   Opa-Locka, FL 33054
      (305) 455-1150 Kasey Cano Business Devel Rep
      Fax: (305) 805-9955
      Email: kcano@nalogistics.com
      Website: www.nalogistics.com
Assist customers with inbound & outbound freight,
manage pick-up & delivery schedules. (Hisp, estab 2004,
empl 45, sales $45,000,000, cert: NMSDC)

3624 Raven Transport Company, Inc.
6800 Broadway Ave   Jacksonville, FL 32254
(904) 425-5230 Andrew Rhodes VP Sales & Mktg
Fax: (904) 781-8946
Email: andrew.rhodes@raventrans.com
Website: www.raventrans.com
Truckload carrier, 48 states authority. (AA, estab 1985, empl 579, sales $85,297,000, cert: NMSDC)

3625 Timus, Inc
8131 Baymeadows Cir W Ste 202 Jacksonville, FL 32256
(904) 641-6206 Mr. Adam P. Kulig VP Business Dev
Fax: (904) 641-6825
Email: Adam.Kulig@timusinc.com
Website: www.timus.com
Full truckload, intermodal (rail). (Nat Ame, estab 1999, empl 5, sales $5,040,000, cert: State)

Georgia

3626 Atlanta Peach Movers, Inc.
2911 Northeast Parkway   Doraville, GA 30360
(770) 447-5121 Orlando Lynch Office Mgr
Fax: (770) 447-5154
Email: olynch@atlpeachmovers.com
Website: www.atlantapeachmovers.com
Moving & storage, furnishings & equipment. (AA, estab 1900, empl 1, sales , cert: NMSDC)

3627 Axiom Logistics LLC
5000 Austell-Powder Springs Rd Ste 189 Austell, GA 30106
(770) 694-6248 Morgan Perry CEO
Fax: (888) 200-6640
Email: morgan@axiomtrans.com
Website: www.axiomtrans.com
Logistics, Dry, frozen & refrigerated truckload, Flatbed, drop deck & double drop, Over-Dimensional, heavy haul & expedited, Power Only, Team & expedited truckload and (LTL) less than truckload services. (Woman/AA, estab 2012, empl 6, sales $1,099,963, cert: NMSDC, WBENC)

3628 Eagle Transportation Services, Inc.
731 Queen City Pkwy Ste 101 Gainesville, GA 30501
(770) 965-1242 Lynn Mull President
Fax: (770) 965-0020
Email: lynn@eagletransportation.com
Website: www.eagletransportation.com
Third party logistics. (Woman/White, estab 1988, empl 6, sales , cert: WBENC)

3629 Efficient Courier & Logistics Services LLC
5475 Tulane Dr Atlanta, GA 30336
(800) 590-2155 Patrick Chukwudolue Exec Director
Fax: (800) 590-2155
Email: partners@ecourierlogistics.com
Website: www.ecourierlogistics.com
Integrated end to logistics & freight services, customized supply chain, warehousing, logistics & delivery. (AA, estab 2013, empl 5, sales , cert: NMSDC)

3630 KCH Trucking, LLC
6695 Peachtree Industrial Blvd Ste 250 Atlanta, GA 30360
(770) 962-6829 Alan Whitten VP sales
Fax: (770) 682-2079
Email: awhitten@kchtrans.com
Website: www.kchtrans.com
National truckload transportation services. (Woman/White, estab 2006, empl 5, sales $8,000,001, cert: WBENC)

3631 MIMCH, Inc. dba GOEH Distribution
200 Piedmont Crt, Ste-B Doraville, GA 30340
(770) 849-0086 Stanley Michel GM
Fax: (770) 849-0820
Email: stmichel@bellsouth.net
Website: www.goehmoving.com
Warehousing, moving & distribution. (Woman/AA, estab 1994, empl 25, sales $485,900, cert: State)

3632 PEI Logistics, Inc.
598 Red Oak Rd Stockbridge, GA 30281
(404) 361-0073 Victoria Carver President
Fax: (678) 278-0020
Email: adobbertin@shippei.com
Website: www.shippei.com
Transportation & logistic services. (Woman/White, estab 1993, empl 35, sales $11,000,000, cert: WBENC)

3633 R2 Trucking Solutions
1882 Princeton Ave,Ste 1 College Park, GA 30337
(770) 892-3699 Amari Ruff CEO
Fax: (770) 892-6366
Email: aruff@r2truckingsolutions.com
Website: www.r2truckingsolutions.com
Global logistics, air, ocean & ground carriers. (AA, estab 2014, empl 22, sales $1,867,989, cert: NMSDC)

3634 Scott Logistics Corp.
375 Technology Pkwy   Rome, GA 30165
(470) 419-6209 Jayme Gauthreaux Director of Natl Sales
Fax:
Email: jayme.gauthreaux@scottlogistics.com
Website: www.scottlogistics.com
Transportation brokerage. (Woman/White, estab 1995, empl 165, sales $155,000,000, cert: WBENC)

3635 Transgroup World Wide Logistics
650 Atlanta S Pkwy, Ste 109   Atlanta, GA 30349
(404) 725-3660 Tamara Barnes President
Fax: (404) 766-0945
Email: tamib.atl@transgroup.com
Website: www.transgroup.cam
Domestic Air: Next flight out, Next Day AM, Second day, 3-5 day service, Air Charters, Express LTL & Full Truckload, Flatbed/Oversize loads, Trade Show Services, Canada/Mexico TransBoarder. (Woman, estab 1986, empl 37, sales $291,000,000, cert: NWBOC)

3636 Upward Global Logistics & Distribution
5421 Legacy Trail   Douglasville, GA 30135
(949) 484-5231 Nick Byers President
Fax: (678) 838-8334
Email: nrbyers@uglad.us
Website: www.uglad.us
Freight Brokerage, transportation solutions to air, ground, rail, expedited, drayage or port logistics; coordinating the movement of freight between plants, ports, warehouses, job sites, or any destination. (As-Pac, estab 2010, empl 6, sales $315,000, cert: 8(a))

Iowa

3637 JMS Transportation Inc.
5650 6th St SW   Cedar Rapids, IA 52404
(800) 877-1529 Riley Larson GM
Fax: (319) 364-0561
Email: rileylarson@jmstransport.com
Website: www.jmstransport.com
Trucking & logistics, asset-based transportation, Midwest regional LTL & FTL dry van freight hauling. (Woman/White, estab 1990, empl 39, sales $19,048,850, cert: NWBOC)

3638 Kirsch Transportation Services, Inc.
25 Main Place Ste 300 Council Bluffs, IA 51503
(712) 396-2120 Tyler Kruse
Fax: (712) 256-0843
Email: tylerk@kirschtrans.com
Website: www.kirschtrans.com
Transportation services, flatbed, dry van & specialized hauling including super loads. (Woman/White, estab 2001, empl 42, sales $41,000,000, cert: NWBOC)

3639 Legacy Logistics Freight, Inc.
500 College Dr, Ste 127B   Mason City, IA 50401
(641) 423-5187 Sarah Novacek President
Fax: (641) 985-2745
Email: sarah@legacylogisticsfreight.com
Website: www.legacylogisticsfreight.com
Freight brokerage, 48 states in the lower continental US. (Woman/White, estab 2006, empl 8, sales , cert: WBENC)

3640 Weinrich Truck Line, Inc.
27932 C 60 P.O. Box 1022 Hinton, IA 51024
(800) 831-0814 Ranae Allen Ops Mgr
Fax: (712) 947-4890
Email: ranaewtl@hotmail.com
Website: www.weinrichtruckline.com
Liquid bulk food grade transportation. (Woman/White, estab 1960, empl 75, sales $9,284,328, cert: WBENC)

Illinois

3641 A & T Trucking Co.
2920 S 19th Ave   Broadview, IL 60155
(708) 344-3770 Marlon K. Hooper VP-Sales
Fax: (708) 344-3773
Email: mkhoopship@yahoo.com
Website:
Local & out of state trucking & warehousing. (AA, estab 1983, empl 45, sales , cert: State, City)

3642 AGT Global Logistics
800 Roosevelt Rd, Building C, Ste 300   Glen Ellyn, IL 60137
(630) 953-4366 Jeff Mock MR
Fax: (630) 953-4381
Email: jeffm@agt3pl.com
Website: www.agt3pl.com
Certified 3rd Party Logistics, air freight carrier, asset based. (Woman/White, estab 2005, empl 21, sales $1,141,103,297, cert: WBENC, NWBOC)

3643 All Girl Transportation & Logistics, Inc
216 S Prater   Northlake, IL 60164
(877) 816-5477 Angela Mock President
Fax: (630) 307-7400
Email: amock@allgirlstrucking.com
Website: www.allgirlstrucking.com
Transportation: ground & ground expedited, air & airfreight, small package, auditing, transportation management services. (Woman/White, estab 2005, empl 30, sales $12,000,000, cert: WBENC)

3644 Box Truck Logistics, LLC
1517 Golfview Court   Glendale Heights, IL 60139
(312) 602-2639 Hayden Lynch President
Fax: (312) 373-9213
Email: hlynch@boxtrucklogistics.com
Website: www.boxtrucklogistics.com
Freight brokerage - FTL, LTL shipments, project freight & out of gauge shipments. (AA, estab 2014, empl 2, sales $85,000, cert: NMSDC)

3645 Chela Logistics Inc.
1521 Brummel Ave   Elk Grove Village, IL 60007
(847) 290-9040 Marcela Orr President
Fax: (847) 290-1050
Email: marcela@chelalogistics.com
Website: www.chelalogistics.com
Local & nationwide transportation. (Woman/White, estab 2001, empl 11, sales $2,500,000, cert: WBENC)

3646 CTL Global
11697 W Grand Ave   Northlake, IL 60164
(708) 223-1179 Josh Miller VP Business Dev
Fax: (708) 223-1179
Email: supplierdiversity@ctlglobalsolutions.com
Website: www.ctlglobalsolutions.com
Fulfillment & logistics, transportation & technology services. (Woman/White, estab 2011, empl 250, sales $49,869,000, cert: WBENC)

3647 DSC Logistics, Inc.
1750 S Wolf Rd   Des Plaines, IL 60018
(847) 390-6800 Tracy Drake Director, Diversity
Fax: (847) 390-7276
Email: tracy.drake@dsc-logistics.com
Website: www.dsclogistics.com
Supply chain mgmt, strategic solutions-based consulting, business process integration, process improvement & management, logistics operations, warehousing, transportation, packaging & fulfillment. (Woman/White, estab 1960, empl 2200, sales $330,000,000, cert: WBENC)

3648 GTS Express, Inc.
13851 S Janas Pkwy   Homer Glen, IL 60491
(844) 487-9777 Olivia Metelanski President
Fax: (708) 377-5703
Email: olivia@gtsexpressinc.com
Website: www.gtsexpressinc.com
Asset based transportation logistics & 3PL. (Woman/White, estab 2013, empl 12, sales $550,000, cert: NWBOC)

3649 Hassett Express, LLC
18W100 22nd St. Ste 109 Oakbrook Terrace, IL 60181
(630) 530-6515 Crissy Floyhar Sr Sales & Mktg Coord
Fax: (630) 530-6538
Email: crissy.floyhar@hassettexpress.com
Website: www.hassettexpress.com
Transportation, Domestic Air Freight, Domestic Ground Freight, White Glove, Logistics Services, International Air, International Moving. (Woman/White, estab 1980, empl 133, sales $56,000,000, cert: WBENC)

3650 Mid-West Moving & Storage, Inc.
1255 Tonne Rd   Elk Grove Village, IL 60007
(847) 593-7201 Luis Toledo President
Fax: (847) 593-7618
Email: diversity@midwestmoving.com
Website: www.midwestmoving.com
Office & residential moving, record storage & destruction, ware housing, distribution & local hauling. (Hisp, estab 1983, empl 100, sales $8,570,165, cert: 8(a))

3651 New Age Transportation, Distribution & Warehousing
1881 Rose Rd   Lake Zurich, IL 60047
(847) 545-9200 Pam Troy VP of Administration
Fax: (847) 545-9201
Email: pamt@newagetransportation.com
Website: www.newagetransportation.com
National & international transportation & logistics: dist, warehousing, fulfillment & e-commerce, expedition & rail shipments, freight bill auditing. (Woman/White, estab 1989, empl 45, sales $28,000,000, cert: WBENC)

3652 Par Logistics, Inc.
1251 N Plum Grove Rd, Ste 120   Schaumburg, IL 60173
(847) 519-1990 Jim Vasquez President
Fax: (847) 519-1995
Email: jvasquez@parlogistics.net
Website: www.parlogsitics.net
Transportation svcs: truckload, domestic air freight, ground expedite, air charter services, int'l air & ocean. (Hisp, estab 2006, empl 8, sales $25,000,000, cert: NMSDC)

3653 Passion Transportation Inc.
145 Sayton Road Ste C Fox Lake, IL 60020
(847) 587-2700 Suzanne Thompson WBE Liasion/ Cstmr Relations
Fax: (847) 587-2703
Email: quotes@passiontrans.com
Website: www.passiontrans.com
Truckload, less than truckload & partial truckloads, air, ocean, expidited, temperature controlled & flatbed freight. (Woman/White, estab 2007, empl 6, sales $4,134,507, cert: WBENC)

3654 Precision Transportation, Inc.
1010 Dixie Highway Ste 309 Chicago Heights, IL 60411
(630) 352-3311 Joyce Michael Division VP
Fax: (866) 651-5919
Email: jmichael@precision-nal.com
Website: www.precision-nal.com
Logistics, transportation, warehousing, project management & inventory control. (Woman/White, estab 1992, empl 10, sales , cert: State, WBENC)

3655   Riverbend Logistics Solutions, Inc.
65 E Ferguson Ave   Wood River, IL 62095
(618) 254-2687 MURDOCK MOSS
Fax: (618) 251-9294
Email: MMOSS@RLS-GLOBAL.COM
Website: www.rls-global.com
Third-party logistics, freight management & shipping.
(Woman/White, estab 1992, empl 8, sales $2,680,000,
cert: State, NWBOC)

3656   Servex, Inc.
1567 Frontenac Rd   Naperville, IL 60563
(630) 369-9500 John Rizek Dir Mktg/sales
Fax: (630) 961-4758
Email: j.rizek@servex.com
Website: www.servex.com
Third party warehousing & warehousing services (Woman/
White, estab 1981, empl 35, sales , cert: CPUC)

3657   Towers Alliance Inc.
4901 W. Quincy   Chicago, IL 60644
(708) 268-1094 John Chambers President
Fax: (407) 287-9197
Email: jchambers@towersalliance.com
Website: www.towersalliance.com
A dynamic minority owned company providing quality,
sustainable goods to our customers. We are committed to
delivering innovative products and services as your supply
chain partner. (AA, estab 2013, empl 5, sales $150,000,
cert: NMSDC)

3658   Williams NationaLease, Ltd.
404 W Northtown Road Ste B Normal, IL 61761
(800) 779-8785 Sandy Hotlen President
Fax: (309) 454-2857
Email: Shotlen@wnlgroup.com
Website: www.wnlgroup.com
Truck leasing & rental: 130 power units & 180 trailers.
(Woman/White, estab 1984, empl 210, sales $36,000,000,
cert: State, WBENC)

Indiana

3659   Butler Tillman Express Trucking, Inc.
PO Box 1017   Belverly Shores, IN 46301
(219) 764-2100 Sue Lundberg Office Mgr
Fax: (219) 764-2100
Email: info@btexpresstrucking.com
Website: www.btexpresstrucking.com
Tanker trucking, bulk liquid and dry materials.
(Woman/AA, estab 2003, empl 6, sales $388,518, cert:
NMSDC)

3660   Chaser, LLC
415 E 31st St Anderson, IN 46016
(765) 640-8620 Nammy Eskar CEO
Fax: (765) 640-8618
Email: neskar@chaserllc.com
Website: www.chaserllc.com
Transportation & logistics, hauling truckload shipments
of general commodities in both interstate & intrastate
commerce. (As-Ind/As-Pac, estab 2011, empl 50, sales ,
cert: NMSDC)

3661   HeLP Logistics, Inc.
13578 East 131st St Ste #260   Fishers, IN 46037
(866) 504-9620 Lorri Lord CEO
Fax: (866) 504-9621
Email: lorri.lord@helplogistics.com
Website: www.helplogistics.com
Transportation & logistics. (Woman/White, estab 2007,
empl 15, sales $4,800,000, cert: State, WBENC)

3662   Langham Logistics Inc.
5335 W 74th St   Indianapolis, IN 46268
(317) 471-5120 Cathy Langham President
Fax: (317) 471-5120
Email: cathylangham@elangham.com
Website: www.elangham.com
Global freight management: FF, expedite, warehousing,
distribution, fulfillment. (Woman/White, estab 1988,
empl 150, sales $36,114,845, cert: State, WBENC)

3663   Mid-American Specialized Transport, Inc.
2827 W State Rd 66   Rockport, IN 47635
(812) 649-2599 Paula Joyner President
Fax: (812) 649-2598
Email: paula.joyner@mastusa.com
Website: www.mastusa.com
General freight & hazardous materials, transportation
logistics, brokerage, third party logistics & transportation consutling services. (Woman/White, estab 2008,
empl 19, sales $8,000,000, cert: WBENC)

3664   MyWay Logistics LLC
1300 E 86th St, Ste 14 Indianapolis, IN 46240
(888) 557-4213 Emily Lawton Owner
Fax: (317) 550-1560
Email: elawton@myway-logistics.com
Website: www.myway-logistics.com
Non-asset based logistics. Licensed & bonded to service
all 48 states & Canada. (Woman/White, estab 2014,
empl 3, sales $303,030, cert: WBENC)

Kansas

3665 Butler Transport, Inc
347 N James St   Kansas City, KS 66118
(913) 321-0047   Bill Taylor Controller
Fax: (913) 321-2367
Email: billtaylor@butlertransport.com
Website: www.butlertransport.com
Transportation (Woman/White, estab 1991, empl 350, sales $67,000,000, cert: NWBOC)

3666 Gold Star Transportation, Inc.
P.O. Box 11350   Overland Park, KS 66207
(913) 433-4133   Anthony Janiak
Fax: (913) 341-6855
Email: tonyj@goldstartrans.com
Website: www.goldstartransportation.com
Third party transportation logistics. (Woman/White, estab 1982, empl 29, sales $24,781,811, cert: NWBOC)

3667 Nationwide Transportation & Logistics Services Inc
P.O. Box 3190   Shawnee, KS 66203
(913) 888-1685   Kim Isenhower President
Fax: (913) 888-1686
Email: kim@nationwidetransportation.com
Website: www.nationwidetransportation.com
Transportation freight brokerage services. (Woman/White, estab 1998, empl 18, sales , cert: WBENC)

Kentucky

3668 HJI -Vascor Logistics LLC
13200 Complete Court   Louisville, KY 40223
(502) 638-8021   Brian Palmer Sr Mgr inbound logistics
Fax:
Email: bpalmer@vascorltd.com
Website: www.vascorlogistics.com
Transportation services. (Woman/AA, estab 2012, empl 500, sales $20,000,000, cert: WBENC)

3669 Stett Transportation Inc.
224 Grandview Dr   Ft. Mitchell, KY 41017
(859) 384-2400   Chris Jolevski Sales Team Lead
Fax: (859) 384-4748
Email: Chris@stett.net
Website: www.stett.net
Non-asset based 3PL transporting liquid bulk, both Hazmat & non hazardous products. (Woman, estab 1995, empl 24, sales $11,500,000, cert: WBENC)

Massachusetts

3670 ImEx Cargo LLC
480 William F McClellan Hwy   East Boston, MA 02128
(617) 718-4639   Michelle DeFronzo President
Fax:
Email: michelle@imexcargo.com
Website: www.imexcargo.com
Cargo Transportation, Import/Export/Domestic & International Air or Ocean Export, Regional/ National & Local Transportation, Airfreight/ OceanFreight, LTL/ FTL, Warehousing/Distribution/ Packaging. (Woman/White, estab 2000, empl 4, sales $200,000, cert: State, City, WBENC)

3671 Normandin Transportation Services Inc.
148 Ironstone St   Uxbridge, MA 01569
(508) 278-6579   Cynthia Normandin President
Fax: (508) 278-6174
Email: cindy@normandintrans.com
Website: www.normandintrans.com
Transportation & logistics, LTL & truckload service. (Woman/White, estab 2008, empl 12, sales $11,700,000, cert: WBENC)

3672 One World Logistics Inc.
128 Eastern Ave   Chelsea, MA 02150
(617) 567-6800   Michelle Merino President
Fax:
Email: Michelle.Merino@Mainfreightusa.com
Website: www.Mainfreightusa.com
Freight transportation shipping services for domestic, international, air, road & ocean. Local, Nationwide & worldwide services. (Woman/White, estab 2006, empl 11, sales $844,734, cert: State, WBENC)

Maryland

3673 C J International Inc.
519 S Ellwood Ave   Baltimore, MD 21224
(410) 963-3533   Samya Murray Compliance Officer
Fax: (410) 563-6021
Email: sdmurray@cjinternational.com
Website: www.cjinternational.com
Global Logistics: air/ocean/ground freight transportation, warehousing & Customs brokerage services. (Woman, estab 1987, empl 50, sales $3,600,000, cert: WBENC)

3674 Patriot Air Freight, Inc.
806 Cromwell Park Dr   Glen Burnie, MD 21061
(410) 766-2422   Heidi Gordon Acct Exec
Fax:
Email: hgordon@aitworldwide.com
Website: www.aitworldwide.com
Domestic Air Freight, Ground Transportation, International Air & Ocean, Custom House Brokerage, Transborder Services. (Woman/White, estab 1980, empl 16, sales $4,790,000, cert: WBENC)

3675   Velocity Global Logistics, Inc.
       6805 Douglas Legum Dr Ste 201 Elkridge, MD
       21075
       (888) 845-9855 Joseph Armstead President
       Fax:
       Email: joe.armstead@VelocityGlobalLogistics.com
       Website: www.velocitygloballogistics.com
Global transportation. (Woman/AA, estab 2005, empl 2,
sales $158,000, cert: NMSDC)

Michigan

3676   Acme Global Logistics, Inc.
       31500 W 13 Mile Rd, Ste 219   Farmington Hills, MI
       48334
       (844) 260-0463 Corey Dickerson Freight Broker
       Fax: (844) 390-2733
       Email: cdickerson@aglogistics.us
       Website: www.aglogistics.us
Freight Brokerage, Logistics Consulting, Specialized Pick-Up
& Delivery, Intermodal. (AA, estab 2015, empl 6, sales ,
cert: NMSDC)

3677   BLT Logistics LLC
       34450 Goddard Rd   Romulus, MI 48174
       (586) 467-1437 Joe Goryl VP Supply Chain
       Fax:
       Email: JGoryl@BLTship.com
       Website: www.bltship.com
Transportation & logistics services in the U.S., Canada, and
Mexico, domestic intermodal, drayage, air & ocean
forwarding services. (Woman, estab 2014, empl 22, sales
$1,500,000, cert: WBENC)

3678   BNM Transportation Services
       91 N Saginaw, Ste 100   Pontiac, MI 48342
       (888) 621-5592 Marsha Rutherford Owner
       Fax: (866) 945-9462
       Email: m.rutherford@bnmtrans.com
       Website: www.bnmtransportation.com
Third party logistics, warehousing basics, public storage &
order fulfillment for manufacturers. (Woman/AA, estab
2008, empl 45, sales $3,000,000, cert: NMSDC, WBENC)

3679   BNM Transportation Services, LLC
       91 N Saginaw, Ste 100   Pontiac, MI 48342
       (866) 832-7114 Marsha Rutherford Owner
       Fax: (866) 945-9462
       Email: m.rutherford@bnmtrans.com
       Website: www.bnmtransportation.com
Transportation & logistics. (Woman/AA, estab 2008, empl
45, sales $12,000,000, cert: State)

3680   Camryn Logistics LLC
       36500 Ford Rd   Westland, MI 48185
       (866) 670-8680 Jimmie Comer Business Dev Mgr
       Fax: (248) 670-8684
       Email: jcomer@camrynlogistics.com
       Website: www.camrynlogistics.com
Freight management, warehousing, sequencing, parts
assembly, custom packing & transportation. (AA, estab
2008, empl 15, sales $600,000, cert: NMSDC)

3681   D & D Logistics, LLC
       3130 Glade St, Ste A   Muskegon Heights, MI
       49444
       (231) 737-0100 Denise Kanaar CEO
       Fax: (231) 737-0099
       Email: denise.kanaar@d-dlogistics.com
       Website: www.d-dlogistics.com
Logistics services. (Woman/White, estab 2005, empl 12,
sales $16,000,000, cert: WBENC)

3682   E.L. Hollingsworth & Co.
       3039 Airpark Dr N   Flint, MI 48507
       (810) 233-7331 Steven Barr President
       Fax: (810) 233-6725
       Email: sbarr@hollingsworthgroup.com
       Website: www.elhc.net
Transportation services: truckload & expedite delivery,
warehouse & packaging svcs. (Nat Ame, estab 1927,
empl 501, sales $45,000,000, cert: NMSDC)

3683   Eagle Express
       5601 Belleville Rd   Canton, MI 48188
       (800) 933-0215 Leander O Richmond President
       Fax: (800) 397-4792
       Email: lrichmond@eagleexp.com
       Website: www.eagleexp.com
Transportation; trucking (AA, estab 1999, empl 6, sales
$2,400,000, cert: NMSDC)

3684   El Camino Transport Logistics & Management, LLC
       P.O. Box 28   Union Lake, MI 48387
       (248) 242-0047 Mary Kilgore President
       Fax: (248) 366-4083
       Email: mkilgore@elcaminotransport.com
       Website:
Warehousing specializing in pick & pack, kitting,
sequencing & building batches. (Woman/Hisp, estab
2007, empl 4, sales , cert: NMSDC)

3685   EPJ Logistics Inc.
       50270 E Russell Schmidt   Chesterfield Township,
       MI 48051
       (586) 421-1375 Pamela Flynn CEO
       Fax: (586) 598-9101
       Email: pflynn@epjlogistics.com
       Website: www.epjlogistics.com
Domestic & international transportation svcs, warehouse storage, fulfillment, inventory control, design &
layout. (Woman, estab 1998, empl 9, sales $2,200,000,
cert: WBENC)

3686   Expedite Express Transportation Inc.
       20411 W 12 Mile Rd Ste 200 Southfield, MI 48076
       (248) 443-1970 William Hamblin VP
       Fax: (248) 443-1972
       Email: dispatch@expeditexp.com
       Website: www.expeditexp.com
Local & long distance TL & FTL, dedicated, same day & next
day services to small & large businesses within the auto
industry. (Woman/AA, estab 2005, empl 7, sales $622,635,
cert: WBENC)

3687   February 14 Inc.
       4525 - 50th St SE Grand Rapids, MI 49512
       (616) 656-0267 Bridget Carey President
       Fax: (616) 656-9824
       Email: BridgetCarey@FFItransportation.com
       Website: www.FFItransportation.com
Transportation logistics. (Woman/White, estab 1984, empl
75, sales $18,875,000, cert: WBENC)

3688   Go-To Transport
       1320 Washington Avenue P.O. Box 2248 Bay City, MI
       48708
       (989) 891-2521 Allison Short President
       Fax: (989) 891-2057
       Email: ashort@gototransport.com
       Website: www.gototransport.com
Truckload carrier: 48 contiguous states & Canada.
(Woman/White, estab 2003, empl 160, sales $38,900,000,
cert: WBENC)

3689   Gumro and Associates
       1000 We University Dr, Ste 150 Rochester, MI
       48307
       (248) 652-6200 Shawn Krukowski Exec Sales
       Fax: (248) 652-8890
       Email: skrukowski@gumroandassociates.com
       Website: www.gumroandassociates.com
3PL trucking logistics, heavy haul, curtain sides, double
drop, Lift-gate Straight truck & Vans. (Woman/White, estab
1974, empl 15, sales $20,000,000, cert: WBENC)

3690   Hollingsworth Logistics Group, L.L.C.
       14225 W Warren Ave Dearborn, MI 48126
       (313) 768-1306 Greg Martinez Jr Director of Govt
       Sales
       Fax:
       Email: gmartinez@hlgllc.com
       Website: www.hlgllc.com
Warehousing, container management, packaging services,
kit packaing, fullfillment services, direct ship,d istribution,
transportation OTR/LTL. (Nat Ame, estab 1991, empl 1900,
sales , cert: NMSDC)

3691   J-Max Transportation Services, Inc.
       10845 Chicago Dr P.O. Box 350 Zeeland, MI 49464
       (616) 748-8091 Pauline Mitchell Sales/Mktg Mgr
       Fax: (616) 748-8095
       Email: pauline_mitchell@jmaxtransport.com
       Website: www.jmaxtransport.com
Long haul, regional & local transportation, 48-states. (AA,
estab 2001, empl 25, sales , cert: NMSDC)

3692   KACE Logistics, LLC
       862 Will Carleton Rd Carleton, MI 48117
       (734) 946-8600 Paul Pavelich VP Business Dev
       Fax:
       Email: pavelichp@kcintegrated.com
       Website: www.kcintegrated.com
Logistics management, freight brokerage & management, parts sequencing, parts sub assembly, quality
containment & rework
warehousing. (Hisp, estab 2014, empl 125, sales
$27,200,000, cert: NMSDC)

3693   LB Transportation Group & Omni Warehouse
       966 Bridgeview S Saginaw, MI 48604
       (989) 759-5544 Tony Lander CEO
       Fax: (989) 755-3299
       Email: tlander@lb-omni.com
       Website: www.lb-omni.com
Transportation: expediting & dedicated svcs, warehousing, inspection, kitting, assembly, repacking. (Hisp, estab
1976, empl 70, sales $9,859,567, cert: NMSDC)

3694   Mexus Transport, Inc.
       18600 Northville Rd, Ste 900 Northville, MI
       48167
       (248) 344-8060 Alba R. McConell President
       Fax: (248) 344-2802
       Email: alba@mexustransport.com
       Website: www.mexustransport.com
Transportation: general freight, machinery & heavy
haul, Canada, United States & Mexico. (Woman/Hisp,
estab 2003, empl 5, sales $300,000, cert: State)

3695   Northfield Trucking Company, Inc.
       7525 Holland Rd Taylor, MI 48180
       (313) 624-4900 Leigh Ann Vallimont President
       Fax: (313) 624-4918
       Email: leighannl@northfieldtruck.com
       Website: www.northfieldtruck.com
Transportation, regional, long haul & dry freight long
distances operation. (Woman/White, estab 2002, empl
100, sales $12,000,000, cert: WBENC)

3696   O & I Transport Inc.
       P.O. Box 807 Dearborn, MI 48121
       (800) 270-0020 Mike Schofiled Sales Mgr
       Fax: (313) 581-7517
       Email: mschofield@oitransport.com
       Website:
Flatbed trucking. (AA, estab 1981, empl 21, sales
$25,000,000, cert: NMSDC)

3697   Oneida Solutions Group
       10049 Harrison, Ste 500A   Romulus, MI 48174
       (248) 252-2260 Fred Rogers Exec. Dir.
       Fax: (734) 480-4189
       Email: frogers@oneidasolutions.com
       Website: www.oneidasolutions.com
Transportation svcs: intl household & office moving,
project mgmt. (Nat Ame, estab 2001, empl 200, sales
$1,722,279, cert: NMSDC)

3698   Palmer Logistic Services
       27050 Wick Rd   Taylor, MI 48180
       (313) 220-5433 Terri Palmer Burton President
       Fax: (313) 557-5254
       Email: terripb@palmerls.com.com
       Website: www.palmerls.com
Global household relocation, commercial relocation,
regional distribution, trade show transportation & store
fixture distribution. (Woman, estab 2007, empl 12, sales
$27,000,000, cert: WBENC)

3699   Promesa Transportation
       3068 Highland Dr   Hudsonville, MI 49426
       (616) 748-2340 Lon Aguilar
       Fax:
       Email: lonagu@chartermi.net
       Website:
Transportation services. (Hisp, estab , empl 1, sales , cert:
NMSDC)

3700   Renaissance City Transportation
       1457 Bewick   Detroit, MI 48214
       (313) 550-8045 Charlie Hall VP
       Fax: (734) 692-1168
       Email: hall4384@sbcglobal.net
       Website:
Trucking & general warehousing. (AA, estab 1984, empl 4,
sales $79,000, cert: NMSDC)

3701   Rich Davis Enterprises, Inc.
       4831 Wyoming Ave   Dearborn, MI 48126
       (313) 584-3334 Melissa Matsos Acct Exec
       Fax: (313) 584-3337
       Email: melmatsos@richdavistrucking.com
       Website: www.richdavistrucking.com
Transport auto parts, steel, machinery & general commodity freight. (Woman/White, estab 1987, empl 17, sales
$1,995,074, cert: WBENC)

3702   Rodriguez Expedited Freight Systems, Inc.
       9400 Pelham   Taylor, MI 48180
       (800) 718-0066 Dennis Schmidt VP Ops
       Fax: (313) 295-2149
       Email: dschmidt@rodexp.com
       Website: www.rodexp.com
Ground & air expedition: cargo van, cube truck, straight
truck & semi, 48 state authority, plus Canada. (Woman/
Hisp, estab 1992, empl 20, sales $5,600,000, cert: NMSDC)

3703   RSP Express Inc.
       28169 Van Born Road   Romulus, MI 48174
       (734) 578-0799 Maria Pop President
       Fax: (734) 462-4239
       Email: rspexpress1@yahoo.com
       Website: www.rspexpress.com
Brokerage and Transportation Services. (Woman/White,
estab 2006, empl 140, sales $19,896,325, cert: WBENC)

3704   Rush Trucking Corporation
       35160 E. Michigan Avenue   Wayne, MI 48184
       (800) 526-7874 Rob Allgary Director of Sales
       Fax: (734) 641-1470
       Email: rallgary@rushtrucking.com
       Website: www.rushtrucking.com
Truckload transportation, expedited transportation.
(Woman/Nat Ame, estab 1984, empl 950, sales
$125,000,000, cert: NMSDC, WBENC)

3705   Sterling Services Ltd.
       1530 Commor   Hamtramck, MI 48212
       (248) 298-2973 Jason Eddleston VP
       Fax: (248) 298-2977
       Email: jason@sterlingoilchem.com
       Website: www.sterlingoilchem.com
Provides high-quality bulk liquid storage, custom
blending, warehousing & bulk liquid transport services.
(Woman/White, estab 1985, empl 9, sales $2,036,474,
cert: WBENC)

3706   T & M Incorporated
       930 Interchange Dr   Holland, MI 49423
       (269) 751-8050 Helen Zeerip President
       Fax: (269) 751-7592
       Email: helen@teddystransport.com
       Website: www.teddystransport.com
Transportation svcs, expediting to all 48 states &
Ontario/Quebec, Canada, dedicated fleet services, full-
truck load services. (Woman, estab 1982, empl 75, sales
$7,276,168, cert: WBENC)

3707   The Outbound Group
       9900 Harrison   Romulus, MI 48174
       (734) 947-1333 Karl Randolph President
       Fax: (734) 947-1395
       Email: KarlR@outboundgroup.com
       Website: www.outboundgroup.com
Interstate & intrastate motor truck transportation
service, fright brokerage, air freight forwarding services
& warehouseing. (Woman/AA, estab 1982, empl 100,
sales $7,200,000, cert: NMSDC)

3708   Three Star Trucking Co.
       36860 Van Born Rd   Wayne, MI 48184
       (734) 728-5500 Tedd Rowe Logistics Mgr
       Fax: (734) 728-2818
       Email: operations@threestartrucking.com
       Website: www.threestartrucking.com
Transportation svcs; automotive. (Woman/Hisp, estab
1979, empl 60, sales , cert: NMSDC, WBENC)

3709 University Moving & Storage
23305 Commerce Dr Farmington Hills, MI 48335
(248) 949-5755 Ben Cross VP
Fax: (248) 615-4715
Email: bcross@universitymoving.com
Website: www.universitymoving.com
Transportation, moving & storage. (Woman/White, estab 1969, empl 150, sales $14,490,725, cert: WBENC)

3710 Warehouse Properties, Inc.
16000 W. Nine Mile Rd. Ste 302 Southfield, MI 48075
(248) 569-6106 Kathleen Eberle President
Fax: (248) 569-5355
Email: keberle@npotransportation.com
Website: www.npotransportation.com
Truckload transportation services: seating companies, kitting & JIT components. (Woman, estab 1984, empl 4, sales $1,641,592, cert: WBENC)

Minnesota

3711 Copeland Truc-King Inc
5400 Main St NE, Ste 201 Minneapolis, MN 55421
(763) 226-7781 Kevin Horvath Dir Business Dev
Fax: (763) 572-0175
Email: khorvath@copelandtruc-king.com
Website: www.copelandtruc-king.com
Commercial moving & storage, regional transportation, truckload, LTL, distribution, dedicated contract carriage, hazmat. (AA, estab 1985, empl 65, sales $9,700,000, cert: NMSDC)

3712 Jade Logistics, Inc.
1590 Thomas Center Dr Ste 100 Eagan, MN 55122
(651) 405-3141 Ni Corbin Owner
Fax: (404) 920-2741
Email: ni@shipjade.com
Website: www.shipjade.com
Domestic & international freight transportation services. (Woman/As-Pac, estab 2007, empl 15, sales , cert: State, NMSDC)

3713 Malark Logistics
P.O. Box 438 Maple Grove, MN 55369
(763) 428-3564 Brendon Eason Sr Sales Exec
Fax: (763) 428-7361
Email: rgangstee@malark.com
Website: www.malark.com
Logistics, transportation, warehousing, trucking, airfreight, expedited, freight auditing, crating, claims filing, distribution, pick and pack, LTL, tradeshow services, 3PL & 4PL. (Woman/White, estab 1994, empl 60, sales $35,000,000, cert: WBENC)

Missouri

3714 All America Transportation, Inc.
910 S Kirkwood Rd Ste 120 Kirkwood, MO 63122
(314) 835-9499 Lianne Reizer President
Fax: (314) 835-9577
Email: lianne@allamericatrans.com
Website: www.allamericatrans.com
Licensed freight broker, truckload shipments throughout US & Canada. (Woman/White, estab 1996, empl 7, sales , cert: State, WBENC)

3715 Crossland Carriers Inc.
421 Cedar Hills Rd Ozark, MO 65721
(800) 217-0898 Patricia Schmig President
Fax: (417) 485-6165
Email: tschmig@crosslandcarriers.us
Website: www.crosslandcarriers.com
Trucking long haul, short haul, partial truckload, logistics, mobile home, mobile office moves, heavy haul, specialized logistics. (Woman/White, estab 1999, empl 3, sales $1,750,000, cert: State)

3716 LHP Transportation Services, Inc.
2032 E Kearney St Ste 213 Springfield, MO 65803
(972) 812-7370 Greg Gloeckner
Fax: (888) 486-3489
Email: gloeg@lhptransport.com
Website: www.lhptransport.com
Multimodal transportation svcs: truck, rail, LTL, steamship & air, 48 states, Canada, Mexico & abroad. (Woman/As-Ind, estab 1993, empl 9, sales $7,041,226, cert: NMSDC)

3717 Marleon International, LLC
5630 NE Lake Dr Kansas City, MO 64118
(816) 249-2319 Cesar Marquez CEO
Fax: (816) 326-3439
Email: camarquez@mar-leon.com
Website: www.marleoninternational.com
Freight transportation: less than container load, less than truckload, full truckload, flatbed freight, air transportation services, distribution & warehousing services. (Hisp, estab 2005, empl 4, sales $560,000, cert: State, NMSDC)

3718 The Thomas Family Business, Inc.
8194 Lackland Rd Saint Louis, MO 63114
(314) 423-6111 Rolondo Thomas CEO
Fax: (314) 423-6114
Email: rolondo.thomas@ttfbcompanies.com
Website: www.ttfbcompanies.com
Transportation services, local & regional, warehousing, supply chain management & logistics. (AA, estab 2009, empl 7, sales $750,000, cert: City)

3719   ValDivia Enterprises, Inc.
       #5C The Pines Court   St. Louis, MO 63141
       (314) 275-7941 steve ellis VP of sales
       Fax: (314) 453-0893
       Email: steve@valdiviaenterprises.net
       Website: www.valdiviaenterprises.net
Transportation services serving North America & Mexico.
(Woman/Hisp, estab 2006, empl 1450, sales , cert: State)

Montana

3720   Bridger Trnasportation LLC
       186 Garden Dr, Ste 103   Bozeman, MT 59718
       (888) 586-0648 Kyle Pena broker
       Fax:
       Email: orders@bridgertrans.com
       Website: www.bridgertrans.com
Full service logistics, supply chain management, OTR, LTL,
FTL & rail in the U.S. & Canada. (Woman/White, estab
2007, empl 11, sales $10,000,000, cert: WBENC)

3721   Meadow Lark Companies
       935 Lake Elmo Dr   Billings, MT 59105
       (406) 657-8645 Chris Verlanic Director of Freight
       Management
       Fax:
       Email: cverlanic@meadowlarkco.com
       Website: www.meadowlarkco.com
Transportation, Freight Management & Logistics: TL, LTL,
Vans/Reefers, Flatbed & Heavy Haul. (Woman/White,
estab 1983, empl 160, sales $65,000,000, cert: WBENC)

North Carolina

3722   All-State Express, Inc.
       121-I Shields Park Dr   Kernersville, NC 27284
       (336) 992-6880 Sherri Squier President
       Fax:
       Email: sherri@all-stateexpress.com
       Website: www.all-stateexpress.com
Transportation Services, Expedited Trucking, Air Charter,
TruckLoad, Expedite Trucking, Truck Load (TL), Milk Runs,
Dedicated Truck Load, Air Freight, Air Charter, Hazmat
Carrier 48 States, Canada and Mexico. (Woman, estab
1996, empl 28, sales $23,755,580, cert: WBENC)

3723   Cargo Transit Inc.
       P.O. Box 792   Weaverville, NC 28787
       (319) 363-1235 Moe Abu-Nameh Director of
       Business Dev
       Fax: (319) 365-9011
       Email: moe@ic-l.com
       Website:
Truck load & LTL services: dry van, flatbed or temperature
controlled carriers. (Woman/White, estab 1999, empl 20,
sales $10,000,000, cert: State, NWBOC)

3724   Graebel Vanlines Holdings, LLC
       2901 Stewart Creek Blvd   Charlotte, NC 28216
       (704) 281-7129 Colin Holden VP of Corp Sales
       Fax:
       Email: colin.holden@graebelmoving.com
       Website: www.graebelmoving.com
Facility management services, commercial moving
services, warehousing services. (Woman/White, estab
1960, empl 1360, sales $266,000,000, cert: WBENC)

3725   Intermodal Logistics Consulting, Inc.
       301 N Main St, Ste 2409B   Winston-Salem, NC
       27101
       (540) 257-3830 Senanu Ashiabor President
       Fax:
       Email: senanu@imlconsulting.com
       Website: www.imlconsulting.com
Transportation Planning, Travel Demand Modeling and
Forecasting, Data Management and Analytics, Aviation
Systems Modeling, Simulation, and Analysis, and
Technical Research Studies. (AA, estab 2013, empl 2,
sales $200,000, cert: 8(a))

3726   Logical Logistics Solutions
       7508 E Independence Blvd Ste 112 Charlotte, NC
       28227
       (704) 566-4770 Noel Sanchez President
       Fax: (704) 566-4771
       Email: nsanchez@llsolutions.com
       Website: www.llsolutions.com
Logistics services: freight cost reduction & administration, warehousing, consolidation & distribution &
inventory management. (AA, estab 1996, empl 5, sales
$3,128,798, cert: City)

Nebraska

3727   Nationwide Auto Transport, Inc.
       730 Pier 3   Lincoln, NE 68528
       (402) 742-4000 Julie Delp President
       Fax: (402) 939-0519
       Email: nwat90@tahoo.com
       Website: www.nwat.com
Automobile transport services. (Woman/White, estab
2001, empl 8, sales $1,400,000, cert: WBENC, SDB)

New Jersey

3728   Bett-A-Way Traffic Systems Inc.
       110 Sylvania Pl   South Painfield, NJ 07080
       (908) 222-2500 Betty Vaccaro VP
       Fax: (908) 222-2534
       Email: laura.vaccaro@bettaway.com
       Website: www.bett-a-way.com
Logistics management, freight nationwide, truck load &
LTL, dry & refrigerated. (Woman/White, estab 1982,
empl 107, sales , cert: WBENC)

3729 Bohren's Moving & Storage/United Van Lines
3 Applegate Dr   Robbinsville, NJ 08691
(800) 326-4736   Charlene Heath Sales/Mktg Mgr
Fax: (609) 208-1471
Email: cheath@bohrensmoving.com
Website: www.bohrensmoving.com
Transportation & storage svcs; brokerage & international divisions. (Woman/White, estab 1924, empl 90, sales $28,798,613, cert: WBENC)

3730 Ltd Logistics, Inc.
222 Outwater Lane Ste 3   Garfield, NJ 07026
(973) 340-4428   Tracy Flood Transportation Sales Rep
Fax: (973) 340-4423
Email: tracy.flood@ltdnj.com
Website: www.ltdnj.com
Ground & air freight transportation, full truckload & LTL/ partials via over the road, intermodal & air freight. (Woman/White, estab 1995, empl 10, sales $4,922,477, cert: State, City)

3731 One Horn Transportation Inc.
576 Valley Rd, Ste 234   Wayne, NJ 07470
(973) 595-7700   Cheryl Biron President
Fax: (973) 595-7720
Email: cheryl@onehorn.com
Website: www.OneHorn.com
Freight brokerage, flatbed & dry van tractor-trailer services, 48 contiguous states & Canada. (Woman/AA, estab 2005, empl 3, sales $1,067,256, cert: NMSDC, WBENC)

3732 Royal Coachman Worldwide
88 Ford Rd, Unit 26   Denville, NJ 07834
(973) 400-3200   Amy Birnbaum CEO
Fax: (973) 675-4365
Email: amy.birnbaum@royalcoachman.com
Website: www.royalcoachman.com
Corporate limousine & transportation svcs: luxury sedans, stretch limousines, 14 passenger motor coaches. (Woman/White, estab 1969, empl 150, sales $13,034,000, cert: WBENC)

New Mexico

3733 Loadstone Transportation, LLC
1811 Copper Loop, Ste K   Las Cruces, NM 88007
(575) 523-7000   Bridgette Snow Mktg Coord
Fax: (888) 574-9149
Email: bridgette@loadstonetransportation.com
Website: www.loadstonetransportation.com
Transportation services, multitude of local, state, & federal government contracts. (Woman/White, estab 2011, empl 6, sales $5,823,500, cert: State, WBENC)

Nevada

3734 Full Tilt Logistics LLC
150 Isidor Court   Sparks, NV 89441
(702) 852-2228   Mark Piethe Cstmr Management Team
Fax:
Email: office@fulltiltlogistics.com
Website: www.fulltiltlogistics.com
LTL, Partial loads, Full truck load, Rail, Heavy haul. (Woman/White, estab 2014, empl 11, sales $8,000,000, cert: WBENC)

3735 Railroad Industries Inc.
1575 Delucchi Ln, Ste 210   Reno, NV 89502
(775) 329-4855   Anastacia Sullivan Director of Ops
Fax: (775) 329-4844
Email: reg@railroadindustries.com
Website: www.railroadindustries.com
Transportation consulting. (Woman/AA/As-Pac, estab 1983, empl 9, sales $775,382, cert: State)

New York

3736 A & Z Trucking, Inc.
115 Corporate Dr   New Windsor, NY 12550
(845) 569-7299   Tiffany Buxton Broker
Fax: (845) 569-0555
Email: Tiffany@aandztrucking.com
Website: www.AandZtrucking.com
Transportation solutions, temperature-controlled reefer trucks, dry vans, flatbeds, full truckload (TL), less-than-truckload (LTL), refrigerated freight. (Woman/As-Pac, estab 2003, empl 15, sales , cert: NMSDC)

3737 Native Trax Logistics LLC
767 Warren Rd   Ithaca, NY 14850
(607) 319-5122   Ryan Van Alstine GM
Fax: (607) 216-1738
Email: ryan@nativetraxlogistics.com
Website: www.nativetraxlogistics.com
Transportation Management, Nationwide service, Asset tracking & reporting, Driver safety screenings, Driver credential checks, Timely proof of delivery, On call 24 hours. (Nat Ame, estab 2014, empl 5, sales $3,500,000, cert: NMSDC)

3738 Spearhead Transportation Services, Inc.
P.O. Box 1984   Blasdell, NY 14219
(716) 823-4942   Joe Dotterweich CFO
Fax: (716) 823-9315
Email: joed@spearheadlogistics.com
Website: www.spearheadlogistics.com
Transportation & logistics services. (Nat Ame, estab , empl 1, sales $14,000,000, cert: NMSDC)

3739   V G Francis Logistics Inc.
       800 Et 180th St   Bronx, NY 10460
       (866) 970-8866 Victor Francis President
       Fax: (707) 667-1533
       Email: vgfrancislogistics@gmail.com
       Website: www.vgfrancislogistics.com
Transportation, logistics & related information services: air,
rail & sea transportation. (AA, estab 2006, empl 1, sales ,
cert: City, NMSDC)

Ohio

3740   BD Transportation, Inc.
       9590 Looney Rd   Piqua, OH 45356
       (309) 531-1370 Tom Stirnaman Sales
       Fax:
       Email: toms@ptc-inc.net
       Website: www.ptc-inc.net
Dry van freight, 62 tractors & 125 dry van trailers.
(Woman/White, estab 2000, empl 95, sales $14,600,000,
cert: WBENC)

3741   Cam Logistics, LLC
       7800 Robinett Way   Canal Winchester, OH 43110
       (614) 409-1776 Patrick Shea VP
       Fax: (614) 409-1777
       Email: patrick@camlogisticsllc.com
       Website: www.camlogisticsllc.com
Third party logistics, transportation, truckload &
intermodal arrangements. (Woman/White, estab 2006,
empl 9, sales $5,400,000, cert: WBENC)

3742   Cimarron Express Inc.
       21611 State Rt 51   Genoa, OH 43430
       (419) 855-7713 Jim Shepperd VP
       Fax: (419) 855-7510
       Email: jshepperd@cimarronexpress.com
       Website: www.cimarronexpress.com
Motor carrier svcs, truckload. (AA, estab 1984, empl 325,
sales , cert: NMSDC)

3743   Cincinnati's Best Brokerage LLC
       4005 Borman Dr   Batavia, OH 45429
       (513) 478-4559 Brad Judy Mktg Dir
       Fax: (513) 735-0328
       Email: info@burdbrothers.com
       Website:
Third party logistics, truckload-shipping services. (Woman/
White, estab 2003, empl 10, sales $500,000, cert: WBENC)

3744   Debo Enterprises Incorporated
       16021 Dunbury Dr Ste 103 Maple Heights, OH
       44137
       (404) 333-5008 Tommie Rodgers Ops Dir/Co-Owner
       Fax:
       Email: deboenterprise@gmail.com
       Website: www.deboenterprises.com
Logistics & transportation services, Short term & long term
line haul services, railroad/shipyards, Hauling services for
construction worksites. (AA, estab 2001, empl 3, sales
$137,000, cert: State)

3745   H & W Trucking
       15 W Locust St   Newark, OH 43055
       (800) 572-2120 Barcy Vidt President
       Fax:
       Email: barcy@handwtrucking.com
       Website: www.handwtrucking.com
Third party logistics & freight, LTL & rail, US & Canada.
(Woman/White, estab 1979, empl 3, sales $5,300,000,
cert: WBENC)

3746   InterChez Global Services, Inc.
       600 Alpha Pkwy   Stow, OH 44224
       (330) 923-5080 Ivette Tam Exec VP
       Fax: (330) 923-5901
       Email: itam@interchez.com
       Website: www.interchezglobal.com
Logistics engineering, network modeling, logistics
execution, freight bill payment, premium freight
management, logistics consulting, translation, interpretation. (Woman/Hisp, estab 2001, empl 12, sales
$18,000,000, cert: State, NMSDC, WBENC)

3747   Kingsgate Transportation Services LLC
       9100 West Chester Towne Centre   West Chester,
       OH 45069
       (513) 874-7447 AMY BARNETT Managing Partner
       Fax: (513) 874-7653
       Email: abarnett@kingsgatetrans.com
       Website: www.kingsgatetrans.com
Freight services: truck, rail, air or ocean. (Woman/White,
estab 1986, empl 21, sales $19,500,000, cert: WBENC)

3748   Priority Logistics Group
       4667 Malsbary Rd   Cincinnati, OH 45242
       (513) 794-3160 Matt Leahy VP
       Fax:
       Email: matt.leahy@shipplg.com
       Website: www.shipplg.com
Third party logistics services, Expedited Same Day, On
demand expedited service, Next Day Distribution.
(Woman/White, estab 1973, empl 80, sales $6,500,000,
cert: WBENC)

3749   Rush Expediting, Inc.
       P.O. Box 2810 Dayton, OH 45401
       (800) 989-7874 Steve Parker President
       Fax: (937) 297-6200
       Email: parkersl@rush-delivery.com
       Website: www.rush-delivery.com
Freight transportation services. (Woman/White, estab
2004, empl 200, sales $1,000,000, cert: WBENC)

3750 Trio Trucking, Inc.
7750 Reinhold Dr   Cincinnati, OH 45237
(513) 679-7100 Carvel Simmons President
Fax: (513) 821-0230
Email: simmons.ce@onecalldoesall.com
Website: www.trioenterprises.com
Transportation svcs: intermodal & full truckload transportation. (AA, estab 1982, empl 75, sales $18,300,000, cert: State, NMSDC)

Oklahoma

3751 STI Trucking LLC
P.O. Box 700   Kiefer, OK 74041
(918) 446-6181 Sam Mookerjee Accountant
Fax: (918) 446-6186
Email: twyla.johnson@stonetrucking.com
Website: www.stonetrucking.com
Premier legal flatbed, oversize & heavy haul carrier servicing the US, Canada & Mexico. Hot shot trucks, tankers, pole trucks, slick backs, RGN's. (AA, estab 1945, empl 200, sales , cert: NMSDC)

Oregon

3752 Alliance Trucking Inc.
1209 Stowe Ave   Medford, OR 97501
(541)74844 Jordan Kell Acct Exec
Fax: (541) 734-7009
Email: jkell@alliancetrucking.com
Website: www.alliancetrucking.com
Asset-based trucking, haul truckload & LTL shipments via vans, flatbeds, step decks & multi-axle heavy haul trailers, 48 states, Canada & Mexico. (Woman/White, estab 1996, empl 20, sales $9,726,975, cert: State)

3753 Lile International Companies
8060 SW Pfaffle St, Ste 200   Tigard, OR 97223
(503) 726-4800 Diane DeAutremont President
Fax: (503) 726-4893
Email: diane.deautremont@lile.com
Website: www.lile.com
National & international transportation svcs, warehousing, distribution & logistics. (Woman/White, estab 1959, empl 275, sales , cert: WBENC)

3754 Mulino Trading, LLC
16570 SE McLoughlin Blvd   Oak Grove, OR 97267
(503) 786-8000 Mike Theis Agent
Fax: (503) 786-8005
Email: info@mulinotrading.com
Website: www.mulinotrading.com
Freight truck transportation, broker forwarding. (Hisp, estab 2012, empl 6, sales , cert: State)

Pennsylvania

3755 Advanced Shipping Technologies
526 W Ogle St   Ebensburg, PA 15931
(877) 692-0570 Jane Sandifeer VP Business Solutions
Fax: (814) 472-5222
Email: diversity@astship.com
Website: www.astship.com
Third party logistics: on-line transportation management system. (Woman/White, estab 2002, empl 18, sales , cert: WBENC)

3756 Allegheny Valley Transfer Co., Inc.
1512 Lebanon Church Rd   Pittsburgh, PA 15236
(412) 653-1200 Mary Jessup Owner
Fax: (412) 892-2648
Email: alleghenyallied@aol.com
Website: www.pghmover.com
Moving, storage & packing of household & office goods. (Woman/White, estab 1925, empl 45, sales $1,561,882, cert: State, WBENC)

3757 Knichel Logistics
5347 William Flynn Hwy   Gibsonia, PA 15044
(724) 449-3300 Kristy Knichel President
Fax: (724) 449-3310
Email: kknichel@knichellogistics.com
Website: www.knichellogistics.com
Intermodal, drayage & truckload services. (Woman/White, estab 1992, empl 42, sales $52,500,000, cert: WBENC)

3758 Maroadi Transfer & Storage
1801 Lincoln Hwy   North Versailles, PA 15137
(412) 824-4420 Michelle Abraham Dir of Business Devel
Fax: (141) 282-2444
Email: michelle@maroadi.com
Website: www.maroadi.com
Local, interstate & international moving services, office & electronics moving, household goods moving, displays & exhibits. (Woman/White, estab 1967, empl 45, sales $3,800,000, cert: WBENC)

3759 Mustang Expediting, Inc.
35 Stanley Dr   Aston, PA 19014
(610) 497-6360 Weston Stratford Acct Exec
Fax: (610) 497-6370
Email: wstratford@mustangexpediting.com
Website: www.mustangexpediting.com
Regional trucking, warehousing, logistics & distribution. (Woman/White, estab 1982, empl 35, sales $5,900,000, cert: WBENC)

3760   Parks Moving Systems
1234 Wrights Ln   West Chester, PA 19380
(610) 429-4125 Gary Piehler Relocation Consultant
Fax: (724) 553-3987
Email: gary_piehler@parksmoving.com
Website: www.parksmoving.com
Transportation: local, long distance, storage, record storage, trade show moves, etc. (Woman/White, estab 1992, empl 20, sales $1,300,000, cert: WBENC)

3761   Shepherd Transport, LLC
296 Cumberland Rd PO Box 660 Bedford, PA 15522
(814) 623-9346 Sandy Jones CEO
Fax: (814) 623-3947
Email: sandy@shepherdtransport.com
Website: www.shepherdtransport.com
Third party Logistics (3PL), non-asset based platform to serve a variety of transportation requirements. (Woman/White, estab 2008, empl 12, sales $7,682,700, cert: WBENC)

Puerto Rico

3762   PR Global Logistics JP Corporation
200 Rafael Cordero Ave, Ste 140 PMB 223 Caguas, PR 00726
(787) 653-5070 Ivelisse Baba-Portalatin VP
Fax: (787) 653-5070
Email: ivelisse@prgloballogistics.com
Website: www.prgloballogistics.com
Logistics & distribution operations, packaging, quality control, supply chain technology, and organizational excellence. (Woman/Hisp, estab 2007, empl 2, sales , cert: NMSDC)

Rhode Island

3763   Trans-Link LLC
1249 Oaklawn Ave   Cranston, RI 02920
(401) 463-3862 Carla Manni President
Fax: (401) 463-6729
Email: translink01@cox.net
Website: www.translinkllc.com
Transportation & trucking: LTL, truckload, rail & flatbeds, refrigerated & dry freight, 48 states & Canada. (Woman/White, estab 2000, empl 5, sales $5,600,000, cert: State)

South Carolina

3764   Holy City Solutions, LLC
904 Commerce Cir   Charleston, SC 29410
(843) 202-2149 Elizabeth Burton President
Fax: (843) 566-7656
Email: burtonb@holycitysolutions.com
Website: www.holycitysolutions.com
Transportation logistics, warehousing, transportation & consulting. (Woman/White, estab 2006, empl 1, sales $146,610, cert: WBENC)

3765   Kontane Inc.
1000 Charleston Regional Pkwy   Charleston, SC 29492
(843) 352-0011 Rusty Byrd President
Fax: (843) 352-0014
Email: rusty@kontanelogistics.com
Website: www.kontanelogistics.com
Logistics, warehousing & distribution, cross-docking, freight consolidation, import material receipt, line sequencing, parts distribution, development of logistics information systems, sub-assembly & foreign trade zones services. (Woman/White, estab 1975, empl 100, sales $40,000,000, cert: WBENC)

3766   TPS Logistics
P.O. Box 9493   Columbia, SC 29229
(803) 622-2970 Al Stokes VP Sales & Ops
Fax:
Email: alstokes@tpslogisticsinc.com
Website: www.tpslogisticsinc.com
Transportation services. (Woman/White, estab 2004, empl 3, sales $20,000,000, cert: NWBOC)

3767   Warehouse Services, Inc.
58 S Burty Rd   Piedmont, SC 29673
(864) 422-6079 Michelle Dender Mktg Coord
Fax: (864) 422-1562
Email: michelledender@wsi-ismi.com
Website: www.wsionline.com
Warehousing, transportation svcs: distribution, client system integration, domestic & international supply chain (SC) enhancement. (Woman/White, estab 1985, empl 2000, sales $220,000,000, cert: WBENC)

South Dakota

3768   K & J Trucking, Inc.
1800 East 50th St North   Sioux Falls, SD 57104
(605) 332-5531 John Kemp Mktg Mgr
Fax: (605) 332-6016
Email: jkemp@kandjtrucking.com
Website: www.kandjtrucking.com
Long haul & regional refrigerated transportation services. (Woman/White, estab 1979, empl 45, sales $21,235,776, cert: WBENC)

Tennessee

3769 Ewing Moving Services
      4006 Air Park St   Memphis, TN 38118
      (901) 774-2197 Ashleigh Hayes Natl Acct Coord
      Fax: (901) 942-1368
      Email: admin@ewingmovingservice.com
      Website: www.ewingmovingservice.com
Moving & storage services. (AA, estab 1980, empl 57, sales $3,047,104, cert: NMSDC)

3770 Western Express Inc.
      7135 Centennial Place   Nashville, TN 37209
      (615) 720-6133 Jared Holland Natl Acct Mgr
      Fax: (615) 346-1572
      Email: jholland@westernexp.com
      Website: www.westernexp.com
Full truck load carrier operates 3800 power units 48 states, Canada & Mexico border cities. (Woman/White, estab 1991, empl 3600, sales $430,250,000, cert: WBENC)

Texas

3771 A-1 Freeman Relocation
      4727 Macro   San Antonio, TX 78218
      (210) 661-1404 Jonathan Hightower Corporate Relocation & Logistics Consultant
      Fax: (210) 661-1405
      Email: jhightower@a-1freeman.com
      Website: www.a-1freemanrelo.com
Domestic & international household goods moving & transportation services. (Woman/White, estab 1994, empl 450, sales $10,000,000, cert: WBENC)

3772 Action Transportation Services, Inc.
      P.O. Box 15711   Houston, TX 77220
      (713) 673-4817 Lucy Bowerman Sales
      Fax: (713) 422-2556
      Email: actiontransport@sbcglobal.net
      Website: www.actionfrtservices.com
Transportation services: flatbeds, van, stepdecks, hotshots, power only, local & specialized equipment for partial & full loads, US & Canada, 24 hrs a day 7 days a week. (Woman/White, estab 1998, empl 3, sales $245,878, cert: State, WBENC)

3773 Americorp Xpress Carriers
      5201 N Veterans Blvd   Pharr, TX 78577
      (956) 283-0052 Frank Flores President
      Fax: (956) 787-0934
      Email: fflores@axcarriers.com
      Website: www.axcarriers.com
Transportation services. (Hisp, estab 2010, empl 250, sales , cert: NMSDC)

3774 A-Rocket Moving & Storage, Inc.
      3401 Corder St   Houston, TX 77021
      (713) 748-6024 Lewis Grisby VP Ops
      Fax: (713) 747-0975
      Email: rocketsales@arocket.com
      Website: www.arocket.com
Relocation services: material handling & warehousing, local, long-distance & international. (AA, estab 1959, empl 60, sales $3,700,000, cert: State, City, NMSDC)

3775 Cargo One Logistics, LLC
      5802 Val Verde, Ste 165   Houston, TX 77057
      (713) 290-9922 Diego Alexander President
      Fax: (713) 290-9955
      Email: dalexander@cargo1logistics.com
      Website: www.cargo1logistics.com
Transportation services, over the road, full truck load, Mexico, US & Canada. (Hisp, estab 2000, empl 7, sales $4,000,000, cert: NMSDC)

3776 EP Logistics LLC
      9601 Pan American Dr   El Paso, TX 79927
      (915) 881-9100 Ingrid Hurtado Mktg Business Dev Mgr
      Fax: (915) 778-9804
      Email: ingridh@eplogistics.com
      Website: www.eplogistics.com
Warehousing, customs brokerage, sorting/rework services, transportation. (Hisp, estab 2005, empl 50, sales $1,200,000, cert: State, NMSDC)

3777 Expedited Specialized Logistics LLC
      801 Pellegrino Court   Laredo, TX 78045
      (956) 712-8350 Armando Correa Commercial Dir
      Fax: (956) 712-8357
      Email: acorrea@es-logistics.net
      Website: www.es-logistics.net
USA and International Truck Load Transportation Services. Dryvan Trailers Flatbeds Stepdecks double drop open or curtain trailers. RGN Lowboys. (Hisp, estab 2011, empl 30, sales $7,661,250, cert: NMSDC)

3778 Hazel's Hot Shot, Inc.
      1735 W Crosby Rd   Carrollton, TX 75006
      (972) 620-8812 Tracey Harris GM
      Fax: (972) 242-5533
      Email: tracey@hazelshotshot.com
      Website: www.hazelshotshot.com
Expedited freight, 48 contiguous states. (Woman/White, estab 1977, empl 10, sales $6,000,000, cert: State, WBENC)

3779   Intercon Carriers
19810 FM 1472   Laredo, TX 78045
(956) 725-7275   Enrique Serna Managing Partner
Fax: (956) 725-7630
Email: enrique.serna@intercomlogistics.com
Website: www.interconcarriers.com
Transportation & logistics services in the United States, Canada & Mexico. (Hisp, estab 1996, empl 175, sales $17,337,543, cert: State, NMSDC)

3780   Logisti-K USA, LLC
13151 S Unitec   Laredo, TX 78045
(956) 723-7606   Cesar Roberto Flores Director of Inland Forwarding
Fax:
Email: cflores@logisti-k.com.mx
Website: www.logisti-k.com.mx
Truckload, Flatbed, Refrigerated & Intermodal services. (Hisp, estab 2005, empl 30, sales $1,225,062, cert: State, NMSDC)

3781   MagRabbit.com
1464. E Whitestone Ste 1001   Cedar Park, TX 78613
(512) 796-9460   Tommy Hodinh CEO
Fax: (512) 796-9903
Email: thodinh@magrabbit.com
Website: www.magrabbit.com
Global supply chain solutions, air, surface & ocean tranportation. (As-Pac, estab 1991, empl 200, sales $15,000,000, cert: State, NMSDC)

3782   MagRabbit-Alamo Iron Works, LLC
P.O. Box 2341   San Antonio, TX 78298
(210) 704-8520   Wayne Dennis diversity Coord
Fax: (210) 705-8514
Email: wdennis@aiwnet.com
Website: www.magrabbit-aiw.com
Dist industrial supplies, steel service & fabrication, hand & power tools, equipment repair & installation, logistics, transportation & freight forwarding. (As-Pac, estab 2004, empl 150, sales $1,573,543, cert: NMSDC)

3783   Moore Transport of Tulsa LLC
661 N Plano Rd Ste 319   Richardson, TX 75081
(972) 578-0606   Gary Moore Owner
Fax: (972) 633-3726
Email: DANCHASE@mooretransport.com
Website: www.mooretransport.com
Freight transportation. (AA, estab 2005, empl 300, sales $63,000,000, cert: NMSDC)

3784   MW Logistics, LLC
5429 LBJ Freeway Ste #550   Dallas, TX 75240
(423) 243-8021   Jay Olejniczak Business Dev Mgr
Fax: (972) 331-9537
Email: jolejniczak@mwlogistics.com
Website: www.mwlogistics.com
Transportation & logistics: over the road, intermodal & bulk. (AA, estab 2001, empl 17, sales $16,800,000, cert: NMSDC)

3785   Navigator Express
14587 Kelmscot Dr   Frisco, TX 75035
(972) 330-2340   Furqan Khan VP Ops
Fax: (888) 502-5651
Email: ops@navex.us
Website: www.navex.us
Authorized motor carrier, interstate transportation of commodities to all 48 contiguous states. (As-Ind, estab 2009, empl 15, sales $250,000, cert: State)

3786   Pan American Express, Inc.
4848 Riverside Dr   Laredo, TX 78041
(855) 279-8166   Michael Aumiller Director of Sales
Fax: (419) 729-8166
Email: mdapaxi@aol.com
Website: www.panamex-zero.com
International transportation svcs; 48 states, Mexico & Canada. (Hisp, estab 1988, empl 185, sales $43,000,000, cert: NMSDC)

3787   Purpose Transportation, LLC
701 Hanover Dr PO Box 535098   GRAND PRAIRIE, TX 75053
(972) 746-4585   Greg Crawford VP of Sales
Fax: (972) 746-4584
Email: chuck@purposetransportation.com
Website: www.purposetransportation.com
Domestic transportation, freight & logistics services. (Woman/White, estab 2011, empl 10, sales $4,874,185, cert: State, WBENC)

3788   Royal Freight, LP
407 W Sioux Rd   Pharr, TX 78577
(956) 283-2200   Mike Kelley Sales Mgr
Fax: (956) 787-8375
Email: mikek@RoyalFreight.net
Website: www.royalfreight.net
Direct, Truckload, Asset Based Carrier, serving U.S.(48), Canada, and Mexico, Satelitte equipped (tractors and trailers). (Woman/White, estab 2001, empl 350, sales , cert: State)

3789   Russell Transport Inc.
12365 Pine Springs   El paso, TX 79928
(915) 542-1495   Rosa Marin President
Fax: (915) 542-1499
Email: Rmarin@russelltransport.com
Website: www.russelltransport.com
Full TL & logistics. (Woman/Hisp, estab 1992, empl 300, sales $27,000,000, cert: State, NMSDC)

3790   Shire Express Transportation
        6651 Watauga Rd, Ste 48803   Fort Worth, TX 76148
        (214) 243-5872   Brenda Jackson Logistics Coord
        Fax:
        Email: brenda.jackson@landstarmail.com
        Website: www.shireexpressgov.com/
Transportation & logistic services across the United States
and Canada. (AA, estab 2015, empl 7, sales , cert: State)

3791   Siam Logistics LLC
        223 NE Loop 820 Ste 160   Hurst, TX 76053
        (682) 253-3069   Matt Navan Acct Mgr
        Fax: (682) 463-0158
        Email: matthew.navan@siam-logistics.com
        Website: www.siam-logistics.com
Transportation, oversized loads, specialized equipment &
special weight requirements, US, Mexico & Canada.
(Woman/As-Pac, estab 2009, empl 5, sales $1,920,000,
cert: NMSDC)

3792   Southwest Freight Lines
        P.O. Box 371736   El Paso, TX 79936
        (915) 860-8592   Jesus Lares Ops Mgr
        Fax: (915) 860-9606
        Email: jesus.lares@swflines.com
        Website: www.swflines.com
Truckload services, 48 states & Mexico. (Hisp, estab 1988,
empl 300, sales $50,000,000, cert: State)

3793   Spirit Truck Lines
        200 W Nolana   San Juan, TX 78589
        (956) 781-7715   Steve Garza VP Ops & Sales
        Fax: (956) 781-1822
        Email: sgarza@spirittrucklines.com
        Website: www.spirittrucklines.com
Dedicated carrier service, bonded shipmment, expedited
loads, cargo tracking. (Hisp, estab 1990, empl 300, sales
$30,000,000, cert: NMSDC)

3794   Sun City Group Inc
        1009 Myrtle Ave Ste 100 A   El Paso, TX 79901
        (915) 593-5900   Patrick Warrington Director of Sales
        Fax: (915) 593-5903
        Email: pwarrington@suncitygroup.com
        Website: www.suncitygroup.com
Multimodal transportation services, over the road,
intermodal, sea & air. (Hisp, estab 2006, empl 21, sales
$15,000,000, cert: NMSDC)

3795   Sunrise Delivery Inc.
        2020 Lawrence St   Houston, TX 77008
        (713) 864-2020   Lanette Martinez President
        Fax: (713) 864-6055
        Email: lm@sditex.com
        Website: www.sunrisedeliveryinc.com
LTL freight, warehousing & logistics. (Woman/Hisp, estab
1981, empl 15, sales $799,616, cert: City, NMSDC, CPUC,
WBENC)

3796   Swift Logistics, Inc.
        1809 Stoney Brook Dr Ste 204 Houston, TX 77063
        (713) 425-4175   Rosemarie Patterson Logistics
        Consultant
        Fax: (713) 785-4175
        Email: rpatterson@swiftlogisticsinc.com
        Website: www.swiftlogisticsinc.com
Freight brokerage. (Woman/White, estab 2014, empl 4,
sales , cert: WBENC)

3797   Texas Freight
        1207 NE Big Bend Trail, Ste L   Glen Rose, TX
        76043
        (254) 898-1117   Preston Shuffield Broker
        Fax: (254) 898-1177
        Email: preston@texasfreight.net
        Website: www.texasfreight.net
Commercial motor carrier, brokerage authority serving
48 states, flatbeds, drop decks, RGN's, lowboys, and dry
vans. (Woman/White, estab 2002, empl 8, sales , cert:
NWBOC)

3798   Tri Star Freight System Inc.
        5407 Mesa Dr   Houston, TX 77028
        (713) 631-1095   Shana Whittington Admin Asst
        Fax: (713) 631-1099
        Email: shanaw@tristarfreightsys.com
        Website: www.tristarfreightsys.com
Linehaul, FTL & LTL, airport pick up & delivery, drayage,
local & OTR container drayage, warehousing. (Woman/
White, estab 1987, empl 83, sales $32,212,911, cert:
NWBOC)

3799   Verde Logistics, LLC
        9525 Escobar Dr   El Paso, TX 79907
        (915) 791-4034   Holly Webb Business Devel
        Fax: (915) 791-4046
        Email: holly.jones@verdelogistics.com
        Website: www.verdelogisticsllc.com/home
Third party transportation, full truck load van, reefer, flat
bed & heavy haul. (Woman/Hisp, estab 2010, empl 4,
sales $9,035,196, cert: NMSDC, WBENC)

3800   Wilmac Enterprises, LLC
        3753 N Beach St   Fort Worth, TX 76137
        (817) 222-0099   Shirley Nevala-Chavie Business
        Dev
        Fax: (817) 439-0804
        Email: shirleyn@blstx.com
        Website: www.wilmacent.com
Freight transportion. (Woman/Hisp, estab 2008, empl
25, sales , cert: State)

Virginia

3801   High Plains Logistics Consulting, LLC
P.O. Box 8   Highland Springs, VA 23057
(804) 437-0066   Burt Epps VP
Fax: (804) 328-2977
Email: burt_epps@msn.com
Website:
Transprotation brokerage & third party logistics. (Nat Ame, estab 2002, empl 3, sales $8,200,000, cert: NMSDC)

3802   LAS Logistical Services LLC
3031 N Lakebridge Dr   Norfolk, VA 23324
(855) 232-5866   Sam Kearson CEO
Fax: (757) 627-2383
Email: samkearson@laslogistical.com
Website: www.laslogistical.com
Logistic services: land, air & sea. (AA, estab 2012, empl 10, sales $30,000, cert: State)

3803   TH Logistics,LLC
2150 Magnolia St   Richmond, VA 23223
(888) 929-7323   Devon Henry President
Fax:
Email: dhenry@thlogistics.net
Website: www.thlogistics.net
Third party logistics & supply chain services, value added warehousing distribution, contract packaging, product acquisition, transload & transportation. (AA, estab 2016, empl 200, sales $50,000,000, cert: NMSDC)

Washington

3804   Red Arrow Logistics
150 120th Ave NE, Ste F110   Bellevue, WA 98005
(425) 747-7914   Liz Lasater CEO
Fax: (425) 747-7569
Email: ashley.moise@redarrowlogistics.com
Website: www.redarrowlogistics.com
Warehousing & distribution services, vendor compliance programs, ground, sea & air transportation. (Woman/White, estab 2003, empl 8, sales $6,747,398, cert: NWBOC)

3805   VETrans LLC
1420 Meridian E Ste 2   Milton, WA 98354
(253) 833-4688   Vincent W. Santiago Owner
Fax: (253) 363-8656
Email: vince@go-vetrans.com
Website: www.go-VETrans.com
Transportation, railroad transloading, other transporation brokerage services. (Woman/Hisp, estab 2006, empl 2, sales $3,967,124, cert: NMSDC)

Wisconsin

3806   Black River Truck Brokers, LLC
N613 Colonial Ave   Pittsville, WI 54466
(800) 241-2785   Heather Jacobson Owner
Fax: (715) 884-7235
Email: heather.brtb@yahoo.com
Website: www.blackrivertruckbroker.com
Transportation & Logistics Services. (Woman/White, estab 2007, empl 2, sales $4,800,000, cert: State, WBENC)

3807   Trans International, LLC
N93 W16288 Megal Dr   Menomonee Falls, WI 53051
(262) 253-3500   Denise Lawien CSMO
Fax: (262) 253-3515
Email: sales@ticominc.com
Website: www.ticominc.com
Transportation consulting & logistics services: freight pre-audit & payment, post audit, transportation reporting software & tools, freight rating & routing, carrier contract negotiations & general logistics consulting. (Woman/White, estab 1975, empl 100, sales $5,250,000, cert: State, WBENC)

FURNISHINGS
Manufacturers, distributors or importers of furniture for office and home. Also floor and window coverings, light fixtures, household and kitchen accessories such as wastebaskets, planters, dishes, vases, brooms, dustpans, etc. (See also GIFTWARE, ARTS & CRAFTS and OFFICE SUPPLIES categories. NAICS Code 42

Arkansas

3808   Burris Inc.
113 S Arkansas Ave   Russellville, AR 72801
(479) 968-4888 Trolynn McSpadden President
Fax: (479) 968-4937
Email:
Website: www.burrisinc.com
Office supplies & office furniture, panel systems, custom millwork, office layout & design. (Woman/White, estab 1953, empl 15, sales $3,374,600, cert: WBENC)

Arizona

3809   Corporate Interior System
3311 E Broadway Rd, Ste A   Phoenix, AZ 85040
(602) 304-0100 Lisa K Johnson President
Fax:
Email: ljohnson@cisinphx.com
Website: www.cisinphx.com
Office Furniture Dealership, modular and system furniture and accessories, and installation of office furniture and accessories. (Woman/White, estab , empl 1, sales , cert: WBENC)

3810   Dave Scott & Associates, Inc.
P.O. Box 22115   Phoenix, AZ 85028
(602) 971-1600 David R Scott Owner
Fax: (602) 971-2021
Email: dave.scott@davescottassociates.com
Website: www.davescottassociates.com
Office Furniture: Systems, Case Goods, Seating, Specialty; Health Care Furniture; Benches, receptacles, bike racks, ash urns; Millwork; Cell phone Charging Station Kiosks, Playgrounds, Design/space planning, Installation. (AA, estab 1999, empl 6, sales $1,360,539, cert: State, City, NMSDC)

3811   Elontec
5502 W Buckey Rd Ste 100   Phoenix, AZ 85043
(602) 759-5500 Jessica Chappell Inside Sales Mgr
Fax: (602) 759-5501
Email: jchappell@elontec.com
Website: www.elontec.com
Office furniture: cubicles, case goods, private offices, ect. Planning, design, procurement & installation. (Woman/White, estab 1997, empl 65, sales $5,200,000, cert: State, WBENC)

California

3812   Alternative Office Solutions
140 San Pedro Ave, Ste 110   Morgan Hill, CA 95037
(408) 776-2036 Kevin Collier Sales Dir
Fax: (408) 779-2658
Email: kevin@alt-office.com
Website: www.alt-office.com
Office space planning & installation of remanufactured Herman Miller AO1 and AO2 cubicles. (Woman/White, estab 1998, empl 19, sales $2,091,446, cert: CPUC)

3813   American Dawn Inc.
401 W Artesia Blvd   Compton, CA 90220
(310) 609-3222 Mike Maloney Corp Secretary
Fax: (310) 223-2016
Email: mmaloney@americandawn.com
Website: www.americandawn.com
Mfr & dist industrial & hospitality items: linens, towels, etc. (As-Ind, estab 1975, empl 200, sales , cert: NMSDC)

3814   Compact International
16161 Ventura Blvd, Ste 382   Encino, CA 91436
(818) 585-1374 Robert Paul Mktg/sales
Fax: (323) 733-1312
Email: Robert.Paul@CompactIntl.com
Website: www.compactintl.com
Design, mfr & dist commercial furniture, folding chairs & tables. (AA, estab 1998, empl 4, sales $2,050,000, cert: State)

3815   Dawn Medical Inc.
844 Jury Court   San Jose, CA 95112
(408) 280-7676 Gaylene McIntosh President
Fax: (408) 280-1549
Email: caremed.products@yahoo.com
Website:
Anesthesia,& critical care equipment and supplies: blood pressure cuffs ,cables & lead wires laryngoscopes blades, airways, electrodes, labor & delivery/Nursery/NICU products, Bio Medical engineering products (Woman/White, estab 1996, empl 3, sales $375,175, cert: NWBOC)

3816   Decor Interior Design
2937 E 4th St   Los Angeles, CA 90033
(310) 289-2186 Ronda Jackson Principal
Fax: (310) 289-2189
Email: rjackson@designsbydecor.com
Website: www.designsbydecor.com
Interior Design, Custom Furniture, Window Treatments, Project Management, Interior Landscaping. (Woman/AA, estab 1997, empl 28, sales $552,000, cert: State, NMSDC, CPUC, WBENC)

3817　Environments Plus, Inc.
　　　　1700 1st St　San Fernando, CA 91340
　　　　(866) 865-8120　Bryan Migdol Dir Relocation Service
　　　　Fax: (888) 854-0846
　　　　Email: bmigdol@epi-usa.com
　　　　Website: www.Environmentsplus.com
Office Furniture Installation, Office Reconfiguration, Office
Moves, Office Furniture Liquidation, Furniture Storage,
Project Manager,
Design Services, Furniture Lifting. (Woman/White, estab
1992, empl 45, sales $6,500,000,000, cert: CPUC, WBENC)

3818　HSE USA, Inc.
　　　　5709 E 61st St　Commerce, CA 90040
　　　　(323) 278-0888　Nelson Yip President
　　　　Fax: (323) 278-0999
　　　　Email: nelson.yip@hseusa.com
　　　　Website: www.hseusa.com
We carry a large selection of candles for the food-service
and hospitality industries. (As-Pac, estab 2008, empl 10,
sales $4,100,000, cert: NMSDC)

3819　Media Management Systems
　　　　3525 Del Mar Heights Rd, Ste 440　San Diego, CA
　　　　92130
　　　　(858) 792-0029　Chita McCollum Owner
　　　　Fax: (858) 792-9727
　　　　Email: mediamgmts@aol.com
　　　　Website: www.mediamgmtsystems.com
Dist office, computer & industrial furniture; file & storage
surveys, tool cabinets. (Woman/Hisp, estab 1986, empl 1,
sales , cert: State)

3820　Metro Contract Group
　　　　6800 Koll Center Parkway Ste 100　Pleasanton, CA
　　　　94566
　　　　(925) 201-5947　Dwight Jackson President
　　　　Fax: (925) 730-4373
　　　　Email: dwight@metrocontractgroup.com
　　　　Website: www.metrocontractgroup.com
Contract furniture dealer & design firm. (AA, estab 1993,
empl 30, sales $3,010,000, cert: State, NMSDC, CPUC)

3821　Southwest Country
　　　　17940 Ventura Blvd　Encino, CA 91316
　　　　(818) 345-3900　Fred Fuchs Mgr
　　　　Fax: (818) 345-3909
　　　　Email: webmaster@swcountry.com
　　　　Website: www.cowboyindian.com
Mfr & dist southwest, western & country furniture, art &
accessories. (Woman/Hisp, estab 1989, empl 5, sales , cert:
State, City)

3822　Systems Source Inc.
　　　　3161 Michelson Dr Ste 110　Irvine, CA 92612
　　　　(949) 852-0920　Rosemarie Smith CEO
　　　　Fax: (949) 475-5924
　　　　Email: bvente@systemsource.com
　　　　Website: www.systemsource.com
Office furniture, modular furniture systems, demountable
walls, design, installation, refinishing, reupholstery &
service. (Woman/White, estab 1982, empl 60, sales
$40,414,099, cert: CPUC, WBENC)

3823　Systems Source, Inc.
　　　　2100 Main St, Ste 100　Irvine, CA 92614
　　　　(949) 224-0488　Rosemarie Correia President
　　　　Fax:
　　　　Email: rcorreia@systemsource.com
　　　　Website: www.systemsource.com
Contract office furniture, design, installation & service.
(Woman/White, estab 2000, empl 1, sales , cert:
WBENC)

3824　Uniworld Omniport
　　　　690 Garcia Ave Ste A　Pittsburg, CA 94565
　　　　(925) 439-3070　Chris Smead Director of Ops
　　　　Fax: (925) 439-3268
　　　　Email: chris@bbopokertables.com
　　　　Website: www.BBOPokerTables.com
Mfr & dist folding leg & furniture/dining/conference
solid wood poker tables. (As-Pac, estab 2006, empl 5,
sales $1,302,000, cert: NMSDC)

Colorado

3825　Premier Commercial Interiors, Inc.
　　　　6830 N Broadway, Unit H　Denver, CO 80221
　　　　(303) 466-8575　Brenda Jones President
　　　　Fax: (303) 410-1491
　　　　Email: brendaj@pciwindowcoverings.com
　　　　Website: www.pciwindowcoverings.com
Furnish & install window treatments (blinds, roller
shades etc.) and projection screens.　Clean & repair
existing window treatments. (Woman, estab 2004, empl
9, sales , cert: WBENC)

3826　Workplace Elements LLC
　　　　2501 Blake St　Denver, CO 80205
　　　　(303) 471-4334　Cameron Gilbreath Controller
　　　　Fax: (303) 471-4330
　　　　Email: cgilbreath@workplaceelements.com
　　　　Website: www.workplaceelements.com
Office furniture, furniture storage, flooring, carpet,
demountable walls, private office furniture. (Woman/
White, estab 2008, empl 60, sales $38,000,000, cert:
WBENC)

Connecticut

3827　De Clercq Office Group
　　　　1227 Whitney Ave　Hamden, CT 06517
　　　　(203) 230-9380　Deborah Hopewell Declercq
　　　　President
　　　　Fax:
　　　　Email: deb@dog-office.com
　　　　Website: www.dog-office.com
Furniture related consulting services, pre-owned
furniture & furniture rescue. (Woman/White, estab
2001, empl 6, sales $11,311,190, cert: WBENC)

Florida

3828   Above the Sill
       745 C Shamrock Blvd   Venice, FL 34293
       (941) 492-3101 Phillip Barone VP Sales and Mktg
       Fax: (941) 492-3102
       Email: phil@abovethesill.net
       Website: www.abovethesill.net
Cubicle Curtains and track fabrication and installation,
vertical blinds, roller shades, solar shades, mini blinds, faux
wood blinds, solar panels, shutters, venetian blinds, etc.
(Woman/White, estab 2004, empl 4, sales , cert: State)

3829   Berwin, Inc.
       3501 Commerce Pkwy   Miramar, FL 33025
       (954) 499-6677 Nancy Wolfe A/R Specialist
       Fax: (954) 499-8376
       Email: nancy.wolfe@jcwhite.com
       Website: www.jcwhite.com
Design, dist, install & service office furniture, walls &
floors. (Woman, estab 1978, empl 103, sales $43,000,000,
cert: State)

3830   Business Interior Group, Inc.
       93 Rosehill Crescent Ct   Debary, FL 32713
       (386) 668-9387 John North President
       Fax: (386) 668-2717
       Email: big32779@aol.com
       Website:
Office furniture & installation, cubicles, seating,
casegoods, etc. (AA, estab 2003, empl 2, sales , cert: State)

3831   Cadence Keen Innovations d/b/a CKI Solutions
       1645 Palm Beach Lakes Blvd #210   West Palm
       Beach, FL 33401
       (561) 249-2219 Gregg Saxton
       Fax: (561) 429-4578
       Email: gregg.s@ckisolutions.us
       Website: www.ckisolutions.us
Bed doubling systems, mattress & pillow protectors,
mattress protection systems, disposable luggage protection systems. (Woman/White, estab 1996, empl 6, sales
$2,211,409, cert: NWBOC)

3832   Cubicle Curtain Factory
       7810 S Dixie Hwy   West Palm Beach, FL 33405
       (800) 588-9296 Stephanie Serio President
       Fax: (866) 804-5692
       Email: stephanie@cubiclecurtainfactory.com
       Website: www.cubiclecurtainfactory.com
Mfr & dist hospital cubicle curtains, window draperies, bed
covers, shower curtains, blackout & disposable curtains.
(Woman/White, estab 2004, empl 23, sales $2,673,550,
cert: State)

3833   Furniture Installation Solution Inc
       4740 NW 15th Ave Ste D Fort Lauderdale, FL 33309
       (954) 638-2432 Donovan Williams Ops Mgr
       Fax:
       Email: info@myfis.biz
       Website: www.myfis.biz
Install, reconfigure & relocate panel (cubicle) system &
case good furniture. (AA, estab 2008, empl 10, sales
$2,400,000, cert: NMSDC)

3834   HNM Global Logistics
       9603 Satellite Boulevard Ste150 Orlando, FL
       32837
       (407) 472-7576 Tony McGee CEO
       Fax: (407) 472-8955
       Email: tmcgee@gohnm.com
       Website: www.gohnm.com
Dist & install furniture supplies, furniture, fixtures &
equipment. (AA, estab 2004, empl 10, sales $5,600,000,
cert: NMSDC)

Georgia

3835   Contract Business Interiors, Inc.
       3455 N Desert Dr, Bldg 3, Ste 103   East Point, GA
       30344
       (404) 684-0800 Michael Murphy
       Fax: (404) 684-0802
       Email: michael@contractbusinessinteriors.com
       Website:
Contract furniture dealer: office case goods, modular
systems, seating, auditorium, lecture hall/training room,
dormitory, lockers & signage, interior design, space
layout, specification, installation, reconfiguration,
furniture restoration. (AA, estab 2001, empl 5, sales
$1,200,000, cert: State)

3836   Corporate Environments of GA, Inc.
       1636 Northeast Exprwy   Atlanta, GA 30329
       (404) 679-8999 Alison Rutledge Sr Acct Mgr
       Fax: (404) 679-8950
       Email: arutledge@corporateenvironments.com
       Website: www.corporateenvironments.com
Dist office furniture. (Woman/White, estab 1973, empl
37, sales $47,200,000, cert: WBENC)

3837   Nance Carpet & Rug Inc.
       201 Nance Road   Calhoun, GA 30701
       (706) 629-7731 Trenna Smith Natl Accts Specialist
       Fax: (706) 629-4864
       Email: Trenna.smith@nancecarpet.com
       Website: www.nancefloors.com
Dist area rugs, carpet remnants, carpet by the roll,
carpet tiles & carpet base. (Woman/White, estab 1972,
empl 300, sales $19,000,000, cert: WBENC)

3838   Table Decor International Inc.
       2748 S Cobb Industrial Blvd   Smyrna, GA 30082
       (770) 432-1156 Lynn Wells President
       Fax: (770) 436-9463
       Email: tdi@tabledecor.com
       Website: www.tabledecor.com
Design & mfr specialty table lighting & unique center-
pieces & table accessory items. (Woman/White, estab
1984, empl 5, sales $750,000, cert: WBENC)

3839   Zig Zag Inc.
4300 Westpark Dr, SW   Atlanta, GA 30336
(404) 629-2621   Gokul Nair President
Fax: (404) 704-0845
Email: gokul@zzincorporation.com
Website: www.zzincorporation.com
Mfr patio cushions, rugs, door mats & general safety items. (As-Ind, estab 2008, empl 10, sales $13,000,000, cert: NMSDC)

Illinois

3840   Phoenix Woodworking Corporation
P.O. Box 459   Woodstock, IL 60098
(815) 338-9338   Sandra Pierce President
Fax: (815) 338-9383
Email: spierce@phoenixwoodworking.com
Website: www.phoenixwoodworking.com
Custom & commercial cabinetry & casework, reception centers, filing cabinets, wooden lockers & millwork, custom desks & wooden store fixtures. (Woman/White, estab 1996, empl 10, sales , cert: State, WBENC)

3841   Resource One
321 E Adams   Springfield, IL 62701
(217) 753-5742   Cynthia Davis President
Fax: (217) 753-5748
Email: cdavis@resourceoneoffice.com
Website: www.resourceoneoffice.com
Dist office furniture, carpet, wallcovering, window treatments, refurbishment services, furniture, space-planning & interior design, furniture installation. (Woman/White, estab 1987, empl 22, sales $8,000,000, cert: State, WBENC)

Indiana

3842   Commercial Office Environments Inc.
7301 Zionsville Road   Indianapolis, IN 46268
(317) 876-9200   James Bednarski Acct Exec
Fax:
Email: james@coeindy.com
Website: www.coeindy.com
Furniture & storage equipment, design, install furniture & storage solutions. (Woman/White, estab 1989, empl 29, sales $13,000,000, cert: State)

3843   Lapsley Inc.
1002 E Rudisill Blvd   Fort Wayne, IN 46806
(260) 745-3265   Donita Mudd President
Fax: (260) 745-2800
Email: dmudd@lapsleyinc.com
Website: www.lapsleyinc.com
Furnish & install window treatments: blinds, shades, draperies, manual or motorized, projection screens, cubicle curtains & cubicle tracks. (Woman/AA, estab 2003, empl 4, sales $140,000, cert: State, 8(a))

3844   Office and Business Resources LLC
244 McConnell Dr   New Albany, IN 47150
(502) 333-8907   Kahy Brown President
Fax:
Email: kbrown@officeandbusinessresources.com
Website: www.officeandbusinessresources.com
Office furniture assembly & installation, furniture systems (cubicles), office relocations & interoffice relocations, space planning & design. (Woman/White, estab 2012, empl 4, sales $60,000, cert: NWBOC)

3845   TLS by Design, LLC
10737 Sand Key Circle   Indianapolis, IN 46256
(765) 683-1971   Jeff Day Dir
Fax: (765) 683-1972
Email: sales@tlsbydesign.com
Website: www.tlsbydesign.com
Mfr custom furniture. (Woman, estab 2002, empl 12, sales $780,000, cert: State, WBENC)

Kentucky

3846   Munson Business Interiors
2307 River Rd   Louisville, KY 40206
(502) 588-7368   Susan Lewis Acct Rep
Fax: (502) 589-1317
Email: susan@mbifurniture.com
Website: www.mbifurniture.com
Office furnishings, space planning, design, delivery, installation, project management, warehousing & inventory reports, repair & refinishing, reupholstery panels, chairs & custom furniture. (Woman/White, estab 1986, empl 21, sales $6,376,824, cert: NWBOC)

Louisiana

3847   Contract Furniture Group, LLC
201 James Dr E James BusPk   Saint Rose, LA 70087
(504) 412-0080   Julio Rodriguez President
Fax:
Email: Julio@contractfurnituregroup.com
Website: www.contractfurnituregroup.com
Design & install furniture systems modular furniture, freestanding casegoods, conference room furniture, break rooms, training rooms, healthcare furniture & high density filing systems. (Hisp, estab 2000, empl 20, sales , cert: NMSDC)

Massachusetts

3848   McElroy Scenic Services LLC
P.O. Box 145   Ashley Falls, MA 01222
(413) 229-9920   Noelle LaMuniere President
Fax: (413) 229-9944
Email: noelle@mcelroyscenic.com
Website: www.mcelroyscenic.com
Decor fabrication, set design & fabrication, custom displays, architectural models, exterior & interior signage, custom corporate furniture & staging, museum exhibits. (Woman/White, estab 1999, empl 7, sales $1,200,000, cert: State, WBENC)

3849 Wholesale Distribution
      P.O. Box 1497   Cotuit, MA 02635
      (800) 345-4027 Linda Sharp President
      Fax: (508) 539-9143
      Email: linda@facilitiesfurniture.com
      Website: www.facilitiesfurniture.com
Dist folding, stack, office & classroom chairs, training &
computer, cafeteria & classroom tables & desks, restroom
fixtures & components, lockers, flags, communication
boards. (Woman/White, estab 2001, empl 3, sales , cert:
State, WBENC)

Maryland

3850 Contemporary Business Interiors, LLC
      1369 D Brass Mill Rd   Belcamp, MD 21017
      (410) 272-5559 Christina Kerr Member
      Fax: (410) 272-5535
      Email: Christi@cbillc.com
      Website: www.cbillc.com
Dist business furniture: office, hospitality, bar & restaurant, medical, school, space planning & design, project
mgmt, installation. (Woman, estab 2006, empl 3, sales
$1,300,000, cert: State)

Michigan

3851 Airea
      23231 B Industrial Park Dr   Farmington Hills, MI
      48335
      (248) 426-3711 Nick Piccione Acct Exec
      Fax: (248) 426-5500
      Email: npiccione@aireainc.com
      Website: www.aireainc.com
Modular walls & ceiling systems, raised-access flooring,
floor covering, furniture & lighting. (AA, estab 1995, empl
28, sales $12,000,000, cert: NMSDC)

3852 Designer Installation Services, Inc.
      9685 Harrison St, Ste 200   Romulus, MI 48174
      (313) 582-9310 Robert Corona President
      Fax: (313) 582-9340
      Email:
      danielle.smith@designerinstallationservicesin.com
      Website: www.designerinstallationservicesin.com
Dist commercial office furniture, flooring & ancillary items,
installation, warehousing, asset management, delivery.
(Hisp, estab 1979, empl 25, sales $4,000,000, cert:
NMSDC)

3853 Hercules & Hercules, Inc.
      19055 W Davison   Detroit, MI 48223
      (313) 933-6669 Belinda Jefferson President
      Fax: (313) 933-1801
      Email: bjefferson@herculesandherculesinc.com
      Website: www.herculesandherculesinc.com
Dist maintenance supplies & equip, office supplies &
equip, office furniture. (AA, estab 1979, empl 16, sales
$7,000,000, cert: NMSDC)

3854 ISCG
      612 N Main St   Royal Oak, MI 48067
      (248) 399-1600 Stephanie Chyz President
      Fax: (248) 399-1601
      Email: schyz@iscginc.com
      Website: www.iscginc.com
Contract furnishings (Haworth Preferred Dealer) &
Floorcoverings, Facility Asset Management, Project &
Move Management, Union & Non. (Woman/White,
estab 1976, empl 21, sales $14,000,000, cert: WBENC)

3855 Remco Storage Systems, Inc.
      2328 Livernois Rd Ste 1070 Troy, MI 48083
      (248) 362-0500 Denise Naughton VP
      Fax: (248) 362-7420
      Email: Denise@remcoequipment.com
      Website: www.remcoequipment.com
Storage & retrieval systems: vertical lifts & carousels,
electric lateral filing systems, movable shelving, rotary
files, cabinets, records mgmt systems, color coded
labels, custom filing systems, folders & indexes.
(Woman/White, estab 1976, empl 10, sales $2,000,000,
cert: WBENC)

Minnesota

3856 AIM Global Trading, LLC
      11209 Commerce Dr N   Champlin, MN 55316
      (612)3058021 Mahtab Khan CEO
      Fax: (763) 323-1027
      Email: Linenbay3@gmail.com
      Website: www.aimglobaltrading.com
Mfr & dist 100% cotton terry towel & Polyester/Cotton
Blended Bath Towels, Hand Towels, Wash Cloths, Bath
Mats, Pool Towels, & Bar Mops. (As-Pac, estab 2014,
empl 3, sales , cert: NMSDC)

3857 Electronic Office Environments, Inc.
      264 East Lafayette Frontage Road   Saint Paul, MN
      55107
      (651) 224-0344 Chris Juarez President
      Fax: (651) 224-0258
      Email: EOE@EOEergo.com
      Website: www.EOEergo.com
Ergonomic seating, ESD seating, cleanroom seating,
specialized seating, height adjustable table frames,
office furniture, lounge furniture, cafeteria furniture,
panel systems & accessories. (Hisp, estab 1983, empl 4,
sales , cert: NMSDC)

3858 Ideal Commercial Interiors LLC
      740 Portland Ave. Ste 1418   Minneapolis, MN
      55414
      (612) 759-0955 Rick Harris CEO
      Fax: (612) 886-1410
      Email: rick@icinteriors.net
      Website: www.icinteriors.net
Office furniture, flooring, fixtures, design, space planning, installation, delivery & project management. (AA,
estab 2012, empl 3, sales , cert: NMSDC)

3859   Kelly Computer Supply Co. LLC
       3588 Hoffman Rd East   St. Paul, MN 55110
       (651) 773-1109 Bob Kelly President
       Fax: (651) 773-1381
       Email: bobkelly@kellyrest.com
       Website: www.kellyrest.com
Ergonomic equip; mfr "KellyRest" computer products:
wrist & foot rests, adjustable copy holders, keyboard
drawers & articulating keyboard trays; workstations. (Nat
Ame, estab 1983, empl 10, sales , cert: State, NMSDC,
CPUC)

3860   R and L Woodcraft, Inc
       823 Industrial Park Dr SE   Lonsdale, MN 55046
       (507) 744-2318 Randall Rivers Business Devel
       Fax: (507) 744-2382
       Email: Randall@randlwoodcraft.com
       Website: www.randlwoodcraft.com
Mfr commercial millwork & casework: cabinets,
countertops, workstations, service counters, point of
service counters, tables, booths, upholstered seating,
running trim, trash recepticles, lockers & toilet partitions.
(Woman/White, estab 1986, empl 22, sales $3,600,000,
cert: WBENC)

Mississippi

3861   Commercial Interiors, Inc.
       4277 Espy Ave   Long Beach, MS 39560
       (228) 452-9540 Donna Heath President
       Fax: (228) 452-9541
       Email: donna@cidesigns.net
       Website: www.cidesigns.net
Commercial FF&E contractor. (Woman/White, estab 1990,
empl 3, sales $555,647, cert: State)

3862   Durfold Corporation
       102 Upton Dr   Jackson, MS 39209
       (601) 922-4144 Jim Warren CEO
       Fax: (601) 922-6244
       Email: jwarren@durfold.com
       Website: www.durfold.com
Mfr upholstered healthcare furniture: sleeper chairs &
sofas, trendelenberg recliners, incliners, rocking chairs,
gliders, bariatric seating, patient & guest seating, lounge
seating, lobby furniture & ganged & tandem seating.
(Woman/White, estab 2003, empl 30, sales $3,200,000,
cert: WBENC)

North Carolina

3863   DARRAN Furniture Industries, Inc.
       2402 Shore St   High Point, NC 27263
       (800) 334-7891 Jennifer Hollingsworth President
       Fax: (336) 861-6485
       Email: jlhollingsworth@darran.com
       Website: www.darran.com
Mfr high quality, mid-market wood desk collections,
conferencing solutions, reception stations & seating.
(Woman/White, estab 1977, empl 195, sales $25,559,279,
cert: WBENC)

New Jersey

3864   Arbee Associates
       1531 S Washington Ave   Piscataway, NJ 08854
       (732) 424-3900 Sheri Isler Mgr, New Project
       Devel
       Fax: (732) 752-6034
       Email: sisler@arbee.net
       Website: www.arbeeofficefurniture.com
Office, healthcare & educational furniture (Woman/
White, estab 1973, empl 105, sales $41,844,745, cert:
WBENC)

3865   Concepts Office Furnishings, Inc.
       280 N Midland Ave Bldg J Saddle Brook, NJ 07663
       (201) 727-9110 Zaida Soto President
       Fax: (201) 727-9112
       Email: adesoto@conceptsoffice.com
       Website: www.conceptsoffice.com
Contract office furniture & equipment, project management, furniture installations & re-configurations,
refinishing & reupholstery. (Woman/Hisp, estab 1973,
empl 15, sales $3,200,000, cert: City)

3866   Corporate Facilities of New Jersey, LLC
       6950 Sherman Avenue   Pennsauken, NJ 08110
       (856) 662-5200 Amanda Chevalier Principal
       Fax: (856) 662-5787
       Email: achevalier@cfinj-knoll.com
       Website: www.cfi-knoll.com
Office furniture. (Woman/As-Pac, estab 2004, empl 26,
sales $36,706,991, cert: NMSDC, WBENC)

3867   Global Installation Resources LLC
       18 Robert St   Clifton, NJ 07014
       (973) 494-9680 Krista Korinis President
       Fax:
       Email: kkorinis@gi-resources.com
       Website: www.gi-resources.com
Installation services: office furniture, demountable walls,
signage & laboratory case work installations & project
management services. (Woman/White, estab 2002,
empl 10, sales $1,345,540, cert: State, WBENC)

3868   Image Office Environments, LLC
       1122 Route 22 W   Mountainside, NJ 07092
       (908) 301-0074 Tricia Patricco President
       Fax: (908) 301-0076
       Email: tpatricco@image-office.com
       Website: www.image-office.com
Interior constructions, raised flooring, moveable walls &
furniture. (Woman/White, estab 2005, empl 6, sales
$9,000,000, cert: State, WBENC)

3869   JC Office Consultants
       242 Union Ave   Somerville, NJ 08876
       (732) 667-5151 Jackie Orlando Principal
       Fax: (732) 667-5153
       Email: jackie@jcofficeconsultants.com
       Website: www.jcofficeconsultants.com
Dist office furniture, installation & reconfiguration
services. Space planning & CAD design. (Woman/Hisp,
estab 2009, empl 5, sales $3,000,000, cert: State,
WBENC)

New York

3870 Alianza Services LLC
74 N Broadway 2nd Fl S Nyack, NY 10960
(845) 675-7337 Dawn Cannon VP
Fax: (845) 675-7341
Email: dcannon@alianzacorp.com
Website: www.alianzacorp.com
Dist furniture, budgeting, refurbishing, storage & asset management, rental solutions, service & repair. (Hisp, estab 2006, empl 6, sales $5,100,000, cert: NMSDC)

3871 Architectural Flooring Resources, Inc.
135 W 27th St New York, NY 10001
(212) 290-0200 Mercedes Montano Project Coord
Fax: (212) 290-2855
Email: Mercedes@afrny.com
Website: www.afrny.com
Carpet, carpet tile, vinyl, composition tile, wood, cork, linoleum & specialty flooring. (Woman/Hisp, estab 1993, empl 19, sales $7,896,224, cert: City, NMSDC, WBENC)

3872 Meadows Office Supply Co., Inc.
71 W 23rd St 2nd Fl New York, NY 10010
(212) 741-0333 Rosalie Edson President
Fax: (212) 741-0334
Email: MOFWBE@meadowsoffice.com
Website: www.meadowsoffice.com
Dist Haworth furniture products. (Woman/White, estab 1967, empl 83, sales $70,000,000, cert: State, City, WBENC)

3873 Seating Inc.
P.O. Box 898 Hunda, NY 14517
(585) 468-2875 Emily J Hart Special Projects Coord
Fax: (585) 468-2804
Email: emily@seatinginc.com
Website: www.seatinginc.com
Mfr office seating: ergonomic task, executive, multi-purpose, stools, stacking & nesting chairs. (Woman/White, estab 1987, empl 25, sales , cert: WBENC)

3874 Waldner's
125 Route 110 Farmingdale, NY 11732
(631) 844-9342 Meredith Stern President
Fax: (631) 694-3503
Email: mstern@waldners.com
Website: www.waldners.com
Dist & install office furniture. (Woman/White, estab 1939, empl 107, sales $87,500,000, cert: City, WBENC)

Ohio

3875 APG Office Furnishings
PO Box 631850 Bldg 44, 7th Fl Cincinnati, OH 45263
(513) 239-6814 Connie L. Goins President
Fax: (513) 621-3721
Email: cgoins@apgde.com
Website: www.apgof.com
Dist office furniture, space planning, design, project mgmt svcs & product solutions. (Woman/White, estab 1969, empl 1, sales $50,000,000, cert: State, WBENC)

3876 Budget Office Interiors LLC
1235 Marquette St Cleveland, OH 44114
(216) 566-1540 Susan Hamilton President
Fax: (216) 566-9044
Email: sue.bofc@yahoo.com
Website: www.BudgetOfficeFurnitureCleveland.com
New furniture, used furniture & refinished furniture: cubicles, workstations, space planning, desks, seating, conference rooms, training rooms, break rooms, home offices, telemarketing areas, reception areas, lateral & vertical filing. (Woman/White, estab 2005, empl 4, sales $22,560,700, cert: City)

3877 Clara I. Brown Interiors, Inc. (CIBI)
5305 Courtney Pl Columbus, OH 43235
(614) 224-9180 Clara I. Brown President
Fax: (614) 221-7974
Email: jim@cibiinc.com
Website: www.cibiinc.com
Office Furniture, Carpet & Hard Flooring, Carpet Cleaning, Re-upholstery, Mill Work, De-mountable Walls, Wall Coverings, Window Treatments, Interior Design/Space Planning, Furniture Moves, Warehousing. (Woman/Hisp, estab 1993, empl 12, sales $3,828,904, cert: NMSDC)

3878 HUGE Heating & Cooling Co. Inc.
711 W Bagley Rd Berea, OH 44017
(440) 234-4157 Bob Palka service Mgr
Fax: (440) 234-6608
Email: bob@hugeheating.com
Website: www.hugeheating.com
We service and sell H.V.A.C. heating & cooling equipment for the greater Cleveland northern Ohio area. (Woman/White, estab 1965, empl 20, sales $1,800,000, cert: State)

3879 Interior Services Incorporated dba Enriching Spaces
1360 Kemper Meadow Dr Cincinnati, OH 45240
(513) 851-0933 Dawn Schwartzman President
Fax: (513) 742-6415
Email: dawn@enrichingspaces.com
Website: www.enrichingspaces.com
Office Furniture, Healthcare Furniture, School & University Furniture, Art & Accessories, Carpet Tile, Signage, Interior Design, Branding, Ergonomic Accessories, Ergonomic Chairs, Desks, Workstations, Conference Room. (Woman, estab 1982, empl 1, sales , cert: WBENC)

3880 King Business Interiors, Inc.
6155 Huntley Rd, Ste D Columbus, OH 43229
(614) 430-0020 Darla J. King Owner
Fax: (614) 430-0022
Email: darlaking@kbiinc.com
Website: www.kbiinc.com
Office furniture dealer. (Woman, estab 1998, empl 1, sales , cert: WBENC)

3881 Master Manufacturing Co, Inc.
9200 Inman Ave   Cleveland, OH 44105
(800) 323-5513 Bob Ptacek V.P. Sales
Fax: (216) 641-0537
Email: bptacek@mastermfgco.com
Website: www.mastermfgco.com
Mfr furniture casters & self-stick wheels; felt pads, surface protectors, wobble stoppers; furniture movers; door stops; ergonomic support cushions & wire mgmt channels & grommets. (Woman/White, estab 1951, empl 34, sales , cert: CPUC, WBENC)

3882 RCF Group
2425 W 11th St   Cleveland, OH 44113
(513) 612-7347 Carl Satterwhite President
Fax: (216) 781-8206
Email: carl@thercfgroup.com
Website: www.thercfgroup.com
Design office layout, new furniture, installation, move management & asset management. (AA, estab 2003, empl 104, sales $68,500,000, cert: City, NMSDC)

3883 Vocon Partners, LLC
3142 Prospect Ave   Cleveland, OH 44115
(216) 588-0800 Frank Mercuri CFO
Fax: (216) 588-0801
Email: info@vocon.com
Website: www.vocon.com
Furniture coordination, graphic design. (Woman/White, estab 1987, empl 95, sales $24,992,464, cert: WBENC)

3884 Williams Interior Designs, Inc.
2168 Citygate Dr   Columbus, OH 43219
(614) 418-7250 Carolyn Williams-Francis CEO
Fax: (614) 418-9047
Email: widcarolyn@rrohio.com
Website: www.williamsinteriordesigns.com
Interior design, office furniture, office supplies & window treatments. (Woman/AA, estab 1985, empl 3, sales $2,000,000, cert: State)

Oregon

3885 Carriage Works, Inc.
1877 Mallard Ln   Klamath Falls, OR 97601
(541) 882-0700 Barbara Evensizer President
Fax: (541) 882-9661
Email: info@carriageworks.com
Website: www.carriageworks.com
Mfr carts: food, espresso, kiosks, beverage, bar, vending & display items. (Woman/Nat Ame, estab 1971, empl 30, sales $4,000,000, cert: State)

Pennsylvania

3886 Alpha Office Supplies, Inc.
4950 Parkside Ave Ste 500 Philadelphia, PA 19131
(215) 226-2690 Chester Riddick CEO
Fax: (215) 223-0321
Email: chet.riddick@alphaos.com
Website: www.alphaos.com
Dist office furniture & supplies, paper, computers & accessories; desktop delivery, installation, space planning & project mgmt. (AA, estab 1985, empl 29, sales $26,000,000, cert: NMSDC)

3887 Peerless Wall and Window Coverings, Inc.
3490 William Penn Hwy   Pittsburgh, PA 15235
(412) 823-7660 Bob Cherry Mgr
Fax: (412) 816-3865
Email: sales@peerlesswallpaperandblinds.com
Website: www.peerlesswallpaperandblinds.com
Dist & install wallcoverings, window coverings, blinds, shades, shutters & draperies. (Woman/White, estab 1993, empl 6, sales $761,857, cert: State)

3888 Telrose Corporation
3801 Ridge Ave   Philadelphia, PA 19132
(215) 229-0500 Todd Rose CEO
Fax: (215) 229-0511
Email: toddrose@telrosecorp.com
Website: www.telrosecorp.com
Dist office supplies, equipment & furniture. (AA, estab 1995, empl 19, sales $8,000,000, cert: City, NMSDC)

Puerto Rico

3889 Integrated Design Solutions
90 Carr 165, Ste 405   Guaynabo, PR 00968
(787) 706-0201 Marlen Diaz VP
Fax: (787) 706-0227
Email: mdiaz@ids-pr.com
Website: www.ids-pr.com
Office furniture dealer. (Hisp, estab 1999, empl 17, sales $5,800,000, cert: NMSDC)

Tennessee

3890 Norris Design, LLC
751 Fox Ridge Lane   Caryville, TN 37714
(865) 712-9658 Liz Salem Principal
Fax: (615) 250-7937
Email: liz@norrisdesignco.com
Website: www.norrisdesignco.com
Contract furniture, single office contracts to multi-floor buildings. (Woman/As-Pac, estab 2004, empl 5, sales $2,500,000, cert: State)

Texas

3891 B&H Total Office Solutions
120 Sam Bass Ridge Rd   Southlake, TX 76092
(817) 430-8345 Jeannie Norris President
Fax:
Email: Jeannie@BHOfficeSolutions.com
Website: www.bhofficesolutions.com
New & used Furniture, refurbished cubicles, Space Planning, Furniture Moves. (Woman/White, estab 2006, empl 6, sales $650,000, cert: State)

3892 Business Interiors
1111 Valley View   Irving, TX 75061
(817) 858-2000 Sally Smith President
Fax: (817) 858-2020
Email: ssmith@businessinteriors.com
Website: www.businessinteriors.com
Office furniture sales & services: rental, used sales, installation, reconnfiguration, repair, touch up, carpet sales & installation, relocations, storage, design & space planning. (Woman/White, estab 1968, empl 151, sales $48,000,000, cert: WBENC)

3893 Facilitech Inc. dba Business Interiors
1111 Valley View Ln   Irving, TX 75061
(817) 858-2024 Mar'e VanTilburg
Fax: (817) 858-2020
Email: sales@businessinteriors.com
Website: www.businessinteriors.com
Office furniture: space planning & design, project mgmt, installation, relocation, work process consulting, refurbishing, asset management & rental. (Woman/White, estab 1970, empl 140, sales $51,517,000, cert: WBENC)

3894 Facilities Connection, Inc.
240 E Sunset Rd   El Paso, TX 79922
(915) 833-8303 Patty Holland Branch CEO
Fax: (915) 833-2898
Email: phBranch@facilitiesconnection.com
Website: www.facilitiesconnection.com
Interior design, furniture layout, space planning, project management, office furniture installation, reconfiguration, relocation, interiors, assets maintenance. (Woman/Hisp, estab 1987, empl 25, sales $27,000,000, cert: State)

3895 Facilities Resource Inc.
9737 Great Hills Trail, Ste 305   Austin, TX 78759
(512) 371-1232 Darren Ross Business Devel
Fax:
Email: dross@fri-texas.com
Website: www.fri-texas.com
Office furniture furnishings. Move services & move coordination & planning. Furniture installation, interior design & space planning. (Woman/White, estab 1997, empl 13, sales $1,800,000, cert: State, City)

3896 Facility Interiors Inc.
P.O. Box 201828   Dallas, TX 75320
(972)31914 Charles Griggsby President
Fax: (972)37599
Email: charlesg@fiinc.com
Website: www.facilityinteriors.com
Furniture installation, design, project management, move services, reconfigurations services. (AA, estab 1994, empl 30, sales $80,000,000, cert: State, NMSDC)

3897 Houston Modular Installation
245 Brookhill Dr, Ste 9   Houston, TX 77087
(713) 847-7666 Robert Garza Owner
Fax: (713) 847-7666
Email: rgarza.houstonmodular@yahoo.com
Website:
Modular furniture installation: new installations, reconfigurations inner office moves, re-location moves & deliveries. (Hisp, estab 1999, empl 18, sales , cert: State)

3898 Intelligent Interiors, Inc.
16837 Addison Rd Ste 500   Addison, TX 75001
(214) 239-9886 Mindy Casas President
Fax: (972) 980-1661
Email: mcasas@intelligentinteriors.net
Website: www.intelligentinteriors.net
Contract office furniture, design, installation, repair refurbishing, carpet, window covering. (Woman/Hisp, estab 1996, empl 12, sales $800,000, cert: State, NMSDC)

3899 Modular Installation Services, Inc.
8606 Wall St Ste 150   Austin, TX 78754
(512) 835-7706 Monica Gould
Fax: (512) 835-9763
Email: MPGould@modularinstall.com
Website: www.modularinstall.com
Commercial office furniture installation & reconfiguration services. (Hisp, estab 1996, empl 30, sales $1,300,000, cert: State, NMSDC)

3900 Neutral Posture, Inc.
3904 N. Texas Avenue   Bryan, TX 77803
(979) 778-0502 Rebecca Boenigk CEO
Fax: (979) 778-9389
Email: rboenigk@neutralposture.com
Website: www.NeutralPosture.com
Mfr ergonomic, multipurpose, industrial seating & accessories. (Woman/White, estab 1989, empl 65, sales $12,600,000, cert: WBENC, SDB)

Virginia

3901 Alpha Stone Solutions
2251 Dabney Rd, Ste H   Richmond, VA 23230
(804) 622-2068 Shion Fenty Acct Exec
Fax: (804) 622-2069
Email: SHION@ALPHASTONE.US
Website: www.alphastone.us
Dist granite products, furniture, fixtures & equipment for hotel industry. (Woman/As-Pac, estab 2000, empl 20, sales $2,800,000, cert: State)

3902   Finial Showcase, Inc.
      720 Third St   Vinton, VA 24179
      (540) 982-3593   Whitney Snyder Corp Acct Mgr
      Fax: (540) 982-5691
      Email: sales@finialshowcase.com
      Website: www.finialshowcase.com
Dist accent tables, plant stands, quilt racks, coat racks, dvd/cd cabinets, stacking tables, umbrella stands, waste baskets, desks for home office, magazine racks, luggage racks, mirrors and wall decor, vases, decorative accessories, table lamps. (Woman/White, estab 1982, empl 5, sales $650,000, cert: WBENC)

3903   Votum Enterprises, LLC
      3530 Post Office Rd Ste 5104   Midlothian, VA 23112
      (804) 317-9660   Mark Walton Dir Business Dev
      Fax:
      Email: mark@votument.com
      Website: www.votument.com
Provides cubicle, modular & systems furniture & related services, installations, reconfigurations, disassembly, moving & storage. (AA, estab 2009, empl 3, sales $257,000, cert: State, NMSDC)

Washington

3904   Allied Fuel LLC
      2400 Harbor Ave SW #100   Seattle, WA 98126
      (206) 582-2020   James E Hasty President
      Fax: (206) 582-2029
      Email: james@alliedfuel.net
      Website: www.alliedfuel.net
Fuel (AA, estab 2009, empl 5, sales $51,350,000, cert: NMSDC)

3905   Home and Travel Solutions, LLC dba BedVoyage
      18915 142nd Ave NE, Ste 230   Woodinville, WA 98072
      (425) 949-8216   Sharon Stuart CEO
      Fax: (425) 949-8374
      Email: sharon@bedvoyage.com
      Website: www.bedvoyage.com
Mfr eco-luxury bamboo bed linens, towels & blankets. (Woman/White, estab 2008, empl 12, sales $2,450,000, cert: NWBOC)

Wisconsin

3906   Laacke & Joys LLC
      3205 N 124th St   Brookfield, WI 53005
      (800) 892-5563   Joel Vento VP Sales & Mktg
      Fax: (262) 754-0536
      Email: jsvento@conceptseating.com
      Website: www.conceptseating.com
Mfr 24/7 intensive use ergonomic office chairs used for dispatch, security, control rooms, surveillance. (Woman/White, estab 1900, empl 100, sales $9,000,000, cert: WBENC)

GIFTWARES, ARTS & CRAFTS
Manufacture, distribute and import merchandise as well as cooperatives which produce jewelry, carvings, baskets, greeting cards, etc. NAICS Code 42

Florida

3907 Floral Group, Inc.
      2291 NW 82 Ave   Miami, FL 33122
      (305) 477-5008 Dornett Mullings President
      Fax: (786) 524-0789
      Email: dornett@ floralgroup.net
      Website: www.floralgroup.net
Fresh floral products to supermarket chains, foam arrangements, vase arrangements, hand-tied bouquets, rose bouquets, mixed bouquets. (Woman/AA, estab 2003, empl 12, sales $990,000, cert: NMSDC)

Georgia

3908 Barazzo, LLC
      2221 Peachtree Rd NE Ste D357 Atlanta, GA 30309
      (888) 716-5785 Quiana Lloyd Member
      Fax:
      Email: quiana@barazzo.com
      Website: www.barazzo.com
Custom gift & accessory solutions, corporate brand identity & marketing solutions. (Woman/AA, estab 2009, empl , sales , cert: State, NMSDC, SDB)

3909 Gratitude Goodies, LLC
      433 Canton Rd Ste 315 Cumming, GA 30040
      (770) 886-9598 Diane Campbell Owner
      Fax: (678) 807-5533
      Email: diane@gratitudegoodies.com
      Website: www.GratitudeGoodies.com
Gift basket with chocolate, savory & gift items. (Woman/White, estab 2009, empl 4, sales , cert: WBENC, NWBOC)

Illinois

3910 Pearl's Girl Sweet Treats
      15222 S LaGrange Orland Park, IL 60463
      (708) 460-3960 Jacqueline Jackson Owner
      Fax: (708) 460-3965
      Email: gojackiejackson@aol.com
      Website: www.kilwins.com
Corporate gift baskets: gourmet caramel apples, handmade fudge, carmel corn, brittles, fine chocolates, dipped strawberries & confectins & 32 flavors of koshers icecream. (Woman/AA, estab 2007, empl 16, sales $160,000, cert: NMSDC)

3911 Planet Canit, LLC
      843 Kimball Rd   Highland Park, IL 60035
      (847) 433-1619 Virginia Price
      Fax: (847) 433-3980
      Email: vprice@planetcanit.com
      Website: www.planetcanit.com
Custom decorative tin-ware packaging. (Woman/White, estab 2000, empl 1, sales , cert: WBENC)

Indiana

3912 Trans-Plants Inc.
      1260 S Senate Ave   Indianapolis, IN 46225
      (317) 972-6760 Christine Ernst President
      Fax: (317) 972-6761
      Email: admin@trans-plantsindy.com
      Website: www.transplants-indy.com
Interior plants & maintenance, design & installation. Floral arrangements, gift baskets, corporate & individual gifts. (Woman/White, estab 1986, empl 10, sales $360,786, cert: City)

Massachusetts

3913 Madison Floral, Inc.
      63B Innerbelt Rd Somerville, MA 02143
      (781) 648-2000 Edison Chae President
      Fax: (781) 648-5152
      Email: edison@madisonfloral.com
      Website: www.madisonfloral.com
Floral design: corporate functions, annual meetings, dinner affairs. (As-Pac, estab 2000, empl 5, sales $180,000, cert: State)

Maryland

3914 Copiosity, LLC
      @Pyramid Atlantic Art Center 8230 Georgia Ave, 2nd Fl Silver Spring, MD 20910
      (301) 608-9102 Dianne Harrison Principal
      Fax: (301) 576-5544
      Email: dcharrison@copiosityllc.com
      Website: www.copiositygreetings.com
Greeting products: holiday gift wrapping paper, bags, tags, and decorations; holiday greeting cards; graphic & decorative wall decals; celebration yard signs; and stylish seasonal garden products such as disposable table liners. (Woman/AA, estab 2010, empl 2, sales $12,000, cert: NMSDC, WBENC)

3915 Main Street Embroidery
      85 Main St   Reisterstown, MD 21136
      (410) 833-0414 Carol Payne President
      Fax: (410) 833-0488
      Email: mse@marylandtowns.com
      Website: www.marylandtowns.com
Embroidery, screen printing, heat press, gift card printing.
(Woman/White, estab 1992, empl 2, sales $83,329, cert:
State)

New York

3916 Chocolate Promises, Inc.
      P.O. Box 694   Merrick, NY 11566
      (516) 299-6400 Cindy Zakalik President
      Fax: (516) 688-3923
      Email: cindy@chocolatepromises.com
      Website: www.chocolatepromises.com
Personalized chocolate with edible images. We'll custom
print your full color logo, picture, design and/or special
message directly on delicious chocolate coins, lollipops,
Belgian truffles and more. (Woman/White, estab 2012,
empl 2, sales $26,273, cert: State, City, WBENC)

Ohio

3917 Independence Flowers & Gifts
      6495 Brecksville Rd   Independence, OH 44131
      (216) 524-2800 Laura Gmitro Owner
      Fax: (216) 524-1371
      Email: indyflowers@yahoo.com
      Website: www.independenceflorist.com
Florist & gift shop, fruit baskets, gourmet baskets, custom
baskets, floral arrangements & gifts. (Woman/White, estab
2009, empl 4, sales $280,000, cert: City)

Texas

3918 Dessert Gallery Bakery & Cafe
      P.O. Box 981034   Houston, TX 77098
      (713) 960-4400 Sara Brook CEO
      Fax: (713) 960-4401
      Email: sara@dessertgallery.com
      Website: www.dessertgallery.com
Custom photo & logo cookies & cakes, catering- box
lunches, office birthday cakes, corporate gifts. (Woman/
White, estab 1995, empl 35, sales , cert: WBENC)

HARDWARE & TOOLS DIST.

Distribute hardware: screw machine products, plumbing supplies, safety apparel, ladders, etc. (See also HYDRAULIC & COMPRESSED AIR EQUIPMNET and INDUSTRIAL EQUIPMENT & SUPPLIES). NAICS Code 42

Alabama

3919 Ram Tool & Supply Co., Inc.
4500 5th Ave South Bldg A Birmingham, AL 35222
(205) 599-7085 Ashley Cato Accts Receivable Rep
Fax: (205) 599-7085
Email: ashley.cato@ramtool.com
Website: www.ram-tool.com
Dist construction material, supplies & tools. (Woman, estab 1985, empl 804, sales , cert: WBENC)

Arizona

3920 Machine Works, LLC
3832 E Illini St Phoenix, AZ 85040
(602) 426-1035 Tien Phan Sales/Office Mgr
Fax: (602) 426-1036
Email: tienphan@mworkllc.com
Website: www.machineworksllc.com
Dist aerospace components & assemblies. (As-Pac, estab 1997, empl 12, sales $900,000, cert: NMSDC)

California

3921 ACF Components & Fasteners, Inc.
31012 Huntwood Ave Hayward, CA 94544
(510) 487-2100 Bob Henriquez Exec VP
Fax: (510) 471-7018
Email: bobh@acfcom.com
Website: www.acfcom.com
Dist industrial fasteners, electronic component hardware, wire, industrial supplies, vmi, kitting, kits, fastener plating, fastener patching, fuses, screws, bolts, terminals. (As-Pac, estab 1976, empl 50, sales $13,000,000, cert: CPUC)

3922 B&B Socket Products, Inc.
1919 Nancita Cir Placenta, CA 92870
(714) 985-4360 Robert Huke GM
Fax: (714) 528-8455
Email: rchuke@bbsocket.com
Website: www.bbsocket.com
Dist fasteners, hardware & electronic components. (Woman/White, estab 1976, empl 17, sales , cert: WBENC)

3923 Cordova Bolt, Inc.
5601 Dolly Ave Buena Park, CA 90621
(714) 739-7500 Moses E. Cordova President
Fax: (714) 994-2912
Email: info@cordovabolt.com
Website: www.cordovabolt.com
Dist nuts, bolts, screws, washers, anchors, A325, A490, GR 2-5-8-L9, etc. (Hisp, estab 1975, empl 34, sales , cert: NMSDC, CPUC)

3924 Mackenzie Aircraft Parts, Inc.
1400 Decision St Vista, CA 92081
(760) 727-3775 Toni Mackenzie President
Fax: (760) 727-3599
Email: TONI@MACAIRPARTS.COM
Website: www.macairparts.com
Dist hardware, screws, nuts, bolts, rivets, washers, bearings & electrical parts. (Woman, estab 1979, empl 11, sales $2,500,000, cert: NWBOC)

3925 SATORI SEAL INC
8455 Utica Ave Rancho Cucamonga, CA 91730
(909) 987-8234 Anne Houlihan President
Fax: (909) 945-3005
Email: anne@satoriseal.com
Website: www.satoriseal.com
Dist o-rings, seals, custom molded seals, rotary shaft seals, PTFE seal tape, worm drive hose clamps, gaskets, washers, die cut gaskets, lathe cut gaskets. (Woman/White, estab 1971, empl 8, sales $2,749,793, cert: WBENC)

3926 STX, Inc. DBA Alta Industries
418 Aviation Blvd, Ste E Santa Rosa, CA 95403
(800) 788-0302 Judith DeZinno
Fax: (800) 788-0292
Email: jdezinno@altaindustries.com
Website: www.altaindustries.com
Mfr & dist protective knee pads & elbow pads, tool belts for industrial, construction, safety, military & tactical markets. (Woman/White, estab 1900, empl 1, sales $3,800,000, cert: NWBOC)

3927 Vampire Tools, Inc.
47 Peters Canyon Rd Irvine, CA 92606
(949) 449-5724 Adam Rauh Admin
Fax: (949) 743-2999
Email: adam@vampiretools.com
Website: www.vampiretools.com
Unique pliers for rusted, damaged, stripped screws/nuts/bolts extraction. (Woman/As-Pac, estab 2010, empl 7, sales $400,000, cert: NMSDC, CPUC)

3928　Widespread Industrial Supplies, Inc.
1220 S Boyle Ave   Los Angeles, CA 90023
(310) 793-7315   Josh Dorfman President
Fax: (310) 793-7317
Email: josh.dorfman@widespreadind.com
Website: www.widespreadind.com
Dist industrial supplies: fasteners, cutting tools, electrical, welding, chemical & safety related supplies, hand & power tools. (Woman/White, estab 2002, empl 4, sales $820,341, cert: State, City)

Florida

3929　Arrowhead Global LLC
13575 58th St N Ste 158   Clearwater, FL 33760
(727) 497-7340   Bernard Cooley Sales Mgr
Fax: (727) 361-0105
Email: orders@arrowheadglobal.com
Website: www.arrowheadglobal.com
Dist aerospace, military & commercial fasteners, hardware, connectors, electronic components, aircraft parts, adhesives & information technology products & services. (Nat Ame, estab 2013, empl 7, sales $2,600,000, cert: State)

3930　Consolidated Cordage Corp Inc.
744 Periwinkle St   Boca Raton, FL 33432
(561) 347-7247   Renee Ciaccio Sales Mgr
Fax: (561) 347-0380
Email: INFO@CONSOLIDATEDCORDAGE.COM
Website: www.consolidatedcordage.com
Dist rope, cord, pull cord, twine, elastic shockcord, fall protection safety equip, multe tape, riggings, hoistings, etc. (Woman/White, estab 1993, empl 8, sales , cert: WBENC)

3931　Limitless Investigative Solutions, L.L.C.
11160 Lost Creek Terrace #205   Bradenton, FL 34211
(678) 458-8538   Miguel Caraballo President
Fax: (951) 280-4710
Email: miguel@limitlessinv.com
Website: www.limitlessinv.com
Solid carbide end mills, drills, reamers, burrs, inserts & specials, in house research & development, custom tool design for various applications, ools simulation software. (Hisp, estab 2017, empl 1, sales , cert: State)

3932　Pelican Sales, Inc.
2825 Business Center Blvd Ste C9   Melbourne, FL 32940
(321) 254-9569   Callena Spearman Sales Professional
Fax: (321) 255-1133
Email: sales@pelican-sales.com
Website: www.pelican-direct.com
Dist industrial hardware equipment & supplies. (Woman/White, estab 1993, empl 15, sales $13,000,000, cert: State)

3933　The Bernd Group Inc.
1251 Pinehurst Rd   Dunedin, FL 34698
(727) 733-0122   Pilar Bernd President
Fax:
Email: businessdevelopment@berndgroup.com
Website: www.berndgroup.com
Material handling equip, safety products, hand & power tools, pumps & compressors, motors, generators, electrical hardware, batteries, lighting fixtures, lockers, bins, shelving, lab equip. (Woman/Hisp, estab 1992, empl 66, sales , cert: NMSDC)

3934　Tropic Fasteners LLC
255 Semoran Comerce Pl   Apopka, FL 32703
(407) 703-1582   Judy Watson President
Fax: (407) 703-1590
Email: judy@tropicfast.com
Website: www.tropicfast.com
Dist fastener products. (Woman/White, estab 1995, empl 50, sales , cert: WBENC)

Illinois

3935　Alin Machining Co, Inc. dba Power Plant Services
3131 W Soffel Ave   Melrose Park, IL 60160
(708) 345-8600   Christine Biela Sales Team Lead
Fax: (708) 345-9181
Email: christine@ppsvcs.com
Website: www.ppsvcs.com
Dist fasteners, studs, nuts, washers, bolts & pins, turbine valve parts, stems, discs & bushings, turbine blade mfg, turbine seals & packing, erosion shields. (As-Ind, estab 1998, empl 142, sales $42,000,000, cert: NMSDC)

3936　Hacha Products Corporation
801 North Main St   Wheaton, IL 60187
(844) 422-4287   Kimberly Meek CEO
Fax: (331) 212-4094
Email: kmeek@hachaproducts.com
Website: www.hachaproducts.com
Wire management devices: cable ties, wire nuts, clamps, nuts, bolts, fasteners, shrink tubing. (Woman/Hisp, estab 2015, empl 1, sales $750,000, cert: NMSDC, WBENC)

Indiana

3937　Impex International Inc.
7114 Innovation Blvd   Fort Wayne, IN 46818
(260) 489-3030   Nagin Shah President
Fax: (260) 489-3040
Email: nshah@impexint.com
Website: www.impexint.com
Dist fasteners. (As-Ind, estab 1985, empl 6, sales , cert: State, NMSDC)

3938 Powell Tool Supply Co., Inc.
1338 Mishawaka Ave   South Bend, IN 46615
(574) 289-4811 Cari Eaton CEO
Fax: (574) 289-3504
Email: ceaton@powelltool.com
Website: www.powelltool.com
Dist industrial supplies: cutting tools, abrasives, chemicals, MRO supplies, material handling, janitorial, etc. (Woman/White, estab 1948, empl 20, sales $5,500,000, cert: WBENC)

3939 Quest Safety Products, Inc.
1414 South West St Ste 200 Indianapolis, IN 46225
(317) 594-4500 Sudhansu (Sam) Yadav President
Fax: (317) 594-4501
Email: samy@questsafety.com
Website: www.QuestSafety.com
Dist safety products. (As-Pac, estab 1997, empl 34, sales $13,000,000, cert: NMSDC)

3940 Thompson Distribution Company
2225 N College Ave   Indianapolis, IN 46205
(317) 923-2581 John Thompson President
Fax: (317) 923-4819
Email: johnt@thomdist.com
Website: www.thomdist.com
Dist pipes, valves, pumps, fittings; plumbing, electrical & industrial supplies; fasteners, stainless steel. (AA, estab 2001, empl 14, sales , cert: State, NMSDC)

Kentucky

3941 America's Finest Filters
2910 W Jefferson St   Louisville, KY 40212
(502) 587-1937 Charles Houston Sales Mgr
Fax: (502) 587-1938
Email: cahou65@aol.com
Website:
Dist filters. (AA, estab 1999, empl 5, sales $1,500,000, cert: NMSDC)

3942 Com Serv LLC
10201 Bunsen Way   Louisville, KY 40299
(502) 553-1770 Shiva Dhanapal President
Fax: (502) 969-3718
Email: sdhanapal@component-supply.com
Website: www.component-supply.com
Specialty screws & customs hardware, engineering special fasteners,tubing, plastic parts, plastic injection molds, packaging supply, jigs for paint line applications, jigs & fixtures, returnable containers/totes, stamping. (As-Ind, estab 2000, empl 7, sales $5,435,800, cert: NMSDC)

3943 Sandy Valley Fasteners, LLC
528 BROADWAY St   Paintsville, KY 41240
(606) 788-0222 Christy Henry-Gregory CEO
Fax: (606) 788-7288
Email: christy@sandyvalleyfasteners.com
Website: www.sandyvalleyfasteners.com
Dist commercial & aerospace fasteners & supplies: AN, MS, NAS washers, nuts, bolts, screws, rivets, nutplates, electrical connectors & backshells, tools, raw materials, fittings, tubing, bushings, etc. (Woman, estab 1999, empl 13, sales , cert: WBENC)

Louisiana

3944 Best Bolt & Nut Corp.
2726 Lexington Ave   Kenner, LA 70062
(504) 469-3585 Jason Mangiaracina GM
Fax: (504) 469-3415
Email: jason@bestboltandnut.com
Website: www.bestboltandnut.com
Dist hardware. (Hisp, estab 1988, empl 20, sales , cert: NMSDC)

3945 Lightning Bolt and Supply
10626 S Choctaw Dr   Baton Rouge, LA 70815
(225) 272-6200 Wesley Valverde VP Business Dev
Fax: (225) 272-7001
Email: sharon@lightningboltandsupply.com
Website: www.lightningboltandsupply.com
Dist fasteners, nuts, bolts, hex bolts, lock nuts, lock washers, flat washers, fender washers, clips, retaining rings, hex head bolts, socket head cap screws, buttons, lug nuts, studs, double end studs, latches. (Woman/White, estab 1994, empl 15, sales , cert: WBENC)

Maryland

3946 American General Contractor Inc.
1 Research Ct, Ste 450   Rockville, MD 20850
(301) 202-4511 Linward Hope VP
Fax:
Email: americangeneralmd@yahoo.com
Website: www.americangeneralmd.com
Dist construction materials, thermostats, tools, cement, sheet rock, led lights, hardware nails, screws, toilets, tile, all flooring, hand towels, paper towels. (Woman/As-Ind, estab 2012, empl 2, sales $107,000, cert: State)

3947 Atlantic Hardware Supply
8389 Ardwick Ardmore Rd   Hyattsville, MD 20785
(240) 249-6047 Jon Gray VP
Fax: (240) 249-6069
Email: jgray@atlantic-supply.com
Website: www.atlantic-supply.com
Dist hardware. (Woman/White, estab 2009, empl 6, sales ,
cert: State)

3948 B & B Lighting Supply, Inc.
PO Box 68084   Baltimore, MD 21215
(410) 523-7300 Sharon Bradford CEO
Fax: (410) 664-6600
Email: sbradford@bnblightingsupply.com
Website: www.bnblightingsupply.com
Dist lamps, relamping & energy mgmt, const mgmt & svcs,
provision & professional. (Woman/AA, estab 1994, empl 2,
sales $525,000, cert: State)

3949 JarCo-Fasteners
7909 Marlboro Pike   Forestville, MD 20747
(301) 420-0146 Bill Todd Dir Sales/Mktg
Fax: (301) 420-0149
Email: jrrco@aol.com
Website:
Dist fastener products: fasteners, washers, rivets &
screws, bolts & nuts, anchors. (AA, estab 1999, empl 4,
sales , cert: State)

Michigan

3950 Ewie Co., Inc.
1099 Highland Dr   Ann Arbor, MI 48108
(734) 971-6265 Shoki Mullick Dir of Diversity
Fax:
Email: shoki.mullick@ewie.com
Website: www.ewie.com
Dist cutting tools, abrasives, special tools, chemical/
lubricants. (As-Ind/As-Pac, estab 1981, empl 253, sales
$122,000,000, cert: NMSDC)

3951 Extreme Tooling LLC
48750 Structural Dr   Chesterfield, MI 48051
(586) 232-3618 Kurt Schill President
Fax: (586) 232-3619
Email: kschill@extremetooling.com
Website: www.extremetooling.com
Dist metal removal & industrial supplies, milling, drilling &
industrial products. (Woman/White, estab 2003, empl 5,
sales $3,683,821, cert: WBENC)

3952 Marshall Sales Inc.
14359 Meyers Rd   Detroit, MI 48227
(313) 491-1700 Brian Tupiak Acct Mgr
Fax: (313) 491-6462
Email: btupiak@marshallsales.com
Website: www.marshallsales.com
Fasteners & fastener installation, tooling. (Woman/
White, estab 1956, empl 20, sales , cert: WBENC)

3953 Materials Management Services Inc.
13691 Girardin St   Detroit, MI 48212
(313) 365-1290 Jack Long President
Fax: (313) 365-1296
Email: jlong@mms-inc.com
Website: www.mms-inc.com
Mfr & dist industrial work gloves of fabric & leather in a
variety of styles. Also dist tools, tape, coolant, etc. (AA,
estab 1994, empl 11, sales , cert: NMSDC)

3954 Mer Wil Industries, Inc.
328 S Saginaw St, Ste 902   Flint, MI 48502
(810) 239-0600 Deborah Love Sales Rep
Fax: (810) 239-0660
Email: mwilliams@merwil.com
Website: www.merwil.com
Dist hardware & building supplies. (AA, estab 1983, empl
2, sales , cert: State)

3955 National Industrial Supply Co.
1201 Rochester Rd   Troy, MI 48083
(248) 588-1828 Kathryn Harper President
Fax: (248) 588-6829
Email: kathybrett@nischain.com
Website: www.nischain.com
Dist chain, wire rope, nylons, hardware supplies, etc.
(Woman/Hisp, estab 1981, empl 20, sales $2,000,000,
cert: NMSDC, WBENC)

3956 New Eagle, LLC
3588 Plymouth Rd, Ste 271   Ann Arbor, MI 48105
(734) 929-4557 Mickey Swortzel CEO
Fax:
Email: mswortzel@neweagle.net
Website: www.neweagle.net
Controls system solutions, tools, products & services.
(Woman/White, estab 2008, empl 25, sales $3,874,600,
cert: WBENC)

3957 Northern Industrial Products Corp.
20380 Cornillie Dr   Roseville, MI 48066
(586) 293-9544 Andrew Wilson VP
Fax: (586) 296-5034
Email: awilson@nipcorp.com
Website: www.nipcorp.com
Dist industrial fasteners, tools, rack & shelving, etc. (AA,
estab 1976, empl 17, sales $5,000,000, cert: NMSDC)

3958 Reggie Mckenzie Industrial Materials, Inc.
      34401 Schoolcraft Rd Ste 200 Livonia, MI 48150
      (734) 261-0844 Dan Kapp Office Mgr
      Fax: (734) 261-0040
      Email: dkapp@rmimi.com
      Website: www.reggiemckenzieindustrial.com
Dist MRO, safety & handtools. (AA, estab 2000, empl 3, sales $6,000,000, cert: NMSDC)

Minnesota

3959 Bredemus Hardware Co Inc.
      1285 Sylvan St St. Paul, MN 55117
      (651) 489-6250 Betty Bredemus CEO
      Fax: (651) 489-5502
      Email: betty@bredemus.com
      Website: www.bredemus.com
Dist hardware, hollow metal doors, frames & wood doors. (Woman, estab 1955, empl 29, sales $5,000,000, cert: State, City)

Missouri

3960 AMC Industries, LLC
      4251 N Kentucky Ave Kansas City, MO 64117
      (816) 833-4249 Adam French Dir of Sales
      Fax: (816) 833-0760
      Email: adam@amc-industries.net
      Website: www.amc-industries.net
Dist pipes, valves, fittings, plumbing fixtures, HVAC equipment, HVAC accessories, toilet partitions & washroom accessories. (AA, estab 2001, empl 5, sales $4,400,000, cert: State, City, NMSDC)

North Carolina

3961 ARTU-USA, Inc.
      330 Fields Dr. Aberdeen, NC 28315
      (910) 944-1883 Beverly Tate-Cooper President
      Fax: (910) 944-1884
      Email: beverly@artu.com
      Website: www.artu.com/
Cutting tools, Multi-Purpose Drill Bits, PORC+ Drill Bits, Cobalt Drill Bits, Tungsten Carbide Grit Hole Saws & Saw Blades, SDS Drill Bits, Precision Multi-Purpose Drill Bits & Spline Shanks. (Woman/White, estab 1989, empl 6, sales $1,636,453, cert: State, CPUC, NWBOC)

3962 C & D Industrial Tools & Supplies Inc.
      2415 Penny Road Ste 101 High Point, NC 27265
      (336) 885-6675 Jerry Camp President
      Fax: (336) 885-2292
      Email: jerry@cdi-tools.com
      Website: www.cdi-tools.com
Dist cutting tools: drills, end mills, reamers, taps & dies, precision tools, etc. (AA, estab 1988, empl 4, sales $2,500,000, cert: NMSDC)

3963 Southern Fasteners & Supply, Inc.
      2421 W Clemmonsville Rd Winston-Salem, NC 27127
      (336) 765-1790 Gene Yates VP
      Fax: (336) 265-1794
      Email: gyates@southernfasteners.com
      Website: www.southernfasteners.com
Dist fasteners. (Woman/Nat Ame, estab 1982, empl 101, sales $19,000,000, cert: NMSDC)

New Jersey

3964 Edwards & West, Inc. dba Divspec
      605 Springfield Rd Kenilworth, NJ 07033
      (908)6882550 Doug Burke NC Sales Mgr
      Fax:
      Email: DougB@Divspec.com
      Website: www.divspec.com
Dist threaded rod, strut, strut fittings, and fasteners. (Woman, estab 1980, empl 12, sales $5,913,389, cert: WBENC)

3965 Fastenation, Inc.
      120 Bright Rd Unit 2 Clifton, NJ 07012
      (973) 591-1277 Stephanie Cherepinsky Sales Rep
      Fax: (9) 735-1443
      Email: stephanie@fastenation.com
      Website: www.fastenation.com
Distributor & Converter of VELCRO(R) Brand Fasteners (Die-Cutting, Packaging, Printing, etc.) (Woman/White, estab 1997, empl 28, sales $9,000,000, cert: WBENC)

3966 Lightning Supply, Inc.
      87 Chadwick Rd Ste 200 Teaneck, NJ 07666
      (800) 724-9976 Benjamin Jones President
      Fax: (866) 402-4974
      Email: bjones@lightningsupply.com
      Website: www.lightningsupply.com
Dist safety equip, supplies & protective apparel & fabrics. (AA, estab 1993, empl 4, sales , cert: State)

3967   MF Supply Corp.
     164 Garibaldi Ave   Lodi, NJ 07644
     (973)75411   Robin Lieberman President
     Fax: (973)70869
     Email: robin@mfsupply.com
     Website: www.mfsupply.com
Dist fasteners, Stainless Steel, Inserts & Keenserts, Socket products, Standoffs & Spacers & Mil-Spec fasteners. (Woman/White, estab 1974, empl 5, sales $823,000, cert: State)

New York

3968   Global Connection Co. of America, Inc.
     150-123 Powells Cove Blvd   Whitestone, NY 11357
     (718) 767-5168   Grace King President
     Fax:
     Email: gk@madeinchina.net
     Website: www.glocoamerica.com
Dist hardware & tools. (Woman/As-Pac, estab 1992, empl 3, sales $2,107,046, cert: State, NMSDC)

3969   Henssgen Hardware Corporation
     P.O. Box 2078   Queensbury, NY 12804
     (518) 793-3593   Rachel Novak President
     Fax: (518) 793-0018
     Email: rachel@henssgenhardware.com
     Website: www.henssgenhardware.com
Sources rigging hardware, Snap Hooks, Pulleys (both Fixed Eye and Swivel with Single Sheave and Double Sheave), Quick Links, Shackles, Wire Rope Clips, Drop Forged Clevis Grab & Clevis Slip Hooks. (Woman/White, estab 2000, empl 3, sales $548,000, cert: WBENC)

3970   NY Plumbing Wholesale & Supply, Inc.
     933 Columbus Ave   New York, NY 10025
     (212) 678-4900   Derek Price President
     Fax: (212) 678-4901
     Email: derek@nyps1.com
     Website: www.nyps1.com
Dist plumbing fittings, fixtures, pipe, tools & accessories. (AA, estab 2009, empl 23, sales , cert: City)

3971   South Atlantic Marine Services
     342 Cold Spring Rd   Syosset, NY 11791
     (516) 449-9000   Linda Allen President
     Fax: (516) 921-9391
     Email: southatlantic15@yahoo.com
     Website: www.southatlantic-services.com
Dist lubricants, greases, additives, hardware, bolts fasteners, tools, fittings, safety products, ropes, chains, hoses, twine, clamps rivet, cables, pumps, valves, bearings, tubing, welding supplies, cutting tools. (Woman/White, estab 2000, empl 2, sales $889,255, cert: State, City)

Ohio

3972   CJ Industrial Supply Inc.
     15326 Waterloo Rd   Cleveland, OH 44110
     (216) 481-4448   Tom Frohwerk VP Sales
     Fax: (216) 481-2444
     Email: tom@cjindustrial.com
     Website: www.cjindustrial.com
Industrial hardware, Valves Pumps Steel Fabrication, OSHA Products, Plumbing, Electrical, Cutting Tools, Machine Shop Services, Abrasives, Hand Tools, Power Tools, VOC Compliant Chemicals & Paints, Steel. (Woman/White, estab 1995, empl 8, sales $2,000,000, cert: State, City)

3973   CryoPlus, Inc.
     2429 N Millborne Rd   Wooster, OH 44691
     (330) 683-3375   Kathi Bond President
     Fax: (330) 683-2653
     Email: kathicryo@aol.com
     Website: www.cryoplus.com
Cutting tools, blades, knives, dies & punches. (Woman/White, estab 1994, empl 3, sales $100,000, cert: NWBOC)

3974   General Factory/ WD Supply
     4811 Winton Rd   Cincinnati, OH 45232
     (513) 681-6300   Pat Priko Sales
     Fax:
     Email: patp@gfwdsupply.com
     Website: www.gfwdsupply.com
Dist MRO, welding, cutting tools, hand tools & safety. (Woman/White, estab 2007, empl 32, sales $12,500,000, cert: WBENC)

3975   Power Tool & Supply Co., Inc.
     3699 Leharps Rd   Youngstown, OH 44515
     (330) 792-1487   Linda Richardson Director, Business Dev
     Fax: (330) 792-3687
     Email: linda@powertoolandsupply.com
     Website: www.powertoolandsupply.com
Dist power tools & supplies. (Woman/White, estab 1961, empl 18, sales , cert: State, WBENC)

3976   Queensgate Hardware & Security, Inc.
     1025 Dalton Ave   Cincinnati, OH 45203
     (513) 929-0062   Sarah Back President
     Fax: (513) 929-0064
     Email: sarah@queensgatehardware.com
     Website: www.queensgatehardware.com
Dist commercial grade hardware, wood doors & frames, hollow metal doors & frames, access control systems, toilet partitions & accessories. (Woman/White, estab 2010, empl 3, sales $768,000, cert: WBENC)

3977 River City Building Solutions, LLC
19885 Detroit Rd, Ste 173   Cleveland, OH 44116
(216) 333-1491 Peggy Powers President
Fax: (216) 373-4930
Email: peggy@rivercitybuildingsolutions.com
Website: www.rivercitybuildingsolutions.com
Dist building materials, sustainable materials, paintings & coatings, roofing materials, flooring, HVAC, plumbing materials, electrical / telecommunications wiring. (Woman/White, estab 2011, empl 2, sales , cert: State, City)

Pennsylvania

3978 Hardware & Supply Company of Chester Inc.
Fourth & Edgmont Ave   Chester, PA 19013
(610) 876-6116 Patricia Steinberg CEO
Fax: (610) 872-7544
Email: support@hschester.com
Website: www.hschester.com
Dist maintenenance repair, operational, safety, janitorial, material handling. (Woman/White, estab 1942, empl 11, sales , cert: State)

3979 Keystone Industrial Sales & Service, Inc.
808 N Fourth Ave   Altoona, PA 16601
(814) 949-5900 Tina McMullen President
Fax: (814) 949-5955
Email: tmcmullen@keystoneindustrialss.com
Website:
Dist power tools, hand tools, tool storage, industrial vacuums, filters & floor matting/carpet. (Woman/White, estab 1997, empl 1, sales $251,120, cert: State, WBENC)

Puerto Rico

3980 Industrial Fittings & Valves
P.O. Box 2329   Toa Baja, PR 00951
(787) 251-0840 Jose Merino President
Fax: (787) 251-0980
Email: jmerino@infiva.com
Website: www.infiva.com
Dist industrial valves & fittings. (Hisp, estab 1985, empl 30, sales $6,093,000, cert: NMSDC)

South Carolina

3981 GT Industrial LLC Co.
846 Royle Rd   Ladson, SC 29456
(843) 873-0290 Teresa Gore President
Fax: (843) 875-2376
Email: teresag@gtindustrial.net
Website: www.gtindustrial.com/
Dist tools, cert kits, tape, adhesives, dust masks, respirators, marking crayons, flashlights, batteries, light bulbs. (Nat Ame, estab 1998, empl 6, sales $5,111,180, cert: NMSDC)

3982 Janeice Products Inc. Co.
1084 Williston Road   Aiken, SC 29803
(803) 652-3025 Valeria Castillo Cstmr Service Specialist
Fax: (803) 652-3026
Email: sales@janeiceproducts.com
Website: www.janeiceproducts.com
Dist MRO products: abrasives, cutting tools, fans, hand tools, hardware, ladders, lawn & garden, material handling equip & safety prods. (AA/Hisp, estab 1994, empl 5, sales , cert: NMSDC)

Tennessee

3983 D & J Tool Supply, LLC
P.O. Box 9601   Knoxville, TN 37940
(865) 546-0744 Deanna Maurer Owner
Fax: (865) 546-0776
Email: deanna@djtoolsupply.com
Website: www.djtoolsupply.com
Dist metalworking & fabricating machinery, machine tool accessories, cutting tools, hand & power tools, metalworking fluids, abrasives, safety supplies, welding consumables. (Woman/White, estab 1999, empl 2, sales $386,641, cert: State)

3984 Industrial Supply Solutions, LLC
108 Jasmine Ct   Henderson, TN 37072
(615) 461-7433 Tonya Martinek Managing Partner
Fax:
Email: ISS.martinek@gmail.com
Website:
Power Tools & Metalworking; Cutting Tools; Precision Measuring; Inserts; Abrasives; Pneumatics & Hydraulics; Pumps & Plumbing; HVAC; Electrical; Lighting; Test Instruments; Hand Tools, Power Tools & Fleet/Vehicle Maintenance. (Woman/White, estab 2005, empl 2, sales , cert: WBENC)

Texas

3985   Power Tool Service Co., Inc.
       3718 Polk St   Houston, TX 77003
       (713) 228-0100 JB Robertson VP
       Fax: (713) 228-0619
       Email: sales@powertoolservice.com
       Website: www.powertoolservice.com
Dist, rent & repair tool & equipment, calibration. (Woman/
Hisp, estab 1969, empl 18, sales , cert: State)

3986   PowerOne and Associates, LLC
       12320 Barker Cypress Rd Ste 600-300 Cypress, TX
       77429
       (713) 955-7888 Gus Guerrero BDM
       Fax: (877) 685-9347
       Email: gus@power-one-usa.com
       Website: www.powerone-usa.com
Dist High Temperature Pipe, Hose & Cable Wraps (Safety),
MRO products, Hand Tools, Personal Safety Equipment
(PSE), Power transmission equipment (Safety Couplings,
Metal Bellows Coupling, Locking assemblies). (Hisp, estab
2008, empl 10, sales , cert: NMSDC)

3987   Powr-Guardian, Inc.
       1607 Falcon Dr, Ste 101   DeSoto, TX 75115
       (972) 228-9029 Von Miller President
       Fax: (972) 224-7813
       Email: info@powrguardian.com
       Website: www.powrguardian.com
Dist & service batteries. (AA, estab 1988, empl 11, sales
$1,375,000, cert: State)

3988   Trinity Tape & Marking LLC
       3573 Bennett Rd   Howe, TX 75459
       (903) 532-6068 Carrie Burt Dir of Sales
       Fax: (903) 532-6268
       Email: carrie@trinity-tape.com
       Website: www.trinity-tape.com
Marking flags, inverted marking paint, barricade tape,
underground detectable & non-detectable tape, surveyors
flagging, safety vests, hard hats, hearing protection, fall
protection, safety glasses, first aid kits, conduit, adhesive
tapes, whiskers. (Woman/White, estab 2007, empl 10,
sales $1,200,000, cert: State, WBENC)

Virginia

3989   Apollo Energy Components Inc. t/a Apollo Supply
       2711 Lowesville Rd   Arrington, VA 22922
       (434) 277-5556 Christine Manley President
       Fax: (434) 277-5811
       Email: apollonrg2711@aol.com
       Website: www.apolloenergycomponents.com
Dist fasteners, pipe fittings, valves, high pressure tube
fittings, abrasives, grinding wheels, cutting tools, saw
blades, aerosols. (Woman/White, estab 2009, empl 3,
sales $122,080, cert: State)

3990   Machine Tools of Virginia, Inc.
       8147 Shady Grove Rd   Mechanicsville, VA 23111
       (804) 569-6147 Cindy Waddell President
       Fax: (804) 569-6147
       Email: machinetoolsofva@hotmail.com
       Website: www.machinetoolsofvirginia.com
Dist machine tools: lathes & mills, CNC & standard, lathe
& mill accessories, carbide cutting tools, compressors,
grinders, drills, saws & fabrication equipment. (Woman/
White, estab 2001, empl 4, sales , cert: State)

Washington

3991   The Part Works Inc.
       2900 4th Ave S   Seattle, WA 98134
       (206) 305-0448 Oly Welke Sales & Mktg Mgr
       Fax: (206) 305-5180
       Email: oly@ thepartworks.com
       Website: www.thepartworks.com
Dist plumbing supplies. (Woman/White, estab 1980,
empl 25, sales $5,500,000, cert: City, WBENC)

VALIDATION
data management
EVALUATE
engage strategy
BEST PRACTICES
reporting
data scrubs
SOURCING
SUPPORT

Advocacy.
Support.
Expertise.
Industry Resources.
Seminars & Trainings.
Good to know.

DIR drives supplier diversity success by providing diverse-supplier data management, education and publications to corporations and diverse-owned suppliers.

Get to know what we know about supplier diversity. Visit www.DiversityInfoResources. com to learn more.

DIR
DIVERSITY
INFORMATION
RESOURCES

DIVERSITY recognizes differences, respects individuality & encourages dialog. **INFORMATION** educates & encourages intelligent decisions. **RESOURCES** provide alternatives to create informed solutions. **Work it.**

HARDWARE & TOOLS MFG.

Manufacture fasteners and other screw machine products. Many manufacture tools and hand tools (See also HYDRAULIC & COMPRESSED AIR EQUIPMENT and INDUSTRIAL EQUIPMENT & SUPPLIES). NAICS Code 42

Arizona

3992   B&T Tool & Engineering Inc.
     2618 E Washington St   Phoenix, AZ 85034
     (602) 267-1481   William Meras President
     Fax: (602) 225-9582
     Email: bnttool@aol.com
     Website: www.bnttool.us
Mfr & dist precision cutting tools. (Hisp, estab 1992, empl 21, sales $3,701,273, cert: NMSDC)

3993   Special Carbide Tools
     3153 E 36th St   Tucson, AZ 85713
     (520) 624-0007   Jerry Gamboa CEO
     Fax: (520) 624-1952
     Email: jerry@specialcarbide.com
     Website: www.specialcarbide.com
Mfr special custom carbide cutting tools: standard drills, endmills & reamers. (Hisp, estab 1999, empl 18, sales $2,000,000, cert: NMSDC)

California

3994   Blue Sky Industries
     595 Monterey Pass Rd   Monterey Park, CA 91754
     (213) 620-9950   Denis Gagnier Outside Sales Mgr
     Fax: (213) 620-9953
     Email: dgagnier@blueskyindustries.com
     Website: www.blueskyindustries.com
Cherry & Monogram blind rivets & blind bolts, Shear Pins & Collars Hi-locks, Standard Aerospace Bolts, Screws, Nuts & Washers, Single & Double Oversize fasteners, Bushings, Bearings, Spacers, & Shims. (As-Pac, estab 1995, empl 52, sales $15,000,000, cert: NMSDC)

3995   D-Unique Tools
     5744 International P.O. Box 2112   Oakland, CA 94621
     (510) 569-9961   Nanette Hunter President
     Fax: (510) 569-9963
     Email: nanette@universalsquare.com
     Website: www.universalsquare.com
Mfr & dist tools. (Woman/AA, estab 1991, empl 4, sales $125,536, cert: NMSDC)

Connecticut

3996   Chapman Manufacturing Company
     471 New Haven Rd   Durham, CT 06422
     (860) 349-9228   Jason Camassar VP
     Fax: (860) 349-0084
     Email: jason@chapmanmfg.com
     Website: www.chapmanmfg.com
Mfr screwdriver kits. (Woman/White, estab 1936, empl 13, sales $683,000, cert: CPUC)

Florida

3997   Limitless Investigative Solutions, L.L.C.
     11160 Lost Creek Terrace #205   Bradenton, FL 34211
     (678) 458-8538   Miguel Caraballo President
     Fax: (951) 280-4710
     Email: miguel@limitlessinv.com
     Website: www.limitlessinv.com
Solid carbide end mills, drills, reamers, burrs, inserts & specials, in house research & development, custom tool design for various applications, ools simulation software. (Hisp, estab 2017, empl 1, sales , cert: State)

3998   Raisman Corporation
     5543 NW 72nd Ave   Miami, FL 33166
     (786) 581-3820   Sales
     Fax: (786) 272-5922
     Email: sales@raisman.com
     Website: www.raisman.com
Mfr trimmer heads, spindles, primer bulbs, fuel filters, oil pumps, spark plugs, shock absorbers, mufflers, carburetors, carburetor kits, etc. (Hisp, estab 1998, empl 120, sales $15,000,000, cert: State)

Illinois

3999   Foreman Tool & Mold Company
     3850 Swenson Ave   St. Charles, IL 60174
     (630) 377-6389   Jeff Gardner Sales Mgr
     Fax:
     Email: jgardner@foremantool.com
     Website: www.foremantool.com
Complete 3D part design, Pro-E mold design & layout. (Hisp, estab 1984, empl 80, sales , cert: NMSDC)

4000   Pioneer Service Inc.
     542 Factory Rd   Addison, IL 60101
     (630) 628-0249   Eric Smith Dir, sales/Mktg
     Fax: (630) 628-9343
     Email: esmith@pioneerserviceinc.com
     Website: www.pioneerserviceinc.com
Contract mfr screw machine products & centerless grinding services: shafts, axles, bolts, bushings, dowels, pins, rods, spacers, valve stems, deburring, drilling, flatting, grinding, knurling, slotting, tapping, threading, heat treating. (Woman/White, estab 1990, empl 30, sales $2,300,000, cert: State)

4001   Tag Tool Services, Inc.
     3303 N Main St   East Peoria, IL 61611
     (309) 694-2400   Vonda Jones President
     Fax: (309) 694-2445
     Email: vonda@countyline-tool.com
     Website: www.countyline-tool.com
Cutting tool manufacturing & tool refurbishment, regrind Hobs, Shaper Cutters, Broach Bars, Drills, Rota Broaches, Port Tools, Gun Drills, End Mills, Taps, Reamers, Chamfer Tools, Special Form Tools. (Woman, estab 1984, empl 14, sales $1,200,000, cert: WBENC)

Massachusetts

4002   Electrical Safety Products LLC
     375 Main St   Woburn, MA 01801
     (781) 249-5007   Tom Wilkie Dir of Sales
     Fax: (888) 204-5306
     Email: tom.wilkie@electricalsafety-usa.com
     Website: www.electricalsafety-usa.com
Mfr ASTM F-1505 certified insulated tools. (Woman/White, estab 2009, empl 4, sales $22,000, cert: WBENC)

Michigan

4003   2K Tool LLC
     3025 Madison Ave SE   Wyoming, MI 49548
     (616) 452-4927   Kevin Smith engineering Mgr
     Fax:
     Email: kevin@2ktool.com
     Website: www.2ktool.com
Moldmaker, machining, tooling, plastic injection molds, compression tooling, composite machining, casting machining, small part Injection molding. (Woman/White, estab 2004, empl 19, sales $2,269,151, cert: WBENC)

4004   Anderson Express, Inc.
     580 W Sherman Blvd   Muskegon Heights, MI 49444
     (231) 733-6001   Angel Ball HR Mgr
     Fax:
     Email: aball@andersonexpressinc.com
     Website: www.andersonexpressinc.com
Rapid tooling & tooling prototypes for small & medium projects. (Woman/White, estab 2011, empl 17, sales , cert: WBENC)

4005   Gill Industries, Inc.
     28345 Beck Rd Ste 203   Wixom, MI 48393
     (616) 559-2838   Todd Kobus Sales Mgr
     Fax: (616) 559-8253
     Email: tkobus@gill-industries.com
     Website: www.gill-industries.com
Engineered, mechanical assemblies: prototyping, product & tool design, tool build, engineering, program management, testing & analysis. (Woman, estab 1964, empl 860, sales $138,000,000, cert: WBENC)

4006   Ideal Machine Tool Technologies, LLC
     675 E. Big Beaver Road, STE. 211   Troy, MI 48083
     (248) 792-9061   Vincent H. Hylton Owner
     Fax: (248) 792-9662
     Email: v.hylton@e-imtt.com
     Website: www.e-imtt.com
Commodity management services, program management, engineering services, field services in the machine tool industry. (AA, estab 2010, empl 2, sales , cert: NMSDC)

4007   Micro Fixtures, Inc.
     20448 Lorne   Taylor, MI 48180
     (313) 382-9781   SUE RADER Office Mgr
     Fax: (313) 382-3001
     Email: microfixtures@msn.com
     Website: www.MicroFixtures.com
Design & mfr tools, fixtures, gauges, prototype products. (Nat Ame, estab 1993, empl 4, sales $514,590, cert: NMSDC)

4008   T&D Machine, Inc.
     2485 E Monroe Rd   Tecumseh, MI 49286
     (517) 423-0778   Debra Fowle President
     Fax: (517) 423-0778
     Email: tdmachine@lni.net
     Website: www.tdmachineinc.net
Precision machined products: steel, aluminum, brass & plastic parts, hand tools, scribers, torque, screwdriver, pliers, mirrors, telescoping tools, magnet hand tools, spark plug pliers. (Woman/Hisp, estab 1985, empl 3, sales $200,000, cert: State)

4009   Universal Tool Equipment & Controls, Inc.
6525 Center Dr   Sterlng Heights, MI 48312
(586) 268-4380   Bill Bartolotta VP
Fax: (586) 803-8329
Email: bbartolotta@universaltecinc.com
Website: www.universaltecinc.com
Automation & welding systems, robotics, weld guns, vision systems, sealant systems, drawn arc welders, projection welders, material handling end effectors & welding fixtures. (Woman/AA, estab 2009, empl 29, sales $10,000,000, cert: WBENC)

Minnesota

4010   Carbide Tool Services, Inc.
1020 Lund Blvd   Anoka, MN 55303
(763) 421-2210   Julie Reiling President
Fax: (763) 421-2686
Email: Julie@carbidetool.com
Website: www.carbidetool.com
Mfr & repair indexable cutting tools, live tooling. (Woman/Hisp, estab 1988, empl 40, sales $3,493,686, cert: WBENC)

North Dakota

4011   Posi Lock Puller, Inc.
805 Sunflower Ave   Cooperstown, ND 58425
(701) 797-2600   Tamara Somerville VP
Fax: (701) 797-2706
Email: t.somerville@posilock.com
Website: www.posilock.com
Mfr gear & bearing pullers. (Woman/White, estab 1977, empl 45, sales $3,900,000, cert: City)

New Jersey

4012   JDV Products, Inc.
22-01 Raphael St.   Fair Lawn, NJ 07410
(201) 796-1720   Ron Vradenburg Sales Mgr
Fax: (201) 796-9399
Email: ron@jdvproducts.com
Website: www.jdvproducts.com
Mfr & dist telecom tools: wire wrap & unwrap tools, semi-automatic wire wrap machines, wire strippers, hand & pneumatic power tools, industrial power bits, hand screwdrivers, tool balancer, torque wrenches & accessories, wire & plastics cutting tools. (Woman/White, estab 1995, empl 19, sales , cert: WBENC)

4013   SMG Services, LLC
462 W Lookout Ave   Hackensack, NJ 07601
(201) 937-5378   Sharon Mendoza-Gardner CEO
Fax: (201) 342-2887
Email: smgdiamondtools@gmail.com
Website: www.smgdiamondtools.com
Mfr Diamond Drill Bits, Diamond Plated drill Bits, Diamond Grinding Tools, Cutting Blades, Impregnated Inserts, Brazed Diamond Products, Diamond Core Drills, Diamond Solid Tools, Cstmr specs. (Woman/AA, estab 2009, empl 1, sales $765,000, cert: State)

New York

4014   American Pride Fasteners, LLC
195 S Fehr Way   Bay Shore, NY 11706
(631) 940-8292   Lynda Zacpal President
Fax: (631) 940-8296
Email: lynda@americanpridefasteners.com
Website: www.americanpridefasteners.com
Engineering & mfr miniature screws & miniature fasteners. (Woman/Hisp, estab 2004, empl 24, sales $4,200,000, cert: City)

4015   Burnett Process, Inc.
545 Colfax St   Rochester, NY 14606
(585) 254-8080   Melissa Shea-Brooks Mktg Dev Mgr
Fax: (585) 277-1621
Email: burnettprocesscsr@cannonind.com
Website: www.burnettprocessinc.com
Mfr & dist ozone, pleated, particulate & HEPA filters. (AA, estab 1957, empl 39, sales $6,000,000, cert: NMSDC)

Ohio

4016   AKKO Fastener, Inc.
6855 Cornell Rd   Cincinnati, OH 45242
(513) 489-8300   Art Huge Sales Mgr
Fax: (513) 489-8366
Email: arthuge@comcast.net
Website: www.akkofastener.com
Mfr fastening products: machine screws, tapping screws, plascrews, thread cutting screws, & cold formed metal products. (Woman/Hisp, estab 1967, empl 40, sales $7,000,000, cert: NMSDC)

4017   Cold Headed Fasteners & Assemblies, Inc.
1875 Harsh Ave SE P.O. Box 547   Massillon, OH 44646
(330) 833-0800   Oscar Lee President
Fax:
Email: o.lee@coldheaded.us
Website: www.coldheaded.us
Mfr fasteners & assemblies, sorting & packaging (As-Pac, estab 2002, empl 15, sales , cert: State)

4018   Custom Millcraft Corp.
9092 LeSaint Dr   Fairfield, OH 45014
(513) 874-7080 Jody Corbett President
Fax: (513) 874-7089
Email: jcorbett@custommillcraft.com
Website: www.custommillcraft.com
Mfr wood & plastic laminate store fixtures. (Woman/White, estab 1983, empl 45, sales $4,000,000, cert: WBENC)

4019   M.O.M. Tools, LLC
3659 Green Road Ste 304 Cleveland, OH 44122
(216) 464-2992 Anthony Lockhart
Fax: (216) 803-0211
Email: axlockhart@toolsbymom.com
Website: www.toolsbymom.com/
Mfr dual-head piercing tools & dies. (AA, estab 2003, empl 2, sales , cert: NMSDC)

4020   Master Manufacturing Co, Inc.
9200 Inman Ave   Cleveland, OH 44105
(800) 323-5513 Bob Ptacek V.P. Sales
Fax: (216) 641-0537
Email: bptacek@mastermfgco.com
Website: www.mastermfgco.com
Mfr furniture casters & self-stick wheels; felt pads, surface protectors, wobble stoppers; furniture movers; door stops; ergonomic support cushions & wire mgmt channels & grommets. (Woman/White, estab 1951, empl 34, sales , cert: CPUC, WBENC)

4021   Midwest Ohio Tool Company, Inc.
215 Tarhe Trail   Upper Sandusky, OH 43351
(419) 294-1987 Stephanie Kettels President
Fax:
Email: skettels@midwestohio.com
Website: www.midwestohio.com
Mfr custom cutting tools, metal cutting tools, milling cutters, specialized cutting tools, boring bars, tool holders, industrial tools. (Woman/White, estab 1954, empl 9, sales $500,000, cert: WBENC)

4022   RB Tool & Mfg Co.
2680 Civic Center Dr   Cincinnati, OH 45231
(513) 521-8292 Scott Schaeper Sales/Mktg Mgr
Fax: (513) 521-0407
Email: scott@rbtoolandmfg.com
Website: www.rbtoolandmfg.com
Mfr mills-horizontal and vertical, lathes-CNC and manuals, EDM-wire and sinker, welding, painting. (Woman/White, estab 1957, empl 40, sales $6,000,000, cert: WBENC)

4023   Steam Turbine Alternative Resources
116 Latourette St   Marion, OH 43302
(740) 387-5535 Ken Kubinski Sales Mgr
Fax: (740) 383-2089
Email: ken@starturbine.com
Website: www.starturbines.com
Mfr steam seals, packing, spill strips hardware, oil seals & deflectors, on-site field installation & machining sevices. (Woman/White, estab 1986, empl 40, sales $5,610,000, cert: WBENC)

4024   Stelfast Inc.
22979 Stelfast Pkwy   Strongsville, OH 44149
(877) 619-8231 Todd McRoberts Sales
Fax: (440) 879-0044
Email: toddm@stelfast.com
Website: www.stelfast.com
Import & manufacture fasteners. (As-Pac, estab 1973, empl 80, sales $31,500,000, cert: NMSDC)

4025   Talent Tool & Die, Inc.
777 Berea Industrial Pkwy.   Berea, OH 44017
(440) 239-8777 Mylynh Vu
Fax:
Email: mylynh@talent-tool.com
Website: www.talent-tool.com
Mfr dies, tools & fixtures; metal stamping & laser cutting. (As-Pac, estab 1989, empl 44, sales , cert: NMSDC)

4026   The M.K. Morse Company
1101 Eleventh St SE   Canton, OH 44707
(330) 453-8187 Ryan Rhodes Cstmr Service
Fax:
Email: rhodesr@mkmorse.com
Website: www.mkmorse.com
Mfr saw blades for professionals. Blades for band saws, reciprocating saws, hole saws, hack saws and frames, wood boring bits, portable band saws, metal cutting circular saws & machines. Made from bimetal, carbon steel, carbide tipped & carbide grit. (Woman/White, estab 1963, empl 500, sales $84,000,000, cert: WBENC)

Texas

4027   Arise Solutions Inc.
5862 Cromo Ste 149 El Paso, TX 79912
(915) 345-9134 Daniel Laing President
Fax:
Email: sales@arisesolutions.biz
Website: www.arisesolutions.biz
Custom designed wire harness, cable assembly, bulk wire, signal cable, specialty bolts, screws, Nut Rivets, Inserts, Fasteners, Spacers, Connectors & Fittings for automotive industry. (As-Pac, estab 2012, empl 5, sales $1,000,000, cert: State, NMSDC)

4028 BiTech Tool & Die Inc.
5240 Tetons   El Paso, TX 79904
(915) 757-8001 Maria Castillo
Fax: (915) 757-2753
Email: mcastillo@bitech.net
Website:
Mfr precision tools, crimping applicator die & crimp tooling. (Hisp, estab 1995, empl 35, sales $615,000, cert: NMSDC)

4029 Danrick Industries Inc.
850 Kastrin St   El Paso, TX 79907
(915) 599-2988 Marco Herrera President
Fax:
Email: marcoherrera@danrick.net
Website: www.danrick.net
Mfr tooling & precision machining parts, fabrication of parts & components of terminal crimping. (AA, estab 2002, empl 22, sales , cert: State, NMSDC)

4030 EZKutter Company
3617 Rabbit Lane   Bryan, TX 77808
(979) 778-0825 Dora Loria Owner
Fax: (979) 778-3914
Email: ezkutter@suddenlink.net
Website: www.ezkutter-usa.com
Mfr hand held cutting tools used for cutting heavy plastic straps, strings & shrink wrapping. (Woman/White, estab 1992, empl 2, sales $89,371, cert: State)

4031 Versatech, LLC
315 N Park Dr   San Antonio, TX 78216
(210) 979-2823 Diana Grinman Admin
Fax: (210) 525-1641
Email: dgrinman@pmtool.com
Website: www.versatech-mfg.com
Advanced tooling, plastic injection molds, tools & dies fields. (Hisp, estab 2006, empl 5, sales , cert: NMSDC)

Virginia

4032 Master Gage & Tool Company
112 Maplewood St   Danville, VA 24543
(434) 836-4243 Debbye Lyle President
Fax: (434) 835-0008
Email: debbyel@mastergt.com
Website: www.mastergt.com
Calibration, specialized tooling & gaging products. (Woman/White, estab 1986, empl 26, sales $12,010,000, cert: WBENC)

Wisconsin

4033 R.J. Zeman Tool & Mfg. Co., Inc.
W228 N575 Westmound Dr   Waukesha, WI 53186
(262) 549-4400 Spencer Schreindl President
Fax:
Email: sschreindl@zemantool.com
Website:
Machining, design, mfr & inspect fixtures, special machines, gages, die cast dies, plastic injection molds, permanent molds, core boxes, patterns for sand casting & short and long-run production parts. (Woman/White, estab 1966, empl 48, sales $9,600,000, cert: WBENC)

HYDRAULIC & COMPRESSED AIR EQUIPMENT DIST.

Distributors of compressed air equipment, valves, gaskets, fittings, pumps, meters, hoses, special tools, pipe, etc. (See also HARDWARE & TOOLS, INDUSTRIAL EQUIPMENT & SUPPLIES, INDUSTRIAL MACHINES and MATERIAL HANDLING EQUIPMENT). NAICS Code 42

Alabama

4034   Elle Waterworks Supply, LLC
4000 Eagle Point Corporate Dr   Birmingham, AL 35242
(205) 314-5783   Courtney Myrick Owner
Fax:
Email: cmyrick@ellewws.com
Website: www.ellewws.com
Dist process valves, air valves, control valves, ductile iron pipe, steel pipe, pipe supports & hangers, couplings, adapters, pvc pipe & fittings, ductile iron fittings, hydrants, valve boxes, hardware, bolts, nuts, gaskets, safety equipment. (Woman, estab 2011, empl 2, sales $850,000, cert: State, WBENC)

California

4035   CLEAR Solutions, Inc.
942 Calle Amanecer Ste D   San Clemente, CA 92673
(949) 429-8922   Kristi Sawyer VP
Fax: (949) 606-9999
Email: kristi@clearsolutionscorp.com
Website: www.clearsolutionscorp.com
Dist filters, filter housings, water purification, filtration, separation, process liquid filtration, HVAC, compressed air & gas filtration, sanitary gaskets, flange gaskets, screen gaskets, hose assemblies, tubing, quick disconnect fittings. (Woman, estab 2010, empl 6, sales , cert: WBENC)

4036   The Valve Shop
6070-A Corte Del Cedro   Carlsbad, CA 92024
(760) 438-4840   Ray Herrera President
Fax: (760) 438-4836
Email: rherrera@thevalveshop.com
Website: www.thevalveshop.com
Dist on/off & flow control valves: butterfly valves, check valves, diaphragm valves, float valves, gate valves, globe valves, plug valves, pressure regulators, relief valves, solenid valves, strainers, water valves. (Hisp, estab 2000, empl 7, sales $3,050,985, cert: State)

4037   VIAIR Corporation
15 Edelman   Irvine, CA 92618
(949) 585-0011   Alan Basham Director of Ops
Fax: (949) 585-0188
Email: alanb@viaircorp.com
Website: www.viaircorp.com
Dist Air Compressor, Air Tank, LED Light, Air accessories for automotive industry. (As-Pac, estab 1998, empl 32, sales , cert: NMSDC)

Florida

4038   Amazon Hose and Rubber Company
4105 Seaboard Rd   Orlando, FL 32808
(407) 843-8190   Jim Donlin President
Fax: (407) 422-5577
Email: jimdonlin@amazonhose.com
Website: www.amazonhose.com
Dist industrial & hydraulic hoses & related fittings. (Woman/White, estab 1919, empl 60, sales $12,698,846, cert: City, WBENC)

4039   Industrial Hose & Hydraulics, Inc.
2450 N Powerline Rd   Pompano Beach, FL 33069
(954) 960-0311   Joanne R. Heckman Controller
Fax: (954) 960-0533
Email: joeyheckman@industrialhose.com
Website: www.industrialhose.com
Dist hoses, fittings, clamps, adapters, fuel hose, hose reels, check valves, lubrication supplies, garden hose & pumps. (Woman, estab 1900, empl 1, sales , cert: State, WBENC)

4040   The Bernd Group Inc.
1251 Pinehurst Rd   Dunedin, FL 34698
(727) 733-0122   Pilar Bernd President
Fax:
Email: businessdevelopment@berndgroup.com
Website: www.berndgroup.com
Material handling equip, safety products, hand & power tools, pumps & compressors, motors, generators, electrical hardware, batteries, lighting fixtures, lockers, bins, shelving, lab equip. (Woman/Hisp, estab 1992, empl 66, sales , cert: NMSDC)

Illinois

4041 Bearings & Industrial Supply
      431 Imen Ave   Addison, IL 60101
      (630) 628-1966 Sejal Khandwala Acct Exec
      Fax: (630) 628-0116
      Email: sejal@bearingsnow.com
      Website: www.bearingsnow.com
Dist bearings & power transmission products; pump &
pump repair parts, HVAC & electrical parts. (As-Pac, estab
1982, empl 10, sales , cert: NMSDC)

4042 Chambers Gasket & Manufacturing Co.
      4701 W Rice St   Chicago, IL 60651
      (773) 626-8800 Heide Kenny President
      Fax:
      Email: hkenny@chambersgasket.com
      Website: www.chambersgasket.com
Gaskets; Washers; Strips; Spiral Wound Gaskets; Molded
Gaskets; Waterjet cut parts; pressure sensitve adhesive
added; kitting; special packaging. (Woman/White, estab ,
empl 1, sales , cert: WBENC)

Indiana

4043 MIDpro Fluid Power and Automation
      444 Johnson Ln   Brownsburg, IN 46112
      (317) 852-5920 Cynthia Torrance President
      Fax: (317) 852-2337
      Email: ctorrance@midprofluidpower.com
      Website: www.midprofluidpower.com
Pnuematic, hydraulic, electronic & air systems, conveyors,
blowers, pumps, dryers, filtration, air tools, cylinders,
valves, fittings, power units, PLC controllers, monitors &
touch screens. (Woman/White, estab 1986, empl 11, sales
$5,200,000, cert: WBENC)

Michigan

4044 Chippewa Systems, Ltd.
      24574 Beck   Eastpointe, MI 48021
      (586) 772-1783 Brian Barr VP
      Fax: (586) 772-1783
      Email: chippewasystemsltd@gmail.com
      Website: www.chippewasystems.com
Dist vacuum pumps, compressors, blowers, filters, air
knives. (Woman/Nat Ame, estab 1986, empl 3, sales
$668,000, cert: NMSDC)

4045 Fluid Line Components, Inc.
      638 S Rochester Rd   Clawson, MI 48017
      (248) 583-9070 Mary Schmitt CEO
      Fax: (248) 583-9046
      Email: mary@fluidlinecomponents.com
      Website: www.fluidlinecomponents.com
Dist air cylinders, air valves, air fittings, air filters, air
gauges, air hoist, air hose, air manifolds, air motors, air
drills, air presses, air tanks, air-oil tanks, anti-tie down,
balancers, ball valves, ball vibrators, blow guns, brass
pipe fittings (Woman/White, estab 1972, empl 4, sales
$1,102,252, cert: WBENC)

4046 Service Manufacturing & Supply Co.
      33380 Groesbeck Hwy   Fraser, MI 48026
      (586) 415-0455 Ryan Maggio GM
      Fax: (586) 415-0459
      Email: Sales@servicemanufacturing.com
      Website: www.servicemanufacturing.com
Hydraulic & pneumatic components & accessories,
brass, steel, stainless steel, malleable & galvanized
fittings, JIC 37 degree flare, push-on barbs, adaptors,
solid & union barbs, pipe els & extension adaptors,
hydraulic tubing. (Woman, estab 1957, empl 7, sales
$1,154,683, cert: WBENC)

Minnesota

4047 Chrom Tech, Inc.
      P.O. Box 240248   Apple Valley, MN 55124
      (952) 431-6000 Jessica Kolsky Technical Sales Rep
      Fax: (952) 431-6345
      Email: jessica@chromtech.com
      Website: www.chromtech.com
Dist HPLC & GC instrumentation, supplies & accessories:
autosampler vials, columns, filters, fittings, PEEK tubing
& fittings, solid phase extraction cartridges, protein
crash plates, positive pressure manifolds, evaporators,
syringes, tubing. (Woman, estab 1985, empl 12, sales
$10,538,000, cert: WBENC)

4048 Unique Contracting Service Corp.
      20531 156th St NW   Elk River, MN 55330
      (763) 218-9385 Angel Perez President
      Fax: (763) 262-1151
      Email: angelpeppy1@izoom.net
      Website:
LPGas & NH3 equipment, Fittings, Pipes, High pressure
Hoses, Pumps, Valves, tanks. (Hisp, estab 1987, empl 3,
sales $156,000, cert: State, NMSDC)

North Carolina

4049   Smith Seal of NC
8441 Garvey Dr   Raleigh, NC 27616
(919) 790-1000   Gertraud Smith President
Fax: (919) 878-8377
Email: judysmith@smithseal.com
Website: www.smithseal.com
Dist hydraulic seals, gaskets & packings. (Woman/White, estab 1976, empl 13, sales , cert: WBENC)

New Jersey

4050   Sur-Seal, Inc.
12 Edgeboro Rd Unit 6   East Brunswick, NJ 08816
(732) 651-7070   Gloria Solomon Inside Sales
Fax: (732) 254-2298
Email: glorias@sur-sealinc.com
Website: www.sur-sealinc.com
Dist gaskets, gasket sheet, roll material, mechanical packing, compression packing, mechanical seals (new & repairs), pressure gauges & thermometers (new and repairs), hydraulic packings, o-rings, lantern rings, extrusions. (Woman/White, estab 1979, empl 11, sales $2,263,945, cert: State)

South Carolina

4051   Eastern Power Technologies, Inc.
11 Caledon Court   Greenville, SC 29615
(864) 312-3840   Chet Chea Legal Counsel
Fax:
Email: chet.chea@easternfirst.com
Website: www.easternpowertech.com
Dist industrial & commercial pipes, valves, fittings & commercial plumbing fixtures. (Woman/White, estab 2014, empl 15, sales $250,000, cert: City, WBENC)

4052   Greenville Fluid System Technologies
2516 River Rd   Piedmont, SC 29673
(864) 295-6700   Greg Farley Sales Mgr
Fax: (864) 295-9777
Email: Greg.Farley@SWAGELOK.com
Website: www.swagelok.com/columbiasc
Dist compression & pipe fittings, valves, hoses, tubing, pumps, gauges & regulators, Orbital welding equipment, tube benders, hydraulic swaging units. (Woman/White, estab 2001, empl 18, sales $3,200,000, cert: WBENC)

4053   Wallace Mechanical Supply, Inc.
635 State Road   Cheraw, SC 29520
(843) 537-4277   Wallace Funderburk, Jr President
Fax: (843) 537-4283
Email: inc_wallace@bellsouth.net
Website:
HVAC/Plumbing , Pipe, Valves, and Pipe fittings (AA, estab 1985, empl 2, sales $1,375,463, cert: State, NMSDC)

Texas

4054   Asociar, LLC
2800 E Plano Pkwy   Plano, TX 75074
(214) 918-1013   Betty Manetta CEO
Fax: (972) 312-0445
Email: cmartinez@asociar1.com
Website: www.asociar1.com
Streamline Supply Chain Management
Total Equipment Rack Integration & Testing
Procure, Rack, Integrate, Deliver, Engineer
Warehousing & Logistics (Woman/Hisp, estab 2012, empl 5, sales $33,500,000, cert: State, NMSDC, WBENC)

4055   Carrco Painting Contractors, Inc.
10944 Alder Cir   Dallas, TX 75238
(214) 624-7560   Rudy Cox Business Dev Mgr
Fax: (214) 624-7562
Email: rcox@carrcopainting.com
Website: www.carrcopainting.com
We are a provider of painting, pressure cleaning, wallcovering, drywall repair, epoxy and urethane floor, specialty coating, wall and ceiling coating, protective coating, Cool Seal Roof Coating and Industrial Painting (Hisp, estab 1994, empl 250, sales $8,000,000, cert: State, City)

4056   CVAL Innovations LLC
9701 Raven Ln   Irving, TX 75063
(214) 699-1326   Jinen Adenwala President
Fax: (972) 789-5169
Email: jinen@cvalinnovations.com
Website: www.cvalinnovations.com
Energy Consumption for Industrial and Commercial customers. We conduct Energy Efficiency Audits, recommend and implement the efficiency measures. (Woman/AA/As-Ind, estab 2009, empl 5, sales $1,093,000, cert: State, NMSDC, SDB)

4057   El Paso Industrial Supplies
119 N Cotton   El Paso, TX 79901
(915) 533-5080   Antonio Herrera Sales Mgr
Fax: (915) 533-4635
Email: sales@epis-usa.com
Website: www.epis-usa.com
Dist pneumatic equipment & parts, sensors, sensors for safety, hydraulic equipments & parts, filters, HEPA filters, work mats, signal towers. (Hisp, estab 1988, empl 16, sales $4,000,000, cert: NMSDC)

4058   Industry Junction, Inc.
       3427 W Kingsley Rd, Ste 6 & 7   Garland, TX 75041
       (972) 926-3526   Rogelio Cabello President
       Fax: (972) 789-5169
       Email: contact@industryjunction.com
       Website: www.industryjunction.com/
Dist fluid power valves, industrial Valves, mallable gittings, stainless steel fittings, hydra-sanitary products. (Hisp, estab 2011, empl 4, sales $4,400,000, cert: State, NMSDC)

4059   iSTAFF Solutions, Inc.
       641 Elderado Pkwy, Ste 322   Mckinney, TX 75070
       (214) 620-2099   Wanda Young VP Ops
       Fax: (866) 289-8804
       Email: wanda.young@istaffsolutions.org
       Website: www.istaffsolutions.org
IT Staffing,
Light Warehouse
Admin. (Woman/AA, estab 2010, empl 20, sales $100,000, cert: State, City)

4060   Lehtola & Cannatti PLLC
       5001 Spring Valley Rd, Ste 400 E   Dallas, TX 75244
       (972) 383-1515   Patricia Lehtola Managing Member
       Fax: (866) 383-1507
       Email: plehtola@lc-lawfirm.com
       Website: www.lc-lawfirm.com
 (Woman, estab , empl 1, sales , cert: NMSDC)

4061   MARS Industries, LLC
       P.O. Box 560   Cedar Creek, TX 78612
       (512) 303-4413   Alvino Rosales President
       Fax: (512) 321-1199
       Email: arosales@marsindustries.us
       Website: www.marsindustries.us
Dist pipe, fittings, valves, etc.for the construction of water & wastewater treatment facilities & water & wastewater utilities. (Hisp, estab 2001, empl 1, sales , cert: State, City)

4062   OnPoint, LLC
       13155 Noel Rd, Ste 900   Dallas, TX 75240
       (972) 918-5154   Amber B D'Amico Partner
       Fax: (972) 918-5101
       Email: amber@onpointlighting.com
       Website: www.onpointlighting.com
Energy-efficient LED lighting, surveys, ROI analysis, best-of-breed American-made products, lighting design, installation &
financing. (Hisp, estab 2011, empl 2, sales $750,000, cert: State)

4063   Professional Choice Fire & Security Systems
       1815 N. Hampton Road   DeSoto, TX 75115
       (972) 298-2303   Dwanald Walker President
       Fax: (972) 298-2305
       Email: dwanald@professionalchoicefire.com
       Website: www.professionalchoicefire.com
Installation, service and repair for fire sprinkler, fire pump, fire alarm systems in the Dallas-Fort Worth metropolitan areas. Testing, inspection and maintenance for fire alarm, sprinkler, fire pumps and backflow detetion equipment. (AA, estab 2004, empl 6, sales $500,000, cert: State, NMSDC)

4064   Texas Seal Supply Co, Inc.
       606 N Great Southwest Pkwy P.O. Box 5726
       Arlington, TX 76011
       (817) 640-1193   Becky Ferrell Mgr
       Fax: (817) 640-1930
       Email: beckyf@texasseal.com
       Website: www.texasseal.com
Dist seals: hydraulic, pneumatic, aerospace, oilfield. (Hisp, estab 1971, empl 13, sales , cert: NMSDC)

Virginia

4065   E&R Minority Supplier LLC
       21290 Hedgerow Terr   Ashburn, VA 20147
       (703) 932-5045   Esvith Palomino-Quillama
       President
       Fax:
       Email: epalomino@erminoritysupplier.com
       Website: www.erminoritysupplier.com
Heavy highway material & industrial hydraulic hoses & fittings. (Hisp, estab 2011, empl 1, sales $60,000, cert: State)

Wisconsin

4066   Anderson Seal Inc.
       16555 W Lincoln   New Berlin, WI 53151
       (262) 821-0344   Jennifer Hansen President
       Fax: (262) 821-0343
       Email: jennifer@andersonseal.com
       Website: www.andersonseal.com
Dist rubber o-rings, custom molded shapes, gaskets, oil seals, kit assemblies, inventory management. (Woman/White, estab 1990, empl 50, sales $27,000,000, cert: WBENC)

Wisconsin

4067　Central Wisconsin Flex
　　　8510 Enterprise Way　Weston, WI 54476
　　　(715) 355-4344　Carmen Sauer VP
　　　Fax: (715) 355-4484
　　　Email: cenflex@cenflex.com
　　　Website: www.cenflex.com
Flexible metal hose, braided metal hose, expansion joints,
exhaust tubing and assemblies, laser cutting, plate rolling,
fab shop, Teflon hoses, machining. (Woman/Hisp, estab
1992, empl 37, sales $8,394,000, cert: NMSDC)

4068　Roeming Industries, Inc.
　　　1133 W Liebau Rd P.O. Box 53092　Mequon, WI
　　　53092
　　　(262) 243-5800　Mary Robertson Owner
　　　Fax: (262) 243-5803
　　　Email: Mroeming@roeming.com
　　　Website: www.roeming.com
Contract sewing on vinyl, leather, Kevlar, fiberglass, plastics
and fabric. Distributor of hydraulic packing, seals, and
packing. Gasket cutting. Rubber to metal bonding.
(Woman/White, estab 1955, empl 13, sales $1,600,000,
cert: WBENC)

HYDRAULIC & COMPRESSED AIR EQUIPMENT MFG.

Manufacturers of compressed air equipment, valves, gaskets, fittings, pumps, meters, hoses, special tools, pipe, etc. (See also HARDWARE & TOOLS, INDUSTRIAL EQUIPMENT & SUPPLIES, INDUSTRIAL MACHINES and MATERIAL HANDLING EQUIPMENT). NAICS Code 42

Arizona

4069   Stenzel Sealing Solutions, LLC
16809 N 53rd Ave, Ste 5   Glendale, AZ 85306
(602) 903-1250   Linda Stenzel Owner
Fax: (602) 903-1045
Email: Linda@AZStenzel.com
Website: www.stenzelsealingsolutions.com
Fluid sealing solutions: Gaskets, Seals, Pump/Valve Packing, Duct/Pipe Expansion Joints, Valves, Pipe, Fittings, Flanges & Steam Traps. (Woman/White, estab 2012, empl 4, sales $1,925,914, cert: CPUC, WBENC)

California

4070   Dexen Industries, Inc.
9220 Norwalk Blvd   Santa Fe Springs, CA 90670
(562) 699-8490   Yu-Shan Teng President
Fax: (562) 699-8471
Email: info@dexen.com
Website: www.dexen.com
Mfr gas valves. (As-Pac, estab 1988, empl 17, sales $11,000,000, cert: CPUC)

Colorado

4071   Die Cut Technologies/Denver Gasket
10943 Leroy Dr   Northglenn, CO 80233
(303) 452-4600   Evelyn Meyers CEO
Fax: (303) 452-4135
Email: evelyn@diecuttech.com
Website: www.diecuttech.com
Mfr gaskets, die cut parts & converted non-metallic materials. Also dist sponge, foam tapes rubber, bridge bearing pads, expansion joints, impact attenuators & adhesives, contract assembly & packaging svcs. (Hisp, estab 1961, empl 20, sales $2,524,000, cert: NMSDC, SDB)

Illinois

4072   Cylinders Inc.
580 W 5th Ave   Naperville, IL 60563
(630) 357-5649   Cynthia Crawford President
Fax: (630) 357-5754
Email: cindy@cylindersinc.com
Website: www.cylindersinc.com
Repair & recondition hydraulic & pneumatic cylinders. (Woman/White, estab 23, empl 7, sales $1,440,992, cert: WBENC)

Kentucky

4073   SealingLife Technology
1141 Red Mile Rd Ste 201   Lexington, KY 40504
(859) 977-6640   Danette Wilder CEO
Fax: (859) 977-6644
Email: wilderdj@sealinglife.com
Website: www.sealinglife.com
Fabricate, mfr & dist sealing, shielding & coating solutions, O-rings, gaskets, molded parts, extrusions, RFI/EMF shielding, vacuum coating & encapsulating. (Woman/AA, estab 2008, empl 9, sales $1,200,000, cert: NMSDC, SDB)

Louisiana

4074   Treco Stainless Solutions, LLC
366 Technology Lane   Gray, LA 70359
(985) 858-2880   Brenna Treland Owner/Sales
Fax: (985) 858-2883
Email: brenna@trecostainless.com
Website: www.trecostainless.com
Stainless Steel Compression fittings, Stainless Steel Instrumentation fittings, Tubing & Piping, Autoclave fittings (up to 60K PSI), Gauges, Hydraulic Hoses, Quick Connects. (Woman/White, estab 2014, empl 3, sales , cert: WBENC)

Maryland

4075   Phelps Industrial Products
6300 Washington Blvd   Elkridge, MD 21075
(410) 796-2222   Gina Lehman CEO
Fax: (410) 796-1277
Email: gmlehman@phelpsgaskets.com
Website: www.phelpsgaskets.com
Mfr, fabricator & dist Gaskets, Compression Packing, O' Rings, Molded Parts & Sealing Devices. (As-Pac, estab 1945, empl 15, sales , cert: State)

Minnesota

4076   Water Technology Resources
9201 E Bloomington Fwy, Ste Z   Bloomington, MN 55420
(952) 641-9004   Sally Waldor President
Fax: (952) 885-9173
Email: sallywaldor@wtrvalves.com
Website: www.wtrvalves.com
Mfr industrial valves. (Woman/White, estab 2009, empl 5, sales $1,000,000, cert: State)

North Carolina

4077 Raleigh-Durham Rubber & Gasket Co., Inc.
P.O. Box 90397   Raleigh, NC 27675
(919) 781-6817 Judy Hooks President
Fax: (919) 781-3243
Email: judyh@raleighdurhamrubber.com
Website: www.raleighdurhamrubber.com
Mfr & dist rubber gaskets. (Woman, estab , empl 1, sales , cert: WBENC)

Ohio

4078 Trident Fluid Power, LLC
P.O. Box 368   Middletown, OH 45042
(513) 217-4999 Sandy Ewen GM
Fax: (513) 217-6222
Email: sewen@tridentfluidpower.com
Website: www.www,Tridentfluidpower.com
Replace, overhaul, manufacture, fluidpower components (cylinders, pumps, valves, systems), field service, trouble shoot, design, engineer, all coke oven equipment & operations, machine, welding, fabricating. (Woman/White, estab 2006, empl 17, sales $2,000,000, cert: WBENC)

Oklahoma

4079 PT Coupling Co.
P.O. Box 3909   Enid, OK 73702
(580) 237-4033 James Matthew Parrish President
Fax:
Email: credit03@ptcoupling.com
Website: www.ptcoupling.com
Mfr industrial hose couplings used in the transfer of fluid & dry products at medium to low pressure. (Nat Ame, estab 1951, empl 390, sales $60,000,000, cert: NMSDC)

Tennessee

4080 Pioneer Air Systems, Inc.
210 Flat Fork Rd   Wartburg, TN 37887
(423) 346-6693 Sam Basseen CEO
Fax: (423) 346-3865
Email: sam@pioneerair.com
Website: www.pioneerair.com
Convert CO to CO2 in compressed air to make it suitable for breathing air purposes, clean & dry Nitrogen, Natural Gas, Hydrogen, Helium, Ethylene, Seal Gas, OxyPurge (with MONEL vessels & Teflon lined piping) etc. (As-Ind, estab 1980, empl 25, sales , cert: NMSDC)

Texas

4081 Corley Gasket Company
P.O. Box 271124   Dallas, TX 75227
(214) 388-7437 Jody Anderson Office Mgr
Fax: (214) 388-0619
Email: janderson@corleygasket.com
Website: www.corleygasket.com
Mfr gaskets. (Woman/White, estab 1975, empl 19, sales $1,941,386, cert: State, CPUC)

4082 OG Energy Solutions LLC
1836 Snake River Rd Ste A Katy, TX 77449
(832) 644-0121 Federico Zamar Regional Sales Rep
Fax: (832) 550-2539
Email: fzsales@ogenergys.com
Website: www.ogenergys.com
Pipes, tubes, fitting, flanges; Valves; Automation & Instrumentation (transducers, sensors, transmitters, panels); Heat Exchanger Equipment & Parts; Seals & Gaskets; Non-toxic, environmentally-safe cleaners, degreasers & solvents. (Woman/Hisp, estab 2010, empl 8, sales $600,000, cert: WBENC)

4083 Piping Technology and Product Inc.
3701 Holmes Rd   Houston, TX 77051
(713) 731-0030 Justin Long Business Dev Mgr
Fax: (713) 731-8640
Email: info@pipingtech.com
Website: www.pipingtech.com
Custom Engineered Hot/Cold Insulated Pipe Shoes and Supports, Fabric Expansion Joints/Metal Bellows, ASME Certified Pressure Vessels, and ASME-U-Stamp rated Hydraulic and Mechanical Snubbers, Custom Engineered (As-Ind/As-Pac, estab 1978, empl 750, sales $50,000,000, cert: NMSDC)

Wisconsin

4084 Husco Automotive, LLC
2239 Pewaukee Rd   Waukesha, WI 53188
(262) 953-6400 Jonathan Hassert Acct Mgr
Fax: (262) 953-6399
Email: jon.hassert@huscoauto.com
Website: www.huscoauto.com
Design, develop & mfr electro-hydraulic solenoid valves & electro-magnetic solenoid actuators. (Hisp, estab 1946, empl 1015, sales $238,000,000, cert: NMSDC)

INDUSTRIAL EQUIPMENT & SUPPLIES

Manufacturers and distributors of food service and restaurant equipment, drive belts, aircraft parts, motors, industrial batteries, underground mining equipment, heaters, bearings, spark plug cleaner, traffic control signs, etc. (See also HARDWARE & TOOLS, HYDRAULIC & COMPRESSED AIR EQUIPMENT, INDUSTRIAL MACHINES and MATERIAL HANDLING EQUIPMENT). NAICS Code 42

Alabama

4085   Alabama Safety Products Inc.
150 Supply Room Rd   Oxford, AL 36203
(256)80963   Tracy Rouse President
Fax: (256) 831-9735
Email: tracyr@alabamasafety.com
Website: www.alabamasafety.com
Dist safety supplies, safety audits, hand protections surveys, respirator fit-testing. (Woman/Nat Ame, estab 1992, empl 8, sales , cert: NMSDC)

4086   Cornerstone Supply, Inc.
340 Production AVe   Madison, AL 35758
(256) 461-4147   Bonnie Powers President
Fax:
Email: bonnie@cornerstone-supply.com
Website: www.cornerstone-supply.com
Dist military fasteners, electronic components, MRO equipment & supplies. (Woman, estab 1986, empl 11, sales , cert: WBENC)

4087   Elle Waterworks Supply, LLC
4000 Eagle Point Corporate Dr   Birmingham, AL 35242
(205) 314-5783   Courtney Myrick Owner
Fax:
Email: cmyrick@ellewws.com
Website: www.ellewws.com
Dist process valves, air valves, control valves, ductile iron pipe, steel pipe, pipe supports & hangers, couplings, adapters, pvc pipe & fittings, ductile iron fittings, hydrants, valve boxes, hardware, bolts, nuts, gaskets, safety equipment. (Woman, estab 2011, empl 2, sales $850,000, cert: State, WBENC)

Arizona

4088   Air Energy Systems & Services
4202 E Superior Ave, Ste 3   Phoenix, AZ 85040
(602) 454-0210   Patricia Bewley Owner
Fax: (602) 454-0213
Email: pbewley@aesas.com
Website: www.aesas.com
Dist & install commerical, industrial & HVAC air filters, energy products, IAQ products, UVC producst, energy audits. (Woman/Nat Ame, estab 1997, empl 15, sales $2,300,000, cert: NMSDC, WBENC)

4089   Diversified Diamond Products
4634 E Mountain View Ct   Phoenix, AZ 85028
(480) 443-4899   Mary Dillon CEO
Fax: (480) 483-1673
Email: mdillon@diversifieddiamond.com
Website: www.diversifieddiamond.com
Dist safety supplies & equipment, vests, gloves, respirators, test meters, locks, cable protection, prescription safety glasses, fall protection, ear protection, face masks, cutting tools, abrasives, work holding, metal working. (Woman/White, estab 1989, empl 6, sales $1,295,404, cert: WBENC)

4090   Industrial Specialties Supply, Inc.
3941 E 29th St, Ste 606   Tucson, AZ 85711
(520) 745-5800   Alan Davila Mgr
Fax:
Email: indussupply@live.com
Website: www.indussupplyinc.com
Solenoid valves, PLC components, Conveyor belts, Steam traps, High Pressure Valves, Sanitary/Food grade fittings, valves & tubing, industrial concrete coatings, personal safety equipment, Gas detectors. (Hisp, estab 2001, empl 2, sales $1,438,845, cert: State, City)

California

4091   Able Industrial Products, Inc.
2006 S Baker   Ontario, CA 91761
(909) 930-1585   Courtney Salvidar Sales/Mktg
Fax: (909) 930-1587
Email: courtneys@able123.com
Website: www.able123.com
Mfr & convert thermal management materials: gap pads, interface pads & various non-metallic gaskets. (Woman/Hisp, estab 1974, empl 40, sales $3,800,000, cert: NMSDC)

4092   Brandon Supply Corporation
14120 Gannet St, Unit 101   Santa Fe Springs, CA 90670
(562) 921-0407   Clarence D. Scott President
Fax: (562) 921-5945
Email: cdavis@brandonsupplycorp.com
Website: www.brandonsupply.com
Dist pipes, valves, fittings, waterworks, material handling, safety line, industrial supplies. (AA, estab 1980, empl 9, sales $1,500,000, cert: State)

4093   Empire Safety & Supply
10624 Industrial Ave   Roseville, CA 95678
(800) 995-1341   Monette Crawford CEO
Fax: (888) 882-9060
Email: monette@empiresafety.com
Website: www.empiresafety.com
Dist environmental health & safety products. (Woman, estab 1992, empl 14, sales $6,000,000, cert: CPUC)

4094   FTG, Inc.
       12750 Center Court Dr S Ste 280 Cerritos, CA 90703
       (562) 865-9200 Pino Pathak President
       Fax: (562) 403-1700
       Email: pino@ftginc.com
       Website: www.ftginc.com
Mfr air filters, oil filters, fuel filters, filtration products,
custom engineered parts. (As-Pac, estab 1992, empl 20,
sales $3,000,000, cert: NMSDC)

4095   Harris Industrial Gases
       8475 Auburn Blvd   Citrus Heights, CA 95610
       (916) 725-2168 Tim Lettich GM
       Fax: (916) 725-2117
       Email: tlettich@harrisgas.com
       Website: www.harrisgas.com
Dist welding & industrial equipment & industrial gases.
(Woman/White, estab 1936, empl 20, sales $5,000,000,
cert: State, CPUC)

4096   Jeyco Products, Inc.
       1221 Cushman Ave   San Diego, CA 92110
       (619) 260-1075 John Johnson Sales Mgr
       Fax: (619) 260-0072
       Email: sales@jeyco.com
       Website: www.jeyco.com
Dist industrial MRO supplies: cutting tools, abrasives,
fittings, fasteners, aerosol & bulk chemicals, electrical
maintenance supplies, janitorial cleaning supplies &
equipment, stainless steel food grade products, food grade
chemicals. (Woman/White, estab 1977, empl 10, sales
$3,500,000, cert: CPUC)

4097   Liberty Glove, Inc.
       433 Cheryl Lane   City of Industry, CA 91789
       (800) 327-8333 Ken Tran Natl Sales Mgr
       Fax:
       Email: kentran@libertyglove.com
       Website: www.libertyglove.com
Dist safety industrial products. (Woman/As-Pac, estab
1988, empl 70, sales , cert: NMSDC)

4098   Paramount Safety Supply
       14516 Crenshaw Blvd   Gardena, CA 90249
       (866) 200-2975 Joel Pulgarin President
       Fax: (310) 361-8330
       Email: info@paramountsafetysupply.com
       Website: www.paramountsafetysupply.com
Personal Protective Equipment, Fall Protection Systems,
Gas Monitors/Sniffers, Disaster Preparedness, Emergency
Response Supplies, Confined Space Entry/Rescue, Rescue
& Descent Systems, Construction Safety. (Hisp, estab 2015,
empl 1, sales $500,000, cert: State, CPUC)

4099   R.J. Safety Supply Company Inc.
       7320 Convoy Court   San Diego, CA 92111
       (858) 541-2880 Diane Rodriguez VP
       Fax: (858) 541-2898
       Email: drodriguez@rjsafety.com
       Website: www.rjsafety.com
Dist safety supplies: PPE products, respiratory, confined
space, fall protection, blowers, first aid, gloves, boots,
rainwear, protective clothing, hazardous material
containers, signs, traffic control, safety cabinets, gas
detectors. (Woman, estab 1959, empl 17, sales , cert:
CPUC)

4100   Widespread Industrial Supplies, Inc.
       1220 S Boyle Ave   Los Angeles, CA 90023
       (310) 793-7315 Josh Dorfman President
       Fax: (310) 793-7317
       Email: josh.dorfman@widespreadind.com
       Website: www.widespreadind.com
Dist industrial supplies: fasteners, cutting tools, electrical, welding, chemical & safety related supplies, hand &
power tools. (Woman/White, estab 2002, empl 4, sales
$820,341, cert: State, City)

Connecticut

4101   IBC - Industrial Supply Plus
       2 Creamery Brook   East Granby, CT 06026
       (860) 246-1618 Ron Nunez CEO
       Fax: (203) 286-1081
       Email: rnunez@industrialbuyers.com
       Website: www.industrialbuyers.com
Dist maintenance, repair, operations, production,
bearing & power transmission supplies, technical
support, inventory control & mgmt, product support &
service, consolidated invoicing & sales reporting,
minority credits, standardization & rationalization. (Hisp,
estab 1999, empl 15, sales $8,200,000, cert: NMSDC)

Florida

4102   Arroyo Process Equipment Inc.
       1550 Centennial Blvd   Bartow, FL 33830
       (863) 533-9700 Diane Schleicher President
       Fax: (863) 533-4907
       Email: diane@arroyoprocess.com
       Website: www.arroyoprocess.com
Dist pumps, tanks, mixers, meters, filters, water treatment equip. (AA/As-Pac/Hisp, estab 1968, empl 32, sales
$15,576,805, cert: NMSDC)

4103   O.T. Trans Inc.
　　　201 Babock St   Melbourne, FL 32901
　　　(321) 259-9880 Dean Danner Business Dev Mgr
　　　Fax: (321) 259-4828
　　　Email: ddanner@ottrans.com
　　　Website: www.ottrans.com
Industrial machinery & equip, material handling, hand
tools, wiring supplies, safety & rescue equip, tool &
hardware boxes, abrasive materials, cabinets, lockers, bins
& shelving, winches, hoists, cranes & derricks. (Hisp, estab
1993, empl 15, sales $5,000,000, cert: NMSDC)

4104   Pelican Sales, Inc.
　　　2825 Business Center Blvd Ste C9 Melbourne, FL
　　　32940
　　　(321) 254-9569 Callena Spearman Sales
　　　Fax: (321) 255-1133
　　　Email: sales@pelican-sales.com
　　　Website: www.pelican-direct.com
Dist industrial hardware equipment & supplies. (Woman/
White, estab 1993, empl 15, sales $13,000,000, cert: State)

4105   Silver Wings Aerospace
　　　25400 SW 140th Ave   Princeton, FL 33032
　　　(305) 258-5950 Eduardo Montalvo President
　　　Fax: (305) 258-5953
　　　Email: Eddie@silverwingsaerospace.com
　　　Website: www.silverwingsaerospace.com
Dist & repair aircraft parts. (Hisp, estab 2007, empl 16,
sales $12,765,527, cert: NMSDC)

Georgia

4106   A.D.A. Supplies & Leasing Services, Inc.
　　　205 Old Perry Rd   Bonaire, GA 31005
　　　(478) 329-8896 Ima McLean Business Dev Mgr
　　　Fax: (478) 329-8897
　　　Email: ima.mclean@adasupply.com
　　　Website: www.adasupply.com
Dist safety supplies & equip: respiratory protection, fall
protection gear, eye & ear plugs & muffs protection,
welding equipment & fire safety, gloves. (Woman/As-Pac,
estab , empl 1, sales $2,500,000, cert: State)

4107   Control Specialties, Inc.
　　　2503 Monroe Dr Gainesville, GA 30507
　　　(770) 532-7736 Janice Moody CSr
　　　Fax: (770) 535-0536
　　　Email: janice@control-specialties.com
　　　Website: www.control-specialties.com
Dist pumps, instrumentation, filtration, controls, valves,
energy audits, utility consultations. (Woman/White, estab
1987, empl 4, sales $1,965,970, cert: WBENC)

4108   Covenant Distributors, Inc.
　　　1227 Augusta West Pkwy   Augusta, GA 30909
　　　(706) 610-2207 Mark Pugh Contract Admin
　　　Fax:
　　　Email: mark@ecovenant.net
　　　Website: www.ecovenant.net
Dist valves, pumps, element filters. (AA, estab 1999, empl
7, sales $360,000, cert: State)

4109   DBS Manufacturing, Inc.
　　　45 SouthWoods Pkwy   Atlanta, GA 30354
　　　(404) 768-2131 Nicole McDermott NWBOC
　　　Admin
　　　Fax:
　　　Email: nwboc@dbsmfg.com
　　　Website: www.dbsmfg.com
Water & Waste Water Treatment Clarifiers & Thickener;
Water & Waste Water Treatment Clarifiers & Thickeners
Bolt-In Retrofit Drive Units; Trickling Filters; Aeration
Equipment; Mixing Equipment. (Woman/White, estab
1975, empl 30, sales $9,000,000, cert: NWBOC)

4110   H&S Supply Co., Inc.
　　　528 N Main St   Moultrie, GA 31768
　　　(229) 985-4575 Randy Blanchett Mgr
　　　Fax: (229) 890-3200
　　　Email: rblanchett@hssupplyco.com
　　　Website: www.hssupplyco.com
Dist plumbing & HVAC supplies, drilling supplies. (Nat
Ame, estab 1969, empl 10, sales $40,000,000, cert:
State)

4111   HeatRep, LLC
　　　400 Galleria Pkwy, Ste 1500   Atlanta, GA 30339
　　　(404) 989-5457 Christie Karis Owner
　　　Fax:
　　　Email: ckaris@heatrep.com
　　　Website: www.heatrep.com
Industrial equipment supplies, heat exchangers, fired
heaters, electric heaters, economizers, condensers,
liquid filtration, gas filtration, strainers, automatic
strainers, filter separators, knockout tanks, reactors,
pulsation bottles, custom fabrication (Woman, estab
2011, empl 1, sales , cert: WBENC)

4112   KACO Supply Company
　　　2968-C Ask Kay Dr   Smyrna, GA 30082
　　　(770) 435-8902 Kay Williams President
　　　Fax: (770) 435-2309
　　　Email: kaco@mindspring.com
　　　Website: www.kacosupplycompany.com
Dist institutional food, paper & plastic products, janitorial supplies, kitchenwares & equipment. (Woman/AA,
estab 1991, empl 5, sales $1,449,460, cert: City, NMSDC)

4113   Stag Enterprise, Inc.
　　　383 Wilbanks Dr   Ball Ground, GA 30107
　　　(770) 720-8888 Rachel Niederer VP Ops
　　　Fax: (770) 720-8887
　　　Email: racheln@stagenterprise.com
　　　Website: www.stagenterprise.com
Dist industrial supplies, slitting tapes. (Woman/As-Pac,
estab 1993, empl 21, sales $22,000,000, cert: NMSDC,
WBENC)

Iowa

4114   Molded Products, Inc.
1112 Chatburn Ave   Harlan, IA 51537
(800) 435-8957   Sheri Tyrrel Mktg/sales Mgr
Fax: (800) 227-7935
Email: mpc@moldedproducts.com
Website: www.moldedproducts.com
Dist ancillary supplies, access sites, luer lock caps, transducer protectors, tube occluding forceps, hansen connectors, recirculation sets, patented tandem dialysis supplies, specialty connectors, dialyzer holders, fistula pressure clamps. (Woman/White, estab 1986, empl 46, sales $4,030,797, cert: State)

Illinois

4115   AMSYSCO, Inc.
1200 Windham Pkwy   Romeoville, IL 60446
(630) 296-8383   Neel Khosa VP
Fax: (630) 296-8380
Email: nkhosa@amsyscoinc.com
Website: www.amsyscoinc.com
Dist post-tensioning tendons used in concrete reinforcement, barrier cable used in parking garage restraint systems. (As-Pac, estab 1981, empl 30, sales $18,697,191, cert: NMSDC)

4116   Emergent Safety Supply
1055 Kingsland Dr   Batavia, IL 60510
(630) 406-9666   Jerry Hill VP
Fax: (630) 406-6195
Email: jhill@emergentsafety.com
Website: www.Emergentsafety.com
Dist PPE, FR Clothing, Traffic Safety Products, Safety Signage, Spill Containment, Repertory Products. (Woman/White, estab 1985, empl 28, sales $12,200,000, cert: State, WBENC)

4117   Equity Industrial
2000 S 25th Ave Unit A   Broadview, IL 60155
(708) 450-0000   Robert Butler President
Fax: (708) 450-0001
Email: KevinDonnelly@equityind.com
Website: www.equityind.com
Dist industrial supplies. (Woman/AA, estab 1996, empl 7, sales $4,675,276, cert: NMSDC)

4118   Freedom Air Filtration Inc.
1712 Arden Place   Joliet, IL 60435
(877) 715-8999   Linda Freveletti President
Fax: (815) 744-8999
Email: linda@freedomairfiltration.com
Website: www.freedomairfiltration.com
HVAC supplies & services. (Woman/White, estab 2004, empl 5, sales $850,000, cert: WBENC)

4119   Howe Corporation
1650 N Elston Ave   Chicago, IL 60642
(773) 235-0200   Tammy Phillips VP Finance & Treasurer
Fax: (773) 235-0269
Email: tammy@howecorp.com
Website: www.howecorp.com
Mfr Flake ice makers, refrigeration & ammonia pump out compressors & refrigeration pressure vessels. (Woman/White, estab 1912, empl 37, sales $10,000,000, cert: WBENC)

4120   Inter-City Supply Company, Inc.
8830 S Dobson Ave   Chicago, IL 60619
(773) 731-8007   Jackie Dyess President
Fax: (773) 731-9115
Email: intercity@ameritech.net
Website: www.intercity-supply.com
Dist janitorial, safety & food service. (Woman/AA, estab 1979, empl 10, sales $5,300,000, cert: City, NMSDC)

4121   International Filter Manufacturing Corporation
713 W Columbian Blvd P.O. Box 549   Litchfield, IL 62056
(217) 324-2303   Cecilia Ewing Hayes President
Fax: (217) 324-2390
Email: ifmpres@consolidated.net
Website: www.ifm-corp.com
Mfr air filters for heavy-duty equip: transit vehicles, coal mining. Also dist HVAC, industrial & specailty filters. (Woman/AA, estab 1987, empl 35, sales , cert: State)

4122   ITA, Inc.
150 Pierce Road, Ste 550   Itasca, IL 60143
(281) 712-7608   Ritu Agrawal Director of Mktg
Fax: (847) 364-1183
Email: ragrawal@itaoffice.com
Website: www.itaoffice.com
Dist Industrial Equipment, Printers, Production Simulation Software, Hazardous & remote sensing robots, Oil filtration equipment, R&D Equipment, Chemiluminesent Oxidation Analyzers, Ferro Magnetic Detector, Automation MRO Products. (As-Pac, estab 1980, empl 10, sales $2,500,000, cert: NMSDC)

4123   JM Industrial Supply
2323 Lakeshore   Pekin, IL 61554
(309) 346-5796   Daniel Whitford Sales
Fax: (309) 347-5700
Email: daniel@jmindsupply.com
Website: www.jmindsupply.com
Dist MRO mill supplies company. (AA, estab 1986, empl 11, sales $10,500,000, cert: State)

4124   One Way Safety, LLC
418 Shawmut Ave   LaGrange, IL 60525
(708) 579-0229   Anne Callaghan Sales Mgr
Fax: (708) 579-0746
Email: anne@onewaysafety.com
Website: www.onewaysafety.com
Dist PPE, gas detection, fall protection, supplied air, respiratory equipment & uniforms, rescue teams, respiratory fit testing, safety training, safety equipment repair & rental, safety supervisors. (Woman/White, estab 2013, empl 20, sales $2,500,000, cert: WBENC)

4125   Permatron
2020 Touhy Ave   Elk Grove Village, IL 60007
(847) 434-1421   Leslye Sandberg President
Fax: (847) 434-1429
Email: lsandberg@permatron.com
Website: www.permatron.com
Mfr air filters, air intake filters, equip protection filters. (Woman/White, estab 1957, empl 40, sales , cert: WBENC)

4126   Production Distribution Companies
9511 S Dorchester ave   Chicago, IL 60628
(708) 489-0195   Cleo Downs President
Fax: (708) 489-0196
Email: cleo@pdcompanies.org
Website: www.pdcompanies.org
Dist electrical, industrial supplies, tools & equipment. (AA, estab 2004, empl 9, sales $5,400,272, cert: City, NMSDC)

4127   Supplied Industrial Solutions, Inc.
1635 West 1st St Ste 151   Granite City, IL 62040
(618) 452-8151   Stephen Brock President
Fax: (618) 257-8013
Email: sbrock@supplied-industrial.com
Website: www.supplied-industrial.com
Dist industrial supplies: hose, fittings, valves, safety supplies. (AA, estab 2003, empl 5, sales $240,000, cert: State)

4128   Wabash Transformer (PowerVolt and Ensign Corp)
300 W. Factory Rd.   Addison, IL 60101
(630) 628-9999   Ajay Sharma VP Sales and Mktg
Fax: (630) 628-9922
Email: ajays@wabashtransformer.com
Website: www.wabashtransformer.com
Mfr power transformers: medical, dental, HVAC, controls, packaging & automation equipment. (As-Pac, estab 1966, empl 33, sales $3,200,000, cert: NMSDC)

Indiana

4129   Courtney Material Handling, Inc.
P.O. Box 6925   South Bend, IN 46660
(574) 231-0094   Beth Courtney President
Fax: (574) 231-0736
Email: beth@cmhionline.com
Website: www.cmhionline.com
Dist safety items: hard hats, vests, safety glasses, gloves, tools, fire & detection, bins, cabinets, carts, casters, chairs & stools. (Woman/White, estab 2003, empl 2, sales $213,673, cert: State)

4130   GM Supply Company, Inc.
6321 E 30th St Ste 205   Indianapolis, IN 46219
(317) 898-3510   Steven Batts Business Devel
Fax: (317) 898-4366
Email: steveb@gmsupplyco.com
Website: www.gmsupplyco.com
Integrated supply services, commodity management services, component assembly services, distribution of cutting tools, abrasives, safety supplies, MRO, packaging, tools, janitorial, electrical, plumbing, power transmission, bearings. (AA, estab 1992, empl 12, sales $22,000,000, cert: NMSDC)

4131   Gripp Inc.
17322 Westfield Park Rd   Westfield, IN 46074
(317) 896-3700   Judy Gripp President
Fax:
Email: JudyG@grippinc.com
Website: www.grippinc.com
Dist, service, install & calibrate environmental monitoring equipment, open & and closed pipe flow monitoring & wastewater sampling. (Woman/White, estab 1992, empl 10, sales , cert: State, City)

4132   Powell Tool Supply Co., Inc.
1338 Mishawaka Ave   South Bend, IN 46615
(574) 289-4811   Cari Eaton CEO
Fax: (574) 289-3504
Email: ceaton@powelltool.com
Website: www.powelltool.com
Dist industrial supplies: cutting tools, abrasives, chemicals, MRO supplies, material handling, janitorial, etc. (Woman/White, estab 1948, empl 20, sales $5,500,000, cert: WBENC)

4133   RFS Group
P.O. Box 68506   Indianapolis, IN 46268
(317) 507-3165   Ramon Morrison Principal
Fax:
Email: rmorrison@meticulousdb.com
Website: www.meticulousdb.com
Dist maintenance, janitorial & cleaning supplies, equipment & accessories. Also wholesale distributes office, foodservice and safety supplies. (AA, estab 2007, empl 6, sales $3,500,000, cert: State, City)

4134   Team Cruiser Supply LLC
P.O. Box 88255   Indianapolis, IN 46208
(317) 423-2430   Christopher Barney President
Fax: (317) 423-8963
Email: mbarney@teamcruiser.com
Website: www.tcsupplylogistics.com
Dist industrial products. (AA, estab 2013, empl 5, sales $3,345,000, cert: NMSDC)

4135 Worldwide Filters, LLC
3318 Pagosa Court Indianapolis, IN 46201
(317) 808-3719 Dawn Codozor Sales Mgr
Fax: (317) 808-3722
Email: frank@worldwidefilters.com
Website: www.worldwidefilters.com
Dist filters: commercial, industrial & residential, HEPA filters, air, oil, hydraulic & fuel vehicle filters, water filtration systems. (AA, estab 2004, empl 5, sales $250,000, cert: NMSDC)

Kansas

4136 Touch Enterprises LLC
117 N Cooper St Olathe, KS 66061
(913) 440-0770 Camilo Fernandez Sales Andmin
Fax: -
Email: cfernandez@touchenterprises.com
Website: www.touchenterprises.com/shop
Dist industrial products, safety products, medical supplies, vet supplies, MRO supplies. (As-Pac, estab 2007, empl 15, sales $3,000,000, cert: NMSDC)

Kentucky

4137 Industrial Electronics LLC dba Indel-USA
10312 Bluegrass Pkwy Louisville, KY 40299
(888) 499-4877 Vadim Nazarenko Owner
Fax: (502) 499-4876
Email: indel@indel-usa.com
Website: www.indel-usa.com
Repair, troubleshooting, retrofitting & design services for industrial electronic equipment. (Woman/White, estab 2005, empl 4, sales , cert: State)

4138 United American Supply, LLC
100-C Dewey Dr Nicholasville, KY 40356
(859) 881-1850 Albert Taylor Managing Partner
Fax: (859) 885-1687
Email: al@unitedamericansupply.com
Website: www.unitedamericansupply.com
Dist safety supplies (PPE), machined parts & sanitary maintenance supplies. (AA, estab 2008, empl 8, sales $1,600,000, cert: NMSDC)

Louisiana

4139 Brewster Procurement Group, Inc.
401 W Main St Lafayette, LA 70501
(337) 291-9009 V. Janet Brewster CEO
Fax: (337) 291-9010
Email: janet@brewsterprocurement.com
Website: www.brewsterprocurement.com
Dist MRO, mill & industrial supplies, electrical, tools, safety products, buyout services. (Woman/Hisp, estab 1999, empl 8, sales $113,609,858, cert: NMSDC, WBENC)

4140 Precision Air & Liquid Solutions, LLC
1905 W Thomas St, Ste D271 Hammond, LA 70401
(504) 208-1525 Cynthia Bourg Chief Exec Mgr
Fax: (985) 878-2014
Email: cyndibourg@precisionair-liquid.com
Website: www.precisionair-liquid.com
Dist ventilation fans, fan parts, filtration, replacement filters, cartridges, housings, compressors, turbines & engines, dust, fume & mist control products & flow monitoring equipment. (Woman/White, estab 2003, empl 2, sales $550,000, cert: State, WBENC)

Massachusetts

4141 New England Die Cutting, Inc.
96 Milk St Methuen, MA 01844
(978) 686-6332 Kimberly Abare President
Fax: (978) 686-9912
Email: kabare@nedc.com
Website: www.nedc.com
Mfr gaskets, seals & insulators, die cutting, waterjet cutting & laser etching. (Woman/White, estab 1982, empl 28, sales $3,900,000, cert: WBENC)

Michigan

4142 Choctaw-Kaul Distribution Company
3540 Vinewood Detroit, MI 48208
(313) 895-3165 Caitlin Johnson Cstmr Dev Mgr
Fax: (313) 894-7977
Email: cjohnson@choctawkaul.com
Website: www.choctawkaul.com
Mfr gloves & safety products, mgmt svcs, janitorial svcs, industrial specialty cleaning, paint booth cleaning, chemical mgmt, recycling, filter maintenance, truck repair, construction mgmt, parking lot maintenance, temp manpower, etc. (Nat Ame/As-Ind/As-Pac/Canadian Aboriginal, estab 1998, empl 350, sales $107,000,000, cert: NMSDC)

4143 Extreme Tooling LLC
48750 Structural Dr Chesterfield, MI 48051
(586) 232-3618 Kurt Schill President
Fax: (586) 232-3619
Email: kschill@extremetooling.com
Website: www.extremetooling.com
Dist metal removal & industrial supplies, milling, drilling & industrial products. (Woman/White, estab 2003, empl 5, sales $3,683,821, cert: WBENC)

4144 IMC Products, Inc.
2743 Henry St, Ste 130   Muskegon, MI 49441
(877) 625-8743 Irmgard Cooper President
Fax: (888) 811-9860
Email: irmgard.cooper@imc-products.com
Website: www.imc-products.com
Assembly & kit packaging, contract administration, warehouse & distribution. (AA, estab 1990, empl 12, sales $1,900,000, cert: NMSDC)

4145 JISI Group, LLC
6043 18 Mile Rd   Sterling Heights, MI 48314
(586) 239-9016 Amber Amato President
Fax: (586) 464-3574
Email: a.amato@jisisupply.com
Website: www.jisisupply.com
Concrete construction & repair products. (Woman/White, estab 2014, empl 2, sales $446,000, cert: WBENC)

4146 Mahar Tool Supply Company, Inc.
7105 Nineteen Mlle Rd   Sterling Heights, MI 48314
(586) 997-2584 Dave Plosky Exec VP of Sales
Fax: (586) 997-3447
Email: dp@mahartool.com
Website: www.mahartool.com
Dist industrial products & MRO supplies, commodity management, integrated supply, technical staffing, engineering support. (Woman/White, estab 1947, empl 142, sales $115,200,000, cert: WBENC)

4147 Master Pneumatic Detroit, Inc.
6701 Eighteen Mile Road   Sterling Heights, MI 48314
(586) 254-1000 Wendy Goscenski Mgr
Fax: (586) 254-6055
Email: WGoscenski@aol.com
Website: www.masterpneumatic.com
Mfr filters, regulators & lubrication systems for compressed air systems. (Woman/White, estab 1950, empl 56, sales $6,500,000, cert: WBENC)

4148 National Integrated Systems
4622 Runway Blvd   Ann Arbor, MI 48108
(313) 817-0066 Jay Park Sales
Fax: (313) 817-0072
Email: jpark@nisusa.com
Website: www.nisusa.com
Dist coated pipe & components, used for modular pipe racking systems. (As-Pac, estab 2003, empl 10, sales , cert: NMSDC)

4149 Safety Services, Inc.
5286 Wynn Rd   Kalamazoo, MI 49048
(269) 382-1052 Kathryn Bowdish CEO
Fax: (269) 382-6414
Email: info@safetyservicesinc.com
Website: www.safetyservicesinc.com
Dist industrial safety equipment: personal protective equipment, gloves, first aid, fall protection, confined space equipment, handling, storage, instrumentation, spill control. (Woman/As-Pac, estab 1948, empl 28, sales , cert: WBENC)

4150 The Safety Source, LLC
35320 Forton Court   Clinton Township, MI 48035
(586) 648-7132 Elizabeth VanSickle President
Fax: (586) 716-2471
Email: elizabeth@safetysourcellc.com
Website: www.safetysourcellc.com
Dist industrial safety supplies, first aid supplies & miscellaneous MRO supplies. (Woman/White, estab 2006, empl 6, sales $2,200,000, cert: WBENC)

Minnesota

4151 Allied Electrical & Industrial Supply Company Inc.
6112 14th St W   St. Louis Park, MN 55416
(763) 544-3600 Valerie McKissack President
Fax: (763) 544-3601
Email: vmckissack@allied-electrical.com
Website: www.allied-electrical.com
Dist medical, industrial, electrical, safety, janitorial & construction supplies. (Woman/AA, estab 1994, empl 6, sales $832,000, cert: NMSDC)

4152 Northern Traffic Supply Inc.
2740 N Ferry St   Anoka, MN 55303
(763) 576-1200 Brent Gummert CEO
Fax: (763) 576-1414
Email: brentg@ntsindustries.com
Website: www.ntsindustries.com
Dist traffic control devices, mfr road, building & parking lot signage, safety vests, safety signs, ear protection, eye protection, safety gloves. (Nat Ame, estab 1998, empl 14, sales $1,400,000, cert: State)

4153 Safety Signs
19784 Kenrick Ave   Lakeville, MN 55044
(952) 469-6700 Sue Blanchard President
Fax: (952) 469-6689
Email: sueblanchard@safetysigns-mn.com
Website: www.safetysigns-mn.com
Traffic safety equipment and svcs specializing in traffic control, permanent signs, pavement striping, pavement stripe removals & safety apparel. (Woman/White, estab 1993, empl 28, sales , cert: State, City)

Missouri

4154 Alliance Industries LLC
2959 N Martin Ave   Springfield, MO 65803
(417) 863-6315 Maynard Larson Ops/purch Mgr
Fax: (417) 863-6339
Email: mlarson@allianceind.com
Website: www.allianceind.com
Remanufacture OEM torque converters. (Woman/AA, estab 2002, empl 20, sales , cert: WBENC)

4155　Controlled Environment Products, Inc.
　　　3851 NE Kimball Dr　Kansas City, MO 64161
　　　(816) 453-8900　Marilyn Townsend CEO
　　　Fax: (816) 453-7077
　　　Email: marilyn@netcep.com
　　　Website: www.netcep.com
Dist safety supplies, personal protection equip, disposable
Tyvek coverall, gloves, ergonomic seating, paper towels,
tissue, Kleenex, handsoap, jan/san chemicals, etc.
(Woman/AA, estab 1989, empl 11, sales $7,100,000, cert:
NMSDC)

4156　King Filtration Technologies, Inc.
　　　1255 Research Blvd　Saint Louis, MO 63132
　　　(800) 999-8441　Jim Seidel VP of Sales
　　　Fax: (314) 432-5147
　　　Email: sales@kingfiltration.com
　　　Website: www.kingfiltration.com
Dist filtration products. (Woman, estab 1960, empl 30,
sales , cert: WBENC)

4157　Millennium Industrial Equipment, LLC
　　　1475 Legacy Circle　Fenton, MO 63026
　　　(314) 574-2047　Tony Estopare President
　　　Fax: (636) 226-4207
　　　Email: testopare@miequipment.com
　　　Website: www.millennium-industrial-
　　　equipment.com
Manufacturer's Rep, Bulk Solids (Dry) Material Handling,
Air Handling, and Air Pollution Control Equipment. (As-Pac,
estab 2002, empl 4, sales $630,862, cert: State)

4158　National Material Supply Co, LLC
　　　2206 Sidney St　St. Louis, MO 63104
　　　(314) 865-1644　Kevie Hendrix
　　　Fax: (314) 865-5837
　　　Email: sales@nmsupply.com
　　　Website: www.nmsupply.com
Dist industrial supplies, products & safety equipment. (AA,
estab 1997, empl 5, sales $1,500,000, cert: State)

4159　Stainless Integrity
　　　5464 S Woodcliffe Dr　Springfield, MO 65804
　　　(417) 773-6383　Vickie Norton President
　　　Fax:
　　　Email: vlnorton@stainlessintegrity.com
　　　Website: www.stainlessintegrity.com
Dist stainless steel nickel alloy ASME pressure vessels &
tanks; bioreactor & fermenter skids; field repair; field
modification & field erection, tank cleaning & inspection,
powder hoppers & bins. (Woman/White, estab 2010, empl
1, sales , cert: WBENC)

Mississippi

4160　MS Rubber Company
　　　715 E McDowell Rd　Jackson, MS 39204
　　　(601) 948-2575　Susan Foster GM
　　　Fax: (601) 360-1703
　　　Email: sfoster@msrubber.com
　　　Website: www.msrubber.com
Dist rubber hoses, hydraulic hoses, belting, plastic,
gaskets, safety supplies, o'rings, general hoses, hose
fittings, clamps, rubber tubing, matting, sheet packing,
rainsuit, gloves & boots. (Woman/White, estab 1963,
empl 14, sales $1,300,000, cert: CPUC)

North Carolina

4161　EMI Supply
　　　5502 Cannon Dr　Monroe, NC 28110
　　　(704) 721-3641　Susan Richardson CEO
　　　Fax: (704) 721-3644
　　　Email: srichardson@emisupply.com
　　　Website: www.emisupply.com
Dist electrical & industrial supplies: abrasives, adhesives,
chemicals, cutting tools, safety, tapes. (Woman/White,
estab 1990, empl 7, sales , cert: WBENC)

4162　GP Supply Company
　　　501 E Washington St　Greensboro, NC 27401
　　　(336) 274-7615　Antonio Wallace CEO
　　　Fax: (336) 370-4715
　　　Email: awallace@gpsupplycompany.com
　　　Website: www.gpsupplycompany.com
Dist mechanical supplies, industrial supplies, commercial
plumbing supplies, pipe, valves, fittings, fixtures. (AA,
estab 2014, empl 35, sales $14,000,000, cert: State,
NMSDC)

New Hampshire

4163　Quintana Associates, Inc.
　　　8 Puzzle Lane　Newton, NH 03858
　　　(978) 689-4411　Jorge Cruz Sales and Acct Rep
　　　Fax: (978) 689-7674
　　　Email: jorgec@qaisupply.com
　　　Website: www.quintanasupply.com
Dist industrial supplies: safety, janitorial, packaging,
material handling equipment, office & clean room
supplies. (Hisp, estab 1991, empl 20, sales $8,717,183,
cert: NMSDC)

New Jersey

4164 Automotive and Industrial Equipment LLC
43 Wilkeshire Blvd   Randolph, NJ 07869
(973) 343-6432 Vijay Srinivasan President
Fax: (855) 343-6432
Email: autoandindustrialinc@gmail.com
Website: www.ai-equip.com
Dist materials, tools, equipment & supplies to laboratories, government facilities & private facilities. (As-Pac, estab 2011, empl 1, sales $375,891, cert: State)

4165 BKC Industries, Inc.
3288 Delsea Dr Ste B Franklinville, NJ 08322
(856) 694-9400 Karen Harrison-Carter President
Fax: (856) 694-9403
Email: bkcindustrial@comcast.net
Website: www.bkcindustries.com
Dist industrial plant supplies, safety supplies, packaging materials & construction materials. (Woman/AA, estab 1998, empl 3, sales $1,200,000, cert: State, 8(a))

4166 Centryco Inc.
300 W Broad St   Burlington, NJ 08016
(609) 386-6448 Mary Gordon President
Fax: (609) 386-6739
Email: mtg@centryco.com
Website: www.centryco.com
Mfr point of operation barriers for machinery & equipment: bellows, way covers, telescoping covers, flat bellows & screens, spring guards/covers. (Woman/White, estab 1949, empl 32, sales $3,910,958, cert: WBENC)

4167 Forty Nine Corp.
P.O. Box 2325   Paterson, NJ 07509
(201) 791-0584 Michael Temkin VP
Fax:
Email: mct@49corp.com
Website: www.49corp.com
Mfr safety, warning & protective flags, tapes & tarpaulins for electric utilities & telephone companies. (Woman/White, estab 1900, empl 1, sales $500,000, cert: State, WBENC)

New York

4168 Active Fire Extinguisher Co., Inc.
5-16 47th Ave   Long Island City, NY 11101
(718) 729-0450 Mildred Munich President
Fax: (718) 729-3910
Email: mmunich@activefire.com
Website: www.activefire.com
Dist fire extinguishers, pre-engineered automatic kitchen range hood systems, cabinets, fire hoses. (Woman/White, estab 1942, empl 13, sales $2,600,000, cert: City)

4169 AMKO Trading
129-09 26th Avenue Unit D Flushing, NY 11354
(718) 505-8401 Tae S Rim Sales Mgr
Fax: (718) 505-8466
Email: trim@amkotrading.com
Website: www.amkotrading.com
Dist commercial kitchen equipment. Electric & Gas Rice cookers, Electric rice warmer, Steam pans, PC food pans, Noodle making machines, Stock pots. (Woman/As-Pac, estab 2001, empl 8, sales $1,000,000, cert: NMSDC)

4170 J.T. Systems, Inc.
8132 Oswego Rd, Rt 57   Liverpool, NY 13090
(315) 622-1980 Jit Turakhia President
Fax: (315) 622-2998
Email: info@jtsystemsinc.com
Website: www.jtsystemsinc.com
Mfr air pollution control equipment: cyclones, scrubbers & baghouses, fans, ventilation, blowers, etc. (As-Pac, estab 1980, empl 5, sales , cert: State)

4171 JHP Industrial Supply Co., Inc.
312 W Taylor St   Syracuse, NY 13202
(315) 422-0050 Robert Jenkins Sales Rep
Fax:
Email: j.robert3@verizon.net
Website:
Dist plumbing & heating supplies, industrial & construction related products. (AA, estab 1981, empl 7, sales , cert: State)

4172 Legacy Construction, LLC
85 Milton Ave   Sag Harbor, NY 11963
(917) 560-5593 Stephen Watson CFO
Fax:
Email: swatson@twcurban.com
Website: www.twcurban.com
Dist construction material & supplies. (AA, estab 2004, empl 2, sales $10,000, cert: State)

4173 Mechanical Heating Supply, Inc.
476 Timpson Pl   Bronx, NY 10455
(718) 402-9765 Frank Rivera President
Fax: (718) 585-1682
Email: frank@mechheat.com
Website: www.mechheat.com
Dist heating equipment & supplies. (Hisp, estab 1989, empl 11, sales $12,800,000, cert: City)

4174 R. Kraft, Inc.
129 Shorecliff Dr   Rochester, NY 14612
(585) 621-6946 Ralph Kraft President
Fax: (585) 621-2778
Email: clnrmsrvs@aol.com
Website: www.cleanroomservices.com
Dist cleanroom systems, components, furnishings, cleanroom cert, personnel training, consulting, design assistance, troubleshooting. (Nat Ame, estab 1977, empl 1, sales , cert: State)

4175 Strategic Procurement Group
36 harbor park Dr port washington, NY 11050
(516) 479-3778 Donna Kay President
Fax: (516) 626-5141
Email: kayd@strategicprocurement.us
Website: www.strategicprocurement.us
Dist MRO supplies. (Woman/As-Pac, estab 2002, empl 10, sales $13,000,000, cert: NMSDC, WBENC)

4176 Wats International Inc.
200 Manchester Rd Poughkepsie, NY 12603
(845) 473-2106 Josh Anselmo President
Fax: (845) 473-2153
Email: Josh.anselmo@watsinternational.com
Website: www.watsinternational.com
Dist janitorial, office & MRO supplies. (AA, estab 1980, empl 8, sales , cert: State, City, NMSDC)

Ohio

4177 All Contractors Supply LLC
12147 Girdled Rd Concord Township, OH 44077
(440) 853-8795 Kim Gilmore President
Fax: (216) 820-4362
Email: kg@allcontractorssupply.com
Website: www.allcontractorssupply.com
Dist plastic pipe, concrete, sealers, coatings, rebar, concrete cure, structural steel, expansion joint materials, drainage pipe, epoxy, grouts and waterproofing. (Woman/White, estab 2011, empl 1, sales $400,000, cert: City)

4178 Benchmark Industrial Supply, LLC
1913 Commerce Rd P.O. Box 367 Springfield, OH 45504
(937) 325-1001 Ron Tenkman Natl sales Mgr
Fax: (937) 328-6477
Email: rtenkman@benchmarkindustrial.com
Website: www.benchmarkindustrial.com
Dist safety products & industrial supplies. (Woman/White, estab 2003, empl 18, sales $5,000,000, cert: State, WBENC)

4179 Hydro Dyne Inc.
225 Wetmore Ave SE P.O. Box 318 Massillon, OH 44646
(330) 832-5076 Kevin Boone Business Dev Mgr
Fax: (330) 832-8163
Email: kevin@hydrodyneinc.com
Website: www.hydrodyneinc.com
Design, mfr & repair shell & tube heat exchangers, condensers, evaporators & feedwater heaters. (Woman/White, estab 1967, empl 30, sales , cert: WBENC)

4180 IPS Group LLC
3254 Hill Ave Toledo, OH 43607
(419) 241-5955 Michele Bighouse CEO
Fax: (419) 241-5040
Email: ipsti@ipstreatment.com
Website: www.ipsgroupllc.com
Derusting, degreasing, washing, deburring, demagnetizing, descaling, pickling, rust inhibiting, surface passivation, chemical paint stripping, bonding removal, assembly, sorting & inspecting, repackaging & shipping. (As-Ind, estab 1994, empl 30, sales $900,000, cert: State)

4181 Niche Consumer Products, LLC
2600 Civic Center Dr Cincinnati, OH 45231
(513)8074174 Benjamin Moore President
Fax: (614) 317-4076
Email: info@nicheconsumerproducts.com
Website: www.nicheconsumerproducts.com
Licenses, distributes and manufactures non-woven consumer products. (AA, estab 2007, empl 5, sales $330,000, cert: State, NMSDC)

4182 PenCo Industrial Supply, Inc.
300 Industrial Pkwy, Unit D Chagrin Falls, OH 44022
(440) 893-9506 Penny Scocos President
Fax: (440) 893-9507
Email: penny@pencosupply.com
Website: www.pencosupply.com
Dist MRO, safety & janitorial supplies: fasteners, cutting tools, abrasives, chemicals, eye & ear protection, gloves, respirators, toilet paper, paper towels, cleaning supplies & chemicals. (Woman/White, estab 2005, empl 5, sales $1,000,000, cert: WBENC)

4183 Quality Building Supplies For Industry, Inc.
17485 Saylor Ln P.O. Box 10 Grand Rapids, OH 43522
(419) 832-2202 Edward haynes CEO
Fax: (419) 832-8106
Email: qualitybldginc@aol.com
Website: www.qualitybuildingsupplies.com
Dist construction & industrial products: rebar, structural steel, piling, tools & hardware. (AA, estab 1978, empl 5, sales $2,300,000, cert: NMSDC)

4184 Superior Industrial Supply & Services Inc.
1717 Indianwood Circle Ste 200 Maumee, OH 43537
(419) 697-3700 Stan McCormick President
Fax: (419) 867-2009
Email: stan.mccormick@siss.cc
Website: www.superiorindustrialsupply.com
Dist janitorial chemicals & equipment, packaging supplies & equipment, paper supplies, mill & crib. (AA, estab 1972, empl 3, sales , cert: NMSDC)

4185   Tradex International Inc.
5300 Tradex Pkwy   Cleveland, OH 44102
(216) 651-4788   Philip A. Baseil COO
Fax: (216) 651-0690
Email: PAB@tradexgloves.com
Website: www.tradexgloves.com
Dist gloves, aprons, shoe covers, bouffant caps, toilet seat covers & wipers. (As-Ind/As-Pac, estab 1988, empl 70, sales , cert: NMSDC)

Oklahoma

4186   Omni Packaging Corporation
12322 E 55th St   Tulsa, OK 74146
(918) 461-1700   Roberta Jones President
Fax: (918) 461-8390
Email: AR@omnipackaging.com
Website: www.omnipackaging.com
Dist adhesives/sealants, hose clamps, expansion joints, gaskets, matting, urethane, protective clothing, plastic, etc. (Woman/Nat Ame, estab 1988, empl 65, sales , cert: NMSDC)

Pennsylvania

4187   Arbill Industries, Inc.
10450 Drummond Rd   Philadelphia, PA 19154
(215) 501-8246   Jessica Thomas Sales Admin
Fax: (800) 423-5367
Email: jthomas@arbill.com
Website: www.arbill.com
Mfr & dist industrial safety products. (Woman/White, estab 1957, empl 76, sales , cert: WBENC)

4188   Electrical Systems & Construction Supplies
5131-37 N 2nd St, Bldg 12   Philadelphia, PA 19120
(215) 324-3291   Bernard Hopewell CEO
Fax: (215) 324-3292
Email: bhopewell@escsinc.net
Website: www.escsinc.net
Dist electrical equipment, construction supplies, wire & cable & lighting. (AA, estab 2003, empl 3, sales $1,440,000, cert: State, City)

4189   General Fire Equipment Company, Inc.
220 Broadway Ave   Aston, PA 19014
(610) 485-8200   Kim McDonnell Exec Asst
Fax: (610) 485-2021
Email: KMcDonnell@GeneralFireEquipment.Net
Website: www.GeneralFireEquipment.Net
Dist, Service & Inspect Fire Extinguishers, Fire Equipment & Fire Surpression Systems. (Woman/White, estab 1975, empl 23, sales , cert: City)

4190   Industrial Piping Systems, Inc.
1250 Toronita St.   York, PA 17402
(717) 846-7473   Christine Wardrop President
Fax: (717) 846-0035
Email: christine.wardrop@ipspipe.com
Website: www.ipspipe.com
Dist pipes, valves, fittings, pumps, heat exchangers, tube, industrial coatings, lubricants. (Woman/White, estab 1982, empl 56, sales $17,574,304, cert: WBENC)

4191   Shah Industrial Sales Inc.
5824 Library Rd   Bethel Park, PA 15102
(412) 831-1224   Barbara Shah President
Fax: (412) 854-1940
Email: kara@shahind.com
Website: www.shahind.com
Dist fasteners, seals, o-rings, gaskets. (As-Ind, estab 1988, empl 2, sales $280,000, cert: State, NMSDC)

4192   Supreme Safety Inc.
21 Richard Road   Warminster, PA 18974
(215) 259-1400   Annette Patchell President
Fax: (215) 259-0594
Email: annette@supremesafetyinc.com
Website: www.supremesafetyinc.com
Dist industrial safety supplies & equipment. (Woman, estab 2004, empl 4, sales $1,400,000, cert: State, WBENC)

4193   Aquatech International Corporation
1 Four Coins Dr   Canonsburg, PA 15317
(724) 746-5300   Francis D'sa Reg sales Mgr
Fax: (724) 746-5359
Email: aic@aquatech.com
Website: www.aquatech.com
Mfr water & waste water treatment equip & systems. ASME tank & piping fabricators. (Woman/As-Ind, estab 1981, empl 450, sales $80,000,000, cert: NMSDC)

Puerto Rico

4194   Interport Trading Corp.
P.O. Box 51958   Toa Baja, PR 00950
(787) 788-8650   Antonio Cruz GM
Fax: (787) 788-8670
Email: acruz@interportpr.com
Website: www.interportpr.com
Dist & service fire prevention equipment: extinguisher, hose, supresion systems, fire alarms, safety equipment: gloves,coveralls,eye protection, ear protection, showers, boots, caps, etc. (Hisp, estab 1989, empl 10, sales $1,448,600, cert: NMSDC)

4195 New York Wiping & Industrial Products, Inc.
698 Calle B San Juan, PR 00920
(787) 273-6363 Dr. Mario Julia President
Fax:
Email: jsantos@nywiping.com
Website: www.nywiping.com
Dist industrial supplies. (Hisp, estab 1989, empl 5, sales ,
cert: NMSDC)

South Carolina

4196 Atlan-Tec, Inc. (Atlantic Technical Sales & Svc)
3215 Bryson Dr Florence, SC 29501
(843) 661-0415 Grace Patterson President
Fax: (843) 665-6012
Email: atlreceivables@aol.com
Website: www.atlan-tec.net
Dist industrial equipment. (Woman/White, estab 1991,
empl 6, sales $3,156,683, cert: State)

4197 Bullzeye Equipment & Supply
PO Box 484 1383 Old Hwy 52 Moncks Corner, SC
29461
(843) 499-2226 Kristie Collins Owner
Fax: (843) 499-2226
Email: kcollins@bullzeyeequipment.com
Website: www.bullzeyeequipment.com
Dist industrial products, welding supplies, janitorial
supplies, safety supplies, packaging supplies, material
handling supplies & construction supplies. (Woman/
White, estab 2012, empl 1, sales , cert: State, SDB)

4198 Carolina Industrial Products, Inc.
1872 Old Dunbar Rd West Columbia, SC 29172
(803)7940008 Dargon Gore President
Fax:
Email: dgore@cipbattery.com
Website: www.cipbattery.com
Dist & service industrial batteries, chargers & handling
equipment. (Woman/White, estab 1983, empl 45, sales ,
cert: WBENC)

4199 Charleston's Rigging and Marine Hardware Inc
P.O. Box 21255 Charleston, SC 29413
(843) 723-7145 Jessica Sage President
Fax:
Email: jsage@charlestonsrigging.com
Website: www.charlestonsrigging.com
Dist rigging & material handling equipment, industrial &
safety products, fabricates custom wire rope, chain, &
nylon slings. (Woman/White, estab 1982, empl 47, sales
$10,000,000, cert: City)

4200 Indcon Inc.
105 Ben Hamby Dr., Ste E 29615 Greenville, SC
29601
(864) 298-8300 Collin Atkins Corporate Counsel
Fax: (864) 534-1493
Email: collin@indconinc.com
Website: www.indconinc.com
Dist industrial maintenance products, lubrication quality,
general equipment maintenance, equipment installation, concrete & industrial repair, maintenance tools &
hardware. (Woman/White, estab 1998, empl 10, sales
$6,000,000, cert: WBENC)

4201 Munaco Sealing Solutions, Inc.
5 Ketron Ct Greenville, SC 29607
(864) 676-2055 Jeff Adams Business Devel
Fax: (864) 676-0177
Email: jeff@munaco-online.com
Website: www.munacosealing.com
Sealing solutions & precision components: gaskets,
custom gaskets, metal seals, piston rings, metal gaskets,
fiber gaskets, spiral-wound gaskets, rubber gaskets,
silicone gaskets, elastomer o-rings, rubber o-rings, FKM,
PTFE. (Woman/White, estab 1995, empl 13, sales
$13,050,000, cert: WBENC)

Tennessee

4202 Dixon Services, Inc.
1315 Farmville Rd Memphis, TN 38122
(901) 345-6608 Charles Dixon President
Fax: (901) 396-0022
Email: charlesrdixon@dixonservicesinc.com
Website: www.dixonservicesinc.com
Dist safety & industrial supplies. (Woman/AA, estab
2000, empl 10, sales , cert: City, NMSDC)

4203 eSpin Technologies, Inc.
7151 Discovery Dr Chattanooga, TN 37416
(423) 267-6266 Jay Doshi President
Fax: (423) 267-6265
Email: jdoshi@exceedfilters.com
Website: www.eSpintechnologies.com
Mfr & dist low energy consuming, high performance
HVAC air filters. (As-Ind, estab 1999, empl 27, sales
$2,160,000, cert: NMSDC)

4204 Government & Industrial Supply, Inc.
401 Leatherwood Creek Rd Pulaski, TN 38478
(931) 424-6067 Randall Manning President
Fax: (931) 424-9057
Email: gisupply@igiles.net
Website: www.gisupplyinc.com
Dist industrial supplies, material handling supplies,
safety supplies, security supplies, hardware items, tools,
abrasives, office furniture & office supplies. (Nat Ame,
estab 1993, empl 5, sales $2,950,000, cert: State)

4205   Porter-Walker LLC
       115 Dyer St Ste 3 Columbia, TN 38401
       (931) 560-2428 Terrence Bybee Strategic Accts
       Mgr
       Fax: (931) 380-1669
       Email: tbybee@porter-walker.com
       Website: www.porter-walker.com
Dist safety, industrial & MRO supplies, supply chain
mgmt. (AA, estab 1907, empl 41, sales $35,000,000,
cert: State, NMSDC)

4206   Sportsdrive LLC
       115 Horne Dr Vonore, TN 37885
       (423) 884-6189 Jennifer Miller
       Fax: (423) 884-6196
       Email: jmiller.sportsdrive@tds.net
       Website:
Mfr felt seals & distribution warehousing of rollled
goods to ISO standards; master scheduling- MRP,
cutting, sewing, inventory control and logistics of
product delivery; dist nonwovens & fire retardants-
squeakstop, rayon/carbon precursor, breather. (As-Pac,
estab 2010, empl 40, sales $1,200,000, cert: NMSDC,
8(a))

4207   Superior Industrial Supply Co.
       2675 Whitman Ave   Memphis, TN 38182
       (901) 327-0450 Rita Montesi CEO
       Fax: (901) 327-0470
       Email: info@superiorindsupply.com
       Website: www.superiorindsupply.com
Dist safety, industrial, janitorial, first aid supplies, fire
protection & AED's. (Woman/White, estab 1981, empl
13, sales $2,500,000, cert: NWBOC)

4208   T G Inc.
       615 Main St   Nashville, TN 37206
       (615) 620-5100 Joseph Towner VP sales
       Fax: (615) 254-4518
       Email: jtowner@t-g-inc.com
       Website: www.t-g-inc.com
Dist industrial & electrical products, construction
supplies, materials & equipment. (Woman/AA, estab
1999, empl 8, sales $2,000,000, cert: NMSDC)

Texas

4209   All-Tex Pipe & Supply, Inc.
       9743 Brockbank   Dallas, TX 75220
       (214) 350-5886 Donna Thompson Exec Asst
       Fax: (214) 350-8988
       Email: donnat@alltexsupply.com
       Website: www.alltexsupply.com
Dist pipe, valves & fittings: acid waste, carbon steel, cast
iron, copper, CPVC, PVC, drainage, stainless steel.
(Woman/White, estab 1973, empl 120, sales
$78,039,000, cert: State, WBENC)

4210   Battery Consulting
       4020 Christopher Way   Plano, TX 75024
       (214) 929-6790 MuMu Moorthi Owner
       Fax: (208) 955-4890
       Email: mumu@battery-consulting.com
       Website: www.battery-consulting.com
Dist batteries. (As-Pac, estab 2001, empl 2, sales
$181,000, cert: State)

4211   CASADA Industrial
       P.O. Box 203161   Austin, TX 78720
       (800) 828-0934 Ernest Anguiano Owner
       Fax: (512) 219-5656
       Email: ernest@casada-industrial.com
       Website: www.casada-industrial.com
Dist industrial supplies. (Hisp, estab 1993, empl 8, sales ,
cert: State)

4212   Dow-Caide Industrial, Inc.
       1534 Sunset Lane   Duncanville, TX 75137
       (972) 421-8662 Michael Downs President
       Fax: (972) 296-4115
       Email: dewaye@sbcglobal.net
       Website: www.dowcaidesupply.com
Dist industrial supplies, industrial equipment, safety
supplies, plastic wrap/sheeting, trashbags, corrugated
boxes, lights/ballasts, food products, chemicals, paper
products, tape, labels, packaging supplies & materials
etc. (AA, estab 2011, empl 2, sales $424,660, cert: State,
NMSDC)

4213   Evco Partners dba Burgoon Company
       P.O. Box 1168   Galveston, TX 77553
       (409) 766-1900 Donna Hanson President
       Fax: (409) 724-0267
       Email: office@burgooncompany.com
       Website: www.burgooncompany.com
Dist industrial supplies & equipment, laboratory &
medical supplies, heavy equipment. (Woman/White,
estab 1988, empl 17, sales $20,981,530, cert: State, City,
WBENC)

4214   Guardian Industrial Supply, LLC
       10629 Metric Blvd   Austin, TX 7878=
       (512) 973-3500 Christina Duncan Managing
       Member
       Fax: (512) 973-3588
       Email: sales@guardian-industrial.com
       Website: www.guardiancatalog.com
Dist industrial supplies: circuit breakers, motor starters,
motor control products, transformers, fuses, safety
switches, wiring devices, plug, receptacles, softstarters,
variable frequency drives, transfer switches, controls,
enclosures, contactors, etc. (Woman/White, estab 2006,
empl 10, sales $3,193,459, cert: WBENC)

4215   I AM Safety
4565 FM 466   Seguin, TX 78155
(832) 715-0375   Lynda President
Fax: (999) 999-9999
Email: lynda@iamsafetytx.com
Website: www.iamsafetytx.com
Safety Training (OSHA), Fire, First Aid/CPR/BBP/AED,
Safety Products. (Woman/White, estab 2011, empl 2,
sales , cert: State, City)

4216   Industrial Water Services
4500 Turf Rd Cordillera de los Andes # 5740-2,   El
Paso, TX 79938
(915) 849-0401   Ruben Diaz President
Fax: (915) 849-6665
Email: rdiaz@industrialwaterservice.com
Website: www.industrialwaterservice.com
Industrial water equipment parts & service. (Hisp, estab
1997, empl 17, sales $3,800,000, cert: NMSDC)

4217   MagRabbit-Alamo Iron Works, LLC
P.O. Box 2341   San Antonio, TX 78298
(210) 704-8520   Wayne Dennis diversity Coord
Fax: (210) 705-8514
Email: wdennis@aiwnet.com
Website: www.magrabbit-aiw.com
Dist industrial supplies, steel service & fabrication, hand &
power tools, equipment repair & installation, logistics,
transportation & freight forwarding. (As-Pac, estab 2004,
empl 150, sales $1,573,543, cert: NMSDC)

4218   Mavich LLC
525 Commerce St.   Southlake, TX 76092
(682) 503-4484   Vincent Manfredini Ops
Fax: (682) 503-6576
Email: Vincent.Manfredini@mavich.com
Website: www.mavich.com
Dist MRO & industrial supplies: electronic components,
connectors, passives, resistors, etc. (Woman/Hisp, estab
2010, empl 10, sales $3,000,000, cert: State)

4219   Pacific Star Corporation
4350 S Wayside Dr STE 106   Houston, TX 77087
(713) 527-0889   Daud Hadi Sales Mgr
Fax: (713) 481-8423
Email: customer@pfstar.com
Website: www.pfstar.com
Industrial supplies, laboratory supplies, medical supplies.
(As-Pac, estab 2005, empl 10, sales $4,000,000, cert: City)

4220   Romar Supply
2468 Fabens   Dallas, TX 75229
(214) 357-2020   Ron Adair VP Ops
Fax: (214) 357-1398
Email: rona@romarsupply.com
Website: www.romarsupply.com
Dist pipe, valves, fittings, steam controls, valve actuation,
stainless piping products, sanitary stainless piping.
(Woman/White, estab 1983, empl 42, sales $17,000,000,
cert: State, WBENC)

4221   Safety Supply, Inc.
12050 Crownpoint, Ste 160   San Antonio, TX
78233
(800) 873-9033   Joan Stafford President
Fax: (800) 873-9036
Email: joan@safetysupplyinc.com
Website: www.safetysupplyinc.com
Dist industrial safety apparel & equipment, fire service &
rescue equipment, environmental & health products.
(Woman/White, estab 1983, empl 11, sales $6,400,000,
cert: State, NMSDC, WBENC)

4222   Supply Innovations Co, LLC
200 Chihuahua St, Ste 100   San Antonio, TX
78207
(210) 225-3194   Nancy Flack Mgr
Fax: (210) 225-8689
Email: nancy@supplyinnovationsllc.com
Website: www.supplyinnovationsllc.com
Dist industrial supplies: tapes, safety , tools , abrasives,
packaging, material handling, hardware,
janitorial, adhesive & aircraft supplies. (Woman/White,
estab 2007, empl 4, sales $1,673,122, cert: State,
WBENC)

4223   TKC Enterprises Inc. dba Batteries Plus
2703 N Beltline Rd   Irving, TX 75062
(972) 256-2073   Stanley Tee Owner
Fax: (972) 252-3775
Email: bplusirv@gte.net
Website: www.batteriesplus.com
Dist batteries. (As-Pac, estab 1994, empl 8, sales
$100,000,000, cert: State, NMSDC)

4224   Track Trading Co./ dba Exaco USA., Exaco Trading
4209 Greystone Dr   Austin, TX 78731
(512) 345-1900   Kim Cook President
Fax: (512) 345-1969
Email: kim@exaco.com
Website: www.exaco.com
Dist metal mixing blades, mixing paint & drywall.
(Woman/White, estab 1987, empl 9, sales $4,800,000,
cert: State, WBENC)

4225   Vernas Ventures LLC
4413 Fairlake Dr P.O. Box 494865   Garland, TX
75043
(972) 303-9102   Verna Melton CEO
Fax: (972) 303-9129
Email: vmgraph@flash.net
Website: www.vernasventures.com
Dist style bags & textile bags, industrial supplies, part
bags, brooms, trash containers, tilt trucks. (Woman/AA,
estab 1988, empl 5, sales $1,949,580, cert: State)

Virginia

4226 Can See Fire Service Co Inc. t/a Fire Solutions
205 Haley Rd   Ashland, VA 23005
(804) 752-2366 Edward Caldas VP Sales
Fax: (804) 752-2899
Email: edward@firesolutionsinc.com
Website: www.firesolutionsinc.com
Install, maintain, service, inspects, relocate & repair fire protection equipment. (Woman/Hisp, estab 1987, empl 53, sales $4,901,793, cert: State, NMSDC, WBENC)

4227 Encompass Supply
8000 Towers Crescent Dr Ste 1350 Vienna, VA 22182
(804) 716-0546 Rudy Burwell President
Fax: (703) 637-1323
Email: rburwell@encompasssupply.net
Website: www.encompasssupply.net
Electrical and industrial supplies, electrical construction & industrial supplies. (AA, estab 2013, empl 3, sales $2,500,000, cert: State)

4228 Parker Battery, Inc.
208 South St   Franklin, VA 23851
(800) 569-6084 Shaun Parker Sales
Fax: (757) 562-3692
Email: shaun@parkerbattery.com
Website: www.parkerbattery.com
Dist batteries, starters & alternators for automotive, commercial & industrial applications. (Woman/White, estab 1990, empl 9, sales $2,000,000, cert: State)

Washington

4229 Birch Equipment Rental & Sales
P.O. Box 30918   Bellingham, WA 98228
(360) 734-5744 Cara Buckingham Information Director
Fax: (360) 734-1105
Email: planning@birchequipment.com
Website: www.birchequipment.com
Dist & rent equipment & machines: aerators, carpet cleaners, boom ifts, large excavators & forklifts. (Woman/White, estab 1972, empl 75, sales $15,000,000, cert: WBENC)

4230 Emerald, Inc.
P.O. Box 14227   Seattle, WA 98168
(206) 767-8909 Victor Servin President
Fax: (206) 767-8078
Email: emeraldinc@msn.com
Website: www.emeraldinc.net
Kitchen Hood Cleaning, Fire Extinguisher Sales/Service, Kitchen Hood Fire System Sales/Service, Safety Equipment Sales. (Hisp, estab 1989, empl 5, sales $300,000, cert: State, City)

4231 Excel Gloves & Safety Supplies, Inc.
6808 26th St E, Ste 102   Fife, WA 98424
(253) 896-1195 Irene Reyes CEO
Fax: (253) 896-1208
Email: glovelady@excelgloves.com
Website: www.excelgloves.com
Import & dist gloves, safety, medical, janitorial & packaging supplies, (Woman/As-Pac, estab 1993, empl 8, sales $2,000,000, cert: State, NMSDC)

4232 Rohtek Automation LLC
9223 NE 174th Pl   Bothell, WA 98011
(425) 318-2179 Oscar Rojas President
Fax:
Email: orojas@rohtek.com
Website: www.rohtekautomation.com
Dist high tech mfg, operating & monitoring solutions. (Hisp, estab 2011, empl 2, sales , cert: State)

Wisconsin

4233 E. R. Abernathy Industrial Inc.
2000 Pewaukee Rd, Ste O   waukesha, WI 53188
(262) 446-3377 Edna Abernathy President
Fax: (262) 446-3366
Email: edna@abernathyco.com
Website: www.abernathyco.com
Dist safety, construction, electrical & industrial supplies. (Woman/AA, estab 1991, empl 10, sales $1,354,000, cert: NMSDC)

4234 First American Engineered Solutions, LLC
136 Jackson St, Ste C   Oshkosh, WI 54901
(920) 231-8501 Gerald Morris President
Fax: (920) 231-8506
Email: gmorris@firstamericanllc.com
Website: www.firstamericanllc.com
Dist electronics, electrical equipment, industrial equipment & supplies, office equipment & supplies & ordnance. (Nat Ame, estab 1997, empl 12, sales $4,500,000, cert: NMSDC, 8(a))

INDUSTRIAL MACHINES

Manufacturers and distributors of ovens, vacuum cleaners, air compressors, blasting machines, food processing equipment, paint mixers, tube flaring machines, etc. (See also HARDWARE & TOOLS, HYDRAULIC & COMPRESSED AIR EQUIPMENT, INDUSTRIAL MACHINES and MATERIAL HANDLING EQUIPMENT). NAICS Code 42

Arizona

4235 STRATCO, Inc.
      14821 N 73rd St   Scottsdale, AZ 85260
      (480) 991-0450 Diane Graham CEO
      Fax: (480) 991-0314
      Email: supplier.diversity@stratcoglobal.com
      Website: www.stratcoglobal.com
Design blending & reaction equipment for grease, lubricants, bio-diesel & petrochemical industries. (Woman/White, estab 1928, empl 16, sales $5,621,643, cert: WBENC)

California

4236 Combustion Associates, Inc.
      555 Monica Circle Corona Corona, CA 92880
      (951) 272-6999 Preeti Chandan Sales/Mktg
      Fax: (951) 272-8066
      Email: pchandan@cai3.com
      Website: www.cai3.com
Food processing systems; integrated skid-mounted process systems; lube oil & gas systems; water heaters & industrial burners; modular aeroderivative power generation systems; packaged. (Woman/As-Ind, estab 1991, empl 45, sales $9,100,000, cert: NMSDC, CPUC)

4237 Lucio Family Enterprises, Inc.
      2150 Prune Ave   Fremont, CA 94539
      (510) 623-2323 Sandra Garcia
      Fax: (510) 623-2357
      Email: sgarcia@compactormc.com
      Website: www.compactormc.com
Mfr waste & recycling equipment: compactors, containers, balers (all sizes), custom fabrication requests. (Woman/Hisp, estab 2006, empl 18, sales $2,500,000, cert: NMSDC)

Illinois

4238 AM Manufacturing Company
      14151 Irving Ave   Dolton, IL 60419
      (708) 841-0959 Edward Mentz President
      Fax: (708) 841-0975
      Email: lserafin@ammfg.com
      Website: www.ammfg.com
Mfr dough processing equipment: dough dividers, dough rounders, pizza / tortilla presses, pizza crust dockers, proofers, cooling conveyors, bagel forming equipment. (Woman/White, estab 1961, empl 30, sales $7,000,000, cert: City)

4239 Apex Beverage Equipment Distribution Group, LLC.
      450 Tower Blvd, Ste 200   Carol Stream, IL 60188
      (877) 901-2739 Christie Tierney President
      Fax: (877) 902-2739
      Email: CTierney@totalapex.com
      Website: www.totalapex.com
Dist beverage equipment, replacement parts & installation products. (Woman/White, estab 2008, empl 11, sales $14,000,000, cert: WBENC)

Indiana

4240 Cici Boiler Rooms Inc.
      7811 Baumgart Rd   Evansville, IN 47711
      (812) 867-0810 Penny Duncan Admin Asst
      Fax: (812) 867-0760
      Email: penny@ciciboilers.com
      Website: www.ciciboilers.com
Boilers, HVAC, Deareators, Water Heaters, Air Conditioning, New Equipment, Parts, Service, (Woman/White, estab 1965, empl 14, sales $4,900,000, cert: State)

4241 Harriman Material Handling
      511 N Range Line Rd   Morristown, IN 46161
      (765) 763-8985 Ashley Larochelle President
      Fax: (765) 763-8986
      Email: ashlar@harrimanmaterialhandling.com
      Website: www.HarrimanMaterialHandling.com
Overhead Cranes, Hoists, Jib Cranes, Monorails, Gantry Cranes, Custom Lifting Devices, Slings/Rigging, Fall Protection Equipment, Crane Components & Parts, Dock Equipment, Storage Equipment, Drum Handling Equipment (Woman/White, estab 2004, empl 5, sales $3,528,300, cert: WBENC)

Michigan

4242 Manufacturers/Machine Builders Services Co.
13035 Wayne Rd   Livonia, MI 48150
(734) 748-3706 Glen Neal Managing Partner
Fax: (734) 261-2569
Email: mmbswork2@sbcglobal.net
Website: www.mmbscorp
Build & service automated machines: pipe, wire, debug & install machines. (Woman/Nat Ame/As-Pac, estab 2002, empl 16, sales $800,000, cert: NMSDC)

4243 Quality Design Services, Inc.
3914 Highwood Pl   Okemos, MI 48864
(614) 946-4749 Ashish Manek Business Dev Mgr
Fax: (517) 349-1179
Email: ashish.manek@qdsautomation.com
Website: www.qdsautomation.com
High production machine electric, hydraulic, pneumatic & lube systems design. (As-Ind, estab 1990, empl 22, sales $250,000, cert: NMSDC)

4244 Tillman Industries dba MEDBIO, Inc.
630 S Division   Grand Rapids, MI 49503
(616) 245-0214 Roosevelt Tillman CEO
Fax: (616) 245-0244
Email: rt@medbioinc.com
Website: www.medbioinc.com
Clean room assembly services, injection molding & medical device mfg. (AA, estab 2002, empl 1, sales , cert: State)

4245 Ultimation Industries LLC
27930 Groesbeck Hwy   Roseville, MI 48066
(586) 771-1881 Jacqueline Canny CEO
Fax: (586) 771-1882
Email: jcanny@ultimationinc.com
Website: www.ultimationinc.com
Design, mfr & install assembly line equipment & services, automation devices & conveyor systems, tire & wheel mounting & inflation devices, tire processing lines, TPMS & soaping machines. (Woman/White, estab 1989, empl 14, sales $4,855,120, cert: WBENC)

Minnesota

4246 DV Roland Enterprises, Inc.
15171 Freeland Ave N   Hugo, MN 55038
(651) 429-9012 Kenny Scamp GM
Fax: (651) 407-7069
Email: Ken@jtservicesinc.com
Website: www.jtservicesinc.com
Dist & service industrial diesel engines & diesel engine parts. Supporting diesel engines for aerial lifts, air compressors, backhoes, dozers, excavators, forklifts, generators, light towers, rollers, skid steer loaders, tractors, welders. (AA, estab 2004, empl 6, sales $1,433,333, cert: City, NMSDC)

Missouri

4247 Erb Equipment Co., Inc.
200 Erb Industrial Dr   Fenton, MO 63026
(636) 349-0200 Gregg Erb Director of Sales
Fax: (636) 349-0874
Email: greggerb@erbequipment.com
Website: www.erbequipment.com
Construction equipment, rent new & used equipment & repair parts, repair & maintenance, Backhoe, Wheel Loaders, Front loaders, excavators, dozers, crawler loaders, skid steer (bobcat), mini excavators & material handlers. (Woman/White, estab 1943, empl 230, sales $134,737,841, cert: WBENC)

4248 TSA Sales Associates, LLC
3466 Bridgeland Dr   Bridgeton, MO 63044
(314) 291-4400 Pamela Sanders Owner
Fax:
Email: psanders@tsasales.com
Website: www.tsasales.com
Air pollution control equipment, dry bulk solids, handling equipment & storage silos & bins. Design dust, fume & mist collecion systems. (Woman/White, estab 2001, empl 5, sales $374,087, cert: State)

New Jersey

4249 Ana M Fisher dba A & A Glove & Safety Co.
20 Richey Ave   West Collingswood, NJ 08107
(800) 854-0060 Ashton Goerge Sales
Fax: (856) 854-6422
Email: ashton@aaglove.com
Website: www.aasafetyindustrial.com
Safety consulting & sourcing, industrial equipment. (Woman/Hisp, estab 1990, empl 5, sales $400,000, cert: State, City)

4250 Hop Industries Corp.
1251 Valley Brook Ave   Lyndhurst, NJ 07071
(201) 438-6200 Melanie Harkin Sales Rep
Fax: (201) 438-9997
Email: mharkin@hopindustries.com
Website: www.hopindustries.com
Laminating Supplies & Equipment: laminating rolls, laminating pouches, pouch laminators, roll laminators, Binding Supplies & Equipment: binding combs, twin wire binding, plastic coil binding. (As-Pac, estab 1977, empl 70, sales $43,697,760, cert: NMSDC)

Ohio

4251 ASD - Automation Systems & Design
6222 Webster St   Dayton, OH 45414
(937) 387-0351 Sunny Kullar CEO
Fax: (937) 387-0357
Email: sunny@asddayton.com
Website: www.asddayton.com
Build, design & integrate custom machines. (As-Ind, estab 2000, empl 14, sales $1,500,000, cert: NMSDC)

4252 OCS Process Systems
24142 Detroit Rd   Westlake, OH 44145
(440) 871-6009 Beth Kloos CEO
Fax: (440) 871-0855
Email: bkloos@ocsprocess.com
Website: www.ocsprocess.com
Engineer, design & install food processing systems: liquid & dry powder processing systems, heat transfer, mixing, batching systems, metering systems, distribution systems, COP, CIP, piping, pumps, valves, welding, fabrication & installation. (Woman/White, estab 1902, empl 40, sales $7,500,000, cert: WBENC)

4253 Planet Products Corporation
4200 Malsbary Rd   Cincinnati, OH 45242
(513) 984-5544 Don McGraw President
Fax: (513) 984-5580
Email: dmcgraw@planet-products.com
Website: www.planet-products.com
Mfr food conveyors: frank loaders, fresh sausage loaders, sandwich assembly automation, string cheese loaders, robotics, tray sealers. (Woman/White, estab 1946, empl 32, sales $4,950,000, cert: State)

4254 Taner Crane & Equipment, LLC
540 E 105th St, Ste 206A   Cleveland, OH 44108
(216) 681-1990 Bobby Hale Ops Mgr
Fax: (216) 707-3717
Email: tanerequipment@sbcglobal.net
Website:
Equipment rental: cranes, lifts, forklifts & light to heavy contruction equipment. (AA, estab 2008, empl 3, sales , cert: State, City)

Pennsylvania

4255 American Kitchen Machinery and Repair Co., Inc.
204 Quarry St   Philadelphia, PA 19106
(215) 627-7760 Andrea Mahon President
Fax: (215) 627-1604
Email: service@akmco.com
Website: www.akmco.com
Parts & service to commercial kitchen equipment: cooking equipment, sanitation & dishwashing equipment, preparation equipment & mixers, refrigeration equipment & ice machines. (Woman/White, estab 1953, empl 45, sales $7,000,000, cert: WBENC)

4256 Gottscho Printing Systems, Inc.
740 Veterans Circle   Warminster, PA 18974
(267) 387-3005 Aimee Hasson President
Fax: (267) 387-3015
Email: sales@gottscho.com
Website: www.gottscho.com
Printing machines, marking machines, bar code printing, ink jet, coding & printing, blister pack printing, hot stamp, thermal printer, T1J printer, C1J printer, flexographic printer, platen printer, UV printer, digital coder, digital printer. (Woman/White, estab 2009, empl 12, sales , cert: WBENC)

Texas

4257 Epcon Industrial Systems, LP
P.O. Box 7060   The Woodlands, TX 77387
(936) 273-3300 Shan Jamaluddin COO
Fax: (936) 273-4600
Email: epcon@epconlp.com
Website: www.epconlp.com
Design, engineer & mfr air pollution control systems, oxidizers, afterburners, deoilers, washlines, spray booths, ovens & furnaces. (As-Pac, estab 1977, empl 99, sales $14,000,000, cert: State, NMSDC)

4258 PLP Enterprises, Inc.
P.O. Box 578   Blue Ridge, TX 75424
(972) 752-4837 Phillip Pulliam VP
Fax: (972) 752-5246
Email: ppulliam@aps-plp.com
Website: www.aps-plp.com
Build Plastic & Stainless Steel Chemical Delivery Systems, Valve Manifold Boxes, Chemical Process Tanks, Process Hoods, Drain Pans, Chemical Carts, Storage Cabinets. PLC Control Systems, Electrical Panels, Sump Systems. (Woman, estab 2000, empl 6, sales $1,100,000, cert: WBENC)

4259 RECS, Inc.
P.O. Box 520   Prosper, TX 75078
(972) 346-3226 Elaine Underwood President
Fax: (972) 346-2600
Email: recsmaterials@windstream.net
Website: www.recsinc.com
Heavy construction rental equipment: excavators, rock chrushers, bulldozers, motorgraders, dumptrucks, backhoes, wheel loader/w bucket & forks, dredging machines, automobile & pickup rental, truck & trailer rental, generators lightplants. (Woman/White, estab 1982, empl 25, sales $5,000,000, cert: State)

Virginia

4260 Century Sales, Inc.
P.O. Box 11743 Roanoke, VA 24022
(540) 562-0847 Herbert Chappelle Owner
Fax: (540) 562-1508
Email: keymike5120@aol.com
Website:
Commercial foodservice equipment, cooking equipment, refrigeration, blast chillers, microwaves, coffee urns, flatware, tables, chairs, salad bars, china, table linen, etc. (AA, estab 1988, empl 2, sales $175,000, cert: State)

4261 Crest Foodservice Equipment Company
605 Jack Rabbit Rd Virginia Beach, VA 23451
(757) 425-8883 Karen Ricketts Business Devel
Fax: (757) 491-7006
Email: karen@cresteq.com
Website: www.crestfoodservice.com
Dist commercial kitchen equipment & ancillary items. (Woman/White, estab 1984, empl 36, sales $11,531,745, cert: State)

4262 E2C Group, LLC
1418 Jacquelin St Richmond, VA 23220
(804) 358-3334 Denise Fields Principal
Fax: (804) 353-1171
Email: dif1@aol.com
Website: www.e2cgroup.com
Dist & install commercial foodservice equipment. (AA, estab 2004, empl 6, sales $2,200,000, cert: State)

4263 VMEK Group LLC
2719 Oak Lake Blvd Midlothian, VA 23112
(804) 349-9001 Adriana Lovvorn Ops Mgr
Fax: (804) 303-3614
Email: Adriana@VMEK.com
Website: www.vmek.com
Build & support high speed industrial machines powered by advanced vision technology & machine design. (Woman/As-Pac, estab 2012, empl 9, sales , cert: NMSDC)

Wisconsin

4264 Accuracy Machine
201 Stange St. Merrill, WI 54452
(715) 722-0825 Kevin Keiser Project Mgr
Fax:
Email: kevin.keiser@accuracymachine.com
Website: www.accuracymachine.com
Mfr machines & specialty parts: converting, printing, coating, paper, material handling, packaging, food grade machine, performance automotive, performance marine, aerospace & powertrain industries. (As-Pac, estab 1994, empl 10, sales , cert: State)

4265 Quintec Integration, Inc.
1600 Paramount Dr Waukesha, WI 53186
(262) 754-5900 Tony Storniolo President
Fax: (262) 754-5907
Email: tstorniolo@quintecconveyor.com
Website: www.quintecconveyor.com
Layout engineering, conveyor hardware, mechanical equipment, electrical controls & programming, mechanical & electrical installation, project management, field training of equipment. (Hisp, estab 1999, empl 7, sales $2,400,000, cert: State)

4266 Trester Hoist Equipment, Inc.
W136 N4863 Campbell Dr, Ste 6 Menomonee Falls, WI 53051
(262) 790-0700 Robyn Vaupel President
Fax: (262) 790-1009
Email: robyn@tresterhoist.com
Website: www.tresterhoist.com
Overhead lifting equipment & service. (Woman/White, estab 1995, empl 11, sales $5,000,000, cert: WBENC)

4267 Wisconsin Oven Distributors LLC
W355 S9075 Godfrey Ln Eagle, WI 53119
(262) 594-3941 Tina M. Binder (Strand) President
Fax: (262) 594-3939
Email: tslaboven@memmertusa.com
Website: www.memmertusa.com
Dist ovens, incubators, climate chambers, humidity chamber, vacuum ovens, water baths, oil baths, CO2 incubators, Paraffin Ovens, Climatic test chambers, sterilizers, glassware washers. (Woman/White, estab 2006, empl 4, sales $2,242,000, cert: WBENC)

INFORMATION TECHNOLOGY: Services

Includes system engineering/design/research, consulting, programming, information/data management, data entry, microfilming, help desk, mobile applications, etc. (See also INFORMATION TECHNOLOGY: Systems/Machines and ENGINEERING, SPECIAL SERVICES). NAICS Code 54

Alaska

4268 Teya Technologies, LLC
       101 E 9th Ave, Ste 9B Anchorage, AK 99501
       (907) 339-4901 Ronald Perry CEO
       Fax: (907) 562-5497
       Email: ron.perry@teyatech.com
       Website: www.teyatech.com
We are a professional service firm that specializes in construction, demolition, project management, custodial and janitorial services, administrative services, product manufacturing, housing maintenance, and conference and event planning/management. (Nat Ame, estab 2005, empl 46, sales $14,422,189, cert: NMSDC)

4269 Tuknik Government Services, LLC
       3800 Centerpoint Dr Ste 502 Anchorage, AK 99503
       (301) 802-3114 Navid Nekoui
       Fax: (407) 270-9241
       Email: nnekoui@koniag.com
       Website: www.tuknikgs.com
Outsourced computer related services, IT support, software installation & security, physical security, program management. (Nat Ame, estab 2014, empl 2, sales , cert: NMSDC)

Alabama

4270 Aetos Systems, Inc.
       1525 Perimeter Pkwy, Ste 115 Huntsville, AL 35806
       (256) 527-7821 Donna Coleman CEO
       Fax: (888) 316-9838
       Email: donna.coleman@aetossystems.com
       Website: www.aetossystems.com
IT, information management, IT systems architecture, business management & engineering services. (Woman/Nat Ame, estab 2007, empl 18, sales $6,346,796, cert: 8(a))

4271 Ariel Information Technology Corporation
       1 Chase Corporate Center Ste 400 Birmingham, AL 35244
       (205) 705-3100 Terry Pennington
       Fax: (888) 705-0335
       Email: tpennington@ariel-it.com
       Website: www.ariel-it.com
Information technology consulting & services, technology staff augmentation, business analysis, requirements management, software design, system design, software development, quality assurance testing, hardware & software procurement. (AA, estab 2009, empl 1, sales , cert: NMSDC)

4272 C E Fallin & Company, LLC
       3814 Meridian St N Huntsville, AL 35811
       (256) 489-4600 Carl Fallin CEO
       Fax: (256) 489-4700
       Email: cefallincpa@comcast.net
       Website: www.6sigmaindustries.com
Management Consulting, Fabrication, Software Development, IT Integration Subject Matter Experts. (AA, estab 1984, empl 10, sales $350,000, cert: State)

4273 Daten System Consulting
       8225 Old Pascagoula Road 36582 Theodore, AL 36582
       (866) 388-3856 Catina Short
       Fax: (866) 388-3856
       Email: cshort@datensys.com
       Website: www.datensystemconsulting.com
Information technology data centric consulting organization. (Woman/AA, estab 2013, empl 5, sales $396,000, cert: State, NMSDC, WBENC)

4274 HCI Management Services
       6767 Old Madison Pike Ste 250 Huntsville, AL 35806
       (256) 763-6671 Bruce Ricker Director
       Fax:
       Email: bricker@allnativegroup.com
       Website: www.allnativegroup.com
Information Technology, IT, Telecommunications, Network Administration, Help Desk, Database, Video Teleconferencing, Health Services, Logistics, Technical Manuals, Financial Management, Program Management, Public Affairs. (Nat Ame, estab 1994, empl 700, sales $24,000,000, cert: 8(a))

4275 Horizon Services Corporation
       4898 Valleydale Rd Ste B-3 Birmingham, AL 35242
       (205) 249-8033 Frank Davis CEO
       Fax: (775) 257-4297
       Email: frank.davis@horizonamerica.net
       Website: www.horizonamerica.net
Technical products & services. (AA, estab 2001, empl 30, sales $2,500,000, cert: City, NMSDC)

4276 M2 Connections, a JKM Consulting, Inc. division
       P.O. Box 3250 Oxford, AL 36203
       (256) 405-0613 Janine Moses President
       Fax: (866) 708-3062
       Email: jkmoses@jkmconsultinginc.com
       Website: www.m2connections.com
Telecom audit detail, network design & support, project management, data management & process engineering. (Woman/White, estab 1998, empl 5, sales , cert: State)

4277 Never Ending Technology, Inc.
       271 Raintree Rd Brownsboro, AL 35741
       (256) 874-2821 Laquita Nelson CEO
       Fax:
       Email: lnelson@net-incorporated.com
       Website: www.net-incorporated.com
IT management & technical experts in supporting network, servers, software, distance learning system, end user computer & mobile devices, A/V in conference rooms & help desk. (Woman/Nat Ame, estab 2012, empl 6, sales , cert: 8(a))

4278　Safety Research Corporation of America, LLC
133 Research Lane　Dothan, AL 36305
(334) 678-7722　Susan Crump CEO
Fax: (334) 678-7705
Email: scrump@srca.net
Website: www.srca.net
Information technology services: software design & development database applications, websites & graphic design services. (Woman/White, estab 1993, empl 20, sales $2,200,000, cert: State)

4279　The Computer Consulting Group
445 Dexter Ave, Ste 4050　Montgomery, AL 36104
(1) 213-9646　Kendra Jenkins Chief Sales & Mktg Officer
Fax: (201) 840-8492
Email: info@ccg-al.com
Website: www.ccg-al.com
A Service Disabled Veteran Owned Small Business. More than 60 years of combined IT security industry and management experience mission to ensure that we serve, secure, and protect our client's information, intelligence, and physical location to the best o (Woman/AA, estab 2013, empl 5, sales , cert: State)

Arkansas

4280　Celerit
2200 N Rodney Parham, Ste 205　Little Rock, AR 72212
(501) 312-2900　Terry Rothwell President
Fax: (501) 312-2999
Email: info@celerit.com
Website: www.celerit.com
IT consulting: full time personnel and custon application development. (Woman/White, estab 1985, empl 50, sales , cert: WBENC)

4281　Inteliblue
15300 Governors Lake Dr　Little Rock, AR 72223
(501) 251-8918　Priyanka kothakanti Mgr
Fax:
Email: priya@inteliblue.com
Website: www.inteliblue.com
IT Consulting/Staffing. (Woman, estab 2012, empl 1, sales , cert: State)

Arizona

4282　Business Partner Solutions Inc.
7362 E Rovey Ave　Scottsdale, AZ 85250
(858) 337-9020　Katherine Bluma CEO
Fax: (866) 322-5620
Email: Kat@businesspartnersolutions.com
Website: www.businesspartnersolutions.com
Asset intelligence, encryption, strong authentication & application security & access control. (Woman/White, estab 2005, empl 5, sales $2,600,000, cert: CPUC, WBENC, SDB)

4283　Centacor, Inc.
135　Chilton Dr　Chandler, AZ 85225
(480) 899-9500　Troy Bryan Mgr
Fax:
Email: info@centacor.com
Website: www.centacor.com
IT products & services. (AA, estab 2009, empl 4, sales $75,000, cert: NMSDC)

4284　Cutting Edge Technologies & Solutions
7406 E Nora St　Mesa, AZ 85207
(888) 832-2090　Wilbert Johnson President
Fax:
Email: wjohnson@cetechs.net
Website: www.cetechs.net
Software Development, Systems Engineering, IV&V, Training & Information Technology, real-time systems, embedded systems and application development to include C++, Java, Ada, UML, C, Fortran, Perl, Python, Corba, VME, Linux, Solaris. (AA, estab 2009, empl 4, sales $250,000, cert: 8(a))

4285　EDB Warehousing and Logistics, LLC
P.O. Box 11363　Chandler, AZ 85248
(800) 370-8670　Eric Bell Owner
Fax: (480) 304-3818
Email: eric.bell@edbwarehousing.com
Website: www.edbwarehousing.com
IT logistics. (AA, estab 2015, empl 2, sales $100,000, cert: NMSDC)

4286　Executive Technology Inc.
4809 E Thistle Landing Dr Ste 100　Phoenix, AZ 85044
(480) 346-7041　Linda Perkins Controller
Fax: (480) 346-7040
Email: lperkins@exectechdirect.com
Website: www.exectechdirect.com
Information technology products & services. (AA, estab 2001, empl 16, sales , cert: NMSDC)

4287　Indidge Systems
130 N Central Ave Ste 201　Phoenix, AZ 85004
(480) 829-0479　Naren Koka President
Fax: (480) 452-1375
Email: marketing@indidge.com
Website: www.itsone.net
IT consulting: enterprise application dev, database dev, web solutions, re-engineering & testing. (As-Ind, estab 1999, empl 30, sales $1,000,000, cert: NMSDC)

4288　Native Technology Solutions Inc.
7065 W Allison Rd　Chandler, AZ 85226
(480) 639-1234　Mabel Tsosie
Fax: (480) 639-1235
Email: mtsosie@gilarivertel.com
Website: www.native-tech.net
Cabling & computing services, structured cabling, phone, security systems, video conferencing, & technology solutions. (Nat Ame, estab 2007, empl 14, sales $4,000,000, cert: State)

4289 QCM Technologies, Inc.
9060 E Via Linda Ste 220 Scottsdale, AZ 85258
(602) 412-3539 Lenny Aupperlee Sales Exec
Fax: (480) 556-6023
Email: laupperlee@qcmtech.com
Website: www.qcmtech.com
IT solutions & services, hardware, software & professional services, design, implement & support enterprise-wide IT solutions. (Hisp, estab 2001, empl 20, sales $12,651,000, cert: NMSDC)

4290 TDR Consulting Inc
951 N Forest Ct   Chandler, AZ 85226
(480) 293-4959 Dean Rosales
Fax: (925) 932-1950
Email: deanrosales@tdrconsultinginc.com
Website: www.tdrconsultinginc.com
Engineering consulting, systems engineering, specification development, requirements traceability, derived requirements, schedule development, milestone tracking, performance tracking & metrics reporting. (Hisp, estab 2013, empl 1, sales , cert: NMSDC)

4291 Tec Global
9674 E Vantage Point Rd   Scottsdale, AZ 85262
(480) 575-4333 Richard Stanford President
Fax: (877) 624-7226
Email: richard.stanford@tecglobalinc.com
Website: www.tecglobalinc.com
Global Supply Chain optimization Company. (AA, estab 1996, empl 3, sales $150,000, cert: NMSDC)

4292 TIPS Consultants LLC
1412 E Michelle Dr   Phoenix, AZ 85022
(713) 307-3362 Dr. Charles Fisher CFO
Fax: (602) 283-4118
Email: Cfisher@tipsconsultants.com
Website: www.tipsconsultants.squarespace.com
Engineering consultant & training services, Enterprise Project Management (EPM) & Earned Value Management (EVM) solutions. (Woman/AA, estab 2015, empl 3, sales , cert: State)

4293 XL Technology Group, LLC
6895 E Camelback Rd Ste 118 Scottsdale, AZ 85251
(602) 324-7474 Michael Brown Director
Fax: (480) 320-3814
Email: michael@xltechnologygroup.com
Website: www.xltechnologygroup.com
IT staffing resources for IT implementations & staff augmentation (contract, contract to hire, & direct hire) . (AA/As-Pac, estab 2010, empl 20, sales $2,600,000, cert: NMSDC)

California

4294 24-Hour Medical Staffing Services, LLC
21700 E Copley Dr Ste 270 Diamond Bar, CA 91765
(909) 895-8960 Myrna Lavapie VP Sales
Fax: (909) 895-8964
Email: myrna@24-hrmed.com
Website: www.24-hrme.com
24-Hour Medical Staffing provides temporary healthcare staffing services to clients on permanent, per diem, travel, and local contract assignment. Services provided are Registered Nurses, Allied, Laboratory, and Administrative staff. 24- Hour Medical is (Woman/As-Pac, estab 2000, empl 150, sales $8,678,030, cert: NMSDC)

4295 360 IT Professionals, Inc.
3031 Tisch Way 110 Plaza West, San Jose, CA 95128   San Jose, CA 95128
(510) 254-3300 Manmeet Manace Bus Dev Exec
Fax: (510) 254-3300
Email: manmeet@360itpro.com
Website: www.360itpro.com/
Programming Languages, .net, Java, PHP, Android, IOS, Python, Ruby, Enterprise Resource Planning SAP, Oracle, Microsoft AX & GP,   Functional IT Positions, Program Managers, Project Managers, Business Analysts & Data. (As-Pac, estab 2013, empl 93, sales $8,948,501, cert: State, NMSDC, SDB)

4296 3K Technologies LLC
161 Mission Falls Ln Ste 201 Fremont, CA 94539
(408) 716-5900 Krishna Chittabathini CEO
Fax: (408) 884-2420
Email: krishna@3ktechnologies.com
Website: www.3ktechnologies.com
Information technology consulting services & staffing. (Woman/As-Ind, estab 2002, empl 65, sales $5,106,000, cert: CPUC)

4297 3S Global Business Solutions
7923 Nita Ave Canoga Park, CA 91304
(818) 453-4403 Sam Mookerjee Dir, Corp affairs
Fax: (360) 899-0364
Email: sam.mookerjee@3sgbs.com
Website: www.3sgbs.com
Information technology resources, staff augmentation, project management, IT training, IT development/ maintenance outsourcing. (As-Ind, estab 2007, empl 12, sales $895,000, cert: State, City, CPUC)

4298 4WardTech Inc.
7317 El Cajon Blvd, Ste 111, La Mesa, CA 91942
La Mesa, CA 91942
(757) 876-1735 Andrew Parker President
Fax:
Email: andrew@4ward.tech
Website: www.4ward.tech
Information Technology solutions & services, Cloud Computing, Internet of Things (IoT), Bluetooth Low Energy (BLE) & Beacons, Machine Learning, Chatbots, Blockchain and Dev, Mobility Platform. (AA, estab 2016, empl 2, sales $100,000, cert: NMSDC, SDB)

4299   AccountSight
       19925 Stevens Creek Blvd Ste 100 Cupertino, CA
       95014
       (408) 560-3900 Anita Bist VP Business Dev
       Fax:
       Email: abist@accountsight.com
       Website: www.accountsight.com
AccountSight time tracking & resource planning software,
SaaS solution, eSign Genie esignature software. (Woman/
As-Ind, estab 2013, empl 20, sales $250,000, cert: NMSDC)

4300   Adroit Resources Inc.
       39500 Stevenson Place, Ste 202 Fremont, CA
       94539
       (510) 573-6102 Prashant Sharma Sr Director
       Fax: (510) 253-0026
       Email: prashant@adroitresources.com
       Website: www.adroitresources.com
Information Technology services. (Woman/As-Pac, estab
2011, empl 75, sales $7,000,000, cert: NMSDC, CPUC)

4301   Agama Solutions Inc.
       39159 Paseo Padre Pkwy Ste 216 Fremont, CA
       94538
       (510) 377-9959 Peter Kalra VP
       Fax: (510) 796-9303
       Email: peter@agamasolutions.com
       Website: www.agamasolutions.com
IT Consulting services in terms of Project based
consulting and Staffing Services of various technical hard
to find skills in the area of Information technology. (As-Pac,
estab 2006, empl 200, sales $3,000,000, cert: State)

4302   Agile Global Solutions, Inc.
       13405 Folsom Blvd, Ste 515 Folsom, CA 95630
       (916) 353-1780 Raja Krishnan President
       Fax: (916) 848-3659
       Email: raja@agileglobal.com
       Website: www.agileglobal.com
IT services (staffing) & turnkey solutions. (Woman/As-Ind,
estab 2003, empl 62, sales $8,300,000, cert: State,
NMSDC, CPUC)

4303   AgileTalent, Inc.
       1900 S Norfolk Ave. San Mateo, CA 94403
       (650) 931-2572 Jay Singh
       Fax: (866) 929-6049
       Email: Jay.Singh@AgileTalentInc.com
       Website: www.agiletalentinc.com
IT contract staffing & recruiting. (As-Ind, estab 2011, empl
48, sales $4,600,000, cert: NMSDC, CPUC)

4304   Agilis Group Inc.
       7968 Arjons Dr Ste 105 San Diego, CA 92126
       (888) 832-4858 Joyce Tang President
       Fax: (619) 550-4677
       Email: jtang@agilisit.com
       Website: www.agilisit.com
Managed IT Services: Consultation, Design, Development,
Deployment, Staffing, Training, Remote Monitoring and
Software Licensing, IT hardware & software products.
(Woman/As-Pac, estab 2006, empl 20, sales $500,000,
cert: 8(a))

4305   AgreeYa Solutions, Inc.
       605 Coolidge Dr Folsom, CA 95630
       (916) 294-0075 Ajay Kaul Managing Partner
       Fax: (866) 886-1555
       Email: sales_americas@agreeya.com
       Website: www.agreeya.com
IT consulting services, staff or project based. (Woman/
As-Pac, estab 1999, empl 1500, sales $107,233,000, cert:
NMSDC, CPUC)

4306   Ahtna Contractors, LLC
       3680 Industrial Blvd Ste 600H West Sacramento,
       CA 95691
       (916) 329-1591 Jessica Vela Admin Asst
       Fax: (916) 329-1592
       Email: jvela@ahtna.net
       Website: www.ahtnacontractors.com
IT Support (Nat Ame, estab 2005, empl 1, sales
$376,178, cert: 8(a))

4307   AKRAYA, Inc.
       2901 Tasman Dr Ste 106 Santa Clara, CA 95054
       (408) 907-6400 Sonu Ratra President
       Fax: (408) 904-6610
       Email: sonu.ratra@akraya.com
       Website: www.akraya.com
IT consulting - Java, Microsoft, databases, Peoplesoft,
Oracle, Siebel, SAP, data warehousing. (Woman/As-Ind,
estab 2001, empl 390, sales $33,430,000, cert: NMSDC,
CPUC, WBENC)

4308   Alicon Group, Inc.
       5405 Alton Pkwy, Ste 5A514 Irvine, CA 92604
       (949) 294-9634 Chris Metzger Ops Coord
       Fax: (888) 522-6413
       Email: chris@alicongroup.com
       Website: www.alicongroup.com
Oracle applications technology consulting. (Woman/Nat
Ame, estab 2001, empl 4, sales $3,980,000, cert:
NMSDC, NWBOC)

4309   Allfon LLC
       2746 Glendon Ave Los Angeles, CA 90064
       (310) 470-7868 Roya Hosseinion President
       Fax: (310) 470-7869
       Email: roya@allfon.com
       Website: www.allfon.com
Systems integration, offshore development, outsourcing
services. (Woman/White, estab 2000, empl 50, sales
$5,390,928, cert: WBENC)

4310   Alpha Omega Solutions, Inc.
       3070 Saturn St, Ste 200 Brea, CA 92821
       (714) 996-8760 Benny Wong President
       Fax:
       Email: bennywong@aosolutions.com
       Website: www.aosolutions.com
Computer software, computer consulting, financial
consulting, automotive business consulting. (As-Pac,
estab 1993, empl 8, sales $1,000,000, cert: NMSDC)

4311	AMBCO Electronics Corporation
	15052 Redhill Ave, Ste D Tustin, CA 92780
	(714) 259-7930 Ada Xiong President
	Fax: (714) 259-1688
	Email: ada@ambco.com
	Website: www.ambco.com
Audiometer Manufacturer. 5 year warranty on all Ambco Audiometers from date of purchased. We repair, service, and calibrate all makes of audiometers. (Woman/As-Pac, estab 1941, empl 4, sales $914,803, cert: State)

4312	Amick Brown LLC
	2500 Old Crow Canyon Road Ste 425 San Ramon, CA 94583
	(925) 820-2000 Karen Gildea Principal
	Fax: (925) 820-2015
	Email: admin@amickbrown.com
	Website: www.amickbrown.com
SAP BI Implementation, SAP HANA, SAP BI, Strategy and Roadmaps, SAP BI Production Support, SAP BI Installations and Upgrade, Reporting, Analytics & Dashboards, SAP BI Training Workshops, SAP BI Security. (Woman/As-Ind, estab 2010, empl 31, sales $7,000,000, cert: State, CPUC, WBENC, SDB)

4313	Apex Computer Systems, Inc.
	13875 Cerritos Corporate Dr Unit A Cerritos, CA 90703
	(562) 926-6820 Ira Klein Director, Partner Alliance
	Fax: (562) 926-0825
	Email: sales@acsi2000.com
	Website: www.acsi2000.com
Computer hardware maintenance & support, managed services, project management, accounting/ERP, EDI, data warehousing, (As-Pac, estab 1984, empl 52, sales $17,010,000, cert: State, NMSDC, CPUC, SDB)

4314	Applied Computer Solutions
	15461 Springdale St. Huntington Beach, CA 92649
	(714) 861-2200 Dennis Di Pietro Mgr. Sales Ops
	Fax: (714) 847-8320
	Email: dennis.dipietro@acsacs.com
	Website: www.acsacs.com
System integration, strategic solutions, enterprise infrastructure, Sun Microsystems, Cisco Systems, HDS, Veritas, Oracle, Network Appliance, Checkpoint, Symantec, StorageTek. (Woman/White, estab 1989, empl 135, sales $265,000,000, cert: CPUC, WBENC)

4315	Ashunya Inc
	642 n. eckhoff St orange, CA 92868
	(714) 385-1900 Melanie Merchant CEO
	Fax: (714) 385-1999
	Email: melaniem@ashunya.com
	Website: www.ashunya.com
Information technology: hardware & software, LAN/WAN wiring, project mgmt, post implementation svcs. (Woman/As-Ind, estab 1993, empl 8, sales $3,000,000, cert: WBENC)

4316	Automae
	7111 Garden Grove Blvd Garden Grove, CA 92841
	(714) 816-3000 Mbuyi Khuzadi CEO
	Fax: (877) 658-5777
	Email: mbuyi@mail.automae.com
	Website: www.automae.com
Technical services: hardware design, systems engineering, software engineering, system safety & health management. (AA, estab 1997, empl 3, sales $80,000, cert: State)

4317	Automatic Door Systems, Inc.
	982 Terminal Way San Carlos, CA 94070
	(650) 592-8282 Thomas C Fenwick VP
	Fax: (650) 595-4825
	Email: accounting@autodoorinc.com
	Website: www.autodoorinc.com
(Woman/White, estab 1971, empl 31, sales , cert: State)

4318	Aviana Global Technologies, Inc.
	915 W Imperial Highway Ste 100 Brea, CA 92821
	(714) 256-9756 Donna Sanchez staffing consultant
	Fax: (714) 674-0279
	Email: donnas@avianaglobal.com
	Website: www.avianaglobal.com
Enterprise planning, reporting, OLAP analysis, dashboards, scorecards, analytics & statutory regulations. (As-Pac, estab 1994, empl 30, sales $53,822,829, cert: CPUC)

4319	Axiom Global Technologies, Inc.
	220 North Wiget Lane Walnut Creek, CA 94598
	(925) 393-5800 Adam Ireland
	Fax: (925) 932-1950
	Email: adam.ireland@axiomglobal.com
	Website: www.axiomglobal.com
Application development, staff augmentation, document management. (Woman/As-Ind, estab 2001, empl 70, sales $6,000,000, cert: NMSDC)

4320	Axxera Inc
	5251 California Ave, Ste 140 Irvine, CA 92617
	(949) 534-3000 Laura Pichardo Senior Mgr
	Fax: (949) 682-2299
	Email: rfp@axxerainc.com
	Website: www.axxerainc.com
Cyber Security, SIEM, anti-trojan, anti-malware, Security Software. (As-Ind, estab 2007, empl 10, sales $3,000,000, cert: State)

4321	Bay Systems Consulting, Inc.
	610 16 St, Ste 409 Oakland, CA 94612
	(800) 510-7754 Jasmine Ali CEO
	Fax: (877) 275-0863
	Email: jasmine@baycareers.com
	Website: www.baysyst.com
Custom software dev, sytem integration, IT / datacenter operations, IT security, application support, system admin, domain svcs, web hosting, data entry & transcription, etc. (Woman/As-Ind, estab 1997, empl 7, sales $240,000, cert: State)

4322　BayInfotech LLC
11501, Dublin Blvd Ste #200　Dublin, CA 94568
(408) 480-8501　Maulik Shyani Sr Acct Mgr
Fax:
Email: maulik@bay-infotech.com
Website: www.bay-infotech.com
Contingent Staffing, Beeline, Infrastructure Management: End-to-End Management, Application, Network, Security, Data Center, Service Desk. (Woman/As-Pac, estab 2011, empl 15, sales $1,101,000, cert: NMSDC, CPUC, WBENC)

4323　Beta Soft Systems Inc.
42808 Christy St Ste 101　Fremont, CA 94538
(510) 744-1700　Bob Hemnani Senior Sales Mgr
Fax: (510) 744-1700
Email: bob@betasoftsystems.com
Website: www.betasoftsystems.com
IT Services & solutions, recruitment, business development, software development & service delivery. (As-Pac, estab 2005, empl 300, sales , cert: State)

4324　BeyondCurious, Inc.
3767 Overland Ave, Ste 115　Los Angeles, CA 90034
(310) 210-1907　Nikki Barua CEO
Fax:
Email: nbarua@beyondcurious.com
Website: www.beyondcurious.com
Design & technology, mobile interfaces. (Woman/As-Ind, estab 2011, empl 9, sales $2,289,210, cert: NMSDC)

4325　Business Talent Group LLC
15332 Antioch St, Ste 20　Pacific Palisades, CA 90272
(1607) 377-1916　Yvonne Spence Corp Paralegal
Fax:
Email: yvonne.spence@businesstalentgroup.com
Website: www.businesstalentgroup.com
(Woman/White, estab 2010, empl 1, sales , cert: WBENC)

4326　California Electronic Asset Recovery (CEAR)
3678 LeMay St　Mather, CA 95655
(916) 388-1777　Stacey Henrikson Corporate Acct Mgr
Fax: (916) 388-1177
Email: shenrikson@cearinc.com
Website: www.cearinc.com
Electronic asset recovery & recycling, Total Solution IT Asset Management & Disposition, E-Waste/E-Asset, ITAD, Data Sanitization, Recovery, Destruction/Shred Remarketing, Test, Repair, Reporting. (As-Pac, estab 2000, empl 65, sales $11,000,000, cert: CPUC)

4327　Celer Systems, Inc.
1024 Iron Point Rd, Ste 100　Folsom, CA 95630
(916) 220-2093　Sree Gaddam VP
Fax: (866) 525-5201
Email: sree.gaddam@celersystems.com
Website: www.celersystems.com
IT consulting services, project management, end to end, application development, testing services, database management, data warehouse, staff augmentation. (Woman/As-Pac, estab 2007, empl 25, sales $3,000,000, cert: NMSDC)

4328　Central Computer Systems Inc.
3777 Stevens Creek Blvd　Santa Clara, CA 95051
(408) 248-5888　Heidi Co CEO
Fax: (408) 246-6239
Email: heidi@centralcomputer.com
Website: www.CentralComputers.com
Custom-build computer systems, repair services, IT services, networking, notebook repair, corporate sales, local government sales, education sales & retail consumer sales. (Woman/As-Pac, estab 1986, empl 80, sales $25,000,000, cert: NMSDC, WBENC)

4329　Cerna Solutions, LLC
3304 Febo Ct　Carlsbad, CA 92009
(442) 222-0303　Michelle Yu CEO
Fax: (714) 990-4073
Email: michelle@cernasolutions.com
Website: www.cernasolutions.com
IT consulting services. (Woman/As-Pac, estab 2012, empl 6, sales , cert: NMSDC)

4330　Certified Independent Adjusters, Inc.
25000 Ave Stanford Ste 224　Valencia, CA 91390
(800) 501-6032　Roosevelt Jackson Owner
Fax: (866) 236-9221
Email: rosey@gociai.com
Website: www.gociai.com
Certified Independent Adjusters, Inc. is a nationwide independent adjusting firm. Our adjusters have over 50 years of experience in Insurance industry.

ï¿½Daily Claims
ï¿½Auto Claims
ï¿½Catastrophes
ï¿½Commercial Claims
ï¿½Li (AA, estab 2010, empl 350, sales $2,300,000, cert: NMSDC)

4331　Citrus Studios, Inc
1512 16th St Ste 3　Santa Monica, CA 90404
(310) 395-9080　Kalika Yap CEO
Fax: (310) 395-9121
Email: design@citrusstudios.com
Website: www.citrusstudios.com
Web design & development. (Woman/As-Pac, estab 1999, empl 6, sales $1,300,000, cert: NWBOC)

4332　Connexus Hub
14252 Culver Dr, Ste #257　Irvine, CA 92604
(949) 415-4364　Daniel Jung Managing Partner
Fax:
Email: dan@connexushub.com
Website: www.connexushub.com
IT solutions products & services that encompass data storage, mobile, cloud technologies, security & networking solutions, IT hardware & software solutions. (Woman/As-Pac, estab 2014, empl 20, sales $1,700,000, cert: CPUC, 8(a), SDB)

4333 CPAC Inc.
4749 E. Wesley Dr   Anaheim, CA 92807
(800) 778-2722 Kara Mack Natl Acct Mgr
Fax: (714) 692-6680
Email: kmack@cpacinc.com
Website: www.cpacinc.com
Technical support, IT solutions. (Woman/White, estab 1993, empl 30, sales $20,000,000, cert: CPUC)

4334 Cyber Professionals Inc. DBA Encore Software Servi
2025 Gateway Pl, Ste 385   San Jose, CA 95110
(408) 573-7337 Radha Krishnan Managing Partner
Fax: (408) 573-7010
Email: rkrishnan@encoress.com
Website: www.encoress.com
Mobility, social commerce, Cloud & analytics IT services. (As-Ind, estab 1998, empl 500, sales $10,679,387, cert: NMSDC)

4335 Danta Technologies
561 Rush Dr   San Marcos, CA 92078
(619) 862-3415 Vishal Bodiwala President
Fax:
Email: sd@dantatechnologies.net
Website: www.dantatechnologies.net
IT applications, Infrastructure, IBM WebSphere, Oracle, Sales Force, IOS developer, Network engineer, Big Data, Hadoop, Java, Angular JS, Node JS, etc. (As-Pac, estab 2013, empl 25, sales $864,000, cert: NMSDC)

4336 Delta Computer Consulting, Inc.
25550 Hawthorne Blvd Ste 106-108 Torrance, CA 90505
(310) 541-9440 Claudia Marroquin Acct Exec
Fax: (310) 541-9330
Email: C.Marroquin@deltacci.com
Website: www.deltacci.com
Human Capital Recruiting & Deployment, IT Staff Recruiting & Augmentation. (Woman/White, estab 1987, empl 165, sales $28,000,000, cert: NWBOC)

4337 DFI Technologies, LLC
1065 National Dr Ste 1 Sacramento, CA 95834
(916) 568-1234 Vieng Phouthachack Tech Sales Eng
Fax: (916) 568-1233
Email: vieng@dfitech.com
Website: www.dfitech.com
High performance computing solutions: Digital Signage, Interactive Kiosk, Gaming, Industrial Automation, Medical Device/Healthcare, Transportation. (As-Pac, estab 1985, empl 70, sales , cert: State)

4338 Digital Mountain
4633 Old Ironsides Dr Ste 401 Santa Clara, CA 95054
(866) 344-3627 Julie Lewis CEO
Fax: (408) 845-9455
Email: supplierdiversity@digitalmountain.com
Website: www.digitalmountain.com
Web-based filtering & review (FileQuest), electronic evidence collection, electronic discovery (including tape restoration), computer forensics, data breach management & expert witness services. (Woman/White, estab 2003, empl 5, sales $2,006,316, cert: State, CPUC, WBENC)

4339 Digital World Alliance, Corp.
2030 Main St, Ste 1300   Irvine, CA 92614
(949) 260-9106 Ken Riley Sr systems & Business Mgr
Fax: (949) 260-9107
Email: kriley@digitalworldalliance.com
Website: www.digitalworldalliance.com
Custom system design, programming, database architectures, security, encryption, VPNs & systems integration. (Woman/As-Pac/Hisp, estab 2003, empl 10, sales $2,000,000, cert: State)

4340 ECommerce Holdings, Inc.
201 Los Gatos Saratoga Rd, Ste 230   Los Gatos, CA 95030
(866) 465-3294 PURNIMA NANDKISHORE President
Fax: (866) 465-3294
Email: PURNIMA@BABYCHANGINGSTATIONS.COM
Website: www.babychangingstations.com
Largest stocking Minority owned distributor of Koala baby changing stations and Bathroom Accessories: Fans, Mirrors, Medicine Cabinets, Soap Dishes, Towel Bars and Rings, Plumbing Fixtures and Parts: Water-free Urinals (Woman/As-Ind, estab 2009, empl 2, sales $840,866, cert: NMSDC, CPUC)

4341 eJangar, Inc.
13700 Altin Pkwy, Ste 154   Irvine, CA 92618
(800) 259-9578 Ayesh Natekal President
Fax:
Email: ayesha@ejangar.com
Website: www.ejangar.com
IT services: staffing, project mgmt, Cloud architect, SFDC Consultants, Sharrepoint Developers, Salesforce developers, .Net, Java, Offshore Development from India, Onsite Services. (Woman/As-Ind, estab 2009, empl 25, sales $250,000, cert: CPUC)

4342 En Pointe Technologies Sales, Inc.
18701 S Figueroa St   Gardena, CA 90248
(310) 337-5200 Michael Rapp VP sales/Mktg
Fax: (310) 725-5240
Email: helpdesk@enpointe.com
Website: www.enpointe.com
IT products & professional services. (As-Ind, estab 1993, empl 1200, sales $347,000,000, cert: NMSDC, WBENC)

4343 eTouch Systems
6627 Dumbarton Circle   Freemont, CA 94555
(510) 795-4800 Amit Shah VP
Fax:
Email: ashah@etouch.net
Website: www.etouch.net
Information technology services - QA, Automation, Manual, Functional, Performance, Specialized testing, Mobile testing, etc. (As-Ind, estab 1997, empl 700, sales $70,000,000, cert: NMSDC)

4344   EUS IT Solutions, LLC
19327 Broadacres Ave   Carson, CA 90746
(562) 731-2244   Donald Hale CEO
Fax: (310) 868-2913
Email: donhale@eusitsolutions.com
Website: www.eusitsolutions.com
IT consulting, IT Support, pc/laptop/workstation support, Hardware/Software support, smartphone support, tablet support, network support, printer support, cloud support, do projects. (AA, estab 2012, empl 5, sales $50,000, cert: NMSDC)

4345   Executive Office Services
P.O. Box 6621   Oakland, CA 94603
(510) 830-9721   Detria Mixon HR consultant
Fax: (614) 224-4857
Email: dmixon@exeservice.biz
Website:
The company provides full service executive human resources business consulting services, Sales & Business Development
Finance /Accounting Healthcare / Human & Social Services Engineering & IT Technology (Woman/AA, estab 2008, empl 1, sales $36,000, cert: NMSDC, CPUC)

4346   EYP, Inc.
235 E Broadway Ste 800-B   Long Beach, CA 90802
(310) 684-3022   Troy DuCre CEO
Fax: (888) 853-6445
Email: tducre@eypinc.com
Website: www.eypinc.com
Workforce Management - IT and engineering contract services, Software as a Service (SaaS), Talent Management and Learning Management,
Management Consulting - Business Process Improvement. (AA, estab 2011, empl 3, sales $146,000, cert: NMSDC)

4347   Flight Light Inc.
2708 47th Ave   Sacramento, CA 95822
(916) 394-2800   isabel martin President
Fax: (916) 394-2809
Email: isabel.martin@flightlight.com
Website: www.flightlight.com
We are manufacturer and distributor of Airfield, Heliport and Obstruction lighting equipment as well as spare parts for all the equipment (Nat Ame, estab 1993, empl 18, sales $5,825,000, cert: State)

4348   FST Services, Inc.
16876 Live Oak St   Hesperia, CA 92345
(760) 948-6546   Scott Van Dagens Acct Mgr & Analyst
Fax: (760) 537-5570
Email: scottv@fsthub.com
Website: www.fuentesandsons.com
FST Services is a Flatbed logistics operation based around the western 11 U.S. We specialize in Partial and FTL shipments in the 400-1200 mile range. (Hisp, estab 2004, empl 60, sales , cert: NMSDC)

4349   Future State
2101 Webster St, Ste 520   Oakland, CA 94612
(877) 614-0222   Shari McAneney Office Mgr
Fax:
Email: certification@futurestate.com
Website: www.futurestate.com
Training svcs, technical writing & information technology consulting svcs. (Woman/White, estab 1986, empl 100, sales $16,000,000, cert: NWBOC)

4350   Gemini Associates Inc.
33 Musick   Irvine, CA 92618
(949) 830-8858   Robert Manciet President
Fax: (949) 830-0858
Email: sales@federalsales.com
Website: www.federalsales.com
Networking & data communications, air blown fiber optics, CAT5 wireless networks, ruggedized CPU, monitor & keyboard. (Hisp, estab 1975, empl 35, sales , cert: State)

4351   Global IT Services
180 Promenade Circle, Ste 300   Sacramento, CA 95834
(916) 414-0311   Shavinder (Shawn) Phagura President
Fax:
Email: sphagura@globalitsvcs.com
Website: www.globalitsvcs.com
IT Staffing Services, Cloud & IT Consulting, and Skilled Staffing Solutions. (As-Ind, estab 2014, empl 15, sales $910,000, cert: State, NMSDC, SDB)

4352   Global Software Resources, Inc.
4447 Stoneridge Dr   Pleasanton, CA 94588
(925) 249-2200   Keith Granucci Dir
Fax: (925) 249-2203
Email: keith@gsr-inc.com
Website: www.gsr-inc.com
Engineering services, plant floor operations. (As-Pac, estab 2003, empl 45, sales $4,000,000, cert: CPUC)

4353   GoAhead Solutions LLC.
400 Oyster Point Blvd Ste 407   South San Francisco, CA 94080
(650) 873-7255   Jaime Mendoza CEO
Fax: (650) 873-7255
Email: jaime@goaheadsolutions.com
Website: www.goaheadsolutions.com
IT Staff Augmentation, Consulting Services, Oracle Software Resell & Oracle Audit Representation. (Hisp, estab 2001, empl 46, sales $12,469,516, cert: NMSDC)

4354   Grove Technical Resources
9035 Rosewood Ave   West Hollywood, CA 90048
(786) 390-7119   Neal Polister President
Fax: (866) 285-9230
Email: ncpolister@grovetr.com
Website: www.grovetechnicalresources.com
Technical staffing & consulting services. (Woman/White, estab 2005, empl 2, sales , cert: CPUC, WBENC)

4355   HB Computers, Inc.
       17131 Beach Blvd, Ste B   Huntington Beach, CA
       92647
       (714) 916-9294 Madiha Rajput CEO
       Fax: (949) 450-1454
       Email: Amir@hbcomputerz.com
       Website: www.hbcomputerz.com
Test & manage networks cables. (Woman/As-Ind, estab
2005, empl 10, sales $268,089, cert: State)

4356   Heritage Global Solutions, Inc.
       230 N Maryland Ave Ste 202 Glendale CA, CA 91206
       (949) 501-1038 Jeff Estep President
       Fax: (818) 240-2611
       Email: jeff.estep@heritageglobal.com
       Website: www.heritageglobal.com
Information technology solutions, staff augmentation. (Nat
Ame, estab 2003, empl 19, sales $2,000,000, cert: State)

4357   Horologiii, Inc.
       270 Corte Colina   Novato, CA 94949
       (510) 764-8500 Rod Nash President
       Fax:
       Email: rod@horologiii.com
       Website: www.horologiii.com
Energy Consulting Services & Information Technology. (AA,
estab 2002, empl 1, sales $60,000, cert: CPUC)

4358   IGIS Technologies Inc.
       10393 San Diego Mission Rd Ste 212 San Diego, CA
       92108
       (619) 640-2330 Andres Abeyta CEO
       Fax: (619) 640-2334
       Email: abeyta@igist.com
       Website: www.igist.com
GIS consulting, training & application development for the
geospatial community. (Hisp, estab 1997, empl 11, sales
$1,000,000, cert: CPUC)

4359   IMPEX Technologies, Inc.
       880 Apollo St Ste 315 El Segundo, CA 90245
       (310) 320-0280 Rajiv Shah President
       Fax: (310) 320-0290
       Email: rshah@impextechnologies.com
       Website: www.impextechnologies.com
Systems integration: computer hardware, software,
consulting & project management, enterprise storage
systems & mgmt, enterprise backup, regulatory compliance, business continuance & disaster recovery, security
solutions & networking. (As-Ind, estab 1992, empl 10,
sales $3,000,000, cert: NMSDC)

4360   IMS
       7755 Center Ave Ste 1100 Huntington Beach, CA
       92647
       (714) 840-3775 Kristi Newman Dir Client Services
       Fax:
       Email: knewman@imssvs.com
       Website: www.imssvs.com
IT Contract, Consulting, Contract-to-Hire & Full Time
placement services. (Woman/White, estab 1973, empl 35,
sales $7,600,293, cert: State)

4361   Information Design Consultants, Inc.
       222 W 6th St, Ste 400   San Pedro, CA 90731
       (310) 707-2532 Debra Hunter President
       Fax: (310) 707-2501
       Email: Debrahunter@idcinc.net
       Website: www.idcinc.net
Project Management; Systems Integration (Woman/AA,
estab 2002, empl 1, sales , cert: CPUC)

4362   Information Management Resources, Inc.
       85 Argonut, Ste 200   Aliso Viejo, CA 92656
       (949) 215-8889 Martha Daniel CEO
       Fax: (949) 215-8890
       Email: jmiller@imri.com
       Website: www.imri.com
Business process mgmt, application integration, systems
integration, data mgmt, operations & network support,
outsourcing, training, programming, etc. (Woman/AA,
estab 1992, empl 60, sales , cert: State)

4363   Infosoft Inc.
       7891 Westwood Dr, Ste 113   Gilroy, CA 95020
       (1408) 659-4326 Raj Chopra VP
       Fax:
       Email: rchopra@infosoft-inc.com
       Website: www.infosoft-inc.com
Information technology staffing & consulting. (As-Ind,
estab 2000, empl 130, sales $16,330,000, cert: NMSDC)

4364   Infoyogi LLC
       2320 #A Walsh Ave   Santa Clara, CA 95051
       (408) 850-1700 Sriram Sundaravaradan Mktg Mgr
       Fax: (408) 516-8945
       Email: info@infoyogi.com
       Website: www.infoyogi.com
Information technology, custom computer programming
services, systems design services. (As-Ind, estab 1995,
empl 15, sales , cert: CPUC)

4365   Integrated Spatial Solutions, Inc.
       13879 Penn St   Whittier, CA 90602
       (562) 693-2253 Julie Henry COO
       Fax:
       Email: jhenry@issi-gis.com
       Website: www.issi-gis.com
Application devel, internet map services, systems
integration, strategic planning, needs assessment, data
conversion, database design, GIS mapping. (Woman/
White, estab 1999, empl 7, sales $841,279, cert: CPUC)

4366   Intelliswift Software, Inc.
       39600 Balentine Dr   Newark, CA 94560
       (510) 370-2619 Mahesh Patil VP
       Fax:
       Email: mahesh.patil@intelliswift.com
       Website: www.intelliswift.com
Systems integration & software services. (As-Pac, estab
2001, empl 1100, sales $59,695,724, cert: NMSDC,
CPUC)

4367   International Word Processing Services, Inc.
P.O. Box 5053   Downey, CA 90241
(562) 900-8359 Mary Jones CEO
Fax: (866) 869-5114
Email: mary.jones@intlword.com
Website: www.intlword.com
Technical word processing, transcription & employment placement. (Woman/AA, estab 1994, empl 2, sales $45,000, cert: State, City, CPUC)

4368   Intrinsyx Technologies
350 N Akron Rd, Bldg.19-102   Moffett Field, CA 94035
(510) 266-2721 Nabil Afifi Business Coord
Fax: (650) 210-9222
Email: nabil@intrinsyx.com
Website: www.intrinsyx.com
Information technology solutions. (Woman/As-Ind, estab 2000, empl 50, sales $7,137,776, cert: State, NMSDC)

4369   IP International, Inc.
1510 Fashion Island Blvd, Ste 104   San Mateo, CA 94404
(650) 403-7840 Margaret Schaninger
Fax: (650) 378-2875
Email: mas@infoplusintl.com
Website: www.infoplusintl.com
IT consulting services: project mgmt & PMO, ERP, help desk & contact center, cost mgmt savings, bill audit & mgmt, ordering & provisioning, business case development, RFP & RFI creation, vendor mgmt & selection. (Woman/White, estab 1986, empl 50, sales $15,000,000, cert: CPUC, WBENC)

4370   IsComp Systems Inc.
5777 W Century Blvd, Ste 560   Los Angeles, CA 90045
(310) 641-3260 Ted Davis President
Fax: (310) 641-4417
Email: iscomp@spicenet.net
Website: www.iscompsystems.com
Unix system integration, systems engineering, software develop, database mgmt. (AA, estab 1986, empl 32, sales , cert: State)

4371   iTalent Corporation
27 Devine St Ste 20 San Jose, CA 95110
(408) 496-6200 Margaret Sanchez Director
Fax: (866) 285-1109
Email: margaret@italentcorp.com
Website: www.italentcorp.com
Global technology consulting services, Software Development Solutions, Innovative & Flexible Consulting Project Resource Solutions, Specialized Practices, Managed Services, Social Knowledge Management, Change Management. (Woman/Hisp, estab 2005, empl 150, sales $20,000,000, cert: NMSDC)

4372   JAUST Consulting Partners Inc.
3150 Almaden Exprwy Sutie 215 San Jose, CA 95118
(408) 805-0901 Gail D'Silva Founder
Fax: (408) 351-4348
Email: gail@jaustpartners.com
Website: www.jaustpartners.com
IT solutions, ERP, CRM, SCM, Analytics & Web services, development & application integration. (As-Ind/Hisp, estab 2005, empl 8, sales , cert: NMSDC)

4373   JBA international LLC
1192 N Lake Ave   Pasadena, CA 91104
(626) 844-1400 Jacqueline Buickians CEO
Fax: (626) 795-9401
Email: vendors@jba.com
Website: www.jba.com
IT consulting & staffing services. (Woman/White, estab 1979, empl 120, sales $15,000,000, cert: CPUC, WBENC)

4374   JE Components Inc.
8709 Aviation Blvd   Inglewood, CA 90301
(310) 645-6021 Joni Paulo President
Fax: (310) 645-6041
Email: joni@jecom.com
Website: www.jecom.com
Resell PC & network hardware. (Woman/AA/As-Ind, estab 1995, empl 7, sales , cert: NMSDC, NWBOC)

4375   Kaygen, Inc.
100 Spectrum Center Dr Ste 890 Irvine, CA 92618
(949) 203-5100 Rashmi Chaturvedi President
Fax: (949) 861-6500
Email: rashmi.chaturvedi@kaygen.com
Website: www.kaygen.com
Oracle Enterprise Resource Planning (ERP). (Woman/As-Pac, estab 2003, empl 25, sales $10,301,583, cert: NMSDC, CPUC)

4376   KT Consulting, Inc.
2545 W 10th St Ste A Antioch, CA 94509
(972) 734-5128 Jonathan Heckmann Acct Mgr
Fax: (972) 734-5139
Email: jheckmann@ktconsultinginc.com
Website: www.ktconsultinginc.com
Information technology & management consulting: IT operations support, project & program mgmt, outsourcing, strategy, performance & operations mgmt, technical writing, IT security, planning, analysis, design, configuration, implementation. (AA, estab 2001, empl 25, sales $39,814,191, cert: State)

4377   Kutir Corporation
37600 Central Ct, Ste 280   Newark, CA 94560
(510) 870-0227 Prathiba Kalyan Sr Business Mgr
Fax: (510) 494-9699
Email: prathiba@kutirtech.com
Website: www.kutirtech.com
Contract & permanent staffing, custom software development, business & technology consulting, systems integration, technical support, admin, testing & support, data warehousing, business intelligence. (As-Ind, estab 2003, empl 40, sales $3,400,000, cert: NMSDC, CPUC, 8(a))

4378 LocalBizNetwork
3141 Stevens Creek Blvd, Ste 358   San Jose, CA 95117
(408) 741-8184 Indu Jayakumar President
Fax: (480) 275-3709
Email: info@localbiznetwork.com
Website: www.localbiznetwork.com
Custom software applications: Internet, Internet based online survey forms, computation of survey data, Internet marketing, SEO, Internet publishing, blogging, website development & hosting. (Woman/As-Ind, estab 2002, empl 22, sales $300,000, cert: CPUC)

4379 Luminous Tec LLC
15481 Red Hill Ave, Ste B   Tustin, CA 92780
(949) 630-0448 Uma Sharma Dir, new Business Devel
Fax:
Email: usharma@luminoustec.com
Website: www.luminoustec.com
IT & non IT staffing & consulting services: project managers, business & technical architects, business analysts, applications development resources, systems integration specialists. (Woman/As-Pac, estab 2006, empl 5, sales $750,000, cert: CPUC)

4380 Maantic Inc.
1202 Kifer Rd   Sunnyvale, CA 94086
(408) 590-7446 HARRY IYER
Fax: (203) 271-8051
Email: hiyer@maantic.com
Website: www.maantic.com/
Implement business applications, BPM, CRM, MDM, ERP, EAI, and BI. (As-Ind, estab 2009, empl 25, sales , cert: NMSDC)

4381 Magellan Solutions USA
100 Old County Rd Ste H Brisbane, CA 94005
(650) 897-5147 Mark Dee CEO
Fax:
Email: mark.dee@magellansolutionsusa.com
Website: www.magellansolutionsusa.com
Call Center, Business Process Outsourcing, Inbound/Outbound Call Center, E-Commerce Support, Data Entry/Processing, Financial/Billing Support, Business Process Management. (As-Pac, estab 2005, empl 600, sales $3,004,000, cert: State)

4382 Medi/Nuclear Corp., Inc.
4610 Littlejohn St   Baldwin Park, CA 91706
(626) 960-9822 Jerry Schoen
Fax: (626) 960-8700
Email: jschoen@medinuclear.com
Website: www.medinuclear.com
Radio-aerosol delivery systems (Woman/White, estab 1973, empl 20, sales $2,418,165, cert: State)

4383 Meijun LLC
9888 Carroll Centre Rd Ste#210   San Diego, CA 92126
(619) 333-8698 Huy Ly
Fax:
Email: hly@meijun.cc
Website: www.meijun.cc
Web development & marketing agency, custom software solutions, web & mobile development, design & strategy, digital marketing services, SEO, content marketing & marketing automation integration. (As-Pac, estab 2011, empl 5, sales , cert: NMSDC, CPUC)

4384 Metabyte Inc.
39350 Civic Center Dr Ste200 Fremont, CA 94538
(510) 494-9700 Unni Krishnan Business Devel Mgr
Fax: (510) 952-3303
Email: unnik@metabyte.com
Website: www.metabyte.com
IT Services, High Technology & ISV, Life Sciences & Healthcare, Manufacturing & Logistics, Banking & Financial Services, Speciality Retail, Telecom & Media. (As-Pac, estab 1993, empl 235, sales , cert: NMSDC)

4385 Mission Critical Technologies, Inc.
2041 Rosecrans Ave Ste 220 El Segundo, CA 90245
(310) 246-4455 Patti Converse
Fax: (310) 246-9540
Email: patti_converse@mctinc.com
Website: www.mctinc.com
Technology solutions: relational database, application design & implementation, custom software dev, outsourcing, offsite dev projects, graphic design & development. (Woman/White, estab 1993, empl 50, sales , cert: WBENC)

4386 mLogica, Inc.
4025 E La Palma Ave, Ste 204   Anaheim, CA 92807
(714) 630-2500 Sales
Fax: (714) 630-2502
Email: ml_accounting@mLogica.com
Website: www.mlogica.com
Enterprise software, remote admin, software development, database management, embedded & mobile solutions. (As-Pac, estab 2004, empl 10, sales $3,572,185, cert: State, City)

4387 MSRCOSMOS LLC
6200 StoneRidge Mall Rd, Ste 300   Pleasanton, CA 94588
(321) 332-6344 Rajkumar Bogam Lead sales
Fax: (925) 219-0934
Email: rajj@msrcosmos.com
Website: www.msrcosmos.com
IT services, mobile application, web applications, cloud solutions, analytics, infrastructure management & offshore consulting. (Woman, estab 2008, empl 84, sales $6,000,000, cert: WBENC)

4388 NexInfo Solutions, Inc.
1851 E First St Ste 900 Santa Ana, CA 92705
(714) 955-6970 Kate Duffy Client Relations
Fax:
Email: kate.duffy@nexinfo.com
Website: www.nexinfo.com
ERP solutions, PLM solutions, Supply Chain Planning, Software implementations, Manged Services, Technical consulting, Functional consulting, Techno Functional Consulting, business process design, Global order promising. (As-Ind, estab 1999, empl 300, sales , cert: NMSDC)

4389 Northbound LLC
961 E Arques Ave   Sunnyvale, CA 94085
(408) 333-9885 Leena Menon Ops Mgr
Fax: (408) 516-9476
Email: supplierdiversity@northboundllc.com
Website: www.northboundllc.com
Information technology contract & full-time placement services. (Woman/As-Ind, estab 1998, empl 150, sales , cert: NMSDC, WBENC)

4390 Omni2max, Inc.
1202 Morena Blvd, Ste 100   San Diego, CA 92110
(619) 269-1663 Javonda Franklin Business Devel Mgr
Fax: (619) 269-2967
Email: javonda.franklin@omni2max.com
Website: www.omni2max.com
Information Assurance, Information Technology, Logistics, Engineering, Contract Management, Help Desk Management & CRM, Systems Engineering, Program Management & Performance Based Acquisition. (AA, estab 2009, empl 25, sales $1,500,000, cert: State, 8(a))

4391 Omnikron Systems Inc.
20920 Warner Center Lane Ste A Woodland Hills, CA 91367
(818) 223-4115 Robin Borough President
Fax: (818) 591-9836
Email: robin.borough@omnikron.com
Website: www.Omnikron.com
Applications development (ERP), database, reporting, business intelligence, operations, infrastructure, security & business personnel. (As-Pac, estab 1980, empl 50, sales $8,000,000, cert: CPUC)

4392 OrangePeople
300 Spectrum Dr Ste 400 Irvine, CA 92618
(949) 667-1762 Natasha Myers VP
Fax: (949) 450-1454
Email: Natasha.Myers@orangepeople.com
Website: www.orangepeople.com
OrangePeople is one of the fastest growing Technology Leadership Services company in America. Our team of consultants bring tremendous hands-on experience in business strategy, architecture, and program management. (As-Pac, estab 2006, empl 70, sales $1,800,000, cert: NMSDC)

4393 Partner Engineering and Science, Inc.
1990 E Grand Ave, Ste 100   El Segundo, CA 90245
(800) 419-4923 Sean Rakhshani Principal
Fax: (866) 928-7418
Email: srakhshani@partneresi.com
Website: www.partneresi.com
Software engineering, modeling & simulation, research & development & consulting services. (Woman/White, estab 2006, empl 120, sales $22,700,000, cert: WBENC)

4394 PC Specialists Inc dbaTechnology Integration Group
10240 Flanders Ct   San Diego, CA 92121
(858) 566-1900 Bruce Geier CEO
Fax: (858) 566-8794
Email: bruce.geier@tig.com
Website: www.tig.com
System integration, engineering, programming, computer software, hardware & furniture, cabling, telephony, help desk. (As-Pac, estab 1983, empl 325, sales $325,000, cert: NMSDC, CPUC)

4395 Perlinski & Company
30025 Alicia Pkwy, Ste 107   Laguna Niguel, CA 92677
(949) 481-5482 Isabel Perlinski CEO
Fax: (949) 481-5483
Email: isabel.perlinski@perlinskico.com
Website: www.perlinskico.com
Perlinski & Company is the culmination of the experience, leadership, skills and capabilities of its founders, partners, board members and strategic partners. Founded in 1989, Perlinski & Company specializes in providing management consulting (Woman/Hisp, estab 1989, empl 2, sales $244,250, cert: NMSDC, WBENC, 8(a))

4396 Pinpoint Resource Group, LLC
1960 E Grand Ave Ste 1260 El Segundo, CA 90245
(310) 356-8123 Felix Lin President
Fax: (310) 868-0663
Email: felix@pinpoint.jobs
Website: www.pinpoint.jobs
Information technology staffing: consultants & direct hire, systems analysts, project managers & management personnel. (As-Pac, estab 2004, empl 15, sales $4,500,000, cert: NMSDC)

4397 Plan b Solutions, Inc.
29222 Rancho Viejo Rd   San Juan Capistrano, CA 92675
(949) 221-9301 Doreen Wakefield CEO
Fax: (949) 769-6199
Email: info@planbsolutions.com
Website: www.planbsolutions.com
IT staffing & professional services, contract, contract-to-hire & permanent placement staffing, process consulting. (Woman/White, estab 2000, empl 20, sales $4,800,000, cert: WBENC)

4398 PM Business Holdings LLC
733 Hindry Ave, Ste C205 Inglewood, CA 90301
(310) 242-3171 Derrick Ferguson CEO
Fax:
Email: pmbh14@gmail.com
Website: www.brilliantmindssolutions.com
Computer Systems Design Services, employment placement & executive search services (AA, estab 2012, empl 1, sales , cert: NMSDC)

4399 Premium Technologies, Inc.
P.O. Box 757 Palm Desert, CA 92261
(760) 340-4603 Stanway Wong President
Fax:
Email: stanwong@premium-technologies.com
Website: www.premium-technologies.com/
Computer software design & development, data integration, physical asset mgmt, computerized maintenance mgmt system (CMMS) & enterprise asset mgmt (EAM) & asset tracking. (As-Pac, estab 1993, empl 1, sales , cert: NMSDC, CPUC)

4400 Propane Studio
1153 Mission St San Francisco, CA 94103
(415)9027958 Neil Chaudhari CXO
Fax:
Email: neil@propanestudio.com
Website: www.propanestudio.com
Websites & Applications, Responsive Websites, Tech Arch Consulting, E-Commerce Development, UX Prototyping & Testing, Mobile Applications, Online Applications, Content Strategy & Migration, CMS Consulting, Strategic Digital Consulting. (As-Ind, estab 2003, empl 20, sales $5,000,000, cert: NMSDC)

4401 Prosum, Inc.
2201 Park Place, Ste 102 El Segundo, CA 90245
(1310) 426-0609 Ravi Chatwani CEO
Fax: (310) 426-0685
Email: ravi.chatwani@prosum.com
Website: www.prosum.com
Technology staffing services, technology consulting services, technology product sales. (AA/Nat Ame/As-Ind/As-Pac/Hisp, estab 1996, empl 250, sales $38,000,000, cert: NMSDC, CPUC)

4402 QualityWorks Consulting Group, LLC
6018 S Citrus Ave Los Angeles, CA 90043
(310) 467-5122 Stacy Kirk CEO
Fax:
Email: skirk@qualityworkscg.com
Website: www.qualityworkscg.com
Automated & manual web testing, Automated & manual mobile testing, Integrated automation test frameworks for web & mobile, DevOps/Continuous Integration Support, API/microservices testing, Agile QA coaching & training. (Woman/AA, estab 2010, empl 31, sales $1,375,000, cert: NMSDC, CPUC, WBENC)

4403 RaviG Inc. dba Salient Global Technologies
510 Garcia Ave, Ste E Pittsburg, CA 94565
(925) 526-1234 Ravikanth Ganapavarapu Pres.
Fax:
Email: rganapa@salientglobaltech.com
Website: www.salientglobaltech.com
End-to-end business applications & IT infrastructure. (As-Ind, estab 1999, empl 55, sales $1,000,000, cert: NMSDC)

4404 Raycom Data Technologies, Inc.
1320 E Imperial Ave El Segundo, CA 90245
(310) 322-5113 Ayaz Pandhiani President
Fax: (310) 322-6025
Email: ayaz@raycomdtech.com
Website: www.raycomdtech.com
Document archiving software, document management services, document scanning, conversion services, microfiche & microfilm. (As-Pac, estab 1978, empl 10, sales $1,165,000, cert: State)

4405 Related Technologies, Inc.
81 Blue Ravine Rd Ste 230 Folsom, CA 95630
(916) 357-5902 Cheryl Borgonah Mgr
Fax:
Email: cherylb@relatedtech.com
Website: www.relatedtech.com/
Technical & Functional SAP consultants, implementations, upgrades, enhancements & support. (Woman/As-Ind, estab 2002, empl 150, sales $1,500,000, cert: CPUC)

4406 RJT Compuquest
222 N Sepulveda Blvd. Ste 2250 El Segundo, CA 90245
(310) 421-1297 Vivek Bhatia Sr Accts Exec
Fax: (310) 421-1297
Email: vivek@rjtcompuquest.com
Website: www.rjtcompuquest.com
IT solutions, SAP, Oracle, WB, web development, CRM & archiving solutions, staff augmentation. (As-Pac, estab 1996, empl 300, sales $46,000,000, cert: NMSDC)

4407 RPM Engineers, Inc.
102 Discovery Irvine, CA 92618
(949) 450-1229 Raymond Phua Principal
Fax: (949) 450-1454
Email: marisolv@rpmpe.com
Website: www.rpmpe.com
RPM Engineers, Inc. was established 1993 in Irvine, California. An engineering firm under the direction of Mr. Raymond Phua, a registered professional engineer in state of California, providing air conditioning (As-Pac, estab 1993, empl 17, sales $1,727,000, cert: State)

4408 SA Technologies Inc.
5201 Great America Pkwy, Ste 441 Santa Clara, CA 95054
(408) 986-0152 Priyanka Joshi President
Fax: (650) 963-3238
Email: priyanka.joshi@satechglobal.com
Website: www.satechglobal.com
Information technology consulting & staffing. (Woman/As-Ind, estab 1900, empl 1, sales $10,800,000, cert: NWBOC)

4409 SD Shredding, Inc.
7263 Engineer Rd Ste C San Diego, CA 92111
(858) 492-9600 Todd M Hoover CFO
Fax: (858) 492-9601
Email: todd.hoover@proshred.com
Website: www.proshred.com
On-site document & computer hard drive shredding. (Woman/White, estab 2010, empl 3, sales $200,000, cert: WBENC)

4410 Sidebench Studios
10317 Washington Blvd. Culver City, CA 90232
(808) 294-5948 Nate Schier Director of Staff & Co-Founder
Fax:
Email: nate@sidebench.com
Website: www.sidebench.com
App design, development & strategy. (As-Pac, estab 2012, empl 13, sales $1,342,459, cert: NMSDC, CPUC)

4411 Sigmaways, Inc.
39737 Paseo Padre Pkwy Fremont, CA 94538
(510) 713-7800 SUJIT GHOSH CEO
Fax: (510) 474-1409
Email: sujit@sigmaways.com
Website: www.sigmaways.com
Software product, technology innovation & staff augmentation. (As-Ind, estab 2006, empl 85, sales $7,200,000, cert: NMSDC)

4412 Sohum Inc
1055 Minnesota Ave, Ste 6 San Jose, CA 95125
(408) 265-2391 Vandana Patil President
Fax: (408) 265-2391
Email: marketing@sohum.biz
Website: www.sohum.biz
Software UX design, web & mobile, Software Design & Development, Cloud based software deployment & monitoring. (Woman/As-Ind, estab 1998, empl 5, sales $300,000, cert: State)

4413 Solugenix Corporation
7700 Irvine Center Dr Ste 800 Irvine, CA 92618
(949) 266-0938 Ramki Venkatraman Director
Fax:
Email: ramki.venkatraman@solugenix.com
Website: www.solugenix.com
Application Lifecycle Management: Project & Requirements Management, Custom Application Development, Testing & Quality Assurance, Change & Release Management, Level 2 & Level 3 Production Support. (As-Ind, estab 2004, empl 52, sales $27,583,910, cert: NMSDC)

4414 Source Diversified, Inc.
1206 Vista Cantora San Clemente, CA 92672
(949) 940-0450 Alfred Ortiz President
Fax: (949) 203-6208
Email: aortiz@sourced.com
Website: www.sourced.com
Command & control systems, security alerting systems, flight test support svcs, aircraft system integration, software dev, construction automation software, network installation, mission control room support svcs. (Hisp, estab 1987, empl 3, sales , cert: State)

4415 SPK and Associates, LLC.
20 S Santa Cruz Ave Ste 300 Los Gatos, CA 95030
(888) 310-4540 Mary Rodrigues Exec Asst
Fax: (888) 246-2096
Email: mrodrigues@SPKAA.COM
Website: www.spkaa.com
Information Technology (IT), Infrastructure, IT Services (implementation, support, training, data migration), IT Staffing through a MSP, Large Data Storage/Management, Network Management, Product Development, Software Programming, Web Administrators (Woman/White, estab 2003, empl 17, sales $2,882,705, cert: WBENC)

4416 SRS Consulting Inc.
39465 Paseo Padre Pkwy, Ste 1100 Fremont, CA 94538
(510) 252-0625 Aswath Panduranga Business Dev Mgr
Fax: (510) 252-0626
Email: aswath@srsconsultinginc.com
Website: www.srsconsultinginc.com
IT Development, Custom Software Development, R&D/Product Development/Re-engineering, Testing and Quality Assurance, Network Security Services, ERP/EAI consulting & implementation, CRM, SCP, BPM, CMS, DMS, e-Governance, Mobile Security. (As-Ind, estab 2002, empl 250, sales $46,000,000, cert: NMSDC)

4417 Stealth Network Communication
6900 Koll Center Pkwy, Ste 413 Pleasanton, CA 94566
(925) 846-7018 Dave Drews Dir
Fax: (925) 426-2563
Email: ddrews@stealthnetwork.com
Website: www.stealthnetwork.com
Voice, network & security, telcom technologies, call center efficiencies information, switching systems, project mgmt, technical project mgmt, IP telephony & VOIP design. (Woman/Nat Ame, estab 2001, empl 32, sales $15,000,000, cert: State)

4418 Stratitude
6601 Koll Center Pkwy, Ste 132 Pleasanton, CA 94566
(510) 461-3981 Khannan Sankaran CEO
Fax: (510) 793-8860
Email: khannan@stratitude.com
Website: www.stratitude.com
IT services, implementation & staffing, software advisory, design, development & testing services, SAP, Microsoft, Java, Salesforce.com , Netsuite, Pega BPM, Guidewire Temenos, Veeva. (As-Ind, estab 2006, empl 36, sales $3,600,000, cert: NMSDC)

4419 Sun MicroSolutions Inc.
29 Avanzare St Irvine, CA 92606
(949) 387-9878 Ruchi Mitra CEO
Fax:
Email: ruchi@sunmicrousa.com
Website: www.sunmicrousa.com
IT consulting, staffing & training. (Woman/As-Pac, estab 2000, empl 5, sales $540,000, cert: City)

4420 Sunny City Enterprises, Inc.
959 Mount Whitney Ct   Chula Vista, CA 91913
(619) 250-5970 Francisco Esparza President
Fax: (619) 250-5970
Email: francisco.esparza@sbcitpros.com
Website: www.sbcitpros.com
IT & Telecom services, Software Solutions & Applications,
Staffing Augmentation. (Hisp, estab 2007, empl 10, sales
$1,500,000, cert: NMSDC, CPUC)

4421 SupplierGATEWAY LLC
601 N Parkcenter Dr Ste 102 Santa Ana, CA 92705
(949) 525-9205 Ade Solaru CEO
Fax: (949) 625-8204
Email: ade.solaru@suppliergateway.com
Website: www.suppliergateway.com
Information technology solutions & consulting svcs:
developed SupplierGATEWAYï¿½ an end-to-end collaborative supply chain solution that connects buyers & suppliers
via the Internet. (AA, estab 1900, empl 1, sales $250,000,
cert: NMSDC)

4422 Sycomp a Technology Company., Inc.
950 Tower Lane Ste 1785 Foster City, CA 94404
(650) 312-8174 Stacy Hunter
Fax: (650) 312-8175
Email: shunter@sycomp.com
Website: www.sycomp.com
Design, implement & deliver complex, heterogeneous
Infrastructure, Software & Security technology solutions.
(Woman/As-Pac, estab 1994, empl 80, sales $120,000,000,
cert: NMSDC)

4423 SysIntelli, Inc.
9466 Black Mountain Road, Ste. 200   San Diego, CA
92126
(858) 271-1600 Ravi Hanumara CEO
Fax: (760) 888-1998
Email: sarahg@paraminfosysinc.com
Website: www.sysintelli.com
Software Development Life Cycle, Re-engineering & Legacy
Migration, Database Administration, Quality Assurance
Testing & Validation, E-Commerce, Data Processing,
Software Maintenance & Support. (As-Ind, estab 2005,
empl 55, sales $16,690,351, cert: NMSDC)

4424 Systems Integration Solutions, Inc.
1255 Treat Blvd. Ste 100 Walnut Creek, CA 94597
(952) 220-7549 Nick Bata Reg Acct Dir
Fax: (925) 465-7417
Email: nbata@sisinc.com
Website: www.sisinc.com
IT consulting & executive search services. (As-Pac/Hisp,
estab 1990, empl 150, sales $30,000,000, cert: CPUC)

4425 Tap3Solutions
2279 Eagle Glen Pkwy, Ste 112-444 Corona, CA
92883
(949) 229-1910 Catrina Snell-Rehder President
Fax:
Email: Catrina@Tap3Solutions.com
Website: www.Tap3Solutions.com
Information technology & human capital solutions.
(Woman/AA, estab 2015, empl 2, sales , cert: State, City)

4426 Techlink Systems
1 Post St Ste 300   San Francisco, CA 94104
(415) 944-1624 Jamie Jacobs Mgr, Strategic
Partnerships
Fax: (212) 202-4428
Email: jjacobs@techlinksystems.com
Website: www.techlinksystems.com
Information technology, engineering, scientific & bio-
tech, application development. (Woman/As-Pac, estab
1998, empl 141, sales $31,500,000, cert: NMSDC,
WBENC)

4427 Technology Integration Group
10240 Flanders Ct   San Diego, CA 92121
(858) 566-1900 Bruce Geier CEO
Fax: (858) 566-1243
Email: bgeier@tig.com
Website: www.tig.com
System integration, computer systems, security, storage,
supplies accessories & peripherals. (As-Pac, estab 1983,
empl 386, sales $340,000,000, cert: CPUC)

4428 Technossus LLC
4000 MacArthur Blvd Ste 100 Newport Beach, CA
92660
(949) 769-3522 Dave LaJeunesse Dir of Sales
Fax: (866) 878-3918
Email: info@technossus.com
Website: www.technossus.com
Custom software development, Microsoft technology
stack, application development, desktop, enterprise &
web-based, mobile applications, SharePoint & Dynamics
CRM, proprietary systems development & enhancement. (As-Ind, estab 2008, empl 25, sales $4,700,000,
cert: NMSDC)

4429 Tellus Solutions, Inc
3350 Scott Blvd 34A   Santa Clara, CA 95054
(408) 850-2942 Smita Gautam HR/Business Dev
Fax: (408) 850-2982
Email: smitag@tellussol.com
Website: www.tellussol.com
Information technology services. (Woman/As-Pac, estab
2005, empl 67, sales $5,320,000, cert: NMSDC, WBENC,
8(a))

4430 The LSC Group, Inc.
200 Spectrum Center Dr 3rd Fl Irvine, CA 92618
(800) 572-9280 Troy Humphrey CEO
Fax: (800) 572-9280
Email: troy.humphrey@yourlscgroup.com
Website: www.yourlscgroup.com
Electronic Discovery, Data Collection, Data Processing,
Data Production, Forensic Date Discovery, Litigation
Support, Records Management, Early Case Assessment,
Webhosting, Project Management, Consulting. (AA,
estab 2007, empl 1, sales $125,000, cert: NMSDC, CPUC)

4431   Thomas Gallaway Corp. dba Technologent
       100 Spectrum Center Dr Ste 700 Irvine, CA 92618
       (949) 716-9500 Shari Jones Client Vendor Relations
       Fax: (949) 716-9600
       Email: vendorbids@technologent.com
       Website: www.technologent.com
Sun Microsystems hardware & service, multi vendor
support, Finisar, Sharkrak, Storedge Tek, Oracle & Veritas.
(Woman/White, estab 2002, empl 250, sales
$348,000,000, cert: WBENC)

4432   Thoughtpowers LLC
       1919 Williams St Ste 215 Simi Valley, CA 93065
       (805) 433-4950 Surendra Kulkarni President
       Fax:
       Email: surendra@thoughtpowers.com
       Website: www.thoughtpowers.com
Custom Application IT development & management, IT
consulting services, IT resources, technical resources. (As-
Pac, estab 2008, empl 1, sales , cert: NMSDC)

4433   Trinus Corporation
       225 South Lake Avenue, Ste 1080 Pasadena, CA
       91101
       (818) 246-1143 Harshada Kucheria President
       Fax: (818) 246-3152
       Email: harshada_kucheria@trinus.com
       Website: www.trinus.com
IT consulting & implementation services, business consulting, systems integration & outsourcing. (Woman/As-Ind,
estab 1995, empl 250, sales , cert: NMSDC, CPUC, SDB)

4434   Two Shea Consulting, Inc.
       1009 Oak Hill Rd, Ste 202 Lafayette, CA 94549
       (925) 962-7432 Maureen Shea CEO
       Fax: (240) 465-0660
       Email: Maureen@twoshea.com
       Website: www.twoshea.com
IT consulting & recruiting services. (Woman/White, estab
2000, empl 25, sales $5,000,000, cert: City, WBENC)

4435   United Support Services, Inc.
       713 Mission Ave, Ste C Oceanside, CA 92054
       (760) 688-0115 Michael Fernandez President
       Fax: (760) 688-0111
       Email: sales@usscompany.com
       Website: www.usscompany.com
Training & Education, Information Technology (IT) &
Networks, Cyber Security, Software Devel & Professional
Support, Custom Software Design, Online Education &
Training Programs, Custom Designed Computer Based
Training. (Hisp, estab 2002, empl 8, sales , cert: 8(a))

4436   VARITE, Inc.
       111 North Market St, Ste 730 San Jose, CA 95113
       (408) 977-0700 Adarsh Katyal CEO
       Fax: (408) 977-0760
       Email: katyal@varite.com
       Website: www.varite.com
Technical consulting & staffing, customized onshore, near
shore & offshore solutions. (As-Ind, estab 2000, empl 49,
sales $9,500,000, cert: NMSDC, CPUC)

4437   Versa Shore Inc.
       1999 S Bascom Ave Ste 700 Campbell, CA 95008
       (408) 874-8330 Shawn Rao CEO
       Fax:
       Email: shawnrao@versashore.com
       Website: www.versashore.com
Consulting, staffing & headhunting, Microsoft APS, Data
warehousing, big data, business intelligence, Oracle,
Birst, Tableau, Sql Server, Hadoop, MongoDB, Database,
Java & IT management skills. (As-Ind, estab 2003, empl
10, sales $3,000,000, cert: NMSDC)

4438   Vertisystem Inc.
       39300 Civic Center Dr, Ste 230 Fremont, CA
       94538
       (702) 241-5131 Shaloo Jeswani Sr BDM
       Fax: (510) 474-1440
       Email: shaloo@vertisystem.com
       Website: www.vertisystem.com
Staff Augmentation, Full-Time Placements, contract to
Hire, IT Projects & Consulting. (Woman/As-Pac, estab
2008, empl 120, sales $20,000,000, cert: CPUC)

4439   Vidhwan Inc dba E-Solutions, Inc.
       2 N Market St Ste 400 San Jose, CA 95113
       (408) 239-4647 Eric Kumar Acct Mgr
       Fax: (408) 521-0167
       Email: eric.kumar@e-solutionsinc.com
       Website: www.e-solutionsinc.com
IT & ITES staffing, recruitment & deployment: perma-
nent, contract, contract to hire & project based staffing.
(Woman/As-Ind, estab 2003, empl 450, sales
$22,800,000, cert: NMSDC, CPUC)

4440   Volante Enterprise Consulting
       3863 Millbrae Terr Perris, CA 92571
       (310) 256-9639 Sheila Volante CEO
       Fax:
       Email: sheilavolante@volantenc.com
       Website: www.volantenc.com
Scheduling Management, Risk Management, Systems
Consulting, Microsoft Project Server, Microsoft Project
Professional, Configuration, Office 365 + SharePoint
Configuration, Project Management Office Setup &
Maintenance. (Woman/AA, estab 2014, empl 2, sales ,
cert: State)

4441   VXI Global Solutions, LLC.
       220 W 1st St, 3rd Fl Los Angeles, CA 90012
       (213) 637-1300 Nick Covelli SVP, Sales/Mktg
       Fax: (213) 637-1351
       Email: nick.covelli@vxi.com
       Website: www.vxi.com
Business process & information technology outsourcing,
call center & BPO services, software development,
quality assurance testing & infrastructure outsourcing.
(As-Pac, estab 1998, empl 19500, sales $584,000,000,
cert: NMSDC)

4442 Webbege, Inc.
      7851 Mission Center Ct Ste 108 San Diego, CA
      92108
      (619) 786-7075 Francis Geraci President
      Fax:
      Email: frank.geraci@webbege.com
      Website: www.webbege.com
Web Design, Development, and Online Marketing. (Hisp,
estab 2011, empl 7, sales $300,000, cert: NMSDC)

4443 WINTEC Software Corporation
      3333 Bowers Ave, Ste 189 Santa Clara, CA 95054
      (408) 988-1600 Narender Ramarapu CEO
      Fax: (702) 543-2373
      Email: narender@winteccorp.com
      Website: www.winteccorp.com
Information technology consulting & staffing, contract
computer programming, software application devel &
training, system & database administration. (As-Ind/As-
Pac, estab 1998, empl 56, sales $3,320,000, cert: 8(a))

4444 WMBE Payrolling, Inc dba TargetCW
      3990 Old Town Ave, Ste A206 San Diego, CA 92110
      (888) 388-8873 Benjamin Jack Business Dev
      Fax: (858) 430-5550
      Email: benjamin@targetcw.com
      Website: www.targetcw.com
Payrolling of contingent workers identified by our clients.
Employer of record for temporary workers and contractors
already sourced across the US and overseas. (Woman/
White, estab 2009, empl 12, sales $200,000, cert: State)

4445 Xavient Information Systems, Inc.
      2125 Madera Rd, Ste B Simi Valley, CA 93065
      (805) 955-4140 Melissa Montejano Director Admin
      Fax:
      Email: melissa@xavient.com
      Website: www.xavient.com
Application development & integration, testing & quality
assurance, IT infrastructure support, application support,
core telecom engineering services. (As-Pac, estab 2003,
empl 2200, sales $40,000,000, cert: NMSDC)

4446 Xinnovit Inc.
      21001 San Ramon Valley Blvd, Ste A4-103 San
      Ramon, CA 94583
      (925) 236-2310 Kiran Raja Client Relations Mgr
      Fax: (925) 226-1450
      Email: kiran@xinnovit.com
      Website: www.xinnovit.com
Information technology services: application development,
systems & database management, data warehousing &
quality assurance. (Woman/As-Ind, estab 2002, empl 165,
sales $12,000,000, cert: NMSDC)

4447 Yadari Enterprises
      728 Texas St, Ste 3 Fairfield, CA 94533
      (707) 398-6478 Tara Lynn Gray President
      Fax: (707) 207-4973
      Email: tara@yadari.com
      Website: www.yadari.com
Web devel, database, report writing, business intelligence,
visual data displays, management consulting, graphic
design, electronic health record, diagnostic imaging
systems, laboratory systems, pharmacy systems. (Woman/
AA, estab 2004, empl 3, sales $310,000, cert: State, CPUC)

Colorado

4448 Advance IT Network Solutions LLC
      4600 S Syracuse St Ste 900 Denver, CO 80237
      (303) 846-3071 Dwight Cunningham CEO
      Fax:
      Email: dwight@advanced-it-solutions.com
      Website: www.advanced-it-solutions.com
Computer Systems Design Services, Computer Facilities
Management Services, Security Consulting Services,
Computer & Computer Peripheral Equip & Software.
(AA, estab 2005, empl 3, sales $800,000, cert: City)

4449 Aspen Capital Company, Inc.
      4489 Roaring Fork Court Loveland, CO 80538
      (303) 716-2898 Pegy Tomcheck
      Fax:
      Email: plapp@aspencapitalcompany.com
      Website: www.aspencapitalcompany.com
Custom asset tracking & invoicing solutions, educational
laptop program lease structures, unique iPad refresh
programs, consignment solutions, electronic invoicing &
billing processes, web based equipment stores.
(Woman/White, estab 2001, empl 8, sales $10,385,908,
cert: WBENC, NWBOC)

4450 Aureus Tech Systems, LLC
      17593 E Euclid Ave Aurora, CO 80016
      (816) 373-1979 Sujata Bhattarai CEO
      Fax:
      Email: sujata@aureustechsystems.com
      Website: www.aureustechsystems.com
Customized & needs-based reporting dashboard, Web-
based, & and near real-time reporting tools, overall
performance optimization reducing lag times & frivolous
resource allocation. (Woman/As-Ind, estab 2008, empl
35, sales $2,316,830, cert: WBENC)

4451 BCM Global Technologies Consultants, Inc.
      9457 S University Blvd, Ste 329 Highlands Ranch,
      CO 80126
      (866) 761-8880 Shawn Buchanan President
      Fax: (720) 294-9853
      Email: info@bcmglobaltech.com
      Website: www.bcmglobaltech.com
Provide technical resources & solutions. (Woman/AA,
estab 2008, empl 20, sales $1,550,000, cert: NMSDC,
WBENC, NWBOC, 8(a))

4452 Daniels & Patterson Corporate Search Inc.
      1732 Marion St Denver, CO 80218
      (303) 830-1230 Ruby Chavez Patterson President
      Fax: (303) 832-6162
      Email: dpsearch@nilenet.com
      Website: www.dp-search.com
Permanent & temp human resources providing EDP, MIS,
IS, telecommunications, clerical/office support &
contract personnel. (Woman/Hisp, estab 1985, empl 25,
sales , cert: State)

4453   DCM Technology Solutions, Inc.
17011 Moorside Dr   Parker, CO 80134
(303) 325-5202   Leslie Kleyweg President
Fax: (303) 325-5202
Email: info@dcmsolution.com
Website: www.dcmsolution.com
IT services: staffing, low voltage wiring, networking & computer repair/maintenance. (Woman/White, estab 2002, empl 5, sales $550,000, cert: WBENC)

4454   HD Communications LLC
2140 S Platte River Dr   Denver, CO 80223
(303) 756-4388   Michael Dominguez President
Fax:
Email: mikeh@hdcom.org
Website: www.hdcom.org
Audio Video Design & Installation. (Hisp, estab 2003, empl 10, sales $2,000,000, cert: 8(a))

4455   iBeta, LLC
2675 S Abilene St, Ste 300   Aurora, CO 80014
(303) 627-1110   Curt Dusing II Sales & Mktg Exec
Fax: (303) 627-1221
Email: cdusing@ibeta.com
Website: www.ibeta.com
Testing services: test engineering, automated & manual testing, functionality testing, performance, stress & load testing, hardware & software testing, data conversion testing, usability testing, console certification testing, handheld testing. (Hisp, estab 1999, empl 141, sales $4,500,000, cert: NMSDC)

4456   Istonish
5500 Greenwood Plaza Blvd   Greenwood Village, CO 80108
(720) 529-4550   Shannon Hickey Business Devel Exec
Fax:
Email: shickey@istonish.com
Website: www.istonish.com
Technical resources: staff augmentation, perm placement, vendor mgmt svcs, IT solutions, project based svcs, customer call ctr svcs. (Woman/Nat Ame/Hisp, estab 1990, empl 85, sales $6,883,874, cert: NMSDC)

4457   Jenco Technologies
3720 Sinton Rd, Ste 203   Colorado Springs, CO 80907
(719) 471-1200   Dan McOmber Acct Mgr
Fax: (719) 471-1201
Email: dan@jencotech.com
Website: www.jencotech.com
Hardware & software procurement, LAN connectivity, maintenance & monitoring, computer configurations & maintenance. (Woman/White, estab 2000, empl 5, sales $1,595,000, cert: State)

4458   Managed Business Solutions
12325 Oracle Blvd, Ste 200   Colorado Springs, CO 80921
(719) 314-3400   Jane Kovalik Mktg Mgr
Fax: (719) 314-3499
Email: diversity@mbshome.com
Website: www.mbshome.com
IT managed svcs: IT infrastructure support, multi-vendor/platform system admin, storage mgmt & admin, SAN engineering & design, server consolidation, open view service desk support, project mgmt, data center operations & mgmt. (Nat Ame, estab 1993, empl 101, sales $14,491,000, cert: NMSDC)

4459   Maven Companies
1880 Office Club Pointe   Colorado Springs, CO 80920
(719) 884-0102   Manish Kochhar President
Fax: (719) 884-0101
Email: diversity@mavenco.com
Website: www.mavenco.com
IT consulting, Project Management & Business Analysis (PM Coordination, Change and Release Management, Process Analysis), ERP Development & Support (Oracle, PeopleSoft, SAP),Business Intelligence (Business Objects, Cognos, Microstrategy, Crystal Reports). (As-Pac, estab 2003, empl 30, sales $3,000,000, cert: NMSDC)

4460   Rearden Logic Inc.
2010 E 17th Ave Unit 1   Denver, CO 80206
(720) 515-3289   Kristopher Schehr Principal
Fax:
Email: kschehr@reardenlogic.com
Website: www.reardenlogic.com
Offensive Cyber, Defensive Cyber, Networks, Reverse Engineering, TS//SCI, Software Defined Radio SDR, FPGA, TCP/IP, Coding, C++, Assembly ASM, Training, RF, Radio Frequency, Ettus, USRP, LTE, GSM, GPS, Satellite, IoT, GNURadio, Xmidas. (Hisp, estab 2013, empl 5, sales $537,000, cert: 8(a))

4461   RTL Networks
1391 Speer Blvd #850   Denver, CO 80204
(303) 757-3100   Jason Sand Senior Sales Associate
Fax: (303) 757-4133
Email: jsand@rtl-networks.com
Website: www.rtl-networks.com
Resell hardware & software, network architecture planning, design & implementation, network security, framework dev, program & project mgmt, cable splicing & installation. (AA, estab 2002, empl 50, sales $1,500,000, cert: State)

4462   Software Engineeering Services
7045 Campus Dr Ste 204   Colorado Springs, CO 80920
(719) 548-9839   Robert E. Watts Western Regional Mgr
Fax: (402) 292-3271
Email: bwatts@sessolutions.com
Website: www.sessolutions.com
Software solutions; mainframe programming; databases; data warehousing. (AA, estab 1992, empl 60, sales , cert: State)

4463 Source One Management Inc.
1225 Seventeenth St, Ste 1500   Denver, CO 80202
(303) 832-8600 Larry Woodburn Business Dev Mgr
Fax: (303) 832-1910
Email: lwoodburn@sourceone.com
Website: www.sourceone.com
Contract mgmt admin support svcs: records mgmt, document mgmt, correspondence control, litigation support, information technology, data mgmt, copy & print ctr mgmt, meeting svcs, video conferencing, call ctr, shipping & receiving, bar coding. (Hisp, estab 1985, empl 270, sales $12,758,000, cert: State)

4464 Systems Research Group
740 Wooten Rd, Ste 108   Colorado Springs, CO 80915
(719) 596-0737 Ken Sandoval Dir Business Dev
Fax: (719) 596-8635
Email: ksandoval@srgcorp.com
Website: www.srgcorp.com
IT systems operations & administrative support, reprographics in-house operations. (Hisp, estab 1986, empl 78, sales $7,000,000, cert: State)

4465 The 'Apps' Consultants Inc.
6909 S Holly Circle Ste 350 Centennial, CO 80112
(303) 502-5407 Kiran Pingali President
Fax: (720) 384-0733
Email: kiran@appsconsultants.com
Website: www.appsconsultants.com
IT consulting, ERP/ CRM & Business Intelligence. (Woman/As-Ind, estab 2005, empl 4, sales $546,846, cert: City)

4466 Tukuh Technologies
5045 List Dr   Colorado Springs, CO 80919
(210) 383-5839 Dan Beard Director of Business Devel
Fax:
Email: dan.beard@tepa.com
Website: www.tukuh.com
Information technology, Unmanned aerial systems (UAS) for data collection, Survey support, Remote sensing, GIS, Mapping, GPS, Simulation, Visualization, Analytics, 3D-printed terrain models, GIS-embedded video. (Nat Ame, estab 2013, empl 18, sales $478,000, cert: 8(a))

4467 Y2Fox, Inc
7900 E Union Ave, Ste 1100   Denver, CO 80237
(720) 436-2288 Yaya Bamba Managing Dir
Fax: (800) 385-2745
Email: ybamba@y2fox.com
Website: www.y2fox.com
Strategic software development, Cloud Computing, Cyber Security, OEM (Microsoft, Oracle, and others) Hardware, and Software licensing reseller. Information Technology application support, Big data management. (AA, estab 2008, empl 25, sales , cert: 8(a))

Connecticut

4468 Agilus Global Services, LLC
35 E Main St, Ste 352   Avon, CT 06001
(860) 404-0476 Dennis Williams CEO
Fax: (203) 297-6076
Email: dwilliams@agilusglobal.com
Website: www.agilusglobalservices.com
IT consulting/staffing & recruiting services. (AA, estab 2015, empl 1, sales , cert: NMSDC)

4469 Aquinas Consulting, LLC
154 Herbert St   Milford, CT 06460
(203) 876-7822 Sally Reed Dir of HR
Fax: (203) 876-9804
Email: sreed@aquinasconsulting.com
Website: www.aquinasconsulting.com
IT & engineering consulting & staffing. (Woman/As-Pac, estab 2000, empl 27, sales $3,045,910, cert: State)

4470 Aspire Systems
36 Mill Plain Rd   Danbury, CT 06811
(732) 406-4284 Laura Del Corpo VP Business Devel
Fax:
Email: laura@aspiresystem.com
Website: www.aspiresystem.com
Information Technology, Staff Augmentation, Technology Deployment & Enterprise support. (As-Pac, estab 2002, empl 45, sales $5,000,000, cert: NMSDC)

4471 Dudas IT Resources & Advisory, Inc.
117 Butternut Lane   Stamford, CT 06903
(203) 653-2739 Liz Chait CEO
Fax: (212) 253-4151
Email: liz@zarit.com
Website: www.zarit.org
Information technology staffing & consulting services. (Woman, estab 2005, empl 8, sales $6,389,623, cert: WBENC)

4472 eRichards Consulting LLC
4 Corporate Dr Ste 390 Shelton, CT 06484
(203) 944-0816 Doreen Gebbia President
Fax: (203) 944-0817
Email: dgebbia@e-richards.com
Website: www.e-richards.com
IT consulting: strategic assessment, internet strategy, application development, project management, IT governance, web development & staff augmentation. (Woman/White, estab 1996, empl 3, sales , cert: WBENC)

4473 InfoLynx Services, Inc.
325 Danbury Rd   New Milford, CT 06776
(860) 210-1203 Uelysee Scantling Dir of Sales
Fax: (860) 210-1207
Email: contact@infolynx.com
Website: www.infolynx.com
Technical services: project mgmt, technical configuration, system & application engineering, performance tuning, desktop support. (AA, estab 1994, empl 75, sales $6,200,000, cert: State)

4474   iTech Solutions, Inc.
        8 Hidden Oak Dr Ste 200 Farmington, CT 06032
        (952) 960-7766 Kay Lukas President
        Fax: (860) 371-2317
        Email: klukas@itechsolutions.com
        Website: www.itechsolutions.com
Information technology staffing, consulting & recruting
services. (Woman/White, estab 1995, empl 115, sales
$14,092,608, cert: WBENC)

4475   JANUS Software, Inc. (d/b/a JANUS Associates)
        4 High Ridge Park Stamford, CT 06905
        (203) 251-0234 Brad Mayer Dir of Business Dev
        Fax: (203) 251-0222
        Email: bradm@janusassociates.com
        Website: www.janusassociates.com
Information & telecommunications security solutions; risk
analysis & disaster recovery planning; computer forensics
& fraud investigations; information mgmt strategies;
identity authentication software. (Woman/White, estab
1988, empl 20, sales , cert: State, WBENC)

4476   Nadicent Technologies LLC
        2389 Main St Glastonbury, CT 06033
        (860) 659-2600 Frank Gomes Director
        Fax: (866) 265-9800
        Email: frank.gomes@nadicent.com
        Website: www.nadicent.com
Advanced Managed Security, Conferencing, Video, Web &
Audio, Cloud Services, Disaster Recovery, Help Desk
Services, Microsoft Azure, Office 365 Enterprise Suites,
Data Centers, Colocation, Infrastructure. (As-Pac, estab
2003, empl 10, sales $9,000,000, cert: NMSDC)

4477   OutSecure Inc.
        Shelton Pointe, 2 Trap Falls Rd Ste 401 Shelton, CT
        06484
        (203) 816-8061 Pamela Gupta President
        Fax:
        Email: pamela.gupta@outsecure.com
        Website: www.outsecure.com
Cyber Security assessment & security programs, risk
assessments. (As-Pac, estab 2003, empl 7, sales $300,000,
cert: NMSDC)

4478   PCC Technology Group
        2 Barnard Lane bloomfield, CT 06002
        (860) 466-7261 Jo Gumbs Mktg Coord
        Fax:
        Email: jomal.gumbs@pcctg.com
        Website: www.pcctg.com
Software development. (AA/As-Pac, estab 1995, empl 50,
sales , cert: NMSDC)

4479   PCNet, Inc.
        100 Technology Dr Trumbull, CT 06611
        (203) 452-8559 Erik Soto VP Finance/Ops
        Fax: (203) 452-8656
        Email: eriks@pcnet-inc.com
        Website: www.pcnet-inc.com
Network systems integrator; e-commerce, Internet/
Intranet; resell of personal computer products & svcs.
(Hisp, estab 1993, empl 65, sales $26,000,000, cert:
NMSDC)

4480   Saisystems International
        5 Research Dr Shelton, CT 06484
        (203) 929-0790 Chirag Modi VP Technology
        Services
        Fax: (203) 929-6948
        Email: cmodi@saisystems.com
        Website: www.saisystems.com
Informatation technology consulting: disaster recovery
planning, dataware & database mgmt systems, quality
assurance svcs. (Woman/As-Ind, estab 1987, empl 350,
sales $18,080,000, cert: State, NMSDC)

4481   Source IT Technologies, LLC
        24 East Ave, Ste 244 New Canaan, CT 06840
        (203) 252-0439 Kara Homan CEO
        Fax: (203) 966-0474
        Email: khoman@sourceittech.com
        Website: www.sourceittech.com
Technology solutions. (Woman/White, estab 2012, empl
7, sales $8,696,000, cert: WBENC)

4482   Stratoserve LLC
        18 Colonial Ct Cheshire, CT 06410
        (203) 768-5690 Subroto Roy President
        Fax: (203) 271-8051
        Email: subroto.roy@stratoserve.com
        Website: www.stratoserve.com
consulting, research and training for the following
NAICS codes:541720,541613,611430 and is committed
to provide quick and measurable value to its clients.
(As-Pac, estab 2005, empl 1, sales , cert: NMSDC)

4483   Technosteps LLC
        3 Hayes Ave Unit B Norwalk, CT 06855
        (703) 864-4848 Narayan Venugopal President
        Fax: (866) 496-6797
        Email: Narayan.venugopal@technosteps.com
        Website: www.technosteps.com
IT Staffing. (As-Ind, estab 2012, empl 3, sales $189,000,
cert: State)

4484   Terrelonge Mastercopy Inc.
        45 Church St Suite 302, CT 06906
        (203) 325-4408 Renee Lunchana CMO
        Fax: (203) 547-6007
        Email: rlt@cdmastercopy.com
        Website: www.cdmastercopy.com
CD ROM/DVD ROM replication & duplication services.
(Woman/AA, estab 2000, empl 5, sales $800,000, cert:
State)

4485   The Computer Company, Inc.
        15 Commerce Dr Cromwell, CT 06416
        (860) 635-0500 Eileen Hasson President
        Fax: (860) 635-3550
        Email: ehasson@www.computercompany.net
        Website: www.computercompany.net
Network engineering, internet connectivity, system
firewalls & security, remote system monitoring, IT
outsourcing, custom programming & integration.
(Woman, estab 1995, empl 22, sales $3,750,000, cert:
State, NMSDC)

4486   The Computer Support People, LLC
       16 River St Upper Level Norwalk, CT 06850
       (203) 653-4643 Cassandre Jean Business Dev
       Fax: (203) 653-4698
       Email: Cassandre.Jean@TCSP360.com
       Website: www.tcsp360.com
Managed Computer Services. Computer Software &
Hardware support. (Hisp, estab 2005, empl 8, sales
$419,362, cert: State, NMSDC)

4487   Transcend Business Solutions, LLC
       30 Grassy Plain St, Unit 5A   Bethel, CT 06801
       (203) 790-5222 Linda Rowan President
       Fax: (203) 790-5888
       Email: linda.rowan@transcendbus.com
       Website: www.transcendbus.com
IT consulting firm & employment recruiting. (Woman/
White, estab 2003, empl 10, sales $850,000, cert: WBENC)

4488   Virpie Inc
       1 Reservoir Office Pk, Ste 208 1449 Old Waterbury
       Rd Southbury, CT 06488
       (203) 264-0999 Shre Thammana President
       Fax: (203) 264-1799
       Email: shre@virpietech.com
       Website: www.virpietech.com
Information technology staffing, storage area network
design, architecture & administration, disaster recovery,
database developers & administrators, senior & project
management. (As-Pac, estab 1997, empl 150, sales
$4,725,000, cert: State, NMSDC)

4489   VisionPoint LLC
       152 Rockwell Rd Newington, CT 06111
       (860) 436-9673 Louise Mastroianni Acct Mgr
       Fax: (860) 436-9790
       Email: visionpointct@gmail.com
       Website: www.visionpointllc.com
Technology acquisition, integration, design, installation,
technical meeting support & service. (Woman/White,
estab 2003, empl 24, sales $7,002,015, cert: WBENC)

District of Columbia

4490   A&A
       20 F St NW Ste 700 Washington, DC 20001
       (202) 505-1431 Aditya Dahagam VP - Business &
       Strategy
       Fax: (202) 478-0216
       Email: adahagam@adincorp.com
       Website: www.adincorp.com
ITSM & ITIL process improvement, Software/Application
Development, IT Business Analytics, BPR, Quality Assur-
ance, Systems Engineering, IT & Organizational Strategy.
(As-Ind, estab 2011, empl , sales , cert: State, NMSDC, 8(a),
SDB)

4491   Centricity Technology Partners, Inc.
       621 Quackenbos St NW Washington, DC 20011
       (202) 696-5270 Shonta Williams CEO
       Fax: (202) 827-0091
       Email: swilliams@centricity-us.com
       Website: www.centricity-us.com
Cloud, Mobile & SOA Application Development, Enter-
prise Architecture, Program/Project Management,
Architecture & Engineering, Business Process
Reengineering, Operations & Maintenance, IT Gover-
nance, Independent Validation & Verification. (Woman/
AA, estab 2012, empl 4, sales $1,451,000, cert: WBENC,
8(a))

4492   E-Logic, Inc.
       1025 Connecticut Ave NW Ste 1000 Washington,
       DC 20036
       (202) 499-7837 Luis F Padilla CEO
       Fax: (703) 349-6228
       Email: lpadilla@e-logic.us
       Website: www.e-logic.us
IT Hardware, Software, System Integration, IT Services.
(Hisp, estab 2007, empl 20, sales $8,500,000, cert: 8(a),
SDB)

4493   Evans & Chambers Technology LLC
       635 Florida Ave NW   Washington, DC 20001
       (202) 768-7330 Andre Chambers COO
       Fax:
       Email: andre.chambers@evanschambers.com
       Website: www.evanschambers.com
Software development, Project management, Cloud
computing, Mentor Protege, Insider Threat, Personnel
security, cybersecurity, Immigration, Counterterrorism,
DevOps, Big Data, Mobile, Application development,
Asset Management. (AA, estab 2003, empl 45, sales
$3,372,565, cert: State)

4494   FWG Solutions, Inc.
       1725 I St, NW Ste 520 Washington, DC 20006
       (202) 391-0058 Vincent L. Dixon Capture Exec
       Fax:
       Email: vince.dixon@fwgsolutions.com
       Website: www.fwgsolutions.com
Information Technology (IT) solutions, Cyber Security,
Wireless Systems, and Distributed Antenna Solutions.
(AA, estab 2010, empl 75, sales $5,000,000, cert: 8(a))

4495   Logistics Systems Incorporated
       1100 G St, NW Ste 410 Washington, DC 20005
       (202) 347-0821 Henry Jennings Sr VP Business
       Devel
       Fax: (215) 879-6702
       Email: henry.jennings@logistics-sys.com
       Website: www.logistics-sys.com
LSI offers a full range of technical and management
support services focused on providing integrated
logistics management and life cycle support, information
technology services, and program management support
(AA, estab 2002, empl 125, sales $15,000,000, cert: 8(a))

4496 Optimus Technologies, LLC
      700 12th St NW Ste 700 Washington, DC 20005
      (202) 263-7370 Donald Jones CEO
      Fax: (202) 263-7369
      Email: djones@optimustech.net
      Website: www.optimustech.net
Document scanning, black & white copy, color copy,
records mgmt & retention, electronic data processing,
computer forensics, foreign language document conversion, web hosting, backup tape restoration, document
printing. (AA, estab 2005, empl 20, sales $8,000,000, cert:
NMSDC)

4497 Peak Technology Solutions, Inc.
      1627 K St, NW, Ste 400   Washington, DC 20006
      (202) 776-7196 Mohammad Tariq President
      Fax:
      Email: mtariq@peaktsinc.com
      Website: www.peaktsinc.com
COTS implementation, system integration, database design
& application development services, Geographic Information System (GIS) solutions, and web enabled automation.
(As-Ind, estab 2002, empl 9, sales $645,948, cert: State)

4498 SupreTech, Inc.
      7600 Georgia Ave, NW Ste LL Washington, DC
      20012
      (202) 726-7200 Ignatius Ogu CEO
      Fax: (202) 204-6046
      Email: ig.ogu@supretech.com
      Website: www.supretech.com
Database development, internet/intranet solutions,
custom application devel, switches, routers install, config-
ure & support, information security engineering, LAN/
WAN install & configure, Wi-Fi solutions, document mgmt.
(AA, estab 2003, empl 3, sales $1,531,432, cert: 8(a))

4499 The ELOCEN Group
      1341 H St, NE Ste 301 Washington, DC 20002
      (202) 644-8500 Taryn Lewis Director of Ops
      Fax:
      Email: tarynl@elocengroup.com
      Website: www.elocengroup.com
Program & Project Management, Construction Manage-
ment, Interior Design, Information Technology, Facilities/
Logistics, and Healthcare Facilities/Logistics/Management.
(Woman/AA, estab 2007, empl 62, sales $20,089,894, cert:
State, City, WBENC, 8(a))

4500 The Training Institute of Washington DC
      1801 10 St NW   Washington, DC 20001
      (202) 797-9099 Belinda Pirtle Business Dev Mgr
      Fax: (202) 797-7791
      Email: bpirtle@traindc.com
      Website: www.traindc.com
Customized training, network security & project management certification training, facility rentals & contract
trainers. (AA, estab 2001, empl 2, sales $100,000, cert:
State)

4501 VIRE Consulting Inc.
      730 Quincy St NW   Washington, DC 20011
      (703) 688-3008 Raj Bandi Program Dir
      Fax:
      Email: raj.bandi@vireconsulting.com
      Website: www.vireconsulting.com
IT services & solutions, emerging technologies, rapid
mobile application development, business intelligence &
data analytics. (Hisp, estab 2008, empl 49, sales
$7,000,000, cert: 8(a), SDB)

4502 vTech Solution Inc.
      1100 H Street NW Ste 450 Washington, DC 20005
      (202) 683-9364 Avinash Kumar Sr Client Relation-
      ship Exec
      Fax: (866) 733-4974
      Email: avinashk@vtechsolution.us
      Website: www.vtechsoln.com
IT staffing, permanent & temporary. (Woman/As-Pac,
estab 2006, empl 44, sales $12,000,000, cert: State, SDB)

Delaware

4503 Alpha Technologies USA, Inc.
      704 N King St   Wilmington, DE 19801
      (302) 304-8421 Amrit Gurung COO
      Fax: (908) 847-0395
      Email: amrit@alphaIT.us
      Website: www.alphaIT.us
Information technology staffing & consulting, project
mgmt, software devel, systems integration, datacenter
mgmt. (Woman/Hisp, estab 1997, empl 200, sales
$42,000,000, cert: NMSDC)

4504 DecisivEdge LLC
      131 Continental Dr Ste 409 Newark, DE 19713
      (302) 299-1570 Michele Frayler
      Fax: (302) 299-1578
      Email: michele.frayler@decisivedge.com
      Website: www.decisivedge.com
Business consulting & technology services, business
architecture & performance, business analytics, data
warehouse strategy, design, development & governance,
marketing analytics development. (As-Ind, estab 2007,
empl 41, sales $4,739,862, cert: NMSDC)

4505 Frontier Technologies, Inc.
      1521 Concord Pike Ste 302 Wilmington, DE
      19803
      (302) 225-2530 Reshma Moorthy President
      Fax: (302) 766-7080
      Email: rmoorthy@ftiusa.com
      Website: www.ftiusa.com
Develop & deploy integrated business solutions: front
office apps, IT staff augmentation, CRM, supply chain
mgmt & computer telephony. (Woman/As-Ind, estab
1989, empl 25, sales $8,400,000, cert: City, NMSDC,
WBENC)

4506   LiivData Inc.
        1201 N Orange St Ste 7065 Wilmington, DE 19801
        (302) 235-3040 Dominic Francis Oguejiofo CEO
        Fax:
        Email: dom.francis@liivdata.com
        Website: www.liivdata.com
Information & systems integration, communications
services, Voip technology. (AA, estab 2010, empl 15, sales
$3,850,000, cert: State)

4507   MWIDM Inc.
        913 N Market St, Ste 200   Wilmington, DE 19801
        (302) 298-0101 Amrinder Romana President
        Fax: (302) 298-0102
        Email: amrinder.romana@mwidm.com
        Website: www.mwidm.com
IT services, staffing, consulting and product implementation. (Woman/As-Ind, estab 2004, empl 2800, sales
$69,111,600, cert: NMSDC)

4508   Star Communication, Inc.
        41 Westbridge Rd   Bear, DE 19701
        (302) 836-4054 Larry Whitfield VP
        Fax: (302) 836-8652
        Email: starcomm@starcomm.biz
        Website: www.starcomm.biz
IT business solutions: staffing, developers, technical
architects, database administrators, technical writers,
project managers, help desk personnel. (Woman/AA, estab
2001, empl 7, sales , cert: State)

Florida

4509   A. Harold and Associates, LLC
        7595 Baymeadows Way Ste 100 Jacksonville, FL
        32256
        (904) 535-2290 Andrew E Harold Jr. President
        Fax: (904) 212-0993
        Email: contracts@aha-llc.com
        Website: www.aha-llc.com
Engineering, training, e-learning, software development,
aviation systems, V-22, H-60, project & program mgmt,
technical publications, custom application dev, CBT, WBT.
(AA, estab 2003, empl 260, sales $27,521,267, cert: SDB)

4510   Action 9-A, Inc.
        10416 New Berlin Rd   Jacksonville, FL 32226
        (904) 696-9191 William Valentino President
        Fax: (904) 696-9192
        Email: action9a@earthlink.net
        Website: www.action9astorage.com
Moving totes/dollies rentals; specialized equipment for
modular furniture; breakdown and reconfiguration for
modular furniture systems; corporate moving and storage
(Hisp, estab 1999, empl 12, sales $800,000, cert: NMSDC)

4511   Advanced IT Concepts, Inc.
        1351 Sundial Point   Winter Springs, FL 32708
        (407) 914-2484 Gabriel Ruiz President
        Fax: (321) 323-1376
        Email: eve.maldonado@aitcinc.com
        Website: www.aitcinc.com
Telecommunications & IT services. (Hisp, estab 2006, empl
51, sales $24,860,693, cert: City, 8(a))

4512   Advanced Systems Design, Inc.
        2450 Tim Gamble Pl Ste 200 Tallahassee, FL
        32308
        (850) 385-5129 John Adams VP
        Fax: (850) 385-1934
        Email: john.adams@asd-web.com
        Website: www.asd-web.com
Operational support services, help desk & call centers,
staff augmentation, web-based disease surveillance
applications, network support, design & development,
implementation, monitoring & management. (Nat Ame,
estab 1979, empl 80, sales $7,570,227, cert: State)

4513   Almond Consulting Group
        5472 Baytowne Place   Oviedo, FL 32765
        (407) 602-8540 Derrick Henry President
        Fax:
        Email: derrick.henry@almondconsulting.com
        Website: www.almondconsulting.com
Information technology consulting solutions: Project
Management, Information Assurance, Certification &
Accreditation & Process Improvement. (AA, estab 2001,
empl 1, sales $63,000, cert: State, City, NMSDC)

4514   Amzur Technologies, Inc.
        405 N Reo St Ste # 110 Tampa, FL 33609
        (813) 600-4060 Bala Nemani CEO
        Fax: (813) 600-4061
        Email: supplier@amzur.com
        Website: www.amzur.com
Information technology, information security, anti-virus,
firewalls, operating systems, IT services, Web e-commerce, LAN / WAN, network management, staff augmentation, servers, workflow, imaging, asset management.
(Woman/As-Pac, estab 2004, empl 200, sales
$22,173,714, cert: State, NMSDC)

4515   Auritas
        4907 International Pkwy Ste 1051 Sanford, FL
        32771
        (407) 834-8324 Anne Cross Dir of Mktg
        Fax: (407) 386-7444
        Email: rfp@auritas.com
        Website: www.auritas.com
SAP Consulting Services & Project Management services,
Data Lifecycle Management. (Woman/White, estab
2003, empl 75, sales $7,400,000, cert: WBENC)

4516   Beacon Systems, Inc.
        3928 Coral Ridge Dr   Coral Springs, FL 33065
        (954) 426-1171 Brian Tupiak Contracts Admin
        Fax: (954) 426-1181
        Email: info@beacongov.com
        Website: www.beacongov.com
Information technology training & support, security
systems, program management, performance consulting,
software & program training, systems security, systems
& networking engineering support, web design &
development. (Woman/As-Ind, estab 2005, empl 20,
sales $500,000, cert: State, NMSDC)

4517 BlueStreak Learning, LLC
P.O. Box 110435 Naples, FL 34108
(630) 842-1865 Jennifer De Vries President
Fax: (866) 870-6105
Email: jennifer@bluestreaklearning.com
Website: www.bluestreaklearning.com
Technology-based training programs: needs assessments, e-learning strategy, LMS selection, course development svcs, evaluation/ROI analysis. (Woman/White, estab 2003, empl 3, sales $500,000, cert: WBENC)

4518 Braille Works International, Inc.
941-942 Darby Lake St Seffner, FL 33584
(813) 654-4050 Jeff Frcho Mktg
Fax: (813) 689-8628
Email: jeff@brailleworks.com
Website: www.brailleworks.com
Braille, large print, audio & computerized documents. (Woman/White, estab 1994, empl 12, sales $1,250,000, cert: WBENC)

4519 Business Information Technology Solutions.Com
100 S. Orange Ave Ste 800 Orlando, FL 32801
(407) 363-0024 Amy Seaman Acct Exec
Fax: (407) 363-7471
Email: amy@abtsolutions.com
Website: www.abtsolutions.com
IT staffing. (Woman/White, estab 2000, empl 25, sales $4,700,000, cert: State, City, WBENC, NWBOC)

4520 C&C International Computers and Consultants, Inc.
7777 N Davie Rd Ext Ste 100 A Hollywood, FL 33024
(954) 450-0023 Bill James President
Fax: (954) 450-0024
Email: bjames@ccintercomputers.com
Website: www.ccintercomputers.com
Value Added Reseller (VAR) Services, Support Services & IT Staffing, Computer Installations, Product Rollouts & Deployments, Consulting Services & Project Management, Onsite & Remote Help Desk Support. (Woman/AA, estab 1995, empl 27, sales , cert: State, City, NMSDC)

4521 Carter Brothers Technology
500 W Cypress Creek Rd Ste 650 Fort Lauderdale, FL 33309
(954) 771-0574 Jeff Davis President
Fax: (954) 489-1302
Email: info@carterbrotherstech.com
Website: www.carterbrotherstech.com
IT services & document management solutions. (AA, estab 1990, empl 15, sales $8,000,000, cert: NMSDC)

4522 Corpotel, Inc
2800 Glades Circle Ste. 146 Weston, FL 33327
(954) 364-7045 Elias Benaim Sales
Fax: (954) 385-5215
Email: ebenaim@corpotel.com
Website: www.corpotel.com
Telecom expense mgmt, call accounting, multi-store telecom svcs, call center software dev, bilingual call center outsourcing. (Hisp, estab 2001, empl 15, sales $1,000,000, cert: NMSDC)

4523 Craig Technical Consulting, Inc.
7177 N Atlantic Ave Cape Canaveral, FL 32920
(321) 613-5620 Greg Sheppard Dir, Business Devel
Fax:
Email: greg.sheppard@craigtechinc.com
Website: www.craigtechinc.com
Software Design and Development, Systems Engineering and Integration, Multidisciplinary Engineering, Training and Courseware Development, Modeling and Simulation, Information Technology Support and Integrated Logistics Support. (Woman/Hisp, estab 1999, empl 413, sales , cert: NMSDC, WBENC, SDB)

4524 Curia Document Solutions LLC
815 North Homestead Blvd. Ste #646 Homestead, FL 33030
(888) 516-5193 Lourdes Cox President
Fax: (305) 615-1288
Email: sales@curiausa.com
Website: www.curiausa.com
On-site & Off-site Document Production & Reprographics, Imaging Services, On-site & Offsite Scanning & Data Conversion, Document Utilization & Coding, Document Clustering for Review Prioritization, Auto Coding. (Woman/Hisp, estab 2011, empl 5, sales $100,000, cert: State)

4525 Damasco Design Inc
7136 Crescent Creek Way Coconut Creek, FL 33073
(954) 361-6600 Jorge Castillo President
Fax: (954) 314-0600
Email: jorge@damascodesign.com
Website: www.damasco.io
Web Application solutions & Cloud systems integration. (Hisp, estab 2013, empl 1, sales $91,353, cert: State)

4526 Dbsys Inc.
5224 W State Rd 46, Ste 369 Sanford, FL 32771
(497) 322-7832 Matthew Hudson Field Tech/Mktg
Fax:
Email: matt@dbsys.com
Website: www.dbsys.com
Hardware Solutions, PCs, Notebooks, Storage & File Servers Networking Solutions, Certified Novell Engineer (CNE) on staff Supporting Windows, Sales Solutions. (Woman/White, estab 1990, empl 13, sales $2,200,000, cert: State)

4527 Digital Hands
400 N Tampa St 17th Fl Tampa, FL 33602
(877) 229-8020 Karen Krymski Dir strategic initiatives
Fax: (813) 338-4949
Email: kkrymski@digitalhands.com
Website: www.digitalhands.com
Outsourced IT managed services: IT security (assurance) – enterprise data security, data loss prevention, endpoint security, infrastructure security & management. (Woman, estab 2001, empl 25, sales $2,225,000, cert: WBENC)

4528   Easy Verification Inc.
       7050 W Palmetto Park Rd Ste 15-256 Boca Raton,
       FL 33433
       (877) 904-7770 Lisa Bruno President
       Fax: (888) 908-1020
       Email: lbruno@easyverification.com
       Website: www.easyverification.com
4506-T Fulfillment, IRS Tax Transcript Verification. Income
Verification, SSN & ID Validation. Web-based verification
application. (Woman/White, estab 2006, empl 3, sales ,
cert: State, SDB)

4529   Ebyte Technologies, Inc.
       7855 NW 12th St Ste 214 & 212 Miami, FL 33126
       (786) 358-9300 Rahul Kone Mgr, Business Devel
       Fax: (866) 903-5298
       Email: rahul@ebytetechnologies.com
       Website: www.ebytetechnologies.com
Technology staffing, placing contract, project solutions &
permanent placement opportunities. (Woman/As-Ind,
estab 2009, empl 70, sales $5,400,000, cert: City)

4530   Employer Management Solutions, Inc.
       5550 W Executive Dr Ste 450 Tampa, FL 33609
       (813) 287-2486 Jennifer Johnston
       Fax: (813) 286-9564
       Email: jjohnston@consultems.com
       Website: www.consultems.com
Info technology svcs: enterprise wide initiatives; vendor
selection, software implementation & project planning
svcs. (Woman/White, estab 1998, empl 30, sales
$4,000,000, cert: WBENC)

4531   ExecuSys, Inc.
       551 S Apollo Blvd, Ste 104   Melbourne, FL 32901
       (321) 253-0077 Eddie Haralson President
       Fax: (321) 253-0099
       Email: eharalson@execusys.com
       Website: www.execusys.com
Software engineering & information technology services,
financial management systems support & range operations
cost modelling solutions. (AA, estab 1993, empl 20, sales
$2,155,571, cert: State)

4532   FermiTron, Inc.
       8129 Tumeric Ct   Orlando, FL 32817
       (407) 513-2716 Guilford Cantave President
       Fax: (877) 781-2345
       Email: gcantave@fermitron.com
       Website: www.fermitron.com
Commercial, industrial, medical & military/aerospace
development; R&D, Analog & Digital Circuit Design,
Firmware Development & Implementation, Schematic
Capture, PCB Layout, RF, Wireless, Circuit Prototyping &
Assembly. (AA, estab 2012, empl 1, sales $25,766, cert:
State, NMSDC)

4533   Freedom Solutions LLC
       19046 Bruce B Downs Blvd, Ste 108   Tampa, FL
       33647
       (404) 713-7777 Kelli Covel Dir Business Dev
       Fax: (813) 994-0853
       Email: kcovel@freedomsolutionsllc.com
       Website: www.freedomsolutionsllc.com
IBM Business partner, dist IBM software & hardware,
aintenance, programming services & installation
services. (AA, estab 2002, empl 18, sales $12,000,000,
cert: NMSDC)

4534   GDKN Corporation
       1779 North University Dr Ste 102 Pembroke
       Pines, FL 33024
       (954) 985-6650 Dave Das Staffing Project Coord
       Fax: (954) 985-6652
       Email: ddas@gdkn.com
       Website: www.gdkn.com
Staffing: information technology, engineering, professional, administrative & clerical, IT consulting, custom
application development. (As-Ind, estab 1993, empl 400,
sales $18,000,000, cert: State, NMSDC)

4535   Global Information Technology
       8905 Regents Park Dr Ste 210 Tampa, FL 33647
       (813) 973-1061 Aruna Ajjarapu VP
       Fax: (212) 202-3628
       Email: araj@git-org.com
       Website: www.git-org.com
IT developers, DBA's, project managers & architects.
(Woman/As-Pac, estab 1995, empl 300, sales
$36,000,000, cert: State)

4536   ICG Software Corporation
       2860 W State Rd 84 Ste 113 Fort Lauderdale, FL
       33312
       (305) 933-9100 Tiffany Nutt Office Mgr
       Fax:
       Email: info@icgsoftware.us
       Website: www.icgsoftware.us
Mfr Point of Sale Software & Hardware for the retail and
restaurant industry. (Woman/Hisp, estab 2010, empl 5,
sales $200,000, cert: State)

4537   ITG Global, LLC
       11235 St. Johns Industrial Pkwy N Ste 2A Jackson-
       ville, FL 32246
       (904) 425-4760 Joseph Lukowski CEO
       Fax:
       Email: almaferrante@itgtec.com
       Website: www.itgtec.com
Automation Design, PLC Programming, Software
Development, Technologies Consulting, Motion Design,
Robot programming, MES, OEE, Data Analytics, Condi-
tion Monitoring, Control System Design, UL 508A Panel
Shop, Control Panel. (Woman/Hisp, estab 2003, empl 27,
sales $3,000,000, cert: NMSDC)

4538　Kolter Solutions
　　　3954 Lake Mira Dr　Orlando, FL 32817
　　　(866) 933-6984　Jenny Toney Acct Mgr
　　　Fax: (561) 683-7739
　　　Email: jtoney@koltersolutions.com
　　　Website: www.koltersolutions.com
Information Technology Staff Augmentation, Project
Teams, Application Design and Development (Java, C/C++,
.NET/C#), Business Analysis/Project Management/Program
Management, Quality Assurance, Infrastructure/Network/
Security. (Woman/White, estab 2010, empl 28, sales
$1,300,000, cert: WBENC)

4539　LebenTech Innovative Solutions Inc.
　　　P.O. Box 670832　Coral Springs, FL 33067
　　　(954) 796-7107　Lennox Bennett President
　　　Fax: (954) 323-4784
　　　Email: lennox_bennett@lebentech.com
　　　Website: www.lebentech.com
Technology consultation svcs: CAD designs, product
development, RAMS analysis, R&D, FRACAS implementa-
tion, product validation, reliability testing. (AA, estab 2004,
empl 6, sales $106,250, cert: State)

4540　Lodestar Solutions, Inc.
　　　3212 W Harbor View Ave　Tampa, FL 33611
　　　(813) 415-2910　Heather Cole President
　　　Fax: (866) 697-8824
　　　Email: hcole@lodestarsolutions.com
　　　Website: www.lodestarsolutions.com
IBM business analytics/Cognos reseller & IBM support
renewals, IBM Cognos licenses, TM1, Cognos business
intelligence, FSR, SPSS, Varicent & Cognos planning.
(Woman/White, estab 2004, empl 11, sales $3,949,751,
cert: WBENC)

4541　Mellow Enterprises LLC
　　　201 SW 63rd Ave　Plantation, FL 33317
　　　(954) 312-7175　Helen F Litsky President
　　　Fax: (954) 585-3797
　　　Email: me@mellowllc.com
　　　Website: www.voacorp.com/mellowenterprises.net
Technology, safety & fire related training, medical supplies.
(Woman/AA, estab 2010, empl 1, sales $25,000, cert: City)

4542　N2 Services Inc
　　　13241 Bartram Park Blvd Ste 2301　Jacksonville, FL
　　　32258
　　　(904) 703-4245　Neminathan Ammaiyappan
　　　President
　　　Fax: (866) 778-1020
　　　Email: nemi@n2sglobal.com
　　　Website: www.n2sglobal.com
Software design, development, analysis a& nd consulting
services, internet application development, E-Commerce
solutions, Web 2.0, n-tier architecture & rapid application
development environments. (As-Pac, estab 2004, empl
140, sales $6,580,000, cert: NMSDC)

4543　Noise Consulting Group, Inc.
　　　9280 Bay Plaza Blvd Ste 705　Tampa, FL 33619
　　　(315) 491-0771　Gina Hannah CEO
　　　Fax: (813) 902-6912
　　　Email: gina.hannah@noisetcd.com
　　　Website: www.noisetcd.com
IT staffing, consulting & systems integration, technology
solutions & systems integration & implementation
services. (Woman/AA, estab 2007, empl 38, sales
$1,900,000, cert: State)

4544　Ospro Systems, LLC
　　　1327 LaFayette St Ste C　Cape Coral, FL 33904
　　　(239) 309-0319　Prasad Kasireddy Recruitment
　　　Fax: (866) 908-1231
　　　Email: prasad@osprosys.com
　　　Website: www.osprosys.com
Software Implementations, Software Changes, Custom
Software Development, Software validation/Testing,
Maintenance and Support
Project Management, E-commerce, B2B, B2C, Custom
Web Development, Application Web. (Woman/As-Ind,
estab 2004, empl 70, sales $2,000,000, cert: State,
NMSDC)

4545　Professional Translating Services, Inc.
　　　44 W Flagler St, Ste1800　Miami, FL 33130
　　　(305) 371-7887　Alexandra Hunt Natl Business Dev
　　　Fax: (305) 371-8366
　　　Email: ahunt@protranslating.com
　　　Website: www.protranslating.com
Translate documents, films & websites, interpreting
services & equipment for multilingual meetings.
(Woman/Hisp, estab 1973, empl 100, sales $8,800,000,
cert: NMSDC)

4546　PSR Associates
　　　1170 Peachtree St Ste 1200　Tampa, FL 33647
　　　(404) 600-1043　Stephen Mendoza CEO
　　　Fax: (813) 978-8670
　　　Email: smendoza@PSRAssociates.com
　　　Website: www.psrassociates.com
Information technology, program management, project
management, staff augmentation, web portal, customer
relationship management, IT resources, program testing.
(As-Pac, estab 2003, empl 43, sales $7,900,000, cert:
NMSDC)

4547　Qualex Consulting Services, Inc.
　　　11900 Biscayne Blvd, Ste 801　North Miami, FL
　　　33181
　　　(305) 576-0255　Cecilia Pedrazzoli VP sales/new
　　　Business Dev
　　　Fax: (305) 675-5751
　　　Email: cecilia.pedrazzoli@qlx.com
　　　Website: www.qlx.com
Software solutions & consulting services. (Woman/Hisp,
estab 1995, empl 65, sales $8,100,000, cert: State)

4548   RADgov Inc
       6750 N. Andrews Ave, Ste 200   Fort Lauderdale, FL
       33309
       (954) 938-2800 Pranay mishra Capture Mgr
       Fax: (954) 938-2004
       Email: parcher@radgov.com
       Website: www.radgov.com
IT planning services, system planning, development &
implementation, electronic commerce, training & support,
program management. (Woman/As-Pac, estab 2005, empl
150, sales $15,400,000, cert: NMSDC, WBENC)

4549   Readix Inc.
       4134 SW 131 Ave   Davie, FL 33330
       (954) 636-6983 Javier Abuabara CFO
       Fax: (954) 302-2769
       Email: javier.ab@readixtechnologies.com
       Website: www.readixtechnologies.com
Engineering svcs: electronic design, software development, mechanical design, system integration, embedded
telecommunication, consulting. (Hisp, estab 2003, empl 3,
sales $394,375, cert: State)

4550   RIK Data Solutions Inc.
       8875 Hidden River Pkwy Ste 300 Tampa, FL 33637
       (941) 527-1464 Chris Kambhampati Principal
       Architect
       Fax: (732) 358-1464
       Email: krk@rds-us.com
       Website: www.rds-us.com
Datacenter Systems Integration, Cloud Brokerage Services,
Software Development,
Graphic Art and Design Services (for Web and Promotional
products). (Woman/As-Pac, estab 2012, empl 6, sales
$1,540,000, cert: NMSDC)

4551   Riley Technology Solutions, Inc.
       3030 N Rocky Point Dr W   Tampa, FL 33607
       (813) 908-4190 John Riley President
       Fax: (813) 856-4508
       Email: jerile1@rileyts.com
       Website: www.rileyts.com
Managed IT equipment & services: LAN/WAN, computing
design, custom software solutions & integrating systems,
web-based data mining & reporting. (AA, estab 2002, empl
10, sales $7,500,000, cert: State)

4552   Rudram Engineering, Inc.
       845 Executive Dr, Ste 200   Rockledge, FL 32955
       (317) 313-5393 Stephen Vitch VP Business Devel
       Fax: (317) 299-9131
       Email: svitch@rudramengineering.com
       Website: www.rudramengineering.com
System design, development, verification & validation, EMI
analysis, Concept analysis, trade studies, emerging
technology research, Software development, embedded
system support, Interface identification, definition, design
and system safety. (As-Ind, estab 2015, empl 27, sales
$566,000, cert: State, NMSDC, SDB)

4553   SDI International Corp
       1000 Corporate Dr Ste 200   Ft. Lauderdale, FL
       33334
       (954) 938-5400 Carmen Castillo President
       Fax: (954) 772-5061
       Email: sdidiversity@sdintl.com
       Website: www.sdintl.com
Staffing & business solutions, staff augmentation, e-
vendor mgmt services. (Woman/Hisp, estab 1992, empl
1500, sales $600,000,000, cert: NMSDC, WBENC)

4554   Securance LLC
       13904 Monroes Business Park   Tampa, FL 33635
       (877) 578-0215 Paul Ashe President
       Fax: (813) 960-4946
       Email: supplydiv@securanceconsulting.com
       Website: www.securanceconsulting.com
Independent technology risk consulting & IT auditing.
(AA, estab 2002, empl 35, sales $1,100,000, cert: State)

4555   SGF US Inc.
       501 Golden Isles Dr, Ste 205   Hallandale Beach, FL
       33009
       (954) 454-7676 Mauricio Sion Managing Dir
       Fax: (954) 454-5476
       Email: msion@sgfglobal.com
       Website: www.sgfglobal.com
Technical recruiting & staffing. (Hisp, estab 1997, empl
82, sales $7,125,838, cert: NMSDC)

4556   SGS Technologies
       6817 Southpoint Pkwy, Ste 2104   Jacksonville, FL
       32216
       (904) 332-4534 Arun Venkatesan CEO
       Fax: (904) 687-0178
       Email: bids@sgstechnologies.net
       Website: www.sgstechnologies.net
Custom Software Applications Development, Mobile
Apps Development, Website Design, Digital Marketing,
SEO, Salesforce Implementation, CRM, SharePoint
Development. (As-Pac, estab 2003, empl 150, sales
$15,000,000, cert: State, NMSDC)

4557   Simplified Technologies, LLC
       6310 Techster Blvd, Ste 2   Fort Myers, FL 33966
       (239) 210-9645 Darius Joseph Owner
       Fax:
       Email: darius@simplifiedtech.biz
       Website: www.simplifiedtech.biz
Network & systems integration, Windows Servers, Small
Business Server, SQL Server, Exchange Server, Windows
Desktop, Microsoft Office & Office 365. (AA, estab 2010,
empl 10, sales , cert: State)

4558   Sonoi Solutions LLC
       800 6th St N   St. Petersburg, FL 33701
       (727) 341-5100 Vienggeun Gertsch President
       Fax: (727) 341-5085
       Email: vienggeun.gertsch@sonoisolutions.com
       Website: www.sonoisolutions.com
IT aggregation, logistics & technical services for supply
chain diversification. (Woman/As-Pac, estab 2013, empl
2, sales , cert: NMSDC, WBENC)

4559   Southeastern Aerospace Services, LLC
1816 SW 7th Ave   Pompano Beach, FL 33060
(305) 992-8257   Julian Tucker Acctability Mgr
Fax: (954) 450-0024
Email: sales@southeasternaerospace.com
Website: www.southeasternaerospace.com
Southeastern Aerospace Services, LLC., is a certified FAA Repair Station, FAA 145 Cert 8SIR251C. As an independent MRO facility, we provide repair and overhaul of military and commercial aircraft power generating units, ranging from regional to wide/nar (AA, estab 2016, empl 4, sales , cert: NMSDC)

4560   SpendCheQ, Inc.
3171 Jasmine Dr   Delray Beach, FL 33483
(561) 870-3171   Mary Ellen Mitchell President
Fax:
Email: mmitchell@spendcheq.com
Website: www.spendcheq.com
Integrated supply chain & procurement solutions, Catalog Management, Inventory Data Management, Supplier Information Management & Spend Analysis. (Woman/White, estab 2014, empl 19, sales $321,000, cert: State, WBENC)

4561   SRR International, Inc.
6649 Indian Trail Dr   Loxahatchee, FL 33470
(561) 228-8349   Rekha Jadala President
Fax:
Email: rekha@srrintl.com
Website: www.srrintl.com
Systems Architecture Design, Mobile & Web App Development, Information Architecture, Hardware and Software Maintenance. (Woman/As-Ind, estab 2001, empl 5, sales $750,000, cert: 8(a))

4562   SurfBigData LLC
4474 Foxtail Ln   Weston, FL 33331
(954) 353-5599   Andrew Li CEO
Fax:
Email: service@surfbigdata.com
Website: www.surfbigdata.com
Enterprise Workflow Analysis, Information Technology, Architecture & System Integration, Dev/Ops & Agile Scrum Plan & Management, Web Application Development, Central Information Repository Design, Big Data Platform design. (As-Pac, estab 2015, empl 6, sales $480,000, cert: State)

4563   Synergy Technologies, LLC
9600 W Sample Rd, Ste 207   Coral Springs, FL 33065
(954) 775-0064   Srikaanth Bollampally Program Mgr
Fax: (954) 775-0010
Email: sri.b@synergytechs.net
Website: www.synergyteks.com
Synergy Technologies has excellent domain competencies in verticals such as Banking & Financial Service, Insurance & Healthcare, and Manufacturing. As a diverse end-to-end IT solutions provider, offers a range of expertise aimed at helping customers re-en (Woman/As-Ind, estab 2006, empl 65, sales $5,000,000, cert: NMSDC, WBENC)

4564   System Soft Technologies, Inc
3000 Bayport Dr Ste 840   Tampa, FL 33607
(727) 723-0801   Sreedhar Veeramachaneni CEO
Fax: (813) 289-5359
Email: v.sreedhar@sstech.us
Website: www.sstech.us
Software development & IT services. (As-Pac, estab 2000, empl 45, sales $49,557,339, cert: State, NMSDC)

4565   Techno-Transfers of Florida, Inc.
4609 NW 26th Ave   Boca Raton, FL 33434
(561) 212-2383   Virginia Mendiola Director
Fax:
Email: vmendiola@techno-transfers.com
Website: www.techno-transfers.com
IT personnel for temporary contract, temp-to-perm roles & full-time positions. (Woman/Hisp, estab 1992, empl 6, sales $350,000, cert: State)

4566   Tec-Link
16350 BB Downs Blvd, Ste 48942   Tampa, FL 33646
(813) 929-3222   Derek Holmes President
Fax: (813) 929-3202
Email: derek@tec-link.com
Website: www.tec-link.com
Information technology professional services & consulting. (AA, estab 1999, empl 20, sales $2,000,000, cert: State, NMSDC)

4567   Tenosar Corportation
3259 Progress Dr Ste 142   Orlando, FL 32826
(407) 347-2333   Raymond Negron President
Fax: (407) 442-3000
Email: raymondnegron@tenosar.com
Website: www.Tenosar.com
Software Engineering, customized & legacy system integration. (Hisp, estab 2012, empl 8, sales $160,000, cert: 8(a), SDB)

4568   The Goal Inc.
1408 N. Westshore Blvd Ste 705   Tampa, FL 33607
(813) 319-7015   Mary Kate Gowl Managing Dir
Fax:
Email: mgowl@thegoalinc.com
Website: www.thegoalinc.com
Technology Consulting, Software Development, Security Services, and our Government Practice. (Hisp, estab 1998, empl 250, sales $34,000,000, cert: NMSDC, SDB)

4569   Tropical Surveillance & Investigations, Inc.
1813 N Tampa St   Tampa, FL 33602
(813) 282-0074   JC Dominguez
Fax: (813) 258-8825
Email: jc@tsilegal.com
Website: www.tsilegal.com
providing professional services to large and small business law firms insurance companies and private citizens. TSI Deals with all aspects of PROCESS SERVING AND DOUCMENT REPRODUCTION (Woman/Hisp, estab 2003, empl 15, sales $1,100,000, cert: NMSDC)

4570 Vitaver and Associates, Inc.
      401 E Las Olas Blvd, Ste 1400   Fort Lauderdale, FL
      33301
      (954) 382-0075 Pablo Vitaver CEO
      Fax: (866) 256-6365
      Email: registrations@vitaver.com
      Website: www.vitaver.com
IT staff augmentation & software outsourcing. (Hisp, estab
1993, empl 15, sales $6,917,493, cert: State)

4571 Widescope Consulting And Contracting Services LLC
      14466 Kandi Ct   Largo, FL 33774
      (813) 374-5205 Donald Jackson VP of Ops
      Fax: (727) 648-4552
      Email: donald.jackson@widescopeccs.com
      Website: www.widescopeccs.com/
IT, Cyber Security, Submarine Fiber optic cable route
survey, engineering, professional services and consulting
to government entities and large corporations. (AA, estab
2014, empl 6, sales $85,000, cert: 8(a))

Georgia

4572 1Source International, LLC
      925 Woodstock Rd Ste 150 Roswell, GA 30075
      (770) 733-1202 Margaret Tinsley VP of Ops
      Fax: (770) 676-7264
      Email: mtinsley@1source-intl.net
      Website: www.1sourceinternational.com
Audio, video & conferencing solutions. (Woman/White,
estab 2000, empl 11, sales $6,000,000, cert: WBENC)

4573 24X7SYSTEMS, Inc.
      1080 Holcombe Bridge Rd Bldg 200, Ste 150
      Roswell, GA 30076
      (678) 234-2711 Ranjan Dattagupta EVP
      Fax: (888) 987-7032
      Email: ranjan@24x7systems.com
      Website: www.24x7systems.com
Information technology solutions, Resource Sourcing, PM,
Entr Arch, Application Software Development, Systems
Integration & developing SCAM (Security, Cloud, Analytics
Mobility) emerging solutions. (As-Ind, estab 2000, empl
20, sales $4,000,000, cert: 8(a))

4574 3i People, Inc.
      5755 N Point Pkwy Ste 234 Alpharetta, GA 30022
      (678) 628-4810 Buvi Raj CMO
      Fax: (404) 795-0491
      Email: rbuvi@3ipeople.com
      Website: www.3ipeople.com
IT consulting, application dev, project mgmt & contract
staffing. (As-Pac, estab 2002, empl 220, sales $12,300,000,
cert: NMSDC)

4575 Accretive Technologies, Inc.
      330 Research Ct Ste 250 Norcross, GA 30092
      (678) 328-2440 Claire Ehrhardt President
      Fax: (770) 246-9186
      Email: claire@accretive.com
      Website: www.accretive.com
IT consulting & placement services. (Woman/White, estab
1997, empl 17, sales $1,857,679, cert: WBENC)

4576 Adroix Corp DBA CodeForce 360
      11381 Southbridge Parkway C Corporation
      Alpharetta, GA 30022
      (770) 688-0097 Emy Mathew Client Relationship
      Mgr
      Fax: (770) 410-7737
      Email: sales360@codeforce.com
      Website: www.codeforce.com/
IT Staffing & Talent Management. (As-Ind, estab 2010,
empl 250, sales $30,000,000, cert: NMSDC)

4577 All Points Logistics, Inc.
      2567 Athens Hwy   Gainesville, GA 30507
      (770) 503-7474 Phil Monkress Dir info tech
      Fax: (770) 503-9941
      Email: pmonkress@allpointslogistics.com
      Website: www.allpointslogistics.com
Logistics, supply chain mgmt, inventory control, government property mgmt & physical dist, hardware &
software procurement, integration, maintenance &
warranty, help desk & computer center technical
support, systems admin & mgmt support. (Nat Ame,
estab 1997, empl 110, sales $21,000,000, cert: State)

4578 American CyberSystems (ACS Group)
      2400 Meadowbrook Parkway   Duluth, GA 30096
      (678) 310-1251 Marc Cohen VPGlobal Mktg and
      Communications
      Fax: (770) 623-4314
      Email: diversitysupplier@acsicorp.com
      Website: www.acsicorp.com
IT services: staffing, payrolling, vendor management
services, consulting & business solutions. (As-Ind, estab
1998, empl 12000, sales $683,000,000, cert: NMSDC)

4579 Arete Technology Solutions, Inc. dba STATEMENT
      3379 PeachtreeRdNE Ste 555 Atlanta, GA 30326
      (800) 640-5589 Kendall Flagg Principal
      Fax: (404) 946-0271
      Email: kendall.flagg@statementcorp.com
      Website: www.statementcorp.com
Software & IT consulting, Architecture Custom software
development Automated Testing Continuous Development and Integration Oracle Database Development
noSql Development Services Native tablet/mobile iOS.
(AA, estab 2007, empl 12, sales $1,641,519, cert:
NMSDC)

4580 Arion Systems, Inc.
      2741 Calloway Ct   Duluth, GA 30097
      (770) 569-3434 Michael Brewington II President
      Fax:
      Email: michael.brewington@arioncorp.com
      Website: www.ArionCorp.com
Implementation & systems integration consulting:
business applications & ERP products, PeopleSoft, SAP,
Oracle, Siebel, technology solutions, financials, supply
chain mgmt, human capital mgmt, enterprise performance mgmt. (Woman/AA, estab 2003, empl 10, sales
$2,000,000, cert: NMSDC)

4581   ASAP Solutions Group, LLC
3885 Holcomb Bridge Rd   Norcross, GA 30092
(770) 246-1718   Nancy Williams CEO
Fax: (770) 840-0280
Email: nancy@myasap.com
Website: www.myasap.com
IT staff augmentation. (Woman/White, estab 1989, empl 800, sales $60,000,000, cert: State, WBENC)

4582   Axiom Corporation
3565 Piedmont Rd Two Piedmont Center, Ste. 125
Atlanta, GA 30305
(404) 949-8280   Anterro Graham President
Fax: (404) 995-8887
Email: aagraham@axiom-corp.com
Website: www.axiom-corp.com
Software development & systems integration; IT assessment & planning; software independent verification & validation (AA, estab 1988, empl 26, sales $2,179,697, cert: State)

4583   Bellsoft
3545 Cruse Rd, Ste 102   Lawrenceville, GA 30044
(888) 545-7639   Kannan Ramanathan Dir Client Svcs
Fax: (770) 935-4153
Email: kannanr@ameri100.com
Website: www.ameri100.com/
Implement ERP solutions: JD Edwards, SAP & PeopleSoft. (As-Ind/As-Pac, estab 1996, empl 350, sales $30,000,000, cert: NMSDC)

4584   Blaze Information Systems Inc.
13026 Dartmore Ave   Alpharetta, GA 30005
(877) 877-5293   Smita Deshpande CEO
Fax: (877) 482-5293
Email: smita.deshpande@blazeinfosys.com
Website: www.blazeinfosys.com
Onsite Technical Support, Onsite Temporary Technology Staffing, Remote Temporary Technology Staffing, End-To-End e-Business Solutions. (Woman/As-Pac, estab 2009, empl 5, sales $116,000, cert: State)

4585   BlueFletch LLC
621 North Ave NE Ste A-150   Atlanta, GA 30308
(855) 529-6349   Richard Makerson Managing Partner
Fax: (855) 529-6349
Email: invoices@bluefletch.com
Website: www.bluefletch.com
Mobile software development, program leadership, business analysis, mobile web application development, legacy integration, MDM management & cloud infrastructure integration. (AA, estab 2008, empl 34, sales $2,906,767, cert: NMSDC)

4586   Capricorn Systems, Inc.
3569 Habersham At Northlake Bldg K   Tucker, GA 30084
(678) 514-1080   Charles Goldman VP Sales
Fax: (678) 514-1081
Email: cgoldman@capricornsys.com
Website: www.capricornsys.com
Software consulting: staff augmentation, turnkey custom application develpment & permanent placements, on site, offsite & off-shore. (As-Ind/As-Pac, estab 1991, empl 155, sales $3,250,000, cert: NMSDC)

4587   Cellworx LLC
1005 Alderman Ste 110   Alpharetta, GA 30005
(678) 254-9094   Chandrasekhar Anchala
Fax: (678) 807-2981
Email: csanchala@celworx.com
Website: www.celworx.com
Wireless & wireline technology design, development, validation & realization, Software Defined Network, Cloud & Virtualization. (As-Ind, estab 2008, empl 10, sales $500,000, cert: NMSDC, CPUC)

4588   Charter Global Inc.
One Glenlake Parkway Ste 525   Atlanta, GA 30328
(770) 326-9933   Dev Shah Client Engagement Mgr
Fax: (770) 326-9922
Email: dshah@charterglobal.com
Website: www.charterglobal.com
Software consulting svcs: client server, web based, e-commerce. (As-Ind/As-Pac, estab 1994, empl 1100, sales $45,000,000, cert: NMSDC)

4589   CI² Aviation, Inc.
9 Dunwoody Park Dr, Ste 104   Dunwoody, GA 30338
(770) 425-2267   Michael Baylis CEO
Fax: (770) 396-4260
Email: mbaylis@ci2.com
Website: www.ci2.com
CI² Aviation aspires to be one of the nations leading and award winning aerospace companies. Among areas of involvement in the aerospace industry, CI² Aviation operates 21 Air Traffic Control Towers on behalf of the FAA and other government entities. Th (Woman/AA, estab 1993, empl 160, sales , cert: NMSDC)

4590   CI2, Inc.
200 Galleria Pkwy, Ste 1200   Atlanta, GA 30339
(770) 425-2267   Sharon Mendon VP Business Devel
Fax: (770) 933-9572
Email: info2@ci2.com
Website: www.ci2.com
Systems integration & engineering, telecommunications mgmt. (Woman/AA, estab 1993, empl 83, sales $25,000,000, cert: State, City, NMSDC)

4591   CIYIS LLC
2625 Piedmont Rd NE, Ste 56-287   Atlanta, GA 30324
(844) 442-4947   Christian Sellu CEO
Fax:
Email: chris@ciyis.net
Website: www.ciyis.net
SAP ECC, SAP HANA, Program Management, Technical Advisory, (AA, estab 2013, empl 6, sales $230,000, cert: 8(a))

4592 Competent Systems Inc.
4080 McGinnis Ferry Rd Ste 1504 Alpharetta, GA 30005
(678) 691-7120 Sridhar Konkala Mgr
Fax:
Email: skonkala@competentsystems.com
Website: www.competentsystems.com
Information Technology Consulting, Development, Outsourcing & Technology Staffing. (As-Pac, estab 2004, empl 150, sales $15,000,000, cert: NMSDC)

4593 Concept Software & Services Inc
11600 Atlantis Place Ste E Alpharetta, GA 30022
(770) 300-9486 Ravindra Bhave CEO
Fax: (700) 300-9417
Email: ravi@concept-inc.com
Website: www.concept-inc.com
Software solutions, IT consulting, application outsourcing & enterprise consulting services. (As-Ind, estab 1998, empl 57, sales $7,682,520, cert: NMSDC)

4594 Corpnet Consulting LLC
2300 Lakeview Pkwy, Ste 700 Alpharetta, GA 30009
(678) 795-1612 Faisal Ansari Managing Principal
Fax:
Email: corpnet@corpnetconsulting.com
Website: www.corpnetconsulting.com
Information security & risk management consultancy services, IT platform integration services. (Woman/As-Pac, estab 2008, empl 15, sales $1,300,000, cert: WBENC)

4595 Datamatics Consultants Inc.
3505 Duluth Park Ln Ste 200 Duluth, GA 30096
(770) 232-9460 Frank Kulendran Bus Devel Mgr
Fax: (770) 232-9463
Email: frank@datamatics.us
Website: www.datamatics.us
Business process mgmt, financial mgmt, CRP, ERP, consulting & strategy, architecture & integration, custom systems dev, supply chain mgmt, knowledge mgmt, IT strategy, re-engineering & migration services, maintenance. (As-Ind, estab 1993, empl 95, sales $10,000,000, cert: NMSDC)

4596 Dataset, Inc.
145 Noble Ct Ste 100 Alpharetta, GA 30005
(678) 240-0771 Azhar Syed President
Fax: (678) 802-0562
Email: Azhar_Syed@dataset-inc.com
Website: www.datasetcorp.com
Professional consulting services, software & hardware installation, software training & temporary contractors. (As-Ind, estab 1994, empl 7, sales $3,009,031, cert: NMSDC)

4597 DW Practice, LLC
5901 Peachtree Dunwoody Rd Ste C-160 Atlanta, GA 30328
(678) 999-8197 Rajani Koneru President
Fax: (770) 234-6160
Email: raj.koneru@dwpractice.com
Website: www.dwpractice.com
Software development services, product development services & IT staffing services. (As-Pac, estab 1998, empl 30, sales $4,000,000, cert: NMSDC)

4598 Edge Solutions, LLC
7 Old Roswell St Alpharetta, GA 30009
(888) 861-8884 Theresa Jackson Dir, Strategic Business
Fax: (888) 818-1114
Email: tjackson@edge-solutions.com
Website: www.edge-solutions.com
Data center solutions (hardware & software), Application development tools, cloud computing, virtualization, network security, data storage, backup and recovery, archiving, professional & managed services. (Woman/White, estab 2008, empl 34, sales $36,000,000, cert: WBENC)

4599 Enrich Inc
3655 Brookside Pkwy Ste 265 Alpharetta, GA 30022
(770) 667-0510 Paul Herron VP-Sales & Mktg
Fax: (678) 868-1019
Email: info@enrich.com
Website: www.enrich.com
Software deployment lifecycle in Oracle EBS. (Woman/As-Pac, estab 2004, empl 200, sales $17,624,212, cert: NMSDC)

4600 Exalt Integrated Technologies LLC
P.O. Box 888161 Atlanta, GA 30356
(678) 920-3019 Donald Maycott VP
Fax: (636) 216-4963
Email: dmaycott@exaltit.com
Website: www.exaltit.com
Network business consulting, organizational assessment, IT strategic planning, telecommunications services, security assessment, intrusion detection, firewall & DMZ implementation & management. (Woman/AA, estab 2004, empl 15, sales $1,750,000, cert: NMSDC)

4601 Fabulous Sites, Inc.
160 Clairemont Ave, Ste 555 Decatur, GA 30030
(404) 478-2050 Laron Walker President
Fax: (404) 687-9800
Email: walkerla@sciberus.com
Website: www.sciberus.com
Information technology consulting & software development. (AA, estab 2006, empl 5, sales $1,447,158, cert: NMSDC, 8(a))

4602 Firmament Solutions
510 Plaza Dr College Park, GA 30349
(770) 742-0385 Adrian Andrews President
Fax: (813) 258-8825
Email: aandrews@firmamentsolutions.com
Website: www.firmamentsolutions.com
Managed IT Services, Network Services, CAT3 & CAT6 Install, Hosting Software Service, Break FIX, Fiber Patch Panel, Cloud Services, ISP Services, Conduit/Surface Mount, IT Asset Management, Application Support, Voice/Mobile. (AA, estab 2013, empl 10, sales $89,000, cert: State, City, NMSDC)

4603 Fulcher Interactive Group, Inc.
2132 Weldon St Savannah, GA 31415
(912) 398-3739 Eric Fulcher CEO
Fax:
Email: fulcher2132@hotmail.com
Website:
Applications development, IT staffing, logistics support. (AA, estab 2001, empl 2, sales $1,540,000, cert: State)

4604 Global Resource Manangement, Inc.
5400 Laurel Springs Pkwy Ste 902 Suwanee, GA 30024
(678) 456-6992 Naheed Syed CEO
Fax: (678) 456-6999
Email: naheed1@grmi.net
Website: www.grmi.net
IT consulting, telecommunications & staff augmentation. (Woman/As-Pac, estab 1993, empl 70, sales $2,600,000, cert: NMSDC, WBENC)

4605 Global Technology Services Group
2850 Barrett Lakes Blvd Ste 500 Kennesaw, GA 30144
(404) 551-5189 Jacqueline Holland CEO
Fax:
Email: jacqui@gtservices.net
Website: www.gtservices.net
IT Asset Management, Auditing, Inventory Management, Warehouse & Logistics, Project Management & Deployment, Reverse Logistics & Asset Recovery, NSA Level Data Security, Depot Technology Hardware Repair & Refurbishment. (Woman/White, estab 2010, empl 35, sales $5,482,715, cert: State, WBENC)

4606 GSquared Group, LLC
3180 Northpoint Pkwy, Ste 301 Alpharetta, GA 30005
(404) 698-1810 Joan Guillory CEO
Fax: (770) 760-7470
Email: contactus@gsquaredgroup.com
Website: www.gsquaredgroup.com
Technology Talent Solutions for contract, contract-to-hire & direct hire positions, Technology Consulting Solutions for short-term, high-touch, high-value engagements. (Woman, estab 2010, empl 25, sales , cert: WBENC)

4607 GTS, Inc.
1325 Satellite Blvd Bldg 1600, Ste 1601 Suwanee, GA 30024
(770) 497-8637 Dinesh Raturi President
Fax: (770) 497-8651
Email: dinesh@gtsamerica.com
Website: www.gtsamerica.com
IT staff augmentation, permanent & contract, software development, requirement analysis & design, outsourcing. (Woman/As-Ind, estab 1998, empl 150, sales $16,500,000, cert: NMSDC, WBENC)

4608 Heagney Logan Group, LLC
2002 Summit Blvd Ste 300 Atlanta, GA 30319
(404) 267-1351 Jeannette Weigelt Principal
Fax: (404) 267-1351
Email: info@heagneylogan.com
Website: www.heagneylogangroup.com
Management Consulting, IT Consultant Staffing, Project Management, ERP Consulting, Remote Development, Contract Technical Staffing. (AA, estab 2009, empl 3, sales $924,954, cert: State, City, NMSDC)

4609 HireGenics, Inc.
2400 Meadowbrook Parkway Duluth, GA 30096
(1678) 310-1251 Marc Cohen VP Global Mktg and Communication
Fax: (1770) 623-4314
Email: diversitysupplier@hiregenics.com
Website: www.hiregenics.com
Technology consulting & solutions: onsite, near-shore, off-shore, business intelligence, e-business, database technologies, ERP, CRM. (As-Ind, estab 1998, empl 10000, sales $678,000,000, cert: NMSDC)

4610 HI-TEC Professional Solutions, Inc.
2501 E Piedmont Rd Ste 103 Marietta, GA 30062
(770) 575-5855 Gerry Cameron Acct Mgr
Fax: (770) 575-5856
Email: gerry@hi-tecsolutions.com
Website: www.hi-tecsolutions.com
Technical staffing solutions: engineering, information technology & professional services. (Woman/AA, estab 2004, empl 10, sales $5,200,000, cert: 8(a))

4611 IBEX IT Business Experts, LLC
3295 River Exchange Dr Ste 212 Sandy Springs, GA 30092
(678) 381-4957 Tracey Grace CEO
Fax: (770) 696-1012
Email: TGrace@IBEXPartners.com
Website: www.IBEXPartners.com
IT Service Management, Enterprise Governance, Project Management, IT Security Management. (Woman/AA, estab 2012, empl 12, sales $184,000, cert: NMSDC, WBENC)

4612 Impel Professional Consulting, LLC
7058 Wind Run Way Stone Mountain, GA 30082
(678) 410-9245 Jerome Potts Business Dev Dir
Fax:
Email: info@impelprofessional.com
Website: www.impelprofessional.com
Design & develop end-to-end integrated IT Solutions in ERP (SAP, SAP S/4 HANA, PeopleSoft, Oracle, Workday), BI, CRM Assessment for ERP systems and Business process improvements for SAP IT Road Maps and Best Practices. (Woman/AA, estab 2016, empl 2, sales , cert: State)

4613 INDU LLC dba intiGrow
2760 Peach tree Ind. Blvd, Ste D Duluth, GA 30097
(678) 666-4368 Abhishek Pandey Business Dev Exec
Fax: (877) 712-4769
Email: abhishek.pandey@intigrow.com
Website: www.igrowstaff.com
Managed Security Services, Identity & Access Management, Federated Identity Management, Single Sign On (E-SSO and SSO), Intrusion Detection & Prevention, Vulnerability Assessment & Penetration Testing. (As-Pac, estab 2006, empl 580, sales $13,000,000, cert: NMSDC)

4614 Information Technology Consulting Company
190 Bluegrass Valley Parkway Ste B7 Alpharetta, GA 30005
(614) 207-9475 Gary Kallenbach Sr Procurement Advisor
Fax: (404) 745-8008
Email: gkallenbach@itc2.net
Website: www.itc2.net
IT resource & infrastrucute consulting. (Hisp, estab 2006, empl 8, sales $1,737,450, cert: NMSDC)

4615 InfoSmart Technologies Inc.
5400 Laurel Springs Pkwy Ste 706 Suwanee, GA 30024
(678) 584-5635 Rao Arumilli President
Fax: (678) 584-5640
Email: rao@infosmartsys.com
Website: www.istinc.net
Software consulting business, project management, participation & subcontracting, partnership, staff augmentation, software programming, design & area. (Woman/As-Ind, estab 1998, empl 25, sales $1,108,882, cert: NMSDC)

4616 Intellectual Concepts LLC
3300 Buckeye Rd, Ste 601 Atlanta, GA 30341
(202) 321-4560 DeLois Babiker CEO
Fax: (678) 222-2993
Email: dbabiker@intellectualconcepts.net
Website: www.intellectualconcepts.com
Information management technology, full life-cycle IT services, communication, content, collaboration & conferencing, contract administration, asset management & IT acquisition services. (Woman/AA, estab 2004, empl 7, sales $817,000, cert: City, NMSDC, WBENC, 8(a))

4617 IT Division, Inc.
5955 Parkway North Blvd Unit A Cumming, GA 30040
(678) 649-3022 Jamie Crosby Dir of Sales
Fax: (678) 302-9898
Email: jamiec@itdivisioninc.com
Website: www.itdivisioninc.com
IT staffing & services, application development, application testing & infrastructure services. (Woman/As-Pac, estab 2006, empl 165, sales $9,332,282, cert: State)

4618 K.L. Scott & Associates LLC
235 Peachtree St NE Ste 400 Atlanta, GA 30303
(404) 692-5552 Keith Scott CEO
Fax:
Email: keith.scott@klscottassociates.com
Website: www.klscottassociates.com
Information technology & management consulting, data analytics, analysis, and business growth strategy, Business Process Management (BPM) & (Re)engineering. (AA, estab 2013, empl 10, sales , cert: NMSDC)

4619 Kavi Software Inc.
250 Gladeside Path   Suwanee, GA 30024
(678) 358-4861 Jegannathan Mehalingam President
Fax: (404) 201-2100
Email: mjegann@kavisoft.net
Website: www.kavisoft.net
IT services & temporary staffing: application security implementation. (As-Ind, estab 1999, empl 25, sales $1,500,000, cert: NMSDC)

4620 Komplete Systems Integrators, Inc. (Kompsys)
3300 Cumberland Blvd, Ste 500 Atlanta, GA 30339
(770) 690-4272 Kevin Doby President
Fax: (770) 933-6223
Email: kevin.doby@kompsys.com
Website: www.kompsys.com
IP telephony, network design & implementation, LAN/WAN, wireless, IP communication solutions, remote network operations services, staff augmentation, disaster recovery. (AA, estab 2001, empl 60, sales $7,400,000, cert: State)

4621 Lanin Technologies
730 Stuart Ct Alpharetta, GA 30004
(678) 620-8210 Mariano Saldana VP Ops
Fax:
Email: msaldana@lanintech.com
Website: www.lanintech.com
Software development, IT services, custom software development; primarily web, mobile applications & SAP. (Hisp, estab 2015, empl 3, sales , cert: NMSDC)

4622 LNKE Technologies Inc.
236 Auburn Ave NE Ste 103B Atlanta, GA 30303
(404) 919-5653 Nate Jones Owner
Fax:
Email: najones@LNKETECH.com
Website: www.LNKETECH.com
Cloud Services, Web Development, Web Design, Strategic IT Consulting, Mobile Development, Project Management, Endpoint Support, Software Development, Managed Services, Programming Services, System Engineering, Network Engineering. (AA, estab 2011, empl 4, sales , cert: 8(a))

4623　Management Decisions, Inc. - MDI Group
35 Technology PkwySouth Ste 150　NORCROSS, GA 30092
(770) 416-7949　Joel McCreight Client Mgr/Business Dev
Fax: (770) 416-7323
Email: jmccreight@mdigroup.com
Website: www.mdigroup.com
IT staffing & contracting, project mgmt, vendor mgmt, direct hire, IT staffing. (Woman/White, estab 1900, empl 1, sales $45,800,000, cert: WBENC, NWBOC)

4624　Megasys Inc.
200 Lazy Shade Ct　Duluth, GA 30097
(770) 573-0745　Vandana Raman President
Fax: (770) 495-7576
Email: vandanaraman@megasysinc.org
Website: www.megasysinc.org
Software consulting services, staff augmentation services. (Woman/As-Ind, estab 1995, empl 2, sales $200,000, cert: State)

4625　Metasys Technologies, Inc.
3460 Summit Ridge Pkwy # 401　Duluth, GA 30096
(470) 514-3654　Mark Lee VP of Ops
Fax: (678) 218-1601
Email: info@metasysinc.com
Website: www.metasysinc.com
Information technology svcs: e-business application devel & integration, staff augmentation. (As-Ind, estab 2000, empl 415, sales $47,664,000, cert: NMSDC)

4626　Milletech Systems Inc.
11539 Park Woods Cir, Ste 201　Alpharetta, GA 30005
(770) 619-0095　Nasir Mujawar VP
Fax: (770) 619-2890
Email: nmujawar@milletechinc.com
Website: www.milletechinc.com
IT services: staffing & consultants, outsourcing, ERP solutions & implementation, application support, upgrades, custom application devel, training, QA & testing, systems integration. (Woman/As-Ind, estab 2000, empl 46, sales $3,900,000, cert: NMSDC)

4627　Next Level Business Services Inc.
11340 Lakefield Dr, Ste 200　Johns Creek, GA 30097
(904) 267-0741　Affaque Ahmed Business Developer
Fax: (608) 646-8326
Email: affaque.ahmed@nlbservices.com
Website: www.nlbservices.com
IT Consultancy and BPO Services. (As-Ind, estab 2007, empl 400, sales $110,000,000, cert: State, NMSDC)

4628　Nineteen Eleven Solutions Inc.
12850 Hwy 9 Ste 600-247　Alpharetta, GA 30004
(404) 644-3702　Daud Haseeb Principal
Fax: (678) 868-2371
Email: daud@1911solutions.com
Website: www.nineteenelevensolutions.com/
IT Staffing, ERP (Oracle, PeopleSoft, & SAP), Open Source & Big Data (Hadoop). (AA, estab 2010, empl 9, sales $275,000, cert: NMSDC)

4629　Nutech Systems Inc.
2675 Paces Ferry Rd Ste 460　Atlanta, GA 30339
(770) 434-7063　Nachu Anbil President
Fax: (770) 234-5818
Email: nanbil@nutech-inc.com
Website: www.nutech-inc.com
IT staff augmentation, IT solutions, software development life cycle, support & infrastructure. (As-Ind, estab 1995, empl 120, sales $20,400,000, cert: NMSDC)

4630　Ocher Technology Group, LLC
555 North Point Center E　Alpharetta, GA 30022
(678) 521-6329　Vasudevan Vijayakumar CEO
Fax: (678) 279-5465
Email: vijay_vasudevan@ochertech.com
Website: www.ochertech.com
IT consulting & staffing. (As-Ind, estab 2007, empl 45, sales $4,000,000, cert: NMSDC)

4631　Olivine LLC
970 Peachtree Industrial Blvd. Ste 100　Suwanee, GA 30024
(770) 596-5155　Rajeev Maddur Sr Acct Mgr
Fax:
Email: rajeevm@olivinellc.com
Website: www.olivinellc.com
IT Consulting Services, Contract, Contract to Hire and Direct hire placements. (As-Ind, estab 2006, empl 20, sales $235,000, cert: NMSDC)

4632　Open Systems Inc.
6495 Shiloh Rd #310 Ste 310　Alpharetta, GA 30005
(770) 752-8600　Quentessa Bullock Business Dev Management
Fax: (770) 752-8601
Email: tessa.bullock@opensystemsinc.com
Website: www.opensystemsinc.com
IT consulting & custom software development. (As-Ind, estab 1994, empl 134, sales , cert: NMSDC)

4633　Paramount Software Solutions, Inc
4030 Old Milton Parkway　Alpharetta, GA 30005
(770) 872-7829　Srinivas Kumar Business Dev Mgr
Fax: (770) 234-3823
Email: srinivas@paramountsoft.net
Website: www.paramountsoft.net/
IT Staffing, IT Consulting, Software outsourcing % development services. (As-Ind, estab 1997, empl 120, sales $178,777,000, cert: NMSDC)

4634　PIE Technology Consulting
559 Commons Park Lane　Tucker, GA 30084
(877) 866-2677　Wesner Charlotin Director of Ops
Fax: (877) 866-4784
Email: wesnerc@pietconsulting.com
Website: www.pietconsulting.com
Planning, design, and implementation services for Microsoft products: Active Directory, Exchange, Lync/Skype for Business, SharePoint, and Office 365. (AA, estab 2014, empl 7, sales $554,276, cert: NMSDC)

4635 Precedent Technologies LLC
3330 Cumberland Blvd SE, Ste 500 Atlanta, GA 30339
(770) 303-0223 Patrick Carley
Fax: (800) 272-5124
Email: pfcarley@precedent-tech.com
Website: www.precedent-tech.com
Strategic IT consulting & project management, voice over IP telephone systems installation & support, web services, network design, installation and support, internet security software/services. (AA, estab 2006, empl 3, sales $196,000, cert: NMSDC)

4636 Premier Software Solutions
3707 Main St, Ste 201 College Park, GA 30337
(678) 643-3034 Paul Gupta President
Fax: (888) 212-8669
Email: pgupta@presoftsolutions.com
Website: www.presoftsolutions.com
IT solutions and services provider in the Healthcare IT, Cyber Security, Data Analytics, and Custom Software Development. (Woman/As-Ind, estab 2008, empl 5, sales $500,000, cert: 8(a))

4637 Primus Software Corporation
3061 Peachtree Industrial Blvd Ste 110 Duluth, GA 30097
(678) 336-1871 Satish Anand President, Project Sevices
Fax: (770) 300-0005
Email: supplier.diversity@primussoft.com
Website: www.primussoft.com
J2EE technology implementation, web services, IBM Websphere, MS .NET Web svcs, data warehousing, Oracle & SYBASE, project management, ERP, CRM and SCM technologies. (Woman/As-Pac, estab 1996, empl 220, sales $27,000,000, cert: NMSDC, WBENC)

4638 Prosys Information Systems
6025 The Corners Parkway Ste 120 Norcross, GA 30092
(404) 717-9205 Jenny Woodruff Acct Exec
Fax: (678) 437-1484
Email: stephen.guynn@prosysis.com
Website: www.prosysis.com
IP telephony & wireless, network integration, outsourcing solutions & technical staff augmentation. (Woman/White, estab 1997, empl 425, sales $776,000,000, cert: WBENC)

4639 Pyramid Consulting, Inc.
11100 Atlantis Place Alpharetta, GA 30022
(678) 514-3500 Namita Tirath Exec VP
Fax: (678) 840-2109
Email: PCIStaffing@pyramidci.com
Website: www.pyramidci.com
Information technology consulting: staff augmentation, turnkey IT projects. (As-Ind, estab 1996, empl 1150, sales $193,534,840, cert: NMSDC)

4640 Radiant Technologies, Inc.
5755 Northpoint Pkwy, Ste 30 Alpharetta, GA 30022
(678) 310-2202 Raj G Sales Mgr
Fax:
Email: raj@radianttechs.com
Website: www.radianttechs.com
Executive IT consulting. (Woman/As-Ind, estab 1999, empl 50, sales $4,900,000, cert: NMSDC)

4641 Rapid IT, Inc.
4080 McGinnis Ferry Rd, Ste 1206 Atlanta, GA 30005
(678) 366-3820 Goutham Goli President
Fax: (678) 366-3822
Email: contracts@rapiditinc.com
Website: www.rapiditinc.com
Information Technology. (As-Ind, estab 2006, empl 120, sales , cert: NMSDC)

4642 Renovo Data, Inc.
3121 Maple Dr Ste 200 Atlanta, GA 30305
(404) 935-6363 Charlotta Vinson President
Fax: (404) 935-6363
Email: cvinson@renovodata.com
Website: www.renovodata.com
Data backup & disaster recovery solutions: replication services, virtualization, consulting services. (Woman/As-Pac, estab 2005, empl 9, sales $2,000,000, cert: NMSDC, NWBOC)

4643 ResiliEnt Business Solutions, LLC
11175 Cicero Dr, Ste 100 Alpharetta, GA 30022
(678) 242-5242 Laila Utley CEO
Fax: (866) 470-9843
Email: marketingservices@resilientbiz.com
Website: www.resilientbiz.com
SDLC, Business Intelligence, Enterprise Data Management/Reporting, Data Modeling, Governance, warehousing, cleansing, WebFOCUS, WebQuery, ScoreCards, Dashboards Cognos, MicroStrategy, Mobile Development. (Woman/White, estab 2004, empl 6, sales $1,153,725, cert: WBENC)

4644 RiVi Consulting Group LLC
2475 Northwinds Pkwy, Ste 200 Alpharetta, GA 30009
(678) 643-8133 Bhushan Mocherla CIO/Partner
Fax: (866) 921-7484
Email: bmocherla@rivigroup.com
Website: www.rivigroup.com
Technology solutions: SAP, Peoplesoft & Oracle. (Woman/As-Ind, estab 2002, empl 45, sales $6,217,522, cert: NMSDC, WBENC, 8(a))

4645   RTX Technology Partners, LLC
     400 Perimeter Center Terr NE Ste 900   Atlanta, GA 30346
     (404) 551-5609   M. Hans Delly Managing Dir
     Fax: (877) 789-8249
     Email: m.hans.delly@rtxpartners.com
     Website: www.rtxpartners.com
Global management & technology consulting: business strategy, technology planning & architecture & business process optimization. (AA, estab 2007, empl 25, sales $6,500,000, cert: NMSDC)

4646   Scintel Technologies Inc.
     6340 Sugarloaf Pkwy Ste 200   Duluth, GA 30097
     (678) 775-6874   Shailesh Patel Acct Mgr
     Fax: (678) 802-4770
     Email: s.patel@scintel.com
     Website: www.scintel.com
Application outsourcing & enterprise consulting . (As-Ind, estab 2003, empl 400, sales $17,500,000, cert: NMSDC)

4647   Scope IT Consulting
     3235 Satellite Blvd Bldg 400, Ste 300   Duluth, GA 30096
     (912) 580-5929   Nadir Noorani Principal, Consultant
     Fax:
     Email: nadir.noorani@scopeitconsulting.com
     Website: www.scopeitconsulting.com
Business Process Management, Project Management, Mobility Solutions, BigData Solutions, Cloud Solutions. (Woman/As-Ind, estab 2015, empl 16, sales $200,000, cert: NMSDC)

4648   Serenity Infotech, Inc.
     950 Scales Rd, Ste 104   Suwanee, GA 30024
     (770) 242-9966   Srini Vangimalla Partner
     Fax: (770) 242-9916
     Email: srini@serenityinfotech.com
     Website: www.serenityinfotech.com
Software solutions & consulting services. (As-Pac, estab 1997, empl 120, sales $13,000,000, cert: NMSDC)

4649   Six Consulting, Inc.
     5900 Windward Pkwy, Ste 410   Alpharetta, GA 30005
     (470) 395-0200   Sam Yehya Sr Mgr
     Fax: (678) 831-4501
     Email: strategicaccounts@sixconsultingcorp.com
     Website: www.sixconsultingcorp.com
Custom Application Development & Maintenance, Business Intelligence & Data Warehousing, Enterprise Resource Planning, Business Process Management, Enterprise Content Management. (Woman/As-Ind, estab 2007, empl 72, sales $5,472,009, cert: NMSDC)

4650   SJ Technologies Inc.
     5024 Meadowbrook Circle   Suwanee, GA 30024
     (404) 386-7376   Patrick Henson
     Fax: (800) 574-4518
     Email: patrick.henson@sjtechcorp.com
     Website: www.sjtechcorp.com
Oracle technology consulting, staffing & implementation of comprehensive IT solutions sector. (Woman/As-Pac, estab 2005, empl 1, sales $120,000, cert: 8(a))

4651   Smartecute LLC
     1266 Wt Paces ferry Rd Ste 196   Atlanta, GA 30327
     (404) 939-6303   Sheldon Mundle CEO
     Fax:
     Email: sheldon@smartecute.com
     Website: www.smartecute.com
IT Consulting, IT Advisory, IT Network & Wireless Access Points, IT Unified Communications, Voice Communications & Data, PeopleSoft ERP Consulting, Telecommunications, IT Project Management. (AA, estab 2010, empl 2, sales , cert: NMSDC)

4652   Softech Int'l Resources, Inc.
     3300 Holcomb Bridge Rd, Ste 216 3300 Holcomb Bridge Rd, Ste 216   Norcross, GA 30092
     (770) 447-8002   Balaji HR
     Fax: (404) 592-4697
     Email: supplier@softintl.com
     Website: www.softintl.com
IT consulting, project mgmt, analysis, architectural design, object modeling, application devel. (Woman/As-Ind, estab 1995, empl 40, sales $16,819,906, cert: NMSDC)

4653   Softpath System, LLC
     3985 Steve Reynolds Blvd Bldg C   Norcross, GA 30093
     (404) 315-1555   Sushumna Roy Jalajam President
     Fax: (404) 315-1558
     Email: supplier@softpath.net
     Website: www.softpath.net
IT services: business intelligence & data warehousing. (Woman/As-Pac, estab 1999, empl 500, sales $85,298,260, cert: City, NMSDC, CPUC, WBENC)

4654   Stellar Consulting Solutions, LLC
     2475 NorthWinds Pkwy, Ste 200   Alpharetta, GA 30009
     (678) 777-7411   Varun Jhanjee CEO
     Fax:
     Email: varun@stellarconsulting.com
     Website: www.stellarconsulting.com
Onsite Technology Staff Augmentation, Contract, Contract to Hire & Permanent Placements, C Level executive search. (As-Ind, estab 2015, empl 11, sales , cert: NMSDC)

4655   Strategic Systems & Technology Corporation
     3325 Paddocks Pkwy Ste 250   Suwanee, GA 30024
     (678) 389-7200   Magan McQuiston CEO
     Fax: (770) 645-7317
     Email: magan.mcquiston@sstid.com
     Website: www.sstid.com
Computer database, peripherals, printers, application systems, terminals, network interface hardware, terminal remote job entry. (Woman/White, estab 1999, empl 20, sales $6,200,000, cert: WBENC)

4656   Sun Technologies, Inc.
       3700 Mansell Road Ste#220 Alpharetta, GA 30022
       (770) 418-0434 Joy Bhowmick Business Dev Mgr
       Fax: (770) 361-1368
       Email: supplierdiversity@suntechnologies.com
       Website: www.suntechnologies.com
IT staffing & IT projects. (Woman/As-Ind, estab 1996, empl
500, sales $28,299,878, cert: NMSDC, WBENC)

4657   Symbioun Technologies, Inc.
       4501 Circle 75 Pkwy D4200 Atlanta, GA 30339
       (408) 385-1078 Raj Muppalla Relationship Mgr
       Fax: (866) 579-2744
       Email: srinik@symbiountech.com
       Website: www.symbiountech.com
Information technology consulting, staffing services. (As-
Ind, estab 1993, empl 140, sales $7,900,000, cert: NMSDC)

4658   Synergy America, Inc.
       6340 Sugarloaf Pkwy, Ste 200   Duluth, GA 30097
       (770) 923-9300 Mike Williams CEO
       Fax: (770) 936-1941
       Email: mike@synergyamerica.com
       Website: www.synergyamerica.com
IT services: BPO, healthcare, ERP, e-business, & client
server environments. (As-Ind, estab 1993, empl 50, sales
$3,000,000, cert: NMSDC, 8(a))

4659   TechBios, Inc.
       11800 Amberpark Dr, Ste 130   Alpharetta, GA
       30004
       (770) 569-2721 Larry Parker President
       Fax: (770) 569-0266
       Email: lparker@techbios.com
       Website: www.techbios.com
Information technology contract & permanent staffing;
professional, administrative & clerical staffing, help desk &
customer svc, software engineering, LAN/WAN installation, maintenance, & support, configuration mgmt &
desktop deployment. (AA, estab 2000, empl 18, sales
$1,466,970, cert: State, NMSDC)

4660   The Danby Group, LLP
       3060-A Business Park Dr   Norcross, GA 30071
       (770) 416-9844 Genie Ragin Managing Partner
       Fax: (770) 416-9845
       Email: genie@danbygroup.com
       Website: www.danbygroup.com
Automatic identification technology (AIT) design &
integration, bar code printing stations. (Woman/White,
estab 1982, empl 11, sales $10,000,000, cert: WBENC)

4661   The Ian Thomas Group, LLC
       2870 Peachtree Rd, Ste 417   Atlanta, GA 30305
       (404) 993-5698 Ashonda Davenport Exec Ops Mgr
       Fax:
       Email: ashondadavenport@ianthomasgroup.com
       Website: www.ianthomasgroup.com
Software performance engineering (SPE) services &
solutions: software performance testing, engineering
analysis & optimization, database analysis & tuning &
operational support. (AA, estab 2007, empl 15, sales
$1,451,588, cert: NMSDC, 8(a))

4662   The REIA Corporation
       3348 Fieldwood Dr   Smyrna, GA 33080
       (770) 432-6974 Darnell Clarke CEO
       Fax: (770) 432-0970
       Email: darnell@reiacorp.com
       Website: www.reiacorp.com
Systems software application development & integration, security mgmt & compliance, custom development,
help desk & IT support project & risk management.
(Woman/AA, estab 1992, empl 46, sales $5,868,000,
cert: State, City, 8(a))

4663   Think Development Systems
       6000 Live Oak Pkwy, Ste 102   Norcross, GA 30093
       (770) 723-7777 P I Joy President
       Fax: (770) 723-1530
       Email: joy@thinkdevelopment.com
       Website: www.thinkdevelopment.com
Software development & IT consulting, offshore development, wireless application. (Woman/As-Ind, estab
1998, empl 47, sales $3,085,109, cert: City, NMSDC)

4664   Unicorn Technologies, LLC
       4080 McGinnis Ferry Rd Ste 1203 Alpharetta, GA
       30005
       (678) 825-8143 Sunil Savili President
       Fax: (855) 207-7936
       Email: sales@unicorntek.com
       Website: www.unicorntek.com
IT solutions & staffing services, Fit Gap Analysis, Application Development, Implementation, Upgrades, Quality
Assurance, Maintenance & Support, Project Management. (Woman/As-Ind, estab 2012, empl 60, sales
$3,700,000, cert: State, WBENC, SDB)

4665   Universal Business Solutions, LLC
       4080 McGinnis Ferry Rd Ste 803 Alpharetta, GA
       30005
       (770) 416-9900 Marcie LaRocque COO
       Fax: (770) 416-9931
       Email: mlarocque@ubsolutions.com
       Website: www.ubsolutions.com
Information technology svcs & solutions: ERP & CRM
systems, application systems, web systems, e-business,
security & threat evaluation, telecommunications,
telephony consulting, call & contact centers, infrastructure design, project mgmt. (Nat Ame, estab 1995, empl
34, sales $7,000,000, cert: NMSDC, SDB)

4666   VDart Inc.
       11180 State Bridge Rd Ste 402 Alpharetta, GA
       30022
       (678) 685-8650 Syed Ahmed CEO
       Fax: (866) 431-2320
       Email: d.sid@vdartinc.com
       Website: www.vdartinc.com
Global IT staffing: SAP FICO Functional, SAP ABAP,
Abinitio, Microstrategy, Oracle Applications (SCM, FIN,
MFG, WMS) Functional/Technical, Microsoft,
Middleware, etc. (As-Ind, estab 2007, empl 42, sales ,
cert: NMSDC)

4667   Virtue Group
     5755 N Point Pkwy, Ste 85   Alpharetta, GA 30022
     (678) 578-4554   Lakshmi Manthena President
     Fax: (678) 325-6416
     Email: lmanthena@virtuegroup.com
     Website: www.virtuegroup.com
IT professionals: contract, contract-to-hire & direct hire
basis. (Woman/As-Ind, estab 2002, empl 250, sales
$23,400,000, cert: NMSDC)

4668   Whitty IT Solutions LLC
     260 Peachtree St, NW Ste 2200   Atlanta, GA 30303
     (404) 823-6955   Mrs. Charlie Whitfield CEO
     Fax: (404) 527-6201
     Email: charlie@whittyapps.com
     Website: www.whittyit.solutions
Software engineering & integration, architecture, design,
development & project management, mobile software
solutions. (Woman/AA, estab 2011, empl 2, sales $55,000,
cert: WBENC, 8(a))

4669   XentIT, LLC
     5425 Peachtree Pkwy   Norcross, GA 30092
     (678) 906-4046   Tariq Alvi President
     Fax: (404) 745-8448
     Email: talvi@xentit.com
     Website: www.xentit.com
Value Added Reseller, System Integrator & Cloud Managed
Service provider. (As-Ind, estab 2006, empl 7, sales
$2,247,000, cert: NMSDC)

4670   Xtreme Solutions, Inc.
     1170 Peachtree St, Ste 1875   Atlanta, GA 30309
     (404) 883-2000   Phyllis Newhouse Project Mgr
     Fax: (877) 282-9485
     Email: pnewhouse@xtremesolutions-inc.com
     Website: www.xtremesolutions-inc.com
Engineering & technology services. (Woman/AA, estab
2002, empl 140, sales $800,000, cert: NMSDC)

Hawaii

4671   In the Middle dba HTS Information Systems
     99-1285 Halawa Valley St Ste A7   Aiea, HI 96701
     (808) 535-9700   Stanley Lau President
     Fax: (866) 390-8282
     Email: slau@hitechsupport.net
     Website: www.hitechsupport.net
Technology products & solutions, virtual computing, secure
communications, mobile computing, managed network
services, technical staffing, IT equipment procurement. (As-
Pac, estab 2004, empl 6, sales $1,100,000, cert: State)

4672   Premier Solutions Hi, LLC
     7391 Makaa St, Ste A   Honolulu, HI 96825
     (808) 396-4444   Rob Hardisty VP
     Fax: (877) 882-5184
     Email: rob@premiersolutionshi.com
     Website: www.premiersolutionshi.com
Information technology & and solutions, design, build &
support applications & networks, data security. (Woman/
As-Pac, estab 2007, empl 13, sales $1,600,000, cert: 8(a))

Iowa

4673   Certintell, Inc
     317 6th Ave. Ste 901   Des Moines, IA 50309
     (515) 802-1281   Benjamin Lefever
     Fax: (888) 758-7908
     Email: benjamin@certintell.com
     Website: www.certintell.com
Online & on-demand healthcare delivery services,
software & remote monitoring that benefit patients,
hospitals, employers, payers, physician practice groups
& accountable care organizations. (AA, estab 2014, empl
6, sales , cert: NMSDC)

4674   Nguyen Information Consulting Inc.
     3636 Westown Pkwy Ste 217   West Des Moines,
     IA 50266
     (515) 457-3174   Trich Mullane Sr Business Dev
     Mgr
     Fax: (515) 457-3176
     Email: tmullane@nicwdm.com
     Website: www.nicwdm.com
Information technology consulting svcs: staff
augumentation, technical resources, outsourcing,
contract programming, staffing, web applications, e-
business, network & system admin, system engineering,
technical writing, technical support. (As-Pac, estab 1993,
empl 31, sales $2,455,000, cert: State)

4675   PC Pitstop LLC
     2515 W 22nd St   Sioux City, IA 51103
     (712) 233-4015   Scott Palmer Sales Consultant
     Fax: (712) 233-4015
     Email: scottp@pcpitstop.com
     Website: www.pcpitstop.com/
Security optimization software, PC Matic. (As-Pac, estab
1999, empl 32, sales $11,913,000, cert: NMSDC)

Illinois

4676   3Core Systems, Inc.
     4355 Weaver Pkwy, Ste 330   Warrenville, IL
     60555
     (630) 748-8800   Shyam Reganti Director Sales
     Fax: (847) 556-1234
     Email: shyam.reganti@3coresystems.com
     Website: www.3coresystems.com
Information Technology services, solutions & consulting,
ERP (Enterprise Resource Planning), CRM (Customer
Relationship Management), DW/BI (Data Warehousing
& Business Intelligence), Application Development &
Management. (As-Ind/As-Pac, estab 2004, empl 45, sales
$7,527,541, cert: State)

4677 A1PlusSoft, Inc.
      222 W Merchandise Mart Plaza, Ste 1212 Chicago,
      IL 60654
      (630) 935-6938 Balaji Rengamannar CEO
      Fax: (844) 583-2035
      Email: brengamannar@a1plussoft.com
      Website: www.a1plussoft.com
PCI Compliance assessment, Staff Augmentation, Information & Cloud security consulting, Legacy system transformation/modernization, Data & EMV Migration, Testing & Technical Writing. (As-Ind, estab 2002, empl 5, sales $296,000, cert: State, City, NMSDC)

4678 Accede Solutions Inc.
      164 Ela Rd Inverness, IL 60067
      (844) 522-2333 Rajesh Sethi Managing Partner
      Fax: (877) 677-4891
      Email: raj.sethi@accedesol.com
      Website: www.accedesol.com
IT, Healthcare, Finance & HR staffing & consulting. Enterprise Resource Planning (ERP) Customer relationship management (CRM) Human Resource Management System (HRMS) Software configuration Management (SCM) System. (Woman/As-Ind, estab 2005, empl 32, sales $2,000,000, cert: City, WBENC)

4679 Advantech Solutions Inc.
      2340 S Arlington Heights Rd Ste 270 Arlington Heights, IL 60005
      (847) 690-0255 Michelle Advaney Ops Mgr
      Fax: (847) 690-0095
      Email: aa@atsus.net
      Website: www.atsus.net
Information technology consulting. (Woman/White, estab 1999, empl 38, sales $4,498,633, cert: State)

4680 Ageatia Technology Consultancy Services Inc
      949 N Plum Grove Road Schaumburg, IL 60173
      (847) 517-8415 Chuck Srinivasan President
      Fax: (847) 517-7796
      Email: csrinivasan@ageatia.com
      Website: www.ageatia.com
e-gov, systems integration, database admin, software, implementation, software services, Legacy data, conversions, software devel, custom devel, web devel, systems outsourcing & support, technical support, enterprise, Oracle, Microsoft, PeopleSoft, SAP. (Woman/As-Ind, estab 2005, empl 300, sales $30,000,000, cert: City, NMSDC)

4681 Aloha Document Services
      60 E Van Buren St Ste S-1502 Chicago, IL 60605
      (312) 542-1300 Ginger Peak President
      Fax: (312) 542-0699
      Email: gpeak@alohadocs.com
      Website: www.alohadocs.com
Litigation copying, oversize & digital imaging, presentation, marketing & training materials, multi-media duplication & electronic archiving. (Woman/White, estab 2002, empl 35, sales $2,600,000, cert: City, WBENC)

4682 Ameex Technologies Corp.
      1701 E Woodfield Rd, Ste 710 Schaumburg, IL 60173
      (847) 563-3064 Arockia Preethi Mktg Analyst
      Fax: (847) 890-6996
      Email: vendor.registration@ameexusa.com
      Website: www.ameexusa.com/
Develop content management solutions, web development, maintenance & enhanced services. (As-Pac, estab 2007, empl 180, sales $8,000,000, cert: NMSDC)

4683 Aonsoft International, Inc
      1600 Golf Rd, Ste 1270 Rolling Meadows, IL 60008
      (847) 999-4060 Siddiq Ahmed President
      Fax: (847) 649-2118
      Email: siddiq@aonsoft.com
      Website: www.aonsoft.com
IT Consulting Services & Staff Augmentation Services. (As-Ind, estab 2007, empl 14, sales $661,000, cert: NMSDC)

4684 Aptude, Inc.
      1601 North Bond St, Ste 316 Naperville, IL 60563
      (630) 692-6700 Guy De Rosa Principal
      Fax: (800) 699-0843
      Email: accounts@aptude.com
      Website: www.aptude.com
Remote data capturing applications, ebusiness solutions, customer relationship mgmt solutions, data warehousing & business intelligence, content svcs, CAD/CAM integration, knowledge mgmt solutions. (As-Ind, estab 2001, empl 100, sales $15,300,000, cert: State, City)

4685 ARBA Technology, Inc.
      2760 Forgue Dr Ste 104 Naperville, IL 60564
      (630) 620-8566 Kathy de la Torre Dir Sales/Mktg
      Fax: (630) 396-3300
      Email: kathy@arbapro.com
      Website: www.arbapro.com
Point of Sale (POS), inventory management & cashless payment solutions. (Woman/As-Pac, estab 2007, empl 17, sales $881,670, cert: NMSDC)

4686 Ascent Innovations, LLC
      475 N Martingale Rd Ste 820 Schaumburg, IL 60173
      (847) 572-8000 Sohena Hafiz President
      Fax: (866) 681-9298
      Email: sohena.hafiz@ascentinnov.com
      Website: www.ascentinnov.com
Dynamics AX & Dynamics CRM Consulting, Implementation, Development, Integration, Support, Upgrades, Data Migration, SYSPRO ï¿½ Implementation & Integration, ERP/CRM Integration. (Woman/As-Ind, estab 2009, empl 12, sales $780,000, cert: State, WBENC, 8(a))

4687   Asset Management Concepts
     4654 N Kenmore St   Chicago, IL 60640
     (773) 878-5150   Tommy Thompson President
     Fax: (773) 878-9625
     Email: thomacce@aol.com
     Website:
Design LAN networks, help desk, call center support, custom design systems, IT staffing, dist PCs. (AA, estab 1991, empl 5, sales , cert: State)

4688   Aura Innovative Technology
     223 W Jackson Blvd, Ste 1112   Chicago, IL 60606
     (312) 342-4292   James Chen President
     Fax:
     Email: mmrcela@aurachicago.com
     Website: www.aurachicago.com
Microsoft & AWS consulting & custom software/integration development. (As-Pac, estab 2011, empl 15, sales , cert: City, NMSDC)

4689   Aurora Solutions, Inc.
     1051 Perimeter Dr, Ste 510   Schaumburg, IL 60173
     (847) 274-7777   Sanjeev Srivastava Business Dev
     Fax: (630) 439-1933
     Email: sanjeev@auroraworldwide.com
     Website: www.auroraworldwide.com
Data Mining & Business Analytics, ECommerce & Custom Application Development. (Woman/As-Ind, estab 1997, empl 30, sales $3,500,000, cert: NMSDC, 8(a))

4690   BitWise Inc.
     1515 Woodfield Rd Ste 930   Schaumburg, IL 60173
     (847) 969-1500   Michael Palermo New Business Mgr
     Fax: (847) 969-1544
     Email: john.broshar@bitwiseglobal.com
     Website: www.bitwiseglobal.com
Application development, system maintenance & support, IT consulting. (As-Pac, estab 1996, empl 600, sales $30,000,000, cert: NMSDC)

4691   Bourntec Solutions, Inc.
     1701 E Woodfield Rd Ste 636   Schaumburg, IL 60173
     (224) 232-5090   Srujana Gudur President
     Fax: (847) 594-6066
     Email: ssurya@bourntec.com
     Website: www.bourntec.com
Information technology remote Oracle support services, on-site Oracle implementation & application development services. (Woman/As-Ind, estab 1994, empl 33, sales $4,500,000, cert: State, NMSDC, 8(a))

4692   BTR Solutions, LLC
     1300 Thorndale   Elk Grove Village, IL 60007
     (630) 594-2011   Nina Nielsen Business Devel Mgr
     Fax: (847) 238-9247
     Email: ninan@sipiar.com
     Website: www.sipiar.com
IT Asset Disposition, remarket, redeploy, perform DOD level Data Security. (Woman/White, estab 1988, empl 300, sales , cert: NWBOC)

4693   Clerysys Incorporated
     O'Hare Corporate Towers 10600 W Higgins Rd, Ste 711   Rosemont, IL 60018
     (847) 768-0314   Nicole Lim Business Dev Exec
     Fax: (847) 954-0762
     Email: info@clerysys.com
     Website: www.clerysys.com
Application design & devel, ERP, business intelligence, systems integration, quality assurance, content mgmt & web-based applications,SAP R/3 implementation svcs, ERP, CRM, SRM, PLM, BI & data warehousing. (As-Pac, estab 2005, empl 450, sales $10,000,000, cert: NMSDC)

4694   Cogent Data Solutions LLC
     2500 W Higgins Rd Ste 1165   Hoffman Estates, IL 60169
     (866) 666-1877   Sumanth Yalavarthy VP IT
     Fax: (866) 650-4883
     Email: sumanth@cogentdatasolutions.com
     Website: www.cogentdatasolutions.com
IT services, IT project base & contract staff augmentation, Information management, Infrastructure Management, Data Warehousing, Business Intelligence, QA Testing, Web Development, EHR & EMR. (Woman/As-Ind, estab 2007, empl 89, sales $5,400,000, cert: State, NMSDC, WBENC)

4695   Compact Solutions, LLC.
     Two TransAm Plaza Dr Ste 400   Oakbrook Terrace, IL 60181
     (312) 493-9911   Pankaj Agrawal President/CTO
     Fax: (708) 524-1869
     Email: pankaj.agrawal@compactsolutionsllc.com
     Website: www.compactsolutionsllc.com
Enterprise wide data integration, data management & quality initiatives, data migration/consolidation, data synchronization, master data management & cross-enterprise information integration. (As-Ind, estab 2002, empl 54, sales $5,550,000, cert: NMSDC)

4696   Complex Network Solutions
     7747 W 96th Pl   Hickory Hills, IL 60457
     (708) 233-6222   Eduardo Lopez President
     Fax: (708) 233-6519
     Email: elopez@complexnetwork.com
     Website: www.complexnetwork.com
IT services, routing switching & wireless, desktop & server support. (Hisp, estab 2005, empl 7, sales , cert: NMSDC)

4697   CosaTech, Inc.
     1415 W 22nd St, Tower Fl   Oak Brook, IL 60523
     (630) 684-2331   Ann Le VP
     Fax: (630) 681-2740
     Email: ann.le@cosatech.com
     Website: www.cosatech.com
Information technology services: systems integration & applications, development, quality assurance, managed services, IT staff augmentation, onsite, offsite & offshore applications dev & maintenance. (Woman/As-Pac, estab 1988, empl 350, sales $25,000,000, cert: NMSDC)

4698 CRSGroup, Inc.
One Pierce Place Ste 325 West Itasca, IL 60143
(630) 202-5348 Jean Reith Business Solutions Mgr
Fax: (630) 467-1032
Email: jreith@crscorp.com
Website: www.crscorp.com
Information technology consulting. (AA, estab 1994, empl 311, sales $17,500,000, cert: State, NMSDC)

4699 Cube Hub Inc.
600 N Commons Dr Ste 109 Aurora, IL 60504
(630) 746-1239 Sunil Bakhshi Business Dev Mgr
Fax:
Email: sunil@cube-hub.com
Website: www.cube-hub.com
Technology, Training, Staffing & Professional Services, Staffing/Recruiting services, Software Development, IT, Engineering, Professional, Marketing, Healthcare, Clinical, Scientific, Finance/Audit, Telecommunication, etc. (Woman/AA/As-Ind, estab 2014, empl 28, sales $3,580,640, cert: NMSDC)

4700 Data Defenders, LLC
10 W 35th St, Ste 9F5-1 Chicago, IL 60616
(312) 224-8831 Lester McCarroll Business Dev Mgr
Fax:
Email: lester.mccarroll@data-defenders.com
Website: www.data-defenders.com
Information Security, Managed Technology, Applied Computer Forensics & Professional Services solutions. (AA, estab 2005, empl 14, sales $400,000, cert: State)

4701 DivIHN Integration Inc.
2800 W Higgins Rd Ste 240 Hoffman Estates, IL 60169
(224) 704-1704 Prabhu Jayapal VP
Fax: (847) 841-3796
Email: pjayapal@divihn.com
Website: www.divihn.com
Computer software consulting, staff augmentation, custom software design & development, data management solutions & services. (As-Ind, estab 2002, empl 55, sales $11,200,000, cert: NMSDC)

4702 E Gen Solutions Inc.
One Energy Center Ste 302 Naperville, IL 60532
(630) 299-4433 Allison Reed Govt Acct Mgr
Fax:
Email: adr@egeni.com
Website: www.egeni.com
Information technology consulting, project management, staffing & on-site customized IT programming. (As-Ind, estab 2000, empl 92, sales $1,000,000, cert: 8(a))

4703 Edgilent Corp.
700 Cooper Ct Ste AF Schaumburg, IL 60173
(847) 839-7388 Raj Ponnuswamy President
Fax: (847) 839-7389
Email: rponnuswamy@edgilent.com
Website: www.edgilent.com
Information technology svcs: application development, outsourcing & consulting. (As-Pac, estab 2003, empl 20, sales $2,500,000, cert: NMSDC)

4704 Edify Technologies, Inc.
1952 Mc Dowell Rd, Ste 112 Naperville, IL 60563
(630) 932-9308 Ken Korhorn Acct Exec
Fax:
Email: ken.korhorn@edifytech.com
Website: www.edifytech.com
Software development & consulting, business process automation, SharePoint consulting, custom .NET solutions, testing & quality assurance, project management, staffing, offshore development. (As-Pac, estab 2002, empl 65, sales $4,000,000, cert: State, NMSDC)

4705 Electronic Knowledge Interchange, Co.
33 W Monroe St, Ste 1050 Chicago, IL 60603
(312) 762-0129 Jose Cruz
Fax: (312) 236-2022
Email: jcruz@eki-consulting.com
Website: www.eki-consulting.com
Technology solutions: web portals, e-commerce, knowledge management, employee intranets, workgroup collaboration & process automation technologies. (AA, estab 1996, empl 91, sales $17,105,910, cert: State, City, NMSDC)

4706 Enterprise Solutions Inc
500 E. Diehl Road Ste 130 Naperville, IL 60563
(630) 345-2713 Varun Gandhi Business Dev Mgr
Fax:
Email: bdm@enterprisesolutioninc.com
Website: www.enterprisesolutioninc.com
IT & engineering staffing, direct hire, contract to hire & contract positions. (As-Ind, estab 2000, empl 350, sales $83,874,697, cert: NMSDC, CPUC)

4707 Evanston Technology Partners, Inc.
54 E. 47th St Chicago, IL 60653
(312) 709-8678 Emmanuel Jackson President
Fax: (312) 348-5122
Email: ejackson@evanstontec.com
Website: www.evanstontec.com
Implement & integrate object storage data (partner to Cleversafe). Unified & Real Time Communications platform including Telehealth. (AA, estab 2012, empl 7, sales $120,000, cert: State, NMSDC)

4708 Evolutyz Corp.
1560 Wall St Ste 105 Naperville, IL 60563
(312) 275-5735 Adriana Perez Director of Sales
Fax: (312) 275-5734
Email: adriana@evolutyz.com
Website: www.evolutyz.com
Application Development, ERP, Mobile Apps, ETL/ BI/ DW, Quality Assurance & Testing, Professional Services, Staff Augmentation. (Woman/As-Pac, estab 2011, empl 25, sales $6,051,748, cert: NMSDC)

4709 Excelsior Consulting Services
P.O. Box 325 Clarendon Hills, IL 60514
(973) 447-2575 Dileta Sapokaite Business Mgr
Fax: (630) 214-2086
Email: dileta@excelsiorconsulting.net
Website: www.excelsiorconsulting.net
IT staff & contracting resources. (Woman/As-Ind, estab 2004, empl 2, sales $790,000, cert: State, WBENC, 8(a))

4710 Frontier Technologies LLC
1601 Bond St, Ste 305 Naperville, IL 60563
(630) 687-1606 Richard Ewbank Sales Exec
Fax: (630) 778-5331
Email: richard@frontiertechllc.com
Website: www.frontiertechllc.com/
IT consulting services. (Woman/As-Pac, estab 2002, empl 146, sales , cert: State)

4711 Galmont Consulting, LLC
70 W Madison St, Ste 1400 Chicago, IL 60602
(312) 214-3261 Jeri Smith President
Fax: (312) 214-3110
Email: jerig@galmont.com
Website: www.galmont.com
Software quality assurance, testing & tool automation. (Woman/White, estab 2000, empl 50, sales $5,700,000, cert: WBENC)

4712 Genius Business Solutions, Inc.
3403 76th St Moline, IL 61265
(309) 269-2551 Shivaji Patil IT Practice Head
Fax:
Email: Shivaji@GeniusBSI.com
Website: www.GeniusBSI.com
IT & Engineering Services Consulting, Software licensing, Implementation & Support SAP, Oracle & Windchill, Custom software development, Quality assurance & Testing, End User Training, Strategic Staffing. (As-Ind, estab 2004, empl 60, sales $4,750,000, cert: NMSDC)

4713 Harrington Technology & Associates, Inc dba HTA Technology Security
30 S Wacker Dr, 22 Fl Chicago, IL 60606
(708) 862-6348 Michelle Chaudry CEO
Fax: (708) 868-2404
Email: mchaudry@hta-inc.com
Website: www.hta-inc.com
Technology & information security consulting: risk assessments, protection, independent verification & validation, vulnerability assessments & penetration testing, computer forensics, network & security remediation. (Woman/AA, estab 2001, empl 29, sales $2,778,000, cert: WBENC)

4714 Harris Ice Company
3927 W 5th Ave Chicago, IL 60624
(773) 826-3110 Walker Harris President
Fax: (773) 826-8245
Email: harrisice1@sbcglobal.net
Website: www.harrisicechicago.com
Information technolofy, ice services. (AA, estab 1970, empl 15, sales $1,423,175, cert: City, NMSDC)

4715 HOBI International, Inc.
1202 Nagel Blvd Batavia, IL 60510
(630) 761-0500 Cathy Hill CEO
Fax: (630) 761-0550
Email: chill@hobi.com
Website: www.hobi.com
Recycle electronics, reverse logistics, IT & cellular asset management, resale & re-marketing, data security, data erasure, equipment removal & environmentally safe recycling. (Woman/White, estab 1992, empl 250, sales $42,000,000, cert: WBENC)

4716 Indusa Technical Corp.
1 TransAm Plaza Dr Ste 350 Oakbrook Terrace, IL 60181
(865) 769-0715 Hemant Shah Dir Business Dev
Fax: (630) 424-1800
Email: hemant.shah@indusa.com
Website: www.indusa.com
Information technology consulting & software solutions. (As-Ind, estab 1989, empl 100, sales , cert: NMSDC)

4717 Innovative Systems Group, Inc.
799 Roosevelt Rd Ste 109 Glen Ellyn, IL 60137
(312) 861-1745 Jordan Myers Acct Mgr
Fax: (630) 858-8532
Email: jordanm@innovativesys.com
Website: www.innovativesys.com/
Information systems consulting, full life cycle systems, application dev & support, project mgmt, business systems analysis, staff augmentation, QA & testing svcs, database architecture & admin, network & systems admin, CRM & enterprise systems. (As-Pac, estab 1991, empl 250, sales $20,000,000, cert: City)

4718 Intellisys Technology
2625 Butterfield Rd Ste 128N Oak Brook, IL 60523
(630) 928-1111 Raju Iyer Managing Partner
Fax: (630) 990-1333
Email: riyer@intellisystechnology.com
Website: www.intellisystechnology.com
IT consulting: system integration, application development, QA & testing, embedded system technology & staff augmentation. (As-Ind, estab 1998, empl 300, sales $6,000,000, cert: State)

4719 JRE & Associates Inc.
46 E 26th St Chicago, IL 60616
(312) 326-4327 Jeffrey Edwards CEO
Fax: (312) 326-3131
Email: jedwards@jreitsolutions.com
Website: www.jreitsolutions.com
Logical Identity Controls, Logical Access Control Systems, Telecommunications and Network Security, Computer Operations Security Management, Cryptography & PKI Infrastructure Support (AA, estab 2009, empl 3, sales $150,000, cert: State)

4720 Kaizen Technologies, Inc.
2339 N Kildare Ave Chicago, IL 60639
(773) 934-3010 Usman Hafeez President
Fax:
Email: usman@kaizeninc.co
Website: www.kaizeninc.co
Project Management Consulting & Software Development. (As-Ind, estab 2010, empl 1, sales , cert: 8(a))

4721 KBS
8056 186th St Tinley Park, IL 60487
(708) 720-5981 Anthony R. Kitchens President
Fax: (708) 298-5807
Email: tonyk@kbs.us.com
Website: www.kbs.us.com
Technology products & svcs: desktop & notebook support, network admin, voice, video, data & electricity cabling, RFID tagging, WLAN, LAN, wireless cameras, help desk & end-user technical support. (AA, estab 1992, empl 22, sales $16,710,521, cert: NMSDC)

4722 Kristine Fallon Associates, Inc.
      11 E Adams St, Ste 1100 Chicago, IL 60603
      (312) 360-9600 Angelica Martinez Mktg Coord
      Fax: (312) 360-9601
      Email: amartinez@kfa-inc.com
      Website: www.kfa-inc.com
Information technology consulting services, Building
Information Modeling (BIM / COBie), electronic project
management & collaboration systems, Facility Management Systems & Transit Asset Management database
solutions. (AA, estab 1993, empl 11, sales , cert: City)

4723 LAB Information Technology, Inc.
      154 S Washington St Ste E Carpentersville, IL 60110
      (630) 524-4080 Martin Laster President
      Fax: (630) 570-5300
      Email: martin@labusa.com
      Website: www.labusa.com
IT, outsourcing & managed services. (AA, estab 1999, empl
6, sales $487,500, cert: City, NMSDC)

4724 LCS Entertainment LLC
      4545 S Drexel Chicago, IL 60653
      (773) 330-2440 Chrishon Lampley CEO
      Fax: (773) 826-8245
      Email: chrishon@lovecorkscrew.com
      Website: www.lovecorkscrew.com
LCS Entertainment, LLC offers Love Cork Screw wine to
provide consumers a diverse line of
varietals. Regionally produced, and distributed in Illinois,
each sleek wine bottle offers a colorful, whimsical and fun
experience. (Woman/AA, estab 2014, empl 5, sales
$18,000, cert: NMSDC, WBENC)

4725 Lead IT Corporation
      1999 Wabash Ste 210 Springfield, IL 62704
      (217) 726-7250 Ira Neuman Sales Mgr
      Fax: (801) 705-2524
      Email: ira.neuman@leaditgroup.com
      Website: www.leaditgroup.com
IT staffing & HR, executive search, consulting, computer
programming, IT mgmt, technical consulting. (Woman/As-
Ind, estab 2005, empl 232, sales $23,712,000, cert: State)

4726 LG Associates Inc. dba Asen Computer Associates
      900 N National Pkwy, Ste 155 Schaumburg, IL
      60173
      (847) 995-1300 Liza Brigham Acct Mgr
      Fax: (847) 995-1305
      Email: lbrigham@asen.com
      Website: www.asen.com/
IT & engineering consulting. (Woman/White, estab 1975,
empl 137, sales $5,985,000, cert: WBENC)

4727 Midwest Solution Providers, Inc.
      21720 W Long Grove Rd, Ste C-227   Deer Park, IL
      60010
      (224) 520-1510 Raj Andathode Consultant
      Fax:
      Email: raj@midwest-sp.com
      Website: www.midwest-sp.com
IT Consulting, Database design, database programming,
ETL, solutions using Informatica, Oracle, Teradata, Java,
Web-Services & custom applications. (As-Ind, estab 2004,
empl 1, sales , cert: NMSDC)

4728 Mirage Software Inc
      1701 E Woodfield Rd Ste 200 Schaumburg, IL
      60173
      (224) 232-5090 Tori Johnstin Business Dev
      Fax:
      Email: tjohnstin@bourntec.com
      Website: www.bourntec.com
ERP implementation, ERP upgrades, successful Cloud
migration, E-business, Big Data, BI, IT Security & Managed IT. (Woman/As-Ind, estab 1994, empl 35, sales ,
cert: NMSDC, 8(a))

4729 MVC Consulting Inc.
      203 N LaSalle St Chicago, IL 60601
      (312) 606-5555 Greg Mummert Recruiting Mgr
      Fax: (847) 283-0511
      Email: greg.mummert@mvc-consulting.com
      Website: www.mvc-consulting.com
IT consulting svcs: business intelligence/data warehous-
ing, compliance, ERP, CRM sales force automation,
change mgmt & project based consulting projects.
(Woman, estab 1981, empl 30, sales $2,800,000, cert:
WBENC)

4730 MZI Group Inc.
      1937 W Fulton St Chicago, IL 60612
      (312) 492-8740 Nicole Klimenko VP
      Fax: (312) 201-5226
      Email: nicole@mzigroup.com
      Website: www.mzigroup.com
Electrical, Mechanical, and Building Services Contractor
(Hisp, estab 1999, empl 110, sales $35,877,000, cert:
City, NMSDC)

4731 Netrion Global Solutions, Inc
      451 Dunham Rd Ste 202 St. Charles, IL 60174
      (630) 510-3000 Heather Thompson VP Bus Ops
      Fax: (877) 329-2220
      Email: heather.thompson@netrion.com
      Website: www.netrion.com
IT svcs: ERP implimentation, e-commerce solutions,
database development, project mgmt. (As-Ind, estab
1989, empl 21, sales $1,950,000, cert: NMSDC)

4732 Next Generation, Inc.
      800 West 5th Ave Ste 202 Naperville, IL 60563
      (312) 739-0520 Albert Villanueva Cstmr Relations
      Fax: (312) 739-0523
      Email: avillanueva@nxtgeninc.com
      Website: www.nxtgeninc.com
Customizations, implementation & support Enterprise
Resource Planning software. (Hisp, estab 2001, empl 15,
sales $2,100,000, cert: State)

4733 On the Job Consulting, Inc, DBA Pixo
      121 W Goose Alley Urbana, IL 61801
      (217) 344-0444 Lori Patterson CEO
      Fax:
      Email: info@pixotech.com
      Website: www.pixotech.com
Information technology consulting services. (Woman/
White, estab 1998, empl 15, sales $565,000, cert: State)

4734 OnShore Technology Group, Inc.
505 N Lake Shore Dr Ste 220 Chicago, IL 60611
(312) 321-6400 Valarie King- Bailey CEO
Fax: (312) 321-1450
Email: vkbailey@onshoretech.com
Website: www.onshoretech.com
Applied technology products & svcs: engineering, e-govt support, advanced strategic & tactical mktg svcs, digital media production, enterprise business intelligence solutions, digital home networking. (Woman/AA, estab 2004, empl 6, sales $1,534,540, cert: City, NMSDC, WBENC)

4735 Pace Systems, Inc
2040 Corporate Ln   Naperville, IL 60563
(630) 395-2191 Nick Taylor
Fax: (630) 395-2250
Email: ntaylor@pace-systems.com
Website: www.pace-systems.com
Information technology services & sales. Citrix networking design & consulting. Physical & network security consulting. (As-Pac, estab 1983, empl 32, sales $30,000,000, cert: State, City, NMSDC)

4736 Pinnakle Technologies, Inc.
424 Fort Hill Dr, Ste 134A   Naperville, IL 60540
(630) 352-0070 Ajay Kshatriya President
Fax: (630) 429-9091
Email: ajay.kshatriya@pinnakle.net
Website: www.pinnakle.net
IT project management, staff augmentation, ERPs, web development, databases, business intelligence, infrastructure, etc. (As-Ind, estab 2009, empl 22, sales $4,500,000, cert: 8(a))

4737 Premier Systems, Inc
14489 John Humphrey Ste 202 Ste 202 Orland Park, IL 60462
(708) 349-9200 Tariq Khan Acct Mgr
Fax: (708) 349-2194
Email: tkhan@premiersystemsinc.com
Website: www.premiersystemsinc.com
IT consulting & staffing, project mgmt, systems programming & admin: IBM mainframe midrange, client server, PeopleSoft, SAP & Microsoft based systems; e-commerce devel. (As-Pac, estab 1993, empl 30, sales $2,713,000, cert: City, NMSDC)

4738 Purple Consulting
2539 Lexington Lane   Naperville, IL 60540
(630) 303-2706 Purnima Parashar Principal
Fax:
Email: purnima@consultpurple.com
Website: www.consultpurple.com
Permanent placement of Software Engineers, Network Engineers, Analysts. Positions like Systems Engineers, Project Managers, Trading Engineers, IT Analysts, Business Analysts, Software Engineers, Sales. (Woman/As-Ind, estab 2014, empl 5, sales , cert: City)

4739 Quinnox Inc.
400 N. Michigan Ave Ste 1300 Chicago, IL 60611
(1312) 219-6517 Amar Sowani Sr Mgr
Fax:
Email: amars@quinnox.com
Website: www.quinnox.com
Information technology consulting & staff augmentation services. (As-Ind, estab , empl 1, sales $52,000,000, cert: NMSDC)

4740 RL Canning Inc.
8700 W. Bryn Mawr Ste 120N Chicago, IL 60631
(773) 693-1900 Rachel Canning President
Fax: (773) 693-0207
Email: rachel@rlcanning.com
Website: www.rlcanning.com
Information technology consulting & staffing services. (Woman/Hisp, estab 1999, empl 48, sales $5,000,000, cert: State, City, WBENC)

4741 S & F Software Solutions Inc.
285 Victor Lane   Lake Zurich, IL 60047
(847) 726-2571 Asma Farhin
Fax: (614) 455-8653
Email: afarhin@sandfbizsolutions.com
Website: www.sandfbizsolutions.com
Project Management, Program/Project Management Office (PMO), Enterprise Risk Management, Business Process Re-engineering (BPR), Strategic Business Analysis, Data Management, Enterprise Quality Management. (Woman/As-Ind, estab 2011, empl 2, sales , cert: State, NMSDC, WBENC)

4742 SDA Consulting, Inc.
3011 W 183rd St   Homewood, IL 60430
(708) 372-8809 Shawn Anderson President
Fax: (800) 823-2990
Email: sda@sdaci.com
Website: www.sdaci.com
Technical consulting, staffing, support, development & training, business software, Oracle EBS, PeopleSoft, JDE, Siebel, Hyperion,
Microsoft, SAP, custom software. (Woman/AA, estab 2004, empl 66, sales $9,185,610, cert: State, NMSDC)

4743 SDI Presence LLC
200 East Randolph, Ste 3550   Chicago, IL 60601
(312) 580-7563 Dawn Pfeiffer Sr Proposal Mgr
Fax: (312) 580-7600
Email: dpfeiffer@sdipresence.com
Website: www.sdipresence.com
Traditional or cloud-based systems life-cycle, concept development, systems integration & long-term support. (As-Ind, estab 2015, empl 136, sales , cert: State, NMSDC)

4744   Senryo Technologies
       387 Shuman Blvd, 208e 60563 Naperville, IL 60563
       (630) 355-7429 Nick Georgelos Research Analyst
       Fax: (630) 364-5838
       Email: nick.georgelos@senryo.com
       Website: www.senryo.com
Consulting services: project management, systems
delivery, management consulting, technology consulting,
quality assurance, value management, application integration & business intelligence. (As-Ind, estab 2001, empl 20,
sales , cert: 8(a))

4745   SNtial Technologies, Inc.
       150 N. Michigan Ave Ste 2800 Chicago, IL 60601
       (630) 452-4735 Leon Francisco President
       Fax: (630) 929-8535
       Email: leon.francisco@sntialtech.com
       Website: www.sntialtech.com
Information technology services, custom software development, systems integration & re-engineering. (As-Pac,
estab 2001, empl 8, sales $1,000,000, cert: City, NMSDC)

4746   Software Tech Enterprises, Inc.
       19730 Governors Hwy Ste 5 Flossmoor, IL 60422
       (708) 922-9008 Rolland Craig Business Devel
       Fax:
       Email: rcraig@software-tec.com
       Website: www.software-tec.com
IT management consulting, IT planning, IT governance,
enterprise architecture, service oriented architecture, ERP
strategy & health information technology. (AA, estab 2001,
empl 55, sales $8,000,000, cert: 8(a))

4747   Swoon Group
       300 South Wacker Dr Ste 300 Chicago, IL 60606
       (312) 450-8701 Joseph Matalone VP
       Fax:
       Email: joe.matalone@swoonstaffing.com
       Website: www.swoonstaffing.com
Technical staffing. (Woman/White, estab 2009, empl 71,
sales $33,000,000, cert: WBENC)

4748   Synchronous Solutions, Inc.
       211 W Wacker Dr Ste 300 Chicago, IL 60610
       (312) 252-3700 John Sterling CEO
       Fax: (312) 201-5226
       Email: jsterling@synch-solutions.com
       Website: www.synch-solutions.com
Implementations, integrations & upgrades, ERP software
products, Oracle-PeopleSoft & SAP, functional & technical
Consulting, database admin, application integration,
training, project mgmt, strategic IT outsourcing. (AA, estab
1998, empl 75, sales $14,000,000, cert: State, City)

4749   Synectics Inc.
       135 S LaSalle St Ste 2050 Chicago, IL 60603
       (312) 629-1020 Melissa Lounds Director of Global
       Accts
       Fax: (312) 629-1028
       Email: M_Lounds@synectics.com
       Website: www.synectics.com/
Information technology consulting, staff augmentation.
(Woman/White, estab 1984, empl 300, sales $19,300,000,
cert: CPUC, WBENC)

4750   System Solutions, Inc.
       3630 Commercial Ave   Northbrook, IL 60062
       (847) 272-6160 Oliver Patterson Sr Acct Mgr
       Fax: (847) 272-8465
       Email: oliver.patterson@thessi.com
       Website: www.THESSI.COM
Information technology: enterprise solution products &
architecture, consulting, staffing, network design &
implementation, hardware & software procurement,
onsite installation services. (As-Pac, estab 1987, empl
20, sales $24,000,000, cert: State, NMSDC)

4751   TechCircle, Inc.
       500 N Michigan Ave Ste 600 Chicago, IL 60611
       (312) 767-5653 Aakash Gajera President
       Fax: (312) 767-5652
       Email: agajera@techcircleinc.com
       Website: www.techcircleinc.com
Information technology consulting & staff augmentation
services, project/program management, business system
analysis, quality assurance, verification & validation. (As-
Ind, estab 2015, empl 4, sales $300,000, cert: State,
NMSDC)

4752   Technical Source, Inc.
       1447 E Rosita Dr   Palatine, IL 60074
       (847) 705-1730 Jerri Gutwein President
       Fax:
       Email: jgutwein@computerrelocation.com
       Website: www.computerrelocation.com
PC Disconnect/Reconnect Corporate Relocation Add,
Moves, Changes. Project Management Information
Technology, IT Management, Help Desk & Support
Disaster Recovery. (Woman/White, estab 1999, empl 54,
sales $1,025,201, cert: City, WBENC)

4753   TransTech, LLC
       248 Spring Lake Dr   Itasca, IL 60143
       (630) 228-8880 Cynthia Conroy Sales Admin
       Fax: (630) 250-8777
       Email: cconroy@transtechit.com
       Website: www.transtechit.com
Informational technology staffing solutions. (Woman/
White, estab 1990, empl 100, sales $34,600,000, cert:
WBENC)

4754   VIVA USA Inc.
       3601 Algonquin Road Ste 425 Rolling Meadows,
       IL 60008
       (847) 368-0860 Vasanthi Ilangovan President
       Fax: (847) 368-0864
       Email: vilangovan@viva-it.com
       Website: www.viva-it.com
IT svcs, custom software dev, IT staffing, offsite &
offshore IT project outsourcing. (Woman/As-Ind, estab
1996, empl 380, sales $25,000,000, cert: City, NMSDC,
CPUC, WBENC)

4755   Von Technologies, LLC
       1193 Old Creek Ct   Woodridge, IL 60517
       (630) 985-8474 Michelle Vondrasek President
       Fax: (866) 604-8822
       Email: vondrasek.michelle@vontechnologies.com
       Website: www.vontechnologies.com
Network solutions: infrastructure design, implementation, management, refresh, software & hardware configuration, wireless solutions. (Woman/White, estab 2006, empl 23, sales , cert: State, WBENC)

Indiana

4756   Alliance Group Technologies Company-Calumet, Inc.
       911 Broad Ripple Ave, Ste B   Indianapolis, IN 46220
       (317) 254-8285 Brian Crump Director-Business Dev
       Fax: (317) 254-8339
       Email: bcrump@alliancegrouptech.com
       Website: www.alliancegrouptech.com
Engineering consulting & technical staffing solutions. (Nat Ame, estab 1975, empl 215, sales , cert: NMSDC)

4757   Anchor Point Technology Resources, Inc
       9510 N MERIDIAN ST Ste 200 Indianapolis, IN 46260
       (317) 225-4141 Rachael Schatko President
       Fax: (866) 242-1821
       Email: diversity@anchorpointtr.com
       Website: www.anchorpointtr.com/
Engineering & IT solutions, IT staffing, contract, C2D, Permanent Placement, Engineering Staffing & Executive Placement. (Woman, estab 2004, empl 140, sales $12,500,000, cert: State)

4758   Data Integration Consulting, Inc.
       7399 N. Shadeland Ave Ste 312 Indianapolis, IN 46250
       (317) 894-2623 Tim Thompson President
       Fax: (317) 894-2223
       Email: tthompson@dataic.com
       Website: www.dataic.com
IT consulting, web application development, desktop application development, computer programming, network design & administration, database design & administration. (AA, estab 2003, empl 1, sales $68,000, cert: State)

4759   GuideSoft Inc. dba Knowledge Services
       5875 Castle Creek PkwyN Dr Ste 400 Indianapolis, IN 46250
       (317) 578-1700 Cindy Davis Director
       Fax: (317) 578-7600
       Email: cindyd@knowledgeservices.com
       Website: www.knowledgeservices.com
IT staffing; IT training development. project mgmt, application development, tier I-III help desk & desktop support. (Woman/White, estab 1994, empl 130, sales $13,186,909, cert: State)

4760   Guilford Group LLC
       615 W Carmel Dr, Ste 130   Carmel, IN 46032
       (317) 814-1060 Rajan Kapur Director
       Fax: (317) 814-1044
       Email: rajkapur@guilfordgroup.com
       Website: www.guilfordgroup.com
Information technology consulting, IT project management, enterprise application development, mobile development, data management, staffing, cloud storage, systems integrations, web development & graphic design resources. (As-Ind, estab 2003, empl 30, sales $2,922,823, cert: State, NMSDC)

4761   GyanSys Inc.
       702 Adams St   Carmel, IN 46032
       (317) 580-4200 Padmaja Una CFO
       Fax: (317) 663-1027
       Email: hr.us@gyansys.com
       Website: www.gyansys.com
Global systems integration: SAP & Microsoft products, mobile platforms. (Woman/As-Ind, estab 2005, empl 500, sales $17,000,000, cert: State, WBENC)

4762   JumpStart Point of Arrival, LLC
       9801 Fall Creek Rd, Ste 410   Indianapolis, IN 46256
       (317) 777-1995 Ek-Leng Chua-Miller CEO
       Fax: (317) 578-2969
       Email: ek-leng@jumpstartpoa.biz
       Website: www.jumpstartpoa.biz
Statistical analysis, data analysis, database marketing, data mining, statistical modeling, regression analysis (Woman/As-Pac, estab 2005, empl 2, sales $442,000, cert: State, NMSDC, WBENC)

4763   LHP Software, LLC
       1888 Poshard Dr   Columbus, IN 47203
       (812) 418-6331 Kandace Yamcharern Mgr Payment Process
       Fax:
       Email: kandace.y@lhpes.com
       Website: www.lhpsoftware.com
Custom software solutions: embedded software, communication software, internet software, testing. (As-Pac, estab 2001, empl 210, sales $26,893,359, cert: NMSDC)

4764   Morse Communications Inc.
       8207 Linden Ave   Munster, IN 46321
       (219) 314-6029 Tim Kerrick Sr Acct Mgr
       Fax: (321) 255-0198
       Email: tkerrick@morsecom.com
       Website: www.morsecom.com
Systems integration, communications, networking & electronic safety & security. (Woman/White, estab 1994, empl 75, sales $17,000,000, cert: State)

4765 Phelco Technologies, Inc.
9801 Fall Creek Rd #131 Indianapolis, IN 46256
(317) 898-0334 Tasha Phelps CEO
Fax: (317) 536-3743
Email: tasha@phelco.com
Website: www.phelco.com
Network infrastructure, disaster recovery, off-site data backup, web development. (Woman/AA, estab 1997, empl 1, sales $50,000, cert: State)

4766 Pinnacle Mailing Products, LLC
7701 W Kilgore Ave, Ste 5   Yorktown, IN 47396
(765) 405-1194 Kim Laffoon Owner
Fax: (765) 405-1196
Email: kimlaffoon@pinnaclemailing.com
Website: www.pinnaclemailingproducts.net
Address correction & shipping software solutions. (Woman/White, estab 2009, empl 6, sales $195,000, cert: State)

4767 RCR Technology Corporation
251 N Illinois St Ste 1150, North Tower Indianapolis, IN 46204
(317) 624-9500 Robert Reed CEO
Fax: (317) 631-3345
Email: rreed@rcrtechnology.com
Website: www.rcrtechnology.com
Information technology consulting, network design, application services & project management. (AA, estab 1997, empl 150, sales $18,000,000, cert: State, City, NMSDC)

4768 Ryan Consulting Group, Inc.
7914 North Shadeland Avenue, Ste 200   Indianapolis, IN 46250
(317) 541-9300 Aisha Washington proposal Mgr
Fax: (317) 541-9339
Email: awashington@consultrcg.com
Website: www.consultrcg.com
Information technologies, systems integration, design & consulting. (AA, estab 2001, empl 106, sales $15,604,064, cert: State, City, NMSDC)

4769 STLogics
9449 Priority Way West Dr Ste 110 Indianapolis, IN 46240
(800) 505-0357 Sandeep Allam President
Fax: (866) 896-0246
Email: procurement@stlogics.com
Website: www.stlogics.com
IT consulting, staff augmentation, managed IT solutions, project management, web & software development, quality assurance, Java applications, sharepoint, SAP, ERP, datawarehouse & network administration. (Woman/As-Ind, estab 2004, empl 120, sales $19,000,000, cert: NMSDC, WBENC)

Kansas

4770 3 Fuerzas Technology Solutions, LLC
14013 Outlook Overland Park, KS 66223
(913) 744-1163 Shawn Hashmi VP Program Management
Fax: (916) 421-3700
Email: shashmi@edzsystems.com
Website: www.edzsystems.com
Software Development, IT Consulting Services, Intelligent Resource Management System (Intelligent RMS. (Woman/Hisp, estab 2015, empl 5, sales $201,000, cert: NMSDC, WBENC)

4771 Complete Carpet Care Inc.
324 Fawn Valley Court   Lansing, KS 66043
(913) 351-3550 Brad Turner President
Fax: (913) 351-3550
Email: bradsmegastore@gmail.com
Website: www.notcompletewithoutyou.com
Hi! This is Brad Turner. Thanks very much for your interest in professional carpet cleaning. I am grateful for the opportunity to provide you with information about carpet cleaning and help you choose a carpet cleaning company. (AA, estab 1993, empl 10, sales $315,689, cert: NMSDC)

4772 Evolv Solutions, LLC.
9401 Indian Creek Pkwy, Ste 250 Overland Park, KS 66210
(913) 553-1041 Aaron Williams Bus Dev Mgr
Fax: (913) 469-8909
Email: awilliams@evolvsolutions.com
Website: www.evolvsolutions.com
IT & document mgmt solutions, project mgmt & outsourcing, enterprise solutions, web devel, system integration, tech communication, office assessment, asset mgmt, etc. (AA, estab 2001, empl 56, sales $18,500,000, cert: NMSDC)

4773 IT Consulting Services, Inc.
901 Kentucky St Ste 105 Lawrence, KS 66044
(913) 972-2321 Kishor Gohel COO
Fax: (785) 371-2951
Email: kgohel@itcscorp.net
Website: www.itcscorp.net
Software Engineering: Application Development (Web, non-Web, Mobile, SharePoint, e-commerce), Legacy systems & data migration, System Integration (SOA based & FOSS Custom Solutions). (Woman/As-Ind, estab 2004, empl 6, sales $156,456, cert: State, 8(a))

4774 JMA Chartered
10551 Barkley St Ste 400 Overland Park, KS 66212
(913) 722-3252 Sanjay Chopra Dir Western Reg
Fax: (913) 432-6667
Email: schopra@jmait.com
Website: www.jma-it.com
Infomration technology: systems integration, IT infrastructure planning, IT facilities management, network design & implementation, IT security audits & staff supplementation. (As-Pac, estab 1994, empl 250, sales $13,900,000, cert: NMSDC, CPUC)

4775   Perfect Output, LLC
        9200 Indian Creek Pkwy Ste 400 Overland Park, KS
        66210
        (913) 317-8400 Asya Evans Business Devel Mgr
        Fax: (913) 317-8489
        Email: aevans@perfectoutput.com
        Website: www.perfectoutput.com
Document output devices: printers, fax machines, & digital
multi-functional devices, develop & implement document
management strategies. (AA, estab 1997, empl 70, sales
$20,000,000, cert: State, NMSDC)

4776   Saicon Consultants, Inc.
        9300 W 110th St Ste 650 Overland Park, KS 66210
        (816) 553-2670 Rick wilbanks VP Business Devel
        Fax: (913) 451-1126
        Email: rwilbanks@saiconinc.com
        Website: www.saicon.com/index.php
IT consulting: ERP, client server devl, & admin. (Woman/As-
Ind, estab 1998, empl 550, sales $65,000,000, cert: NMSDC)

4777   Technology Group Solutions, LLC
        14649 W 95th St Lenexa, KS 66215
        (913) 451-9900 Doug Floersch President
        Fax: (913) 451-9907
        Email: dfloersch@tgs-kc.com
        Website: www.tgs-kc.com
Information technology soutions. (Woman/AA, estab 2005,
empl 30, sales $82,151,244, cert: NMSDC, WBENC, 8(a))

4778   Vedainfo Inc
        10500 Barkley St Ste 110 Overland Park, KS 66212
        (302) 357-9017 Salman Mohammed VP Business Dev
        Fax: (302) 634-0307
        Email: salman@us.vedainfo.com
        Website: www.vedainfo.com
IT development & software consulting, staffing, design,
development & maintenance of high-end business enabling
IT systems. (Woman/As-Pac, estab 2006, empl 130, sales
$9,400,000, cert: CPUC)

4779   Veracity Consulting, Inc.
        15516 W 81st St, Ste 195 Lenexa, KS 66219
        (913) 579-9242 Angela Hurt CEO
        Fax: (866) 407-6834
        Email: angela.hurt@engageveracity.com
        Website: www.veracityconsulting.us
IT contracting services: process improvement, PMO, project
Mgt, custom computer programming, systems administration & information security. (Woman/Nat Ame, estab 2006,
empl 26, sales , cert: WBENC)

Kentucky

4780   AnITConsultant, LLC
        P.O. Box 22998 Owensboro, KY 42304
        (270) 883-1450 Whaylon Coleman Owner
        Fax: (888) 391-4068
        Email: it@anitconsultant.com
        Website: www.anitconsultant.com
IT solutions & consulting services, Game Dev, Social Media
Consulting , Microsoft Application Development, Mobile &
Tablet Apps. (AA, estab 2010, empl 1, sales , cert: State)

4781   CEEJS Software
        3406 Greentree Rd Lexington, KY 40517
        (859) 576-6790 Eddie Sanford President
        Fax: (859) 971-0361
        Email: esanford@ceejs.com
        Website: www.ceejs.com
Information technology: design, development, maintenance & support software applications. (AA, estab 1996,
empl 11, sales $6,404,000, cert: State)

4782   Etisbew Technology Group Inc.
        7031 Glen Arbor Dr Florence, KY 41042
        (502) 386-4999 Raj Pakala CEO
        Fax: (253) 540-6073
        Email: bizteam@etisbew.com
        Website: www.etisbew.com
E-Business solutions, e-business strategy, architecture &
process automation, web based applications development & maintenance. (As-Pac, estab 2000, empl 150,
sales $5,321,106, cert: NMSDC)

4783   V-Soft Consulting Group Inc.
        2115 Stanley Gault Pkwy, Ste 200 Louisville, KY
        40223
        (502) 425-8425 Vincel Anthony Natl Business Dev
        Mgr
        Fax: (502) 412-5869
        Email: vanthony@vsoftconsulting.com
        Website: www.vsoftconsulting.com
Information technology staffing & consulting services:
temporary, contract & permanent placement. (Woman/
As-Pac, estab 1997, empl 230, sales , cert: NMSDC)

Louisiana

4784   A-B Computer Solutions, Inc.
        P.O. Box 1851 Mandeville, LA 70470
        (985) 624-3092 Jason Brady President
        Fax: (985) 624-3994
        Email: jasonb@a-bcomputers.com
        Website: www.a-bcomputers.com
Information technology solutions & consulting. (Woman,
estab 1997, empl 13, sales $3,060,000, cert: WBENC)

4785   Barrister Global Services Network Inc
        42548 Happywoods Road Hammond, LA 70403
        (985) 365-0806 Melissa Dobson Director of
        Service Solutions
        Fax: (985) 310-5533
        Email: mdobson@barrister.com
        Website: www.barrister.com
Information technology services. (Woman/White, estab
1982, empl 147, sales $17,000,000, cert: WBENC)

4786   ComTec Consultants Inc.
        2400 Veterans Memorial Blvd Ste 205 Kenner, LA
        70062
        (972) 338-3533 Vijay Saradhi VP
        Fax: (504) 910-3010
        Email: vijay@comtecinfo.com
        Website: www.comtecinfo.com
Information technology & business process services.
(Woman/As-Ind, estab 1996, empl 635, sales
$62,550,319, cert: NMSDC)

4787   Morine Networking, Inc.
P.O. Box 363   Opelousas, LA 70570
(337) 942-1790 Rodney Morine VP
Fax: (866) 878-6745
Email: rodney@morinetrucking.com
Website: www.morinenetworking.com
We are a freight brokering company providing 3rd party property logistics (Woman/AA, estab 2007, empl 2, sales , cert: State, NMSDC)

4788   MSF Global Solutions, LLC
201 St. Charles Ave, Ste 2500   New Orleans, LA 70170
(504) 872-0641 Marseyas Fernandez CEO
Fax: (504) 301-4856
Email: marseyas@msfglobal.net
Website: www.msfglobal.net
Geospatial & location based software & data development, mobile website & app development, staffing & training support services, data & business intelligence services, web & custom software design & development services. (AA, estab 2003, empl 5, sales $400,000, cert: State)

4789   Trendsic Corporation
311 Veterans Blvd Ste A Denham Springs, LA 70726
(225) 490-9505 Jelani Clark President
Fax: (225) 490-9506
Email: jelani@trendsic.com
Website: www.Trendsic.com
Software engineers, application support, integration, testing, deployment & software management systems (applications) & system software tools. (AA, estab 2006, empl 9, sales $976,415, cert: State)

4790   Vinformatix, LLC
5615 Corporate Blvd Ste 500A Baton Rouge, LA 70808
(225) 810-3550 Padma Vatasavai CEO
Fax: (225) 810-3851
Email: padma@vinformatix.com
Website: www.vinformatix.com
Custom-built software applications for web & mobile platforms (including OS/Android/Windows mobile apps), software lifecycle services, requirements analysis, design, coding, testing, QA/QC, training & maintenance. (Woman/As-Ind, estab 2008, empl 20, sales $1,050,000, cert: NMSDC, WBENC)

Massachusetts

4791   Advans IT Services, Inc.
65 Boston Post Rd W Ste 390 Marlborough, MA 01752
(508) 624-9900 Paul Angelo CRM Mgr
Fax: (508) 624-9905
Email: pangelo@advansit.com
Website: www.AdvansIT.com
IT infrastructure, project management & software development & offshore support. (As-Pac, estab 2009, empl 205, sales $21,000,000, cert: State, NMSDC)

4792   Advoqt, LLC
10 Guest St Ste 290 Boston, MA 02135
(617) 307-7770 Reinier Moquete CEO
Fax: (617) 307-7771
Email: info@advoqt.com
Website: www.advoqt.com
Systems integration & technology advisory firm focused on Hybrid Cloud Computing. (Hisp, estab 2012, empl 10, sales $40,000, cert: State)

4793   Aquent LLC
501 Boylston St Third Fl Boston, MA 02116
(202) 808-0557 Jennifer Cousins Director, Staffing Solutions Dev
Fax: (877) 430-8724
Email: jcousins@aquent.com
Website: www.aquent.com
Graphic designers, web designers, production artists, presentation graphics experts, writers & project managers: freelance, permanent & temporary-to-permanent basis. (Woman/As-Ind, estab 1986, empl 7000, sales $311,000,000, cert: NMSDC)

4794   Cambridge Computer Services, Inc.
271 Waverley Oaks Ste 301 Waltham, MA 02452
(781) 250-3000 Karen King Cstmr Advocate
Fax: (781) 250-3342
Email: kking@cambridgecomputer.com
Website: www.cambridgecomputer.com
Data storage & data protection solutions: SAN, NAS, backup, cloud, solid state, archiving solutions, research data management, scientific workflow, metadata, tiered storage, chargebacks, archiving & cloud storage. (Woman/White, estab 1991, empl 74, sales , cert: State, WBENC)

4795   CTS Services Inc.
260 Maple St   Bellingham, MA 02019
(508) 528-7720 Michelle Carlow President
Fax: (508) 966-9734
Email: mcarlow@ctsservices.com
Website: www.ctsservices.com
Computer, printer & peripheral repair: touch screen displays, barcode scanning equipment, receipt printer. (Woman/White, estab 1989, empl 22, sales $2,775,000, cert: State)

4796   Cube Intelligence Corporation
12 Brattle Lane   Arlington, MA 02474
(617) 275-8254 Hemant Verma President/Chief Technology Officer
Fax: (617) 314-6239
Email: hsverma@cubeic.com
Website: www.cubeic.com
IT consulting and Staffing augmentationsvcs: data warehousing, data integration, data profiling, data quality, master data management, ODS, Operational Data Stores, Data Mart, Star Schema. (As-Ind, estab 2001, empl 2, sales $178,654, cert: State, NMSDC, 8(a))

4797 Deerwalk, Inc.
430 Bedford St   Lexington, MA 02420
(781) 325-1775 Jeffrey Gasser President
Fax: (617) 307-7771
Email: jgasser@deerwalk.com
Website: www.deerwalk.com
Global data analytics, big data technology & web based data analytics apps, healthcare data analytics, population management & controlling healthcare costs. (As-Ind, estab 2010, empl 400, sales $7,450,000, cert: NMSDC)

4798 Distributed Technology Associates
1740 Massachusetts Ave   Boxborough, MA 01719
(978) 274-0462 Sanjay Tikku President
Fax: (801) 505-0315
Email: office@dtainc.us
Website: www.dtainc.us
Database & systems services, Oracle & SQL Server databases, Linux, Solaris & Windows platforms. (As-Ind, estab 1997, empl 7, sales $2,114,602, cert: State, NMSDC)

4799 Dnutch Associates, Inc.
301 Broadway   Methuen, MA 01844
(978) 687-1500 Stephen Payne President
Fax: (978) 687-1540
Email: spayne@dnutch.com
Website: www.dnutch.com
Networking & systems integration solutions. (Woman/AA, estab 1993, empl 8, sales $550,000, cert: State, WBENC, 8(a))

4800 Executive Analytics & Design, Inc.
10 Malcolm X Blvd   Boston, MA 02119
617-445-52 Josie Haywood
Fax: 617-445-52
Email: eadtech@msn.com
Website: www.eadtech.com
Network installation, maintenance & external client interfaces, training, support & outsourcing, project mgmt, web site hosting, etc. (Woman/AA, estab 1998, empl 3, sales , cert: State)

4801 Fenco Global Industries Corp.
1 Federal St   Springfield, MA 01105
(413) 308-8800 Fenella Sitati President
Fax:
Email: fenella@winningtek.com
Website: www.winningtek.com
Technology hardware for application security, datacenters & cloud virtualization, F5 Networks, VMware, Palo Alto, Cisco Networks, RedHat, Microsoft, NetApp, EMC, HP, IBM, Dell & ExtraHop. (Woman/AA, estab 2009, empl 5, sales $450,000, cert: NMSDC)

4802 Hawkins Point Partners LLC
7 Technology Dr   North Chelmsford, MA 01863
(781) 640-0893 Heather Morris Kyer Sr principal
Fax:
Email: hmorriskyer@hawkinspointpartners.com
Website: www.hawkinspointpartners.com
IT consulting, outsourcing reset, application modernization, information mgmt, mobile solutions & enterprise architecture & integration. (Woman/White, estab 2012, empl 5, sales , cert: State, WBENC)

4803 Inspiration Zone, LLC
Two Heritage Dr, Ste 302   Quincy, MA 02171
(617) 328-0953 Juliette Mayers CEO
Fax: (617) 328-0769
Email: info@inspirationzonellc.com
Website: www.inspirationzonellc.com
Inspiration Zone provides strategic advisory services primarily for HR/Talent, Diversity, and Inclusion and has expertise in Multicultural Marketing and Leadership Development. We offer training and inspirational talks including workshops and speaking eng (AA, estab 2011, empl 1, sales $130,000, cert: State, NMSDC)

4804 IntePros Incorporated
750 Marrett Road Ste 301 Lexington, MA 02421
(612) 916-7387 Jeffrey Anderson Branch Mgr
Fax:
Email: janderson@intepros.com
Website: www.intepros.com
Provide contracted IT consultants, software development lifecycle, network infrastructure & security. (Woman/White, estab 1996, empl 350, sales $55,400,000, cert: WBENC)

4805 Interactive Tactical Group
55 Wallace St   Somerville, MA 02144
(617) 500-7520 Michael Quan President
Fax: (617) 500-7520
Email: mike@tacticalvr.com
Website: www.tacticalvr.com
Interactive panoramic imaging for military, security & industrial organizations. DotProduct3D hand held 3D scanner, DotProduct3D hand held 3D scanner, DPI-7, uses Android tablet & Kinect sensor. (As-Pac, estab 2000, empl 1, sales $150,500, cert: State, NMSDC)

4806 M & R Consultants Corporation
700 Technology Park Dr Ste 203 Billerica, MA 01821
(781) 273-5050 Brendan Farrand Sales Dir
Fax: (781) 273-5051
Email: bfarrand@mrccsolutions.com
Website: www.mrccsolutions.com
IT consulting: software engineering, client server technology, internet & intranet, network admin, project mgmt, product dev. (As-Ind, estab 1996, empl 700, sales $20,000,000, cert: State)

4807 Martindale Associates, Inc.
65 Avco Rd, Unit M   Bradford, MA 01835
(978) 372-2120 Laurie Hall President
Fax: (978) 372-6537
Email: lmh@martindaleassoc.com
Website: www.martindaleassoc.com
Automated machine & process control systems, data acquisition systems, barcode data collection, inventory & asset tracking, RFID, mobile device management, handheld computers & systems integration.
(Woman/Nat Ame, estab 1976, empl 7, sales $1,525,041, cert: State)

4808 On Track Consulting
317 Eliot St Milton, MA 02186
(617) 653-1409 Janet McCloskey President
Fax: (617) 433-2953
Email: jmccloskey@ontrackconsult.com
Website: www.ontrackconsult.com
Information management services, big data, data ware-
housing, business intelligence & data management.
(Woman/White, estab 1997, empl 1, sales $3,157,077,
cert: State, WBENC)

4809 Online Computer Prodcuts, Inc.
672 Pleasant St Norwood, MA 02062
(781) 255-9100 Harry Butters Acct Mgr
Fax: (781) 255-9191
Email: hbutters@online-computer.com
Website: www.online-computer.com
Information technology support products, services &
solutions. (Woman/White, estab 1987, empl 24, sales
$14,075,000, cert: WBENC)

4810 Onyx Spectrum Technology, Inc. dba Shearwater EM
78 Fisher Ave Boston, MA 02120
(617) 407-2826 Adrienne R. Benton President
Fax: (617) 507-0779
Email: abenton@onyxspectrum.com
Website: www.onyxspectrum.com
Technical consulting services: data analysis, information
security, business process improvement & regulatory
concerns. (Woman/AA, estab 2004, empl 5, sales
$726,000, cert: State)

4811 ResourceSoft, Inc.
33 Boston Post Rd W Ste 230 Marlborough, MA
01752
(508) 787-0882 Pyi Phyo VP
Fax: (508) 861-0220
Email: pyi@resourcesoft.com
Website: www.resourcesoft.com
Custom computer programming svcs: MS .NET, JAVA/J2EE,
quality assurance. (Woman/As-Pac, estab 1999, empl 55,
sales $5,711,183, cert: State, NMSDC)

4812 SAI Enterprises, Inc.
35 Corporate Dr, 4th Fl Burlington, MA 01803
(781) 685-4988 Ajay Rangu Dir
Fax: (781) 998-4767
Email: ajay@saiamerica.com
Website: www.saiamerica.com
Information technology products, infrastructure services,
custom computer programming, staffing, ecommerce
design & consulting services. (As-Ind, estab 2004, empl 10,
sales $1,500,000, cert: State)

4813 Scitics Inc.
436 Central St Acton, MA 01720
(978) 844-1258 Joan Yu President
Fax:
Email: jyu@sciticsinc.com
Website: www.sciticsinc.com
Data analytics, data exploration & discovery, data processing, hosting & related services, custom computer programming services, dashboard & customized business intelligence reports, predictive modeling. (Woman/As-Pac, estab
2010, empl 3, sales $128,170, cert: State, WBENC)

4814 Shred King Corporation
60 McGrath Hwy Quincy, MA 02169
(617) 221-1600 Donald Cornell GM
Fax: (617) 770-4158
Email: info@shred-king.com
Website: www.shred-king.com
Document destruction services. (Woman/White, estab
2006, empl 10, sales $160,200, cert: State)

4815 Sigma Systems, Inc.
201 Boston Post Rd W Ste 201 Marlborough, MA
01752
(508) 925-3200 Mohan Nannapaneni EVP & CTO
Fax: (508) 449-9339
Email: mohan@sigmainc.com
Website: www.sigmainc.com
IT consulting, project mgmt, application dev, network
mgmt, database mgmt & support, staffing services,
custom application dev, data warehousing, business
intelligence, CRM, ERP, EAI, quality assurance, systems
admin, web dev & custom MIS. (Woman/As-Ind, estab
1994, empl 97, sales $11,150,000, cert: State, NMSDC)

4816 SJB Enterprises, Inc. dba Sandra Network
25 Goodale St Peabody, MA 01960
(978) 535-0202 Sandra Batakis President
Fax: (978) 336-8560
Email: wbe@sandranetwork.com
Website: www.sandranetwork.com
IT consulting: PC repair, training & networks. (Woman/
White, estab 1998, empl 3, sales $155,000, cert: State,
WBENC)

4817 Softlinx, Inc.
100 Riverpark Dr North Reading, MA 01864
(978) 881-0575 Helen Kim Contract Mgr
Fax: (978) 664-0181
Email: hkim@softlinx.com
Website: www.softlinx.com
Software, IT development, consulting & training. (As-
Pac, estab 1993, empl 15, sales $1,530,000, cert:
NMSDC, WBENC)

4818 Solidus Technical Solutions, Inc.
17 Forsythia Rd Leominster, MA 01453
(866) 765-4387 Jill Blagsvedt Bus Dev Specialist
Fax: (781) 538-0602
Email: solidussmallbd@solidus-ts.com
Website: www.solidus-ts.com
Software & systems engineering, life cycle, radar,
sensors, fault tolerant, mission planning, intelligence
systems, embedded software, networking, integration &
test. (Woman/White, estab 2001, empl 95, sales , cert:
WBENC)

4819 Soltrix Technology Solutions Inc.
14 Vernon St Ste 215 Framingham, MA 01701
(774) 293-1293 Raghu Nandan President
Fax: (866) 520-4756
Email: raghu.nandan@soltrixsolutions.com
Website: www.soltrixsolutions.com
Custom software application design & development
services. (Woman/As-Ind, estab 2007, empl 3, sales
$50,000, cert: State)

4820   Stellar Corporation
594 Marrett Rd   Lexington, MA 02421
(781) 863-0101   Swapan Roy President
Fax: (781) 863-1151
Email: sroy@stlr.net
Website: www.stlr.net
software - custom application development, reengineering, database
engineering - structural engineering (As-Pac, estab 2002, empl 7, sales $614,678, cert: State)

4821   Stemac Inc
30 Evergreen Dr   Bridgewater, MA 02324
(508) 331-1410   Jane McCarthy President
Fax:
Email: jane@stemacinc.com
Website: www.stemacinc.com
IT placement, pre screened Supply Chain & SAP Talent, Customer Service & Consultative. (Woman/White, estab 2013, empl 2, sales $400,000, cert: WBENC)

4822   TalentBurst, Inc
679 Worcester Road   Natick, MA 01760
(614) 382-8840   Jamie Jacobs Director of Strategic Partnerships
Fax: (508) 319-3065
Email: jamie.jacobs@talentburst.com
Website: www.talentburst.com
Information technology staff augmentation, lifesciences, business & regulatory compliance, accounting, finance & IT solutions services. (Nat Ame, estab 2002, empl 1389, sales $66,700,000, cert: State, NMSDC, CPUC)

4823   Tanisha Systems Inc.
75 Federal St Ste 1330   Boston, MA 02110
(617) 729-0260   Gorav Aggarwal VP
Fax: (617) 801-8880
Email: gaggarwal@tanishasystems.com
Website: www.tanishasystems.com
Custom application development & end-to-end IT services. (As-Ind, estab 2002, empl 80, sales $9,700,000, cert: State)

4824   tCognition, Inc.
70 Kemble St Ste#201   Boston, MA 02119
(617) 552-5002   Rita Shah CEO
Fax: (617) 830-0813
Email: rita.shah@tcognition.com
Website: www.tCognition.com
IT/software consulting & outsourcing services. (As-Ind, estab 2003, empl 65, sales $3,159,484, cert: State, NMSDC)

4825   Vernance, LLC
745 Atlantic Ave   Boston, MA 02111
(936) 647-3376   Pedro Marcano CEO
Fax: (877) 777-6143
Email: pmarcano@vernance.com
Website: www.vernance.com
Cyber & Physical Security Risk Management consulting services. (Hisp, estab 2014, empl 3, sales $350,000, cert: State, NMSDC)

Maryland

4826   5 Star Consulting Group, LLC.
3261 Old Washington Rd Ste 2020   Waldorf, MD 20602
(301) 216-3839   Lethia Dargin President
Fax: (301) 710-0639
Email: ldargin@5StarConsultingGrp.com
Website: www.5StarConsultingGrp.com
Systems Integration & Design, Computer Integration, SCCM, Software deployment, Software packaging, Server maintenance, troubleshooting, configuration & build. IT Consulting, software & hardware support. (Woman/AA, estab 2013, empl 5, sales , cert: State, SDB)

4827   Acela Technologies, Inc.
5115 Pegasus Ct, Ste A   Frederick, MD 21704
(301) 846-9060   Carole Derringer CEO
Fax: (301) 846-9062
Email: cderringer@acelatechnologies.com
Website: www.acelatechnologies.com
Wireless solutions engineering & integration, wireless internet services, VoIP, VoWiFi, wireless video surveillance. (AA, estab 2002, empl 20, sales $3,834,797, cert: State)

4828   Advanced Engineering Design, Inc.
6525 Belcrest Road Ste 426   Hyattsville, MD 20782
(301) 683-2112   Reginald Waters CEO
Fax: (240) 465-0653
Email: rwaters@aedworld.com
Website: www.aedworld.com
Central office & data center engineering services: site surveys, computer-aided-design drafting, equipment inventories & assessments, records development & space planning. (AA, estab 1991, empl 60, sales $2,480,000, cert: State, City, NMSDC)

4829   Alliance Technology Group, LLC
7010 Hi Tech Dr   Hanover, MD 21076
(410) 712-0270   Cynthia Miles Corporate Admin
Fax:
Email: vendorrelations@alliance-it.com
Website: www.alliance-it.com
End-to-end storage technology solutions, computer, monitor & printer repair, network peripherals, system upgrades, backup & recovery engineering, data storage assessments. (Woman/White, estab 1987, empl 83, sales $36,903,666, cert: WBENC)

4830   Alphatech Systems And Consulting Inc.
762 Perthshire Place   Abingdon, MD 21009
(269) 274-7877   Deepak Sharma CEO
Fax:
Email: deepak.sharma@alphatechglobal.com
Website: www.alphatechglobal.com
Information Technology Managed Services, Business Process Management, System Engineering, Big Data Analytics & Field Communication Technologies. (As-Ind, estab 2006, empl 20, sales , cert: 8(a))

4831 ALTEK Information Technology, Inc.
      241 E Fourth St, Ste 205   Frederick, MD 21701
      (301) 695-4440 Anne Lipman CEO
      Fax: (301) 695-9390
      Email: cardinalhealth@al-tekinc.com
      Website: www.al-tekinc.com
Information technology staffing & project management:
contract, contract to hire or direct hire. (Woman/White,
estab 2004, empl 150, sales $15,000,000, cert: State,
WBENC)

4832 Altus Technology Solutions
      1121 Annapolis Rd, Ste 211   Odenton, MD 21113
      (443) 321-2069 David Brashear President
      Fax: (443) 296-8393
      Email: dbrashear@AltusTS.com
      Website: www.altusts.com
Mission-critical services & IT solutions. (AA, estab 2004,
empl 32, sales $5,618,000, cert: 8(a))

4833 Apex IT Services
      5999 Harpers Farm Rd Ste E250 Columbia, MD
      21044
      (508) 863-2733 Nagesh Gorantla President
      Fax:
      Email: nagesh@apex-its.com
      Website: www.apex-its.com
IT service solution provider, responsive customer service,
innovative technical solutions & targeted risk management
strategies. (As-Ind, estab 2005, empl 25, sales $2,354,343,
cert: 8(a))

4834 Applications Alternatives, Inc.
      P.O. Box 4238 Upper Marlboro, MD 20775
      (301) 350-4752 David Kiasi-Barnes
      Fax: (360) 886-1350
      Email: david.kiasi@appalt.com
      Website: www.appalt.com
Information technology applications consulting in the area
of informational survey processing. (AA, estab 1987, empl
2, sales $48,961, cert: State)

4835 Applied Development LLC
      7 S Front St Ste 200 Baltimore, MD 21202
      (410) 571-4016 Kimberly Citizen
      Fax: (360) 886-1350
      Email: kcitizen@applied-dev.com
      Website: www.applied-dev.com
Process improvement, automation, analytics & cyber
security, project management, business process improvement, strategic communications, cybersecurity & administrative support. (Woman/AA, estab 2011, empl 12, sales
$687,000, cert: State, City, NMSDC, 8(a))

4836 Applied Wireless LAN, Inc.
      1627 Yale Pl Rockville, MD 20850
      (301) 424-6857 Jonathan Walker, Sr. CEO
      Fax: (301) 424-7937
      Email: jwalker@appliedwlan.com
      Website: www.appliedwlan.com
Wireless & wired LAN installation, site survey design,
hardware, systems integration, network maintenance, etc.
(AA, estab 2001, empl 3, sales , cert: State)

4837 A-Team Solutions
      12507 Marlow Rd   Fulton, MD 20759
      (702) 224-8243 Craig Chung Ops Coord
      Fax: (202) 517-9172
      Email: cchung@a-teamsolutions.com
      Website: www.a-teamsolutions.com
Mission oriented business integrated services, management consulting, training, professional support, administrative & information technology. (As-Pac, estab 2004,
empl 60, sales , cert: State)

4838 Avance IT Solutions LLC
      7 Gondola View Court   Woodstock, MD 21163
      (443) 955-5107 Antoinette Gardner CEO
      Fax: (480) 247-5791
      Email: partner@avanceits.com
      Website: www.avanceitsolutions.com
IT consulting services, project management, training,
technology assessments, programming, helpdesk,
testing & deployment. (Woman/AA, estab 2007, empl 5,
sales , cert: State)

4839 BITHGROUP Technologies, Inc.
      113 W Monument St   Baltimore, MD 21201
      (410) 962-1188 Robert Wallace President
      Fax: (410) 962-6535
      Email: robertwallace@bithgroup.com
      Website: www.bithgroup.com
Information Technology Consulting, Network Engineering, Application Development, Wireless Infrastructure
Development, e-learning (AA, estab 1992, empl 70, sales
, cert: State, NMSDC)

4840 Brooks Logic LLC
      4640 Forbes Blvd Ste 320 Lanham, MD 20706
      (301) 358-2600 Tchikaya Brooks Sr partner
      Fax: (240) 837-0241
      Email: tbrooks@brookslogic.com
      Website: www.brookslogic.com
Custom developed IT solutions. (AA, estab 1996, empl 3,
sales $5,265,000, cert: State)

4841 Business Integra Technology Solutions, Inc.
      6550 Rock Spring Dr Ste 600 Bethesda, MD 20817
      (301) 474-9600 Yashika Prabhakar Bus Dev Mgr
      Fax: (301) 474-9651
      Email: BIStates@businessintegra.com
      Website: www.businessintegra.com
Staff augmentation services, information technology
consulting. (Woman/As-Pac, estab 2001, empl 450, sales
$63,000,000, cert: WBENC)

4842 Business One Consulting, Inc.
      11111 Flanagan Lane   Germantown, MD 20876
      (703) 786-6476 Harish Rao VO/COO
      Fax: (703) 815-6602
      Email: hrao@biz-one.biz
      Website: www.biz-one.biz
Management & technology consulting firm, Program
Management, Performance Metrics/Balanced Scorecard,
Business Process Analysis & Development, Enterprise
Services. (As-Ind, estab 2003, empl 10, sales $1,247,000,
cert: State)

4843 CAEI Inc.
      9256 Bendix Rd, Ste 102   Columbia, MD 21045
      (443) 319-5381 Derrick Burnett Sr Business Devel.
      Exec
      Fax: (443) 283-8430
      Email: dburnett@caeiinc.com
      Website: www.caeiinc.com
Help Desk and Customer Service call center
Personnel and management, in addition to our Help Desk
Tier I, Tier II and Tier III experience and past performance.
(AA, estab 2011, empl 125, sales $6,500,000, cert: State,
NMSDC)

4844 Carson Solutions, LLC
      16701 Melford Blvd. Ste. 431   Bowie, MD 20715
      (800) 480-7132 Eugene Carson President
      Fax: (240) 407-0773
      Email: eugene@carsonsolutionsllc.com
      Website: www.carsonsolutionsllc.com
Information technology solutions & administrative support.
(AA, estab 2000, empl 10, sales $1,850,000, cert: State)

4845 Cinnity LLC
      10809 Boswell Lane   Potomac, MD 20854
      (301) 642-6595 Aboje Jay Ameh President
      Fax:
      Email: jay@cinnity.com
      Website: www.cinnity.com
Design, develop & implement user-centered software
solutions: web-based applications, Content Management
Systems, Graphical User Interfaces, Interactive Training
Software & data visualization. (AA, estab 2007, empl 2, sales
$130,000, cert: 8(a))

4846 Cyber Management Systems
      11504 Eastern Red Cedar Ave   Clinton, MD 20735
      (301) 613-3717 Cory Coleman CEO
      Fax:
      Email: corycoleman@cybermss.com
      Website: www.cybermanagementsystems.com
Information Technology consulting, Enterprise IT Systems
Monitoring, Management Consulting & IT Consulting. (AA,
estab 2014, empl 1, sales , cert: State)

4847 Cybern Consulting Group, LLC
      13615 Triadelphia Mill Rd   Clarksville, MD 21029
      (410) 379-0545 Serif Mumuney President
      Fax: (410) 970-4656
      Email: serif.mumuney@cyberngroup.com
      Website: www.cyberngroup.com
Develop applications using Business Process Management
tools running on finely tuned Databases. (AA, estab 2004,
empl 8, sales $400,050, cert: State, 8(a))

4848 Dakota Consulting Inc.
      1110 Bonifant St, Ste 310   Silver Spring, MD 20910
      (240) 839-7812 Lori Renner CEO
      Fax: (301) 328-5297
      Email: lori.renner@dakota-consulting.com
      Website: www.Dakota-Consulting.com
Information technology management, telecommunications
& networking. (Woman/White, estab 2004, empl 93, sales
$10,834,069, cert: State)

4849 Davis Unlimited Information Technologies, Inc.
      9532 Whitehurst Dr   Owings Mills, MD 21117
      (301) 637-5411 Denise Davis CEO
      Fax: (301) 637-5412
      Email: duit@duit.us
      Website: www.duit.us
IT modernization & Software Engineering, secure
software, vulnerability analysis, custom modular code
that is scalable, reusable & maintainable for UNIX,
LINUX & Microsoft platforms, GOTs & COTS, requirements analysis. (Woman/AA, estab 2010, empl 10,
sales $1,200,000, cert: 8(a))

4850 DB Commercial Group LLC
      8401 Colesville Rd Ste 310 Silver Spring, MD
      20910
      (301) 363-2790 Kim Harwell CEO
      Fax: (301) 329-6922
      Email: kim.harwell@dbcommercialgroup.com
      Website: www.dbcommercialgroup.com
IT Services, Staff Augmentation, Systems Engineering,
Cyber Security, Application Development, Cloud
Computing & Multimedia Services. (AA, estab 2014,
empl 20, sales $10,000,000, cert: NMSDC)

4851 Dhaivat Maharaja Enterprises Inc.
      6 Latimore Ct   Reisterstown, MD 21136
      (443) 650-8287 Dhaivat Maharaja CEO
      Fax:
      Email: dhaivat.maharaja@dhaivat.com
      Website: www.dhaivat.com
Enterprise resource planning (ERP), customer relationship management (CRM), Cloud architecture, unified
computing system (UCS), online course development,
service-oriented architecture (SOA). (As-Pac, estab
2006, empl 3, sales , cert: State)

4852 DK Consulting, LLC
      10380 Old Columbia Rd Ste 100 Columbia, MD
      21046
      (443) 552-5851 Dana Kerr CEO
      Fax: (443) 283-4010
      Email: contacts@dkconsult.net
      Website: www.dkconsult.net
Management & technological solutions services.
(Woman/White, estab 2003, empl 9, sales $818,570,
cert: State, City)

4853 Douglas Consulting & Computer Services, Inc.
      3108 Timanus Ln, Ste 100   Baltimore, MD 21244
      (410) 298-3812 James Douglas President
      Fax: (410) 298-1804
      Email: jdouglas@douglasccs.com
      Website: www.douglasccs.com
Computer systems integration, ecommerce, web &
database design, LAN/WAN/MAN & sec, document
imaging & data capture, auto workflow, custom
application dev. (AA, estab 1985, empl 45, sales , cert:
State)

4854   Dream Management Inc.
       210 W 28th St Baltimore, MD 21211
       (443) 552-5512 Joseph DeCarlo President
       Fax: (443) 957-1817
       Email: jdecarlo@dream-mgmt.com
       Website: www.dream-mgmt.com
Transportation services, including but not limited to,
shuttle services, wheelchair equipped vehicle services,
passenger vans, passenger buses, passenger motor coach
buses, sedan vehicles, and limousine (Hisp, estab 1999,
empl 63, sales $2,500,000, cert: State)

4855   Eigennet LLC
       13508 Wisteria Dr Germantown, MD 20874
       (240) 476-5094 Godfrey Pereira President
       Fax: (703) 738-7557
       Email: gpereira@eigennet.com
       Website: www.eigennet.com
We are pleased to inform you that Eigennet LLC is now
certified Minority Business Enterprise and is participating
in all IT supplier diversity programs and staffing models.
We request you to include us in any staffing needs that
mandate diversity certific (Nat Ame, estab 2016, empl 25,
sales , cert: State, NMSDC)

4856   Encore Solutions Inc.
       12300 Twinbrook Parkway, Ste 330 Rockville, MD
       20852
       (301) 998-6191 Gary Lewis President
       Fax: (301) 576-5473
       Email: glewis@encore-solu.com
       Website: www.encore-solu.com
Technology solutions: systems engineering, acquisition &
logistics support, program management & administrative
services, records information management. (Woman/AA,
estab 2001, empl 3, sales $502,789, cert: State, NMSDC,
WBENC)

4857   ERPMatrix LLC
       3620 Turbridge Dr Burtonsville, MD 20866
       (240) 396-4380 Shams Abedin Managing Partner
       Fax: (866) 702-7470
       Email: sa@erpmatrix.com
       Website: www.erpmatrix.com
Staffing, enterprise architecture/integration, software
devel, database & IT support. (As-Ind, estab 2005, empl 4,
sales $178,191, cert: State)

4858   GenRev Technologies, LLC
       7620 Serenade Circle Clinton, MD 20735
       (202) 528-3082 Caleb Baity CEO
       Fax:
       Email: calebbaity@GenRevTechnologies.com
       Website: www.GenRevTechnologies.com
Network installation of CAT 5e/CAT6/Fiber/Copper cabling,
cisco switch installation, IP address schemas, IP subnetting,
ACAS scanning, HBSS, IAVA/IAVM patch management, help
desk support, windows server mgmt. (AA, estab 2006,
empl 2, sales , cert: 8(a))

4859   Infinite Computer Solutions Inc.
       15201 Diamondback Dr Ste 125 Rockville, MD
       20850
       (215) 262-8027 John Stritzl Director Sales
       Fax: (301) 330-8501
       Email: partnership@infinite.com
       Website: www.infinite.com
Applications development, network engineering/
operations, help desk support; e-business, client/server
& mainframe solutions; network & system migrations;
LAN/WAN/MAN svcs. (As-Ind, estab 2001, empl 5400,
sales , cert: NMSDC)

4860   Information Protection Solutions
       1997 Annapolis Exchange Pkwy Ste 300 Annapo-
       lis, MD 21401
       (240) 345-4212 Todd Chamberlain CEO
       Fax: (240) 607-6727
       Email: info@ips314.com
       Website: www.ips314.com
Cyber Security • Cloud security • Continuous Monitoring
Strategies • Cyber Security Policy Development • System
Hardening Implementation • Vulnerability Analysis
Information Assurance: • FedRAMP compliance • NIST
800-53 Rev 4 to Rev 5 Prep • Risk Mgmt. (AA, estab
2014, empl 3, sales $90,000, cert: State, NMSDC, 8(a))

4861   Information Security Enterprise Consulting, LLC
       6701 Democracy Blvd Bethesda, MD 20814
       (301) 337-2527 Jason Peterson CEO
       Fax:
       Email: jpeterson@isec-cybersecurity.com
       Website: www.isec-cybersecurity.com
Cyber security, design, develop, deploy, operate &
maintain defensive security measures. (AA, estab 2007,
empl 20, sales $2,500,200, cert: State, NMSDC)

4862   ITnova
       108 Old Solomons Island Rd Ste L10 Annapolis,
       MD 21401
       (443) 906-6073 Sandra Seldes CEO
       Fax:
       Email: cseldes@itnovaconsulting.com
       Website: www.itnovaconsulting.com
IT and Engineering consulting, Software Development
Life Cycle (SDLC), project management, cybersecurity,
business re-engineering, organizational change management, quality assurance. (Woman/Hisp, estab 2014,
empl 20, sales , cert: 8(a))

4863   JuneGem Technologies, Inc.
       3601 Hamilton St Ste 201 Hyattsville, MD 20782
       (301) 864-2321 Stephanie Thomas Business Dev
       Mgr
       Fax: (888) 408-7436
       Email: hr@junegemtech.com
       Website: www.junegemtech.com
Information Technology and Enterprise Resource
Planning (ERP) solutions, project management, business
process engineering, and software & systems development. (Woman/AA, estab 2011, empl 10, sales
$333,686, cert: State)

4864 Jupiter LLC
   12021 Eaglewood Ct Silver Spring, MD 20902
   (240) 316-2943 E Alex Jupiter President
   Fax:
   Email: alexj@jupitercybsec.com
   Website: www.jupitercybsec.com
Risk assessment, analysis & management; control vulner-ability assessment, data & functional specification; IS/IT security scope management, features, architecture & design; cyber incident response planning; software capability maturity assessment. (AA, estab 2013, empl 3, sales , cert: State, City)

4865 MASAI Technologies Corporation
   201B Broadway St Frederick, MD 21701
   (301) 694-2751 Masai Troutman CEO
   Fax: (301) 694-0909
   Email: masai@masai-tech.com
   Website: www.masai-tech.com
Specialized Staffing & Enterprise Resource Planning (ERP) SAP Software System Integration, implementation & operational services. (AA, estab 1997, empl 15, sales $2,000,000, cert: State, NMSDC)

4866 MORI Associates, Inc.
   3202 Tower Oaks Blvd, Ste 200 Rockville, MD 20852
   (301) 468-6674 Michael Robertson Ops Mgr
   Fax: (301) 230-1733
   Email: mrobertson@moriassociates.com
   Website: www.moriassociates.com
Internet svcs & total system solutions: client server, e-commerce, hardware, networking, programming, software, system reengineering, web technology. (Woman/White, estab 1997, empl 105, sales $14,000,000, cert: State)

4867 Neo Technologies, Inc.
   2901 Druid Park Dr, Ste C104 Baltimore, MD 21215
   (410) 728-9104 Ronald Curry CEO
   Fax: (410) 728-9106
   Email: rcurry@neotechs.com
   Website: www.neotechs.com
Network svcs, routers, bridges, gateways, transmitting equip, analysis, programming LAN integration, software engineering. (AA, estab 1990, empl 8, sales $800,000, cert: State)

4868 NucoreVision, Inc
   4601 Forbes Blvd, Ste 310 Lanham, MD 20706
   (301) 577-3999 Yolanda Murphy
   Fax: (301) 577-5114
   Email: ymurphy@nucorevision.com
   Website: www.nucorevision.com
Cybersecurity, Agency IT Operations, IT Program / Project Management, Management Consulting, IT Services & Solutions. (AA, estab 1996, empl 25, sales $1,900,000, cert: NMSDC)

4869 Nu-Pulse Technologies, Inc.
   21 Industrial Park Dr Ste 101 Waldorf, MD 20602
   (301) 374-2534 E. Renee Ingram President
   Fax: (301) 374-2584
   Email: ringram@nu-pulse.com
   Website: www.nu-pulse.com
Information technology svcs: software design & devel, LAN/WAN design & implementation, database design & devel, project mgmt. IT security, fire protection engi-neering, voice guidance exit systems, electronic door locks. (AA, estab 1998, empl 39, sales $3,000,000, cert: State)

4870 Omega Micro Services
   P.O. Box 1271 Bowie, MD 20721
   (240) 602-8624 Paulson Obiniyi CEO
   Fax: (301) 925-2123
   Email: info@omicroservices.com
   Website: www.omicroservices.com
Technical Services and Consulting, Enterprise Architec-ture, Data & Media Sanitization, Web site Design and development, Project and Program Management, Staffing Augmentation, Content Production, Enterprise Content Management. (AA, estab 2007, empl 2, sales , cert: State)

4871 Peyak Solutions, Inc.
   9250 Bendix Rd N, Ste 150 Columbia, MD 21045
   (800) 958-2188 Leah Conover CEO
   Fax: (443) 899-9306
   Email: leah.conover@peyaksolutions.com
   Website: www.peyaksolutions.com
IT consulting & support services: network design, procurement & installation, desktop, internet & data-base application dev, project & program management, hardware recycling & confidential data destruction. (Woman/Nat Ame, estab 2007, empl 2, sales $195,000, cert: State, City, 8(a))

4872 Planned Systems International, Inc.
   10632 Little Patuxent Pkwy, Ste 200 Columbia, MD 21044
   (410) 964-8000 Terry Lin CEO
   Fax: (410) 946-8001
   Email: TLIN@PLAN-SYS.COM
   Website: www.plan-sys.com/
Providing Healthcare IT, management consulting, IT solutions & services. (As-Pac, estab 1988, empl 350, sales $105,101,730, cert: State)

4873 Pn Automation
   1521 S Edgewood St Baltimore, MD 21227
   (410) 409-6730 Nitin Baviskar COO
   Fax: (877) 570-4579
   Email: nitin@pnautomation.com
   Website: www.pnautomation.com
Software development & IT service. (As-Ind, estab 2004, empl 25, sales $600,000, cert: State)

4874   Pramac Engineering LLC
       2000 Astilbe Way   Odenton, MD 21113
       (410) 409-9772 Kevin Ruffin CEO
       Fax:
       Email: kfruffin@pramacengineering.com
       Website: www.pramacengineering.com
Java and C/C++ object oriented design and development,
web applications Model/View/Controller (MVC) development, Niagara Files development, Commercial Off the
Shelf (COTS) Integration, Systems Integration and 508
Compliance application implementation. (AA, estab 2017,
empl 1, sales $121,000, cert: State)

4875   ProSync Technology Group, LLC
       6021 University Blvd, Ste 300   Ellicott City, MD
       21043
       (410) 772-7969 Keith Slack VP Business Dev
       Fax: (410) 772-7967
       Email: keith.slack@prosync.com
       Website: www.prosync.com
Information technology & infrastructure, enterprise
information systems services & solutions, adaptive
engineering products & svcs, data & signal processing
products. (As-Pac, estab 2000, empl 45, sales $4,000,000,
cert: State)

4876   Qlaire Systems Incorporated
       11002 Veirs Mill Rd Ste 700 Silver Spring, MD 20902
       (301) 873-1972 Uma Subramanian President
       Fax: (301) 528-5526
       Email: umas@qlaire.com
       Website: www.qlaire.com
Web Application, Web design, E-Business, BPR, Search &
Analytics Services, Portal Services, PMO Support, Process
Improvement, IV&V, Enterprise Architecture, ERP solu-
tions, CRM applications, 508 compliance, C&A, Security.
(Woman/As-Ind, estab 2008, empl 8, sales $420,000, cert:
8(a))

4877   Rahman LLC
       10025 Governor Warfield Pkwy Ste 212 Columbia,
       MD 21044
       (443) 283-7000 Mohammad Rahman Owner
       Fax: (443) 283-8430
       Email: rahman@rahmanllc.com
       Website: www.rahmanllc.com
Intellectual property, patents, trademarks, copyrights,
trade secrets, legal, strategy, valuation, IP (As-Ind, estab
2008, empl 3, sales $49,000, cert: State, NMSDC)

4878   Reliable Government Solutions Inc.
       3002 Gazebo Ct   Silver Spring, MD 20904
       (800) 767-0896 Chieu Le President
       Fax: (866) 585-2176
       Email: chieule@rgsfederal.com
       Website: www.rgsfederal.com
Data warehouse, development, architecture & admin,
financial applications, IT audits, JCIDS documentation,
network admin & security, testing, program & project
mgmt, equirements analysis, SME, training, web development. (As-Pac, estab 2001, empl 5, sales $317,842, cert:
City)

4879   Rescon Inc.
       4526 Cheltenham Dr,   Bethesda, MD 20814
       (301) 330-5265 Prem Singh CEO
       Fax:
       Email: resconinc@aol.com
       Website: www.resconisit.com
IT technology consulting & staffing, project management, software architects, programmers, systems admin,
network engineers, software quality assurance. (As-Ind,
estab 1998, empl 14, sales $2,000,000, cert: State)

4880   Right Choice Computers & Networks, LLC
       P.O. Box 5324   Capitol Heights, MD 20791
       (301) 839-4905 Pamela Mitchell President
       Fax: (301) 839-5135
       Email: contactus@rchoicecn.com
       Website: www.rchoicecn.com
Software & applications, mainframe Legacy Systems,
networks topologies, computer hardware & accessories,
help desk & support, network installation. (Woman/AA,
estab 1994, empl 1, sales , cert: State)

4881   RTH Solutions LLC
       10320 Little Patuxent Pkwy, Ste 200   Columbia,
       MD 21044
       (240) 638-1222 Tanisha Lockett COO
       Fax: (240) 638-1222
       Email: tanisha.lockett@rthsolutions.com
       Website: www.rthsolutions.com
Mgmt consulting, staffing & training, business & IT
Service mgmt process consulting, ITIL, Project mgmt,
Cyber Resilia, DevOps, Lean IT, and Scrum. (Woman/AA,
estab 2006, empl 2, sales $44,819, cert: State, WBENC,
NWBOC)

4882   Secure Technologies LLC
       5160 Squawroot Ct   Indian Head, MD 20640
       (301) 613-6605 James Hoxsie Business Devel
       Fax:
       Email: jim.hoxsie@securetechnologiesllc.net
       Website: www.securetechnologiesllc.net
IT consulting & solutions. (Woman/AA, estab 2007, empl
6, sales $575,000, cert: 8(a))

4883   Shakthy Information Systems, Inc.
       13910 Falconcrest Rd   Germantown, MD 20874
       (240) 355-6184 Susheela Palaniswamy CEO
       Fax: (301) 916-8696
       Email: hr@shakthy.com
       Website: www.shakthy.com
Custom software dev services & solutions. (Woman,
estab 2000, empl 5, sales $350,000, cert: State)

4884   Sustainable Approach Consulting
       9319 Kendal Circle   Laurel, MD 20723
       (240) 696-3000 Carol Morgan President
       Fax:
       Email: cmorgan@sustainac.com
       Website: www.sustainac.com
Project Management Enterprise Infrastructure Setup,
Maintenance Technology, Business Strategy Migrations,
Upgrades Business Intelligence Big Data SAP Applications
Cloud Application Solution Mgr Configuration. (Woman/
AA, estab 2009, empl 5, sales , cert: 8(a))

4885　Sympora Technologies
5431 Woodland Blvd Ste B Oxon Hill, MD 20745
(800) 568-9965 Dean Matthews President
Fax: (301) 505-2838
Email: dean.matthews@sympora.com
Website: www.sympora.com
Software development, information technology, web-based training & information security services. (AA, estab 2000, empl 3, sales $158,325, cert: State)

4886　TASA Information Technology Group
9111 Edmonston Rd, Ste 402 Greenbelt, MD 20770
(240) 599-7030 Jamar Spruill
Fax: (713) 995-8765
Email: contracts@tasait.com
Website: www.tasait.com
IT Systems Design & Integration, IT architecture, LAN, hardware & software requirements, system cost, acquisition, implementation & maintenance. (AA, estab 2006, empl 13, sales $3,607,578, cert: 8(a))

4887　Technology Engineering Associates, LLC
2275 Research Blvd, Ste 500 Rockville, MD 20850
(240) 603-6563 Lloyd Tang President
Fax: (301) 960-5802
Email: lloyd.tang@tea-llc.com
Website: www.tea-llc.com
Software development, data management, operations management & technical leadership. (As-Pac, estab 2006, empl 4, sales $850,000, cert: 8(a))

4888　The Aspen Group, Inc.
1100 Wayne Ave Ste 1200 Silver Spring, MD 20910
(410) 308-0629 Christina Fitts Exec VP
Fax: (240) 839-5526
Email: cfitts@theaspengroupinc.com
Website: www.theaspengroupinc.com
Information technology consulting & services. (Woman/AA, estab 1988, empl 400, sales $38,481,357, cert: NMSDC, WBENC)

4889　The net.America Corporation
16201 Trade Zone Ave, Unit 112 Upper Marlboro, MD 20774
(301) 218-4559 Yasmin Hines Business Devel asst
Fax: (301) 618-6457
Email: yasmin.hines@netamerica.net
Website: www.discovernetamerica.com
Information technology solutions, contact centers & help desk, information technology, health services, program management, peer review & grants management. (Woman/AA, estab 2000, empl 51, sales $8,226,437, cert: State)

4890　The Squires Group
128 Lubrano Dr, Ste 102 Annapolis, MD 21401
(410) 224-7779 Nancy Squires CEO
Fax: (410) 224-5755
Email: nancy@squiresgroup.com
Website: www.squiresgroup.com
ERP staffing & consulting svsc: process reengineering, change mgmt, implementation, upgrades & web-enabled integration. (Woman/White, estab 1994, empl 75, sales , cert: WBENC)

4891　Thomas & Herbert Consulting LLC
1010 Wayne Ave, Ste 460   Silver Spring, MD 20910
(301) 578-4004 Frederick Schaefers Business support Mgr
Fax: (301) 578-4008
Email: fred.schaefers@thcllc.com
Website: www.thcllc.com
Enterprise architecture, e-government, business realignment, managed services. (AA, estab 1996, empl 100, sales , cert: State)

4892　TISTA Science and Technology Corporation
1201 Seven Locks Rd Ste 350 Rockville, MD 20850
(301) 968-3435 Ahmed Ali CEO
Fax:
Email: aali@tistatech.com
Website: www.tistatech.com
Information technology & professional services, cyber security, software & database development, engineering support, network & critical infrastructure protection, IT operations & maintenance. (As-Pac, estab 2005, empl 150, sales $22,000,000, cert: State)

4893　TMCS, LLC
6910 Wade Ave Ste A Clinton, MD 20735
(301) 686-8417 Tynnetta McBeth CEO
Fax: (301) 868-7861
Email: tmcbeth@tmcsllc.com
Website: www.tmcsllc.com
Technical & management consulting, design & implementation of LAN/WAN solutions, security, communicatons & mobility, virtual data center solutions, hardware & software resales. (Woman, estab 2008, empl 3, sales $160,000, cert: State, 8(a))

4894　Unatek, Inc.
1100 Mercantile Lane Ste 115-A Largo, MD 20774
(301) 583-4629 Charles Iheagwara Dir
Fax:
Email: ciheagwara@unatek.com
Website: www.unatek.com
Information technology consulting. (AA, estab 1996, empl 15, sales $1,860,000, cert: State, 8(a))

4895　Vangel Inc.
3020 Nieman Ave Baltimore, MD 21230
(410) 644-2600 Valerie Androutsopoulos Principal
Fax: (410) 644-1186
Email: valerie@vangelinc.com
Website: www.vangelinc.com
Data destruction & recycling services: on-site & off-site paper shredding, off-site non-paper storage, media shredding. (Woman/White, estab 1988, empl 15, sales $1,642,150, cert: State)

4896   Victory Global Solutions, Inc.
       5950 Symphony Woods Rd, Ste 211   Columbia, MD
       21044
       (410) 884-9310 Angela Brown CEO
       Fax: (410) 884-9311
       Email: abrown@victorygs.com
       Website: www.victorygs.com
Information technology & networking integration services,
systems engineering, integration & consulting. (Woman/
AA, estab 2001, empl 30, sales $26,000,000, cert: State,
WBENC)

4897   VVL Systems & Consulting, LLC
       8840 Stanford Blvd Ste 1550 Columbia, MD 21045
       (410) 864-8659 Vinnie Lima Managing Dir
       Fax: (410) 630-7321
       Email: vlima@vvlsystems.com
       Website: www.vvlsystems.com
Information technology & consulting, cloud services,
infrastructure & end-user optimization. (Hisp, estab 2008,
empl 6, sales $950,000, cert: State, 8(a))

4898   Web Traits, Inc.
       9423 Eagleton Lane   Montgomery Village, MD
       20886
       (240) 731-6120 Bhaskar Roy President
       Fax: (240) 668-9848
       Email: bhaskar.roy@web-traits.com
       Website: www.web-traits.com
Information systems security & operations (ISSO), cyber
security, network operations management, virtualization,
certification & accreditation (C&A), independent verification & validation (IV&V). (As-Ind, estab 2007, empl 7, sales
$960,000, cert: State, 8(a))

4899   Williams Consulting, LLC
       5523 Research Park Dr Ste 310 Baltimore, MD
       21228
       (855) 597-9666 Antoinette Williams CEO
       Fax:
       Email: awilliams@williamsconsultingllc.com
       Website: www.williamsconsultingllc.com/
Healthcare Policy, Planning, Health Plan Operations & large
scale enterprise transformational IT Projects. (Woman/AA,
estab 2013, empl 6, sales $280,000, cert: 8(a))

4900   WITS, LLC
       5070 Wabash Ave Blg A, Ste 201 Baltimore, MD
       21225
       (443) 919-0113 Vijay Williams CEO
       Fax: (443) 926-0297
       Email: vwilliams@witsbusiness.com
       Website: www.witsbusiness.com
IT services, Software Engineering, Systems Engineering,
Systems Administration, Database Management,
Virtualization, Project management, Systems Integration,
Information Assurance, and Cyber analysis. (AA, estab
2007, empl 5, sales , cert: 8(a))

Maine

4901   CST2000 dba iCST IT Solutions
       100 Brickhill Ave Ste C, Lower Level South
       Portland, ME 04106
       (207) 221-2952 Sasha Asdourian Finance Mgr
       Fax: (207) 772-7364
       Email: Finance@i-cst.com
       Website: www.i-cst.com
Software testing & IT solutions: ASP, client server,
database, IT staffing, .NET, internet, Java, network
admin, mainframe, migration, etc. (As-Pac, estab 1997,
empl 70, sales $6,050,000, cert: State)

Michigan

4902   Acro Service Corporation
       39209 W. Six Mile Rd.   Livonia, MI 48152
       (734) 591-1100 Baidaa Betty Regional Mgr
       Fax: (713) 789-3144
       Email: bbetty@acrocorp.com
       Website: www.acrocorp.com
Staff augmentation: engineering, information technology, light industrial, clerical. Outsourcing; offshore
application dev; IT, engineering, project mgmt consulting. (As-Ind, estab 1982, empl 1000, sales $232,670,000,
cert: NMSDC)

4903   All About Technology
       6450 Michigan Avenue   Detroit, MI 48210
       (313) 965-5543 Willie Brake Mgr
       Fax: (313) 965-5851
       Email: isupply@all-about-technology.com
       Website: www.all-about-technology.com
Computer Sales, Service, Training & Upgrades. Data
Backup & Recovery, Wireless Networking, Microsoft,
Adobe, Quicken, Value Added Reseller, Computer
Insurance, Website Maintenance & Design. (AA, estab
2001, empl 7, sales $210,000, cert: State, NMSDC, SDB)

4904   Allegiance Technologies Inc.
       140 Edgelake Dr   Waterford, MI 48327
       (248) 425-0252 Matthew Montpas President
       Fax: (248) 682-9710
       Email: matt.montpas@allegiance-tech.com
       Website: www.allegiance-tech.com
SAP consulting & implementation. (Hisp, estab 1998,
empl 10, sales $594,447, cert: NMSDC)

4905   Alliance Technology Solutions, LLC
       540 N.Lapeer Road #379 Lake Orion, MI 48359
       (248) 364-2195 Margie Garza-Carlson President
       Fax: (248) 364-9607
       Email: mcarlson@ats.biz
       Website: www.ats.biz
Ebusiness infrastructure solutions: server consolidation,
high availability, Tivoli storage mgr, firewall & security,
enterprise storage & networks. (Woman/Hisp, estab
2002, empl 7, sales $5,862,867, cert: State)

4906 AltaFlux Corporation
3250 W Big Beaver Rd Ste 342 Troy, MI 48084
(248) 850-2298 John Morrison Natl Sales Mgr
Fax: (248) 850-2299
Email: john.morrison@altaflux.com
Website: www.altaflux.com
Business Transformation Consulting, Complete SaaS Solutions, Cloud Computing Solutions, Specialized Technology Staffing, SAP, Oracle, Google Apps, Dell Boomi, OrangeScape (Woman/As-Ind, estab 2006, empl 48, sales $5,000,000, cert: NMSDC)

4907 Blue Chip Talent
43252 Woodward Ave, Ste 240 Bloomfield Hills, MI 48302
(248) 630-7170 Steve Gaura Sr Director of IT Services
Fax: (248) 858-7724
Email: steveg@bctalent.com
Website: www.bctalent.com
Information technology project based services, project management, staff augmentation services & security consulting. (Woman/White, estab 1994, empl 204, sales $18,100,000, cert: WBENC, NWBOC)

4908 Broadgate Inc.
830 Kirts Blvd, Ste 400 Troy, MI 48084
(248) 918-0110 Kashi Kotha Director
Fax: (800) 531-8659
Email: kashi@broadgateinc.com
Website: www.broadgateinc.com
IT Profetional services, consulting, project services & software development. (Woman/As-Ind, estab 2006, empl 70, sales $5,000,000, cert: NMSDC)

4909 BSC Solutions, Inc.
1000 John R. Rd, Ste 203 Troy, MI 48083
(810) 449-3640 Jody Kapale Business Dev Mgr
Fax:
Email: jody@bsc-us.com
Website: www.BSCSolutionsInc.com
ERP Implementation & support PeopleSoft, Oracle, SAP, CRM - Siebel & Salesforce, Staff Augmentation/Custom Application Development, Java, .Net, C#, EDI, Data Warehousing, BI, Big Data, Cloud based applications. (As-Ind, estab 1999, empl 200, sales $11,143,000, cert: NMSDC)

4910 CADworks Solutions, Inc.
43422 W Oaks Dr, Ste 326 Novi, MI 48377
(248) 910-9988 James Vaughn Jr. President
Fax: (248) 449-4296
Email: jamesv@cadwrx.com
Website: www.cadwrx.com
CAD systems integration, lifecycle mgmt consulting. (AA, estab 1995, empl 5, sales $153,000, cert: NMSDC)

4911 CAEtech International, Inc.
43000 W 9 Mile Rd, Ste 305 Novi, MI 48375
(248) 342-7661 Vic Havele President
Fax:
Email: havelev@caetech.com
Website: www.caetech.com
Contract & direct placement staffing svcs, engineering svcs, IT svcs. (As-Ind, estab 1989, empl 55, sales , cert: NMSDC)

4912 CIBER, Inc.
300 Galleria Officentre Southfield, MI 48034
(248) 204-1713 Derrick Ryskamp Sr Client Partner
Fax: (303) 220-7100
Email: vhickman@ciber.com
Website: www.ciber.com
Software Eng., Systems Eng., Software and Systems Test, Configuration Mgmt, Systems Anaylsis, Intelligence, Data Warehousing, Business Intelligence, Network Security, Network Engineering, Information Technology (As-Ind, estab 1900, empl 1, sales $600,000,000, cert: NMSDC)

4913 CnC Controls
5745 W Maple #217 West Bloomfield, MI 48322
(248) 681-7722 Abizer Rasheed President
Fax: (248) 681-9632
Email: arasheed@cnccontrolsusa.com
Website: www.cnccontrolsusa.com
Information technology: installation, repairs & maintenance services. (Woman/As-Ind, estab 1983, empl 10, sales $1,500,000, cert: NMSDC, WBENC)

4914 Cogent Integrated Business Solutions, Inc.
2855 Coolidge Hwy Ste 112 Troy, MI 48084
(248) 649-4444 Srini Thonta Dir SAP Solutions
Fax: (248) 659-1516
Email: sthonta@cogentIBS.com
Website: www.cogentIBS.com
IT services & solutions, SAP services. (Woman/As-Pac, estab 2005, empl 30, sales $3,795,325, cert: WBENC)

4915 Communications Professionals, Inc.
2265 Livernois Rd Troy, MI 48083
(248) 557-0100 Andrew Wallace CEO
Fax: (248) 557-8700
Email: awallace2@cpgp.com
Website: www.cpgp.com
Information technology: development, implementation & application, hardware, software & technological analysis. (AA, estab 1997, empl 15, sales $15,000,000, cert: NMSDC)

4916 CompuSoft Integrated Solutions, Inc.
31500 W 13 Mile Rd Ste 200 Farmington Hills, MI 48334
(248) 538-9494 Pratap Koganti CEO
Fax: (248) 538-8435
Email: pkoganti@compusoft-is.com
Website: www.compusoft-is.com
Internet & intranet, e-commerce dev, ERP, Oracle, SAP, PeopleSoft, client/server software. (As-Ind, estab 1997, empl 80, sales $8,500,000, cert: State, NMSDC)

4917 Computech Corporation
W 100 Kirby St Detroit, MI 48202
(248) 622-1420 Sai Kancharla Project Mgr
Fax: (248) 594-4855
Email: sai.kancharla@computechcorp.com
Website: www.computechcorp.com
Information technology staffing & project svcs: custom programming, enterprise resource planning, CRM, ebusiness, database programming. (As-Ind/As-Pac, estab 1996, empl 250, sales $1,200,000, cert: NMSDC)

4918 Dechen Consulting Group, Inc.
37185 Fox Chase Farmington Hills, MI 48331
(248) 346-4590 Raj Dechen President
Fax: (248) 661-4888
Email: rdechen@dcg-us.com
Website: www.dcg-us.com
IT professional staffing & project-based implementation, PeopleSoft, SAP & Oracle software application packages, staff augmentation services, design, develop & implement Business Intelligence. (As-Ind, estab 1998, empl 30, sales $4,100,000, cert: NMSDC)

4919 DPM Consulting Services, Inc.
5440 Corporate Dr Sutie 125 Troy, MI 48098
(24) 897-8667 Gary Gozdor Business Dev Mgr
Fax: (248) 740-8846
Email: ggozdor@dpmcs.com
Website: www.dpmcs.com
Program & project managers, business intelligence & data mgmt, Legacy, business analysts, executive search, network & technical support, database dev & admin, ebusiness & offshore staffing resources. (Woman/White, estab 1992, empl 120, sales , cert: WBENC)

4920 Emergent Systems Corp.
3 Parklane Blvd Ste 1120 West Dearborn, MI 48126
(313) 996-8285 Saleem Qureshi VP - Engineering
Fax: (313) 996-8287
Email: SaleemQ@emergentsys.com
Website: www.EmergentSys.com
Engineering, design, product development & styling, CAD/CAM/CAE consulting, software development, engineering design staffing, tooling design, offshore capability, engineering software products, KBE, knowledge management. (As-Ind, estab 1997, empl 40, sales $7,000,000, cert: NMSDC)

4921 Epitec
24800 Denso Dr Ste. 150 Southfield, MI 48033
(469) 454-3649 Kelleen Young
Fax: (800) 647-1898
Email: businessdevelopment@epitec.com
Website: www.epitec.com
IT staff augmentation. (AA, estab 1978, empl 1000, sales $75,000,000, cert: NMSDC)

4922 ESM Group LLC
43422 W Oaks Dr, Ste 298 Novi, MI 48377
(248) 921-7452 Jayme Rossiter President
Fax: (248) 344-9304
Email: jrossiter@esmonline.com
Website: www.esmonline.com
Information technogy services & staffing. (Woman/White, estab 1992, empl 23, sales $1,800,000, cert: WBENC)

4923 Excel Technical Services, Inc.
200 Kirts Blvd Ste A Troy, MI 48084
(248) 310-9413 Pat Kirby Managing Dir
Fax: (248) 290-0508
Email: patkirby@exceltechnical.com
Website: www.exceltechnical.com
Technical staffing & document management svcs, supplier quality & development. (Hisp, estab 1998, empl 30, sales $2,500,000, cert: NMSDC)

4924 GDI Infotech, Inc.
3775 Varsity Dr Ann Arbor, MI 48108
(734) 477-6900 Vishal Chaubal Dir
Fax: (734) 477-7100
Email: vishal@gdii.com
Website: www.gdii.com
Enterprise information technology consulting & services. (As-Ind, estab 1993, empl 125, sales $10,200,000, cert: NMSDC)

4925 HCL Global Systems, Inc.
24543 Indoplex Circle Ste 220 Farmington Hills, MI 48334
(248) 473-0720 Prasad Gadde President
Fax:
Email: gadde@hclglobal.com
Website: www.hclglobal.com
IT Consulting & Staffing. (As-Pac, estab 2005, empl 1170, sales $78,000,000, cert: NMSDC)

4926 HRU Technical Resources
3451 Dunckel Road Ste 200 Lansing, MI 48911
(517) 272-5888 Todd Briggs V.P. Business Dev
Fax: (517) 272-5880
Email: briggs.todd@hru-tech.com
Website: www.hru-tech.com
Engineering, IT, design, mfg, technical staffing services: contract or direct hire. (Woman/White, estab 1980, empl 215, sales $20,500,517, cert: WBENC)

4927 ICONMA, LLC
850 Stephenson Hwy Ste 612 Troy, MI 48083
(804) 916-0905 Sumit Bhandari Business Dev Mgr
Fax: (248) 583-1929
Email: sumit@iconma.com
Website: www.iconma.com
IT consultant staffing: contract, contract to hire & fulltime.
(Woman/White, estab 2000, empl 2046, sales $245,822,661, cert: WBENC)

4928 Iknowvate Technologies, Inc.
17197 N Laurel Park Dr, Ste 307 Livonia, MI 48152
(734) 432-0634 Sriram Rajakumar Sales Dir
Fax: (734) 432-1602
Email: rkumar@iknowvate.com
Website: www.iknowvate.com
IT staff augmentation, application dev, maintenance & support, project mgmt, real time embedded systems, e-strategize, portals, implement & deploy SCM, CRM, ERP packaged solutions, business intelligence solutions, etc. (As-Pac, estab 2001, empl 40, sales $2,000,000, cert: NMSDC)

4929 Infomatics Inc.
31313 Northwestern Hwy, Ste 219   Farmington Hills, MI 48334
(248) 865-0300   Ragan Raghunathan Founder
Fax: (248) 865-0058
Email: Rajan@infomatinc.com
Website: www.infomatinc.com
Information technology staffing, web technologies, Java, J2EE , ERP/CRM-Oracle, SAP, database administration, Oracle, DB2 SQL Server, content management. (Woman/As-Ind, estab 1998, empl 225, sales $25,000,000, cert: NMSDC)

4930 Information Systems Resources
1800 Bailey St   Dearborn, MI 48124
(131) 430-2267   Eric Levy Business Dev Mgr
Fax: (131) 430-2267
Email: elevy@is-resources.com
Website: www.is-resources.com
Computer asset mgmt services, professional services, lifecycle mgmt, dist hardware & software.
(AA, estab 1989, empl 48, sales $4,856,426, cert: NMSDC)

4931 Internet Operations Center, Inc.
200 Galleria Officentre Ste 109   Southfield, MI 48034
(248) 204-8800   Rhonda Hall Business Mgr
Fax: (248) 204-8801
Email: thayward@iocenter.net
Website: www.iocenter.net
Managed internet service provider, web development, help center, EDI, TPP appilcation development. (As-Pac, estab 1996, empl 56, sales , cert: NMSDC)

4932 IP Consulting, Inc.
3635 29th St   Kentwood, MI 49512
(616) 855-9967   Cherri Mosey VP
Fax: (616) 828-4417
Email: cherri.mosey@ipconsultinginc.com
Website: www.ipconsultinginc.com
Information technology solutions, design, implementation & support services. (Hisp, estab 2006, empl 10, sales $1,400,000, cert: NMSDC, 8(a))

4933 IPS Technology Services
363 West Big Beaver Road Ste 100   Troy, MI 48084
(248) 835-9895   Pradip Sengupta President
Fax: (248) 526-9001
Email: info@ipstechnologyservices.com
Website: www.ipstechnologyservices.com
Information technology services: customer systems development, CAD/CAM/CAE/PDM svcs, systems integration, HR technology implementation, consulting, & ERP implementation. (As-Pac, estab 2000, empl 22, sales $1,200,000, cert: NMSDC)

4934 JRD Systems, Inc.
42450 Hayes Rd Ste 3   Clinton Township, MI 48038
(586) 416-1500   Melissa Husmillo
Fax: (586) 416-1600
Email: contact@jrdsi.com
Website: www.jrdsi.com
Information technology solutions, services, & staffing. (As-Ind/As-Pac, estab 2000, empl 80, sales $5,500,000, cert: State, NMSDC)

4935 Logic Solutions, Inc.
2929 Plymouth Rd Ste. 207   Ann Arbor, MI 48105
(734) 930-0009   Grace Lee CFO
Fax: (734) 930-9005
Email: grace@logicsolutions.com
Website: www.logicsolutions.com
Custom web based software development & integration. (As-Pac, estab 1995, empl 104, sales $8,261,867, cert: NMSDC)

4936 Millennium Software Inc.
2000 Town Center Dr Ste, 300   Southfield, MI 48075
(248) 213-1800   Anu Anand President
Fax: (248) 213-1802
Email: anu@webmsi.com
Website: www.webmsi.com
IT consulting, project developemnt, contract programming, web designing. (As-Pac, estab 1996, empl 165, sales $23,129,824, cert: NMSDC, WBENC)

4937 Miracle Software Systems, Inc.
45625 Grand River Avenue   Novi, MI 48374
(248) 412-7217   Ashok Meduri Software Maintenance Renewal Rep
Fax: (248) 350-2575
Email: ameduri@miraclesoft.com
Website: www.miraclesoft.com/
IT consulting: SAP, Oracle, PeopleSoft, JDEdwards, Solaris, J2EE. webMethods, MQ, EAI, Cognos, MicroStrategy, VB, ASP,.Net, SQL, Siebel, Informatica, TIBCO, Vitria, etc. (As-Ind/As-Pac, estab 1994, empl 2500, sales $172,000,000, cert: NMSDC)

4938 Nueva Vision, LLC
1041 Main St   Royal Oak, MI 48067
(313) 336-6135   Brian Callaghan President
Fax:
Email: briancallaghan@yahoo.com
Website:
Engineering, Consulting, Information Technology, Automotive Engineering, Aerospace Engineering, Industrial Engineering, Software, Programming, Web Development, Application Develop, System Design, Disaster Recovery, Global Supply Chain Management. (Hisp, estab , empl 1, sales , cert: NMSDC)

4939 Ocean Inc. dba Omega Systems
5324 Plainfield Ave NE   Grand Rapids, MI 49525
(616) 361-6677   Nadeem Hamid President
Fax: (616) 363-9430
Email: nadeem.hamid@oceaninc.com
Website: www.oceaninc.com
Computer solutions, components, notebooks, printers, assembly, packing & configuration, web development, web hosting, surveillance camera solutions & installation.
(As-Ind, estab 1984, empl 8, sales $600,000, cert: NMSDC)

4940 Ojibway, Inc.
3720 High St Ecorse, MI 48229
(248) 526-0555 James Richardson Acct Exec
Fax: (248) 689-1789
Email: jrichardson@theojibwaygroup.com
Website: www.theojibwaygroup.com
Information technology, leasing & financial services,
computer equipment & services. (Nat Ame, estab 1988,
empl 13, sales $3,500,000, cert: NMSDC)

4941 Open Systems Technologies DE, LLC
605 Seward NW, Ste 101 Grand Rapids, MI 49504
(616) 574-3500 David Gerrity Exec Dir
Fax: (616) 574-3520
Email: dgerrity@ostusa.com
Website: www.ostusa.com
Resell computer hardware & software, business process
solutions, data center solutions, application development,
managed services. (Nat Ame, estab 1997, empl 110, sales
$68,873,026, cert: NMSDC)

4942 OpenLogix Corporation
28345 Beck Rd Ste 308 Wixom, MI 48393
(919) 200-4333 Rick Pardy Acct Mgr
Fax: (248) 679-3038
Email: mbe@open-logix.com
Website: www.open-logix.com
SOA, business integration, portals & business intelligence,
SAP, WebSphere, web svcs, webMethods, Java/J2EE,
Informatica, business objects.. (As-Ind, estab 2006, empl
45, sales $18,000,000, cert: NMSDC)

4943 Peer Solutions Group, Inc.
30777 Northwestern Hwy Ste 107 Farmington Hills,
MI 48334
(248) 522-7767 Mohamed Irfan Peeran CEO
Fax:
Email: mpeeran@peersolutionsgroup.com
Website: www.peersolutionsgroup.com
IT Consulting Staffing, Recruiting, Project Management,
Technology Consulting. (As-Ind, estab 2002, empl 60, sales
$5,412,715, cert: NMSDC)

4944 PeoplePlus software Inc.
3131 South State St. Ste 250 Ann Arbor, MI 48108
(734) 531-6620 Tom Bastian Solutions Consultant
Fax: (734) 531-6621
Email: tbastian@peopleplussoftware.com
Website: www.peopleplussoftware.com
Software design & development, SaaS cloud supply chain
software. IT staffing, Mobile app development. (Woman/
As-Ind, estab 2007, empl 35, sales $1,000,000, cert:
NMSDC)

4945 Preferred Data Systems, LLC
39100 Country Club Dr Ste 200 Farmington Hills, MI
48331
(248) 522-4442 Chad Muncy
Fax: (248) 553-6460
Email: cmuncy@pdsnetworking.com
Website: www.pdsnetworking.com
IT networking infrastructure & consulting services.
(Woman/Nat Ame, estab 1982, empl 12, sales $510,000,
cert: NMSDC)

4946 PROLIM Global Corporation
30445 Northwestern Hwy Ste 380 Farmington
Hills, MI 48334
(248) 522-6959 Prabhu Patil President
Fax: (800) 515-6821
Email: prabhu.patil@prolim.com
Website: www.prolim.com
IT & PLM solutions & consulting services. (As-Ind, estab
2005, empl 350, sales $2,333,950, cert: NMSDC)

4947 Pro-Motion Technology Group
29755 Beck Rd Wixom, MI 48393
(248) 560-0521 Brian Flewelling Acct Mgr
Fax: (248) 694-0911
Email: hello@promotion.tech
Website: www.promotion.tech
Audiovisual technology solutions. (Woman/White, estab
2002, empl 45, sales $25,000,000, cert: WBENC)

4948 Pure Data Services LLC
4459 13th St Wyandotte, MI 48192
(734) 283-3000 Katie Chambers Owner
Fax: (734) 283-3144
Email: katie.chambers@puredataservices.com
Website: www.puredataservices.com
Document destruction services. (Woman, estab 2014,
empl 5, sales , cert: WBENC)

4949 Ragha Systems, LLC
8390 Warwick Groves Ct Grand Blanc, MI 48439
(810) 694-6551 Veera R Thota CEO
Fax: (810) 344-9356
Email: vthota@raghasys.com
Website: www.raghasys.com
IT solutions. (Woman/As-Ind, estab 2002, empl 5, sales ,
cert: NMSDC, WBENC)

4950 Ramsoft Systems, Inc..
29777 Telegraph Rd Ste 2250 Southfield, MI
48034
(248) 354-0100 Rama Gudivada COO
Fax: (248) 354-3626
Email: rama@ramsoft.net
Website: www.ramsoft.net
IT solutions, staff augmentation: onsite, offsite,
nearshore, offshore projects. (Woman/As-Pac, estab
1993, empl 100, sales , cert: NMSDC)

4951 Rapid Global Business Solutions, Inc.
1200 Stephenson Highway Troy, MI 48083
(248) 589-1135 Vivek Thakur Business Dev Mgr
Fax: (248) 589-1329
Email: vt@rgbsi.com
Website: www.rgbsi.com
Engineering svcs: staffing, mechanical, electrical &
electronics, mfg, automotive, design & release, embed-
ded systems, systems modeling & simulation, CAD/CAM/
CAE/PIM svcs, software dev, contract & permanent. (As-
Ind/As-Pac, estab 1997, empl 1800, sales $80,000,000,
cert: NMSDC)

4952   Real World Technologies Inc.
     28423 Orchard Lake Rd Ste 203   Farmington Hills, MI 48334
     (248) 987-6008   Vishnu Jampala President
     Fax: (248) 779-1789
     Email: vishnujam@rwts.net
     Website: www.rwts.net/
Information Technology Solutions & Business Analyst solutions, Application development, Enterprise resource planning, Data-Warehousing, Customer Relationship Management, Business Analysis, Project Management. (As-Pac, estab 2005, empl 40, sales $3,155,012, cert: State, City, NMSDC, SDB)

4953   Rumba Solutions, LLC
     44648 Mound Rd, Ste 190   Sterling Heights, MI 48314
     (248) 978-3674   Jibu Joseph Managing Dir
     Fax:
     Email: Jibu.Joseph@rumbasolutions.com
     Website: www.rumbasolutions.com
Application development, staff augmentation & consulting services, Mobile, Web Applications (Cloud and On premise), IoT, Identity & Access Management, Portal Development. (As-Ind, estab 2010, empl 50, sales , cert: NMSDC)

4954   ShoreWise Consulting LLC
     2609 Crooks Rd Unit 116   Troy, MI 48084
     (416) 879-8443   Greg Bhatia President
     Fax:
     Email: greg.bhatia@shorewiseconsulting.com
     Website: www.shorewiseconsulting.com
IT Recruitment & Staff Augmentation, Requirements Analysis & Project Management, Software Quality Assurance & Testing, Business Intelligence & Reporting Solutions, Automated Document & Content Management Solutions. (As-Ind, estab 2012, empl 18, sales $650,000, cert: NMSDC)

4955   Skansoft Inc.
     4681 Amberwood Ct   Rochester, MI 48306
     (248) 276-4770   Srividya Sadasivam President
     Fax: (248) 659-1789
     Email: srividya@skandasoftinc.com
     Website: www.skandasoftinc.com
Integrated information technology consulting & placement services, IT professionals. (Woman/As-Ind, estab 2006, empl 11, sales $1,118,340, cert: NMSDC)

4956   SmartIT Pros Inc.
     6001 N Adams Rd, Ste 205 Women Owned Certified Organization   Bloomfield Hills, MI 48304
     (734) 238-1553   David Thomas Director - Sales
     Fax: (187) 763-6359
     Email: dave.thomas@smartitpros.com
     Website: www.smartitpros.com
IT & Business Services, Application & Business process services. (As-Ind, estab 2012, empl 10, sales $3,500,000, cert: WBENC)

4957   SoftCorp International, Inc.
     2838 E Long Lake Ste 236 Troy, MI 48085
     (248) 918-2224   Raja Puli President
     Fax:
     Email: vinod@softcorpinc.com
     Website: www.softcorpinc.com
Staff augmentation, permanent & temporary IT resources. (As-Ind, estab 1997, empl 87, sales $6,100,000, cert: NMSDC)

4958   SoftPath Technologies LLC
     16801 Newburgh Rd, Ste 112   Livonia, MI 48154
     (248) 522-7011   Rohith Thumma Regional Sales Mgr
     Fax: (248) 295-4458
     Email: supplier@softpathtech.com
     Website: www.softpathtech.com
Global Staffing, Technology, Services & Consulting. (As-Ind, estab 2006, empl 150, sales $6,012,589, cert: NMSDC)

4959   SunSoft Technologies Inc.
     21772 Manchester Ct   Farmington Hills, MI 48335
     (248) 426-9805   Rashmi Upadhyaya President
     Fax: (888) 587-9060
     Email: rashmiu@sunsoft.us
     Website: www.sunsofttechnologies.com
Engineering & IT staffing. (Woman/As-Pac, estab 2000, empl 45, sales $3,705,233, cert: NMSDC)

4960   Synergy Computer Solutions, Inc,
     30700 Telegraph Rd Ste #2615   Bingham Farms, MI 48025
     (248) 723-7220   Ruslan Avshalumov Accountant
     Fax: (248) 723-5372
     Email: ravshalumov@synergycom.com
     Website: www.synergycom.com
Information techology & engineering consulting & staffing: implementation & integration, infrastructure support, web solutions, project mgmt, data warehousing, EDI, off shore devel. (As-Pac, estab 1995, empl 250, sales $16,000,000, cert: NMSDC)

4961   Synova Inc.
     1000 Town Center Ste 700   Southfield, MI 48075
     (248) 281-2500   Iain McKendrick Director of Automotive and Manufacturing
     Fax:
     Email: imckendrick@synovainc.com
     Website: www.synovainc.com
IT contract staffing & professional svcs. (As-Pac, estab 1998, empl 1800, sales $117,000,000, cert: NMSDC)

4962   Syntel Inc.
     525 E Big Beaver Third Fl   Troy, MI 48083
     (602) 391-8868   ShyamSundar Dittakavi Director-Lifesciences
     Fax: (248) 619-2800
     Email: Vendor_Registration@syntelinc.com
     Website: www.syntelinc.com
IT lifecycle solutions, applications outsourcing, development, enhancements, maintenance, integration & technology transformation & support. (As-Pac, estab 1980, empl 22114, sales $923,828,000, cert: NMSDC)

4963   Syntel, Inc.
        525 E Big Beaver Third Fl Troy, MI 48083
        (248) 619-2800 Michael Voss VP Strategic Sourcing
        Fax: (248) 619-2888
        Email: Vendor_Registration@syntelinc.com
        Website: www.syntelinc.com
IT & knowledge process services. (As-Pac, estab 1980,
empl 24537, sales $968,600,000, cert: NMSDC)

4964   Systems Technology Group, Inc. (STG)
        3001 W. Big Beaver Road STE 500 Troy, MI 48084
        (248) 712-6702 Anup Popat CEO
        Fax: (248) 643-9250
        Email: apopat@stgit.com
        Website: www.stgit.com
Application software development outsourcing svcs: onsite
& offshore. (As-Ind/As-Pac, estab 1985, empl 600, sales
$102,000,000, cert: NMSDC)

4965   Systems Technology International, Inc.
        39555 Orchard Hill Pl, Ste 530 Novi, MI 48375
        (248) 735-3900 Rodney Tesarz Dir of Sales
        Fax: (248) 735-3934
        Email: rodney.tesarz@sti-world.com
        Website: www.sti-world.com
Information technology & engineering: contract staffing,
off shore services, software development & testing,
engineering design & diagnostics. (AA, estab , empl 1, sales
$7,500,000, cert: NMSDC)

4966   Technosoft Corporation
        1 Towne Square 6th Fl Southfield, MI 48076
        (248) 603-2666 Radhakrishnan Gurusamy CEO
        Fax: (248) 603-2599
        Email: supplierdiversity@technosoftcorp.com
        Website: www.technosoftcorp.com
Information technology staffing, IT consulting, system
integration & business process outsourcing. (Woman/As-
Pac, estab 1996, empl 4000, sales $123,867,758, cert:
NMSDC)

4967   The Bartech Group, Inc.
        27777 Franklin Rd, Ste 600 Southfield, MI 48034
        (248) 208-4515 Michelle Hyland Dir Sales & Mktg
        Fax:
        Email: bartechinfo@bartechgroup.com
        Website: www.bartechgroup.com
Contract & temporary staffing svcs: technical, office,
computer & utility support svcs, facilities mgmt, IT solutions & support. (AA, estab 1977, empl 2972, sales , cert:
NMSDC)

4968   Touch World, Inc.
        31500 W 13 Mile Rd Ste 101 Farmington Hills, MI
        48334
        (248) 539-3700 Gordon McKenna President
        Fax: (248) 539-4700
        Email: gordon.mckenna@touchworld.com
        Website: www.touchworld.com
Computer software consulting & staff augmentation svcs:
ERP, Client Server, Microsoft, UNIX, workflow, supply chain
mgmt, ILVS, EDI , barcoding, RFID, Gentran, Future 3,
Harbinger, Mercator, Trinary, AS 400, mainframe products.
(As-Pac, estab 1996, empl 17, sales $1,550,000, cert:
NMSDC)

4969   Trillium Teamologies Inc.
        219 S Main St Royal Oak, MI 48067
        (248) 584-2080 Greg Stanalajczo COO
        Fax: (248) 584-2250
        Email: stano@trilliumteam.com
        Website: www.trilliumteam.com
IT solutions: 2D & 3D animations, web dev, flash
animations, IT consulting, e-commerce, project mgmt,
systems integration & software dev, etc. (Woman/White,
estab 1996, empl 63, sales , cert: WBENC)

4970   TTi Global
        6001 N. Adams Road Ste 185 Bloomfield Hills, MI
        48304
        (248) 853-5550 April Bousamra Controller
        Fax: (248) 853-2411
        Email: abousamra@tti-global.com
        Website: www.tti-global.com
Training design, development & delivery, outsourcing
services, staffing services. (Woman/White, estab 1976,
empl 780, sales $38,100,000, cert: WBENC)

4971   Unified Business Technologies Inc.
        315 Indusco Ct Troy, MI 48083
        (248) 677-9550 Allyssia Gutierrez Sales Rep
        Fax: (248) 588-1834
        Email: allyssia.gutierrez@ubtus.com
        Website: www.emd.ubtus.com
Software consulting services & staffing. (Woman/As-Pac,
estab 1997, empl 150, sales , cert: WBENC)

4972   V2Soft Inc.
        300 Enterprise Court Bloomfield Hills, MI 48302
        (248) 904-1702 Varchasvi Shankar President
        Fax: (248) 281-5269
        Email: vs@v2soft.com
        Website: www.v2soft.com
Software business solutions, consulting, contract
services & staff augmentation, project outsourcing,
offshore development. (As-Ind, estab 1998, empl 1000,
sales $25,500,000, cert: NMSDC)

4973   Vision Information Technologies, Inc.
        3031 W Grand Blvd, Ste 600 Detroit, MI 48202
        (313) 420-2000 Christine Rice President
        Fax: (313) 420-2001
        Email: info@visionit.com
        Website: www.visionit.com
IT staffing, e-business consulting & web application dev.
(Hisp, estab 1997, empl 1000, sales $209,000,000, cert:
NMSDC)

4974   Vivek Systems, Inc.
        2163 Avon Industrial Dr Rochester Hills, MI
        48309
        (248) 293-1070 Bose Vivek President
        Fax: (248) 293-1075
        Email: bvivek@viveksystems.com
        Website: www.viveksystems.com
CAD/engineering solution company. (As-Ind, estab ,
empl 1, sales $1,080,000, cert: NMSDC)

4975 WebRunners, Inc. dba W3R Consulting
      1000 Town Center Ste 1150 Southfield, MI 48044
      (248) 358-1002 Eric hardy CEO
      Fax: (248) 358-1005
      Email: corporateinfo@w3r.com
      Website: www.w3r.com
Infrastructure planning & design, custom hosting solutions,
directory svcs design, systems admin,
middleware & database support, metrics tools, monitoring
& reporting, firewall mgmt & security,
VPN architecture, application integration. (AA, estab 1995,
empl 400, sales $36,500,000, cert: NMSDC)

4976 Weldon Enterprise Global IT, LLC
      3031 W Grand Blvd, Ste 695   Detroit, MI 48202
      (313) 687-4990 Markeith Weldon CEO
      Fax: (313) 486-0063
      Email: mweldon@weglobalit.com
      Website: www.weglobalit.com
IT managed services, technical staffing & non technical
staffing. (AA, estab 2011, empl 10, sales $1,000,000, cert:
NMSDC)

4977 WIT Inc.
      900 Tower Dr Ste 325 Troy, MI 48098
      (248) 641-5900 Quaid Saifee President
      Fax: (248) 641-0227
      Email: quaid@witinc.com
      Website: www.witinc.com
Web site design & development, internet branding, graphic
design, content management solutions, database design &
consulting, web application development, training, web
collaboration. (As-Ind, estab 1996, empl 20, sales
$2,500,000, cert: NMSDC)

4978 Youngsoft Inc.
      49197 Wixom Tech Dr Ste B Wixom, MI 48393
      (248) 675-1200 Chris Reaume Director of Sales Ops
      Fax: (248) 675-1163
      Email: chrisr@youngsoft.com
      Website: www.youngsoft.com
Information technology services: staffing support, consulting, solution design & development. (As-Ind, estab 1996,
empl 130, sales $11,690,000, cert: NMSDC)

Minnesota

4979 Active-Duty
      12996 Eastview Ct   Apple Valley, MN 55124
      (952) 322-3662 Gregory St.James President
      Fax:
      Email: gstjames@active-duty.us
      Website: www.active-duty.us
Project management, information technology, research &
development. (AA/Nat Ame, estab 2001, empl 1, sales ,
cert: State)

4980 Agilea Solutions, Inc.
      7205 Ohms Lane Ste 200 Edina, MN 55439
      (866) 800-1897 Marce Roth CEO
      Fax: (866) 800-1898
      Email: contact@agileasolutions.com
      Website: www.agileasolutions.com
IT consulting firm, systems integration, implement &
support enterprise software applications. (Woman/As-
Pac, estab 2005, empl 65, sales $10,500,000, cert:
NMSDC, WBENC)

4981 Analysts International Corporation (AIC)
      7700 France Ave S Ste 200 Minneapolis, MN
      55435
      (800) 800-5044 Marc Cohen VP Global Mktg
      Fax: (952) 897-4555
      Email: diversitysupplier@acsicorp.com
      Website: www.analysts.com
Information technology (IT) services. (As-Ind, estab
1900, empl 1, sales , cert: NMSDC)

4982 Analytiks International, Inc.
      10 S Fifth St Ste 720 Minneapolis, MN 55402
      (612) 305-4312 Mike Regan Mktg & Sales
      Fax: (866) 347-2021
      Email: mregan@aii-3.com
      Website: www.aii-3.com
SAS consulting & resource placement services. (As-Ind,
estab 2004, empl 6, sales $200,000, cert: NMSDC)

4983 Arrowhead Promotion & Fulfillment Co., Inc.
      1105 SE 8th St   Grand Rapids, MN 55744
      (218) 327-1165 Katie Prokop Christmas CEO
      Fax: (218) 327-2576
      Email: katie@apfco.com
      Website: www.apfco.com
Software development, customized reporting, fulfillment activities. (Woman/White, estab 1983, empl 300,
sales $16,000,000, cert: WBENC)

4984 Backbone Consultants
      50 S 6th St Ste 1360 Minneapolis, MN 55402
      (612) 568-7167 Walter Zuniga Managing Partner
      Fax:
      Email: info@backboneconsultants.com
      Website: www.backboneconsultants.com
IT Audit Outsource & Co-source, IT Risk Assessment &
Advisory, IT Sourcing Risks, Information Security Risk
Assessment, Financial Institutions Data Privacy (GLBA)
Reviews. (As-Pac/Hisp, estab 2008, empl 13, sales
$1,897,914, cert: State)

4985 Barnes Business Solutions, Inc.
      4857 Island View Dr Mound, MN 55364
      (630) 715-4452 Maria Barnes President
      Fax: (866) 715-5442
      Email: mbarnes@BarnesBusinessSolutions.com
      Website: www.BarnesBusinessSolutions.com
Core competency: Custom programming services,
Microsoft Access databases, SQL Server databases,
Microsoft Excel tools & macros,
Microsoft Office integration, Windows-based software
solutions. (Woman/White, estab 2008, empl 1, sales
$139,235, cert: WBENC)

4986 BCforward
7701 France Ave S Ste 325   Edina, MN 55435
(952) 229-8887 Roy Larson Senior Acct Mgr
Fax: (952) 229-8888
Email: roy.larson@bcforward.com
Website: www.bcforward.com
IT consulting & staffing. (AA, estab 1998, empl 275, sales $2,500,000, cert: NMSDC)

4987 BPK Inc.
12800 Whitewater Dr, Ste 100   Minnetonka, MN 55439
(612) 293-7585 Rajeev Bhatia CEO
Fax: (615) 649-0561
Email: rajeev@bpktech.com
Website: www.bpktech.com
IT Consulting, Agile, Software Development, IT Services, Financial consulting, Staff augmentation, Staffing solutions, Java, .Net, Project Manager, Sap, SQ, Investment management, Wealth management. (As-Ind, estab 2006, empl 10, sales $4,000,000, cert: NMSDC)

4988 BTM Global Consulting LLC
330 S Second Ave Ste 450 Minneapolis, MN 55401
(612) 238-8801 Lesli Hines President
Fax: (612) 216-5304
Email: lesli.hines@btmgcs.com
Website: www.btmgcs.com
Custom application development, software development, integration, implementation. (As-Pac, estab 2004, empl 85, sales $5,100,000, cert: NMSDC)

4989 Business Technology Solutions, Inc.
7441 Windmill Dr   Chanhassen, MN 55317
(612) 208-7287 Brian Hugh President
Fax: (214) 481-7032
Email: brian.hugh@btsbiz.com
Website: www.btsbiz.com
Information systems integration/dev, project management, business/system analysis, large-scale application/ infrastructure upgrades, packaged software evaluation/ selection & database performance analysis & tuning. (As-Pac, estab 1996, empl 2, sales $290,804, cert: State)

4990 Clarity Tek, Inc.
2859 Aspen Lake Dr NE   Blaine, MN 55449
(612) 567-0835 Abida Banu President
Fax: (866) 868-4515
Email: abida.banu@claritytek.com
Website: www.claritytek.com/
Placement, Recruiting, IT Consulting, IT Services, Staff augmetation, IT Contractor Services, Software development services, Software maintenance services. (Woman/ As-Pac, estab 2012, empl 4, sales $56,561, cert: City)

4991 CS Solutions, Inc.
3440 Federal Dr, Ste 100   Eagan, MN 55122
(651) 271-4477 Sonia Stephen Staffing Mgr
Fax: (651) 344-1100
Email: sonia@cssoln.com
Website: www.cssolutionsinc.com
IT consulting, staff augmentation, project outsourcing, solution design & develop, data warehousing & admin, e-commerce security, web develop. (As-Ind/As-Pac, estab 1996, empl 30, sales , cert: NMSDC)

4992 Denysys Corporation
2400 Blaisdell Ave Ste 202 Minneapolis, MN 55404
(612) 869-7617 Philip Denny President
Fax: (866) 671-0076
Email: philip.denny@denysys.com
Website: www.ww.denysys.com
Information technology, administrative & management consulting services. (AA, estab 1991, empl 35, sales $4,100,540, cert: State)

4993 Docunet Corporation
2435 Xenium Ln N   PLYMOUTH, MN 55441
(800) 936-2863 Wendy Morical President
Fax: (763) 475-1516
Email: wnm@docunetworks.com
Website: www.docunetworks.com
Digital printing: black & white, color, database management, direct mail & fulfillment. (Woman/White, estab 1991, empl 12, sales $1,780,000, cert: WBENC)

4994 E-Comm Systems, Inc.
1728 Ashland Ave   St. Paul, MN 55104
(612) 875-5531 Ruben Benegas President
Fax: (612) 875-5531
Email: ruben.benegas@e-commsystems.com
Website: www.e-commsystems.com
IT security, risk management, security assessment reports, remediation efforts, identification of mitigating controls & security planning, implement security policies. (Hisp, estab 1999, empl 5, sales $120,001, cert: NMSDC)

4995 Enclipse Corp.
331 2nd Ave S Ste 703 Minneapolis, MN 55401
(612) 360-4713 Mohammed Halim Client Relationship Mgr
Fax: (925) 226-4723
Email: halimm@enclipse.com
Website: www.enclipse.com
Professional consulting svcs, managed svcs & solutions design & development: identifying organizational strategies & objectives, design, develop & implement end-to-end software solutions. (As-Pac, estab 2002, empl 128, sales $10,000,000, cert: NMSDC)

4996 Genisys Technologies, Inc.
3545 Plymouth Blvd, Ste 115   Plymouth, MN 55447
(763) 205-4883 Mohan Dhavileswarapu CEO
Fax: (763) 205-4949
Email: mohan@genisystechnologies.com
Website: www.genisystechnologies.com
Management, IT staffing & solutions, business information, system design, planning, development & implementation. (As-Ind, estab 2013, empl 15, sales $2,000,000, cert: NMSDC)

4997 Horizontal Integration
1660 Hwy 100 Ste 200 St. Louis Park, MN 55416
(612) 392-7581 Kate Schmaltz Dir Staffing Ops
Fax: (952) 835-4574
Email: kschmaltz@horizontalintegration.com
Website: www.horizontalintegration.com
Information technology staff augmentation , software design & devel, e-commerce, crm apps, enterprise arcitecture & enterprise app integration, business performance mgmt app, custom business apps, web app information architecture & creative design. (As-Pac, estab 2003, empl 632, sales $83,667,089, cert: NMSDC)

4998 Icon IT Group
3025 Hatbor Ln N, Ste 324 Plymouth, MN 55447
(612) 207-4778 Shaik Ahmed President
Fax:
Email: ahmed@iconitgroup.com
Website: www.iconitgroup.com
E-verify Software Development, Web Technologies, ERP Packages, Data Warehousing, Business Intelligence, Business Analysis & Quality Assurance. (As-Ind, estab 2013, empl 11, sales $1,200,000, cert: NMSDC)

4999 Ideal System Solutions, Inc.
5610 Rowland Rd Ste 150 Minnetonka, MN 55343
(888) 696-1044 Elise M Hernandez President
Fax: (218) 568-7781
Email: sales@idealssi.com
Website: www.idealssi.com
Dist servers, workstations, pcs, parts, upgrades, memory, storage, networking components & peripherals, consulting, system planning & integration, network design & set up, maintenance & training. (Woman/Hisp, estab 1997, empl 32, sales $25,661,586, cert: NMSDC, WBENC)

5000 ILM Professional Services, Inc.
5221 Viking Dr Ste 300 Edina, MN 55435
(952) 960-2220 Lee Ann Villella Acct Exec
Fax:
Email: leeann.villella@ilmservice.com
Website: www.ilmservice.com
Integrated, custom web & mobile applications, consulting, project outsourcing on & offsite. (As-Ind, estab 2002, empl 30, sales $4,100,000, cert: NMSDC)

5001 Infinity Systems, Inc.
P.O. Box 43925 Brooklyn Park, MN 55443
(612) 819-3940 Michael Perkins Dir Business Devel
Fax: (763) 424-4844
Email: mperknoll@aol.com
Website: www.isimetrics.com
Internet security software. (AA, estab 1993, empl 10, sales , cert: NMSDC)

5002 IPCS
600 S Hwy 169 Ste 1595 Minneapolis, MN 55426
(952) 541-4888 Kuldeep Dhar Sr VP
Fax: (952) 541-1222
Email: kuldeep@ipcs.net
Website: www.ipcs.net
Software development & consulting: on-site, off-site & off-shore IT contract programming, e-commerce applications, data warehousing, application development, database admin, package implementations. (Woman/As-Pac, estab 1996, empl 51, sales $4,900,000, cert: State)

5003 Jeevtek Inc.
7160 Cahill Rd, Ste 238 Edina, MN 55439
(612) 440-0123 Suneel Gundlapalli President
Fax:
Email: sg@jeevtek.com
Website: www.jeevtek.com/
IT staff augmentation & custom software development services, Java, J2EE, web applications, eCommerce, databases, SQL, ERP (Oracle, SAP), .NET, Cloud etc. (As-Ind, estab 2015, empl 2, sales $230,000, cert: City, WBENC)

5004 KCS
2395 Ariel St N, Ste A Saint Paul, MN 55109
(651) 777-9119 Dorothy C. Richburg CEO
Fax: (651) 389-0208
Email: drichburg@keystonecs.com
Website: www.keystonecs.com
IT consulting, technical services, IT training. (Woman/AA, estab 1987, empl 45, sales $9,894,985, cert: State, NMSDC, WBENC)

5005 Net Anchor, Inc.
202 N 22nd Ave Minneapolis, MN 55411
(612) 425-2200 Keni Fegbeboh
Fax: (612) 436-2201
Email: kenfegb@netanchor.com
Website: www.netanchor.com
Software & hardware procurement, Help desk support, IT Managed Services, IT Staff Augmentation, Remote monitoring, IT Network Architecture, Network Design & Installation, IT Infrastructure & Data Center, Custom hardware software application development. (AA, estab 2006, empl 1, sales $15,455, cert: NMSDC)

5006 New Horizons Computer Learning Center Minnesota
2915 Commers Dr Ste 500 Eagan, MN 55121
(651) 900-7203 Sammy Peterson Dir of Ops
Fax: (651) 365-1078
Email: speterson@newhorizonsmn.com
Website: www.newhorizonsmn.com
IT training. (Woman/White, estab 2010, empl 18, sales $3,554,749, cert: WBENC)

5007 Performix Business Services
9100 W Bloomington Fwy, Ste 159 Bloomington, MN 55431
(952) 888-2791 Sunil Bafna Owner
Fax: (952) 400-8008
Email: sbafna@performixbiz.com
Website: www.performixbiz.com
Software consulting, application integration, database integration, ecommerce application, enterprise application. (As-Ind/As-Pac, estab 1997, empl 13, sales $1,650,000, cert: State, NMSDC)

5008 Pinnacle Consulting Solutions
17761 Cascade Dr Eden Prairie, MN 55347
(952) 292-4556 Ranja Tarafder CEO
Fax: (999) 999-9999
Email: ranja@pinnacleconsultingsolutions.com
Website: www.pinnacleconsultingsolutions.com
IT staffing & consulting, Project/Program Management, ITIL Process Management, Application Development, Software Development Life Cycle, Database Design & Development, Business Intelligence, Business Analysis/ Data Analysis. (Woman/As-Ind, estab 2014, empl 2, sales $150,000, cert: NMSDC, WBENC)

5009 Pleasant Consulting, LLC
9145 Lyndale Ave S Bloomington, MN 55420
(952) 484-4373 Marty Pleasant President
Fax: (952) 516-5945
Email: marty@pleasantconsulting.com
Website: www.pleasantconsulting.com
Contract & temporary IT staff, contract to hire staff. (Woman/White, estab 2012, empl 17, sales $900,000, cert: WBENC)

5010 Premier Transportation
999 American Blvd E Minneapolis, MN 55420
(800) 899-7433 Nicole French VP Sales & Mktg
Fax: (161) 272-4126
Email: sales@premiertrans.com
Website: www.premiertrans.com
Tele-Consultants, Inc. (TCI) is a woman-owned small business, established in 1985. TCI provides program management, system engineering, integrated logistics, cyber security, software development and support, training, technical publications, Foreign Milit (Woman, estab 1988, empl 75, sales $3,800,000, cert: WBENC)

5011 Procellis Technology Inc.
901 Marquette Ave Suire 1500 Minneapolis, MN 55402
(612) 430-9505 Damian Young
Fax: (626) 357-0079
Email: damian.young@procellis.com
Website: www.procellis.com
IT services, servers, storage, virtualization, backup, disaster recovery & cloud services. (AA, estab 2013, empl 6, sales , cert: NMSDC)

5012 SDK Software Inc aka Sudhko Inc.
11322 86th Ave N Maple Grove, MN 55369
(763) 657-7272 Hema Arumilli President
Fax: (763) 657-1890
Email: sdkhr@sdksoft.com
Website: www.sdksoft.com
Software development svcs, staff augmentation & project mgmt. (Woman/As-Ind, estab 1993, empl 100, sales $13,350,000, cert: City, NMSDC)

5013 Select Source International
13911 Ridgedale Dr, Ste 230 Minnetonka, MN 55305
(952) 546-3300 Mandeep Sodhi CEO
Fax: (952) 546-3500
Email: sales@selectsourceintl.com
Website: www.SelectSourceIntl.com
Temporary Staffing, Information Technology Staffing, Information Technology Services, Engineering Services, Financial Services, Government Services, Retail Services, Energy & Utility Services, Application Development, Mobile Development. (As-Ind, estab 2000, empl 773, sales $74,018,880, cert: NMSDC)

5014 TAJ Technologies, Inc.
7900 International Dr Ste 405 Bloomington, MN 55425
(651) 405-7411 K.C. Sukumar President
Fax: (651) 688-8321
Email: kcs@tajtech.com
Website: www.tajtech.com
E-business solutions, e-commerce applications, client/ server programming, on-site, off-site & offshore. (As-Ind, estab 1987, empl 208, sales $27,000,000, cert: NMSDC)

5015 Tartan Marketing, Inc.
10467 93rd Ave N Maple Grove, MN 55369
(763) 391-7575 Margie MacLachlan CEO
Fax: (763) 777-8647
Email: info@tartanmarketing.com
Website: www.tartanmarketing.com
We are a full service B2B agency that specializes in helping food, technology and service companies energize their brands and grow their businesses. We employ a completely integrated marketing approach where strategy drives creative execution (Woman/ White, estab 1999, empl 14, sales $2,038,340, cert: WBENC)

5016 Technical Information & Professional Solutions Inc
15600 35th Ave N Ste 203 Plymouth, MN 55447
(763) 557-7010 Adnan (AJ) Jalil Sales and Mktg Mgr
Fax: (763) 557-7015
Email: aj@tips2e.com
Website: www.tips2e.com
Technical staffing: short & long term contract, contract to hire & direct placement staff. (As-Ind, estab 1995, empl 89, sales $9,374,046, cert: NMSDC)

5017 Technology Solutions Group LLC
60 S 6th St Ste 2800 Minneapolis, MN 55402
(888) 733-4599 Alexandra Farnsworth CEO
Fax:
Email: ali@tsg-mn.com
Website: www.tsg-mn.com/
BI/Data Mining, IoT & Software Development, Business Intelligence, BI/Data mining, Analytics, Internet of Things, Mobile App Development, Software Development, Web Development, QA/testing. (Woman/White, estab 2013, empl 1, sales $616,140, cert: WBENC)

5018 The MACRO GROUP, Inc.
1200 Washington Ave S Ste 350 Minneapolis, MN 55401
(612) 332-7880 Dawn Kuzma President
Fax:
Email: dkuzma@macrogroup.net
Website: www.macrogroup.net
Project/Program Management, Business Analysis, Process Improvement, Web Application Devel, Application Integration, Electronic Content Management/Electronic Document Management, Technical Analysis & Design, Client/Service Application Devel. (Woman/White, estab 1987, empl 35, sales $3,700,000, cert: City)

5019 Titan Data Group Inc.
6043 Hudson Rd, Ste 399-E Woodbury, MN 55125
(651) 493-0039 Viswanathan Subramanian Pres.
Fax: (651) 493-0149
Email: vish@titandata.com
Website: www.titandata.com
Business strategy, IT consulting, process improvement & technology development. (Woman/As-Ind, estab 2002, empl 20, sales $3,917,883, cert: NMSDC)

5020 Transcomp Inc.
2974 Rice St St Paul, MN 55113
(651) 628-4000 Marnie Ochs-raleigh CEO
Fax: (651) 628-4004
Email: marnie@evolve-systems.com
Website: www.evolve-systems.com
Web development, shopping carts, event management interfaces, Content Management Systems (CMS) & payment forms. (Woman/White, estab 1993, empl 10, sales $875,007, cert: WBENC)

5021 TSG Server and Storage
10 2nd St NE, Ste 214 Minneapolis, MN 55413
(612) 465-0800 Mike DuBois COO
Fax:
Email: info@tsg-usa.com
Website: www.tsg-usa.com
Solution Integrator & infrastructure, Hyper-converged infrastructure, cloud and security, networking, storage, server & software, cloud storage, back up & recovery, cybersecurity, IBM Power Systems, IBM Storage. (As-Pac, estab 2001, empl 11, sales , cert: State, City)

5022 Twin Cities Solutions, Inc.
P.O. Box 21975 Eagan, MN 55121
(952) 583-0367 Scott Miller CFO
Fax: (612) 605-0150
Email: smiller@twincs.com
Website: www.twincs.com
IT consulting: .Net developers, Java developers, business analysts & project managers. (Woman, estab 2000, empl 10, sales $970,000, cert: State)

5023 UpNet Technologies, Inc.
7825 Washington Ave S Ste 450 Minneapolis, MN 55439
(952) 944-2345 Kevin Amys Controller
Fax: (952) 486-7610
Email: kevin.amys@upnettec.com
Website: www.upnettec.com
Information technologies: EDI, XML, CIDX , EDIFACT and Rosetta net. (Woman/As-Pac, estab 2000, empl 25, sales $3,200,000, cert: NMSDC, WBENC)

5024 Virtelligence, Inc
6216 Baker Road Ste 100 Eden Prairie, MN 55346
(952) 548-6600 Akhtar Chaudhri CEO
Fax: (952) 548-6620
Email: achaudhri@virtelligence.com
Website: www.virtelligence.com
Management consulting & technology solutions: project mgmt, enterprise software dev & integration, business intelligence & data warehousing, application outsourcing, staffing. (As-Ind/As-Pac, estab 1998, empl 150, sales $27,100,000, cert: NMSDC)

5025 Virtual Matrix Corporation (dba 1 Source, Inc.)
7200 France Ave S Ste 324 Edina, MN 55435
(952) 835-6400 Bill Hohn Director
Fax: (952) 487-2277
Email: hohnb@vmatrixcorp.com
Website: www.1Source.net
IT staffing/consulting, SAP, ABAP, Java, PHP, Oracle, Microsoft products (.NETs). (As-Ind, estab 2002, empl 78, sales $3,500,000, cert: State, City, NMSDC)

5026 Visual Consultants, Inc.
4900 Hwy 169 N, Ste 307 New Hope, MN 55428
(763) 533-1000 Bala Akkina VP
Fax: (877) 841-4152
Email: bala@visual-consultants.com
Website: www.visual-consultants.com
IT solutions, enterprise IT applications development & IT consulting services. (Woman/As-Pac, estab 2003, empl 42, sales $3,500,000, cert: NMSDC)

5027 Word Tech Secretarial Service Inc.
6825 York Place N Minneapolis, MN 55429
(612) 349-9214 Patty Mesenbrink President
Fax: (763) 549-0796
Email: wordtec000@aol.com
Website: www.wordtechsecretarialservice.com
Audio Transcription, Digital transcription, Video tran-scription, transcription, document preparation, audio and video transcription. (Woman/White, estab 1986, empl 3, sales , cert: State, City, SDB)

5028 Xylo Technologies Inc.
2434 Superior Dr NW Ste 105 Rochester, MN 55901
(507) 289-9956 Dharani Ramamoorthy President
Fax: (507) 289-9957
Email: dharani@xylotechnologies.com
Website: www.xylotechnologies.com
IT consulting, web & client/server technolgies, custom software dev & system integration services. (As-Pac, estab 2000, empl 60, sales $7,043,821, cert: NMSDC)

5029 YFI Technologies
1422 Thomas Ave Saint Paul, MN 55104
(651) 645-4987 Reynaldo Lyles President
Fax: (651) 340-0336
Email: rlyles@yourfutureimage.com
Website: www.YFItechnologies.com
Mobile & wireless solutions: PDA's, palm devices, custom software design, mobile database synchroniza-tion, IT consulting & staff augmentation. (AA, estab 1994, empl 8, sales $183,000, cert: NMSDC)

Missouri

5030 Advanced Resources Group, Inc.
687 Trade Center Blvd Ste 110 Chesterfield, MO 63005
(636) 777-4141 Sonya Gotto CEO
Fax: (636) 777-4142
Email: marketing@advr.com
Website: www.advr.com
Contract engineers & IT consultants. (Woman/White, estab 2002, empl 450, sales $12,000,000, cert: CPUC, WBENC)

5031 Application Engineering Group
12300 Old Tesson Rd, Ste 100-G   St. Louis, MO 63128
(314) 842-9110 Chris Rakel Sr Acct Mgr
Fax:
Email: chris.rakel@aeg-inc.com
Website: www.aeg-inc.com
Provide contract, contract to hire & direct hire IT employment services. (Hisp, estab 1992, empl 35, sales , cert: State)

5032 Ares Construction Co, LLC
4900 Lawn Ave   Kansas City, MO 64130
(816) 285-5933 Quinton Fears CEO
Fax: (816) 861-2300
Email: qfears@aresconst.com
Website: www.aresconst.com
Electrical contracting, satellite dishes, computer consulting, network design & installation, web design, data recovery, customer training, structured cabling & phone systems. (AA, estab 2002, empl 7, sales $85,000, cert: State, City)

5033 Byrne Software Technologies, Inc.
16091 Swingley Ridge Rd Ste 200 Chesterfield, MO 63017
(636) 537-2505 Tom Allen VP
Fax: (636) 537-2666
Email: tra@byrnesoftware.com
Website: www.byrnesoftware.com
IT consulting & software development; custom applications, web sites, Windows applications. (Woman/White, estab 1985, empl 55, sales $6,538,000, cert: State)

5034 C-Edge Software Consultants LLC
655 Craig Rd Ste 220 Creve Coeur, MO 63141
(314) 254-7551 Sekhar Prabhakar CEO
Fax: (314) 254-7551
Email: sekhar@cedgecorp.com
Website: www.cedgecorp.com
Project mgmt, software application development, infrastructure consolidation, database mgmt, systems integration. (As-Ind, estab 2004, empl 40, sales $5,000,000, cert: 8(a))

5035 Communitronics Corp.
970 Bolger Court   Fenton, MO 63026
(314)7717160 Rita Leitensdorfer CEO
Fax: (314) 771-9144
Email: rital@communitronics.com
Website: www.communitronics.com
Audio Visual Systems, VTC Systems, Secure/Non-Secure VTC, Enterprise Collaboration, Video/Media Walls, Project Engineering, Custom AV Applications, Service Contracts, FTEs, Information Assurance Compliance (Woman/White, estab 1969, empl 11, sales $2,000,000, cert: State, WBENC)

5036 Data Dynamics, Inc.
500 Oak Leaf Manor Court Ste 1 St. Louis, MO 63021
(314) 607-3758 Thomas Van Cleave Mgr Business Devel
Fax: (636) 394-8175
Email: thomas.vancleave@datadynamics-inc.com
Website: www.datadynamics-inc.com
IT consulting, software development, web applications, mobile apps, web sites& custom software development, infrastructure, PCs, server, networks, routers, etc. (Woman/As-Ind, estab 1996, empl 2, sales $195,836, cert: State)

5037 Digital Partners Incorporated
8008 Carondelet Ave Ste 103 Saint Louis, MO 63105
(314) 863-8008 Matina Koester President
Fax: (314) 863-8018
Email: matina@dpipro.com
Website: www.dpipro.com
System Integration. (Woman/White, estab 1994, empl 11, sales $8,500,000, cert: WBENC)

5038 Document Imaging Systems of St. Louis
1463 S Vandeventer Ave   St. Louis, MO 63110
(314) 531-0167 Adrienne Williams President
Fax: (314) 533-0616
Email: awilliams@disrepro.com
Website: www.disrepro.com
blueprint document reproduction, project collaboration & document management solutions. (Woman/AA, estab 1995, empl 8, sales $4,095,761, cert: State, City, NMSDC)

5039 ECCO Select
4100 N. Mulberry Dr Ste 105   Kansas City, MO 64116
(816) 960-3800 Jeanette Prenger President
Fax: (816) 960-3804
Email: jprenger@eccoselect.com
Website: www.eccoselect.com
Project management, security consulting, network security admin, system security audits. (Woman/Hisp, estab 1995, empl 171, sales $28,172,000, cert: State, NMSDC, WBENC)

5040   Ferguson Consulting Inc.
       1350 Timberlake Manor Pkwy Ste 450 Chesterfield,
       MO 63017
       (636) 728-4408 Paul Woolverton VP Govt Sector
       Fax:
       Email: pwoolverton@fergcons.com
       Website: www.fergusonconsultinginc.com
IT solutions. (Woman/White, estab 1993, empl 110, sales ,
cert: State)

5041   Geodata IT
       555 Washington Ave, Ste 310   St. Louis, MO 63101
       (217) 390-8085 Justin Bennett President
       Fax: (314) 403-7981
       Email: justin@geodatait.com
       Website: www.geodatait.com
Agile Software Dev, Data Center Consolidation & Cloud
Services, Big Data & Data Analytics, Systems Engineering &
Integration, Program & Project Mgmt, Enterprise Content
Management, Data & Information Engineering. (Hisp,
estab 2012, empl 4, sales $120,000, cert: NMSDC, 8(a))

5042   Information Solutions Design
       2122 Kratky Rd Ste 250 St. Louis, MO 63114
       (314) 429-3311 Timothy Slater CEO
       Fax: (314) 429-3790
       Email: tim.slater@newhorizonsstl.com
       Website:
Information technology svcs: network & server consolidation, web & portal development, application & database
development. (AA, estab 2005, empl 35, sales $1,500,000,
cert: NMSDC)

5043   Ingenuity Consulting Partner, Inc.
       410 B SE 3rd St, Ste 102   Lee's Summit, MO 64081
       (816) 272-8145 Brenda Riggs CEO
       Fax: (816) 875-4582
       Email: briggs@ingenuityconsulting.com
       Website: www.ingenuityconsulting.com
Software development & application integration, web &
mobile applications. (Woman/White, estab 2002, empl 22,
sales $1,155,578, cert: State)

5044   Kelly Mitchell Group, Inc.
       8229 Maryland Ave   Clayton, MO 63105
       (314) 727-1700 Cassandra Sanford
       Fax: (314) 727-0107
       Email: cassandra.sanford@kellymitchell.com
       Website: www.kellymitchell.com
Technology consulting: staff augmentation, project
solutions, managed outsourcing & strategic consulting.
(Woman/White, estab 1998, empl 2000, sales
$72,000,000, cert: CPUC, WBENC)

5045   NextGen Information Services Inc.
       906 Olive St Ste 600 Saint Louis, MO 63101
       (314) 588-1212 Christy Herschbach Admin Asst
       Fax: (314) 588-1211
       Email: supplierdiversity@nextgen-is.com
       Website: www.nextgen-is.com
IT consulting services: project mgmt, custom application
dev, legacy transition svcs & staff augmentation, staff
augmentaion. (Woman/Hisp, estab 1997, empl 300, sales ,
cert: State, City, WBENC)

5046   Optitek, Inc.
       2001 S Hanley Rd Ste 250 Brentwood, MO 63144
       (314) 644-2880 Ricki McGuire President
       Fax: (314) 644-7727
       Email: ricki@optitek.com
       Website: www.optitek.com
Electronic remittance processing, electronic lockbox
services, forms processing, legal services & electronic
document management systems. (Woman/White, estab
1992, empl 30, sales $1,796,300, cert: WBENC)

5047   Pace Solutions, Inc.
       1065 Executive PkwySte 225   St. Louis, MO 63141
       (314) 560-9641 Clint Kleinsorge Dir Business Dev
       Fax: (314) 667-3020
       Email: clint@pacesi.com
       Website: www.pacesi.com
Information Technology staffing & consulting services.
(Woman/As-Ind, estab 2011, empl 55, sales $5,000,000,
cert: NWBOC)

5048   PSRI TecHnologies LLC
       113 Eastland Dr   Jefferson City, MO 65101
       (573) 636-9696 Natasha Conley President
       Fax: (573) 636-5407
       Email: cconley@psritech.com
       Website: www.psritech.com
Information technology/staff augmentation, project
management & call center/help desk operations.
(Woman/AA, estab 2001, empl 5, sales $197,053, cert:
State)

5049   Rose International, Inc.
       16401 Swingley Ridge Rd Ste 300 Chesterfield,
       MO 63017
       (636) 812-4000 Himanshu Bhatia Owner/Founder
       Fax: (636) 812-0076
       Email: sales@roseIT.com
       Website: www.roseIT.com
Information systems consulting, software devlopment,
computer programming & maintenance. (Woman/As-
Pac, estab 1993, empl 3500, sales $233,000,000, cert:
State, NMSDC, WBENC)

5050   Saigan Technologies Inc.
       2300 Main St Ste 900 Kansas City, MO 64108
       (816) 303-1301 Julie Robertson Client Engage-
       ment Mgr
       Fax: (816) 222-0477
       Email: Diversity@SaiganTech.com
       Website: www.saigantech.com
Information technology IT services & solutions. (Woman/
As-Pac, estab 2004, empl 31, sales $1,701,826, cert:
State, NMSDC, WBENC)

5051   ServeKool Technologies LLC
       287 Arbor Trails Dr   Ballwin, MO 63021
       (636) 207-8055 Lovelina Bhagat President
       Fax:
       Email: info@servekool.com
       Website: www.servekool.com
Custom software development, application support
outsourcing & staffing services. (Woman/As-Ind, estab
2013, empl 2, sales , cert: NMSDC)

5052   Strategic Staffing Solutions
       120 S. Central Avenue   St. Louis, MO 63105
       (630) 546-1784 Denice Olson VP
       Fax: (313) 965-9967
       Email: dolson@strategicstaff.com
       Website: www.strategicstaff.com
Information technology consulting. (Woman/White, estab
1990, empl 2700, sales $642,000,000, cert: WBENC)

5053   TechGuard Security LLC
       28 Hawk Ridge Blvd, Ste 107   Lake St. Louis, MO
       63367
       (636) 489-2230 Suzanne Magee CEO
       Fax: (443) 453-5700
       Email: info@techguardsecurity.com
       Website: www.techguard.com
IT networking & security services: vulnerability assessments; policy development; secure network infrastructure
design; security awareness training; intrusion detection;
business continuity/disaster recovery; 24x7 incident
response. (Woman/White, estab 2000, empl 45, sales
$7,550,000, cert: State)

5054   TechnoSmarts, Inc.
       16090 Swingley Ridge Rd Ste 330 St.Louis, MO
       63017
       (636) 519-0814 Rao Vallabhaneni President
       Fax: (636) 536-1414
       Email: rao@technosmarts.com
       Website: www.technosmarts.com
IT consulting & staffing services. (As-Ind, estab 1997, empl
30, sales , cert: State, NMSDC)

5055   The Newberry Group, Inc.
       2440 Executive Dr, Ste 208   St. Charles, MO 63303
       (636) 928-9944 Brenda Newberry President
       Fax: (636) 928-8899
       Email: bnewberry@thenewberrygrp.com
       Website: www.thenewberrygrp.com
Information systems consulting, software devel, LAN/WAN
planning, installation & support, & permanent placement.
(Woman/AA, estab 1996, empl 78, sales $3,100,000, cert:
State)

5056   TurnGroup Technologies, LLC
       2811 Locust St   St. Louis, MO 63103
       (314) 289-8734 Kim St. Onge Business Dev Mgr
       Fax: (314) 289-8735
       Email: kim@turngroup.com
       Website: www.turngroup.com
Database development, hardware/software support,
internet solutions, LAN/WAN, programming, website
development. (AA, estab 2002, empl 9, sales $225,000,
cert: City)

5057   Unitech Consulting, LLC dba Chameleon
       3207 Washington Ave   St. Louis, MO 63103
       (314) 773-7200 Mary Burgess Bus Dev Specialist
       Fax: (314) 773-6306
       Email: sales@chameleonis.com
       Website: www.chameleonis.com
Program management, software development & integration & infrastructure support services. (Hisp, estab 2003,
empl 75, sales $7,742,000, cert: NMSDC)

5058   World Wide Technology, Inc.
       One World Wide Way   Maryland Heights, MO
       63146
       (314) 656-0034 Javon Coleman Corporate
       Supplier Diversity Mgr
       Fax: (314) 919-1550
       Email: javon.coleman@wwt.com
       Website: www.wwt.com
VAR and Systems Integrator providing technology
products, professional services, and supply chain
solutions to customers around the globe. (AA, estab
1900, empl 4000, sales $10,777,032,808, cert: NMSDC)

Mississippi

5059   Applied Geo Technologies, Inc.
       404 Industrail Rd   Choctaw, MS 39350
       (601) 663-7415 Tim Magnusson GM
       Fax: (601) 663-7488
       Email: tmagnusson@appliedgeotech.com
       Website: www.appliedgeotech.com
Digital mapping services: conversion, parcel mapping,
feature extraction, aerial & satellite image
orthophotography production. (Nat Ame, estab 2001,
empl 26, sales $4,545,061, cert: State)

5060   Omni Sourcing, Inc.
       1230 Raymond Road; Box 6   Jackson, MS 39204
       (713) 628-6929 John Perkins President
       Fax: (713) 628-6929
       Email: jperkins@omnisourcing.net
       Website: www.omnisourcing.net
Systems integration & quality management, service
assurance mgmt & testing, sourcing value creation,
business & technology performance improvement,
program & project mgmt. (AA, estab 2012, empl 30,
sales $3,600,000, cert: NMSDC)

Montana

5061   S & K Global Solutions, LLC
       145 S Lake Crest, Ste 2   Polson, MT 59860
       (281) 468-7565 David Dean Senior Program Mgr
       Fax:
       Email: ddean@skgs-llc.com
       Website: www.skglobalsolutions.com
Logistics, engineering, telecommunications, and information technology (IT). (Nat Ame, estab 2005, empl 250,
sales $21,000,000, cert: 8(a))

5062   S & K Technologies
       63066 Old Hwy 93   St. Ignatius, MT 59865
       (406) 745-7500 Dermot O'Halloran Sr VP IT Ops
       Fax: (406) 745-7506
       Email: dohall@sktcorp.com
       Website: www.sktcorp.com
Information technology engineering svcs, software dev,
technical manuals, software integration, web site design,
web application dev, internet mgmt, program mgmt,
logistical support, systems mgmt, integration, installation & training. (Nat Ame, estab 1999, empl 300, sales
$67,403,178, cert: State)

North Carolina

5063 3 Birds Marketing, LLC
505-B W Franklin St   Chapel Hill, NC 27516
(919) 913-2750 Layton Judd Co-Founder/President
Fax: (919) 913-2751
Email: layton@3birdsmarketing.com
Website: www.3birdsmarketing.com
Technology, software, integrated marketing platform, marketing, digital marketing, multichannel marketing, email marketing, email newsletters, digital newsletters, social media management, social media marketing. (Woman, estab 2009, empl 60, sales $3,769,500, cert: WBENC, NWBOC)

5064 Active Ergonomics, Inc.
6501 Creedmoor Rd Ste 101 Raleigh, NC 27613
(919) 676-8211 Shannon A Powell President
Fax: (919) 676-8265
Email: SPOWELL@ACTERGO.COM
Website: www.actergo.com
Office ergonomic software to help increase worker productivity and reduce repetitive stress injuries. (Woman/Hisp, estab 1997, empl 4, sales $934,000, cert: NMSDC, WBENC)

5065 Alliance of Professionals & Consultants, Inc.
8200 Brownleigh Dr   Raleigh, NC 27617
(301) 922-1848 Carla Griffin Business Dev Mgr
Fax: (919) 510-9668
Email: cgriffin@apcinc.com
Website: www.apcinc.com
Requirements analysis, network architecture definitions & enhancements, information technology, hardware & software upgrades, modifications, installation, operation & maintenance. (Nat Ame, estab 1993, empl 724, sales $70,684,230, cert: NMSDC)

5066 Banerasoft Inc.
5710 W Gate City Blvd Ste K, #279 Greensboro, NC 27407
(864) 787-5408 Brenda Zamzow Sales & Cstmr Relations Mgr
Fax:
Email:
Website: www.banerasoft.com
Technology Consulting/Outsourcing, Software Development, App Development for all iOS & Android devices, Data Analytics & Business Intelligence, QA & Solutions Integration. (As-Ind, estab 2012, empl 35, sales $310,000, cert: NMSDC)

5067 Barrchin, Inc.
14133 Kennington Park Dr Ste 305 Raleigh, NC 27614
(919) 630-5128 Janet Barrett President
Fax:
Email: JBarrett@barrchin.com
Website: www.barrchin.com
Information Technology (IT) & Management consulting. (Woman/AA, estab 2013, empl 4, sales , cert: State, City)

5068 Carolina IT Professionals, Inc.
243 W Catawba Ave   Mount Holly, NC 28120
(704) 827-8102 David McConnell VP Mktg
Fax: (704) 825-0199
Email: Mac.McConnell@citpinc.com
Website: www.citpinc.com
Information technology staff augmentation, solutions & consulting, permanent placements. (Woman/White, estab 2001, empl 160, sales $19,009,811, cert: WBENC)

5069 Ciber Global LLC
2501 Aerial Center Pkwy#103   Morrisville, NC 27560
(919) 880-9805 Jay Horowitz Acct Director
Fax:
Email: jhorowitz@ciber.com
Website: www.ciber.com
IT solutions & consulting: application mgmt, systems integration, project outsourcing, packaged solutions implementation, business process outsourcing & embedded systems solutions. (As-Ind, estab 1990, empl 3000, sales $300,000,000, cert: NMSDC)

5070 Clark-Powell Associates, Inc.
920 Blairhill Rd Ste 112 Charlotte, NC 28217
(704) 525-4223 Cindy Gibson inside sales
Fax: (704) 525-7147
Email: cgibson@clark-powell.com
Website: www.clark-powell.com
Design, integration & maintenance of AV systems for presentation, videoconferencing, video broadcast & production. (Woman, estab 1983, empl 62, sales $20,000,000, cert: State)

5071 Clinton Gaddy Inc.
717 Green Valley Rd Ste 200 Greensboro, NC 27408
(336) 355-8708 Will Gaddy CEO
Fax:
Email: wmgaddy@gsostaffing.com
Website: www.gsostaffing.com
Contract IT Staffing/Temporary Labor: Systems Analyst, API Development, Data Analyst, Software Developers, DevOps, Lead Architects, IT Audit Managers, Change Management, Incident/Change Management, Technical Lead, IT Directors, Solution Architect. (AA, estab 2017, empl 2, sales , cert: State)

5072 COMNet Group, Inc.
301 McCullough Dr, Ste 400   Charlotte, NC 28262
(704) 909-2792 Ana Sai President
Fax: (866) 678-9041
Email: ana@comnetgroup.com
Website: www.comnetgroup.com
IT Technology & training services: ERP, offshoring/outsourcing, agile program management & complex software development & delivery. (Woman/As-Ind, estab 2005, empl 20, sales $216,422, cert: NMSDC, WBENC)

5073 DD Consulting and Management
13016 Eastfield Rd Ste 200-272 Huntersville, NC 28078
(704) 909-2970 Walter Great
Fax:
Email: walter@ddconsultingservice.com
Website: www.DDConsultingservice.com
IT consulting, data storage, data backup, physical surveillance data, digital evidence & security-sensitive digital data. (AA, estab 2001, empl 3, sales , cert: NMSDC)

5074 DynPro
7412 Chapel Hill Rd Raleigh, NC 27607
(919) 747-7114 Michael Kallam VP-Business Dev
Fax: (919) 233-9313
Email: mkallam@dynpro.com
Website: www.dynpro.com
Design & implement internet applications & web-enable, enterprise solutions, SAP, People Soft & Oracle application mgmt outsourcing, technical svcs, staff augmentation, project mgmt, help desk support. (As-Ind/As-Pac, estab 1996, empl 90, sales $3,695,000, cert: NMSDC)

5075 Empores LLC
11020 David Taylor Dr Charlotte, NC 28262
(703) 409-4945 Satish Prasad Ramamurthy VP Business Devel
Fax: (540) 301-2800
Email: satish@emporesllc.com
Website: www.emporesllc.com
Voltage optimization, intelligent PF correction, KVAR improvements, cloud based energy monitoring & automatic techniques. (As-Ind/As-Pac, estab 2012, empl 5, sales , cert: State, City)

5076 Infestus Inc.
P.O. Box 222 McLeansville, NC 27301
(202) 794-7280 Glasco Taylor CEO
Fax:
Email: glasco.taylor@calibertec.com
Website: www.calibertec.com/
IT staffing: Cyber Security, Data Center(Virtualization, Storage, SAN, Networking, Server Hardware, Linux, etc), Infrastructure Networking. (AA, estab 2014, empl 5, sales $200,000, cert: NMSDC)

5077 IT People Corporation
One Copley Pkwy. Ste #216 Morrisville, NC 27560
(919) 806-3535 Sai Nidamarty Business Dev
Fax: (919) 806-2299
Email: sai@itpeoplecorp.com
Website: www.itpeoplecorp.com
Information technology staffing, consulting & outsourcing services. (Woman/As-Ind, estab 1999, empl 153, sales $7,459,294, cert: State, NMSDC)

5078 J2 Associates, LLC
900 S. Wilmington St, Ste 207 Raleigh, NC 27601
(919) 949-4707 John Johnston President
Fax: (866) 264-5252
Email: jjohnston@j2assoc.com
Website: www.j2assoc.com
IT, Systems Integration, audio visual systems, cabling, VTC, network engineers, sharepoint, cyber security, help desk, systems administration & web development. (AA, estab 2008, empl 18, sales $2,800,000, cert: 8(a))

5079 MSys Inc.
5540 Centerview Dr, Ste 200 Raleigh, NC 27606
Ste 200 Raleigh Raleigh, NC 27606
(919) 234-7581 Raj Thiyagarajan Director
Fax: (510) 280-7352
Email: register@msysinc.com
Website: www.msysinc.com
Software consulting,custom programming & development, web development. (As-Ind, estab 1994, empl 37, sales $220,000, cert: NMSDC)

5080 Paula P. White and Associates, Inc dba DataMasters
P.O. Box 14548 Greensboro, NC 27415
(336) 373-1461 Dana White Director, Ops
Fax: (336) 373-1501
Email: dwhite@datamasters.com
Website: www.datamasters.com
IT staffing, contract, staff augmentation & permanent or direct hire positions. (Woman/White, estab 1971, empl 25, sales $2,500,000, cert: State)

5081 QCentric Consultants, LLC
624 Tyvola Rd, Ste 103-177 Charlotte, NC 28217
(800) 260-5728 Nuradin Kariye Managing Partner
Fax: (866) 430-3843
Email: admin@qcentricconsultants.com
Website: www.qcentricconsultants.com
IT staffing & technology solutions. (AA, estab 2009, empl 45, sales $92,000, cert: State)

5082 Quantum Technology Group, LLC
P.O. Box 762 Cornelius, NC 28031
(800) 918-3510 Adam Jones President
Fax: (800) 928-5430
Email: amjones@qtg-llc.com
Website: www.qtg-llc.com
IT, cabling infrastructure, IP converged telephony systems, voice mail solutions, access control, paging systems, mass notification systems, video telecon, CATV. (AA, estab 2007, empl 16, sales $338,454, cert: 8(a))

5083 Queen Associates Inc.
201 S Tryon St Ste 875 Charlotte, NC 28202
(704) 943-9232 Robin Pugh President
Fax: (704) 331-0633
Email: robin.pugh@queenassociates.com
Website: www.queenassociates.com
Integrated business & technology services: project mgmt, business analysis, software design & development, quality assurance, database modeling & design, database admin, architecture, network infrastructure, network design & support, etc. (Woman/White, estab 2000, empl 125, sales $15,202,394, cert: WBENC)

5084 Refulgent Technologies Inc.
      112 South Tryon St Ste 1270 Charlotte, NC 28284
      (704) 405-4238 Horace Worley President
      Fax: (980) 939-6292
      Email: horace.worley@refulgent-tech.com
      Website: www.refulgent-tech.com
IT consulting & staffing services, application development
& staffing. (Woman/As-Pac, estab 2005, empl 22, sales
$1,157,433, cert: NMSDC)

5085 Sajiton LLC
      301 McCullough Dr Ste 400 Charlotte, NC 28262
      (888) 828-7991 Nicole Williams Managing Dir
      Fax: (888) 481-0778
      Email: nicole.williams@sajiton.com
      Website: www.sajiton.com
Custom Mobile & Web Application Development, Big Data,
Data Analytics, Data Engineering, Data Integration, Master
Data Management. Data Encryption, Data Security in the
Cloud & On Premise - CyberSecurity. (Woman/AA, estab
2014, empl 1, sales , cert: NMSDC, WBENC)

5086 Saponi Industries, Inc.
      3229 Goslen Dr   Pfafftown, NC 27040
      (336) 770-5321 Deborah Bare Owner
      Fax: (866) 765-7370
      Email: lynn@saponi-industries.com
      Website: www.saponi-industries.com
Saponi Industries is a brokerage company that provides
competitive products by shopping the insurance market
for the customer. Group products include: Universal life,
whole life, term life, accident, critical illness, dental, cancer
and long term care. (Woman/Nat Ame, estab 2010, empl
2, sales $54,000, cert: NMSDC)

5087 Technology Concepts & Design, Inc.
      4510 Weybridge Ln   Greensboro, NC 27407
      (336) 232-5800 Lisa Cain CFO
      Fax: (336) 232-5850
      Email: l_cain@tcdi.com
      Website: www.tcdi.com
Advanced application & system design services,
eDiscovery, review & production & large-scale case
management products & services to help effectively
manage and reduce costs associated with significant
litigation and investigations. (As-Pac, estab 1988, empl 69,
sales , cert: NMSDC)

5088 Telecom Sales & Marketing, Inc.
      P.O. Box 1454 High Point, NC 27261
      (336) 882-6113 Don Taylor President
      Fax: (336) 882-6713
      Email: don@tsmtelecom.com
      Website: www.tsmtelecom.com
Dist telecommunications parts & equipment, telephone
headsets. (AA, estab 1979, empl 6, sales $1,380,000, cert:
State)

North Dakota

5089 Laducer & Associates, Inc.
      201 Missouri Dr   Mandan, ND 58554
      (701) 667-1980 James Laducer President
      Fax: (701) 667-2970
      Email: boston@laducer.com
      Website: www.laducer.com
Data input & comprehensive processing; mgmt & admin
computer based work environments; business devel &
consulting svcs. (Nat Ame, estab 1985, empl 175, sales
$8,136,389, cert: State)

Nebraska

5090 Client/Server Software Solutions
      5069 S 108th St   Omaha, NE 68137
      (402) 393-8059 Lisa Wolford CEO
      Fax: (402) 393-1825
      Email: lisa@csss.net
      Website: www.csss.net
Technology consulting & IT solutions, short long term,
contract-to-hire & permanent placement. (Woman/
White, estab 1997, empl 15, sales , cert: State)

New Hampshire

5091 Advanced Presentation Systems dba CCS
      132 Northeastern Blvd   Nashua, NH 03062
      (978) 256-2001 Chris Gamst VP
      Fax: (978) 256-2002
      Email: cgamst@ccsprojects.com
      Website: www.ccsnewengland.com
Audio visual system design, integration, sales, service &
installation for boardrooms, conference rooms, training
rooms & auditoriums. (Woman/As-Ind, estab 1998, empl
23, sales , cert: State)

5092 Apollo Professional Solutions, Inc.
      29 Stiles Rd Ste 302 Salem, NH 03079
      (866) 277-3343 Bruce Thomason VP
      Fax: (603) 890-6668
      Email: bthomason@apollopros.com
      Website: www.apollopros.com
Recruited & payrolled engineering & information
technology temporary personnel. (Woman/White, estab
1983, empl 20, sales $12,000,000, cert: State)

5093 Dataservinc
      1 Tara Blvd, Ste 102 Nashua, NH 03062
      (603) 557-0600 Anil Kumar VP Business Dev
      Fax: (866) 703-9670
      Email: contact@dataservinc.com
      Website: www.dataservinc.com
IT staffing & IT software development. (Woman/As-Ind,
estab 2005, empl 100, sales $7,000,000, cert: State)

5094 Digital Prospectors Corp.
100 Domain Dr Ste 103 Exeter, NH 03833
(603) 772-2700 Chris Roos Principal
Fax: (603) 772-2828
Email: croos@dpcit.com
Website: www.dpcit.com
Permanent & temporary IT staffing. (Woman/White, estab 1999, empl 120, sales $50,201,563, cert: WBENC)

5095 Paramount Technology Solutions LLC
63 Emerald St, Ste 442 Keene, NH 03431
(281) 617-1400 Beth Wright Dir of Finance & Admin
Fax:
Email: beth.wright@acuitycloudsolutions.com
Website: www.acuitycloudsolutions.com
Computer software consulting services. (Woman/White, estab 2008, empl 25, sales , cert: WBENC)

5096 Patriot Cyber Defense
80 Winkley Farm Lane Rochester, NH 03867
(603) 231-7000 Jennifer Caron CEO
Fax:
Email: jennifer.caron@patriotcyberdefense.com
Website: www.patriotcyberdefense.com
DFARS Cyber Compliance, Cyber Security Consulting, Security Program Deployments, Managed Security Monitoring , CISO Support, Security Staff Augmentation, Security Gap Analysis & Needs & Risk Assessments. (Woman/White, estab 2017, empl 4, sales , cert: State)

5097 SCA Technica, Inc.
P.O. Box 3148 Nashua, NH 03061
(603) 321-6536 David Murotake President
Fax: (603) 222-2098
Email: dmurotak@scatechnica.com
Website: www.scatechnica.com
Research & development, high assurance & secure software defined radio, wireless computing system, develop embedded communications software systems. (As-Pac, estab 2002, empl 5, sales $611,320, cert: State)

5098 Universal Software Corporation
20 Industrial Park Dr Nashua, NH 03062
(603) 324-4004 Sonu Khanna Sr Mgr
Fax: (603) 598-0851
Email: sonuk@universal-sw.com
Website: www.universal-sw.com
Information technology: staff augmentation, project mgmt, project & offshore outsourcing, embedded systems & hardware design, Oracle/MS SQL, .Net framework, open source tools, WinNT, Solaris, Unix, Linux. (As-Pac, estab 1992, empl 58, sales , cert: State)

New Jersey

5099 1st Choice Financial Group LLC
1121 Asbury Avenue Asbury Park, NJ 07712
(717) 599-1907 Kathrina Nease CEO
Fax:
Email: knease@1stchoicefg.com
Website: www.1stchoicefg.com
IT solutions & program/project management. (Woman/White, estab 2006, empl 10, sales $500,000, cert: State)

5100 20/20 Solutions, Inc.
33 Wilson Dr Unit D Sparta, NJ 07871
(973) 383-8703 Jody Torre President
Fax: (973) 383-5114
Email: j.torre@20-20solutions.com
Website: www.20-20solutions.com
Website development, website management, search engine optimization, website design, website hosting, computer programming, computer repair, computer training, computer equipment, computer maintenance, computer support. (Woman/White, estab 1999, empl 10, sales $450,000, cert: WBENC)

5101 22nd Century Technologies, Inc.
1 Executive Dr Ste 285 Somerset, NJ 08873
(732) 507-7048 Neil Watson Mgr Sales
Fax: (732) 537-0888
Email: neil@tscti.com
Website: www.tscti.com
Computer programming & consulting, IT support. (As-Ind, estab 1997, empl 1800, sales $59,000,000, cert: NMSDC)

5102 Actuan Global LLC
4 Debra Ct Scotch Plains, NJ 07076
(908) 443-1180 Talib Morgan President
Fax:
Email: talib.morgan@actuanglobal.com
Website: www.actuanglobal.com
Digital innovation & technology consulting, mobile, personalization, marketing automation, content management, social media, data & digital systems. (AA, estab 2011, empl 1, sales , cert: NMSDC)

5103 Adaptive Tech Resources Inc.
4400 Route 9 South Ste 1000 Freehold, NJ 07728
(732) 683-0800 Roland Williams CEO
Fax: (732) 683-1888
Email: Roland.Williams@atrstaffing.com
Website: www.atrstaffing.com
IT consulting/contract & full time staffing services. (AA, estab 1996, empl 3, sales $862,000, cert: NMSDC)

5104 Advanced Technology Solutions, Inc.
251 Monmouth Road Ste 1A Oakhurst, NJ 07755
(732) 918-4664 Michele Kieffer Mgr Business Dev
Fax: (732) 918-4666
Email: michele@atsolutions.com
Website: www.atsolutions.com
IT consulting: software devel, system & network engineers, project managers, etc. (Woman/White, estab 1995, empl 200, sales , cert: State, City, WBENC, NWBOC)

5105 Agnosco Technologies Inc.
6 Thornhill Dr Lumberton, NJ 08048
(877) 933-5439 Kiran Khan Ops Mgr
Fax: (609) 751-0156
Email: kiran@agnoscotech.com
Website: www.agnoscotech.com
Information technology recruitment consultancy services: permanent, temporary & contract positions, executive search & outplacement services & solutions. (Woman/As-Pac, estab 2013, empl 50, sales , cert: State)

5106　AIT Global Inc.
228 Route 34　Matawan, NJ 07747
(732) 997-9917　Mittal Shah VP
Fax: (732) 583-8122
Email: mittals@aitglobalinc.com
Website: www.aitglobalinc.com
IT Staffing & Solutions, Contract, Contract to Hire or Full-time Placements. (Woman/As-Ind, estab 2003, empl 135, sales $14,800,000, cert: NMSDC, WBENC)

5107　AITA Consulting Services Inc.
6-80 Towne Center Dr North Brunswick　New Jersey, NJ 08902
(732) 658-4471　Ranjith kumar Business Dev Mgr
Fax: (732) 357-3807
Email: ranjith@aitacs.com
Website: www.aitacs.com
IT staffing services, Corp To Corp, W2, 1099, contract, full time, contract to hire, Business Intelligence, Big Data, Web development, J2EE, Microsoft technologies, Quality Assurance & Oracle Applications, SAP, Mobile Apps. (Woman/As-Ind, estab 2006, empl 182, sales $6,100,000, cert: NMSDC, WBENC)

5108　Alliance Sourcing Network Inc
40 Galesi Dr Ste 2　Wayne, NJ 07470
(201) 438-2005　Heather Milanak CEO
Fax: (866) 292-7960
Email: hmilanak@asn-corp.com
Website: www.asn-corp.com
IT consulting services: application design, client server design, database admin & hardware design & support, network admin. (Woman/White, estab 2006, empl 26, sales $7,913,098, cert: WBENC)

5109　AppliedInfo Partners, Inc.
28 World's Fair Dr　Somerset, NJ 08873
(732) 507-7316　Betty Lau CEO
Fax: (732) 805-0637
Email: blau@appliedinfo.com
Website: www.appliedinfo.com
Software & web dev, computer & IT products & services, marketing communications. (Woman/As-Pac, estab 1990, empl 50, sales $10,000,000, cert: NMSDC, WBENC)

5110　Arborsys Group
3131 Princeton Pike, Bldg 4, Ste 210　Lawrenceville, NJ 08648
(609) 843-0225　Vsau Ranganathan Partner
Fax:
Email: vranganathan@arborsys.com
Website: www.arborsys.com
Business & IT consulting, content lifecycle management, collaboration, business process management, portal solutions & electronic records management. (Woman/As-Pac, estab 2004, empl 50, sales $5,300,000, cert: State, NMSDC)

5111　Artech Information Systems LLC
360 Mt. Kemble Ave Ste 2000　Morristown, NJ 07960
(973) 998-5004　Vinu Varghese Dir New Bus Dev
Fax:
Email: rfp@artech.com
Website: www.artech.com
Network infrastructure mgmt, web applications dev, content mgmt, design, internet infrastructure design devel & maintenance, multitier architecture, client server, software applications, systems devel & support. (Woman/As-Ind, estab 1992, empl 7800, sales $465,000,000, cert: NMSDC, CPUC, WBENC)

5112　Astir IT Solutions
50 Cragwood Rd Ste 219　South Plainfield, NJ 07080
(908) 279-8670　Robert Markowitz Exec VP
Fax: (908) 279-8667
Email: bobm@astirit.com
Website: www.astirit.com
IT consulting, staffing & outsourced software development. (Woman/As-Ind, estab 2001, empl 300, sales $30,700,000, cert: State, NMSDC)

5113　Atlas Data Systems DBA Atlas
400 Connell Dr Ste 6000　Berkeley Heights, NJ 07922
(908) 519-8013　Lisa Wickey Acct Exec
Fax: (908) 286-1019
Email: lisa.wickey@chooseatlas.com
Website: www.chooseatlas.com
Information technology consulting: internet, e-commerce, infrastructure & RDMS consulting. (Woman/White, estab 1998, empl 350, sales $31,900,000, cert: State, WBENC)

5114　Atlas Systems, Inc.
5 Independence Way Ste 309　Princeton, NJ 08540
(609) 452-0101　Robin Grossman Business Dev Mgr
Fax: (609) 452-2290
Email: robin.grossman@atlassystems.com
Website: www.atlassystems.com
IT Services Solutions, Product Development, Maintenance, Data Base Management, BI, Spend Analytics, Sourcing, Supplier/Vendor Management, Contract Management, P2P- iBuy- Order management. (Nat Ame, estab 2003, empl 300, sales , cert: NMSDC)

5115　Aumtech, Inc.
710 Old Bridge Turnpike　East Brunswick, NJ 08816
(732) 254-1875　Tom Porter COO
Fax: (732) 254-2081
Email: tporter@aumtech.com
Website: www.aumtech.com
IVR & VoIP network solution: speech recognition, touchtone input, VXML programming tools. (As-Ind/As-Pac, estab 1988, empl 38, sales $2,120,000, cert: NMSDC)

5116   Avenues International Inc.
       4 Restrick Court   Princeton Junction, NJ 08550
       (609) 945-1160 Anupam Gupta Director
       Fax: (609) 228-6647
       Email: anupam@avenuesinc.com
       Website: www.avenuesinc.com
IT consulting services: Data Analytics, Business Intelligence, Data Warehousing, Big Data Solution & Management Reporting Solutions. (As-Ind, estab 1994, empl 15, sales $1,847,886, cert: NMSDC)

5117   Bardess Group, Ltd.
       15 Morey Ln, Ste 100   Randolph, NJ 07869
       (973) 895-3500 Barbara Pound Pres Consult Svcs
       Fax: (973) 895-1900
       Email: barbara@bardess.com
       Website: www.bardess.com
Data revitalization, business process design & information technology. (Woman/White, estab 1997, empl 25, sales , cert: WBENC)

5118   Blue Planet Solutions Inc.
       36 Route 10 W, Ste E   East Hanover, NJ 07936
       (973) 581-1500 Pradeep Darbhe Resource Mgr
       Fax: (973) 240-0010
       Email: pradeep@blueplanetsolutions.com
       Website: www.blueplanetsolutions.com
Outsource software development & maintenance, contract programmers, offshore programming. (Woman/As-Ind, estab 1997, empl 20, sales , cert: State)

5119   BNG Consulting, Inc.
       12 Sandhill Ct   Jamesburg, NJ 08831
       (732) 631-0003 Biswatosh Guha VP
       Fax: (732) 656-0019
       Email: guha@bngconsulting.com
       Website: www.bngconsulting.com
Business intelligence, data warehousing, reporting/ ETL tools, database admin, support, development, maintenanance, enhancements, architecture & design, data modeling. (As-Pac, estab 2003, empl 65, sales $7,000,000, cert: State)

5120   Cardinal Technology Solutions Inc.
       1100 Cornwall Rd, Ste 113   Monmouth Junction, NJ 08852
       (732) 821-7400 Abhay Srivastava Director
       Fax: (732) 820-2331
       Email: srivasta@cardinaltsinc.com
       Website: www.cardinaltsinc.com
IT and Engineering Staffing and consulting services. (As-Ind, estab 2004, empl 22, sales $8,000,000, cert: NMSDC)

5121   Caresoft Inc.
       220 Lincoln Blvd Ste 300 Middlesex, NJ 08846
       (732) 764-9500 Dhaval Desai Business Dev Mgr
       Fax: (877) 738-7842
       Email: ddesai@caresoftinc.com
       Website: www.caresoftinc.com
Information technology staff augmentation. (As-Ind, estab 1994, empl 189, sales $9,000,000, cert: NMSDC)

5122   Cavalier IT Inc.
       One Evertrust Plaza Ste 1105 Jersey City, NJ 07302
       (201) 589-4767 Manikandan Padmanabhan Sr VP
       Fax:
       Email: mani@cavalieritinc.com
       Website: www.cavalieritinc.com
Technology staffing & consulting. (As-Pac, estab 2005, empl 500, sales $50,100,000, cert: State, NMSDC)

5123   Chenoa Information Services, Inc.
       10 Parsonage Rd Ste 312 Edison, NJ 08837
       (732) 549-6800 Michael Fortino EVP Client Solutions
       Fax: (732) 549-6041
       Email: mfortino@chenoainc.com
       Website: www.chenoahealth.com
Information technology solutions & staff augmentation. (As-Ind, estab 1998, empl 600, sales $17,000,000, cert: State, NMSDC)

5124   Client Solution Architects
       142 W Upper Ferry Rd   West Trenton, NJ 08628
       (609) 638-3304 Neftali Arroyo CEO
       Fax: (703) 852-4447
       Email: larroyo@csaassociates.com
       Website: www.csaassociates.com
Information technology: Manugistics, SAP, Logility, i2. (Hisp, estab 2003, empl 28, sales $3,390,000, cert: State)

5125   CNC Consulting
       50 E Palisades Ave Ste 422 Englewood, NJ 07631
       (201) 541-9122 Wade Mcmurray Business Dev Mgr
       Fax: (201) 541-9128
       Email: wmcmurray@cncconsulting.com
       Website: www.cncconsulting.com
IT professionals for consulting contracts. (AA, estab 1996, empl 25, sales $3,000,000, cert: State)

5126   Collab USA, LLC
       9 Haypress Rd   Cranbury, NJ 08512
       (609) 488-6400 Sam Matreja VP
       Fax: (609) 751-9366
       Email: sam@collabclinical.com
       Website: www.collabclinical.com
IT consulting, software development & technology services. (Woman/As-Ind, estab 2009, empl 47, sales $4,470,000, cert: NMSDC)

5127   Collabera
       110 Allen Road   Basking Ridge, NJ 07920
       (973) 889-5200 Hauleen Petrossi Business Dev Mgr
       Fax: (973) 292-2838
       Email: collaberainfo@collabera.com
       Website: www.collabera.com
Information technology & management svcs, customized software solutions, business solutions, implementation, maintenance, support, etc. (As-Pac, estab 1991, empl 15000, sales $585,000,000, cert: NMSDC)

5128   Combined Computer Resources, Inc.
     120 Wood Ave S, Ste 408 P.O. Box 5002 Iselin, NJ 08830
     (732) 632-2502 Laura Palamara Controller
     Fax: (732) 632-2939
     Email: laurap@combinedcomputer.com
     Website: www.combinedcomputer.com
Information technology consulting: data processing, right-to-hire & full time placement services. (Woman/White, estab 1994, empl 107, sales $16,500,000, cert: State)

5129   Communication Experts, Inc.
     51 Cragwood Rd Ste 304 South Plainfield, NJ 07080
     (908) 512-9129 Shirish R. Nadkarni CEO
     Fax: (732) 516-0608
     Email: SRN@comexpinc.com
     Website: www.comexpinc.com
I help clients identify and solve problems using analytical abilities I have developed through management education, decades of working with small and large companies and from my own experience of founding and running software product and service companie (As-Ind, estab 2003, empl 8, sales $1,704,000, cert: NMSDC)

5130   CompuPlus International Inc.
     94 Lilac Lane Paramus, NJ 07652
     (626) 755-0607 David Wei President
     Fax: (888) 670-9070
     Email: davidw@cp-intl.com
     Website: www.cp-intl.com
IT staffing & IT consulting, recruitment & service. (As-Pac, estab 1990, empl 7, sales $1,625,219, cert: State)

5131   Comrise Technology, Inc.
     1301 State Route 36, Ste 9 Concord Center, Bldg 2 Hazlet, NJ 07730
     (732) 203-6236 Michael Ferrara Ops Officer
     Fax: (732) 739-1996
     Email: SupplierDiversity@comrise.com
     Website: www.comrise.com
Staff supplementation, IT mgmt consulting, project outsourcing & recruiting svcs. (As-Pac, estab 1984, empl 150, sales $13,000,000, cert: NMSDC)

5132   Connexions Data Inc.
     241 Main St, Ste 206 Hackensack, NJ 07601
     (201) 210-8938 Raghu Menon CFA
     Fax:
     Email: raghu.menon@cdatainc.com
     Website: www.cdatainc.com
Information technology consulting & integration services, SAP, Oracle & Cloud computing. (As-Ind, estab 2004, empl 48, sales , cert: State)

5133   Consolidated Energy Design, Inc.
     1933 Hwy 35 Ste 105, No. 367 Wall, NJ 07719
     (732) 681-8800 Rey Montalvo President
     Fax: -
     Email: reym@cedinternational.com
     Website: www.cedinternational.com
FADRS® (pronounced faders) Smart Grid and Smart Micro Grid technology. (Hisp, estab 1987, empl 2, sales $101,432, cert: NMSDC)

5134   Corporate Training Group, Inc.
     120 Wood Ave S Ste 405 Iselin, NJ 08830
     (732) 635-9033 Kathleen Harvey Sr Acct Exec
     Fax: (732) 635-9032
     Email: kharvey@ctgtraining.com
     Website: www.ctgtraining.com
Technical & business end user training on Microsoft, Java, J2EE, Linux, Oracle solutions. (Woman/White, estab 1991, empl 8, sales $2,000,000, cert: State, WBENC)

5135   Cosmic Software Technology, Inc.
     14 Benedek Rd   Princeton, NJ 08540
     (609) 430-8284 Ranvir Sinha CEO
     Fax: (609) 430-8285
     Email: ranvir@cosmic-usa.com
     Website: www.cosmic-usa.com
System programming, database analysis, design, dev & admin, documentation & content mgmt, software analysis & design, system analysis & architecture, systems integration, interface design & dev, ERP/CRM implementations. (As-Ind, estab 1999, empl 15, sales $950,000, cert: State, 8(a))

5136   Crave InfoTech LLC
     15 Corporate Place S Ste 104 Piscataway, NJ 08854
     (253) 310-5371 Vrushali Nistane President
     Fax:
     Email: vrushali@craveinfotech.com
     Website: www.craveinfotech.com
Global software and technology services. (As-Ind, estab 2007, empl 75, sales $2,500,000, cert: State, NMSDC)

5137   Crescens Inc.
     1200 Route 22 East, Ste 2000-2176   Bridgewater, NJ 08807
     (732) 305-2858 Sophia Samuel President
     Fax: (732) 305-2861
     Email: supplier@crescensinc.com
     Website: www.crescensinc.com
IT consulting, application development, maintenance, product engineering services, testing, business intelligence, packaged applications & staffing. (Woman/As-Ind, estab 2002, empl 25, sales $550,000, cert: State, NMSDC)

5138   Crystal Data LLC
     1 Eves Dr Ste 145 Marlton, NJ 08053
     (732) 766-9292 Monika Anand CEO
     Fax: (773) 409-3875
     Email: monika.anand@crystaldatasystems.net
     Website: www.crystaldatasystems.net
IT Staffing & Services. (Woman/As-Ind, estab 2008, empl 40, sales $3,009,933, cert: State, City, WBENC)

5139   CSF Technologies Inc.
     1427 Cranleigh Ln   Williamstown, NJ 08094
     (888) 495-7561 Curtis Freeman President
     Fax: (609) 543-6100
     Email: cfreeman@csftechnologies.com
     Website: www.csftechnologies.com
IT staffing solutions. (AA, estab 2002, empl 2, sales $110,000, cert: State)

5140   cyberThink, Inc.
       685 Route 202/206 Ste 101   Bridgewater, NJ 08807
       (908) 429-8008 Raj Thind Director
       Fax: (908) 429-8004
       Email: rajveer.thind@cyberthink.com
       Website: www.cyberthink.com
IT auditing & assessment, project mgmt, app devel &
integration, infrastructure architecture & deployment,
database modeling, data warehousing, business intelligence, quality assurance, ebusiness, collaboration &
knowledge mgmt, network & sys admin. (As-Ind/As-Pac,
estab 1996, empl 220, sales $25,100,000, cert: State,
NMSDC)

5141   Databased Solutions Inc.
       1200 Route 22 E Ste 2000 Bridgewater, NJ 08807
       (215) 366-2732 Ila Choudhary VP Ops
       Fax: (732) 875-0371
       Email: ila.choudhary@dbsiservices.com
       Website: www.dbsiservices.com
IT svcs, staffing augmentation, IT products. (As-Ind, estab
1995, empl 20, sales $860,000, cert: NMSDC)

5142   Datanomics, Inc.
       991 US Hwy 22 West Ste 301 Bridgewater, NJ 08807
       (908) 707-8200 Lori Vail CEO
       Fax: (908) 707-9600
       Email: vail@datanomics.com
       Website: www.datanomics.com
IT staffing, helpdesk, desktop support,
administration, technical writers, validation specialists,
business/systems
analysts, programmers, mainframe, client/server, & web.
(Woman/White, estab 1982, empl 100, sales , cert: State)

5143   Decentxposure LLC
       75 Gorge Rd   Edgewater, NJ 07020
       (201) 313-1100 Joseph Confreda VP of Finance
       Fax: (201) 840-8492
       Email: jconfreda@dxagency.com
       Website: www.dxagency.com
Todayï¿½s customer wants more than your product or
service, they want a relationship, a 1:1 connection where
you keep track of their preferences, the details of past
transactions, and anticipate their desires. (Woman/Hisp,
estab 2004, empl 45, sales $15,300,000, cert: NMSDC,
WBENC)

5144   DIVERSANT, LLC
       331 Newman Springs Rd Bldg 3, 2nd Fl, Ste 350 Red
       Bank, NJ 07701
       (732) 222-1250 Charlean Parks Mktg Mgr
       Fax: (732) 222-4050
       Email: cparks@diversant.com
       Website: www.diversant.com
IT staffing & solutions. (AA, estab 2005, empl 1300, sales
$171,611,584, cert: NMSDC)

5145   EmployVision, Inc.
       1100 Cornwall Road Ste 115 Monmouth Junction,
       NJ 08854
       (732) 422-7100 Ash Geria Managing Dir
       Fax: (732) 422-7162
       Email: ash@emplolyvision.com
       Website: www.employvision.com
Information technology, recruitment, RPO, IT consulting,
staffing. (Woman/As-Pac, estab 2005, empl 10, sales
$15,000,000, cert: State)

5146   Entrophase Solutions
       19 Washington Rd   Princeton Junction, NJ 08550
       (732) 734-9119 Mark Conover Business Devel
       Exec
       Fax:
       Email: mark.conover@entrophase.com
       Website: www.entrophase.com
SAP, SharePoint, CFR compliance, Regulatory and
compliance services, cGMP, GLP, GCP, Systems Engineering, IT Infrastructure Support, Enterprise Support, and
Data Center Support , Program/Project Management.
(As-Ind, estab 2005, empl 15, sales $2,000,000, cert:
8(a))

5147   eTeam, Inc.
       1001 Durham Ave Ste 201 South Plainfield, NJ
       07080
       (732) 248-1900 Ann Thakur Dir Strategic Accts
       Fax: (908) 757-0800
       Email: rfp@eteaminc.com
       Website: www.eteaminc.com
IT, Business Consulting, Management Consulting. (As-
Ind, estab 1999, empl 1300, sales $85,000,000, cert:
NMSDC, CPUC)

5148   Evergreen Technologies LLC
       2050 Route 27, Ste 202   North Brunswick, NJ
       08902
       (732) 422-1500 Lisa Ferrara Client Relationship
       Mgr
       Fax:
       Email: lisa@evergreentechnologies.com
       Website: www.evergreentechnologies.com
Provides top-notch IT talent with a depth of knowledge
in the latest cutting-edge technologies. (Woman/As-Ind,
estab 1998, empl 80, sales $3,154,475, cert: State,
NMSDC, WBENC)

5149   Excelgens, Inc.
       5 E Main St, 2nd Fl Ste 6B Denville, NJ 07834
       (973) 370-8081 Mona Krishan President
       Fax: (973) 695-1343
       Email: mona@excelgens.com
       Website: www.excelgens.com
Information technology solutions & services. (Woman/
As-Pac, estab 2011, empl 100, sales $8,500,000, cert:
WBENC)

5150 ExterNetworks Inc.
10 Corporate Place S, Ste 1-05 Piscataway, NJ 08854
(908) 751-0875 Abdul Moiz Senior Director
Fax: (732) 465-0005
Email: mmoiz@externetworks.com
Website: www.externetworks.com
Staff augumentation, IT professional services, managed services. (Woman/As-Pac, estab 2001, empl 205, sales $20,000,000, cert: CPUC)

5151 Fabergent, Inc.
63 Ramapo Valley Rd, Ste 214 Mahwah, NJ 07430
(201) 378-0036 Ratna Silpa Gorantla President
Fax: (201) 328-3179
Email: Ratna@fabergent.com
Website: www.fabergent.com
Contract & full-time positions IT staffing in Java, .Net, SharePoint, SAP, Oracle, BI, Analytics, networking & IT security. (Woman/As-Pac, estab 2005, empl 125, sales , cert: State)

5152 Fortidm Technologies LLC
103 Carnegie Center Ste 300 Princeton, NJ 08540
(609) 851-7190 Hariram Hari President
Fax: (609) 935-3245
Email: chari@fortidm.com
Website: www.fortidm.com
IT Program management, information security advisory, identity & access management, secured SDLC, vulnerability management services. (Woman/As-Ind, estab 2005, empl 9, sales $900,000, cert: State, City, 8(a), SDB)

5153 Futran Solutions Inc.
2025 Lincoln Hwy STE 110, Edison, NJ 08817 Ste 110 Edison, NJ 08817
(908) 279-3112 Jyoti Vazirani President
Fax:
Email: apankaj@futransolutions.com
Website: www.futransolutions.com
IT services, information technology services. (As-Ind, estab 2010, empl 150, sales $7,000,000, cert: State, NMSDC)

5154 FYI Systems Inc.
3799 Route 46 E Parsippany, NJ 07054
(973) 909-0390 Mindy Zaziski
Fax: (973) 331-9055
Email: colleen.luzaj@fyisolutions.com
Website: www.fyisolutions.com
IT solutions: corporate performance mgmt, business intelligence, analytics, data warehousing, web dev, systems integration, project mgmt, applications support, testing, etc. (Woman/White, estab 1984, empl 100, sales $14,500,000, cert: WBENC)

5155 Global IT Solutions, Inc.
200 Centennial Avenue Ste 200 Middlesex, NJ 08846
(732) 667-3578 William Moore President
Fax: (732) 377-2099
Email: info@globalitsolutionscorp.com
Website: www.globalitsolutionscorp.com
Software development life cycle. (AA, estab 2008, empl 2, sales , cert: State, NMSDC)

5156 Global World Solutions
1 Phoenix Dr Lincoln Park, NJ 07035
(551) 206-4432 Maurice Lash President
Fax: (973) 832-7035
Email: Maurice@globalworldstaffing.com
Website: www.globalworldstaffing.com
Network deployment life cycle, cabling and security system. (AA, estab 2004, empl 3, sales $600,000, cert: NMSDC)

5157 Globalnest LLC
281 State Route 79, Ste 208 Morganville, NJ 07751
(732) 333-1901 Durga P Mikkilineni Partner
Fax: (732) 333-5946
Email: durgam@globalnest.com
Website: www.globalnest.com
IT staffing, software development & design. (As-Ind/As-Pac, estab 2005, empl 170, sales $12,000,000, cert: NMSDC, CPUC)

5158 Government Systems Technologies, Inc.
3159 Schrader Rd Dover, NJ 07801
(973) 361-2627 Prashanth Kalnad Mgr, Finance and Contracts
Fax: (973) 695-2007
Email: accounting@gstiusa.com
Website: www.gstiusa.com
Consulting services, software products, full service SAP implementations & offshore development and support. (Woman/As-Ind, estab 2002, empl 46, sales $16,367,405, cert: NMSDC)

5159 Hired by Matrix, Inc.
266 Harristwon Rd Ste 202 Rochelle Park, NJ 07452
(201) 587-0777 Jennifer Catanese Supplier Diversity & Business Devel
Fax: (201) 291-8614
Email: jcatanese@hiredbymatrix.com
Website: www.hiredbymatrix.com
IT consulting svcs & permanent placements. (Woman/White, estab 1986, empl 275, sales $23,000,000, cert: WBENC)

5160 Ideal Data Inc.
420 River Rd North Arlington, NJ 07031
(201) 998-9440 Linda Ferreira President
Fax: (201) 998-5590
Email: linda@idealdata.com
Website: www.idealdata.com
Data processing svcs: data entry, inventory, word processing, mailing lists, surveys, tax rebates, traffic studies, etc. (Woman/Hisp, estab 1987, empl 5, sales $350,000, cert: State, NMSDC)

5161 iii Technologies Inc.
100 Horizon Center Blvd, Ste 100 Hamilton, NJ 08691
(609) 901-8000 Deepak Mandrekar President
Fax:
Email: drman@iiitech.com
Website: www.iiitech.com
IT & SAP transformation projects, SAP program management, project management, architecture & implementation consulting. (As-Ind, estab 2005, empl 1, sales $150,000, cert: State, NMSDC)

5162 InfoQuest Consulting Group Inc.
68 Culver Road Ste 106 Monmouth Junction, NJ 08852
(609) 409-5151 Vinita Lobo Business Mgr
Fax: (609) 409-5155
Email: vinita@infoquestgroup.com
Website: www.infoquestgroup.com
IT contract staffing: ERP, CRM, business intelligence, infrastructure management, industry verticals. (Woman/As-Ind, estab 1994, empl 40, sales , cert: City, NMSDC)

5163 Inforeem
One Quality Pl Edison, NJ 08820
(732) 494-4100 Bhal Deshpande CEO
Fax: (732) 791-4777
Email: bhal@inforeem.com
Website: www.inforeem.com
IT consulting services. (As-Pac, estab 2004, empl 40, sales $3,000,000, cert: State)

5164 Innospire Systems Corporation
281 State Route 79 Morganville, NJ 07751
(732) 858-1740 Raj Durai President
Fax: (732) 862-3279
Email: vrm@innospire.com
Website: www.innospire.com
IT consulting, custom application development & advanced analytics solutions, Predictive Analytics, Enterprise Performance Management, Mobile & Custom Application development. (As-Ind, estab 1996, empl 5, sales $355,480, cert: NMSDC)

5165 Instaknow.com, Inc.
180 Talmadge Rd, Ste 32 Edison, NJ 08817
(908) 650-9598 Paul Khandekar CEO
Fax: (908) 834-0949
Email: pkhandekar@instaknow.com
Website: www.instaknow.com
Artificial Intelligence software solutions. (As-Ind, estab 1999, empl 3, sales $293,478, cert: NMSDC, CPUC)

5166 Integration International Inc.
160 Littleton Rd Ste 106 Parsippany, NJ 07054
(973) 796-2301 Pratap Jayakar COO
Fax: (888) 308-8444
Email: pratap.jayakar@i3intl.com
Website: www.i3intl.com
IT infrastructure planning & implementation, software dev, ERP design & deployment, offshore software development & network monitoring. (Woman/As-Ind, estab 2000, empl 190, sales $17,000,000, cert: NMSDC)

5167 International Digital Systems
400 Kelby St, 6th Fl Fort Lee, NJ 07024
(201) 983-7700 Anthony Han CEO
Fax: (201) 482-6446
Email: ahan@idigitalsystems.com
Website: www.idigitalsystems.com
Server, Network management, Helpdesk, Desktop Support. Microsoft .Net C# based system development. Data Cabling, Data Center build up, SAN, NAS, Server & Network Hardware Resell. (As-Pac, estab 2005, empl 20, sales $1,883,584, cert: State)

5168 International Information Technology Team
45 Campus Dr Edison, NJ 08837
(732) 417-9301 Balaji Ravi President
Fax: (732) 417-5141
Email: balaji.ravi@i2t2.com
Website: www.i2t2.com
IT Consulting, HRIS services, software implementation & staffing support services. (As-Ind, estab 1997, empl 36, sales $3,005,097, cert: State)

5169 International Technology Solutions, Inc.
2000 Cornwall Road Ste 220 Monmouth Junction, NJ 08852
(732) 754-7019 Brian Armstrong Director, Business Dev
Fax: (732) 960-1823
Email: brian@itcsolutions.com
Website: www.itcsolutions.com
Information technology consulting & software development services. (As-Ind/As-Pac, estab 1998, empl 165, sales , cert: NMSDC)

5170 Intuity Technologies, LLC
One Gateway Center Ste 2600 Newark, NJ 07102
(201) 880-0774 Max Bhavnani VP Ops
Fax: (201) 621-4303
Email: mbhavnani@intuitytech.com
Website: www.intuitytech.com
IT Services, Oracle Hyperion tool-set (Essbase, Planning, HFM, DRM/MDM Financial Reporting) & Oracle Business Intelligence (OBIEE, Staff Augmentation, Implementations, Infrastructure, Performance Tuning. (As-Ind, estab 2005, empl 12, sales $1,100,000, cert: State)

5171 iQuanti, Inc.
111 Town Square Place Ste 710 Jersey City, NJ 07310
(718) 223-3403 Vish Sastry CEO
Fax: (877) 350-4239
Email: supplier@iquanti.com
Website: www.iquanti.com/
Web analytics, web development, web design, online marketing, search engine optimization, pay per click. (As-Ind, estab 2008, empl 205, sales $5,867,132, cert: NMSDC)

5172 ISES, Inc
      372 Rte 22 West   Whitehouse Station, NJ 08889
      (800) 447-4737 Kathleen Sullivan Director
      Fax: (800) 788-4737
      Email: ksullivan@isesincorporated.com
      Website: www.isesincorporated.com
Information technology consulting: esolutions &
ecommerce, B2B, knowledge mgmt, customer relationship
mgmt, application dev & support, database dev & admin,
data warehousing, telecommunications, systems support
& admin. (Woman/White, estab 1980, empl 142, sales
$20,000,000, cert: WBENC)

5173 IT by Design
      120 Wood Ave S Ste 608 Iselin, NJ 08830
      (646) 380-0688 Kam Attwal CEO
      Fax: (646) 349-2572
      Email: kkaila@itbd.net
      Website: www.itbd.net
Infrastructure management, virtualization/cloud computing, data center hosting, managed backups, implementa-
tions/migrations & 24x7x365 Live Help Desk. (Woman/As-
Ind, estab 2003, empl 100, sales $3,000,000, cert: WBENC)

5174 IT Staffing, Inc.
      5 Bliss Court Ste 200 Woodcliff Lake, NJ 07677
      (201) 505-0493 Jerry G. Myers Director, Business
      Dev
      Fax: (201) 586-0389
      Email: jerry.myers@itstaffinc.com
      Website: www.itstaffinc.com
Strategic contract sourcing, consulting, staff augmentation,
managed teams & outsourcing. (Woman, estab 1998, empl
78, sales $11,500,000, cert: State)

5175 ITM Information & Technology Management
      6 Kilmer Rd   Edison, NJ 08817
      (732) 339-9801 Jeffrey Snow Business Dev Mgr
      Fax: (732) 339-9809
      Email: jeffs@itmsys.com
      Website: www.itmsys.com
Computer consulting, applications development, QA,
infrastructure support, SAP implimentation, database
administration, maintanance & support, data warehousing, technical support. (Woman/As-Ind, estab 1989, empl
40, sales $2,750,000, cert: State, NMSDC)

5176 Kavayah Solutions Inc.
      5 Independence Way, Ste 360   Princeton, NJ 08540
      (609) 919-9797 Vivek Casula Principal
      Fax:
      Email: vivek.casula@kavayahsolutions.com
      Website: www.kavayahsolutions.com
Enterprise application management (development and
maintenance) & project management services, technology
solutions, staff augmentation. (As-Ind, estab 2006, empl
10, sales $1,224,316, cert: State)

5177 LexHarbor, LLC
      1974 State Route 27   Edison, NJ 08817
      (626) 427-2674 Akshat Tewary Director
      Fax:
      Email: info@lexharbor.com
      Website: www.lexharbor.com
Information technology services. (As-Ind, estab 2007,
empl 2, sales $100,000, cert: NMSDC)

5178 Link2consult, Inc.
      1 Bridge Plaza Ste 275   Fort Lee, NJ 07024
      (201) 308-9101 PETER MCCREE President
      Fax: (201) 308-9101
      Email: PETER.MCCREE@LINK2CONSULT.COM
      Website: www.link2consult.com
Information technology consulting: PeopleSoft, human
resources & finance solutions. (AA, estab 1992, empl 35,
sales $5,800,000, cert: State, NMSDC, CPUC)

5179 Logistic Solutions Inc.
      216 Stelton Rd Ste 2 Piscataway, NJ 08854
      (732) 743-2300 Al Limaye President
      Fax: (732) 457-0016
      Email: al.limaye@logistic-solutions.com
      Website: www.logistic-solutions.com
Information technologies, Mobile (iPhone, Android,
Blackberry/RIM) content aggregation services. (As-Pac,
estab 1990, empl 715, sales $140,000,000, cert: NMSDC)

5180 Maestro Technologies, Inc.
      510 Thornall St Ste 375 Edison, NJ 08837
      (908) 458-8600 Kamal Bathla Managing Dir
      Fax: (732) 902-6755
      Email: kamal.s.bathla@maestro.com
      Website: www.maestro.com
Actuarial Sciences, Big Data & and Technologies, Data
Science, IT Services. (Woman/As-Ind, estab 2003, empl
63, sales $6,800,000, cert: State, City, NMSDC)

5181 Makro Technologies, Inc.
      One Washington Park, Ste 1303   Newark, NJ
      07102
      (973) 481-0100 Pritesh Dholakia Business Dev
      Fax: (973) 481-1020
      Email: pritesh.dholakia@makrocare.com
      Website: www.makrocare.com
Information technology, IT staffing services. (As-Ind,
estab 1996, empl 650, sales $45,000,000, cert: State)

5182 Marlabs Inc.
      One Corporate Place S Piscataway, NJ 08854
      (732) 694-1000 Danielle Jennings Assoc Business
      Devel Mgr
      Fax: (732) 676-7992
      Email: danielle.jennings@marlabs.com
      Website: www.marlabs.com
Information technology services & solutions: IT strategy
consulting, resources & staff augmentation, application
dev, business intelligence solutions, SAP & Oracle, ERP/
CRM systems, data warehousing. (As-Pac, estab 1996,
empl 2100, sales $92,000,000, cert: NMSDC)

5183   MARVEL INFOTECH Inc.
45 Knightsbridge Road Ste 101 Piscataway, NJ 08854
(732) 906-0444 Venkat Bokka President
Fax: (732) 875-0333
Email: vbokka@marvelinfotech.com
Website: www.marvelinfotech.com
Information technology staffing, consulting. (As-Pac, estab 2000, empl 25, sales $1,850,000, cert: NMSDC)

5184   MashPoint, LLC
100 Wood Ave S Ste 109 Iselin, NJ 08830
(732) 515-7171 KJ Saini President
Fax: (732) 379-4131
Email: kjsaini@mashpoint.com
Website: www.mashpoint.com
Staffing services, data management, data quality, data security, business intelligence, web & mobile development & internet marketing services. (As-Ind, estab 2011, empl 55, sales $797,510, cert: NMSDC)

5185   Masterex Technologies, Inc.
379 Princeton-Hightstown Rd, Bldg 2   Cranbury, NJ 08512
(302) 632-9532 Sunny Gupta Business Devel Mgr
Fax: (206) 203-4270
Email: info@masterexinc.com
Website: www.Masterexinc.com
IT staffing , application development, project management, framework, on-shore & offshore testing & QA services. (Woman/As-Ind, estab 2002, empl 60, sales $5,000,000, cert: State)

5186   Mercury Systems, Inc.
5 Independence Way Ste 140 Princeton, NJ 08540
(609) 937-2801 Wing Li Admin Mgr, VP
Fax: (609) 243-0235
Email: wli@mercurysystemsinc.com
Website: www.mercurysystemsinc.com
Consulting, IT Staffing & IT Placement services. (As-Pac, estab 1999, empl 170, sales $10,000,000, cert: State)

5187   microMEDIA Imaging Systems, Inc.
300-2 Route 17 South, Ste 4   Lodi, NJ 07644
(973) 685-5164 Joseph Wise President
Fax:
Email: jwise@imagingservices.com
Website: www.imagingservices.com
Document conversion & scanning services, Data Capture, Data Migration, Document Hosting. (Woman/White, estab 1993, empl 85, sales $3,200,000, cert: State, City)

5188   Millennium Info Tech. Inc.
101 Morgan Lane Ste 204 Plainsboro, NJ 08536
(609) 750-7120 Ramana Krosuri President
Fax: (609) 750-1114
Email: ramana@mitiweb.com
Website: www.mitiweb.com
Application Development, Business Analysis/Project Management, Business Intelligence, Data/Database Management,
 Document Management, ERP, ETL, Information Security/Compliance, Migration Services. (As-Ind, estab 1999, empl 150, sales $9,500,000, cert: State)

5189   Mindlance, Inc.
1095 Morris Avenue, Unit 101A   Union, NJ 07083
(201) 204-9752 Vik Kalra Managing Dir
Fax: (201) 386-0553
Email: cws@mindlance.com
Website: www.mindlance.com
IT contigent staffing, offshore recruitment, IT permanent placement, software, semiconductor, finance & insurance. (As-Ind, estab 1999, empl 2000, sales $161,000,000, cert: NMSDC)

5190   MKI Group, LLC dba IS3 Solutions
740 Broad St Ste 1 Shrewsbury, NJ 07702
(732) 945-0403 John Marshall President
Fax:
Email: sraffetto@is3sol.com
Website: www.is3sol.com
IT solutions, Services & Staffing programs. (AA, estab 2010, empl 220, sales , cert: NMSDC)

5191   Momento USA LLC
440 Benigno Blvd Unit A, 2nd Fl Bellmawr, NJ 08031
(856) 432-4774 Hasheem Himmati Director
Fax:
Email: info@momentousa.com
Website: www.momentousa.com
Project Management, Application Development, Business Analysis, Systems Analysis, System Design, ERP, Database Administration, Systems Engineering, Systems Maintenance, Systems Testing, Systems Architecture, Systems Administration. (As-Pac, estab 2009, empl 28, sales $2,128,413, cert: NMSDC)

5192   MSquare Systems Inc.
35 Journal Sq, Ste 415   Jersey City, NJ 07306
(201) 290-6728 Muthu Natarajan President
Fax: (415) 259-5762
Email: info@msquaresystems.com
Website: www.msquaresystems.com
IT consulting services. (As-Pac, estab 2005, empl 5, sales $403,967, cert: NMSDC)

5193   Mutex Systems Inc.
50 Cragwood Rd Ste 224 South Plainfield, NJ 07080
(908) 822-8515 Bill Scharnikow BDM
Fax: (908) 822-8719
Email: bill.scharnikow@mutexsystems.com
Website: www.mutexsystems.com
IT staff augmentation & consulting . (Woman/As-Ind, estab 1999, empl 100, sales $10,000,000, cert: State)

5194   NatSoft Corporation
1075 Easton Ave, Tower 3 Ste 4 Somerset, NJ 08873
(732) 939-2969 Rakesh Kotha Business Dev Mgr
Fax:
Email: rakeshkv@natsoft.us
Website: www.natsoft.us
Software dev, IT consulting, Enterprise application development, ERP implementation & support, Quality assurance services on offshore/Onsite/Nearshore model. (As-Pac, estab 2004, empl 300, sales , cert: State)

5195 NCS Technologies, Inc.
15 Corporate Place S Piscataway, NJ 08854
(732) 562-8880 Christine Arce' VP Business Dev
Fax: (732) 562-8883
Email: carce@ncstech.com
Website: www.ncstech.com
Data warehousing, business intelligence, enterprise
architecture, process engineering & enterprise security.
(Hisp, estab 1984, empl 155, sales $29,000,000, cert:
NMSDC)

5196 Neo Tech Solutions, Inc.
1 Cragwood Rd Ste 301 South Plainfield, NJ 07080
(917) 385-8717 Krishna Reddy CEO
Fax: (240) 595-6134
Email: kreddy@neotechusa.com
Website: www.neotechusa.com
IT, telecommunications, program & project management:
ASP.NET, ASP, HTML, DHTML, VBScript, JavaScript, SOAP,
ADO.NET, ActiveX, ADO, RDO, DAO, MTS, ODBC, OLEDB,
MSOffice, MS-Visual Source Safe, VB.NET, C#, C++, Cobol,
VB 6.0,XML, XSLT, SQL. (As-Ind, estab 1996, empl 63, sales ,
cert: NMSDC)

5197 NetTarius Technology Solutions, LLC
35 College Dr   East Orange, NJ 07017
(973) 788-1955 Derrick Law President
Fax: (617) 572-3673
Email: sdiversity@nettarius.net
Website: www.nettarius.com
Business Strategy, Technology Design & Integration, Fiber
Wireless Broadband, Data Network, Video Technology,
Web & Application Development, Cloud Services, Installa-
tion & Support. (AA, estab 2003, empl 5, sales $300,000,
cert: NMSDC)

5198 New Instruction, LLC
615 Valley Rd   Upper Montclair, NJ 07043
(973) 744-3339 Maria Esteves Director of Training
Fax: (973) 744-2129
Email: maria@newinstruction.com
Website: www.newinstruction.com/
Instructor-led technology training: systems & software
engineering, project management, programming languages, internet security, telecommunications & networking, management & leadership skills. (Woman/White,
estab 1978, empl 5, sales $2,130,000, cert: WBENC)

5199 NewAgeSys, Inc.
600 Alexander Rd, Ste 3-3   Princeton Junction, NJ
08540
(609) 919-9800 Greeshma Digi Sales Coord
Fax: (609) 919-9830
Email: contact@newagesys.com
Website: www.newagesys.com
Validation & quality mgmt svcs, custom application devel,
SAP upgrade & support svcs, information security, infrastructure services. (Woman/As-Ind, estab 1994, empl 190,
sales $20,000,000, cert: NMSDC, WBENC)

5200 NexAge Technologies USA Inc.
75 Lincoln Hwy Ste 104 Iselin, NJ 08830
(732) 494-4944 Suresh Kumar CEO
Fax: (732) 494-4555
Email: minoritymanager@nexageusa.com
Website: www.nexageusa.com
IT staffing & consulting, software applications. (As-Pac,
estab 2001, empl 65, sales , cert: State, NMSDC)

5201 NIKSUN Inc.
100 Nassau Park Blvd 3rd Fl Princeton, NJ 08540
(609) 936-9999 Christopher Dervishian VP Ops
Fax: (609) 419-4260
Email: cdervish@niksun.com
Website: www.niksun.com
Develop real time & forensics-based cybersecurity,
network performance management & mobility solutions.
(As-Ind, estab 1997, empl 175, sales , cert: NMSDC)

5202 NPD Global Inc.
3 Lincoln Hwy Ste 102 Edison, NJ 07018
(732) 902-6342 Nagesh Davuluri President
Fax: (732) 902-6343
Email: ndavuluri@npdglobal.com
Website: www.npdglobal.com
IT staffing & recruiting services. (Nat Ame, estab 2006,
empl 30, sales $6,000,000, cert: NMSDC)

5203 Optima Global Solutions, Inc.
3113 Princeton Pike Bldg. 3, Ste 207
Lawrenceville, NJ 08648
(609) 586-8811 Rajesh Sinha Federal Business
Specialist
Fax: (609) 935-0529
Email: rajesh@optimags.com
Website: www.optimags.com
IT staffing, BPM, Data Warehousing, Business Intelli-
gence, Microsoft & Enterprise Mobility. (As-Ind, estab
2001, empl 10, sales $3,186,483, cert: NMSDC, 8(a))

5204 Paxton Consultants Limited Liability Company
50 Brandywine Rise   Green Brook, NJ 08812
(831) 210-8850 Anand Emmanuel CEO
Fax: (408) 647-1304
Email: anand.emmanuel@paxtonconsultants.com
Website: www.paxtonconsultants.com
Information Technology (IT) Consulting & Staffing
Solutions. (As-Ind, estab 2007, empl 2, sales , cert: State)

5205 Peri Software Solutions
570 Broad St   Newark, NJ 07102
(973) 735-9500 Rosemarie Lederer Sr Acct Mgr
Fax: (973) 547-3310
Email: rlederer@perisoftware.com
Website: www.perisoftware.com
Open source solutions, IT staff augmentation, offshore
business outsourcing, custom application development.
(Woman/As-Pac, estab 1999, empl 700, sales
$12,631,398, cert: NMSDC)

5206 Pioneer Data Systems, Inc.
379 Thornall St   Edison, NJ 08837
(732) 603-0001 Naushad Mulji Director
Fax: (732) 603-3990
Email: nmulji@pioneerdata.com
Website: www.pioneerdata.com
Client-server, e-business, data warehousing, CRM & ERP. (As-Ind, estab 1995, empl 100, sales $5,000,000, cert: NMSDC)

5207 Platys Group
100 Franklin Square Dr   Somerset, NJ 08873
(908) 888-6007 Darren Cobb VP buisness Devel
Fax: (908) 636-2593
Email: dcobb@platysgroup.com
Website: www.platygroup.com
IT consulting & software solutions. (Woman/As-Pac, estab 2008, empl 140, sales $10,000,000, cert: State)

5208 Presafe Technologies, LLC
P.O. Box 5872   Somerset, NJ 08875
(732) 887-2442 Robert V Jones CEO
Fax: (888) 305-8782
Email: rvjones@presafetech.com
Website: www.presafetech.com
Cybersecurity architecture & design; Secure network planning & design, enterprise system design, network builds, migration upgrades; Data center planning design, consolidation migrations & relocations; network & performance mgmt. (AA, estab 2010, empl 2, sales , cert: State)

5209 Princeton IT Services, Inc.
3525 Quakerbridge Rd, Ste 1400   Hamilton, NJ 08619
(609)80058 Ravi Karamsetty CEO
Fax:
Email: ravi@princetonits.com
Website: www.princetonits.com
Database Consulting, Data modeling, Development, Administration, Capacity Planning, Replication, HA, DR, Oracle Database, Linux System Administration, Linux Engineering, Security, Single sign-on, Cloud Deployments. (As-Pac, estab 2008, empl 10, sales , cert: State)

5210 Princeton Web Systems Inc.
1901 N Olden Ave Ext, Ste 8A   Ewing, NJ 08618
(888) 485-9040 Bhavesh Senedhun CEO
Fax: (800) 610-5305
Email: bhavesh@princetonwebsystems.com
Website: www.princetonwebsystems.com
Custom software development, software & application development, website design, mobile app development, IT staff augmentation, staffing & networking solutions. (As-Ind/As-Pac, estab 2014, empl 25, sales $1,000,000, cert: State)

5211 Prudentia Group, LLC
101 Hudson St Ste 2100   Jersey City, NJ 07302
(201) 479-2372 Vladimir Laguerre
Fax: (646) 496-9128
Email: vlaguerre@prudentia-grp.com
Website: www.prudentia-grp.com
Pharmacovigilance (PV) process & technology services, operational improvements, inspection readiness, system selection, upgrades (for both ARISg and Argus), data migrations & managed services. (AA/As-Ind, estab 2012, empl 22, sales $5,800,000, cert: NMSDC)

5212 Rang Technologies Inc.
15 Corporate Place South Ste #356   Piscataway, NJ 08854
(732) 475-4375 Jigar Patel Exec VP
Fax: (732) 947-4653
Email: sales@rangtech.com
Website: www.rangtech.com/
Analytics & Data Science solutions & comprehensive IT staffing services. (As-Ind, estab 2005, empl 292, sales $16,270,066, cert: State, NMSDC)

5213 Rangam Consultants Inc.
270 Davidson Ave Ste 103   Somerset, NJ 08873
(908) 704-8843 Hetal Parikh President
Fax: (908) 253-6550
Email: hetal@rangam.com
Website: www.rangam.com
IT staffing & outsourced web application development services. (Woman/As-Ind, estab 1995, empl 750, sales $23,000,000, cert: State, NMSDC, CPUC, WBENC)

5214 Rapid Response Computer Service Inc.
2313 Route 33   Robbinsville, NJ 08691
(609) 945-2389 Terry Ikey Owner
Fax: (609) 223-3961
Email: tikey@rapidresponsecs.com
Website: www.rapidresponsecs.com
Software development, website design, network installation & support & compuer repair. (Woman/White, estab 2004, empl 12, sales $750,000, cert: State)

5215 RCI Technologies, Inc.
1133 Green St   Iselin, NJ 08830
(732) 382-3000 Anisa Balwani President
Fax: (732) 839-0448
Email: raj@rci-technologies.com
Website: www.rci-technologies.com
Custom software development & IT staffing, consulting services. (Woman/As-Pac, estab 1983, empl 43, sales , cert: State, NMSDC, WBENC)

5216 Real Soft Inc.
68 Culver Road Ste 100   Monmouth Junction, NJ 08852
(609) 409-3636 Joel Jerva VP
Fax: (609) 409-3637
Email: joel@realsoftinc.com
Website: www.realsoftinc.com
Software development, consulting & staffing, offshore resources, turnkey dev, voice solutions, IVR, VXML. (As-Ind/As-Pac, estab 1991, empl 450, sales $23,000,000, cert: NMSDC)

5217   RedSalsa Technologies, Inc.
12 Roszel Rd Ste A-204   Princeton, NJ 08540
(609) 243-9603   Kiran Vallurupalli CEO
Fax: (609) 243-0400
Email: k_vallurupalli@redsalsa.com
Website: www.redsalsa.com
IT consulting services: internet & e-business consulting, system integration, custom application development & application management. (As-Ind/As-Pac, estab 1993, empl 120, sales , cert: NMSDC)

5218   Reliant Tech., Inc.
2137 Route 35 Ste 365   Holmdel, NJ 07733
(732) 583-6244   Subhash Kothari President
Fax: (732) 583-5702
Email: skothari@relianttech.com
Website: www.relianttech.com
Application development, technical training, Sun Solaris, HP UX certified. (As-Ind/As-Pac, estab 1985, empl 30, sales $3,000,000, cert: State)

5219   Resource Logistics, Inc.
505 Thornall St   Edison, NJ 08837
(732) 553-0566   Rajesh Rane AVP
Fax: (732) 553-0568
Email: rajesh@resource-logistice.com
Website: www.resource-logistics.com
IP Services with following industry verticals,ie: Banking and Finance, Clinical Databases and Bioinformatics. (As-Ind, estab 2002, empl 1, sales , cert: State)

5220   Revision Technologies Inc.
10 Station Place, Ste 3   Metuchen, NJ 08840
(732) 261-9239   Raja Balan President
Fax: (813) 258-8825
Email: raja.balan@revisiontek.com
Website: www.revisiontek.com
Data Center Design, support, maintenance.Networking, IP and SAN products, Project management, Storage Area Networking architect, planning, implementation, system analysis, Big Data, Cloud implementation & support services. (As-Ind, estab 2006, empl 4, sales $17,792,057, cert: NMSDC)

5221   Samiti Technologies, Inc.
2 Lincoln Highway Ste 401   Edison, NJ 08820
(732) 516-0066   Parmi Cheema President
Fax: (732) 391-6683
Email: parmicheema@samitimail.com
Website: www.samititechnology.com
Software development & consulting services. (Woman/As-Pac, estab 2003, empl 70, sales $11,502,000, cert: State)

5222   Satnam Data Systems, Inc.
220 Davidson Ave Ste 318   Somerset, NJ 08873
(732) 961-8383   Parita Patel Dir Business Dev
Fax:
Email: Parita@Satnam.com
Website: www.satnam.com
Technology Consulting, Professional & Outsourcing services, Staff Augmentation, Custom Dev Services, Software Integration, Custom Solution Svcs,Business Applications, Database Dev. (Woman/As-Pac, estab 1994, empl 23, sales $6,500,000, cert: State, NMSDC, CPUC)

5223   Scadea Solutions Inc
100 Franklin Square Dr Ste 304   Somerset, NJ 08873
(609) 937-6699   Sreekanth Akkapalli CEO
Fax: (888) 396-1230
Email: sreekanth@scadea.net
Website: www.scadea.net
ERP, Consulting & Outsourcing Services. (Woman/As-Ind, estab 2011, empl 150, sales $9,000,000, cert: WBENC)

5224   Scalable Systems Inc.
15 Corporate Place South Ste 222   Piscataway, NJ 08854
(732) 333-3191   Suman Bajaj Acct Mgr
Fax: (732) 909-2732
Email: sumanb@scalable-systems.com
Website: www.scalable-systems.com
Software consulting, development & IT outsourcing, offshore & onshore software solutions & integration services. (As-Ind, estab 2005, empl 30, sales $3,000,000, cert: State, NMSDC)

5225   Scalar Solutions, LLC.
330 Changebridge Rd, Ste 101   Pinebrook, NJ 07058
(973) 767-3260   Mariana C Mgr Sales
Fax:
Email: sales@scalarsol.com
Website: www.scalarsol.com
IT consulting/staffing, end-to-end IT consulting services, Software Development Services (Java, Dot Net Platform), Database & Data warehouse development (SQL Server, Oracle, MPP Systems, Cloud, Hadoop Big data), Database Administration. (As-Ind, estab 2013, empl 2, sales , cert: State)

5226   SEAL Consulting Inc.
105 Fieldcrest Ave 4th FL, Raritan Plaza 3   Edison, NJ 08837
(732) 947-4901   John Beaumont VP
Fax: (732) 417-9655
Email: info@sealconsult.com
Website: www.sealconsult.com/
Systems integration, implementation services & staffing: ERP, APO, SEM, BW and SRM. (As-Ind, estab 1996, empl 400, sales $50,000,000, cert: NMSDC)

5227   Seven Seven Softwares, Inc.
217 E Main St   Rockaway, NJ 07866
(973) 586-1817   Adela Sering VP / Global HR Director
Fax: (973) 586-6964
Email: dsering@77soft.com
Website: www.77soft.com
Information technology, business process outsourcing & call center services. (Woman/As-Pac, estab 1996, empl 335, sales , cert: State)

5228 Silicon Alley Group, Inc.
      1 Austin Ave. 2nd Fl Iselin, NJ 08830
      (732) 326-1600 Terrance L Sprinkle Bus Dev Mgr
      Fax: (732) 875-1060
      Email: tsprinkle@sag-inc.com
      Website: www.sag-inc.com
IT services & solutions. (Woman/As-Pac, estab 2003, empl
30, sales $1,901,608, cert: State, 8(a))

5229 Smart Source Technologies, Inc.
      622 Georges Rd Ste 203 North Brunswick, NJ 08902
      (732) 729-7700 Shaan Kelly Acct Rep
      Fax: (732) 729-7705
      Email: subcontract@smartsourcetec.com
      Website: www.smartsourcetec.com
IT staffing, application & web development, database
administration & development, data warehousing &
systems administration, business analyst & project
management. (Woman/As-Ind, estab 1999, empl 52, sales
$6,000,000, cert: State)

5230 Software Synergy, Inc.
      151 Highway 33 E Ste 252 Manalapan, NJ 07726
      (732) 617-9300 Rose Oxley CEO
      Fax: (732) 617-1396
      Email: rmo@ssi-corp.com
      Website: www.ssi-corp.com
IT: automate key business processes, modernize legacy
systems, integrate multi system & technology environments, data translations. (Woman/White, estab 1990,
empl 10, sales $1,500,000, cert: WBENC)

5231 Software Technology, Inc.
      100 Overlook Center Ste 200 Princeton, NJ 08540
      (609) 858-0630 Scott Mandel VP Sales
      Fax: (815) 331-3861
      Email: scott.mandel@stiorg.com
      Website: www.stiorg.com
IT staffing services. (Woman/As-Ind, estab 2004, empl 45,
sales , cert: NMSDC)

5232 Solutions3 LLC
      637 Wyckoff Ave PMB 352 Wyckoff, NJ 07481
      (845) 365-0675 Dianne McKim Exec Business Admin
      Fax: (201) 891-5316
      Email: dianne.mckim@solutions3llc.com
      Website: www.solutions3llc.com
Enterprise Network & Systems Management (architecture
and implementation), IT Service Management, Service
Desk & associated process definitions (Incident & Problem
Management, Change & Configuration Management).
(Woman/White, estab 2003, empl 18, sales $2,707,834,
cert: State)

5233 SPHERE Technology Solutions
      525 Washington Blvd. Ste 2635 Jersey City, NJ
      07310
      (201) 659-6204 George Nikanorov Director
      Fax:
      Email: george.nikanorov@sphereco.com
      Website: www.sphereco.com
Data Governance, Security & Compliance centering on
structured & un-structured data. (Woman/White, estab
2009, empl 22, sales $6,448,680, cert: State, WBENC)

5234 Spruce Technology, Inc.
      1149 Bloomfield Ave Ste G Clifton, NJ 07012
      (781) 413-5527 Srini Penumella CEO
      Fax: (201) 338-6260
      Email: spenumella@sprucetech.com
      Website: www.sprucetech.com
Information technology consulting svcs: systems
deployment, server infrastructure, technology deployment, network infrastructure, executive, management &
general support. (As-Ind, estab 2006, empl 69, sales
$8,259,406, cert: State, NMSDC)

5235 Sunrise Systems, Inc.
      105 Fieldcrest Ave. Ste 504   Edison, NJ 08837
      (732) 395-4446 SANDY BALDINO Senior Acct Exec
      Fax: (732) 603-2208
      Email: SANDY@SUNRISESYS.COM
      Website: www.sunrisesys.com
IT systems integration, systems integration. (As-Ind,
estab 1990, empl 500, sales , cert: NMSDC)

5236 Synergem, Inc.
      2323 Randolph Avenue   Avenel, NJ 07001
      (732) 225-0001 Amy Silverman President
      Fax: (732) 225-7555
      Email: amysilverman@synergem.com
      Website: www.synergem.com
Duplicate DVD's, CD's & USBs, custom packaging, custom
printing, fulfillment & distribution. (Woman/White,
estab 1985, empl 26, sales $7,344,330, cert: WBENC)

5237 Systemart, LLC
      140 Littleton Rd, Ste 303   Parsippany, NJ 07054
      (973) 917-4848 Nitin Shah President
      Fax: (973) 695-6363
      Email: mbe@systemart.com
      Website: www.systemart.com
IT related services, custom software dev, business
process mgmt svcs. (Woman/As-Ind, estab 1999, empl
75, sales $5,800,000, cert: State, NMSDC)

5238 SystemGuru,Inc.
      900 Rte 9 N Ste 205 Woodbridge, NJ 07095
      (732) 326-3951 Nitin Sohal Business Dev Mgr
      Fax: (732) 879-0326
      Email: nitin.sohal@systemguru.com
      Website: www.systemguru.com
Web enabled application development, data modeling &
enterprise data architecture, application design &
architecture. (As-Pac, estab 2000, empl 100, sales
$8,907,001, cert: City)

5239 Techdemocracy LLC
      499 Thomall St, Ste 301   Edison, NJ 08837
      (732) 439-5534 Madhukar Malladi Dir
      Fax: (732) 549-7020
      Email: madhukar@techdemocracy.com
      Website: www.techdemocracy.com
Information technology, custom application develop-
ment, quality testing, identity management solutions.
(Woman/As-Ind, estab 2000, empl 185, sales
$10,000,000, cert: State)

5240   Technology Concepts Group International, LLC
       285 Davidson Ave, Ste 501   Somerset, NJ 08873
       (732) 659-6035 Elizabeth Shelton Exec Admin Asst
       Fax: (732) 659-6036
       Email: eshelton@technologyconcepts.com
       Website: www.technologyconcepts.com
E-business solutions, web design & hosting, systems
integration, desktop support. (Woman/AA, estab 2008,
empl 8, sales , cert: NMSDC)

5241   TechnoSphere, Inc.
       21 Addison Rd   Bergenfield, NJ 07621
       (201) 384-7400 Aureo Capiral President
       Fax: (201) 648-7892
       Email: aureo.capiral@technosphere.com
       Website: www.technosphere.com
IT staffing, contracting, contract programming svcs. (As-
Pac, estab 1994, empl 26, sales $4,171,947, cert: State,
NMSDC)

5242   Technovision, Inc.
       10 Stuyvesant Ave   Lyndhurst, NJ 07071
       (732) 381-0200 Anju Aggarwal President
       Fax: (732) 381-0207
       Email: anju@etechnovision.com
       Website: www.etechnovision.com
IT Consulting. (Woman/As-Ind, estab 1995, empl 35, sales
$3,000,000, cert: State, WBENC)

5243   The Roy Consulting Group, LLC
       103 Carnegie Center Ste 300 Princeton, NJ 08540
       (609) 955-3549 Mickey Shah Managing Dir
       Fax:
       Email: mickey.shah@process-stream.com
       Website: www.process-stream.com
Life Sciences IT Solutions, Quality Management & Custom
Development Systems. (As-Ind, estab 2008, empl 25, sales
, cert: NMSDC)

5244   The Sourcium Group
       833 Blanch Ave   Norwood, NJ 07648
       (201) 447-1777 Gabriella Lombardi CEO
       Fax: (201) 447-6414
       Email: gabriella.lombardi@sourcium.net
       Website: www.sourcium.net
IT procurement, project management, desktop svcs, staff
augmentation. (Woman/White, estab 2002, empl 12, sales
, cert: WBENC)

5245   Twintron Data Systems Inc.
       1 Evans Dr., Ste 111   Marlton, NJ 08053
       (856) 952-8506 Dayal Nagasuru President
       Fax:
       Email: dayal.nagasuru@twintron.com
       Website: www.twintron.com
IT services (Java, C++, SQL, Big Data, .NET, Web Applica-
tions). (As-Ind, estab 2004, empl 5, sales $500,000, cert:
NMSDC)

5246   Urooj LLC
       301 Route 17N Ste 800 Rutherford, NJ 07070
       (201) 966-7861 Salman Mohammed CEO
       Fax:
       Email: salman@urooj.net
       Website: www.urooj.net
IT solutions, IT staffing, project architecture, design &
analysis, project administration & management, web
paradigm, e-commerce & web applications, networking
& system administration, RF engineering, database
admin & management. (As-Ind, estab 2002, empl 40,
sales $2,154,929, cert: State, City, NMSDC)

5247   US Tech Solutions, Inc.
       10 Exchange Place, Ste 1710   Jersey City, NJ
       07302
       (201) 524-9600 Manoj Agarwal President
       Fax: (201) 524-9601
       Email: sales@ustechsolutions.com
       Website: www.ustechsolutions.com
IT solutions: consulting, outsourcing, software development, engineering, systems integration, ERP, customer
relationship management, supply chain mngt, product
development, & electronic commerce. (As-Ind, estab
2000, empl 3800, sales $410,000,000, cert: NMSDC)

5248   Vedicsoft Solutions Inc.
       100 Wood Ave, Ste 200   Iselin, NJ 08830
       (732) 906-3200 Sam Vaghela Strategic Business
       Alliance Mgr
       Fax: (732) 906-3210
       Email: sam@vedicsoft.com
       Website: www.vedicsoft.com
IT technologies: ERP, data warehousing, web & client/
server technologies. (As-Ind, estab 1999, empl 300, sales
$54,000,000, cert: NMSDC)

5249   Ventures Unlimited Inc.
       309 Fellowship Rd, Ste 200   Mount Laurel, NJ
       08054
       (201) 377-5954 Rajesh Varma President
       Fax: (888) 534-5731
       Email: rvarma@vui-inc.com
       Website: www.vui-inc.com
IT consulting services: enterprise application services,
product life cycle management, business process
modeling. (As-Ind, estab 2004, empl 162, sales
$4,500,000, cert: State, NMSDC, 8(a))

5250   Vichara Technologies Inc.
       5 Marine View Plaza Ste 312 Hoboken, NJ 07030
       (201) 850-1912 Atul Jain CEO
       Fax: (201) 850-1916
       Email: payables@vichara.com
       Website: www.vichara.com
Software development services for financial institutions,
banks & asset management firms, hedge funds, private
equity firms. (As-Pac, estab 2000, empl 15, sales
$7,259,788, cert: NMSDC)

5251 VNB Consulting Services, Inc.
100 Menlo Park Ste 302B Edison, NJ 08837
(732) 474-0700 Nirav Shah Dir HR & Finance
Fax:
Email: info@vnbconsulting.com
Website: www.vnbconsulting.com
IT services, Business Intelligence, Analytics, CRM, Marketing & Application Integration solutions. (As-Ind, estab 2007, empl 25, sales $2,000,000, cert: State)

5252 XL Impex Inc DBA Atika Technologies
5 Independence Way Ste 300 Princeton, NJ 08540
(732) 907-9001 Ashish Dua President
Fax: (973) 577-6989
Email: ash@atikaservices.com
Website: www.atikatech.com
CRM recruiting, staff augmentation, IT services & Digital Marketing. (As-Pac, estab 2008, empl 22, sales $1,770,777, cert: NMSDC)

5253 Xybion Corporation & Subsidiaries
2000 Lenox Dr, Ste 101 Lawrenceville, NJ 08648
(609) 512-5790 Rose Ann McBride Personnel Admin
Fax: (609) 482-3823
Email: rmcbride@xybion.com
Website: www.xybion.com
Preclinical Data Management and Analysis Software (Pristime); Quality & Process Management software; Enterprise Content Management Software, Data Migration & Federation. (As-Ind/As-Pac, estab 1975, empl 109, sales , cert: NMSDC)

5254 Xybion Medical Systems Corporation
2000 Lenox Dr Ste 101 Lawrenceville, NJ 08648
(609) 512-5790 Nagraj Lanka Business Dev Dir
Fax:
Email: nlanka@xybion.com
Website: www.xybion.com
Compliance/software & services solutions, data migration, data content & compliance management, enterprise asset management, pre-clin/R&D, quality management, validation/software testing & IT consulting services. (As-Ind, estab 1977, empl 33, sales $7,751,400, cert: State, NMSDC)

5255 York Telecom Corporation
81 Corbett Way Eatontown, NJ 07724
(732) 413-6000 Rebecca Kane Contracts Specialist
Fax: (732) 413-6060
Email: mbe@yorktel.com
Website: www.yorktel.com
Visual communications applications: videoconferencing, streaming media, distance learning, consulting, integration, design, training, project mgmt, on-site & remote support services. (As-Pac, estab 1985, empl 302, sales $125,000,000, cert: NMSDC)

5256 Z&A Infotek Corporation
35 Waterview Blvd 2nd Fl Parsippany, NJ 07054
(917) 751-2299 John Pezzullo EVP
Fax: (973) 299-3980
Email: johnp@znainc.com
Website: www.znainc.com
IT, consulting & software, ERP & CRM, web enabling applications, RDBMS, project management, network infrastructure tools & management. (As-Ind, estab 2003, empl 90, sales $7,500,000, cert: NMSDC, 8(a))

Nevada

5257 A.R. Acosta, Ltd. dba Alisa Acosta Business Conslt
18124 Wedge Pkwy   Reno, NV 89511
(702) 203-4382 Alisa Acosta President
Fax: (775) 853-9646
Email: alisaa@earthlink.net
Website: www.AlisaAcostaConsulting.com
Business consulting: process reengineering, documentation, process mapping, project management, develop training curriculum & conducting training. (Woman/Hisp, estab 1998, empl 1, sales $55,000, cert: State, 8(a))

5258 American Project Management LLC
11700 W Charleston Blvd, Ste 170-315   Las Vegas, NV 89135
(702) 220-4562 Jane Lee Managing Partner
Fax: (702) 220-9784
Email: jlee@apmlasvegas.com
Website: www.apmlasvegas.com
Project Scheduling & Cost Control, Earned Value Management System (EVMS) Implementation, Computer Programming & Embedded Software Development Services & Staff Augmentation. (Woman/As-Pac, estab 2003, empl 2, sales , cert: NMSDC, NWBOC)

5259 Blue Fields Digital LLC
3172 N Rainbow Blvd, Ste 1120   Las Vegas, NV 89108
(949) 344-2996 Akilah Kamaria Data Security Consultant
Fax:
Email: akilahk@bluefieldsdigital.com
Website: www.bluefieldsdigital.com
Cybersecurity solutions, security risk assessments, third-party risk management, security engineering & cyber security awareness training. (Woman/AA, estab 2015, empl 2, sales , cert: City)

5260 ECF Data LLC
6149 S Rainbow Blvd, Ste 400   Las Vegas, NV 89118
(702) 664-0075 Joseph Henderson
Fax: (713) 429-1812
Email: jhenderson@ecfdata.com
Website: www.ecfdata.com
Polycom telephones & video equipment, Audio Codes, Dialogic, Acme Packet voice gateways, HP, Dell, Lenovo Server Hardware, Cisco, Juniper, HP network switches and Routers, Contact Center, Voice Response Applications. (AA, estab 2010, empl 4, sales $220,000, cert: NMSDC, 8(a))

5261   Ingenarius, Inc.
    29 N 28th St, Ste 14E   Las Vegas, NV 89101
    (702) 763-1419   Ishmael Thomas President
    Fax:
    Email: ishmaellthomas@ingenarius.com
    Website: www.solutions.oracle.com/scwar/scr/
    Partner/SCP
Software product life cycle (SPLC) services & enterprise
Java software development services, embedded, mobile,
big data & the Internet of Things (IoT), analysis, design,
construction, operation, configuration & maintenance.
(AA, estab 2013, empl 1, sales , cert: State)

5262   Intelligent Image Management Inc.
    2850 W Horizon Ridge Pkwy Ste 200   Henderson, NV
    89052
    (801) 906-9517   Shuvo Rahman VP Business Dev
    Fax: (702) 446-8310
    Email: shuvo@iimdirect.com
    Website: www.capturedata.com
Business Process Outsourcing (BPO) & document management, data entry, indexing, data conversion, data mining,
call center, post scan processing, back office. (As-Ind, estab
1999, empl 3, sales $5,000,000, cert: NMSDC)

5263   OCAA Solutions LLC
    170 S Green Valley Pkwy, Ste 300   Henderson, NV
    89012
    (702) 900-2733   Foma Odje
    Fax: (866) 523-5745
    Email: odje@ocaasolutions.com
    Website: www.ocaasolutions.com
Identity Management Solutions, Single Sign-On Solutions,
Custom Software Development, Enterprise Architecture
Design, Technical Writing, Remote DBA Services, Business
Analysis, Personal GPS Trackers. (AA, estab 2011, empl 3,
sales $500,446, cert: NMSDC)

5264   Spartacus Consulting, Inc.
    7521 W Lake Mead Blvd Ste 300   Las Vegas, NV
    89128
    (702) 997-4132   Henry Lowery Managing Dir
    Fax:
    Email: henry@scicpa.com
    Website: www.scicpa.com
AGILE Project Management Methodology for Software
Development Lifecycle, design, configuration, develop-
ment & support. (Woman/AA, estab 2003, empl 18, sales
$13,000,000, cert: State)

5265   XIOSS, Inc.
    4730 S. Fort Apache Rd Ste 300   Las Vegas, NV
    89147
    (952) 941-4000   Susie Galyardt Founder, President &
    CEO, XIOSS
    Fax: (952) 942-0000
    Email: susie.galyardt@xioss.com
    Website: www.xioss.com
IT storage solutions: data & network architecture, data
management, infrastructure management, systems
architecture & disaster recovery. (Woman/White, estab
2008, empl 11, sales $6,000,000, cert: WBENC)

New York

5266   A-1 Technology Inc.
    115 Broadway, 13th Fl   New York, NY 10006
    (212) 397-7481   Ishwari Singh President
    Fax: (212) 931-8530
    Email: ishwari.singh@a1technology.biz
    Website: www.a1technology.com
Website design, iPhone programming, mobile programming, application development, database , networking,
quality assurance. (As-Ind, estab 2001, empl 45, sales
$4,500,000, cert: City)

5267   ADDO, LLC
    155 W 118th St, Ste 1   New York, NY 10026
    (212) 933-0670   S Courtney Booker, CEO
    Fax: (212) 591-7951
    Email: courtney@theaddo.com
    Website: www.theaddo.com
From determining your brand's effectiveness to creating
a distinctive experience for your customers, ADDO's
comprehensive services will enable you to strengthen
your brand's position in the multicultural and niche
marketplaces. (AA, estab 2006, empl 1, sales $53,750,
cert: City, NMSDC)

5268   Admiral Courier Services Inc.
    18 W 30th St 2nd Fl   New York, NY 10001
    (212) 714-3581   Ray Rafeek Owner
    Fax: (212) 504-3184
    Email: ruqayyah@admiralstaffinginc.com
    Website: www.admiralstaffinginc.com
Admiral Courier Services, Inc. is a same day on demand
Courier / Delivery service located in midtown Manhat-
tan, in the heart of the big apple. We are fully computerized, with state-of-the-art-tracking and dispatch systems,
and operate on a (AA, estab 2005, empl 25, sales , cert:
City, NMSDC)

5269   Aimssoft Consultants Inc.
    13760 45th Ave Ste- 6 -C   Flushing, NY 11355
    (718) 762-2370   Ambreen Imran President
    Fax:
    Email: imran@aimssoftconsultant.net
    Website: www.aimssoftconsultant.net
Aimssoft serves the business clients by locating a
professional candidates, Interviewing and screening
candidates, setting up interviews if necessary Administering all hiring paperwork. (As-Pac, estab 2013, empl
45, sales $357,809, cert: NMSDC)

5270   American Technical Services, Inc.
    59,Hilldale Rd   New York, NY 11507
    (347) 282-7137   Nitin Dave President
    Fax:
    Email: atscorp@gmail.com
    Website:
Information Technology staffing, consulting &
outsourcing services. (As-Pac, estab 1997, empl 3, sales ,
cert: State, City, NMSDC)

5271 ASI System Integration, Inc.
48 W 37th St   New York, NY 10018
(212) 736-0111 Rick Lisker Dir bd/Mktg
Fax: (212) 629-3944
Email: rlisker@asisystem.com
Website: www.asisystem.com
IT technology sourcing/procurement, support services, consulting & integration, asset disposition & recycling, technical staffing. (As-Pac, estab 2005, empl 625, sales , cert: City, NMSDC)

5272 Ask IT Consulting Inc
33 Peachtree St., Ste 100   Holtsville, NY 11742
(631) 649-1313 Manisha Gupta President
Fax: (631) 803-4488
Email: commercial@askitc.com
Website: www.askitc.com
Information technology services. (Woman/As-Ind, estab 2008, empl 10, sales $3,311,713, cert: State, City, SDB)

5273 Bell Services Group, Inc.
88 Hunns Lake Rd   Stanfordville, NY 12581
(800) 645-8191 Justin Macedonia President
Fax: (800) 600-2216
Email: jmacedonia@bellservicesgroup.com
Website: www.bellservicesinc.com
Converting words into various types of tangible media. Specifically, Bell provides Transcription, Closed Captioning, Foreign Language Subtitling and Court Reporting services. (AA, estab 2003, empl 68, sales $2,100,000, cert: State)

5274 BruteForce Solutions Inc
545 8th Ave, Ste 540   New York, NY 10018
(212) 658-0277 Khurshedur Rahman President
Fax: (718) 717-8780
Email: info@bruteforcesolution.com
Website: www.bruteforcesolution.com/bfs/
Staffing & consulting, Information Technology (IT) solutions. (As-Ind, estab 2010, empl 14, sales $1,093,686, cert: State)

5275 Compulink Technologies, Inc.
214 W 29th St Ste 201   New York, NY 10001
(212) 695-5465 Rafael Arboleda CEO
Fax: (212) 695-5560
Email: rafael@compu-link.com
Website: www.compu-link.com
Cabling, network consulting, wireless networks, fiber optic cabling, LAN/WAN, computer hardware, software. (Woman/Hisp, estab 1989, empl 15, sales $5,000,000, cert: State, City)

5276 Connect Technology Solutions
550 W Old Country Rd, Ste 307   Hicksville, NY 11801
(516) 433-7707 Donna Chaimanis President
Fax:
Email: donnac@connectts.com
Website:
Information technology consulting & staffing services: technical staffing, executive recruiting, project mgmt, process reengineering, networking& system admin, software development & web design. (Woman/White, estab 1998, empl 30, sales $1,084,139, cert: State)

5277 Controls and Automation Consultants LLC
100 N Main St, Ste L06   Elmira, NY 14901
(800) 430-4021 Tangela Nixon CEO
Fax: (800) 436-7801
Email: tnixon@controls-automation.com
Website: www.controls-automation.com
IT Staffing
Hybrid Technical Staffing TM
Project Management & Control
Electrical Engineering
Automation Engineering (AA, estab 2005, empl 4, sales $1,000,000, cert: State, NMSDC)

5278 Corporate Computer Solutions
55 Halstead Ave   Harrison, NY 10528
(914) 835-1105 Larry Grippo VP of Sales
Fax: (914) 835-5947
Email: lgrippo@corporatecomputersol.com
Website: www.corporatecomputersol.com
Computer-based business solutions. (Woman/White, estab 1986, empl 18, sales $12,000,000, cert: State, City, WBENC)

5279 Crossfire Consulting
1940 Commerce St   Yorktown Heights, NY 10598
(917) 701-4905 Beth Boyce Senior Acct Exec
Fax: (914) 364-7917
Email: beth@crossfireconsulting.com
Website: www.crossfireconsulting.com
IT Consulting, Development & Staff Augmentation, consulting, development, program management & onshore outsourcing. (Woman/White, estab 2000, empl 25, sales , cert: State, City, CPUC, WBENC, NWBOC)

5280 Deltronix Technologies Inc.
251 New Karner Road   Albany, NY 12205
(518) 713-5140 Snekalatha Jegadeesan President
Fax: (518) 670-2819
Email: hr@deltronixtech.com
Website: www.deltronixtech.com
IT Staff Augmentation: Java, .NET, Siebel, SAP, Peoplesoft, CRM, Database, Kofax, Testing etc. (Woman/As-Pac, estab 2012, empl 15, sales $888,071, cert: State)

5281 Derive Technologies
110 William St   New York, NY 10038
(347) 532-5025 Jemal Alford Sr Acct Exec
Fax: (212) 363-6214
Email: jalford@derivetech.com
Website: www.derivetech.com
Hardware fullfillment, computer integration service, iinfrastructure, desktop & printer support. (As-Ind, estab 1986, empl 110, sales $58,000,000, cert: NMSDC)

5282 Doddi Information Technologies
24 Picture Lane   Hicksville, NY 11801
(646) 330-5354 David Trotman Director Business Dev
Fax:
Email: david.trotman@dodditech.com
Website: www.dodditech.com
Professional Services and Software development. (As-Ind, estab 2013, empl 10, sales , cert: NMSDC)

5283 Donnelly & Moore Corporation
75 Carolina Dr   New City, NY 10956
(845) 304-8344 Tracy Stein CEO
Fax: (845) 708-0111
Email: tracys@donmor.com
Website: www.donmor.com
IT consulting & full time IT staffing: GUI dev, internet & intranet application dev, quality assurance testing, help desk & desk top support, database dev & administration. (Woman/Hisp, estab 1997, empl 50, sales $10,000,000, cert: State, City, NMSDC)

5284 Eclaro International
450 Seventh Ave Ste 1102 New York, NY 10123
(212) 258-2626 Rick Cafiero VP
Fax: (212) 258-2115
Email: rcafiero@eclaroit.com
Website: www.eclaroit.com
Information technology staffing & software development services. (As-Pac, estab 1900, empl 1, sales $23,100,000, cert: State, City, NMSDC)

5285 eiWorkflow Solutions, LLC
125 Wolf Rd   Albany, NY 12205
(518) 240-1155 John Andrew CEO
Fax: (614) 455-8653
Email: info@eiworkflowsolutions.com
Website: www.eiworkflowsolutions.com/
Cloud software consulting, Workflow Management, Customer Service Management, Customer Relationship Management & Human Resource Management. (As-Ind, estab 2006, empl 7, sales $450,000, cert: NMSDC)

5286 Elite Technical Services, Inc.
3281 Veterans Memorial Hwy Ste E17 Ronkonkoma, NY 11779
(631) 256-1399 Donna Keller President
Fax: (631) 256-1574
Email: dkeller@elitetechnical.com
Website: www.elitetechnical.com
Technical consultants & staff augmentation services: information technology, networking & engineering. (Woman/White, estab 1992, empl 88, sales $14,500,000, cert: State, WBENC)

5287 emedia, LLC
274 Madison Avenue Ste 1202 New York, NY 10017
(212) 774-6100 Shari Lowsky Director, Client Relations
Fax: (212) 645-2901
Email: slowsky@emediaweb.com
Website: www.emediaweb.com
Design, build, integrate & maintain custom software applications, Enterprise Resource Planning (ERP) systems, Enterprise Content Management (ECM) systems, Customer Relationship Management (CRM) systems. (Woman, estab 1996, empl 8, sales $1,000,000, cert: State, City, WBENC)

5288 Episerve Corp.
266 Midwood St   Brooklyn, NY 11225
(917) 921-2644 Sony Titus President
Fax:
Email: info@episervecorp.com
Website: www.episervecorp.com
Training, consulting, system integration & managed services. (Woman/AA, estab 2003, empl 6, sales $245,000, cert: City)

5289 Espirit Systems, LLC
14 Penn Plaza Ste 2105 New York, NY 10122
(212) 631-0188 Sales
Fax: (212) 631-0190
Email: amcclean@eliteconsulting.com
Website: www.eliteconsulting.com
Application architect & dev, database dev, network admin & architects, systems admin, business analysts, mainframe. (AA, estab 1997, empl 10, sales $5,000,000, cert: State)

5290 Expinfo, Inc.
1621 Central Ave   Albany, NY 12205
(518) 459-4100 Tiya Bhattacharya CEO
Fax: (518) 459-4141
Email: contracts@expinfo.com
Website: www.expinfo.com
Information technology staffing, HR consulting, custom computer programming, computer systems design, web development & graphic design, custom application development. (Woman/As-Pac, estab 2005, empl 21, sales $1,800,000, cert: State, City)

5291 Fair Pattern Inc.
1460 Broadway   New York, NY 10036
(800) 906-1656 Simon Islam Managing Dir
Fax:
Email: simon@fairpattern.com
Website: www.fairpattern.com
IT staffing, web & mobile application, software engineering & project management. (As-Ind, estab 2015, empl 22, sales $650,000, cert: NMSDC)

5292 Fast Lane Interactive
P.O. Box 987 New York, NY 11225
(646) 389-8495 Shalonda Hunter Founder
Fax:
Email: contactus@flitimes.com
Website: www.flitimes.com
Digital Media & Advertising, Content Development, Web, Mobile, Tablet Device Dev & Services, Software Development, Web Security, Information Security, Cloud Services (Email, Web Storage, Telecomm, Data Center Migration). (Woman/AA, estab 2015, empl 5, sales , cert: NMSDC)

5293 Financial Technologies Inc
305 Madison Ave, Ste 4600 New York, NY 10165
(212) 485-9842 Young Lee CEO
Fax:
Email: hlee@sciostrategy.com
Website: www.ScioStrategy.com
IT consulting services, web/mobile applications & back end data management & integration solutions. (Woman/As-Pac, estab 2006, empl 3, sales $527,935, cert: State)

5294 Galica, LLC
620 Park Ave, Ste 216   Rochester, NY 14607
(585) 319-9301 Carlos Perez Principal
Fax: (800) 600-2216
Email: galicaehs@gmail.com
Website: www.galicalean.com
Galica LLC provides bilingual (Spanish/English) Strategy Support and Lean Facilitation using The Toyota KATA teachings. Rapid Improvement Event Facilitation Lean Program dev Training on Strategy development (Hisp, estab 2009, empl 1, sales $50,000, cert: State, NMSDC)

5295 GCom Software, Inc.
24 Madison Ave   Albany, NY 12203
(518) 869-1671 Manish Garg Acct Mgr
Fax: (518) 869-1673
Email: manish@gcomsoft.com
Website: www.gcomsoft.com
IT Staff Augmentation, fixed cost deliverable, project based services, Web based application development, Data warehousing, Network support, server , security, virtualization, Quality/Testing. (As-Ind, estab 2005, empl 130, sales , cert: State)

5296 GENESYS Consulting Services, Inc.
1 Marcus Blvd, Ste 102   Albany, NY 12205
(518) 459-9500 Leo Pfohl VP
Fax: (518) 459-9501
Email: Leo@genesysonline.com
Website: www.genesysonline.com
Information Technology consulting services, design, develop, implement & maintain technology solutions. (Woman/White, estab 1987, empl 84, sales $12,500,717, cert: State, City)

5297 Globalquest
435 Lawrence Bell Dr, Ste 7   Williamsville, NY 14221
(716) 635-9820 Lynn Dearmyer Business Dev Mgr
Fax: (716) 635-9834
Email: Ldearmyer@globalquestinc.com
Website: www.globalqueststaffing.com
IT staffing: contract, contract-to-hire, direct & payroll. (Woman/White, estab 1994, empl 120, sales $24,000,000, cert: State, City)

5298 Granwood Inc
61-43 186th St   Fresh Meadows, NY 11365
(718) 640-2828 Glen Greene Managing Dir
Fax:
Email: ggreene@granwoodinc.com
Website: www.granwoodinc.com
Information technology consulting & staffing. (AA, estab 2005, empl 12, sales $745,000, cert: State, City, NMSDC)

5299 Green Point Technology Services LLC
555 Theodore Fremd Ave Ste A102   Rye, NY 10580
(212) 913-0500 Shirley Sharma President
Fax: (646) 217-3141
Email: shirley@greenpointglobal.com
Website: www.greenpointglobal.com/
Legal and Compliance, Regulatory Tracking, Publishing & Editorial services, Software Development, Professional development. (Woman/As-Ind, estab 2001, empl 350, sales $3,200,000, cert: State)

5300 ImageWork USA LLC
170 Hamilton Ave, Ste 301   White Plains, NY 10601
(914) 681-0700 Cecilia Bikkal President
Fax:
Email: cbikkal@imagework.com
Website: www.imagework.com
Full life Cycle Recruitment, IT services, IT; Documentation Scanning; Printing; Computing. (Woman/Hisp, estab 2009, empl 1, sales $35,000, cert: State, City)

5301 Indotronix International Corporation
687 Lee Rd, Ste 250   Rochester, NY 14606
(845) 473-1137 Venkat S Mantha President
Fax: (845) 473-1197
Email: bd@iic.com
Website: www.iic.com
Software applications, e-business initiatives, IT consulting, customer interaction management. (As-Ind, estab 1986, empl 900, sales $55,000,000, cert: State, NMSDC, CPUC)

5302 InnoSoul, Inc.
24 Fairfield Ave   Albany, NY 12205
(518) 400-0425 Rashi Shamshabad President
Fax:
Email: innosoul@gmail.com
Website: www.innosoul.com
Software Product Development & IT Consulting Services, IT Staffing. (Woman/As-Ind, estab 2003, empl 20, sales $4,000,000, cert: State, City, WBENC)

5303 Integrated Systems Management
303 S Broadway, Ste 101   Tarrytown, NY 10591
(914) 332-5590 Dean Menon Business Dev Mgr
Fax: (914) 332-5766
Email: dmenon@ismnet.com
Website: www.ismnet.com
IT solution services & IT staffing: network security, ERP, CRM softwares. (Woman/As-Pac, estab 1989, empl 35, sales $5,550,000, cert: State)

5304 Integrity Communications
130 Route 209   Port Jervis, NY 12771
(845) 649-5387 Wayne Murray President
Fax: (845) 856-2328
Email: wmurray@integritycom.net
Website: www.integritycom.net
Systems integration & installation, structured network cabling for computer, LAN networks, voice/data. (AA, estab 2003, empl 2, sales $41,000, cert: State)

5305 Jasper Solutions Inc.
21 Melville Rd Cross Hunter Lane Huntington Station, NY 11746
(631) 514-8106 Anshuman Patel President
Fax: (631) 759-3805
Email: contracts@jaspersolutions.com
Website: www.jaspersolutions.com
Enterprise storage, network monitoring, security, private & public Cloud, networking, disaster recovery, application integration, data warehousing, data mining, database implementation, virtualization, hybrid Cloud, Cisco. (As-Ind, estab 2002, empl 3, sales $300,000, cert: State)

5306 Jean Martin Inc.
551 Fifth Ave, Ste 1425 New York, NY 10176
(212) 883-1000 Shawn Kumar CEO
Fax: (212) 883-1003
Email: shawnk@jeanmartin.com
Website: www.jeanmartin.com
Information technology consulting services. (As-Ind, estab 1997, empl 150, sales $16,000,000, cert: City)

5307 JSL Computer Services, Inc.
437 E Allen St Hudson, NY 12534
(518) 828-7761 Ed Grossman VP
Fax: (518) 828-7517
Email: ed@jslinc.com
Website: www.jslinc.com
E-commerce, web design & dev, JAVA, systems programming, analysis & business requirements, project mgmt, software testing & quality assurance, documentation, database design, data modeling & warehousing, network engineering. (Woman/White, estab 1978, empl 39, sales $3,610,079, cert: City)

5308 KDI Technology Solutions, Inc
412 Broadway 2nd Fl New York, NY 10113
(646) 724-0875 John Thomas President
Fax:
Email: jthomas@kditek.com
Website: www.kditek.com
Database design & development, mobile applications, web development, business & systems analysis. (AA, estab 2007, empl 1, sales $100,000, cert: State, City)

5309 Maureen Data Systems, Inc.
307 W 38th St Ste 1801 New York, NY 10018
(646) 744-1000 Robert Irvin Dir, Govt channels
Fax: (212) 328-1713
Email: rirvin@mdsny.com
Website: www.mdsny.com
Systems integrator & VAR, UC, Cloud computing, virtualization & storage, networking & security. (Woman/White, estab 1994, empl 24, sales $8,500,000, cert: State, City)

5310 Motivate Design, LLC
111 John St, Ste 450 New York, NY 10038
(646) 400-5108 Laura Haykel Client Experience Dir
Fax: (314) 770-0661
Email: Laura@motivatedesign.com
Website: www.motivatedesign.com
Motivate Design is a user experience (UX) research, design, and staffing* agency in New York City. We know that great customer experience doesn't just happen. It is the result of deep and empathetic thinking, research and design. We help companies shape t (Woman/As-Ind, estab 2009, empl 15, sales $4,000,000, cert: WBENC)

5311 Navatar Consulting Group Inc.
44 Wall St, 12 Fl New York, NY 10005
(212) 461-2140 Saket Misra Mgr Ops
Fax: (212) 461-2141
Email: smisra@navatargroup.com
Website: www.navatargroup.com
On-demand CRM, ERP & supply chain. (As-Pac, estab 2002, empl 25, sales $820,000, cert: State)

5312 Netfast Technology Solutions Inc.
589 8th Avenue 22nd Fl New York, NY 10018
(212) 792-5200 Navid Nawaz Mgr
Fax: (212) 213-1152
Email: nnawaz@netfast.com
Website: www.netfast.com
Information security consulting & network integration. (As-Pac, estab 1994, empl 25, sales $13,800,000, cert: City, NMSDC)

5313 New York Technology Partners
332 Jefferson Rd Rochester, NY 14623
(585) 300-4720 Mohan Kanala VP
Fax: (201) 474-8533
Email: mohan@nytp.com
Website: www.nytp.com
Software consulting, onsite, offsite, and offshore, IT & Business Consulting, IT Integration, Project mgmt. (As-Pac, estab 1999, empl 280, sales $3,000,000, cert: NMSDC)

5314 Panther Solutions, LLC
1001 Lee Rd P.O. Box 60375 Rochester, NY 14606
(585) 546-7163 Daryll (Tony) Jackson President
Fax: (866) 557-4877
Email: supplierdiversity@panthersolutions.biz
Website: www.panthersolutions.biz
Account management, custom data programming. (AA, estab 2005, empl 45, sales , cert: NMSDC)

5315 Prista Technologies, LLC
235 Harrison St, Ste 57 Syracuse, NY 13202
(315) 746-0713 Lynna Cekova CEO
Fax: (813) 855-5665
Email: lynna@pristatech.com
Website: www.pristatech.com
Full Stack & Lifecycle Software Application Dev, Enterprise Systems, Relational/Non-relational Databases, Scalable Middleware, Data Analysis/Analytics, Big Data, Amazon Web Svcs, Graphical User Interfaces &Experience. (Woman, estab 2014, empl 1, sales , cert: State)

5316 Quantilus Inc.
115 Broadway Ste 1202 New York, NY 10006
(212) 768-8900 Debarshi Chaudhury Dir Bus Dev
Fax: (866) 275-7226
Email: debarshi.chaudhury@quantilus.com
Website: www.quantilus.com
IT Strategy, Implementation, Custom Development, Machine Vision, Publishing, Education, Artificial Intelligence, Natural Language Processing3. (As-Ind, estab 2004, empl 22, sales $7,213,447, cert: State, City, NMSDC)

5317 RMK Consulting, Inc.
2 Oregon Hollow Rd Armonk, NY 10504
(914) 765-0075 Debra DeWitt Acct Exec
Fax: (914) 273-1535
Email: info@rmkconsulting.com
Website: www.rmkconsulting.com
BPO & IT consulting, outsourcing & consulting svcs, staff augmentation, managed svcs & project sourcing solutions, on-site, near-site & off-shore staffing. (Woman, estab 1998, empl 127, sales $30,000,000, cert: WBENC)

5318   SD Services Inc.
3149 Wilmarth Pl   Wantagh, NY 11793
(516) 633-5229 Shashi Malik President
Fax: (516) 221-8210
Email: shashi.malik@sdservicesinc.us
Website: www.sdservicesinc.us
Custom software dev, website design & dev, application dev, website optimization. (Woman/As-Ind, estab 2001, empl 1, sales $700,000, cert: State, City)

5319   Sharp Decisions, Inc.
1040 Avenue of the Americas 17th Fl New York, NY 10018
(212) 403-7557 Edward McCann Managing Dir
Fax: (212) 656-1083
Email: emccann@sharpdecisions.com
Website: www.sharpdecisions.com
Computer consulting: staff augmentation & contract programming, systems integration, data networks design, development & implementation, business continuity planning, security & firewall design & dev, vendor product evaluation. (Woman/White, estab 1990, empl 330, sales $60,000,000, cert: WBENC, NWBOC)

5320   Silverman Shin & Byrne PLLC
88 Pine St, 22nd Fl New York, NY 10005
(212) 779-8600 Gerard Crowe Partner
Fax: (212) 779-8858
Email: gcrowe@silverfirm.com
Website: www.silverfirm.com
Corporate/Commercial realm, we represent small start-up companies to multinationals alike in both tranactional adn litigation. In the Insurance/Tort defense realsm, we represent a host of insurance carriers, municipalites, and privately insured (AA/As-Pac/Hisp, estab 1986, empl 46, sales $9,188,231, cert: NMSDC)

5321   Siwel Consulting, Inc.
213 West 35th St Ste 12 West New York, NY 10001
(212) 691-9326 Michael LaPayower Senior Accountant
Fax: (212) 741-9590
Email: mlapayower@siwel.com
Website: www.siwel.com
Information technology: contract & fulltime staffing, IBM Premier VAR, ELA & software license, asset management, Linux, VOIP, VMware, server, storage & networking. (Woman/White, estab 1992, empl 30, sales $52,780,000, cert: WBENC)

5322   Softpath Systems Inc.
75 Maiden Lane, Ste 903 New York, NY 10038
(212) 405-1894 Shiv Mgr
Fax:
Email: shiv@softpathsystems.com
Website: www.softpathsystems.com
IT & supply chain staffing. (As-Pac, estab 1997, empl 150, sales $300,000, cert: State)

5323   Software Guidance & Assistance, Inc.
200 White Plains Road Tarrytown, NY 10591
(914) 960-3193 Jose Munoz Acct Mgr
Fax:
Email: josem@sgainc.com
Website: www.sgainc.com
IT professionals: programmers, analysts, senior project managers, operating systems, programming, networking, application software & hardware skills & certifications. (Woman/White, estab 1981, empl 500, sales $100,000,000, cert: City, WBENC)

5324   Source Of Future Technology (SOFT), Inc.
333 Hudson St Ste 202 New York, NY 10013
(212) 633-1515 Cathy Grubiak President
Fax: (212) 633-6429
Email: cgrubiak@soft-inc.com
Website: www.softinc.com
Computer technology solutions: project life cycle. (Woman/White, estab 1981, empl 75, sales $6,000,000, cert: State, WBENC)

5325   Sphynx Software Solutions LLC
59 Lafayette Ave Ste 2D Brooklyn, NY 11217
(917) 705-5548 Yonas Keflemariam CEO
Fax:
Email: yonas@sphynxsoftware.com
Website: www.sphynxsoftware.com
Technology solutions, enterprise architecture, local & offshore software development resources & technical staff augmentation. (AA, estab 2007, empl 3, sales $33,943, cert: City, NMSDC)

5326   Sutherland Global Services
1160 Pittsford-Victor Rd   Pittsford, NY 14534
(585) 586-5757 Steve Sandt Business Dev Mgr
Fax: (585) 419-3799
Email: sandts@sutherlandglobal.com
Website: www.sutherlandglobal.com
Business process outsourcing & call ctr svcs: technical & customer support, systems integration & application development. (As-Ind, estab 1986, empl 33000, sales $500,500,000, cert: NMSDC)

5327   SVAM International Inc.
233 East Shore Rd, Ste 201   Great Neck, NY 11023
(516) 466-6655 Manav Bhasin Managing Dir
Fax: (516) 466-8260
Email: manav@svam.com
Website: www.svam.com
IT staff augmentation, custom software dev, web enabling technologies, workflow automation, content management. (As-Pac, estab 1994, empl 600, sales $35,600,000, cert: State, NMSDC)

5328   Techolution LLC
3 World Financial Ctr 24th Fl New York, NY 10281
(201) 417-7240 Zachary Kissel Office Mgr
Fax:
Email: zak@techolution.com
Website: www.techolution.com
Digital transformation: web & mobile, migrating server farms & applications to the cloud (public or private). (As-Pac, estab 2014, empl 50, sales $1,500,000, cert: NMSDC)

5329 Ubiqus
61 Broadway Ste 1400 New York, NY 10003
(212) 964-6400 Tammy Whelan SMR
Fax: (212) 964-6448
Email: infousa@ubiqus.com
Website: www.ubiqus.com
IT staff augmentation. (Woman, estab 1996, empl 240,
sales $20,182,200, cert: WBENC)

5330 URimagination, Inc.
18 E 41st St Ste 1703 New York, NY 10017
(212) 729-9558 Alf Baez CEO
Fax: (877) 210-4269
Email: info@urimagination.com
Website: www.urimagination.com
Information technology solutions: custom application
development, systems integration, maintenance spanning.
(Hisp, estab 2007, empl 7, sales $500,000, cert: City,
NMSDC)

5331 Vernalis Group Inc
353 Lexington Ave, Ste 1604   New York, NY 10016
(647) 923-1903 Nanda Rajasek COO
Fax:
Email: nanda.rajasek@vernal.is
Website: www.vernalisengg.com
Global software & engineering solutions, Microsoft, IBM,
JEE, openSource, Mobile, Business Intelligence, Enterprise
Application Integration. (As-Ind, estab 2012, empl 300,
sales $4,440,000, cert: NMSDC)

5332 VQV Services LLC
204 Forrest Pointe Dr   East Greenbush, NY 12061
(201) 920-6170 Khuhsbooben Patel President
Fax:
Email: khush@vqvservices.com
Website: www.vqvservices.com
Quality Engineer, Validation Engineer, Qualification
Specialist, Information Technology consultants. (Woman/
As-Pac, estab 2016, empl 2, sales $50,000, cert: State)

5333 www.datrose.com
660 Basket Road, www.datrose.com   Webster, NY
14580
(585) 265-1780 Eunice Sonneville Business Dev Mgr
Fax: (585) 265-4016
Email: esonneville@datrose.com
Website: www.datrose.com
Facilities support mgmt svcs: mailing-repro & steno;
computer hardware & software; programming; data
processing; systems design. (AA, estab 1976, empl 360,
sales $23,505,000, cert: State)

5334 Xperteks Computer Consultancy, Inc.
1001 Avenue of the Americas, Ste 2301   New York,
NY 10018
(212) 206-6262 Marcial Velez CEO
Fax: (212) 206-6261
Email: vstella@xperteks.com
Website: www.xperteks.com
Apple, PC & network managed services, IT services. (Hisp,
estab 2002, empl 17, sales $2,500,000, cert: City, NMSDC)

Ohio

5335 Accelerated Business Results an A Fox Corporation
1530 Sycamore Ridge Dr   Maineville, OH 45039
(513) 774-8608 Amy Fox Owner
Fax: (513) 774-8904
Email: amy.fox@acceleratedbr.com
Website: www.acceleratedbr.com/what-we-do/
Customized content development, design & develop
instructor-led training programs, e-Learning solutions &
blended learning solutions. (Woman, estab 2002, empl
11, sales $1,678,119, cert: WBENC)

5336 AespaTech, LLC
23800 Commerce Park, Ste A   Beachwood, OH
44122
(216) 928-1919 Parul Jain President
Fax: (216) 765-0667
Email: parul@aespatech.com
Website: www.aespatech.com
Information Technology Consulting & Training Services.
(Woman/As-Pac, estab 2014, empl 1, sales $200,000,
cert: State, City, WBENC)

5337 Alego Health
24651 Center Ridge Rd Ste 400 Westlake, OH
44145
(440) 617-6516 Jonathan Levoy VP
Fax: (440) 617-6512
Email: jlevoy@alegohealth.com
Website: www.alegohealth.com
Healthcare IT, EMR Training, EMR Implementation, EMR
Analysts, Hardware Support, Hardware, Software, IT
Analysts, IT, Mobile Technology (Woman/White, estab
2004, empl 127, sales $11,500,000, cert: WBENC)

5338 American Business Solutions, Inc.
8850 Whitney Dr   Lewis Center, OH 43035
(614) 310-4471 Larry Bame Director, Business
Dev
Fax: (888) 699-8866
Email: Larry@absi-USA.com
Website: www.absi-usa.com
Technology Services & Solutions, Business Intelligence &
Database Management, Organizational Change Manage-
ment, Mobile Application Development, Project Man-
agement & Support, Quality Assurance & Testing, Cloud
Computing Services. (As-Ind, estab 1998, empl 85, sales
$20,000,000, cert: State, NMSDC)

5339 Ardent Technologies Inc.
6234 Far Hills Ave   Dayton, OH 45459
(937) 312-1345 Vas Appalaneni President
Fax: (937) 312-1346
Email: ohbids@ardentinc.com
Website: www.ardentinc.com
ITservices & project management, software development & maintenance, systems
analysis, turnkey project implementations, data services
(modeling, management and migration),
project outsourcing services. (As-Ind, estab 2000, empl
60, sales $7,300,000, cert: State, SDB)

5340 ASC Associates, Inc.
110 Clearbrook Lane   Aurora, OH 44202
(216) 496-2773 Shashi Jina President
Fax: (330) 995-0184
Email: sjina@ascassociates.com
Website: www.ascassociates.com
IT services, custom systems development (COBAL, JAVA, .NET), ERP implementations. Oracle, SAP & related databases (Oracle 9, 10g, SQL). (As-Ind, estab 2001, empl 15, sales $300,000, cert: State)

5341 Ascendum
10290 Alliance Rd   Cincinnati, OH 45242
(513) 792-5100 Tara Heiner Business Devel Exec
Fax: (513) 792-5105
Email: tara.heiner@ascendum.com
Website: www.ascendum.com
IT solutions, technology-inspired solutions to business-driven challenges. (As-Ind, estab 2008, empl 1500, sales $80,000,000, cert: State, NMSDC)

5342 Barcode Industrial Systems, Inc.
8044 Montgomery road Ste 700 Cincinnati, OH 45236
(513) 772-5252 Juan Merchan Business Dev Mgr
Fax: (513) 772-5544
Email: Contracts@BISLabels.com
Website: www.BISLabels.com
Mobile data transaction systems, wireless & batch data capture applications: inventory, shipping, receiving & warehouse mgmt via Internet. (AA/Hisp, estab 1990, empl 16, sales $1,010,000, cert: NMSDC)

5343 Cadre Computer Resources Co.
201 E 5th St, Ste 1800 Cincinnati, OH 45202
(513) 762-7350 Kristen Norris Mktg
Fax:
Email: kristen.norris@cadre.net
Website: www.cadre.net
Network & information security solutions, design, assessment, installation, training & support of information security systems. (Woman/White, estab 2001, empl 52, sales $43,383,000, cert: WBENC, NWBOC)

5344 CDO Technologies, Inc.
5200 Springfield St Ste 320 Dayton, OH 45431
(937) 258-0022 Valerie Smith Contracts Admin
Fax: (937) 258-1614
Email: valerie.smith@cdotech.com
Website: www.cdotech.com
Information engineering; computer networks; network mgmt; design; software engineering; programming; communications; telecommunications; system engineering & admin; bar codes; biometric authentication, etc. (AA, estab 1995, empl 185, sales $36,136,518, cert: State)

5345 Chagrin Consulting Services Inc.
1795 South Belvoir Blvd. South Euclid, OH 44121
(216) 514-3301 Ann Allard President
Fax: (216) 803-4952
Email: ahallard@chagrinconsulting.com
Website: www.chagrinconsulting.com
IT consulting & staffing. (Woman/White, estab 1993, empl 12, sales $2,451,851, cert: WBENC)

5346 ClemCorp
714 E Monument Ave   Dayton, OH 45402
(937) 531-6645 Kevin Clemons CEO
Fax: (937) 262-8322
Email: Kevin.Clemons@ClemCorp.com
Website: www.ClemCorp.com
IT solution & services: rational capabilities, enterprise architecture, GCSS, web dev, graphic design, document mgmt, network design & admin, software dev, project mgmt, system design, life cycle application support. (AA, estab 2005, empl 12, sales $300,000, cert: State, 8(a))

5347 Corbus, LLC
1129 Miamisburg Centerville Rd 45449 West Carrollton, OH 45449
(513) 703-2929 Jerry Teuschler Director, Strategic Sales Dev
Fax:
Email: corbusconnects@corbus.com
Website: www.corbus.com
Software development, offshore IT support, testing & quality solutions, staff augmentation. (As-Ind/As-Pac, estab 1994, empl 600, sales , cert: NMSDC)

5348 Cybervation, Inc.
4150 Tuller Rd, Ste 204   Dublin, OH 43017
(614) 818-9061 Purba Majumder President
Fax: (614) 389-1225
Email: pmajumder@cybervationinc.com
Website: www.cybervationinc.com
Technology Services, Website Development, custom Software Programming, Graphics Design, Animation, Video, Transcription, Data Entry & Internet Marketing. (Woman/As-Pac, estab 1998, empl 32, sales , cert: State, NMSDC, WBENC)

5349 Cynergies Solutions Group
26301 Curtiss-Wright Pkwy Ste 400 Richmond Heights, OH 44143
(440) 565-0168 Debbie Holy President
Fax: (440) 461-2615
Email: debbie_holy@cynergies.net
Website: www.cynergies.net
Information technology staffing: consulting, contracting, permanent, executive placement, contract-to-hire, software devel & training. (Woman/White, estab 1997, empl 62, sales , cert: WBENC)

5350 Dedicated Tech Services, Inc.
545 Metro Place S Ste 100 Dublin, OH 43017
(614) 309-0059 Patricia Lickliter President
Fax: (614) 298-0878
Email: sales@dedicatedtechservices.com
Website: www.dedicatedtechservices.com
Application Design & Development, Service Oriented Architecture (SOA), Database Design & Development, Client/Server & N-Tier Development, Web & Web Service Development, Data Warehousing Solutions. (Woman/As-Ind, estab 2008, empl 25, sales $1,940,000, cert: State, WBENC, NWBOC)

5351   Deemsys Inc.
800A Cross Pointe Rd   Columbus, OH 43230
(614) 322-9929 RT Rajan
Fax: (614) 322-9945
Email: raj@deemsysinc.com
Website: www.deemsysinc.com
Application design, dev & implementation, Systems integration/consolidation, Re-engineering, Implementation, Feasibility & requirement analysis. (Woman/As-Ind, estab 2004, empl 82, sales $7,550,000, cert: State, NMSDC)

5352   DevCare Solutions
131 N High St Ste 640 Columbus, OH 43215
(614) 285-2714 Ron Vogel Sr Business Dev Mgr
Fax: (614) 867-9367
Email: rvogel@devcare.com
Website: www.devcare.com
On-site/offshore development of software solutions & Staff Augmentation consultants. (Woman/As-Pac, estab 1995, empl 263, sales $11,320,000, cert: State, WBENC)

5353   Development Consultants Inc.
24940 Patrick Brush Run Rd   Marysville, OH 43040
(937) 246-2193 Kauser Kabealo President
Fax: (855) 746-5324
Email: kauser@devconinc.com
Website: www.devconinc.com
Large-enterprise computer software & infrastructure services, software architectural design & dev, capability & process maturity, enterprise resource planning, infrastructure design, capacity planning & disaster recovery svcs. (Woman/As-Ind, estab 2001, empl 8, sales , cert: 8(a))

5354   Echo Imaging Inc.
2645 Wooster Rd   Rocky River, OH 44116
(440) 356-4720 Barbara Milloy President
Fax: (440) 356-4731
Email: barbara@echoimg.com
Website: www.echoimg.com
Replication svcs: CD-R, CD-ROM, DVD-R, mini CD's, business card CD's & diskette duplication, full color custom printed packaging. (Woman/White, estab 1997, empl 1, sales $801,642, cert: WBENC)

5355   Evanhoe & Associates, Inc.
5089 Norman Blvd.   Dayton, OH 45431
(937) 528-5806 Marty Pendergrass VP Contracts/Admin
Fax: (937) 235-8692
Email: Marty.Pendergrass@evanhoe.com
Website: www.evanhoe.com
Data management, software development, business process reengineering & modeling & simulation. (As-Pac, estab 1996, empl 35, sales $6,051,297, cert: State)

5356   EXCEL Management Systems, Inc.
691 N High St, 2nd Fl Columbus, OH 43215
(614) 224-4007 Curtis Jewell
Fax: (614) 224-4857
Email: curtis@emsi.com
Website: www.emsi.com
Project mgmt, BPR/BPI, document imaging, EC/EDI, systems design dev & legacy data conversion services. (AA, estab 1989, empl 130, sales $13,000,000, cert: State)

5357   Expeed Software LLC
659 Lakeview Plaza Blvd, Ste K   Worthington, OH 43085
(614) 371-4791 Rao Chejarla President
Fax:
Email: rao.chejarla@expeedsoftware.com
Website: www.expeedsoftware.com
Custom Application Development, Mobile Application Development, Application Integration, Data Warehousing and Business Intelligence, Independent Software, Verification/Quality Assurance, Project Management. (As-Pac, estab 2008, empl 35, sales $735,000, cert: State, NMSDC)

5358   Fiducia TechneGroup LLC
3838 Eileen Dr   Cincinnati, OH 45209
(513) 418-8217 Alma Bartos CEO
Fax: (281) 454-7513
Email: amartinez@fiduciatg.com
Website: www.fiduciatg.com
Engineering Services, Reliability (Products, Processes and Software), Implement Reliability Life Cycle Management & Benchmarking. (Woman/Hisp, estab 2014, empl 2, sales $100,000, cert: NMSDC, WBENC)

5359   Flairsoft, LTD
7720 Rivers Edge Dr Ste 200 Columbus, OH 43235
(614) 207-0764 Sharon Fraley Sr Business Devel Mgr
Fax: (614) 573-7255
Email: sharon.fraley@flairsoft.net
Website: www.flairsoft.net
Information Technology, e-Business, Professional Services, Systems Integration & Business Process Re-Engineering. (As-Ind, estab 2001, empl 100, sales $8,000,000, cert: NMSDC)

5360   Global Associates, Inc.
7160 Corporate Way   Dayton, OH 45459
(937) 312-1204 Kevin Toshok Dir, Solutions Sales
Fax:
Email: ktoshok@gassociates.com
Website: www.gassociates.com
IT Consulting, Staff Augmentation, Project Outsourcing & Offshore software design & testing. (Woman/As-Ind, estab 1996, empl 8, sales $15,000,000, cert: NMSDC)

5361   IdentiPhoto Company Ltd.
1810 Joseph Lloyd Pkwy   Willoughby, OH 44094
(440) 306-9000 Pamela Johnson GM
Fax: (440) 306-9001
Email: pam@identiphoto.com
Website: www.identiphoto.com
Badging, tracking, verification systems, photo ID systems ID badges, ID software ID supplies, ID badge attachments, ID cards, visitor management software/systems, card printers, perimeter management systems, smart cards, proximity. (Woman/White, estab 1969, empl 15, sales $2,252,840, cert: WBENC)

5362 Integrated Solutions and Services
4055 Executive Park Dr, Ste 450 Cincinnati, OH 45241
(513) 769-3913 Clarence McGill
Fax: (513) 769-3782
Email: rmcgill@iss-unlimited.com
Website: www.iss-unlimited.com
Information technology hardware integration, network server mgmt, help desk svcs, LAN/WAN, database dev & mgmt, system application support. (AA, estab 1999, empl 5, sales , cert: State)

5363 JASStek, Inc.
555 Metro Place N Ste 100 Dublin, OH 43017
(614) 808-3600 Praveen Tummalla Business Dev Mgr
Fax: (614) 808-3599
Email: praveen@jasstek.com
Website: www.jasstek.com
Information technology consulting, project staffing, IT staffing, contract programming, contract consultants, technology consultants & contract to hire consultants. (Woman/As-Pac, estab 2012, empl 9, sales $24,000, cert: State, NMSDC, WBENC)

5364 Lightwell Inc.
565 Metro Place S Ste 220 Columbus, OH 43017
(614) 310-2700 Bryan Scott Acct Exec
Fax:
Email: bryan.scott@lightwellinc.com
Website: www.lightwellinc.com
EDI, B2B integration, order management, ecommerce, business management, and supply chain management services. (Woman, estab 1998, empl 225, sales $39,000,000, cert: WBENC)

5365 Logic Soft, Inc.
5900 Sawmill Rd, Ste 200 Dublin, OH 43017
(614) 884-5544 Louis Viciedo Business Dev Mgr
Fax: (614) 884-5540
Email: louis.viciedo@logicsoftusa.com
Website: www.logicsoftusa.com
IT Managed Services, monitor program activity, detailed program analysis & benchmarking, invoicing, robust supplier management & total workforce solutions. (As-Ind, estab 1997, empl 50, sales $15,000,000, cert: State)

5366 LRSolutions, LLC dba Lyon Recruiting Solutions
6908 Engle Rad #CC Middleburg Heights, OH 44130
(440) 403-9241 Linda Gutekunst CEO
Fax: (440) 243-3777
Email: Linda@LRSolutions.net
Website: www.LRSolutions.net
IT staffing & solutions: permanent placement, staff augmentation & project-based solutions. (Woman/White, estab 2006, empl 4, sales $382,000, cert: State, NWBOC)

5367 Marinar Technology Co LLC dba VantageOne Software
33801 Curtis Blvd, Ste 112 Eastlake, OH 44095
(440) 354-1458 Erica Martin CEO
Fax: (440) 639-1987
Email: erica.francis@vantageonesoftware.com
Website: www.vantageonesoftware.com
IT service engineers & technicians, infrastructure expansion, data migration, system security, disaster planning or basic workstation & server optimization. (Woman/White, estab 1994, empl 10, sales $900,000, cert: State, WBENC)

5368 Marketing & Engineering Solutions
625 Bear Run Lane 625 Bear Run Lane Lewis Center, OH 43035
(740) 201-8112 Hiten Shah President
Fax: (866) 877-3585
Email: hshah@mesinc.net
Website: www.mesinc.net
Information technology, outsourcing, customer survey processing, database maintenance, OCR & ICR data processing, call center, data processing, data entry, rebate processing. (AA/As-Ind, estab 1999, empl 110, sales $2,700,000, cert: NMSDC)

5369 MAX Technical Training Inc.
4900 Parkway Dr   CINCINNATI, OH 45040
(513) 322-8888 Patricia Miller CEO
Fax: (513) 322-8898
Email: patricia@maxtrain.com
Website: www.maxtrain.com
IT programmers & developers training. (Woman/White, estab 1998, empl 12, sales $1,950,556, cert: WBENC)

5370 MCB Consulting, Inc.
501 Evans Ln Dayton, OH 45459
(937) 291-2751 B. Michael Bennett III CEO
Fax: (530) 325-5716
Email: michaelbennett@ameritech.net
Website:
Information technology solutions, Oracle, DB2, IBM 360, software process, software methodology, program mgmt, enterprise architecture, logistics, education, analysis, design, testing, implementation, installation, data modeling, database admin. (Woman/AA, estab 1998, empl 10, sales , cert: State, 8(a))

5371 MediaScript, LLC
3982 Powell Rd, Ste 235 Powell, OH 43065
(614) 551-3549 Angela Horne CEO
Fax:
Email: angela@mediascriptllc.com
Website: www.mediascriptllc.com
Media webinar technology: distance education, online learning & training. (Woman/White, estab 2009, empl 3, sales $165,000, cert: WBENC)

5372   MurTech Consulting LLC
       4807 Rockside Rd, Ste 250   Independence, OH
       44131
       (216) 328-8580 Ailish Murphy President
       Fax: (216) 328-8910
       Email: amurphy@murtechconsulting.com
       Website: www.murtechconsulting.com
Information technology consulting & placement services.
(Woman/White, estab 2000, empl 25, sales $14,200,000,
cert: WBENC)

5373   Myca Multimedia and Training Solutions, LLC
       4555 Lake Forest Dr Ste 650 Cincinnati, OH 45242
       (513) 608-6033 Patricia Massey President
       Fax: (888) 699-9794
       Email: pmassey@mycagroup.com
       Website: www.mycalearning.com
Interactive & engaging eLearning tools, computer & cloud-
based eLearning courseware on harassment prevention,
culture & inclusion, bullying. (Woman/White, estab 1991,
empl 15, sales $984,166, cert: WBENC)

5374   Net Activity
       9535 Midwest Ave, Ste 114   Garfield Heights, OH
       44125
       (216) 503-5150 John Marion CFO
       Fax: (216) 503-5148
       Email: info@netactivity.us
       Website: www.netactivity.us
Hardware & Software reseller, VoIP Phone Systems; hosted
& on-site, Connectivity; dedicated data & voice communication, Cloud Back-up; proprietary infrastructure &
Microsoft Azure, Remote network & hardware managed
services. (As-Ind, estab 2002, empl 11, sales $1,377,695,
cert: 8(a), SDB)

5375   N-ovation Technology Group
       10 W. 2nd St Ste 2201 Dayton, OH 45402
       (937) 886-4850 Dwayne Coker CEO
       Fax:
       Email: sales@n-ovationtech.com
       Website: www.n-ovationtech.com
Network Design, Architecture & Integration services, Data
Center Solutions, Cyber Security, Wireless DAS deployment, Cloud strategy, Infrastructure Program Management, Process Management & Quality Assurance, Vendor
Management. (AA, estab 2015, empl 5, sales $10,000,000,
cert: City, NMSDC)

5376   Precise Infotech Inc.
       7315 Royal Portrush Dr   Solon, OH 44139
       (440) 265-0402 Kashifa Ahmed President
       Fax:
       Email: kahmed@preciseinfotech.com
       Website: www.preciseinfotech.com
Software development & consulting. (Woman/As-Pac,
estab 2004, empl 2, sales $274,121, cert: State)

5377   Professional Consulting Technology, LLC
       526 South Main St Ste 230   Akron, OH 44311
       (404) 433-4677 Ronald Moore President
       Fax: (330) 752-4936
       Email: ronmoore@procon-technologies.com
       Website: www.procon-technologies.com
Information Technology & Security, Network Design,
Installation, Operation & Maintenance, Governance Risk
Management & Compliance, Managed Services, Infor-
mation Technology Staff Augmentation. (AA, estab 2011,
empl 5, sales $201,850, cert: State)

5378   Promark Custom Solutions LLC
       8 Prestige Plaza, Ste 110   Springboro, OH 45342
       (937) 557-0333 Lisa Johnson President
       Fax: (888) 437-8352
       Email: ljohnson@promarkcs.com
       Website: www.promarkcs.com
Office Productivity, Cyber Security, Security Certifica-
tions, IT Certifications, IT Skills, and Business Skills.
(Woman/White, estab 1995, empl 1, sales $49,000, cert:
WBENC)

5379   R.Dorsey & Company, Inc.
       400 W Wilson Bridge Rd Ste 105 Worthington,
       OH 43085
       (614) 486-8900 Joyce Dorsey CEO
       Fax: (866) 457-7323
       Email: jcdorsey@dorseyplus.com
       Website: www.dorseyplus.com
Network Architecture, Application Architecture, Service
Oriented Architecture, Data Warehouse, Hosting,
Security, Data Backup, Outsourcing (Woman/White,
estab 1996, empl 30, sales , cert: WBENC, 8(a))

5380   Record Express, LLC
       4295 Armstrong Blvd   Batavia, OH 45103
       (513) 685-7329 Nadine Albenze-Smith CEO
       Fax: (513) 685-7330
       Email: nalbenze@recordexpressllc.com
       Website: www.recordexpressllc.com
Record retrieval & document management: insurance
defense, personal injury, medical malpractice, tobacco,
product liability, construction, asbestos, finance &
banking, toxic tort, environmental. (Woman/White,
estab 2003, empl 33, sales $1,500,000, cert: State)

5381   Solutions For You Inc.
       470 Olde Worthington Rd Ste 200 Westerville, OH
       43082
       (614) 410-6648 Robert Johnson
       Fax: (614) 410-6649
       Email: robertj@sfyi.com
       Website: www.sfyi.com
Information Technology consulting: Full cycle product
development, Business Analysis, Quality Assurance,
Project Management, Security (data, network, database), Open Source (language, tools, software), data
analysis, Electronic Data Interchange. (Woman/AA, estab
1999, empl 4, sales $423,027, cert: State, City, NMSDC)

5382 StarTech Consulting, Inc.
      6746 Rivercrest Dr, Ste 100 Cleveland, OH 44141
      (440) 546-9500 Joe Bains President
      Fax:
      Email: jbains@startech-consult.com
      Website: www.startech-consult.com
Staff Augmentation, Web applications, Mobile applications, Database development/administrators, Project Managers, Business Analysts, Quality Assurance, etc. (As-Ind, estab 1998, empl 6, sales $2,107,771, cert: State)

5383 Strategic Systems, Inc.
      485 Metro Place S Ste 270 Dublin, OH 43017
      (614) 973-7981 Fred Shafer VP of sales
      Fax: (614) 413-2832
      Email: fred@strsi.com
      Website: www.strsi.com
Staff Augmentation for Information Technology, Project Management, Hybrid Staff Aumentation, Contract to Hire, and Platform Development/Delivery. (Woman/As-Ind, estab 2004, empl 175, sales $19,000,000, cert: State, NMSDC)

5384 TechSoft Systems, Inc.
      10296 Springfield Pike Ste 400 Cincinnati, OH 45215
      (513) 772-5010 Clifford A. Bailey CEO
      Fax: (513) 772-5032
      Email: cabailey@techsoftsystems.com
      Website: www.techsoftsystems.com
IT Consultants/Staffing, On-Site Support (desktop, network, help desk), Remot Support, Manages Services, Hardware & Software purchasing. (AA, estab 1983, empl 30, sales , cert: City, NMSDC)

5385 TMH Solutions LLC
      4176 Menderes Dr Powell, OH 43065
      (614) 581-4450 Theresa Harris President
      Fax: (740) 881-3264
      Email: theresa@tmhsolutions.com
      Website: www.tmhsolutions.com
Resell software & services, management & information technology solutions. (Woman/AA, estab 2010, empl 3, sales $5,800,000, cert: State, City, NMSDC)

5386 TPSi, LLC
      11590 Century Blvd Cincinnati, OH 45246
      (877) 682-5300 Matt Bender President
      Fax: (513) 346-2786
      Email: mbender@tpsinc.com
      Website: www.tpsinc.com
Technical staffing & engineering services. (Woman/White, estab 2000, empl 25, sales $2,300,000, cert: WBENC)

5387 UNICON International, Inc.
      241 Outerbelt St Columbus, OH 43213
      (614) 861-7070 Michael McAlear VP
      Fax: (614) 861-7096
      Email: mcalear@unicon-intl.com
      Website: www.unicon-intl.com
Information technology solutions. (Woman/As-Pac, estab 1990, empl 300, sales $31,000,000, cert: NMSDC, WBENC)

5388 Vertex Computer Systems, Inc.
      2245 Enterprise Pkwy E, Ste A Twinsburg, OH 44087
      (330) 963-0044 Venkit Raman CEO
      Fax: (330) 963-3566
      Email: vertex.rfp@vertexcs.com
      Website: www.vertexcs.com
IT development & outsourced services: web, database & middleware. (As-Ind, estab 1989, empl 200, sales $400,000,000, cert: State)

5389 Warwick Communications, Inc.
      405 Ken Mar Parkway Broadview Heights, OH 44147
      (216) 787-0300 Heidi Murphy Principal
      Fax: (216) 830-8505
      Email: hmurphy@warwickinc.com
      Website: www.warwickinc.com
Information technology managed services, telephone systems, VOIP systems, cloud/hosted systems, wireless systems, data switching equipment, call recording software, support desk services, call accounting systems, call center software. (Woman/White, estab 1960, empl 40, sales $6,245,000, cert: State)

Oklahoma

5390 Aero Tech Service Associates, Inc.
      909 S Meridian Ave, Ste 200 Oklahoma City, OK 73108
      (405) 946-2872 John Howard CEO
      Fax: (405) 946-2889
      Email: atsa@atsainc.com
      Website: www.atsainc.com
Aviation systems requirements, systems engineering & operations, information technology, communications, technical training, technical & administrative svcs & support. (AA, estab 1991, empl 180, sales , cert: State)

5391 Delaware Resource Group of Oklahoma LLC
      3220 Quail Springs Parkway Oklahoma City, OK 73134
      (405) 721-7776 Meredith Kemp Prog Mgmt Asst
      Fax: (405) 721-7779
      Email: meredith.kemp@drgok.com
      Website: www.drgok.com/
Contract instruction services, computer based training, curriculum development & maintenance, computer training materials devel & contract operations maintenance svcs. (Nat Ame, estab 2002, empl 200, sales $21,569,317, cert: NMSDC)

5392 Muscogee International LLC.
      1018 S Wood Dr Okmulgee, OK 74447
      (918) 752-3150 Mike Duke Business Dev Mgr
      Fax: (918) 758-1458
      Email: mduke@muscogeeinternational.com
      Website: www.muscogeeinternational.com/
IT, telecom, data, security, audio video, low voltage specialty, cyber security, consulting, programming, engineering, design, procurement, management, support (Nat Ame, estab 2011, empl 24, sales $10,161,321, cert: 8(a))

5393 Muscogee Nation Business Enterprise
P.O. Box 147   Okmulgee, OK 74447
(918) 752-3150 Woody Anderson Sales Mgr
Fax: (918) 758-1458
Email: wanderson@mnbe.com
Website: www.mnbe.com
Program mgmt, system engineering & integration, information technology, project admin & mgmt, architectural design & engineering, telecommunications, fire & security total integrated systems, surveillance, CCTV & access control. (Nat Ame, estab 1999, empl 100, sales $19,000,000, cert: State)

5394 Xyant Technology, Inc.
710 ASP Ave Ste 500 Norman, OK 73069
(405) 209-7371 Sowmya Sridhar President
Fax: (405) 447-8394
Email: sowmyas@xyant.com
Website: www.xyant.com
IT consulting & staff augmentation solutions: application implementation & deployment, maintenance & support, networking svcs, migration upgrades. (As-Pac, estab 1995, empl 50, sales $2,000,000, cert: NMSDC)

Oregon

5395 Cayuse Technologies, LLC
72632 Coyote Rd   Pendleton, OR 97801
(541) 278-8200 Heather Collins Dir. Business Dev
Fax: (541) 278-8470
Email: heather.collins@cayusetechnologies.com
Website: www.cayusetechnologies.com
Technology Platforms: Java and .NET-Operating Systems: UNIX and Windows-Programming Languages: Java, J2EE, PL/SQL, ASP, C, C+, C++, C#, VB, COBOL, TAL, TACL-Open Source Frameworks; Hibernate, Spring. (Nat Ame, estab 2006, empl 240, sales $15,063,354, cert: State, NMSDC)

5396 Dravon Medical, Inc.
11465 SE Hwy 212 P.O. Box 69 Clackamas, OR 97015
(503) 656-6600 Richard Parker CFO
Fax: (503) 655-5229
Email: admin@dravon.us
Website: www.dravon.com
manufacturer of medical & health care products including true blue clamps
and medical bags ranging from blood handling to collection. (Woman/White, estab 1974, empl 22, sales $2,804,000, cert: State)

5397 Everest Consultants, Inc.
1500 NW Bethany Blvd Ste 235 Beaverton, OR 97006
(503) 643-3990 Ranya Edupuganti President
Fax: (503) 643-3991
Email: ranya@everestinc.com
Website: www.everestinc.com
Software consulting, offshore software dev, systems integration & IS/IT staff augmentation. (Woman/As-Ind, estab 1993, empl 65, sales $9,500,000, cert: NMSDC)

5398 iBridge, LLC
15725 SW Greystone Ct Ste 200 Beaverton, OR 97006
(503) 906-3930 Desh Urs President
Fax: (503) 906-3931
Email: bids@ibridgellc.com
Website: www.ibridgellc.com/
Digitizing, converting, data processing all forms of information, electronic, paper, microfilm, voice or video, e cleanse, format & verify data. (As-Ind, estab 2004, empl 16, sales , cert: State)

5399 Martin's Got You Covered
P.O. Box 3764 Portland, OR 97208
(503) 289-0278 Donald Martin President
Fax: (503) 289-6698
Email: donald@martinsgotyoucovered.com
Website: www.martinsgotyoucovered.com/
Computer hardware & software, custom-build laptops, notebooks, tablet pcs, monitors, modems, presentation equipment, servers. (AA, estab 2002, empl 1, sales , cert: State)

5400 Mavensoft Technologies
15248 NW Greenbrier Pkwy   Beaverton, OR 97006
(503) 629-4855 Anu Mallavarapu Acct Mgr
Fax: (503) 296-2337
Email: anu@mavensoft.com
Website: www.mavensoft.com
IT services, software development, QA, Cloud Engineering, Project Management, Java, .NET, PHP, Angular JS, HP ALM, Selenium, BI Analytics, E-commerce, IBM Websphere, SAP Hybris, Oracle ATG, Magento. (As-Ind, estab 2004, empl 30, sales $2,400,000, cert: NMSDC)

5401 Protech Excellens Inc.
1500 NW Bethany Blvd Ste 200 Beaverton, OR 07006
(866) 688-8843 Ben Condol CEO
Fax:
Email: Ben@protechexcellens.com
Website: www.protechexcellens.com
Oracle Databases, Oracle Middleware, Oracle applications, Oracle Engineered Systems, Oracle storage, Oracle support. PeoleSoft, Fusion, EBS, CRM. (Woman/As-Pac, estab 2007, empl 2, sales $170,000, cert: State)

5402 Rapid External Solutions, Inc.
9450 SW Gemini Dr Ste 61944 Beaverton, OR 97008
(617) 616-0986 Vic Gupta Dir
Fax: (888) 516-4305
Email: info@r-e-s.com
Website: www.r-e-s.com
ERP Applications staffing: Oracle, SAP, PeopleSoft, JDE, Siebel, Microsoft. (As-Ind, estab 2009, empl 13, sales $11,000,000, cert: NMSDC)

5403   Triad Technology Group
       10300 SW Greenburg Rd, Ste 560   Portland, OR
       97223
       (503) 293-9547 Regina Shapiro Acct Mgr
       Fax: (503) 293-9546
       Email: kelley@go2triad.com
       Website: www.triadtechnology.com
Information technology staffing & recruiting services.
(Hisp, estab 1989, empl 30, sales $3,700,000, cert: State)

Pennsylvania

5404   Abator Information Services, Inc.
       615 South Avenue   Pittsburgh, PA 15221
       (412) 271-5922 Joanne E. Peterson CEO
       Fax: (412) 271-5833
       Email: joanne@abator.com
       Website: www.abator.com
Information technology & systems projects. (Woman/
White, estab 1983, empl 4, sales $901,392, cert: State,
WBENC)

5405   ABOUT-Consulting LLC
       330 Kennett Pike, Ste 205   Chadds Ford, PA 19317
       (610) 388-9455 Frances Gatto CEO
       Fax: (610) 388-9454
       Email: fgatto@about-consulting.com
       Website: www.about-consulting.com
Project mgmt, internet, intranet & extranet design & dev,
business apps & databases, help desk, network systems
engineering, architecture & admin, operations & technical
svcs.
(Woman/White, estab 2002, empl 20, sales $3,000,000,
cert: WBENC)

5406   AptoTek Inc.
       2026 Milta Hill Rd   Romansville, PA 19320
       (610) 241-2603 Joe Johnbosco CEO
       Fax:
       Email: joe.johnbosco@aptotek-inc.com
       Website: www.aptotek-inc.com
Custom Application Development, CRM Solutions, IT staff
augmentation, IT outsource Services, Application/software
support & maintenance contracts, IT strategy solutions.
(As-Ind, estab 2015, empl 1, sales , cert: NMSDC)

5407   Aspect Consulting, Inc.
       20140 Valley Forge Circle   King of Prussia, PA 19406
       (610) 783-0600 Nicole Gantzhorn Business Dev Rep
       Fax: (610) 783-5155
       Email: ngantzhorn@aspect-consulting.com
       Website: www.aspect-consulting.com
Technical Staffing, Data Management, Business Intelli-
gence, Configuration, Data Warehouse Development,
Database Administration, Oracle, SQL Server, Custom
Software Development, Application Design & Architecture.
(Woman/White, estab 1994, empl 40, sales $5,300,000,
cert: WBENC)

5408   Cogent Infotech Corporation
       1035 Boyce Rd Ste 108 Pittsburgh, PA 15241
       (412) 835-2700 Manu Mehta President
       Fax: (412) 774-1515
       Email: manu.mehta@cogentinfo.com
       Website: www.cogentinfo.com
IT services, systems integration, technical/functional IT
consulting, staff augmentation. (As-Ind, estab 2003,
empl 120, sales $7,100,000, cert: State, NMSDC)

5409   Cognis IT Advisors LLC
       1735 Market St Ste A-485 Philadelphia, PA 19103
       (215) 557-4455 Mike Thomas CEO
       Fax: (215) 557-4456
       Email: mthomas@cognisit.com
       Website: www.cognisit-advisors.com
Information Technology (IT) Services. (AA, estab 2007,
empl 4, sales $489,000, cert: NMSDC)

5410   Computer Enterprises Inc. (CEI)
       1000 Omega Dr Ste. 1150 Pittsburgh, PA 15205
       (412) 571-3686 Jim Kusnir Controller
       Fax: (412) 341-3087
       Email: jkusnir@ceiamerica.com
       Website: www.ceiamerica.com
Software consulting & system integration services,
custom applications & systems software programming
services & Internet systems consulting services. (As-Pac,
estab 1900, empl 1, sales $49,500,000, cert: NMSDC)

5411   CREDO Technology Solutions, Inc.
       110 Sunset Ave Ste 101 Harrisburg, PA 17112
       (717) 657-7017 Missy Flexman Dir Mktg &
       Communications
       Fax:
       Email: mflexman@credotsinc.com
       Website: www.credotsinc.com
IT project solutions, ERP software implementations &
upgrades. (As-Ind, estab 2010, empl 42, sales
$3,130,000, cert: State, NMSDC)

5412   Eminent Group, Inc
       2 Walnut Grove Rd Ste 130 Horsham, PA 19044
       (267) 387-6487 Katherine Moore CEO
       Fax:
       Email: kmoore@egiusa.com
       Website: www.egiusa.com
Transportation Management Systems Implementation,
Global Trade Management Systems Implementation,
Outsourcing:
Transportation Operational Planning, Transportation
Optimization. (Woman/White, estab 2002, empl 38,
sales $7,104,089, cert: WBENC)

5413   Genzeon Corporation
       559 W Uwchlan Ave Ste 120 Exton, PA 19341
       (610) 441-7308 Jessica Thomas COO
       Fax: (302) 691-1453
       Email: jessica.thomas@genzeon.com
       Website: www.genzeon.com
Technology solutions, custom application development,
performance engineering & human capital solutions.
(As-Ind/As-Pac, estab 2009, empl 50, sales $10,000,000,
cert: NMSDC)

5414　Hanabi Networks Systems, LLC
150 N Radnor Chester Rd, Ste F200　Radnor, PA 19087
(484) 381-0698　Tariq Yusufzai VP Business Dev
Fax:
Email: tyusufzai@ehanabi.com
Website: www.ehanabi.com
Analyze, design, install, configure, manage & repair global network infrastructure & application components. (As-Pac, estab 2016, empl 2, sales $120,000, cert: NMSDC)

5415　I&I Software, Inc.
2571 Baglyos Circle, B-32　Bethlehem, PA 18020
(610) 882-9699　Sebas Abraham VP Mktg
Fax: (610) 882-4341
Email: sebastian@iandisoft.com
Website: www.iandisoft.com
IT Services on COTS products, ERP, CRM, Business Intelligence, Network & Systems Administration, DBA, Project Management Services & Application Development. (As-Pac, estab 2001, empl 48, sales $8,343,201, cert: State)

5416　iBusiness Solution, LLC
5000 Lenker St　Mechanicsburg, PA 17050
(717) 724-7865　Narendra Ghuge
Fax: (408) 904-5798
Email: sales@ibusinesssolution.com
Website: www.ibusinesssolution.com
IT consulting, technology services, staffing & outsourcing. (As-Ind, estab 2000, empl 54, sales $9,000,000, cert: State, NMSDC)

5417　ImageTech Systsems, Inc.
3913 Hartzdale Dr　Camp Hill, PA 17011
(717) 761-5900　RJ Oommen Principal
Fax:
Email: rjo@imagetechsys.com
Website: www.imagetechsys.com
Enterprise Content Management (ECM) & Business Process automation technologies. (As-Ind, estab 1994, empl 7, sales $2,000,000, cert: State, NMSDC)

5418　Independent Computer Consulting Group, Inc.
1 Ivybrook Blvd Ste 177　Warminster, PA 18974
(215) 675-9149　Mihir Shah Sr Business Dev Mgr
Fax: (215) 675-5756
Email: mshah@iccg.com
Website: www.iccg.com
LX, SA, M3 products implementation, upgrades & support, WMS/PkMS, WMOS, SCALE, DOM implementations, upgrades & support, Business Intelligence, Qlik, Cognos & Micro Strategy
SAP suite of applications. (Woman/As-Ind, estab 1988, empl 100, sales , cert: WBENC)

5419　Iron Lady Enterprises Inc.
1943 Poplar St, 2nd Fl　Philadelphia, PA 19130
(267) 973-8626　Dianna Montague CEO
Fax: (215) 564-5531
Email: Dianna.Montague@IronladyEnterprises.com
Website: www.ironladyenterprises.com/
Ironworking services, IT services (Woman/AA, estab 2011, empl 2, sales , cert: City, NMSDC)

5420　JCW Computer Consulting, LLC
7478 Rhoads St, Ste C　Philadelphia, PA 19151
(215) 879-6701　Carl Johnson Sales Assoc
Fax: (215) 879-6702
Email: carl@jcwcc.com
Website: www.jcwcc.com
Computer consulting: Microsoft, IBM & Compaq solutions, workstation & server product lines. (AA, estab 1992, empl 3, sales , cert: City, NMSDC)

5421　KORYAK Consulting, Inc.
2003 Kinvara Dr　Pittsburgh, PA 15237
(412) 364-6600　Suresh Ramanathan CEO
Fax: (412) 364-6601
Email: sramanathan@koryak.com
Website: www.koryak.com
Management & IT consulting: business & IT strategy dev, supply chain enhancement, E-business integration, Oracle app implementation & outsourcing, systems dev & integration. (As-Ind, estab 2000, empl 25, sales $3,000,000, cert: State, NMSDC)

5422　Lim, Norris & Associates
12 Fox Hunt Cir　Plymouth Meeting, PA 19462
(610) 825-6730　Yvonne Norris President
Fax: (601) 825-0394
Email: ynorris@limnorris.com
Website: www.limnorris.com
IT, strategic planning & organization design. (Woman/AA/As-Ind, estab 1994, empl 3, sales $953,000, cert: City)

5423　Logix Guru LLC
3821 Old William Penn Hwy　Murrysville, PA 15668
(724) 733-4500　Singh Ajmani Business Dev Mgr
Fax: (724) 387-2451
Email: Ajmani@logixguru.com
Website: www.logixguru.com
IT consulting & staff augmentation, engineering, administrative, information technology. (As-Ind, estab 2000, empl 20, sales $4,200,000, cert: State, NMSDC)

5424　M.A.P. Consulting Services, Inc.
520 South 3rd St　Philadelphia, PA 19147
(215) 315-4175　Peggy Pacella CEO
Fax: (215) 315-4175
Email: ppacella@mapconsult.com
Website: www.mapconsult.com
IT staffing & consulting, ERP & EDI specialists, project mgmt expertise, data warehousing. (Woman/White, estab 1997, empl 2, sales $201,000, cert: WBENC)

5425　Mastech Digital Technologies, Inc.
1305 Cherrington Parkway Bldg 210, Ste 400 Moon Township, PA 15108
(412) 787-9559　Abhishek Jain Engagement Mgr
Fax: (412) 494-9272
Email: abhishek.jain@mastechdigital.com
Website: www.mastechdigital.com
IT services: usiness intelligence, data warehousing, architecture & web svcs, enterprise resource planning, custom applications, dev & maintenance, migration, re-engineering, project mgmt, ebusiness solutions. (As-Ind, estab 1986, empl 750, sales $123,400,000, cert: NMSDC)

5426 Minitab Inc.
Quality Plaza 1829 Pine Hall Road   State College, PA 16801
(814) 238-3280 Justin Callahan Sr Reg Sales Mgr
Fax: (814) 239-1702
Email: jcallahan@minitab.com
Website: www.minitab.com
IT products and services. (Woman/White, estab , empl 1, sales , cert: WBENC)

5427 Momentum, Inc.
2120 Market St Ste 100 Camp Hill, PA 17011
(717) 214-8000 Scott Reilly Exec Director
Fax: (717) 214-8004
Email: momentum@m-inc.com
Website: www.m-inc.com
IT & management consulting, process improvement, project mgmt & implementation support. (Woman/White, estab 1998, empl 54, sales $9,304,338, cert: State, City)

5428 Ohm Systems, Inc.
955 Horsham Rd Ste 101 Horsham, PA 19044
(215) 675-2766 Praful Patel President
Fax: (215) 675-2767
Email: ppatel@ohmsysinc.com
Website: www.ohmsysinc.com
Software dev, support, maintainance, R&D, web, consulting, FAA, telecom, protocols, client/server. (As-Ind, estab 1998, empl 89, sales $4,147,335, cert: State, NMSDC)

5429 OPTiMO Information Technology LLC
240 Market St, Ste 112 P.O. Box 770 Bloomsburg, PA 17815
(877) 564-8552 Michael Miguelez CEO
Fax: (877) 564-8552
Email: mmiguelez@optimo-it.com
Website: www.optimo-it.com
Web / Mobile application development, UI/UX system integration, database development, agile project/program management, digital forensic investigations, eDiscovery processing & hosted review. (Hisp, estab 2008, empl 50, sales $5,000,000, cert: 8(a))

5430 Partner's Consulting, Inc.
2004 Sproul Road, Ste 206   Broomall, PA 19008
(215) 939-6294 Matthew Robbins Engagement Mgr
Fax:
Email: mrobbins@partners-consulting.com
Website: www.partners-consulting.com
Information technology recruiting for full-time, temp-to-perm & contract positions. (Woman/White, estab 2006, empl 40, sales $6,000,000, cert: State, WBENC)

5431 PC Network Inc.
1315 Walnut St Ste 1402 Philadelphia, PA 19107
(267) 236-0015 Charlotte Anne Veazie General Counsel
Fax: (267) 236-0016
Email: charlotte.veazie@pcn-inc.com
Website: www.pcn-inc.com
IT Staffing Services, Managed Service Delivery & Business Process Outsourcing, Technology Deployments, Deskside Support, Data Center Operations. (Woman/White, estab 1988, empl 76, sales $7,340,000, cert: State, WBENC)

5432 Pierson Computing Connection, Inc.
6 N Frederick St Mechanicsburg, PA 17055
(717) 796-0493 Debra Pierson President
Fax: (717) 796-0692
Email: dpierson@piersoncci.com
Website: www.piersoncci.com
Project mgmt, multi-site IT & related installations, printers, cash registers, PC equipment, cabling, networking equipment, etc. (Woman/White, estab 1993, empl 47, sales $4,250,000, cert: State, WBENC)

5433 Probitas Technology Inc.
3544 N Progress Ave Ste 104 Harrisburg, PA 17110
(717) 773-4208 Benjamin Williams President
Fax: (717) 910-0283
Email: sales@probitastek.com
Website: www.probitastek.com
Computer networking design, installation & maintenance, electronic security. (AA, estab 2004, empl 8, sales $600,000, cert: State, City)

5434 PRWT Services, Inc.
1835 Market St Ste 800 Philadelphia, PA 19103
(215) 569-8810 Rose Braverman SVP, Strategic Planning & Ops
Fax: (215) 569-9893
Email: Rose.Braverman@prwt.com
Website: www.prwt.com
Information & document processing; lockbox processing; call ctr customer care & service; facilities mgmt; web & telephone-based fulfillment; telecommunications construction; help desk functions & toll collections operations. (AA, estab 1988, empl 1000, sales $69,800,000, cert: City, NMSDC)

5435 Relevante, Inc
1235 Westlakes Dr Ste 280 Berwyn, PA 19312
(484) 403-4100 William Brassington CEO
Fax: (610) 565-4990
Email: wbrassington@relevante.com
Website: www.relevante.com
Accounting & technology consultants. (As-Ind, estab 2002, empl 130, sales $6,100,000, cert: NMSDC)

5436 River Development Corporation
2005 Garrick Dr Pittsburgh, PA 15235
(412) 243-2005 Cheryl McAbee
Fax: (412) 243-0433
Email: crmcabee@riverdevcorp.com
Website:
Records storage: off site, web access inventory, media vault storage & delivery, scan & index, data vaulting, shredding. (Woman/AA/Nat Ame, estab 1996, empl 4, sales $45,000, cert: State, City, NMSDC)

5437 RST Solutions Inc.
1005 Azlen Lane Ste 114 Chalfont, PA 18914
(610) 613-8699 Rajan Kaistha VP
Fax: (610) 672-9985
Email: rajan@rstsolutions.com
Website: www.rstsolutions.com
ERP services, implementations, upgrade, integrations, JDE Mobile Apps, FRICE/COMLI, etc. (Woman/As-Ind, estab 2003, empl 18, sales $5,000,000, cert: WBENC)

5438   Sigma Resources LLC
7950 Saltsburg Rd   Pittsburgh, PA 15239
(412) 712-1019 Andreas Knispel VP consulting
Fax: (412) 712-1033
Email: aknispel@sigma-resources.com
Website: www.sigma-resources.com/
IT consulting services. (Woman/As-Pac, estab 1998, empl 24, sales $9,000,000, cert: State, WBENC)

5439   Simminger Trucking Ltd.
10 Courtney Lane   Media, PA 19063
(610) 566-1346 Steven E Simminger II Owner
Fax: (610) 771-4102
Email: info@simmingertrucking.com
Website: www.simmingertrucking.com
(AA, estab 2008, empl 1, sales $116,017, cert: State)

5440   SoftSages, LLC
17 Mystic Lane, Ste 2A   Malvern, PA 19355
(484) 604-0603 Jiraj Ruparelia VP
Fax:
Email: jiraj@softsages.com
Website: www.softsages.com
Software Development Consultants, programming, Database Developments, Networking & mobile development, custom software & security solutions. (As-Pac, estab 2005, empl 25, sales $8,000,000, cert: State, NMSDC, WBENC)

5441   solutions4networks, Inc.
1501 Reedsdale St Ste 2001 PIttsburgh, PA 15233
(412) 638-4341 Michele McGough CEO
Fax:
Email: michele@s4nets.com
Website: www.s4nets.com
Data, voice, wireless & network security consulting: network assessments & design, security assessments, IPv6 planning, MPLS, QoS, project mgmt, product selection, RFP devel. (Woman/White, estab 2000, empl 24, sales $8,103,000, cert: State, WBENC)

5442   Strother Enterprises Inc.
100 S Broad St Ste 2130 Philadelphia, PA 19110
(215) 564-5538 Ernest L Strother CEO
Fax: (215) 564-5531
Email: elstrother@strotherenterprises.com
Website: www.strotherenterprises.com
Food Service Management; Facilities Management; Commissary Services; Staffing and Training. Knowledge of government contracts, knowledge of compliance and regulatory standards and long-standing (AA, estab 1990, empl 26, sales $3,409,222, cert: State, City, NMSDC)

5443   SwitchLane Inc.
5 Christy Dr Ste 303 Chadds Ford, PA 19317
(267) 297-0790 Meera Kalyani President
Fax: (877) 203-7131
Email: meera@switchlane.com
Website: www.switchlane.com
IT staffing & consulting services. (Woman, estab 2010, empl 10, sales $1,312,407, cert: State, WBENC)

5444   Symphony Enterprises LLC
P.O. Box 16140 Pittsburgh, PA 15242
(412) 212-0135 Amit Kumar Sales & Business Dev
Fax: (412) 774-9230
Email: amit@symphonyenterprises.com
Website: www.symphonyenterprises.com
IT staffing & consulting services. (Woman/As-Ind, estab 2004, empl 4, sales $120,000, cert: State)

5445   Synergy EnterPrize, LLC
1150 First Ave, Ste 501   King of Prussia, PA 19406
(215) 279-1440 Jonathan Ngah Principal
Fax: (877) 735-4342
Email: jngah@synergy-ia.com
Website: www.synergy-ia.com
Audit Support, IT Management & Governance, Business Process Improvement, Project Management, Fraud Risk & Vulnerability Assessment solutions. (AA, estab 2011, empl 10, sales $450,000, cert: 8(a))

5446   Systems Staffing Group   Inc.
910 E. Main St Ste 201 Norristown, PA 19401
(1111) 111-1111 Beth Verman CEO
Fax: (610) 668-8102
Email: bverman@systemsstaffinggroup.com
Website: www.systemsstaffinggroup.com
Information technology staffing: consultants & permanent employees. (Woman/White, estab 2000, empl 30, sales $15,000,000, cert: WBENC)

5447   Tan Check Consolidated, Inc.
2 Silver Trail Circle Ste 101 Newtown, PA 18940
(215) 860-5031 Rebecca Smith Senior Acct Mgr
Fax: (215) 860-7173
Email: rsmith@tcci.com
Website: www.tcci.com
IT Staffing, IT Management, Consulting, Permanent Placement, Temp to Perm, Executive Search, Software Development. (Woman/White, estab 2001, empl 75, sales $6,850,000, cert: State, WBENC)

5448   Techwave Consulting Inc.
1 E Uwchlan Ave   Exton, PA 19341
(484) 873-4602 Jalpesh Thaker Mgr
Fax: (484) 872-8716
Email: infoNA@techwave.net
Website: www.techwave.net/
Software consulting & staffing services: SAP (BI, BO, BPC, BPM & BW), Oracle (OBIEE), Cognos & BPM products & services. (Woman/As-Ind, estab 2004, empl 150, sales $11,000,000, cert: State)

5449   The United Solutions Group Inc.
1101 W Hamilton St Ste 351 Allentown, PA 18101
(267) 401-1300 Sri Vadi Director of Govt Relations
Fax: (267) 339-6111
Email: gov@tusgi.com
Website: www.usgit.com
Database Design and Development, Data Warehouse Design, WEB Based Application Development, WEB Administration, Legacy Migration Strategies, Facility Management,Software Development. (As-Ind, estab 2002, empl 24, sales $2,535,000, cert: State, NMSDC, SDB)

5450   Trecom System Group, Inc.
       700 E Township Line Rd Ste 205 Havertown, PA
       19083
       (610) 328-7971 Phil Gring COO
       Fax: (800) 610-4508
       Email: pgring@trecomsystems.com
       Website: www.trecomsystems.com
Internet Services, Network Services and Support, Help-
Desk Management, Data Entry, Computer Facility Opera-
tions, Staff Augmentation, Program Management Support,
Documentation, Software Application Development. (AA,
estab 2009, empl 37, sales , cert: State, NMSDC)

5451   TreCom Systems Group
       99 November Dr   Camp Hill, PA 17011
       (717) 319-0711 Phillip Gring COO
       Fax:
       Email: pgring@trecomsystems.com
       Website: www.trecomsystems.com
Information technology consulting svcs: software dev &
design, enterprise architecture, training, help desk,
programming, networking, documentation, software
testing, staff augmentation, contract programming, Oracle
authorized reseller. (AA, estab 2009, empl 58, sales
$7,000,000, cert: State, NMSDC)

5452   Tri-force Consulting Services Inc.
       650 North Cannon Avenue   Lansdale, PA 19446
       (215) 362-2611 Manish Gorawala President
       Fax: (267) 200-0026
       Email: mgorawala@triforce-inc.com
       Website: www.triforce-inc.com
Information technology consulting: Java, J2EE, .NET, QA &
open source technologies based business applications
solutions. (As-Ind, estab 2000, empl 15, sales $220,000,
cert: State, NMSDC)

5453   TriLogic Corporation
       161 Hillpointe Dr   Canonsburg, PA 15317
       (724) 745-0200 Gary Grabowski oper Mgr
       Fax: (724) 745-5950
       Email: ggrabowski@tri-logic.com
       Website: www.tri-logic.com
Design, install & maintain LAN/WANs; wireless networking,
IP telephony, virtual private networks. (AA, estab 1981,
empl 35, sales , cert: NMSDC)

5454   Urban Harvest Partnership, LLC
       6050 Osage Ave   Philadelphia, PA 19143
       (610) 482-4284 Jonathan Ford Principal
       Fax: (215) 701-8732
       Email: ford@uhpwireless.com
       Website: www.urbanharvestllc.com
Technology services: desktop & network services, secure
wireless networking, cabling services, voice, data & audio/
video installations. (AA, estab 2003, empl 7, sales
$960,000, cert: State)

5455   YIKES, Inc.
       204 E Girard Ave   Philadelphia, PA 19125
       (215) 238-8801 Mia Levesque Co-Owner
       Fax: (215) 238-8802
       Email: info@yikesinc.com
       Website: www.yikesinc.com
Web design & development services, WordPress,
Custom web design, website maintenance, ecommerce,
web/database integration, ColdFusion, custom-built
web-based applications, content management systems.
(Woman/Nat Ame/As-Pac, estab 1996, empl 5, sales
$664,693, cert: City, WBENC)

5456   ZIOS Corporation
       211 N Camac St   Philadelphia, PA 19107
       (215) 988-9467 Eileen Hing CEO
       Fax: (215) 988-9488
       Email: ec.hing@zios3.com
       Website: www.zios3.com
Information technology: software, hardware & wireless
telecom services. (Woman/As-Pac, estab 1999, empl 1,
sales $70,000, cert: State)

5457   Zodiac Solutions Inc.
       270 Lancaster Ave Ste h-2 Malvern, PA 19355
       (484) 550-6482 Ravi Kukreja VP Ops
       Fax: (866) 655-7805
       Email: ravi@zodiac-solutions.com
       Website: www.zodiac-solutions.com
IT staff augmentation , IT solutions services, managed
services, project management, software development,
knowledge process outsourcing, management consulting. (As-Ind, estab 2011, empl 70, sales $4,751,993, cert:
NMSDC)

Puerto Rico

5458   Beryllium Corporation
       P.O. Box 5938   Caguas, PR 00726
       (787) 744-5729 Jorge Normandia CEO
       Fax: (615) 649-0561
       Email: info@berylliumpr.com
       Website: www.berylliumpr.com
Custom Software Design & Development, Pharmaceuti-
cal/Medical Devices Industries, Manufacturing Execution
Systems Integrators. (Hisp, estab 1998, empl 8, sales
$756,288, cert: NMSDC)

5459   CIC Construction Group, SE
       P.O. Box 29726   San Juan, PR 00929
       (787) 287-3540 Jose Torrens VP
       Fax: (787) 287-3555
       Email: jtorrens@cic-pr.com
       Website: www.cicconstruction.com/
General contractors doing construction at pharmaceuticals, hotels, hospitals etc. (Hisp, estab 1983, empl 480,
sales $70,743,703, cert: NMSDC)

5460   Ideal Engineering Solutions, PSC
RR 3 Box 7266   Cidra, PR 00739
(787) 378-2948   Ismael Robles President
Fax: (787) 739-4736
Email: irobles.ies@gmail.com
Website: www.idealengineeringsolutions.com
General Construction, Electrical and Mechanical Installations, Instrumentation and Control Systems, Gypsum Board works. (Hisp, estab 2007, empl 5, sales $300,000, cert: NMSDC, 8(a))

5461   Integrated Services for Productivity & Validation
Acuarela St, Ste 3A Urb Munoz Rivera   Guaynabo, PR 00969
(787) 789-4778   Luis Baez Principal
Fax: (787) 789-4778
Email: lmbaez@is-pv.com
Website: www.is-pv.com
Technology, Management, Systems & Productivity Improvement projects. (Hisp, estab 2007, empl 25, sales $2,280,441, cert: NMSDC)

5462   Integrated Technology & Compliance Services
PMB 470 Box 4956   Caguas, PR 00726
(939) 579-3846   Ismael Aviles COO
Fax:
Email: ismael.aviles@itcspr.com
Website: www.itcspr.com
Information Technology Consulting & cGMP Validation Consulting & Compliance services. (Hisp, estab 2005, empl 10, sales $977,456, cert: NMSDC)

5463   Jays and Fancy Interiors, Inc.
2A-16 Ave. Carlos Javier Andaluz   Bayamon, PR 00956
(787) 786-9411   Gavin Davis President
Fax: (787) 778-3808
Email: gdavis@jaysandfancy.com
Website: www.jaysandfancy.com
General contracting, interior finishes, concrete, masonry, cold formed metal framing, drywall, plaster, gypsum board, tiling, resilient flooring, Nora, installation, acoustical. (Hisp, estab 2001, empl 25, sales $5,200,000, cert: NMSDC)

5464   JC Automation, Corp.
Calle D #27-C Urb. Los Maestros   Humacao, PR 00791
(787) 719-7315   Juan Senquiz GM
Fax: (787) 716-4871
Email: jsenquiz@jcapr.cmom
Website: www.jcapr.com
IT Management, Compliance & Manufacturing System Services, Application Design & Development, Systems Integration. (Hisp, estab 1997, empl 40, sales $4,700,000, cert: NMSDC)

5465   Mirus Consulting Group Corp
P.O. Box 851   Humacao, PR 00792
(787) 285-0992   Giovanni Gomez Dir
Fax: (787) 850-7771
Email: ggomez@miruspr.com
Website: www.miruspr.com
Computer system validation & information technology consulting services. (Hisp, estab 2001, empl 25, sales $2,900,000, cert: NMSDC)

5466   Real Physics, Inc.
1056 Munoz Riviera Ave Ste 903   San Juan, PR 00927
(787) 469-1359   Pedro Torres President
Fax: (888) 828-0106
Email: ptorres@realphysics.net
Website: www.realphysics.net
Project management, IT consulting, outsourcing, appraisal, validation, aerial photography, scheduling services, quality & logistics audits. (Hisp, estab 2007, empl 3, sales , cert: NMSDC)

5467   Weil Group, Inc.
Urb. Villa Blanca Calle Aquamarina #78 Ste 1 Caguas, PR 00725
(787) 633-0025   Milagros del R Gonzalez GM
Fax: (787) 286-1833
Email: mgonzalez@weilgroup.com
Website: www.weilgroup.com
Temporary employment agency, outsourcing IT & automation services: management and/or admin, help desk, servers, WAN, email system, desktop, maintenance, backup & restore. (Hisp, estab 1994, empl 50, sales $11,000,000, cert: NMSDC)

Rhode Island

5468   Artifex Technology Consulting, Inc.
614 George Washington Hwy   Lincoln, RI 02865
(401) 723-6644   Jenna Schmidt President
Fax: (401) 723-2225
Email: jenna@artifextech.com
Website: www.artifextech.com
Custom software solutions & graphic design. (Woman/White, estab 2002, empl 13, sales $2,380,350, cert: WBENC)

5469   Granger Warburton Consulting, LLC
79 West St   East Greenwich, RI 02818
(401) 965-1288   Bethany Warburton Principal Consultant
Fax:
Email: bethany@grangerwarburton.com
Website: www.grangerwarburton.com
Learning management system design & deployment, elearning creation, software application development, project management, business analysis, change management, documentation & process design. (Woman/White, estab 2013, empl 2, sales $127,000, cert: State)

South Carolina

5470   Blue Eye Soft Corp.
2541 N Pleasantburg Dr, Ste 158   Greenville, SC 29609
(937) 581-7110 Srikanth Kodeboyina Managing Partner
Fax:
Email: sri@blueyesoft.com
Website: www.blueyesoft.com
IT Consulting Software solutions, BI Analytics, CRM, Scalable Architecture, Health IT, Program& Project Management, Human Resource Consulting. (As-Pac, estab 2017, empl 9, sales , cert: NMSDC)

5471   Datasoft Technologies Inc.
34 Parkway Commons Way   Greer, SC 29650
(864) 278-0608 Jayadev Manyapu President
Fax: (877) 888-7207
Email: jmanyapu@datasoft-tech.com
Website: www.datasoft-tech.com
Software devel & consulting: system integration, engineering & architecture, project mgmt, analysis & design. (As-Ind, estab 1994, empl 31, sales $3,130,849, cert: NMSDC)

5472   Globalpundits Technology Consultancy Inc.
4715D Sunset Blvd   Lexington, SC 29072
(803) 354-9400 Manoj Devulapalli President
Fax: (803) 996-1055
Email: manoj@globalpundits.com
Website: www.globalpundits.com
Computer programming services, software design services, project management, business analysts, database administrations, contract engineering, mechanical engineers, stress engineers, electrical engineers, aeronautical engineers, CAD. (As-Pac, estab 2000, empl 146, sales $11,000,000, cert: State, NMSDC)

5473   Ishpi Information Technologies, Inc.
496 Bramson Court   Mt. Pleasant, SC 29464
(843) 329-4100 Pat Stanton Director of Ops
Fax: (888) 388-5152
Email: pat.stanton@ishpi.net
Website: www.ishpi.net
System engineering & integration, information & assurance & enterprise architecture. (Nat Ame, estab 2006, empl 58, sales $550,000, cert: State)

5474   Synesis International, Inc.
30 Creekview Ct   Greenville, SC 29615
(864) 288-1550 Ricardo Studart President
Fax: (864) 288-7650
Email: Rstudart@synesisintl.com
Website: www.synesisintl.com
Information technology: ERP, MES, business analytics, EDI, bar code & quality control systems. (Hisp, estab 1994, empl 28, sales $3,500,000, cert: NMSDC)

Tennessee

5475   Conch Technologies, Inc.
6750 Poplar Ave, Ste 711   Memphis, TN 38138
(901) 827-5183 Ray Scott VP Natl sales
Fax: (901) 754-6890
Email: contact@conchtech.com
Website: www.conchtech.com
IT consultants & contract programming, pc/client servers, internet/intranet, B2B & e-commerce. (Woman/As-Pac, estab 2004, empl 55, sales $1,700,000, cert: State, NMSDC)

5476   MCH Corporation
P.O. Box 720   Sweetwater, TN 37874
(865) 388-2727 Mike Hamilton President
Fax: (423) 337-7223
Email: mhamilton@visualc.com
Website: www.visualc.com
Data extraction & conversion, document scanning, OCR & ICR processing, litigation support svcs, reverse engineering , data transformation, data capturing & harvesting. (Nat Ame, estab 1998, empl 3, sales $372,000, cert: State)

5477   Redbird Technology Inc.
2505 Blair Blvd   Nashville, TN 37212
(404) 386-3073 Gary Campbell Dir Business Dev
Fax: (770) 926-3251
Email: gcampbell@rbti.com
Website: www.rbti.com
Develops software technologies used in the aerospace & defense industry. (Nat Ame, estab 1993, empl 3, sales $220,000, cert: State)

5478   Stragistics Technology, Inc.
6263 Poplar Avenue, Ste 950   Memphis, TN 38119
(901) 309-5550 Hughetta Dudley CEO
Fax: (901) 309-2228
Email: hdudley@stragistics.com
Website: www.stragistics.com
Technology solutions, data integration, migration, eCommerce, infrastructure management, proprietary software, SDLC, systems integration. (Woman/AA, estab 1997, empl 8, sales $379,010, cert: State, City, NMSDC, WBENC)

5479   Zycron, Inc.
413 Welshwood Dr   Nashville, TN 37211
(615) 251-9588 Rochelle Taylor VP of Ops
Fax: (615) 251-9577
Email: rtaylor@zycron.com
Website: www.zycron.com
System integration,technical consulting, supplemental staffing, configuration mgmt, software analysis, system design & facilities mgmt. (AA, estab 1991, empl 300, sales $29,245,696, cert: State)

Texas

5480 A1 Shredding Inc.
P.O. Box 460085   Houston, TX 77056
(832) 545-3949 Christopher Passmore President
Fax:
Email: cpassmore@a1shreddinginc.com
Website: www.a1shreddinginc.com
Document shredding, paper recycling, paper destruction & shredding, IT/computer services. (AA, estab 2007, empl 1, sales , cert: State)

5481 AACANN Mechanical, Inc.
12718 Robert E. Lee   Houston, TX 77044
(281) 458-2258 Larry Cannon President
Fax: (713) 456-2788
Email: aacann@ymail.com
Website: www.aacann.com
Service, repair, installation, maintenance and zone comfort controls/design of HVACR systems designed for industrial and offshore accommodations along with process cooling systems. (AA, estab 1982, empl 4, sales $642,000, cert: NMSDC)

5482 Accolite Inc.
16479 Dallas North Pkwy, Ste 350   Addison, TX 75001
(469) 235-9316 Matthew McKinley VP Business Devel
Fax: (972) 200-7063
Email: Matthew.McKinley@Accolite.com
Website: www.accolite.com
Contingent staffinng services: contract, contract to hire & permanent candidates for IT. (As-Pac, estab 2006, empl 280, sales $12,000,000, cert: State, NMSDC)

5483 Ace Delivery
7308 Gaines Mill Ln   Austin, TX 78745
(512) 326-3553 Tammie Garcia Office Mgr
Fax: (512) 326-3531
Email: viaace1@gmail.com
Website: www.acedeliveryatx.com
Ace Delivery we specilize in the medical supply chains. We help with delivering medical products to all hospitals and supply chains. We have a 100 mile radius from downtown Austin. We are vendors to Seton Family of Hospitals, St Davids (Woman/Hisp, estab 1980, empl 7, sales $947,931, cert: City)

5484 Addison Stuart
566 Homewood Dr   Coppell, TX 75019
(847) 707-0429 Christina Kolassa Owner
Fax:
Email: ckolassa@addisonstuart.com
Website: www.addisonstuart.com
Information technology, PPM implementation using CA Clarity & Oracle PPM tools. (Woman/White, estab 2012, empl 4, sales $200,000, cert: WBENC)

5485 Advent Global Solutions, Inc
12777 Jones Rd, Ste 445   Houston, TX 77070
(281) 640-8934 Chet Mann VP Client Services
Fax: (832) 678-2368
Email: chet.mann@adventglobal.com
Website: www.adventglobal.com
ERP implementation, IT development & systems integration, SAP technology. (As-Ind, estab 1997, empl 1500, sales $182,000,000, cert: NMSDC)

5486 Akorbi (Elahi Enterprises dba Akorbi)
6504 International Pkwy Ste 1500 Plano, TX 75093
(214) 256-9222 Cheryl Parker Natl Director of Client Partnerships
Fax: (214) 256-9222
Email: cparker@akorbi.com
Website: www.akorbi.com
IT consulting & recruitment: information technology, telecommunications, professional services & language solutions, technical staffing, professional placements, custom application development & business communications. (Woman/AA, estab 2003, empl 964, sales $34,000,000, cert: NMSDC)

5487 Alphaworks LLC
1600 10th St, Ste B Plano, TX 75074
(972) 509-8837 Don R Joe Ops Mgr
Fax: (972) 509-8831
Email: rodney.joe@alphaworksnow.com
Website: www.alphaworksnow.com
IT hardware, software & services: HP, Oracle, SAP, Cisco & TDi. (As-Pac, estab 2010, empl 16, sales $3,000,000, cert: NMSDC)

5488 Al-Razaq Computing Services
6001 Savoy, Ste 505   Houston, TX 77036
(713) 839-9613 Vicki Semander Contract vehicle spec
Fax: (713) 839-9931
Email: vsemander@al-razaqcomputing.com
Website: www.al-razaqcomputing.com
Database mgmt, systems network integration, computer hardware & software, educational product dev & training, financial mgmt, budget dev & execution package, software dev & computer programming. (AA, estab 1993, empl 48, sales $3,167,414, cert: State, City, NMSDC)

5489 American Unit, Inc.
2901 N Dallas Pkwy Ste 333 Plano, TX 75093
(9723) 983-3355 Ramana Mgr
Fax: (214) 889-9666
Email: ramana@americanunit.com
Website: www.americanunit.com
Enterprise & e-business implementation, upgrade, & production support services. (As-Pac, estab 2003, empl 365, sales $30,000,000, cert: State)

5490 Amtek Consulting LLC
18170 Dallas Pkwy Ste 104 Dallas, TX 75287
(214) 680-6111 Satya Movva President
Fax: (214) 975-1041
Email: smovva@amtekconsulting.com
Website: www.amtekconsulting.com
IT consulting services, system design & implementation, client-Server solutions, application development, systems maintenance/operations support. (As-Ind, estab 2004, empl 42, sales $1,727,782, cert: NMSDC)

5491 Applied Training Resources Inc.
6405 Cypresswood Dr, Ste 250 Spring, TX 77379
(281) 370-9540 Rose Bradshaw Controller
Fax:
Email: atr@globalxlr.com
Website: www.atrco.com
Lifecycle management systems: procedure & policy management, editing, procedure workflow (MOC), periodic review, incident investigation, action tracking & integrated learning management. (Woman/White, estab 1990, empl 43, sales $6,580,266, cert: WBENC)

5492 Argus Talent, LLC
11739 Willcrest Houston, TX 77031
(713) 465-5985 Zeyn Patel President
Fax: (713) 465-7545
Email: info@argustalent.com
Website: www.argustalent.com
Document, Records & Electronic Content Management (ECM) systems, custom computing services, system design services, and staff augmentation services. (As-Ind/Hisp, estab 1989, empl 20, sales $500,000, cert: State, NMSDC)

5493 Armstrong Archives, LLC
1515 Crescent Dr Carrollton, TX 75006
(972) 242-7179 Sherri Taylor President
Fax: (972) 245-9788
Email: Hub@aarchives.com
Website: www.armstrongarchives.com
Secure & Reliable Record Storage, Document Storage, Document Management, Document Scanning, Paper Shredding & Distribution. (Woman/White, estab 1996, empl 13, sales $3,585,450, cert: WBENC)

5494 Aspiryon, LLC
711 Nolana, Ste 103-F McAllen, TX 78504
(919) 900-8622 Neil Crisman GM
Fax:
Email: sales@aspiryon.net
Website: www.aspiryon.net
Information security solutions. (Woman/Hisp, estab 2011, empl 12, sales $2,000,000, cert: State)

5495 Assent Solutions LLC
27311 Bentridge Park Ln Katy, TX 77494
(713) 853-9288 Venkata Reka VP
Fax: (713) 338-2678
Email: reka@assentsolutions.com
Website: www.assentsolutions.com
Information Technology Consulting, Staffing Augmentation, IT Staffing Services, Custom Software Application Development, Web Development. (Woman/As-Ind, estab 2009, empl 10, sales $588,751, cert: City)

5496 Associates Systems LLC
750 S Mac Arthur Blvd Ste 100 Coppell, TX 75019
(972) 241-4436 Pavan Akula Dir of Sales
Fax: (972) 241-4439
Email: pavan.akula@associatessystems.com
Website: www.associatessystems.com
Information technology solutions & services. (Woman/As-Pac, estab 2002, empl 40, sales , cert: State, NMSDC)

5497 Austin Tele-Services Partners, LP dba Genesis ATS
4209 S Industrial Dr Ste 300 Austin, TX 78744
(512) 437-3041 Patrick Manning VP Business Dev
Fax: (512) 329-8091
Email: pmanning@genesis-ats.com
Website: www.genesis-ats.com
IT, Networking, Telecommunications & Computer related equipment & services. (Hisp, estab 2003, empl 45, sales $25,000,000, cert: State, NMSDC)

5498 Axis Technologies
5904 Chapel Hill Blvd Ste 205 Plano, TX 75093
(972) 473-3633 Dana Bower CEO
Fax:
Email: dbower@axistec.com
Website: www.axistec.com
Contract consulting: PLM, PDM, CRM/ERP Seibel, SAP, Peoplesoft. (Woman/White, estab 1900, empl 1, sales $1,675,000, cert: NMSDC)

5499 Bastion Technologies, Inc.
17625 El Camino Real Houston, TX 77058
(281) 283-9330 Jorge Hernandez President
Fax: (281) 283-9333
Email: jhernandez@bastiontechnologies.com
Website: www.bastiontechnologies.com
Engineering design, analysis, systems engineering, information technology applications, engineering research, mechanical engineering, structural engineering, safety & reliability engineering, systems safety, hazard analysis. (Hisp, estab 1998, empl 400, sales $42,711,000, cert: State, NMSDC)

5500 Bestica, Inc.
3463 Magic Dr Ste 303 San Antonio, TX 78229
(210) 614-4198 Harvinder Singh CEO
Fax: (210) 399-0694
Email: harvinder@bestica.com
Website: www.bestica.com
IT consulting & staffing firm. (As-Ind, estab 2005, empl 185, sales $7,500,000, cert: NMSDC, 8(a))

5501 Bravo Technical Resources
4835 LBJ Fwy Ste 1000 Dallas, TX 75244
(972) 419-1655 Kristen Lindner
Fax: (972) 419-1654
Email: klindner@bravotech.com
Website: www.bravotech.com
IT & engineering staffing: contract, contract to hire, direct hire. (Woman/White, estab 1995, empl 10, sales $9,800,000, cert: State, WBENC)

5502 BroadAxis Inc.
2591 Dallas Pkwy Ste 300 Frisco, TX 75034
(215) 280-1992 Nazish Imran Technical Recruiter
Fax:
Email: nazish@broadaxis.com
Website: www.broadaxis.com
Technology solutions, infrastructure & security projects, IT projects & staffing. (As-Ind, estab 2014, empl 5, sales , cert: State, NMSDC)

5503 Calpion Inc.
4835 Lyndon B Johnson Freeway Ste 515 Dallas, TX 75244
(469) 242-6056 Thomas John President
Fax: (469) 242-6078
Email: thomas@calpion.com
Website: www.calpion.com
IT consulting & staffing, software development, SAP testing & consulting, Cloud based server & IT resources. (As-Ind, estab 2004, empl 50, sales $2,400,000, cert: State, NMSDC)

5504 Caravan Consulting, LLC
16947 Old Pond Dr   Dallas, TX 75248
(469) 525-6518 Richard Bird Mgr
Fax: (866) 383-1507
Email: rbird@caravanconsulting.com
Website: www.caravanconsulting.com
Infrastructure Architecture, Data Modeling, Database Management, ETL Architecture & Development, Data Warehouse Architecture & Development. (AA, estab 2009, empl 1, sales $318,000, cert: NMSDC)

5505 Carter Scholer Arnett Hamada & Mockler PLLC
8150 N Central Expressway Ste 500 Dallas, TX 75206
(214) 550-8188 Helen Gilliland Partner
Fax: (214) 730-5026
Email: helen@carterscholer.com
Website: www.carterscholer.com
Legal Services (Woman/AA/As-Ind, estab 2012, empl 14, sales $6,000,000, cert: NMSDC)

5506 Castillo & Associates
6942 FM 1960 E., Ste 290   Humble, TX 77346
(281) 852-7487 Mike Castillo President
Fax: (281) 812-7288
Email: mike.a.castillo@cainfotech.com
Website: www.cainfotech.com
Engineering & technical support services: network infrastructure, telecommunications systems & services, enterprise application support & IT risk analysis. (Hisp, estab 1998, empl 16, sales $3,200,000, cert: State, City)

5507 CBI Consulting Group
9609 Asheboro St Frisco, TX 75035
(956) 559-0454 Heriberto Estrada President
Fax:
Email: heriberto.estrada@cbiconsultinggroup.com
Website: www.cbiconsultinggroup.com
IT professional services, SAP solutions, implementation, system upgrades, education, support, and custom development. (Hisp, estab 2014, empl 5, sales $350,000, cert: State, NMSDC)

5508 CES Network Services, Inc.
P.O. Box 810256   Dallas, TX 75381
(972) 241-3683 Enrique Flores President
Fax: (972) 241-8973
Email: ehflores@cesnetser.com
Website: www.cesnetser.com
Network engineering services, LAN, WAN & MAN, cell site planning & desig, RFI / EMI analysis, CADD services, satellite design, microwave radio, topographic map studies, digital terrain studies. (Nat Ame/Hisp, estab 1988, empl 11, sales $6,200,000, cert: State, City)

5509 CESCO, Inc.
11969 Plano Rd Ste 130 Dallas, TX 75243
(214) 824-8741 Billie Bryant Schultz CEO
Fax: (214) 824-0490
Email: bbryant@cesco-inc.com
Website: www.cesco-inc.net
Dist & service fax, printers & copiers, pens, paper, furniture, etc. (Woman/White, estab 1965, empl 24, sales $8,844,935, cert: State, WBENC)

5510 Cima Solutions Group, Ltd.
118 Lynn Avenue Ste 300 Lewisville, TX 75057
(972) 499-8261 John Alday President
Fax: (866) 259-0320
Email: jalday@cimasg.com
Website: www.cimasg.com
IT optization & business continuity. (Hisp, estab 2005, empl 11, sales $2,374,624, cert: State, City, NMSDC)

5511 CIS Cenergy International Services
12650 Crossrroads Park Dr Houston, TX 77065
(713) 965-6200 June Ressler President
Fax: (713) 965-6204
Email: christine.lujan@cenergyintl.com
Website: www.cenergyintl.com
Information technology consulting services: outsourcing, software development, PC repairs & network support, training, project mgmt, GIS consulting, web development, system support, repair & maintenance. (Woman/White, estab 2006, empl 20, sales $100,000, cert: WBENC)

5512 ClearRES LLC
800 E Campbell Rd Ste 170 Richardson, TX 75081
(214) 455-7860 Dhanya Yalamanchi CEO
Fax:
Email: dhanya@clearRES.com
Website: www.ClearRES.com
IT services & solutions, fixed priced projects, strategic staffing, onshore, offshore developed centers. (Nat Ame, estab 2015, empl 3, sales $100,000, cert: State, NMSDC)

5513 Cognitive Technologies, Inc.
115 Wild Basin Rd S Ste 104 Austin, TX 78746
(512) 380-1204 Karen McGraw CEO
Fax: (512) 233-0098
Email: kmcgraw@cognitive-technologies.com
Website: www.cognitive-technologies.com
Project management, project recovery, business process redesign, implementation planning, change management, testing. (Woman/White, estab 2001, empl 10, sales $800,000, cert: City)

5514   CompQsoft, Inc.
       505N Sam Houston Pkwy East Ste 682 Houston, TX
       77060
       (832) 932-8732 Franklin Benjamin Business Dev
       Mgr
       Fax: (281) 968-2077
       Email: franklinb@compqsoft.com
       Website: www.compqsoft.com
Mobile computing solutions, custom programming,
network support, e-commerce solutions, QA testing svcs,
staffing, on-site training. (As-Ind, estab 1997, empl 120,
sales $12,000,000, cert: City, NMSDC)

5515   Consultis
       8700 Tesoro Dr, Ste 360   San Antonio, TX 78217
       (210) 930-1640 Jason Schweitzer Acct Mgr
       Fax: (210) 930-1042
       Email: info@consultis.com
       Website: www.consultis.com
Information technology staffing, staff augmentation,
outsourcing & direct hires. (Woman/White, estab 1984,
empl 150, sales $13,000,000, cert: WBENC)

5516   Coptic Communications, Inc. dba Wave Technology
       2340 E Trinity Mills Rd Ste 240 Carrollton, TX 75006
       (972) 820-6950 Phillip Radcliff VP Business Devel
       Fax: (214) 722-1279
       Email: pradcliff@wavehitech.com
       Website: www.wavehitech.com
Voice, data, cabling, inside & outside plant design, PC's,
network appliances, servers, printers, routers, switches &
network design, systems integration, network admin &
configuration mgmt, database dev, email & calendaring,
systems upgrades & support. (Woman/White, estab 1990,
empl 12, sales $3,000,000, cert: State)

5517   Corporate Records Management Inc.
       3141 Hansboro Ave   Dallas, TX 75233
       (214) 333-3453 Denise Chadima Owner
       Fax: (214) 467-3453
       Email: denise@crmfiles.com
       Website: www.crmfiles.com
Record storage, archiving, secured shredding, back up tape
rotation. (Woman/White, estab 1998, empl 12, sales
$764,220, cert: State)

5518   Critical Start LLC
       6100 Tennyson Pkwy Ste 250 Plano, TX 75024
       (214) 810-6760 Tera Davis Managing Dir
       Fax: (214) 919-4050
       Email: tera.davis@criticalstart.com
       Website: www.criticalstart.com
Network security products & services: risk, compliance,
governance; threat management & incident response.
(Woman/White, estab 2012, empl 10, sales , cert: State)

5519   CRV, Inc.
       3407 Northeast Pkwy, Ste 170   San Antonio, TX
       78218
       (210) 828-8552 Glenda Anzualda Project Mgr
       Fax: (210) 828-5042
       Email: glendaa@crvinc.com
       Website: www.crvinc.com
Network consulting, resell Cisco, Dell, Hewlett Packard/
Compaq, IBM & Minolta/QMS, printer repair & maintenance agreements, voice & data circuits, audio visual
integration & rental svcs. (Hisp, estab 1993, empl 15,
sales $8,858,797, cert: State)

5520   Dallas Digital Services
       5316 Bransford Road   Colleyville, TX 76034
       (817) 577-8794 Howie Evans VP
       Fax: (817) 503-9970
       Email: hevans@ddserv.com
       Website: www.ddserv.com
IT storage products: Fibre Channel & iSCSI devices, data
center design solutions, Quantum, OverlandStorage,
EMC, SUN, Tek-Tools, Qlogic, Legato, Cisco, NEOScale.
(Woman/Nat Ame, estab 1996, empl 14, sales
$4,600,000, cert: State, WBENC)

5521   Decca Consulting LLC
       14090 SW Freeway Ste 300 Sugar Land, TX 77478
       (832) 561-0634 Nayeem Amin Managing Partner
       Fax: (832) 201-7233
       Email: amin@deccaconsulting.com
       Website: www.deccaconsulting.com
IT staffing & solutions. (Woman/As-Ind, estab 2007,
empl 25, sales $1,850,000, cert: State, NMSDC)

5522   Decision Tree Technologies
       306 Thunderbird Ln   El Paso, TX 79912
       (512) 294-0604 Bryyan Ritter Client Mgr
       Fax:
       Email: ritter@dtreetech.com
       Website: www.dtreetech.com
Data center, contact center, IT security, networking &
related IT technologies. (Woman/White, estab 1989,
empl 10, sales $8,100,000, cert: State)

5523   Defense Support Services, Inc.
       3212 Bishop Dr Arlington, TX 76010
       (817) 261-0233 Deon Moses President
       Fax: (817) 861-5147
       Email: dmoses@dss-inc.net
       Website: www.dss-inc.net
Aircraft hardware logistics & distribution, IT design &
services, communications. (AA, estab 1998, empl 10,
sales $3,000,000, cert: NMSDC)

5524   Digital Consulting & Software Services, Inc.
       2277 Plaza Dr Ste 275 Sugar Land, TX 77479
       (713) 982-8034 Patricia Patterson CEO
       Fax: (281) 243-2506
       Email: pmpatter@dcss.com
       Website: www.dcss.com
Management consulting, professional technical serivces.
(Woman/White, estab 1900, empl 1, sales $30,241,907,
cert: WBENC)

5525   Direct Line To Compliance, Inc.
9555 W Sam Houston Pkwy S, Ste 333   Houston, TX 77099
(713) 777-3522 Micha Adeeko Business Devel Mgr
Fax: (866) 433-0740
Email: michael.adeeko@dl2c.com
Website: www.dl2c.com
Software & consulting (ColorCodeIT and ChameleonDocs), form automation, electronic document handling & compliance program software. (Woman/AA, estab 2008, empl 17, sales $1,363,745, cert: State, NMSDC)

5526   doc2e-file,Inc.
4500 S. Wayside Dr Ste 102 Houston, TX 77087
(713) 649-2006 Sherry McManus President
Fax: (713) 649-2033
Email: sherrymcmanus@doc2e-file.com
Website: www.doc2e-file.com
Document scanning & indexing, e-records mgmt, systems & equipment. (Woman/White, estab 1999, empl 35, sales $2,700,000, cert: State, WBENC)

5527   Dployit, Inc.
15305 Dallas Parkway Ste 300 Addison, TX 75001
(214) 646-6525 Ralph Harper President
Fax: (214) 646-6523
Email: rharper@dployit.com
Website: www.dployit.com
Deploy information systems, IT staff augmentation, asset management. (AA, estab 2000, empl 20, sales $500,000, cert: State, NMSDC)

5528   Dynamic Computing Services
3307 Northland Dr, Ste 250   Austin, TX 78731
(800) 345-1275 Jenelle Thomas Director, Business Dev
Fax: (800) 800-9790
Email: jenelle@dcshq.com
Website: www.dcshq.com
Information technology placements services. (Woman/White, estab 1990, empl 152, sales $13,926,270, cert: State)

5529   ECOM Consulting, Inc.
2828 W Parker Rd Ste 224 Plano, TX 75075
(972) 578-0191 Baku Kshatriya President
Fax: (469) 361-7309
Email: baku@ecomconsultinginc.com
Website: www.ecomconsultinginc.com
Technical consulting services & staff augmentation. (As-Ind, estab 1995, empl 72, sales , cert: State, NMSDC)

5530   eConsulting Partners Global, Inc
10000 North Central Exprwy Ste 400 Dallas, TX 75231
(214) 680-0982 Jade Tran Principal
Fax: (888) 727-5705
Email: jade.tran@ecpgi.com
Website: www.ecpgi.com
System Integration, Enterprise Application Architecture, Service-Oriented Architecture, and IT Security (Cyber Security, Information Assurance, Computer Forensics). (Woman/As-Pac, estab 2006, empl 20, sales $300,000, cert: State)

5531   Eco-Worx, Inc.
860 Kastrin   El Paso, TX 79907
(915) 633-1411 Peter Reyes President
Fax: (915) 599-1330
Email: peter.reyes@ecoworxinc.com
Website: www.ecoworxinc.com
Energy Assessments
Lighting Designs
ROI Assessments
Lighting Installations
Sensors and Controls Installations (Hisp, estab 2007, empl 20, sales $443,000, cert: NMSDC)

5532   eDataWorld LLC
2770 Main St Ste 229 Frisco, TX 75033
(206) 504-8739 Bhujang Karakavalasa Director
Fax: (469) 575-9333
Email: Bhujang.K@edataworld.com
Website: www.edataworld.com
IT consulting, software development & service. (Woman/As-Pac, estab 2005, empl 100, sales $2,000,000, cert: NMSDC)

5533   ElectroSystems Engineers Inc.
4141 Pinnacle St, Ste 208   El Paso, TX 79902
(915) 587-7902 Benita R Munoz Director of Ops
Fax: (915) 587-7768
Email: brmunoz@esei.com
Website: www.esei.com
Information technology, integrated solutions, telecommunications engineering, software design, management & consulting, test & evaluation support & intelligence training. (Hisp, estab 1994, empl 20, sales $1,441,208, cert: NMSDC)

5534   Elise Resources, Inc.
950 Echo Lane Ste 200 Houston, TX 77024
(281) 313-4422 Nadia Clark CEO
Fax: (713) 955-7991
Email: nadia@eliseresources.com
Website: www.eliseresources.com
call center that specializes in the handling of inbound and outbound customer service and sales related calls. We do this by employing quality staff and by utilizing the best technology available related to training (AA, estab 2015, empl 1, sales $75,000, cert: State)

5535   Endata Corporation
3217 Thorne Hill Ct Richardson, TX 75082
(214) 603-4456 Ricardo Rossi CTO
Fax: (405) 603-8970
Email: ricardo@endata.com
Website: www.endata.com
Information Technology Professional Services, machine learning, sentiment analysis, predictive data analytics, web & app development, artificial intelligence for web, mobile & cloud applications. (Woman/Hisp, estab 1997, empl 2, sales $370,808, cert: State, NMSDC)

5536   Enovox Technical Group, LLC
          1775 St. James Place, Ste 120   Houston, TX 77584
          (832) 736-5869 Michael Wilson President
          Fax: (713) 968-4690
          Email: mike@enovox.com
          Website: www.enovox.com
IT consulting & technology svcs, telecommunication svcs &
network equip, program/project mgmt & outsourcing. (AA,
estab 2011, empl 2, sales $100,000, cert: State, City)

5537   Enterprise IT Experts LLC dba EITE LLC
          4017 Duclair Dr   McKinney, TX 75070
          (248)4947474 Ravi Vegesna Managing Partner
          Fax:
          Email: ravi@eitellc.com
          Website: www.enterpriseitexperts.com
Information Technology & Computer Software services:
Enterprise Architecture, SAP Implementations, Upgrades,
Technology Upgrades, Microsoft Technologies - Sharepoint
& Office 365, Cloud Architecture, Integration & Custom
development. (As-Ind, estab 2011, empl 228, sales
$8,700,000, cert: State, NMSDC)

5538   eXcellence in IS Solutions, Inc.
          9800 Northwest Fwy Ste 305 Houston, TX 77092
          (713) 862-9200 Joan Khosla Treasurer
          Fax: (877) 486-8015
          Email: jkhosla@x-iss.com
          Website: www.x-iss.com
Integrate, manage & maintain HPC cluster systems,
monitor, report & deliver analytics. (As-Ind/Hisp, estab
2001, empl 17, sales $1,859,000, cert: State, City, NMSDC)

5539   Fidelis Companies
          2800 N Dallas Pkwy Ste 250 Plano, TX 75093
          (972) 392-9230 Bryce Shields BusinessDev Mgr
          Fax: (972) 392-9255
          Email: Bshields@fideliscompanies.com
          Website: www.fideliscompanies.com
IT Consulting for Oracle, PeopleSoft, Hyperion, SAP.
(Woman/White, estab 2000, empl 25, sales $4,000,000,
cert: State, WBENC)

5540   Fuse Solutions Inc.
          4100 Midway Rd Ste 2120 Carrollton, TX 75007
          (214) 687-7393 Jay Jordan COO
          Fax:
          Email: Jay@fusesolutions.com
          Website: www.fusesolutions.com
Strategic consulting, enterprise service delivery, vendor &
asset management. (Woman/White, estab 2014, empl 25,
sales , cert: State, WBENC)

5541   Genesis Networks Enterprises, LLC
          600 N Loop 1604 E   San Antonio, TX 78232
          (770) 329-6538 Jason McGinnis Dir Vendor Engage-
          ments
          Fax: (210) 489-6612
          Email: jason.mcginnis@genesisnet.com
          Website: www.genesisnet.com
Software development, software testing, systems integrator, proto-type development, security, system application
mgmt, application mgmt, business process flow, event
mgmt, exception mgmt. (Hisp, estab 2001, empl 771, sales
$1,100,000,000, cert: State, NMSDC, CPUC)

5542   Genesis Networks Integration Services, LLC
          600 N. Loop 1604 East   San Antonio, TX 78232
          (210) 489-6600 Nicole Nash supplier diversity
          asst
          Fax: (210) 489-6612
          Email: nicole.nash@genesisnet.com
          Website: www.genesisnet.com
Provides engineering, furnish & installation services for
data & phone networks, network management architecture, implementation & support, information systems
security management, server & virtualization management. (Hisp, estab 2010, empl 77, sales $16,526,811,
cert: State, NMSDC)

5543   GeoPropel, LLC
          16225 Park Ten Place Ste 500 Houston, TX 77084
          (713) 338-3441 Aditya Tadakaluru Managing
          Member
          Fax: (281) 858-2323
          Email: aditya@geopropel.com
          Website: www.geopropel.com
Technology solutions, staffing & recruiting, enterprise
GIS, application development & geospatial solutions.
(As-Pac, estab 2011, empl 3, sales $1,240,270, cert:
State)

5544   Gill Digital Services, LLC
          4100 Spring Valley Road, Ste 920   Dallas, TX
          75244
          (214) 653-8352 Barbara Gill President
          Fax:
          Email: bgill@gilldigital.com
          Website: www.gilldigital.com
Document Scanning, Database Software, Disaster
Recovery Services, Court Reporting (Woman/White,
estab , empl 1, sales , cert: State, WBENC)

5545   Global IT, Inc.
          1303 W Walnut Hill Ln Ste 360 Irving, TX 75038
          (972) 871-9292 Sales
          Fax: (972) 751-5222
          Email: info@globalitinc.com
          Website: www.globalitinc.com
Information technology: ERP packages, SAP, Oracle Apps
& PeopleSoft. (As-Ind, estab 1999, empl 182, sales
$13,400,000, cert: State)

5546   GS Infovision LLC dba Global Systems LLC
          1200 Walnut Hill Lane, Ste 2220 Irving, TX 75038
          (214) 717-4344 Shekhar Gupta VP
          Fax: (240) 554-2470
          Email: account@globalsyst.com
          Website: www.globalsyst.com
IT Consulting, Staffing, BPO, IT Consulting, temporary,
contract, temp to perm & permanent staffing solutions.
(Woman/As-Pac, estab 2005, empl 110, sales
$11,000,000, cert: NMSDC)

5547 Guardian Zone LLC
        4843 Colleyville Blvd Ste 251-155 Colleyville, TX
        76034
        (866) 866-8731 Sheryl Maas CEO
        Fax:
        Email: spmaas@guardianzone.com
        Website: www.guardianzone.com
Security & protection software, wireless software, security
services. (Woman/AA, estab 2016, empl 5, sales , cert:
State, WBENC)

5548 Hacware, Inc.
        1212 E Arapaho Rd Ste 204 Richardson, TX 75081
        (214) 662-8332 Tiffany Ricks CEO
        Fax:
        Email: tiffany@hacware.com
        Website: www.hacware.com
Mobile applications and emerging technology solutions.
(AA, estab 2017, empl 8, sales , cert: WBENC)

5549 Hy-Density Imaging
        1850 Hunter Dr, Ste 108 El Paso, TX 79915
        (915) 593-7007 Steve Madrid Owner
        Fax: (915) 590-7739
        Email: Steve_hdcpr@sbcglobal.net
        Website:
Service/Sales: Computers & Printers, IT equipment sales,
Data & Voice Cabling, Remove viruses, General Computer
and Printer repair, Data recovery, Laptop repair (power
Jacks, Lcd screen replacements. (Hisp, estab 1994, empl 3,
sales $187,000, cert: State)

5550 iBizSoft
        9300 Wade Blvd Ste 301 Frisco, TX 75035
        (214) 705-3623 Sandeep Kuttiyatur President
        Fax: (214) 975-1291
        Email: vendor@ibizsoftinc.com
        Website: www.ibizsoftinc.com
Enterprise application services: system integration &
solution development for Oracle ERP, CRM, Endeca & ATG
implementation. (As-Ind, estab 2001, empl 100, sales
$6,000,000, cert: State)

5551 ICC Software
        4837 Frost Hollow Dr Plano, TX 75093
        (214) 227-9559 Anthony Johnson President
        Fax: (214) 227-9560
        Email: ajohn@iccsoftware.net
        Website: www.iccsoftware.net
Document management, biometrics & document conversion software, programming, risk analysis, & project
management. (AA, estab 2001, empl 3, sales $74,000, cert:
State)

5552 Imagetek Office Systems
        630 Westway Place, Ste 500 Arlington, TX 76018
        (817) 465-2450 Cindy Munson Cstmr Care Coord
        Fax: 817465-159
        Email: cmunson@imagetekos.com
        Website: www.imagetekos.com
Extensive managed document, print services and software
solutions. (Woman/White, estab 2000, empl 61, sales ,
cert: State, WBENC)

5553 Independent Professional Management
        9525 Katy Freeway, Ste 435 Houston, TX 77024
        (713) 973-7400 Andy Bishop VP - Resource Mgmt
        Fax:
        Email: andy.bishop@ipm-inc.com
        Website: www.ipm-inc.com
IT Staffing, SAP programers, developers & consultants.
(Woman/White, estab 1992, empl 9, sales , cert: State,
WBENC)

5554 Infobeam Technologies LLC
        1333 Corporate Dr, Ste 262 Irving, TX 75038
        (972) 365-9928 Jay Gajavelli Director
        Fax: (800) 724-8380
        Email: jay.gajavelli@infobeamtech.com
        Website: www.infobeamtech.com
IT consulting. (As-Pac, estab 2009, empl 15, sales , cert:
State)

5555 Infolob Solutions, Inc.
        909 Lake Carolyn Parkway Ste 120 Irving, TX
        75039
        (972) 535-5559 Vijay Cherukuri CEO
        Fax: (888) 228-4125
        Email: vijay@infolob.com
        Website: www.infolob.com
Database services, RAC, Exadata, SOA, Oracle Fusion,
Ebusiness, OBIEE, BI, DW, OLTP, networking, J2EE,
replication. (Woman/As-Ind, estab 2009, empl 130, sales
$14,279,837, cert: State, NMSDC)

5556 Inoditech LLC, dba Camino Information Services
        14340 Torrey Chase Blvd Ste 210 Houston, TX
        77014
        (281) 742-9560 Lam Nguyen CEO
        Fax: (832) 666-3909
        Email: lam.nguyen@caminois.com
        Website: www.caminois.com
Custom software development & mobile applications.
(Woman/As-Pac, estab 2012, empl 22, sales $1,273,000,
cert: State, NMSDC)

5557 Instant Data Technologies
        85 NE Loop 410, Ste. 405 San Antonio, TX 78216
        (210) 344-0012 Bede Ramcharan CEO
        Fax: (210) 344-3540
        Email: bramcharan@indatatech.com
        Website: www.indatatech.com
Physical inventory, RFID technology, asset valuation &
tracking, supplier integration, barcoding, asset procurement, tagging & management, inventory mgmt software. (AA/As-Pac, estab 2001, empl 31, sales
$11,999,837, cert: State, NMSDC, SDB)

5558 Intras LLC
        101 E Park Ste 769 Plano, TX 75074
        (972) 422-1022 Elvan Jones
        Fax: (714) 550-4973
        Email: elvanj@intras-it.com
        Website: www.intras-it.com
Global integrator of technology solutions, technology
hardware & applications develop, IT products, IT
Services, IT Consulting & IT Managed services. (AA, estab
2010, empl 10, sales $3,000,000, cert: State, NMSDC)

5559   IPM Asset Solutions, Inc.
        9525 Katy Freeway Ste 435 Houston, TX 77024
        (713) 973-7400 Andy Bishop VP - Resource Management
        Fax: (713) 973-0460
        Email: andy.bishop@ipm-inc.com
        Website: www.ipmasset.com
Asset management & tracking utilizing bar code & Radio Frequency Identification (RFID) technology. (Woman/White, estab 2006, empl 9, sales , cert: State)

5560   JB Software and Consulting, Inc.
        807 Soapberry Dr   Allen, TX 75002
        (469) 878-3639 Jaber Hussain VP Business Devel
        Fax: (214) 432-3747
        Email: jaber@jbsac.com
        Website: www.jbsac.com
Information technology services & staff augmentation. (Woman/As-Ind, estab 2004, empl 10, sales , cert: NMSDC, CPUC, 8(a))

5561   JG Haney & Associates LLC
        9711 Haven Crossing Court   Houston, TX 77065
        (281) 653-2441 Joyce Haney CEO
        Fax: (281) 653-2134
        Email: haney@jghaneyassociates.com
        Website: www.jghaneyassociates.com
Telecommunications Services, IT products & services, data acquisition systems, telemetry products, circuit card assemblies, shipping containers, test set cases, special nonmetallic, preformed packing material & acquisition program management. (Woman/AA, estab 2011, empl 2, sales $300,000, cert: 8(a))

5562   KEDAR Integration Services, Inc.
        405 State Hwy 121 Bypass Ste A250 Lewisville, TX 75067
        (972) 317-3577 Charles Williams
        Fax:
        Email: charles@KEDARit.com
        Website: www.kedarit.com
IT financial management, cost optimization; business process management; lean transformation; and training. (AA, estab 1900, empl 1, sales $586,858, cert: State)

5563   Kreative Zeno Systems, Inc.
        12019 Colwick   San Antonio, TX 78216
        (877) 768-1574 Thomas Dooley VP
        Fax: (800) 274-9626
        Email: tomd@kreativesystemsinc.com
        Website: www.kreativesystemsinc.com
Provide SCSI disk drive assemblies. (Woman, estab 2010, empl 7, sales $160,000, cert: State)

5564   Managed Staffing Inc
        15851 Dallas Pkwy| Ste 450, Addison Dallas, TX 75001
        (469) 608-7015 Mark Miller Sr Mgr
        Fax: (888) 703-0185
        Email: mark@managedstaffing.com
        Website: www.managedstaffing.com
IT consulting: contract, contract to hire, or direct placement, outsourcing. (Woman/As-Ind, estab 2007, empl 300, sales $39,300,000, cert: NMSDC, WBENC)

5565   MB Five Consulting LLC
        8013 Blue Hole Ct   McKinney, TX 75070
        (972) 895-2414 Andre Ketter Mgr
        Fax: (972) 895-2415
        Email: aketter@mb5consulting.com
        Website: www.mb5consulting.com
IT Services & Industrial Automation services, desktop & server support, Networking & software development. (AA, estab 2014, empl 1, sales $220,000, cert: State, NMSDC)

5566   Michael Resource Group LLC
        1325 Daja Lane Ste 604 Grand Prairie, TX 75050
        (888) 313-8688 Brandon Russell
        Fax: (888) 313-8688
        Email: brussell@mrgroupllc.com
        Website: www.mrgroupllc.com
Management Consulting. We match the worldï¿½s most dynamic and innovative leadership professionals recruiting and staffing firm that focuses on matching and the placement of IT Leadership professionals. With more than eight years of (AA, estab 2014, empl 4, sales $100,000, cert: State, NMSDC)

5567   Milner & Schooley LLC
        14000 S Hwy 95   Coupland, TX 78615
        (512) 914-4061 Sheri Milner Mgmt Services
        Fax: (253) 541-7867
        Email: slmilner@milnerschooley.com
        Website: www.milnerschooley.com
Information technology svcs: ERP CIS/CRM. (Woman/White, estab 2005, empl 2, sales $165,000, cert: State)

5568   MRI Technologies
        17047 El Camino Real Ste 200 Houston, TX 77058
        (281) 786-2000 Debbie Kropp CEO
        Fax:
        Email: dkropp@mricompany.com
        Website: www.mricompany.com
Information systems, engineering, planning & integration, logistics, configuration & data management & project management. (Woman/White, estab 1988, empl 110, sales $9,957,839, cert: State)

5569   Mshana Group LLC dba AriesPro
        19901 Southwest Frwy Sugar Land, TX 77479
        (281) 410-6930 Shivani Sangari Dir Business Dev
        Fax:
        Email: shivani.sangari@ariespro.com
        Website: www.ariespro.com
Information technology consulting: SAP, HANA, BW, ERP, CRM, SCM, Business Objects, FICO, Oracle, Teradata, Big Data, Microsoft, IBM, Java, Microstrategy, Cognos, Hadoop, DB2, DataStage, Informatica, Netezza, Tivoli, Unix, WebSphere. (Woman/As-Ind, estab 2011, empl 5, sales $460,000, cert: City)

5570 New Renewable Energy Technologies, LLC dba
NERETEC
4102 Amhurst Dr   Highland Village, TX 75077
(217) 299-7789 Phil Fosso Principal
Fax:
Email: fosso@neretec.com
Website: www.neretec.com
Project Mgmt, Application Dev, Technology Migration/
Upgrade, Application Maintenance & Support, IT Assess-
ments/Planning, Independent Verification &Validation,
Business Intelligence/Data Warehouse, Architecture (SOA).
(AA, estab 2010, empl 2, sales $154,000, cert: State)

5571 NewData Strategies
5339 Alpha Rd Ste 200 Dallas, TX 75240
(972) 735-0001 Kristen Scott Director of Sales
Fax: (972) 735-8008
Email: tpope@newdata.com
Website: www.newdata.com
IT consulting, placement & education. (Woman/White,
estab 1989, empl 70, sales $7,384,599, cert: WBENC)

5572 Newt Global Consulting
1300 W Walnut Hill Lane Ste 230 Irving, TX 75038
(972) 887-3159 Rajiv Chum Director Ops
Fax: (214) 260-6051
Email: rchum@newtglobalcorp.com
Website: www.newtglobal.com
Java / J2EE application devel, Microsoft .NET framework,
service oriented architecture, wireless & mobile application devel, database devel, business intelligence, project
mgmt & quality assurance. (Woman/As-Ind, estab 2004,
empl 390, sales $16,800,700, cert: State, NMSDC, CPUC)

5573 Next Generation Technology Inc.
6060 N Central Exprwy, Ste 560   Dallas, TX 75206
(214) 800-2893 Ray Richardson President
Fax: (214) 800-2805
Email: rrichardson@nexgentech.us
Website: www.nexgentech.us
Resell Hewlett Packard products, UPS back-up power for
Liebert, APC & Powerware, digital video surveillance
systems, IT consulting. (AA, estab 2003, empl 5, sales ,
cert: State, SDB)

5574 Nomotion Software, LLC
6243 Cypress Cir   San Antonio, TX 78240
(210) 710-2800 Orlando Padilla President
Fax: (888) 810-9120
Email: opadilla@nomotion.net
Website: www.nomotion.net
Information security consulting & software development,
application security design, assessment, and remediation.
(Hisp, estab 2012, empl 4, sales $400,000, cert: 8(a))

5575 Object Information Services, Inc.
1755 North Collins Blvd #220   Richardson, TX
75080
(214) 335-6632 Mohammad Hafizullah President
Fax: (888) 393-4021
Email: mhafiz@objectinformation.com
Website: www.objectinformation.com
Information technology recruiting. (As-Ind, estab 1995,
empl 42, sales $3,449,325, cert: State, NMSDC)

5576 Omega Business Systems
P.O. Box 8297 Fort Worth, TX 76124
(817) 492-4249 Norman Labrosse President
Fax: (817) 492-4250
Email: norman@omegabiz.com
Website: www.omegabiz.com
Network solutions & technical services. (As-Ind, estab
1992, empl 6, sales $2,000,000, cert: State, City, NMSDC,
SDB)

5577 On Air Solutions, Inc.
5415 Chevy Chase   Houston, TX 77056
(713) 961-3990 Becky Martin Dir
Fax: (832) 615-3062
Email: bmartin@onairsol.com
Website: www.onairsol.com
Wireless infrastructure projects & telecommunications
svcs: in-building wireless system engineering & installation, tower erection/construction; site maintenance, site
acquisition, project management. (Woman/White, estab
2003, empl 6, sales $56,000, cert: State)

5578 Oveana
123 W Mills Ave, Ste 400   El Paso, TX 79901
(915) 533-0549 Bill Randag Business Dev
Fax:
Email: bill.randag@oveana.com
Website: www.oveana.com
Document mgmt, data processing, mail room processing, scanning, data storage, data entry, data capture &
destruction, call center. (Woman/Hisp, estab 2013, empl
2200, sales , cert: State)

5579 OverNite Software Inc.
1212 N Velasco, Ste 110   Angleton, TX 77515
(979) 849-2002 David Stark Mktg Dir
Fax: (979) 848-2448
Email: david.stark@overnitecbt.com
Website: www.overnitecbt.com
Computer-based performance systems. (Hisp, estab
1995, empl 55, sales , cert: State)

5580 Principle Information Technology
9301 Southwest Fwy Ste 475 Houston, TX 77074
(832) 434-4016 Nickell Cheruku President
Fax: (832) 849-1119
Email: reddy@principleinfotech.com
Website: www.principleinfotech.com
SAP Services, Oracle Service, Big Data, Cloud
Mobility, Luxon. (As-Pac, estab 2009, empl 157, sales ,
cert: State, City, NMSDC, 8(a))

5581 Pure Business Solutions, LLC
219 Gessner Rd   Houston, TX 77024
(713) 750-9500 Andrea Hite CEO
Fax:
Email: ahite@purebizsolns.com
Website: www.purebizsolns.com
IT Operations Management Software, IT Service Man-
agement, Discovery, Configuration Management
Database, Application & Service Modeling, IT Operations
& Business Analytics, Performance and Availability
Management. (Woman/White, estab 2015, empl 1, sales
, cert: State, WBENC)

5582   Quality High-Tech Services, Inc.
       11807 Forestgate Dr   Dallas, TX 75243
       (972) 231-6696 Mary Rogers President
       Fax: (972) 231-6699
       Email: m.rogers@qht.com
       Website: www.QHT.com
IT services and repairs. (Woman/White, estab 1987, empl
17, sales $2,492,492, cert: State)

5583   RD Data Solutions
       2340 E Trinity Mills Ste 349 Carrollton, TX 75006
       (972) 899-2334 Reuben D'Souza CEO
       Fax:
       Email: reuben.dsouza@rddatasolutions.com
       Website: www.rddatasolutions.com
Technology staffing: SAP & ERP. (Woman/As-Pac, estab
2002, empl 26, sales $25,000,000, cert: State, NMSDC)

5584   Remedy Technological Services, L.P.
       501 N 4th St   Killeen, TX 76541
       (254) 213-4740 Christopher Walton VP & Legal
       Counsel
       Fax: (254) 634-3998
       Email: cwalton@centextech.com
       Website: www.centextech.com
Information Technology, Software Engineering, Project
Management, Database Management, ERP Solutions, Data
Warehouse & Business Intelligence, Web & App Develop-
ment, Internet Marketing & Network Administration. (As-
Ind, estab 2006, empl 50, sales $1,300,000, cert: State,
8(a))

5585   Research Analysis and Maintenance, Inc.
       9440 Viscount Blvd, Ste 200   El Paso, TX 79925
       (915) 592-7047 Richard Jones Contracts Admin
       Fax: (915) 595-0559
       Email: jonesr@ramincorp.com
       Website: www.ramincorp.com
IT services, networking & telecommunications, software
development, systems integration & information management. (Woman, estab 1982, empl 650, sales $62,000,000,
cert: State)

5586   Resolve Tech Solutions
       15851 Dallas Pkwy, Ste 1103   Addison, TX 75001
       (703) 995-7377 Justin Palmer Business Devel Mgr
       Fax:
       Email: justin.palmer@resolvetech.com
       Website: www.resolvetech.com/
Information Technology Staffing, Consulting Services and
Implementation. (As-Ind, estab 1996, empl 25, sales
$3,000,000, cert: State)

5587   RSI Solutions Inc.
       3607 Summer Ranch Dr   Katy, TX 77494
       (832) 506-0868 Raj Srivastava Principal
       Fax:
       Email: raj@rsisolutions.net
       Website: www.rsisolutions.net
Enterprise Resource Planning (ERP) based solutions to
both public and private sector entities, SAP BW, HANA.
(As-Ind, estab 2011, empl 2, sales $254,000, cert: State,
SDB)

5588   Saratoga Software Solutions, Inc.
       555 Republic Dr. Ste 200 Plano, TX 75074
       (469) 301-1515 Arlene Carter President
       Fax: (469) 916-3022
       Email: arlene.carter@teamsaratoga.com
       Website: www.saratogasoftwaresolutions.com
IT staff augmentation: contract, contract-to-hire &
permanent. (Woman/White, estab 1900, empl 1, sales
$1,400,000, cert: State)

5589   Sasaki Evolutionary Integration Services, LLC
       P.O. Box 340562   Austin, TX 78734
       (512) 263-7347 Todd Sasaki CEO
       Fax:
       Email: todd.sasaki@TeamSEIS.com
       Website: www.TeamSEIS.com
Business automation & modeling/simulation for decision
support & project/program management. (As-Pac, estab
2009, empl 6, sales $452,500, cert: 8(a))

5590   Shirley Hollywood & Associates, Inc.
       17585 State Hwy 19 Ste 100 Canton, TX 75103
       (972) 287-8834 Stacie Hollywood-Baber President
       Fax:
       Email: stacie@shirleyhollywoodinc.com
       Website: www.shirleyhollywoodinc.com
SAP curriculum devel & training delivery resources.
(Woman/White, estab 1996, empl 5, sales $5,000,000,
cert: State, WBENC)

5591   Simplistek, LLC
       5050 Quorum Dr, Ste 700   Dallas, TX 75254
       (469) 675-3594 Xavier Hurd VP of Talent Acquisi-
       tion
       Fax:
       Email: xhurd@simplistekit.com
       Website: www.simplistekit.com
ERP Implementation & support, business process
improvement, utilities business consulting & staff
augmentation for all areas of Information Technology
(IT). (AA, estab 2014, empl 3, sales $1,200,000, cert:
State, NMSDC)

5592   Skylla Engineering Ltd.
       316 Main St   Humble, TX 77338
       (228) 344-5449 Tim Brogdon Exec VP
       Fax: (281) 446-6580
       Email: BrogdonT@skyllaeng.com
       Website: www.skyllaeng.com
Systems engineering, software & hardware design,
systems integration, configuration control, program
mgmt, acquisition planning & mgmt, program planning,
scheduling & resource mgmt. (Hisp, estab 2004, empl
110, sales $12,800,000, cert: State)

5593   SOAL Technologies, LLC.
       8801 Research Blvd, Ste 104   Austin, TX 78758
       (512) 270-6700 Ahmed Moledina CEO
       Fax: (866) 516-4415
       Email: amoledina@soaltech.com
       Website: www.soaltech.com
Information technology development & consulting. (As-
Ind, estab 2009, empl 40, sales $4,783,993, cert: City)

5594 Software Professionals, Inc.
1029 Long Prairie Rd Ste A Flower Mound, TX 75022
(972) 355-0054 Reena Batra CEO
Fax: (214) 260-1112
Email: reena@spius.net
Website: www.spius.net
Systems integration & computer programming svcs: client/server & mainframe environ; facilities mgmt, help desk support & training; business re-engineering & total quality mgmt. (Woman/As-Ind, estab 1992, empl 100, sales $15,000,000, cert: State, NMSDC, WBENC)

5595 Softway Solutions, Inc.
7324 Southwest Frwy Ste 1600 Houston, TX 77074
(281) 914-4381 Robert Goady VP Client Services
Fax: (815) 331-3861
Email: Robert@softwaysolutions.com
Website: www.softway.com
Website design & development, Internet marketing services, graphics design & multimedia. (As-Pac, estab 2003, empl 65, sales $5,800,000, cert: NMSDC)

5596 SPAR Information Systems
7800 Dallas Pkwy, Ste 120 Plano, TX 75024
(201) 528-5324 Abraham Regan VP IT Talent Acquisition
Fax: (201) 528-5307
Email: abraham.regan@sparinfosys.com
Website: www.sparinfosys.com
IT Services. (Woman, estab 2012, empl 380, sales $30,000,000, cert: State)

5597 Storage Assessments LLC
P.O. Box 864017 Plano, TX 75086
(972) 578-2708 Carolyn Chambers CEO
Fax: (972) 767-0555
Email: cc@storageassessments.com
Website: www.storageassessments.com
Resell, design & support computer storage related products: database, backup & recovers, disaster recovery & file management. (Woman/White, estab 2003, empl 6, sales $4,774,271, cert: State, WBENC)

5598 STS Systems Integration, LLC
1077 Central Pkwy S Bldg A, Ste 150 San Antonio, TX 78232
(210) 888-2631 Dan Beard Sr program Mgr
Fax:
Email: daniel.beard@ssi-anc.com
Website: www.ssi-anc.com
System engineering, performance, mission readiness & sustainment for weapon systems, propulsion systems & information systems. (Nat Ame, estab 2011, empl 143, sales $13,000,000, cert: 8(a))

5599 Swift Pace Solutions, Inc
600 E John Carpenter Frwy Ste 175 Irving, TX 75062
(972) 714-0000 Pratima Upadhya Client Partner
Fax: (972) 767-0975
Email: pratima@spsolinc.com
Website: www.spsolinc.com
IT Services Consulting, Oracle Gold Partner, SAP Partner, Horton Works Partner Migrate, Integrate & Build Custom Apps. (Woman/As-Ind, estab 2013, empl 12, sales $2,000,000, cert: State, NMSDC)

5600 Talent Logic Inc.
2313 Timber Shadows Dr Ste 200 Kingwood, TX 77339
(281) 358-1858 Hilda Roper VP
Fax: (281) 358-8145
Email: hroper@talentlogic.com
Website: www.talentlogic.com
Computer consulting & programming svcs. (As-Ind, estab 1984, empl 300, sales $17,500,000, cert: NMSDC)

5601 Taylor Smith Consulting, LLC
16800 Greenspoint Park Dr, STE 155N Houston, TX 77060
(713) 937-3111 Tracy Smith CEO
Fax: (713) 937-3486
Email: staylor@taylorsmithconsulting.com
Website: www.taylorsmithconsulting.com
Business Development
Training
Call/Customer Service Center Operations
Staffing
Contracting Services (Woman/AA, estab 2006, empl 1200, sales $18,001,317, cert: State, City, NMSDC)

5602 Technology Asset LLC
789 N Grove Rd, Ste 103 Richardson, TX 75081
(972) 318-2600 Tom Earley Reg sales Mgr
Fax: (214) 318-2602
Email: tearley@globalassetonline.com
Website: www.globalassetonline.com
Eco-Friendly IT lifecycle management. (Woman/Nat Ame, estab 2010, empl 40, sales $12,500,000, cert: State)

5603 Technology for Education
658 Alliance Pkwy Hewitt, TX 76643
(254) 741-2450 Brandy Mynar-Olson Sales Mgr
Fax: (254) 299-1396
Email: sales@tfeconnect.com
Website: www.tfe-wordpress.tfeconnect.com
Structured cabling & networking, Data Center, IP Communications, Audio Visual & Physical Security. (Woman/White, estab 1998, empl 50, sales $31,709,451, cert: State, WBENC)

5604 Techway Services
12880 Valley Branch Ln Ste 100 Farmers Branch, TX 75234
(855) 832-4929 Cathi Coan President
Fax: (214) 988-2697
Email: cathi@techwayservices.com
Website: www.techwayservices.com
E-data destruction services & used computer asset remarketing. (Woman/White, estab 2004, empl 32, sales $607,751,300, cert: State, WBENC)

5605 TekFokus Inc.
1950 N Stemmons, Ste 2062 Dallas, TX 75207
(214) 800-5643 Steve Lindley Business Dev Mgr
Fax: (214) 800-5645
Email: slindley@tekfokus.com
Website: www.tekfokus.com
Microsoft IT training & consulting. (Hisp, estab 2003, empl 12, sales $1,650,000, cert: State)

5606 TELA Technologies, Inc.
        10310 Harwin Dr. East Wing Houston, TX 77036
        (713) 863-1411 Jaime Flores President
        Fax: (866) 763-1490
        Email: jflores@telatechnologies.com
        Website: www.telatechnologies.com
Document management solutions, electronic document
storage & retrieval solutions. (Hisp, estab 2003, empl 15,
sales $1,050,000, cert: State, NMSDC)

5607 Telecopy, Inc.
        2280 Springlake Rd Ste 104 Dallas, TX 75234
        (972) 432-8384 Marsha Davidson President
        Fax: (972) 432-9312
        Email: marsha@telecopy.com
        Website: www.telecopy.com
CD, DVD, video & audio duplication. (Woman/White, estab
1979, empl 6, sales $717,000, cert: State, WBENC)

5608 The Ternio Group LLC
        8285 El Rio Ste 120 Houston, TX 77054
        (210) 519-7933 Luis Romero Principal
        Fax:
        Email: lromero@terniogroup.com
        Website: www.terniogroup.com
Consulting & project management services: supply chain,
logistics, distribution, medical-surgical & pharmacy
inventory management, consignment, resource management, data processing, data cleansing, e-commerce, ERP.
(Hisp, estab 2012, empl 10, sales $1,960,000, cert: State)

5609 Themesoft Inc.
        13601 Preston Rd, Ste W860 Dallas, TX 75240
        (972) 474-8787 Pascal Vinoth Director
        Fax: (972) 474-8888
        Email: vinoth@themesoft.com
        Website: www.themesoft.com
Custom Software Development & Consulting, Java, J2EE,
SAP, Networking, Infrastructure, QA, Project Management.
(Woman/As-Ind, estab 2004, empl 200, sales $42,845,261,
cert: State, NMSDC, WBENC)

5610 Third Term Inc.
        6 Meadowridge Pl the Woodlands, TX 77381
        (713) 357-6666 Carolina Denkler Project Mgr
        Fax: (713) 955-4994
        Email: carolina.denkler@thirdtermlearning.com
        Website: www.thirdtermlearning.com
eLearning, computer based training, web based Training,
Learning Management Systems, LMS. (Hisp, estab 2013,
empl 2, sales $266,000, cert: NMSDC)

5611 Thurstfield Roman
        6113 Covington Dr Rowlett, TX 75089
        (214) 335-2806 Courtney Davis President
        Fax: (972) 692-7603
        Email: cdavis@thurstfieldroman.biz
        Website:
Secure on-site/off-site document shreddiing services. (AA,
estab 2001, empl 3, sales $36,500, cert: State)

5612 Traveling Coaches Inc.
        2805 Dallas Pkwy Ste 150 Dallas, TX 75093
        (214) 742-6224 Lyndi Lockhart Acct Mgr
        Fax:
        Email: llockhart@travelingcoaches.com
        Website: www.travelingcoaches.com
Software, consulting, integration & training. (Woman,
estab 1995, empl 35, sales $10,637,000, cert: State,
WBENC)

5613 Tunabear, Inc.
        13155 Noel Rd Ste 900 Dallas, TX 75240
        (888) 923-8889 James Knowles
        Fax: (888) 923-8889
        Email: james@tunabear.com
        Website: www.tunabear.com
Staff Augmentation, Project Management, Upgrades,
Implementation, Development, Strategy Development,
Infrastructure Planning, Training / Change Management,
Technologies, Peoplesoft, Hyperion / Data Warehousing.
(As-Pac, estab 2010, empl 6, sales $1,444,000, cert:
State)

5614 Unified Services of Texas, Inc.
        2110 Greenbriar Dr   Southlake, TX 76092
        (817) 481-9510 Marshall Ryan President
        Fax: (817) 488-1729
        Email: mryan@ust-inc.com
        Website: www.ust-inc.com
Retail and fleet Fuel system design and installation,
including tanks, piping, dispensers, canopies, electrical
and concrete (Nat Ame, estab 1991, empl 18, sales
$4,100,000, cert: State)

5615 VCM Technologies, Inc.
        25 Highland Park Village, Ste 100-149   Dallas, TX
        75205
        (817) 571-6335 Kerry Williams CEO
        Fax: (817) 571-6337
        Email: kerry.williams@beaconsystems.com
        Website: www.beaconsystems.com
Information technology staff augmentation, SAP
consultants. (Woman/White, estab 2002, empl 6, sales
$14,200,000, cert: WBENC)

5616 Vensiti Inc
        300 East Royal Lane Ste 104 Irving, TX 75039
        (972) 887-7995 Vijaya Saradhi Sr Director Staffing
        Fax: (972) 887-8585
        Email: saradhi.v@vensiti.com
        Website: www.vensiti.com
Information tehcnology staffing & consulting services.
(Woman/As-Ind, estab 2004, empl 52, sales $4,340,000,
cert: State)

5617 Verge Information Technologies, Inc.
        1305 Cheyenne Trail   Corinth, TX 76210
        (214) 206-8885 Mark McLaughlin Ops Mgr
        Fax: (866) 268-8397
        Email: mark@vergeit.com
        Website: www.vergeit.com
Information technology & IS consulting & staff augmentation. (Nat Ame, estab 2000, empl 15, sales $1,600,000,
cert: State)

5618 Versacom LLC
      8111 LBJ Freeway, Ste 685   Dallas, TX 75251
      (972) 479-0202 Sales
      Fax: (972) 479-0303
      Email: info@versacomllc.com
      Website: www.versacomllc.com
Networking, LANs, WANs & WLANs, voice & data integration, develop, implement & maintain integrated programs,
hardware & software support. (Woman/As-Ind, estab
2005, empl 50, sales $1,544,000, cert: WBENC)

5619 Virtuo Group Corporation
      6700 Woodlands Pkwy Ste 230-322 The Wood-
      lands, TX 77382
      (281) 298-8571 Theresa Blackwell CEO
      Fax: (281) 298-8571
      Email: tblackwell@virtuogroup.com
      Website: www.virtuogroup.com
PMO, Cyber Security, application modernization, migration
& consolidation technology services. (Woman/AA, estab
2001, empl 35, sales $3,800,000, cert: City, NMSDC)

5620 VKNetworks IT Solutions
      638 Quail Run Dr   Murphy, TX 75094
      (469) 323-3345 Dr. Rajan Subramanian President
      Fax:
      Email: drrajs@vknetworks.com
      Website: www.vknetworks.com
IT/SAP STAFFING & Consulting, SAP Projects, AM, AD.
Big Data, SAP HANA, S/4 HANA, SAP Vistex, EDI, Business
Intelligence and Analytics, BW4HANA, ERP, BPC, HCM, SAP
Fiori, RDS, POC, HEC, BI Reporting (Webi, Crystal Reports,
Dash Boards. (Woman/As-Ind, estab 1999, empl 10, sales ,
cert: State)

5621 Wise Men Consultants Inc
      1500 S Dairy Ashford Ste 285 Houston, TX 77077
      (281) 953-4500 Rosa Delgado-Batchan Exec Asst
      Fax: (888) 553-7758
      Email: rosa.batchan@wisemen.com
      Website: www.wisemen.com
IT staffing, project mgmt, team leads, onshore & offshore
custom software development. (Woman/As-Ind, estab
1997, empl 220, sales , cert: NMSDC, WBENC)

5622 XBI Tech Corporation
      7670 Woodway Dr, Ste 370   Houston, TX 77063
      (713) 999-1286 Trieu Nguyen CEO
      Fax:
      Email: trieu.nguyen@xbitech.com
      Website: www.xbitech.com
Comprehensive web development & management
services: web design & development, accessibility, web
content management, web training, maintenance &
support, web application/software development &
business intelligence. (As-Pac, estab 2007, empl 5, sales
$1,300,000, cert: State)

5623 XTGlobal, Inc.
      2701 N Dallas Pkwy, Ste 550 Plano, TX 75093
      (972) 755-1800 Ananth Ramaswamy President
      Fax: (972) 267-7201
      Email: ananth@xtglobal.com
      Website: www.xtglobal.com
Professional design, development, integration & support
services: Microsoft. NET, SQL, BizTalk, SharePoint, .NET
Web-based & Desktop Application development. (As-
Ind, estab 1998, empl 170, sales $26,500,000, cert:
State, NMSDC)

5624 YASME Soft Inc.
      1212 Corporate Dr Ste 150 Irving, TX 75038
      (214) 529-3693 Sandeep Kilaru President
      Fax: (972) 767-0592
      Email: sam@yasmesoft.com
      Website: www.yasmesoft.com
IT consulting solution services: Oracle, SAP, Microsoft &
IT staff augmentation. Application devel, maintenance &
support, enterprise applications, practices, consulting.
(As-Ind, estab 2007, empl 70, sales $6,000,000, cert:
State, NMSDC)

Utah

5625 Global Consulting International Inc.
      270 East 100 South   Salt Lake City, UT 84111
      (801) 707-4463 Michelle Dennis Mgr, Business
      Dev
      Fax: (801) 364-1152
      Email: Michelle.Dennis@GCI-USA.com
      Website: www.GCI-USA.com
Oracle's e-business solutions. (As-Ind, estab 2005, empl
210, sales $10,662,180, cert: State)

5626 Rylex Consulting LLC
      1785 East 1450 South Ste 140 Clearfield, UT
      84015
      (801) 820-5221 Steven Noyce Exec VP
      Fax: (801) 820-6370
      Email: steven.noyce@rylex.com
      Website: www.rylex.com
IT help desk management support, Network design &
administration, System / server administration, Software
engineering & development (ASP.net, C#, C++) Hill AFB,
Web application development. (Woman/As-Pac, estab
2004, empl 45, sales $5,000,000, cert: State)

5627 Toyakoi Ventures, LLC
      95 Bridger Cir Woodland Hills, UT 84653
      (801) 634-4194 Elliot Collins President
      Fax:
      Email: ecollins@Toyakoi.com
      Website: www.toyakoi.com
SAP consulting & full-service background checks. (Nat
Ame, estab 2010, empl 12, sales $664,000, cert: 8(a))

Virginia

5628　Aarisha Inc.
　　11890 Sunrise Valley Dr Ste 201 Reston, VA 20191
　　(703) 579-8510 Shailesh Akhouri President
　　Fax: (206) 203-2532
　　Email: supplier@aarisha.com
　　Website: www.aarisha.net
Software development life cycle, Oracle Fusion Middle ware Administration, Oracle Fusion Middle ware Development, Oracle Database Administration, Business Intelligence and Data warehousing, Software Development. (As-Pac, estab 2005, empl 6, sales $1,059,708, cert: NMSDC)

5629　ACI Solutions Inc.
　　131 E Broad St Falls Church, VA 22046
　　(703) 766-4070 Jovan Silva Business Dev Mgr
　　Fax: (703) 531-1962
　　Email: Jsilva@acisolutions.net
　　Website: www.acisolutions.net
IT, data & voice networking products & services. (AA/As-Pac, estab 2001, empl 25, sales $125,000, cert: NMSDC)

5630　Advanced Computer Concepts
　　7927 Jones Branch Dr Ste 600 N Mclean, VA 22102
　　(571) 395-4117 Mark Braxton Sr Acct Exec
　　Fax: (703) 525-9300
　　Email: bill@acconline.com
　　Website: www.acconline.com
IT hardware, software sales & network engineering services, wireless network design & implementation, IT security, IT storage systems, VOIP design & implementation. (Woman/White, estab 1982, empl 45, sales $55,000,000, cert: WBENC)

5631　Advinti Technical Solutions, Inc.
　　P.O. Box 37 Bealeton, VA 22712
　　(702) 261-7090 Maurice Nowlin President
　　Fax: (877) 287-8785
　　Email: maurice@advinti.com
　　Website: www.advinti.com
Information technology systems integration, consulting & technical training. (AA, estab 2006, empl 2, sales , cert: State)

5632　AEi International LLC
　　7686 Richmond Hwy, Ste 118 Alexandria, VA 22306
　　(410) 988-3966 Jenna Reese CEO
　　Fax:
　　Email: jenna.reese@aeiintl.com
　　Website: www.aeiintl.com
Management consulting & technology, strategic consulting, digital experience & enterprise technology related-services, staff augmentation. (Woman/AA, estab 2007, empl 12, sales $1,200,000, cert: 8(a))

5633　Affigent, LLC
　　13873 Park Center Rd Ste 127 Herndon, VA 20171
　　(301) 305-9513 Joe Clagett Acct Exec
　　Fax:
　　Email: joe.clagett@affigent.com
　　Website: www.affigent.com
Dist IT product & systems integration. (Nat Ame, estab 2004, empl 5, sales , cert: NMSDC)

5634　AhaApps LLC
　　11608 Timberton Ct Glen Allen, VA 23060
　　(804) 366-9979 Satish Reddy CEO
　　Fax: (866) 929-6049
　　Email: satish@ahaapps.com
　　Website: www.ahaapps.com
Design & build mobile applications for iOS (iPhone, iPad), Android phone & tablets, web applications, ASP.NET, ASP.NET MVC, Ruby on Rails, Java, Salesforce.com implementation & integration. (As-Pac, estab 2010, empl 15, sales $245,146, cert: State, NMSDC)

5635　All Native, Inc.
　　1229 King St 2nd Fl Alexandria, VA 22314
　　(703) 838-8902 Joe Harrison Exec Director
　　Fax: (703) 838-8908
　　Email: jharrison@allnativegroup.com
　　Website: www.allnativeinc.com
Information Technology & Infrastructure, transport Systems, Network Administration, IT Infrastructure Installation, LAN/WAN Services, Database Administration, Help Desk, Asset Management, Information Assurance. (Nat Ame, estab 2008, empl 488, sales , cert: 8(a))

5636　Alliant Global Strategies Inc.
　　4607 W. Broad St Richmond, VA 23230
　　(804) 283-2203 James Wallace
　　Fax: (804) 342-0053
　　Email: jwallace@alliantglobalstrategies.com
　　Website: www.alliantglobalstrategies.com
Business process outsourcing (BPO) & technology training solutions. (AA, estab 2011, empl 5, sales $137,000, cert: State, NMSDC)

5637　Ampcus Inc.
　　14900 Conference Center Dr, Ste 500 Ste 500 Chantilly, VA 20151
　　(703) 436-9405 Jay Paige Business Dev Mgr
　　Fax: (703) 956-6996
　　Email: jay.paige@ampcus.com
　　Website: www.ampcus.com
Information technology and application development services that are aligned with our clients business objectives. (Woman/As-Ind, estab 2004, empl 1200, sales $70,790,000, cert: NMSDC, CPUC, WBENC)

5638　Apex CoVantage
　　198 Van Buren St Ste 200 Herndon, VA 20170
　　(703) 709-3000 MIKE LOHNEIS Director , Proposal & Contract
　　Fax: (703) 709-8242
　　Email: MLOHNEIS@APEXCOVANTAGE.COM
　　Website: www.apexcovantage.com
Process engineering, knowledge & content management, imaging, document management, forms processing & digital assets creation, engineering: data conversion, purification & conflation, work order posting, inspections, audits. (As-Ind, estab 1988, empl 2500, sales , cert: State, NMSDC)

5639   Applied Integrity Consulting, LLC
       40646 Weaver Ct   Leesburg, VA 20175
       (703) 868-3886 Loan Clarke CEO
       Fax:
       Email: lclarke@aic-llc.us
       Website: www.aic-llc.us
Enterprise IT & Software Engineering support and services.
Expertise in Microsoft technologies. (Woman/As-Pac, estab
2011, empl 2, sales , cert: State)

5640   Archura, LLC
       673 Potomac Station D, Ste 808   Leesburg, VA
       20176
       (703) 728-1302 Kurt McHenry COO
       Fax: (703) 738-7406
       Email: kurt.mchenry@archura.com
       Website: www.archura.com
lifecycle requirements of wire-line, wireless and optical
networks, design, deploy, maintain and manage large and
small scale public & private network infrastructures. We
provide scalable integration and network support services
(AA, estab 2005, empl 85, sales $7,200,000, cert: State)

5641   Astyra Corporation
       411 East Franklin St, Ste 105   Richmond, VA 23219
       (804) 433-1117 Lee Rattigan Director of Fulfillment
       Fax: (804) 433-1101
       Email: lrattigan@astyra.com
       Website: www.astyra.com
IT staff augmentation & IT solutions: Medicaid & HIPAA
application development & project management. (AA,
estab 1997, empl 150, sales $15,000,000, cert: State,
NMSDC, SDB)

5642   Atlantic Resource Group, Inc.
       4880 Cox Rd, Ste 105   Glen Allen, VA 23060
       (804) 262-4400 Deborah J. Dowdy President
       Fax: (804) 262-4559
       Email: Debbie@AtlanticResource.com
       Website: www.atlanticresource.com
Information technology, staff augmentation & project
mgmt. (Woman/White, estab 1990, empl 45, sales , cert:
WBENC)

5643   BAI, Inc.
       4600 Duke St, Ste 303   Alexandria, VA 22304
       (703) 461-4713 Mindy Cookmeyer VP
       Fax: (703) 461-4719
       Email: cookmeyerm@bai-inc.net
       Website: www.bai-inc.net
Program mgmt & policy, implementation, security & info
technology. (Hisp, estab 1999, empl 70, sales , cert: State)

5644   Balance Technology Group, Inc.
       8136 Old Keene Mill Rd Ste A207 Springfield, VA
       22152
       (703) 451-8675 Tracy Betts CEO
       Fax: (703) 783-0392
       Email: tracy.betts@balanceinteractive.com
       Website: www.balanceinteractive.com
Web design & development agency. (Woman/White, estab
1997, empl 13, sales $1,600,000, cert: WBENC)

5645   Benten Technologies
       13996 Parkeast Circle 105 Herndon, VA 20171
       (703) 788-6560 Tony Ma President
       Fax: (703) 560-0297
       Email: tonyma@bententech.com
       Website: www.bententech.com
IT consulting. (As-Pac, estab 2000, empl 4, sales
$2,050,615, cert: State)

5646   Biswas Information Technology Solutions Inc.
       2612 Litchfield Dr   Herndon, VA 20171
       (202) 203-0982 Sumita Biswas
       Fax: (703) 860-2829
       Email: sbiswas@b-itsinc.com
       Website: www.b-itsinc.com
Database centric applications, dbase mgmt & development. (Woman/As-Ind, estab 2006, empl 5, sales
$383,733, cert: NMSDC, WBENC, 8(a))

5647   BlueAlly Technology Solutions, LLC
       8609 Westwood Center Dr Ste 100 Vienna, VA
       22182
       (919) 249-1509 Hope Jepson Proposal and
       Certification Mgr
       Fax: (919) 858-0552
       Email: HJepson@blueally.com
       Website: www.blueally.com
Big Data, Business Intelligence, Micro Strategy cognos,
project management office model. (As-Pac, estab 2010,
empl 55, sales $46,000,000, cert: NMSDC)

5648   Burke Consortium, Incorporated
       5500 Cherokee Ave, Ste 510   Alexandria, VA
       22312
       (703) 941-0600 Thomas Nodeen COO
       Fax: (703) 941-0704
       Email: tnodeen@bcinow.com
       Website: www.bcinow.com
Information technology solutions, software development, cyber security, independent verification &
validation. (Woman/White, estab 1982, empl 44, sales
$10,500,000, cert: WBENC)

5649   Capital Legal Solutions dba Capital Novus
       10521 Rosehaven St Ste 300 Fairfax, VA 22030
       (703) 226-1500 Ramesh Purohit Business Dev
       Mgr
       Fax: (703) 226-1550
       Email: rpurohit@capitalnovus.com
       Website: www.capitalnovus.com
Forensic data collection from project sites around the
world, data preservation, processing, and presentation,
web hosting services & loading (Woman/As-Ind, estab
2002, empl 250, sales $21,560,000, cert: State, WBENC)

5650   Centurion Consulting Group, LLC
       13800 Coppermine Rd Ste 190 Herndon, VA
       20171
       (571) 375-8179 Theresa Zandi Principal
       Fax: (703) 935-2510
       Email: theresa.zandi@centurioncg.com
       Website: www.centurioncg.com
IT/Professional staffing. (Woman/White, estab 2016,
empl 43, sales , cert: State)

5651 CEXEC Inc.
11440 Commerce Park Dr Ste 600 Reston, VA 20191
(703) 766-8489 Mike Klazas Dir of Mktg
Fax: (703) 766-8539
Email: mike.klazas@cexec.com
Website: www.cexec.com
IT svcs, telecommunications, LAN/WANs, networking. (Nat Ame, estab 1976, empl 144, sales , cert: State)

5652 Cheshil Consultants, Inc.
8136 Old Keene Mill Rd, Ste B-201 Springfield, VA 22152
(703) 569-8763 Chet Bhimani President
Fax: (703) 569-3122
Email: cvbhimani@ccione.com
Website: www.ccione.com
Information technology consulting. (As-Ind, estab 1991, empl 13, sales $1,226,303, cert: State)

5653 Citadel Logic
26 Town Center Way, Ste 236 Hampton, VA 23666
(757) 864-0905 Miranda Nichols VP plans/programs
Fax:
Email: info@citadellogic.com
Website: www.citadellogic.com
Cyber security, IT, intelligence, command & control, UAS/RPA operations & support, energy security/management, logistics & emergency management support. (AA, estab 2009, empl 6, sales $400,000, cert: State)

5654 Commonwealth Copy Products dba Commonwealth Digital Office Solutions
21205 Ridgetop Circle Sterling, VA 20166
(240) 401-4776 Mark Harris Dir Major Accts
Fax: (703) 450-5781
Email: markh@commonwealthdigital.com
Website: www.commonwealthdigital.com
Document management systems managed network services, managed print services, records retention, systems integration hardware and software. (Woman/White, estab 1977, empl 80, sales $21,000,000, cert: State)

5655 CompuGain LLC
13241 Woodland Park Rd, Ste 100 Ste 100
Herndon, VA 20171
(703) 956-7005 Manita Hota VP Client Dev
Fax: (703) 956-7059
Email: srinivasa.chowdary@Compugain.com
Website: www.compugain.com
Application development, business intelligence, data management, systems integration, project management, support & maintenance services. (As-Ind, estab 2000, empl 500, sales $57,400,000, cert: NMSDC)

5656 Conviso Inc.
312 E Main St, Ste 200 Luray, VA 22835
(703) 980-7074 Uday Malhan President
Fax:
Email: umalhan@convisoinc.com
Website: www.convisoinc.com
Application Development & Maintenance lication security & applications portfolio rationalization, .NET, Java, PeopleSoft, Systems Integration. (As-Ind, estab 2010, empl 18, sales $1,590,000, cert: State)

5657 CoreLogix Consulting Inc.
1900 Campus Commons Dr Reston, VA 20191
(703) 665-0813 Inderbir Singh President
Fax:
Email: inder@clx-inc.com
Website: www.clx-inc.com
IT & Management Consulting, Program Management, Project Management, Subject Matter Expertise, Applications Programming, System Programming, Database Administration
Network Engineering, Technical Writing, Quality Assurance. (As-Pac, estab 2011, empl 25, sales , cert: State)

5658 CoreLogix Consulting Incorporation
1900 Campus Commons Dr Ste 100 Reston, VA 20191
(703) 665-0813 Inderbir Singh President
Fax:
Email: inder@clx-inc.com
Website: www.clx-inc.com
IT & management consulting services. (As-Ind, estab 2011, empl 25, sales $1,400,000, cert: State)

5659 Corporate Leads, Inc.
2009 Mara Park Pl Williamsburg, VA 23185
(757) 220-8215 Luis Long President
Fax: (757) 220-8516
Email: LongL@CorporateLeads.com
Website: www.CorporateLeads.com
Corporate Leads, Inc. is a contingency search firm specializing in the global placement of Junior Military Officers and business experienced managers, supervisors, engineers, and technicians. (Hisp, estab 1997, empl 2, sales $462,000, cert: State)

5660 CurtMont Global Services, Inc.
9501 Hull St Rd, Ste D Richmond, VA 23236
(804) 982-9349 Curtiss Stancil President
Fax: (804) 745-0982
Email: cstancil@curtmont.com
Website: www.curtmontglobalservices.com
Contracted foodservices, facility management, and transportation support services through our operating companies (CurtMont Foodservices and TransitServcorp). We are minority owned certified in 20 states in the USA. (AA, estab 2014, empl 105, sales $2,000,000, cert: State)

5661 Cyber Clarity Inc.
15722 Ryder Court Haymarket, VA 20169
(571) 982-6710 Ed Kraemer VP
Fax:
Email: ed@cyberclarity.com
Website: www.cyberclarity.com
Cyber Intelligence, Operational Continuity, Computer network Defense, Incident Response & Compliance. (Woman/White, estab 2011, empl 12, sales $1,700,000, cert: State, City)

5662　Cynet Systems Inc.
21000 Atlantic Blvd #740　Sterling, VA 20166
(571) 645-5910　Arpit Paul Talent Management
Fax: (866) 838-0907
Email: arpitp@cynetsystems.com
Website: www.cynetsystems.com
IT & engineering staffing consulting, direct/full time hiring, contract (temp hiring) or contract to hire services. (As-Ind, estab 2010, empl 798, sales $52,500,000, cert: NMSDC, CPUC)

5663　Data Concepts
4405 Cox Rd Ste 140　Glen Allen, VA 23060
(804) 968-4700　Dennis Woomer Dir Business Dev
Fax: (804) 968-7900
Email: dennis.woomer@dataconcepts-inc.com
Website: www.dataconcepts-inc.com
Application development, Microsoft, Java & Mobile technologies.. (Woman/White, estab 1997, empl 20, sales $15,000,000, cert: State)

5664　Dataline Inc.
9830 Mayland Dr Ste J　Richmond, VA 23233
(804) 270-4900　John Cumberland Sr Acct Mgr
Fax: (804) 270-1091
Email: john.cumberland@dataline.com
Website: www.dataline.com
Applications development, collaborative tools & help desk consulting. (Hisp, estab 1960, empl 450, sales , cert: State)

5665　Deque Systems, Inc.
2121 Cooperative Way Ste 210　Reston, VA 20191
(703) 225-0380　Preety Kumar CEO
Fax: (703) 225-0387
Email: preety.kumar@deque.com
Website: www.deque.com
IT consulting & services. (Woman/As-Ind, estab 1999, empl 25, sales $1,745,001, cert: State, WBENC)

5666　Digilent Consulting, LLC
2612 Amanda Ct　Vienna, VA 22180
(412) 657-2219　Vinny Raj Managing Dir
Fax: (412) 657-2219
Email: vinnyraj@digilentconsulting.com
Website: www.digilentconsulting.com
SMAC (Social, Mobile, Analytics and Cloud), Cyber Security expertise/capabilities. (Woman/As-Ind, estab 2006, empl 5, sales $450,000, cert: State, NMSDC)

5667　Digital Intelligence Systems LLC, d.b.a DISYS
8270 Greensboro Dr Ste 1000　McLean, VA 22102
(818) 481-5556　Arthur Levitt Exec Director, Strategic Acco. & MSP Alliance
Fax: (800) 854-7254
Email: Vizient@disys.com
Website: www.disys.com
Information technology service, staff augmentation & recruitment, hardware & software, wireless & mobile systems design, implementation & mgmt. (As-Pac, estab 1994, empl 4234, sales $333,266,296, cert: NMSDC)

5668　DISYS Solutions, Inc.
4151 Lafayette Center Dr Ste 600　Chantilly, VA 20151
(703) 802-0500　Vinu Luthra COO
Fax: (800) 601-2944
Email: Supplier.Diversity@disyssolutions.com
Website: www.disyssolutions.com
Information technology products & services. (As-Ind, estab 2010, empl 45, sales $62,000,000, cert: State)

5669　Diverse Solutions Group Inc.
12185 Balls Ford Rd　Manassas, VA 20109
(571) 921-4801　Steve ForUs President
Fax: (215) 879-6702
Email: SForUs@DSGinc-USA.com
Website: www.diversesolutionsgrp.com
Industrial Security Services, Security Management and Support Services utilizing the latest technologies and proven practices to comply with HSPD-12 and FIPS 201-2 compliance. (Woman/Hisp, estab 2010, empl 6, sales $474,000, cert: 8(a), SDB)

5670　Dorkin Inc.
1103 W Broad St　Falls Church, VA 22046
(202) 657-9907　Stephanie Juniel President
Fax:
Email: sjuniel@dorkin.net
Website: www.dorkin.net/
Project Management Software, HR staffing software, Data Encryptions software, Access Development, Asset Management, Business Intelligence, Cloud & Virtualization, Content Management Systems, Custom Software. (Woman/AA, estab 2012, empl 11, sales $60,000, cert: 8(a))

5671　E&E Enterprises Global Inc.
2017 Cunningham Dr, Ste 213　Hampton, VA 23666
(757) 826-9532　Ernest Green CEO
Fax: (757) 265-9750
Email: egreen@eeenterprisesinc.com
Website: www.eeenterprisesinc.com
Broadband internet satellite communications systems, digital satellite television, web based & computer based training products & programs, IT solutions, WiFi & wireless technologies. (AA, estab 1997, empl 11, sales $2,000,000, cert: State)

5672　End-to-End Computing, LLC
6024 Craig St　Springfield, VA 22150
(571) 449-6554　Esteve Mede CEO
Fax:
Email: emede@eecomputing.com
Website: www.eecomputing.com
Vendor agnostic solutions, infrastructure solution, network architectureand design, network security architecture, unified communications, data center design, Cloud data center design, information assurance, policy implementation & procedure. (AA, estab 2012, empl 4, sales , cert: State)

5673 Enterprise Architecture and Information Management
9220 Treasure Oak Ct Lorton, VA 22079
(703) 725-3801 Arulkumar Selvappan President
Fax: (703) 485-3422
Email: aselvappan@eaaim.com
Website: www.eaaim.com
Enterprise architecture solutions, actionable enterprise architecture, information & data architecture, application architecture, metadata management, repository support. (As-Ind, estab 2006, empl 2, sales $350,000, cert: 8(a))

5674 Enterprise ITech Corp.
10014 Manor Pl Fairfax, VA 22032
(703) 731-7881 Pals Nagaraj
Fax: (888) 688-4925
Email: pnagaraj@enterpriseitech.com
Website: www.enterpriseitech.com
Full Software Development Lifecycle, Business Analytics, Business Intelligence, Enterprise Web Development, Enterprise Legacy System Modernization, Mobile application development, Database Design, Data Warehouse ETL. (As-Ind, estab 2000, empl 2, sales $300,000, cert: State, NMSDC)

5675 ESC, Inc.
2451 Crystal Dr Ste 775 Arlington, VA 22202
(703) 291-6706 Maggie Harris CEO
Fax: (703) 291-6731
Email: harris_maggie@escinc1.com
Website: www.escinc1.com
Information Technology, Information Security & Assurance, Cyber Security, Network Security, Certifications & Accreditation, Access Control, Investigative & Adjudication, Information Sharing, Portfolio Management. (Woman/AA, estab 1992, empl 110, sales $7,000,000, cert: State)

5676 EsteemLogic
722 E Market St Leesburg, VA 20176
(571) 235-9284 Kristina Francis CEO
Fax:
Email: kfrancis@esteemlogic.com
Website: www.esteemlogic.com
IT consulting and training firm that implements sustainable, scalable solutions to ensure organizations optimize engagement with its people, customers and the communities they serve. (AA, estab 2017, empl 2, sales , cert: State, WBENC)

5677 ETELIC Inc.
5388 Twin Hickory Rd Glen Allen, VA 23059
(866) 240-3395 Mark Murphy President
Fax: (866) 591-5906
Email: mark.murphy@etelic.com
Website: www.etelic.com
Computer programming svcs: systems design, facilities management, consulting, database & data warehouse. (As-Pac, estab 2004, empl 20, sales $2,400,000, cert: State, NMSDC)

5678 EvereTech LLC
2705 Main Sail Ct Henrico, VA 23233
(804) 986-9998 Andrew Everett Principal
Fax:
Email: andrew.everett@everetech.com
Website: www.everetech.com
Systems Administration & Engineering , Network Design, Network Administration & Network Engineering, Software Development & Engineering, Project Management, COTS/GOTS Systems Integration & Configuration. (AA, estab 2014, empl 7, sales $300,000, cert: State)

5679 eWaste Tech Systems, LLC
501 E Franklin St Ste 726 Richmond, VA 23219
(804) 716-3577 Felipe Wright Managing Member
Fax: (804) 521-4295
Email: fwright@ewastetech.com
Website: www.ewastetech.com
Green Information technology sustainability & asset mgmt, data destruction & disposition services, electronic waste disposal. (AA, estab 2012, empl 16, sales $225,000, cert: State, NMSDC)

5680 Eyak Technology
22980 Indian Creek Dr Ste 400 Dulles, VA 20166
(703) 481-0050 Susan Stepanski Business Dev Mgr
Fax: (703) 481-0703
Email: susan.stepanski@eyaktek.com
Website: www.eyaktek.com
IT products, information assurance, help desk, networking, storage solutions, satellite & LMR communications, wireless, physical security, critical infrastructure design & construction, medical staffing, enironmental mediation. (Nat Ame, estab 2002, empl 170, sales $225,000,000, cert: 8(a))

5681 Force 1 Global, LLC
1050 Temple Ave Ste 214 Colonial Heights, VA 23834
(804) 723-1164 DeAlteman Beasley CEO
Fax:
Email: dbeasley@force1global.com
Website: www.force1global.com
Staffing, outsourcing & technology integration. (AA, estab 2014, empl 1, sales , cert: State, NMSDC)

5682 G2 Global Solutions, LLC
202 Church St SE Ste 538 Leesburg, VA 20176
(703) 349-7787 Elizabeth Lauren Galati CEO
Fax: (877) 934-8713
Email: lgalati@g2gs.net
Website: www.g2gs.net
Cyber Exploitation, Information Technology Services, Intelligence. (Woman/Hisp, estab 2012, empl 86, sales $8,000,000, cert: State, 8(a), SDB)

5683   G2 Ops Inc.
205 Business Park Dr   Virginia Beach, VA 23462
(757) 965-8330 Robert Gregorio COO
Fax: (757) 965-8331
Email: bobg@g2-ops.com
Website: www.g2-ops.com
Model based systems engineering & cybersecurity, acquiring data, modeling systems & processes, identifying cyber vulnerabilities, performing analyses, identifying capability gaps and/or areas for improvement. (Woman/White, estab 2005, empl 15, sales $2,200,000, cert: State, WBENC)

5684   Geologics Corporation
5285 Shawnee Rd, Ste 300   Alexandria, VA 22312
(978) 524-8152 John Hildreth Director - Consulting Services
Fax:
Email: jhildreth@geologics.com
Website: www.geologics.com
Technical services: systems engineering, spacecraft, space systems, software dev, science applications. (Hisp, estab 1989, empl 500, sales $79,434,480, cert: NMSDC)

5685   Global Geographic Inc.
11511 Cavalier Landing Ct   Fairfax, VA 22030
(703) 594-5181 Sameer Chandra VP
Fax: (866) 247-4528
Email: schandra@globalgeographic.com
Website: www.globalgeographic.com
=> IT Services
•Resourcing (Temporary / Full Time)
•Customized Software Development
•Program and Project Management
Our IT Services is managed by our Vice President who is a seasoned IT professional with over 20 years of rich experience in IT industry (As-Pac, estab 2006, empl 3, sales $99,243, cert: State, NMSDC)

5686   Global Technology Solutions, LLC
108 E Grace St, Ste 01   Richmond, VA 23219
(804) 343-7400 Anthony Long
Fax: (804) 343-0014
Email: aelong@gtsnetwork.com
Website: www.gtsnetwork.com
Systems design & implementation, project mgmt, network security & mgmt, business transformation outsourcing, software design & implementation. (AA, estab 2003, empl 10, sales $600,000, cert: State)

5687   Gupton & Associates, Inc.
901 N Pitt St Ste 230 Alexandria, VA 22314
(703) 419-3048 Clara Lee Client Engagement Mgr
Fax:
Email: clarablee@guptonassociates.com
Website: www.guptonassociates.com
Program/Project Management; Application Architecture; Information Assurance/Cyber Security; Network Services; Virtualization & Consolidation; Cloud Computing; Engineering Services; Data Analysis & Generation. (Woman, estab 2002, empl 5, sales $19,200,000, cert: State)

5688   Hanusoft Inc.
7206 Impala Dr, Ste 214   Richmond, VA 23228
(804) 484-2400 Bala Kamuju President
Fax: (804) 441-8263
Email: kamuju@hanusoftinc.com
Website: www.hanusoftinc.com
Computer related services, implementation requirements, computer applications, implementing customize hardware systems, updating & modifying existing programs. (As-Ind, estab 2005, empl 46, sales $4,816,708, cert: State)

5689   HarmonyTech
2010 Corporate Ridge Ste 700 McLean, VA 22102
(703) 405-4587 Nat Vinod President
Fax:
Email: nat.vinod@harmonytech.com
Website: www.harmonytech.com
SQL/NoSQL/XML development, Microsoft Dynamics, Sharepoint, Secure Enterprise Search, Azure, AWS, 508 accessibility,mobile apps,enterprise architecture, server & desktop hardening, Agile/Scrum, Native Xamarin, Program Management. (As-Ind, estab 1995, empl 30, sales $3,500,000, cert: 8(a))

5690   HyperGen Inc.
7810 Carvin St   Roanoke, VA 24019
(540) 992-6500 Sherry Dyer VP sales
Fax: (540) 992-6563
Email: sales@hypergeninc.com
Website: www.hypergeninc.com
PeopleSoft® functional & technical consulting svcs: implementation, upgrade, system analysis, custom developed. (Woman/White, estab 1992, empl 25, sales $2,000,000, cert: State, WBENC)

5691   Idexcel, Inc.
459 Herndon Parkway, Ste 10   Herndon, VA 20170
(703) 230-2607 Prasad Alapati President
Fax: (703) 562-1933
Email: palapati@idexcel.com
Website: www.idexcel.com
Staff augmentation, software development, network design, systems integration & business process improvement. (As-Ind, estab 1998, empl 615, sales $44,830,000, cert: NMSDC)

5692   ILM Corporation
1551 Jefferson Davis Hwy, Ste 200
Fredericksburg, VA 22401
(540) 898-1406 Jason Cohen President
Fax:
Email: bids@ilmcorp.com
Website: www.ilmcorp.com
Document & data capture services. (As-Pac, estab 1976, empl 15, sales $3,000,000, cert: State)

5693 INADEV Corporation
1651 Old Meadow Rd Ste 205 McLean, VA 22102
(703) 286-0860 Scott Armstrong Chief Strategy Officer
Fax:
Email: scott.armstrong@inadev.com
Website: www.inadev.com
Application Modernization & Development, cloud & mobile enablement, Software Architecture, Design, Implementation, & Integration, Native & Hybrid Apps, Content Management Systems, Dashboard. (As-Ind, estab 2001, empl 65, sales $6,000,000, cert: State, 8(a))

5694 Inficare, Inc.
22375 Broderick Dr Ste 225 Dulles, VA 20166
(703) 404-4402 Paul Turner VP
Fax: (703) 544-1048
Email: paul@inficaretech.com
Website: www.inficaretech.com
IT consulting, staff augmentation. (As-Ind, estab 2001, empl 40, sales $4,783,000, cert: State)

5695 Innovative Computing & Applied Technology
11490 Commerce Park Dr, Ste 530 Reston, VA 20191
(703) 391-1600 Bruce Freedman VP of Corporate Devel
Fax: (703) 391-1601
Email: bruce.freedman@incatech-corp.com
Website: www.incatech-corp.com
Web Design & Development, Enterprise Web Content Management, User Interface (UI)/User Experience (UX) Design, Full Life Cycle Software Devel, Microsoft SharePoint Development & Administration. (Woman, estab 2007, empl 20, sales , cert: 8(a))

5696 Innovative Technology Application, Inc. (ITA)
6551 Loisdale Ct Springfield, VA 22150
(703) 924-9200 Jim Clifford strat Business Dev
Fax: (703) 455-4049
Email: jimc@itapages.com
Website: www.itapages.com
Computer based training; multimedia presentations; interactive full motion video training; PC; multimedia graphics applications; CD-ROM production; simulations; 3D imagery devel; full text search & retrieval databases; etc. (As-Pac, estab 1995, empl 113, sales $25,000,000, cert: State)

5697 Inscope Internatioinal, Inc.
12018 Sunrise Valley Dr Ste 100 Reston, VA 20191
(703) 480-3280 Chris Barlow Acct Exec
Fax: (703) 348-2729
Email: cbarlow@inscopeinternational.com
Website: www.inscopeinternational.com
IT strategy, deployment & operations, enterprise application, integration, data & COTS solutions. (AA, estab 1997, empl 100, sales $33,301,501, cert: NMSDC)

5698 Integrated Support Systems Inc (ISSi)
P.O. Box 2402 Arlington, VA 22202
(703) 892-6100 Frank Duron CEO
Fax: (703) 892-9200
Email: fduron@integratedsupport.com
Website: www.integratedsupport.com
Web design, develop & content mgmt, imaging, form conversion, records & docuemnt mgmt, workflow & litigation solutions, systems integration & custom solutions. (Hisp, estab 1984, empl 22, sales $2,334,042, cert: NMSDC)

5699 IntellecTechs, Inc.
195 S Rosemont Rd Virginia Beach, VA 23455
(757) 962-2487 Jeri Prophet CEO
Fax:
Email: contracts@intellectechs.com
Website: www.intellectechs.com
Information technology (IT), logistics, program management, training & testing & professional services. (Woman/White, estab 2008, empl 30, sales $1,500,000, cert: 8(a))

5700 iQuasar, LLC
6 Pidgeon Hill Dr Ste 305 Sterling, VA 20165
(703) 962-6001 Amin Bhat Chief Business Officer
Fax: (703) 773-6970
Email: amin.bhat@iquasar.com
Website: www.iQuasar.com
Information technology solutions & services, IT consulting, staffing & recruitment services. (As-Pac, estab 2004, empl 15, sales $2,070,152, cert: State, NMSDC)

5701 Iron Horse Computers, Inc.
8328-A Traford Ln Springfield, VA 22152
(703) 866-6413 Joe Whitford Office Mgr
Fax: (703) 866-6418
Email: billing@ih-online.com
Website: www.ih-online.com
LAN/WAN; network utilities, CAD, GIS, hardware, software, parts, supplies, system integration, consulting, telephone integration, imaging, repairs. (Hisp, estab 1990, empl 3, sales $1,600,000, cert: State)

5702 IT Data Consulting LLC
11951 Freedom Dr, Ste 1300 Reston, VA 20190
(202) 999-9184 Benny Asnake CEO
Fax: (866) 758-0865
Email: Benny@it-dc.com
Website: www.it-dc.com
Enterprise Business Solutions, Enterprise Data Management, Cloud/Web/Mobile/Database Solution Development. (AA, estab 2010, empl 8, sales $570,000, cert: 8(a), SDB)

5703 iWorks Corporation
1889 Preston Shite Dr Ste 100 reston, VA 20191
(571) 485-2004 Jothi Radhakrishnan Sr VP
Fax: (866) 574-2310
Email: Jradhakrishnan@iworkscorp.com
Website: www.iworkscorp.com
Information technology consulting & staff augmentation. (As-Ind, estab 2005, empl 9, sales $8,000,000, cert: State)

5704   JPI Technology LLC
       9720 Capital Court, Ste 301   Manassas, VA 20155
       (703) 828-5651 Haris Perwaiz VP
       Fax: (202) 688-1905
       Email: harris@jpitechnology.com
       Website: www.jpitechnology.com
Information consulting, contracting, application development, e-commerce/ERP, application integration, infrastructure & staff augmentation. (Woman/As-Ind, estab 2011, empl 9, sales $1,300,000, cert: State)

5705   Key Concepts Knowledgebase LLC
       4031 University Dr   Fairfax, VA 22030
       (703) 966-1364 Kim de Peiza President
       Fax: (703) 385-5843
       Email: kdepeiza@keyknowledgebase.com
       Website: www.keyknowledgebase.com
Technical and customer centric documentation, SOPsService Desk supportLAN/WAN Infrastructure and Systems Administration supportSoftware Web Development, SOA development, mobile computing, Web 2.0 (AA, estab 2004, empl 10, sales $450,000, cert: NMSDC, 8(a))

5706   Knowledge Connections, Inc.
       610 Herndon Pkwy Ste 900A Herndon, VA 20170
       (571) 203-9120 Marion Bonhomme-Knox President
       Fax: (571) 203-8809
       Email: marion.bk@theknowledgeconnection.com
       Website: www.knowledgeconnector.com
Systems engineering & telecommunications. (Woman/AA, estab 1996, empl 150, sales $4,000,000, cert: State)

5707   Knowledge Information Solutions, Inc.
       227 S Rosemont Rd   Virginia Beach, VA 23452
       (757) 463-0033 Terry Kreamer CFO
       Fax: (757) 463-3971
       Email: terry.kreamer@kisinc.net
       Website: www.kisinc.net
Information technology products & services: inside/outside plant cabling & wireless solutions, security systems, telephone systems, computer products & services, web development, data base dev & mgmt, network architecture & engineering. (Woman/Hisp, estab 1983, empl 100, sales $30,200,000, cert: State)

5708   Lancesoft, Inc.
       13454 Sunrise Valley Dr Ste 120 Herndon, VA 20171
       (703) 674-4565 Prashant Arni VP Strategic Client Rel
       Fax: (703) 935-0339
       Email: marketing@lancesoft.com
       Website: www.lancesoft.com
IT software, staffing & project execution. (Woman/As-Ind, estab 2000, empl 1386, sales $68,000,000, cert: NMSDC)

5709   Loyola Enterprises Inc.
       2984 S Lynnhaven Rd Ste 101 Virginia Beach, VA 23452
       (757) 498-6118 Benito Loyola President
       Fax: (757) 498-6110
       Email: benito@loyola.com
       Website: www.loyola.com
TS/SCI, Modeling & Simulation Information Technology, Web Portal and Multimedia. (Hisp, estab 1991, empl 30, sales $7,325,312, cert: State)

5710   MAI Enterprises, Inc.
       P.O. Box 1194 Annandale, VA 22003
       (703) 750-2228 Bonnie Norem President
       Fax: (703) 750-0097
       Email: bonnie@maienterprises.com
       Website: www.maienterprises.com
System engineering, graphic illustration, desktop publishing, proposals, tech editing & writing, computer hardware & software products. (Woman/White, estab 1986, empl 15, sales $763,400, cert: State)

5711   Management Support Technology, Inc. (MSTI)
       3701 Pender Dr Ste 505 Fairfax, VA 22030
       (703) 385-5841 Norris Middleton President
       Fax: (703) 385-5843
       Email: nmiddleton@msti-net.com
       Website: www.msti-net.com
Information Management Support Incident Management, Problem Management, Change Management, Configuration Management, Asset Management, enterprise desktop Systems (AA, estab 1989, empl 125, sales $115,798,643, cert: State)

5712   Maven Inc
       161 Fort Evans Rd, NE Ste 205 Leesburg, VA 20176
       (202) 888-7159 Venkat Mallasani President
       Fax: (855) 466-2636
       Email: vm@maven-federal.com
       Website: www.maven-federal.com
Computer Programming Services, Systems Design Services, Facilities Management Services, Management Consulting Services. (As-Pac, estab 2010, empl 10, sales $1,400,000, cert: 8(a))

5713   McKinney & McKinney Technical Services, Inc.
       3122 Golansky Blvd Ste 202 Woodbridge, VA 22192
       (703) 580-1995 Michelle McKinney CEO
       Fax: (703) 580-1975
       Email: mmckinney@mmtsi.com
       Website: www.mmtsi.com
Engineering, systems engineering, software development, and Tier I, II, and III Help Desk Support. We provide systems engineering support for FAA Air Traffic Management systems (Woman/AA, estab 1989, empl 15, sales $1,600,000, cert: State)

5714   Meta Dimensions Inc.
       7115 Leesburg Pike, Ste 213 Falls Church, VA 22043
       (571) 969-4140 Amit Prakash President
       Fax: (703) 981-9042
       Email: amit@metadim.com
       Website: www.metadim.com
Analytics service, Big Data Lake, Data Visualization, Enterprise Information Management, Intelligent Enterprise Roadmap, Master Data Management. (Woman/As-Ind, estab 2007, empl 85, sales $2,064,955, cert: State, NMSDC, WBENC)

5715 MicroHealth, LLC
8245 Boone Blvd, Ste 706   Vienna, VA 22182
(855) 294-3547   Jutta Whitfield Business Dev Mgr
Fax:
Email: jutta.whitfield@microhealthllc.com
Website: www.microhealthllc.com
Health information technology & health information management. (As-Pac, estab 2010, empl 71, sales , cert: 8(a))

5716 MicroTechnologies, LLC
8330 Boone Blvd, Ste 600   Vienna, VA 22182
(703) 891-1073   Aaron Drabkin SVP of Contracts
Fax: (703) 891-1074
Email: adrabkin@microtech.net
Website: www.MicroTech.net
Program mngt, database mgnt & admin, change mgnt & process re-engineering, sys eng svcs, info sys sustainment & support, IT svcs & solns, collaboration svcs & info sharing apps, network solns & sys modernization, & IT enterprise transformation. (Hisp, estab 2004, empl 420, sales $780,000,000, cert: State, NMSDC)

5717 Mosaic Solutions, Inc.
209 Elden St, Ste 204   Herndon, VA 20170
(703) 707-1680   Vikash Nangalia Program Mgr
Fax: (703) 707-1683
Email: vikash@mosaic-us.com
Website: www.mosaic-us.com/
Systems integration, program mgmt, enterprise resource mgmt, customer relationship mgmt, data mgmt, database admin & warehousing, knowledge mgmt, networking, desktop & help desk svcs, business process outsourcing & supply chain mgmt. (As-Ind, estab 1996, empl 17, sales $1,170,660, cert: NMSDC)

5718 NETHOST, Inc.
1750 Tysons Blvd. Ste 1500 McLean, VA 22102
(571) 236-0781 Ikram Koreshi CEO
Fax: (703) 738-7736
Email: ikoreshi@nethostus.com
Website: www.nethostus.com
Network systems & data communication, engineering, business processes, ERP & CRM functional areas & technical consulting. (As-Ind, estab 2002, empl 3, sales $300,000, cert: State)

5719 NetVision Resources, Inc.
2201 Cooperative Way, Ste 600   Herndon, VA 20171
(703) 342-4284 Vishnu Seri VP
Fax: (703) 378-5147
Email: vseri@netvisionresources.com
Website: www.netvisionresources.com
Information technology svcs: staff augmentation, on-site, off-site & off-shore software development. (As-Ind, estab 1999, empl 100, sales $15,500,000, cert: NMSDC)

5720 NexThreat LLC
12110 Sunset Hills Rd Ste 600 Reston, VA 20190
(571) 989-0577 Ruben Gavilan CEO
Fax:
Email: Ruben@NexThreat.com
Website: www.Nexthreat.com
Cyber Security. Emerging SIEM Tool Optimization (Splunk, Qradar, Arcsight Partner), Insider Threat Detection, Incident Response, SOC/NOC Support Services, Continuous Data Analytics, IA, IT Security, Vulnerability Assessments. (Hisp, estab 2016, empl 13, sales $400,000, cert: State)

5721 Nirvana International Inc.
2108 Gunnell Farms Dr   Vienna, VA 22181
(571) 215-0072 Pritish Nawlakhe President
Fax:
Email: pritish@nirvana-international.com
Website: www.nirvana-international.com
Oracle EBS/ERP Solutions, INFOR Solutions, Program & Project Management, Staff Augmentation, PCI Compliant Credit Card Solutions, Business Intelligence & Analytics solutions, Social Media Integration. (Woman/As-Ind, estab 2012, empl 5, sales $158,000, cert: State)

5722 OSI Federal Technologies, Inc.
42020 Village Center Plaza, Ste 120-154   Stone Ridge, VA 20105
(703) 940-5879 Hans Sugatan Sales
Fax: (571) 210-4733
Email: hsugatan@osifederal.com
Website: www.osifederal.com
Information Technology, Systems Integration. (Woman, estab 1988, empl 9, sales $9,000,000, cert: State)

5723 Pan Asia Resources Pte Ltd.
44031 Pipeline Plaza Ste 305 Ashburn, VA 20147
(571) 269-2778 Aparnaa Vinod President
Fax: (703) 880-7134
Email: aparnaa@panasiagroup.net
Website: www.panasiaresources.com
Information Technology, Marketing & Telecommunications. (Woman/As-Ind, estab 2003, empl 35, sales , cert: State)

5724 PeopleNTech LLC
1604 Spring Hill Rd, Ste 302   Vienna, VA 22182
(703) 373-7329 Mohit Kumar Dir Recruiting Svcs
Fax:
Email: mohit@peoplentech.com
Website: www.peoplentech.com/index.php
IT & Engineering solutions, Development, Outsourcing & Consulting. (Woman/As-Pac, estab 2005, empl 92, sales $9,600,000, cert: State)

5725 Pioneer Corporate Services Inc.
44345 Premier Plaza, Ste 120   Ashburn, VA 20147
(703) 726-1653 Purna Dokku CEO
Fax:
Email: purna@pcservicesinc.com
Website: www.pcservicesinc.com/contactus.php
Software Integration, Database Services, Managed Services, IT Consulting Services. (As-Ind, estab 2002, empl 90, sales , cert: 8(a))

5726 PL Systems LLC
14570 Woodland Ridge Dr   Centreville, VA 20121
(703) 598-2333 Donald Jung President
Fax:
Email: jung.donald@plsystems.net
Website: www.plsystems.net
IT services: infrastructure support, applications development, web services, Cloud based tools, CMMI level II, PMI & PMP certified staff, Global IT deployments, advanced systems design & delivery. (As-Pac, estab 2004, empl 25, sales $2,000,000, cert: 8(a))

5727 Pretek Corporation
800 Corporate Dr Ste 301 Stafford, VA 22554
(703) 855-7148 Dilip Goyal Exec Dir
Fax:
Email: dilip@pretek.com
Website: www.pretek.com
Enterprise architecture, agile application development, DevOps, enterprise data management, IT infrastructure, systems engineering, and security. (As-Ind, estab 2002, empl 25, sales $2,800,000, cert: State, 8(a))

5728 Protege LLC
12359 Sunrise Valley Dr Ste 260 Reston, VA 20191
(703) 953-2535 Shyam Monaysar Sr Business Devel Mgr
Fax:
Email: shyam@protegellc.com
Website: www.protegellc.com
Web/Application Development (.Net, Java, J2EE, JSP, HTML, DHTML, CSS, Ajax, Flash, C#, C++, C), Web Services(WebLogic, WebSphere, Apache, TeamSite, Windows Administration), SharePoint (Developers, Administrators). (Woman/As-Ind, estab 2004, empl 60, sales $3,500,000, cert: State)

5729 Qassurance Technology Inc.
5821 Maybrook Court   Glen Allen, VA 23059
(814) 441-9634 Gurushyam Mony CEO
Fax:
Email: support@qassurancetechnology.com
Website: www.qassurancetechnology.com
Information technology consulting services. (As-Ind, estab 2012, empl 2, sales $145,000, cert: State)

5730 QSACK & Associates, Inc.
2111 Wilson Blvd, Ste 700   Arlington, VA 22201
(703) 351-5035 C. Anthony Cusack CEO
Fax: (703) 526-9781
Email: cac@qsack1.com
Website: www.qsack1.com
Professional, information technology & business support services, systems integration; information assurance; systems security services; information technology services, program & project management. (AA, estab 2001, empl 35, sales $3,879,000, cert: State)

5731 RazorX2, LLC
403 Old Dominion Ave   Herndon, VA 20170
(703) 464-9829 Mary Flaherty Business Dev Mgr
Fax:
Email: mflaherty@razorx2.net
Website: www.razorX2.net
Full-cycle Software Development, Tier 1, 2 & 3 level Help Desk Support, IT Program Management & Support, Technologies & Methodologies. (Woman/As-Pac, estab 2004, empl 30, sales , cert: 8(a))

5732 Red Jacket Systems, LLC
13912 Cristo Ct Centreville, VA 20120
(703) 623-9982 Rex Lallmang President
Fax: (703) 815-4748
Email: rex@redjacketsystems.com
Website: www.redjacketsystems.com
IT professional svcs: software engineering, IVV&V, project management, QA, CM, training, helpdesk, web development. (Nat Ame, estab 2002, empl 4, sales $210,000, cert: State)

5733 Reed Integration, Inc.
7007 Harbour View Blvd Ste 117 Suffolk, VA 23435
(757) 638-3238 Steve Waddell VP strategy
Fax: (757) 638-3239
Email: swaddell@reedintegration.com
Website: www.reedintegration.com
Systems engineering & project management. (Woman/White, estab 2002, empl 40, sales $5,000,000, cert: State)

5734 Savi Solutions, Inc.
8200 Greensboro Dr, Ste 900   McLean, VA 22102
(571) 258-7602 Smita Iyer CEO
Fax:
Email: siyer@savisolutions.biz
Website: www.savisolutions.biz
Strategic Planning, Program/Project Management, Merger & Acquisition Support, Systems Implementation (ERP/CRM/SCM), Cloud Based Implementation Solutions, Business Requirement Analysis, System Design and Development. (As-Ind, estab 2010, empl 3, sales $552,551, cert: WBENC)

5735 Secured Network Solutions, Inc.
929 Ventures Way Ste 113 Chesapeake, VA 23320
(757) 819-7647 Alphonzo Barney President
Fax: (888) 785-8447
Email: team@teamsns.com
Website: www.eamsns.com
Telecommunications & information technology: cabling, design, install, fiber optics single/multi-strand, fiber fusion & splicing, LAN/WAN/wireless network engineering, drafting & information systems security. (AA, estab 2006, empl 11, sales , cert: State)

5736   Shivan Technologies, Inc.
       12818 Owens Glen Dr   Fairfax, VA 22030
       (703) 595-6879 Rekha Bathula President
       Fax:
       Email: contact@stgxinc.com
       Website: www.stgxinc.com
IT, Network Mgmt, Computer Facilities Mgmt, Program
Mgmt, Consulting, Admin & Professional Support Svcs, Info
Assurance, Enterprise Architecture, Cloud. (Woman/As-
Pac, estab 2007, empl 4, sales , cert: State, 8(a))

5737   SilTek, Inc.
       13454 Sunrise Valley Dr Ste 250 Herndon, VA 20171
       (703) 620-9130 Silvia M. Park President
       Fax: (703) 620-5285
       Email: info@siltek.com
       Website: www.siltekinc.com
Computer hardware, IT svcs, systems integration, computer training. (Woman/As-Pac, estab 1997, empl 1, sales
$43,443, cert: State)

5738   Simba Enterprises LLC
       21 Fort Evans Rd, Ste F   Leesburg, VA 20176
       (703) 782-4042 Ali Sajjad CEO
       Fax:
       Email: asajjad@simbacom.net
       Website: www.simbacom.net
Satellite-based telecommunications & information technology solutions worldwide. (As-Ind, estab 2005, empl 10,
sales $3,500,000, cert: State)

5739   Solvitur Systems LLC
       202 Church St SE Ste 526 Leesburg, VA 20176
       (703) 348-3544 Ade Odutola Managing Dir
       Fax: (703) 777-4402
       Email: aodutola@solvitursystems.com
       Website: www.solvitursystems.com
Regulatory Compliance & Security Assessments, Privacy
Impact Analysis, Cloud Security Services, FedRAMP, CSA,
Assessment & Authorization, Independent Verification &
Validation. (AA, estab 2007, empl 5, sales $230,000, cert:
State)

5740   Spurgetech, LLC
       21580 Atlantic Blvd, Ste 220B   Sterling, VA 20166
       (703) 652-6576 Susetha Balabishegan President
       Fax:
       Email: susetha@spurgetech.com
       Website: www.spurgetech.com
Information Technology Consulting, contract & permanent
staffing solutions, On-site, off-site or remote, ERP Resources, SAP, Oracle & Peoplesoft. (Woman/As-Pac, estab
2006, empl 5, sales $900,000, cert: State, WBENC)

5741   Stanton Secure Technologies, LLC
       2054 S Shirlington Rd   Arlington, VA 22204
       (703) 568-0553 Lisa Wallace CEO
       Fax:
       Email: johnson@sst-llc.com
       Website: www.sst-llc.com
Information Assurance services, training & security
management, Cyber Security Program Management,
Assessment & Authorization, Security Engineering,
Remediation Solutions, Security Awareness & Training.
(Woman/AA, estab 2005, empl 2, sales $180,000, cert:
State)

5742   Strategic Operational Solutions, Inc.
       8391 Old Courthouse Rd Ste 300 Vienna, VA
       22182
       (703) 942-8590 Brennan Reif Business Ops
       Analyst
       Fax:
       Email: brennan.reif@stopso.com
       Website: www.stopso.com
Acquisition Support & Logistics, Biometrics & Identity
Management, Information Assurance & Cybersecurity,
Information Technology, Policy & Analysis Support,
Intelligence, Security, Critical Infrastructure, Force
Protection/Anti-Terrorism. (As-Pac, estab 2006, empl
250, sales $24,000,000, cert: State)

5743   Summit Information Solutions, Inc.
       4870 Sadler Road Ste 102 Glen Allen, VA 23060
       (804) 201-4356 Vickie Quigg Comm & Mktg Mgr
       Fax: (804) 201-4382
       Email: vickie.quigg@summitis.com
       Website: www.summitis.com
Enterprise Architecture; Change Management; Informa-
tion Technology; SCORM; Virtual; 3D; Training; Atomic
Layering; ALD; Banking; Finance; Aerospace Engineering;
Big Data; Data Analytics; Resource Management;
Portfolio Management; Cloud; Procurement; AGIL.
(Woman/As-Ind, estab 2002, empl 44, sales $8,981,247,
cert: State)

5744   Sygna Technologies Inc
       4000 Legato Rd Ste 1100 Fairfax, VA 22033
       (571) 445-4800 Paul Shakya President
       Fax:
       Email: paul@sygnatechnologies.com
       Website: www.sygnatechnologies.com
Temporary contract IT Staffing. (As-Ind, estab 2014, empl
1, sales , cert: State)

5745   Symposit LLC
       4809 Eisenhower Ave Ste B3 Alexandria, VA
       22304
       (571) 224-4739 Bobby Bermudez President
       Fax:
       Email: bobby.bermudez@symposit.com
       Website: www.symposit.com
Cloud Solutions & Applications, Cloud Office Productivity
Integration, Email Migration Services,
Virtual Machines / Virtual Desktop Infrastructure,
Windows & Linux Servers, Network & Wireless Infra-
structure, Business Applications, Content Management.
(Hisp, estab 2009, empl 6, sales $400,000, cert: 8(a))

5746   Synapse Business Systems
       11350 Random Hills Rd, Ste 800   Fairfax, VA
       22030
       (703) 782-0007 Sanjay Kumar Sales Head
       Fax: (703) 880-7166
       Email: sanjay@synapsebsystems.com
       Website: www.synapsebsystems.com
Staff Augmentation, Experienced, dedicated and
qualified core staffs, Network of IT Professional, System-
atic and well-defined process to recruit and hire new
talent. (Woman/As-Ind, estab 2013, empl 63, sales
$2,911,046, cert: City, NMSDC, WBENC)

5747   Synaptein Solutions Inc.
       1568 Spring Hill Road Ste 402 Mclean, VA 22102
       (703) 209-2350 Sharad Dayma CEO
       Fax: (888) 906-7153
       Email: sharad.d@synap-one.com
       Website: www.synapteinsolutions.com
Staff Augmentation & Resource Planning Services, BPM
Solutions, Product Development, Customer Support,
Professional Services, Enterprise Solutions Provider,
Business Intelligence & DSS, Off-& and On-site. (As-Ind,
estab 2011, empl 15, sales $1,196,000, cert: State,
NMSDC, 8(a))

5748   Talteam,Inc
       13800 Coppermine Rd Ste 120 Herndon, VA 20171
       (703) 501-0906 Reggie Mathew CEO
       Fax: (703) 995-0917
       Email: regi@talteam.com
       Website: www.talteam.com
IT professional Services, Salesforce & Java technologies.
(Woman/As-Ind, estab 2011, empl 65, sales $5,000,000,
cert: WBENC)

5749   Team Askin Technologies, Inc
       13135 Lee Jackson Memorial Hwy Ste 340 fairfax,
       VA 22033
       (703) 230-0111 steve askin COO
       Fax:
       Email: steve.askin@teamaskin.com
       Website: www.teamaskin.com
Software engineering & development, electronic com-
merce (Internet and Intranet Web Sites, G2C,G2G), Java
Applets, XML, Graphical User Interface (GUI), Front Page,
Cold Fusion, Dreamweaver. (Woman/Hisp, estab 1992,
empl 50, sales $9,000,000, cert: State, WBENC)

5750   Techead
       111 N 17th St Richmond, VA 23219
       (804) 782-6971 Philise Conein CEO
       Fax: (804) 782-2033
       Email: philise@techead.com
       Website: www.techead.com
IT staff augmentation svcs, web & graphics training,
website devel, Linux platform. (Woman/White, estab 1988,
empl 250, sales $7,037,139, cert: State, WBENC)

5751   Technalink, Inc.
       8000 Towers Crescent Dr Ste 600 Vienna, VA 22182
       (703) 627-1916 Alka Dhillon CEO
       Fax: (703) 883-0424
       Email: adhillon@technalink.net
       Website: www.technalink.net
Informaiton technology staffing solutions. (Woman/As-Ind,
estab 2000, empl 20, sales , cert: State)

5752   Technatomy Corporation
       3900 Jermantown Rd Ste 420 Fairfax, VA 22030
       (703) 268-5525 Nadeem Butler Managing Dir
       Fax: (703) 268-5530
       Email: nbutler@technatomy.com
       Website: www.technatomy.com
Information technology, program mgmt, logistics &
engineering. (As-Ind, estab 2000, empl 11, sales
$2,900,000, cert: State)

5753   Technical Expert Consulting LLC
       5765-F Burke Centre Pkwy, Ste 182   Burke, VA
       22015
       (202) 905-2392 Al Bradley President
       Fax:
       Email: al.bradley@tecincorp.com
       Website: www.tecincorp.com
Data Management, Business Intelligence & Systems
Integration services. (AA, estab 2002, empl 6, sales
$2,226,378, cert: 8(a))

5754   Technogems Inc.
       14039 Compton Heights Ct   Clifton, VA 20124
       (703) 856-3350 Jean Meslie President
       Fax:
       Email: jean.meslie@technogemsinc.com
       Website: www.technogemsinc.com
Android application dev, web application dev & maintenance, mobile applications & wireless protocols,
business intelligence & data analysis, interactive application dev,
database design & implementation. (As-Pac, estab 2007,
empl 3, sales $253,000, cert: 8(a))

5755   Technology Assurance Group, Inc.
       2114 Tomlynn St Richmond, VA 23230
       (804) 323-7480 Angela Taylor CEO
       Fax: (804) 355-9716
       Email: ahtaylor@tagva.com
       Website: www.tagva.com
Systems integration: LAN/WAN, VP & wireless networks,
bandwidth mgmt tools, file & directory svcs, storage,
messaging, databases, IP telephony, desktop support.
(Woman/White, estab 2002, empl 10, sales $850,000,
cert: State)

5756   The Mt. Olivet Group, LLC
       P.O. Box 56415 Virginia Beach, VA 23456
       (757) 271-8681 Jon McGlothian President
       Fax: (757) 271-1598
       Email: jon@tmogllc.com
       Website: www.tmogllc.com
The Mt Olivet Group, LLC (TMOG) is set up as a Project
Management Office. As such we provide power,
lighting, security and data products. We provide
training and development services as well as execute
(AA, estab 2007, empl 2, sales $59,000, cert: State)

5757   Total System Services US, Inc.
       1900 Campus Commons Dr #100   Reston, VA
       20191
       (703) 732-6063 Aniths Paalepu President
       Fax: (925) 932-1950
       Email: anithapaalepu@tsysus.com
       Website: www.tsysus.com
IT consulting solutions, distributed operating & comput-
ing systems, storage, networking, systems knowledge.
(Woman/As-Pac, estab 2012, empl 3, sales $76,000, cert:
NMSDC)

5758 True Information Assurance, LLC
7790 Abbey Oaks Court   Manassas, VA 20112
(703) 795-0535 Steven Covey CEO
Fax: (571) 535-5064
Email: coveys@true-ia.com
Website: www.true-ia.com
IT, Cybersecurity, Management Consulting, Cybersecurity program management, certification & accreditation (e.g., FISMA, DIACAP, FIPS, NIST, RMF), security engineering, risk assessment & management. (AA, estab 2007, empl 30, sales $12,000,000, cert: 8(a))

5759 US Websoft Corp.
2430 Birch Cove Rd   Herndon, VA 20171
(703) 318-0103 Guru Nagaraja VP
Fax: (703) 232-1065
Email: gnagaraja@us-websoft.com
Website: www.us-websoft.com
Information technology products & services. (Woman/As-Pac, estab 2000, empl 3, sales , cert: State)

5760 USM Business Systems, Inc.
14175 Sullyfield Circle Ste 400 Chantilly, VA 20151
(832) 881-7903 USM Business Systems SVP Business Dev
Fax: (703) 263-2113
Email: joshuar@usmsystems.com
Website: www.usmsystems.com
Staffing & implementation solutions, computer software programming, application dev, web dev, data warehouse dev & ERP implementations. (As-Ind, estab 1999, empl 125, sales $45,000,000, cert: State)

5761 Vigintis LLC
4000 Legato Rd, Ste 1100   Fairfax, VA 22033
(703) 395-3044 Subodh Dash President
Fax:
Email: corporate@vigintis.us
Website: www.vigintis.us
Agile Program & Project Mgmt, Software Engineering & Product Dev, Solution Architecture & Technology Consulting, System & Application Integration, Cloud Solutions & Svcs. Database Design, Mgmt & Implementation, DevOps (As-Pac, estab 2004, empl 3, sales $460,000, cert: 8(a))

5762 Weiatech, LLC
22584 Hammersmith Pl   Ashburn, VA 20148
(703) 665-9603 Akomala Akouete Operation Director
Fax: (703) 782-9307
Email: aakouete@weiatech.com
Website: www.weiatech.com
Information technology equipment, solutions, and services. (AA, estab 2016, empl 5, sales , cert: State)

5763 Wiltex Incorporated
1012 Oaklawn Ave   Norfolk, VA 23504
(757) 961-3734 Lois S. Williams CEO
Fax: (757) 627-5333
Email: lwilliams@wiltexinc.com
Website: www.wiltexinc.com
Desktop, server & network mgmt, LAN/WAN, database mgmt, application development. (Woman/AA, estab 1999, empl 5, sales $2,039,000, cert: State)

5764 Worldgate, LLC
1760 Reston Pkwy Ste 312 Reston, VA 20190
(703) 349-0493 Justin Zubrick Director, Client Services
Fax:
Email: jzubrick@worldgatellc.com
Website: www.worldgatellc.com
IT systems integration consulting, technology platforms, operating systems & infrastructures, data warehouse, business intelligence, ERP, project managment, call center/service desk. (Woman/White, estab 2002, empl 20, sales $1,200,000, cert: State, WBENC)

5765 Zillion Technologies, Inc.
45189 Research Pl Ste 150 Ashburn, VA 20147
(703) 592-6949 Mariya Anthony Business Dev Mgr
Fax: (703) 349-6527
Email: anthony@zilliontechnologies.com
Website: www.zilliontechnologies.com
Business consulting & technology solutions, strategic outsourcing & application mgmt. (As-Ind, estab 2002, empl 125, sales $18,026,547, cert: State, NMSDC, SDB)

5766 Zolon Tech
13921 Park Center Rd Ste 500 Herndon, VA 20171
(703) 636-7370 Goutham Amarneni President
Fax: (703) 636-7377
Email: supplier.diversity@zolon.com
Website: www.zolontech.com
IT consulting: integration, unification, secure & customized, applications & enterprise software. (As-Ind, estab 1998, empl 623, sales $57,987,454, cert: NMSDC)

5767 Zolon Tech Solutions, Inc.
13921 Park Center Rd Ste 500 Herndon, VA 20171
(703) 636-7639 Sam Mallipeddi Director
Fax: (703) 636-7370
Email: supplierdiverstiy@zolon.com
Website: www.zolon.com
IT services, custom application dev, application management, business intelligences, enterprise application/ERP & engineering services. (As-Ind/As-Pac, estab 1998, empl 250, sales $61,670,000, cert: NMSDC)

Vermont

5768 iTech US, Inc.
20 Kimball Ave, Ste 303N   S Burlington, VT 05403
(802) 383-1500 Kishore Khandavalli CEO
Fax: (802) 383-1501
Email: kk@itechus.com
Website: www.itechus.com
Software consulting services, application development, business process outsourcing solutions & offshore project development. (As-Pac, estab 2001, empl 1150, sales $53,000,000, cert: NMSDC)

Washington

5769 ABN Technologies
8650 Martin Way E Ste 211 Lacey, WA 98516
(253) 964-1745 Trena Payton President
Fax: (253) 964-1837
Email: operations@abntec.com
Website: www.abntec.com
IT project management, IT infrastructure. (Woman/AA, estab 2003, empl 10, sales $1,783,564, cert: State)

5770 Advanced Technology Computers, Inc.
824 Grimes Rd Bothell, WA 98012
(425) 486-6045 Andre Tyson Owner
Fax: (425) 486-2773
Email: andre@atcdirect.com
Website: www.atcdirect.com
Information technology systems integration, networking & information security. (AA, estab 1996, empl 3, sales , cert: 8(a))

5771 Amreli Technology Solutions, LLC
17530 NE Union Hill Rd, Ste 290 Redmond, WA 98052
(425) 881-6971 Atul Hirpara CEO
Fax:
Email: atul@amrelitech.com
Website: www.amrelitech.com
IT intelligence, dashboards & scorecards, software, integration of disparate systems & applications. (As-Pac, estab 2004, empl 32, sales $3,400,000, cert: State, NMSDC)

5772 Axelerate
13401 Bel Red Rd, Ste B8 Bellevue, WA 98005
(425) 429-6720 Julie Campbell Sr Client Services Mgr
Fax:
Email: Julie.Campbell@axelerate.com
Website: www.axelerate.com
IT consulting & staffing. (Woman/White, estab 2003, empl 5, sales , cert: WBENC)

5773 Azimuth Group
777 108th Ave NE, Ste 1830 Bellevue, WA 98004
(425) 395-4867 Jeff Steffens Supplier Acct Exec
Fax:
Email: jeff.steffens@azimuth-grp.com
Website: www.azimuth-grp.com
IT consulting, big data/insight, customer experience, IT infrastructure & cloud, outsourcing & managed services engagement. (Hisp, estab 2016, empl 4, sales $240,000, cert: NMSDC)

5774 BiSoft Consultancy Services
16310 NE 80th St, Ste 104 Redmond, WA 98052
(401) 450-1672 Balaji Udayshankar CEO
Fax:
Email: bala@bisoftllc.com
Website: www.bisoftllc.com
Information technology svcs, website design, wed development & maintenance, SEO optimization, application software. (As-Ind, estab 2015, empl 1, sales $2,000,000, cert: NMSDC)

5775 Eastside Groups LLC
P.O.Box 165 Mercer Island, WA 98040
(206) 466-6649 Jessie Wang Owner
Fax:
Email: main@catandena.com
Website: www.catandena.com
Software solutions, financial applications, web sites & web services, from stand-alone scale to enterprise scale. (Woman/As-Pac, estab 2014, empl 1, sales , cert: State)

5776 ELYON International Inc.
1111 Main St, Ste 610 Vancouver, WA 98660
(360) 696-5892 Carmen Nazario President
Fax: (360) 906-0219
Email: carmen@elyoninternational.com
Website: www.elyoninternational.com
Consulting & technology svcs: software devel, systems integration, offshore solutions delivery. (Woman/Hisp, estab 1997, empl 145, sales $2,080,500, cert: State)

5777 General Microsystems Inc.
3220 118th Ave SE Bellevue, WA 98005
(425) 644-2233 Earl Overstreet President
Fax: (425) 644-7244
Email: earl@gmi.com
Website: www.gmi.com
Information technology: systems, storage management solutions. (AA, estab 1983, empl 13, sales $32,330,000, cert: State, NMSDC)

5778 Hansell Tierney, Inc.
2955 80th Ave SE Ste 205 Mercer Island, WA 98040
(206) 232-3080 Monica Gardenier Bus Dev Mgr
Fax: (425) 444-6951
Email: mgardenier@hanselltierney.com
Website: www.hanselltierney.com
IT consulting services & recruiting. (Woman/White, estab 2001, empl 35, sales $2,800,000, cert: State)

5779 i9 Systems, Inc.
16928 NE 38th Place Bellevue, WA 98008
(206) 412-7918 Sukhjot Basi CEO
Fax: (216) 472-7918
Email: basi@i9systems.com
Website: www.i9systems.com
Staffig, consulting, software development & testing, program/project management, database & network administrations, business requirements, full software development life cycle. (Woman/As-Ind, estab 1999, empl 16, sales $500,000, cert: State)

5780 Idea Entity Corporation
16625 Redmond Way Ste M 009 Redmond, WA 98052
(425) 454-2905 John Strathy CFO
Fax: (425) 458-6995
Email: john.strathy@ideaentity.com
Website: www.ideaentity.com
Project, staff, dev, testing, onsite, offsite, offshore, application developmen, custom application development & packaged solution integration. (As-Ind, estab 2006, empl 45, sales $706,000, cert: State, NMSDC)

5781   InConsulting Inc.
         12901 181st Ave NE   Redmond, WA 98052
         (425) 281-7284 Aparna Mahadevan CEO
         Fax:
         Email: services@inconsultinginc.com
         Website: www.inconsultinginc.com
Information staffing & placement, IT services, Consulting,
Systems planning, Web Design & development. (Woman/
As-Ind, estab 2010, empl 40, sales $40,000, cert: State)

5782   Kaasm, LLC
         900 1st Ave S, Ste 302   Seattle, WA 98134
         (206) 735-3882 Shawn Sandoval President
         Fax: (206) 735-3882
         Email: shawns@kaasm.com
         Website: www.kaasm.com
SCADA software, Industrial computers, networking
components, alarm notification software & Enterprise
Asset Management. (Hisp, estab 2013, empl 3, sales
$150,000, cert: City, NMSDC)

5783   Kathcart Open Systems & Consulting, Inc.
         17311 135th Ave NE, Ste B500   Woodinville, WA
         98072
         (425) 402-0258 Kathy Cartwright CEO
         Fax: (425) 402-0633
         Email: kathy@dimension-systems.com
         Website: www.dimension-systems.com
Information technology consulting services. (Woman/
White, estab 1993, empl 20, sales $42,000,000, cert:
WBENC)

5784   Martirx Infotech LLC
         1017 4th Ave E Ste 6 Olympia, WA 98506
         (360) 545-4089 Narasimha Varakantham CEO
         Fax: (360) 524-2297
         Email: reddy@matrixinf.com
         Website: www.matrixinf.com
Information technology services, contingent workforce
staffing solutions, technology support, consulting &
development, software to hardware. (Woman/As-Ind,
estab 2014, empl 3, sales $105,253, cert: State)

5785   Nvelup Consulting
         19125 North Creek Parkway Ste 120 Bothell, WA
         98011
         (206) 419-2584 Chris Barrios CEO
         Fax: (425) 285-7005
         Email: chris@nvelupconsulting.com
         Website: www.nvelupconsulting.com
Performance Management (Budgeting, Planning &
Forecasting) & Business Intelligence (Data Analysis &
Reporting) solutions. (Nat Ame/Hisp, estab 2014, empl 15,
sales $936,000, cert: State, NMSDC, SDB)

5786   Online Training Solutions, Inc.
         P.O. Box 951 Bellevue, WA 98009
         (888) 308-6874 Joan Preppernau President
         Fax: (888) 308-6875
         Email: biz@otsi.com
         Website: www.otsi.com
Publishing & programming services. (Woman/White, estab
1987, empl 13, sales $1,120,873, cert: WBENC)

5787   P2 Solutions Group LLC
         2296 W Commodore Way, Ste 300   Seattle, WA
         98199
         (206) 226-8433 Tonjia Borland
         Fax: (206) 260-7208
         Email: tborland@p2solutionsgroup.com
         Website: www.p2solutionsgroup.com
Technical, system administrator, programming, developer, engineering, finance, marketing & project management staff. (Hisp, estab 2002, empl 120, sales
$10,600,000, cert: City, NMSDC)

5788   PeopleTech Group
         15809 Bear Creek Pkwy Ste 410 Redmond, WA
         09-82
         (425) 444-6174 Mark W. Meyer Exec VP
         Fax: (253) 563-1177
         Email: mark.meyer@peopletech.com
         Website: www.peopletech.com
ERP Services, Oracle, PeopleSoft, SAP, Microsoft Dynam-
ics, Implementation, Upgrade, Application Development,
Testing & Consulting, Big Data, DWH & BI, OBIEE, BO,
Micro Strategy, Microsoft. (Woman/As-Ind, estab 2006,
empl 1200, sales $22,000,000, cert: State)

5789   Prowess Consulting, LLC
         5701 Sixth Ave S Ste 374 Seattle, WA 98108
         (206) 443-1117 Aaron Suzuki CEO
         Fax:
         Email: info@prowesscorp.com
         Website: www.prowesscorp.com
Content program management, technical content
development & editing, training content development,
IT & content systems management & digital marketing
services. (As-Pac, estab 2003, empl 80, sales
$11,800,000, cert: State, NMSDC)

5790   S3Global Consulting Services, LLC
         10532 82nd Ave Court SW   Lakewood, WA 98498
         (877) 470-1900 Morris Sterling III, MBA CEO
         Fax:
         Email: morris.sterling@s3goglobal.com
         Website: www.s3goglobal.com
Information technology & business-based enterprises,
project, program & product management, technical
writing & communications, continuous process improvement, business analysis & intelligence. (Woman/AA,
estab 2012, empl 5, sales $52,000, cert: State, City)

5791   ScrumPoint
         1110 112th Avenue Northeast Ste 350 Bellevue,
         WA 98052
         (509) 714-4842 Michael Mpare President
         Fax:
         Email: michael@scrumpoint.com
         Website: www.scrumpoint.com
Custom software applications, SSIS & SSRS management,
SharePoint portals, custom web applications, Windows
Azure Cloud Services. (AA, estab 2011, empl 6, sales ,
cert: NMSDC)

5792   Synergistics, Inc.
114 Columbia Point Dr Ste A Richland, WA 99352
(800) 875-7921 Kim DeTienne VP
Fax: (509) 946-2213
Email: Kim@syngt.com
Website: www.syngt.com
Customized software & project management. (Hisp, estab 2003, empl 12, sales $1,010,000, cert: State)

5793   Tam Partners Consulting, LLC
18350 204th Ave NE Woodinville, WA 98077
(425) 998-8401 Lisa Tam Founder
Fax:
Email: lisatam@tpartnerscg.com
Website: www.tpartnerscg.com
Engineering: Power BI, Excel Power Pivot, ETL, SSIS, SSAS, T-SQL, Data Marts, Data Warehouse, SQL Server Management Studio, Business Intelligence Development StudioBig Data Analytics: JSon, HiveQL, Microsoft Azure HDInsight | Cloud Hadoop, Azure Managem (Woman, estab 2016, empl 1, sales $114,784, cert: WBENC)

5794   Teleion Consulting
1110 Dexter Ave N Seattle, WA 98109
(206) 601-3350 Alison Small Director, Business Devel
Fax:
Email: alison@teleionconsulting.com
Website: www.teleionconsulting.com
Hosted & managed IT solutions, business intelligence, data management, marketing campaign, risk & compliance solutions. (As-Pac, estab 2008, empl 60, sales $11,000,000, cert: NMSDC)

5795   TripleNet Technologies, Inc.
1122 E Pike St, Ste 509 Seattle, WA 98122
(206) 260-8998 Hans Gomez President
Fax: (206) 260-8998
Email: hansgomez@triplenettech.com
Website: www.triplenettech.com
IT staffing, network architecture & design, software development, wireless network design & implementation, data storage plan, disaster recovery. (Hisp, estab 1997, empl 18, sales $500,000, cert: State, City, NMSDC)

5796   TSS Redmond
8461 154th Ave NE, Bldg G Redmond, WA 98052
(425) 749-3030 Lisa Roeder CEO
Fax: (425) 660-8200
Email: lroeder@tssredmond.com
Website: www.tssredmond.com
Software, computer, technical development, soft skills, project management, business development & leadership training. (Woman/White, estab 2000, empl 20, sales $700,000, cert: State)

5797   Zones, Inc.
1102 15th St SW Auburn, WA 98001
(253) 205-3167 Kate Rhoades Supplier Diversity Program Mgr
Fax:
Email: diversity@zones.com
Website: www.zones.com
Information technology products & services, resell computer hardware & software. (As-Ind/As-Pac/Hisp, estab 1986, empl 1666, sales $1,380,000,000, cert: NMSDC)

Wisconsin

5798   Abaxent LLC
N28 W23050 Roundy Dr. Ste 200 Pewaukee, WI 53072
(414) 587-2950 Adonica Randall President
Fax: (262) 650-6530
Email: arandall@abaxent.com
Website: www.abaxent-global.com
Information technology services, project management, software development, network engineering & consulting/design. (Woman/AA, estab 2002, empl 10, sales $664,306, cert: State, NMSDC, WBENC)

5799   Adam Information Technologies LLC
402 Gammon Pl Madison, WI 53719
(608) 237-1416 Ricky Shaik
Fax: (608) 237-2211
Email: ricky@adaminfotech.com
Website: www.adaminfotech.com
Information Technology and Non-IT manpower services where our clients excel in deliverable s. (As-Pac, estab 2007, empl 127, sales $8,000,000, cert: State)

5800   Comcentia, LLC
1025 W Glen Oaks Lane Ste 211 Mequon, WI 53092
(414) 871-1100 Darrell Caldwell President
Fax: (877) 780-1102
Email: info@comcentia.com
Website: www.comcentia.com
IT Consulting, Custom Applications & Database Development, Custom web based or windows desktop application development, Application Management of Existing Systems, Ongoing & and ad hoc changes. (AA, estab 2006, empl 6, sales $612,112, cert: NMSDC, 8(a))

5801   Excel Global Solutions Inc.
2727 N Grandview Blvd Ste 117 Waukesha, WI 53188
(262) 347-4911 Jerry Sorci VP
Fax:
Email: jerry.sorci@excelglobalsolution.com
Website: www.excelglobalsolution.com
IT services, solutions & products, Big Data Predictive intelligence Product, Automated Application Testing Product, Vehicle Maintenance Management Product. (Woman/As-Pac, estab 2010, empl 250, sales $2,100,000, cert: State)

5802 Malleswari Inc.
      11512 N Port Washington Rd, Ste 101-I   Mequon,
      WI 53092
      (262)33480 Trinadha Pattem
      Fax: (866)39918
      Email: trinadha@malleswari.com
      Website: www.malleswari.com
End to End SAP ERP/SRM/BI/Mobile Technology Solutions.
(Woman/As-Ind, estab 2004, empl 5, sales $2,350,227,
cert: State, City, NMSDC)

5803 Valicom Corp
      2923 Marketplace Dr Ste 104 Fitchburg, WI 53719
      (800) 467-7226 Chantel Soumis Mktg
      Fax: (608) 227-0118
      Email: marketing@valicomcorp.com
      Website: www.valicomcorp.com
IT & telecom invoice audit & management: RFP facilitation,
contract negotiation & management, network design &
engineering, help desk, invoice payment & general ledger
coding. (Woman/White, estab 1991, empl 20, sales , cert:
State)

5804 Wissen Infotech Inc
      2325 Parklawn Dr Ste G Waukesha, WI 53186
      (262) 510-2900 Upendra Rachupaly Ops Mgr
      Fax: (262) 782-7544
      Email: upendra.rachupally@wisseninfotech.com
      Website: www.wisseninfotech.com
IT services, onsite, offsite & offshore service, End to end
Mobility application, development, Analytics, Cloud
Management, Media & Entertainment, Embedded Sys-
tems, Big data & Hadoop.
Enterprise Resource Planning, Remote Infrastructure
Management (As-Ind, estab 2001, empl 800, sales
$12,000,000, cert: State, NMSDC)

West Virginia

5805 Fusion Plus Solutions Inc.
      17 Cherokee Dr   Moundsville, WV 26041
      (732) 250-9048 Mark Thomas Director
      Fax:
      Email: mark@fusionplusinc.com
      Website: www.fusionplusinc.com
IT Staff Augmentation, Information Technology Solutions,
Consulting/Staffing Services, System Integration, Software
Products. (Woman/As-Pac, estab 2009, empl 1000, sales
$3,000,000, cert: State)

> ## INFORMATION TECHNOLOGY: Supplies
> Manufacture or distribute magnetic media supplies such as , disketts, paper, printers, fascimilies, toner cartridges, keyboards, computer peripherials. NAICS Code 42

Arizona

5806   Centacor, Inc.
135 Chilton Dr   Chandler, AZ 85225
(480) 899-9500   Troy Bryan Mgr
Fax:
Email: info@centacor.com
Website: www.centacor.com
IT products & services. (AA, estab 2009, empl 4, sales $75,000, cert: NMSDC)

5807   Cybergear, Inc.
6640 E Baseline Rd Ste 102   Mesa, AZ 85206
(480) 926-6470   Danette Carnahan President
Fax: (480) 507-0484
Email: danette@cybergearusa.com
Website: www.cybergearusa.com
Dist computer hardware, consumer electronics, electronic test & measurement, computer software & software licensing, POS/bar code equipment, wireless voice/data products & services. (Woman/White, estab 1998, empl 7, sales $2,800,000, cert: State, City, WBENC, 8(a))

5808   ESI Ergonomic Solutions, LLC
4030 E Quenton Dr Ste 101   Mesa, AZ 85215
(480) 517-1871   Carol Keogh CEO
Fax: (480) 517-1872
Email: ckeogh@esiergo.com
Website: www.esiergo.com
Mfr & dist articulating arms, keyboard platforms, flat screen monitor arms & ergonomic accessories. (Woman/White, estab 1988, empl 25, sales $15,000,000, cert: NWBOC)

5809   Herco Technology div. of Hernandez Companies
3734 E Anne St   Phoenix, AZ 85040
(602) 438-7825   Mike Pena Acct Exec
Fax: (602) 438-6558
Email: info@hernandezcompanies.com
Website: www.hernandezcompanies.com/
Dist computer & networking cable & cable accessories: fiber optic cables, coaxial, custom assemblies, racks, shelving, wire mgmt, Cat5E patch cables. (Woman/Hisp, estab 1975, empl 75, sales $150,000, cert: NMSDC)

5810   LEEO Industries
6868 N 7th Ave Ste 205   Phoenix, AZ 85013
(800) 584-5554   Pierre Tousant GM
Fax: (602) 548-5591
Email: sales@leeo-industries.com
Website: www.leeo-industries.com
Dist office & information technology products: barcoding equipment & printers, cables, network hubs & interface cards, power supplies, CPUs. (AA, estab 2002, empl 6, sales $200,000, cert: State)

California

5811   Alliant Event Services
196 University Pkwy   Pomona, CA 91768
(909) 354-4469   Pat Davis Sr sales Mgr
Fax: (909) 622-3917
Email: pat.davis@alliantevents.com
Website: www.AlliantEvents.com
Rental technology & event production solutions: laptop & desktop computers, printers, copiers, audio-visual, sound & lighting products. (As-Ind, estab 2003, empl 38, sales $4,150,000, cert: State)

5812   CDCE Inc.
22755-G Savi Ranch Pkwy   Yorba Linda, CA 92887
(714) 282-8881   Kim Hufford Natl Acct Mgr
Fax: (714) 282-1501
Email: khufford@cdce.com
Website: www.cdce.com
Wireless, computer vehicle installations, ruggedized notebooks & tablets. (Woman/White, estab 1984, empl 25, sales , cert: CPUC, WBENC)

5813   Computer 1 Products of America, Inc.
11135 Rush St, Unit A   South El Monte, CA 91733
(626) 213-2407   Robert Edwards Small Business Coord
Fax: (626) 213-2444
Email: robert@computer1products.com
Website: www.c1psolutions.com
Dist computer hardware, software, networking, electronic components, audio visual, printers & supplies. (Woman/Hisp, estab 1992, empl 25, sales $10,000,000, cert: 8(a))

5814   ComputerSuppliers.Com
7377 Convoy Court, Ste A   San Diego, CA 92111
(858) 268-7370   Jay Satpute Bids specialist
Fax: (858) 268-7371
Email: bids@computersupplies.com
Website: www.computersupplies.com
Dist inks, toners, monitor filters, furniture, pens, printers, ribbons, and storage media such as DVD, CD, LTO, SDX, AIT, 4mm & 8mm cartridges. (Woman/As-Ind, estab 2002, empl 7, sales $6,000,000, cert: City)

5815   Conversions Technology
          1740 Emerson Ave   Oxnard, CA 93033
          (800) 596-2037 Kevin Williams VP Sales
          Fax: (919) 585-4391
          Email: Kevin@ConversionsTechnology.com
          Website: www.ConversionsTechnology.com
Mfr & dist cable accessory & PC peripheral components.
(Woman/Nat Ame, estab 2006, empl 25, sales $1,000,000,
cert: CPUC)

5816   GC Micro Corporation
          3910 Cypress Dr   Petaluma, CA 94954
          (800) 426-4276 Ashley Huff Acct Mgr
          Fax: (707) 789-0700
          Email: ahuff@gcmicro.com
          Website: www.gcmicro.com
Dist personal computers, microcomputer hardware,
software, peripherals, IBM, HP, AST, Epson authorized
dealer. (Woman/Hisp, estab 1986, empl 35, sales , cert:
CPUC, WBENC)

5817   Kambrian Corporation
          2707 E Valley Blvd   West Covina, CA 91792
          (626) 374-3933 Cathy Hsieh CEO
          Fax: (626) 964-4447
          Email: cathyh@kambrian.com
          Website: www.kambrian.com
Resell IT products: software, hardware & services.
(Woman/As-Pac, estab 2009, empl 7, sales $10,469,102,
cert: NMSDC, WBENC, 8(a))

5818   MelroseMAC, Inc.
          6614 Melrose Ave   Hollywood, CA 90038
          (323) 937-4600 Sandy Nasseri CEO
          Fax: (323) 937-4664
          Email: sandy@melrosemac.com
          Website: www.melrosemac.com
Resell Apple products. (Woman/White, estab 2003, empl
80, sales $55,000,000, cert: CPUC, WBENC)

5819   Mobile ID Solutions, Inc.
          1574 N Batavia St, Ste 1   Orange, CA 92867
          (714) 922-1134 Rick Fahilga Acct Exec
          Fax: (714) 532-4234
          Email: rfahilga@mobileidsolutions.com
          Website: www.mobileidsolutions.com
Mobile Computers, printers. Barcode Printers, Scanners,
verifiers. ID Card Printers and supplies. IP Cameras. Cellular
Routers, modem, POS Equipment, Satellite phones. (As-
Pac, estab 2004, empl 9, sales $4,800,000, cert: NMSDC)

5820   Mobilematics, Inc.
          2528 Qume Dr, Ste 2   San Jose, CA 95131
          (408) 609-1220 Dominick Borrello Business Devel
          Mgr
          Fax:
          Email: dominick@mobilematics.us.com
          Website: www.mobilematics.us.com
IT hardware & software. (Woman/As-Ind, estab 2012,
empl 5, sales $100,000,000, cert: NMSDC, CPUC,
WBENC)

5821   New Century Technologies Inc.
          4290 Kendall St   San Diego, CA 92109
          (800) 457-4313 Peter Steiner COO
          Fax: (866) 237-5403
          Email: peter@nctsolution.com
          Website: www.nctsolution.com
Toner cartridges, office supplies/products, office
equipment, office furniture, janitorial supplies,
breakroom supplies, industrial supplies/products, hard
drive, memory, IT products that offers hardware,
software, related services. (Woman/As-Pac, estab 2006,
empl 3, sales $1,391,800, cert: 8(a))

5822   On-Site LaserMedic Corp.
          21540 Prairie St, Unit D   Chatsworth, CA 91311
          (818) 772-6911 Gail Solomon CEO
          Fax: (818) 349-8111
          Email: SD@onsitelasermedic.com
          Website: www.onsitelasermedic.com
Laser printer, fax & deskjet service & repair, dist toner.
(Woman/White, estab 1992, empl 46, sales $5,318,472,
cert: WBENC)

5823   Performance Designed Products
          14144 Ventura Blvd Ste 200 Sherman Oaks, CA
          91423
          (479) 445-8612 Theresa Harrell Natl Acct Mgr
          Fax:
          Email: theresa.harrell@pdp.com
          Website: www.pdp.com
Design & mfr video game peripherals & accessories: PS2,
PS3, PSP PS Vita, Xbox, Xbox 360, Wii, Wii U, 3DS, DS
Lite. (Woman, estab 1990, empl 200, sales , cert:
WBENC)

5824   PNH Technology, Inc.
          15375 Barranca Pkwy Ste F-108 Irvine, CA 92618
          (949) 614-4102 Thacher Grauer Office Mgr
          Fax: (949) 297-2424
          Email: thacher@pnhtech.com
          Website: www.pnhtech.com
Dist servers, rack, tower, blades, memory, hard drives,
server accessories, storage (SAN, NAS, DAS), storage
accessories. networking switches, routers, firewalls,
network accessories, desktops, PCs & laptops. (As-Pac,
estab 2008, empl 6, sales $3,000,000, cert: State)

5825 Saitech Inc.
      42640 Christy St   Fremont, CA 94538
      (510) 440-0256 Ernesto Juarez Business Dev
      Fax: (510) 440-0257
      Email: ernesto@esaitech.com
      Website: www.esaitech.com
Dist telecom, network & computer components & equipment. (As-Ind/As-Pac, estab 2002, empl 18, sales $19,500,000, cert: NMSDC, CPUC)

5826 Source Graphics
      1530 N. Harmony Circle   Anaheim, CA 92807
      (714) 701-1500 Sy Hussaini Sr Acct Mgr
      Fax: (714) 701-1505
      Email: sy.h@sourcegraphics.com
      Website: www.sourcegraphics.com
Dist & svc plotter scanners, printers & digitizers. (As-Pac, estab 1989, empl 10, sales , cert: CPUC)

5827 Southland Technology Inc.
      8053 Vickers St   San Diego, CA 92111
      (858) 634-4136 Jack Lowrey Acct Exec
      Fax: (858) 694-0938
      Email: jlowrey@southlandtechnology.com
      Website: www.southlandtechnology.com
Computer, computer hardware, software, cables, peripherals, IT, information technology, audio, video, A/V, sound systems, servers, storage, virtualization, fiber cables, workstations, notebooks, voip, projectors, monitors. (Woman/As-Pac, estab 2001, empl 43, sales $45,000,000, cert: CPUC)

5828 Varitek, Inc.
      1100 E. Orangethorpe Ave Ste 195 Anaheim, CA 92801
      (714) 224-0361 Moe Moalemi VP
      Fax: (714) 224-0414
      Email: moalemi@varitekinc.com
      Website: www.varitekinc.com
Dist & service network solutions, computers, printers, barcode printers, plotters, point of sale, copiers, faxes, office equipment consumables. (Woman/Nat Ame, estab 1982, empl 12, sales $1,030,000, cert: State)

5829 ViewSonic Corporation
      381 Brea Canyon Rd   Walnut, CA 91789
      (909) 444-8613 Julie Yao Legal Asst
      Fax: (909) 869-7958
      Email: legal@viewsonic.com
      Website: www.viewsonic.com
Dist visual display technology products: liquid crystal displays, LCD, monitors, cathode ray tube, CRT, monitors, projectors, LCD TVs, plasma displays, tablet personal computers & PCs, wireless monitors. (As-Pac, estab 1987, empl 700, sales $1,093,000,000, cert: NMSDC)

5830 Vision Specialties, Inc.
      10330 Regis Ct   Rancho Cucamonga, CA 91730
      (800) 499-8176 Donn DeMarzio VP
      Fax: 888581-220
      Email: donn.demarzio@visionspecialties.com
      Website: www.visionspecialties.com
Mfr & dist Category Cable, HDMI Cable, Audio/Video Cable, Batteries, Injection Molding products & services. (Woman/White, estab 1995, empl 14, sales $6,000,000, cert: CPUC)

5831 Zetta Pros - Total IT Solutions
      2201 E Willow St, Ste D232   Signal Hill, CA 90755
      (562) 252-3673 Sarom Hong CEO
      Fax: (562) 252-3659
      Email: sarom.hong@zettapros.com
      Website: www.zettapros.com
Computers, hardware, software, printers, computer peripherals, cables. (Woman/As-Pac, estab 2005, empl 4, sales $600,000, cert: NMSDC, CPUC, 8(a))

Colorado

5832 Image Projections West, Inc.
      14135 E 42nd Ave Ste 40 Denver, CO 80239
      (888) 576-9477 Kedar Morarka CEO
      Fax: (303) 576-6630
      Email: josephF@ipwusa.com
      Website: www.ipwusa.com
Mfr advance technology toner cartridges. (As-Ind, estab 1996, empl 172, sales $31,200,000, cert: NMSDC)

5833 SK&T Integration Inc.
      10495 S Progress Way, Ste 104   Parker, CO 80134
      (720) 851-9108 Kathy Lawson President
      Fax: (720) 851-8663
      Email: kathy@skandt.com
      Website: www.skandt.com
Dist stock & custom labels, ribbons, bar code & specialty printers, asset tracking & inventory management systems, bar coding software, scanners, mobile computers & wireless switches. (Woman/White, estab 1997, empl 10, sales $3,200,000, cert: WBENC)

5834 Systec101
      1027 Fenwick Dr   Fort Collins, CO 80524
      (970) 646-2706 Murat Yildirim Owner
      Fax:
      Email: murat.yildirim@systec101.com
      Website: www.systec101.com
Dist networking equipment, manufacture & resell, cat5e, cat6, cat6a cables & accessories. (As-Ind, estab 2012, empl 3, sales $120,000, cert: State)

Connecticut

5835   Hartford Toner & Cartridge
6 Wapping Rd   Broad Brook, CT 06016
(860) 292-1280 Timothy Golubeff Sr sales
Fax: (860) 292-1281
Email: tgolubeff@hartfordtoner.com
Website: www.hartfordtoner.con
Hp authorized service center, repair laser printers & supplies.
(Woman/White, estab 1998, empl 9, sales $1,000,100, cert: State)

District of Columbia

5836   Borrowed Time Enterprises, Inc.
4460 Alabama Ave, SE   Washington, DC 20019
(202) 581-0406 Vanessa Brooks CEO
Fax: (202) 239-0582
Email: borrowedte@rcn.com
Website: www.btenterprise.us
Dist computers, parts, software & hardware, office supplies, digital signage & content management software installation & services. (Woman/AA, estab 1999, empl 1, sales $127,000, cert: State, City)

5837   Mall Lobby.com, Inc.
1775 Eye St, NW Ste 1150 Washington, DC 20006
(301) 807-2422 Lang Maith CEO
Fax: (202) 595-0426
Email: lang.maith@malllobby.com
Website: www.malllobby.com
Dist computers, software, network equipment, office products, electronics, cellular phones, pagers, merchant accounts, microfilm/microfiche, CD/DVD production, etc. (AA, estab 1995, empl 15, sales $500,000, cert: State)

FLorida

5838   American Data & Computer Products, Inc.
4505 Town N Country Blvd   Tampa, FL 33615
(800) 367-2461 Robert Castro President
Fax: (813) 886-2802
Email: rcastro@adcpi.com
Website: www.adcpi.com
Dist computer systems, software & peripheral components. (Hisp, estab 1988, empl 15, sales $25,000,000, cert: State)

5839   BIT DIRECT
2202 N Westshore Blvd, Ste 200   Tampa, FL 33607
(813) 343-0879 Duane Turner Senior VP & GM
Fax: (813) 996-2140
Email: duane@bitdirect.com
Website: www.bitdirect.com
Dist audio & headsets, digital cameras, LCD & plasma TV's & projectors, handheld computers, removable media, optical dives, keyboards & mice, software & licenses, flash drives, cables, hard drives, media tapes, computer furniture. (Woman/White, estab 2002, empl 11, sales $700,000,000, cert: City, WBENC)

5840   Card Quest, Inc.
6630 Rowan Rd   New Port Richey, FL 34655
(727) 816-8401 Shannon Capshaw President
Fax: (727) 841-8427
Email: sales@cardquest.com
Website: www.cardquest.com
Dist proximity cards, readers, photo ID printers, ribbons, accessories, cards. (Woman/White, estab 2001, empl 4, sales $750,000, cert: State)

5841   Chilcott, Inc.
15751 Sheridan St, Ste 3158   Fort Lauderdale, FL 33331
(786) 351-8298 Allyson Ameideiras VP
Fax:
Email: admin@chilcottinc.com
Website: www.chilcottinc.com
Computer hardware, software, peripherals,   Mobile Command Centers, Satellite Service & Equipment, Helicopter Training & Equipment/Parts & Mutualink Interoperability Systems. (Hisp, estab 2012, empl 8, sales , cert: 8(a))

5842   Innovative Software Solution
3762 NW 124th Ave   Coral Springs, FL 33065
(954) 800-7552 Kareline Duverge Office Mgr
Fax: (954) 800-7556
Email: kduverge@isoftwaresolution.com
Website: www.isoftwaresolution.com
Mfr ink & toner cartridges. Authorized distributors of HP, Lexmark & Ricoh products & supplies, general office supplies, toner & ink cartridges. (Woman/AA, estab 2012, empl 15, sales $1,590,000, cert: State, NMSDC)

5843   Laser Products, Inc.
11975 SW 142nd Terrace Unit 105 Miami, FL 33186
(305) 235-9544 Wendy K. Rudman President
Fax: (305) 235-7132
Email: laser@laser-products.com
Website: www.ww.laser-products.com
Digital imaging products, parts & supplies: copier, fax, printer, wide-format, high speed, ink, toner, ribbons, software, registration & warranty. (Woman, estab 1990, empl 4, sales $801,011, cert: State)

5844 LRE Inc. dba Lee Ryder Lamination
   6187 NW 167th St Unit H-10 Miami, FL 33015
   (305) 893-2762 Lee Ryder President
   Fax: (305) 893-2775
   Email: office@leeryder.com
   Website: www.leeryder.com
Computerized photo id systems & supplies: Hid Global, Edisecure, Magicard, Eltron, Fargo, Nisca, Zebra, Evolis, Datacard. retractable id badge reels, laminator, pouch laminator, roll laminator, laminating pouches, laminating roll (Woman/Nat Ame, estab 1980, empl 2, sales , cert: State, City)

5845 R&D Systems Group, Inc.
   19140 SW 24th St   Miramar, FL 33029
   (305) 528-9402 patricia Garcia Acct Exec
   Fax: (954) 447-4256
   Email: pgarcia@rdsgi.com
   Website: www.rdsgi.com
Resell IBM software & hardware. (Woman/Hisp, estab 2004, empl 6, sales $400,000, cert: NMSDC)

Georgia

5846 Eastern Data, Inc.
   4386 Park Dr   Norcross, GA 30093
   (770) 279-8888 JoAnn Pfeiffer Natl Accts Mgr
   Fax:
   Email: jo.pfeiffer@ediatlanta.com
   Website: www.ediatlanta.com
Dist computer systems, components & peripherals. (Woman/As-Pac, estab 1997, empl 27, sales $20,906,578, cert: NMSDC, WBENC)

5847 Worldwide Audio Visual Services Inc
   5040 Bakers Ferry Rd SW   Atlanta, GA 30336
   (404) 745-9842 Bradford McWhorter CEO
   Fax: (404) 346-7711
   Email: brad@atlanta-audiovisual.com
   Website: www.atlantaav.com
Audio visual equipment, audio reinforcement, video production, lighting design & corporate set design. (AA, estab 2005, empl 8, sales $374,970, cert: NMSDC)

5848 XentIT, LLC
   5425 Peachtree Pkwy   Norcross, GA 30092
   (678) 906-4046 Tariq Alvi President
   Fax: (404) 745-8448
   Email: talvi@xentit.com
   Website: www.xentit.com
Value Added Reseller, System Integrator & Cloud Managed Service provider. (As-Ind, estab 2006, empl 7, sales $2,247,000, cert: NMSDC)

Illinois

5849 Data Media Products, Inc.
   1946 Lehigh Ave, Ste B   Glenview, IL 60025
   (847) 729-2020 Caryl Galassini President
   Fax: (847) 729-7074
   Email: cgalassini@datamediaproducts.com
   Website: www.datamediaproducts.com
Dist blank audio/video tapes, dvds, cds, data backup tapes, printer & toner cartridges. (Woman/White, estab 1900, empl 1, sales $5,569,000, cert: State, City)

5850 Flexaco, Inc.
   936 W Lake St   Roselle, IL 60172
   (630) 529-4510 Donna Fiedler President
   Fax: (630) 529-4825
   Email: donnafiedler@flexaco.com
   Website: www.flexaco.com
Dist flexographic & rotogravure printers: 10 color printing, 2 color backside printing, surface & reverse printing, laminating, shrink sleeves, lidding material, paper, poly, foil & poly. (Woman/White, estab 1981, empl 5, sales $1,000,000, cert: WBENC)

5851 Mercommbe Inc.
   2101 Estes Ave   Elk Grove Village, IL 60007
   (847) 290-0368 Eric Moe Sales
   Fax: (847) 290-0365
   Email: eric@mercommbe.com
   Website: www.mercommbe.com
Dist datacom & networking products; fiber optic, structured wiring, low voltage cable & connectors. (Woman/Hisp, estab 1989, empl 7, sales $5,686,000, cert: State, City, NMSDC)

5852 MNJ Technologies Direct
   1025 Busch Pkwy   Buffalo Grove, IL 60089
   (847) 634-0700 Susan Kozak President
   Fax: (847) 876-5603
   Email: skozak@mnjtech.com
   Website: www.mnjtech.com
Dist computer hardware, software & peripheral products. (Woman/White, estab 2002, empl 85, sales $25,000,000, cert: WBENC)

5853 RPT Toner LLC
   475 Supreme Dr   Bensenville, IL 60106
   (630) 694-0400 Jamie Luety Sr VP sales/Mktg
   Fax: (630) 694-9060
   Email: jamie@rpttoner.com
   Website: www.rpttoner.com
Re-manufacture laser toner cartridges. (As-Ind, estab 1900, empl 1, sales $10,770,000, cert: NMSDC)

Indiana

5854 ASAP Identification Security, Inc.
212 W 10th St, Ste F-100   Indianapolis, IN 46202
(317) 488-1030 Sheila Brown President
Fax: (866) 671-9230
Email: sbrown@asapident.com
Website: www.asapident.com
Photo ID printers, supplies, service, software and accessories. (Woman/White, estab 1982, empl 3, sales , cert: State, WBENC)

5855 Convenient Tape & Supplies LLC
545 Industrial Dr   Carmel, IN 46032
(317) 846-0335 Jennifer Pippen President
Fax: (317) 846-0553
Email: jencts1@sbcglobal.net
Website: www.sundsales.com
Distributors of point-of-sale (pos) paper rolls, cash register rolls, printer ribbons, toner cartridges, ink-jet cartridges, printer cleaning supplies, scale labels, industrial bar code labels, pos printers to small computer printer users. (Woman/White, estab 2002, empl 3, sales $244,000, cert: State)

Kansas

5856 Inland Associates, Inc.
18965 W 158th St   Olathe, KS 66062
(913) 764-7977 Peggy Meader President
Fax: (913) 764-8721
Email: pmeader@inlandassoc.com
Website: www.inlandassoc.com
Dist computer peripherals, data communications equipment. (Woman/White, estab 1969, empl 7, sales $5,000,000, cert: WBENC)

Louisiana

5857 Dempsey Business Systems of Louisiana
1321 Second St, Ste B   Alexandria, LA 71301
(318) 604-6061 Freddie Price, Sr. President
Fax: (318) 561-4326
Email: fprice@dempseybus.com
Website: www.dempseybus.com
Dist Computer & Computer Peripheral equipment & software, custom computer programing services, computer systems design services, computer facilities management services, information technology value added reseller. (AA, estab 2004, empl 1, sales $278,789, cert: NMSDC)

5858 The Lazers Edge LLC
2168 Airline Dr, Ste C   Bossier City, LA 71111
(318) 742-6232 Sandra Nix Owner
Fax: (318) 742-7010
Email: nix@lazers-edge.com
Website: www.lazers-edge.com
Remanufactured Toner cartridges, laser printer service & repair. (Woman/White, estab 1989, empl 7, sales , cert: City)

Massachusetts

5859 Alpha Identification, Inc.
7 Spanish River Rd   Grafton, MA 01519
(508) 839-6144 Frank Ng Treasurer
Fax: (508) 839-6145
Email: alphaidinc@gmail.com
Website: www.alphaidinc.com
Dist photo ID equip & supplies for employee & student ID badges: Polaroid films, cameras, laminators, die-cutters, etc. (Woman/As-Pac, estab 1987, empl 2, sales $918,810, cert: State, City, CPUC)

5860 Encore Images
21 Lime St   Marblehead, MA 01945
(781) 631-4568 Laurel Mervis President
Fax: (781) 631-7200
Email: laurel.mervis@encoreimages.com
Website: www.encoreimages.com
Remanufacture toner cartridges: monochrome & color laser printers, copiers & facsimile machines. (Woman, estab 1989, empl 14, sales $2,020,000, cert: State)

5861 Pro AV Systems, Inc.
275 Billerica Road Ste 3 Chelmsford, MA 01824
(978) 692-5111 Kimberly Bishop President
Fax: (978) 692-5252
Email: kbishop@proavsi.com
Website: www.proavsi.com
Dist audiovisual products & installation services. (Woman/As-Ind, estab 2006, empl 58, sales $16,100,000, cert: State)

Maryland

5862 Cartridge Technologies, Inc. dba CTI
15738 Crabbs Branch Way   Rockville, MD 20855
(301) 417-8057 Kevin Brooks Federal Acct Mgr
Fax: (301) 417-7204
Email: kevinb@ctimd.com
Website: www.ctimd.com
Laser/Color Printers and Fax Machines, Maintenance/Warranty Service and manufactures the Optima brand Toner Cartridge. (Woman/Hisp, estab 1989, empl 25, sales , cert: WBENC)

5863   Laser Printers Plus
P.O. Box 264   Greenbelt, MD 20768
(301) 933-9007   Sales
Fax: (301) 933-9011
Email: info@laserprintersplus.com
Website: www.laserprintersplus.com
Dist new & remanufactured laser & toner cartridges, drum units, fusers, ribbons, developers, parts. (As-Ind, estab 1998, empl 4, sales $500,000, cert: State)

Michigan

5864   Audio Visual Equipment & Supplies, Inc.
25325 Shiawassee Circle Southfield, MI 48033
(800) 296-5446   Carol Kirkland VP
Fax: (313) 347-8592
Email: carol@aveofficesupplies.com
Website: www.aveofficesupplies.com/
Dist office supplies, office furniture, office equipment, audio visual equipment, computer equipment & supplies, printer equipment & supplies, paper, janitorial supplies, first aid supplies. (Woman/AA, estab 1990, empl 6, sales , cert: NMSDC, WBENC)

5865   Computer Group, Inc.
41252 Vincenti Court Ste 200   Novi, MI 48375
(248) 888-6900   Beverly Ricci VP Sales
Fax:
Email: bev@compgroup.com
Website: www.compgroup.com
Dist micro computer hardware, software, peripherals & supplies, MS Access databases programming. (AA, estab 1982, empl 10, sales $800,000, cert: NMSDC)

5866   Data Ranger Computer Products
P.O. Box 835 507 E Main St   Manchester, MI 48158
(734) 428-8551   Andrea Ranger Owner
Fax: (734) 428-8561
Email: andrea@datarangercomputerproducts.com
Website: www.datarangercomputerproducts.com
Dist computer, pos, barcoding & imaging supplies, hardware/equipment & peripherals, toner, ink, ribbons, backup media, paper, labels, custom forms, printers, cables, scanners, networking hardware, monitors, computers, etc. (Woman/White, estab 2002, empl 2, sales , cert: WBENC)

5867   JEM Computers, Inc. dba JEM Tech Group
23537 Lakepointe   Clinton Township, MI 48036
(586) 783-3400   Denise Bonino Sales Support
Fax: (586) 783-3430
Email: d.bonino@jemtechgroup.com
Website: www.jemtechgroup.com
Dist IT products: toners, tape backup media, printers, cables, monitors, bar code readers, backup libraries, furniture, switches, hubs, racks, projectors, hardware & software, etc. (Woman/White, estab 1979, empl 14, sales $7,100,000, cert: WBENC)

5868   M.O.R.E. Computer Supplies, LLC
384 Park   Troy, MI 48083
(248) 733-9011   Jim Williams CEO
Fax: (248) 733-9016
Email: steve@more-office.biz
Website: www.more-office.biz
Dist computer supplies. (AA, estab , empl 1, sales $16,000,000, cert: NMSDC)

5869   Micro Wise, Inc.
21421 Hilltop Dr, Unit 4   Southfield, MI 48034
(248) 350-0066   Dan Mamman Sales Mgr
Fax: (248) 350-0068
Email: dan@microwise.net
Website: www.microwise.net
Resell computers, servers & networking gear, POS, access-control, PC repairs, upgrades, service, leasing & disposal. (Woman/As-Ind, estab 1989, empl 9, sales , cert: NMSDC)

5870   Mikan Corporation
1271 Industrial, Ste 3   Saline, MI 48176
(734) 944-9447   Maggie Stevens President
Fax: (734) 944-9442
Email: maggie@mikancorp.com
Website: www.mikancorp.com
Remanufacture laser toner cartridges. (Woman/White, estab 1990, empl 7, sales $1,726,617, cert: WBENC)

5871   Open Systems Technologies DE, LLC
605 Seward NW, Ste 101   Grand Rapids, MI 49504
(616) 574-3500   David Gerrity Exec Dir
Fax: (616) 574-3520
Email: dgerrity@ostusa.com
Website: www.ostusa.com
Resell computer hardware & software, business process solutions, data center solutions, application development, managed services. (Nat Ame, estab 1997, empl 110, sales $68,873,026, cert: NMSDC)

5872   The Computer Group, Inc.
32985 Hamilton Ct. Ste 135   Farmington Hills, MI 48331
(248) 888-6900   Phillip Ingram President
Fax: (248) 888-6925
Email: phil@compgroup.com
Website: www.compgroup.com
Computer systems, copy machines, computer peripherals, computer software networking products. (AA, estab 1982, empl 9, sales $525,000, cert: NMSDC)

Minnesota

5873 All Media Supplies Inc.
4902 NE Tri Oak Cir S Wyoming, MN 55092
(763) 413-1907 Rita Morse President
Fax: (763) 645-5485
Email: rita@allmediasuppliesinc.com
Website: www.allmediasuppliesinc.com
Dist computer media supplies. (Woman/White, estab 1997, empl 1, sales , cert: WBENC)

5874 All Media Supplies, Inc
4902 NE Tri Oak Circle South   Wyoming, MN 55092
(763) 413-1907 Rita Morse President
Fax: (763) 413-1539
Email: shelly@allmediasuppliesinc.com
Website: www.allmediasuppliesinc.com
Dist magnetic computer products: 4MM,8MM,CD-Rom, labels & racking. (Woman/White, estab 1997, empl 5, sales $729,000, cert: WBENC)

5875 Best Datacom, Inc.
8405 First Ave NE   Stacy, MN 55079
(715) 398-0342 Doug Anderson Acct Mgr
Fax: (651) 408-0500
Email: doug@best-datacom.com
Website: www.best-datacom.com
Computer & network hardware & peripheral products, copper & fiber cable assemblies, cabinets/racks & computer/network enclosures. (Woman/As-Pac, estab 2007, empl 3, sales $264,000, cert: NMSDC)

5876 CaDan Technologies
4131 Old Sibley Memorial Hwy Ste 200 Eagan, MN 55122
(952) 278-0560 Tom Kreiling Sales
Fax: (651) 681-8078
Email: sales@cadan.com
Website: www.cadan.com
Computer hardware, software & services, new & refurbished hardware, hardware/software installations, new site setups or site tear downs. (Woman/White, estab 1992, empl 32, sales $9,300,000, cert: WBENC)

5877 Kelly Computer Supply Co. LLC
3588 Hoffman Rd East   St. Paul, MN 55110
(651) 773-1109 Bob Kelly President
Fax: (651) 773-1381
Email: bobkelly@kellyrest.com
Website: www.kellyrest.com
Ergonomic equip; mfr "KellyRest" computer products: wrist & foot rests, adjustable copy holders, keyboard drawers & articulating keyboard trays; workstations. (Nat Ame, estab 1983, empl 10, sales , cert: State, NMSDC, CPUC)

5878 Magnetic Products and Services, Inc.
7600 Boone Ave N Ste 1 Brooklyn Park, MN 55428
(800) 447-1277 Michelle Morey VP
Fax:
Email: mmorey@mpsinc.org
Website: www.mpsinc.org
Dist electrical products & computer supplies: magnetic tapes, cartridges, optical disks, etc. (Woman/White, estab 1989, empl 14, sales $9,520,000, cert: WBENC)

Missouri

5879 Desktop Color Systems
1675 Larkin Williams Rd   Fenton, MO 63122
(636) 343-4600 Maryann Gephardt CEO
Fax: (636) 343-4644
Email: info@dtcolor.com
Website: www.dtcolor.com
Resell imaging supplies & office equipment hardware, service agreements, break-fix & warranty service. (Woman/White, estab 1993, empl 5, sales $1,546,000, cert: WBENC)

5880 Huber & Associates, Inc.
1400 Edgewood Dr   Jefferson City, MO 65109
(573) 634-5000 Elizabeth Huber CEO
Fax: (573) 634-5500
Email: ehuber@teamhuber.com
Website: www.teamhuber.com
Dist IBM hardware, software, maintenance & services. (Woman/White, estab 1986, empl 80, sales $36,332,740, cert: State, WBENC)

5881 Missouri Office Systems & Supplies, Inc.
941 W 141st Terrace Ste B Kansas City, MO 64145
(816) 761-5152 Virgie Dillard President
Fax: (816) 761-5170
Email: VLD@8asupplier.com
Website: www.8asupplier.com
Dist office supplies, furniture, ethernet, media, printers, software, hardware, ribbons, fax, scanners, computers, typewriters, routers, hubs, toners, servers. (Woman/AA, estab 1993, empl 9, sales $8,775,113, cert: State, City, NMSDC)

North Carolina

5882 Carolina Cartridge Systems, Inc.
516 E Hebron St Charlotte, NC 28273
(704) 347-2447 Sharon Summers CEO
Fax: (704) 347-8946
Email: sharon.summers@ccsinside.com
Website: www.ccsinside.com
Mfr toner cartridges. (Woman/White, estab 1991, empl 35, sales $2,200,000, cert: State, WBENC)

5883　Key Services, Inc.
　　　3921 Westpoint Blvd　Winston-Salem, NC 27103
　　　(336) 397-2129　Lisa Hodges President
　　　Fax: (336) 768-2201
　　　Email: lhodges@key-services.com
　　　Website: www.key-services.com
Dist & repair computer hardware & software, displays, touchscreens, printers, scanners, barcoding products & networking equipment. (Woman/White, estab 1976, empl 35, sales $10,000,000, cert: WBENC)

Nebraska

5884　The EW Armstrong Industries Inc.
　　　3702 Burr Oak Dr　Bellevue, NE 68123
　　　(402) 291-4982　Carole Armstrong CEO
　　　Fax: (402) 291-4982
　　　Email: carolea@ewaindustries.com
　　　Website: www.ewaindustries.com
Computer equipment, supply sales & services. (AA, estab 2012, empl 3, sales , cert: State)

New Hampshire

5885　110 Technology LLC
　　　27 Technology Way Millyard Technology Park
　　　Nashua, NH 03060
　　　(603) 886-2800　Gary Nicoll Sales Mgr
　　　Fax: (603) 886-2890
　　　Email: sales@110technology.com
　　　Website: www.110technology.com
Resell information technology products: Hewlett Packard, IBM, Dell, Apple, Microsoft, Cisco, 3Com, APC, Philips, Xerox, NEC, Infocus, Intel, Viewsonic. (Woman/Hisp, estab 2004, empl 8, sales $11,000,000, cert: NMSDC, WBENC)

5886　Tape Services, Inc.
　　　15 Londonderry Rd, Unit 11　Londonderry, NH 03053
　　　(603) 425-2202　Bryan Webb Sales Mgr
　　　Fax: (603) 425-2220
　　　Email: bwebb@tapeservices.com
　　　Website: www.tapeservices.com/
Pro Audio; Videotape; Back Up Tape; Data Media;Hard Drives; CD;Computer Media; Digital Media; Pro Tape; Professional Media; Recording Media; Computer Media; Data Migration; DBeta; DVCam; DVCPro; DVD; Glyph; G-Tech. (Woman/White, estab 1989, empl 8, sales $4,314,589, cert: WBENC)

New Jersey

5887　Baanyan Software Services, Inc.
　　　399 Thornall St, 1st Fl　Edison, NJ 08837
　　　(732) 439-3841　Steve Kasarsky VP Sales
　　　Fax: (866) 841-9545
　　　Email: skasarsky@baanyan.com
　　　Website: www.baanyan.com
IT staffing, ERP, BI, Data Warehousing, Cloud and Mobile Computing, and Big Data. (Woman/As-Ind, estab 2009, empl 100, sales $7,091,695, cert: City, NMSDC)

5888　DATA Inc. USA
　　　72 Summit Ave　Montvale, NJ 07645
　　　(201) 802-9800　George Nikanorov Head of Mktg
　　　Fax: (201) 802-9808
　　　Email: george@datacusa.com
　　　Website: www.datainc.biz
IT solutions: staff augmentation & custom application development solutions. (As-Pac, estab 1983, empl 400, sales $49,079,601, cert: State, NMSDC)

New York

5889　BXI Consultants, Inc.
　　　33 Peuquet Pkwy　Tonawanda, NY 14150
　　　(716) 693-0343　Ingrid Charlton President
　　　Fax: (716) 693-0130
　　　Email: icharlton@bxiconsultants.com
　　　Website: www.bxiconsultants.com
Xerox copying, printing & scanning. (Woman/As-Pac, estab 1993, empl 15, sales , cert: State)

5890　Empress Media, Inc.
　　　306 W 38th St, 4 Fl　New York, NY 10018
　　　(212) 643-4898　David Miller President
　　　Fax: (212) 643-4894
　　　Email: empressmedia@cs.com
　　　Website:
Dist recording media, video, audio & data. (Woman/As-Pac, estab 1998, empl 25, sales , cert: State)

5891　Garic, Inc.
　　　26 Broadway Ste 961　New York, NY 10004
　　　(646) 487-0103　Patrick O'Keefe Principal
　　　Fax: (646) 227-1128
　　　Email: patrick@garicinc.com
　　　Website: www.garicinc.com
Technology leasing & computer remarketing, financial services, computer & telecommunications equipment, computers, telephone systems, switches, networks, peripherals, etc. (AA/Hisp, estab 2000, empl 7, sales $5,000,000, cert: State, City, NMSDC)

5892 Gholkar's, Inc.
      7321 State Rt 251   Victor, NY 14564
      (585) 924-2050 Preeya Gholkar President
      Fax: (585) 924-2084
      Email: info@gholkars.com
      Website: www.gholkars.com
Dist computer supplies: magnetic media, CAD plotter
paper, ribbons, barcode labels, & ribbons. (As-Ind, estab
1988, empl 7, sales $3,400,000, cert: State)

5893 GT Business Supplies LLC
      115-13 Linden Blvd   South Ozone park, NY 11420
      (718) 659-9165 Jodhan Basanta Managing Dir
      Fax: (718) 233-2721
      Email: jodhanb@gttoner.com
      Website: www.gttoner.com
Dist printers, ink cartridges & toners. (Hisp, estab 2003,
empl 4, sales $400,000, cert: City)

5894 Hugo Neu Recycling, LLC
      249 E Sandford Blvd   Mount Vernon, NY 10550
      (917) 566-8464 Joseph Claiborne Director, sourcing
      Fax: (914) 530-2355
      Email: info@hugoneu.com
      Website: www.hugoneurecycling.com
IT asset disposal & advance electronic e-waste recycler.
(Woman/As-Pac, estab 2009, empl 90, sales , cert: NMSDC,
WBENC)

5895 New Computech, Inc.
      39 Broadway Ste 1630 New York, NY 10006
      (212) 406-1801 Mona Abraham President
      Fax: (212) 406-1799
      Email: mona@newcomputech.com
      Website: www.newcomputech.com
Resell computer hardware & software products. (Woman/
AA, estab 1996, empl 12, sales $1,500,000, cert: City)

5896 Pioneer Business Systems
      165 W 29th St   New York, NY 10001
      (212) 594-2614 James Breland Dir Business Dev
      Fax: (212) 564-9336
      Email: jamesb@pioneercopier.com
      Website: www.pioneercopier.com
Lease, rentals, purchase copiers, prints, scanners, MFP
equipment, wide format printers. Service copiers, printers,
fax & MFP equipment. (As-Pac, estab 2009, empl 12, sales
$13,500,000, cert: City, NMSDC)

5897 Sidewinder Holdings, Inc.
      245 Mineola Blvd   Mineola, NY 11501
      (516) 742-1700 Stacey Rose President
      Fax: (516) 742-1716
      Email: srose@cartridgeworldusa.com
      Website: www.cartridgeworldusa.com/store76
Dist laser, toner & inkjet cartridges for printers, copiers &
fax machines. (Woman/AA, estab 2005, empl 5, sales
$211,429, cert: City, NMSDC)

Ohio

5898 Integrated Business Supplies Inc.
      17381 Old Tannery Trail   Chagrin Falls, OH 44023
      (440) 498-3888 Judy Wardley VP
      Fax: (440) 498-8889
      Email: judyw@misibs.com
      Website: www.askibs.com
Dist computers & equipment, office machines, supplies,
paper, furniture, vellum. (Woman/White, estab 1990,
empl 5, sales $546,600, cert: State, City)

5899 SpaceBound, Inc.
      280 Opportunity Way   LaGrange, OH 44050
      (440) 355-8008 Cindi Duesler Sales Mgr
      Fax: (440) 355-8009
      Email: govtbids@spaceboundsolutions.com
      Website: www.spaceboundsolutions.com
Computer hardware, software, peripherals, accessories,
electronics, office supplies, office equipment, audio,
video, cameras, phones telephone, etc. (Woman/White,
estab 1987, empl 49, sales , cert: WBENC)

5900 WMG, LLC
      P.O. Box 3115   Dayton, OH 45401
      (937) 268-0773 William Michael Green CEO
      Fax:
      Email: info@WMGreensales.com
      Website: www.WMGreensales.com
Office equipment, hardware & doftware multifunctional
devices, copiers, scanners, plotters & faxes. (AA, estab
2011, empl 1, sales $1,250,000, cert: State, City,
NMSDC)

Oklahoma

5901 Miami Business Services, Inc.
      28 N Main   Miami, OK 74354
      (918) 541-2195 Gary Shelton econ Dev Mgr
      Fax: (918) 542-3967
      Email: gshelton@mn-e.com
      Website: www.mbs.mn-e.com
Dist office products, remanufactured & compatible
imaging products. (Nat Ame, estab 1987, empl 5, sales
$263,158, cert: State)

Pennsylvania

5902 Parmetech, Inc.
      137 W Eagle Ave   Havertown, PA 19083
      (610) 446-4000 Ana Fernandez-Parmet President
      Fax: (610) 449-3349
      Email: afparmet@parmetech.com
      Website: www.parmetech.com
Dist printers, scanners, multifuction machines & storage
devices. (Woman/Hisp, estab 1991, empl 23, sales
$4,900,000, cert: NMSDC, WBENC)

Rhode Island

5903 NetCablesPlus Inc.
P.O. Box 7815 Cumberland, RI 02864
(401) 475-6040 John Rodrigues President
Fax: (401) 475-6041
Email: sales@netcablesplus.com
Website: www.netcablesplus.com
Network & PC cables & accessories, ethernet, fiber optic, USB, firewire. (Hisp, estab 2004, empl 3, sales $135,000, cert: State)

Tennessee

5904 Columbia Data Systems, Inc.
2002 Oakland Pkwy Columbia, TN 38401
(931) 381-4660 Julie Baker President
Fax: (931) 380-1212
Email: julie.baker@edge.net
Website: www.cdsmicro.com
Dist & service computer & peripherals. (Woman/White, estab 1983, empl 3, sales $308,690, cert: State)

5905 Guy Brown, LLC
7111 Commerce Way Brentwood, TN 37027
(615) 777-1500 Lauren Cooley Sales & Mktg Mgr
Fax: (615) 777-1501
Email: sales@guybrown.com
Website: www.guybrown.com
Mfr recycled laser toner cartridges & office products. (Woman/Hisp, estab 1997, empl 115, sales $205,956,925, cert: NMSDC, WBENC, SDB)

5906 Laser Recharge Inc.
485 E South St Ste 100 Collierville, TN 38017
(901) 853-0742 John Ferris VP
Fax: (901) 853-1501
Email: jferris@laser-recharge.com
Website: www.laser-recharge.com
Laser Printers, Ink Jet Printers, Copiers, Fax, Machines, Multi Function Machines, Scanners, Digital Senders, Plotters, Printer & Copier Supplies, Printer Repair Service. (Woman/White, estab 1986, empl 11, sales $2,780,000, cert: State)

5907 Unistar-Sparco Computers, Inc.
7089 Ryburn Dr Millington, TN 38053
(901) 872-2272 Tessa Horowitz Mktg & Business Dev Exec
Fax: (901) 872-8482
Email: teresa@sparco.com
Website: www.sparco.com
IT solutions, hardware, computer systems, desktops, notebooks, thin clients, tablet PCs, PDAs, workstations, rack-mount servers, blade servers, monitors, displays, Plasma TVs, LCD monitors, flat-screen monitors, LCD TVs. (As-Pac, estab 1992, empl 35, sales , cert: State, NMSDC)

Texas

5908 ARDETECH Industries, Inc.
11526 Pagemill Rd Dallas, TX 75243
(800) 821-5678 Bill Nist Sales Rep
Fax: (214) 349-9496
Email: info@ardetech.com
Website: www.ardetech.com
Dist IT products, cable assemblies, computer peripherals, data & telecomm supplies. (Woman/White, estab 1996, empl 14, sales $2,415,008, cert: State)

5909 CompuPro Global
15720 Park Row Ste 400 Houston, TX 77084
(713) 934-9633 Randy Pfeiffer VP Business Develop
Fax: (713) 934-9644
Email: ginnib@compuproglobal.com
Website: www.compuproglobal.com
Dist computer tape, computer media, computer accessories, hardware, toner, wide format printer supplies (Woman/White, estab 1999, empl 9, sales $5,600,000, cert: State, WBENC)

5910 Designs That Compute
1778 N Plano Rd, Ste 211B Richardson, TX 75081
(214) 276-0124 Gregg Coapman technical sales consultant
Fax: (214) 276-0123
Email: sales@visionality.com
Website: www.visionality.com
Videoconferencing & audio/visual solutions, digital signage, interactive whiteboards & displays, video walls, projectors/screens, audio/speakers, recording, streaming video. (Woman/White, estab 1986, empl 14, sales $5,400,000, cert: State)

5911 ELP Enterprises, Inc.
9346 Rosstown Way Houston, TX 77080
(832) 969-9947 Martha Ceballos CEO
Fax: (713) 463-5682
Email: mceball@aol.com
Website: www.elpenterprisesinc.com
Dist computer supplies. (Woman/Hisp, estab 1999, empl 2, sales $813,923, cert: City)

5912 JHJ Computer Supplies, Inc.
3901 Arlington Highlands Blvd. Ste 200 Arlington, TX 76013
(817) 861-0888 Jessie Hampton President
Fax:
Email: jhampton@jhjcs.com
Website: www.jhjcs.com
Dist computer supplies: printers, keyboards, flash drives, ink & toner cartridges, magnetic media, media storage, anti-glare screens, mouse pads, optical mouse devices, wireless devices, computer bags, USB cables. (Woman/AA, estab 2007, empl 2, sales $352,000, cert: State)

5913 Meridian Office Systems, Inc.
      4113 Lindbergh Dr   Addison, TX 75001
      (972) 690-3661 Jeff Emery Mgr
      Fax:
      Email: jemery@meridianoffice.com
      Website: www.meridianoffice.com
Sell, lease, rent, repair, service & maintenance office
copiers, laser printers & multifunction color copiers.
(Woman/As-Pac, estab 1994, empl 15, sales $3,200,000,
cert: State)

5914 OAS Computer Supplies
      3333 Earhart Dr, Ste 120   Carrollton, TX 75006
      (972) 267-8020 Susan Considine Sales Exec
      Fax: (972) 267-8028
      Email: sales@oas-supplies.com
      Website: www.oas-supplies.com
Resell office supplies & computer supplies. (Woman/
White, estab 1986, empl 12, sales $150,500,000, cert:
State)

5915 Patriot Group, Ltd.
      5000 Terminal St   Bellaire, TX 77401
      (713) 664-1172 Lois Livingston Acct Mgr
      Fax: (713) 664-9126
      Email: llivingston@patriotgroup.com
      Website: www.patriotgroup.com
Dist business equipment, equipment supplies, service and
support. (Woman/White, estab 1979, empl 22, sales
$5,137,000, cert: State)

5916 RLS Interests, Inc.
      10402 Harwin Dr   Houston, TX 77036
      (713) 933-0934 Michael Chang
      Fax: (713) 933-1030
      Email: directron@globalxlr.com
      Website: www.directron.com
DIY computer components, CPUs, memory, hard drives,
optical drives, hardware & software, pre-built systems,
notebooks, netbooks, tablets, peripherals & accessories.
(As-Pac, estab 1990, empl 157, sales $51,100,000, cert:
NMSDC)

5917 Southwest Office Systems, Inc.
      13960 Trinity Blvd   Dallas, TX 76040
      (817) 510-2177 Karl Duncan Acct Mgr
      Fax:
      Email: Kduncan@sostexas.com
      Website: www.Sostexas.com
Copiers, printers, print management, plotters, digital white
boards. (Hisp, estab 1964, empl 55, sales $5,000,000, cert:
State, NMSDC)

5918 TAPEANDMEDIA.COM, LLC
      450 Colorado Dr   Cedar Creek, TX 78612
      (877) 938-0901 Bennie Wallace VP
      Fax: (512) 448-0708
      Email: bennie@tapeandmedia.com
      Website: www.tapeandmedia.com
Dist blank media: computer back-up tapes, video tapes,
audio tapes, DVD's, CD's, DVD/CD cases. (Woman/White,
estab 2000, empl 6, sales $5,000,000, cert: State)

Virginia

5919 Advanced Business Software Consulting LLC dba
      NCN
      11890 Sunrise Valley Dr, Ste 515   Reston, VA
      20191
      (703) 298-2468 Sharon Muniz CEO
      Fax:
      Email: sharon@ncntechnology.com
      Website: www.ncntechnology.com
Mobile & web application development, SharePoint
services. (Woman/Hisp, estab 2006, empl 3, sales
$520,000, cert: State, WBENC, 8(a), SDB)

5920 Computer Upgrade King, LLC
      1555 Standing Ridge Dr Ste A-1 Powhatan, VA
      23139
      (800) 985-9364 Robert Robinson VP
      Fax: (800) 985-9489
      Email: sales@computerupgradeking.com
      Website: www.cukusa.com/
Computers (laptops, desktops), Custom Desktops,
Components, Cases, Laser Etching. (Woman/As-Pac,
estab 2008, empl 45, sales $846,956, cert: State)

5921 Metropolitan Technology Solutions Corp.
      3633 Brockenbrough Dr   Dumfries, VA 22026
      (703) 946-6565 Russell Henderson CEO
      Fax: (703) 441-9194
      Email: hendersonr@mts2003.com
      Website: www.mtsitcorp.com
Dist hardware & software products, office supplies, IT
consulting. (Woman/AA, estab 2003, empl 11, sales
$169,000, cert: State)

Washington

5922 EC Corporation Export
      22307 Marine View Dr S   Des Moines, WA 98198
      (206) 878-3321 Patricio Mendoza Mgr
      Fax: (253) 214-1299
      Email: patricio@eccomputer.com
      Website: www.eccomputer.com
Computers Peripherals, Cartridges, Office Supply,
External hard drives, Keyboard, Mouse, Monitors,
Software, Licenses, Office Supplies, PC'S. (Hisp, estab
1991, empl 4, sales $250,000, cert: State, City)

5923   Evergreen Computer Products Inc
       2720 1st Ave S   Seattle, WA 98134
       (206) 624-3722 Barbara Anderson VP
       Fax: (206) 340-1635
       Email: banderson@evergreencomp.com
       Website: www.evergreencomp.com
Printer repair services. (Woman/AA, estab 1977, empl 10,
sales $10,116,295, cert: State, NMSDC)

Wisconsin

5924   Cartridge Savers, Inc.
       2801 Coho St Ste 206 Madison, WI 53713
       (608) 663-5126 Thomas Wangard President
       Fax: (608) 227-7285
       Email: tom.w@cartridgesavers.com
       Website: www.cartridgesavers.com
Dist remanufactured & new laser printer toner cartridges,
laser printers. (Hisp, estab 1994, empl 8, sales $6,843,995,
cert: State, NMSDC)

INFORMATION TECHNOLOGY: Systems/Machines
Design, manufacture, lease and/or distribute information processing systems, machines and components. Many of these firms also distribute information processing supplies. (See also INFORMATION TECHNOLOGY: Services and INFORMATION TECHNOLOGY: Supplies). NAICS Code 33

California

5925   CB Technologies, Inc.
       750 The City Dr South Ste 225 Orange, CA 92868
       (714) 573-7733 Dwanna Lynch Director/ Corporate Relations
       Fax: (714) 573-7752
       Email: dwanna.lynch@cbtechinc.com
       Website: www.cbtechinc.com
Information technology hardware. (Woman/Hisp, estab 2001, empl 40, sales $1,400,000, cert: CPUC, WBENC)

5926   DuraTech USA, Inc.
       6765 Westminster Blvd Ste 314 Westminster, CA 92683
       (831) 419-8179 Skip Howland Govt Business Dev
       Fax: (866) 704-9132
       Email: showland@duratechusa.com
       Website: www.Duratechusa.com
Dist semi rugged & MIL-STD 810F laptops, rugged & submersible tablet pc's. (Woman/As-Pac/Hisp, estab 2005, empl 3, sales $1,293,628, cert: State)

5927   Elgin Micro
       14271 Jeffrey Rd Ste 247 Irvine, CA 92620
       (949) 878-7461 Daniel Laterneau Sales Dir
       Fax: (855) 693-5446
       Email: dan@elginmicro.com
       Website: www.elginmicro.com
Dist HP, IBM, SUN Microsystems (Oracle), Dell, Cisco, Emulex, Qlogic, Juniper, EMC, NetApp, Nortel, Lenovo, Toshiba, Acer, Operating systems, Security, Applications, Design, Accounting, Training & Utilities. (Woman/Hisp, estab 2012, empl 8, sales , cert: NMSDC)

5928   JE Components Inc.
       8709 Aviation Blvd   Inglewood, CA 90301
       (310) 645-6021 Joni Paulo President
       Fax: (310) 645-6041
       Email: joni@jecom.com
       Website: www.jecom.com
Resell PC & network hardware. (Woman/AA/As-Ind, estab 1995, empl 7, sales , cert: NMSDC, NWBOC)

5929   Performance Designed Products
       14144 Ventura Blvd Ste 200 Sherman Oaks, CA 91423
       (479) 445-8612 Theresa Harrell Natl Acct Mgr
       Fax:
       Email: theresa.harrell@pdp.com
       Website: www.pdp.com
Design & mfr video game peripherals & accessories: PS2, PS3, PSP PS Vita, Xbox, Xbox 360, Wii, Wii U, 3DS, DS Lite. (Woman, estab 1990, empl 200, sales , cert: WBENC)

5930   RICOM
       26062 Merit Circle Bldg. 108 Laguna Hills, CA 92653
       (949) 788-9939 Isaac Buchanan Acct Exec
       Fax: (949) 788-9940
       Email: isaac@ricom.net
       Website: www.shopricom.com
Computers: Cisco; IBM; Hewlett Packard; Emulex; Sun Microsystems; Dell; EMC; Nimble Storage; F5 Networks; VMware; citrix. (Woman/Hisp, estab 1998, empl 9, sales $13,000,000, cert: NMSDC, CPUC, WBENC)

Colorado

5931   SF&B, LLC
       9585 Niwot Rd   Longmont, CO 80504
       (240) 566-6778 Elizabeth LaRock Mgr
       Fax: (720) 208-0613
       Email: elarock@sfbllc.com
       Website: www.sfbllc.com
Dist top-tier computer hardware. (Woman, estab 2011, empl 5, sales , cert: WBENC)

Connecticut

5932   PCNet, Inc.
       100 Technology Dr   Trumbull, CT 06611
       (203) 452-8559 Erik Soto VP Finance/Ops
       Fax: (203) 452-8656
       Email: eriks@pcnet-inc.com
       Website: www.pcnet-inc.com
Network systems integrator; e-commerce, Internet/Intranet; resell of personal computer products & svcs. (Hisp, estab 1993, empl 65, sales $26,000,000, cert: NMSDC)

Florida

5933 United Data Technologies
8825 NW 21 Terrace Doral, FL 33172
(305) 882-0435 Mariana Lugaro Mgr Sales Ops
Fax: (305) 882-0436
Email: sales.operations@udtonline.com
Website: www.udtonline.com
Dist, install & repair IT equipment: desktops, laptops, servers, printers, switches, peripherals, & audio visual equipment. (Hisp, estab 1995, empl 94, sales , cert: State)

Georgia

5934 American Megatrends Inc.
5555 Oakbrook Pkwy, Ste 200   Norcross, GA 30093
(770) 246-8600 Srivatsan Ramachandran Dir Business Dev
Fax: (770) 326-9153
Email: srivatsanr@ami.com
Website: www.ami.com
Mfr key hardware & software solutions, StorTrends, IP Storage Area Network (IP-SAN) and Network Attached Storage (NAS) solutions, Aptio and AMIBIOS system software and firmware, MegaRAC remote management software & firmware. (As-Ind, estab 1985, empl 1345, sales $10,000,000, cert: NMSDC)

5935 Eastern Data, Inc.
4386 Park Dr   Norcross, GA 30093
(770) 279-8888 JoAnn Pfeiffer Natl Accts Mgr
Fax:
Email: jo.pfeiffer@ediatlanta.com
Website: www.ediatlanta.com
Dist computer systems, components & peripherals. (Woman/As-Pac, estab 1997, empl 27, sales $20,906,578, cert: NMSDC, WBENC)

Illinois

5936 Koi Computers Inc.
200 W North Ave   Lombard, IL 60148
(630) 627-8811 Ayde Chavez Acct Rep
Fax: (630) 627-8877
Email: ayde@koicomputer.com
Website: www.koicomputer.com
Dist computers, servers, printers, copiers, digital imaging & networking equipments. (Woman/As-Ind, estab 1995, empl 6, sales $7,500,000, cert: State)

Indiana

5937 Professional Information Systems
232 S Linda St P.O. Box 619 Hobart, IN 46342
(219) 947-4349 Paulette Hill President
Fax: (219) 947-5668
Email: paulette@proinfosys.com
Website: www.proinfosys.com
Hardware & software, build customize computers or prebuilt computers. (Woman/White, estab 1992, empl 4, sales $172,000, cert: State, 8(a))

5938 Qumulus Solutions LLC
101 N Michigan St Ste 300 South Bend, IN 46601
(574) 208-6772 Russell Ford President & COO
Fax: (574) 208-6777
Email: rford@qumulussolutions.com
Website: www.qumulussolutions.com
Resell servers, storage, data backup hardware & software. (AA, estab 2010, empl 7, sales $644,000, cert: State, NMSDC)

Kansas

5939 ProActive Solutions Inc.
5625 Foxridge Dr   Mission, KS 66202
(913) 948-8000 Dean Thiede Exec VP
Fax: (913) 831-7744
Email: dthiede@proactivesolutions.com
Website: www.proactivesolutions.com
IBM Hardware Power, System i, AS400, System p, RS6000, System x, Storage, SAN, Lotus, Domino, Notes, Websphere, Tivoli, TSM, VMWare, virtualization, Disaster Recovery, DR, High Availability, HA, Business Continuity, BC, Linux, (Woman/White, estab 1996, empl 30, sales $45,029,277, cert: CPUC, WBENC)

Massachusetts

5940 Concord Information Systems, LLC
165 Middlesex Turnpike Ste 201 Bedford, MA 01730
(781) 863-7200 Suzanne Hiniker Partner
Fax: (781) 863-1717
Email: suzy@concordinfo.com
Website: www.concordinfo.com
Computers, laptops, tablets, servers, monitors, printers, networking hardware, cloud & email services & technical consulting services. (Woman/White, estab 1994, empl 10, sales $10,000,000, cert: State)

5941 Fenco Global Industries Corp.
1 Federal St Springfield, MA 01105
(413) 308-8800 Fenella Sitati President
Fax:
Email: fenella@winningtek.com
Website: www.winningtek.com
Technology hardware for application security, datacenters & cloud virtualization, F5 Networks, VMware, Palo Alto, Cisco Networks, RedHat, Microsoft, NetApp, EMC, HP, IBM, Dell & ExtraHop. (Woman/AA, estab 2009, empl 5, sales $450,000, cert: NMSDC)

5942 Pyramid Technology Services, Inc.
10 Riverbank Rd, Ste 200 Maynard, MA 01754
(877) 289-7874 Claudia Nimar President
Fax: (978) 897-9611
Email: claudia@pyramiddec.com
Website: www.pyramiddec.com
Resell new, used & refurbished computer equipment: Sun, HP, Digital & Compaq systems, Cisco, Enterasys & Cabletron networking lines. (Woman/White, estab 1989, empl 12, sales , cert: State)

Michigan

5943 Dynamic Computer Corporation
23400 Industrial Park Ct Farmington Hills, MI 48335
(248) 473-2200 Farida Ali Acct Mgr
Fax: (248) 473-2201
Email: fali@dcc-online.com
Website: www.dcc-online.com
Dist IT equipment: HP/Compaq, Dell, IBM, Microsoft, Symantec & Gateway. (Woman/As-Ind, estab 1979, empl 24, sales $27,000,000, cert: NMSDC)

Minnesota

5944 SHI International Corp.
45 South 7th St Ste 2240 Minneapolis, MN 55402
(651) 485-5436 Dustin Branan Enterprise Acct Exec
Fax:
Email: dustin_branan@shi.com
Website: www.shi.com
Dist computer software, hardware, peripherals, networking products, accessories & IT lifecycle services. (Woman/As-Pac, estab 1989, empl 3500, sales $8,500,000,000, cert: NMSDC, CPUC, WBENC)

5945 Vaske Computer Inc
2310 W County Rd D Ste 110 St. Paul, MN 55112
(651) 633-6446 Shaun Stefano CEO
Fax: (651) 633-6446
Email: smstefano@collier-it.com
Website: www.collier-it.com
Computer maintenance; HP & Sun Microsystems computer equipment. (Woman, estab 1993, empl 22, sales $17,000,000, cert: State)

New Jersey

5946 CPI (USA) Inc.
6 Doreen Court Edison, NJ 08820
(732) 494-0007 Deepak Advani
Fax: (732) 494-0007
Email: Dadvani@cpiusainc.com
Website: www.cpiusainc.com
Workstations, Laptops, Servers, Tablets, Multifunction Printers, Held Workstations, CCTV
Phone Systems (Panasonic, Mitel), Enterprise Business, Industry Standard Servers and Options
Routers & Add On, Switches & Add On, UPS & Generators. (Woman/As-Pac, estab 1997, empl 2, sales $375,000, cert: NMSDC)

New York

5947 Empire Electronics Inc.
103 Fort Salonga Rd Northport, NY 11768
(631) 544-9111 Nancy Pavis / Krista Fisher
Fax: (631) 544-9015
Email: kfisher@empireusa.com
Website: www.empireusa.com
Dist information technology equip, computer hardware & components. (Woman/White, estab 1983, empl 10, sales $4,400,000, cert: City, WBENC)

5948 Ergonomic Group, Inc.
609-3 Cantiague Rock Rd Westbury, NY 11590
(516) 746-7777 Keith Trotte Sr Acct Director
Fax: (516) 746-7809
Email: keith.trotte@ergogroup.com
Website: www.ergogroup.com
Resell computer equipment, peripherals & computer related services. (Woman/White, estab 1984, empl 139, sales , cert: WBENC)

Ohio

5949 Northern Technical Group LLC
14500 Industrial Ave N Maple Heights, OH 44137
(216) 662-0561 Mary Fink President
Fax: (866) 289-2079
Email: mfink@northerntechnicalgroup.com
Website: www.northerntechnicalgroup.com
IT Asset Management, removal, audit, sanitizing, remarketing & recycling of computer related asset. (Woman/White, estab 2003, empl 17, sales $921,316, cert: NWBOC)

Texas

5950   Computize Inc.
  80 E. McDermott Dr.   Allen, TX 75002
  (972) 437-3100 Bennie Moore Sr Sales Dir
  Fax: (972) 437-3777
  Email: benniem@computize.com
  Website: www.computize.com
Resell computers. (Woman/As-Pac, estab 1982, empl 125, sales $4,000,000, cert: State, WBENC)

5951   Cytec Software Systems Inc.
  10877 Sanden Dr   Dallas, TX 75238
  (214) 349-8881 Oscar De Leon President
  Fax: (214) 349-8994
  Email: oscar@cytecsys.com
  Website: www.cytecsys.com
Mfr & integrate industrial network computers, RAID servers & rugged portable computers, custom hardware & software devel. (Hisp, estab 1984, empl 18, sales , cert: State)

5952   M&A Technology Inc.
  2045 Chenault Dr   Carrollton, TX 75006
  (888) 639-4438 Donna Shepard Exec VP
  Fax: (972) 490-5813
  Email: dshepard@macomp.com
  Website: www.macomp.com
Custom intergration, servers, workstation, high performance intergrating, data center, on line back up, disater recovery. (AA, estab 1984, empl 137, sales $75,000,000, cert: State)

Virginia

5953   US21, Inc.
  2721 Prosperity Ave, Ste 300   Fairfax, VA 22031
  (703) 560-0021 Bassel Shubassi Business Devel Officer
  Fax: (703) 560-2336
  Email: info@us21.com
  Website: www.us21.com
Dist IT hardware: SMB & Enterprise. (Woman/White, estab 1998, empl 20, sales $10,000,000, cert: State)

5954   Video & Telecommunications, Inc.
  5427-A Backlick Rd   Springfield, VA 22151
  (703) 658-0304 Justin Larkin Sr Acct Mgr
  Fax: (703) 658-1829
  Email: JustinL@vti2.com
  Website: www.vti2.com
Dist PCs, ATs, microcomputers, laptops, printers, modems, multiplexers, fiber optics, ASCII & ANSI terminals, disk drives, etc. (Nat Ame, estab 1982, empl 20, sales , cert: State)

INSURANCE COMPANIES
Firms carry life, accident, auto and health insuance policies. Most are licensed in several states. NAICS Code 52

California

5955   Flexon Technologies Inc.
       7901 Stoneridge Dr, Ste 404   Pleasanton, CA 94588
       (510) 648-8878 Sandeep Singh VP - Sales
       Fax: (186) 693-6496
       Email: ken@flexontechnologies.com
       Website: www.flexontechnologies.com
Our offerings are designed to cater to the entire range of clients' technology needs. We deliver end-to-end solutions that can build, manage and support our customers' IT systems across the entire value chain infrastructure, applications and business pro (As-Ind, estab 2015, empl 52, sales $1,500,000, cert: NMSDC)

5956   Merriwether & Williams Insurance Services
       550 Montgomery St Ste 550 San Francisco, CA 94111
       (415) 986-3999 Donna Hart CEO
       Fax: (415) 986-4421
       Email: dhart@imwis.com
       Website: www.imwis.com
Commercial insurance marketing & placements, surety bonding, OCIP, third party admin. (Woman/AA, estab 1997, empl 35, sales $2,292,090, cert: NMSDC, CPUC)

5957   Mudrasys Inc.
       6200 Stoneridge Mall Rd, Ste 300   Pleasanton, CA 94588
       (925) 353-3888 Narsi Ayyagari CEO
       Fax: (188) 826-6512
       Email: narsi@mudrasys.com
       Website: www.mudrasys.com
AgeAlert is the first thermal age sensor for use in predicting remaining thermal life of propellants as well as other thermally degradable components in ordnance and aircraft and other aerospace platforms. These sensors, weighing less than 1/4 gram, elim (Woman/As-Ind, estab 2009, empl 59, sales $4,200,000, cert: NMSDC, CPUC)

5958   Progressive Technology Solutions
       500 E Calaveras   Milpitas, CA 95035
       (408) 507-7106 Rumi Bordoloi Acct/Relationship Mgr
       Fax: (408) 850-1799
       Email: HR@ptsol.com
       Website: www.ptsol.com
Business, Functional Technical consultants and permanent staff/workforce. AP, Oracle, Internet Technology, Data Management and Analysis, ETL and Datawarehousing, Release and Change Management. (Woman/As-Ind, estab 2002, empl 50, sales $6,650,000, cert: NMSDC)

5959   Sovereign Employee Benefits, Inc.
       10630 Town Center Dr, Ste 113   Rancho Cucamonga, CA 91730
       (909) 948-7779 Katie King Owner
       Fax: (909) 948-7769
       Email: melissadickson@sebins.com
       Website: www.sebins.com
Insurance brokerage services: group medical, customized employee benefit packages, liability, workers' comp & consulting services. (AA, estab 1982, empl 10, sales , cert: CPUC)

Florida

5960   Epiphany Insurance Company LLC
       6073 NW 167 St, Ste C7   Hialeah, FL 33015
       (305) 783-1487 Martine Miller Mgr
       Fax: (305) 676-9040
       Email: epiphanyinsures@gmail.com
       Website: www.epiphanyinsures.com
Health and Life Insurance, Group Benefits, Supplemental Benefits, Dental & Vision. (Woman/AA, estab 2017, empl 4, sales $10,000, cert: State, SDB)

Georgia

5961   AEGIAS Corporation
       3500 Lenox Rd, Ste 1500   Atlanta, GA 30326
       (404) 419-2173 Mary L Beachum President
       Fax: (706) 863-8959
       Email: mbeachum@aegias.com
       Website: www.aegias.com
Employee benefits & financial risk consulting: group health & dental insurance, self-funded plans, life and AD&D, short & long term disability, vision plans, employee assistance programs. (AA, estab 2003, empl 11, sales $392,902, cert: State)

5962   Atlanta Life Insurance Company
       100 Auburn Ave NE   Atlanta, GA 30303
       (404) 654-8893 Leonard Grimes President
       Fax: (404) 654-8955
       Email: lgrimes@atlantalife.com
       Website: www.atlantalife.com
Financial services, employee benefits, reinsurance, asset mgmt, etc. (AA, estab 1905, empl 150, sales , cert: NMSDC)

5963   Benalytics Consulting Group, LLC
       1850 Parkway Place SE Ste 730 Marietta, GA 30067
       (770) 420-0525 Charles Atkinson Principal
       Fax: (770) 420-0535
       Email: catkinson@benalytics.com
       Website: www.benalytics.com
Benefit consulting & insurance brokerage services. (AA, estab 2005, empl 12, sales $1,196,531, cert: NMSDC, SDB)

5964 JLM Risk Management Group
      201 17th St Ste 300 Atlanta, GA 30363
      (404) 874-2929 Joseph L Moore
      Fax: (404) 874-2923
      Email: jmoore@jlmriskmgmt.com
      Website: www.jlmriskmanagementgroup.com
Property, casualty, life & employee benefits insurance
brokerage. Risk management, claims management & loss
control consultation. (AA, estab 1996, empl 7, sales
$600,000, cert: NMSDC)

5965 Premier Benefit Consultants, Inc.
      2470 Windy Hill Rd Ste 300 Marietta, GA 30068
      (678) 794-8104 Maureen Jurgelas President
      Fax: (770) 973-1563
      Email: Maureen@Premierbenefit.com
      Website: www.Premierbenefit.com
Insurance agency & consulting: group medical, dental,
vision plans, LTD, STD, life insurance, AD&D, etc. (Woman/
White, estab 2000, empl 4, sales $240,000, cert: WBENC)

Illinois

5966 CS Insurance Strategies
      542 S Dearborn St   Chicago, IL 60605
      (312) 566-9700 Charles Smith CEO
      Fax: (312) 566-0965
      Email: csmith@csstrategy.com
      Website: www.csstrategy.com
Comprehensive risk management, commercial insurance &
group employee benefit solutions. (AA, estab 2006, empl
4, sales $500,000, cert: City)

5967 Insurers Review Services, Inc.
      225 N Michigan Ave Ste 902 Chicago, IL 60601
      (312) 938-0900 Alvin Robinson President
      Fax: (312) 938-3552
      Email: arobin3172@aol.com
      Website: www.insurersreviewservices.com
Insurance coverages, employee benefits, property coverages, special events, travel accident insurance & expatriate
benefits. (AA, estab 1983, empl 5, sales $450,000, cert:
State, City, NMSDC)

5968 Lambent Risk Management Services, Inc.
      33 N. La Salle St Ste 1150 Chicago, IL 60602
      (866) 419-1415 Shirley Evans-Wofford CEO
      Fax: (312) 220-0117
      Email: shirley_evans@lambent-rms.com
      Website: www.lambent-rms.com
Insurance brokerage: property & casualty, third party
theft, construction builders risk, insurance bonding, travel
accident, healthcare & life, 401(k). (Woman/AA, estab
2000, empl 21, sales $2,433,496, cert: State, City)

Louisiana

5969 1st Team Insurance Agency
      3745 Choctaw Dr   Baton Rouge, LA 70805
      (225) 806-6923 Harold Williams Owner
      Fax: (225) 372-8105
      Email: hwilliams@1stteaminsurance.com
      Website: www.1stteaminsurance.com
Property & casualty insurance, property management,
public relations, lobbying. (AA, estab 2005, empl 3, sales
$350,000, cert: State)

Michigan

5970 Brownrigg Companies LTD
      840 W Long Lake Rd Ste 100 Troy, MI 48098
      (248) 373-5580 Nancy Brownrigg CEO
      Fax: (313) 638-2046
      Email: nbrownrigg@brownrigg.com
      Website: www.brownrigg.com
Specialty insurance. (Woman/White, estab 1990, empl
14, sales $11,000,000, cert: WBENC)

5971 Custom Results Corporate Consulting LLC
      101 W Big Beaver Rd Ste 115 Troy, MI 48084
      (248) 572-1160 Diane Christensen President
      Fax: (248) 509-8765
      Email: diane@customresults.com
      Website: www.customresults.com
Insurance, design, implementation, service & communication of Employee Benefit Plans & Retiree Medicare
Advantage plans. (Woman, estab 2001, empl 6, sales ,
cert: WBENC)

5972 Employee Solve
      725 S Adams Ste L-140 Southfield, MI 48009
      (248) 438-0096 Kenneth Hurtt, RHU, REBC
      President
      Fax: (248) 479-2585
      Email: info1@employeesolve.com
      Website: www.employeesolve.com
Health & welfare plans for employer groups. (AA, estab
1987, empl 6, sales $3,000,000, cert: NMSDC)

5973 GOSS LLC
      600 Renaissance Ctr, Ste 1200   Detroit, MI 48243
      (313) 446-9636 Vincent Davis Dir of Mktg
      Fax: (313) 446-9706
      Email: vdavis@gossllc.com
      Website: www.gossllc.com
Commercial risk & risk consulting svcs: group benefits,
property, casualty, liability, E&O, D&O, workers comp,
business auto, etc. (AA, estab 2001, empl 7, sales
$37,150,000, cert: NMSDC)

5974 Laurie Sall & Associates
201 West Big BeaverRd#300 Troy, MI 48084
(248) 641-2755 Laurie Sall President
Fax: (248) 641-1441
Email: LAURIE@LAURIESALL.COM
Website: www.lauriesall.com
Life, disability & health insurance. (Woman/Hisp, estab 1980, empl 3, sales $8,532,047, cert: NMSDC, WBENC)

5975 ReviewWorks
21500 Haggerty Rd Ste 250 Northville, MI 48167
(248) 848-5067 Carolyn Lahousse President
Fax: (248) 848-9508
Email: carolyn_lahousse@reviewworks.com
Website: www.reviewworks.com
Medical cost containment solutions & disability services for workers' compensation, LTD & auto injury related claims & claimants. (Woman/White, estab 1989, empl 70, sales $11,650,921, cert: WBENC)

5976 The Dearborn Agency
22691 Michigan Ave Dearborn, MI 48124
(313) 562-8373 Wendy Beaver Sales Mgr
Fax: (313) 562-5371
Email: wendyb@dearbornagency.com
Website: www.dearbornagency.com
Insurance. (Woman/White, estab 1924, empl 10, sales , cert: WBENC)

5977 The Goss Group, Inc.
600 Renaissance Center Dr Ste 1200 Detroit, MI 48243
(313) 446-9636 Cindy Smith Sr VP
Fax: (734) 747-6553
Email: csmith@gossllc.com
Website: www.gossllc.com
Commercial insurance agency. (AA, estab 1995, empl 3, sales $333,876, cert: City)

Minnesota

5978 Integrated Benefits Group, Inc.
601 Carlson Pkwy Ste 1097 Hopkins, MN 55305
(952) 449-5290 Deborah J. Dybdahl CEO
Fax: (952) 449-5291
Email: deborah@integratedbenefitsgroup.com
Website: www.integratedbenefitsgroup.com
Auto/home, legal, long term care, critical illnesss, supplemental disability, retirement planning, PET, etc. (Woman/White, estab 1992, empl 16, sales $550,000, cert: WBENC)

Ohio

5979 Pinkney-Perry Insurance Agency, Inc.
2143 Stokes Blvd Cleveland, OH 44106
(216) 795-1995 Patricia L. Welcome VP
Fax: (216) 795-1014
Email: pwelcome@pinkney-perry.com
Website: www.pinkney-perry.com
Insurance. (AA, estab , empl 1, sales , cert: NMSDC)

Rhode Island

5980 Axiom Actuarial Consulting
26 Knapton St Barrington, RI 02806
(860) 550-0740 Carlos Fuentes President
Fax:
Email: carlos-fuentes@axiom-actuarial.com
Website: www.axiom-actuarial.com
Actuarial consulting: dental & vision coverages, pension, life insurance, employee benefits, special risk insurance, reinsurance, investment, finance & strategy. (Hisp, estab 2008, empl 4, sales $75,000, cert: 8(a))

Tennessee

5981 Diversity Benefits
230 N 4th Ave, Ste 162 Nasville, TN 37219
(615) 515-3329 David Carter President
Fax:
Email: davidc@diversitybenefits.net
Website: www.diversitybenefits.net
Health insurance/self-funded health plans, Prescription drug coverage, Reinsurance ,Dental insurance, Vision insurance, Life and AD&D insurance, Disability insurance, Voluntary benefits, Retirement plans. (AA, estab 2012, empl 2, sales $24,750, cert: NMSDC)

Texas

5982 CPR Insurance Group LLC
600 E John Carpenter Frwy Ste 365 Irving, TX 75062
(972) 887-3660 Les Titus President
Fax: (972) 887-3669
Email: ltitus@cprins.com
Website: www.cprins.com
Insurance claims: property, liability/casualty & auto claims. (AA/Hisp, estab 2013, empl 19, sales $1,200,000, cert: State)

LABORATORY/SCIENTIFIC SUPPLIES & SERVICES
Manufacture or distribute products or provide services for scientific laboratories. Products include glassware, disposables, chemicals, safety items. etc. NAICS Code 33

California

5983   Accurate C&S Services, Inc.
       8105 Edgewater Dr #225 Oakland, CA 94621
       (510) 387-0324 Regina Jones President
       Fax: (510) 777-0905
       Email: rjones@accuratemgmt.com
       Website: www.accureatecsservices.com
Drug & alcohol testing. (Woman/AA, estab 2006, empl 15, sales $1,700,000, cert: State, NMSDC, WBENC, 8(a))

5984   BC Laboratories, Inc.
       4100 Atlas Court Bakersfield, CA 93308
       (800) 878-4911 Mark Ellis Business Devel Dir
       Fax: (661) 327-1918
       Email: mark.ellis@bclabs.com
       Website: www.bclabs.com
Analytical Services for Groundwater, Drinking Water, Wastewater, Soils & Air, Certified Testing Services, Sampling & Monitoring. (Woman/White, estab 1949, empl 97, sales $1,000,000,000, cert: CPUC)

5985   BIO PLAS, Inc.
       4340 Redwood Hwy Ste A1 San Rafael, CA 94903
       (415) 472-3777 Jeananne McGrath VP
       Fax: (415) 472-3758
       Email: jam@bioplas.com
       Website: www.bioplas.com
Mfr disposable laboratory supplies. (Woman/White, estab 1977, empl 10, sales , cert: State)

5986   Brylen Technologies
       275 Orange Ave Santa Barbara, CA 93117
       (805) 692-9300 Barbara Tzur President
       Fax: (805) 692-1966
       Email: barbara.tzur@brylen.com
       Website: www.brylen.com
Calibration & testing laboratory, clean room & clean bench certifications, calibration is electro-magnetic, thermodynamics, dimensional, angle, & mechanical areas, calibrate equipment. (Woman/White, estab 1985, empl 10, sales $519,692, cert: State)

5987   Comprehensive Drug Testing, Inc. (CDT, Inc.)
       P.O. Box 11869 Santa Ana, CA 92711
       (800) 440-3784 Kim Jasper President
       Fax: (714) 852-5201
       Email: kimj@cdtsolutions.com
       Website: www.cdtsolutions.com
Substance abuse program management, drug testing, collections, laboratory, education. (Woman/White, estab 1985, empl 13, sales $2,400,000, cert: State, CPUC)

5988   Core Diagnostics
       3535 Breakwater Ave Hayward, CA 94545
       (650)5329500 Krishnamurthy Balachandran CEO
       Fax: (650) 532-9550
       Email: balachandran@corediagnostics.net
       Website: www.corediagnostics.net
Laboratory offering biomarker analysis & translational research support for studies ranging from early discovery to analyses of Phase III clinical trial samples. (As-Ind, estab 2009, empl 12, sales $3,259,000, cert: NMSDC)

5989   Discount Lab Supplies
       3201 Verdant Way San Jose, CA 95117
       (408) 246-4024 Stacey Blanding President
       Fax: (408) 521-0669
       Email: stacey@discountlabs.com
       Website: www.discountlabs.com
Dist lab products: cryogenic storage vessels, DI water systems, furnaces, harvey sterilizers, incubators, NANOpure water systems, ovens, rotators & rockers, spectrophotometers, turner fluorometers, ultrasonic cleaners. (Woman, estab 2004, empl 1, sales $56,500, cert: NMSDC)

5990   Fulgent Therapeutics LLC
       4978 Santa Anita Ave Ste 205 Temple City, CA 91780
       (626) 350-0537 Joe Roach VP
       Fax: (626) 454-1667
       Email: joeroach@fulgentdiagnostics.com
       Website: www.fulgentdiagnostics.com
Hereditary genetic testing. (As-Pac, estab 2013, empl 30, sales $1,000,000, cert: NMSDC)

5991   Orange Coast Analytical, Inc.
       3002 Dow Ave, Ste 532 Tustin, CA 92780
       (714) 832-0064 Cindy Noorani President
       Fax: (714) 832-0067
       Email: cindyn@ocalab.com
       Website: www.ocalab.com
Environmental & analytical testing laboratory, organic & inorganic testing-water, waste water, soil, air, industial, chemical & food products. (Woman, estab 1990, empl 15, sales $1,450,178, cert: State, CPUC)

5992   Pure Lab Solutions, Inc.
       4901 Morena Blvd., #118 San Diego, CA 92117
       (619) 840-5858 Pam Wammes President
       Fax: (619) 275-2926
       Email: pwammes@purelabsolutions.com
       Website: www.purelabsolutions.com
Dist Sartorius lab equipment, ultrapure water purification & lab bench scales. (Woman/White, estab 2012, empl 2, sales $19,911, cert: WBENC)

5993 The Andwin Corp.
6636 Variel Ave   Canoga Park, CA 91303
(818) 999-2828 Arnie Shedlow Sr VP sales
Fax: (818) 226-4125
Email: jpalaganas@andwin.com
Website: www.andwinsci.com
Dist medical & lab supplies & product kits: boxes, labels, bar codes, instruction inserts & kit components. (Woman/White, estab 1950, empl 98, sales $32,000,000, cert: WBENC)

Connecticut

5994 PRO Scientific Inc.
99 Willenbrock Rd   Oxford, CT 06478
(203) 267-4600 Holly Archibald Sales Dir
Fax: (203) 267-4606
Email: sales@proscientific.com
Website: www.proscientific.com
Mfr PRO Scientific laboratory equipment, PRO homogenizers, mixers, shakers & stirrers. Dist Andreas Hettich Centrifuges. (Woman/White, estab 1992, empl 15, sales , cert: State)

Florida

5995 Algon Corporation
12000 SW 132 Court   Miami, FL 33186
(305) 253-6901 Eduardo Suarez-Troconis Director
Fax: (305) 253-6952
Email: edal@algon.com
Website: www.algon.com
Chemical raw materials, laboratory supplies & machine parts. (Woman/Hisp, estab 1989, empl 24, sales $20,570,883, cert: NMSDC)

5996 Kramer Laboratories, Inc.
400 University Dr Ste 400 Coral Gables, FL 33134
(800) 824-4894 Myrna Patterson Sales Mgr
Fax: (305) 223-5510
Email: mpatterson@kramerlabs.com
Website: www.kramerlabs.com
Fungi Nail Brand, Safetussin CD Cough Relief/Nasal Decongestant Formula, Safetussin DM Cough Formula. (Woman/Hisp, estab 1987, empl 14, sales , cert: NMSDC, WBENC)

5997 VetMeds, Inc.
8950 SW 74th Court Ste 2201 Miami, FL 33156
(786) 220-3634 Andria Nelson President
Fax: (786) 513-8096
Email: vetmeds@gmx.com
Website: www.vetmedsinc.biz
Dist medical equipment, medical apparel, wound care supplies, medical furniture, exam room supplies, extrication-patient transport equipment, surgical gloves, IV therapy & laboratory supplies. (Woman/AA, estab 2012, empl 5, sales $65,000, cert: State)

Indiana

5998 Mectra Labs, Inc.
P.O. Box 350   Bloomfield, IN 47424
(812) 384-3521 Lorena Terhune Mktg Mgr
Fax: (812) 384-8518
Email: lorena@mectralabs.com
Website: www.mectralabs.com
Mfr disposable laparoscopic instruments & accessories. (As-Pac, estab 1988, empl 21, sales $2,206,670, cert: NMSDC)

Massachusetts

5999 Cross-Spectrum Acoustics Inc
P.O. Box 90842   Springfield, MA 01139
(413) 315-5770 Herbert Singleton Managing Partner
Fax: (413) 315-5770
Email: dbe@csacoustics.com
Website: www.csacoustics.com
Acoustical consulting, noise and vibration control, sound measurements, noise & vibration mitigation. (AA, estab 2003, empl 1, sales $45,000, cert: State)

Maryland

6000 Quality Biological, Inc.
7581 Lindbergh Dr   Gaithersburg, MD 20879
(301) 840-9331 Basile Whitaker VP Ops
Fax: (301) 840-0743
Email: whitakerb@qualitybiological.com
Website: www.qualitybiological.com
Mfr tissue culture & molecular biology products, bacteriological plates, dist Corning glass & plastics, Corning lab equipment, Microflex gloves & JT Baker chemicals. (Woman/AA, estab 1983, empl 24, sales , cert: NMSDC)

6001 The Perara Group Inc.
1610 Professional Blvd Stes E & F Crofton, MD 21114
(410) 451-4141 Yancey Brown Telecomm Dir
Fax: (410) 451-4410
Email: ybrown@peraragroup.com
Website: www.peraragroup.com
DNA research support, genetic models, bio-analytical chemistry models, metabolism & pharmacokinetics, oncology models, toxicology, lab diagnostics, vaccine & vector safety, bio-safety testing. (Woman/AA, estab 2001, empl 7, sales $1,700,000, cert: State)

6002   Trinity Sterile, Inc.
201 Kiley Dr   Salisbury, MD 21801
(410) 860-5123   Crystal Lutz VP Sales
Fax: (410) 860-2913
Email: crystal.lutz@trinitysterile.com
Website: www.trinitysterile.com
Production & sterilization equipment: clinical kits, trays or instruments. (As-Ind, estab 2004, empl 100, sales , cert: NMSDC)

Michigan

6003   Forensic Fluids Laboratories Inc.
225 Parsons St   Kalamazoo, MI 49007
(269) 492-7700   Bridget Lemberg CEO
Fax: (269) 492-7704
Email: blemberg@forensicfluids.com
Website: www.Forensicfluids.com
Drug testing & screening. (Woman/White, estab 2005, empl 80, sales $19,861,000, cert: WBENC)

6004   RTI Laboratories, Inc.
33080 Industrial Rd   Livonia, MI 48150
(734) 422-8000   Kae Trojanowski President
Fax: (734) 422-5342
Email: ktrojanowski@rtilab.com
Website: www.rtilab.com
Analytical testing laboratory: environmental, chemical & metallurgical testing, environmental compliance field sampling services. (As-Ind, estab 1986, empl 40, sales $5,000,000, cert: NMSDC, SDB)

6005   Structural Testing Laboratory
397 Washington St, Ste B   Brighton, MI 48116
(734) 476-9882   Tracy LaCroix Owner
Fax: (734) 476-9882
Email: sales@stlbrighton.com
Website: www.stlbrighton.com
Vibration & shock testing services for automotive, aerospace & defense, transportation & packaging & military. (Nat Ame, estab 2005, empl 3, sales , cert: NMSDC)

Minnesota

6006   LKT Laboratories, Inc.
545 Phalen Blvd   Saint Paul, MN 55130
(651) 644-8424   Luke Lam President
Fax:
Email: llam@lktlabs.com
Website: www.lktlabs.com/
Mfr biochemicals for life science research, inhibitors, activators, modulators, and many other high purity small molecules, phytochemical isolation and analysis. (As-Pac, estab 1990, empl 11, sales $1,300,000, cert: NMSDC)

Missouri

6007   HERA Laboratory Planners
411 N. Tenth St, Ste 400   St. Louis, MO 63101
(314) 289-9202   Laurie Sperling President
Fax: (314) 289-6167
Email: lauries@herainc.com
Website: www.herainc.com
Laboratory planning, design, programming & equipment planning. (Woman/White, estab 1996, empl 22, sales $4,879,377, cert: State, WBENC)

North Carolina

6008   LJP Lab LLC
495-S Arbor Hill Rd   Kernersville, NC 27284
(336) 992-3902   Thomas Stith President
Fax: (336) 992-3906
Email: tstith@ljplab.com
Website: www.ljplab.com
Urine drug screen & confirmation services. (As-Pac, estab 2017, empl 6, sales $500,000, cert: State)

Nebraska

6009   Midland Scientific Inc.
1202 South 11th St   Omaha, NE 68108
(402) 346-8352   David Ellis VP of Sales
Fax: (402) 346-7694
Email: dellis@midlandsci.com
Website: www.midlandsci.com
Dist lab supplies & equipment. (Woman/White, estab 1975, empl 104, sales , cert: WBENC, NWBOC)

New Jersey

6010   BioRepository Resources, LLC
755 Central Ave, Unit 3   New Providence, NJ 07974
(908) 790-8890   Catherine Chin CEO
Fax: (908) 790-8899
Email: cchin@brr.us.com
Website: www.brr.us.com
Long term storage of biological & clinical trial samples: blood, plasma, urine, tissue, biomarkers, retain drug product, API, pathology slides, blocks. (Woman/As-Pac, estab 2008, empl 2, sales , cert: State)

6011 Laboratory Disposable Products
1 Como Court Towaco, NJ 07082
(973) 335-2966 Cindy Beatty President
Fax: (973) 335-2466
Email: mail@labdisposable.com
Website: www.labdisposable.com
Laboratory Disposable Products. (Woman/White, estab 1979, empl 10, sales $3,549,720, cert: City, WBENC)

6012 Neta Scientific, Inc.
4206 Sylon Blvd Hainesport, NJ 08036
(609) 265-8210 Winfred Sanders, PhD President
Fax: (609) 265-8213
Email: sales@netascientific.com
Website: www.netascientific.com
Dist laboratory instruments & supplies safety & environmental supplies. (Woman/AA, estab 1999, empl 40, sales $56,751,411, cert: State, NMSDC, WBENC)

6013 Sarchem Laboratories, Inc.
5012 Industrial Rd Farmingdale, NJ 07727
(732) 938-2777 Arun Kumar VP
Fax: (732) 938-3777
Email: arun.kumar@sarchemlabs.com
Website: www.sarchemlabs.com
Custom Synthesis, Process development from concept to lab scale preparation, Contract Research and Development. Supply small scale diagnostic reagents, chemical reagents and EPA samples in customer required ampules. (Woman/As-Ind, estab 1984, empl 6, sales $1,215,000, cert: NMSDC)

Ohio

6014 Crawford & Associates Services, LLC
100 E Campus View Blvd Ste 250 Columbus, OH 43235
(614) 557-1498 Troy Crawford Principal
Fax: (614) 438-2626
Email: tcrawford@cas-associates.com
Website: www.cas-associates.com
Commercial & Industrial Commissioning of Mechanical/Electrical/Plumbing Systems, including Heating, Ventilating and Air Conditioning Systems and Building Automatic Temperature Control Systems. (AA, estab 2007, empl 5, sales $293,055, cert: 8(a))

6015 DHDC Engineering Consulting Services, Inc.
2390 Advanced Business Center Dr Columbus, OH 43228
(614) 527-7656 Savvas Sophocleous President
Fax: (614) 527-7489
Email: sophocleous@dhdcinc.com
Website: www.dhdcinc.com
Laboratory testing services, geotechnical (engineering, drilling, and laboratory) & subsurface utility engineering (SUE). (As-Pac, estab 2012, empl 15, sales $500,000, cert: State)

6016 Midtown Scientific, Inc.
4415 Euclid Ave, Ste 343 Cleveland, OH 44103
(216) 431-0110 Darlene Darby Baldwin CEO
Fax: (216) 431-0128
Email: ddarbywatt@aol.com
Website: www.midtownscientific.com
Dist scientific laboratory research supplies & equipment, chemicals. (Woman/AA, estab 2002, empl 4, sales $98,000, cert: City)

6017 Nnodum Pharmaceuticals Corp.
483 Northland Blvd Cincinnati, OH 45240
(513) 861-2329 Nnodum Iheme President
Fax: (513) 861-3629
Email: n.iheme@nnodumpharma.com
Website: www.nnodumpharma.com
Research, development & mfg over the counter & generic pharmaceuticals: prenatal Vitamins, dialysis vitamins, topical analgesics, lotions & creams for diabetic patients. (AA, estab 1997, empl 10, sales $30,000,000, cert: State, 8(a))

Pennsylvania

6018 Hayes
157 S Broad St, Ste 200 Lansdale, PA 19446
(215) 855-0615 Glenn Phillips Dir, Provider Sales
Fax: (215) 855-5218
Email: gphillips@hayesinc.com
Website: www.hayesinc.com
Devices, procedures, drugs/biologics, laboratory equipment & genetic tests. (Woman, estab 1989, empl 60, sales , cert: WBENC)

6019 MB Research Laboratories
1765 Wentz Rd Spinnerstown, PA 18968
(215) 536-4110 Betty Salyer Accts Receivable
Fax:
Email: blandis@mbresearch.com
Website: www.mbresearch.com
Contract Research Toxicology Laboratory. (Hisp, estab 1972, empl 28, sales , cert: WBENC)

Puerto Rico

6020 Instrumed Services Corp.
10th St O 14 Castellana G Carolina, PR 00983
(787) 257-9249 Luis Peña President
Fax:
Email: luis.pena@instrumed.net
Website: www.instrumed.net
Sales, Service, Validation and Calibration of Laboratory Equipments. (Woman/Hisp, estab 1999, empl 10, sales $138,603, cert: NMSDC)

6021   J.C. Gonzalez, Inc.
2 St KM 178.2 Interior BO. Minillas Alto San German, PR 00683
(787) 892-0047 Julio C. Gonzalez Santiago CEO
Fax: (787) 264-3816
Email: sales@jcgonzalezinc.com
Website: www.jcgonzalezinc.com
Dist & service scientific & research equipment, laboratory equipment & consumables, microscopes, stereoscopes, freezers, refrigerators. (Hisp, estab 2001, empl 6, sales $865,047, cert: NMSDC, SDB)

Tennessee

6022   Safety Plus, LLC
P.O. Box 2549 Chattanooga, TN 37409
(423) 822-0487 Alexa Wardlaw VP/Member
Fax: (423) 822-0547
Email: alexa@safetyplusllc.com
Website: www.safetyplusllc.com
Safety solutions: fume hood, biosafety cabinet & clean air bench testing & maintenance, employee training, lab design & equipment recommendations. (Woman/White, estab 2005, empl 7, sales $284,017, cert: WBENC)

6023   Scientific Sales, Inc.
130 Valley Ct   Oak Ridge, TN 37830
(800) 229-7252 Vicki Dyer President
Fax: (865) 483-0241
Email: vdyer@scisale.com
Website: www.scisale.com
Dist laboratory supplies, equipment, chemicals, safety, industrial & environmental products. (Woman/Nat Ame, estab 1987, empl 24, sales , cert: NMSDC)

6024   The Premier Group
4600 Cromwell Ave, Ste 101   Memphis, TN 38118
(901) 346-9002 JW Gibson CEO
Fax: (901) 346-6642
Email: jwgibson@gibsoncompanies.com
Website: www.gibsoncompanies.com
Dist medical supplies, laboratory & scientific equipment & related supplies. (AA, estab 1900, empl 1, sales $8,692,576, cert: NMSDC)

Texas

6025   Food Safety Net Services (FSNS)
199 W Rhapsody   San ANtonio, TX 78216
(210) 308-0675 Timothy Santy Director of Ops
Fax: (210) 525-1702
Email: Tim.Santy@fsns.com
Website: www.fsns.com
Microbiological testing & chemical analysis. (Woman/White, estab 1999, empl 500, sales $33,916,912, cert: WBENC)

6026   Fox Scientific, Inc.
8221 East FM 917   Alvarado, TX 76009
(800) 369-5524 Jetta Lewis Sales
Fax: (817) 783-3571
Email: paisleyg@foxscientific.com
Website: www.foxscientific.com
Dist laboratory supplies, equipment & chemicals. (Hisp, estab 1988, empl 21, sales $5,420,000, cert: State, City, NMSDC)

6027   Pacific Star Corporation
4350 S Wayside Dr STE 106   Houston, TX 77087
(713) 527-0889 Daud Hadi Sales Mgr
Fax: (713) 481-8423
Email: customer@pfstar.com
Website: www.pfstar.com
Industrial supplies, laboratory supplies, medical supplies. (As-Pac, estab 2005, empl 10, sales $4,000,000, cert: City)

6028   Products Unlimited, Inc.
P.O. Box 339 Justin, TX 76247
(940) 648-3073 Susan Raithel Sales Mgr
Fax: (940) 648-3407
Email: sraithel@products-unlimited.com
Website: www.products-unlimited.com
Dist medical, lab & safety supplies & equipment. (Woman/White, estab 1992, empl 7, sales $5,020,000, cert: State)

Virginia

6029   United Lab Company
103 Arrow Ct Ste B Yorktown, VA 23693
(757) 806-6230 Wendy Wood VP
Fax: (757) 257-0073
Email: wendy.wood@unitedlabco.com
Website: www.unitedlabco.com
Laboratory appliances & instruments. (Woman/White, estab 2008, empl 2, sales $1,962,425, cert: State)

Wisconsin

6030   Scientific Molding Corporation, Inc.
330 SMC Dr   Somerset, WI 54025
(715) 247-3500 Rochelle Livingston Paralegal
Fax: (715) 247-3611
Email: rochelle.livingston@smcltd.com
Website: www.smcltd.com
Design, molding & assembly enterprise, project integration, validation & quality controls, packaging & labeling & sterilization management. (As-Ind, estab 1988, empl 1200, sales , cert: State, NMSDC)

Alabama

6031   Springer Equipment Co., Inc.
       4263 Underwood Industrial Dr   Birmingham, AL 35210
       (205) 951-3675 Annette Springer CEO
       Fax:
       Email: annettes@springerequip.com
       Website: www.SpringerEquipment.com
New & used forklift equipment sales, service, parts rentals & leasing. (Woman/White, estab 1992, empl 52, sales $17,696,746, cert: WBENC)

California

6032   Bench-Tek Solutions, LLC
       525 Aldo Ave   Santa Clara, CA 95054
       (408) 653-1100 Maria Castellon CEO
       Fax: (408) 653-1103
       Email: mcastellon@bench-tek.com
       Website: www.bench-tek.com
Custom workbenches, materials handling & storage. (Woman/Hisp, estab 2002, empl 16, sales $4,000,000, cert: NMSDC, CPUC, WBENC)

6033   Can Lines Engineering
       9839 Downey-Norwalk Rd   Downey, CA 90241
       (800) 233-4597 Erik Koplien
       Fax: (562) 869-5293
       Email: erik.koplien@canlines.com
       Website: www.canlines.com
Engineer, design, fabricate, install & service container & material operational & conveying systems. (Hisp, estab 1960, empl 100, sales , cert: NMSDC)

6034   ELA Enterprises
       1813 Lexington Dr   Fullerton, CA 92835
       (714) 738-0397 Lisa alkoraishi President
       Fax:
       Email: lisaa@elaent.com
       Website: www.elaent.com
Design & mfr custom material handling solutions: dollies, service carts, platform trucks, hand trucks, electric tugs, tow vehicles, trailers, food containers, packaging for transportation & storage solutions. (Woman/Hisp, estab 2006, empl 2, sales $115,000, cert: CPUC, WBENC)

6035   Quality Material Handling
       900 W Foothill Blvd   Azusa, CA 91702
       (626) 812-9722 Julia Pinto President
       Fax: (626) 812-6544
       Email: qmh@qmhinc.com
       Website: www.qmhinc.com
Material handling equipment distribution & services, pallet racking, boltless shelving, yard ramps, warehouse racks, pallet rack installation, city permits, high pile & fire permits. (Woman/Hisp, estab 1991, empl 40, sales , cert: CPUC)

Colorado

6036   Advanced Manufacturing Technology For Bottles, Inc.
       3920 Patton Ave   Loveland, CO 80538
       (970) 612-0315 Jamie Maier Accting
       Fax: (970) 612-0320
       Email: jmaier@amtcolorado.com
       Website: www.amtcolorado.com
Mfr conveyor systems, integrated systems, conveyors, controls & mechanical & electrical installation services, primarily for the packaging industry. (Woman/White, estab 1996, empl 57, sales , cert: WBENC)

Connecticut

6037   Warner Specialty Products, Inc.
       40-B Montowese Ave   North Haven, CT 06473
       (203)69030 Jack Norton VP
       Fax: (203)69023
       Email: amy@warnerspecialty.com
       Website: www.warnerspecialty.com
Dist material handling & ergonomic equipment solutions. (Woman/White, estab 1991, empl 8, sales $4,228,000, cert: WBENC)

Florida

6038   BMG Conveyor Services of Florida Inc
       5010 16th Ave S   Tampa, FL 33619
       (813) 247-3620 Stephenie Davis Director
       Fax: (813) 248-5716
       Email: sdavis@bmgtampa.com
       Website: www.bmgtampa.com
Conveyor services, hot vulcanizing conveyor belting. (Woman/White, estab 1970, empl 11, sales $1,625,000, cert: City, WBENC)

6039 TriFactor Solutions, LLC
2401 Drane Field Rd Lakeland, FL 33811
(863) 646-9671 JJ Phelan Managing Member
Fax: (863) 644-8329
Email: jjphelan@TriFactor.com
Website: www.trifactor.com
Material handling systems, services, parts & integrations: conveyors, racking, palletizers, diverters, storage systems, pallets, work stations. (Woman/White, estab 2007, empl 25, sales $756,831, cert: State, WBENC)

Georgia

6040 Atlanta Caster & Equipment
1810-E Auger Dr Tucker, GA 30084
(770) 492-0682 John Brumbaugh Govt Sales Mgr
Fax: (770) 492-9210
Email: atlantacaster@atlantacaster.com
Website: www.atlantacaster.com
Dist casters, wheels & non-powered material handling equipment. (Woman/White, estab 1986, empl 8, sales $2,010,000, cert: WBENC)

6041 Material Handling Inc.
P.O. Box 1045 Dalton, GA 30722
(706) 278-1104 William Gleaton CFO
Fax: (706) 278-0460
Email: billgleaton@mhiusa.net
Website: www.mhiusa.net
New & used lift trucks, lift truck parts, service, maintenance, rental & leasing. (As-Ind, estab 1975, empl 93, sales $28,444,451, cert: NMSDC)

Illinois

6042 Midway Industrial Equipment Inc..
660 Heartland Dr Sugar Grove, IL 60554
(630) 466-7700 Dawn Adams President
Fax: (630) 466-8484
Email: dawn@midwaylift.com
Website: www.midwaylift.com
Material Handling Services, sales, service, rental & parts for forklifts, scrubbers, aerial. (Woman/White, estab 2003, empl 60, sales $10,500,000, cert: State)

6043 Stevenson Crane Service, Inc.
410 Stevenson Dr Bolingbrook, IL 60440
(630) 972-9199 Donna Stevenson President
Fax: (630) 972-0303
Email: donna@stevensoncrane.com
Website: www.stevensoncrane.com
Material handling equipment: truck cranes, carrydeck cranes, crawler cranes, rough terrain cranes, material & personnel hoists, material handlers, scissor lifts & boom lifts. (Woman/White, estab 1989, empl 85, sales $17,779,999, cert: WBENC)

Indiana

6044 Courtney Material Handling, Inc.
P.O. Box 6925 South Bend, IN 46660
(574) 231-0094 Beth Courtney President
Fax: (574) 231-0736
Email: beth@cmhionline.com
Website: www.cmhionline.com
Dist safety items: hard hats, vests, safety glasses, gloves, tools, fire & detection, bins, cabinets, carts, casters, chairs & stools. (Woman/White, estab 2003, empl 2, sales $213,673, cert: State)

6045 Handling Technologies, Inc.
51024 Portage Road South Bend, IN 46628
(866) 518-8108 Scott Fowler VP
Fax: (866) 518-5816
Email: sfowler@handlingtechnologies.com
Website: www.HandlingTechnologies.com
Dist material handling products - shelving, racking systems, decking, conveyor systems, shop equipment (i.e., carts, bins, tables, hoists). (Woman, estab , empl 12, sales , cert: WBENC)

6046 Harriman Material Handling
511 N Range Line Rd Morristown, IN 46161
(765) 763-8985 Ashley Larochelle President
Fax: (765) 763-8986
Email: ashlar@harrimanmaterialhandling.com
Website: www.HarrimanMaterialHandling.com
Overhead Cranes, Hoists, Jib Cranes, Monorails, Gantry Cranes, Custom Lifting Devices, Slings/Rigging, Fall Protection Equipment, Crane Components & Parts, Dock Equipment, Storage Equipment, Drum Handling Equipment (Woman/White, estab 2004, empl 5, sales $3,528,300, cert: WBENC)

6047 Meyer Material Handling Products Inc.
P.O. Box 47366 Indianapolis, IN 46247
(317) 786-9214 Carolyn F. Meyer Chairman
Fax: (317) 788-3784
Email: cfmeyer@meyermat.com
Website: www.meyermat.com
Material handling equipment. (Woman/White, estab 1974, empl 11, sales , cert: WBENC)

Michigan

6048 Brooks & Perkins, Inc. dba B&P Manufacturing
8051 E Boon Rd Cadillac, MI 49601
(231) 306-3828 Lia K. Lipar Dir Military Sales & Contracts
Fax: (231) 775-0013
Email: lia.krantz@bpmfg.com
Website: www.bpmfgdefense.com
Mfr heavy duty aluminum material handling equipment: hand trucks, convertible dollies & brake trucks, dock boards & dock plates. (Woman/White, estab 1995, empl 65, sales $11,747,633, cert: State)

6049 Dynamic Conveyor Corp
5980 Grand Haven Rd Muskegon, MI 49441
(800) 640-6850 Tracy Powers Business Devel
Fax:
Email: tpowers@dynamicconveyor.com
Website: www.dynamicconveyor.com
Quality built radius turns, metal detection, clean room, water tanks, cooling fans, box filling, split belt, ergonomic tilt, etc. (Woman, estab 1991, empl 24, sales $5,700,000, cert: WBENC)

6050 ECI Unlimited, Inc.
110 Trealout Dr Ste 102 Fenton, MI 48430
(810) 354-2775 Lance Stokes President
Fax: 248-360-40
Email: powertrain@ecienv.com
Website: www.ecipowertrain.webs.com
Install & refurbish material handling & machine loading & unloading equipment: chain conveyors, roller conveyors, pallet conveyors, accumulating conveyors, overhead conveyors, inverted conveyors, skillet conveyors, assembly machines. (AA, estab 1993, empl 4, sales $40,000, cert: NMSDC)

6051 Econobuild, LLC
21060 Bridge St Southfield, MI 48033
(248) 799-7500 Ramiro Salazar Managing Member
Fax: (248) 356-0349
Email: rsalazar@econobuild.com
Website: www.econobuild.com
Material handling equip: flow-thru racks, rack systems, industrial carts, fork-free environment, plant engineering, facility improvements. (As-Pac, estab 1999, empl 15, sales $3,100,000, cert: NMSDC)

6052 Technical Conveyor Group, Inc.
5918 Meridian Blvd. Ste 2 Brighton, MI 48116
(810) 229-5811 Rob Tarrien President
Fax: (810) 229-5811
Email: rtarrien@tcginc.org
Website: www.tcginc.org
Material handling systems: floor conveyors, overhead/inverted power & free systems, chain-on-edge systems, AGV, electrified monorails, indexing systems, AS/AR systems. (Nat Ame, estab 2000, empl 5, sales $650,956, cert: NMSDC)

6053 Ultimation Industries LLC
27930 Groesbeck Hwy Roseville, MI 48066
(586) 771-1881 Jacqueline Canny CEO
Fax: (586) 771-1882
Email: jcanny@ultimationinc.com
Website: www.ultimationinc.com
Design, mfr & install assembly line equipment & services, automation devices & conveyor systems, tire & wheel mounting & inflation devices, tire processing lines, TPMS & soaping machines. (Woman/White, estab 1989, empl 14, sales $4,855,120, cert: WBENC)

6054 Valmec Inc.
1274 S Holly Rd Fenton, MI 48430
(810) 629-8750 Krystn Tatus CEO
Fax: (810) 629-3522
Email: valmec@comcast.net
Website: www.valmecinc.com
Material handling & packaging, conveyors, returnable packaging, installation, tear-outs & complete system integration. (Woman/White, estab 1971, empl 5, sales $1,344,664, cert: WBENC)

Minnesota

6055 J & B Equipment Company, Inc.
8200 Grand Ave S Bloomington, MN 55420
(952) 884-2040 David Heggem VP/COO
Fax:
Email: office@jbeq.com
Website: www.jbeq.com
Design & sell engineered overhead crane & monorail systems; hoists; lift tables; specialty carts; and engineered ergonomic material handling systems. (AA/As-Pac, estab 1961, empl 10, sales , cert: NMSDC)

Missouri

6056 C&B Lift Truck Service, Inc.
6250 Knox Industrial Dr High Ridge, MO 63049
(314) 781-5438 Melinda Barbaglia Owner
Fax: (314) 781-5630
Email: sales@cbforklift.com
Website: www.cbforklift.com
Dist & service forklifts, aerial/scissor lifts, sweepers, scrubbers, golf carts, dollies, dock equipment, warehouse & distribution equipment (Woman/White, estab 1976, empl 12, sales $1,000,000, cert: State)

North Carolina

6057 Guna Enterprises, Inc.
1104 Commercial Ave Charlotte, NC 28205
(704) 358-8787 Sales
Fax: (704) 358-8788
Email: info@GandRcasters.com
Website: www.gandrcasters.com
Mfr industrial, institutional, special & custom made casters, wheels & floor locks. (Woman/As-Ind, estab 1994, empl 60, sales $2,400,000, cert: State)

6058　WARP Services, LLC
1316 Providence Rd   Charlotte, NC 28207
(888) 547-9277 Dr. Patrick LaRive CEO
Fax: (413) 541-7742
Email: patrick@warprobotics.com
Website: www.warprobotics.com
Intall, repair & replace conveyors, motors, compressors, electrical safety equip, material handling, industrial robotics, laser navigation, anything mechanical or electrical. (Woman/AA, estab 2005, empl 4, sales $298,000, cert: State, NWBOC)

New Jersey

6059　Hu-Lift Equipment
400 Apgar Dr, Unit F   Somerset, NJ 08873
(908) 874-5585 Ming Gang Guo Mgr
Fax:
Email: mgguo@hu-liftusa.com
Website: www.hu-liftusa.com
Dist material handling products: lift table, cart, platform trucks, furniture movers, skid lifters, highlifts, scale jacks, hydraulic jacks, skates,pallet trucks, industrial class portable air conditioners, pallet tilters, forklift jacks. (As-Pac, estab 1999, empl 5, sales , cert: State)

6060　JDB Equipment Company, Inc.
116 W Almond St   Vineland, NJ 08360
(856) 264-0314 Jennifer Sexton President
Fax: (856) 691-4071
Email: jdbequipment@hotmail.com
Website:
Rent scissor lifts, boom lifts, aerial lifts, man lifts, forklifts & aerial work platforms. (Woman/White, estab 2001, empl 3, sales $592,000, cert: State)

Ohio

6061　Caster Connection, Inc.
2380 International St   Columbus, OH 43228
(800) 544-8978 Joe Lyden Director of Sales
Fax: (888) 852-7202
Email: joe.lyden@casterconnection.com
Website: www.casterconnection.com
Mfr & dist institutional & industrial casters and wheels, hand trucks, pallet jacks, dollies & manual materials handling products. (Woman/White, estab 1987, empl 36, sales , cert: WBENC)

6062　MYCA Material Handling Solutions, Inc.
4555 Lake Forest Dr Ste 650 Cincinnati, OH 45242
(513) 608-6033 Patricia Massey President
Fax: (888) 699-9794
Email: pmassey@mycagroup.com
Website: www.mycagroup.com
Material handling equipment, lift trucks, safety programs & safety equipment, training, warehouse systems, conveyor systems. (Woman/White, estab 2004, empl 38, sales $4,600,000, cert: WBENC)

6063　WHM Equipment Co.
11775 Enterprise Ave   Cincinnati, OH 45241
(513) 771-3200 Joan Morgan President
Fax: (513) 771-3244
Email: joan@whmequipment.com
Website: www.whmequipment.com
Design, fabricate & assemble conveyors & material handling systems. (Woman/White, estab 1968, empl 12, sales $1,920,869, cert: WBENC)

Pennsylvania

6064　Shingle Belting
420 Drew Ct   King of Prussia, PA 19406
(610) 239-6667 Jeff Jensen
Fax: (610) 239-6668
Email: jjensen@shinglebelting.com
Website: www.shinglebelting.com
Dist industrial conveyors & power transmission belting. (Woman/White, estab 1979, empl 31, sales , cert: WBENC)

Tennessee

6065　Southfork Lift Truck, Inc.
3070 Sidco Dr   Nashville, TN 37204
(615) 647-9615 Jennifer Dickson Mktg Mgr
Fax: (615) 840-6185
Email: jennifer.dickson@southforklifttruck.com
Website: www.SouthforkLiftTruck.com
Forklift & material handling equipment sales, service, parts, rentals & leasing. (Woman/White, estab 2014, empl 10, sales $1,700,000, cert: State, WBENC)

Texas

6066　Casters of Amarillo Inc.
1520 S Polk St   Amarillo, TX 79101
(806) 373-2884 Karen Hicks President
Fax: (806) 373-7544
Email: karenh@casterama.com
Website: www.casterama.com
Dist material handling equipment: casters & industrial wheels, freight, dock & warehouse equipment, drum handling equipment, wire & steel shelving & pallet rack, steel & aluminum hand trucks, appliance trucks & specialty hand trucks. (Woman/White, estab 1974, empl 5, sales $649,054, cert: State)

6067   Design Associates International, Inc
       11615 Forest Central Dr, Ste 101   Dallas, TX 75243
       (214) 720-6083 Lucia Fredenburgh President
       Fax: (214) 979-9006
       Email: luciaf@daiinc.com
       Website: www.daiinc.com
Dist materials handling equipment: casters, wheels, carts, dollies, hand trucks, facilities planning & design. (Woman/Hisp, estab 1994, empl 8, sales $1,250,000, cert: State)

6068   Mighty Lift Inc.
       PO Box 14998 Portland, OR 97238 Houston, TX 77221
       (713) 668-0263 Helen Fu President
       Fax: (713) 668-1965
       Email: helenfu@mightylift.com
       Website: www.mightylift.com
Dist pallet jacks, lifting tables, hand trucks, casters and wheels, wire containers, wire partitions, pallet racks & guard rails, electric personnel & burden carriers & scooters. (Woman/As-Pac, estab 2002, empl 15, sales $4,042,931, cert: State, NMSDC, WBENC)

6069   Permian Machinery Movers Inc.
       2200 W Interstate 20   Odessa, TX 79763
       (432) 333-1777 Robert M. Chavez President
       Fax: (432) 580-3777
       Email: robert@permianmachineryinc.com
       Website: www.permianmachineryinc.com
Dist, rent & lease forklifts. (Hisp, estab 1981, empl 45, sales $11,100,000, cert: State)

6070   Texas Storage Systems
       P.O. Box 751632   Houston, TX 77075
       (713) 991-1089 Karen Cato Owner
       Fax: (713) 991-3971
       Email: tssinc@ymail.com
       Website: www.catoindustries.com
Material handling & warehouse equipment. (Woman/AA, estab 2010, empl 5, sales $100,000, cert: State)

6071   Walter Terry Distributor, Inc.
       2420 LOUISIANA A111   Houston, TX 77006
       (713) 227-6369 Fairlynn Ryberg President
       Fax: (713) 223-5805
       Email: lryberg@WTstraps.com
       Website: www.wtstraps,com
Material Handling Equipment, Cargo Control Systems, vending trucks, appliance trucks, dollies, ramps, bars, nets, furniture pads, plastic mattress & furniture bags, packaging items, Load Control/Protection items & Wheelchair Restraint. (Woman/White, estab 1965, empl 3, sales $863,762, cert: State, City)

Utah

6072   Conveyors & Equipment, Inc.
       3580 S 300 W   Salt Lake City, UT 84115
       (801) 263-1843 Ginger Goyzueta President
       Fax: (801) 266-6727
       Email: goyzuetag@conveyequip.com
       Website: www.conveyequip.com
Conveyor design, service & installation, Conveyor belt supply, service & installation, Material handling equipment, Ergonomic solutions. (Woman, estab 1972, empl 32, sales $6,600,000, cert: State)

Washington

6073   Washington Liftruck
       700 S Chicago   Seattle, WA 98108
       (206) 762-2040 Jeff Darling VP
       Fax: (206) 767-6280
       Email: darling@forkliftsamerica.com
       Website: www.washingtonlift.com
Dist forklifts & material handling equipment. (Woman/White, estab 1973, empl 34, sales $21,260,000, cert: City, WBENC)

MEASURING INSTRUMENTS
Manufacturers and distributors of counters and timers, X-ray spectrometers, voltage and frequency indicators, gas analyzers, thermocouples, thermometers, etc. (See also OPTICAL EQUIPMENT, ELECTRONIC categories and HARDWARE & TOOLS). NAICS Code 42

Alaska

6074   Delta Leasing LLC
       8101 Dimond Hook Dr   Anchorage, AK 99507
       (907) 771-1300 Sam Amato VP
       Fax: (907) 771-1380
       Email: lmorgan@deltaleasing.com
       Website: www.deltaleasing.com
Delta Leasing provides professional commercial leasing services of vehicles, equipment for major industries including oil and gas, construction, mining, as well as many others. (Nat Ame, estab 2002, empl 32, sales $13,000,000, cert: NMSDC)

California

6075   Alloy Valves and Control
       3210 S Susan St   Santa Ana, CA 92704
       (714) 427-0877 Phyllis Abrams Dir of Sales & Mktg
       Fax: (714) 427-6392
       Email: pabrams@avcovalve.com
       Website: www.avcovalve.com
Design & mfr ball valves & flow measurement products, manual & automated ball valve assemblies. (Woman, estab 2000, empl 15, sales , cert: State)

6076   Brylen Technologies
       275 Orange Ave   Santa Barbara, CA 93117
       (805) 692-9300 Barbara Tzur President
       Fax: (805) 692-1966
       Email: barbara.tzur@brylen.com
       Website: www.brylen.com
Calibration & testing laboratory, clean room & clean bench certifications, calibration is electro-magnetic, thermodynamics, dimensional, angle, & mechanical areas, calibrate equipment. (Woman/White, estab 1985, empl 10, sales $519,692, cert: State)

6077   RHF, Inc.
       16202 Keats Circle   Westminster, CA 92683
       (714) 848-9367 Robert Friesen President
       Fax: (714) 848-4028
       Email: rhf.radar@earthlink.net
       Website: www.radaretc.com
Repair & calibration of speed radar & lidar equipment. (Woman/White, estab 1983, empl 3, sales $300,000, cert: State)

6078   STB Electrical Test Equipment, Inc.
       1666 Auburn Ravine Rd   Auburn, CA 95603
       (530) 823-5111 Patricia Tavare President
       Fax: (530) 823-2971
       Email: pat@stbinc.com
       Website: www.stbinc.com
Mfr phasing voltmeters, voltage detectors, voltage sensors, ground detectors, clamp-on ammeters, phase rotation meters, ground cable testers, drain tools. (Woman/White, estab 1979, empl 6, sales $1,329,220, cert: State, CPUC)

6079   Vanguard Instruments Company, Inc.
       1520 S. Hellman Ave   Ontario, CA 91761
       (513) 477-2965 Timm Smith Natl Sales Mgr
       Fax: (909) 923-9391
       Email: timm.s@vanguard-instruments.com
       Website: www.vanguard-instruments.com
Mfr measuring & testing electricity & electrical signal instruments. (As-Pac, estab 1993, empl 11, sales , cert: CPUC)

Connecticut

6080   Environics, Inc.
       69 Industrial Park Rd E   Tolland, CT 06084
       (860) 872-1111 Cathy Dunn CEO
       Fax: (860) 870-9333
       Email: cdunn@environics.com
       Website: www.environics.com
Design, mfr, dist & service computerized gas flow instruments, gas mixing systems, gas on-demand systems, gas calibration systems, gas dilution systems, gas flow management systems. (Woman/White, estab 1986, empl 20, sales $3,000,000, cert: State)

Florida

6081   Diverse Services USA, Inc.
       11111 N 46th St   Tampa, FL 33617
       (813) 988-6000 Michael Schmidt VP
       Fax: (818) 885-5855
       Email: michael.schmidt@diverseservicesusa.com
       Website: www.diverseservicesusa.com
Mfr & install all signs: interior, exterior, graphics, LED message centers, millwork (counters, cabinetry), architectural imaging (ACM panel systems, awnings) and lighting (general illumination, specialty/accent, energy savings (Hisp, estab 2009, empl 650, sales $152,000,000, cert: NMSDC)

6082   Technical Maintenance Inc.
       P.O. Box 76010   Tarpon Springs, FL 34688
       (727) 526-3200   Michael Floyd VP
       Fax: (727) 526-4150
       Email: Michael.Floyd@tmicalibration.com
       Website: www.tmicalibration.com
Calibrate test & measurement equipment (Woman/White,
estab 1991, empl 140, sales , cert: WBENC)

Georgia

6083   Georgia Time Recorder Co., Inc.
       722 Collins Hill Rd Ste H-283 Lawrenceville, GA
       30046
       (770) 444-2879 Andrea Drath President
       Fax: (678) 407-4145
       Email: Andrea@GeorgiaTime.com
       Website: www.georgiatime.com
Time & Attendance, Time clocks, Wireless Synchronized
clocks & master clocks, Temperature Sensors, temp/
humidity sensors, CO2 sensors, emergency lighting, event
monitoring. (Woman/White, estab 1982, empl 6, sales
$550,000, cert: WBENC)

Illinois

6084   B&B Instruments, Inc.
       145 W Taft Dr   South Holland, IL 60473
       (708) 596-1700 Wesley Yee President
       Fax: (708) 596-1755
       Email: wesyee@bbinstruments.com
       Website: www.bbinstruments.com
Dist pressure, temperature, level, flow, humidity gauges &
instrumentation, NiST shop calibrations, testing type
calibrators. (As-Pac, estab 1972, empl 100, sales , cert:
NMSDC)

6085   Connor-Winfield Corp.
       2111 Comprehensive Dr   Aurora, IL 60505
       (630) 851-4722 Gordon Olp Reg sales Mgr
       Fax: (630) 851-5040
       Email: golp@conwin.com
       Website: www.conwin.com
Quartz crystals, oscillators & timing synchronization
modules. (Woman/White, estab 1963, empl 250, sales
$20,050,000, cert: CPUC)

Indiana

6086   AFC International
       PO Box 894   DeMotte, IN 46310
       (219) 987-6825 Pamela Seneczko
       Fax: (219) 987-6826
       Email: pjseneczko@afcintl.com
       Website: www.afcintl.com
Gas detectors, respiratory protection, detector tubes,
self contained breathing apparatus, heat stress monitors, CO detectors, toxic gas detectors. (Woman/White,
estab 1992, empl 6, sales $3,000,000, cert: WBENC)

6087   The CREW Corporation
       7768 Zionsville Rd Ste 150 Indianapolis, IN 46268
       (317) 713-7777 Kathy Reehling President
       Fax: (317) 713-7701
       Email: kreehling@crewcorp.com
       Website: www.crewcorp.com
Validation services: qualification testing & validation,
change control, FAT & SAT, IQ/OQ/PQ protocols &
execution, instrument calibration, supporting documentation. (Woman/White, estab 1992, empl 85, sales
$7,263,156, cert: State, WBENC)

Louisiana

6088   A-T Specialties, LLC
       P.O. Box 4157   New Orleans, LA 70178
       (504) 828-1424 Tony Asberry, Jr President
       Fax: (504) 831-4664
       Email: tony.asberry@atspecialties.com
       Website: www.atspecialties.com
Dist measurement & controls, level, pressure, temperature, flow & position. (AA, estab 2002, empl 2, sales
$1,350,000, cert: State)

Michigan

6089   Hines Industries, Inc.
       793 Airport Blvd. Ann Arbor, MI 48108
       (734) 769-2300 Beverly Monge Sales Admin
       Fax: (734) 996-9192
       Email: ddonall@hinesindustries.com
       Website: www.hinesindustries.com
Balancing machines, rebuild balancing equipment &
balancing instrumentation services, balancing equipment design innovation & manufacturing process
improvement. (Woman/White, estab 1971, empl 25,
sales $8,400,000, cert: WBENC)

6090   M & B Holdings, LLC
       5594 E Ten Mile Rd   Warren, MI 48091
       (586) 427-9971 Brian McMillan GM
       Fax: (586) 427-9974
       Email: bmcmillan@gsnscorp.com
       Website:
Gage Commodity Management, Gage Purchasing, Gage
Design & Manufacturing. (As-Ind, estab 2005, empl 31,
sales $4,420,017, cert: NMSDC)

6091   Omni-Tech Sales, Inc.
       31189 Schoolcraft Rd   Livonia, MI 48150
       (734) 425-5730 Deborah Denne CEO
       Fax: (734) 261-6337
       Email: omnitech_sales@ameritech.net
       Website: www.omnitech-sales.com
Dist precision measuring equipment, CMM's, Vision
Systems, Roundness & Form Measurement, Surface Finish
equipment & fixturing, Hardness Testers, Optical Compara-
tors. (Woman/White, estab 1988, empl 6, sales
$3,975,637, cert: WBENC)

6092   River City Metrology LLC
       2215 29th St SE, Ste B1   Grand Rapids, MI 49508
       (616) 530-4899 Victor Barker Owner
       Fax: (616) 530-4891
       Email: vbarker@rcmetrology.com
       Website: www.rcmetrology.com
Dimensional Inspection, CMM calibration & sales, Dimensional inspection product sales. (As-Pac, estab 2004, empl
5, sales , cert: NMSDC)

6093   Standard Scale & Supply Co.
       25421 Glendale   Redford, MI 48239
       (313) 255-6700 John Bowman GM
       Fax: (313) 255-6799
       Email: jbowman@standardscale.com
       Website: www.standardscale.com
Dist & service weight-based measuring equipment &
accessories. (Hisp, estab 1946, empl 12, sales $2,000,000,
cert: NMSDC)

6094   Universal Tool Equipment & Controls, Inc.
       6525 Center Dr   Sterlng Heights, MI 48312
       (586) 268-4380 Bill Bartolotta VP
       Fax: (586) 803-8329
       Email: bbartolotta@universaltecinc.com
       Website: www.universaltecinc.com
Automation & welding systems, robotics, weld guns, vision
systems, sealant systems, drawn arc welders, projection
welders, material handling end effectors & welding
fixtures. (Woman/AA, estab 2009, empl 29, sales
$10,000,000, cert: WBENC)

North Carolina

6095   Measurement Controls, Inc.
       P.O. Box 562775   Charlotte, NC 28256
       (704) 921-1101 Paresh Patel President
       Fax: (704) 921-1010
       Email: sales@measurementcontrols.com
       Website: www.measurementcontrols.com
Refurbish, mfr & dist rotary, diaphragms & turbine gas
meters, meter sets with regulators, filters & by-pass,
install index, connections, swivels, nuts, & washers,
electro mechanical correctors, dust caps & blind disc.
(As-Ind, estab 1999, empl 9, sales $400,000, cert: State,
City, NMSDC)

Ohio

6096   AVM Industries
       30505 Bainbridge Rd, Ste 100   Solon, OH 44139
       (440) 349-1849 Linda Holt Dir
       Fax: (440) 349-8589
       Email: lholt@hawthornmc.com
       Website: www.avminc.com
Mfr & dist climate control actuators & counterbalancing
systems for the automotive, commercial & aftermarket
industries. (As-Pac, estab 2006, empl 376, sales
$34,000,000, cert: NMSDC)

6097   Cincinnati Control Dynamics Inc.
       4924 Para Dr   Cincinnati, OH 45237
       (513) 242-7300 Jeff Bao President
       Fax: (513) 242-5691
       Email: jbao@ccdi1.com
       Website: www.airflowmachines.com
Non-destructive air flow test equipment for
turbine engines, customized air flow solutions, nacelle
testing, leak testing & pressure testers. (As-Pac, estab
1977, empl 10, sales $1,900,000, cert: State)

6098   Cooper Atkins
       11353 Reed Hartman Hwy Ste 110 Cincinnati, OH
       45241
       (847) 373-2033 Glenn Marcus Sr VP sales
       Fax: (847) 715-9624
       Email: gmarcus@cooper-atkins.com
       Website: www.cooper-atkins.com
Wireless temperature / environmental monitoring
systems, software, hardware, installation & support.
(Woman/White, estab 1900, empl 140, sales , cert:
WBENC)

6099 Intek, Inc.
751 Intek Way   Westerville, OH 43082
(614) 895-0301 Audrey Myers Cstmr Service
Fax: (614) 895-0319
Email: amyers@intekflow.com
Website: www.intekflow.com
Mfr & dist thermal low flow meters & switches, measures liquid flow rates, also mfr RheoVac line of vacuum monitoring equipment. (As-Pac, estab 1976, empl 20, sales , cert: City)

Puerto Rico

6100 Instrumentation Corps, Inc.
P.O. Box 2116   Barceloneta, PR 00617
(787) 970-0746 Juan Oliveras President
Fax: (787) 970-0759
Email: jaoliver@instrumentationcorps.com
Website: www.instrumentationcorps.com
Process instrumentation & weight scales sales, installation, configuration, calibration & certification svcs, equipment repair & technical services. (Hisp, estab 1998, empl 40, sales $4,851,214, cert: NMSDC)

6101 PAS Technologies, Inc.
9 Pedro Arzuaga W   Carolina, PR 00984
1 787-752-2370 Alfredo Agelviz President
Fax:
Email: alfredo.agelviz@pastechnologies.com
Website: www.pastechnologies.com
Dist & service instrumentation & control products. (Hisp, estab 1993, empl 3, sales $1,300,000, cert: NMSDC)

Texas

6102 DDLS Group, LLC
5734 Trowbridge   El Paso, TX 79925
(915) 881-0281 Dalia De Los Santos Owner
Fax: (915) 881-0280
Email: dalia@fas-tes.com
Website:
- Drug & Alcohol Policy Development - Workplace Drug Screen Programs - Random Drug Screen Programs - Urine & Saliva Drug Screens
- BAT Breath Alcohol Testing - Post Accident Testing - Background Checks (Woman/Hisp, estab 2012, empl 1, sales , cert: State, NMSDC)

Wisconsin

6103 Precision Metrology, Inc.
7350 N Teutonia Ave   Milwaukee, WI 53209
(414) 351-7420 Carol Shipley President
Fax: (414) 351-7429
Email: carol@precisionmetrology.com
Website: www.precisionmetrology.com
Calibrate & repaire precision measuring instruments. (Woman/White, estab 1980, empl 93, sales , cert: WBENC)

> ## MEDICAL SUPPLIES & SERVICES
> Manufacturers and distributors of over the counter drugs, dental supplies, diagnostic equipment and supplies, glass containers, labwear, veterinary products, latex, hospital supplies & apparel, etc. NAICS Code 32

Alabama

6104 Hygia Health Services, Inc.
434 Industrial Lane   Birmingham, AL 35211
(865) 755-3181 Glenn Chenot Natl Business Dir
Fax: (205) 314-3959
Email: glenn.chenot@hygia.net
Website: www.hygia.net
Reprocessed, non-invasive, non-critical medical devices. (Woman/White, estab 1999, empl 120, sales $3,000,000, cert: State)

6105 Medical Place
350 Industrial Park Blvd.   Montomery, AL 36117
(334) 241-0807 Shanavian Strickland
Fax: (334) 262-8576
Email: sstrickland@medicalplace.net
Website: www.medicalplace.net
Dist medical, laboratory, respiratory, scientific, telemedicine equipement & supplies. (AA, estab 1983, empl 25, sales $22,100,000, cert: NMSDC)

6106 VELOX Integration Services, LLC
600 S Court St, Ste 322   Montgomery, AL 36104
(334) 233-3328 Sherrell Love CEO
Fax: (334) 613-2813
Email: sherrell@veloxintegration.com
Website: www.veloxintegration.com
Dist medical supplies & equipment, construction management. (Woman/AA, estab 2014, empl 2, sales , cert: State)

Arizona

6107 CJPS Healthcare Supplies & Equipment LLC
14201 N Hayden Rd Bldg B4 Scottsdale, AZ 85260
(480) 939-4362 Christophe Sevrain President
Fax: (480) 939-5010
Email: christophe@cjps-healthcare.com
Website: www.CJPS-Healthcare.com
Dist VitalPoint remote monitoring system, enables comprehensive measurement across 9 vitals in one device. (Woman/As-Pac, estab 2009, empl 10, sales $250,000, cert: NMSDC)

6108 Magnum Medical LLC
3265 N Nevada St Chandler, AZ 85225
(800) 336-9710 Omar Hameed Mktg Dir
Fax: (480) 633-2525
Email: ohameed@magnummed.com
Website: www.magnummed.com
Import & dist surgical instruments, plastic instruments & related items. (As-Ind, estab 1984, empl 9, sales $3,000,000, cert: NMSDC)

California

6109 Abell Marketing Group, Inc.
15057 Avenida De Las Flores   Chino Hills, CA 91709
(909) 456-8905 James Lohan Project Mgr
Fax: (888) 304-1065
Email: james@abellmarketinggroup.com
Website: www.abellmarketinggroup.com
Protective clothing & medical/industrial nitrile, vinyl & latex gloves. (Woman/White, estab 1998, empl 2, sales $375,000, cert: WBENC)

6110 Active Potential Inc.
7898 Ostrow St Ste G San Diego, CA 92111
(858) 292-4128 Anna Pollard CEO
Fax: (858) 292-4833
Email: anna@activepotentialmedical.com
Website: www.activepotentialmedical.com
Safety devices, Arc Flash protection, Emergency & Exam room supplies, Emergency preparedness, Ergonomics, Eye protection & accessories, Fall protection, Fire protection, Safety storage, Work wear, Gloves & hand protection. (Woman/AA, estab 2006, empl 7, sales $247,300, cert: NMSDC, CPUC)

6111 Advanced ImmunoChemical, Inc.
111 W Ocean Blvd, 4th Fl   Long Beach, CA 90802
(562) 434-4676 Anne Tolles, M.Sc. President
Fax:
Email: atolles@advimmuno.com
Website: www.advimmuno.com
Mfr laboratory reagents for In vitro diagnostics & research, Cardiac Disease, Tumor Markers, Metabolic Syndrome, Inflammation, Emerging Infectious Diseases, Biowarfare Threats, Hormones, Autoimmune Disease, Neuroscience. (Woman/White, estab 1986, empl 2, sales $58,500, cert: WBENC)

6112 Ames Medical Equipment, Inc.
301 N Jackson Ave, Ste 7A   San Jose, CA 95133
(408) 942-9000 Mike Patel Treasurer
Fax: (408) 251-1015
Email: mspatel101@hotmail.com
Website: www.AlliancemedsupplyCom
Dist durable medical equipment & supplies. (Woman/As-Pac, estab 2005, empl 2, sales $40,000, cert: State)

6113 Axiom Medical, Inc.
19320 Van Ness Ave   Torrance, CA 90501
(310) 533-9020 Denisse Blanc
Fax: (310) 533-8127
Email: sales@axiommed.com
Website: www.axiommed.com
Mfr silicone & PVC disposable wound drainage catheters. (Woman, estab 1976, empl 25, sales , cert: State)

6114 BioMed Resources Inc.
      6646 Doolittle Ave   Riverside, CA 92503
      (310) 323-3888 Lisa Liu CEO
      Fax: (951) 343-8888
      Email: lisal@bmres.com
      Website: www.bmres.com
Dist specimen containers, transfer pipettes, conical tubes, irrigation syringes, lab jackets, lab coats, isolation gowns & cover gowns. (Woman/As-Pac, estab 2002, empl 15, sales $4,300,000, cert: NMSDC)

6115 Broadline Medical, Inc.
      2100 Atlas Rd, Ste E   Richmond, CA 94806
      (510) 662-5270 Georgia W. Richardson President
      Fax: (510) 895-1784
      Email: grichardson@broadline.com
      Website: www.broadline.com
Dist disposable medical apparel: headwear, footwear, labcoats & lab jackets, OR towels, lap sponges, gowns & non sterile kits. (Woman/AA, estab 1994, empl 10, sales $3,000,000, cert: NMSDC)

6116 Duncan & Duncan Medical, Inc.
      911 Marina Way S Unite E2 Richmond, CA 94804
      (510) 799-0100 Luta Duncan President
      Fax: (415) 366-1577
      Email: glovesbylu@aol.com
      Website: www.duncanmeds.com
Medical, surgical, laboratory supplies & equipment, medical books, cleaning supplies, housekeeping supplies, apparel, gloves, incontinence, textiles, orthopedic , nutritional & feeding supplies, personal hygiene, physical therapy. (Woman/AA, estab 2011, empl 3, sales $429,000, cert: CPUC)

6117 EMS Safety Services, Inc.
      1046 Calle Recodo Ste K San Clemente, CA 92673
      (800) 215-9555 Marian Lepore CEO
      Fax: (949) 388-2776
      Email: bids@emssafety.com
      Website: www.emssafetyservices.com
Training curriculums & products: CPR, AED, First Aid & Bloodborne Pathogens. (Woman/As-Pac, estab 1993, empl 18, sales $2,700,000, cert: NMSDC, CPUC, WBENC)

6118 Flying Medical USA
      18187 Valley   La Puente, CA 91744
      (855) 227-3080 Conrad Reveles Sales Exec
      Fax: (626) 648-6483
      Email: sales3@flyingmedusa.com
      Website: www.flyingmedusa.com
Mfr medical supplies: band aid, ice packs, finger splints, etc. (As-Pac, estab 2008, empl 4, sales , cert: State)

6119 Hand and Hand Medical
      822 Wakefield Dr   Oakdale, CA 95361
      (209) 322-2699 Sharon Devereaux CEO
      Fax: (209) 847-1365
      Email: Dwight@handandhand.com
      Website: www.handandhandmed.com
Dist surgical post-op "JP Drain" Management Systems, unique effective product, US Patent Awarded 2015. (Woman/White, estab 2016, empl 3, sales $750,000, cert: WBENC)

6120 Hospital Systems, Inc.
      750 Garcia Ave   Pittsburg, CA 94565
      (925) 427-7800 Kathie Campbell VP Ops
      Fax: (925) 427-0800
      Email: kcampbell@hsiheadwalls.com
      Website: www.HSIheadwalls.com
Mfr patient headwalls, patient service columns, Isolated power panels, patient care systems & neo natal. Dist hospital accessories. (Woman/White, estab 1900, empl 1, sales $5,511,866, cert: State, WBENC)

6121 IDEAON
      1855, Gateway Blvd Ste 170 Concord, CA 94520
      (925) 465-2175 Shankar Krishna Director
      Fax: (408) 904-5798
      Email: shankar@ideaoninc.com
      Website: www.ideaoninc.com
Custom Computer Programming Services
Technology Staffing
eLearning, Virtual Training Development
Custom Content Develpment
Course Development
Training Services: Instructor Led Training, Web Based Training and Education Courses, Course Development and (As-Ind, estab 2003, empl 5, sales $1,500,000, cert: NMSDC)

6122 Legend Medical Devices Inc.
      16714 E Johnson Dr   City Of Industry, CA 91745
      (626) 350-9733 Mark Sevilla Dir of Sales
      Fax: (626) 350-9731
      Email: msevilla@legendmd.com
      Website: www.legendmd.com
Mfr & dist CPAP, anesthesia, respiratory care & infection control products. (Woman/As-Pac, estab 2006, empl 8, sales $1,500,000, cert: CPUC)

6123 Small Beginnings, Inc.
      17229 Lemon St Ste B2 Hesperia, CA 92345
      (760) 949-7707 Kelly Brockelmeyer Exec Admin
      Fax: (760) 948-1916
      Email: kelly@small-beginnings.com
      Website: www.small-beginnings.com
Mfr Neonatal Intensive Care Unit disposable products: diapers, photo-therapy masks, suction devices, pacifiers, & meconium aspirators. (Woman/White, estab 2001, empl 8, sales $1,071,101, cert: WBENC)

6124 The Andwin Corp.
      6636 Variel Ave   Canoga Park, CA 91303
      (818) 999-2828 Arnie Shedlow Sr VP sales
      Fax: (818) 226-4125
      Email: jpalaganas@andwin.com
      Website: www.andwinsci.com
Dist medical & lab supplies & product kits: boxes, labels, bar codes, instruction inserts & kit components. (Woman/White, estab 1950, empl 98, sales $32,000,000, cert: WBENC)

6125   Total Resources International
420 S Lemon Ave   Walnut, CA 91789
(909) 594-1220   Andre Dela Victoria Sales Mgr
Fax: (909) 468-2820
Email: andrev@totalresourcesintl.com
Website: www.totalresourcesintl.com
Mfr First Aid Kits & Emergency Survival Essentials. (As-Pac, estab 1990, empl 150, sales $13,000,000, cert: NMSDC)

Colorado

6126   in3corp Inc.
1750 30th St, Ste 216   Boulder, CO 80301
(303) 448-1191   Patricia Gilpin Acct Coord
Fax: (720) 565-3559
Email: gilpin@in3corp.com
Website: www.in3corp.com/
Our firm has a variety of capabilities to help audit supplier invoice payments. Our projects find transaction errors in order to deliver lost money to clients; but we also reinforce existing best practices, identify new optimization strategies (Hisp, estab 2000, empl 79, sales $2,200,000, cert: NMSDC)

6127   LifeHealth LLC
5951 S Middlefield Rd, Ste 102   Littleton, CO 80123
(303) 730-1902   Margot Langstaff Managing Partner
Fax: (303) 798-5829
Email: margot@lifehealthcorp.com
Website: www.lifehealthcorp.com
Clinical health care services & solutions. (Woman/White, estab 2004, empl 5, sales $870,000, cert: WBENC)

6128   Relius Medical LLC
615 Wooten Rd Ste 150   Colorado Springs, CO 80915
(719) 725-6444   Lauralee Martin Owner
Fax:
Email: LMartin@ReliusMed.com
Website: www.reliusmed.com
Orthopedic Medical Device Manufacturer: Implants, External Fixation Devices, Instrumentation. (Woman/White, estab 2014, empl 125, sales $1,010,907,952, cert: WBENC)

6129   The Medcom Group, Ltd.
541 East Garden Dr, Unit Q   Windsor, CO 80550
(970) 674-3032   John Bergsten Natl Accts Mgr
Fax: (970) 674-3061
Email: jbergsten@medcomgroup.com
Website: www.medcomgroup.com
Dist orthopedic rehabilitative equipment. (Woman/White, estab 1988, empl 24, sales $2,500,000, cert: WBENC)

Connecticut

6130   Quaisar Enterprises LLC dba Health Products ForYou
82 North St   Danbury, CT 06810
(203) 616-2850   Masarrat Quaisar Dir of Sales
Fax: (203) 616-2851
Email: masarrat@healthproductsforyou.com
Website: www.healthproductsforyou.com
Dist medical equipment & supplies. (Woman/As-Ind, estab 2002, empl 12, sales $11,000,000, cert: State)

District of Columbia

6131   Medical Supply Systems, Inc.
3182 Bladensburg Rd NE P.O. Box 41456   Washington, DC 20018
(202) 832-5000   Janice Littlejohn President
Fax: (202) 832-5565
Email: medsupsys2@aol.com
Website:
Dist general medical & surgical supplies & equipment, mortuary supplies, laboratory supplies. (Woman/AA, estab 1985, empl 5, sales $1,499,998, cert: State)

Delaware

6132   AquaCast Liner LLC
364 E Main St Ste 422   Middletown, DE 19709
(855) 938-2278   Mark Monahan VP
Fax: (302) 778-7911
Email: markm@aquacastliner.com
Website: www.aquacast.com
Mfr waterproof cast liners for fracture care management. (Woman/White, estab 2011, empl 15, sales , cert: State)

6133   Med-Tech Equipment, Inc.
2207 Concord Pike Ste 135   Wilmington, DE 19803
(800) 322-2609   David Gentile VP
Fax:
Email: info@buymedtech.com
Website: www.buymedtech.com
Dist, service & maintain sport medicine modalities & training equipment: Electrotherapy Ultrasound, Stim, Laser and Combo units, Hydrotherapy Whirlpools, Traction/Decompression Systems, Treatment Tables, Extremity Testing Systems. (Woman/White, estab 1989, empl 2, sales $250,000, cert: State)

Florida

6134 AmCar Group, LLC
342 Pike Rd, Ste 19   West Palm Beach, FL 33411
(954) 557-8697 Herbert Bernard Co-Owner
Fax: (407) 536-5001
Email: amcarmedical@gmail.com
Website:
Dist disposable/consumable medical
supplies, medical equipment. (AA, estab 2013, empl 3,
sales , cert: State)

6135 American Medicals
8900 Corporate Square Court   Jacksonville, FL
32216
(904) 636-9451 B G Bihani President
Fax:
Email: bg.bihani@americanmedicals.com
Website: www.americanmedicals.com
Mfr & dist medical, surgical & healthcare products. (As-
Ind, estab 2001, empl 3, sales , cert: State)

6136 American Purchasing Services
10315 USA Today Way   Miramar, FL 33025
(305) 364-0888 Akhil Agrawal President
Fax: (305) 364-0877
Email: akhil.agrawal@american-depot.com
Website: www.american-depot.com
Dist medical supplies. (As-Ind/As-Pac, estab 1990, empl 94,
sales , cert: NMSDC)

6137 Anexa Biomedical, Inc.
40423 Air Time Ave   Zephyrhills, FL 33542
(813) 780-7927 Lenny Budloo President
Fax: (813) 780-7930
Email: lenny@anexabiomedical.com
Website: www.anexabiomedical.com
Mfr USP Sterile Saline and Sterile Water solutions for
moistening of wound dressings, wound debridement, and
device irrigation. (Hisp, estab 2010, empl 8, sales , cert:
State)

6138 Bayside Medical Supply Company, Inc.
3924 W Palmetto St   Tampa, FL 33607
(813) 879-2731 Reginald Nickson CEO
Fax: (813) 879-0540
Email: rjnickson@netzero.net
Website: www.baysidemedicalsupply.com
Dist disposable & durable medical supplies & equipment:
furniture, bandages, exam room, gloves, orthopaedic,
needles, syringes, point of care testing, infection control,
instruments, surgical supplies, respiratory, personal care,
etc. (AA, estab 1990, empl 1, sales $1,100,000, cert: State)

6139 Care-Full Products
3905 Tampa Rd, Ste 432   Oldsmar, FL 34677
(813) 602-2824 Colleen Meloff President
Fax:
Email: cmeloff@carefullproducts.com
Website: www.carefullproducts.com
Mfr CareFull Catch disposable specimen cup holder.
(Woman/White, estab 2015, empl 1, sales $10,000, cert:
NWBOC)

6140 Carter-Health Disposables LLC
4201 Vineland Road Ste I-13-14 Orlando, FL
32811
(407) 296-6689 Nancy Berrios Office Admin
Fax: (407) 296-6693
Email: nancy@carterhealth.com
Website: www.carter-health.com
Disposable medical supplies & medical devices, Phar-
macy support products & consultation, Disposable, high
quality, low-lint, non-woven gowning apparel, Lab Coats,
Isolation Gowns & Coveralls, shoe covers, hair covers.
(Woman/AA, estab 2009, empl 4, sales $1,900,000, cert:
NMSDC, WBENC)

6141 Customed USA, LLC
10805 Southport Dr   Orlando, FL 32824
(407) 850-5558 Milexis Torres Dir of Sales
Fax: (407) 850-5557
Email: milexis.torres@prhospital.com
Website: www.customedhealing.com
Dist hospital, medical supplies, imaging products,
custom surgical products. (Hisp, estab 2010, empl 240,
sales $1,100,000, cert: NMSDC)

6142 EncompasUnlimited, Inc.
2219 Whitfield Park Dr   Sarasota, FL 34243
(941) 751-3385 Marybeth Flynn VP
Fax: (941) 727-7986
Email: marybeth@encompasunlimited.com
Website: www.encompasunlimited.com
Dist endoscopy accessories, specimen caddies, multiple
glove dispenser boxes, endoscopy wedges & headrests.
(Woman/White, estab 1977, empl 4, sales $2,400,000,
cert: NWBOC)

6143 Healthcare Supply Solutions, Inc.
13949 Alvarez Rd Ste 100 Jacksonville, FL 32218
(904) 638-5520 Lara Cheek
Fax: (904) 638-5522
Email: Lcheek@hssone.com
Website: www.hssone.com
Dist healthcare products & services. (Hisp, estab 2008,
empl 14, sales $10,000,000, cert: NMSDC)

6144 HNM Medical USA
20855 NE 16th Ave Ste C15 Miami, FL 33179
(866) 291-8498 Yoav Anisz President
Fax:
Email: yanisz@hnmmedical.com
Website: www.hnmmedical.com
Dist medical equipment and supplies. (Hisp, estab 2004,
empl 5, sales $7,000,000, cert: NMSDC)

6145 Kramer Laboratories, Inc.
400 University Dr Ste 400 Coral Gables, FL 33134
(800) 824-4894 Myrna Patterson Sales Mgr
Fax: (305) 223-5510
Email: mpatterson@kramerlabs.com
Website: www.kramerlabs.com
Fungi Nail Brand, Safetussin CD Cough Relief/Nasal
Decongestant Formula, Safetussin DM Cough Formula.
(Woman/Hisp, estab 1987, empl 14, sales , cert: NMSDC,
WBENC)

6146   Lifeline Pharmaceuticals LLC
       1301 NW 84th Ave Ste 101 Miami, FL 33126
       (877) 430-6337 Benjamin Rivera Jr SVP
       Fax: (305) 643-6929
       Email: ben@lifelinepharm.com
       Website: www.lifelinepharm.com
Dist medical supplies & equipment, medical-surgical products, specialty pharmaceuticals, anesthesia, controlled medications, blood & plasma products, generic & branded chemotherapy products, vaccines, albumin, IVIG. (AA, estab 2006, empl 37, sales $29,000,000, cert: State, NMSDC)

6147   Medgluv Inc.
       5607 Hiatus Road, Ste 200   Tamarac, FL 33321
       (954) 586-5309 Jerry Leong CEO
       Fax: (954) 586-5310
       Email: Jleong@medgluv.com
       Website: www.medgluv.com
Mfr & dist examination gloves. (As-Pac, estab 2001, empl 6, sales $10,500,000, cert: State, NMSDC)

6148   Medical Support International, LLC
       2626 Sawyer Terr   Wellington, FL 33414
       (561) 337-4866 Edgar Rivera CEO
       Fax: (561) 282-6285
       Email: edgar.rivera@medsupportintl.com
       Website:
Dist medical, dental, veterinary, surgical & hospital supplies & equipment. (Hisp, estab 2009, empl 2, sales , cert: NMSDC)

6149   Med-Lab Supply Co., Inc.
       923 NW 27th Ave   Miami, FL 33125
       (305) 642-5144 Lucas Diaz VP Sales
       Fax: (305) 541-0832
       Email: lucas.diaz@med-lab.com
       Website: www.med-lab.com
Dist & service Siemens medical equipment. (Hisp, estab 1964, empl 79, sales $25,000,000, cert: NMSDC)

6150   Surgimed Corporation
       1303 NW 78th Ave   Doral, FL 33126
       (305) 594-1121 Luis Arias VP
       Fax: (305) 594-4334
       Email: larias@surgimedcorp.com
       Website: www.surgimedcorp.com/
Dist endotracheal tubes, stylets, guedels, suction catheters, tracheostomy tubes, endobroncheal tubes, foley catheters, urinary collection bags, leg bags, urine meters, pediatric urine collectors, foley Catheterization trays, irrigation syringes & trays. (Hisp, estab 1981, empl 13, sales $4,000,000, cert: NMSDC)

6151   Teknia Networks & Logistics, Inc.
       10451 66th St N Pinellas Park, FL 33782
       (813) 918-8417 Jorge Monsalve President
       Fax: (727) 290-9852
       Email: laura@teknialogistics.com
       Website: www.TEKNIANETWORKS.COM
Teknia Networks and Logistics provides rental of machinery, copiers, printers, material handling machines like Toyota foklifts, racking systems, power generators (Hisp, estab 2010, empl 10, sales $5,000,000, cert: NMSDC)

6152   US Medical International LLC
       6989 NW 82nd Ave   Miami, FL 33166
       (305) 468-3248 Ryan Kissane Sales/Ops Mgr
       Fax: (305) 468-3242
       Email: ryan@usmedicalintl.com
       Website: www.usmedicalintl.com
Mfr & dist disposable medical supplies. (Hisp, estab 2009, empl 3, sales , cert: State, NMSDC)

6153   VetMeds, Inc.
       8950 SW 74th Court Ste 2201 Miami, FL 33156
       (786) 220-3634 Andria Nelson President
       Fax: (786) 513-8096
       Email: vetmeds@gmx.com
       Website: www.vetmedsinc.biz
Dist medical equipment, medical apparel, wound care supplies, medical furniture, exam room supplies, extrication-patient transport equipment, surgical gloves, IV therapy & laboratory supplies. (Woman/AA, estab 2012, empl 5, sales $65,000, cert: State)

Georgia

6154   American Clinics for Preventive Medicine
       1343 Terrell Mill Rd Ste 100 Marietta, GA 30067
       (767) 836-3477 Juanita Cato Office Asst
       Fax:
       Email: americanclinicpm@gmail.com
       Website: www.acpm.net
Provide physical exams, alternative medical treatment options, nutritional infusion therapy, high dose Vitamin C infusions, primary prevention exams, alternative complimentary cancer therapies, detoxification programs. (AA, estab 1985, empl 10, sales , cert: State)

6155   Attain Med, Inc.
       5825 Glenridge Dr NE Bldg 4, Ste 106 Atlanta, GA 30328
       (770) 288-2466 Charles Stafford VP Diversity Partnerships
       Fax: (888) 288-2181
       Email: charles.stafford@attainmed.com
       Website: www.attainmed.com
Dist pharmaceuticals. (AA/As-Ind/Hisp, estab 2008, empl 16, sales $8,000,000, cert: NMSDC, 8(a))

6156   Canterbury Pointe LLC
       3350 Riverwood Parkway, Ste 1900   Atlanta, GA 30339
       (770) 633-2570 Diane P. Dixon President
       Fax: (678) 426-8845
       Email: diane.dixon@canterburypointe.com
       Website: www.cpointellc.com
Medical Supplies, Pharmacy Benefit Management, Energy Management & Insurance Services. (Woman/AA, estab 2015, empl 1, sales $70,000, cert: WBENC)

6157 DOC Development Inc
      2500 Park Central Blvd Ste 30035 Decatur, GA
      30094
      (678) 509-1501 Radcliff Quarterman COO
      Fax: (678) 509-1505
      Email: rquarterman@doc-development.com
      Website: www.doc-development.com
Medical Supplies. (AA, estab 2001, empl 7, sales
$110,000,000, cert: 8(a))

6158 MedX Diagnostic Solutions, LLC
      2004 Eastview Pkwy Ste 108 Conyers, GA 30013
      (770) 278-0199 Gerald Patterson COO
      Fax: (609) 773-0126
      Email: gpatterson@medxghs.com
      Website: www.medxghs.com
Dist healthcare materials, supplies, furniture, diagnostic
kits, biomedical equipment services & repairs. (Woman/
AA, estab 2014, empl 3, sales , cert: NMSDC)

6159 UNYTER Enterprises
      912 Holcomb Bridge Rd Ste 301 Roswell, GA 30076
      (800) 704-8875 Tony Rayfus President
      Fax: (888) 840-1265
      Email: info@unyter.com
      Website: www.unyter.com
Dist pharmaceuticals, medical/surgical supplies & equipment. (AA, estab 2009, empl 2, sales $223,500, cert: State)

6160 Vanguard Safety Company LLC
      P.O. Box 608 Savannah, GA 31402
      (912) 236-1766 Howard Genser Jr. Exec VP/COO
      Fax: (912) 238-3072
      Email: howardg@vanguardsafetyco.com
      Website: www.vanguardsafetyco.com
Dist occupational health & safety products. (AA, estab
1985, empl 21, sales $8,700,000, cert: NMSDC)

6161 WellSol Medical Inc.
      1261 LaVista Rd, Ste D1 Atlanta, GA 30324
      (855) 935-5765 William Moylan CFO
      Fax:
      Email: bill@wellsolmed.com
      Website: www.wellsolmed.com
Dist medical equipment. (Hisp, estab 2015, empl 4, sales ,
cert: NMSDC)

Iowa

6162 Dermatologic Lab & Supply, Inc.
      608 13th Ave Council Bluffs, IA 51501
      (712) 323-3269 Kara Torpy Mktg Dir
      Fax: (712) 323-1156
      Email: questions@delasco.com
      Website: www.delasco.com
Dist dermatologic supplies: chemicals, cosmetic supplies,
cryosurgery, melanoma detection, electrosurgery, cautery,
examination supplies, surgical instruments, exam lighting,
sharps, sterilization supplies, wound care. (Woman/White,
estab 1980, empl 45, sales , cert: WBENC)

Illinois

6163 Cura Surgical Inc.
      2571 Kaneville Ct Geneva, IL 60134
      (630) 232-2510 Lynn Uvodich Controller
      Fax: (630) 232-8005
      Email: luvodich@curasurgical.com
      Website: www.curasurgical.com
Dist surgical & burn wound dressings (Hisp, estab 2006,
empl 10, sales $5,261,075, cert: NMSDC)

6164 Global Medical Services LLC
      707 Davis Rd, Ste 102B Elgin, IL 60123
      (224) 238-3273 Kelvin Udogu CEO
      Fax: (224) 535-8197
      Email: kudogu@gmail.com
      Website: www.globalmedsllc.com
Dist pharmaceuticals & medical equipment. (Woman/
AA, estab 2009, empl 5, sales $450,000, cert: 8(a))

6165 JERO Medical Equipment & Supplies, Inc.
      4108 W Division St Chicago, IL 60651
      (312) 829-5376 Julia Bowens President
      Fax: (312) 829-5671
      Email: juliabowens@jeromedical.com
      Website: www.jeromedical.com
Mfr disposbable wearing apparels, kit assembler, 1st aid,
disaster, admission. (AA, estab 1987, empl 24, sales
$4,000,000, cert: City)

6166 MAC Medical Supply Co.
      525 W Monroe St Ste 2360 Chicago, IL 60661
      (773) 650-9400 Millie Maddocks CEO
      Fax: (773) 843-2201
      Email: millie.maddocks@macmed.com
      Website: www.macmed.com
Dist medical & safety supplies; cleaning products.
(Woman/White, estab 2000, empl 14, sales $14,000,000,
cert: WBENC)

6167 MC Squared Medical, Inc.
      7801 Industrial Dr Ste F Spring Grove, IL 60081
      (815) 322-2485 Jody McCrea President
      Fax: (815) 425-1801
      Email: jodymccrea@gmail.com
      Website: www.mc-squared-group.com
Dist peripheral nerve products, Neurolac nerve tube
conduit & Vivosorb nerve tube wrap to prevent adhe-
sions. (Woman/White, estab 2011, empl 3, sales
$20,000, cert: State)

6168 Medefil, Inc.
      405 Windy Point Dr Glendale Heights, IL 60139
      (630) 682-4600 Praveen Aggarwal Exec VP
      Fax: (630) 681-9100
      Email: contracts@medefilinc.com
      Website: www.medefilinc.com
Mfr prefilled syringes filled with saline & hepain for IV
flush. (As-Ind, estab 1998, empl 95, sales $23,000,000,
cert: NMSDC)

6169   MedGyn Products, Inc.
100 W Industrial Rd   Addison, IL 60101
(630) 627-4105   Aarathi Singh President
Fax: (630) 627-0127
Email: asingh@medgyn.com
Website: www.medgyn.com
Dist disposables, medical devices, diagnostic equipment & surgical/procedure instruments. (As-Ind, estab 1975, empl 50, sales , cert: NMSDC)

6170   Nexus Pharmaceuticals, Inc.
175 East Hawthorn Pkwy   Vernon Hills, IL 60640
(847) 996-3797   Joseph Marchese Chief Commercial Officer
Fax: (847) 996-3799
Email: jvmarchese@nexuspharma.net
Website: www.nexuspharma.net
Mfr sterile generic injectable pharmaceuticals. (Woman/As-Ind, estab 2003, empl 5, sales $750,000, cert: WBENC)

6171   Novo Surgical, Inc.
700 Commerce Dr Ste 500   Oak Brook, IL 60523
(877) 860-6686   Abed Moiduddin VP Business Dev
Fax: (877) 806-8686
Email: abed.moiduddin@novosurgical.com
Website: www.novosurgical.com
Custom instrument design & mfg, premium, specialty surgical instrumentation. (As-Pac, estab 2009, empl 35, sales , cert: NMSDC)

6172   Omar Supplies, Inc.
4601 S. Cottage Grove Ave. #53452   Chicago, IL 60653
(708) 922-4277   Andre Fair President/Director of Worldwide Sales
Fax: (708) 922-9077
Email: afair@omarinc.com
Website: www.omarinc.com
Dist disposable gloves, clear & protective clothing, medical, lab & safety supplies, first aid kits, film/shrink wrap, corrugated boxes & garbage can liners. (AA, estab 1997, empl 20, sales $25,000,000, cert: NMSDC)

6173   Tetra Medical Supply Corp.
6364 W Gross Point Rd   Niles, IL 60714
(800) 621-4041   Mike Imhoff Director of Mktg
Fax: (847) 647-9034
Email: mike@tetramed.com
Website: www.tetramed.com
Mfr & dist medical supplies. (Woman/White, estab 1913, empl 12, sales $5,500,000, cert: WBENC)

Indiana

6174   Bryton Corporation
4001 Methanol Ln   Indianapolis, IN 46268
(317) 334-8700   James Waldrop Controller
Fax: (317) 334-8787
Email: J.waldrop@brytoncorp.com
Website: www.brytoncorp.com
Mfr & dist medical equipment, supplies & accessories. (Woman/White, estab 1981, empl 40, sales $7,500,000, cert: City)

Kentucky

6175   Blu Pharmaceuticals
301 Robey St   Franklin, KY 42134
(270) 586-6386   Bill Luster Contract Mgr
Fax: (270) 586-6389
Email: jfurlong@blurx.us
Website: www.blurx.us
mfr & dist generic pharmaceuticals. (Woman/Hisp, estab 2006, empl 15, sales $39,613,667, cert: State)

6176   Marian Medical, Inc.
319 Westport Dr   Louisville, KY 40207
(502) 425-6363   Lisa Stewart Clinical Sales Mgr
Fax: (502) 425-6543
Email: lisa@marianmedicalonline.com
Website: www.marianmedicalonline.com
Neonatal products: Enteral System, Urinary Catheters, Urinary Collection Kit, Circumcision Tray, Chest Tube Kit, Exchange Transfusion Tray, Blood Administration Syringe Sets, PICC Procedure Kits. (Woman/White, estab 1995, empl 4, sales , cert: City)

Louisiana

6177   Carousel Medical Equipment LLC
2138 Wooddale Blvd Bldg B, Ste 13   Baton Rouge, LA 70806
(225) 216-0360   Lizzset Gordon Owner
Fax: (225) 216-0380
Email: carouselmedical@bellsouth.net
Website: www.carouselmedical.com
Dist medical equipment & supplies. (Woman/AA, estab 2007, empl 2, sales $49,000, cert: 8(a))

Massachusetts

6178   Genesis Medical Products, Inc.
40 Farm Hill Rd   Wrentham, MA 02093
(877) 933-5437   Kevin Kelliher Principal
Fax: (508) 883-2515
Email: Genesismedical@aol.com
Website: www.iGenesisMedical.com
Dist neonatal, pediatric, labor & delivery soft goods. (Woman, estab 1996, empl 10, sales $300,000, cert: State)

6179   Shinemound Enterprise Inc.
17A Sterling Rd   North Billerica, MA 01862
(978) 436-9980   Gloria Shiao VP
Fax: (978) 436-9983
Email: info@shinemound.com
Website: www.shinemound.com
Mfr latex & non-latex products: disposable PVC, synthetic, vinyl & nitrile, CPE & PE gloves. (As-Pac, estab 1988, empl 6, sales , cert: State)

6180 Westnet Inc.
      55 North St   Canton, MA 02021
      (781) 828-7772 Gordon Thompson CEO
      Fax: (781) 828-2011
      Email: gordon@westnetmed.com
      Website: www.westnetmed.com
Dist medical/surgical supplies & equipment; life science
products & industrial paper. (AA, estab 1994, empl 34,
sales , cert: NMSDC)

Maryland

6181 1st Needs Medical LLC
      7003 Glenn Dale Rd Ste 151 Glenn Dale, MD 20769
      (301) 928-2557 Vernon White Partner
      Fax:
      Email: vernon.white@1stneedsmedical.com
      Website: www.1stneedsmedical.com
Durable Medical Equipment & daily use medical supplies.
(AA, estab 2014, empl 2, sales , cert: State, City, NMSDC)

6182 Asclepius Solutions Inc.
      3510 Raymoor Rd   Kensington, MD 20895
      (301) 685-3557 Deven Shah VP
      Fax: (646) 219-2840
      Email: deven.shah@asclepius.net
      Website: www.asclepius.net
Clinical Trials Support Solutions & Services, Protocol
Lifecycle Management, Clinical Monitoring, Clinical Data
Management, Safety Reporting, Electronic Data Capture,
Dictionary Management, Patient Registration. (Woman/As-
Ind, estab 2003, empl 15, sales , cert: State)

6183 Lifeline Medical Services, Inc.
      2955 Mercy Lane   Cheverly, MD 20785
      (301) 386-0000 Eze Nwoji President
      Fax: (301) 386-0002
      Email: eze@lifelinemeds.com
      Website: www.lifelinemedicalsupplies.com
Dist automatic sanitary shoe dispenser, hand held EKG
monitor, ambulatory product, bathroom product, gloves,
dental supplies, woundcare supplies, diagnotics equipment, medical apparels hospital beds & accessories. (AA,
estab 2003, empl 4, sales $385,000, cert: State)

6184 The McConnell Group, Inc.
      1901 Research Blvd Ste 502 Rockville, MD 20850
      (301) 309-8310 Irving W. McConnell CEO
      Fax: (301) 309-8314
      Email: imcconnell@themccgroup.com
      Website: www.themccgroup.com
Dist laboratory & medical supplies. (AA, estab 1996, empl
200, sales , cert: State)

6185 Universal Medical Associates, Inc.
      111 Hamlet Hill Rd Ste 710 Baltimore, MD 21210
      (443) 765-9366 Renee Parks
      Fax: (443) 708-7754
      Email:
      ReneeParks@UniversalMedicalAssociates.com
      Website: www.UniversalMedicalAssociates.com
Medical & surgical implants, osteobiologics & regenera-
tive medicine products, Osteobiologics, Sports Medicine
Allografts, Synthetic Biologics & Regenerative Tissue
products. (AA, estab 2010, empl 3, sales $621,930, cert:
NMSDC)

Michigan

6186 J and B Medical Supply Company Inc.
      50496 W Pontiac Trail   Wixom, MI 48393
      (248) 896-6200 Mark David Ohio Territory Mgr
      Fax:
      Email: mdavid@jandbmedical.com
      Website: www.jandbmedicalsupply.com
Dist Medical Surgical & Emergency Medical Supplies.
(Woman/White, estab 1996, empl 265, sales $925,000,
cert: WBENC)

6187 OCS Inc.
      916 Fremont St   Bay City, MI 48708
      (989) 714-0719 Amy Swackhamer Dir of commu-
      nications
      Fax: (989) 390-5900
      Email: amy@ocsmgt.com
      Website: www.ocsmgt.com
Medical & vocational management, occupational
therapy consultating & cost containment services.
(Woman/White, estab 2010, empl 12, sales $1,000,000,
cert: WBENC)

6188 Revive Surgical Instrument Service & Repair, LLC
      201 Streamview Ct   Canton, MI 48188
      (734) 796-3143 Freda Crawley President
      Fax: (855) 573-8483
      Email: info@revivesurgicalinstrumentrepair.com
      Website:
      www.revivesurgicalinstrumentrepair.com
Surgical instrument repair. (Woman/AA, estab 2011,
empl 3, sales $243,000, cert: WBENC)

6189 TerryWorldWide, LLC
      6505 Grandville Ave   Detroit, MI 48228
      (313) 974-8341 Terry Willis CEO
      Fax:
      Email: terry@terryworldwide.com
      Website: www.terryworldwide.com
Dist CanAm Medical/SiO2 Ultra Thin Liquid Glass
Coatings. (AA, estab 2010, empl 1, sales , cert: NMSDC)

6190   Veteran Medical Products, Inc.
     813 Franklin St SE   Grand Rapids, MI 49507
     (616) 451-8486   Roosevelt Tillman President
     Fax: (616) 454-8642
     Email: rt@veteranmedical.com
     Website: www.veteranmedical.com
Disposable medical supplies. (AA, estab 2005, empl 2, sales $100,000, cert: NMSDC)

Minnesota

6191   Global International LLC
     1305 Larc Industrial Blvd   Burnsville, MN 55337
     (651) 333-4581   Ambrose Kpoto Dir of Market & Business Devel
     Fax: (877) 758-5066
     Email: ambrose@fgmmedical.com
     Website: www.fgmmedical.com
Dist medical, dental, and pharmaceuticals. (AA, estab 2014, empl 25, sales $5,000,000, cert: NMSDC)

6192   Kelco Supply Company
     7700 Setzler Pkwy N   Minneapolis, MN 55445
     (763) 493-1260   Alicia Carr CEO
     Fax: (763) 493-1261
     Email: alicia@kelcosupply.com
     Website: www.kelcosupply.com
Dist post mortem equipment & supplies, prep room products. (Woman, estab 1939, empl 17, sales $6,733,300, cert: City, WBENC)

6193   NavasDRSTi, LLC
     1714 Basswood Court   Carver, MN 55315
     (888) 628-2860   Yog Ohneswere CEO
     Fax: (612) 234-4804
     Email: yohnes@navadrsti.com
     Website: www.navadrsti.com
Electro-Surgical Units, Cardio-Vascular & Cardiology Equipment & Instruments, Radiology, Ultrasound, Diagnostic Imaging & Testing Equipment, Orthopedic Devices, Implants & Tools, Surgical Equipment, Instruments, Supplies & Disposables. (As-Ind, estab 2016, empl 2, sales , cert: State)

6194   Ulmer Pharmacal
     1614 Industry Ave W   Park Rapids, MN 56470
     (218) 732-2656   Brent Swanson CFO
     Fax: (218) 732-5300
     Email: bswanson@lobanaproducts.com
     Website: www.ulmerpharmacal.com
Mfr premium cleaning & infection control products, patient lubricating jellies & skin care products.. (Woman/White, estab 2013, empl 10, sales $520,000, cert: State)

Missouri

6195   Controlled Environment Products, Inc.
     3851 NE Kimball Dr   Kansas City, MO 64161
     (816) 453-8900   Marilyn Townsend CEO
     Fax: (816) 453-7077
     Email: marilyn@netcep.com
     Website: www.netcep.com
Dist safety supplies, personal protection equip, disposable Tyvek coverall, gloves, ergonomic seating, paper towels, tissue, Kleenex, handsoap, jan/san chemicals, etc. (Woman/AA, estab 1989, empl 11, sales $7,100,000, cert: NMSDC)

6196   Emed Medical Company
     11551 Adie Rd   Maryland Heights, MO 63043
     (314) 739-6815   Susan Jones Mgr Supplier Diversity
     Fax: (314) 344-4303
     Email: sjones@emedmedical.com
     Website: www.emedmedical.com
Dist pharmaceuticals, medical related products & specialty pharmacy services. (AA, estab 1999, empl 10, sales $26,000,000, cert: State, NMSDC)

6197   I.V. House, Inc.
     418 Seven Gables Ct   Chesterfield, MO 63017
     (314) 453-9200   Angela Cressey President
     Fax: (314) 453-9576
     Email: angela@ivhouse.com
     Website: www.ivhouse.com
Mfr & dist I.V. House Ultra Dressings & Ultra Domes, IV site protectors for all ages. (Woman/White, estab 1991, empl 3, sales , cert: State)

6198   SimmCo Distribution
     4813 Lee Ave   St. Louis, MO 63115
     (314) 389-3630   Shaun Simms President
     Fax: (314) 282-0670
     Email: info@simmcodistribution.com
     Website: www.simmcodistribution.com
Dist Medical Devices, Medical Supplies & Pharmaceuticals. (AA, estab 2012, empl 5, sales $50,000, cert: State, City)

North Carolina

6199   Make It Market USA
     10612 Providence Rd Ste D343   Charlotte, NC 28277
     (877) 647-7639   Kate Liddle Founder, Sr Partner
     Fax:
     Email: kliddle@makeitmarketusa.com
     Website: www.makeitmarketusa.com
InjuryShield is a thermoplastic-based, self-contained wound & splinting system that is biocompatible, radiolucent, latex-free. (Woman/White, estab 2014, empl 2, sales $115,000, cert: State)

New Jersey

6200 Amneal Pharmaceuticals
400 Crossing Blvd 3rd Fl Bridgewater, NJ 08807
(908) 947-3120 Brown Massey Director, Sales
Fax: (770) 984-8997
Email: bmassey@amneal.com
Website: www.amneal.com
Develop, mfg & dist generic pharmaceutical products. (As-Ind, estab 2002, empl 4727, sales , cert: NMSDC)

6201 Case Medical Inc.
19 Empire Blvd   South Hackensack, NJ 07606
(201) 313-1999 Steven Beltis Contract Mgr
Fax: (201) 373-9090
Email: sbeltis@casemed.com
Website: www.casemed.com
Mfr decontamination & sterilization products. (Woman/White, estab 1992, empl 37, sales $7,000,000, cert: State, WBENC)

6202 Cenmed Enterprises
121 Jersey Ave   New Brunswick, NJ 08901
(732) 447-1100 Rizwan Chaudhry Ops
Fax: (732) 249-0008
Email: rizwan@cenmed.com
Website: www.cenmed.com
Dist medical supplies, laboratory supplies, hospital supplies, surgical supplies, emt supplies, safety supplies, fire supplies. (Woman/As-Ind, estab 1992, empl 25, sales $8,400,000, cert: State, City, NMSDC, WBENC, SDB)

6203 Discovery ChemScience LLC
66 Witherspoon St, Ste 1100   Princeton, NJ 08542
(609) 475-5097 Qun Sun President
Fax:
Email: qsun@dischemsci.com
Website: www.dischemsci.com
Provide discovery, medicinal chemistry & custom synthesis CRO services. (As-Pac, estab 2004, empl 2, sales $2,900,000, cert: NMSDC)

6204 NEXT Medical Products Company, LLC
45 Columbia Rd   Branchburg, NJ 08876
(908) 722-4549 John Buday Dir Cstmr Service
Fax: (908) 218-3715
Email: jbuday@nextmedicalproducts.com
Website: www.nextmedicalproducts.com
Mfr Clear Image & LithoClear Ultrasound Gel brands, sterile & non-sterile single patient packets. (Woman/As-Pac, estab 2012, empl 12, sales $5,000,000, cert: WBENC)

6205 Precision Medical Devices, Inc.
121 Jersey Ave   New Brunswick, NJ 08901
(732) 447-2587 Lynn Indyk Business Dev Mgr
Fax:
Email: lindyk@pmdmfg.com
Website: www.pmdinstruments.com
Mfr medical devices, instrument systems & clinical products, surgical instruments. (As-Ind, estab 2008, empl 6, sales $275,000, cert: NMSDC)

6206 Siris Pharmaceutical Services
75 North St Ste 1 Bloomsbury, NJ 08804
(908) 479-1331 Andrew Voigt Business Dev
Fax: (908) 479-1280
Email: andrewv@sirispharma.com
Website: www.sirispharma.com
Clinical packaging, distribution, drug storage, and drug returns/destruction services. (Woman/White, estab 2001, empl 12, sales $672,000, cert: WBENC)

6207 United Medical Supplies Inc.
25 Craig Place   North Plainfield, NJ 07059
(908) 757-0075 Raman Alaigh CEO
Fax: (908) 757-0079
Email: RayAlaigh@UnitedMedSupplies.com
Website:
Dist synthetic, latex & nitrile exam gloves, walkers, wheelchairs, bathroom accessories, bath benches, commodes, rollators, crutches, disposable medical supplies, alternating pressure relief mattress, overlay mattress. nebulizers, oxygen tubing. (Woman/As-Pac, estab 2007, empl 4, sales , cert: State)

New Yrok

6208 Alpha Medical Distributor, Inc.
60-B Commerce Place Unit B Hicksville, NY 11801
(516) 681-5290 Jonathan Lee President
Fax: (516) 681-5291
Email: alphameddis@aol.com
Website: www.MortuarySuppliesUSA.com
Dist body bags, cadaver bags, transport bags & mortuary supplies. (Woman/As-Pac, estab 2000, empl 4, sales $500,000, cert: State)

6209 BFFL Co., LLC
20 Kensington Rd   Scarsdale, NY 10583
(914) 713-8550 Elizabeth Thompson CEO
Fax: (914) 713-8549
Email: drelizabeth@bfflco.com
Website: www.bfflco.com
Surgical Bras, surgical vests, compression bras, comfort and recovery garments, compression wear, hospital gowns, orthopedic dressings. (Woman/White, estab 2011, empl 5, sales $1,549,736, cert: WBENC)

6210 Danlee Medical Products, Inc.
6075 E Molloy Rd, Ste 5 Bldg. 5 Syracuse, NY 13211
(315) 431-0143 Joni Walton Ops
Fax: (315) 431-0149
Email: joni@danleemedical.com
Website: www.danleemedical.com
Mfr custom hook-up kits, boxer shorts & endoscopy shorts, disposable pouches for holter & event recording, disposable scrubs & disposable blood pressure cuff liners. (Woman/White, estab 1994, empl 13, sales $2,900,000, cert: State)

6211 Medi-Tech International Corp.
26 Court St, Ste 1301 Brooklyn, NY 11242
(718) 272-6390 Victoria Lamantia COO
Fax: (718) 855-1618
Email: Vicky.LaMantia@medi-techintl.com
Website: www.medi-techintl.com
Mfr wound management products. (Woman/White, estab 1971, empl 29, sales $4,000,000, cert: WBENC)

6212 Robert Busse & Co., Inc. dba Busse Hospital Dispos
75 Arkay Dr Hauppauge, NY 11788
(800) 645-6526 Ray O'Hara VP
Fax: (631) 435-4721
Email: rohara@busseinc.com
Website: www.busseinc.com
Mfr disposable medical supplies: apparel, procedural kits, post mortem bags, ice bags, suction products, pain management kits, diagnostic kits, sterile drapes & towels, etc. (Woman/White, estab 1964, empl 270, sales $37,150,000, cert: WBENC)

6213 Silarx Pharmaceuticals, Inc.
19 West St Spring Valley, NY 10977
(845) 325-4020 George Hauss RA/QA Coord
Fax: (845) 352-4037
Email: ghauss@silarx.com
Website: www.silarx.com
Mfr liquid generic pharmaceutical & nutritional supplements. (As-Ind, estab 1985, empl 40, sales $11,130,742, cert: NMSDC)

6214 SS Elder In-Home Care, Inc.
145-69 167th St Jamaica, NY 11434
(718) 949-3316 Alisha Hall President
Fax: (718) 819-7506
Email: sselderinc@gmail.com
Website: www.sselderinc.com
Medical Equipment, Medical Supplies, Health Care. (AA, estab 2014, empl 3, sales , cert: City)

6215 X-GEN Pharmaceuticals, Inc.
300 Daniel Zenker Dr. Horseheads, NY 14845
(607) 562-2700 April King Contracts, Medicaid and Licensing Mgr
Fax: (607) 562-2760
Email: aking@x-gen.us
Website: www.x-gen.us
Mfr & dist generic pharmaceuticals (Woman, estab 2003, empl 32, sales $57,250,000, cert: WBENC)

Ohio

6216 AMedEquip
7031 Corporate Way Ste 201 Cincinnati, OH 45459
(513) 988-8550 Faisal Ali Dir of Ops
Fax: (888) 224-5006
Email: faisal@amedequip.com
Website: www.amedequip.com
Dist medical & lab equipment & supplies. (Woman/As-Ind, estab 2007, empl 2, sales $100,000, cert: State, NMSDC)

6217 C&M Medical Supply, Inc.
8600 S Wilkinson Way, Ste C Perrysburg, OH 43551
(419) 872-0033 Creston Tarrant President
Fax: (419) 872-0044
Email: CTarrant@cmmedicalsupply.com
Website: www.cmmedicalsupply.com
Diagnostic & respiratory equipment & supplies, advanced woundcare, latex, vinyl & nitrile exam gloves, ultrasound & electro medical products, portable EKG, spirometry, holter, blood pressure & oximetry. (AA, estab 2005, empl 8, sales $486,000, cert: State, NMSDC)

6218 Cincinnati Sub-Zero Products, LLC
12011 Mosteller Rd Cincinnati, OH 45241
(513) 772-8810 Matt McCurdy Cstmr Service & Natl Accts Mgr
Fax: (513) 772-9119
Email: mmccurdy@genthermcsz.com
Website: www.cszindustrial.com
Hyper-Hypothermia systems for use in hosptials before during and after surgery. Patient temperature controll. (Woman/White, estab 1940, empl 200, sales , cert: City)

6219 Kadiri Health, LLC
301 W 1st St., Ste 100 Dayton, OH 45402
(937) 404-2005 Christopher Cox
Fax: (718) 402-3934
Email: ccox@kadirihealth.com
Website: www.kadirihealth.com
Dist medical, laboratory, scientific, diagnostic, & research equipment, supplies & furniture. (AA, estab 2015, empl 4, sales $99,000, cert: NMSDC)

6220 Nnodum Pharmaceuticals Corp.
483 Northland Blvd Cincinnati, OH 45240
(513) 861-2329 Nnodum Iheme President
Fax: (513) 861-3629
Email: n.iheme@nnodumpharma.com
Website: www.nnodumpharma.com
Research, development & mfg over the counter & generic pharmaceuticals: prenatal Vitamins, dialysis vitamins, topical analgesics, lotions & creams for diabetic patients. (AA, estab 1997, empl 10, sales $30,000,000, cert: State, 8(a))

6221 Procura Select
30700-E Carter St Solon, OH 44139
(440) 248-1622 Patricia Palermo President
Fax: (440) 248-5483
Email: ppalermo@procuraselect.com
Website: www.procuraselect.com
Dist medical carts, shelving, storage & organization products. (Woman/White, estab 2014, empl 3, sales $10,000, cert: WBENC)

6222 Pyramid Enterprise Supplies
32593 Haverhill Dr Solon, OH 44139
(440) 248-7008 Linda Colson Owner
Fax:
Email: pyramid44139@yahoo.com
Website:
Pharmaceuticals, supplies, gowns, surgery sets & supplies, bedding, curtains, trays & kitchen items. (Woman/AA, estab 2000, empl 1, sales $869,018, cert: State)

6223 Reidy Medical Supply, Inc.
      P.O. Box 713079 Cincinnati, OH 45271
      (330) 686-4485 Ted Stitzel President
      Fax:
      Email: tstitzel@reidymed.com
      Website: www.reidymed.com
Dist disposable medical supplies. (Woman, estab 1992, empl 26, sales $9,000,000, cert: State)

6224 SGM Contracting Inc.
      9485 Root Rd PO Box 39374 North Ridgeville, OH 44039
      (216) 337-0742 Regina Morris Owner
      Fax: (440) 748-3349
      Email: gmorris@INTEGRITY.COM
      Website: www.sgmcontracting.com
Engineered medical support systems: cath, x-ray, surgical & exam light supports, operable walls & specialty support systems. (Woman/White, estab 2008, empl 3, sales $265,000, cert: City)

Oregon

6225 Ascent Group Medical LLC
      1631 NE Broadway St, Ste 308 Portland, OR 97211
      (888) 386-1112 Nuradin Kariye CEO
      Fax: (971) 275-1737
      Email: nuradin@ascentgroupmedical.com
      Website: www.ascentgroupmedical.com
Dist medical surgical supplies, equipment & medical staffing. (AA, estab 2011, empl 1, sales , cert: State)

Pennsylvania

6226 Coleman Laboratories
      1150 First Ave, Ste 501 King of Prussia, PA 19406
      (267) 644-7767 Le-Jun Yin President
      Fax: (484) 727-8828
      Email: lejun.yin@colemanlabs.com
      Website: www.colemanlabs.com
Develop & mfr IV status monitors. The LM series Fluid Level Monitor is a passive sensing device that alarms when the infusion fluid level is low. The device provides both visual and audible alarms when preset condition is met. (As-Pac, estab 2010, empl 4, sales $200,000, cert: NMSDC)

6227 Gray Physicians Supply, Inc.
      1330 Graham Ave Windber, PA 15963
      (814) 254-2188 Bethany Gray President
      Fax: (814) 509-6228
      Email: grayphysiciansupply@verizon.net
      Website: www.gpsmedicalonline.com
Dist stethoscopes, syringes, gauze, bandages, blood pressure cuffs, exam tables, latex & latex free gloves, sterile gloves. (Woman/White, estab 2012, empl 1, sales $107,000, cert: State)

6228 Hayes
      157 S Broad St, Ste 200 Lansdale, PA 19446
      (215) 855-0615 Glenn Phillips Dir, Provider Sales
      Fax: (215) 855-5218
      Email: gphillips@hayesinc.com
      Website: www.hayesinc.com
Devices, procedures, drugs/biologics, laboratory equipment & genetic tests. (Woman, estab 1989, empl 60, sales , cert: WBENC)

6229 Total Scope, Inc.
      17 Creek Pkwy Boothwyn, PA 19061
      (800) 471-2255 Denis Kennedy Natl Acct Mgr
      Fax: (800) 448-2680
      Email: dkennedy@totalscopeinc.com
      Website: www.totalscopeinc.com
Direct repair facility for flexible endoscopes, rigid endoscopes & surgical cameras. (Woman/White, estab 1992, empl 42, sales $7,127,486, cert: WBENC)

Puerto Rico

6230 Cesar Castillo, Inc.
      361 Calle Angel Buonomo St Tres Monjitas Industrial Pk Hato Rey, PR 00917
      (787) 999-1616 Luis Vazquez VP
      Fax:
      Email: lvazquez@cesarcastillo.com
      Website: www.cesarcastillo.com
Dist pharmaceutical products, health & beauty care, consumer goods, Specialty Pharmaceutical Products to Physicians and Specialty Pharmacies. (Hisp, estab 1946, empl 400, sales $177,000,000, cert: NMSDC)

6231 J.C. Gonzalez, Inc.
      2 St KM 178.2 Interior BO. Minillas Alto San German, PR 00683
      (787) 892-0047 Julio C. Gonzalez Santiago CEO
      Fax: (787) 264-3816
      Email: sales@jcgonzalezinc.com
      Website: www.jcgonzalezinc.com
Dist & service scientific & research equipment, laboratory equipment & consumables, microscopes, stereoscopes, freezers, refrigerators. (Hisp, estab 2001, empl 6, sales $865,047, cert: NMSDC, SDB)

6232 R & G Clean Room Laboratory, Inc.
      Ave Esmeralda #53 PMB 112 Guaynabo, PR 00969
      (787) 993-1781 Ruben Gomez President
      Fax: (787) 633-0029
      Email: rgomez@crlrd.com
      Website: www.cleanroomlab.com
R & G Clean Room Laboratory, Inc provides specialty laboratory and clean room products to Biotech, Medical Devices, Animal Research and Pharmaceutical. (Hisp, estab 2007, empl 10, sales $700,000, cert: NMSDC)

6233 Steri-Tech Inc.
Road 701 Km. 0.7, Salinas Ind. Park   Salinas, PR 00751
(787) 824-4040 Juan Arguelles Managing Dir
Fax: (787) 824-5552
Email: jarguelles@steri-tech.com
Website: www.steri-tech.com
Dist cleanroom products & contract sterilization services. (Hisp, estab 1986, empl 30, sales $3,020,000, cert: NMSDC)

South Carolina

6234 Cambridge Marketing, Inc.
P.O. Box 4481   Rock Hill, SC 39732
(803) 328-3167 Carol Ballard Owner
Fax: (803) 328-8140
Email: carolcmi@aol.com
Website: www.cambridgemarketingcorp.com
Dist hospital products: custom sterile kits, suture removal kits & ER kits. (Woman/Nat Ame, estab 1983, empl 2, sales $326,813, cert: State)

6235 Carolina Diagnostic Solutions
100 Old Cherokee Rd Ste F 301 Lexington, SC 29072
(803) 360-3410 Amanda Clark President
Fax: (877) 400-8388
Email: amanda@carolinadxsol.com
Website: www.carolinadiagnosticsolutions.com/
Pulmonary diagnostic related equipment, supplies, consultation & clinical service, body box/ plethysmography, gas measurement (FRC lung volumes, diffusing capacity), Spirometry equipment, handheld spirometer, portable spirometer. (Woman/White, estab 2014, empl 2, sales $99,000, cert: State)

6236 CPT Medical
6000 Pelham Rd   Greenville, SC 29615
(866) 584-3713 Connie Liesman CEO
Fax: (770) 234-4008
Email: cliesman@cptmed.com
Website: www.cptmed.com
Mfr surgical packs, kits, trays (sterile & non sterile), laboratory services. (Woman/White, estab 2010, empl 1, sales , cert: State)

6237 Professional Healthcare Services LLC
1007 Pendleton St   Greenville, SC 29601
(864) 505-6747 Doris Haley President
Fax: (864) 370-1201
Email: dhaley@phsonline.com
Website: www.phsonline.com
Alcohol & drug screening, pre employment physicals & health screening & health fairs, injury management programs & medical case management, On Site nursing care. (Woman/AA, estab 1998, empl 7, sales $259,000, cert: NMSDC)

Tennessee

6238 Global Industrial Components Inc.
705 S College St   Woodbury, TN 37190
(615) 563-5120 David W. Vance Automtive Product Mgr
Fax: (615) 563-5121
Email: dvance@gic-co.com
Website: www.gic-co.com
Dist medical kits, ER kits, roadside emergency kits, dental & medical supplies & equipment, component hardware. (Hisp, estab 1994, empl 47, sales $14,900,000, cert: NMSDC)

6239 GQSI
3777 Winchester Rd Ste 1 Memphis, TN 38118
(901) 365-9566 Williette Graham President
Fax:
Email: willgraham@gqsi.net
Website: www.gqsi.net
Engineering & technical services, medical devices, process & special processes equipment & validation, laser marking, CMM inspection services, product inspection, engineering support, supplier support services. (Woman/AA, estab 2005, empl 6, sales $160,000, cert: State)

6240 International Medical & Laboratory Supply, LLC
9093 Valkrie Lane   Lakeland, TN 38002
(901) 377-0191 Michael Tharps VP
Fax: (901) 377-0750
Email: michaeltharps@bellsouth.net
Website: www.internationalmedlab.com
Dist medical, safety, automotive, print management & labopratory supplies. (AA, estab 2004, empl 2, sales , cert: NMSDC)

6241 MRP, LLC dba Aquabiliti & AmUSA
5209 Linbar Dr Ste 640 Nashville, TN 37211
(615) 833-2633 Timir Patel CEO
Fax: (615) 425-2772
Email: accounts@aquabiliti.com
Website: www.aquabiliti.com
Mfr terminally sterilized pre-filled flush syringes used for maintaining IV (intravenous) catheter patency. (AA/As-Ind/As-Pac/Hisp, estab 2005, empl 25, sales $8,016,000, cert: NMSDC)

6242 The Premier Group
4600 Cromwell Ave, Ste 101   Memphis, TN 38118
(901) 346-9002 JW Gibson CEO
Fax: (901) 346-6642
Email: jwgibson@gibsoncompanies.com
Website: www.gibsoncompanies.com
Dist medical supplies, laboratory & scientific equipment & related supplies. (AA, estab 1900, empl 1, sales $8,692,576, cert: NMSDC)

Texas

6243 Alea Health dba Kersh Health
2600 Technology Dr, Ste 100   Plano, TX 75074
(469) 241-2500 Bruce Brown VP Advanced Clinical Services
Fax:
Email: program.coordinator@aleahealth.com
Website: www.kershhealth.com
Population health management, Health Risk Assessment, Diabetes Disease Management, Weight Loss, Stop Smoking, Activity Monitoring, Wellness Programs. (Nat Ame, estab 2015, empl 37, sales , cert: City)

6244 Alert Services, Inc.
P.O. Box 1088   San Marcos, TX 78666
(830) 372-3333 Sharon Morin Bid Agent
Fax: (830) 372-1447
Email: orders@alertservices.com
Website: www.alertservices.com
Dist sports medicine. (Woman/White, estab 1967, empl 25, sales $10,000,000,000, cert: State)

6245 Bracane Company, LLC
2300 McDermott, Ste 200-142   Plano, TX 75025
(888) 568-4271 Pamela Nelson President
Fax: (972) 727-6239
Email: pjnelson@bracaneco.com
Website: www.bracaneco.com
Dist medical supplies: lab equipment, Iv pumps, hospital beds, lab kits and supplies. (Woman/AA, estab 2002, empl 7, sales $211,000, cert: State, NMSDC, WBENC)

6246 Cina Pharamceutical
15622 Silver Ridge Dr, Ste B   Houston, TX 77090
(281) 602-3492 Mel Martino Office Mgr
Fax: (281) 602-3496
Email: mmartino.cinapharma@gmail.com
Website:
Dist pharmaceuticals. (AA, estab 2014, empl 15, sales $2,000,000, cert: State)

6247 Dalton Medical Corp.
1435 Bradley Lane, Ste 100   Carrollton, TX 75007
(972) 418-5129 Jim Lein President
Fax: (972) 248-0880
Email: jim@daltonmedical.com
Website: www.daltonmedical.com
Dist bariatric wheelchairs; walking aids, rollators, forearm rollators, walkers, and U-shape moving walkers with seat; cane stand; knee walker; foot pillow; acrylic medicine organizer; DryAid incontinence supply, protective underwear. (As-Pac, estab 1993, empl 35, sales $1,003,000, cert: State, NMSDC)

6248 GTL Supply Solutions, LLC
101C N Greenville Ave, Ste 423   Allen, TX 75002
(972) 359-7300 Famira Green Inside Sales Acct Mgr
Fax: (972) 359-1648
Email: fgreen@gtlsolutions.com
Website: www.gtlsolutions.com
Dist medical supplies & equipment. (Woman/AA, estab 2007, empl 10, sales $2,300,000, cert: State)

6249 Instrument Specialists, Inc.
32390 IH 10 West   Boerne, TX 78006
(800) 537-1945 Lori Brown VP Business Dev
Fax: (830) 249-9433
Email: Lori@isisurgery.com
Website: www.isisurgery.com
Endoscopic repairs, operating room supplies & surgical instrument cleaners. (Woman/White, estab 1978, empl 19, sales $2,877,906, cert: State, WBENC)

6250 Jackson & Associates, Inc.
8633 Schumacher Ln   Houston, TX 77063
(713) 777-1155 Saul Szub President
Fax: (713) 777-1450
Email: Saul@Dealmedical.com
Website: www.dealmedical.com
Dist medical, dental, surgical, pharmaceuticals, beauty, health & safety supplies & equipment. (Hisp, estab 1998, empl 6, sales $1,210,000, cert: State, City)

6251 MDD Marketing Inc.
5773 Woodway, Ste 214   Houston, TX 77057
(713) 647-8240 Dereck Dietrich Acct Mgr
Fax: (713) 647-9294
Email: dereck.dietrich@sterlingtonmedical.com
Website: www.aedtoday.com
AEDs and Manual Defibrillators. (Woman, estab 2000, empl 7, sales $2,000,000, cert: State)

6252 MJW Medical Solutions, Inc.
45 NE Loop 410, Ste 250   San Antonio, TX 78216
(210) 858-8997 Michael Williams CEO
Fax: (210) 858-6286
Email: mjwmedsol@att.net
Website: www.mjwmedicalsolutions.com
Medical equipment & supplies. (AA, estab 2006, empl 7, sales $3,500,000, cert: State)

6253 Mpulse Healthcare, LLC
54 Sugar Creek Center Ste 300 Sugarland, TX 77478
(281) 277-4410 Tyrone Dixon CEO
Fax: (281) 605-5598
Email: tdixon@mpulsehealth.com
Website: www.mpulsehealth.com
Dist medical, veterinary, dental, athletic & scientific supplies, products & equipment. (AA, estab 2005, empl 2, sales $100,000, cert: State, NMSDC)

6254 MRC - Medical Research Consultants
10550 Richmond Avenue Ste 310 Houston, TX 77042
(713) 528-6326 Gretchen Watson CEO
Fax: (713) 522-7386
Email: gwatson@mrchouston.com
Website: www.mrchouston.com
Medical litigation support services: nurse reviews, mass tort expertise, record retrieval & document management. (Woman/White, estab 1983, empl 268, sales $9,164,882, cert: WBENC)

6255   Pacific Star Corporation
     4350 S Wayside Dr Ste 106   Houston, TX 77087
     (713) 527-0889   Daud Hadi Sales Mgr
     Fax: (713) 481-8423
     Email: customer@pfstar.com
     Website: www.pfstar.com
Industrial supplies, laboratory supplies, medical supplies.
(As-Pac, estab 2005, empl 10, sales $4,000,000, cert: City)

6256   Prestige Ameritech LTD
     7201 Iron Horse Blvd   North Richland Hills, TX
     76180
     (817) 427-7200   Steven LaBracke Natl Dir of sales
     Fax:
     Email: stevel@prestigeameritech.com
     Website: www.prestigeameritech.com
Mfr surgcal masks & face shields. (Nat Ame, estab 2005,
empl 50, sales $7,000,000, cert: State)

6257   Products Unlimited, Inc.
     P.O. Box 339   Justin, TX 76247
     (940) 648-3073   Susan Raithel Sales Mgr
     Fax: (940) 648-3407
     Email: sraithel@products-unlimited.com
     Website: www.products-unlimited.com
Dist medical, lab & safety supplies & equipment. (Woman/
White, estab 1992, empl 7, sales $5,020,000, cert: State)

Virginia

6258   Best Medical International, Inc.
     7643 Fullerton Rd   Springfield, VA 22153
     (703) 451-2378   Manny Subramanian VP
     Fax: (703) 451-0196
     Email: manny@teambest.com
     Website: www.teambest.com
Develop, mfr & dist medical equipment & supplies. (As-
Ind, estab 1977, empl 120, sales , cert: State, NMSDC)

6259   Evident, Inc.
     739 Brooks Mill Rd   Union Hall, VA 24176
     (800) 576-7606   Michael Grimm President
     Fax: (540) 576-3942
     Email: michael@evident.cc
     Website: www.ShopEVIDENT.com
Crime scene & forensic identification products: fingerprint
products, evidence supplies, DNA collection materials,
identification equipment, & crime scene kits for police &
law enforcement. (Woman/White, estab 1992, empl 15,
sales , cert: State)

6260   JKICT, Inc.
     11240 Waples Mill Rd Ste 400   Fairfax, VA 22030
     (703) 474-4924   Jay Kim President
     Fax: (703) 825-1711
     Email: jeakuk@gmail.com
     Website: www.jkict.net
Digital X-Ray Imaging System, High frequency X-Ray
generator, Digital Radiology System, ECG Electrodes, ESU
Pencils, ESU Plates, TENS/EMS Units, Cutaneous Electrodes, Robotic Assisted Gait Training System. (As-Pac,
estab 2008, empl 2, sales , cert: State)

6261   M.E.Z Distributors LLC
     45910 Transamerica Plaza Ste 104   Sterling, VA
     20166
     (703) 821-6760   Adeel Shah President
     Fax: (703) 821-6952
     Email: adeel@sterlingsurgical.com
     Website: www.sterlingsurgical.com
Dist medical supplies, medical equipment & equipment
maintenance/service. (As-Ind, estab 2011, empl 7, sales
$1,700,000, cert: State)

6262   Reliant Medical Supply
     1431 Abingden Road   W. Chesterfield, VA 23236
     (804) 814-3180   stacey worthington Owner
     Fax: (804) 739-5377
     Email:
     staceyworthington@reliantmedicalsupply.com
     Website: www.reliantmedicalsupply.com
Dist medical supplies. (Woman/White, estab 2008, empl
2, sales , cert: State)

6263   Triton Light Medical, LLC
     8412 MacAndrew Terr   Chesterfield, VA 23838
     (804) 543-8137   Kennon Artis Principal
     Fax:
     Email: kennon@tritonlightmedical.com
     Website: www.tritonlightmedical.com
Dist our proprietary line of instruments crafted in
Tuttlingen, Germany, the global center of first-quality,
surgical-grade instruments and operating room (OR)
equipment. (AA, estab 2017, empl 1, sales $33,000, cert:
State, NMSDC)

Washington

6264   Anesthesia Equipment Supply, Inc.
     24301 Roberts Dr   Black Diamond, WA 98010
     (253) 631-8008   Glynis Wileman
     Fax: (360) 886-1350
     Email: gwileman@aesol.com
     Website: www.trucuff.com
Dist custom medical equipment. (Woman/White, estab
1967, empl 15, sales , cert: WBENC)

6265   Attunix Corporation
     405 114th Ave SE Ste 110   Bellevue, WA 98004
     (206) 774-3163   Matt O'Donnell CEO
     Fax: (310) 533-8127
     Email: matto@attunix.com
     Website: www.attunix.com
Custom Development, Portals and Web, Cloud Integra-
tion, and Mobile Solutions, Program Management.
Technology capabilities include Microsoft .Net, SQL
Server, Windows Phone 7, SharePoint (Hisp, estab 2006,
empl 12, sales $1,935,000, cert: State, NMSDC)

6266 Summit Imaging
      15000 Woodinville Redmond Rd Bldg B, Ste 800
      Woodinville, WA 98072
      (866) 586-3744 Jessica Curtiss Cstmr Outreach
      Coord
      Fax: (425) 491-7004
      Email: sales@mysummitimaging.com
      Website: www.mysummitimaging.com
Ultrasound transducers & parts. (As-Ind, estab 2006, empl
41, sales , cert: NMSDC)

Wisconsin

6267 Alpha Source Inc.
      6619 W Calumet Rd   Milwaukee, WI 53223
      (800) 654-9845 Norine Carlson-Weber
      Fax: (414) 760-2070
      Email: norine.carlson-weber@alphasource.com
      Website: www.alphasource.com
Mfr medical batteries, dist medical lighting, diagnostic
instruments, repair parts for medical equipment. (Woman/
White, estab 1986, empl 40, sales $18,219,000, cert:
WBENC)

6268 Fox Converting, Inc.
      P.O. Box 12795   Green Bay, WI 54307
      (920) 434-5272 Doreen Sorenson Accts Mgr
      Fax: (920) 434-5273
      Email: alexandra.vertz@foxconverting.com
      Website: www.foxconverting.com
Sterilization Bags/Envelopes, 8" & 16" Swabs -Sterilizable,
CSR Sterilizer Wraps, Hospital Bedside Disposal Bags, X-Ray
Envelopes. (As-Pac, estab 1960, empl 60, sales
$15,150,000, cert: State)

METAL CASTING
Non-ferrous foundries and molds. (Also see six other METAL categories). NAICS Code 33

California

6269　JDH Pacific Inc.
　　　14821 Artesia Blvd.　La Mirada, CA 90638
　　　(562) 207-1764　David Unger Sales Mgr
　　　Fax: (562) 926-8066
　　　Email: dunger@jdhpacific.com
　　　Website: www.jdhpacific.com
Cast & forged components. (As-Pac, estab 1989, empl 35, sales $18,000,000, cert: NMSDC)

6270　KFM International Industries, Inc.
　　　20277 Valley Blvd, Ste L　Walnut, CA 91789
　　　(626) 369-9556　Dennis Boribor engineer
　　　Fax: (909) 598-5811
　　　Email: dennis@kfmii.com
　　　Website: www.kfmii.com
Casting: Sand Cast, Die Casting, Investment Casting & Permanent Mold Forging: Hot & Cold Formed Sheet Metal Stamping Machining: CNC,Turning & Milling Powder Metal. (Woman/As-Pac, estab 2000, empl 6, sales $2,500,000, cert: City, CPUC)

Illinois

6271　Calumet Brass Foundry, Inc.
　　　14610 Lakeside Ave　Dolton, IL 60419
　　　(708) 344-7874　Dawn Stromberg President
　　　Fax:
　　　Email: dawn@calumetbrassfoundry.com
　　　Website: www.calumetbrassfoundry.com
Mfr bushings, bearings, liners & guides, bronze sand casting, foundry. (Woman/Hisp, estab , empl 1, sales , cert: WBENC)

Michigan

6272　Aerostar Manufacturing
　　　28275 Northline Rd　Romulus, MI 48174
　　　(734) 942-8440　Robert Johnson VP
　　　Fax: (734) 942-1947
　　　Email: rjohnson@aerostarmfg.com
　　　Website: www.aerostarmfg.com
CNC machining assembly, prototyping, machine castings & forgings, sand casting. (As-Ind/As-Pac, estab 1970, empl 170, sales $18,000,000, cert: NMSDC)

6273　DEE & Associates
　　　1665 Devonshire Dr　Troy, MI 48098
　　　(248) 641-0668　Pradeep Korgavkar Dir
　　　Fax: (248) 641-0040
　　　Email: pkorgavkar@aol.com
　　　Website:
Warehouse NAAMS standard products, import castings, machine castings, aluminum machined castings. (Woman/As-Ind, estab 1995, empl 2, sales $1,200,000, cert: NMSDC)

6274　GK Tech, LLC
　　　3331 W Big Beaver Rd Ste 106　Troy, MI 48084
　　　(248) 494-1960　Kelly Choi
　　　Fax: (509) 371-5153
　　　Email: kellychoi@gktechusa.com
　　　Website: www.gktechllc.com
Marketing specialist, consulting, business development, forging, die-casting, stamping, spring, magnesium pulley, rubber bushing, fasteners, machining, plastic injection molding. (Woman/As-Pac, estab 2015, empl 3, sales $64,000, cert: NMSDC)

6275　Lucerne International
　　　40 Corporate Dr　Auburn Hills, MI 48326
　　　(248) 674-7210　Karen Ryan Finance Mgr
　　　Fax: (248) 674-7215
　　　Email: kryan@lucerneintl.com
　　　Website: www.lucerneintl.com
Advanced metal forming components & assemblies, body structures, chassis systems & powertrain systems. Mfg aluminum & steel forgings, stampings, aluminum & zinc die castings & steel. (Woman, estab 1993, empl 58, sales , cert: WBENC)

METAL COATING
Includes plating, polishing, spray painting, metal finishing, paint stripping, de-oiling, anodizing, etc. (Also see six other METAL categories). NAICS Code 33

Arizona

6276 Best Finishing, Inc.
7670 E Broadway Blvd Ste 203 Tucson, AZ 85710
(520) 546-7763 Chris Schlesinger President
Fax: (520) 546-7765
Email: chris@bestfinishing.com
Website: www.bestfinishing.com
Metal finishing, polishing & buffing: aluminum castings, exhaust systems, metal moldings, body hardware, stampings, aluminum heads & blocks, magnesium components, closures. (Woman/White, estab 2000, empl 5, sales $985,981, cert: WBENC)

Connecticut

6277 Colonial Coatings, Inc.
66 Erna Ave Milford, CT 06460
(203) 783-9933 Russell Colon President
Fax: (203) 876-7680
Email: russ@colonialcoatings.com
Website: www.colonialcoatings.com
HAE Magnesium anodize, paint sealants, plasma & high temperature coatings. (Hisp, estab 1982, empl 50, sales $8,000,000, cert: NMSDC)

Florida

6278 AmeriCoat Corporation
2935 Barneys Pumps Pl Lakeland, FL 33812
(863) 667-1035 Shrikant Desai President
Fax: (863) 667-0289
Email: americoatusa@yahoo.com
Website: www.ameri-coat.com
Powder coating, fluoropolymers, metal finishing, coating, blasting, stripping. (As-Ind, estab 1995, empl 5, sales $277,169, cert: State)

Illinois

6279 Advance Coating Solutions
748 E Sunnyside Ave Libertyville, IL 60048
(847) 732-1118 Joseph Webb CEO
Fax: (847) 918-0444
Email: joseph@acsco.us
Website: www.acsco.us
Epoxy coating solutions. (AA, estab 2008, empl 7, sales $91,937, cert: State, NMSDC)

Indiana

6280 Danco Anodizing
2450 Deelyn Dr Warsaw, IN 46580
(574) 269-5900 Dean Zentz VP Ops
Fax: (574) 269-5966
Email: info@danco.net
Website: www.danco.net
Aluminum anodizing, anodizing, stainless steel, citric & nitric passivation electropolishing . (Woman/White, estab 1971, empl 150, sales $15,000,000, cert: WBENC)

6281 Riepen LLC.
P.O. Box 2050 Warsaw, IN 46581
(574) 269-5900 Tim Zentz Sales Mgr
Fax: (574) 269-5966
Email: tim.z@danco.net
Website: www.danco.net
Titanium Anodize (Type 2 & Color), Aluminum Anodize, Electropolish, Passivation (Nitric & Citric), Laser Marking, Electroless Nickel, Chemfilm, NDT Services, Low Friction Chrome Coating & metal finishing services. (Woman, estab 1971, empl 100, sales , cert: WBENC)

Massachusetts

6282 The Falmer Associates, Inc.
96 Swampscott Rd Unit 10 Salem, MA 01970
(978) 745-4000 Stacy Ames President
Fax: (978) 745-4077
Email: sames@falmer.com
Website: www.falmer.com
Machining, grinding & thermal spray coating svcs: metal, ceramic & carbide coatings, wear, corrosion, erosion, galling, thermal insulation or conduction, electrical insulation or conduction, anti-skid. (Woman/White, estab 1961, empl 7, sales $400,000, cert: WBENC)

Michigan

6283 Dhake Industries
15169 Northville Rd   Plymouth, MI 48170
(734) 420-0101 Arjun Dhake VP
Fax: (734) 420-3210
Email: adhake@dhakeindustries.com
Website: www.dhakeindustries.com
Mfr automotive coatings. (As-Ind, estab 1979, empl 25, sales $12,000,000, cert: NMSDC)

6284   Great Lakes Finishing, Inc.
510 W Hackley Ave   Muskegon, MI 49444
(231) 733-9566 Diana Bench President
Fax: (231) 733-4226
Email: dbench@greatlakesfinishinginc.com
Website: www.greatlakesfinishinginc.com
Alkaline and Chloride zinc plating. Barrel plating for small parts. Rack plating for parts up to 12' long. Two automatic lines. RoHS compliant. Chromates: bright, yellow, black and olive drab. (Woman, estab 2002, empl 12, sales $1,000,000, cert: WBENC)

6285   Jackson Tumble Finish
1801 Mitchell St Jackson, MI 49203
(517) 787-0368 Denise L. Losey President
Fax: (517) 787-8752
Email: denise@jacksontumble.com
Website: www.jacksontumble.com
Zinc phosphate, fine, med, heavy grain; calcium modified fine grain phosphate, manganese phosphate, phos. and lube, black oxide, tumble and vibratory deburr, shot blast, glass bead, acid pickle, wash/degrease, and passivate, sort and packaging. (Woman/White, estab 1956, empl 45, sales $4,700,000, cert: WBENC)

Minnesota

6286   Coating Solutions, Inc.
13525 Fenway Blvd N Hugo, MN 55038
(651) 762-5700 Kimberly Northrop CFO
Fax: (651) 762-8555
Email: knorthrop@coatingsolutions.com
Website: www.coatingsolutions.com
DuPont teflon industrial coatings. (Woman/White, estab 1995, empl 7, sales , cert: WBENC)

New Jersey

6287   Karnak Corporation
330 Central Ave Clark, NJ 07066
(800) 526-4236 Sarah Jane Jelin President
Fax: (732) 388-9422
Email: sjjelin@karnakcorp.com
Website: www.karnakcorp.com
Protective roof coatings, reflective roof coatings, aluminum coatings, elastomeric coatings, Energy Star & LEED compliant coatings, dampproofing, waterproofing, flashing cements, primers, sealants, membranes, reinforcing fabrics. (Woman/White, estab 1933, empl 97, sales $79,000,000, cert: WBENC)

Ohio

6288   Cleveland Die & Mfg. Co.
20303 First Ave Middleburg Heights, OH 44130
(440) 243-3404 Marty Curry sales/engineering
Fax:
Email: mcurry@clevelanddie.com
Website: www.clevelanddie.com/
Ecoat & powder coat line, automatic & single hit presses, spot & robotic welders, CNC machining. (Hisp, estab 1973, empl 300, sales $24,000,000, cert: NMSDC)

6289   Great Lakes Maintenance, Inc.
1213 Maple Ave. Hamilton, OH 45011
(513) 423-0800 Marilyn Barlow President
Fax: (513) 423-0888
Email: glmbarlow@hotmail.com
Website: www.greatlakesmtce.com
Tank linings & coatings, abrasive blasting, industrial & maintenance painting, leak repair to live gas, water, sludge, fume exhaust & liquor piping, secondary containment coatings & repairs, fiberglass repairs & fabrications. (Woman/Hisp, estab 1997, empl 14, sales $14,000,000, cert: State, NMSDC, WBENC)

6290   Steelcote, Inc.
215 Eastview Dr Brooklyn Hts., OH 44131
(216) 635-2585 Mohan Kapahi President
Fax: (216) 635-2584
Email: mohan_kapahi@steelcoteinc.com
Website: www.steelcoteinc.com
Anti-corrosion coatings on metal stampings & assemblies. (AA/As-Ind, estab 2002, empl 9, sales $1,000,000, cert: NMSDC)

6291   Westwood Finishing Company
5881 Wolf Creek Pike Trotwood, OH 45426
(937) 854-6608 Marcia Richley Owner
Fax:
Email: marcia1118@aol.com
Website: www.westfinish.com
Apply all types of paint material: wet coating, epoxy, urethane, enamels and copper coatings (EMI and RFI shielding. (Woman/White, estab 1995, empl 11, sales $530,864, cert: WBENC)

South Carolina

6292 JBE, Inc.
P.O. Box 337 512 Hartland Dr Hartsville, SC 29551
(843) 332-0589 John Miller Dir of Business Dev
Fax: (843) 332-0592
Email: johnmiller@jbeinc.net
Website: www.jbeinc.net
Metal finishing; preplate finishing; abrasive blasting, manual & auto buffing, plating needs, chrome, decorative & hard, brite & electroless, silver & tin. Pre-eng bldgs; structure steel & metal fab. Sub-assembly for auto field. (AA, estab 1982, empl 49, sales $348,000,000, cert: NMSDC)

6293 McKechnie Vehicle Components USA, Inc.
12117 CR Koon Hwy Newberry, SC 29108
(803) 364-7417 Jim Palazzolo New Business Devel
Fax: (803) 364-2831
Email: jimpalazzolo@mvcusa.com
Website: www.mvcusa.com
Metal stamping, finishing, automotive stamping, buffing, roll forming, painting, powder painting, acrylic powder paint, assembly, robotic assembly. (Woman/White, estab 1988, empl 310, sales $77,000,000, cert: WBENC)

Tennessee

6294 Y&W Technologies LLC
2883 Director Cove Memphis, TN 38131
(901) 396-3380 Willis Yates President
Fax: (901) 396-3402
Email: wyates@ywtech.com
Website: www.ywtech.com
Chrome plating, titantium anodizing, metal finishing, electroplating, laser marking, critic & nitric passivation. (AA, estab 2001, empl 20, sales $1,250,000, cert: State, City, NMSDC)

Texas

6295 Cimcon Finishing, LLC
2314 Executive Dr Garland, TX 75041
(972) 840-0934 Mike Gilbert VP Sales
Fax:
Email: mike@cimconfinishing.com
Website: www.cimconfinishing.com
Electroplate: hard anodize, anodize, chemfilm, electroless nickel, nickel, tin, zinc, powder coat. (AA, estab 1994, empl 48, sales $3,200,000, cert: NMSDC)

6296 Texas Finishing Company
P.O. Box 59445 Dallas, TX 75229
(972) 416-2961 Carolyn Beard President
Fax: (972) 418-5951
Email: cbeard@texasfinishing.com
Website: www.texasfinishing.com
Paint application & custom metal fabrication. (Woman/White, estab 1982, empl 45, sales , cert: State, WBENC)

Washington

6297 Dunkin & Bush, Inc.
P.O. Box 97080 Kirkland, WA 98083
(425) 885-7064 Deidre Dunkin President
Fax: (425) 885-3790
Email: Ddunkin@dunkinandbush.com
Website: www.dunkinandbush.com
Industrial painting, scaffolding, insulation, rigging, containment, lead abatement, shop coating aplication, concrete restoration, plural applied tank linings, abrasive blasting, specialty blasting, water jetting, high heat coating applications. (Woman/White, estab 2008, empl 300, sales , cert: WBENC)

METAL FABRICATION
Includes tanks and tank liners, steel containers, aircraft framework parts, electronic chassis, work stands, ornamental ironwork, fences, sheet metal components, etc. (Also see six other METAL categories). NAICS Code 33

Alaska

6298   Katmai Support Services, LLC
701 E Tudor Rd, Ste 215   Anchorage, AK 99503
(907) 333-7000   Katherine Tweidt Business Dev
Fax: (907) 333-7099
Email: eric@anc8a.com
Website:
Mfr, overhaul, repair & modification of advanced composites & bonded honeycomb structures for numerous space & airframe applications in new generations of aircraft and space vehicles. (Nat Ame, estab 2003, empl 1, sales $521,411, cert: State)

Alabama

6299   Majestic Solutions, Inc.
241 Production Ave   Madison, AL 35758
(256) 772-3232   Grace Lo President
Fax: (256) 772-3237
Email: grace@majesticsolutionsinc.net
Website: www.majesticsolutionsinc.net
Mfr institutional metal furniture & security products: lockers, bunk beds, electronic enclosures, dayroom tables, benches, access panel, shelves, storage cabinets, railings, stairs, wire mesh partition/fence, tubings. (Woman/As-Pac, estab 2004, empl 10, sales $1,000,000, cert: State, City, SDB)

Arizona

6300   K&R Holdings, Inc.
2322 W Detroit Pl   Chandler, AZ 85224
(480) 236-2682   Wayne Armoogam President
Fax: (480) 857-6177
Email: warmoogam@lumawaresafety.com
Website: www.lumawaresafety.com
Supply and install photoluminescent egress systems for facilities. Our technologies for egress requires no electricity, external power source or batteries to provide the illumination required for safe movement of employees (As-Ind, estab 2007, empl 5, sales $100,000, cert: City, NMSDC)

6301   Kirin Manufacturing
3300 E. 36th St 85713   Tucson, AZ 85268
(520) 940-6278   William Johnson Sales and Mktg
Fax:
Email: william@kirinmfg.com
Website: www.kirinmfg.com
Prototype manufacturing equipment & special equipment for various aerospace OEM's. Form, shape, mill, weld & finish a multitude of materials into an infinite number of fabrications. (Hisp, estab 2011, empl 30, sales $5,178,000, cert: NMSDC)

6302   PVB Fabrications, Inc.
2311 N 14th Ave   Tucson, AZ 85705
(520) 623-3529   Pete Van Bogaert President
Fax: (520) 647-9915
Email: pete@pvbfabs.com
Website: www.pvbfabs.com
Metal fabrication, waterjet cutting & CNC plasma cutting capabilities. (Hisp, estab 2003, empl 39, sales $5,100,000, cert: 8(a))

6303   Vics Welding Company, LLC
8376 N El Mirage Rd Bldg 3   El Mirage, AZ 85335
(623) 925-5696   Victor Valencia President
Fax: (623) 882-3623
Email: vic@vicswelding.com
Website: www.vicswelding.com
Metal fabrication, field welding, structural, piping, ASME pressure vessel repair or manufacturing, aerospace welding. (Woman/Hisp, estab 1996, empl 6, sales $970,000, cert: City)

California

6304   A-1 Truck and Equipment, Inc.
1588 Los Angeles Ave   Ventura, CA 93004
(805) 659-1817   Dan Poole President
Fax:
Email: dan@a1truck.com
Website: www.a1truck.com
Rotating equipment repair, body repair, truck, trailers & equipment blasting & paint repairs, metal fabrication & welding. (Hisp, estab 2008, empl 30, sales $2,200,000, cert: NMSDC)

6305   Bueno Enterprises
25589 Seaboard Ln   Hayward, CA 94545
(510) 782-2225   Lydia Bueno Sec/Treas
Fax: (510) 782-2513
Email: lydia@metalspecialists.com
Website: www.metalspecialists.com
Precision sheet metal, laser cutting, machining & powder coat painting, fabricate metal parts. (Hisp, estab 1988, empl 10, sales , cert: CPUC)

6306   Columbia Sanitary Products, Inc.
1622 Browning   Irvine, CA 92606
(847) 559-6132   Paul Escalera
Fax:
Email: p.escalera@columbiasinks.com
Website: www.columbiasinks.com
Mfr stainless steel products: sinks, wash stations, sink accessories, faucets, heavy-duty forks, shovels, scoops, valves, knife sterilizers & trays. (Woman/White, estab 1949, empl 8, sales , cert: State)

6307   CX Enterprise Inc.
14408 Iseli Rd   Santa Fe Springs, CA 90670
(562) 407-1088   Steve Chin Mgr
Fax: (562) 407-3688
Email: stevechin@cxenterprise.com
Website: www.cxenterprise.com
Steel strapping. (Woman/As-Pac, estab 1991, empl 5, sales $1,771,000, cert: CPUC)

6308 International Rite-Way Products
1725 S Campus Ave   Ontario, CA 91761
(909) 985-8300 Ravi Joshi President
Fax: (909) 985-8388
Email: ravi@intlrwp.com
Website: www.intlrwp.com
Precision aerospace sheet metal mfg: roll forming, hydro-forming, extrusion & skin stretch forming of aerospace components (ribs, spars, brackets, formers, etc.). Complete program management capabilities. (As-Ind, estab 1994, empl 10, sales $1,250,000, cert: 8(a))

6309 Pacific HVAC Depot Corporation
3029 Teagarden St   San Leandro, CA 94577
(510) 346-6500 Phyllis La Voy CEO
Fax: (510) 346-5700
Email: pacifichvacdepot@aol.com
Website: www.pacifichvacdepot.com
Dist hardcast duct sealants, coils & condensers, sheet metal products, fittings & heat ducts. (Woman/Hisp, estab 2000, empl 6, sales $2,300,000, cert: WBENC)

6310 Scott Engineering, Inc.
5051 Edison Ave   Chino, CA 91710
(909) 594-9637 Deborah Davis CFO
Fax: (909) 595-0379
Email: debi@scott-eng.com
Website: www.scott-eng.com
Mfr medium voltage custom fabricated mild steel, stainless steel, & aluminum electrical cabinets & metal fabricated products. (Hisp, estab 1967, empl 75, sales $14,990,887, cert: CPUC)

6311 Tanfel
1945 Camino Vida Roble, Ste J   Carlsbad, CA 92008
(760) 720-9632 Greg Lange Owner
Fax: (760) 720-9706
Email: glange@tanfel.com
Website: www.tanfel.com
Custom metal parts: stamping, extrusion, casting, metal injection molding, machining, turning, prototype to large production with warehousing capabilities. (Hisp, estab 2008, empl 5, sales , cert: NMSDC)

6312 THISAI LLC
1834 Blazewood St   Simi Valley, CA 93063
(747) 206-3886 Ramalingam Subramaniam Owner
Fax:
Email: ram@thisaillc.com
Website: www.thisaillc.com
Electrical products, cables, switches, wire, lighting fixtures, metal products, aluminum, sheet metal, laser cut, bent & fabricated. (As-Ind/As-Pac, estab 2015, empl 2, sales , cert: State)

6313 West Coast Form Grinding
2548 S Fairview St   Santa Ana, CA 92704
(714) 540-5621 Adrian Calderon President
Fax: (714) 540-5620
Email: adrian@precisioncorepins.com
Website: www.precisioncorepins.com
Mfr mold components, core pins, sleeves, ejector pins, luer taper pins. (Hisp, estab 2005, empl 10, sales $1,222,670, cert: NMSDC)

Colorado

6314 Excalibur Machine & Sheet Metal
208 W Buchanan St, Unit C   Colorado Springs, CO 80907
(719) 520-5404 Douglas McDaniel Plant Mgr
Fax: (719) 520-5265
Email: doug@excaliburmfg.com
Website: www.excaliburmfg.com/
Precision machining & sheet metal fabrication, welding, assembly, powder coating. (Hisp, estab 1989, empl 25, sales $2,600,000, cert: NMSDC)

Conencticut

6315 Turbo America Technology, LLC
1400 Old North Colony Rd   Meriden, CT 06450
(860) 970-8777 Liliane Yebarth
Fax: (813) 258-8825
Email: liliane@turboamericatech.com
Website: www.turboamericatech.com
Mfr & repair Industrial Gas Turbine components. (Hisp, estab 2014, empl 5, sales $341,000, cert: NMSDC)

Delaware

6316 M. Davis & Sons, Inc.
19 Germay Dr   Wilmington, DE 19804
(302) 993-3323 Christina MacMillan Mgr of Business Dev
Fax: (302) 998-4984
Email: christina.macmillan@mdavisinc.com
Website: www.mdavisinc.com
Metal fabrication: welding, piping, mechancial installations, sheetmetal, structural steel, tank fabrication & control panels. (Woman/White, estab 1870, empl 325, sales $51,697,420, cert: WBENC)

Florida

6317 Blue Water Dynamics LLC DBA Dougherty Manufacturing
301 S Old County Rd   Edgewater, FL 32132
(386) 316-5939 Davey Carroll Sales Dir
Fax: (386) 957-5464
Email: dcarroll@dougherty-mfg.com
Website: www.doughertymanufacturing.com
Fabricate metals (aluminum, steel & stainless steel) & composites/FRP, engineering, design, tooling, prototyping & manufacturing. (Woman, estab 2010, empl 46, sales $2,500,000, cert: State, WBENC)

6318 Coastal Steel Inc.
      870 Cidco Rd   Cocoa, FL 32926
      (321) 632-8228 Dale Coxwell
      Fax: (678) 807-2981
      Email: dcoxwell@coastalsteelmfg.com
      Website: www.coastalsteel.com
Complex & Iconic Structures (AISC Fabrication & Erection),
Ride & Show (AISC Fabrication & Installation), Machining
(Large Capacity 5 Axis Vertical & Horiz), CMM (Zeiss Contra
G2 & FERO). (Nat Ame, estab 1976, empl 90, sales
$14,000,000, cert: State, NMSDC)

Georgia

6319 Harbor Enterprises, LLC
      1207 Sunset Dr   Thomasville, GA 31792
      (229) 226-0911 Brandy Spradlin CEO
      Fax: (229) 236-0780
      Email: sba@harborenterprisesllc.com
      Website: www.survive-a-storm.com
Wood & metal fabrication, mfr solid steel above ground
safe rooms & underground storm shelters. (Nat Ame,
estab 2009, empl 25, sales $5,500,000, cert: NMSDC)

Iowa

6320 Air Control, Inc.
      80 14th Ave N   Clinton, IA 52732
      (563) 243-7228 Mary Connell President
      Fax: (563) 243-4290
      Email: marypat@acifabricators.com
      Website: www.acifabricators.com
HVAC contracting, specialty steel fabrication, tank fabrication. (Woman/White, estab 1956, empl 45, sales
$8,000,000, cert: 8(a))

6321 EIP Manufacturing, LLC
      2677 - 221st St P.O. Box 336 Earlville, IA 52041
      (800) 942-2226 Kathy Krapfl VP sales/Mktg
      Fax: (563) 923-7525
      Email: kkrapfl@eipmfg.com
      Website: www.eipmfg.com
Steel fabricated components, structural steel, rebar.
(Woman, estab 1975, empl 45, sales $7,700,000, cert:
State)

Idaho

6322 Burly Products, Inc.
      3999 St. Joe Ave   Post Falls, ID 83854
      (208) 262-9531 Stephani Morris Admin Asst
      Fax: (208) 262-9541
      Email: Stephani@Burlyproducts.com
      Website: www.burlyproducts.com
Design & mfr steel & aluminum products. (Nat Ame, estab
2006, empl 18, sales , cert: State)

Illinois

6323 American Chrome Chicago Company, Inc.
      518 Crossroads Pkwy   Bolingbrook, IL 60440
      (630) 685-2200 Linda Hou President
      Fax: (630) 685-2211
      Email: linda.hou@americanchrome.com
      Website: www.americanchrome.com
Dist chrome, stainless steel & PC/ABS chrome products,
mirrors, exhaust products, clam shells for catalytic
converters, shock absorbers & components, rubber
products / bushings, u-joints, grease caps, air tubes,
clutch control rods. (Woman/As-Pac, estab 1983, empl
26, sales $11,695,000, cert: NMSDC, WBENC)

6324 Combined Metals of Chicago LLC
      2401 W Grant Ave   Bellwood, IL 60104
      (708) 547-8800 John Dicello Dir minority Dev
      Fax: (708) 547-1037
      Email: johnd@combmet.com
      Website: www.combmet.com
Stainless steel: flat rolled stainless steel strip, sheet &
foil. (As-Pac, estab 1975, empl 279, sales , cert: NMSDC)

6325 KSO Metalfab, Inc.
      250 Roma Jean Pkwy   Streamwood, IL 60107
      (630) 372-1200 Dora Kuzelka President
      Fax: (630) 372-1251
      Email: dkuzelka@kso.com
      Website: www.kso.com
Precision sheet metal fabrication: short to large runs.
(Woman/White, estab 1973, empl 33, sales $3,700,000,
cert: State)

6326 Patel International
      30 N River Rd Ste 102 Des Plaines, IL 60016
      (847) 795-3006 Steve Gordon Sales Rep
      Fax: (847) 795-0323
      Email: sgordon@patelintl.com
      Website: www.sejasmi.com
Injection molding, aluminum die casting. (As-Ind, estab
2005, empl 65, sales $8,000,000, cert: NMSDC)

6327 Rockford Specialties Company
      5601 Industrial Ave   Rockford, IL 61111
      (815) 877-6000 Lisa Stankey President
      Fax: (815) 877-7435
      Email: lisas@rswire.com
      Website: www.rockfordspecialties.com
Mfr wire, tube & sheet metal custom displays & components, counter racks, free standing floor displays, wire
dividers & aisle extenders, plating & powder painting,
laser cutting, forming & welding, MIG, TIG, resistance &
robotic welding. (Woman/White, estab 1979, empl 45,
sales $10,780,000, cert: WBENC)

6328 W.E.B. Production & Fabricating, Inc.
      448 N Artesian Ave   Chicago, IL 60612
      (312) 733-6800 Maureen Kendziera President
      Fax: (312) 733-6801
      Email: maureenk@webproductionandfabricating.com
      Website: www.webproductionandfabricating.com
Welding, shearing, bending, punching, stamping, &
drilling, MIG/TIG welding, aluminum, stainless & carbon
steel, handrails, guardrails & metal stair frames.
(Woman/White, estab 1993, empl 24, sales $3,068,370,
cert: State)

6329 Young Technology Inc.
      900 W. Fullerton Ave. Addison, IL 60101
      (630) 690-4320 Young Sohn President
      Fax: (630) 543-5883
      Email: youngsohn@ytinc.com
      Website: www.ytinc.com
Mfr molded rubber, plastic & forged steel: shifter knobs,
bezels, decorative molding & cable components, leather
wrapped & chrome plated. (As-Pac, estab 1985, empl 350,
sales $6,000,000, cert: NMSDC)

Indiana

6330 Diversified Quality Services of Indiana, LLC
      1315 W 18th St Anderson, IN 46016
      (765) 644-7712 Sharon Montgomery CEO
      Fax: (765) 641-7784
      Email: sharon.montgomery@dqsicorp.com
      Website: www.dqsicorp.com
Design, prototyping, production, modification & repair
steel racks, containers & dunnage. (AA, estab 2003, empl
123, sales $5,000,000, cert: NMSDC)

6331 Eagle Magnetic Company Inc.
      7417 Crawfordsville Rd Indianapolis, IN 46214
      (317) 297-1030 Ron Jaggers VP Inside Sales
      Fax: (317) 299-1323
      Email: RJaggers@EagleMagnetic.com
      Website: www.eaglemagnetic.com
Magnetic shielding, precision sheet metal fabrication,
precision machining. (Woman/White, estab 1970, empl 39,
sales $3,275,000, cert: State)

6332 Electric Metal Fab, Inc.
      4889 Helmsburg Rd Nashville, IN 47448
      (812) 988-9353 Mandy Chittum President
      Fax: (812) 988-7080
      Email: mandy@electricmetalfab.com
      Website: www.electricmetalfab.com
Mfr Stainless Steel Equip & Products, turn-key conveyor
systems for production lines, specialty products, etc.
Cabinets, Carts, Tables, Racks, Platforms, Lab Furnishings,
etc. (Woman/White, estab 1993, empl 16, sales
$1,177,089, cert: WBENC)

6333 Indiana Bridge-Midwest Steel, Inc.
      1810 S Macedonia Ave Muncie, IN 47307
      (765) 288-1985 Sheryl Bronnenberg Office Mgr
      Fax: (765) 287-1985
      Email: sheryl@indianabridge.net
      Website: www.indianabridge.net/
Fabricate structural steel & rack structures, design build &
erection services. (As-Pac, estab 1900, empl 35, sales
$26,790,376, cert: NMSDC)

6334 Irons Metal Processing LLC
      1605 Adler Cir Ste I Portage, IN 46368
      (219) 764-9999 Earmon Irons CEO
      Fax: (219) 764-5091
      Email: earmon@ironsmetalprocessing.com
      Website: www.ironsmetalprocessing.com
Processed metal products. (AA, estab 2007, empl 3, sales ,
cert: NMSDC)

6335 Lacay Fabrication and Mfg Inc.
      52941 Glenview Dr Elkhart, IN 46514
      (574) 288-4678 Ann Filley President
      Fax: (574) 288-2921
      Email: ann@lacayfab.com
      Website: www.lacayfab.com
Mfr material handling racks, Baskets, Industrial &
Production Welding, Machining, Robotic Welding,
Stamping, Custom Fabrication, Prototyping. (Woman/
White, estab 1975, empl 70, sales , cert: WBENC)

6336 Royalty Investments, LLC
      2476 E US Hwy 50 Seymour, IN 47274
      (812) 358-3534 Marshall Royalty Member
      Fax: (812) 358-2351
      Email: mroyalty@cranehillmachine.com
      Website: www.cranehillmachine.com
Machining, fabricating & assembly: steel, aluminum &
plastic components. Design, engineering & coating
applications. (Woman/White, estab 1989, empl 30, sales
$3,714,618, cert: State)

6337 The Phillips Company, Inc.
      6330 East 100 South Columbus, IN 47201
      (812) 378-3797 Valerie Phillips CEO
      Fax: (812) 378-5941
      Email: valeriephillips@thephillipscompany.com
      Website: www.thephillipscompany.com
Cast iron & aluminum parts: pulleys, lube pumps, oil
coolers, wire harnesses, water pumps, blocks, heads,
gear covers. (Woman/AA, estab 1986, empl 47, sales
$2,800,000, cert: NMSDC)

Kansas

6338 PTMW, Inc.
      5040 NW US HWY 24 Topeka, KS 66618
      (785) 232-7792 Patti jon Goff President
      Fax: (785) 232-7793
      Email: pgoff@ptmw.com
      Website: www.ptmw.com
OEM metal fabrication & assembly: metal parts, enclo-
sures & cases, assembly & powdercoating. (Woman/
White, estab 1983, empl 214, sales $53,000,000, cert:
CPUC, WBENC)

Louisiana

6339 JRE LLC dba Ascension Roofing and Sheet Metal
      2140 S Philippe Ave Gonzales, LA 70737
      (225) 647-3576 Rebecca Evans President
      Fax: (225) 647-6013
      Email: rebevans@ascensionrsm.com
      Website: www.ascensionrsm.com
Metal fabrication: stainless steel, carbon steel, galvanized metal & specialty alloys. (Woman/White, estab
1954, empl 31, sales $2,260,000, cert: WBENC)

6340   New Orleans Copper, Inc.
     827 Tchoupitoulas St   New Orleans, LA 70130
     (504) 525-7426   Pamela Schafer President
     Fax: (504) 529-2904
     Email: pschafer_@bellsouth.net
     Website: www.neworleanscopperinc.com
Pipe & tube bending services. (Woman/White, estab 1956, empl 6, sales , cert: WBENC)

Massachusetts

6341   Heat Exchanger Products Corp.
     55 Industrial Park Rd   Hingham, MA 02043
     (781) 749-0220   Tracy Bonnyman President
     Fax: (781) 740-8738
     Email: hepco@hepcoplugs.com
     Website: www.HeatExchangerProducts.com
Mfr tube plugs for condensers, heat exchangers, boilers in sizes 5/8" up to 1 1/4" in materials; Brass, 316 and 314 Stainless Steel, Titanium and Ultem & Non-Metallic High Performance Polymer plug. (Woman/White, estab 1985, empl 5, sales $300,000, cert: WBENC)

6342   Precision Engineering Inc
     29 Industrial Dr P.O. Box 546   Uxbridge, MA 01569
     (508) 278-5700   Liora Stone President
     Fax: (508) 278-5725
     Email: lstone@precisionengineering.com
     Website: www.precisionengineering.com
Laser cutting, punching, forming, powder coating, AWS-certified welding, spot welding, hardware insertion, finishing (graining/deburring), assembly, kitting, labeling, part marking. (Woman/White, estab 1988, empl 40, sales $6,139,429, cert: State, WBENC)

6343   Wrobel Engineering Co., Inc.
     154 Bodwell St   Avon, MA 02322
     (508) 586-8338   Michael Long General/QA Mgr.
     Fax: (508) 586-8466
     Email: mlong@wrobeleng.com
     Website: www.wrobeleng.com
Mfr precision sheet metal fabricated parts per customer specs, precision machining, milling & turning, metal stamping, long & short runs, tool & die making, assembly mechanical & electrical, welding all materials. (Woman/White, estab 1976, empl 98, sales $14,800,000, cert: State, City)

Maryland

6344   Waltons Welding & Fabrication, Inc.
     155 Prospect Dr   Huntingtown, MD 20639
     (301) 855-2944   Fay Walton President
     Fax: (410) 286-2643
     Email: metalfab@waltonswelding.net
     Website: www.waltonswelding.com
Metal fabrication: elctrode welding, mig welding, tig welding, aluminum welding, stainless steel welding, tourch cutting, saw cutting, plasma cutting, shear cutting, drilling, rolling, bending, sanding, grinding, tapping & punching. (Woman/White, estab 2000, empl 5, sales $154,007, cert: State)

Michigan

6345   Airodyne Industries, Inc.
     95 E 10 Mile Rd   Madison Heights, MI 48071
     (248) 548-3336   Celeste Herpel President
     Fax: (248) 548-3338
     Email: caherpel@airodyne.com
     Website: www.airodyne.com
Mfr & dist aerodynamic & fuel-saving devices. (Woman/White, estab 2004, empl 3, sales $1,265,000, cert: WBENC)

6346   Anderson Express, Inc.
     580 W Sherman Blvd   Muskegon Heights, MI 49444
     (231) 733-6001   Angel Ball HR Mgr
     Fax:
     Email: aball@andersonexpressinc.com
     Website: www.andersonexpressinc.com
Rapid tooling & tooling prototypes for small & medium projects. (Woman/White, estab 2011, empl 17, sales , cert: WBENC)

6347   Clips & Clamps Industries
     15050 Keel St   Plymouth, MI 48170
     (734) 455-0880   Jeff Aznavorian President
     Fax: (734) 455-4270
     Email: jaznavorian@clipsclamps.com
     Website: www.clipsclamps.com
Metal forming, progressive dies, four slide, CNC wire forming, tool building, MIG & TIG welding, tapping, riveting, automated assemblies, prototyping & production volumes, engineering services, design services, sales support. (Woman/White, estab 1954, empl 62, sales , cert: WBENC)

6348   Cortar Laser and Fab. LLC
     12828 Emerson Dr   Brighton, MI 48116
     (248) 446-1110   Livia Walker Managing Member
     Fax: (248) 446-1113
     Email: lwalker@cortarlaser.com
     Website:
Dist precision laser cut blanks & formed sheet metal parts. (Woman/Hisp, estab 2007, empl 4, sales , cert: WBENC)

6349   Dawson Mfg Co. - Benton Harbor Division
     1042 N Crystal Ave   Benton Harbor, MI 49022
     (269) 925-0100   Neil Trivedi VP
     Fax: (269) 925-0997
     Email: neil.trivedi@vibracoustic.com.com
     Website: www.dawsonmfg.com
Mfr body mounts, engine mounts, strut mounts, link assemblies & bushings, dist anti-vibration components, rubber injection molding. (As-Pac, estab 1988, empl 90, sales $36,000,000, cert: NMSDC)

6350 DGH Enterprises, Inc. dba K-O Products Co.
      1225 Milton St   Benton Harbor, MI 49022
      (269) 925-0657 Barbara Herrold CEO
      Fax: (269) 925-9020
      Email: barbaraherrold@koproducts.com
      Website: www.koproducts.com
Metal stampings, welded & fabricated assemblies,
electrical & mechanical assemblies, metal hardware, metal
truck parts & assemblies, metal stamped components for
auto, appliances, off-road equipment, metal welding, mig
welding, spot welding. (Woman/White, estab 1938, empl
28, sales $3,500,000, cert: WBENC)

6351 Gill Industries Inc.
      5271 Plainfield Ave   Grand Rapids, MI 49525
      (616) 559-2700 Regina Wilk Sales Acct Mgr
      Fax:
      Email: rwilk@gill-industries.com
      Website: www.gill-industries.com/
Stamped weldments & structural assemblies, seat, chassis,
body & powertrain structural assemblies, folding head
restraint & seat mechanisms. (Woman/White, estab 1964,
empl 1923, sales $340,000,000, cert: WBENC)

6352 Globe Tech LLC.
      101 Industrial Dr   Plymouth, MI 48170
      (734)6562200 Amanda Menchinger President
      Fax:
      Email: mmenchinger@globe-tech.biz
      Website: www.globe-tech.biz
Machining, fabrication & welding, metal stamping.
(Woman/White, estab 2009, empl 72, sales , cert: WBENC)

6353 Harbin Steel
      440 Burroughs St, Ste 133   Detroit, MI 48202
      (248)9745793 Anthony Harbin President
      Fax:
      Email: Anthony@harbinsteel.com
      Website: www.harbinsteel.com
Miscellaneous/structural steel fabrication & installation.
(AA, estab 2016, empl 1, sales , cert: NMSDC)

6354 HDN F&A, Inc. dba F&A Fabricating
      104 Arbor St   Battle Creek, MI 49015
      (269) 965-3268 Hiep Nguyen President
      Fax: (269) 965-8371
      Email: hiep.nguyen@fa-fabricating.com
      Website: www.fa-fabricating.com
Custom sheet metal fabrication, food grade stainless steel,
dist sheet metal, tubing. (As-Pac, estab 1956, empl 25,
sales $3,000,000, cert: NMSDC)

6355 I F Metalworks
      14009 Achyl   Warren, MI 48313
      (586) 776-8311 Karen Arondoski President
      Fax: (586) 776-8331
      Email: karen@ifmetalworks.com
      Website: www.ifmetalworks.com
Welding, fabrication, design, weldments, assemblies,
prototype, short & long run, decorative, railings, staircases, ballisters, custom furniture, artistic works, architectural, trailers, foodservice production equipment, racks &
repair. (Woman/White, estab 2002, empl 10, sales
$425,000, cert: WBENC)

6356 International Specialty Tube
      6600 Mt. Elliott   Detroit, MI 48124
      (313) 841-6900 Jason VanDeVen Sales Mgr
      Fax: (313) 841-6398
      Email: Quality@ISTube.com
      Website: www.istube.com
Mfr stainless steel tubing for automotive exhaust. (AA,
estab , empl 1, sales $29,000,000, cert: NMSDC)

6357 JLC Group LLC
      287 Executive Dr   Troy, MI 48083
      (248) 792-3281 William Chen Director, Ph.D.
      Fax: (248) 479-1888
      Email: wchen@jlcgroupllc.com
      Website: www.jlcgroupllc.com
Dist casting parts, forging parts & machine finished
parts, plastic injected molds & plastic parts. (Woman/As-
Pac, estab 2010, empl 5, sales , cert: WBENC)

6358 Jorgensen Steel Machining & Fabrication
      PO Box 315   TEKONSHA, MI 49092
      (517) 767-4600 Matt Jorgensen President
      Fax: (517) 767-4616
      Email: mjorgensen@jorgensen-usa.com
      Website: www.jorgensen-usa.com
Design & manufacture contract machinery & contour
formed products for the aviation, space & defense
industries. (Nat Ame, estab 2000, empl 15, sales
$2,400,000, cert: NMSDC)

6359 Midbrook Industrial Washers Inc.
      2080 Brooklyn Rd P.O. Box 867 Jackson, MI 49204
      (517) 787-3481 Rodney Sims Govt & diversity
      sales
      Fax: (517) 787-2349
      Email: rsims@midbrookindustrial.com
      Website: www.midbrookindustrial.com
Custom sheet metal fabrication. (Woman/AA/As-Pac,
estab 2012, empl 70, sales , cert: WBENC)

6360 Mintech LLC
      P.O. Box 428   Niles, MI 49120
      (269) 683-4551 Minnie Warren President
      Fax:
      Email: minnie@mintechllc.com
      Website: www.mintechllc.com
Metal fabrication, stamping, light assembly, sort,
vibratory deburring, rollforming. (Woman/White, estab ,
empl 1, sales , cert: WBENC)

6361 MRD Aerospace, LLC
      23565 Schoenherr Rd   Warren, MI 48089
      (586) 443-5350 Michele Dew Managing Member
      Fax: (586) 443-5360
      Email: r7mdew@aol.com
      Website: www.mrdaerospace.com
Prototype machining, milling, turning, jig grinding, ID/
OD grinding, surface grinding, honing & lapping,
hydraulic cylinder blocks, drive shafts, rotors, housings,
broaching ID splines, valve plates, pistons, sleeved
cylinder blocks, etc. (Woman/White, estab 2011, empl 9,
sales $440,311, cert: WBENC)

6362 Northern Wings Repair, Inc.
      6679 County Rd 392   Newberry, MI 49868
      (906) 477-6176 David Goudreau President
      Fax: (906) 477-6175
      Email: dave@nwrepair.com
      Website: www.nwrepair.com
Mfr, repair & dist commercial & military aircraft parts,
material & services. (Nat Ame, estab 2001, empl 20, sales
$11,650,000, cert: State)

6363 Rochester Tube Products, Ltd.
      51366 Fischer Park Dr   Shelby Township, MI 48316
      (586) 726-4816 Jennie Preston Dir of Mktg
      Fax:
      Email: jennie@rochestertube.com
      Website: www.rochestertube.com
Fabricate steel parts; specifically tube. (Woman/White,
estab 1973, empl 25, sales , cert: WBENC)

6364 Rose-A-Lee Technologies, Inc
      7448 19 Mile Rd   Sterling Heights, MI 48314
      (586) 799-4555 Julie Wood Dir Business Dev
      Fax:
      Email: jwood@rosealeetechnologies.com
      Website: www.rosealeetechnologies.com
CAD design (surface and solid modeling), stamping,
assembly/kitting, tube bending, welding (mig, tig, stud
arc), etc. (Woman, estab 2013, empl 2, sales , cert:
WBENC)

6365 Santanna Tool &Design LLC
      25880 Commerce Dr 48071   Madison Hgts, MI
      48071
      (248) 541-3500 Jamilce & Newton President
      Fax: (248) 541-5095
      Email: jsnewton@santannatool.com
      Website: www.santannatool.com
Design & mfr conveyors, tooling & welding. (Woman/Hisp,
estab 1937, empl 75, sales $1,376,927,385, cert: NMSDC,
WBENC)

6366 The Ideal Group
      2525 Clark St   Detroit, MI 48209
      (313) 842-7290 Linzie Venegas Sales
      Fax: (313) 842-7860
      Email: linzie@idealshield.com
      Website: www.weareideal.com
Architectural & engineering svcs; general contracting &
construction mgmt, rigging. Mfr, dist, fabricate & erect
structural & misc steel. Patent for "Ideal Shield" Protective Guard Rail System. (Hisp, estab 1979, empl 120, sales ,
cert: NMSDC)

6367 Thompson Marketing, LLC
      15890 Sturgeon CT   Roseville, MI 48066
      (248) 761-6802 Derek Thompson President
      Fax: (586) 294-4907
      Email: derek@tmsglobalservices.com
      Website: www.tmsglobalservices.com
Mfr shipping racks & fixtures. (AA, estab 1999, empl 7,
sales $435,000, cert: NMSDC)

Minnesota

6368 JML Fabrication, LLC
      21054 Chippendale Ct   Farmington, MN 55024
      (612) 444-3025 Margo Lackore President
      Fax: (651) 460-3674
      Email: margo@jmlfabrication.com
      Website: www.jmlfabrication.com
Aluminum welding, Aluminum Fabrication, Stainless
steel welding, Stainless steel fabrication, Steel welding,
Steel fabrication, Certified Welding, Bending, Shearing.
MIG/TIG welding, Flux core welding, large structural
steel fabrication. (Woman/As-Pac, estab 2004, empl 7,
sales $1,485,762, cert: WBENC)

6369 Jones Metal Inc.
      3201 3rd Ave   Mankato, MN 56001
      (507) 625-4436 John Clifford Natl Business Devel
      Fax: (507) 625-2994
      Email: jclifford@jonesmetalinc.com
      Website: www.jonesmetalinc.com
Metal fabrication, laser technology, water jet, saw,
punch presses, press brakes, rollers & machining
capabilities. (Woman/White, estab 1942, empl 100, sales
$12,000,000, cert: WBENC)

6370 Wyoming Machine, Inc.
      30680 Forest Blvd P.O. Box 180 Stacy, MN 55079
      (651) 462-4156 Lori Tapani President
      Fax: (651) 462-5238
      Email: ltapani@wyomingmachine.com
      Website: www.wyomingmachine.com
Precision metal fabrication: aser cutting, CNC punching,
forming & welding. (Woman/White, estab 1974, empl
65, sales , cert: WBENC)

Missouri

6371 Sinclair Industries, Inc.
      1317 Kentucky Ave   St. Louis, MO 63110
      (314) 535-6335 Jagdish Hinduja President
      Fax: (314) 535-7848
      Email: sinclair.inc@sbcglobal.net
      Website: www.snclr.com
Metal fabrication. (As-Ind, estab 1978, empl 9, sales
$1,200,000, cert: City)

Montana

6372 Montana Hydraulics, LLC
      888 Florence St   Helena, MT 59601
      (814) 592-5412 Jay Krause Natl Contracts Mgr
      Fax: (406) 449-3465
      Email: mthyd@ironfurnace.com
      Website: www.montanahydraulics.com
Mfr industrial metal, compaction attachments for heavy
equipment (roller compaction buckets & wheels,
vibratory compaction buckets), bedding boxes &
doweling machines, CNC machining, turning & lathe,
manual machining, custom fabrication. (Woman/White,
estab 1998, empl 47, sales $6,027,445, cert: State)

North Carolina

6373 QMF Metal & Electronic Solutions, Inc.
324 Berry Garden Rd   Kernersville, NC 27284
(336) 992-6501 Raymond Polomski Sales Assoc
Fax: (336) 996-1931
Email: rpolomski@qmf-usa.com
Website: www.qmf-usa.com
Custom sheet metal fabrication, punching, forming, welding, robotic welding, machining, hardware installation, wet and powder coat painting, silk screening, mechanical & electronic assembly. (Woman/White, estab 1978, empl 75, sales $7,000,000, cert: WBENC)

New Jersey

6374 Central Metals, Inc.
1054 S 2nd St   Camden, NJ 08103
(856) 963-5844 Susan Vilotti President
Fax: (856) 963-1789
Email: vilotti@aol.com
Website: www.centralmetals.com
Steel fabrication, structural steel, miscellaneous metals, ornamental metals, railings, stairs & iron. (Woman, estab 1981, empl 57, sales $29,770,000, cert: WBENC, NWBOC)

6375 Holtec International
1 Holtec Blvd   Camden, NJ 08104
(856) 797-0900 Myron Kaczmarsky Sales and Mktg Mgr
Fax: (856) 797-0909
Email: m.kaczmarsky@holtec.com
Website: www.holtecinternational.com
Design & mfr storage systems for wet & dry spent nuclear fuel, takes, vessels, hoists, cranes. (As-Pac, estab 1900, empl 1, sales $99,000,000, cert: NMSDC)

New York

6376 ASP Industries
9 Evelyn St   Rochester, NY 14606
(585) 254-9130 Robert Uerkvitz Acct Exec
Fax: (585) 254-9139
Email: robert@aspindustries.com
Website: www.aspindustries.com
Sheet metal fabrication, laser, welding, machine. (Woman/White, estab 1980, empl 25, sales $205,000, cert: State)

6377 Bailey Manufacturing Co., LLC
10987 Bennett State Rd   Forestville, NY 14062
(716) 965-2731 John Hines President
Fax:
Email: bailey03@netsync.net
Website: www.baileymfgcollc.com
Metal Stamping, Sheet Metal Fabrication, Welding, Multi-Part Assemblies, Zinc Plating, Rust Proofing, Quality Inspection, E-Coat Painting. (AA, estab 2002, empl 100, sales $8,500,000, cert: NMSDC)

6378 Technical Welding Fabricators LLC
27 Thatcher St   Albany, NY 12207
(518) 463-2229 Carole Boyer Owner
Fax: (518) 462-1360
Email: caroleboyer@aol.com
Website: www.technicalweldingfabricators.com
Metals & structural steel, railings, columns, beams, repairs. (Woman/White, estab 2006, empl 5, sales $1,600,000, cert: State)

6379 Truform Manufacturing
1500 N Clinton Ave   Rochester, NY 14621
(585) 458-1090 Rick Hardwick Sales Mgr
Fax: (585) 458-1155
Email: rick@randhmarketing.com
Website: www.truformmfg.net
Sheet metal fabrication: metal brackets, panels, covers, boxes & enclosures. (AA, estab 1992, empl 80, sales $27,582,000, cert: State, NMSDC)

Ohio

6380 Armor Metal Group
4600 Mason-Montgomery Rd   Mason, OH 45040
(800) 543-7417 John Ravana Inside sales
Fax: (877) 891-8200
Email: jravana@witt.com
Website: www.witt.com
Fabrication, burn, grind, machining, lathe, blanchard, surface, roll, laser, form, weld, paint, blast. (Woman/White, estab 1950, empl 250, sales $51,000,000, cert: WBENC)

6381 Extol of Ohio, Inc.
208 Republic St   Norwalk, OH 44857
(419) 668-2072 Andrea Buggele Inside Sales
Fax: (419) 663-1992
Email: andrea@extolohio.com
Website: www.extolohio.com
Fabricate & dist thermally efficient, non-wicking rigid pipe insulation products & accessories. (Woman, estab 1985, empl 50, sales $18,939,725, cert: WBENC)

6382 Fabrication Group LLC
3453 W 140th St   Cleveland, OH 44111
(216) 251-1125 Patricia Setlock President
Fax: (216) 251-1135
Email: patty@fabricationgroup.com
Website: www.fabricationgroup.com
Metal fab, welded assemblies, guardrails, handrails, bollards, stair railings, cutting, shearing, roll forming, punch presses, sheet metal fab equip. (Woman/White, estab 2008, empl 10, sales $433,345, cert: WBENC)

6383 Ferragon Corporation
11103 Memphis Ave   Cleveland, OH 44144
(216) 671-6161 Luis J. Gonzalez Mgr
Fax: (216) 671-4078
Email: lgonzalez@ferrousmetalprocessing.com
Website: www.ferrousmetalprocessing.com
Hot roll steel toll processing: pickle, slit, level, shear, decamber & warehousing. (Hisp, estab 1983, empl 144, sales $16,200,000, cert: NMSDC)

6384   Journey Steel, Inc.
        7655 Production Dr   Cincinnati, OH 45237
        (513) 731-2930 Barbara Smith President
        Fax: (513) 731-2936
        Email: bsmith@journeysteel.com
        Website: www.journeysteel.com/
Remodeling & Expanding: retrofit piping, staircases,
overhead walkways. Structural & Mechanical Erector:
mechanical devices & assorted equipment supported &
erected. (Woman/AA, estab 2009, empl 4, sales
$3,900,000, cert: State, NMSDC, WBENC)

6385   KeYAH International Trading, LLC
        4655 Urbana Rd   Springfield, OH 45502
        (937) 399-3140 Ramon Vasquez VP
        Fax: (937) 917-0016
        Email: rvasquez@keyahint.com
        Website: www.keyahint.com
Die cut, RF weld/sonic weld, automotive interior trim
components, sub-assemblies. (Woman/Nat Ame, estab
2000, empl 85, sales $2,000,000, cert: WBENC)

6386   Magni-Power Company
        5511 Lincoln Way E   Wooster, OH 44691
        (330) 264-3637 Kim Coblentz New Business Dev
        Mgr
        Fax: (330) 264-9035
        Email: kcoblentz@magnipower.com
        Website: www.magnipower.com
Metal fabrication & stamping: process steel, aluminum,
stainless steel, CNC punching, forming, laser cutting,
robotic welding, in-house powder coating & assembly. (As-
Ind, estab 1948, empl 230, sales $27,000,000, cert:
NMSDC)

6387   Main Metal Products, Inc.
        8800 US Highway 68 N   West Liberty, OH 43357
        (937) 465-9353 Cynthia Haddix Owner
        Fax: (937) 465-6772
        Email: mmp@loganrec.com
        Website:
Welding & fabricating, custom fixturing, custom
prototyping, automotive rack mfg, rack designs & modifications, material handling products, custom machine
guarding, mig & tig welding. (Woman, estab 1995, empl
17, sales $1,250,000, cert: WBENC)

6388   MCM Industries Co., Inc.
        25825 Science Park Dr Ste 260 Beachwood, OH
        44122
        (216) 292-4708 Gloria Reljanovic Owner
        Fax: (216) 292-4730
        Email: greljanovic@mcmindustries.com
        Website: www.mcmindustries.com
Mfr, dist & import finished steel & plastic parts: precision
& bicycle chains, non-metal chains, steel ball bearings.
(Woman/Hisp, estab 1986, empl 50, sales , cert: NMSDC)

6389   Middletown Tube Works, Inc.
        2201 Trine St   Middletown, OH 45044
        (513) 727-0080 Angela Phillips CEO
        Fax:
        Email: aphillips@middletowntube.com
        Website: www.middletowntube.com
Mfr as-welded steel tubes for Automotive, Appliance,
HVAC and Packaging industries. (Woman/White, estab ,
empl 1, sales , cert: WBENC)

6390   Morrison Metalweld Process Corporation
        3685 Stutz Dr, Ste 102   Canfield, OH 44406
        (330) 702-5188 Robin Eisenbrei CEO
        Fax: (330) 702-5198
        Email: robin@morrisonmetalweld.com
        Website: www.morrisonmetalweld.com
Railroad track & crane rail welding services & products.
(Woman/White, estab 1929, empl 9, sales $2,221,823,
cert: WBENC)

6391   Salinas Inudustries
        1010 N Forth St   Miamisburg, OH 45342
        (937) 866-0886 Robert Salinas President
        Fax: (937) 866-7371
        Email: salinas@infinet.com
        Website:
Mfr sound deadners & insulators for automotive use, die
cut & assemble finished goods. (Hisp, estab 2000, empl
10, sales $754,217, cert: NMSDC)

6392   Shelby Welded Tube
        5578 State Route 61 North   Shelby, OH 44875
        (419) 347-1720 Kelly Kleman Sales
        Fax: (419) 347-5231
        Email: kkleman@shelbytube.com
        Website: www.shelbytube.com
Dist welded steel tubes. (Woman, estab 1967, empl 81,
sales $22,000,000, cert: WBENC)

6393   Thieman Quality Metal Fab, Inc.
        05140 Dicke Rd   New Bremen, OH 45869
        (419) 629-2612 Ben Wissman Sales Mgr
        Fax: (419) 629-3720
        Email: bwissman@thieman.com
        Website: www.thieman.com
Engineering: AutoCAD, 2000i, Solid Edge & Metamation
CAD/CAM Software, Welding:
MIG, TIG, Robotic & Spot welding, Fabrication:
Sawing, Machining, Drilling, Hy Def Plasma, Turret
Punch, Lasers, Press Break. (Woman, estab 1951, empl
90, sales $16,200,000, cert: NWBOC)

6394   Tylok International, Inc.
        1061 E 260th St   Euclid, OH 44132
        (216) 261-7310 Michael Palinkas VP sales
        Fax: (216) 261-7317
        Email: mpalinkas@tylok.com
        Website: www.tylok.com
Mfr stainless steel, brass & steel tube fittings, pipe &
weld fittings, ball valves, needle valves, manifolds &
double block & bleed valves. (Woman/White, estab
1955, empl 75, sales $8,600,000, cert: WBENC)

Oregon

6395   Ebony Iron Works, Inc.
       2401 NW 22nd Ave   Portland, OR 97210
       (503) 224-3038 Edward Holmes President
       Fax: (503) 224-3062
       Email: ebonyiron@aol.com
       Website:
Structural steel fabrication. (AA, estab 1993, empl 25, sales
, cert: State)

6396   General Sheet Metal Works, Inc.
       P.O. Box 1490   Clackamas, OR 97015
       (503) 650-0405 Carol Duncan President
       Fax: (503) 650-0405
       Email: carol@gsmw.com
       Website: www.gsmw.com
Sheet metal fabrication, installation, design & support.
(Woman/White, estab 1932, empl 40, sales $7,620,093,
cert: WBENC)

Pennsylvania

6397   American Roll Suppliers, Inc.
       186 Compass Rd   Parkesburg, PA 19365
       (610) 857-2988 Karen Neuhauser Ruppert President
       Fax: (610) 857-9150
       Email: KNeuhauser@peoplepc.com
       Website:
Metal fabrication & machining. (Woman, estab , empl 1,
sales , cert: WBENC)

6398   Cromedy Construction Corporation
       5702 Newtown Ave   Philadelphia, PA 19120
       (215) 437-7606 Bill Cromedy President
       Fax: (215) 437-7655
       Email: bcromedy@cromedyconstruction.com
       Website: www.cromedyconstruction.com
HVAC, Sheetmetal (AA, estab 2004, empl 15, sales
$14,000,000, cert: State, NMSDC, 8(a))

6399   General Carbide Corporation
       1151 Garden St   Greensburg, PA 15601
       (800) 245-2465 Carrie Gartland Administration Exec
       Fax: (724) 836-1852
       Email: sales@generalcarbide.com
       Website: www.generalcarbide.com
Mfr tungsten carbide preforms & blanks used in wear
resistant, cutting & metal forming operations. (Woman,
estab , empl 1, sales , cert: WBENC)

Puerto Rico

6400   RAC Enterprises, Inc.
       Road 1, KM 24.8   Caguas, PR 00726
       (787) 789-9338 Vivian Carballo President
       Fax: (787) 789-9339
       Email: rac@racsteeldrums.com
       Website: www.racsteeldrums.com
Mfr steel drums, dist plastic, steel & stainless containers, sorbent products, secondary containment: spill
pallets, drain seals. Stormwater management products,
PPE & material handling, monitors. (Hisp, estab 1995,
empl 15, sales $2,300,000, cert: NMSDC)

South Carolina

6401   E=MC4I Inc.
       3216 Industry Dr Ste C North Charleston, SC
       29418
       (843) 225-4091 Jennifer Gomez President
       Fax: (843) 552-4532
       Email: jennifer@emc4i.com
       Website: www.emc4i.com
Metal fabricating: fencing & machine gun mounts,
communication assemblies & military parts. (Woman/
Hisp, estab 1997, empl 30, sales $1,000,000, cert: 8(a))

6402   J.I.T. Manufacturing, Inc.
       428 Oglesby Lane P.O. Box 1017 Cowpens, SC
       29330
       (864) 463-0581 Dan Hunter Production / Sales
       Mgr.
       Fax: (864) 463-0583
       Email: dan@jitmanufacturing.com
       Website: www.jitmfg.net
Laser cutting, welding, forming, CNC punching, CNC
machines, fabrication, sheetmetal, powdercoating,
pressbrakes, modifications, spot welding, control boxes,
mounting plates, brackets, CAD programing, Cad design.
(Woman, estab 1992, empl 22, sales $2,910,792, cert:
City, WBENC)

6403   Lamar's Fabrication, Inc.
       210 Ashley Circle   North Augusta, SC 29841
       (706) 513-1992 Michael Lamar CEO
       Fax: (803) 613-0706
       Email: michael.lfab@gmail.com
       Website: www.LamarsFabrication.com
Process Pipe, Structural Steel, Carbon steel, Stainless
steel, Chromemoly, Inconel, Hastelloy, GTAW, SMAW,
FCAW, CNC Plasma cutting, C.A.D. Detailing and Design,
3D Modeling. (AA, estab 2008, empl 2, sales $27,185,
cert: State, City)

Texas

6404   A & A Aero Structures Inc.
        800 Schneider Bldg M   Cibolo, TX 78108
        (210) 566-3660 Ronald D Atkins Owner
        Fax: (210) 566-3660
        Email: ron@aaaerostructures.com
        Website: www.aaaerostructures.com
Fabricate, assemble & mfr aircraft parts & components.
(AA, estab 2007, empl 4, sales , cert: State)

6405   Advanced Turbine Solutions LLC
        15653 N Brentwood   Channelview, TX 77530
        (314) 494-1900 Tim Donohue InterNatl Sales Mgr
        Fax: (281) 452-2441
        Email: DonohueT@ATSHouston.com
        Website: www.ATSHouston.com
Fabrication, piping, structural & skids, welding, carbon
steel to exotic metals. (As-Pac/Hisp, estab 2010, empl 12,
sales $2,850,000, cert: NMSDC)

6406   GABS LLC
        1011 Regal Row   Dallas, TX 75247
        (972) 354-6512 Dot Haymann CEO
        Fax: (214) 819-9655
        Email: dhaymann@guard-all.com
        Website: www.guard-all.com
Engineer, design & manufacture steel framed, tension
fabric buildings for a multitude of applications. (Woman/
White, estab 2011, empl 45, sales $4,990,000, cert: State,
WBENC)

6407   GST Manufacturing, Ltd.
        4201 Janada St   Haltom City, TX 76117
        (817) 520-2320 Sharrian Lamberth Owner
        Fax: (817) 520-2323
        Email: info@gstmanufacturing.com
        Website: www.gstmanufacturing.com
Metal fabrication, in plant maintenance. (Woman/White,
estab 2000, empl 250, sales $50,800,000, cert: State)

6408   Harris Composites, Inc.
        600 Holmes Dr Granbury, TX 76048
        (817) 279-9546 Debra Harris CEO
        Fax: (817) 573-4974
        Email: hci@itexas.net
        Website: www.harriscomposites.com
Mfr & produce all size composite parts. (Woman, estab
2000, empl 25, sales $3,500,000, cert: State, WBENC)

6409   Llano River Fence Company, LLC
        11418 Lake June Rd   Balch Springs, TX 75180
        (972) 286-4316 Ashanti Smith President
        Fax: (866) 355-6979
        Email: asmith@llanoriverfence.com
        Website: www.llanoriverfence.com
Custom iron products: gates, iron doors, handrails, &
puppy panels, fencing, automatic gates installation &
automatic gate operator maintenance. (Woman/AA, estab
2006, empl 13, sales $1,250,000, cert: State)

6410   Magni-Fab Southwest Company
        P.O. Box 578   Howe, TX 75459
        (903) 532-5533 Wayne Swineford Dir sales/
        Admin
        Fax: (903) 532-6992
        Email: wswineford@mfsw.net
        Website: www.magnifab.com
Sheet metal fabrication, shearing, CNC punching, laser
cutting, stamping, forming, sawing, spot welding, arc
welding, robotic welding, powder coating. (As-Pac,
estab 1971, empl 105, sales $10,350,000, cert: NMSDC)

6411   MagRabbit-Alamo Iron Works, LLC
        P.O. Box 2341   San Antonio, TX 78298
        (210) 704-8520 Wayne Dennis diversity Coord
        Fax: (210) 705-8514
        Email: wdennis@aiwnet.com
        Website: www.magrabbit-aiw.com
Dist industrial supplies, steel service & fabrication, hand
& power tools, equipment repair & installation, logistics,
transportation & freight forwarding. (As-Pac, estab
2004, empl 150, sales $1,573,543, cert: NMSDC)

6412   Quality Fabrication & Design
        955 Freeport Pkwy Ste 400 Coppell, TX 75019
        (972) 304-3266 Alex Pier President
        Fax: (972) 745-2032
        Email: alexpier@quality-fabrication.com
        Website: www.quality-fabrication.com
Mfr custom stainless steel & mild steel equipment:
conveyors, drags, belts & bucket, structural steel
platforms, waterjet cutting & complete food processing
lines. (Hisp, estab 1987, empl 65, sales $6,000,000, cert:
State, NMSDC)

6413   Texas Finishing Company
        P.O. Box 59445   Dallas, TX 75229
        (972) 416-2961 Carolyn Beard President
        Fax: (972) 418-5951
        Email: cbeard@texasfinishing.com
        Website: www.texasfinishing.com
Paint application & custom metal fabrication. (Woman/
White, estab 1982, empl 45, sales , cert: State, WBENC)

Virginia

6414   Metal Tech Inc.
        2629 Richard Ave NE   Roanoke, VA 24012
        (540) 798-4193 Natasha Crowder Project
        Estimator
        Fax: (540) 343-4397
        Email: metaltech@cox.net
        Website: www.metaltechincorporated.com
Custom metal fabrication: sandblasting, punching,
machine cutting, CNC plasma cutting, water jet cutting,
pipe bending, ornamental bender machine, surface
preparation & coating. (Woman/White, estab 1996,
empl 2, sales $150,000, cert: State)

6415   Shickel Corporation
       115 Dry River Rd   Bridgewater, VA 22812
       (540) 828-2536 Don Crawford Sales Mgr
       Fax:
       Email: donc@shickel.com
       Website: www.shickel.com
Custom metal fabricating, engineering, design, project management, welding, fabrication, precision machining, finishing & installation services. (Woman/White, estab 1938, empl 80, sales $11,200,000, cert: State)

6416   Valley Industrial Piping, Inc.
       P.O. Box 1751   Waynesboro, VA 22980
       (540) 942-4469 Michelle Carter President
       Fax: (540) 942-5974
       Email: michelle@valleypipes.com
       Website: www.valleypipes.com
Industrial maintenance, fabricate & install process skid systems, pressure vessels, tank installation & repair, structural steel, carbon & stainless steel platforms, mezzanines, ladders & stairways, piping, in-line instrumentation & equipment installation (Woman/White, estab 2004, empl 10, sales $984,906, cert: State, WBENC)

Vermont

6417   Vermont Precision Tools, Inc.
       10 Precision Ln   Swanton, VT 05488
       (802) 868-4246 Monica Greene President
       Fax: (802) 868-7180
       Email: mgreene@vermontprecisiontools.com
       Website: www.vermontprecisiontools.com
Mfr high quality precision ground medical burr blanks for the OEM medical industry. (Woman/White, estab 1968, empl 190, sales $32,527,681, cert: WBENC)

Washington

6418   JIT Manufacturing
       19510 144th Ave NE, Ste E 7   Woodinville, WA 98072
       (425) 487-0672 Duane Parrish Sales Mgr
       Fax:
       Email: duanep@jit-mfg.com
       Website: www.jit-mfg.com
Aerospace Sheet Metal Manufacturing, complete parts, Punching, Laser, Bending, Forming, Hardware & Assembly, Finish, Chem Treat, Paint, Primer. (Woman, estab 1985, empl 60, sales , cert: State)

Wisconsin

6419   Church Metal Spinning Company
       5050 N 124th St   Milwaukee, WI 53225
       (414) 461-6460 Brenda Birno President
       Fax:
       Email: markv@churchmetal.com
       Website: www.churchmetal.com
Metal fabrications including metal stampings, metal spun, laser cut, press brake parts. Also, complete assembly and welding of multi-part components. (Woman/White, estab 1944, empl 30, sales $6,600,000, cert: State)

6420   Creative CNC LLC
       712 Rose Dr   Hartland, WI 53029
       (262) 347-3939 Janet Murphy President
       Fax: (262) 247-0249
       Email: jmurphy@creativecnc.net
       Website: www.creativecnc.net
Mfr metal parts: aerospace, medical, automotive, turbomachinery, etc. (Woman/White, estab 2010, empl 3, sales , cert: WBENC)

6421   Metal-Era, Inc.
       1600 Airport Rd   Waukesha, WI 53188
       (800) 373-9156 Jody Delie Channel Mktg Mgr
       Fax: (800) 558-2162
       Email: info@metalera.com
       Website: www.metalera.com/Home.aspx
Mfr perimeter edge metal for the low sloped commercial roofing industry. (Hisp, estab 1980, empl 148, sales $36,700,000, cert: State, NMSDC)

6422   Ridgway LLC dba The Price Erecting Co.
       10910 W Lapham St   Milwaukee, WI 53214
       (414) 778-0300 Fred Quilling estimator
       Fax: (414) 778-4787
       Email: fquilling@priceerecting.com
       Website: www.priceerecting.com
Equipment installation & removal, steel erection, fabrication & machining. (Woman/White, estab 1915, empl 40, sales $9,000,000, cert: State)

6423   Safeway Sling USA, Inc.
       6209 Industrial Ct   Greendale, WI 53129
       (414) 421-7303 Susan Szymczak President
       Fax: (414) 421-7523
       Email: sales@safewaysling.com
       Website: www.safewaysling.com
Mfr nylon & polyester web lifting slings, polyester round slings, alloy chain slings, wire rope slings, metal mesh slings & tie down assemblies. (Woman/White, estab 1980, empl 36, sales $6,800,000, cert: WBENC)

METAL STAMPING
Services include forming, welding, tapping, tooling, tube fabrication and bending, etc. (Also see six other METAL categories). NAICS Code 33

California

6424 Proformance Manufacturing, Inc.
1922 Elise Circle   Corona, CA 92879
(951) 279-1230 Tim Borth Technical Sales Mgr
Fax: (951) 734-6542
Email: tborth@proformancemfg.com
Website: www.proformancemfg.com
Precision metal stampings, deep draw parts & machined components & parts. Components formed from flat sheet stock are produced in mechanical & hydraulic presses. (Hisp, estab 1987, empl 21, sales $2,200,000, cert: NMSDC)

6425 Tanfel
1945 Camino Vida Roble, Ste J   Carlsbad, CA 92008
(760) 720-9632 Greg Lange Owner
Fax: (760) 720-9706
Email: glange@tanfel.com
Website: www.tanfel.com
Custom metal parts: stamping, extrusion, casting, metal injection molding, machining, turning, prototype to large production with warehousing capabilities. (Hisp, estab 2008, empl 5, sales , cert: NMSDC)

Connecticut

6426 Hylie Products, Inc.
669 Straits Tpke   Watertown, CT 06795
(860) 274-5447 Bill Thompson CEO
Fax: (860) 945-0411
Email: donna@hylie.com
Website: www.hylie.com
Mfr high-volume, customer-specific, high-precision, quality-critical, metal stampings & progressively drawn eyelets, four-slide stamped & formed parts. (Woman/White, estab 1963, empl 17, sales $2,500,000, cert: WBENC)

6427 WCES, Inc.
225 S Leonard St   Waterbury, CT 06708
(203) 573-1325 Dave Bromley
Fax: (203) 574-2943
Email: dbromley@waterburycontract.com
Website: www.waterburycontract.com
Deep drawn eyelets & metal stampings, die design & manufacture, long run production, assembly, finishing & plating. (Woman/White, estab 1900, empl 1, sales , cert: WBENC)

Georgia

6428 Dixien LLC
5286 Circle Dr   Lake City, GA 30260
(404) 366-7427 Alex Garcia VP Mktg
Fax: (404) 366-2403
Email: agarcia@dixien.com
Website: www.dixien.com
Stamping 100 ton to 1000 ton, welded sub-assemblies, tooling, plastic injection molding, blow molding & vaccum forming. (Hisp, estab 1961, empl 400, sales $25,000,000, cert: NMSDC)

Illinois

6429 Flex-N-Gate Corp.
5663 E 9 Mile Rd   Urbana, IL 61802
(586) 759-8613 Teresa DeStefanis Acct Mgr
Fax:
Email: tdestefanis@flexngate-mi.com
Website: www.flex-n-gate.com
Automotive stampings, injection moldings, functional/mechanical assemblies for OEMs, chrome plating & painting parts . (As-Ind, estab 1978, empl 9200, sales , cert: State)

6430 North Star Stamping & Tool, Inc.
1264 Industrial Dr   Lake in the Hills, IL 60156
(847) 658-9400 Catherine O'Brien
Fax: (847) 658-2610
Email: nstar9400@aol.com
Website: www.northstarstampingandtool.com
Metal stamping & assembly: 32 ton press to 200 ton press. (Woman/White, estab 1993, empl 9, sales , cert: WBENC)

6431 Reliable Machine Company
1327 10th Ave   Rockford, IL 61104
(815) 968-8803 Gloria Pernacciaro CEO
Fax: (815) 968-5902
Email: gloriap@reliablemachine.com
Website: www.reliablemachine.com
Metal Stampings, Part Production Capabilities: Deep draw up to 5 inches, Flat stampings, Stampings with multiple geometric forms, Secondary operations (piercing, staking, trimming and forming). (Woman/White, estab 1921, empl 40, sales $8,000,000, cert: WBENC)

Indiana

6432 Lacay Fabrication and Mfg Inc.
52941 Glenview Dr   Elkhart, IN 46514
(574) 288-4678 Ann Filley President
Fax: (574) 288-2921
Email: ann@lacayfab.com
Website: www.lacayfab.com
Mfr material handling racks, Baskets, Industrial & Production Welding, Machining, Robotic Welding, Stamping, Custom Fabrication, Prototyping. (Woman/White, estab 1975, empl 70, sales , cert: WBENC)

Michigan

6433 Apex Spring & Stamping
11420 First Ave   Grand Rapids, MI 49534
(616) 453-5463 Doug Furness Sales/Eng Mgr
Fax: (616) 453-4221
Email: djf@apexspring.com
Website: www.apexspring.com
4 slide & vertislide, CNC winders, stamping presse to 110 ton & various assembly equipment, in-house tool room, proto-type capability. (As-Pac, estab 1977, empl 40, sales $12,000,000, cert: NMSDC)

6434 Atlas Tool Inc.
29880 Groesbeck Hwy   Roseville, MI 48066
(586) 778-3570 Douglas Flanagan Business Dev Mgr
Fax: (586) 778-3931
Email: doug@atlastool.com
Website: www.atlastool.com
Stamping dies, service parts production, prototype parts, machining, engineering, die repair. (Woman/White, estab 1962, empl 200, sales , cert: WBENC)

6435 BAE Industries Inc.
26020 Sherwood Ave   Warren, MI 48091
(586) 475-9600 Roger Clark Director of Business Dev
Fax: (248) 475-9908
Email: rwclark@marisaind.com
Website: www.baeind.com
Metal stamped components & mechanical assemblies, CNC mills & lathes, wire EDM, manual & robotic welders. (Hisp, estab 1970, empl 409, sales $69,753,365, cert: NMSDC)

6436 Delaco Steel Corporation
8111 Tireman, Ste 1   Dearborn, MI 48126
(313) 491-1200 Michael Roualet VP of Quality
Fax: (313) 491-6210
Email: mike.roualet@delacosteel.com
Website: www.delacosteel.com
Dist & process steel & aluminum. Blanking, warehousing, slitting, stampings, etc. (Woman/Hisp, estab 1974, empl 650, sales , cert: NMSDC, WBENC)

6437 DGH Enterprises, Inc. dba K-O Products Co.
1225 Milton St   Benton Harbor, MI 49022
(269) 925-0657 Barbara Herrold CEO
Fax: (269) 925-9020
Email: barbaraherrold@koproducts.com
Website: www.koproducts.com
Metal stampings, welded & fabricated assemblies, electrical & mechanical assemblies, metal hardware, metal truck parts & assemblies, metal stamped components for auto, appliances, off-road equipment, metal welding, mig welding, spot welding. (Woman/White, estab 1938, empl 28, sales $3,500,000, cert: WBENC)

6438 Die Cad Group
3258 Clear Vista Court NE   Grand Rapids, MI 49525
(616)3652454 Bobbie Blanton President
Fax:
Email: bobbie@diecadgroup.com
Website: www.diecadgroup.com
Product & process simulation, tool & die design, mold design, special purpose machine design, transfer press simulation, die details sourcing, metal stamping die design, metal stamping process development, stamped parts formation. (Woman/White, estab 1995, empl 41, sales $8,150,746, cert: WBENC)

6439 GK Tech, LLC
3331 W Big Beaver Rd Ste 106 Troy, MI 48084
(248) 494-1960 Kelly Choi
Fax: (509) 371-5153
Email: kellychoi@gktechusa.com
Website: www.gktechllc.com
Marketing specialist, consulting, business development, forging, die-casting, stamping, spring, magnesium pulley, rubber bushing, fasteners, machining, plastic injection molding. (Woman/As-Pac, estab 2015, empl 3, sales $64,000, cert: NMSDC)

6440 Globe Tech LLC.
101 Industrial Dr   Plymouth, MI 48170
(734)6562200 Amanda Menchinger President
Fax:
Email: mmenchinger@globe-tech.biz
Website: www.globe-tech.biz
Machining, fabrication & welding, metal stamping. (Woman/White, estab 2009, empl 72, sales , cert: WBENC)

6441　Lapeer Metal Stamping Companies, Inc.
　　　930 S Saginaw St　Lapeer, MI 48446
　　　(810) 664-8588　Joe Wierbicki VP Sales
　　　Fax: (810) 664-9351
　　　Email: jwierbicki@lapeermetal.com
　　　Website: www.lapeermetal.com
Mfr metal stampings & assemblies: seat frame assemblies,
dash panels assemblies, heat shields, fuel tank straps,
pedals, brake, clutch, latches & hinges, crossmembers, air
bag components & structural body components. (Hisp,
estab 1960, empl 500, sales $101,781,836, cert: NMSDC)

6442　Lucerne International
　　　40 Corporate Dr　Auburn Hills, MI 48326
　　　(248) 674-7210　Karen Ryan Finance Mgr
　　　Fax: (248) 674-7215
　　　Email: kryan@lucerneintl.com
　　　Website: www.lucerneintl.com
Advanced metal forming components & assemblies, body
structures, chassis systems & powertrain systems. Mfg
aluminum & steel forgings, stampings, aluminum & zinc
die castings & steel. (Woman, estab 1993, empl 58, sales ,
cert: WBENC)

6443　Mico Industries, Inc.
　　　2929 32nd St SE　Kentwood, MI 49512
　　　(616) 245-6426　Tracy DeKlein VP Technical Sales
　　　Fax: (616) 245-2661
　　　Email: tdeklein@micoind.com
　　　Website: www.micoindustries.com
Mfr metal stampings, welding, assemblies. (Hisp, estab
1983, empl 75, sales $12,000,000, cert: NMSDC)

6444　Motor City Stamping
　　　47783 N Gratiot Ave　Chesterfield Twp, MI 48051
　　　(586) 949-8420　Paul Lachowicz Controller
　　　Fax:
　　　Email: plachowicz@mcstamp.com
　　　Website: www.mcstamp.com
Medium stampings & multi-welded assemblies. (Woman,
estab 1969, empl 350, sales $48,000,000, cert: WBENC)

6445　Proos Manufacturing, Inc.
　　　1037 Michigan St NE　Grand Rapids, MI 49503
　　　(616) 454-5622　Amy Engelsman CEO
　　　Fax: (616) 458-5316
　　　Email: aengelsman@proos.com
　　　Website: www.proos.com
Metal stampings & assemblies. (Woman, estab 1919, empl
1, sales , cert: WBENC)

6446　PTM Corporation
　　　6560 Bethuy　Fair Haven, MI 48023
　　　(248) 670-2650　Nicole Robinson Sales
　　　Fax: (586) 725-2147
　　　Email: nrobinson@ptmcorporation.com
　　　Website: www.ptmcorporation.com
Metal stamping, production up to 600 ton, prototype/low
volume up to 1000 ton, tool design & build, laser, EDM,
CNC, welding & assemblies. (Woman/White, estab 1972,
empl 196, sales $60,000,000, cert: WBENC)

6447　Quasar Industries, Inc.
　　　1911 Northfield Dr　Rochester Hills, MI 48309
　　　(248) 852-0300　Shane Majesky Quality/Safety Mgr
　　　Fax: (248) 852-0442
　　　Email: quality@quasar.com
　　　Website: www.quasar.com
Prototypes, hydroforming, tube processing, deep draw
& exotic metal stampings, laser cutting & welding,
robotic welding, assemblies, fixture design & mfg,
inspection, short run production, CNC machining, wire
EDM & waterjet cutting. (Woman/White, estab 1967,
empl 79, sales $13,000,000, cert: WBENC)

6448　Rose-A-Lee Technologies, Inc
　　　7448 19 Mile Rd　Sterling Heights, MI 48314
　　　(586) 799-4555　Julie Wood Dir Business Dev
　　　Fax:
　　　Email: jwood@rosealeetechnologies.com
　　　Website: www.rosealeetechnologies.com
CAD design (surface and solid modeling), stamping,
assembly/kitting, tube bending, welding (mig, tig, stud
arc), etc. (Woman, estab 2013, empl 2, sales , cert:
WBENC)

6449　Roth-Williams Industries Inc. dba Lunar Industries
　　　34335 Groesbeck Hwy　Clinton Township, MI
　　　48035
　　　(586) 792-0090　Patricia Williams President
　　　Fax: (586) 792-0098
　　　Email: pat@lunarind.com
　　　Website: www.lunarind.com
Design & mfr custom tooling, fixtures, gages, stamping
dies, prototype parts & stamped metal parts. (Woman/
White, estab 1966, empl 16, sales $2,351,954, cert:
WBENC)

Minnesota

6450　Bokers Inc.
　　　3104 Snelling Ave　Minneapolis, MN 55406
　　　(800) 448-7492　Linda Demma CFO
　　　Fax: (612) 729-8910
　　　Email: ldemma@bokers.com
　　　Website: www.bokers.com
Mfr precision metallic & non-metallic stampings &
washers. (Woman/AA, estab 1919, empl 110, sales , cert:
WBENC)

6451　Top Tool Company
　　　3100 84th Lane Northeast　Blaine, MN 55449
　　　(763) 786-0030　Duane Kari Sales Mgr
　　　Fax: (763) 786-0066
　　　Email: dakari@toptool.com
　　　Website: www.toptool.com
Dies, precision metal stampings & wire EDM, exotic &
precious metals, platinum, iridium, titanium, MP35N,
copper alloys, phos bronze, gold & silver plating.
(Woman/White, estab 1966, empl 30, sales $4,427,000,
cert: State)

Missouri

6452 Thiel Tool & Engineering Co., Inc.
4622 Bulwer Ave   St. Louis, MO 63147
(314) 241-6121 Gary Shamel Sales Mgr
Fax: (314) 241-2954
Email: gshamel@thieltool.com
Website: www.thieltool.com
Automotive stampings & sub-assemblies. (Woman, estab 1945, empl 42, sales $10,000,000, cert: WBENC)

New York

6453 Bailey Manufacturing Co., LLC
10987 Bennett State Rd   Forestville, NY 14062
(716) 965-2731 John Hines President
Fax:
Email: bailey03@netsync.net
Website: www.baileymfgcollc.com
Metal Stamping, Sheet Metal Fabrication, Welding, Multi-Part Assemblies, Zinc Plating, Rust Proofing, Quality Inspection, E-Coat Painting. (AA, estab 2002, empl 100, sales $8,500,000, cert: NMSDC)

6454 Cannon Industries, Inc.
525 Lee Rd   Rochester, NY 14606
(585) 254-8080 Reggie Cannon President
Fax: (585) 254-1352
Email: rcannon@cannonind.com
Website: www.cannonind.com
Sheet metal fabrication, welding fabrication, laser & plasma cutting, metal stamping, CNC machining & turning, mechanical assembly, spot welding. (AA, estab 1979, empl 104, sales $16,000,000, cert: NMSDC)

Ohio

6455 Die-Mension Corporation
3020 Nationwide Pkwy   Brunswick, OH 44212
(330) 273-5872 Karen Thompson President
Fax: (330) 273-8275
Email: karen@diemension.com
Website: www.diemension.com
Mfr & design precision progressive die & metal stampings. (Woman/White, estab 1985, empl 15, sales $1,200,000, cert: WBENC, NWBOC)

6456 GB Manufacturing Company
100 Adams St   Delta, OH 43515
(419) 822-5323 Teresa Elling
Fax: (419) 822-5440
Email: apetree@gbmfg.com
Website: www.gbmfg.com
Stamping, laser blanking, fabrication & assembly, tool making, robotic & hand welding, spot welding, press braking, productin machining, prototyping. (As-Pac/Hisp, estab 1975, empl 85, sales $24,500,000, cert: NMSDC)

6457 Green Rock Lighting, LLC
3175 W 33rd St   Cleveland, OH 44109
(216) 651-6446 Tina Haddad CEO
Fax: (216) 281-2420
Email: thaddad@greenrocklighting.com
Website: www.greenrocklighting.com
Laser cutting, wire bending & forming, press brake, spinning, stamping, mig, tig & stick welding, spot welding, machining, destructive & non-destructive testing, packaging & assembly. (Woman, estab 2011, empl 20, sales $150,000, cert: State, WBENC)

6458 Hamlin Acquisition, LLC dba Hamlin Steel Products
2741 Wingate Ave   Akron, OH 44314
(330) 753-7791 Lal Tekchandani President
Fax: (330) 753-5577
Email: JKunczt@hnmetalstamping.com
Website: www.hamlinsteel.com
Small to medium size metal stampings, assembly & robotic welding capabilities. (As-Ind, estab 1953, empl 95, sales $15,000,000, cert: NMSDC)

6459 Hamlin Newco, LLC
2741 Wingate Avenue   Akron, OH 44314
(216) 924-5449 Rick Sadd Sales Mgr
Fax: (330) 753-5577
Email: ricksadd@gmail.com
Website: www.hnmetalstamping.com/
Metal stampings & welded assemblies with presses up to 800 tons for the automotive industry. (As-Pac, estab 1945, empl 105, sales $16,000,000, cert: NMSDC)

6460 Magni-Power Company
5511 Lincoln Way E   Wooster, OH 44691
(330) 264-3637 Kim Coblentz New Business Dev Mgr
Fax: (330) 264-9035
Email: kcoblentz@magnipower.com
Website: www.magnipower.com
Metal fabrication & stamping: process steel, aluminum, stainless steel, CNC punching, forming, laser cutting, robotic welding, in-house powder coating & assembly. (As-Ind, estab 1948, empl 230, sales $27,000,000, cert: NMSDC)

6461 Tech-Matic Industries, Inc.
17941 Englewood Dr   Middleburg Heights, OH 44130
(440) 826-3191 Kathleen Byrnes President
Fax: (440) 239-7399
Email: kbyrnes@tc-tm.com
Website: www.tc-tm.com
Metal stamping for automotive industry. (Woman/White, estab 1985, empl 9, sales $4,000,000, cert: WBENC)

6462   Wrena, LLC dba Angstrom-USA, LLC
      265 Lightner Rd   Tipp City, OH 45371
      (937) 667-4403   Nagesh Palakurthi CEO
      Fax:
      Email: pyenger@wrenallc.com
      Website: www.angstrom-usa.com
Stampings, tubular products, machining, welding, robotic welding, steel forgings (Warm & Cold), aluminum forgings, assemblies, plastic injection molding, needle bearings, starter assemblies (As-Pac, estab 2011, empl 46, sales , cert: NMSDC)

6463   Zip Tool & Die Inc.
      12200 Sprecher Ave   Cleveland, OH 44135
      (216) 267-1117   Victor De Leaon CEO
      Fax: (216) 267-5466
      Email: vdeleon@tritonduro.com
      Website: www.ziptool.com
Engineering, Prototyping, Metal Forming, Metal Stamping & Tool & Die solutions. (Hisp, estab 1968, empl 10, sales $650,000, cert: NMSDC)

Pennsylvania

6464   Spalding Automotive, Inc.
      1011 Cedar Ave   Croydon, PA 19021
      (215) 826-4061   Vincent Florio Business Dev
      Fax: (267) 550-9008
      Email: vflorio@spaldingautomotive.com
      Website: www.spaldingautomotive.com
Metal stampings, roll form components, welding, mechanical assemblies & design & build tooling. (Hisp, estab 1987, empl 75, sales $18,518,000, cert: NMSDC)

6465   Tottser Tool and Manufacturing
      1630 Republic Rd   Huntingdon Valley, PA 19006
      (215) 357-7600   Linda Macht President
      Fax: (215) 357-9215
      Email: lmacht@tottser.com
      Website: www.tottser.com
Metal stampings, tool & die. (Woman/White, estab , empl 1, sales , cert: WBENC)

South Carolina

6466   McKechnie Vehicle Components USA, Inc.
      12117 CR Koon Hwy   Newberry, SC 29108
      (803) 364-7417   Jim Palazzolo New Business Devel
      Fax: (803) 364-2831
      Email: jimpalazzolo@mvcusa.com
      Website: www.mvcusa.com
Metal stamping, finishing, automotive stamping, buffing, roll forming, painting, powder painting, acrylic powder paint, assembly, robotic assembly. (Woman/White, estab 1988, empl 310, sales $77,000,000, cert: WBENC)

Wisconsin

6467   Church Metal Spinning Company
      5050 N 124th St   Milwaukee, WI 53225
      (414) 461-6460   Brenda Birno President
      Fax:
      Email: markv@churchmetal.com
      Website: www.churchmetal.com
Metal fabrications including metal stampings, metal spun, laser cut, press brake parts. Also, complete assembly and welding of multi-part components. (Woman/White, estab 1944, empl 30, sales $6,600,000, cert: State)

6468   Universal Die & Stampings
      735 15th St   Prairie du Sac, WI 53555
      (608) 643-2477   Karl Andersson Sales Mgr
      Fax: (608) 643-2024
      Email: kanders@unidie.com
      Website: www.unidie.com
Precision, high volume metal stamping, full tooling. (Woman/White, estab 1967, empl 32, sales $6,000,000, cert: City)

METAL, GENERAL MACHINING

Job shops, prototypes, short and long run production work. Tool and dies, jigs and fixtures, electromechanical assemblies, etc. (Also see six other METAL categories). NAICS Code 33

Alaska

6469　Superior Machine & Welding Inc.
1745 Ship Ave　Anchorage, AK 99501
(907) 277-3538　Jantina Lunsford President
Fax: (907) 277-4999
Email: smwjal@acsalaska.net
Website: www.superiormachine.net
Machine & welding. (Woman/White, estab 1950, empl 10, sales , cert: WBENC)

Alabama

6470　Theonics Incorporated
12525 Memorial Pkwy SW　Huntsville, AL 35803
(256) 885-3500　Shelley Coxwell President
Fax: (256) 885-3563
Email: shelley.coxwell@theonicsinc.com
Website: www.theonicsinc.com
Precision machining, CMM inspection & assembly of complex hardware. (Woman/White, estab 2012, empl 18, sales $1,300,000, cert: WBENC)

Arkansas

6471　Conway Machine, Inc.
192 Commerce Rd　Conway, AR 72032
(501) 327-1311　Anthony Davis President
Fax: (501) 327-5711
Email: tonyd@conwaymachine.com
Website: www.ConwayMachine.com
Precision milling & turning machining. (Woman/White, estab 1970, empl 25, sales $2,400,000, cert: WBENC)

Arizona

6472　J.B.'s Precision Industries
2320 W Parkside Lane　Phoenix, AZ 85027
(623) 581-9088　Steve Hoffner GM
Fax: (623) 581-3688
Email: steve@jbsprecision.com
Website: www.jbsprecision.com
CNC machining, 4 mills, 3 lathes & multiple manual machines. (Woman/White, estab 1966, empl 11, sales $1,400,000, cert: State)

6473　State Technology & Manufacturing
2555 E University Dr　Phoenix, AZ 85034
(602) 275-0990　Ruben Cadena CEO
Fax: (602) 275-0991
Email: ruben@azsip.com
Website: www.azsip.com
Machinng, mill, lathe, CNC, welding, fabricating, dist steel, copper, brass, bronze, stainless steel, aluminum. (Hisp, estab 2003, empl 21, sales $3,000,000, cert: State, City, NMSDC)

California

6474　3D Machine Company, Inc.
4790 E Wesley Dr　Anaheim, CA 92807
(714) 777-8985　Maria Falcusan President
Fax: (714) 777-8987
Email: costel@3dmachineco.com
Website: www.3dmachineco.com
CNC machining, 5-axis CNC capability, CAD/CAM software, precision-machined parts & assemblies. (Woman, estab 1996, empl 35, sales , cert: CPUC)

6475　A Better Affect, Inc. dba ABACORP CNC
9165 Independence Ave　Chatsworth, CA 91311
(818) 771-7671　Kim Frankel President
Fax: (818) 772-1745
Email: kim@abacorpcnc.com
Website: www.abacorpcnc.com
CNC machining services. (Woman/White, estab 1998, empl 33, sales $2,365,000, cert: NWBOC)

6476　ACC Precision, Inc.
321 Hearst Dr　Oxnard, CA 93030
(805) 278-9801　Arturo Alfaro GM
Fax: (805) 278-9841
Email: aalfaro@accprecision.com
Website: www.accprecision.com
Precision manufacturing & assembly: CNC Turning, CNC Milling, DNC Software Tooling & measuring machines. (Hisp, estab 1998, empl 22, sales $1,867,833, cert: 8(a))

6477　Acutek US
1488 E Valencia Dr　Fullerton, CA 92831
(714) 278-0912　Charley Yoo Owner
Fax: (714) 278-9217
Email: cyoo@acutekus.com
Website: www.acutekus.com
CNC milling, turning: aluminum, steel, titanium, copper, brass. 3 & 4 axis programming tooling fixtures, electronic file transfer. (As-Pac, estab 2003, empl 60, sales $10,700,000, cert: CPUC)

6478 Aranda Tooling, Inc.
15301 Springdale St   Huntington Beach, CA 92649
(714) 379-6565 Gerrard Connolly GM
Fax: (714) 379-6570
Email: gerrard.connolly@arandatooling.com
Website: www.arandatooling.com
Medium to high production metal stamping, assembly, robotic welding, tooling, EDM, prototypes. (Hisp, estab 1975, empl 125, sales , cert: NMSDC)

6479 Azachorok Contract Services LLC
320 Grand Cypress Ave Ste 502 Palmdale, CA 93551
(661) 951-6566 Gene Souza Mgr
Fax: (661) 951-6576
Email: gsouza@azachorok.com
Website: www.azcsllc.com
Precision CNC machining & turning, aircraft structures, machined housings, castings, aluminum, steel, titanium, copper, brass etc. (Nat Ame, estab 1998, empl 12, sales $550,000, cert: 8(a), SDB)

6480 Bay Tank and Boiler Works
825 W 14th St   Eureka, CA 95501
(707) 443-0934 Amandy Massey Office Mgr
Fax: (707) 443-0989
Email: info@BTMetals.com
Website: www.baytankandboilerworks.com
Carbon Steel Products Stainless Steel Products Aluminum Products Rebar Industrial Fasteners (Stock and Custom) We specialize in Made in the USA Certified Welding Drilling, Milling, Plasma Cutting, Oxy Fuel Cutting, laser Forming, Press (Woman/White, estab 1956, empl 7, sales $500,000, cert: CPUC)

6481 Bishop-Wisecarver Corporation
2104 Martin Way   Pittsburg, CA 94565
(888) 580-8272 Barbara Williams Supplier Diversity Admin
Fax: (925) 439-5931
Email: bwilliams@bwc.com
Website: www.bwc.com
Mfr linear & rotary motion components, custom engineering services, bearings, vee guide wheels, linear guides, linear actuator, custom machine shop, XYZ systems, gantry, rotary tables, custom assembly, linear slides, linear bearing, dualvee. (Woman/White, estab 1950, empl 58, sales $21,000,000, cert: WBENC)

6482 California Machine Specialties
12282 Colony Ave   Chino, CA 91710
(909) 464-0405 Anand Jagani Owner
Fax: (909) 464-2256
Email: anand@calmachine.com
Website: www.calmachine.com
Precision machining, CNC milling, 4 axis milling, CNC turning, machining of castings & forgings, bar & plate stocks, mechanical assemblies, brazed assemblies, hardware installation, bushing & bearing installation, adhesive bonding. (As-Ind, estab 1977, empl 19, sales $1,500,000, cert: State)

6483 Dinucci Corporation
1057 Shary Cir   Concord, CA 94518
(925) 798-3946 Gabriela Dinucci COO
Fax: (925) 798-3896
Email: gabriela@dinuccicorp.com
Website: www.dinuccicorp.com
Machine shop; computerized mfg & precision prototypes. (Woman/Hisp, estab 1978, empl 25, sales $4,227,662, cert: NMSDC)

6484 Fabtronics, Inc.
5026 Calmview Ave   Baldwin Park, CA 91706
(626) 962-3293 David K. Thompson VP of Ops
Fax: (626) 814-4768
Email: contact@fabtronics.com
Website: www.fabtronics.com
Precision sheet metal mfg, CNC turret punching, spot welding, enclosures, tubular frame weldments, skins & chassis. (Hisp, estab 1976, empl 14, sales $3,500,000, cert: NMSDC)

6485 G.B.F. Enterprises, Inc.
2709 S Halladay St   Santa Ana, CA 92705
(714) 979-7131 Keith Garrison VP
Fax: (714) 979-1815
Email: keith@gbfenterprises.com
Website: www.gbfenterprises.com
Mfr precision lathe & mill parts per customer specifications. (Woman/White, estab 1976, empl 24, sales $2,194,551, cert: State)

6486 Hunter Hawk, Inc.
1842 Taft St   Concord, CA 94521
(925) 798-4950 Sandy Hunter President
Fax: (925) 798-5250
Email: sandy@hunterhawk.com
Website: www.hunterhawk.com
Precision mechanical components, fabrication, reverse engineering, documentation, critical inventory & equipment boxes. (Woman/White, estab 1994, empl 4, sales $1,886,100, cert: State, CPUC, WBENC)

6487 Infinity Precision Inc.
6919 Eton Ave   Canoga Park, CA 91303
(818) 447-3008 Evelina Martirosova President
Fax: (818) 812-5677
Email: evelina@ipinc-usa.com
Website: www.ipinc-usa.com
Hydroforming, Machined parts per print, CAD/CAM/ CNC Machining, 5-Axis Water Jet Cutting, Honing, Sheet Metal Fabrication (Woman/Hisp, estab 1996, empl 10, sales $1,200,000, cert: State)

6488 Ingels Engineering Inc.
1828 Evergreen St   Duarte, CA 91010
(626) 256-1967 Enilde Ingels VP
Fax: (626) 256-1910
Email: eeemachineshop@earthlink.net
Website: www.ingelsengineeringservices.com
Machining & engineering consulting services, specialized medical devices, prototype works, short run productions in Stainless Steel, Aluminum, Delrin, Brass, Copper or plastics. (Woman/Hisp, estab 1997, empl 7, sales $230,000, cert: State, City)

6489 International Rite-Way Products
1725 S Campus Ave   Ontario, CA 91761
(909) 985-8300 Ravi Joshi President
Fax: (909) 985-8388
Email: ravi@intlrwp.com
Website: www.intlrwp.com
Precision aerospace sheet metal mfg: roll forming, hydro-forming, extrusion & skin stretch forming of aerospace components (ribs, spars, brackets, formers, etc.). Complete program management capabilities. (As-Ind, estab 1994, empl 10, sales $1,250,000, cert: 8(a))

6490 JB Manufacturing
2814 Aiello Dr Ste D San Jose, CA 95111
(408) 281-9994 Jim Ogawa GM
Fax: (408) 493-4262
Email: jim@jb-mfg.com
Website: www.jb-mfg.com
CNC milling & turning, 5 CNC vertical mills & 1 CNC lathe. (As-Pac, estab 1985, empl 4, sales $325,000, cert: NMSDC)

6491 KFM International Industries, Inc.
20277 Valley Blvd, Ste L   Walnut, CA 91789
(626) 369-9556 Dennis Boribor engineer
Fax: (909) 598-5811
Email: dennis@kfmii.com
Website: www.kfmii.com
Casting: Sand Cast, Die Casting, Investment Casting & Permanent Mold Forging: Hot & Cold Formed Sheet Metal Stamping Machining: CNC,Turning & Milling Powder Metal. (Woman/As-Pac, estab 2000, empl 6, sales $2,500,000, cert: City, CPUC)

6492 LT CNC Machining, Inc.
7945 Silverton Ave, Ste 1103   San Diego, CA 92126
(858) 586-7705 Liem Phan President
Fax: (858) 586-7702
Email: liem@ltmachininginc.com
Website: www.ltmachininginc.com
CNC milling & machining. (Woman/As-Pac, estab 2006, empl 7, sales $800,000, cert: State)

6493 M&L Precision Machining
18655 Madrone Pkwy   Morgan Hill, CA 95037
(408) 436-3955 Mike Sullivan Business Specialist
Fax: (408) 782-9780
Email: mikes@mlprecision.com
Website: www.mlprecision.com
Precision machining done with over 55 mills and multiple lathes. (Woman/White, estab 1971, empl 110, sales $18,000,000, cert: WBENC)

6494 Machining Solutions Inc.
22122 S Vermont Ste F Torrance, CA 90502
(310) 787-1790 Edward Dennis President
Fax: (310) 787-7631
Email: edward.dennis@machining-sol.com
Website: www.machining-sol.com
Machining: stainless steel, titanium, Inconel & other high temperature grades. (AA/As-Pac, estab 1998, empl 4, sales $512,000, cert: NMSDC)

6495 Mirofine Company
1940 W 144th St   Gardenia, CA 90249
(310) 327-2622 Wayne Perez President
Fax: (310) 327-1942
Email: mirofine@mirofine.com
Website: www.mirofine.com
CNC precision turning & milling. (Hisp, estab 1970, empl 6, sales , cert: State)

6496 Nichols Manufacturing, Inc.
913 Hanson Ct   Milpitas, CA 95035
(408) 945-0911 Maria Nichols President
Fax: (408) 945-8127
Email: lnichols@nicholsmfg.com
Website: www.nicholsmfg.com
Machined parts & fasteners, CNC mills, conventional mills & lathes. (Woman/Hisp, estab 1978, empl 17, sales $1,800,000, cert: State)

6497 Qualitask, Inc.
2840 E Gretta Lane   Anaheim, CA 92806
(714) 237-0900 Som Suntharaphat President
Fax: (714) 237-0979
Email: soms@qualitask.net
Website: www.qualitask.com
CNC Milling & Turning, Research & Development, Prototype & Production Machining, Jigs & Fixtures, steel, stainless steel, titanium, aluminum, plastics. (As-Pac, estab 1992, empl 30, sales $1,187,381, cert: NMSDC)

6498 Spec-Metal Inc.
PO Box 660536   Arcadia, CA 91066
(626) 301-7969 Evelyn Chen
Fax: (626) 303-8878
Email: evelync@spec-metal.com
Website: www.Spec-Metal.com
Machine metal precision machined parts: aluminum, brass, copper, carbon steel & stainless steel. Engineering design, product development, manufacturing, logistics & customer service. (Woman/As-Pac, estab 2008, empl 4, sales $2,600,000, cert: NMSDC)

6499 UDASH Corp.
200 N Ashdale Ave   Los Angeles, CA 90049
(310) 472-2798 George Melamed Tech Sales
Fax: (310) 472-2570
Email: udash26@hotmail.com
Website: www.udash.com
CNC milling, turning & 5-axis machining. (Woman/As-Ind, estab 1981, empl 6, sales , cert: State)

Colorado

6500 Excalibur Machine & Sheet Metal
208 W Buchanan St, Unit C Colorado Springs, CO 80907
(719) 520-5404 Douglas McDaniel Plant Mgr
Fax: (719) 520-5265
Email: doug@excaliburmfg.com
Website: www.excaliburmfg.com/
Precision machining & sheet metal fabrication, welding, assembly, powder coating. (Hisp, estab 1989, empl 25, sales $2,600,000, cert: NMSDC)

Florida

6501 Custom Manufacturing & Engineering, Inc.
3690 70th Ave North Pinellas Park, FL 33781
(727) 547-9799 Fred Munro VP
Fax: (727) 541-8822
Email: fmunro@custom-mfg-eng.com
Website: www.custom-mfg-eng.com
Subassemblies, turn-key, integrated test systems & process equip. (Woman/White, estab 1997, empl 40, sales $8,100,000, cert: WBENC)

6502 KN Machine & Tool, Inc.
3125 Jupiter Park Circle Ste 4 Jupiter, FL 33458
(561) 748-3035 Ron Passino Ops Mgr
Fax: (561) 748-3036
Email: ron@knmachine.com
Website: www.knmachine.com
High Speed Machining on Milling machines capable of handling parts up 40"x20"x20".
Turning w/ Live Tooling up to 2-5/8" Bar Capacity and up to 12" O.D. Turning. (As-Pac, estab 2000, empl 10, sales $1,300,000, cert: State)

6503 Mashack & Associates, Inc.
503 Tuscanny St Brandon, FL 33511
(813) 662-7353 Brenda Rhym President
Fax: (813) 662-7353
Email: bdrhym@verizon.net
Website:
CNC machining & printed circuit board assembly. (Woman/AA, estab 1998, empl 2, sales $105,000, cert: 8(a))

6504 Skill-Metric Machine and Tool, Inc.
1424 Gwenzell Ave Delray Beach, FL 33444
(561) 454-8895 Anthony Kresty COO
Fax: (561) 272-7166
Email: akresty@skill-metric.com
Website: www.skill-metric.com
Jet engine tooling, ground support equipment, munitions handling equipment, airframe components, precision machined parts. (Woman/AA/As-Ind, estab 1978, empl 30, sales $4,600,000, cert: State)

6505 Velezco Inc.
4401 112th Terrace N, Unit F Clearwater, FL 33762
(727) 571-1026 Travis Smith Office Mgr
Fax: (727) 571-1096
Email: travis@velezco.com
Website: www.velezco.com
CNC & manual machining. (Hisp, estab 2002, empl 6, sales $344,642, cert: State)

Georgia

6506 Omni Machine Works, Inc.
30 Chamisa Rd Covington, GA 30016
(770) 385-1331 Claudia Engelbracht CEO
Fax: (770) 385-1361
Email: claudia@omnimachineworks.com
Website: www.omnimachineworks.com.
Mfr machine parts, replacement OEM parts, repair parts, sub assemblies, complete assemblies & prototypes, welding, fabrication, machine rebuilding, assembly, engineering & design. (Woman/Hisp, estab 1996, empl 15, sales $1,847,000, cert: NMSDC, WBENC)

Iowa

6507 Indoshell Precision Technologies, LLC
435 Precision Pkwy Story City, IA 50248
(713)9926666 Ramki Ramakrishan Owner
Fax:
Email: paul.diggins@isptglobal.com
Website: www.isptglobal.com
Precision machine aluminum and steel, CNC Turning Centers and Swiss Turning Centers; Multi axis CNC HMC and VMC Machining Centers with pallet changers; as well as lapping, honing and grinding work centers. (As-Ind, estab 2009, empl 75, sales $12,000,000, cert: NMSDC)

Illinois

6508 ADC LP
1720 Wolf Rd Wheeling, IL 60090
(847) 541-3030 Patrick Tang President
Fax: (847) 439-3032
Email: PTang@adclp.com
Website: www.adclp.com
High pressure aluminum die casting, CNC machining, automated assembly. (As-Pac, estab 1991, empl 243, sales $35,000,000, cert: NMSDC)

6509 Craftsman Custom Metals, LLC
3838 N River Rd   Schiller Park, IL 60176
(847) 655-0040 William Johnson Bus Dev Mgr
Fax: (847) 678-4469
Email: wjohnson@ccm.com
Website: www.ccm.com
Custom chassis & enclosures, cabinets, brackets, structural components, OEM's & EMS's, prototype development, precision milling, metal stamping, testing, weilding, engineering support, mechanical & electro-mechanical assembly. (Hisp, estab 1953, empl 65, sales $10,000,000, cert: NMSDC)

6510 Edmik Inc.
3850 Grove Ave   Gurnee, IL 60031
(847) 263-0460 Heidi Knill VP
Fax: (847) 263-0504
Email: edmik@edmik1.com
Website: www.edmik1.com/
Production, custom tooling, machinery & engineering, CAD/CAM, contract & production assembly, industrial appliances, machining & tooling services. (Woman/Hisp, estab 1957, empl 32, sales $3,200,000, cert: NMSDC)

6511 KDL Machining, Inc.
1917 S 2nd St Pekin, IL 61554
(309) 477-3036 Deborah Lutz President
Fax: (309) 477-3063
Email: kdl@grics.net
Website:
Portable machining, turning, welding, boring, milling, pump repair, piercing & forming, die fabrication & repair, large shafting, mold building & repair, production, grinding, vertical machining production work, industrial repair work. (Woman/White, estab 1998, empl 12, sales $827,551, cert: NWBOC)

6512 KrisDee & Associates, Inc.
755 Schneider Dr   South Elgin, IL 60177
(847) 608-8300 Hermann VP
Fax: (847) 608-8400
Email: gregg.m@krisdee.com
Website: www.krisdee.com
Precision machining of non ferrous prismatic components. (Nat Ame, estab 1983, empl 65, sales $14,000,000, cert: NMSDC)

6513 Lakeview Precision Machining, Inc.
751 Schneider Dr   South Elgin, IL 60177
(847) 742-7170 Debra Sommers President
Fax: (847) 742-8088
Email: debbie@lakeviewprecision.com
Website: www.lakeviewprecision.com
CNC precision machining. (Woman/White, estab 2006, empl 15, sales $1,600,000, cert: WBENC)

6514 Machined Products Co.
2121 Landmeier Rd   Elk Grove Village, IL 60007
(847) 718-1300 Mohammed Qureshi President
Fax: (847) 718-1307
Email: mirna@machinedproducts.com
Website: www.machinedproducts.com
Machine iron, steel & aluminum. (As-Ind, estab 1958, empl 100, sales , cert: NMSDC)

6515 Microtech Machine Company, Inc.
222 Camp McDonald Rd   Wheeling, IL 60090
(847) 870-0707 Elizabeth A. Iwanicki CEO
Fax: (847) 870-1177
Email: microcamp@aol.com
Website: www.microtech-machine.com
Engineering services & precision machined prototype & production components, precision machining, machine design & building, assembly & welding. (Woman/White, estab 1984, empl 22, sales $4,000,000, cert: NWBOC)

6516 Monnex Precision Inc.
476 Diens Dr   Wheeling, IL 60090
(847) 478-1800 James E. Wallace Sr. President
Fax: (847) 478-1850
Email: jwallace@monnex.net
Website:
Metals, die casting, stampings & fasteners. (AA/As-Pac, estab 1985, empl 620, sales $5,000,000, cert: NMSDC)

6517 Multitech Industries, Inc.
350 Village Dr   Carol Stream, IL 60188
(630) 784-9200 Nick S. Anastopoulos Business Acct Mgr
Fax: (630) 784-9225
Email: nick@multitechind.com
Website: www.multitechind.com
Wire forms, castings, forgings, stampings, machining, cold-heading. (As-Ind, estab 1993, empl 60, sales $100,000,000, cert: NMSDC)

6518 Pioneer Service Inc.
542 Factory Rd   Addison, IL 60101
(630) 628-0249 Eric Smith Dir, sales/Mktg
Fax: (630) 628-9343
Email: esmith@pioneerserviceinc.com
Website: www.pioneerserviceinc.com
Contract mfr screw machine products & centerless grinding services: shafts, axles, bolts, bushings, dowels, pins, rods, spacers, valve stems, deburring, drilling, flatting, grinding, knurling, slotting, tapping, threading, heat treating. (Woman/White, estab 1990, empl 30, sales $2,300,000, cert: State)

6519 Precise Products Inc.
3286 Talbot Ave P.O. Box 310 Warrenville, IL 60555
(630) 393-9698 Ernest Tucker CEO
Fax: (630) 393-6819
Email: PreciseProducts@ameritech.net
Website:
Automatic screw & CNC machined parts. (AA, estab 1966, empl 30, sales $3,000,000, cert: NMSDC)

6520　Tuson Corporation
　　　　475 Bunker Court　Vernon Hills, IL 60061
　　　　(847) 816-8800　Michael Jin Sales Mgr
　　　　Fax: (847) 816-8801
　　　　Email: michael-jin@tuson.com
　　　　Website: www.tuson.com
Precision CNC machining, powdered metal, forging,
casting, gear, hydraulic relief valve assembly, pump, motor
& cylinder components, electric motor. (As-Pac, estab
1987, empl 200, sales $29,000,000, cert: NMSDC)

Indiana

6521　A&A Custom Automation, Inc.
　　　　2125 Bergdolt Rd　Evansville, IN 47711
　　　　(812) 464-3650　Bill Frey Sales Rep
　　　　Fax: (812) 464-3651
　　　　Email: bfrey@aacustomautomation.com
　　　　Website: www.AAcustomautomation.com
Precision CNC machining, steel fabrication, design, mfg &
rebuild automated equipment, mechanical & electrical
engineering, (Woman/White, estab 1989, empl 55, sales ,
cert: NWBOC)

6522　Accutech Mold & Machine, Inc.
　　　　2817 Goshen Rd　Fort Wayne, IN 46808
　　　　(260) 471-6102　Darrin Geiger VP
　　　　Fax: (260) 471-8584
　　　　Email: dgeiger@accutechmoldinc.com
　　　　Website: www.accutechmoldinc.com
Plastic injection molding, Insert plastic injection molder of
cables/connectors, rapid prototype tooling builder/
injection molding, production machining of brass, aluminum & metals, prototype machining of brass, aluminum &
metals. (Woman/White, estab 1996, empl 70, sales
$3,000,000, cert: WBENC)

6523　AMG Engineering & Machining, Inc.
　　　　4030 Guion Ln　Indianapolis, IN 46268
　　　　(317) 329-4000　Chris Chadd Business Dev
　　　　Fax: (317) 329-4010
　　　　Email: cchadd@amgindy.com
　　　　Website: www.amgindy.com
Mfr & design machined components, fluid controls &
connectors, adapters, fittings, plugs, check valves, gas
regulators & pressure relief valves. (AA, estab 1989, empl
46, sales , cert: NMSDC)

6524　Brinly-Hardy Company
　　　　3230 Industrial Pkwy　Jeffersonville, IN 47130
　　　　(812) 218-7219　Scott Whitehouse Sales Mgr
　　　　Fax: (812) 218-6085
　　　　Email: swhitehouse@brinly.com
　　　　Website: www.brinly.com
Bending & forming, welding, powder painting, assembly &
packaging. (Woman/White, estab 1839, empl 150, sales
$28,000,001, cert: WBENC)

6525　Exacto, Inc. of South Bend
　　　　1137 S Lafayette Blvd　South Bend, IN 46601
　　　　(574) 288-4716　Barbara Jordan CEO
　　　　Fax: (574) 288-5780
　　　　Email: bjordan@exacto-inc.com
　　　　Website: www.exacto-inc.com
CNC turning, CNC milling, OD/ID grinding, lapping &
honing (Woman/White, estab 1970, empl 52, sales
$4,000,000, cert: WBENC)

6526　Mercer Machine
　　　　1421 S Holt Rd　Indianapolis, IN 46241
　　　　(317) 441-0877　Joe Robinson VP sales
　　　　Fax: (317) 846-1697
　　　　Email: jrobinson@mercermachine.net
　　　　Website: www.mercermachine.net
CNN machining. (Woman/White, estab 1954, empl 20,
sales $2,000,000, cert: WBENC)

6527　Precision Cadcam, Inc.
　　　　8446 Brookville Rd　Indianapolis, IN 46239
　　　　(317) 353-8058　Darryl Williams President
　　　　Fax: (317) 353-1895
　　　　Email: precisioncadcam@sbcglobal.net
　　　　Website: www.pccinc.org
Precision maching and molding, tool & dies. (AA, estab
2004, empl 2, sales $170,000, cert: NMSDC)

6528　Royalty Investments, LLC
　　　　2476 E US Hwy 50　Seymour, IN 47274
　　　　(812) 358-3534　Marshall Royalty Member
　　　　Fax: (812) 358-2351
　　　　Email: mroyalty@cranehillmachine.com
　　　　Website: www.cranehillmachine.com
Machining, fabricating & assembly: steel, aluminum &
plastic components. Design, engineering & coating
applications. (Woman/White, estab 1989, empl 30, sales
$3,714,618, cert: State)

6529　Sceptre Mechanical Inc.
　　　　93 E County Rd, Ste 200 N　Rockport, IN 47635
　　　　(812) 649-9820　Mickey Toler GM
　　　　Fax: (812) 649-9809
　　　　Email: mickey.toler@sceptremech.com
　　　　Website: www.sceptremech.com
Industrial maintenance & machining services, dist &
repair industrial tools. (Woman/Nat Ame, estab 1991,
empl 45, sales , cert: State, WBENC)

Louisiana

6530　P&R Accessories, LLC
　　　　15396 Hwy 90　Paradis, LA 70080
　　　　(985) 758-5558　Philip Strother Owner
　　　　Fax: (985) 758-5551
　　　　Email: philip@acu-jet.com
　　　　Website: www.pandraccessories.com
Mfr & construction: naval ship computer simulation,
injected molded plastics, lasercutting, waterjet machining, EDM machining, circuit board printing, pulsed laser
deposition mfg of composites & superconductors. (Nat
Ame, estab 2002, empl 4, sales $490,566, cert: 8(a))

6531 Vast Industries
108 Venus St Ste 200 Morgan City, LA 70380
(985) 312-1592 Yvette Archuleta-Tudury Owner
Fax: (985) 395-1940
Email: Yvette@Vast-Ind.com
Website: www.Vast-Ind.com
Wire EDM & precision machined parts manufacturing, custom product design, reverse engineering & aluminum & steel fabrication. (Woman/Nat Ame/Hisp, estab 2007, empl 7, sales $600,000, cert: NMSDC, WBENC, 8(a))

Massachusetts

6532 Boulevard Machine & Gear, Inc.
785 Page Blvd Springfield, MA 01104
(413) 788-6466 Susan Kasa President
Fax: (413) 734-6814
Email: skasa@boulevardmachine.com
Website: www.boulevardmachine.com/
Mfr aerospace, defense, paper & commercial parts, precision machining, CNC turning, lathe & milling, manual lathes & millers, grinding, splines, rack cutting, turning, honing, stamping & assembly. (Woman/White, estab 1954, empl 20, sales , cert: WBENC)

6533 D&R Products Co, Inc.
455 River Rd Hudson, MA 01749
(978) 562-4137 Cece Newman CEO
Fax: (978) 562-4745
Email: cnewman@drproducts.com
Website: www.drproducts.com
Precision machined products: stainless steels, titanium & exotics; CNC turning, milling, wire EDM, grinding, welding, electropolishing & lasermarking. (Woman/As-Ind/Hisp, estab 1938, empl 65, sales $11,000,000, cert: WBENC)

6534 Fitz Machine Inc.
4 Railroad Ave Wakefield, MA 01880
(781) 245-5966 Kathleen Fitzgerald President
Fax: (781) 245-5967
Email: kathleen@fitzmachine.com
Website: www.fitzmachine.com
Precision CNC machined components, multi axis capabilities, prototype & production machining, long & short production runs, in-house tooling design. (Woman/White, estab 1994, empl 15, sales $1,300,000, cert: WBENC)

6535 M&K Engineering
66 Concord St North Reading, MA 01864
(978) 276-1973 Gene Ungvarsky Business Dev/Mktg Mgr
Fax: (978) 276-1996
Email: gene@mkeng.com
Website: www.mkeng.com
Precision machining: CNC & swiss screw CNC. (Woman/White, estab 1990, empl 28, sales $4,464,492, cert: NMSDC)

6536 PremaTech Advanced Ceramics
2 Coppage Dr Worcester, MA 01603
(508) 791-9549 Thomas Shearer Dir Business Dev
Fax: (508) 793-9814
Email: info@prematechac.com
Website: www.PremaTechAC.com
Fabricate technical ceramics, sapphire, composite & exotic materials, machining & grinding, ceramic components, refractories, cordierite, kiln furniture, porous metal parts, stainless steel, bronze & titanium filters, zinc, zinc selenide. (Woman/White, estab 1980, empl 35, sales $3,525,000, cert: WBENC)

6537 Wrobel Engineering Co., Inc.
154 Bodwell St Avon, MA 02322
(508) 586-8338 Michael Long General/QA Mgr.
Fax: (508) 586-8466
Email: mlong@wrobeleng.com
Website: www.wrobeleng.com
Mfr precision sheet metal fabricated parts per customer specs, precision machining, milling & turning, metal stamping, long & short runs, tool & die making, assembly mechanical & electrical, welding all materials. (Woman/White, estab 1976, empl 98, sales $14,800,000, cert: State, City)

Maryland

6538 FlexFit Hose LLC
7948 E. Baltimore St. Baltimore, MD 21224
(410) 327-0758 Arjun Radhakrishnan Managing Partner
Fax: (410) 327-0759
Email: sales@flexfithose.com
Website: www.flexfithose.com
CNC Swiss machining, MNT, Female NPT, Female JIC, Tube Adaptors, Tri-Clamps, Mini Tri-Clamps. (AA, estab 2008, empl 4, sales $974,000, cert: NMSDC, SDB)

6539 Ray Machine Inc.
12 Lynbrook Rd Baltimore, MD 21220
(410) 686-6955 Dan Solomon GM
Fax: (410) 686-5860
Email: dsolomon@rayamch.com
Website: www.raymachine.com
CNC & conventional machining; precision sheet metal fab, welding, mechanical & elec assembly, etc. (As-Ind, estab 1950, empl 42, sales $4,711,000, cert: NMSDC)

Michigan

6540 2K Tool LLC
3025 Madison Ave SE Wyoming, MI 49548
(616) 452-4927 Kevin Smith engineering Mgr
Fax:
Email: kevin@2ktool.com
Website: www.2ktool.com
Moldmaker, machining, tooling, plastic injection molds, compression tooling, composite machining, casting machining, small part Injection molding. (Woman/White, estab 2004, empl 19, sales $2,269,151, cert: WBENC)

6541 Accu-Shape Die Cutting, Inc.
      4050 Market Place Dr   Flint, MI 48507
      (810) 230-2445 Joe Brooks New Business Devel
      Fax: (248) 334-7540
      Email: joebrooks@accushape.com
      Website: www.accushape.com
Large parts a specialty up to 84" x 75" in size with kiss
cutting capability from larger roll stock. Lamination of
pressure sensitive adhesives up to 54" wide. Slitting and
Sheeting of rolled goods up to 85" wide. (AA, estab 1998,
empl 36, sales $3,200,000, cert: NMSDC)

6542 Action Tool & Machine Inc.
      5976 Ford Ct   Brighton, MI 48116
      (810) 229-6300 Doug Lademan Dir, minority
      Business Dev
      Fax: (810) 229-6414
      Email: actiontool@actiontoolmachine.com
      Website: www.actiontoolmachine.com
Machining & assembly svcs: build-to-print, part-to-print
reverse engineering svcs. (As-Pac, estab 1993, empl 30,
sales $3,700,000, cert: NMSDC)

6543 Aerostar Manufacturing
      28275 Northline Rd   Romulus, MI 48174
      (734) 942-8440 Robert Johnson VP
      Fax: (734) 942-1947
      Email: rjohnson@aerostarmfg.com
      Website: www.aerostarmfg.com
CNC machining assembly, prototyping, machine castings &
forgings, sand casting. (As-Ind/As-Pac, estab 1970, empl
170, sales $18,000,000, cert: NMSDC)

6544 ALBAH Manufacturing Technologies Corp.
      1985 Ring Rd   Troy, MI 48083
      (519) 972-7222 Kofi Adomako VP
      Fax: (519) 972-9954
      Email: kadomako@albah.com
      Website: www.albah.com
Automation & robotics, machine load/unload, material
handling, assembly, dispensing, palletizing & material
removal. (Woman/AA, estab 1992, empl 27, sales
$5,000,000, cert: NMSDC)

6545 Alphi Manufacturing, LLC
      576 Beck St   Jonesville, MI 49250
      (517)8499945 Ed Carter Dir Diversity Devel
      Fax: (626) 964-4447
      Email: ecarter@crownegroupllc.com
      Website: www.alphimfg.com/
Fabrication (bending, piercing, end forming, miter cutting,
welding) of ferrous and non-ferrous tubalur products.
Fabricated exhaust components, Fabricated structural
components. (Nat Ame, estab 1959, empl 125, sales
$19,939,913, cert: NMSDC)

6546 Aluminum Blanking Company, Inc
      360 W Sheffield   Pontiac, MI 48340
      (248) 338-4422 Michael Rutkowski VP Finance &
      Admin
      Fax: (248) 338-9779
      Email: mrutkowski@albl.com
      Website: www.albl.com
Leveling, Blanking, lubing, edge-trimming and slitting of
Aluminum, Stainless and other surface sensitive materi-
als. (Woman/White, estab 1979, empl 120, sales
$9,864,397, cert: WBENC)

6547 Axly Tool & Bushing
      700 E Soper Rd   Bad Axe, MI 48413
      (989) 269-9702 Mark Tomlinson Project Leader
      Fax: (989) 269-9021
      Email: mtomlinson@geminigroup.net
      Website: www.geminigroup.net
CNC machining, contract machining. (Woman, estab
1970, empl 70, sales $25,000,000, cert: WBENC)

6548 Aztec Manufacturing Corporation
      15378 Oakwood Dr   Romulus, MI 48174
      (734) 942-7433 Richard Johnson President
      Fax: (734) 942-9499
      Email: rjohnson@aztecmfgcorp.com
      Website: www.aztecmfgcorp.com
Machined aluminum, ductile iron castings & forgings.
(Hisp, estab 1983, empl 55, sales $25,000,000, cert:
NMSDC)

6549 CKS Precision Machining
      700 E Soper Rd   Bad Axe, MI 48413
      (989) 269-9702 Frank Gerbig Dir of Sales
      Fax: (989) 269-9021
      Email: Fgerbig@geminigroup.net
      Website: www.ckstool.com
CNC machining: lathe, mill, grind & heat treating.
(Woman/White, estab 1979, empl 100, sales
$15,709,000, cert: WBENC)

6550 Clips & Clamps Industries
      15050 Keel St   Plymouth, MI 48170
      (734) 455-0880 Jeff Aznavorian President
      Fax: (734) 455-4270
      Email: jaznavorian@clipsclamps.com
      Website: www.clipsclamps.com
Metal forming, progressive dies, four slide, CNC wire
forming, tool building, MIG & TIG welding, tapping,
riveting, automated assemblies, prototyping & production volumes, engineering services, design services, sales
support. (Woman/White, estab 1954, empl 62, sales ,
cert: WBENC)

6551 Costello Enterprises, LLC
      56358 Precision Dr   Chesterfield Township, MI
      48051
      (586) 615-6307 Tom Orban VP
      Fax:
      Email: torban@costelloenterprises.com
      Website: www.costelloenterprises.com
CNC machining & dimensional inspection services. (Hisp,
estab 2000, empl 25, sales , cert: NMSDC)

6552   Costello Machine LLC
       56358 Precision Dr   Chesterfield, MI 48051
       (586) 749-0136 Frank Keena Ops Mgr
       Fax: (586) 749-0139
       Email: fkeena@costellomachine.com
       Website: www.costellomachine.com
Precision machining, boring mill & assemblies. (Hisp, estab 2000, empl 25, sales $3,500,000, cert: NMSDC)

6553   Dalany Metal Products Inc.
       4450 13th St   Wyandotte, MI 48192
       (734) 282-6666 Al Yglesias President
       Fax: (734) 282-7004
       Email: al.yglesias@dalany.com
       Website: www.dalany.com
Machine formed metal parts: cold heading, rod heading, wire forming, stampers & screw machine, grooves, reamed holes, cross holes, plating. (Hisp, estab 2004, empl 9, sales $525,000, cert: NMSDC)

6554   Dienamic Tool Corporation
       4541 Patterson Ave SE   Kentwood, MI 49512
       (616) 954-7882 Rogelio (Roger) Ramirez President
       Fax: (616) 954-7883
       Email: rramirez@dienamictoolcorp.com
       Website: www.dienamictoolcorp.com
Die Build, Reverse Engineering, CNC Machining, Fixture Build. (Hisp, estab 1998, empl 16, sales $1,856,444, cert: NMSDC)

6555   Dowding Industries
       503 Marilin   Eaton Rapids, MI 48827
       (517) 663-5455 Roger Cope VP of Sales
       Fax: (517) 663-0533
       Email: roger@willowhill.net
       Website: www.dowdingindustries.com
CNC machining, milling & boring. (Woman/White, estab 1965, empl 150, sales $300,000, cert: WBENC)

6556   GK Tech, LLC
       3331 W Big Beaver Rd Ste 106 Troy, MI 48084
       (248) 494-1960 Kelly Choi
       Fax: (509) 371-5153
       Email: kellychoi@gktechusa.com
       Website: www.gktechllc.com
Marketing specialist, consulting, business development, forging, die-casting, stamping, spring, magnesium pulley, rubber bushing, fasteners, machining, plastic injection molding. (Woman/As-Pac, estab 2015, empl 3, sales $64,000, cert: NMSDC)

6557   Jolico/J-B Tool, Inc.
       4325 22 Mile Rd   Utica, MI 48317
       (586) 739-5555 Patricia Wieland President
       Fax: (586) 739-4840
       Email: PWieland@jolico.com
       Website: www.jolico.com
CNC turning, vertical, multipallet machining, welding, suface, wet & blanchard grinding. (Woman/White, estab 1963, empl 38, sales $6,000,000, cert: WBENC)

6558   KJL Industries, Inc.
       44057 Phoenix Dr   Sterling Heights, MI 48314
       (586) 803-1818 Kristin Wikol President
       Fax: (586) 803-1087
       Email: kwikol@kjlindustries.com
       Website: www.kjlindustries.com
Precision machining, tight tolerance, complex parts. (Woman, estab 1984, empl 15, sales $2,000,000, cert: WBENC)

6559   Maya Jig Grinding & Gage Co.
       20770 Parker Rd   Farmington Hills, MI 48336
       (248) 471-0802 Jeff Beier VP
       Fax: (248) 471-1156
       Email: jbeier@mayagage.com
       Website: www.MayaGage.com
Automatic gages, variable gages, functional gages, hand gages, masters, fixtures & tooling. (Woman, estab 1976, empl 20, sales $3,000,000, cert: WBENC)

6560   MRD Aerospace, LLC
       23565 Schoenherr Rd   Warren, MI 48089
       (586) 443-5350 Michele Dew Managing Member
       Fax: (586) 443-5360
       Email: r7mdew@aol.com
       Website: www.mrdaerospace.com
Prototype machining, milling, turning, jig grinding, ID/OD grinding, surface grinding, honing & lapping, hydraulic cylinder blocks, drive shafts, rotors, housings, broaching ID splines, valve plates, pistons, sleeved cylinder blocks, etc. (Woman/White, estab 2011, empl 9, sales $440,311, cert: WBENC)

6561   Pioneer Machine & Tech
       1167 East 10 Mile Rd   Madison Heights, MI 48071
       (248) 546-4451 Jeffery Harris President
       Fax: (248) 546-4952
       Email: jharris@pioneermachinetech.com
       Website: www.pioneermachinetech.com
Machining: custom & precision machining, fabrication, grinding & repair of components & fixtures. (AA, estab 1998, empl 15, sales $1,500,000, cert: NMSDC)

6562   Precision Components Manufacturing, LLC
       35855 Stanley   Sterling Heights, MI 48312
       (586) 939-8500 Tommy Longest CEO
       Fax: (586) 939-7635
       Email: tommy@pcmfettes.com
       Website: www.pcmfettes.com
Mfr cast tooling, castings iron/aluminum, steel forging, fully machined castings & assembly, ferrous & nonferrous products, forging, sand & die casting. (AA, estab 2009, empl 30, sales $7,010,000, cert: NMSDC)

6563   ProMax Engineering, LLC
       7522 Baron Dr   Canton, MI 48187
       (734) 468-0146 Jeff Hampton Dir Sales/Mktg
       Fax:
       Email: jeff@betasales.com
       Website:
Machining: castings, forgings, powder metal & cold formed steel. (As-Pac, estab 1999, empl 75, sales $15,000,000, cert: NMSDC)

6564　Quasar Industries, Inc.
　　　1911 Northfield Dr　Rochester Hills, MI 48309
　　　(248) 852-0300　Shane Majesky Qualtiy/Safety Mgr
　　　Fax: (248) 852-0442
　　　Email: quality@quasar.com
　　　Website: www.quasar.com
Prototypes, hydroforming, tube processing, deep draw &
exotic metal stampings, laser cutting & welding, robotic
welding, assemblies, fixture design & mfg, inspection,
short run production, CNC machining, wire EDM &
waterjet cutting. (Woman/White, estab 1967, empl 79,
sales $13,000,000, cert: WBENC)

6565　Robinson Industries, Inc.
　　　3051 W Curtis Rd P.O. Box 521　Coleman, MI 48618
　　　(989) 465-6111　Marvin Ries Sales
　　　Fax: (989) 465-1217
　　　Email: mries@robinsonind.com
　　　Website: www.robinsonind.com
Custom design & mfg, vacuum forming, injection molding,
extrusion, tool & die shop. (Woman/White, estab 1950,
empl 200, sales $28,348,370, cert: WBENC)

6566　Sequoia Tool
　　　44831 North Groesbeck Hwy　Clinton Township, MI
　　　48036
　　　(586) 463-4400　James Coates Acct Mgr
　　　Fax: (586) 463-2696
　　　Email: bcoates@sequoiatool.net
　　　Website: www.sequoiatool.net
Mfr prototype sheet metal stampings & assemblies, low
volume production and short run svcs. (Nat Ame, estab
1988, empl 65, sales $10,000,000, cert: NMSDC)

6567　Steadfast Engineered Products, LLC
　　　775 Woodlawn Ave　Grand Haven, MI 49417
　　　(616) 846-4747　Jay Cutie Managing Partner
　　　Fax: (616) 846-4750
　　　Email: jcutie@steadfastep.com
　　　Website: www.steadfastep.com
Screw machine products, turned parts. (AA/Hisp, estab
1986, empl 12, sales $6,000,000, cert: NMSDC)

6568　Sure Solutions LLC
　　　5385 Perry Dr　Waterford, MI 48329
　　　(248) 674-7210　Art Huge Sales
　　　Fax: (586) 254-5359
　　　Email: info@suresolutionsmbe.com
　　　Website: www.suresolutionsmbe.com/
Stampings, plating, coatings, roll forming, machining,
castings, forgings, assembly, packaging, warehousing &
distribution, containment. (Woman/As-Ind, estab 1990,
empl 25, sales $8,250,000, cert: WBENC)

6569　Systrand Manufacturing Corporation
　　　19050 Allen Rd　Brownstown, MI 48329
　　　(734) 479-8100　Jim Meadows Director of Finance
　　　Fax: (734) 479-8107
　　　Email: jim.meadows@systrand.com
　　　Website: www.systrand.com
High volume machining: cast iron, aluminum, steel &
powdered metal components. (Woman/Nat Ame, estab
1982, empl 200, sales $65,000,000, cert: NMSDC, WBENC)

6570　T&D Machine, Inc.
　　　2485 E Monroe Rd　Tecumseh, MI 49286
　　　(517) 423-0778　Debra Fowle President
　　　Fax: (517) 423-0778
　　　Email: tdmachine@lni.net
　　　Website: www.tdmachineinc.net
Precision machined products: steel, aluminum, brass &
plastic parts, hand tools, scribers, torque, screwdriver,
pliers, mirrors, telescoping tools, magnet hand tools,
spark plug pliers. (Woman/Hisp, estab 1985, empl 3,
sales $200,000, cert: State)

6571　Trutron Corporation
　　　274 Executive Dr　Troy, MI 48083
　　　(248) 583-9166　Lisa Kingsley President
　　　Fax: (248) 583-4750
　　　Email: lkingsley@trutron.com
　　　Website: www.trutron.com
Precision machining, CNC turning, milling, grinding:
pressure plates, valve plates, wafer plates, cam rings,
rotors, housings, manifolds, radial rings, levers, sleeves,
actuator pistons, tooling & gauging. (Woman/White,
estab 1967, empl 26, sales $5,239,911, cert: WBENC)

6572　United Manufacturing Network Inc.
　　　12 Lincoln St　Mt. Clemens, MI 48043
　　　(586) 468-7443　Cathy DeNardo President
　　　Fax: (866) 674-7481
　　　Email: cathydenardo@comcast.net
　　　Website: www.unitedmanufacturingnetwork.com
Design & build fixtures & gages, tool & dies injection
molds, molded parts & rapid prototype, CNC machining,
turning, milling & boring mill, OD, ID, surface &
centerless grinding, precision jig grinding & wire EDM.
(Woman/White, estab 2004, empl 3, sales $104,202,
cert: WBENC)

6573　West Michigan Flocking
　　　78277 CountyRd378　Covert, MI 49043
　　　(269) 639-1634　Garrett Fox VP of Sales
　　　Fax: (269) 764-0025
　　　Email: gfox@wmflocking.com
　　　Website: www.wmflocking.com
Object flocking, injection molding, in-line attachment
assembly, sub assembly & sonic welding. (AA, estab
1978, empl 50, sales $4,500,000, cert: NMSDC)

6574　Witco Inc.
　　　6401 Bricker Rd　Avoca, MI 48006
　　　(810) 387-4231　Tom Kean Sales Engineer
　　　Fax: (810) 387-4145
　　　Email: tomk@witcoinc.com
　　　Website: www.witcoinc.com
CNC precision machine parts: milling, turning, grinding,
gear shaping & assembly. (Woman/White, estab 1977,
empl 60, sales $7,000,000, cert: WBENC)

6575   Zoatex
       510 Savage Rd   Belleville, MI 48111
       (734) 697-5555 Hamid Servati Partner
       Fax: (734) 697-6633
       Email: hservati@zoatex.com
       Website: www.zoatex.com
Manufacturing & machining, powertrain devel, emissions, durability testing, project mgmt, prototyping. (As-Ind, estab 2002, empl 20, sales $2,100,000, cert: NMSDC)

Minnesota

6576   Columbia Precision Machine Corp.
       1309 Larc Industrial Blvd   Burnsville, MN 55337
       (952) 890-1003 Sales
       Fax: (952) 890-3820
       Email: info@columbiapmc.com
       Website: www.columbiapmc.com
Precision machine shop: milling, turning, light assembly, prototype, small batch, production qtys. MIL-I-45208A. (AA, estab 1983, empl 20, sales $1,400,000, cert: NMSDC)

6577   Lake Country Machining
       P.O. Box 127   Two Harbors, MN 55616
       (218) 834-7033 Clara Mikkelsen CEO
       Fax: (218) 834-7044
       Email: clara@lakecountrymachining.net
       Website: www.lakecountrymachining.net
Precision machining: aluminum, stainless steel & non-ferrous machining. (Woman/White, estab 2001, empl 5, sales , cert: State)

6578   Mack Engineering Corporation
       3215 E 26th St   Minneapolis, MN 55406
       (612) 721-2471 Jennifer Salisbury President
       Fax: (612) 721-8774
       Email: Info@MackEngineering.com
       Website: www.mackengineering.com
Mfr precision-machined components utilizing a dock to stock quality system. (Woman/White, estab 1943, empl 30, sales , cert: WBENC)

6579   Metal Craft Machine & Engineering, Inc.
       13760 Businesss Center Dr   Elk River, MN 55330
       (763) 441-1855 Trisha Mowry CEO
       Fax: (763) 441-0798
       Email: trisha@metal-craft.com
       Website: www.metal-craft.com
Contract manufacturing & engineering design: CNC milling & turning, multi-tasking machining, 7-axis CNC grinding, wire EDM, swiss gundrilling, laser & GTAW (Tig.), welding blasting, deburring, & finishing. (Woman/White, estab 1978, empl 185, sales , cert: WBENC)

6580   Miller Machine Company
       14105 Commerce Dr   Becker, MN 55308
       (763) 263-0091 Cynthia Wahl President
       Fax:
       Email: cyndiw@millermachinecompany.com
       Website: www.millermachinecompany.com
CNC mills & lathes, brown & sharpe screw machines, automatice saws, bridgeports, hardinges. (Woman/White, estab 1944, empl 15, sales $1,764,305, cert: WBENC)

6581   Modern Manufacturing & Engineering, Inc.
       9380 Winnetka Ave N   Brooklyn Park, MN 55445
       (612) 781-3347 Nancy Lien Berndt President
       Fax: (612) 781-0030
       Email: nancyl@mmeincmn.com
       Website: www.mmeincmn.com
Precision custom machining, milling, turning, grinding, assembly, plating, painting. (As-Pac, estab 1958, empl 160, sales $25,000,000, cert: NMSDC)

6582   Northern U & S, Inc. dba Quali-Mac, Inc.
       9208 James Ave S, Ste 11   Bloomington, MN 55431
       (952) 881-6677 Shawn Thai President
       Fax: (952) 881-3208
       Email: shawnt@qualimac-inc.com
       Website: www.qualimac-inc.com
Precision, CNC machining, metal/plastic machining, turning, vertical milling, protoype, production machining. (As-Pac, estab 1974, empl 7, sales $400,000, cert: NMSDC)

6583   Riverside Manufacturing, Inc.
       14280 Sunfish Lake Blvd NW   Ramsey, MN 55303
       (763) 274-2193 Mic Wieshaar President
       Fax: (763) 274-2195
       Email: riversidemnf@earthlink.net
       Website: www.riversidemnf.com
CNC machining, complex horizontal machining. (Nat Ame, estab 1997, empl 15, sales $3,450,000, cert: NMSDC)

Missouri

6584   Stemmerich Inc.
       4728 Gravois Ave   St. Louis, MO 63116
       (314) 832-7726 Lisa Ruff Sales Mgr
       Fax: (314) 832-7799
       Email: lruff@stemmerich.com
       Website: www.stemmerich.com
CNC precision edge grinding & shaping. (Woman/White, estab , empl 1, sales $7,850,000, cert: NWBOC)

Montana

6585 Montana Hydraulics, LLC
     888 Florence St Helena, MT 59601
     (814) 592-5412 Jay Krause Natl Contracts Mgr
     Fax: (406) 449-3465
     Email: mthyd@ironfurnace.com
     Website: www.montanahydraulics.com
Mfr industrial metal, compaction attachments for heavy equipment (roller compaction buckets & wheels, vibratory compaction buckets), bedding boxes & doweling machines, CNC machining, turning & lathe, manual machining, custom fabrication. (Woman/White, estab 1998, empl 47, sales $6,027,445, cert: State)

North Carolina

6586 C & J Machine Company Inc.
     3519 Philadelphia Ch Rd Dallas, NC 28034
     (704) 922-5913 Amy Hunt President
     Fax: (704) 922-5202
     Email: cjmachinecompany@gmail.com
     Website:
Mfr machine parts & fixtures, tool & dies, CRS, HRS, tool steel, plastics, copper, bronze, stainless steel. (Woman/White, estab 1976, empl 4, sales $350,000, cert: State)

New Hampshire

6587 Maclean Precision Machine
     1928 Village Rd P.O. Box 70 Madison, NH 03849
     (603) 367-9011 Deborah Folsom President
     Fax: (603) 367-8617
     Email: d.folsom@macleanprecision.com
     Website: www.macleanprecision.com
Precision machining, tight tolerance parts, Titanium, Inconel, Stainless Steel, Aluminum, Castings, Bar Stock & Plate. (Woman/White, estab 1977, empl 33, sales $3,800,000, cert: NWBOC)

New Jersey

6588 Arlington Machine & Tool
     90 New Dutch Ln Fairfield, NJ 07004
     (973) 276-1377 Susan Blanck President
     Fax: (973) 276-1378
     Email: sblanck@arlingtonmachine.com
     Website: www.arlingtonmachine.com
CNC machining & turning, manufacturing, assemblies & systems. (Woman/White, estab 1963, empl 100, sales $16,000,000, cert: State, WBENC)

6589 Computa-Base Machining
     411 N Grove St P.O. Box 340 Berlin, NJ 08009
     (856) 767-3509 Agustin Rosado President
     Fax: (856) 767-8541
     Email: cbmpresident@computabase.com
     Website: www.computabase.com
Close tolerance, special metals, nickel, inconell, kamenell, etc. (Hisp, estab 1981, empl 20, sales $1,000,000, cert: NMSDC, SDB)

6590 Kaizen Technologies Inc.
     1 Lincoln Hwy, Ste 10 Edison, NJ 08820
     (732) 452-9555 Prakash Bahumanyam VP
     Fax: (732) 452-9559
     Email: prakashb@kaizentek.com
     Website: www.kaizentek.com
Precision machining, tooling, jigs & fixtures. (As-Ind, estab 1995, empl 150, sales $11,000,000, cert: State)

New Mexico

6591 Las Cruces Machine, Mfg. & Engineering
     6000 S Main, Ste B Mesilla Park, NM 88047
     (575) 526-1411 Rod Mitchell President
     Fax: (575) 526-8520
     Email: rmitchell@lascrucesmachine.com
     Website: www.lascrucesmachine.com
CNC precision machining capabilities. (Woman/White, estab 1975, empl 40, sales $3,907,000, cert: WBENC)

New York

6592 Cannon Industries, Inc.
     525 Lee Rd Rochester, NY 14606
     (585) 254-8080 Reggie Cannon President
     Fax: (585) 254-1352
     Email: rcannon@cannonind.com
     Website: www.cannonind.com
Sheet metal fabrication, welding fabrication, laser & plasma cutting, metal stamping, CNC machining & turning, mechanical assembly, spot welding. (AA, estab 1979, empl 104, sales $16,000,000, cert: NMSDC)

6593 Greno Industries Inc.
     P.O. Box 542 Schenectady, NY 12301
     (518) 393-4195 Joe Vainauskas VP of Ops
     Fax:
     Email: jvainauskas@greno.com
     Website: www.greno.com
Contract OEM machining, milling & turning services, CAD/CAM capabilities, modern equipment. (Woman/White, estab 1961, empl 65, sales $15,500,000, cert: WBENC)

6594 Indimet Inc.
     50 Main St, Ste 1260 White Plains, NY 10606
     (914) 831-6500 Himanshu Trivedi Sales Engineer
     Fax: (914) 831-5500
     Email: himanshu-trivedi@indimet.com
     Website: www.indimet.com
Contract manufacturer, screw machining, forging, cold forging, casting, heat treatments, electroplating, metal components & machined components. (As-Ind, estab 1990, empl 8, sales $6,500,000, cert: NMSDC)

6595   Ingleside Machine Company, Inc.
       1120 Hook Rd   Farmington, NY 14425
       (585) 924-3046 Gary Veomett
       Fax: (585) 924-7904
       Email: office@inglesidemachine.com
       Website: www.Inglesidemachine.com
CNC milling, turning, sheet metal fabrication, welding, finishing & assembly. (Woman/White, estab 1974, empl 85, sales , cert: State)

Ohio

6596   Action Precision Products Inc.
       100 E North Ave Box 188 Pioneer, OH 43554
       (419) 737-2348 Linda Heisler President
       Fax: (419) 737-3039
       Email: linda@actionprecision.com
       Website: www.actionprecision.com
Machining: low volume, high tolerance blue print items, steel, brass, bronze & plastics, CNC turning, milling & grinding operations. (Woman/White, estab 1972, empl 10, sales $1,020,000, cert: WBENC)

6597   Chippewa Industries, Inc. dba, Seaport Mold & Casting
       1309 West Bancroft St   Toledo, OH 43606
       (419) 243-1422 Jeff St. Louis President
       Fax: (419) 243-4445
       Email: jstlouis@chippewaindustries.com
       Website: www.chippewaindustries.com
CNC Machining, vertical and horizontal 3 Axis, 4 Axis and 5 Axis CNC machining capabilities. We provide Billet, Sand Castings, Metal Castings, Aluminum Castings, Investment Castings, Plaster Casting, Die Casting, Prototype, and Short to Medium Production. (Nat Ame, estab 2015, empl 25, sales $6,000,000, cert: NMSDC)

6598   Cleveland Die & Mfg. Co.
       20303 First Ave   Middleburg Heights, OH 44130
       (440) 243-3404 Marty Curry sales/engineering
       Fax:
       Email: mcurry@clevelanddie.com
       Website: www.clevelanddie.com/
Ecoat & powder coat line, automatic & single hit presses, spot & robotic welders, CNC machining. (Hisp, estab 1973, empl 300, sales $24,000,000, cert: NMSDC)

6599   EnKon, LLC dba Broadway
       6344 Webster St   Dayton, OH 45414
       (937) 890-2221 Jodi Walters Member
       Fax: (937) 890-5678
       Email: jodi.walters@enkonllc.com
       Website: www.broadwaymold.com
Injection molds, components, mold repairs, Precision Fabrication,
CNC Machining, welding, turning, Electrode manufacturing, EDM'ING, Wire EDM, Polish, Milling, OD, ID, and surface grinding, Design. (Woman, estab 1955, empl 12, sales , cert: WBENC)

6600   GB Manufacturing Company
       100 Adams St   Delta, OH 43515
       (419) 822-5323 Teresa Elling
       Fax: (419) 822-5440
       Email: apetree@gbmfg.com
       Website: www.gbmfg.com
Stamping, laser blanking, fabrication & assembly, tool making, robotic & hand welding, spot welding, press braking, productin machining, prototyping. (As-Pac/Hisp, estab 1975, empl 85, sales $24,500,000, cert: NMSDC)

6601   Green Rock Lighting, LLC
       3175 W 33rd St   Cleveland, OH 44109
       (216) 651-6446 Tina Haddad CEO
       Fax: (216) 281-2420
       Email: thaddad@greenrocklighting.com
       Website: www.greenrocklighting.com
Laser cutting, wire bending & forming, press brake, spinning, stamping, mig, tig & stick welding, spot welding, machining, destructive & non-destructive testing, packaging & assembly. (Woman, estab 2011, empl 20, sales $150,000, cert: State, WBENC)

6602   Industrial Machining and Design Services, Inc.
       2007 South Ave   Youngstown, OH 44502
       (330) 747-4637 Robert Hill Jr. CEO
       Fax: (330) 747-3286
       Email: rahilljr@imds-ohio.com
       Website: www.imds-ohio.com
Precision machining, CNC, high tolerance machining: forgings, castings, bearings, land vehicles, brakes, calipers, rotor castings, etc. (AA, estab 1991, empl 10, sales $1,050,000, cert: State)

6603   Kaskell Manufacturing, Inc.
       240 Hiawatha Trail   Springboro, OH 45066
       (937) 704-9700 Brian Harris VP
       Fax: (937) 704-9710
       Email: bharris@kaskellmfg.com
       Website: www.kaskellmfg.com
CNC machining, milling & turning. (Woman/White, estab 2000, empl 12, sales $1,250,000, cert: WBENC)

6604   Lewis Unlimited, Inc.
       3690 Orange Place   Beachwood, OH 44122
       (216) 514-8282 Joseph Lewis, Jr. President
       Fax: (216) 514-8283
       Email: jlewis@lewisunlimited.com
       Website: www.lewisunlimited.com
CNC precision machined components, multi axis machining centers, single & multi-spindle screw products, CNC Swiss machined components. (AA, estab 1991, empl 10, sales $6,043,537, cert: State)

6605 Magni-Power Company
5511 Lincoln Way E   Wooster, OH 44691
(330) 264-3637 Kim Coblentz New Business Dev Mgr
Fax: (330) 264-9035
Email: kcoblentz@magnipower.com
Website: www.magnipower.com
Metal fab & stamping: process steel, aluminum, stainless steel, CNC punching, forming, laser cutting, robotic welding, in-house powder coating & assembly. (As-Ind, estab 1948, empl 230, sales $27,000,000, cert: NMSDC)

6606 Mantych Metalworking, Inc.
3175 Plainfield Rd   Dayton, OH 45432
(937) 258-1373 Bill Sewell Sales
Fax: (937) 258-3771
Email: bill@mantych.net
Website: www.mantych.net
Precision CNC machining & sheet metal fabrication. (Woman/White, estab 1971, empl 34, sales $8,000,000, cert: WBENC)

6607 Ohio Transitional Machine & Tool Inc.
3940 Castener St   Toledo, OH 43612
(419) 476-0820 Marten Whalen President
Fax: (419) 476-1621
Email: ohiotransitional@hotmail.com
Website: www.ohiotransitional.com
CNC milling & turning, wire EDM, boringmill, general machining, blanchard grinding, 3D machining, jigs & fixtures, prototypes, R&D, welding, painting & assembly. (Nat Ame, estab 1985, empl 10, sales $800,000, cert: NMSDC)

6608 Schnipke Engraving Co. Inc.
14223Rd24 P.O. Box 278 Ottoville, OH 45876
(419) 453-3376 Ellie Halter CEO
Fax: (419) 453-3876
Email: ehalter@schnipkeengraving.com
Website: www.schnipkeengraving.com
Precision injection molding, tool design & build, precision assembly, insert molding, overmolding. (Woman/White, estab 1962, empl 350, sales $33,592,463, cert: WBENC)

6609 Vantage Agora
23811 Chagrin Blvd Ste 244 Beachwood, OH 44122
(888) 246-7211 Sudhir Achar President
Fax:
Email: Sudhir@vantageagora.com
Website: www.vantageagora.com
Mfr turned parts, machining, hot & cold forging, printing, precision parts. (As-Ind, estab 2004, empl 19, sales $3,697,558, cert: NMSDC)

6610 Wrena, LLC dba Angstrom-USA, LLC
265 Lightner Rd   Tipp City, OH 45371
(937) 667-4403 Nagesh Palakurthi CEO
Fax:
Email: pyenger@wrenallc.com
Website: www.angstrom-usa.com
Stampings, tubular products, machining, welding, robotic welding, steel forgings, aluminum forgings, assemblies, plastic injection molding, needle bearings, starter assemblies (As-Pac, estab 2011, empl 46, sales , cert: NMSDC)

Oregon

6611 Browns Machine and Hydraulic
90500B Hwy 99N   Eugene, OR 97402
(541) 344-1466 Kevin Brown President
Fax: (541) 344-7161
Email: kevin@brownsmachine.com
Website: www.brownsmachine.com
Custom machining, first article inspections, material certifications. (Nat Ame, estab 2003, empl 18, sales $24,000, cert: State)

6612 Hy Speed Machining, Inc.
353 California Ave   Grants Pass, OR 97526
(541) 476-0769 Rachel Chamberland HR Mgr
Fax: (541) 476-7993
Email: rachelc@hyspeedmachining.com
Website: www.hyspeedmachining.com
Machine shop specializing in machined parts; all materials; close tolerance, high volume. (Woman/Hisp, estab 1984, empl 19, sales $3,049,034, cert: State)

Pennsylvania

6613 Acutec Precision Aerospace Inc.
13555 Broadway   Meadville, PA 16335
(814) 336-7274 Rich Shaffer Senior Acct Mgr
Fax: (814) 724-6495
Email: rshaffer@acutecprecision.com
Website: www.acutecprecision.com
Milling, turning, grinding, honing, lapping, EDM & light assembly of aluminum, titanium, stainless steel, inconel, hastalloy, hastx, plastics. (Woman/White, estab 1988, empl 470, sales $70,364,000, cert: WBENC)

6614 Agape Precision Manufacturing, LLC
320 Circle of Progress Dr Ste 108 Pottstown, PA 19464
(484) 824-3134 Dana Wolfe President
Fax: (484) 300-4125
Email: dana.wolfe@agapeprecision.com
Website: www.agapeprecision.com
Machining, fabrication, bending, assemblies, hardware, some special processes, brackets, prototyping, metals, delron, plastics, aerospace manufacturing. (Woman/White, estab 2006, empl 11, sales $1,100,000, cert: State)

6615 American Roll Suppliers, Inc.
186 Compass Rd   Parkesburg, PA 19365
(610) 857-2988 Karen Neuhauser Ruppert Pres.
Fax: (610) 857-9150
Email: KNeuhauser@peoplepc.com
Website:
Metal fabrication & machining. (Woman, estab , empl 1, sales , cert: WBENC)

6616 Amity Industries
491 Old Swede Rd   Douglassville, PA 19518
(610) 385-6075 Monica Lubinsky CEO
Fax: (610) 385-6079
Email: mlubins@amityindustries.com
Website: www.amityindustries.com
Custom fabrication, machining & assembly. (Nat Ame, estab 1973, empl 45, sales $10,000,000, cert: NMSDC)

6617 Atlas Machining & Welding, Inc.
777 Smith Lane   Northampton, PA 18067
(610) 262-1374 Andrew Weiss Project Mgr
Fax: (610) 262-5202
Email: info@atlasmw.com
Website: www.atlasmw.com
CNC machine & steel fabrication, vertical & horizontal boring mills, vertical machine centers, lathes & turning. (Woman/White, estab 1981, empl 65, sales $13,000,000, cert: NWBOC)

6618 C.A. Spalding, Co.
1011 Cedar Ave   Croydon, PA 19021
(215) 850-5777 Javier Kuehnle CEO
Fax: (215) 826-4053
Email: nteubert@spaldingautomotive.com
Website: www.caspalding.com
High-precision forming, laser cutting & bracket machining. (Hisp, estab 1938, empl 30, sales $18,231,344, cert: NMSDC)

6619 D & R Machine Co.
1330 Industrial Hwy   Southampton, PA 18966
(215) 526-2080 Nelson Redante Mgr, Business Dev
Fax: (215) 526-2084
Email: nelsonredante@drmachine.com
Website: www.drmachine.com
Mfr precision machine parts to cstmr specs. (Hisp, estab 1971, empl 38, sales , cert: NMSDC)

Puerto Rico

6620 EngiWorks Corp.
P.O. Box 8728   Caguas, PR 00725
(787) 703-0288 Yanira Delgado Admin Asst
Fax:
Email: yanira@engiworks.com
Website: www.engiworks.com
3D CAD tools, 3D Printing & CNC manufacturing technologies. (Hisp, estab 2000, empl 12, sales , cert: NMSDC)

6621 SQS, Inc. (Successful Quality Systems)
Palmas Industrial Park Road 869 KM. 2.0 Street 4
Catano, PR 00962
(787) 275-2424 Wilda Aguirre President
Fax: (787) 275-2428
Email: wildaaguirre@sqswarehouse.com
Website: www.sqswarehouse.com
Specialized Storage and Inventory Management Services of materials and products for the pharmaceutical, medical devices, biotech and consumer industries as well as to the safe-guarding of documents (Woman/Hisp, estab 2003, empl 8, sales $2,500,000, cert: NMSDC)

Rhode Island

6622 East Bay Manufacturing
400 Franklin St   Bristol, RI 02809
(401) 254-2960 Randy Medina GM
Fax: (401) 254-2962
Email: randy@eastbaymfg.com
Website: www.eastbaymfg.com
CNC machining & fabrication resources. (Hisp, estab 1985, empl 14, sales , cert: State)

South Carolina

6623 Bunty, LLC
444 Fairforest Way   Greenville, SC 29607
(864) 567-0498 Rajeev Jindal President
Fax: (864) 752-1244
Email: rajeev@buntyllc.com
Website: www.buntyllc.com
Precision machined components, assemblies, metal fabrication, jigs & fixtures, forgings, castings, dies, re-engineered OEM parts, CNC milling, CNC turning. (As-Pac, estab 2000, empl 10, sales $1,600,000, cert: NMSDC)

6624 J.I.T. Manufacturing, Inc.
428 Oglesby Lane P.O. Box 1017 Cowpens, SC 29330
(864) 463-0581 Dan Hunter Production / Sales Mgr.
Fax: (864) 463-0583
Email: dan@jitmanufacturing.com
Website: www.jitmfg.net
Laser cutting, welding, forming, CNC punching, CNC machines, fabrication, sheetmetal, powdercoating, pressbrakes, modifications, spot welding, control boxes, mounting plates, brackets, CAD programing, Cad design. (Woman, estab 1992, empl 22, sales $2,910,792, cert: City, WBENC)

6625   Secondary Solutions, Inc.
     101 Northeast Dr   Spartanburg, SC 29303
     (864) 494-5337   Mark Mahaffey Sales
     Fax: (864) 494-5337
     Email: markmahaffey@secondarysolutionsinc.net
     Website: www.ssiservesyou.net
Machining, fabrication, drilling, tapping, grinding, warehousing, assembly, boring, wire marking, wire harness assembly, 3rd party inspection services, buffing, polishing, packaging. (Woman, estab 1997, empl 10, sales $550,000, cert: WBENC)

Tennessee

6626   Engineered Mechanical Systems
     118 Parmenas Lane PO Box 4958   Chattanooga, TN 37405
     (423) 624-3300   Brenna Fairchild CEO
     Fax: (423) 648-4367
     Email: brenna@emsfab.com
     Website: www.emsfab.com
Design & build custom machines/equipment, multiple lasers & CNC sheet metal machines, certified welders. (Woman/Nat Ame, estab 1990, empl 67, sales $13,000,000, cert: State)

6627   Gonzalez Group LLC/
     237 Kraft St P.O. Box 360   Clarksville, TN 37040
     (517) 542-2928   Felix Gonzalez CEO
     Fax: (517) 542-3850
     Email: fg@gonzalezmfg.com
     Website: www.gonzalezmfg.com
Mfr precision turned machined parts. (Hisp, estab 1974, empl 135, sales $14,000,000, cert: NMSDC)

Texas

6628   365 Machine Inc.
     27890 Commercial Park Lane   Tomball, TX 77375
     (281) 378-7811   Billy Helveston VP Sales/Mktg
     Fax: (281) 378-7810
     Email: billy@365-machine.com
     Website: www.365-machine.com
Precision CNC machining, 4 CNC lathes, 5 CNC mills, horizontal mill. (Woman, estab 2013, empl 13, sales $1,200,000, cert: State, WBENC)

6629   Aero CNC, Inc.
     960 S Burleson Blvd   Burleson, TX 76028
     (817) 295-0184   Chris Layne GM
     Fax: (817) 447-2741
     Email: clayne@aerocnc.com
     Website: www.aerocnc.com
Aerospace machined parts, exotic metals & swarf contour machining. (Woman/Nat Ame, estab 1981, empl 30, sales $4,250,000, cert: State)

6630   Best Sheet Metal Solutions
     923 KCK Way, Ste A   Cedar Hill, TX 75104
     (214) 384-1951   Jacob Bell Owner
     Fax: (972) 293-6922
     Email: jacob@bestsheetmetalsolutions.com
     Website: www.bestsheetmetalsolutions.com
Close Tolerance CNC Machining, CNC Vertical Machining Center & Haas CNC Horitzonal Turning Center (Lathe), Machine Heat Sinks, Buss bar, Surfacing, Profiling, Casting Molds, (AA, estab 2008, empl 3, sales $150,000, cert: NMSDC)

6631   Buks Tool Company, Inc.
     6410-X Langfield Rd   Houston, TX 77092
     (713) 974-5187   Danielle Buks President
     Fax:
     Email: danielle@bukstool.com
     Website: www.bukstool.com
CNC Machining, Conventional machining, coordinate measuring machine, welding, grinding, boring, jig bore, tooling, design, EDM, sawing, hydrostatic pressure testing, high pressure pumps, components & assemblies. (Woman/White, estab 1978, empl 22, sales , cert: WBENC)

6632   Coastal Machine & Mechanical, LLC
     14004 S Hwy 288B   Angleton, TX 77515
     (979) 848-8900   Mike Adams GM
     Fax: (979) 849-9325
     Email: madams@coastalmandm.com
     Website: www.coastalmandm.com
Custom machining & fabrication, millwright & welding services, maintenance services & balancing, rebuild pumps, gearboxes, ASME "R" stamp certificate. (Hisp, estab 2010, empl 28, sales , cert: State)

6633   Cutting Source Precision, Inc.
     14011 Fm 529 Bldg B   Houston, TX 77065
     (281) 859-2900   Larry Boyd Dir Govt sales
     Fax: (281) 859-2922
     Email: info@cspmachine.com
     Website: www.cspmachine.com
Machining, CNC milling & turning, waterjet saw cutting, carbon, aluminum, stainless, Monel, Inconel, Ferrilum, Titanium, Delrin, & Duplex. (Woman/White, estab 2000, empl 20, sales $1,900,000, cert: NWBOC)

6634   Gretna Machine Shop, Inc.
     3450 Lang Rd   Houston, TX 77092
     (713) 690-7328   Nancy Perez VP
     Fax: (713) 690-7350
     Email: nancy@gretnamachine.com
     Website: www.gretnamachine.com
CNC turning machines, CAD/CAM software programming, Sawing, Marking, Deburring services, Real-time order tracking, Worldwide Packaging & Delivery. (Woman/Hisp, estab 1980, empl 52, sales $9,000,000, cert: WBENC)

6635 Guzman Manufacturing, Inc.
      4206 Industrial St   Rowlett, TX 75088
      (972) 475-3003 Annabell Acuna Office Mgr
      Fax: (972) 475-4530
      Email: info@gzmfg.com
      Website: www.gzmfg.com
Machine shop: precision sheet metal, spot welding, CNC, etc. (Hisp, estab 1975, empl 15, sales , cert: State)

6636 Mentco Inc.
      15926 University Oak   San Antonio, TX 78249
      (210) 494-3100 Matt Weber Sr Mgr
      Fax: (609) 773-0126
      Email: matt.weber@mentco.com
      Website: www.mentcoinc.com
Mfr high precision, tight tolerance machined parts from bar stock, castings or forgings. Stainless Steel, (all grades), Inconel, Monel, Hastelloy, 15-5PH, 17-4PH, Titanium, Aluminum, Copper, Brass, Bronze. (As-Ind, estab 2006, empl 55, sales , cert: State, NMSDC)

6637 QMF Steel, Inc.
      3846 IH-30 East P.O. Box 460 Campbell, TX 75422
      (903) 455-3618 Sherrill Lester President
      Fax: (903) 455-9282
      Email: sherrill@qmfsteel.com
      Website: www.qmfsteel.com
CNC plate saw precision cutting, CNC plasma cutting, CNC machining, CNC lathe/turning, bundle cutting, threading, polishing: aluminum, stainless, hot roll, cold roll, alloy, magnesium, brass, copper & other metal products. (Woman/White, estab 1994, empl 25, sales , cert: State, NWBOC)

6638 Spring International
      23594 Dogwood Trail Dr Ste A Hockley, TX 77447
      (281) 966-5109 Spring Wasserman President
      Fax: (281) 259-2021
      Email: spring@springintl.net
      Website: www.springintl.net
Machining, turn key, assembly, coat. etc. (Woman/AA, estab 2014, empl 5, sales $500,000, cert: State)

6639 Standard Industrial Products Company
      12610 Galveston Rd   Webster, TX 77059
      (281) 480-8711 Walter Gomez Dir Operation & Mktg
      Fax: (281) 480-8656
      Email: wgomez@sipco-mls.com
      Website: www.sipco-mls.com
Engineering, Electro - Mechanical Design, Validation & System Integration, CNC Milling, CNC Turning, Sawing, Mechanical System assembly & integration, Gearing - Design, Sourcing, Assembly & System Integration. (Hisp, estab 1984, empl 15, sales $2,099,000, cert: NMSDC)

6640 Systems Integration, Inc.
      7316 Business Pl   Arlington, TX 76001
      (817) 468-1494 Rhonda Smith Acct Mgr
      Fax: (817) 468-7975
      Email: rsmith@sitexas.com
      Website: www.sitexas.com
Engineering & Design, Reverse Engineering, Fabrication, Installation, Structural & Civil, Manufacturing, Machinery, Mechanical, CNC Machining, Electrical & Controls, Test Structures, Tooling. (Hisp, estab 1992, empl 20, sales $4,000,000, cert: State)

6641 VLJ Inc. dba Smith Tool & Mfg.
      116 Regency Dr   Wylie, TX 75098
      (972) 442-4673 Kevin Hefley Sales Mgr
      Fax: (972) 442-1925
      Email: smithtoolsales@airmail.net
      Website: www.smithtoolmfg.com
Precision sheet metal mfg, stamping, tool & die, laser cutting, spinning, maching, turning. (Woman/White, estab 2001, empl 35, sales $570,000, cert: State)

Virginia

6642 High-Tech Machine Mfg, Inc.
      11010 Trade Rd   North Chesterfield, VA 23236
      (804) 794-8640 Cheryl Cacciotti President
      Fax: (804) 379-7490
      Email: c.cacciotti@earthlink.net
      Website: www.high-techmachine.com
Production machining, swiss screw machine, CNC milling & turning, stock & release program. (Woman/White, estab 1984, empl 10, sales $1,100,000, cert: State, WBENC)

6643 Metal Tech Inc.
      2629 Richard Ave NE   Roanoke, VA 24012
      (540) 798-4193 Natasha Crowder Project Estimator
      Fax: (540) 343-4397
      Email: metaltech@cox.net
      Website: www.metaltechincorporated.com
Custom metal fabrication: sandblasting, punching, machine cutting, CNC plasma cutting, water jet cutting, pipe bending, ornamental bender machine, surface preparation & coating. (Woman/White, estab 1996, empl 2, sales $150,000, cert: State)

Washington

6644 Premier Manufacturing
      1711 N Madison   Liberty Lake, WA 99019
      (509) 993-6800 Britt La Chance Sales Dir
      Fax:
      Email: britt@premier-manufacturing.com
      Website: www.premier-manufacturing.net
Mfr precision sheet metal products. (Woman/White, estab 2001, empl 100, sales $8,486,433, cert: WBENC)

Wisconsin

6645   American Metal Technologies LLC
8213 Durand Ave   Sturtevant, WI 53177
(262) 633-1756 San Santharam President
Fax: (262) 637-9706
Email: san@amermetals.com
Website: www.amermetals.com
Precision CNC machining & assembly: ferrous & non-ferrous components, fluid retention components, FEAD brackets & vibration dampening products. (As-Pac, estab 2000, empl 142, sales $25,500,000, cert: NMSDC)

6646   Bothe Associates Inc.
6901-46th St   Kenosha, WI 53144
(262) 656-1860 Cathryn Bothe President
Fax: (262) 656-1858
Email: c.bothe@bothe.com
Website: www.bothe.com
Machine shop & assembly: prototype, short & long run metal & plastic parts, high tolerance, tooling lathes, mills. (Woman/White, estab 1950, empl 40, sales $5,487,258, cert: State, WBENC)

6647   Cardinal Components, Inc.
N59W13500 Manhardt Dr   Menomonee Falls, WI 53051
(262) 437-1510 Leann Kurey President
Fax: (262) 252-5033
Email: nelsonm@cardinalcomponents.com
Website: www.cardinalcomponents.com
Dist Metal Components: Rivet-Nut Fasteners; Precision Machining: CNC Turning and Milling; Metal Fabrication: Brake Press, Laser, Stamping and Welding-Spot; Wire Forming and Springs. (Woman/White, estab 1983, empl 17, sales $7,000,100, cert: CPUC)

6648   eTek Tool and Manufacturing LLC
N37 W5677 Hamilton Rd   Cedarburg, WI 53012
(262) 377-4150 Christopher Ernster Partner
Fax: (262) 377-4150
Email: chris@etektool.com
Website: www.eTekTool.com
CNC machining, fabrication & tooling. (Woman/White, estab 2011, empl 2, sales , cert: State)

6649   Global Precision Group, LLC
S84W19120 Enterprise Dr   Muskego, WI 53150
(262) 679-9411 Chris Lauria Key Acct Mgr
Fax: (262) 679-9411
Email: clauria@globalprecisiongroup.com
Website: www.globalprecisiongroup.com
Tier 1 and Tier 2 CNC machining, ITAR Military certified. (Woman, estab 2008, empl 25, sales , cert: WBENC)

6650   Mantz Automation
1630 Innovation Way   Hartford, WI 53027
(262) 224-7528 Gary Sonnenburg Sales Rep
Fax: (262) 673-0377
Email: tnewman@mantzautomation.com
Website: www.mantzautomation.com
Machining components: alloys, design & build tooling, gages, fitures, CNC machinery, 5 axis machinng centers. (Woman/Hisp, estab 1986, empl 105, sales $22,300,000, cert: State, NMSDC)

6651   R.J. Zeman Tool & Mfg. Co., Inc.
W228 N575 Westmound Dr   Waukesha, WI 53186
(262) 549-4400 Spencer Schreindl President
Fax:
Email: sschreindl@zemantool.com
Website:
Machining, design, mfr & inspect fixtures, special machines, gages, die cast dies, plastic injection molds, permanent molds, core boxes, patterns for sand casting & short and long-run production parts. (Woman/White, estab 1966, empl 48, sales $9,600,000, cert: WBENC)

6652   Stanek Tool Corporation
2500 S Calhoun Rd   New Berlin, WI 53151
(262) 786-0120 Paul Bartkowiak VP - Workholding
Fax: (262) 786-8236
Email: pbartkowiak@stanektool.com
Website: www.stanektool.com
Design & build machining fixtures, plastic molds, & precision machined parts & assemblies. (Woman/White, estab 1924, empl 50, sales $10,000,000, cert: WBENC)

METAL RAW STOCK
Includes distributors of metal sheets, plates, rods, pipe, etc. Many can provide cutting and other metal processing services. (Also see six other METAL categories). NAICS Code 33

Arizona

6653 HiTemp Management Consulting, Inc.
      4650 S Coach Dr Ste 120 Tucson, AZ 85714
      (520) 807-6157 Carlos Ruiz CEO
      Fax: (520) 807-2370
      Email: carlos@htmetals.com
      Website: www.htmetals.com
Raw Material Distribution, Aluminum, Stainless Steel, Specialty Steels, Brass, Bronze, Superalloys, Titanium, Abrasive waterjet cutting,
Cut to length band saw cutting. (Hisp, estab 2003, empl 6, sales $1,440,000, cert: 8(a))

6654 K&R Holdings, Inc.
      2322 W Detroit Pl Chandler, AZ 85224
      (480) 236-2682 Wayne Armoogam President
      Fax: (480) 857-6177
      Email: warmoogam@lumawaresafety.com
      Website: www.lumawaresafety.com
Supply and install photoluminescent egress systems for facilities. Our technologies for egress requires no electricity, external power source or batteries to provide the illumination required for safe movement of employees (As-Ind, estab 2007, empl 5, sales $100,000, cert: City, NMSDC)

California

6655 California Metal & Supply Inc.
      10230 Freeman Ave Santa Fe Springs, CA 90670
      (800) 707-6061 Kenneth Minkyu Lee President
      Fax: (800) 707-3439
      Email: klee@californiametal.com
      Website: www.CaliforniaMetal.com
Titanium, Inconel, Aluminum, Stainless, Magnesium Sheet, Plate, Bar, Tube & Tubing, Pipe, Tubing: Stainless, Carbon Steel, Aluminum, Brass, Valves. (As-Pac, estab 1984, empl 12, sales $60,000,000, cert: NMSDC)

6656 Carnegie Metals Inc.
      2700 Rose Ave, Ste J Long Beach, CA 90755
      (562) 989-6431 Carl Grigsby President
      Fax: (562) 989-6432
      Email: carl@carnegiemetals.com
      Website: www.carnegiemetals.com
Scrap & surplus metals, ferrous & non-ferrous scrap, aluminum & titanium, clean, strip, sort, separate & process metals. (AA, estab 1993, empl 2, sales , cert: State)

6657 Global Steel Alliance Corp.
      14241 E Firestone Blvd, Ste 400 La Mirada, CA 90638
      (562) 293-4086 Keith Shiozaki President
      Fax: (562) 293-4089
      Email: keith@steel-alliance.net
      Website: www.steel-alliance.net
Dist carbon steel pipe. (As-Pac, estab 2008, empl 3, sales $3,370,000, cert: NMSDC)

6658 International Metal Source
      17605 Fabrica Way Ste E & F Cerritos, CA 90703
      (714) 676-5669 Jaymee Del Rosario CEO
      Fax: (888) 880-6404
      Email: Jaymee@imetalsource.com
      Website: www.imetalsource.com
Dist Aluminum, Nickel, Titanium, Stainless Steel, High-Temperature & Specialty Steels, Ferrous, Non-Ferrous & Non-Metallic Raw Material in Sheet, Plate, Rod, Bar, Extrusions, Tubes & Formed Shapes. (Woman/As-Pac, estab 2009, empl 10, sales $889,000, cert: CPUC, SDB)

6659 Southern California Metals, Inc.
      9900 Bell Ranch Dr Santa Fe Springs, CA 90670
      (562) 941-1616 Alisa Thorpe President
      Fax: (562) 941-2709
      Email: alisa@socalmetals.com
      Website: www.socalmetals.com
Dist alloys, steels, stainless steels, titanium, nickel based alloys, aluminum & copper alloys in plate, sheet, bar, extrusion, forgings & castings, plastic lexan sheets, aviation rivets, nuts, fasteners, screws & seat tracks. (Woman/White, estab 1995, empl 15, sales $4,001,000, cert: State, CPUC)

Florida

6660 Aluminum Distributing, Inc. dba ADI Metal
      2930 SW Second Ave Fort Lauderdale, FL 33315
      (954) 523-6474 Betsy McGee President
      Fax: (954) 779-7355
      Email: betsy@adimetal.com
      Website: www.adimetal.com
Dist aluminum for the marine and industrial markets. (Woman/White, estab 1958, empl 16, sales $5,300,000, cert: State, WBENC)

6661 ASM Aerospace Specifications Metals, Inc.
      2501 NW 34th Place, B28 Pompano Beach, FL 33069
      (954) 977-0666 Douglas Bridges Sales
      Fax: (954) 977-3858
      Email: dbridges@aerospacemetals.com
      Website: www.aerospacemetals.com
Dist raw materials: aircraft quality metals, sheet, plate, rod, wire, bar, tubing & extruded shapes. (Woman/Hisp, estab 2001, empl 14, sales $7,000,000, cert: NMSDC)

6662   Manzi Metals, Inc.
       15293 Flight Path Dr   Brooksville, FL 34604
       (352) 277-5852 Dorsey Peterson Small Business
       Specialist
       Fax: (352) 799-8244
       Email: dpeterson@manzimetals.com
       Website: www.manzimetals.com
Dist aerospace & commercial metals: aluminum, stainless,
alloy steel, copper, brass, titanium, high temps in sheet,
plate, bar, rod, hex, tube, etc. forgings, castings, ingots,
billets.
 (Woman/AA, estab 1993, empl 10, sales $3,600,000, cert:
State, City, NMSDC, SDB)

Georgia

6663   Pacesetter Steel Service, Inc.
       1045 Big ShantyRdNW   Kennesaw, GA 30144
       (770) 919-8000 Dawne Knerr Credit
       Fax: (678) 581-8800
       Email: dknerr@teampacesetter.com
       Website: www.teampacesetter.com
Flat rolled products: minimum & zero spangled Galvanized-
chemically or non-chemically treated, Galvannealed,
Bonderized, Cold Rolled, Aluminized & Galvalume steel.
(Woman/White, estab 1977, empl 140, sales
$205,000,000, cert: WBENC)

Illinois

6664   Elgiloy Specialty Metals
       1565 Fleetwood Dr   Elgin, IL 60123
       (847) 695-1900 Margaret Wilson Wire Sales Rep
       Fax: (847) 695-0169
       Email: margaretw@elgiloy.com
       Website: www.elgiloy.com
Strip, wire, rod & bar specialty alloys; various gauges/
diameters and widths. Strip: rolling, slitting, annealing.
Wire/bar/rod: drawing, annealing. In-house lab. (As-Pac,
estab 1975, empl 75, sales , cert: NMSDC)

6665   HL Metals, LLC
       910 Spruce St   Winnetka, IL 60093
       (312) 590-3360 Hui Lin Lim President
       Fax: (847) 859-5875
       Email: hlim@hlmetalsllc.com
       Website: www.hlmetalsllc.com
Dist P1020 aluminum sows/aluminum sheet ingot.
(Woman/As-Pac, estab 2007, empl 1, sales $55,000,000,
cert: CPUC, NWBOC)

6666   Nak-Man Corporation
       5677 W Howard   Niles, IL 60714
       (847) 673-7377 Perry Nakachi President
       Fax: (847) 673-2358
       Email: nakmancorp@aol.com
       Website:
Dist carbon steel, stainless steel, structural steel,
aluminum, copper, brass, bronze, plastics, machined &
fabricated parts. (As-Pac, estab 1989, empl 12, sales
$4,796,534, cert: City, NMSDC)

6667   National Material Company, L.L.C.
       1965 Pratt Blvd   Elk Grove Village, IL 60007
       (847) 806-4742 Jim Osborne Dir. Minority Dev
       Fax: (847) 806-7220
       Email: josborne@nmlp.com
       Website: www.nmlp.com
Steel service & processing. (As-Pac, estab 1999, empl
299, sales $370,000,000, cert: NMSDC)

6668   National Material Trading, LLC
       1965 Pratt Blvd   Elk Grove Village, IL 60007
       (847) 806-4742 Jim Osborne Director of Minority
       Dev
       Fax: (847) 806-7220
       Email: josborne@nmlp.com
       Website: www.nationalmaterialtrading.com
Dist carbon flat rolled steel. (As-Pac, estab 1964, empl
12, sales , cert: NMSDC)

6669   North States Steel Corp.
       12255 Highway 173   Hebron, IL 60034
       (815) 648-1500 Sandra Myers President
       Fax: (815) 648-4185
       Email: smyers@northstatessteel.com
       Website: www.northstatessteel.com
Hot rolled, cold rolled, aluminum stainless steel sheets.
(Woman/White, estab 1971, empl 25, sales $14,000,000,
cert: State, WBENC, SDB)

6670   S & S International,Inc.
       457 St. Paul Blvd   Carol Stream, IL 60188
       (708) 805-5701 Rich Isom Sr Acct Exec
       Fax:
       Email: icemanandfamily1@msn.com
       Website: www.ssistainless.com
Dist stainless steel: sheet, plate, strip, coil, bars, structural shapes, square & rectangular tubing, pipe &
fittings, aluminum sheet, strip & coil. (As-Ind/As-Pac,
estab 1991, empl 105, sales $30,000,000, cert: NMSDC)

Indiana

6671 Advanced Metal Services, LLC
2324 Longleaf Dr   Fort Wayne, IN 46804
(260) 625-5046 Jason L. Redden, Jr. Exec VP
Fax: (260) 625-8046
Email: slyred01@aol.com
Website:
Metal recycling; dist flat rolled steel (Hisp, estab 1999, empl 2, sales , cert: NMSDC)

6672 Eagle Steel Products, Inc.
5150 Loop Rd   Jeffersonville, IN 47130
(812) 282-7090 Gary Shumate GM Sales
Fax: (812) 282-5873
Email: gshumate@eaglesteelproducts.com
Website: www.eaglesteelproducts.com
Mfr strip steel; flat rolled products, blanking; covered barge & rail loading & unloading svcs, warehousing, etc. (Woman/As-Pac, estab 1982, empl 83, sales $32,000,000, cert: NMSDC)

Maryland

6673 Inkomparable
10440 Little Patuxent Pkwy Ste 300 Columbia, MD 21046
(877) 673-5050 Curtis Kelly President
Fax: (810) 385-9280
Email: Curtis@inkomparable.com
Website: www.inkomparable.com
(AA, estab , empl 1, sales , cert: NMSDC)

Michigan

6674 Delaco Steel Corporation
8111 Tireman, Ste 1   Dearborn, MI 48126
(313) 491-1200 Michael Roualet VP of Quality
Fax: (313) 491-6210
Email: mike.roualet@delacosteel.com
Website: www.delacosteel.com
Dist & process steel & aluminum. Blanking, warehousing, slitting, stampings, etc. (Woman/Hisp, estab 1974, empl 650, sales , cert: NMSDC, WBENC)

6675 H&H Metal Source
1909 Turner Ave NW   Grand Rapids, MI 49504
(616) 364-0113 JR Hartman Ops Mgr
Fax: (616) 364-0904
Email: jr@hhmetalsource.com
Website: www.hhmetalsource.com
Flat rolled steel in coil or blanks. (Woman/White, estab 1992, empl 30, sales $38,000,000, cert: WBENC)

6676 Instramed
3071 Commerce Dr. Ste. C Ft. Gratiot, MI 48059
(800) 451-5840 Cori May President
Fax: (810) 385-9280
Email: allinfo@instramedinc.com
Website: www.instramedinc.com
Scrap metal & recyclable materials, ferrous & non-ferrous scrap metal. (Woman, estab 1987, empl 1, sales , cert: NWBOC)

6677 National Material Co.
1505 N Dixie Dr, Ste 2   Monroe, MI 48162
(734) 384-9720 John Allen Sales Rep
Fax: (734) 384-9788
Email: jballen53@msn.com
Website: www.nmcmonroe.com
Steel coil, sheet, blank, painted steel, galvanized, aluminum,stainless HSLA, CS, DS. (As-Pac, estab , empl , sales $750,000,000, cert: NMSDC)

6678 Scion Steel
21555 Mullin Ave   Warren, MI 48089
(800) 288-2127 Micky Tschirhart VP
Fax: (586) 755-4064
Email: mtschirhart@scionsteel.com
Website: www.scionsteel.com
Full line steel service center - processed & fabricated to order. (Hisp, estab 1984, empl 51, sales , cert: NMSDC)

6679 Torch Steel Sales LLC
18501 Krause St   Riverview, MI 48193
(734) 783-2018 Cristina Simone Owner
Fax: (734) 783-9797
Email: csimone@torchsteelsales.com
Website: www.torchsteelsales.com
Steel service center: slitting, blanking, shearing, & slearing of non-ferrous flat rolled steel products, Hot Rolled, Cold Rolled, Hot Dipped Galvanized, Electro Galvanized, Galvanneal, & Aluminized. (Woman/White, estab 2013, empl 2, sales $700,600, cert: WBENC)

North Carolina

6680 Accro-Met, Inc.
3406 Westwood Industrial Dr   Monroe, NC 28110
(704) 283-2111 Andrea Doolittle Sales
Fax: (704) 283-2112
Email: alm@accromet.com
Website: www.accromet.com
Dist metal: stainless, nickel, aluminum, copper, brass, bronze, sheet, plate, bar, shapes. (Woman/White, estab 1988, empl 15, sales $6,000,000, cert: WBENC)

New Jersey

6681 L-E-M Plastics& Supply Inc.
255 Highland Cross   Rutherford, NJ 07070
(201) 933-9150 Ellen Pietrowitz-Phillips President
Fax: (201) 933-9154
Email: ellenp@l-e-mplastics.com
Website: www.l-e-mplastics.com
Fabriate & dist raw material plastic & rubber, Sheet, rod, tubing & film cut to size. Machining of all plastic, build to print. Steel rule die punching of thin plastic & rubber. (Woman/White, estab 1974, empl 12, sales $1,200,000, cert: WBENC)

New York

6682 O.S.S. Metals Inc.
14939 Guy R Brewer Blvd   Jamaica, NY 11434
(718) 553-2054 Sattesh Singh CEO
Fax: (718) 553-2092
Email: sattesh@ossmetals.com
Website: www.ossmetals.com
Provide raw material: Aluminum, Stainless Steel, Titanium, Carbon Steel & specialty alloys. (As-Ind, estab 2012, empl 3, sales $750,000, cert: State)

Ohio

6683 CT Metal Source
9551 St Christine Ct   Sylvania, OH 43560
(419) 779-6172 Chad Crooks President
Fax: (419) 720-7801
Email: ccrooks@ctmetalsource.com
Website: www.ctmetalsource.com
Dist metal castings, rail car parts, vent registers & steel coils. (Hisp, estab 2005, empl 5, sales $7,000,000, cert: NMSDC)

6684 Ferrolux Metals Co. of Ohio, LLC
8055A Highland Pointe Pkwy   Macedonia, OH 44056
(330) 468-1008 Mark Nester GM
Fax: (330) 468-1308
Email: mnester@ferrolux.com
Website: www.ferrolux.com
Dist flat rolled processed steel, Cold rolled, Coated, Slitting & Inspection, Storage, Transportation. (Hisp, estab 2004, empl 22, sales , cert: NMSDC)

6685 MasterSource Co., Inc.
1208 Massillon Rd Ste #2 Akron, OH 44306
(800) 968-1718 Tracy Skinner Cstmr Service
Fax: (330) 794-8833
Email: tracy@mastersourceco.com
Website: www.mastersourceco.com
Aluminum, brass, bronze, copper, alloy & carbon steel, nylon, stainless, tool steel: bar, rod, plate, sheet, tube, foil, wire, structural shapes, bushings. (Woman/As-Pac, estab 1992, empl 4, sales $1,090,000, cert: State)

6686 New Concepts, Inc.
34208 Aurora Rd Box 160 Solon, OH 44139
(440) 542-9510 Sudarshan Sathe President
Fax: (440) 542-9505
Email: sudarshan@new-concepts.net
Website: www.new-concepts.net
Aluminum products: cones, shot, nuggets, briquettes, metallurgical coke, mid-volatile coal. (As-Pac, estab 1990, empl 3, sales $123,905,402, cert: NMSDC)

6687 Nu Tek Steel, LLC
6180 American Road   Toledo, OH 43612
(419) 724-0891 Sarah Bates President
Fax: (419) 724-0884
Email: sarah.bates@ntsteel.net
Website: www.ntsteel.net
Steel services: slitting, pickling, blanking, leveling, special bar quality, construction & medical. (Woman/AA, estab 2000, empl 10, sales $4,300,000, cert: State, WBENC)

6688 Slice Of Stainless Inc.
1015 Seabrook Way   Cincinnati, OH 45245
(513) 943-1290 Jim Schneible Sales Mgr
Fax: (513) 943-1267
Email: jim@sliceofstainless.com
Website: www.sliceofstainless.com
Dist stainless steal & high nickel alloys sheet & plate. (Woman/White, estab 1992, empl 20, sales $7,100,000, cert: WBENC)

6689 Texas Specialty Metals, Inc.
4989 FM 1461   McKinney, TX 75071
(972) 347-5557 Andy Dimock Mgr
Fax: (877) 213-4929
Email: andy@txspec.com
Website: www.texasspecialtymetals.com
Stainless steel, aluminum & steel, titanium, nickel, invar, vespel & alloys. (Woman/Nat Ame, estab 1998, empl 3, sales $250,000, cert: State)

Virginia

6690 United Scrap Metal
      2900 Terminal Avenue   Richmond, VA 23234
      (434) 430-1039 Owen Tomlinson Recycling Consult-
      ant
      Fax:
      Email: otomlinson@unitedscrap.com
      Website: www.unitedscrap.com
Metal recycling. (Woman/White, estab 1978, empl 170,
sales , cert: WBENC)

METAL, WIRE PRODUCTS
See six other METAL categories. NAICS Code 33

California

6691   Calmont Wire & Cable
       420 E Alton Ave   Santa Ana, CA 92707
       (714) 549-0336 Barbara Monteleone CEO
       Fax: (714) 549-4028
       Email: bobbem@calmont.com
       Website: www.calmont.com
Custom mfr precision wire & cable, including high-flex &
high-temp Silicone & FEP. (Woman/White, estab 1958,
empl 32, sales , cert: State)

6692   Top-Shelf Fixtures
       5263 Schaefer Ave   Chino, CA 91710
       (909) 627-7423 Michelle Burguan Controller
       Fax: (909) 591-1418
       Email: sprochnow@topshelffixtures.com
       Website: www.topshelffixtures.com
Wire fabrication: sheet metal & structural steel for
gondola shelving. (Hisp, estab 2002, empl 123, sales
$8,500,000, cert: NMSDC)

Georgia

6693   Healthier & Happier, Inc.
       1853 Whitehall Forest Ct.   Atlanta, GA 30316
       (678) 900-6617 Jing Carter-Lu President
       Fax:
       Email: Jing.Carter-Lu@healthier-happier.com
       Website: www.healthier-happier.com
Dist wire rope, steel rope, carbon spring steel wire, bead
wire, hose wire, plastic coated wire rope, PC stranded
wire, bunched wire, galvanized stranded wire & zinc-plated
steel wire. (Woman/As-Pac, estab 2003, empl 2, sales
$120,000, cert: City)

Illinois

6694   Solar Spring & Wire Forms
       345 Criss Circle   Elk Grove Village, IL 60007
       (847) 437-7838 Aida Carrera Director of Global
       Sales
       Fax:
       Email: acarrera@solarspring.com
       Website: www.solarspring.com
Mfr springs, wire forms & stampings. (Hisp, estab 1979,
empl 110, sales $11,100,000, cert: NMSDC)

Louisiana

6695   Vast Industries
       108 Venus St Ste 200 Morgan City, LA 70380
       (985) 312-1592 Yvette Archuleta-Tudury Owner
       Fax: (985) 395-1940
       Email: Yvette@Vast-Ind.com
       Website: www.Vast-Ind.com
Wire EDM & precision machined parts manufacturing,
custom product design, reverse engineering & aluminum
& steel fabrication. (Woman/Nat Ame/Hisp, estab 2007,
empl 7, sales $600,000, cert: NMSDC, WBENC, 8(a))

Massachusetts

6696   Springfield Spring
       311 Shaker Road P.O. Box 505 Longmeadow, MA
       01028
       (413) 525-6837 Norman Rodriques President
       Fax: (413) 525-6895
       Email: pat@springfieldspring.com
       Website: www.springfieldspring.com
Mfr precision engineered compression springs, torsion
springs, extension springs, wire forms, fourslide-
produced stampings, assemblies. (Hisp, estab 1942,
empl 39, sales $7,200,000, cert: NMSDC)

Ohio

6697   MCM Industries Co., Inc.
       7800 Finney Ave   Cleveland, OH 44105
       (216) 641-6300 Abby Werner VP
       Fax: (216) 641-6318
       Email: awerner@northcoastspring.com
       Website: www.mcmindustries.com
Wire & spring forming. (AA/Hisp, estab 1980, empl 25,
sales , cert: NMSDC)

6698   Mid West Fabricating
       313 N Johns St   Amanda, OH 43102
       (740) 969-4411 Dave Gallimore Business Dev
       Fax: (740) 969-4433
       Email: dgallimore@midwestfab.com
       Website: www.midwestfab.com
Cold formed rod & wire products, fasteners, CNC
wireforming, cold forming. (Woman/White, estab 1945,
empl 200, sales $32,000,000, cert: WBENC)

Oklahoma

6699 Ebsco Spring Company, Inc.
4949 S 83rd Ave E   Tulsa, OK 74145
(918) 628-1680 Todd Pfeifer Sales
Fax: (918) 628-0382
Email: toddp@ebscospring.com
Website: www.ebscospring.com
Mfr & engineer custom, high quality compression, extension & torsion springs. (Woman/White, estab 1940, empl 75, sales $6,500,000, cert: WBENC)

Pennsylvania

6700 LEM Products, Inc.
301 S Main St Ste 2 East Doylestown, PA 18901
(800) 220-2400 Maureen O'Connor CEO
Fax: (267) 880-6731
Email: moconnor@lemproductsinc.com
Website: www.lemproductsinc.com
Mfr wire identification safety products: wire marker cards & books, voltage markers, transformer marking, hand writeable cable markers, laser coded bar codes, lockout tags, roll
dispensers, heat shrinkables, etc. (Woman/White, estab 1900, empl 1, sales $5,500,000, cert: CPUC, WBENC)

6701 R.A.W. Consulting, LLC
126 Mervis Dr   Beaver Falls, PA 15010
(724) 384-1559 Robert Washington President
Fax:
Email: rawconsultantsllc@gmail.com
Website: www.R-A-W-LLC.com
Distribution & warehousing of Stainless & alloy tubing, Cold rolled wire, Metal grating, Deformed wire. (AA, estab 2013, empl 3, sales $309,996, cert: State, NMSDC)

Texas

6702 M3 Associates, Inc.
P.O. Box 224075   Dallas, TX 75222
(214) 339-2117 Yvonne Newhouse President
Fax: (214) 331-1457
Email: yvonne@m3associatesinc.com
Website: www.m3associatesinc.com
Distributor of wire, cable, tubing, sleeving, solder sleeves, heat shrink molded, shapes, boots (Woman/AA, estab 1988, empl 5, sales , cert: State)

Virginia

6703 Jo Kell Inc.
1716 Lambert Ct   Chesapeake, VA 23320
(904) 260-8420 Patricia Galiney
Fax: (904) 260-8401
Email: customerservice@jokell.com
Website: www.jokell.com
Dist electrical apparatus & equipment, wiring supplies & related equipment. (Woman/White, estab 1977, empl 50, sales $30,383,075, cert: WBENC)

OFFICE SUPPLIES
Manufacturers and distributors of office supplies and equipment: rubber stamps, writing implements, binders and portfolios, business forms, calculators, envelopes, tape, ink, office machines and furniture, toner cartridges, printers, etc. NAICS Code 42

Arkansas

6704 Burris Inc.
113 S Arkansas Ave   Russellville, AR 72801
(479) 968-4888 Trolynn McSpadden President
Fax: (479) 968-4937
Email:
Website: www.burrisinc.com
Office supplies & office furniture, panel systems, custom millwork, office layout & design. (Woman/White, estab 1953, empl 15, sales $3,374,600, cert: WBENC)

6705 Goddess Products, Inc.
6142 Getty Dr   North Little Rock, AR 72117
(501) 372-4002 Andrew Sigeti Acct Mgr
Fax: (501) 372-4066
Email: asigeti@ussco.com
Website: www.goddessproductsinc.com
Dist office products, office equipment, office furniture, computer peripherals, janitorial supplies & safety equipment. (Woman/AA, estab 2006, empl 5, sales $375,000, cert: WBENC)

California

6706 Big Red Print Solutions, LLC
2100 Sawtelle Blvd Ste 201 Los Angeles, CA 90025
(213) 985-7201 Rudy Wrabel Director
Fax:
Email: rudy@bigredink.com
Website: www.bigredink.com
Dist office equipment, supplies & technology products. (Woman, estab 2010, empl 7, sales $1,100,000, cert: NMSDC, CPUC)

6707 Garza Industries
1870 N Glassell St   Orange, CA 92865
(714) 769-2777 James Garza
Fax: (714) 769-2770
Email: james@garzaindustries.com
Website: www.garzaindustries.com
Dist office supplies: copy paper, laser toner cartridges, fax & copier supplies, furniture, direct mail svcs, commercial printing, corporate apparel, promotional items. (Woman/Hisp, estab 1991, empl 35, sales , cert: CPUC)

6708 Kleenslate Concepts, LP
14997 Camage Ave, Unit B   Sonora, CA 94370
(209) 588-0375 Julia Rhodes CEO
Fax: (209) 588-9677
Email: julia@kleenslate.com
Website: www.kleenslate.com
Dist attachable white board markers erasers, white board products (Woman/As-Pac/Hisp, estab 2001, empl 12, sales $1,200,000, cert: WBENC)

6709 New Century Technologies Inc.
4290 Kendall St   San Diego, CA 92109
(800) 457-4313 Peter Steiner COO
Fax: (866) 237-5403
Email: peter@nctsolution.com
Website: www.nctsolution.com
Toner cartridges, office supplies/products, office equipment, office furniture, janitorial supplies, breakroom supplies, industrial supplies/products, hard drive, memory, IT products that offers hardware, software, related services. (Woman/As-Pac, estab 2006, empl 3, sales $1,391,800, cert: 8(a))

6710 Z Venture Capital Frontiers, Inc.
1625 W Vernon Ave   Los Angeles, CA 90062
(323) 596-4690 Karim Zaman President
Fax: (323) 596-4695
Email: karim@thezamangroup.com
Website: www.thezamangroup.com
Dist office supplies, inkjet, laser, toner cartridge, thermal fax ribbon. (AA, estab 1997, empl 2, sales $1,300,000, cert: State, City, CPUC, 8(a))

Colorado

6711 CADDO Design Inc. dba CADDO Solutions
2760 W 5th Ave   Denver, CO 80204
(303) 534-3252 Donald Kelin CEO
Fax: (303) 534-6962
Email: dkelin@caddosolutions.com
Website: www.caddosolutions.com
Dist office products, office furniture, coffee & refreshments, ad specialty items, printing, print management. (Nat Ame, estab 1990, empl 45, sales $5,000,000, cert: State)

6712 Faison Office Products Company
3251 Revere St, 2nd Fl Aurora, CO 80011
(303) 945-6438 Susan Manuello Acct Developer
Fax: (303) 365-4588
Email: SManuello@faisonopc.com
Website: www.faisonopc.com
Dist office supplies & furniture; word processing & data processing supplies & furniture. (AA, estab 1981, empl 40, sales , cert: NMSDC)

District of Columbia

6713 The Hamilton Group
4406 Gault Place NE   Washington, DC 20019
(202) 689-4304 Kaari Hamilton President
Fax: (202) 204-6083
Email: kayhhpbp@verizon.net
Website: www.thehamiltongroupllc.net
Dist office supplies, advertisement & promotional products, office equipment & clothing wearables. (Woman/AA, estab 2007, empl 1, sales $731,000, cert: City, NMSDC)

Florida

6714 Apex Office Products, Inc.
5209 N Howard Ave   Tampa, FL 33603
(800) 227-1563 Aurelio Llorente, Jr President
Fax:
Email: allorentejr@apexop.com
Website: www.apexofficeproducts.com
Dist office supplies & furniture, data supplies & furniture, paper products, rubber stamps. (Woman/Hisp, estab 1981, empl 55, sales , cert: State, NMSDC)

6715 J&E Office Supplies, Inc.
7911 NW 72ND Ave, Unit 110A   Medley, FL 33166
(305) 887-7339 Jaime Hernandez Owner
Fax: (305) 882-1558
Email: jeoffice@mindspring.com
Website: www.biggestbook.com/index.faces
Office supplies & office furniture. (Hisp, estab 1985, empl 4, sales $2,500,000, cert: State)

6716 MarkMaster, Inc.
11111 N 46th St   Tampa, FL 33617
(813) 988-6000 Deborah Jordan Sales Rep
Fax: (813) 985-6860
Email: sales@markmasterinc.com
Website: www.markmasterinc.com
Mfr rubber stamps, engraved & screened signage & badges; industrial marking equip. (Hisp, estab 1933, empl 65, sales $8,700,993, cert: NMSDC)

6717 Source One Distributors, Inc.
3125 Fortune Way, Ste 1   Wellington, FL 33414
(561) 296-0520 Mark Llano CEO
Fax: (561) 514-1021
Email: mllano@buysourceone.com
Website: www.buysourceone.com
Dist office products & furniture, safety & janitorial products, light sticks, snap light, cyalume, camo face paint. (Hisp, estab 2003, empl 5, sales $1,800,000, cert: State)

Georgia

6718 ABC Laser USA, Inc.
6000 G Unity Dr   Norcross, GA 30092
(770) 448-5867 Kammie Lee Acct Mgr
Fax: (770) 448-6253
Email: kmichell@abclaserusa.com
Website: www.abclaserusa.com
Office Supplies, Ink, Toner, Furniture, Paper, Disc, Printers, Faxes, Pens, Pencils, Maintenance, Service, Janitorial Supplies, Cleaners, Toilet Paper, Paper Towels, Recycle Toner, Hewlett Packard, Lexmark, Dell, Canon. (Woman/As-Pac, estab 1996, empl 6, sales $2,006,890, cert: City)

6719 Freeman Forms & Supplies dba MySupplies
800 Doug Davis Dr   Atlanta, GA 30354
(404) 768-2387 Nancy Freeman Balkcom President
Fax: (404) 768-0420
Email: nancy@mysupplies.com
Website: www.mysupplies.com
Dist office product & furniture. (Woman/White, estab 1970, empl 22, sales $6,000,000, cert: State)

6720 Peachtree Supplies, Inc.
233 Peachtree St NE, Ste 1265   Atlanta, GA 30303
(404) 963-2410 Al Graham President
Fax: (404) 393-9793
Email: agraham@peachtreesupplies.com
Website: www.peachtreesupplies.com
Office supplies, furniture, ink & toner, paper, cleaning supplies, technology. (Woman/AA, estab 2009, empl 10, sales $1,350,000, cert: NMSDC)

Iowa

6721 Bailey Office Equipment, Inc.
123 E 2nd St P.O. Box 661 Ottumwa, IA 52501
(800) 728-0407 Linda Gardner President
Fax: (641) 684-4297
Email: Linda@baileyoffice.com
Website: www.baileyoffice.com
Dist office supplies, business machines, office furniture, cleaning supplies, safety equipment & breakroom essentials. (Woman/White, estab 1925, empl 10, sales $2,798,000, cert: WBENC)

Illinois

6722 Bren Products
437 E 103rd St   Chicago, IL 60628
(773) 568-9900 Rochelle Gary Comptroller
Fax: (773) 568-9894
Email: brenprod@sbcglobal.net
Website:
Dist office machines & supplies, office furniture, custom printing, file folders & envelopes, recycling containers & supplies. (AA, estab 1994, empl 3, sales $5,600,000, cert: NMSDC)

6723   Logsdon Office Supply
       111 S Fairbank   Addison, IL 60101
       (847) 593-8282 Jack Dern VP
       Fax:
       Email: jdern@logsdonofficesupply.com
       Website: www.logsdonofficesupply.com
Dist office supplies. (AA, estab 1966, empl 25, sales
$7,000,000, cert: City, NMSDC)

6724   National Office Works, Inc.
       1965 W Pershing Rd   Chicago, IL 60612
       (312) 455-9343 Joanna Davidson President
       Fax:
       Email: joanna.davidson@nationalofficeworks.com
       Website: www.nationalofficeworks.com
Dist office supplies. (Woman/White, estab 2006, empl 11,
sales $750,000, cert: State, WBENC)

6725   Pointe International
       234 Oakwood Road   Lake Zurich, IL 60047
       (847) 550-7001 Sheila Liao President
       Fax: (847) 550-7102
       Email: sheila.liao@pointecompany.com
       Website: www.pointecompany.com
Mfr & dist wooden case pencils, mechanic pencils, desk
stapler, office supplies & promotional items. (Woman/As-
Pac, estab 1997, empl 12, sales $1,800,000, cert: NMSDC,
WBENC)

6726   Taylor Made Business Solutions LLC
       318 W. Adams St 16th Fl Chicago, IL 60606
       (312) 803-5635 Evonne Taylor CEO
       Fax: (312) 803-5639
       Email: etaylor@tmbsllc.com
       Website: www.TMBSLLC.com
Dist general office supplies, office furniture, break room &
janitorial supplies. (Woman/AA, estab 2011, empl 3, sales
$2,762,000, cert: State, NMSDC)

6727   Working Hands, Inc.
       39W254 Sheldon Ct   Geneva, IL 60134
       (630) 270-1097 Maureen Vedder President
       Fax:
       Email: maureen@workinghandsinc.com
       Website: www.workinghandsinc.com
GBC equipment & supplies, copier tabs, laminating rolls &
pouches, clear presentation covers, black composition
back covers prepunched, binding coils, 3 ring clear view
binders, plain or mylar docucopy copier tabs. (Woman/
White, estab 2003, empl 2, sales $250,000, cert: NWBOC)

Indiana

6728   Kramer & Leonard, Inc.
       312 Roberts Rd   Chesterton, IN 46304
       (219) 926-1171 Mary Fox President
       Fax:
       Email: mfox@kramerleonard.com
       Website: www.kramerleonard.com
Office products, office supplies, computer supplies,
office furniture, commercial interior design services,
copier sales, copier service. (Woman, estab , empl 1,
sales , cert: State, WBENC)

6729   Media Hub, LLc dba Office Hub
       60 E Washington St   Shelbyville, IN 46176
       (317) 398-3070 Shannon Huber CEO
       Fax: (317) 398-6418
       Email: shannonhuber@iwantmysupplies.com
       Website: www.officehubonline.com
Office supplies, printing and promotional products.
(Woman, estab 2006, empl 7, sales $941,136, cert:
State)

6730   OfficeWorks Services LLC
       12000 Exit Five Pkwy   Fishers, IN 46037
       (317) 577-3519 Joyce Posson VP Admin
       Fax: (317) 577-3550
       Email: jposson@officeworks.net
       Website: www.officeworks.net
Dist office furniture & material handling equip. (Hisp,
estab 1984, empl 55, sales $25,000,000, cert: State,
NMSDC)

6731   Rite Quality Office Supplies, Inc.
       710 N Washington St   Kokomo, IN 46901
       (765) 459-4788 Douglas Vaughn President
       Fax: (765) 459-8262
       Email: riteq@netusa1.net
       Website: www.ritequality.com
Dist office & janitorial supplies & office furniture. (AA,
estab 1989, empl 10, sales , cert: State, NMSDC)

Massachusetts

6732   New England Office Supply
       135 Lundquist Dr   Braintree, MA 02184
       (866) 636-7872 Peter Tracy Ops Director
       Fax: (888) 636-7329
       Email: petert@neosusa.com
       Website: www.neosusa.com
Dist office computer supplies & furniture. (Woman/As-
Ind, estab 1993, empl 75, sales , cert: State)

Maryland

6733   Rudolph's Office & Computer Supply, Inc.
       5020 Campbell Blvd Ste C Baltimore, MD 21014
       (410) 931-4150 Henry Dow VP sales
       Fax: (410) 931-4158
       Email: henry@rudolphsupply.com
       Website: www.rudolphsupply.com
Dist office, computer & janitorial supplies, custom stamps,
office furniture, space planning. (Woman/White, estab
1980, empl 60, sales $1,600,000, cert: State)

6734   Sue-Ann's Office Supply, Inc.
       4147 Hayward Ave   Baltimore, MD 21215
       (410) 664-6226 Beverly Williams CEO
       Fax: (410) 664-6086
       Email: bwms@sueannsofficesupply.com
       Website: www.sueannsofficesupply.com
Dist office products; office furniture; workstations;
computer products. (Woman/AA, estab 1986, empl 5, sales
$1,503,484, cert: State, City)

Michigan

6735   Audio Visual Equipment & Supplies, Inc.
       25325 Shiawassee Circle, 3203   Southfield, MI
       48033
       (800) 296-5446 Carol Kirkland VP
       Fax: (313) 347-8592
       Email: carol@aveofficesupplies.com
       Website: www.aveofficesupplies.com/
Dist office supplies, office furniture, office equipment,
audio visual equipment, computer equipment & supplies,
printer equipment & supplies, paper, janitorial supplies,
first aid supplies. (Woman/AA, estab 1990, empl 6, sales ,
cert: NMSDC, WBENC)

6736   Hercules & Hercules, Inc.
       19055 W Davison   Detroit, MI 48223
       (313) 933-6669 Belinda Jefferson President
       Fax: (313) 933-1801
       Email: bjefferson@herculesandherculesinc.com
       Website: www.herculesandherculesinc.com
Dist maintenance supplies & equip, office supplies &
equip, office furniture. (AA, estab 1979, empl 16, sales
$7,000,000, cert: NMSDC)

6737   Kamar Office Express
       1280 E Big Beaver Rd   Troy, MI 48083
       (866) 996-8952 Kevin Monreal President
       Fax: (800) 428-0357
       Email: kevinm@oexusa.com
       Website: www.oexusa.com
Dist office supplies & furniture. (AA, estab 2005, empl 15,
sales , cert: NMSDC)

6738   KamarOE
       1280 E Big Beaver Ste A Troy, MI 48083
       (866) 996-8952 Devin Durrell
       Fax: (877) 792-8110
       Email: devind@kamaroe.com
       Website: www.kamaroe.com
Dist office supplies. (AA, estab 2005, empl 10, sales ,
cert: NMSDC)

6739   Nationwide Envelope Specialists, Inc.
       1259 Doris Rd   Auburn Hills, MI 48326
       (248) 373-0111 David Dzuris
       Fax: (248) 373-0194
       Email: sales@nespn.com
       Website: www.nespn.com
Printed & plain envelopes: special sizes & windows;
commercial, booklet & open-end. (Hisp, estab 1990,
empl 16, sales $5,200,000, cert: NMSDC)

6740   Remco Storage Systems, Inc.
       2328 Livernois Rd Ste 1070 Troy, MI 48083
       (248) 362-0500 Denise Naughton VP
       Fax: (248) 362-7420
       Email: Denise@remcoequipment.com
       Website: www.remcoequipment.com
Storage & retrieval systems: vertical lifts & carousels,
electric lateral filing systems, movable shelving, rotary
files, cabinets, records mgmt systems, color coded
labels, custom filing systems, folders & indexes.
(Woman/White, estab 1976, empl 10, sales $2,000,000,
cert: WBENC)

6741   Rubber Stamps Unlimited, Inc.
       334 S Harvey St   Plymouth, MI 48170
       (888) 451-7300 Maryellen Lewandowski Presi-
       dent
       Fax: (800) 451-7677
       Email: mlew@thestampmaker.com
       Website: www.thestampmaker.com
Custom rubber stamps, self inking stamps, date stamps,
seals, embossers & signs in one day. (Woman/White,
estab 1993, empl 12, sales $3,306,000, cert: WBENC)

6742   Workplace Integrators
       30700 Telegraph, Ste 4800   Bingham Farms, MI
       48025
       (248) 430-2345 Joe Eatman President
       Fax:
       Email: jeatman@wp-int.com
       Website: www.wp-int.com
Dist office supplies: paper, writing instruments, folders,
technology products, fastners, etc. (AA, estab 1938,
empl 1, sales $50,000,000, cert: NMSDC)

Minnesota

6743   American Diversity Business Solutions
106 First St SE PO Box 337   Glenwood, MN 56334
(320) 634-9805   Erica Van Beck President
Fax: (320) 634-0001
Email: adbsmail@americanmin.com
Website: www.americandiv.com
Dist custom business forms, office supplies, & promotional items. (Woman/White, estab 1992, empl 15, sales $23,941,250, cert: WBENC)

6744   Crown Marking, Inc.
4270 Dahlberg Dr   Golden Valley, MN 55422
(763) 543-8243   Gregg Prest Treasurer
Fax: (763) 543-8244
Email: gprest@crownmarking.com
Website: www.crownmarking.com
Mfr & dist rubber & photopolymer stamps, daters, embossers & related stamping supplies. (Woman, estab 1928, empl 9, sales $5,000,000, cert: WBENC)

6745   Innovative Office Solutions, LLC
151 E Cliff Rd   Burnsville, MN 55337
(952) 808-9900   Kathy Hovde Senior Acct Exec, Sales & Diversity
Fax: (952) 894-7153
Email: khovde@innovativeos.com
Website: www.innovativeos.com
Dist office, school, janitorial supplies & furniture. (Woman/White, estab 2001, empl 213, sales $100,000,000, cert: WBENC)

6746   Smead Manufacturing Company
600 Smead Blvd   Hastings, MN 55033
(651) 437-4111   Michelle Hanson
Fax: (651) 437-9134
Email: michelle.hanson@smead.com
Website: www.smead.com
Mfr & dist office filling supplies, systems & record mgmt software. (Woman/White, estab 1906, empl 2800, sales $225,000,000, cert: WBENC)

Missouri

6747   Missouri Office Systems & Supplies, Inc.
941 W 141st Terrace Ste B   Kansas City, MO 64145
(816) 761-5152   Virgie Dillard President
Fax: (816) 761-5170
Email: VLD@8asupplier.com
Website: www.8asupplier.com
Dist office supplies, furniture, ethernet, media, printers, software, hardware, ribbons, fax, scanners, computers, typewriters, routers, hubs, toners, servers. (Woman/AA, estab 1993, empl 9, sales $8,775,113, cert: State, City, NMSDC)

6748   Offices Unlimited Inc.
2127 William St   Cape Girardeau, MO 63703
(573) 332-0202   Celeste "Sally" LeGrand Owner
Fax: (573) 332-0606
Email: Sally@officesunlimited.com
Website: www.officesunlimited.com
Office supplies, stationary, office furniture, office partitions, panel systems, office equipment, copiers, faxes, toners, medical supplies, break room furniture, break room foods, janitorial products. (Woman/White, estab 2001, empl 6, sales $2,000,000, cert: State)

Montana

6749   e Office Supply
117 N 24th Ave   Bozeman, MT 59718
(888) 603-0274   Louis Bowker Owner
Fax: (406) 586-4932
Email: bowker@eofficesupply.biz
Website: www.eofficesupply.biz
Dist office products, computer supplies & equipment. (Nat Ame, estab 2003, empl 1, sales , cert: State)

North Carolina

6750   American Product Distributors, Inc.
8350 Arrowridge Blvd   Charlotte, NC 28273
(704) 522-9411   Ray Kennedy CEO
Fax: (704) 525-1975
Email: registration@americanproduct.com
Website: www.americanproduct.com
Dist office imaging supplies, remanufactured toner cartridges, cut sheet paper, wide format paper, rolled paper & ribbons, business & manufacturing labels. (AA, estab 1992, empl 50, sales $40,000,000, cert: NMSDC)

6751   Kennedy Office Supply Inc.
4211-A Atlantic Ave   Raleigh, NC 27604
(919) 878-5400   Linda McCotter Accting Mgr
Fax: (919) 878-4088
Email: lmccotter@kennedyoffice.com
Website: www.kennedyofficesupply.com
Dist office supplies, breakroom products, technology & janitorial supplies. (Woman/White, estab 1960, empl 50, sales $13,200,000, cert: State)

New Jersey

6752   Corporate Diversity Solutions
615 Franklin Turnpike Ste 5   Ridgewood, NJ 07450
(201) 444-1506   Stacey Scarpa President
Fax: (866) 249-9969
Email: stscarpa@corporatediversitysolutions.com
Website: www.corporatediversitysolutions.com
Dist stationery & office supplies. (Woman/White, estab 2009, empl 7, sales $4,300,000, cert: WBENC)

6753 CSS Building Services Inc.
12 Stults Rd, Ste 132   Dayton, NJ 08810
(732) 246-0554 Vic Tartara Sales
Fax: (732) 342-8004
Email: lcoury@cssbuildingservices.com
Website: www.cssofficesupply.com
Dist office supplies. (Hisp, estab 2004, empl 25, sales , cert: WBENC)

6754 Officemate International Corporation
90 Newfield Ave   Edison, NJ 08837
(732) 225-7422 Sharon Kiefer Natl Sales Mgr
Fax: (732) 225-6466
Email: skiefer@officemate.com
Website: www.officemate.com
Mfr & dist office supply products. (As-Pac, estab 1978, empl 100, sales , cert: State, NMSDC)

New Mexico

6755 Desert Paper & Envelope Company, Inc.
2700 Girard Blvd NE   Albuquerque, NM 87107
(800) 228-2298 Pam Lucero VP Finance
Fax: (505) 884-1093
Email: pam@desertpaper.com
Website: www.desertpaper.com
Mfr & print envelopes. (Woman/Hisp, estab 1973, empl 40, sales $5,435,600, cert: NMSDC, WBENC)

6756 Midway Office Supply Inc.
5900 Midway Park Blvd NE   Albuquerque, NM 87109
(505) 345-3414 Mike Sei President
Fax: (505) 343-1590
Email: mikesei@midwayos.com
Website: www.midwayos.com
Dist office supplies. (As-Pac/Hisp, estab 1980, empl 10, sales $9,000,000, cert: NMSDC)

6757 Stride, Inc.
1021 Carlisle Blvd SE   Albuquerque, NM 87106
(505) 232-3201 Jessica Miera President
Fax: (505) 232-3204
Email: info@strideinc.com
Website: www.strideinc.com
Mfr & dist writing instruments, binders & office products: pens & markers for wood finishes, parts marking, black light, crafts, photographic, cosmetics, cleaning devices & voter marking pens. (Woman/White, estab 1988, empl 14, sales $4,472,495, cert: State, WBENC)

New York

6758 Asian & Hispanic Trading & Consulting Inc.
37 West 39th St Ste 503 New York, NY 10018
(212) 252-8988 Franco Nidea Business Devel
Fax: (269) 982-4189
Email: franco.nidea@aandhtc.com
Website: www.aandhtc.com
Dist office supplies, furniture, computer equipment, and promotional products. (Woman/As-Pac, estab 2016, empl 4, sales $320,000, cert: City)

6759 Ebony Office Products, Inc.
10-17 44th Ave   Long Island City, NY 11101
(718) 706-8200 Michael Ukhueduan Dir Bus Dev
Fax: (718) 784-9113
Email: info@ebonyproducts.com
Website: www.ebonyproducts.com
Dist office supplies, office furniture, computer supplies, printing services. (AA, estab 1982, empl 10, sales $1,500,000, cert: State, City)

6760 Proftech LLC
200 Clearbrook Rd   Elmsford, NY 10523
(800) 937-8354 Jose Monteil President
Fax: (800) 937-8353
Email: jmontiel@proftech.com
Website: www.proftech.com
Dist office supplies; computer supplies; packaging supplies; drafting & art supplies; furniture; janitorial supplies; remanufactured toner cartridges. (Hisp, estab 1998, empl 55, sales , cert: State, City, NMSDC)

6761 Royal Automation Supplies
1982 Crotona Pkwy   Bronx, NY 10460
(718) 842-5900 David Changar VP
Fax: (718) 842-6965
Email: royalautomation@aol.com
Website: www.royalautomation.com
Dist paper & office supplies. (As-Ind, estab 1954, empl 5, sales $1,200,000, cert: NMSDC)

6762 S & B Computer & Office Products Inc.
17 Wood Road Ste 700 Round Lake, NY 12151
(518) 877-9500 Seema Nepal President
Fax: (518) 877-3800
Email: seema@sbcomputers-office.com
Website: www.sbcomputers-office.com
Dist office & computer supplies, office furniture & promotional products. (Woman/As-Ind, estab 1989, empl 9, sales $5,695,685, cert: State)

Ohio

6763 BoLinds Solutions Services, Inc.
850 Euclid Ave, Ste 1314　Cleveland, OH 44114
(216) 479-0290　Sales Sales
Fax: (330) 468-7939
Email: service@bolinds.com
Website: www.bolinds.com
Dist office products, office furniture, remanufactured & compatible toner cartridges, fax machines & office equipment repair. (Woman/AA, estab 1990, empl 6, sales , cert: State, NMSDC)

6764 Office Partners, LLC
826 E Edgerton　Bryan, OH 43506
(419) 636-7260　Cookie Lehman President
Fax: (419) 636-8210
Email: cookie1@bright.net
Website: www.officepartnersonline.com
Office products. (Hisp, estab 2002, empl 3, sales , cert: NMSDC)

6765 Quality Ribbons and Supplies Co.
2769 Commercial Rd　Cleveland, OH 44113
(216) 579-6200　Jacqueline Litz Owner
Fax:
Email: jackielitz@qr-s.com
Website: www.qr-s.com
Dist office, computer & janitorial supplies & small equip. (Woman/White, estab 1982, empl 5, sales , cert: City)

6766 SeaGate Office Products, Inc.
1044 Hamilton Dr　Holland, OH 43528
(419) 861-6161　Connie Leonardi President
Fax: (419) 861-6060
Email: cleonardi@seagateop.com
Website: www.seagteop.com
Dist office supplies: copy & writing paper, pens, post it notes, toner cartridges, ink, stamps, computer supplies, promotional items, mugs, golf balls and, pens, uniforms, desk accessories, binder clips, pencils, staples, tape & dispensers. (Woman/White, estab 1985, empl 30, sales $5,300,000, cert: WBENC)

6767 Signal Office Supply, Inc.
415 W Benson St　Cincinnati, OH 45215
(513) 821-2280　Matt Thiergartner VP Contract sales
Fax: (513) 821-2242
Email: matt@signaloffice.com
Website: www.signaloffice.com
Dist office products, furniture, computers, etc. (Woman/White, estab 1958, empl 1, sales , cert: State)

Oklahoma

6768 Miami Business Services, Inc.
28 N Main　Miami, OK 74354
(918) 541-2195　Gary Shelton econ Dev Mgr
Fax: (918) 542-3967
Email: gshelton@mn-e.com
Website: www.mbs.mn-e.com
Dist office products, remanufactured & compatible imaging products. (Nat Ame, estab 1987, empl 5, sales $263,158, cert: State)

Pennsylvania

6769 Alpha Office Supplies, Inc.
4950 Parkside Ave Ste 500　Philadelphia, PA 19131
(215) 226-2690　Chester Riddick CEO
Fax: (215) 223-0321
Email: chet.riddick@alphaos.com
Website: www.alphaos.com
Dist office furniture & supplies, paper, computers & accessories; desktop delivery, installation, space planning & project mgmt. (AA, estab 1985, empl 29, sales $26,000,000, cert: NMSDC)

6770 SUPRA Office Solutions, Inc.
5070 Parkside Ave Ste 3200　Philadlephia, PA 19131
(855) 777-8772　Charles Carter COO
Fax: (267) 275-8883
Email: execs@supraos.com
Website: www.supraos.com
Office supplies, office furniture, janitorial & break-room, paper & paper products, technology items, medical & chemical supplies. (AA, estab 2011, empl 16, sales $19,000,000, cert: State, NMSDC)

6771 Telrose Corporation
3801 Ridge Ave　Philadelphia, PA 19132
(215) 229-0500　Todd Rose CEO
Fax: (215) 229-0511
Email: toddrose@telrosecorp.com
Website: www.telrosecorp.com
Dist office supplies, equipment & furniture. (AA, estab 1995, empl 19, sales $8,000,000, cert: City, NMSDC)

South Carolina

6772 Ebony Holding
1204 Lexington Ave Unit 1, A-2　Irmo, SC 29063
(803) 798-7777　Pam Heirs Acct Exec
Fax: (803) 798-7823
Email: pamh@jmgrace.com
Website: www.jmgrace.com
Office Supplies & Furniture, Business Machines, Printing, Promotional Items, Embroidered Apparel, Janitorial Supplies, Breakroom Items, Safety Equipment. (Woman/AA, estab 2013, empl 7, sales $590,692, cert: State)

Tennessee

6773   Guy Brown, LLC
       7111 Commerce Way   Brentwood, TN 37027
       (615) 777-1500 Lauren Cooley Sales & Mktg Mgr
       Fax: (615) 777-1501
       Email: sales@guybrown.com
       Website: www.guybrown.com
Mfr recycled laser toner cartridges & office products.
(Woman/Hisp, estab 1997, empl 115, sales $205,956,925,
cert: NMSDC, WBENC, SDB)

Texas

6774   2M Business Products
       2630 Nova Dr   Dallas, TX 75229
       (972) 484-0000 Ali Mamdani GM
       Fax: (972) 484-1234
       Email: ali@2mbp.com
       Website: www.2mbp.com
Dist office supplies, computer supplies, office furniture,
new & remanufactured toner cartridges. rubber stamps,
printing. (As-Ind, estab 1980, empl 8, sales $2,000,000,
cert: NMSDC)

6775   Dallas Paper & Packaging
       880 Gerault Rd   Flower Mound, TX 75028
       (817) 422-3089 Nemosthenes Baker Owner
       Fax:
       Email: nemo@dallaspaperpackaging.com
       Website: www.dallaspaperpackaging.com
Dist toner & ink cartridges, trash bags, food gloves, white
T-shirts, grey sweat pants, shirts, drinking water carts,
janitorial supplies, ribbons, first aid kits, popcorn, hazard &
medical supplies. (AA, estab 1984, empl 2, sales $745,963,
cert: State, NMSDC)

6776   EIS Office Solutions, Inc.
       5803 Sovereign Dr, Ste 214   Houston, TX 77036
       (713) 484-7300 Judy Lanum Acct Exec
       Fax: (713) 484-5634
       Email: judy.lanum@secor.cc
       Website: www.eisoffice.net
Provide OEM & Compatible printer ink & toner cartridges,
office supplies. (As-Pac, estab 2004, empl 11, sales
$1,700,000, cert: State)

6777   General Office Plus
       1020 W 8th Ave   Amarillo, TX 79101
       (806) 373-2877 Loretta Redmon President
       Fax: (806) 374-0289
       Email: lredmon@generalofficeplus.com
       Website: www.general-officesupply.com/
Dist office supplies, machines, furniture. (Woman/White,
estab 1948, empl 15, sales $1,803,887, cert: State)

6778   Lee Office Solutions
       202 Travis ST, Ste 205   Houston, TX 77002
       (713) 227-1010 Cathleen Nguyen Exec Asst
       Fax: (713) 227-8615
       Email: cathleen@leeofficesolutions.com
       Website: www.leeofficesolutions.com
Dist office supplies & products, electronics, furniture,
paper, facilities mgmt & system design. (As-Pac, estab
1970, empl 5, sales $308,647, cert: NMSDC)

6779   Longhorn Office Products, Inc.
       2210 Denton Dr. Ste. 109   Austin, TX 78758
       (512) 672-4567 Marcia Winkler CEO
       Fax: (512) 672-4444
       Email: mswinkler@longhornop.com
       Website: www.longhornop.com
Dist office products & furniture. (Woman/White, estab
1999, empl 13, sales $2,386,005, cert: State, City,
WBENC)

6780   PD Morrison Enterprises, Inc. dba PDME
       1120 Toro Grande Blvd Bldg 2, Ste 208 Cedar
       Park, TX 78613
       (512) 750-3598 Tom Suhy Natl Acct Mgr
       Fax: (512) 219-0901
       Email: tsuhy@pdme.com
       Website: www.pdme.com
Dist office & computer supplies, office furniture. (AA,
estab 1994, empl 21, sales , cert: State, NMSDC)

6781   R.W. Gonzalez Office Products, Inc.
       600 Congress Ave 14th Fl Austin, TX 78701
       (512) 717-6623 Pamela Gonzalez VP
       Fax: (512) 300-2500
       Email: diversity@gonzalezop.com
       Website: www.MBEpartners.com
Dist office products. (Hisp, estab 2002, empl 7, sales ,
cert: State, NMSDC)

6782   Reliant Business Products, Inc
       10641 Haddington Dr, Ste 100   Houston, TX
       77043
       (713) 980-7140 Steven Woodall V.P. of Sales & I.T.
       Fax:
       Email: stevenw@rbp.com
       Website: www.rbp.com
Office Products, Office Supplies, Industrial Supplies,
HS&E, MRO, Office Furniture, Coffee Service, Break
Room Supplies, Printing. (Nat Ame, estab 1984, empl 17,
sales $7,000,000, cert: State, NMSDC)

6783   Summus Industries, Inc.
       245 Commerce Green Blvd Ste 155 Sugar Land,
       TX 77478
       (281) 640-1765 Rodney Craig CEO
       Fax: (281) 640-1766
       Email: rcraig@summusindustries.com
       Website: www.summusindustries.com
Dist office supplies. (AA, estab 1997, empl 21, sales
$21,000,000, cert: State, City, NMSDC)

6784 Tejas Office Products, Inc.
     1225 W 20th St Houston, TX 77008
     (713) 864-6004 Stephen M. Fraga President
     Fax: (713) 864-5562
     Email: stephenf@tejasoffice.com
     Website: www.tejasoffice.com
Dist office products. (Hisp, estab 1962, empl 50, sales ,
cert: NMSDC, 8(a))

6785 Today's Business Solutions
     1919 Lubbock St. Houston, TX 77007
     (713) 861-8508 Priscilla Luna VP
     Fax: (713) 861-8638
     Email: priscilla@tbstx.com
     Website: www.tbstx.com
Dist office supplies. (Hisp, estab 2003, empl 13, sales
$31,582,773, cert: State, City, NMSDC)

Virginia

6786 Access Office Products
     6 W Cary St Richmond, VA 23220
     (804) 767-7211 AJ Scott President
     Fax:
     Email: aj@accessofficeproducts.com
     Website: www.accessofficeproducts.com
Dist office supplies, technology & furniture. (AA, estab
2009, empl 2, sales $119,231, cert: State, NMSDC)

6787 Ball Office Products, LLC
     2218 Tomlyn St Richmond, VA 23230
     (804) 204-1774 Melissa Ball Managing Member
     Fax: (804) 204-1597
     Email: melissa@ballop.com
     Website: www.ballop.com
Dist business furniture & office supplies. (Woman/White,
estab 2000, empl 17, sales $7,050,591, cert: State,
WBENC)

6788 Corporate Office Solutions, LLC
     4094 Majestic Lane Ste 333 Fairfax, VA 22033
     (703) 352-2029 Katrina Funkhouser President
     Fax: (703) 352-8103
     Email: KF@cosdirect.com
     Website: www.cosdirect.com
Dist computer products, office equipment & supplies,
printer service, computer repair, networking & office
furniture. (Woman/As-Ind, estab 1996, empl 8, sales
$2,386,109, cert: State)

6789 Envelopes Only Plus, Inc.
     133 Roxbury Industrial Ctr Charles City, VA
     23030
     (804) 966-5479 Stuart Peyton GM
     Fax: (804) 966-5496
     Email: stuart@envelopesonly.com
     Website: www.envelopesonly.com
Dist envelopes: commercial, coin, catalog, booklet.
(Woman/AA/Nat Ame/As-Pac/Hisp, estab 1984, empl
32, sales $4,625,000, cert: State)

6790 Snap Office Supplies, LLC
     9710 Farrar Court Ste M Richmond, VA 23236
     (804) 794-9387 Andy Todd VP of Sales
     Fax: (804) 379-5765
     Email: andy@snapsupplies.com
     Website: www.snapsupplies.com
Dist Office & Point-of-Sale supplies. (Woman/White,
estab 1980, empl 7, sales $1,500,000, cert: State)

6791 TSRC, Inc.
     P.O. Box 1810 Ashland, VA 23005
     (804) 412-1200 David Johnson Acct Mgr
     Fax: (804) 752-0072
     Email: djohnson@thesupplyroom.com
     Website: www.thesupplyroom.com
Dist office supplies & furniture. (Woman/White, estab
1986, empl 187, sales $45,000,000, cert: State)

Washington

6792 Keeney's Office Supply, Inc.
     P.O. Box 848 Redmond, WA 98073
     (425) 869-7555 Maureen Condit Acctg Mgr
     Fax: (425) 556-1742
     Email: maureenc@keeneys.com
     Website: www.keeneys.com
Dist office supplies & office interiors. (Woman/White,
estab 1947, empl 30, sales $8,641,836, cert: State)

Wisconsin

6793 H.Derksen & Sons Co., Inc.
     250 Industrial Dr Omro, WI 50310
     (920) 685-4000 Mike Willeford VP
     Fax:
     Email: mike@hderksen.com
     Website: www.hderksen.com
Pressure sensitive labels, wide format digital printing,
business forms, computer paper, paper & packaging
products, mobility solutions, bar code label printers, bar
coding software. (Nat Ame, estab 1900, empl 11, sales
$8,000,000, cert: NMSDC)

OPTICAL EQUIPMENT
Manufacturers of optical supplies, coatings, components, precision optics, lenses, glass blanks, prescribed safety glasses, optical filters, components for thin film technology, ion beam guns, laser components. NAICS Code 42

California

6794   Clariti Eyewear, Inc.
       940 Ajax Ave   City of Industry, CA 91748
       (800) 372-6372   Dominique Yonemoto President
       Fax: (888) 277-7001
       Email: gene@claritieyewear.com
       Website: www.claritieyewear.com
Eyeglasses, Optical frames, Eyeglass frames, Eyewear, Sunglasses, Eyeglass cases, Cleaning cloths, Cleaning Kit. (Woman/As-Pac, estab 1993, empl 14, sales $3,219,627, cert: State, NMSDC)

Indiana

6795   Armada Optical Services, Inc.
       701 N Weinbach Ave Ste 410   Evansville, IN 47711
       (812) 476-6623   Julia Coakley GM
       Fax: (812) 476-6680
       Email: jcoakley@armadaoptical.com
       Website: www.armadaoptical.com
Safety prescription eyewear, mfr plastic, polycarbonate, trilogy & other products. (Woman/White, estab 1990, empl 11, sales $99,500, cert: State)

Michigan

6796   Heritage Vision Plans, Inc.
       One Woodward Avenue Ste 2020   Detroit, MI 48226
       (313) 863-1633   Leonard T. Barnes VP Sales & BD
       Fax: (313) 863-5134
       Email: lbarnes@heritagevisionplans.com
       Website: www.heritagevisionplans.com
Optical goods & services: eye exams, frames, lenses & contact lenses. (AA, estab 1975, empl 18, sales $9,952,609, cert: NMSDC)

Pennsylvania

6797   SlateBelt Safety
       1694 Southlawn Dr   Lancaster, PA 17603
       (888) 642-0001   Robert D Williams President
       Fax: (888) 642-0001
       Email: robert@slatebeltsafety.com
       Website: www.slatebeltsafety.com
Dist occupational safety prescription eyewear. (AA, estab 2006, empl 21, sales $1,600,000, cert: NMSDC)

Texas

6798   Adair Visual, Inc.
       3550 W 7th St   Fort Worth, TX 76107
       (817) 377-3500   Alyce Jones President
       Fax: (817) 737-3157
       Email: melanie@adaireyewear.com
       Website: www.adaireyewear.com
Protective eyewear & surgical loupes. (AA, estab 1980, empl 6, sales $1,484,023, cert: State, NMSDC)

PACKAGING & PACKING SERVICES & SUPPLIES

Contract packaging and crating, shrink or blister packaging and bagging. Also included are manufacturers and distributors of foam packaging, rope and twine, bottles, shrink wrap, etc. (See also BOXES & BAGS). NAICS Code 32

Alabama

6799 ARD Logistics, LLC
10098 Brose Dr   Vance, AL 35490
(205) 393-5207 Courtney Waters Sales & Mktg Rep
Fax:
Email: cwaters@ardlogistics.com
Website: www.ardlogistics.com
Distribution operations: sequencing, sub-assembly, warehousing, inventory mgmt, shipping & receiving materials handling maintenance, packaging & repackaging, transportation mgmt, transportation svcs. (AA, estab 1998, empl 900, sales $68,717,549, cert: NMSDC)

6800 Containers Plus, Inc.
3068 Alabama Hwy 53   Huntsville, AL 35806
(256) 746-8002 Ajesh Khanijow Business Devel
Fax:
Email: akhanijow@containersplususa.com
Website: www.containersplususa.com
Wooden crates, pallets, cardboard boxes, heat shrink, milspec packaging, packaging, RFID, UID, Mil-std-129, mil-std-2073, warehousing, logistics, hazmat packaging. (As-Pac, estab 2014, empl 5, sales $180,000, cert: NMSDC)

6801 Prystup Packaging Products, Inc.
101 Prystup Dr P.O. Box 1039 Livingston, AL 35470
(205) 652-9583 Erin McGahey Natl Acct Rep
Fax: (205) 652-2696
Email: emcgahey@prystup.com
Website: www.prystup.com
Mfr folding paper cartons: food, consumer goods & electronics. (Woman/Nat Ame, estab 1980, empl 160, sales $30,418,102, cert: NMSDC, WBENC)

6802 The Trinity Design Group, LLC
1107 Dowzer Ave   Pell City, AL 35125
(205) 338-6888 Fernando Valentin CEO
Fax: (205) 338-6898
Email: fvalentin@thetrinitydesigngroup.com
Website: www.thetrinitydesigngroup.com
Design, mfr & copack packaging, corrugated, paper, plastics, point of purchase & promotional materials. (AA/Hisp, estab 2004, empl 15, sales $2,028,500, cert: NMSDC)

Arkansas

6803 Alliance Rubber Company, Inc.
210 Carpenter Dam Rd   Hot Springs, AR 71901
(501) 262-2700 Sheryl Koller Natl Accts
Fax: (501) 262-3948
Email: skoller@alliance-rubber.com
Website: www.rubberband.com/
Mfr & dist mailing, packaging & shipping products. (Woman/White, estab 1923, empl 175, sales $35,529,619, cert: WBENC)

6804 Sigma Supply North America
824 Mid America Blvd   Hot Springs, AR 71913
(501) 760-1151 Brooke Griffin Natl Acct Mgr
Fax: (501) 760-1521
Email: Supplierdiversity@sigmasupply.com
Website: www.sigmasupply.com
Packaging solutions, turnkey solution for warehouse equipment, bulk storage, individual shipment packaging, labeling & inventory control. (Woman/White, estab 2003, empl 205, sales $205,750,000, cert: WBENC)

Arizona

6805 All-Pac Distributng LLC
4859 E Gleneagle Dr Chandler, AZ 85249
(480) 861-0842 Adam Snow Sales Mgr
Fax: (480) 792-1666
Email: asnow@allpaconline.com
Website: www.allpaconline.com
Mfr & dist returnable plastic packaging, injection molding, compression molding. (Woman/White, estab 2001, empl 3, sales $1,150,000, cert: NWBOC)

6806 La Fiesta Label & Packaging Systems
6162 W Detroit St   Chandler, AZ 85226
(480) 785-3900 Kirk Valadez VP Ops
Fax: (480) 785-3901
Email: kvaladez@lafiestalabel.com
Website: www.lafiestalabel.com
Mfr shrink sleeves, unsupported film pouches & packets, pressure sensitive labels, fold out coupons, cartons, static cling, consecutive number, UV & laminate coating. (Hisp, estab 1985, empl 20, sales , cert: NMSDC)

California

6807 Alom Technologies Corporation
48105 Warm Springs Blvd   Fremont, CA 94539
(510) 360-3600 Lisa Dolan VP Supply Chain Strategy
Fax: (510) 226-7617
Email: customerservice@alom.com
Website: www.alom.com
Fulfillment, assembly, contract packaging, video & audio tape duplication, CD & DVD duplication (Woman/White, estab 1997, empl 107, sales $53,000,000, cert: WBENC, NWBOC)

6808 Atlantis Paper & Packaging
13405 Benson Ave   Chino, CA 91710
(909) 591-1809 James Montano Sales Rep
Fax: (909) 591-2087
Email: james@atlantispkg.com
Website: www.atlantispkg.com
Dist packaging products & machinery, corrugated boxes, stretch wrap, poly bags, ice pages, tape, cold storage, pallets, etc. (Hisp, estab 1984, empl 15, sales $15,000,000, cert: NMSDC)

6809 Corporate Packaging, Inc.
1555 S Archibald Avenue   Ontario, CA 91761
(909) 390-1112 Craig Johnson VP
Fax: (909) 390-1113
Email: craig@corporatepackaginginc.com
Website: www.corporatepackaginginc.com
Contract packaging & promotional packaging services. (Woman/White, estab 1989, empl 50, sales $2,000,000, cert: State)

6810 Future Commodities Int'l Inc.
10676 Fulton Ct   Rancho Cucamonga, CA 91730
(909) 987-4258 Matthew Lim VP of Ops
Fax: (909) 987-5189
Email: mlim@bestpack.com
Website: www.bestpack.com
Mfr & import carton sealing equipment, carton sealing tape. (As-Pac, estab 1984, empl 14, sales $10,200,000, cert: NMSDC)

6811 Industrial Container Corporation
2015 Acacia Court   Compton, CA 90220
(310) 763-3550 Josh Rodgers Ops
Fax: (310) 763-3760
Email: sales@industrialcontainer.com
Website: www.industrialcontainer.com
Packaging design services & protective packaging, Customer Design/CAD Documentation, Prototyping, Performance Certification, Manufacturing Responsibility, Total Quality control, Supply Chain Management, Maquiladora/JIT & warehousing. (Hisp, estab 1971, empl 35, sales , cert: NMSDC)

6812 PKG Packaging
311 Hearst Dr   Oxnard, CA 93030
(805) 278-6648 Carlos Rodriguez Cstmr Service Mgr
Fax: (805) 278-6649
Email: c.rodriguez@pkgpackaging.com
Website: www.pkgpackaging.com
Design, mfr & dist packaging material. (Woman/Hisp, estab 1987, empl 10, sales $3,805,000, cert: NMSDC, WBENC)

6813 Premier Packaging/Assembly div of Haringa Inc.
14422 Best Ave   Santa Fe Springs, CA 90670
(562) 802-2765 Vicki Haringa CEO
Fax: (562) 404-9596
Email: vharinga@premierpkg.com
Website: www.premierpkg.com
Packaging services. (Woman/White, estab 1987, empl 6, sales $13,882,899, cert: WBENC)

6814 Thoro Packaging
1467 Davril Cir   Corona, CA 92880
(951) 278-2100 Andrea Percy Mktg Liaison
Fax: (951) 278-2198
Email: apercy@thoropkg.com
Website: www.thoropkg.com
Mfr & print custom folding cartons. (Woman/White, estab 1967, empl 184, sales $29,750,000, cert: WBENC)

6815 TransPak
2111 Abalone Ave   Torrance, CA 90501
(424) 731-2301 Amber Griggs Business Dev Mgr
Fax: (424) 731-2301
Email: amber.griggs@transpak.com
Website: www.transpak.com
Mfr wood crates & crating systems, custom packaging solutions, logistics, transportation & rigging services. (Woman/White, estab 1952, empl 800, sales $120,000,000, cert: WBENC)

6816 Uniq Seal, LLC
5753-G Santa Ana Canyon Rd   Anaheim, CA 92807
(714) 299-5899 Jacek Zdzienicki VP sales
Fax: (949) 388-6372
Email: jacek@nafm.com
Website: www.nafm.com
Contract sleeving & shrink labeling, multi-pack assemblies, shrink overwrap, tray assembly, re-packing & special assemblies, casing & cartoning, displays assembly, packaging R&D, fulfillment. (Woman/As-Pac, estab 1993, empl 7, sales $3,500,000, cert: NMSDC)

Colorado

6817 Craters and Freighters
331 Corporate Circle, Ste J   Golden, CO 80401
(720) 287-7805 Chad Brockmeyer Natl Sales Mgr
Fax:
Email: chad@cratersandfreighters.com
Website: www.cratersandfreighters.com
Custom wood crating, plastic hard cases and freight services. (Woman/White, estab 1990, empl 12, sales $55,000,000, cert: WBENC)

6818 Die Cut Technologies/Denver Gasket
10943 Leroy Dr   Northglenn, CO 80233
(303) 452-4600 Evelyn Meyers CEO
Fax: (303) 452-4135
Email: evelyn@diecuttech.com
Website: www.diecuttech.com
Mfr gaskets, die cut parts & converted non-metallic materials. Also dist sponge, foam tapes rubber, bridge bearing pads, expansion joints, impact attenuators & adhesives, contract assembly & packaging svcs. (Hisp, estab 1961, empl 20, sales $2,524,000, cert: NMSDC, SDB)

6819 Rocky Mountain Pioneer, LLC
13802 E 33rd Pl, Unit B   Aurora, CO 80011
(303) 371-6070 Diane Hamilton Acct Mgr
Fax: (303) 371-6169
Email: diane@pioneerdenver.com
Website: www.hpcorporategroup.com
Custom & stock packaging materials: corrugated boxes, folding carton, bubble, foam protective packaging, shrink & stretch films, banding & tapes, fulfillment services. (Woman, estab 2004, empl 9, sales $5,000,000, cert: WBENC)

6820 Summit Container Corporation
901Synthes Ave Monument, CO 80132
(719) 481-8400 Adam Walker CEO
Fax:
Email: awalker@summitcontainer.com
Website: www.summitcontainer.com
Packaging solutions, custom packaging, warehousing, distribution, assembly & kitting, (AA, estab 1989, empl 200, sales , cert: NMSDC)

6821 Universal Packaging
11440 E 56th Ave Denver, CO 80239
(303) 373-2523 Karen Millwater VP
Fax: (303) 373-2524
Email: kmillwater@upc-solutions.com
Website: www.universalpackagingcorp.com
Dist industrial packaging supplies: bubble, foam, tape, stretch, shrink wrap, banding, bags, cable ties, boxes, styrofoam, rolled corrugated, mailing tubes, etc. (Woman/White, estab 1980, empl 17, sales $4,525,000, cert: City)

Connecticut

6822 Eastern Bag & Paper Company, Inc.
200 Research Dr Milford, CT 06460
(203) 878-1814 Meredith Reuben CEO
Fax: (203) 783-9824
Email: mreuben@ebpsupply.com
Website: www.ebpsupply.com
Dist paper, packaging & allied products. (Woman, estab 1918, empl 270, sales $196,987,948, cert: WBENC)

6823 New England Packaging Co. LLC
119 Sherman Ct Fairfield, CT 06824
(203) 256-2350 Mark Hyman President
Fax: (203) 256-2351
Email: mark@zero-contact.com
Website: www.zero-contact.com
Dist corrugated & paper products. (Hisp, estab 1997, empl 6, sales $200,000, cert: NMSDC)

6824 Penmar Industries, Inc.
35 Ontario St Stratford, CT 06615
(203) 853-4868 Ed Rodriguez President
Fax: (203) 855-8136
Email: eddy@penmar-industries.com
Website: www.penmar-industries.com
Mfr & convert custom labels & tapes, dist packaging materials, carton sealing tapes, cartons & shipping room supplies. (Hisp, estab 1964, empl 15, sales $2,900,000, cert: NMSDC)

Florida

6825 3 Points Packaging LLC
3505 NW 123rd St Miami, FL 33167
(305) 624-8343 Noel Bosh President
Fax: (305) 624-8929
Email: info@3pointspackaging.com
Website: www.3PointsPackaging.com
Packaging & janitorial products. (AA, estab 2011, empl 2, sales $660,000, cert: NMSDC)

6826 All American Containers, Inc
9330 NW 110th Ave Miami, FL 33178
(305) 913-0624 Richard Cabrera VP Int'l Division
Fax: (305) 888-4133
Email: richardc@americancontainers.com
Website: www.americancontainers.com
Dist packaging supplies. (Woman/Hisp, estab 1991, empl 284, sales , cert: NMSDC)

6827 Diverse Solution and Supplies
7305 Lismore Ct. Orlando, FL 32835
(407) 256-2653 Carolyn Griffin President
Fax: (407) 298-9871
Email: carolyn.griffin@div-erse.com
Website: www.div-erse.com
Dist packaging & facility supplies: stretch wrap, corrugated, tapes, cushioning, bundling material, void fill, floor cleaning equip, mats, bags, etc. (Woman/White, estab 2013, empl 2, sales $279,000, cert: WBENC)

6828 FlexSol Packaging Corp.
1531 NW 12th Ave Pompano Beach, FL 33069
(800) 325-7740 Bonni O'Connell Dir Sales/Mktg
Fax: (800) 828-0530
Email: BonniO@FlexSolPackaging.com
Website: www.flexsolpackaging.com
Mfr flexible packaging & value-added plastic films, custom bags & film, shrink & hood films, performance & barrier films & can liners. (As-Pac, estab 2009, empl 425, sales , cert: NMSDC)

6829 National Packaging, LLC
6346-65 Lantana Rd, Ste 126 Lake Worth, FL 33463
(561) 968-4420 Kerry Lowe Mgr
Fax: (734) 264-4420
Email: klowe@nationalpack.net
Website: www.nationalpack.net
Flexible packaging, Bag films. (Woman/AA, estab 2006, empl 2, sales , cert: NMSDC)

6830 Secure Applications, LLC
6010 Presidential Circle Zephyrhills, FL 33540
(732) 874-0954 Gina Uzzolino President
Fax: (813) 355-3591
Email: guzzolino@secureapplications.net
Website: www.secureapplications.net
Packaging materials for Product Security, Tamper Evident, Non-Tamper Evident tapes & labels, security bags, stretch film & Temperature Monitoring Systems for cold chain applications as well as security containers & seals. (Woman/White, estab 2011, empl 2, sales $150,000, cert: State, CPUC)

6831 Soule Company
4322 Pet Lane Lutz, FL 33559
(813) 907-6005 Roger Boldizsar Dir of Sales
Fax: (813) 907-6091
Email: roger.boldizsar@soulecompany.com
Website: www.soulepackaging.com
Dist packaging products: crates, corrugated cartons, military type board, hard & soft cases, foams, bubble, tapes, poly bags, ect. (Woman/White, estab 1957, empl 31, sales $10,000,000, cert: WBENC)

Georgia

6832 Alliance Packaging Group, Inc.
940 Sherwin Pkwy, Ste 100 Buford, GA 30517
(770) 309-1012 Michelle Calvert CEO
Fax: (770) 904-0306
Email: mcalvert@alliancepkggroup.com
Website: www.alliancepkggroup.com
Packaging, janitorial & shipping supplies. (Woman/White, estab 2007, empl 5, sales $2,733,290, cert: WBENC)

6833 Containers Unlimited, Inc.
400 Claridge Trace Atlanta, GA 30331
(714) 734-8608 C. Eric Jones President
Fax: (775) 269-9139
Email: chuck@containersunlimited.net
Website: www.containersunlimited.net
Diat stock & custom boxes & packaging materials. (AA, estab 1999, empl 4, sales , cert: State)

6834 E. Smith Box, Inc.
1875 Rockdale Industrial Blvd Conyers, GA 30012
(770) 388-7787 Jaquacer Middlebrooks President
Fax: (770) 388-7889
Email: sales@esmithbox.com
Website: www.esmithbox.com
Mfr corrugated boxes. (AA, estab 1987, empl 35, sales $20,384,000, cert: NMSDC)

6835 FilmLOC Inc.
4190 Thurmon Tanner Pkwy Flowery Branch, GA 30542
(404) 892-8778 Shirl Handly President
Fax: (404) 874-1654
Email: shirl@filmloc.com
Website: www.filmloc.com
Mfr Intelli-Plac¿½ placards for labeling & re-labeling reusable containers, totes & pallets, shelves, equipment, racking, manufactured goods in process, shipping crates. (Woman/Hisp, estab 2002, empl 5, sales $749,359, cert: WBENC)

6836 Meristem Packaging Company LLC
10882 Crabapple Rd Ste 4 Roswell, GA 30075
(770) 998-7120 Nate Carter Supply Chain Mgr
Fax: (770) 998-7124
Email: ncarter@meristempkg.com
Website: www.meristempkg.com
Packaging, folding cartons/boxes, plastic bags & styrofoam coolers. (AA/Hisp, estab 2009, empl 5, sales $7,444,000, cert: NMSDC)

6837 Palmetto Industries International, Inc.
6001 Horizon West Pkwy Grovetown, GA 30813
(828) 808-2574 Jerry Edmonds Regional Acct Mgr
Fax: (706) 737-7995
Email: jerry@palmetto-industries.com
Website: www.palmetto-industries.com
Mfr & dist polymer & paper packaging products. (As-Ind/As-Pac, estab 1994, empl 500, sales $20,000,000, cert: NMSDC)

6838 SquarePac Ltd.
7115 Oak Ridge Parkway Ste 110 Austell, GA 30168
(770) 617-5688 Walter Griggs CFO
Fax: (404) 920-2141
Email: admin@squarepac.us
Website: www.squarepac.us
Returnable packaging & material handling solutions, eco-friendly containers & packaging, totes, pallets & metal racks. (AA, estab 2013, empl 8, sales , cert: NMSDC, SDB)

Illinois

6839 Alta Packaging, Inc.
150 Chaddick Dr Wheeling, IL 60090
(847) 215-2582 Jill Zienkiewicz
Fax: (827) 215-2577
Email: jillz@altapackaging.com
Website: www.altapackaging.com
Dist industrial packaging supplies. (Woman/White, estab 1995, empl 10, sales $5,276,581, cert: WBENC)

6840 BAF Packaging, LLC
1053 E. 95th St. Chicago, IL 60619
(888) 225-8221 Valerie Matthews President
Fax: (888) 225-8221
Email: vam@bafpack-rite.com
Website: www.bafpack-rite.com
Contract Packaging, shrink wrap packaging, Light industrial assembly, Fulfillment, Distribution warehouse capabilities. (Woman/AA, estab 2013, empl 3, sales $350,000, cert: NMSDC)

6841 Cano Container Corporation
3920 Enterprise Court Aurora, IL 60504
(630) 585-7500 Juventino Cano President
Fax: (630) 585-7501
Email: juventino@canocontainer.com
Website: www.canocontainer.com
Mfr corrugated shipping containers. (Hisp, estab 1986, empl 2, sales $20,000,000, cert: NMSDC)

6842 Carter Paper & Packaging, Inc.
3400 SW Washington St Peoria, IL 61607
(309) 637-7711 Mike Krost Sales
Fax: (309) 637-7748
Email: mike@carterpaper.com
Website: www.erpaper.com
Dist paper & plastic packaging, bags, towels, wipers, tissue, VCI paper, loose fill, foam, tape, adhesives & specialty items. (Woman/White, estab 1957, empl 18, sales , cert: WBENC)

6843 Commercial Bag Company
1 Paper Chase Normal, IL 61761
(309) 862-0144 Steve Barger VP of Sales
Fax: (309) 888-9087
Email: sbarger@commercialpackaging.com
Website: www.commercialpackaging.com
Flexible Packaging, stand up pouches, Bulk Bags/Totes, Woven Poly Bags, Multiwall Bags. (Woman/White, estab 1984, empl 49, sales $95,000,000, cert: WBENC)

6844   Cross Packaging Supply, Inc.
     968 Dundee Ave Ste B   Elgin, IL 60120
     (847) 780-7225   AJ Loredo President
     Fax:
     Email: aloredo@crosspackaging.com
     Website: www.crosspackaging.com
Packaging supplies: boxes, paper, tape, stretch film, bubble wrap, poly bags, bubble mailers, mailers, labels, can liners. (Hisp, estab 2013, empl 2, sales $500,000, cert: NMSDC)

6845   Dynamic Packaging
     1248 W Jackson Blvd, Ste 2E   Chicago, IL 60607
     (312) 374-4445   Elson Seale President
     Fax: (312) 374-4447
     Email: elson@dynam-pak.com
     Website: www.dynam-pak.com
Dist industrial & janitorial supplies: corrugated boxes, tape, stretch-film, shrink-film, poly-bags, bubble wrap. (Woman/AA, estab 2014, empl 5, sales $250,000, cert: NMSDC)

6846   H&H Sorting Services
     1021 St. Charles St   Elgin, IL 60120
     (847) 741-8479   Jeanne Hintz President
     Fax:
     Email: Jeanne@hhsort.com
     Website: www.hhsort.com
Sorting & inspection, assembly, packaging, labeling of fasteners & molded plastics & other pre-manufactured parts. (Woman/White, estab 1989, empl 48, sales $1,737,436, cert: WBENC)

6847   Magenta LLC
     15160 New Avenue   Lockport, IL 60441
     (773) 777-5050   Jennifer Smith Mktg Director
     Fax: (773) 777-4055
     Email: jsmith@magentallc.com
     Website: www.magentallc.com
Design, develop & mfr injection molded components, packaging, closures and containers. (Woman/White, estab 1969, empl 81, sales $16,880,000, cert: WBENC)

6848   Midwest Mailing & Shipping Systems Inc.
     3006 Gill St, Ste A   Bloomington, IL 61704
     (309) 661-1144   Dave Rappa VP sales
     Fax: (309) 661-1148
     Email: dave@midwestmailing.com
     Website: www.midwestmailing.com
Dist mailing systems, folder inserters, letter openers, inbound letter & parcel tracking systems, shipping systems, addressing systems, CASS/PAVE certified software, electronic scales, shredders, pressure sealers, bursters, collators, etc. (Woman/White, estab 1988, empl 9, sales $1,650,000, cert: WBENC)

6849   Numeridex, Inc.
     632 Wheeling Rd   Wheeling, IL 60090
     (847) 541-8840   Alberto Hoyos President
     Fax: (847) 541-8392
     Email: debbie@numeridex.com
     Website: www.numeridex.com
Dist labeling & bar code products: thermal transfer printers, labels, ribbons, scanners, packaging & shipping supplies, corrugated cartons, stretch film, carton sealing tape. (Hisp, estab 1967, empl 10, sales $2,370,000, cert: NMSDC)

6850   Planned Packaging of Illinois Corp.
     19558 S Harlem Ave Ste 5   Frankfort, IL 60423
     (815) 277-5270   Jack Callham Exec VP
     Fax: (815) 277-5280
     Email: vianney@ppoic.com
     Website: www.ppoic.com
Dist industrial packaging supplies: corrugated boxes, film, foams, pallets, etc. (AA, estab 2001, empl 13, sales $15,000,000, cert: NMSDC)

6851   Poly-Pak and Ship, Inc.
     2021 Illini Ave   Vandalia, IL 62471
     (618) 283-2397   JoAnn Boggs President
     Fax: (618) 283-4948
     Email: joannboggs@polypakusa.com
     Website: www.polypakusa.com
Warehousing, packaging, labeling, addressing, mailing, distribution printed matter, direct mail svcs. (Woman/White, estab 1985, empl 85, sales $2,658,671, cert: State, City, WBENC)

6852   Primary Resources Inc.
     405 Busse Road   elk Grove Village, IL 60007
     (847) 808-7684   Enza Fragassi President
     Fax: (847) 808-7686
     Email: enza@primarypkg.com
     Website: www.primaryresources.net
Corrugated packaging, fibre board slip sheets, folding cartons, corrugated, chip partitions, flexible films, barrier bags, pouches, bundling, film products, shrink, stretch, polyethylene, labels, tamper evident products, bio-degradable materials. (Woman/Hisp, estab 2001, empl 10, sales , cert: NMSDC)

6853   Scout Sourcing, Inc.
     1580 N. Northwest Hwy #217   Park Ridge, IL 60068
     (847) 698-3340   Nancy Walsh President
     Fax: (708) 836-4398
     Email: agitzke@scoutsourcinginc.com
     Website: www.scoutsourcinginc.com
Dist paper & packaging. (Woman/White, estab 2006, empl 6, sales $95,000,000, cert: WBENC)

6854   Service Packaging Design, Inc.
     6238 Lincoln Ave   Morton Grove, IL 60053
     (847) 966-6556   Norman Croft President
     Fax: (847) 966-6658
     Email: ncroft@servicepackaging.com
     Website: www.servicepackaging.com
Mfr & dist corrugated boxes, wood products, tags & labels, gum & poly tape, stretch wrap. (AA, estab 1982, empl 7, sales $1,250,000, cert: NMSDC)

6855   TransWorld Plastic Films, Inc.
     150 N 15th St   Rochelle, IL 61068
     (815) 561-7117   Rodolfo Hernandez Business Dev
     Fax: (815) 561-7120
     Email: rhernandez@transworldplasticfilms.com
     Website: www.transworldplasticfilms.com
Polyethylene film for the automotive, tire & rubber industries used in the manufacturing & packaging process. (Woman/Hisp, estab 2007, empl 31, sales , cert: NMSDC)

6856   Trinity Graphic & Packaging Solutions, LLC
       28W031 Greenview Ave   Warrenville, IL 60555
       (630) 393-7550 Leonard Hardy President
       Fax: (630) 847-2811
       Email: len.hardy@trinitygraphic.net
       Website: www.trinitygraphic.net
Dist thermal transfer ribbons, thermal transfer printers,
thermal transfer print heads, printed labels, warehouse
labels, promotional labels. (AA/Nat Ame, estab 2001, empl
1, sales , cert: State)

Indiana

6857   AIM Solutions, Inc.
       P.O. Box 340   McCordsville, IN 46055
       (239) 316-0004 John Laakso Director
       Fax:
       Email: john.laakso@aimsolutionsinc.net
       Website: www.aimsolutionsinc.net
Packaging & shipping supplies, pallets, boxes, film, bubble
sheet stock, package automation engineering, foam,
packaging equipment, plastic trays, labeling products &
equipment, tape. (As-Pac, estab 2006, empl 7, sales
$1,500,000, cert: State)

6858   Brown Tape Products Company
       8909 Sargent Rd   Indianapolis, IN 46256
       (866) 276-9682 Janice Brown President
       Fax: (317) 570-4475
       Email: janbrown@browntapeproducts.com
       Website: www.browntapeproducts.com
Adhesive tape, cardboard boxes, mailers, steel banding,
plastic banding, banding tools, stretch film, bubble pack,
foam packaging, tape dispensers, newsprint, nylon cable
ties, rolled corrugated, packing slip envelopes, plastic bags.
(Woman/White, estab 1984, empl 5, sales $1,000,000,
cert: City)

6859   Morales Group, Inc.
       5628 W 74th St   Indianapolis, IN 46278
       (317) 334-0950 Seth Morales Sales Mgr
       Fax: (317) 337-0849
       Email: smorales@moralesgroup.net
       Website: www.moralesgroup.net
Assembly, packaging & warehousing services, Point of
Purchase display assembly, Kitting, Literature collation,
insertion, Sort/rework. (Hisp, estab 2003, empl 28, sales
$14,900,000, cert: State, NMSDC)

6860   Premier Business Solutions
       3202 N Kenmore 46628 South Bend, IN 46628
       (574) 232-8840 Joyce Manthay President
       Fax: (574) 232-8841
       Email: joyce@premierbus.com
       Website: www.premierbus.com
Fulfillment & marketing services: product & literature
fulfillment, rebate & free offer processing, network
programs, lead mgmt programs, pick pack, warehousing &
inventory management.
We help our clients execute all facets of their marketing
plan. (Woman/White, estab 2001, empl 15, sales , cert:
WBENC)

6861   The Servants, Inc.
       3145 Lottes Dr   Jasper, IN 47546
       (812) 634-2201 Jerome Balbach Controller
       Fax: (812) 634-2730
       Email: jerome@servants.com
       Website: www.servants.com
Corrugated packaging & packaging accessories.
(Woman/AA, estab 1973, empl 55, sales $10,000,000,
cert: NWBOC)

6862   Vesta Ingredients, Inc.
       5767 Thunderbird Rd   Indianapolis, IN 46236
       (317) 895-9000 Michael Ball Sr Sales Exec
       Fax: (317) 895-9340
       Email: michael@vestaingredients.com
       Website: www.vestaingredients.com
Contract manufacturing & packaging. (As-Pac, estab
1997, empl 20, sales , cert: NMSDC)

Kentucky

6863   Chavira Packaging Products, Inc.
       701-4 Dishman   Bowling Green, KY 42104
       (877) 823-1316 Dawn Dodd President
       Fax: (270) 781-7725
       Email: chavirapackaging@bellsouth.net
       Website:
Dist shipping & packaging material: wood pallets, crates,
dunnage & industrial lumber. (Hisp, estab 1900, empl 1,
sales , cert: NMSDC)

6864   CSS Distribution Group, Inc.
       3600 Chamberlain Ln Ste 216 Louisville, KY 40241
       (502) 423-1011 Sandy Allemang CEO
       Fax: (502) 423-1033
       Email: sandya@customersourcingsolutions.com
       Website: www.customersourcingsolutions.com
Dist packaging tape, edge protector, pallets, packaging &
automation equipment, forklift software tracking
program. (Woman/White, estab 2006, empl 12, sales
$2,200,000, cert: WBENC)

6865   Kyana Packaging & Industrial Supply, Inc.
       2501 Ampere Dr   Louisville, KY 40291
       (502) 992-3333 Kimberly Osborne CEO
       Fax: (502) 992-3342
       Email: kim@kyanaind.com
       Website: www.kyanaind.com
Dist packaging & shipping supplies: boxes, tape, stretch
wrap, bubble wrap, strapping, adhesives, air pillow
machines, stretch wrappers, strapping machines,
automatic tape machines, shrink wrap equipment &
film, poly bags, plastic films. (Woman/White, estab
1976, empl 37, sales $9,737,350, cert: WBENC)

6866   P3 Protective Packaging Products
       P.O. Box 3583 Louisville, KY 40201
       (502) 357-6872 Anne Sizemore VP
       Fax:
       Email: annes@p3products.com
       Website: www.p3products.com
Expendable/Returnable Packaging & design. Retail
package. (Woman/White, estab 2001, empl 22, sales
$7,000,000, cert: WBENC)

Louisiana

6867 IPC Louisiana LLC
2015 Chanute Dr Alexandria, LA 71303
(318) 473-0400 Mark Vassar VP sales/Mktg
Fax: (219) 764-5091
Email: mark.vassar@ipcboxes.com
Website: www.ipcboxes.com
Mfr corrugated packaging, brown box & multicolor packaging, POP's. (AA, estab 2004, empl 30, sales $17,000,000, cert: NMSDC)

Massachusetts

6868 Lancaster Packaging, Inc.
560 Main St, Ste 2 Hudson, MA 01749
(978) 562-0100 Marianne Lancaster President
Fax: (978) 568-8423
Email: mlancaster@lancasterpackaging.com
Website: www.lancasterpackaging.com
Dist bank tamper evident bags, file storage boxes, corrugated materials, stretch wrap, shipping supplies. (Woman/AA, estab 1989, empl 10, sales $12,180,000, cert: NMSDC)

Maryland

6869 projectWorks, LLC
6900 English Muffin Way, Ste E Frederick, MD 21703
(301) 682-4800 Michelle Stephens CEO
Fax: (541) 962-0588
Email: michelle@projectworks.com
Website: www.projectworks.com
Fulfillment & marketing support svcs: warehouse & distribution, assembly & order fulfillment, printing & direct mail, eCommerce & inventory mgmt, advertising specialties & premiums. (Hisp, estab 1998, empl 7, sales $808,117, cert: State)

6870 Vac Pac, Inc.
150 W Ostend St, Ste 160 Baltimore, MD 21230
(410) 685-5181 Hessa Tary CEO
Fax: (410) 332-4536
Email: hessa.tary@vacpacinc.com
Website: www.vacpacinc.com
Print & convert flexible packaging, poly, polyprop, polyester, cellophane, nylon
high temeprature. (Woman/White, estab 1949, empl 25, sales $4,000,000, cert: WBENC)

Michigan

6871 Aldez Containers, LLC
4260 Van Dyke, Ste 109 Almont, MI 48003
(586) 243-0596 Diane Pattison VP
Fax: (269) 924-0433
Email: dpattison@aldezcontainers.com
Website: www.aldezcontainers.com
Mfr corrugated packaging & dunnage, service parts packaging. (Woman/Hisp, estab 1998, empl 78, sales $10,000,000, cert: NMSDC)

6872 Bay Corrugated Container, Inc.
1655 W 7th St P.O. Box 667 Monroe, MI 48161
(734) 243-5400 Judy Thoma Exec Admin
Fax: (734) 243-2499
Email: jthoma@baycorr.com
Website: www.baycorr.com
Mfr corrugated boxes/folding cartons, corrugated pallets, corrugated interior packaging materials, stretchwrap, chipboard, board coatings, linerboard/fine paper, stickers, labels, etc. (Woman/Hisp, estab 1964, empl 275, sales $61,371,243, cert: NMSDC, WBENC)

6873 Contract Source & Assembly Inc.
5230 33rd St SE Grand Rapids, MI 49512
(616) 897-2185 Bryce Cooper
Fax: (913) 677-3358
Email: bryce@contractmi.com
Website: www.contractmi.com
Light Manufacturing & Contract Assembly, Contract Packaging & Inventory Management, Supply Chain Management, Inspection & Re-work. (As-Pac, estab 2001, empl 13, sales $18,000,000, cert: NMSDC)

6874 Diversity Products
32031 Howard St Madison Heights, MI 48071
(248) 585-1200 Darlene Fleser Ops Dir
Fax: (248) 585-1212
Email: dfleser@diversityproducts.com
Website: www.diversityproducts.com
Packaging engineering support, cost reduction, vendor consolidation, packaging program mgmt, returnable container repair, cleaning & tracking, inventory management. (Woman/AA, estab 1998, empl 35, sales $9,000,000, cert: NMSDC)

6875 Galaxy Forest Products LLC
1655 W 7th St Monroe, MI 48161
(734) 243-5400 Judy Thoma Exec Admin
Fax: (734) 243-2499
Email: jthoma@galaxyforestproducts.com
Website: www.galaxytforestproducts.com
Packaging materials, pulp, microflute, consumer boxes, corrugated containers, slip sheets, folding cartons, corner/angle protectors, dunnage packaging. (Woman/Hisp, estab 2005, empl 1, sales $2,058,358, cert: NMSDC)

6876 Genesee Packaging Inc.
2010 N Dort Hwy Flint, MI 48506
(810) 514-1883 Ken Miller Sales Mgr
Fax: (810) 235-0350
Email: kmiller@genpackaging.com
Website: www.genpackaging.com
Packaging supplies & services. (Woman/AA, estab 1979, empl 125, sales $14,500,000, cert: WBENC)

6877 Harbor Foam, Inc.
2950 Prairie St SW, Ste 300 Grandville, MI 49418
(616) 855-8150 Laura Kuperus Owner
Fax: (616) 855-8149
Email: Harborfoam@hotmail.com
Website:
Dist polystyrene foam, white ridgid foam used for packaging & insulation. (Woman, estab 2007, empl 8, sales $500,000, cert: WBENC)

6878 Integrated Packaging Company
6400 Harper Ave   Detroit, MI 48211
(612) 802-1736 Jeffrey Laney Strategic Accts Mgr
Fax: (763) 497-8081
Email: jeff.laney@ipcboxes.com
Website: www.ipcboxes.com
Packaging solutions, packaging & displays, Design, Concept & Development. (AA, estab 1992, empl 200, sales $20,000,000, cert: NMSDC)

6879 Packaging Integration, LLC
13235 Avalon Ct   Brighton, MI 48116
(248) 437-1900 Scott Bradford President
Fax: (248) 437-1901
Email: scott.bradford@packagingintegration.com
Website: www.packagingintegration.com
Dist packaging materials. (Hisp, estab 2005, empl 5, sales $5,000,000, cert: NMSDC)

6880 Patriot Packaging Solutions and Consulting
269 Walker St, Ste 522   Detroit, MI 48207
(313) 580-1538 Jay Jackson VP
Fax: (734) 453-5196
Email: jay.jackson@patriotgm1.com
Website: www.patriotpackagingsolutionsconsuting.com
Packaging services: corrugated box, bulk boxes, displays, single face, bubble wrap, stretch wrap, trays, sheets, tape & labels. (AA, estab 2011, empl 4, sales $500,250, cert: NMSDC)

6881 Peach State Packaging Solutions
8803 Cairn Hwy   Elk Rapids, MI 49629
(819) 599-2594 Lisa McCririe President
Fax: (810) 222-4106
Email: lmccririe@peachstatepackagingsolutions.com
Website: www.peachstatepackagingsolutions.com
Dist packaging supplies. (Woman/White, estab 2006, empl 1, sales $800,000, cert: WBENC)

6882 Pro-Pak Products, Ltd.
17580 Helro Dr   Fraser, MI 48026
(586) 415-1500 Nancy Stachnik President
Fax: (586) 415-1504
Email: Propakltd@aol.com
Website: www.propakproductsltd.com
Packaging supplies & services. (Woman/White, estab 1993, empl 5, sales , cert: NWBOC)

6883 Quixerve Corporation
341 N Helmer Rd   Springfield, MI 49037
(269) 441-0700 Linda Gillett President
Fax: (269) 441-0701
Email: lgillett@quixerve.com
Website: www.quixerve.com
Printing, Labeling, Packaging, Fulfillment, Warehousing, Inventory Control, Distribution. (Woman/White, estab 2003, empl 3, sales $225,000, cert: WBENC)

6884 Ryan Industries, Inc.
30369 Beck Rd   Wixom, MI 48382
(248) 926-5254 Brenda Ryan President
Fax: (248) 926-8115
Email: bryan@ryanind.net
Website: www.ryanind.net
Warehousing, packaging, light assembly, kitting, distribution, rework. (Woman/AA, estab 1995, empl 10, sales , cert: NMSDC, WBENC)

6885 STEWART Industries, LLC
150 McQuiston Dr   Battle Creek, MI 49037
(269) 998-0608 Matt Amos Business Dev Mgr
Fax: (269) 660-0421
Email: mamos@stewartindustriesusa.com
Website: www.stewartindustriesusa.com
Third party inspection, sorting, rework, light assembly, packaging. (AA, estab 2000, empl 60, sales $37,615,000, cert: NMSDC)

6886 Tabb Packaging Solutions
41605 Ann Arbor Rd Ste 2   Plymouth, MI 48170
(734) 254-0251 Julie Kavulich Business Devel Mgr
Fax: (734) 254-0257
Email: jkavulich@tabbpackaging.com
Website: www.tabbpackaging.com
Post Consumer Recycled Materials, HDPE & PET, Primary Processing Operations, Market Color Concentrates & Additives, Packaging Materials & Label Substrate (IML), Virgin & PCR Pre-blend Resins. (Woman/White, estab 2007, empl 7, sales , cert: WBENC)

6887 Valmec Inc.
1274 S Holly Rd   Fenton, MI 48430
(810) 629-8750 Krystn Tatus CEO
Fax: (810) 629-3522
Email: valmec@comcast.net
Website: www.valmecinc.com
Material handling & packaging, conveyors, returnable packaging, installation, tear-outs & complete system integration. (Woman/White, estab 1971, empl 5, sales $1,344,664, cert: WBENC)

6888 Venchurs, Inc.
800 Liberty St   Adrian, MI 49221
(517) 264-4392 Erica Wilt Program Mgr
Fax: (517) 265-7468
Email: esellers@venchurs.com
Website: www.venchurs.com
Custom package design & flexible packaging solutions. (Hisp, estab 1973, empl 86, sales , cert: NMSDC)

6889 Whisper Creative Products, Inc.
1585 Wells Rd   Dundee, MI 48131
(734) 529-2734 Dolores Rodriguez CEO
Fax: (734) 529-8525
Email: whisper@cass.net
Website:
Packaging supplies, expendable & returnable packaging. (Woman/Hisp, estab 1997, empl 10, sales $300,000, cert: NMSDC, WBENC)

6890   World Corrugated Container
P.O. Box 840   Albion, MI 49224
(517) 629-9400   Tara Saumier Human Resources
Fax: (517) 629-9415
Email: tsaumier@worldcorrugated.com
Website: www.worldcorrugated.com
Mfr & dist corrugated containers. (Woman/Hisp, estab 1991, empl 40, sales $7,900,000, cert: WBENC)

Minnesota

6891   Independent Packing Services, Inc.
7600 32nd Ave N   Crystal, MN 55427
(763) 425-7155   Joseph Wallace President
Fax: (763) 425-0451
Email: jwallace@ipsipack.com
Website: www.ipsipack.com
Mfr industrial crating for domestic & export shipments; electronics & fragile artwork. (AA, estab 1976, empl 60, sales , cert: NMSDC)

6892   Polybest, Inc.
2962 Cleveland Ave N   Roseville, MN 55113
(651)6331688   Zongzhao Li President
Fax: (651) 633-9190
Email: johnli@polybestinc.com
Website: www.polybestinc.com
Mfr packaging materials such as all kinds of plastic and compostable bags, hazard trash bags, disposal bags, trash canliners, wrapping film, etc. (As-Pac, estab 2006, empl 4, sales $1,234,157, cert: NMSDC)

6893   Promotion Management Center, Inc.
31205 Falcon Ave PO Box 245   Stacy, MN 55079
(651) 462-6415   Eric Scheid Acct Exec
Fax: (651) 462-4118
Email: eric@pmci.us
Website: www.pmci.us
Fulfillment, direct mail, sweepstakes, packaging. (Woman/White, estab 1983, empl 40, sales $4,000,000, cert: City, WBENC)

6894   SeaChange Print Innovations
14505 27th Avenue North   Plymouth, MN 55447
(763) 586-3700   Ann Marie Keene Business Dev
Fax:
Email: annmarie.keene@seachangemn.com
Website: www.seachangemn.com
Folding carton & marketing print production, Folding Carton Packaging, Marketing Printing, Commercial Printing, Direct Mail Printing, Digital Printing. (Woman/White, estab 2014, empl 90, sales $13,100,000, cert: WBENC)

6895   TJ's Packaging Inc
19950 177th St NW   Big Lake, MN 55309
(763) 241-2022   Kristy Murray COO
Fax:
Email: tfarrington@tjpackaging.com
Website: www.tjpackaging.com
Packaging supplies & automated packaging equipment. (Woman/White, estab 1998, empl 4, sales $1,935,193, cert: WBENC)

Missouri

6896   Bennett Packaging of Kansas City, Inc.
220 NW Space Center Cir   Lee's Summit, MO 64064
(816) 379-5001   Traci Strickert Director of Mktg
Fax: (816) 379-5003
Email: traci.strickert@bpkc.com
Website: www.BennettKC.com
Design & mfr corrugated boxes, point-of-purchase displays, co-packing, fulfillment, warehousing & distribution. (Woman/White, estab 1987, empl 240, sales $65,153,256, cert: WBENC)

6897   Crossroads USA
14004 Century Lane   Grandview, MO 64030
(816) 767-8008   Jason Begnaud Director of Sales
Fax: (816) 767-8012
Email: service@bestwaylogistics.com
Website: www.bestwaylogistics.com/
Single source packaging & shipping solutions nationwide. (Woman/White, estab 2000, empl 14, sales $5,050,000, cert: WBENC)

6898   Signature Packaging and Paper, LLC
1302 Lenco Ave   Jackson, MO 63755
(314) 330-8085   Leon Vinson Regional Sales Mgr
Fax: (573) 243-0057
Email: lvinson@signaturepackaging.net
Website: www.signaturepackaging.net
Dist corrugated packaging, partitians & POP displays. (AA, estab 2003, empl 56, sales $29,200,000, cert: State)

6899   Swan Packaging Inc.
PO Box 1558   St. Louis, MO 63026
(314) 771-9777   Mary Swanson President
Fax: (844) 273-8526
Email: mswanson@swanpackaginginc.com
Website: www.swanpackaginginc.com
Dist shrink sleeves, lidding films, printed rollstock & pouches, rotogravure & flexographic printing, multilayer films, extrusion & off-line lamination, films, paper & foil. (Woman/White, estab 1999, empl 6, sales $3,519,000, cert: WBENC)

Mississippi

6900   Innpack LLC
10511 High Point Rd   Olive Branch, MS 38654
(901) 949-4977   Jin Ahn CFO
Fax: (901) 774-6201
Email: jahn@innpack.com
Website: www.innpack.com
Mfr & dist packaging solutions: burlap, cotton, PP woven, laminated & FBIC bags. (As-Pac, estab 1997, empl 20, sales $9,000,000, cert: NMSDC)

North Carolina

6901 AAKCo. Packaging
256 Highgate Circle   Wake Forest, NC 27587
(919) 609-7486 Danielle Kerner CEO
Fax:
Email: aakcopackaging@outlook.com
Website:
Packaging for pharmaceutical products. (Woman/White, estab 2015, empl 1, sales , cert: WBENC)

6902 Carolina Industrial Resources, Inc
4303 Oak Level Rd   Rocky Mount, NC 27803
(800) 849-1819 Margaret Hoyle President
Fax: (252) 446-3776
Email: tphoyle@cir-poly.com
Website: www.cir-poly.com
Dist polyethylene plastic packaging products. (Woman/White, estab 1986, empl 359, sales $155,000,000, cert: WBENC)

6903 PolySi Technologies, Inc.
5108 Rex McLeod Dr   Sanford, NC 27330
(919) 775-4989 Lynn Richardson Ops Mgr
Fax: (919) 775-2460
Email: lynn@polysi.com
Website: www.polysi.com
Mfr silicone, synthetic greases & silicone fluids, industrial packaging, retail packaging, contract filling & custom packaging. (Woman/White, estab 1995, empl 25, sales $7,000,000, cert: WBENC)

6904 SLR Designs, LLC
11220 Elm Lane, Ste 200   Charlotte, NC 28277
(704) 546-8448 Linda Tilley Managing Member
Fax: (877) 307-8728
Email: linda@slrdesignsllc.com
Website: www.slrdesignsllc.com
Design & dist customer packaging, PVC, mPE & phthalate free materials. (Woman/White, estab 2011, empl 4, sales $3,247,681, cert: WBENC)

6905 Southern Film Extruders, Inc.
2319 English Rd   High Point, NC 27265
(800) 334-6101 John Barnes VP Finance
Fax: (336) 885-8838
Email: sales@southernfilm.com
Website: www.southernfilm.com
Extrudes polyethylene packaging films using LDPE, LLDPE,HDPE and Metallocene resins for packaging applications, shrink film, film for bags, laminations etc. (Hisp, estab 1965, empl 150, sales $65,000,000, cert: NMSDC)

Nebraska

6906 Frontier Bag Company, Inc
2520 Grant St   Omaha, NE 68111
(402) 342-0992 Rendell Gines Reg sales Mgr
Fax: (402) 342-2107
Email: jplee@frontierbagco.com
Website: www.frontierbagco.com
Dist plastic bags & packaging, film wrap & shrink wrap. (Woman/AA, estab 1946, empl 15, sales $1,430,000, cert: WBENC)

New Jersey

6907 Accurate Box Company
86 Fifth Ave   Paterson, NJ 07524
(197) 334-5200 Stuart Pollack Sales Rep
Fax: (973) 345-2006
Email: sschlossman@accuratebox.com
Website: www.accuratebox.com
Litholaminated E, B & F flute packaging & displays. (Woman/White, estab 1944, empl 275, sales , cert: WBENC)

6908 Alpha Industries Inc. dba Sigma Stretch Film
Page and Schuyler   Lyndhurst, NJ 07071
(214) 799-3975 John Buchan Mgr strategic Accts
Fax: (918) 446-4920
Email: johnbuchan@sigmaplastics.com
Website: www.sigmaplastics.com
Mfr custom barrier & sealant mono & co-ex blown films for dry,frozen, refrigerated & liquid food applications.. (As-Pac, estab 1997, empl 70, sales $57,500,000, cert: NMSDC)

6909 Argent Associates, Inc.
140 Fieldcrest Ave   Edison, NJ 08837
(732) 512-9009 William Donadio VP Supply Chain
Fax: (732) 512-9549
Email: bdonadio@argentassociates.com
Website: www.argentassociates.com
Inventory mgmt, warehousing, dist, logistics, packaging, installation & commercial construction. (Woman/Hisp, estab 1998, empl 30, sales $181,676,013, cert: NMSDC, WBENC)

6910 Creative Packaging Solutions Corporation
5 W First St   Keyport, NJ 07735
(732) 335-3700 Coni Lefferts President
Fax: (732) 264-3655
Email: ConiLefferts@usa.com
Website: www.packaging-usa.com
Dist packaging containers, parts & components: bottles, jars, flexible tubes, rigid tubes aand canister, caps, sprayers, lotion pumps, folding boxes, rigid gift set up boxes, ribbons, thermoformed blisters and trays. (Woman/White, estab 2003, empl 2, sales $176,677, cert: State, WBENC)

6911 G&T Trading International
128 Circle Ave   Clifton, NJ 07011
(973) 340-8003 George Chen President
Fax: (973) 340-8013
Email: philipgttic@gmail.com
Website: www.gttic.com
Dist stretch film, wooden pallets, chipboard, stretch film equip, annual equipment audits, shrink film, shrink wrap & bundling equip, carton sealing & bagging equip, supporting films & tapes. (As-Pac, estab 1977, empl 6, sales $23,987,513, cert: State, NMSDC)

6912 Pro Pack Inc.
500 W Main St   Wyckoff, NJ 07481
(201) 337-1001 Peter Quercia CEO
Fax:
Email: peter@shrinkfilm.com
Website: www.shrinkfilm.com
Packaging materials, form, fill & seal systems, doy-pack systems, metal detectors & check
weighers, labeling systems, clip & twist systems, shrink wrappers, carton sealers, stretch wrappers, strapping machines, conveyors, band sealers, filling systems. (Woman/White, estab 1976, empl 10, sales $4,000,000, cert: WBENC)

6913 Products Distribution, Inc.
7 Santa Fe Way Ste 701 Cranbury, NJ 08512
(609) 655-1341 Dawn Dunbar President
Fax: (609) 655-4917
Email: requests@productsdistribution.com
Website: www.productsdistribution.com
Warehousing, distribution, fulfillment, assembly, kitting, pick pack, container unloading, palletizing, ingredient storage, bulk storage, EDI, custom assembly, display assembly, GWP assembly, rack storage, raw material storage. (Woman/White, estab 1979, empl 7, sales $1,119,000, cert: WBENC)

6914 Quality Packaging Specialists International, LLC
2030 US 130 N   Florence, NJ 08518
(609) 273-6364 Jeff Lemke Sales Exec
Fax: (609) 239-0228
Email: jlemke@qpsiusa.com
Website: www.qpsiusa.com
Packaging & fulfillment, merchandising displays, contract packaging, logistics & distribution services. (AA, estab 1972, empl 1500, sales $300,000,000, cert: NMSDC)

6915 RKS Plastics Inc.
100 Jersey Ave   New Brunswick, NJ 08903
(800) 635-9959 Sudhir Shah President
Fax: (732) 828-7703
Email: srshah@rksplastics.com
Website: www.rksplastics.com
Dist polyethylene & polyproylene bags, drum/box liners, sheeting & tubing, zipper lock bags, anti-static bags, printed bags, wicket/staple pack, stretch wrap & tapes. In addition, we also offer design services. (As-Pac, estab 1993, empl 7, sales $4,223,000, cert: NMSDC)

6916 SunFlex Packagers Inc.
2 Commerce Dr   Cranford, NJ 07016
(908) 709-1500 Manny Patel CEO
Fax: (908) 709-1525
Email: mannypatel@sunflexpackagers.com
Website: www.sunflexpackagers.com
Convert & dist flexible packaging material: roll form, bags & specialty pouches. (As-Ind, estab 2002, empl 15, sales , cert: NMSDC)

Nevada

6917 West Pack Industries, LLC.
2225 E Greg St, Ste 107   Sparks, NV 89431
(775) 351-3345 James Alford GM
Fax: (775) 251-2346
Email: james@westpackcopack.com
Website: www.westpackcopack.com/
Flexible packaging, contract packaging, dry product filling, mixing, blending. Stand up pouch filling, Vertical Form Fill Seal filling, volume metric filling, scale filling. Snack Foods, candy, confectionery, powdered beverages. (Nat Ame, estab 2003, empl 44, sales $1,850,000, cert: NMSDC)

New York

6918 Berry Industrial Group, Inc.
30 Main St   Nyack, NY 10960
(845) 353-8338 Debra Berry CEO
Fax: (845) 353-8333
Email: debra.berry@berryindustrial.com
Website: www.berryindustrial.com
Mfr, recycle & dist industrial shipping pallets. (Woman/White, estab 1984, empl 6, sales , cert: WBENC)

6919 Bluepack
215 John Glenn Dr   Amherst, NY 14228
(716) 923-0032 Helen Ma President
Fax: (716) 923-0034
Email: hma@bluepackinc.com
Website: www.bluepackinc.com
Mfr printed & unprinted shrink labels, neck bands & safety seals. We have 8 color flexo and rotogravure presses. (Woman/As-Pac, estab 1999, empl 65, sales $10,000,000, cert: NMSDC)

6920 Diamond Packaging
111 Commerce Dr   Rochester, NY 14623
(585) 334-8030 Dennis Bacchetta Director of Mktg
Fax: (585) 334-9141
Email: sales@diamondpkg.com
Website: www.diamondpackaging.com
Contract mfg & packaging services: automatic cartoning, bagging bar coding, blister sealing, EAS source tagging, flexible packaging, form, fill & seal, fulfillment, labeling, POP displays, product assembly, RF sealing, shrink wrapping & skin packaging. (Woman/AA, estab 1911, empl 262, sales $61,584,000, cert: WBENC)

6921 Eltrex Industries, Inc.
65 Sullivan St   Rochester, NY 14605
(585) 454-6100 Avis Williams Business Dev Mgr
Fax: (585) 263-7766
Email: avis.williams@eltrex.com
Website: www.eltrex.com
Mechanical & electromechanical assemblies, remanufacturing, kitting & logistics services: material purchasing & consignment, packaging & distribution, warehousing. (AA, estab 1968, empl 200, sales $18,000,000, cert: State)

6922 Ongweoweh Corp
5 Barr Road   Ithaca, NY 14850
(607) 266-7070 Alison Meyer Supplier Diversity
Mgr
Fax: (607) 266-7085
Email: ameyer@ongweoweh.com
Website: www.ongweoweh.com
Mfr & dist wooden pallets & specialty containers. (Nat Ame, estab 1978, empl 96, sales $162,289,435, cert: NMSDC)

6923 Prism Packaging
70 E Sunrise Hwy, Ste 611   Valley Stream, NY 11581
(516)52080 Randi Norfleet Exec Director
Fax: (516) 568-2036
Email: RNorfleet@witlogistics.com
Website: www.walkerscm.com
Print, packaging & logistics solutions. (AA, estab 2015, empl 1, sales , cert: NMSDC)

6924 The Standard Group
1010 Northern Blvd Ste 236 Great Neck, NY 11021
(718) 310-5512 James Gregory Acct Exec
Fax:
Email: jamesg@thestandardgroup.com
Website: www.thestandardgroup.com
Folding carton, specialty printed packaging & paperboard converter. (Hisp, estab 1932, empl 130, sales $35,000,000, cert: NMSDC)

6925 Universal Packaging Systems
6080 Jericho Turnpike   commack, NY 11725
(404) 554-0770 David Boone Natl Acct Mgr
Fax: (404) 554-0786
Email: dboone@paklab.com
Website: www.paklab.com
Contract manufacturing & flexible film, extended gamut flexographic printing of roll stock & pouches with gussets & fitments. (AA, estab 1987, empl 600, sales $116,400,000, cert: NMSDC)

6926 Walker SCM
70 E Sunrise Hwy Ste 611 Valley Stream, NY 11581
(516) 568-2080 Maria Hill Director of Sales
Fax: (516) 568-2036
Email: mhill@walkerscm.com
Website: www.walkerscm.com
Assembly & contract packaging services. (AA, estab 1999, empl 450, sales $54,129,000, cert: NMSDC)

Ohio

6927 Accel Inc.
9000 Smith's Mill Road   New Albany, OH 43054
(614) 656-1100 Tara Abraham Co-CEO
Fax: (614) 656-1119
Email: tabraham@accel-inc.com
Website: www.accel-inc.com
Contract packaging & fulfillment svcs: design, sourcing, assembly, shrink-wrapping, warehousing, dist & e-fulfillment svcs. (Woman/AA/As-Ind, estab 1995, empl 400, sales $21,492,000, cert: WBENC)

6928 Allied Shipping and Packaging Supplies
3681 Vance Rd   Moraine, OH 45439
(937) 222-7422 Shelly Heller President
Fax: (937) 222-7470
Email: sheller@asapi.com
Website: www.asapi.com
Dist packaging supplies: special size boxes, printed boxes, printed tape, special inserts or cell partitions, printed poly bags or special size poly bags. (Woman/White, estab 1982, empl 12, sales $4,337,543, cert: WBENC)

6929 Arrowhead Packaging Services
P.O. Box 1284   Perrysburg, OH 43551
(419) 344-7373 Brian Deiger VP sales
Fax:
Email: brian@apackserv.com
Website: www.apackserv.com
Packaging & packaging services, fulfillment operations, sequencing, storage & logistics. (AA, estab 2010, empl 2, sales $120,000, cert: NMSDC)

6930 Bickley Innovations, LLC
607 Redna Terr, Ste 700   Cincinnati, OH 45215
(513) 655-6074 Kendra Alexander President
Fax: (513) 889-4180
Email: information@bickleyllc.com
Website: www.bickleyllc.com
Dist packaging & industrial supplies. (Woman/AA, estab 2015, empl 1, sales $80,000, cert: NMSDC, WBENC)

6931 Custom Paper Tubes
15900 Industrial Pkwy Cleveland, OH 44135
(216) 362-2964 Emily Miller Mktg Mgr
Fax: (216) 362-2980
Email: emiller@custompapertubes.com
Website: www.custompapertubes.com
Produce sustainable, recyclable & biodegradable packaging for all types of products. (Woman/AA/Hisp, estab 1964, empl 25, sales $5,500,000, cert: WBENC, SDB)

6932 Forest City Companies, Inc.
3607 W 56th St Cleveland, OH 44102
(216) 634-9000 Anthony Galang President
Fax:
Email: tgalang@forestcityco.com
Website: www.forestcityco.com
Military packaging service & supplies, laser marking services, wood boxes, export packing & crating, hazmat packaging service & supplies, induatrial sewing, bellows, insulated blankets. (AA, estab 1993, empl 14, sales $3,600,000, cert: NMSDC)

6933 Joshen Paper and Packaging
5800 Grant Ave   Cuyahoga Heights, OH 44105
(216) 441-5600 Anthony Salyers
Fax: (216) 441-0743
Email: greiser@joshen.com
Website: www.joshen.com
Dist packaging supplies, bags, office supplies, custom printing, sanitation, chemicals & floor care programs. (Woman/White, estab 1988, empl 152, sales $180,500,000, cert: NWBOC)

6934　LEFCO Worthington, LLC
18451 Euclid Ave   Cleveland, OH 44112
(216) 432-4422 Larry Fulton President
Fax: (216) 432-4424
Email: Larry.Fulton@LEFCOWorthington.com
Website: www.LEFCOWorthington.com
Dist wooden crates, OSB Boxes, custom pallets, sub-assembly & packaging services. (AA, estab 2003, empl 30, sales $3,600,000, cert: State, NMSDC)

6935　TrueChoicePack Corp.
1285 Lyons Rd, Bldg H   Dayton, OH 45458
(937) 630-3832 Heena Rathore President
Fax: (800) 307-0681
Email: hrathore@truechoicepack.com
Website: www.truechoicepack.com
Mfr environmentally friendly green packaging products, biodegradable & compostable food service packaging & disposable products. (AA/As-Ind, estab 2008, empl 10, sales $50,560,000, cert: NMSDC)

Oregon

6936　Yoshida Foods International
8440 NE Alderwood Rd, Ste A   Portland, OR 97220
(503) 872-8450 Junki Yoshida Sales Mgr
Fax: (503) 872-8498
Email: junki.yoshida@yoshida.com
Website: www.yoshidafoodsinternational.com
Liquid hot-fill bottling, industrial packaging, portion packaging. (As-Pac, estab 1982, empl 241, sales , cert: NMSDC)

Pennsylvania

6937　Alpine Packaging Inc.
4000 Crooked Run Rd   North Versailles, PA 15137
(412) 664-4000 Jan Lehigh President
Fax: (412) 664-0691
Email: jlehigh@alpinepackaging.com
Website: www.alpinepackaging.com
Packaging supplies & services. (Woman/White, estab 1972, empl 38, sales $14,180,198, cert: WBENC)

6938　Carlisle Packaging Company, Inc.
750 Claremont Rd P.O. Box 85 Carlisle, PA 17013
(717) 249-2444 Ed Schimmel CEO
Fax: (717) 249-6834
Email: eschimmel@carlislecontainer.net
Website: www.carlislecontainer.net
Mfr corrugated packaging & displays. (Woman/White, estab 1965, empl 40, sales $7,173,000, cert: State, WBENC)

6939　Evco Industries, Inc.
126 Talbot Ave   Holmes, PA 19043
(610) 586-9842 Kathleen Evans President
Fax: (610) 586-0167
Email: kitty@evcoindustries.com
Website: www.evcoindustries.com
Dist industrial packaging products: adhesives, adhesive applicating equipment, marking/coding equipment & drying systems. (Woman/White, estab 1979, empl 8, sales $2,230,099, cert: WBENC)

6940　Kalstar Enterprises, LLC
P.O. Box 931 Scranton, PA 18501
(973) 553-5370 Adam Zaranski Director Client Solutions
Fax: (570) 207-2244
Email: adam.zaranski@kalstar.com
Website: www.kalstar.com
Packaging, kitting other labor services to manufacturing companies. (Woman/White, estab 2004, empl 206, sales $33,600,000, cert: WBENC)

6941　S&G Corrugated Packaging
195 Slocum St   Swoyersville, PA 18704
(570) 287-1718 Earl Sampson CEO
Fax: (570) 287-1720
Email: sgcorrugated@verizon.net
Website: www.s-gcorrugatedpackaging.com
Mfr corrugated cartons & corrugated sheets: assembled partitions, corrugated trays, half slotted cartons, one & five panel folders, scored sheets, coated pads, telescoping cartons, die cutting items, slip sheets, packaging tapes. (AA, estab 2007, empl 10, sales , cert: NMSDC)

6942　Union Packaging, LLC
6250 Baltimore Avenue   Yeadon, PA 19050
(610) 622-7001 Michael K. Pearson President
Fax: (610) 622-7006
Email: mpearson@unionpkg.com
Website: www.unionpkg.com
Mfr folding cartons, paperboard printing & converting. (AA, estab 1999, empl 82, sales $9,287,115, cert: NMSDC)

6943　Wexler Packaging Products
777M Schwab Rd   Hatfield, PA 19440
(800) 878-3878 Tara Utain V.P. Sales & Mktg
Fax: (215) 631-9705
Email: tara@wexlerpackaging.com
Website: www.wexlerpackaging.com
Packaging products. (Woman/White, estab 1974, empl 20, sales $8,000,000, cert: WBENC)

Puerto Rico

6944 3A Press
P.O. Box 47   Lajas, PR 00667
(787) 899-0110 Marie Rosado President
Fax: (787) 899-0155
Email: mrosado@3apress.com
Website: www.3apress.com
Mfr & print pharmaceutical, commercial & folding cartons, inserts, stitched & perfect bound booklets/magazines, printed literature. (Hisp, estab 1996, empl 126, sales $11,200,000, cert: NMSDC)

6945 Flexible Packaging Company, Inc.
KM 5 1 BO Guaragua RR 176 Bayamon Gardens Station Bayamon, PR 00959
(787) 622-7225 Esteban Serrano Sales Mgr
Fax: (787) 622-7247
Email: eserrano@flepak.com
Website: www.flepak.com
Flexible packaging solutions. (Hisp, estab 1976, empl 170, sales , cert: NMSDC)

6946 Inter-Strap Packaging Systems
P.O. Box 12367   San Juan, PR 00914
(787) 771-5230 Antonio Fernández GM
Fax: (787) 765-2130
Email: afernandez@inter-strap.com
Website: www.inter-strap.com
Dist packaging equipment & materials. (Woman/Hisp, estab 1991, empl 18, sales $6,317,564, cert: NMSDC)

6947 Johnny Rullan & Co.,
Road # 1 Km. 20.9 RR-3 Box 3710   San Juan, PR 00926
(787) 789-3050 Julio Pizarro Accting Clerk
Fax: (787) 789-3099
Email: accountsreceivable@johnnyrullan.com
Website: www.johnnyrullan.com
Packaging equipment sales & service. (Hisp, estab 1970, empl 25, sales , cert: NMSDC)

Rhode Island

6948 Banneker Industries, Inc.
582 Great Rd, Ste 101   North Smithfield, RI 02896
(603) 819-6966 Joe Cefalo Sales & Mktg Mgr
Fax:
Email: marketing@banneker.com
Website: www.banneker.com
Supply chain management services: e-business services, assembly & packaging, bar coding, dist packaging materials, third party logistics (3PL), warehousing, material flow & inventory management. (Woman/AA, estab 1991, empl 72, sales $10,072,400, cert: NMSDC, WBENC)

South Carolina

6949 Alpha Pack LLC
P.O. Box 30266   Charleston, SC 29417
(843) 737-3931 Carver Wright Jr. Owner
Fax: (843) 620-1055
Email: Wright.pkg@alphapackllc.com
Website: www.alphapackllc.com
Flexible packaging,polybags, shrink bags, printed bags, tubing, vci bags, sheeting & can liners. (AA, estab 2012, empl 2, sales , cert: NMSDC)

6950 Progressive Packaging
1224 Old Stage Rd   Greenville, SC 29681
(864) 271-8106 Mark Hutcherson Sales Exec
Fax: (864) 967-2244
Email: hutcherson64@gmail.com
Website: www.progpack.com
Corrugated packaging, boxes, sheet plant, assembly. (Woman/White, estab 1996, empl 55, sales $19,000,000, cert: WBENC)

6951 Solution Packaging LLC
2131 Woodruff Rd, Ste 196   Greenville, SC 29607
(864) 313-9595 Joe Nichol VP Sales
Fax:
Email: joe@solutionplastics.net
Website: www.solutionplastics.net
Mfr & dist polyethylene based end product & solutions, packaging, poly film, etc. (Woman/Hisp, estab 2013, empl 2, sales , cert: WBENC)

6952 WDS, Inc.
1414 Village Harbor Dr   Lake Wylie, SC 29710
(803) 619-0301 Jennfer Maier CEO
Fax: (803) 753-8370
Email: jennifer.maier@womends.com
Website: www.womends.com
Dist industrial supplies: paper products, chipboard, films & plastics. (Woman/White, estab 2007, empl 180, sales $186,000,000, cert: WBENC)

Tennessee

6953 DSI Warehouse Inc
1315 Farmville Rd   Memphis, TN 38122
(901) 345-6608 Debbie Martin President
Fax: (901) 396-0022
Email: debbiemartin@dsiwarehouse.com
Website: www.dsiwarehouseandstorage.com
Warehousing & Storage, Packing & Crating, Packaging & Labeling, Kitting Pack Services, Storage & Handling Equipment & Supplies, Distribution Fulfillment. (Woman/AA, estab 2013, empl 20, sales $1,455,421, cert: NMSDC, WBENC)

6954 Johnson Bryce, Inc.
      276 S Parkway West   Memphis, TN 38109
      (901) 942-6513 Sherry Akins Controller
      Fax: (901) 271-3309
      Email: rpurifoy@johnsonbryce.com
      Website: www.johnsonbryce.com
Mfr flexible packaging. (AA, estab 1991, empl 65, sales
$27,500,000, cert: NMSDC)

6955 Puffy Stuff
      9 Music Square S, Ste 376   Nashville, TN 37203
      (877) 833-9872 Sales
      Fax: (615) 228-6139
      Email: info@puffystufftn.com
      Website: www.puffystufftn.com
Mfr 100% biodegradable packing peanuts. (Woman/White,
estab 2000, empl 20, sales $100,000, cert: State)

6956 Remar Inc.
      6200 E Division St   Lebanon, TN 37090
      (615) 449-0231 Nelson Remus President
      Fax: (615) 449-0774
      Email: nremus@remarinc.com
      Website: www.remarinc.com
Dist blister packaging, fin seal wrap, shrink wrap, inventory
mgmt, point of purchase displays, media replication, direct
mail services, turn key or component projects. (Hisp, estab
1996, empl 125, sales , cert: State, NMSDC)

6957 TSS Industrial Packaging, LLC
      P.O. Box 3181   Jackson, TN 38303
      (888) 424-1946 Michelle Boyd CEO
      Fax: (888) 424-1946
      Email: mboyd@tssip.com
      Website: www.tssip.com
Dist industrial packaging materials: industrial sewing
thread & yarn for closing bags, crepe paper sewing tape,
pull tape, twine, slip sheets, pallet covers, stretch film &
stretch wrap. (Woman/White, estab 2006, empl 8, sales
$3,496,505, cert: State, WBENC)

6958 Worldwide Label & Packaging LLC
      158 Madison Ave Ste 101 Memphis, TN 38103
      (901) 454-9290 Anthony Norris President
      Fax:
      Email: anorris@worldwidebg.com
      Website: www.worldwidebg.com
Mfr printed packaging: pressure sensitive labels, flexible
packaging & continuous roll forms. (AA, estab 2000, empl
20, sales $4,817,859, cert: NMSDC)

Texas

6959 Accredo Packaging, Inc.
      12682 Cardinal Meadow Dr   Sugar Land, TX 77478
      (713) 580-4872 Malcolm Cohn Director of
      Sustainability
      Fax: (281) 980-3012
      Email: mcohn@accredopkg.com
      Website: www.accredopackaging.com
Dist biopolymer resins. (As-Pac, estab 2007, empl 350,
sales $305,000,000, cert: State, NMSDC)

6960 Age Industries, Ltd.
      3601 County Rd, Ste 316C Cleburne, TX 76031
      (281) 799-0935 Max Walls GM/VP Packaging Div
      Fax: (817) 641-2509
      Email: max@ageindustries.com
      Website: www.ageindustries.com
Mfr & dist packaging products. (Woman/White, estab
1974, empl 247, sales $35,331,300, cert: WBENC)

6961 Austin Foam Plastics, Inc.
      2933 AW Grimes Blvd Pflugerville, TX 78660
      (512) 251-6300 Lisa Carnett Project Leader
      Fax: (512) 251-9222
      Email: lisa.carnett@a-f-p.com
      Website: www.a-f-p.com
Packaging Design and testing; logistics; sustainable
solutions; manufacturing - corrugated (boxes; die cut;
pallets; solid fiber folding cartons) wood (custom crates;
pallets; floating pallets) custom cases; custom cushions;
plastic corrugated; sourcing ((Woman/White, estab
1978, empl 228, sales , cert: WBENC)

6962 B.A.G. Corp.
      1155 Kas Dr. Ste 170 Richardson, TX 75081
      (214) 340-7060 Sherlene A Wegner Mktg Asst
      Fax:
      Email: sherlene@bagcorp.com
      Website: www.bagcorp.com
Bulk handling & supply chain solutions. (Woman/White,
estab 1969, empl 100, sales $70,000,000, cert: WBENC)

6963 Castle Business Solutions, LLC
      2777 North Stemmons Frwy Ste 1242 Dallas, TX
      75207
      (214) 599-2880 Sharon King CEO
      Fax:
      Email: sharon@castlebusinesssolutions.net
      Website: www.castlebusinesssolutions.com/
Directory & mailing list publishing, direct mail advertising, packaging & labeling services, warehousing &
storage, custom computer programming services, data
processing, hosting & related services. (Woman/AA,
estab 2010, empl 3, sales $615,880, cert: State, NMSDC,
NWBOC)

6964 CCA Distributions
      12832 Tierra Karla Dr   El Paso, TX 79938
      (915) 239-1870 Carlos Camarena Owner
      Fax: (100) 000-0000
      Email: carlos@ccadistributions.com
      Website: www.ccadistributions.com
Dist Packaging Material: Stretch Film, Kraft Paper, Tape,
Poly Strapping, Metal Strapping, Boxes, Kraft Paper
Tubes, Chipboard. Poly Sheeting, Poly Bags, and more.
(Woman/Hisp, estab 2007, empl 2, sales $85,000, cert:
State, NMSDC)

6965   Diamond Display Group Partners, Inc.
       2637 Summit Ave Ste 303 Plano, TX 75074
       (972) 636-0781 Glenn Towery Project Mgr & Sales
       Fax: (972) 636-3665
       Email: Glenn@ddg-corp.com
       Website: www.diamonddisplaygroup.com
Corrugated & permanent displays & packaging, shipper
style corrugated displays & POS signage, styrene,
foamboard, vinyl, acrylic and metal. (Woman/White, estab
2003, empl 5, sales , cert: State, WBENC)

6966   Guardian Packaging Industries, LP
       3615 Security St Garland, TX 75042
       (214) 349-1500 Susan Stuart President
       Fax: (214) 349-1584
       Email: gbutterfield@guardianpackaging.com
       Website: www.guardianpackaging.com
Design & manufacture protective packaging, Polyurethanes, Polyethylene's, Expanded Polystyrene, Rigid
Urethanes and all Military Spec Foams, corrugated box
shop. (Woman/White, estab 2005, empl 35, sales
$3,900,000, cert: State, WBENC)

6967   International Print & Packaging, Inc.
       951 Hwy 183 N.   Liberty Hill, TX 78642
       (512) 515-6333 Shelly Armstrong Digital Solutions
       Specialist
       Fax: (512) 778-5101
       Email: shelly@dle-corp.com
       Website: www.ipp-corp.com
Mfr flexible packaging: labels, stickers, decals, shrink film,
printed film, lidding materials, POP products, displays,
table tents, shelf strips, hang tags, folding cartons, self
sufficient manufacturing, inhouse graphics design department. (Woman/White, estab 1996, empl 90, sales , cert:
State)

6968   Komplete Group, Inc.
       202 N Great Southwest Pkwy   Grand Prairie, TX
       75050
       (214) 252-8102 Tariq Usmani Diversity Coord
       Fax: (214) 646-9922
       Email: tusmani@kpak.com
       Website: www.kpak.com
Food copackaging, packaging equipment & supplies,
thermoforming, commercial printing. (As-Pac, estab 1995,
empl 150, sales $781,401, cert: State, NMSDC)

6969   New Century Packaging Systems, LLC
       401 N Carrol Ave, Ste 124 401 N Carroll Ave, #124
       Southlake, TX 76092
       (972) 725-0311 Vanessa Brown GM
       Fax: (972) 961-3587
       Email: vbrown@newcenturypkg.net
       Website: www.newcenturypkg.net
Dist packaging materials & packaging equipment. (AA,
estab 1972, empl 5, sales $2,002,000, cert: State, NMSDC)

6970   Premier LogiTech
       1100 Avenue T Grand Prairie, TX 75050
       (972) 606-1234 Scott Paul President
       Fax: (972) 606-1677
       Email: spaul@premierlogitech.com
       Website: www.premierlogitech.com
Kitting packaged goods into boxes, bags, displays, gift
sets or other kits, packaging, heat shrinking, blister
bagging & clam shelling. (Woman/White, estab 1995,
empl 129, sales $14,000,410, cert: SDB)

6971   Southwest Packaging Solutions, LLC
       2472 Southwell Rd   Dallas, TX 75229
       (903) 440-3628 Edgar Sotelo President
       Fax: (214) 902-7999
       Email: edgar@southwestpackaging.net
       Website: www.southwestpackaging.net
Contract packaging services, printed registered film
packaging services, warehousing, display building,
bundling, reverse logistics, blister pack, skin pack, mfg
consulting for improved efficiencies. (Hisp, estab 2009,
empl 30, sales $1,800,000, cert: NMSDC)

Washington

6972   Kalani Packaging, Inc.
       2525 W Casino Rd, Ste 8C   Everett, WA 98204
       (425) 347-0330 Shelly Dickson
       Fax: (425) 347-0118
       Email: shelly@kalanipkg.com
       Website: www.kalanipkg.com
Dist packaging supplies: tape, stretch wrap, shipping
labels, poly bags & sheeting, boxes, bubble wrap &
custom printed labels. Also dist janitorial supplies,
boxes & bags. (As-Pac, estab 2000, empl 12, sales , cert:
NMSDC, 8(a))

Wisconsin

6973   A&M Integrated Packaging
       1645 Bergstrom Rd   Neenah, WI 54956
       (920) 751-1043 Terry Spielbauer Sales Mgr
       Fax: (920) 751-1279
       Email: terry.spielbauer@menasha.com
       Website:
Packaging: cartons, shrink wrap, liquid & dry filling,
pouching, assembly, form, fill & seal, stuffing, bagging,
repacking, labeling, blister & skin packaging, point-of-
purchase displays, promotional mass mailing, e-commerce fulfillment, etc. (Woman/AA, estab 1968, empl
10, sales , cert: NMSDC)

6974 Chryspac - Quality Custom Solutions
      130 W Edgerton Avenue Ste 130 Milwaukee, WI
      53207
      (414) 372-0541 Warren Scurlock Business Dev Mgr
      Fax: (414) 744-8605
      Email: Sales@Chryspac.com
      Website: www.chryspac.com
Packaging & assembly: quality inspection, containment
sorting, assembling, re-work, reclamation, shrink wrapping
& labeling. (AA, estab 2000, empl 50, sales $816,456, cert:
NMSDC)

6975 Pac Basic
      S10744 State Rd 93   Eleva, WI 54738
      (715) 552-1722 Mindy Pedersen President
      Fax: (715) 552-9722
      Email: mpedersen@pacbasic.com
      Website: www.pacbasic.com
Packaging, corrugated, molded pulp & other various
protective materials. (Woman/White, estab 2007, empl 4,
sales $1,978,000, cert: WBENC)

6976 Packaging Specialties Inc.
      W130 N10751 Washington Dr   Germantown, WI
      53022
      (262) 512-1261 Hugh Ahn President
      Fax: (262) 512-1665
      Email: hahn@packaging-specialties.com
      Website: www.packaging-specialties.com
Dist packaging systems & materials. (As-Pac, estab 1973,
empl 30, sales , cert: NMSDC)

6977 TechniSource Services Group
      1025 S Moorland Rd 2057 Brookfield, WI 53005
      (800) 864-2317 James Nguyen VP Sales
      Fax: (262) 785-1477
      Email: james@technisourcegroup.com
      Website: www.technisourcegroup.com
Dist packaging products & services: stretch films, shrink
film, poly films, carton sealers, erectors, stretch wrappers,
tapes & adhesives, corrugated & fiber boxes. (Woman/As-
Pac, estab 1994, empl 50, sales $25,000,000, cert: NMSDC)

6978 Twin River LLC
      2721 Harvey St   Hudson, WI 54016
      (715) 381-3067 Kathy Enerson President
      Fax: (715) 377-0432
      Email: kathyb@twinriverllc.com
      Website: www.twinriverllc.com
Packaging, fulfillment, high-speed shrink wrapping, blister
pack, clamshells, poly & paper banding, labeling,
barcoding, kitting, assembly, distribution, warehousing,
POP displays, quality inspections & mailings. (Woman/
White, estab 2009, empl 8, sales $357,450, cert: WBENC)

PAINT, GLUES & TILES
Manufacturers of paint, varnish, sealers, solvents, adhesives, etc. NAICS Code 42

California

6979 Ferco Color
2315 Baker Ave   Ontario, CA 91761
(909) 930-0773 Jennifer Thaw President
Fax: (909) 930-0775
Email: info@fercocolor.com
Website: www.fercocolor.com/
Mfr color & additives for plastics, bottles, closures. (Woman/White, estab 1994, empl 48, sales $16,000,000, cert: WBENC)

6980 Genard, inc. dba Lennova
1717 Boyd St   Santa Ana, CA 92705
(562) 860-3213 Tony Genova VP Sales & Mktg
Fax: (562) 860-6913
Email: tony@lennova.net
Website: www.lennova.net
Install epoxy & urethane protective floor & wall coatings. (Hisp, estab 2000, empl 15, sales $2,387,000, cert: CPUC)

Illinois

6981 Budnick Converting Inc.
200 Admiral Weinel Blvd   Columbia, IL 62236
(800) 282-0090 Lori Baltz Acct Mgr
Fax: (618) 281-6308
Email: samwi@budnickconverting.com
Website: www.budnickconverting.com
Convert & dist adhesive tapes & foams, cutting, slitting, laminating, printing & spooling. (Woman/White, estab 1952, empl 85, sales $20,000,000, cert: WBENC)

Kentucky

6982 TSP Solutions
7057 Production Court   Florence, KY 41042
(859) 384-1548 Charles Mcgregor President
Fax: (859) 384-1493
Email: charlie@tspsolutions.biz
Website: www.tspsolutions.biz
Mfr commercial printing specialty & adhesive coatings, standard commodity coatings, Gloss, non-gloss products. (AA, estab 2009, empl 10, sales $5,000,000, cert: NMSDC)

Ohio

6983 Westwood Finishing Company
5881 Wolf Creek Pike   Trotwood, OH 45426
(937) 854-6608 Marcia Richley Owner
Fax:
Email: marcia1118@aol.com
Website: www.westfinish.com
Apply all types of paint material: wet coating, epoxy, urethane, enamels and copper coatings (EMI and RFI shielding. (Woman/White, estab 1995, empl 11, sales $530,864, cert: WBENC)

Oregon

6984 YOLO Colorhouse LLC
519 NE Hancock St, Ste B   Portland, OR 97212
(503) 493-8275 Rick Barnard VP Ops
Fax: (503) 232-0445
Email: rick@colorhousepaint.com
Website: www.colorhousepaint.com
Premium paints: no-VOC, low-odor & earth friendly. (Woman/White, estab 2006, empl 11, sales $780,000, cert: WBENC)

Puerto Rico

6985 Lanco Manufacturing Corp.
Urb. Aponte 5   San Lorenzo, PR 00954
(787) 736-4221 Nelson Soto Category Mgr
Fax: (787) 736-5313
Email: nsoto@lancopaints.com
Website: www.lancopaints.com
Paints (Water and Oil Based), Enamels, Caulking, Spackling, Wood Stains, Wood Fillers, Adhesive, Roof Sealers, Concrete Bonding Agents and Solvents(Paint removers, Lacquer Thinners, Mineral Spirits). (Hisp, estab 1978, empl 250, sales $69,320,794, cert: NMSDC)

Virginia

6986 Creative Maintenance Solutions, LLC
1171 Polk Rd   Edinburg, VA 22824
(540) 984-8172 Nancy Barnett
Fax: (540) 984-8231
Email: nancy@cmsolutionsus.com
Website: www.cmsolutionsus.com
Dist polymer/epoxy & coatings. (Woman/White, estab 2007, empl 1, sales $10,000, cert: State)

Washington

6987 Dunkin & Bush, Inc.
P.O. Box 97080   Kirkland, WA 98083
(425) 885-7064 Deidre Dunkin President
Fax: (425) 885-3790
Email: Ddunkin@dunkinandbush.com
Website: www.dunkinandbush.com
Industrial painting, scaffolding, insulation, rigging, containment, lead abatement, shop coating aplication, concrete restoration, plural applied tank linings, abrasive blasting, specialty blasting, water jetting, high heat coating applications. (Woman/White, estab 2008, empl 300, sales , cert: WBENC)

California

6988 American Textile Systems, Inc. DBA American Paper
13151 Midway Place   Cerritos, CA 90703
(562) 229-0036 Mike Khan VP Corporate Markets
Fax: (562) 229-0533
Email: mike@amtexsys.com
Website: www.amtexsys.com
Healthcare & hospitality related textile & paper products.
(As-Ind, estab 1993, empl 25, sales $20,000,000, cert:
State)

6989 DD Office Products, Inc
5025 Hampton St   Los Angeles, CA 90058
(323) 973-4569 John Kim GSA Contract Admin
Fax: (323) 973-4569
Email: johnk@libertypp.com
Website: www.libertypp.com
Dist office paper. (As-Ind, estab 2001, empl 14, sales
$36,617,778, cert: NMSDC)

Florida

6990 Konie Cups International, Inc.
9001 NW 105th Way   Medley, FL 33178
(786) 337-7967 Fiorella Roversi Sales Analyst
Fax:
Email: fiorellaroversi@koniecups.com
Website: www.koniecups.com
Mfr paper cone cups & funnels. (Hisp, estab 1991, empl
56, sales $9,223,670, cert: NMSDC)

Georgia

6991 Sierra International LLC
9308 Industrial Dr   Covington, GA 30014
(770) 786-5301 Darryl Jackson Dir outside sales
Fax: (770) 786-5302
Email: dmjackson@sierrainternationalllc.com
Website: www.sierrainternationalllc.com
Mfr paper cups & paper plates. Dist foam/plastic, utensils,
tissue, paper towels & other foodservice disposable items.
(AA, estab 2007, empl 5, sales , cert: State)

6992 South Coast Paper LLC
2300 Windy Ridge Pkwy, Ste 830   Atlanta, GA
30339
(770) 933-3411 LaJoia Broughton Supplier Diversity
Fax: (770) 644-2743
Email: supplierdiversity@southcoastpaper.com
Website: www.southcoastpaper.com
Mfr & convert uncoated, coated, photographic & digital
paper grades, cut, wrap, package, palletize & ship product.
(AA, estab 2000, empl 49, sales $18,000,000, cert: NMSDC)

Illinois

6993 Gorilla Paper Inc.
1125 Lunt Ave   Elk Grove Village, IL 60007
(773) 789-8113 Su Chang Lim President
Fax:
Email: suchang@gorillapaper.com
Website: www.gorillapaper.com
POS Thermal Paper rolls, carbonless paper rolls. (As-Pac,
estab 2009, empl 3, sales $18,598,936, cert: NMSDC)

6994 Montenegro Paper, Ltd.
25 E Main St. #205 Roselle, IL 60172
(630) 894-0350 Ed Enciso President
Fax: (630) 894-0095
Email: mbe@montenegro-inc.com
Website: www.montenegropaper.com
Dist commercial printing paper & packaging supplies.
(Hisp, estab 1996, empl 6, sales $23,173,000, cert: State,
City, NMSDC)

6995 Norwood Paper
7001 W 60th St   Chicago, IL 60674
(773) 788-1508 Laura Martin Natl Acct Mgr
Fax: (773) 788-1528
Email: Laura@norwoodpaper.com
Website: www.norwoodpaper.com
Dist non-box related packaging chipboard, skid liners,
dust covers, interleavers, divider sheets, pallet liners,
pallet pads. (Woman/White, estab 1972, empl 1, sales
$8,000,000, cert: WBENC)

Michigan

6996 Paperworks, Inc.
15477 Woodrow Wilson St   Detroit, MI 48238
(800) 243-1424 Katrece Business Unit Mgr
Fax: (313) 867-6540
Email: customerservice@pwi-inc.com
Website: www.dchem.com
Dist paper & related products & office supplies. (AA,
estab 1981, empl 23, sales $26,000,000, cert: NMSDC)

Minnesota

6997 ecoThynk
607 Dayton Avenue   Saint Paul, MN 55012
(612) 605-4885 Gale Ward President
Fax: (612) 392-8924
Email: gale@ecoenvelopes.com
Website: www.ecothynk.com
Mfr reusable envelopes. (Woman/White, estab 2002,
empl 5, sales $210,000, cert: WBENC)

North Carolina

6998 New Generation Product, Inc.
5736 N Tryon St Ste 223B Charlotte, NC 28213
(704) 596-5327 Donald Allen Black President
Fax: (704) 295-0134
Email: don.black@NewGenProduct.com
Website: www.NewGenProduct.com
Provide biomass papers made from recycled agricultural
fibers. (AA, estab 2010, empl 1, sales $24,000, cert:
State, CPUC)

New Hampshire

6999   Gorham Paper and Tissue LLC
       72 Cascade Flats   Gorham, NH 03581
       (603) 342-2000 Wayne Johnson Sales
       Fax:
       Email: wayne.johnson@gorhampt.com
       Website: www.gorhampt.com
Mfr specialty paper, tissue & towel papers, baking (baking cups, release papers) or food applications like tray liners, food bags & pouches that require grease resistance or wets strength. (Woman/White, estab 2011, empl 200, sales , cert: WBENC)

New Jersey

7000   The Fisher Group
       P.O. Box 1653   Dover, NJ 07802
       (973) 442-3000 Irving Fisher Managing Partner
       Fax: (973) 442-3005
       Email: irving@fisherpaper.net
       Website: www.fisherpaper.net
Dist paper. (AA, estab 2000, empl 4, sales $3,556,001, cert: NMSDC)

New Mexico

7001   Roses Southwest Paper, Inc.
       1701 2nd St SW   Albuquerque, NM 87102
       (734) 968-8103 James Hinkle NSM
       Fax: (505) 242-0342
       Email: jmhinkle@aol.com
       Website: www.rosessouthwest.com
Mfr sanitary paper products: hard roll towels, multi fold towels, jumbo roll toilet tissue, standard roll toilet tissue, facial tissue, seat covers, dispenser napkins, dinner napkins, cocktail napkins, kitchen roll towels. (Hisp, estab 1984, empl 215, sales $58,980,000, cert: NMSDC)

New York

7002   Impact Enterprises, Inc.
       11 Horse Hill Lane   Warwick, NY 10990
       (845) 988-1900 Ralph Salisbury Sr VP
       Fax: (845) 988-1910
       Email: rsalisbury@impactenterprises.com
       Website: www.impactenterprises.com
Mfr custom binder covers, award covers, presentation folders, portfolio covers, sales kits & other custom covers. (Woman/White, estab 1987, empl 8, sales $2,500,000, cert: WBENC)

7003   Mrs. Paper
       31 West 34th St, Ste 8044   New York, NY 10001
       (212) 532-7777 Marion Hindenburg President
       Fax: (212) 532-7779
       Email: marion@mrspaper.com
       Website: www.mrspaper.com
Dist copy & computer paper, janitorial/sanitary supplies & advertising specialties. (Woman/White, estab 1982, empl 3, sales $4,082,000, cert: City, WBENC)

Ohio

7004   The Millcraft Paper Company
       6800 Grant Ave   Cleveland, OH 44105
       (216) 441-5500 Lisa Rogala Corp Business Dev
       Fax: (216) 441-4128
       Email: rogalal@millcraft.com
       Website: www.millcraft.com
Paper converting, mfr envelopes, printing, inventory management. (Woman/White, estab 1920, empl 225, sales $139,988,865, cert: WBENC)

7005   World Pac Paper, LLC
       1821 Summit Rd, Ste 317   Cincinnati, OH 45237
       (513) 779-9595 Edgar Smith CEO
       Fax: (513) 362-2736
       Email: elsmith@worldpacpaper.com
       Website: www.worldpacpaper.com
Dist printing & packaging papers. (AA, estab 2004, empl 22, sales $71,084,762, cert: NMSDC)

Pennsylvania

7006   Max International
       2360 Dairy Rd   Lancaster, PA 17603
       (800) 233-0222 Tiffanie Shaud Mktg Dir
       Fax: (717) 898-0970
       Email: tjs@maxintl.com
       Website: www.maxintl.com
Roll paper converting: standard & special sizes, slittering, 4-color printing. (Woman/White, estab 1992, empl 22, sales $7,500,000, cert: WBENC)

Texas

7007   Hogan Paper Co.
       6904 Hillcroft Dr   Austin, TX 78724
       (512) 926-6134 Alfred Hogan Owner
       Fax: (512) 926-0066
       Email: ahogan3@austin.rr.com
       Website:
Dist toilet tissue, paper towels, plastic trashliners, & copier paper. (AA, estab 1983, empl 3, sales $24,779,577, cert: State)

7008   J R Rodriguez International Corporation
       4541 Leston St   Dallas, TX 75247
       (214) 905-5086 Jim Lohr Natl Acct Mgr
       Fax: (214) 905-5095
       Email: jim@interconpaper.com
       Website: www.interconpaper.com
Printing paper, rolls & sheets: offset, gloss & matte/dull, board, Hi-Brite, groundwood coated, newsprint, digital sizes, cut size xerographic, slitting & rewinding. (Hisp, estab 1998, empl 61, sales $25,100,000, cert: NMSDC)

7009   Pearle, Inc.
       3660 Richmond Ave Ste 370 Houston, TX 77046
       (832) 304-9571 Erskine Black Jr. President
       Fax:
       Email: eblack@pearle-inc.com
       Website: www.pearle-inc.com
Dist disposable paper goods. (AA, estab 2013, empl 1, sales , cert: State, City, NMSDC)

PHOTOGRAPHY, MOTION & STILL
Commercial photographers. Includes aerial photography, topographic mapping, film processors, photo labs, corporate and professional photography. NAICS Code 54

California

7010   Number 3 Inc.
108 W 2nd St, Ste 706   Los Angeles, CA 90012
(323) 646-8764 Kal Yee
Fax: (586) 461-1175
Email: kal@kalyee.com
Website: www.kalyee.com
Photography & videography. (As-Pac, estab 2000, empl 2, sales $100,000, cert: CPUC)

Florida

7011   APImaging, Inc.
19 SW 6th St   Miami, FL 33130
(305) 373-4774 Diana Herrera VP Sales
Fax: (305) 358-8345
Email: dianah@apimaging.com
Website: www.apimaging.com
Photo imaging & photo finishing services, commercial printing, studio photography, self adhesive signs & graphics, directional signs, posters, point of purchase signs, graphic displays, graphic design, trade shows & exhibits. (Woman/Hisp, estab 2013, empl 22, sales , cert: WBENC)

7012   Kerrick Williams Photography LLC
811 Hickory Glen Dr   Seffner, FL 33584
(813) 571-3768 Kerrick Williams Owner
Fax: (866) 571-7149
Email: Kerrick@KerrickWilliams.com
Website: www.KerrickWilliams.com
Corporate Photography, Video Production: special event coverage, advertising, marketing archival. Onsite printing, Executive portraits, Head Shots, group functions. (AA, estab 1992, empl 1, sales $50,000, cert: State, City, NMSDC)

Illinois

7013   McLaren Photographic LLC
1482 Armstrong Court   Elk Grove Village, IL 60007
(847) 668-8615 Fiona McLaren Owner
Fax:
Email: fmclaren@mclarenphotographic.com
Website: www.mclarenphotographic.com
HD video, time-lapse, commercial photography, gigapanography & virtual mobile tours, commercial photographic services with portable studios & editing capabilities. (Woman/White, estab 2009, empl 1, sales $30,000, cert: WBENC)

7014   Powell Photography, Inc.
531 S Plymouth Court, Ste 101   Chicago, IL 60605
(312) 922-6366 Victor Powell President
Fax: (312) 622-6066
Email: vpowell@powellphotography.com
Website: www.powellphotography.com
Photography, photography services, digital imaging & retouching, photo composition, video, multi-media & graphics pre-production. (AA, estab 1976, empl 3, sales $440,000, cert: State, NMSDC)

Massachusetts

7015   Melvin's Photo
34 Frank st   Watertown, MA 02472
(617) 942-3432 Melvin Guante Owner
Fax:
Email: Melvin@melvinsphoto.com
Website: www.Melvinsphoto.com
Portrait photographic studios, still or video photography, business portrait, commercial, real estate & corporate event. (Hisp, estab 2001, empl 1, sales $87,000, cert: State)

Minnesota

7016   Code Creative Services
6001 Code Ave   Edina, MN 55436
(952) 922-8348 Erin Schwind Owner
Fax:
Email: erin@codecreativeservices.com
Website: www.codecreativeservices.com
Photography production, Estimating, Crew Sourcing, Location Scouting, Casting, Talent Negotiations, Budget Management, Catering, Travel Arrangements, Props, Permits & Insurance & Billing. (Woman, estab 2012, empl 1, sales $120,262, cert: WBENC)

Nevada

7017   Infinity Enterprises, Inc.
3347 S Highland Dr, Ste 304   Las Vegas, NV 89109
(702) 837-1128 Audrey Dempsey President
Fax: (702) 837-1132
Email: audrey@infinity-photo.com
Website: www.infinity-photo.com
Photography & graphic design: conventions & special events, food, corporate headshots, products & architecture, private sittings, weddings & retouching, web & print design, company branding, logo design & marketing, video editing. (Woman/White, estab 1993, empl 5, sales $532,467, cert: WBENC)

7018 Square Shooting
1800 Industrial Rd, Ste 103 Las Vegas, NV 89102
(702) 721-9893 Jennifer Burkart Managing Partner
Fax:
Email: jennifer@squareshooting.com
Website: www.squareshooting.com
Commercial photography, professional photographer,
executive portrait photography, architecture, interior
design, editorial, food & cocktail photography, advertising,
fashion, lifestyle, resort, product, photography studio.
Established in 2013, Square (Woman/White, estab 2013,
empl 2, sales $80,157, cert: WBENC)

New York

7019 5th Avenue Digital
231W 29th St, Ste 1006 New York, NY 10001
(212) 741-6427 Caitlin Elby Corporate Sales Assoc
Fax:
Email: caitlin@5thavenuedigital.com
Website: www.5thavenuedigital.com
Corporate photography: promotional & marketing events,
meetings & conventions, galas & award ceremonies,
headshots, group photos & product shots. (Woman/White,
estab 2008, empl 5, sales $2,560,552, cert: WBENC)

7020 Adrienne Nicole Productions, LLC
14 Dekalb Ave 3rd Fl Brooklyn, NY 11201
(646)5994911 Adrienne Nicole Exec Producer
Fax:
Email: info@producedbyanp.com
Website: www.producedbyanp.com
Videography, aerial video, drone video photography, drone
photography, progress photos, story development, pre-
production, post-production, motion graphics and animation, casting, photography, progress photos. (Woman/AA,
estab 2011, empl 1, sales $986,000, cert: State, City,
NMSDC)

7021 E. Lee White Photography, LLC
116 Duane St, 3rd F New York, NY 10007
(917) 584-8000 E. Lee White President
Fax: (480) 393-5704
Email: lee@leewhite.com
Website: www.leewhite.com
Advertising photography, executive portraits. (AA, estab
2004, empl 1, sales $40,000, cert: NMSDC)

Ohio

7022 The Couple Creative Imagery & Design, LLC
9912 Atena Rd Ste 2 Cleveland, OH 44105
(216) 271-0654 Theresa Highbaugh Co-Owner
Fax: (216) 271-0654
Email: thecouple@roadrunner.com
Website:
Photography & graphic design services. (AA, estab 2009,
empl 2, sales $26,601, cert: City)

Washington

7023 Mike Nakamura Photography LLC
7414 337th Place SE Fall CIty, WA 98024
(425) 260-4033 Mike Nakamura Owner
Fax:
Email: mike@mikenakamuraphotography.com
Website: www.mikenakamuraphotography.com/
Headshots, event & lifestyle photography, aerial &
commercial photography. (As-Pac, estab 2013, empl 1,
sales $110,000, cert: NMSDC)

PLASTIC PRODUCTS
Manufacturers and distributors of plexiglass, plastic, rubber and fiberglass products. Products range from supplies to aircraft and automobile parts, housewares and apparel accessories. NAICS Code 42

Arizona

7024　4front Tooling LLC dba 4front Manufacturing
3820 E Watkins St　Phoenix, AZ 85034
(480) 966-1088　Joseph Baiz Owner
Fax: (480) 966-1270
Email: joebaiz@4frontmfg.com
Website: www.4frontmfg.com
Plastic injection mold making, molding prototype & production, stampings, assembly & decorating. (Hisp, estab 2008, empl 20, sales $2,595,172, cert: NMSDC)

7025　All-Pac Distributng LLC
4859 E Gleneagle Dr　Chandler, AZ 85249
(480) 861-0842　Adam Snow Sales Mgr
Fax: (480) 792-1666
Email: asnow@allpaconline.com
Website: www.allpaconline.com
Mfr & dist returnable plastic packaging, injection molding, compression molding. (Woman/White, estab 2001, empl 3, sales $1,150,000, cert: NWBOC)

California

7026　Benchmark Displays LLC
44-311 Monterey Ave　Palm Desert, CA 92260
(760) 775-2424　Bonnie Miller VP of Sales
Fax:
Email: bonnie@benchmarkdisplays.com
Website: www.benchmarkdisplays.com
Mfr soft & hard vinyl store merchandising products, acrylic pos displays & fixtures, stock & custom molded & fabricated plastic literature holders. (Woman/White, estab 2009, empl 5, sales $161,553,552, cert: WBENC)

7027　Fairway Injection Molding Systems, Inc.
20109 Paseo Del Prado　Walnut, CA 91789
(909) 595-2201　David Cockrell VP - General Mgr
Fax:
Email: dcockrell@fairwaymolds.com
Website: www.fairwaymolds.com
Plastic injection molding. (As-Pac, estab 2006, empl 72, sales , cert: NMSDC)

7028　L.W. Reinhold Plastics
8763 Crocker St　Los Angeles, CA 90003
(562) 862-2714　Everett Woolum engineering Mgr
Fax: (562) 862-1683
Email: brenda@rpiplastics.com
Website: www.rpiplastics.com
Injection molded thermosets & thermoplastics, compression molded thermosets & transfer molded thermoset, prototyping, machining. (Woman/Hisp, estab 1943, empl 26, sales $1,800,000, cert: NMSDC)

7029　Myers Stevens Group, Inc.
7137 Telegraph Rd　Montebello, CA 90640
(323) 721-8552　Victor Parker President
Fax: (323) 721-8554
Email: vparker@myersstevensgroup.com
Website: www.myersstevensgroup.com
Mfr, dist & repackage disposable plastic products & devices: test tubes, pipets, containers & support racks. (AA, estab 2001, empl 11, sales $902,500, cert: NMSDC)

7030　Plastek Cards, Inc.
24412 S Main St Ste 104　Carson, CA 90745
(888) 762-2737　Mark Robinson Director of Mktg
Fax:
Email: mark.robinson@plastekcards.com
Website: www.plastekcards.com
Blank, white PVC plastic cards with & without a magnetic strip, high coercivity Hi-Co or low coercivity Lo-Co. (As-Pac, estab 2004, empl 51, sales , cert: NMSDC)

7031　Plastikon Industries, Inc.
688 Sandoval Way　Hayward, CA 94544
(989) 525-3310　Ron Yerrick Sales Specialist
Fax: (510) 400-1133
Email: ryerrick@plastikon.com
Website: www.plastikon.com
Custom injection molding of thermal plastic products & packaging. (Nat Ame, estab 1984, empl 100, sales $38,000,000, cert: NMSDC)

7032　Weldon Works, Inc.
1650 Mabury Rd　San Jose, CA 95133
(408) 251-1161　Jennifer Easom CEO
Fax: (408) 251-1162
Email: jenn@weldonworks.com
Website: www.weldonworks.com
Plastic Fabrication & Signage, Interior & Exterior Signs, ADA Signage, Lobby Signs, Window Graphics & Lettering, Menu Boards, Isle Signage, Banner, Stencils, Reflective Road Work/ Parking Signs, Full Color Digital Printing. (Woman/White, estab 1982, empl 3, sales $100,000, cert: State)

7033　Wright Engineered Plastics, Inc.
3663 N Laughlin Road Ste 201　Santa Rosa, CA 95403
(707) 575-1218　Mike Nellis VP mfg
Fax: (707) 575-3128
Email: mnellis@wepmolding.com
Website: www.wepmolding.com
Plastic injection molding & contract manufacturing. (Woman, estab 1970, empl 48, sales $5,040,000, cert: CPUC)

Florida

7034 American Tool and Mold LLC
1700 Sunshine Dr   Clearwater, FL 33765
(727) 447-7377 Phil Gaitan Dir of Sales
Fax: (727) 447-0125
Email: pgaitan@a-t-m.com
Website: www.atmmolding.com
Design & construct complex, precision, multi-cavity plastic injection molding, thin-wall, stack, hot runner, unscrewing & two-shot molds built with the latest methods & technologies available. (Woman, estab 1992, empl 220, sales , cert: WBENC, NWBOC)

7035 JTF Ventures, LLC
7545 W 2 Ct   Hialeah, FL 33014
(305) 556-5156 Tania Garza President
Fax: (305) 556-6973
Email: tania.garza@advak.com
Website: www.advak.com
Full service thermoform manufacturing company specializing in heavy guage polymer manipulation. (Woman/Hisp, estab 2006, empl 11, sales $1,200,000, cert: State)

7036 Plastec USA Inc.
7752 NW 74th Ave   Miami, FL 33166
(513) 708-9091 Julio Mejia Dir Reg sales
Fax: (513) 231-1920
Email: julio.mejia@mejiatechnologies.com
Website: www.plastecusa.com
Dist plastics processing machinery, ancillary equipment, spare parts & MRO services, chemicals & plastic goods. (Hisp, estab 1985, empl 23, sales $20,000,000, cert: NMSDC)

7037 Precision Tool and Mold, Inc.
12050 44th St N   Clearwater, FL 33762
(727) 573-4441 Sherry Mowery President
Fax: (727) 573-0777
Email: sherry@precisiontoolmoldinc.com
Website: www.precisiontoolmoldinc.com
Design build & run plastic injection molded parts. Small to medium sized molds. Assembly work, pad printing, over molding & insert molding. (Woman/White, estab 1981, empl 30, sales $2,665,365, cert: State, WBENC)

Georgia

7038 Citation Plastics, LLC
5828 Riverstone Circle   Atlanta, GA 30339
(248) 798-7705 Gregory Collingwood President
Fax: (678) 402-8975
Email: gregcollingwood@citationplastics.com
Website: www.citationplastics.com
Dist Plastic Resins: High Density Polyethylene (HDPE)- Polypropylene (PP)- Talc & Glassed Filled Polypropylene- Glass Filled Nylon 6 & 66 (AA, estab 1998, empl 7, sales $189,000, cert: NMSDC)

7039 Dixien LLC
5286 Circle Dr   Lake City, GA 30260
(404) 366-7427 Alex Garcia VP Mktg
Fax: (404) 366-2403
Email: agarcia@dixien.com
Website: www.dixien.com
Stamping 100 ton to 1000 ton, welded sub-assemblies, tooling, plastic injection molding, blow molding & vaccum forming. (Hisp, estab 1961, empl 400, sales $25,000,000, cert: NMSDC)

7040 Joyce Fabrication LLC dba Custom Plastics & More
2625 Jason Industrial Pkwy #700 Winston, GA 30187
(770) 577-0661 Gail Moore President
Fax: (770) 577-0668
Email: gailmoore@customplasticsandmore.com
Website: www.customplasticsandmore.com
Rigid plastic fabrication, hand cut sheet plastic; die stamped parts, CNC or hand routed plastic. (Woman/White, estab 2004, empl 4, sales $318,365, cert: WBENC)

7041 Marglen Industries
1748 Ward Mountain Rd   Rome, GA 30161
(706) 295-5621 Ben McElrath President
Fax:
Email: bmcelrath@marglen.us
Website: www.marglen.us
Recycle PET plastic containers, convert recycled PET water & soda bottles into cleaned washed flake, then convert the clean washed flake into a FDA approved, high IV, melt filtered pellet that can be used to make new bottles. (Woman/White, estab 1971, empl 150, sales $62,513,555, cert: WBENC)

7042 Standridge Color Corp.
1196 E Hightower Trail   Social Circle, GA 30025
(770) 464-3362 Sherry Waters President
Fax:
Email: swaters@standridgecolor.com
Website: www.standridgecolor.com
Mfr pellitized plastic pellets and color concentrates for the plastics industry. (Woman/White, estab , empl 1, sales , cert: WBENC)

7043 United Seal & Rubber Co. Inc.
7025 C Amwiler Industrial Dr   Atlanta, GA 30360
(770) 729-8880 Kathy Alonso VP/General Mgr
Fax: (770) 729-8992
Email: kalonso@unitedseal.com
Website: www.unitedseal.com
Mfr seals, gaskets, custom molded rubber parts, EMI Shielding products, lathe cut seals, extrusions, rubber to metal bonded parts, spliced & vulcanized parts. (Hisp, estab 1974, empl 28, sales $8,000,000, cert: NMSDC, SDB)

Iowa

7044 Engineered Plastic Components Inc.
1408 Zimmerman Dr S   Grinnell, IA 50112
(641) 236-3100 Jeremy Barger Sales
Fax: (641) 236-3555
Email: jbarger@epcmfg.com
Website: www.epcmfg.com
Mfr wire harness cover caps, injection molding. (As-Ind, estab 1998, empl 500, sales $200,000,000, cert: NMSDC)

Illinois

7045 All Foam Products Co.
2546 Live Oak Ln   Buffalo Grove, IL 60089
(847) 913-9341 Marvin Steinlauf VP sales
Fax: (847) 913-0731
Email: sales@allfoam.com
Website: www.allfoam.com
Mfr poly foams, polyester, polyethylene, tool drawer foam liners, cross linked polyethylene, EPS, foam balls, laminating, die cutting, flocking. (Woman/White, estab 1977, empl 24, sales $3,945,000, cert: NWBOC)

7046 Amtec Molded Products, Inc.
1355 HolmesRdUnit A Elgin, IL 60123
(815) 226-0187 Adithya Jayakar Sales Mgr
Fax: (815) 226-0276
Email: adithyaj@amtecmolded.com
Website: www.amtecmolded.com
Plastic injection molding, insert molding, pad printing & sub-assemblies. (As-Ind, estab 1998, empl 35, sales $3,862,500, cert: NMSDC)

7047 Best Foam Fabricators, Inc.
9633 S Cottage Grove   Chicago, IL 60628
(773) 721-1006 Aqui Hasty Mktg
Fax: (773) 721-5257
Email: aqui@bff.com
Website: www.bff.com
Mfr thermoforming, high speed die cutting, heat sealing, CNC machining & injection molding. (Woman/AA, estab 1981, empl 60, sales $14,750,000, cert: NMSDC)

7048 Cope Plastics Inc.
P.O. Box 368   Godfrey, IL 62002
(618) 467-7357 Susanne Simon COO
Fax: (618) 466-0221
Email: susannes@uniteddisplaycraft.com
Website: www.copeplastics.com
Plastic stock shapes (rod, sheet & tube) distribution & fabrication. (Woman/White, estab 1946, empl 350, sales $86,000,000, cert: NWBOC)

7049 E James & Co.
6000 S Oak Park Ave   Chicago, IL 60638
(773) 788-1881 Mike Romano
Fax: (773) 788-9134
Email: mike.romano@ejames.com
Website: www.ejames.com
Mfr & dist rubber & plastic products: V belts, rubber hose, plastic hose & hose assemblies. (Hisp, estab 1955, empl 14, sales $2,200,000, cert: NMSDC)

1330 Holmes Rd   Elgin, IL 60123
(847) 531-9500 Bill Bernardo Sales
Fax: (847) 531-9530
Email: bbernardo@ebco-inc.com
Website: www.ebco-inc.com
Rubber products: molded, extruded, rubber bonded, metal vibration isolators & plastic extrusions. (Hisp, estab 1951, empl 30, sales $15,700,000, cert: NMSDC)

7051 Elas Tek Molding Inc.
7517 Meyer Rd   Spring Grove, IL 60081
(815) 675-9012 Richard Davis Sales
Fax: (815) 675-9263
Email: rdavis@rtdelastek.com
Website: www.rtdelastek.com
Liquid silcone rubber & thermoplastic elastomer components. (Woman/Nat Ame, estab 1985, empl 20, sales $100,000,000, cert: NMSDC)

7052 First American Plastics Molding Enterprise
810 Progressive Ln   South Beloit, IL 61080
(815) 624-8538 Steven McGaw sales engineer
Fax: (815) 624-8572
Email: info@firstamericanplastic.com
Website: www.firstamericanplastic.com
Custom plastic injection molding. (Nat Ame, estab 1993, empl 130, sales $12,000,000, cert: NMSDC)

7053 HST Materials, Inc.
1631 Brummel Avenue   Elk Grove Village, IL 60007
(847) 640-1803 Kathryn Miller President
Fax: (847) 640-1830
Email: kmiller@hstmaterials.com
Website: www.hstmaterials.com
Custom die-cutting & fabrication of non-metallics, including sponge & dense rubber, plastic, films & tapes used as gaskets & sealing devices. (Woman/White, estab 1987, empl 20, sales $4,428,617, cert: WBENC)

7054 LSL Industries, Inc.
5535 N Wolcott Ave   Chicago, IL 60640
(773) 878-1100 Kat Logan Director of Natl Accts
Fax: (773) 878-9100
Email: kat.logan@lslhealthcare.com
Website: www.lslhealthcare.com
Mfg plastics & procedural kit assembly & packaging. (As-Ind, estab 1983, empl 130, sales , cert: NMSDC)

7055 Magenta LLC
15160 New Avenue   Lockport, IL 60441
(773) 777-5050 Jennifer Smith Mktg Director
Fax: (773) 777-4055
Email: jsmith@magentallc.com
Website: www.magentallc.com
Design, development & mfr injection molded components-primarily packaging— closures and containers. (Woman/White, estab 1969, empl 81, sales $16,880,000, cert: WBENC)

7056 Midwest Insert Composite Molding & Assembly Corp.
3940 Industrial Ave   Rolling Meadows, IL 60008
(847) 818-8444 Chirag Patel President
Fax:
Email: chirag.pate@micmolding.com
Website: www.micmolding.com
Mfr plastic injection molded products. (As-Ind, estab 2015, empl 23, sales $2,526,000, cert: NMSDC)

7057 Shamrock Plastics, Inc.
P.O. Box 3530   Peoria, IL 61612
(309) 243-7723 Rhonda Jones Cstmr liaison
Fax: (309) 243-5852
Email: rhonda@shamrockplastics.net
Website: www.shamrockplastics.net
Mfr custom, vacuum & pressure formed plastic parts. (Woman/White, estab 1968, empl 25, sales $4,000,000, cert: State)

7058 Thermal-Tech Systems, Inc.
750 W Hawthorne Lane   West Chicago, IL 60185
(630) 639-5115 Joe Majchrowski Sales
Fax: (630) 639-5119
Email: jm@thermal-tech.com
Website: www.thermal-tech.com
Dist plastic injection molders, service and repair of manifolds. (Woman/White, estab 1986, empl 10, sales $2,500,000, cert: WBENC)

7059 TransWorld Plastic Films, Inc.
150 N 15th St   Rochelle, IL 61068
(815) 561-7117 Rodolfo Hernandez Business Dev
Fax: (815) 561-7120
Email: rhernandez@transworldplasticfilms.com
Website: www.transworldplasticfilms.com
Polyethylene film for the automotive, tire & rubber industries used in the manufacturing & packaging process. (Woman/Hisp, estab 2007, empl 31, sales , cert: NMSDC)

7060 Young Technology Inc.
900 W. Fullerton Ave.   Addison, IL 60101
(630) 690-4320 Young Sohn President
Fax: (630) 543-5883
Email: youngsohn@ytinc.com
Website: www.ytinc.com
Mfr molded rubber, plastic & forged steel: shifter knobs, bezels, decorative molding & cable components, leather wrapped & chrome plated. (As-Pac, estab 1985, empl 350, sales $6,000,000, cert: NMSDC)

Indiana

7061 A. H. Furnico, Inc.
6425 English Ave. Unit 1A Indianapolis, IN 46278
(317) 802-9363 Benjamin Liu President
Fax: (317) 802-9382
Email: ben.liu@ahfurnico.com
Website: www.ahfurnico.com
Polystyrene extruded mouldings with PVC veneers. (As-Pac, estab 1999, empl 5, sales $3,880,000, cert: NMSDC)

7062 Accutech Mold & Machine, Inc.
2817 Goshen Rd   Fort Wayne, IN 46808
(260) 471-6102 Darrin Geiger VP
Fax: (260) 471-8584
Email: dgeiger@accutechmoldinc.com
Website: www.accutechmoldinc.com
Plastic injection molding, Insert plastic injection molder of cables/connectors, rapid prototype tooling builder/ injection molding, production machining of brass, aluminum & metals, prototype machining of brass, aluminum & metals. (Woman/White, estab 1996, empl 70, sales $3,000,000, cert: WBENC)

7063 Calico Precision Molding, LLC
1211 Progress Rd   Fort Wayne, IN 46808
(260) 484-4500 Nancy Rivera Sales Rep
Fax: (260) 484-4405
Email: nancyr@calicopm.com
Website: www.calicopm.com/
Custom plastic injection molding. (AA, estab 2001, empl 28, sales , cert: NMSDC)

7064 Hi-Tech Foam Products, LLC
One Technology Way   Indianapolis, IN 46268
(317) 615-1515 John Metaxas VP
Fax: (317) 618-1520
Email: jmetaxas@hitechfoam.com
Website: www.hitechfoam.com
Convert, design, package, mold, form, cut & route foam rubber. Laminating foam to foam, foam to corrugated, foam to plastic. Protective, cushioning, acoustical, thermal, polyethylene, polyurethane, crosslink, EVA, EDPM rubber. (AA, estab 11, empl 35, sales $6,000,000, cert: NMSDC)

7065 Lorentson Manufacturing Co., Inc.
P.O. Box 932   Kokomo, IN 46903
(765) 452-4425 John Routt VP / COO
Fax:
Email: jroutt@lorentson.com
Website: www.lorentson.com
Design & build plastic injection molds, injection molding machines. (Woman/White, estab 1949, empl 100, sales $16,000,000, cert: WBENC)

7066 Tomken Plastic Technologies, Inc.
4601 N Superior Dr.   Muncie, IN 47303
(765) 284-2472 Kevin Undem Sales/Engineering
Fax: (765) 284-1277
Email: kevinu@tomkenplastics.com
Website: www.tomkenplastics.com
Precision plastic injection molding, tooling, & injection molding. (Woman/White, estab 1960, empl 40, sales $6,000,000, cert: WBENC)

7067 Vidal Plastics, LLC
318 Main St Ste 207 Evansville, IN 47708
(812) 431-8075 Alfonso Vidal President
Fax:
Email: alfonso@vidalplastics.com
Website: www.vidalplastics.com
Dist resins, from prime raw materials to recycled compounds. (Hisp, estab 2009, empl 2, sales , cert: NMSDC)

Louisiana

7068 Noble Plastics Inc.
318 Burleigh Lane Grand Coteau, LA 70541
(337) 662-5374 Sandy Rowell Inside sales
Fax: (337) 662-5339
Email: sandy@nobleplastics.com
Website: www.nobleplastics.com
SPE, MAPP, ASME, Product design, Contract manufacturing, Scientific molding, Inspection, Assembly & fulfillment, Automation systems. (Woman/White, estab 2000, empl 30, sales $4,900,000, cert: WBENC)

Massachusetts

7069 Polyneer, Inc.
259D Samuel Barnet Blvd   New Bedford, MA 02745
(508) 998-5225 Nancy DeOliveira Cstmr Service
Fax: (508) 998-5440
Email: Ndeoliveira@polyneer.com
Website: www.polyneer.com
Design & mfg polymeric products. (Hisp, estab 2001, empl 39, sales $2,600,000, cert: NMSDC)

7070 TPE Solutions, Inc.
3 Patterson Rd   Shirley, MA 01464
(978) 425-3033 Jonas Angus President
Fax: (978) 425-3037
Email: jonas.angus@tpesinc.com
Website: www.tpesinc.com
Design, mfr & dist Thermoplastic elastomers (TPEs). (AA, estab 2004, empl 5, sales $3,000,000, cert: NMSDC)

Michigan

7071 Accu-Mold, LLC
7622 S Sprinkle Rd   Portage, MI 49002
(269) 323-0388 Dave Felicijan President
Fax: (269) 323-9865
Email: davidf@accu-moldinc.com
Website: www.accum-moldinc.com
Overmold & two shot mold, hybrid metal/plastic parts, high & low pressure plastic injection molds, machined plastic or metal parts, SLA plastic parts, metal-to-plastic conversions. (Nat Ame, estab 1977, empl 15, sales $4,118,893, cert: NMSDC)

7072 Ammex Plastics
725 Ternes Dr   Monroe, MI 48162
(734) 241-9622 David Ayala President
Fax: (734) 241-9632
Email: dfaammex@provide.net
Website:
Mfr & design plastic injection molded parts. (Hisp, estab 1999, empl 17, sales $3,300,000, cert: NMSDC)

7073 Argent International
41016 Concept Dr   Plymouth, MI 48170
(734) 582-9800 Tomas Flores Sales Mgr
Fax: (734) 582-9999
Email: tflores@argent-international.com
Website: www.argent-international.com
Die cut foam, felt, fabric adhesive. (Woman/White, estab 1976, empl 120, sales , cert: WBENC)

7074 Atlantic Precision Products
51234 Filomena Dr   Shelby Twp, MI 48315
(586) 532-9420 Rob Pryomski GM
Fax: (586) 532-9424
Email: rpryomski@atlanticpp.com
Website:
Custom injection molding, functional/decorative plastics, insert molding, welding, sonic, vibration, heatstaking, assembly. Fully certified CMM Lab with color approval capabilities. (Woman/Hisp, estab 2004, empl 26, sales $5,200,000, cert: NMSDC)

7075 Colonial Plastics, Inc
51734 Filomena Dr   Shelby Township, MI 48315
(586) 991-5150 Michele Simo
Fax: (586) 991-5075
Email: mms@colgrp.com
Website: www.colgrp.com
Injection, compression, blow, vacuum, prototype, hybrid, bridge & production molds, machining, assemblies, tryouts, product developement, product design & sorting. (Woman/White, estab 1988, empl 110, sales $8,200,000, cert: WBENC)

7076 Concordant Healthcare Solutions, Inc.
200 E. Big Beaver   Troy, MI 48083
(248) 321-3899 James P Young CEO
Fax: (248) 267-9641
Email: jyoung@concordanthealth.com
Website: www.concordanthealth.com
NCQA Certified in Patient Centered Medical Home Recognition for PCPs and Specialists. Staff training in cultural competency and communication skills. Improve hospital HCAHPS total performance scores. (AA, estab 2009, empl 8, sales $26,500, cert: NMSDC)

7077 Diversified Engineering & Plastics
1801 Wildwood Ave   Jackson, MI 49202
(517) 789-8118 Anita Quillen President
Fax:
Email: aquillen@deplastics.com
Website: www.wwww.deplastics.com
Plastic Injection Molding, Design/Engineering Services, Plastic Part Assembly. (Woman/Hisp, estab 2010, empl 130, sales $14,497,480, cert: NMSDC)

7078 DN Plastics
1415 Steele Ave SW   Grand Rapids, MI 49507
(616) 942-6060 Raj Agrawal President
Fax: (616) 642-6010
Email: raj@dnplasticscorp.com
Website: www.dnplasticscorp.com
Polymer compounding for custom & toll manufacturing, Thermoplastic Elastomers (TPE), Thermoplastic Olefins (TPO) & filled Polypropylene compounds. (As-Ind, estab , empl 1, sales , cert: NMSDC)

7079 Eagle Fasteners
185 Park Dr   Troy, MI 48083
(248) 373-1441 Theresa C. Srock President
Fax: (248) 373-1212
Email: TSrock@eaglefasteners.com
Website: www.eaglefasteners.com
Custom injection molded plastic parts, design & fabricate tooling. (Woman/White, estab 1976, empl 9, sales , cert: WBENC)

7080 Elite Mold & Engineering
51548 Filomena Dr   Shelby Township, MI 48315
(586) 314-4000 Daniel Mandeville Sales Engineer
Fax: (586) 314-3000
Email: DJ@teameliteonline.com
Website: www.teameliteonline.com
Dist close tolerance plastic parts for the automotive, consumer product, electronic & medical device industries. (Nat Ame, estab 1982, empl 34, sales $3,576,887, cert: NMSDC)

7081 Engineered Plastic Products
699 James L. Hart Pkwy   Ypsilanti, MI 48197
(734) 483-2500 Aschandria Fisher Business Mgr
Fax: (734) 483-2325
Email: afisher@eppmfg.com
Website: www.eppmfg.com
Injection molded plastic assembly & sequencing. (AA, estab 1987, empl 500, sales $50,000,000, cert: NMSDC)

7082 Gemini Plastics, Inc.
4385 Garfield St   Ubly, MI 48475
(248) 435-7271 Melanie Cappello Mgr, New Business Devel
Fax:
Email: Melaniecappello@geminigroup.net
Website: www.geminigroup.net
Mfr engineered plastic extrusion products: transportation, medical, lawn & garden, consumer, & appliance. (Woman/White, estab 1972, empl 110, sales $60,000,000, cert: WBENC)

7083 Intex Technologies LLC
3133 Highland Blvd   Hudsonville, MI 49426
(616) 662-0276 Kevin Ryan Sales Dir
Fax: (616) 662-0276
Email: kevin.ryan@intextech.net
Website: www.intextech.net
Mfr integral skin flexible foam automotive interior parts: arm rests, center console, console door, sun visor, steering wheel, soft-touch points on door handles, cup holders, seals, jounce bumpers & insulation components. (Hisp, estab 2008, empl 36, sales $14,800,000, cert: NMSDC)

7084 Jenerxx Inc.
307 West Sixth St Ste 209   Royal Oak, MI 48067
(810) 225-1600 Paul Chaplin Acct Mgr
Fax:
Email: paul@jenerxx.com
Website: www.jenerxx.com
Dist injection grade resins ranging from engineered plastics to commodities. (Woman, estab 2000, empl 5, sales $760,000, cert: WBENC)

7085 JLC Group LLC
287 Executive Dr   Troy, MI 48083
(248) 792-3281 William Chen Director, Ph.D.
Fax: (248) 479-1888
Email: wchen@jlcgroupllc.com
Website: www.jlcgroupllc.com
Dist casting parts, forging parts & machine finished parts, plastic injected molds & plastic parts. (Woman/As-Pac, estab 2010, empl 5, sales , cert: WBENC)

7086 Latin American Industries, LLC
1036 Ken-O-Sha Industrial Dr SE   Grand Rapids, MI 49508
(616) 301-1878 Scott Bigger GM
Fax: (616) 301-2566
Email: sbigger@laiinc.net
Website: www.laiinc.net
Plastic injection molding & assembly, molding machines. (Woman/Hisp, estab 2000, empl 10, sales $1,000,000, cert: NMSDC)

7087 Polymerica Limited Co. LLC
26909 Woodard Ave   Huntington Woods, MI 48070
(248) 542-2000 Marilyn M. Kunz President
Fax:
Email: mkunz@globalent.org
Website:
Mfr plastics, automotive extruded plastic parts, co-extrusions, flocking, steel inserts, extruded sheet plastic. (Woman/White, estab , empl 1, sales , cert: WBENC)

7088 Premier Plastic Resins, Inc.
3079 S Baldwin Rd   Orion, MI 48359
(248)84515 Michelle Cloutier Sales Engineer
Fax:
Email: mcloutier@premierplasticresins.com
Website: www.premierplasticresins.com
Dist thermoplastic resins for injection molding. ABS, Nylon, Polycarbonate, PBT, Acetal. Automotive approved grades. Prime branded materials available, such as DuPont, Sabic, Covestro, etc. (Woman, estab 2007, empl 5, sales $1,200,000, cert: WBENC)

7089 Primera Plastics
3424 Production Court   Zeeland, MI 49464
(616) 748-6248 Noel Cuellar President
Fax: (616) 748-1174
Email: noelc@primera-inc.com
Website: www.primera-inc.com
Plastic injection molding & assembly. (Hisp, estab 1994, empl 140, sales , cert: NMSDC)

7090 Quality Assured Plastics, Inc.
1200 Crandall Pkwy Lawrence, MI 49064
(269) 674-3888 Annette Crandall President
Fax:
Email: acrandall@qapinc.com
Website: www.qapinc.com
Custom injection molding, insert/overmolding, & assembly capabilities, molding commodity & engineering resins, Nylon, TPE, ABS, PEEK, Valox, Polystyrene, HDPE, TPO & Polypropylene. (Woman/White, estab 1986, empl 60, sales $5,200,000, cert: WBENC)

7091 Western Diversified Plastics LLC
53150 N. Main St.   Mattawan, MI 49071
(269) 668-3377 George Kawwas Dir Business Dev
Fax: (269) 668-5132
Email: george.kawwas@westerndp.com
Website: www.westerndp.com
Mfr close tolerance injection & insert molded electro-mechanical components, engineering grade plastic resin. (AA, estab 2005, empl 75, sales , cert: NMSDC)

7092   Williamston Products, Inc.
       845 Progress Ct   Williamston, MI 48895
       (517) 655-2131 Nigam Tripathi President
       Fax: (517) 655-2021
       Email: nigam@wpius.com
       Website: www.wpius.com
Blow mold, injection mold, foaming, hand wrapping,
cutting, trim, sewing, lamination, prototyping, assembly.
(As-Ind, estab 2006, empl 450, sales $42,000,000, cert:
NMSDC)

Minnesota

7093   Classic Acrylics Inc.
       11040 Industrial Circle NW   Elk River, MN 55330
       (763) 241-5242 Kathy Berg Sales Exec
       Fax: (763) 241-9155
       Email: Kberg@classicacrylics.com
       Website: www.classicacrylics.com
Plastic fabrication: POP & POS displays, acrylic cereal
boxes, literature & brochure holders, advertising &
specialty items, sign holders, screened acrylic signs, display
cases, food service bins, LED lighting. (Hisp, estab 1998,
empl 25, sales $4,000,000, cert: NMSDC)

7094   Steinwall
       1759 116th Ave   Coon Rapids, MN 55448
       (800) 229-9199 Jake Northrup sales engineer
       Fax:
       Email: jnorthrup@steinwall.com
       Website: www.steinwall.com
Custom thermoplastic injection molding, full service
plastics manufacturing, 30 ton to 1750 ton injection press
size capabilities, 2-shot molding, production automation,
engineering, tooling, injection molding, quality and
inspection. (Woman/White, estab 1965, empl 120, sales
$20,000,000, cert: State)

7095   Thermotech, Inc.
       1302 S 5th St Hopkins, MN 55343
       (734) 634-1816 Andrea Hinrichs
       Fax: (734) 451-1228
       Email: andrea.hinrichs@thermotech.com
       Website: www.thermotech.com
Mfr precision plastic parts, thermoplastic molding,
thermoset molding, insert molding, two-shot molding,
micromolding & assembly. (As-Ind, estab 1949, empl 522,
sales $83,000,000, cert: NMSDC)

7096   TMI Coatings, Inc.
       3291 Terminal Dr St. Paul, MN 55121
       (651) 452-6100 Tracy Gliori President
       Fax: (651) 452-0598
       Email: tmi@tmicoatings.com
       Website: www.tmicoatings.com
Protective coatings & linings, spray on urethane foam
insulation, chemical resistant floor coverings & containment dike linings. (Woman/White, estab 1985, empl 75,
sales $12,162,000, cert: WBENC)

North Carolina

7097   Central Carolina Products
       250 W Old Glencoe Rd   Burlington, NC 27217
       (336) 226-0005 Jason Greenhill President
       Fax: (336) 226-0403
       Email: jgreenhill@isotechintl.com
       Website: www.centralcarolinaproducts.com
Plastic injection molding: assembly & finishing capabilities. (Hisp, estab 1993, empl 72, sales , cert: NMSDC)

7098   Core Technology Molding Corp
       4300 Piedmont Pkwy   Greensboro, NC 27410
       (336) 708-2673 Geoff Foster CEO
       Fax: (336) 632-0192
       Email: geoff.foster@coretechnologycorp.com
       Website: www.coretechnologycorp.com
Plastic injection molded parts. (AA, estab 2006, empl 14,
sales $4,000,000, cert: NMSDC)

7099   Raleigh-Durham Rubber & Gasket Co., Inc.
       P.O. Box 90397   Raleigh, NC 27675
       (919) 781-6817 Judy Hooks President
       Fax: (919) 781-3243
       Email: judyh@raleighdurhamrubber.com
       Website: www.raleighdurhamrubber.com
Mfr & dist rubber gaskets. (Woman, estab , empl 1, sales
, cert: WBENC)

7100   RubberMill, Inc.
       9897 Old Liberty Rd   Liberty, NC 27298
       (704) 458-2653 Shawn Baldwin Sales Mgr
       Fax: (336) 622-1685
       Email: sbaldwin@rubbermill.com
       Website: www.rubbermill.com
OEM custom parts: solid and sponge rubber, foams &
nonwovens. Gaskets and Seals, Custom Molded Parts,
Acoustical Insulation Parts, Urethane Products, Balls, Lab
Stoppers, Cleanout Balls. (Woman/White, estab 1987,
empl 56, sales $11,000,000, cert: WBENC)

Nebraska

7101   Lenco, Inc. - PMC
       10240 Deer Park Rd   Waverly, NE 68462
       (402) 786-2000 Clarke McGuire VP
       Fax: (402) 786-5050
       Email: cmcguire@pmc-group.com
       Website: www.lencopmc.com
Dist defect-free molded & assembled products, injection
molding. (As-Ind, estab 1963, empl 160, sales , cert:
State, NMSDC)

New Jersey

7102 L-E-M Plastics& Supply Inc.
255 Highland Cross Rutherford, NJ 07070
(201) 933-9150 Ellen Pietrowitz-Phillips President
Fax: (201) 933-9154
Email: ellenp@l-e-mplastics.com
Website: www.l-e-mplastics.com
Fabriate & dist raw material plastic & rubber, Sheet, rod, tubing & film cut to size. Machining of all plastic, build to print. Steel rule die punching of thin plastic & rubber. (Woman/White, estab 1974, empl 12, sales $1,200,000, cert: WBENC)

7103 Sigma Extruding Corp. DBA Sigma Stretch Film
808 Page Avenue, Bldg 8 Lyndhurst, NJ 07071
(201) 507-9100 Maria Samuelson
Fax: (201) 507-0447
Email: maria.samuelson@sigmaplastics.com
Website: www.sigmastretchfilm.com
Mfr plastics. (As-Pac, estab 1988, empl 354, sales $396,000,000, cert: NMSDC)

New York

7104 Extreme Molding LLC
25 Gibson St Watervliet, NY 12189
(518) 266-6261 Joanne Moon Managing Partner
Fax: (518) 266-6263
Email: joanne@extrememolding.com
Website: www.extrememolding.com
Injection molding: silicone, TPE, floropolymers, teflon, polycarbonate, polypropelene, Ultem, CAD design, material selection assistance, rapid prototyping, overmolding, compression molding, packaging. (Woman, estab 2002, empl 20, sales $1,000,000, cert: State)

7105 Mechanical Rubber Products Company, Inc.
77 Forester Ave, Ste 1 Warwick, NY 10990
(845) 986-2271 Cedric Glasper President
Fax: (845) 986-0399
Email: alisa.sherow@mechanicalrubber.com
Website: www.mechanicalrubber.com
Mfr elastomeric (rubber) products. (AA, estab 1995, empl 21, sales $945,000, cert: NMSDC)

Ohio

7106 Advanced Engineering Solutions Incorporated
250 Advanced Dr Springboro, OH 45066
(937) 743-6900 Scott Paulson Business Dev
Fax: (909) 752-7716
Email: spaulson@aesi-usa.com
Website: www.advancedinternational.com
Tooling, CNC, punch press, subassembly, automated equipment, injection molded plastics. (Woman/As-Pac, estab 1995, empl 35, sales $2,250,000, cert: NMSDC)

7107 Axium Plastics LLC
9005 Smiths Mill Rd N Johnstown, OH 43031
(678) 464-2259 Tammy Hoffman Bus Devel Mgr
Fax:
Email: thoffman@axiumplastics.com
Website: www.axiumplastics.com
Extrusion Blow Molding, Injection Stretch Blow Molding, Injection Molding, Modeling, Design, Silk Screening, Pressure Sensitive Labeling (As-Ind, estab 2010, empl 250, sales $102,000,000, cert: NMSDC)

7108 Composite Technologies LLC
401 N Keowee St Dayton, OH 45404
(937) 228-2880 Karen Pierce Sales & Mktg Mgr
Fax: (937) 228-9184
Email: kpierce@ctcplastics.com
Website: www.ctcplastics.com
Mfr plastic pallets made from 100% recycled plastic, compression & injection molding, of plastic parts made from recycled & virgin materials. (As-Pac, estab 1994, empl 150, sales $21,980,540, cert: NMSDC)

7109 Cox Financial Corporation
105 E Fourth St Cincinnati, OH 45202
(513) 621-1771 Ethan Cox CEO
Fax: (800) 493-3977
Email: ethancox@coxfinco.com
Website: www.coxfinco.com
Long Term & Short Term Disability Plans - Cox Financial provides plans that are customized to fit your organizations needs offered at premium discounts. (AA, estab 1972, empl 12, sales $1,436,689, cert: NMSDC)

7110 EnKon, LLC dba Broadway
6344 Webster St Dayton, OH 45414
(937) 890-2221 Jodi Walters Member
Fax: (937) 890-5678
Email: jodi.walters@enkonllc.com
Website: www.broadwaymold.com
Injection molds, components, mold repairs, Precision Fabrication,
CNC Machining, welding, turning, Electrode manufacturing, EDM'ING, Wire EDM, Polish, Milling, OD, ID, and surface grinding, Design. (Woman, estab 1955, empl 12, sales , cert: WBENC)

7111 Ernie Green Industries
2030 Dividend Dr Columbus, OH 43228
(614) 949-1714 Bill Dunlevy VP Sales & Mktg
Fax:
Email: bdunlevy@egindustries.com
Website: www.egi.net/
Plastic injection molding, paint, pad print, silk screen, hot stamp, graphic emblems, sonic welding, chrome plating, assembly, bar code labeling, shrink wrap & kit/unitized packaging. (AA, estab 1987, empl 450, sales $28,000,000, cert: NMSDC)

7112   HESS Advanced Technology, Inc.
P.O. Box 17669   Dayton, OH 45417
(937) 268-4377   Frederick Edmonds CEO
Fax: (937) 263-5258
Email: fred.edmonds@gmail.com
Website: www.plastikleen.net
Mfr protective coatings: surveillance cameras, lens/domes, PC's, laptops, PDA's, plasma screens & anti-microbial skin protector. (AA, estab 1997, empl 8, sales $3,508,718, cert: NMSDC)

7113   Industry Products Company
500 Statler Rd   Piqua, OH 45356
(937) 778-0585   Aaron Blakely Sales Specialist
Fax: (937) 660-9411
Email: ablakely@industryproductsco.com
Website: www.industryproductsco.com
Mfr precision die-cut & formed products, gasket & sealing products, rubber-coated steel & alloys, compressed fiber, cork, neoprene, phenolic, nylon, Mylar, felts, PE, PP, rubber, etc. (Woman/White, estab 1966, empl 450, sales $80,000,000, cert: WBENC)

7114   Jensar Manufacturing LLC
1230 Expressway South Dr   Toledo, OH 43608
(419) 727-8320   Luis Villaflor President
Fax: (419) 727-9320
Email: jensar@sbcglobal.net
Website:
Mfr plastic injection molded products. (As-Pac, estab 1996, empl 4, sales $1,228,000, cert: NMSDC)

7115   MVP Plastics, Inc.
15005 Enterprise Way   Middlefield, OH 44062
(440) 834-1790   Darrell McNair President
Fax: (440) 834-0718
Email: darrellm@mvpplastics.com
Website: www.mvpplastics.com
Custom injection molding, decorating & assembly of plastics components. (AA, estab 2009, empl 30, sales $20,000,000, cert: NMSDC)

7116   PMC SMART Solutions LLC
9825 Kenwood Rd Ste 302   Cincinnati, OH 45242
(513) 557-5222   Lisa Jennings CEO
Fax:
Email: ljennings@pmcsmartsolutions.com
Website: www.pmcsmartsolutions.com
Development engineering, contract manufacturing & injection molding services for medical device, transportation & commercial electronics markets. (Woman/White, estab 1929, empl 200, sales $33,000,000, cert: WBENC)

7117   Polymer Technologies
1835 James Pkwy   Heath, OH 43056
(740) 929-5500   Sharad Thakkar President
Fax: (740) 929-5500
Email: sharad@polymertechnologiesinc.com
Website: www.polymertechnologiesinc.com
Provide reprocessed & wide spec resins, form, film. powder, parts & return back in certified pellet form. (As-Ind, estab 2002, empl 38, sales $7,000,000, cert: NMSDC)

7118   Shirley K's Storage Trays LLC
P.O. Box 2519   Zanesville, OH 43702
(740) 868-8140   Devin Hall Sales & Mktg Coord
Fax: (740) 868-8142
Email: devin.hall@shirleyks.com
Website: www.shirleyks.com
Mfr storage products, high-impact polystyrene or high-density polyethylene; labeling tags, casters, locking lids & imprinting. (Woman/White, estab 2013, empl 8, sales $1,410,400, cert: WBENC)

7119   Tessec LLC
5679 Webster St   Dayton, OH 45414
(938) 985-3552   Siamak Hashimi President
Fax:
Email:
Website: www.tessec.com
Plastic injection molding precision machining. (AA, estab 2007, empl 17, sales $3,450,000, cert: NMSDC, 8(a))

7120   Tom Smith Industries, Inc.
500 Smith Dr   Clayton, OH 45315
(937) 832-1555   James Pugh Sales Mgr
Fax: (937) 832-1577
Email: jpugh@tomsmithindustries.com
Website: www.tomsmithindustries.com
Design & build plastic injection molds. Custom injection molding of thermoplastics; assemble computer components. (Woman/Nat Ame, estab 1980, empl 125, sales $22,200,000, cert: WBENC)

7121   Triple Diamond Plastics, Inc.
405 N Pleasantview Dr   Liberty Center, OH 43532
(941) 484-7750   Josh Purdy VP
Fax: (941) 484-2749
Email: josh.purdy@tdplastics.com
Website: www.tdplastics.com
Mfr structural foam, multiple plastic pallets & collapsible bins, large plastic contract products. (Woman/White, estab 2005, empl 35, sales $3,500,000, cert: WBENC)

Oklahoma

7122   DA/PRO Rubber Inc.
601 N Poplar Ave   Broken Arrow, OK 74012
(918) 258-9386   Gretchen Brauninger CEO
Fax: (918) 258-3286
Email: gbrauninger@daprorubber.com
Website: www.daprorubber.com
High quality rubber, TPE & plastic custom components, diaphragms, seals, connectors, custom molded shapes, rubber-to-metal parts & molded to precision tolerances. (Woman/White, estab 1961, empl 320, sales , cert: WBENC)

Oregon

7123 Griffith Rubber Mills
2625 NW Industrial   Portland, OR 97296
(503) 226-6971 Rick McClain Corporate Quality Mgr
Fax: (503) 226-6976
Email: rickm@griffithrubber.com
Website: www.griffithrubber.com
Custom rubber products (Woman/White, estab 1911, empl 250, sales , cert: NWBOC)

7124 Warm Springs Composite Products
Highway 26, Bldg 8   Warm Springs, OR 97761
(541) 553-1143 Charles Currier CFO
Fax: (541) 553-1145
Email: curriercw@bendnet.com
Website: www.wscp.com
Composite panel mfg & product devel: thermal setting, thermal plastic, radio frequncy & cold pressing processes, ballistic & non-ballistic fabrics laminiation, s-glass, e-glass, spectra, dynema, kevlar. (Nat Ame, estab 1994, empl 50, sales $6,200,000, cert: 8(a))

Pennsylvania

7125 Pittsburgh Plastics Manufacturing
140 Kriess Rd   Butler, PA 16001
(724) 789-9300 Emily Crawford Acct Mgr
Fax:
Email: ecrawford@pittsburghplastics.com
Website: www.pittsburghplastics.com
Polyurethanes, TPEs, Silicones, Hydrogels & Foams. (Woman, estab 1977, empl 100, sales , cert: WBENC)

7126 PMC-Polymer Products Company, Inc.
100 Station Ave   Stockertown, PA 18083
(610) 759-3690 Don Barber Business Mgr
Fax: (610) 759-3692
Email: donbarber@pmc-group.com
Website: www.polymerproductscompany.com/index.htm
Design & develop additive masterbatches & ignition resistant thermoplastic compounds. (As-Ind, estab 1965, empl 75, sales $25,500,000, cert: NMSDC)

7127 Precise Plastics, Inc.
7700 Middle Rd P.O. Box R Fairview, PA 16415
(814) 474-5504 Charlotte Farrell President
Fax: (814) 474-2758
Email: char.farrell@ppi-erie.com
Website: www.ppi-erie.com
Injection molding manufacturer. Non Clean room medical. Design - Build and Run Capability. (Woman/White, estab 1969, empl 15, sales $2,498,070, cert: State)

Puerto Rico

7128 Vassallo International
1000 St 506   Cotolaurel, PR 00780
(787) 848-1515 Rafael Vassallo CEO
Fax: (787) 848-3666
Email: faelo@vassalloindustries.com
Website: www.vassallointernational.com
Lines of PVC & plastics, Water Tanks. (Woman/Hisp, estab 1962, empl 90, sales $15,000,000, cert: NMSDC)

South Carolina

7129 Milagro Packaging LLC
60 Fairview Church Road   Spartanburg, SC 29306
(864) 578-0085 Jill McCurry
Fax: (864) 582-1178
Email: jillm@concept-pkg.com
Website: www.milagro-pkg.com
Mfr corrugated & solid fiber boxes, polystyrene foam products & urethane foam products. (Hisp, estab 2001, empl 425, sales $94,873,435, cert: NMSDC)

Tennessee

7130 Innovative Plastics
2900 Old Franklin Rd   Antioch, TN 37013
(404) 402-8062 Tom Florence Sales
Fax: (615) 501-9101
Email: tomf4plastics@aol.com
Website: www.innovative-plastics.com
Custom thermoform & RF contract packaging: PVC, PETG, Styrene, Barex & HDPE. (Woman/White, estab 1985, empl 350, sales , cert: NWBOC)

Texas

7131 Austin Foam Plastics, Inc.
2933 AW Grimes Blvd   Pflugerville, TX 78660
(512) 251-6300 Lisa Carnett Project Leader
Fax: (512) 251-9222
Email: lisa.carnett@a-f-p.com
Website: www.a-f-p.com
Packaging Design and testing; logistics; sustainable solutions; manufacturing - corrugated (boxes; die cut; pallets; solid fiber folding cartons) wood (custom crates; pallets; floating pallets) custom cases; custom cushions; plastic corrugated; sourcing ((Woman/White, estab 1978, empl 228, sales , cert: WBENC)

7132 Belco Manufacturing Company, Inc.
2303 Taylor's Valley Rd   Belton, TX 76513
(254) 933-9000 Steve Macy President
Fax:
Email: sales@belco-mfg.com
Website: www.belco-mfg.com
Industrial fiberglass reinforced plastics products. (Woman/White, estab , empl 1, sales , cert: WBENC)

7133 CamLow, LLC
105 S Friendswood Dr, Ste B   Friendswood, TX 77546
(281) 474-2613   Karen Wiest President
Fax: (281) 664-3471
Email: kawiest@camlow.com
Website: www.camlow.com
Polyurethane spray foam insulation, closed cell spray foam, open cell spray foam, roof spray foam insulation, hurricane protection, hurricane panels, storm panels, storm shutters, roll down shutters, accordian shutters, stainless steel screens. (Woman/White, estab 2005, empl 4, sales $317,000, cert: State, City)

7134 Idea Planet, LP
6001 Summerside Dr Ste 204   Dallas, TX 75252
(972) 380-9867   Michael Flecker President
Fax: (972) 380-1915
Email: mflecker@ideaplanetinc.com
Website: www.ideaplanetinc.com
Plastic injected molding, resin, metal & glass manufacturing. (Woman/White, estab 1999, empl 18, sales $19,000,000, cert: WBENC)

7135 Mexican Technologies Co
8650 Yermoland Dr   El Paso, TX 79907
(915) 595-2285   Alfredo Baca Sales Mgr
Fax: (915) 592-7350
Email: abaca@uniqueproductsinc.com
Website: www.uniqueproductsinc.com
Die cutting, converting, lamination, plastic fabrication, extrusion & coextrusion, slitting, sewing. (Hisp, estab 2002, empl 20, sales , cert: State)

7136 Nicor Inc.
100 Commons Rd, Ste 7-355   Dripping Springs, TX 78620
(707) 484-0835   Jeff Cook VP sales/Mktg
Fax: (512) 276-2033
Email: jeffacook@nicorinc.net
Website: www.nicorinc.net
Custom injection molding, polymer replacement meter pit lids that are traffic rated. (Woman/White, estab 1988, empl 5, sales $2,000,000, cert: State)

7137 Precision Mold & Tool Group
315 N Park Dr   San Antonio, TX 78216
(210) 525-0094   Domingo Auces Director of Mktg
Fax: (210) 525-1561
Email: dhauces@pmtool.com
Website: www.precision-group.com
Injection molding & mold making. (Woman/White, estab 1985, empl 36, sales $6,505,000, cert: WBENC)

7138 Premier Polymers LLC
16800 Imperial Valley, Ste 200   Houston, TX 77060
(281) 902-0909   Melwani Kwan Supply Chain Mgr
Fax: (832) 212-8882
Email: mkwan@premierpolymers.com
Website: www.premierpolymers.com
Dist Plastic Resin. (As-Pac, estab 2009, empl 22, sales , cert: State, NMSDC)

7139 Rhino Contractors
26163 Altas Palmas Rd   Harlingen, TX 78552
(956) 535-3699   Brandon Russell Director
Fax: (956) 412-6240
Email: Brandon@rhino-rgv.com
Website: www.rhino-plastics.com
Mfr ABS plastic substrate made out of 100% post consumer e-waste (electronic) plastics. (Woman/White, estab 2003, empl 8, sales $1,600,000, cert: 8(a))

Utah

7140 Kaddas Enterprises, Inc.
255 N. Apollo Rd. Ste 500   Salt Lake City, UT 84116
(801) 972-5400   Patrick Scott Dir of Sales
Fax: (801) 972-3200
Email: patricks@kaddas.com
Website: www.kaddas.com
Custom Thermoforming, Pressure Forming, Hand Fabrication, 5-Axis CNC Router, Master CAM, Solid Works Modeling, 3-Axis CNC Router, vacuum formed or hand fabricated polymer solutions. (Woman/White, estab 1966, empl 28, sales $4,296,559, cert: CPUC, WBENC)

Virginia

7141 Dynaric Inc.
5740 Bayside Rd   Virginia Beach, VA 23455
(757) 363-5851   Kenny Samdahl Cstmr svc Mgr
Fax: (757) 363-8016
Email: kens@dynaric.com
Website: www.dynaric.com
Mfr plastic strapping & strapping systems. (Hisp, estab 1973, empl 150, sales $122,000,000, cert: NMSDC)

7142 Polyfab Display Company
14892 Persistence Dr   Woodbridge, VA 22191
(703) 497-4577   Al Parker Owner
Fax:
Email: al@polyfab-display.com
Website: www.polyfab-display.com
Mfr & dist acrylic fabricated products: point-of-purchase displays (countertop, wall-mount, slatwall and free-standing), fixtures, signage, protective covers & medical device holders. (AA, estab 1987, empl 15, sales $1,189,000, cert: State, NMSDC)

Wisconsin

7143 Custom Service Plastics, Inc.
1101 S Wells St   Lake Geneva, WI 53147
(262) 248-9557   Minoo Seifoddini President
Fax: (262) 248-9603
Email: john@csplastics.com
Website: www.csplastics.com
Plastics injection molding: autotmotive & non automaotive parts & assemblies. (Woman/As-Pac, estab , empl 160, sales $12,000,000, cert: NMSDC, WBENC)

7144   Molded Dimensions, Inc.
       701 Sunset Rd   Port Washington, WI 53074
       (262) 284-9455 Sue Bialzik Cstmr Service
       Fax: (262) 284-0696
       Email: sue@moldeddimensions.com
       Website: www.moldeddimensions.com
Rubber & polyurethane custom molded components.
(Woman/White, estab 1952, empl 70, sales $12,500,000,
cert: WBENC)

7145   Shell Plastics LLC
       1010 Valley Rd P.O. Box 515 Plymouth, WI 53073
       (920) 893-6281 Mary Beth Dellger President
       Fax: (920) 893-5427
       Email: marybeth@shellplastics.com
       Website: www.shellplastics.com
Job Shop, Plastic Fabrication, Screen Printing, Vacuum
Forming, CNC routing, Heat Bending, Cold Bending, Flame
Polishing, Solvent Bonding, Laminating, Spray Painting, Die
Cutting, Buffing, Drape Forming, Assembly, Packaging,
Fulfillment. (Woman/White, estab 1953, empl 15, sales
$2,924,884, cert: WBENC)

7146   SMC Ltd.
       330 SMC Dr   Somerset, WI 54025
       (978) 422-6800 Eugene Puckhaber Corporate
       Controller
       Fax: (978) 422-3395
       Email: eugene.puckhaber@smcltd.com
       Website: www.smcltd.com
Contract manufacturing & molding services, design,
engineering, thermoplastic molding including insert &
two-shot, micro molding. (As-Ind, estab 1989, empl 700,
sales , cert: State, NMSDC)

> ## PRINTING & ENGRAVING
> Full service printers with layout, composition, binding and trimming, digital, multi-color, large format, etc. Also included are silkscreen printers, nameplate and trophy engravers, manufacturers or distributors of labels, decals and pressure sensitive materials. NAICS Code 32

Arizona

7147   Sapphire Printing Group, Inc.
3800 N. 38th Avenue   Phoenix, AZ 85019
(714) 941-9534   Kenn Gary Director of Sales
Fax: (909) 456-2159
Email: kenng@sapphireprinting.com
Website: www.sapphireprinting.com
Commercial web printing, mailing & fulfillment services. (Woman/White, estab 2004, empl 115, sales $22,000,000, cert: CPUC)

7148   Squala LLC
2909 E Broadway   Phoenix, AZ 85040
(602) 547-7020   Angela Lawrence Dir Natl sales
Fax:
Email: alawrence@sherrimayco.com
Website: www.sherrimayco.com
Brand dev, graphic design, copy writing, direct marketing campaigns, websites, mobile, data analytics & public relations, web, sheetfed, digital variable, large format, flexo, retail packaging & folding cartons. (Woman/White, estab 2010, empl 10, sales $3,550,646, cert: WBENC)

California

7149   Acme Press Inc., dba California Lithographers
2312 Stanwell Dr   Concord, CA 94520
(925) 682-1111   Mardjan Taheripour VP
Fax: (925) 682-9991
Email: mardjan@calitho.com
Website: www.Calitho.com
Commercial printing, digital printing, fulfillment, mailing, packaging. (Woman, estab 1976, empl 75, sales $11,530,090, cert: WBENC)

7150   Clear Image Printing, Inc.
12744 San Fernando Road Bldg #2   Sylmar, CA 91342
(818) 630-7670   Gene Byrne Dir, Mktg/sales
Fax: (818) 547-4685
Email: eugene@clearimageprinting.com
Website: www.clearimageprinting.com
Offset sheet fed & digital printing, Brochures, Catalogues, Direct mail campaigns, Special Packaging, Books, Foil stamping, Die-cutting, Posters, Large Format Banners, Graphic Design, Modern-Media. (As-Pac, estab 2008, empl 45, sales $5,005,000, cert: CPUC)

7151   Digital Mania, Inc.
455 Market St Ste 180   San Francisco, CA 94105
(415) 896-0500   Darius Meykadeh CEO
Fax: (415) 896-2656
Email: copymat@copymatsf.com
Website: www.copymat1.com
Indoor & outdoor signs, brochures, booklets, RFPs, oversized prints, desktop publishing & design, mailing services, newsletters, name tents, name badges, conference materials, etc. (As-Ind, estab 1994, empl 20, sales $4,000,000, cert: City)

7152   Digital Services Enterprises
40 Tesla, Ste B   Irvine, CA 92618
(949) 387-6200   Steve Morgan Sales Mgr
Fax: (949) 387-6300
Email: steve@sirspeedyprinter.com
Website: www.sirspeedyprinter.com
Offset printing, digital printing, color copies, photocopying, promotional products, Signs, banners, posters, floor graphics, direct mail, fulfillment, high speedy copies, training manuals, human resource manuals, direct marketing. (Woman/White, estab 1974, empl 17, sales $2,757,000, cert: CPUC)

7153   Dulco Printing
740 E Belmont Ave   Fresno, CA 93701
(559) 266-8245   Kipp Weber President
Fax: (559) 266-2844
Email: info@dulcoprinting.com
Website: www.dulcoprinting.com
Commercial printing, collating & binding: books, manuals & full color promotional material. (Woman/White, estab 2002, empl 4, sales , cert: State)

7154   Essence Printing
151 Mitchell Ave   South San Francisco, CA 94080
(650) 952-5072   Bau-Lin Yueh President
Fax:
Email: baulin@essenceprinting.com
Website: www.essenceprinting.com
Printing: marketing material, brochures, datasheets, newsletters, tradeshow posters, business cards, letterheads, etc. (As-Pac, estab 1976, empl 60, sales , cert: NMSDC, CPUC)

7155   Financial Statement Services, Inc.
3300 S Fairview St   Santa Ana, CA 92704
(714) 436-3300   Michael Perales Business Dev
Fax: (714) 436-3396
Email: info@fssi-ca.com
Website: www.fssi-ca.com
Printing, mailing & electronic invoices, statements, bills & marketing communications. (Woman/White, estab 1980, empl 187, sales $5,000,000, cert: WBENC)

7156   Fong & Fong Printers and Lithographers
3009 65th St   Sacramento, CA 95820
(707) 761-7831   Karen Cotton Controller
Fax: (916) 739-0350
Email: kcotton@fongprinters.com
Website: www.fongprinters.com
Commercial printing services: sales literature, brochures, folders, packaging, annual reports, data sheets, direct mail & posters. (Woman/As-Pac, estab 1962, empl 51, sales $12,000,000, cert: CPUC)

7157   Fruitridge Printing and Lithograph
3258 Stockton Blvd   Sacramento, CA 95820
(916) 452-9213   Karen Young VP
Fax: (916) 452-6020
Email: karen@fruitridge.com
Website: www.fruitridge.com
Commercial offset and digital printing, in house bindery & mailing capabilities. (Woman, estab 1970, empl 35, sales $5,100,000, cert: CPUC)

7158 Gibraltar Graphics
5075 Brooks St   Montclair, CA 91763
(909) 624-6171 Hector Rosado Sales Mgr
Fax: (909) 624-6362
Email: hectorr@gprint4u.com
Website: www.gPrint4u.com
Printing, inhouse bindery, heatset web presses, pick up and delivery, brochures, envelopes, laser forms, newsletters, booklets, scratch pads, laser forms, (Hisp, estab 1989, empl 18, sales $410,000, cert: CPUC)

7159 Image Quest Plus, LLC
215 No Marengo Ave.   Pasadena, CA 91101
(626) 744-1333 Margaret Floyd Member
Fax: (626) 744-9905
Email: Margaret@iqcopy.com
Website: www.iqcopy.com
Photocopy services: document reproduction, scanning & imaging, color copies, wideformat printing, binding, off-site document reproduction. (Woman/AA, estab 1998, empl 3, sales , cert: NMSDC, CPUC)

7160 Impact Printing
23278 Bernhardt St   Hayward, CA 94545
(510) 783-7977 Sarah Elder VP sales
Fax: (510) 783-9699
Email: impactprint@impactprint.com
Website: www.impactprint.com
Digital & offset printing, full bindery, graphics. (Woman, estab 1985, empl 25, sales $2,500,000, cert: CPUC)

7161 Ink Link, Incorporated
351 Oak Place, Ste J   Brea, CA 92821
(714) 256-9700 Linda Brooking CEO
Fax: (714) 256-9701
Email: linda@myinklink.com
Website: www.myinklink.com
Commercial printing: banners, signs, displays, floor graphics. (Woman/White, estab 2003, empl 4, sales $850,000, cert: State, CPUC, WBENC)

7162 International Diversified Marketing, Inc.
1809 Carnegie Ave   Santa Ana, CA 92705
(714) 550-4971 Jan Northcutt
Fax: (714) 550-4973
Email: jn@comfortfirst.us
Website: www.ComfortFirstProducts.com
Comfort First Filtered Diffuser™If you want to go GREEN and save energy, improve employee comfort and health, all while improving indoor air quality, this diffuser is the solution you've been looking for. (Woman/White, estab 2003, empl 3, sales $269,700, cert: WBENC)

7163 Lester Lithograph Inc. (dba Castle Press)
1128 N Gilbert St   Anaheim, CA 92801
(714)4913981 Larry Lester Retired
Fax:
Email: Amy@castlepress.com
Website: www.castlepress.com
Commercial printing. (Woman/White, estab 1980, empl 45, sales $5,500,000, cert: CPUC, WBENC)

7164 Marina Graphic Center, Inc.
12903 Cerise Ave   Hawthorne, CA 90250
(310) 970-1777 Glen Momary Sr Acct Exec
Fax: (310) 263-1777
Email: glenm@marinagraphics.com
Website: www.marinagraphics.com
Commercial Printing, Pre-Press, Offset Printing, Digital Printing, Mail fulfillment & Mailing services, Full Bindery, Letterpress, Die Cutting & Embossing. (Woman, estab 1964, empl 125, sales $14,000,000, cert: WBENC)

7165 Metropolitan West, Inc.
11901 Santa Monica Blvd, Ste 350   Los Angeles, CA 90025
(310) 829-5701 Kelly Taylor President
Fax: (310) 373-4693
Email: nikki@metwest.com
Website: www.metwest.com
Dist film products: solar, safety, anti-graffiti, designer, custom & digital film. (Woman/White, estab 1992, empl 5, sales $1,200,000, cert: WBENC)

7166 Monarch Litho, Inc.
1501 Date St   Montabella, CA 90640
(323) 727-0300 Gerry Lewis Acct Exec
Fax: (323) 720-1169
Email: gerry.lewis@monarchlitho.com
Website: www.monarchlitho.com
Printing svcs: small & large format sheet fed press; digital pre-press (Hisp, estab 1974, empl 275, sales , cert: NMSDC, CPUC)

7167 PGI - Pacific Graphics, Inc.
14938 Nelson Ave   City of Industry, CA 91744
(626) 336-7707 Eddy O. Salas GM
Fax: (626) 336-6627
Email: eddy@pacgraphics.com
Website: www.pacgraphics.com
Printing & graphics, business forms, etc. (Woman/Hisp, estab 1989, empl 25, sales $3,350,000, cert: City, NMSDC, CPUC, SDB)

7168 Photomation
2551 W La Palma Ave   Anaheim, CA 92801
(714) 236-2121 Francisco Flores Production Mgr
Fax: (714) 527-6489
Email: fflores@photomation.com
Website: www.photomation.com
Digital Graphics, Trade show, Digital Imaging, Photographics prints, Banners, POP displays, Standees, Wallcovering, Large wall Murals, Lobby art, Custom framing, Awards and recognition, office décor. (Woman/White, estab 1955, empl 21, sales , cert: State, CPUC, WBENC)

7169 Precise Panel Engraving, Inc.
12881 Western Ave, Unit B   Garden Grove, CA 92841
(714) 898-6510 Joan VonKarvaly President
Fax:
Email: precisepanel@verizon.net
Website: www.government-vendor.us/precisepanel
Industrial engraving: signs, labels, nameplates, control panels; sheet metal fab; metal & plastic panel machining; mylar & metal marking. (Woman/White, estab 1978, empl 7, sales $255,000, cert: CPUC)

7170 Summit Graphics Inc.
11354 Burbank Blvd, Ste A   North Hollywood, CA 91601
(818) 753-5075 Jorge Ververa VP minority Business Devel
Fax: (818) 753-4857
Email: jorge@summit-graphics.net
Website: www.summit-graphics.net
Medium to large runs in offset, digital & large format printing: mailers, inkjet address, brochures, catalogues, booklets, bindery, die-cutting, packaging, coallating, hand fulfillment. (Hisp, estab 2001, empl 4, sales $1,436,504, cert: State, NMSDC)

7171 Transworld Printing Services, Inc.
2857 Transworld Dr   Stockton, CA 95206
(209) 982-1511 Daphyne Brown CEO
Fax: (209) 982-1458
Email: daphyne@tpslabels.com
Website: www.tpslabels.com
Flexographic & digital label manufacturer. (Woman/AA, estab 1996, empl 15, sales $2,065,000, cert: NMSDC, NWBOC)

Colorado

7172 DT Investments Inc. dba Beacon Printing Inc.
2161 S Platte River Dr   Denver, CO 80223
(303) 922-4384 Terri Witt CEO
Fax: (303) 922-2137
Email: beacon.sales@qwestoffice.net
Website: www.beaconprintingdenver.com
Printing services, large format sheetfed, digital, full color, PMS color, pocket folders, post cards, letterhead, envelopes, posters, booklets, annual reports, brochures, forms, rack cards, pamphlets, catalogs, tabs, loose leaf, inserts. (Woman/Nat Ame, estab 1995, empl 10, sales $1,200,000, cert: City)

7173 Mar-Tek Industries, Inc.
3545 S Platte River Dr   Englewood, CO 80110
(303) 789-4067 Irene Smith President
Fax: (303) 789-9296
Email: irene@mar-tekind.com
Website: www.mar-tekind.com
Mfr & dist screen printed & digital graphic labels, decals, overlays. (Woman/White, estab 1987, empl 45, sales $4,500,000, cert: WBENC)

Connecticut

7174 Enhance a Colour Corp.
43b Beaver Brook Road   Danbury, CT 06810
(203) 748-5111 Lenore Nespoli Sales Mgr
Fax: (203) 730-8413
Email: Lnespoli@eacgs.com
Website: www.eacgs.com
Large format digitally printed graphics, printing dyesub fabrics & carpets up to 16' wide, UV printing, full color & white ink direct to rigid and flexible substrates, pressure sensitive, regular & mesh substrates. (Woman/White, estab 1988, empl 32, sales $4,014,058, cert: WBENC)

7175 Kool Ink/Sir Speedy Printing
21 Old Windsor Rd   Bloomfield, CT 06002
(860) 242-0303 Mark Jacobs Owner
Fax: (860) 286-0343
Email: mark@sirspeedy.cc
Website: www.sirspeedy.com
Offset printing, copying, black & white, color, scanning, posters banners & signs. (AA, estab 2001, empl 15, sales $3,500,000, cert: State, NMSDC)

7176 Turnstone Inc. dba Alphagraphics
915 Main St   Hartford, CT 06103
(860) 247-3766 Doug Baumgardner VP Sales
Fax: (860) 247-5764
Email: us667@alphagraphics.com
Website: www.hartford.alphagraphics.com
Brochures, Reports, Training books, Posters, Reports, mailings. Forms, labels, Flyers, Design Services. Fulfillment, Signs & banners, marketing material. (Woman/White, estab 1989, empl 23, sales $3,100,000, cert: WBENC)

Florida

7177 Alpha Press, Inc.
3804 N John Young Pkwy, Ste 2   Orlando, FL 32804
(407) 299-2121 John Latorre GM
Fax: (407) 299-8137
Email: sales@alphapressfl.com
Website: www.alphapressfl.com
Four color press: brochures, business cards, envelopes, pamplets, magazines & publications. (Woman/Hisp, estab 1996, empl 5, sales $870,000, cert: City)

7178 APImaging, Inc.
19 SW 6th St   Miami, FL 33130
(305) 373-4774 Diana Herrera VP Sales
Fax: (305) 358-8345
Email: dianah@apimaging.com
Website: www.apimaging.com
Photo imaging & photo finishing services, commercial printing, studio photography, self adhesive signs & graphics, directional signs, posters, point of purchase signs, graphic displays, graphic design, trade shows & exhibits. (Woman/Hisp, estab 2013, empl 22, sales , cert: WBENC)

7179 Bellak Color
P.O. Box 227656   Miami, FL 33222
(305) 854-8525 Manny Fernandez VP
Fax: (305) 858-8783
Email: manny@bellak.com
Website: www.bellak.com
Commerical sheet-fed printing - print publications, magazines, brochures, rack brochures, catalogs, stationery packages, POS pieces, postcards, pamplets, invitations, folders. (Hisp, estab 1960, empl 47, sales $6,500,000, cert: NMSDC)

7180 Colonial Press International, Inc.
3690 NW 50th St   Miami, FL 33142
(540) 347-1402 Jeff Statler EVP Corporate Sales
Fax: (305) 637-9324
Email: jstatler@colonialpress.com
Website: www.colonialpressintl.com
Printing svcs: web & sheet fed, 4-6 color, brochures, rack cards, magazines, etc. (Hisp, estab 1952, empl 221, sales $31,000,000, cert: NMSDC)

7181 Innovative Printing & Graphics
310 S Federal Hwy   Boynton Beach, FL 33435
(561) 742-2977 Amy Bernard Sales Assoc
Fax: (561) 740-3833
Email: info@ipgprinting.com
Website: www.ipgprinting.com
Commercial printing: full color, magazines, NCR forms, pocket folders, postcard mailiers, letterhead, invitations, etc. (Woman, estab 2006, empl 9, sales $250,000, cert: City)

7182 Lawton Printers, Inc.
649 Triumph Court   Orlando, FL 32804
(407) 260-0400 Kimberly Lawton Koon President
Fax: (407) 260-1321
Email: kimberly@lawtonprinters.com
Website: www.LawtonPrinters.com
Printing ; offset, digital & wide-format printing equipment. (Woman/White, estab 1900, empl 27, sales $3,600,000, cert: State, WBENC)

7183 NIS Print
1809 S Division Ave   Orlando, FL 32805
(407) 423-7575 Sheryl Batchelder President
Fax: (407) 423-1464
Email: sheryl@nisprint.com
Website: www.nisprint.com
Specialty Binding, Employee Handbooks, Training Manuals, Sales Presentations, Specialty Boxes, Custom Index Tabs, Guestroom Compendiums, Custom Index Tabs, Commercial Printing. (Woman/White, estab 1986, empl 17, sales $53,713, cert: WBENC)

7184 Quadco Printing & Signs
8953 NW 23rd St   Doral, FL 33172
(305) 519-1234 Jorge Quadreny President
Fax: (305) 470-2329
Email: jorge@quadcoonline.com
Website: www.quadcoonline.com
Full color printing services, advertising specialties, promotional items, trade show & retractable banner stands. (Hisp, estab 1982, empl 8, sales $140,000,000, cert: State)

7185 Sol Davis Printing, Inc.
5205 N Lois Ave   Tampa, FL 33614
(813) 353-3609 Solomon E. Davis President
Fax: (813) 353-8559
Email: soldavis.print@verizon.net
Website: www.soldavisprinting.com
Offset printing: 1, 2, 3 & 4 color process, graphic design, typesetting & bindery services. (Woman/AA, estab 1999, empl 9, sales , cert: State, City, NMSDC)

7186 Solo Printing, Inc.
7860 NW 66th St 33166   Miami, FL 33166
(305) 594-8699 Lorenzo Cosio Acct Exec
Fax: (305) 599-5245
Email: lorenzo@soloprinting.com
Website: www.soloprinting.com
Commercial printing, binding & fullfillment. (Hisp, estab 1984, empl 143, sales $49,000,000, cert: NMSDC)

7187 Vista Color Corporation
1401 NW 78th Ave   Miami, FL 33126
(305) 635-2000 Catherine Finnemore Sr Acct Exec
Fax: (305) 635-1985
Email: cfinnemore@vistacolor.com
Website: www.vistacolor.com
Pre-press & printing svcs. (Hisp, estab 1968, empl 120, sales $22,000,000, cert: NMSDC)

Georgia

7188 American Reprographics Corporation
7800 Jett Ferry Rd   Atlanta, GA 30350
(770) 394-2465 Mindy Godwin President
Fax:
Email: mindy@arcinatlanta.com
Website: www.arcinatlanta.com
Full service printing: business cards, letterhead, envelopes, check stock, brochures, mailings, graphic design services. (Woman/White, estab 1978, empl 3, sales , cert: WBENC)

7189 Barcode Warehouse
101 Smoke Hill Lane Ste 130 Woodstock, GA 30188
(678)33560 Margie Benton VP Sales Ops
Fax: (678) 391-3561
Email: mbenton@barcodewarehouse.biz
Website: www.barcodewarehouse.biz
Mfr labels & tags, full color product branding labels, blank labels & tags for variable data printing. (Woman/White, estab 2004, empl 18, sales $4,225,778, cert: WBENC)

7190 Basiqa, LLC
1555 Oakbrook Dr Ste 135   Norcross, GA 30093
(678) 824-6460 Winston Dzose VP Digital Mktg
Fax: (678) 824-6467
Email: winston@basiqa.com
Website: www.basiqa.com
Direct mail, advertising, material preparation services for mailing or other direct distribution, digital printing. (AA, estab 2009, empl 16, sales $3,000,000, cert: NMSDC)

7191 Dixie Graphics
2074 E Park Dr NE   Conyers, GA 30013
(770) 972-2354 Denise Hindle COE
Fax: (678) 750-0046
Email: dhindle@dixiegraphicsinc.com
Website: www.dixiegraphicsinc.com
Commercial offset printing & large format, graphics design & full mail room capabilities. (Woman/White, estab 1980, empl 14, sales $2,012,337, cert: WBENC)

7192 LittKare, LLC
      200 Cobb Pkwy N Ste 130 Marietta, GA 30062
      (770) 693-1767 Littie Brown President
      Fax: (770) 693-1582
      Email: lbrown@speedpro.com
      Website: www.speedpromarietta.com
Large format digital printing: banners, posters, signs, trade
show displays & banner stands, vehicle wraps, vinyl
lettering, wall, window & floor graphics. (Woman/AA,
estab 2010, empl 2, sales $373,880, cert: NMSDC, WBENC)

7193 Matoaka Enterprises, LLC
      2455 Bridlewood Dr   Smyrna, GA 30080
      (404) 932-6825 Julie Custalow Owner
      Fax: (888) 430-6737
      Email: julie@matoaka.com
      Website: www.matoaka-ent.com
Large format graphics, banners, signs, window clings,
vehicle wraps, LEED certified wall paper, custom printed
litho & digital printing, custom printed promotional items,
apparel. (Woman/Nat Ame, estab 2010, empl 1, sales
$181,611, cert: NMSDC)

7194 NorthStar Print, LLC
      6050 Peachtree Pkwy Ste 240 Norcross, GA 30092
      (770) 490-6251 Jacki Suckow President
      Fax: (770) 225-0155
      Email: jacki@northstarprint.net
      Website: www.northstarprint.net
Print & promotional products, marketing materials,
traditional business forms, POP items, promotional items
& just-in-time digital printing, distribution & kitting
services. (Woman/White, estab 1991, empl 8, sales
$3,000,000, cert: NWBOC)

7195 PrinTech Label Corporation
      2550 Collins Springs Dr   Smyrna, GA 30080
      (404) 792-1133 Kelly Weaver CFO
      Fax: (404) 792-7370
      Email: kelly@printechlabel.com
      Website: www.printechlabel.com
Pressure senstive labels, custom printed tags, 4 color
process, 6 color capability, hot stamp labels, cold foil
labels, UL registered label vendor, IRC's, IRC, redeemable
coupons, silver coupon, thermal transfer blanks, direct
thermal blanks. (Woman/Nat Ame, estab 1993, empl 14,
sales $1,701,002, cert: WBENC)

7196 Printing and Marketing Services, Inc.
      1500 Southland Circle, Ste A   Atlanta, GA 30318
      (404) 724-9080 Brian McDaniel Sr Acct Mgr
      Fax:
      Email: bmcdaniel@alphagraphics.com
      Website: www.us756.alphagraphics.com
Printing: digital color, digital black & white, offset printing,
envelopes, stationery, large format signs & banners. (AA,
estab 2015, empl 13, sales $1,695,647, cert: NMSDC)

7197 The Printing People, Inc.
      3427 Oakcliff Rd. Ste 112 Doraville, GA 30340
      (770) 452-7561 Misael Millan VP
      Fax: (770) 451-5758
      Email: misa@printingpeople.com
      Website: www.printingpeople.com
Commercial offset & digital printing: brochures, postcards,
catalogs, posters, folders, manuals & stationery. (Hisp,
estab 1980, empl 13, sales $1,400,000, cert: NMSDC)

Iowa

7198 Promotion Support Services, Inc.
      1320 W Kimberly Rd   Davenport, IA 52806
      (563) 362-6002 Terance VanWinkle Director
      Fax:
      Email: TVanWinkle@PSS-Inc.Net
      Website: www.pss-inc.net
Offset printing, Digital printing (static & variable),
Commercial printing, Transactional print & mail services,
Transcription Services, Data capture, Medical Transcrip-
tion, Outbound call center, warehousing, Fulfillment,
Kitting. (Woman/White, estab 1989, empl 56, sales
$5,600,000, cert: WBENC)

Illinois

7199 AmeriPrint Corporation
      1401 W Diggins St   Harvard, IL 60098
      (800) 366-8573 Taylor Schulty Marking/Sales Dir
      Fax:
      Email: taylors@ameriprint.com
      Website: www.ameriprint.com
Continuous forms & checks, snap sets, laser cut-sheets,
booked & padded sets, integral card forms & labels,
decals, re-positionable labels, key tags, magnets,
thermal labels, barcoding, jumbo numbering & rolls.
(Woman/White, estab 1990, empl 63, sales $8,603,265,
cert: NWBOC)

7200 Clyde Printing Company
      3520 S Morgan   Chicago, IL 60609
      (773) 847-5900 Colleen Woulfe President
      Fax: (773) 847-6470
      Email: clydeprint@sbcglobal.net
      Website: www.clydeprinting.com
Sheet fed commercial printing, conventional & digital
printing, fullfillment & mailing. (Woman/White, estab
1942, empl 10, sales $792,852, cert: WBENC)

7201 ComGraphics Inc.
      329 W 18th St, 10 Fl   Chicago, IL 60616
      (312) 226-0900 Lydia Erickson CFO
      Fax: (312) 226-9411
      Email: LydiaE@cgichicago.com
      Website: www.cgichicago.com
Digital printing svcs, folding & inserting operations,
internet hosting, statement processing, web statement,
laser svcs, invoicing, marketing & fulfillment, data
archiving, scanning svcs, direct mail. (Woman/White,
estab 1980, empl 55, sales , cert: WBENC)

7202 Consolidated Printing Company
      5942 N Northwest Hwy   Chicago, IL 60631
      (773) 631-2800 Marilyn Jones President
      Fax: (773) 631-2822
      Email: marilyn@consolidatedprinting.net
      Website: www.consolidatedprinting.net
Commercial printing includes: design, computer to plate,
color digital, offset short & long run: advertising materials, annual reports, banners, brochures, booklets,
buttons, business cards, conference materials, digital
printing, door hangers. (Woman/White, estab 1973,
empl 15, sales , cert: State, WBENC)

7203   D&D Business Inc. dba DDI Printing
       7830 Quincy St   Willowbrook, IL 60527
       (630) 734-1455 Darmi Parikh CEO
       Fax: (630) 734-1476
       Email: darmi@ddimage.com
       Website: www.ddimage.com
Graphic design, Commercial colored printing, digital
printing, full bindery & fullfillment. (Woman/As-Pac, estab
1994, empl 5, sales $560,000, cert: State, City, NMSDC)

7204   Envelopes Only, Inc.
       2000 Park Ave   Streamwood, IL 60107
       (630) 213-2563 Fran Kowal Acct Mgr
       Fax: (630) 213-7455
       Email: fran@envelopesonly.net
       Website: www.envelopesonly.net
Printing envelopes & letterheads. (Woman/White, estab
1983, empl 24, sales $7,287,492, cert: State, WBENC)

7205   Krick Enterprises, Inc.
       1548 Ogden Ave   Downers Grove, IL 60515
       (630) 515-1085 Reggie Godfrey President
       Fax: (630) 515-1087
       Email: reggie@krickinc.com
       Website: www.signsnowdownersgrove.com
Graphic Design & Layout, commercial & digital printing.
Signs & Posters, Brochures, Business Cards, Training
Manuals & materials, Promotional items. (Woman/As-Pac,
estab 1991, empl 7, sales $600,000, cert: State, NMSDC)

7206   LabelQuest Inc.
       493 W. Fullerton Ave.   Elmhurst, IL 60126
       (630) 833-9400 Patricia Vandenberg President
       Fax: (630) 833-9421
       Email: labelquest@sbcglobal.net
       Website:
Custom printing & print management: offset, flexo, screen
& digital printing, safe storage & fulfillment capabilities.
(Woman/White, estab 1996, empl 4, sales $1,646,670,
cert: WBENC)

7207   M & R Graphics
       2401 Bond St   University Park, IL 60466
       (708) 534-6621 Keith Reimel VP
       Fax: (708) 534-6756
       Email: kreimel@mrgraphics.biz
       Website: www.mrgraphics.biz
Mfr pressure sensitive labels & flexographic printing.
(Woman/AA, estab 1989, empl 17, sales , cert: NMSDC)

7208   MOTR GRAFX, LLC
       7430 N Lehigh Ave   Niles, IL 60714
       (847) 600-5656 Lissette Herin VP
       Fax: (847) 655-6130
       Email: lherin@motrgx.com
       Website: www.motrgrafx.com
Print/media production, design, print, finishing, fulfillment
& distribution, digital, sheet fed, large format, web
printing, screen printing, direct mail, POP/packaging
services. (Woman/Hisp, estab 2011, empl 10, sales
$2,980,000, cert: City, NMSDC)

7209   Printing Master Services
       6370 W Emerald Pkwy   Monee, IL 60449
       (708) 534-8535 Gary De La Fuente President
       Fax: (708) 534-8538
       Email: gary@printingmasterservices.com
       Website: www.printingmasterservices.com
Commercial sheetfed printing: books, brochures,
posters, displays, manuals, banners, window displays,
coupons, adslicks, digital printing & proofing, cd duplication & website design. (Hisp, estab 1978, empl 13, sales
$2,050,000, cert: State)

7210   Richards Graphic Communications, Inc.
       2700 Van Buren St   Bellwood, IL 60104
       (708) 731-2103 Mary Lawrence President
       Fax:
       Email: MaryL@rgcnet.com
       Website: www.rgcnet.com
Printing & communications, creative concept development, language translations, digital imaging, printing,
finishing & mailing. (Woman/White, estab 1925, empl
23, sales $4,400,000, cert: State, WBENC)

7211   Shree Ganesha, Inc.
       311 S Wacker Dr   Chicago, IL 60606
       (312) 408-1080 Tina Kuvadia Production Mgr
       Fax: (312) 408-1079
       Email: printxpress@printx-press.com
       Website: www.printx-press.com
Offset printing, copying, binding, large format, digital
printing & graphic designing capabilities. (Woman/As-
Pac, estab 2008, empl 9, sales $10,001, cert: City)

7212   Signcraft Screenprint, Inc.
       100 AJ Harle Dr   Galena, IL 61036
       (815) 777-3030 Sandy Redington President
       Fax: (815) 777-0740
       Email: sandy@signcraftinc.com
       Website: www.signcraftinc.com
Custom screen printing, mfr pressure sensitive decals,
signs & anti-skid plates. (Woman/White, estab 1947,
empl 133, sales $11,500,000, cert: State)

7213   Sunrise Hitek Service, Inc.
       5915 N Northwest Hwy   Chicago, IL 60631
       (773) 792-8880 Mark Finch VP
       Fax: (773) 792-8881
       Email: mfinch@sunrisedigital.us
       Website: www.sunrisehitek.com
Large format printing; displays, exhibit boards, POP
displays, signs, floor graphics, etc. (As-Pac, estab 1987,
empl 15, sales $3,700,000, cert: State, NMSDC)

7214   THM Creative, Inc. dba Advanced Imaging Inc.
       1944 University Lane   Lisle, IL 60532
       (630) 969-1300 Tim Donnell Sales
       Fax: (630) 969-1975
       Email: tim@aiprolab.com
       Website: www.aiprolab.com
Digital Color Lab, Photographic Printing & Processing,
Enlargements to 30x40, Inkjet/Giglee Printing, Online
Order Fulfillment. (Woman, estab 1994, empl 6, sales ,
cert: NMSDC)

7215　Wyka LLC d/b/a Edison Graphics
　　　1515 S Mt. Prospect Rd　Des Plaines, IL 60018
　　　(847) 298-0740　Larae J. Breitenstein CEO
　　　Fax: (847) 298-9507
　　　Email: larae@edison-graphics.com
　　　Website: www.edison-graphics.com
Printing svcs: 6 colors & coater sheet fed printing, in-house finishing, cutters, MBO folders, stitcher, digital printing & wide format printing. (Woman/White, estab 1998, empl 14, sales $3,215,000, cert: WBENC)

Indiana

7216　Fineline Printing Group
　　　8081 Zionsville Rd　Indianapolis, IN 46268
　　　(317) 802-1964　Richard Miller President
　　　Fax: (317) 870-4410
　　　Email: richardm@FinelinePrintingGroup.com
　　　Website: www.FinelinePrintingGroup.com
Commercial sheetfed printing, inhouse bindery, mailing svcs, prepress svcs: scanning, design, ctp & high end color corrections. (Woman/Hisp, estab 1981, empl 60, sales $10,000,000, cert: NMSDC)

7217　International Label Mfg.
　　　1925 S 13th St　Terre Haute, IN 47802
　　　(800) 525-8469　Lisa Gonzales VP
　　　Fax: (812) 232-3402
　　　Email: lisagonzales@internationallabelmfg.com
　　　Website: www.internationallabelmfg.com
Custom label mfr & commercial printer. (Woman/White, estab 1972, empl 18, sales $2,900,000, cert: State)

7218　Miles Printing Corporation
　　　4923 W 78th St　Indianapolis, IN 46268
　　　(317) 870-6145　Wendy Miles Robbins Owner
　　　Fax: (317) 243-8575
　　　Email: wmiles@milesprinting.com
　　　Website: www.milesprinting.com
Commercial printing, offering digital, multi-color UV sheet-fed, large format printing, complete bindery, mailing & fulfillment capabilities. (Woman/White, estab 2006, empl 38, sales $13,600,000, cert: State)

7219　Nicholson Printing Inc.
　　　209 Eastern Blvd　Jeffersonville, IN 47130
　　　(812) 283-1200　Chris Nicholson VP
　　　Fax: (812) 284-3705
　　　Email: chris@nicholsonprinting.com
　　　Website: www.nicholsonprinting.com
Commercial & quick printing, graphic design, full-color printing, disk to print, digital color, digital black & white, copying, letterheads, envelopes, business cards, memos, business forms, carbonless forms, time cards, folders, books. (Woman, estab 1979, empl 12, sales $1,118,000, cert: State)

7220　Offset House Printing, Inc.
　　　9374 Castlegate Dr　Indianapolis, IN 46256
　　　(317) 849-5155　Jay Williamson Acct Mgr
　　　Fax: (317) 842-3324
　　　Email: jwilliamson@offsethouse.biz
　　　Website: www.offsethouseinc.com
Commercial printing, graphic design & direct mail capabilities. (Woman/White, estab 1964, empl 13, sales , cert: State)

7221　Printing Inc of Louisville Kentucky
　　　1600 Dutch Lane Ste A　Jeffersonville, IN 47130
　　　(502) 368-6555　Maureen Minogue Mgr Business Devel
　　　Fax: (812) 284-4683
　　　Email: maureen.minogue@prettyincredible.com
　　　Website: www.prettyincredible.com
Print, fulfillment, distribution, marketing consulting, project management, direct mail with management of distributions, inventory & fulfillment of literature, bindery & kit packing. (Woman, estab 1971, empl 19, sales $3,000,000, cert: State)

7222　Thomas E. Slade, Inc.
　　　6220 Vogel Road　Evansville, IN 47715
　　　(812) 437-5233　Lisa Slade President
　　　Fax: (812) 491-3850
　　　Email: tom@sladeprint.com
　　　Website: www.sladeprint.com
Printing, graphic design, website design, wide format posters & banners, mailing, promotional products, letterhead, envelopes, business cards, labels, tags, inserts, marketing services, augmented reality, QR codes for tracking, signs. (Woman/White, estab 1993, empl 17, sales $2,500,000, cert: State)

7223　Town & Country Printing
　　　1001 E Summit St　Crown Point, IN 46307
　　　(219) 924-0441　Debera Hinchy President
　　　Fax: (219) 924-1302
　　　Email: dhinchy@tandcii.com
　　　Website: www.townandcountryprinting.com
Commercial printing - offset & digital. Traditional, large/grand format printing. Full color business cards, stationery, notepads, banners, indoor and outdoor signage, brochures, booklets, wall and floor graphics, decals (window, wall, floor). (Woman/White, estab 1970, empl 18, sales $1,800,000, cert: WBENC)

7224　UN Communications Group, Inc.
　　　1429 Chase Court　Carmel, IN 46032
　　　(317) 218-8262　Denise Purvis President
　　　Fax: (317) 573-0239
　　　Email: dpurvis@uncommgroup.com
　　　Website: www.uncommgroup.com
Commercial, digital & wide format print services, mailing services, brochures, catalogs & annual reports, banners, vehicle wraps & tradeshow signage. (Woman/White, estab 1975, empl 32, sales $4,500,000, cert: State, City, WBENC)

7225　Valley Screen Process Company, Inc.
　　　58740 Executive Dr　Mishawaka, IN 46544
　　　(574) 256-0901　Karen Barnett CEO
　　　Fax: (574) 255-7966
　　　Email: karenb@valleyscreen.com
　　　Website: www.valleyscreen.com
Commercial screen & digital printing. (Woman/White, estab 1967, empl 50, sales $7,445,882, cert: WBENC)

Kansas

7226 Total Print Solutions, Inc.
3220 W 121st Terr Leawood, KS 66209
(913) 481-7393 Constance Kingsley President
Fax: (913) 327-1251
Email: ckingsley@tpsmidwest.com
Website: www.tpsmidwest.com
Commercial printing, pharma labels, digital print, magazine type publications, business forms, direct mail, warehousing & distribution. (Woman/Hisp, estab 2000, empl 2, sales $800,000, cert: State, NMSDC)

Kentucky

7227 EDJ Inc.
8158 Mall Rd Florence, KY 41042
(859) 525-1199 Maureen Schuler President
Fax: (859) 525-3342
Email: maureen.schuler@fastsigns.com
Website: www.fastsigns.com/226
Banners, posters, foam boards, decals, site signs, dimensional logos, coroplast signs, now hiring signs, production boards, & tradeshow products and graphics. (Woman/White, estab 1995, empl 5, sales $856,000, cert: WBENC)

7228 Larger than Life Printing, LLC
10626 Worthington Ln Prospect, KY 40059
(502) 592-0399 Siri Seidt President
Fax: (502) 290-4305
Email: siri@insightbb.com
Website: www.ltlco.com
Large format printing, digital printing, banners, displays, tradeshow/event products, custom fabrications. (Woman/Nat Ame, estab 2005, empl 2, sales $30,000, cert: NMSDC)

7229 Multi-Craft Litho, Inc.
131 E Sixth St Newport, KY 41072
(859) 655-8863 Debbie Simpson President
Fax: (859) 581-8722
Email: dsimpson@multi-craft.com
Website: www.multi-craft.com
Commercial printing: pocket folders, annual reports, posters, brochures, sell sheets, packaging, etc. (Woman/White, estab 1955, empl 50, sales $9,500,000, cert: WBENC)

Louisiana

7230 Advanced Graphic Engraving, LLC
3105 Melancon Rd Broussard, LA 70518
(337) 364-1991 Monica Duplantis Mgr
Fax: (337) 364-1951
Email: monica@tagsfast.com
Website: www.tagsfast.com
Industrial Engraving: Safety Signage, Architectural signage, Vinyl signs & decals, Master/Well Control Panels, Sub Sea Well Control Panels, Flow Schematics, Data Tags, Operating Instruction Tags, Dual Language Tags, Angle Indicators, Crane Hand Signals. (Woman/White, estab 1997, empl 21, sales $2,000,000, cert: WBENC)

7231 Walle Corporation
600 Elmwood Park Blvd Harahan, LA 70123
(504) 734-8000 Dave Taylor Business Dev
Fax: (504) 733-2513
Email: dave_taylor@walle.com
Website: www.walle.com
Lithographic & flexographic label printing. (Woman/White, estab 1900, empl 175, sales , cert: WBENC)

Massachusetts

7232 Adam Graphic Corporation
63 N Washington St North Attleboro, MA 02760
(508) 699-2089 Nancy Ruo President
Fax: (508) 699-2672
Email: nancy@adamgraphic.com
Website: www.adamgraphic.com
Printing, print management, forms, envelopes, marketing brochures, folders, binders, ID cards, labels, commerical print, digital print, signage, mailings, fulfillment, kitting, warehousing, on-line ordering, promotional products. (Woman, estab 1985, empl 5, sales $1,193,045, cert: State, WBENC)

7233 CSW Inc.
45 Tyburski Rd Ludlow, MA 01056
(800) 800-9522 Scott Ellison VP Sales
Fax: (413) 583-6387
Email: scotte@cswgraphics.com
Website: www.cswgraphics.com
Packaging pre press, design, flexo plates, cutting dies. (Woman/White, estab 1936, empl 150, sales $16,160,013, cert: State, WBENC)

7234 Gangi Printing, Inc.
17 Kensington Ave Somerville, MA 02145
(617) 776-6071 Stephen Gangi Sales
Fax: (617) 776-6084
Email: steve@gangiprinting.com
Website: www.gangiprinting.com
Promotional printing & book binding services, printed apparel, trade show displays & direct mail pieces. (Woman/White, estab 1972, empl 9, sales $1,200,000, cert: State)

7235 Print & More Associates
143 North St Mattapoisett, MA 02739
(617) 899-3664 Fred Ford Sales Rep
Fax: (508) 758-9594
Email: frford@p-massociates.com
Website: www.p-massociates.com
Commercial printing, stationary, brochures, catalogs, window displays, POP, floor mats & banners. (AA, estab 2005, empl 6, sales $1,000,000, cert: NMSDC)

7236 Pyramid Printing and Advertising Inc
58 Mathewson Dr Weymouth, MA 02189
(781) 337-7609 Bill Scheufele Sales Rep
Fax: (781) 337-1046
Email: bill@pyramidprinting.net
Website: www.pyramidprinting.net
Multicolor offset & digital graphics. (Woman/White, estab 1978, empl 14, sales $1,400,000, cert: State)

7237   Schmidt Printing, Inc.
237 Chandler St   Worcester, MA 01609
(508) 752-7600   Ariel Schmidt Dir Sales/Mktg
Fax: (508) 752-7601
Email: ariel@schmidtprinting.ink
Website: www.schmidtprinting.ink
Eight Color Offset Printing, HP Indigo Printing, Variable
Data Printing, Stochastic Screening, Online Remote
Proofing, In-House Mailing Services, Full Service Bindery &
Fulfillment. (Hisp, estab 2011, empl 2, sales $54,307, cert:
NMSDC)

7238   Shafiis' Inc.
P.O. Box 215   East Longmeadow, MA 01028
(413) 224-2100   Jennifer Shafii CEO
Fax: (413) 224-2150
Email: jennifer@tigerpress.com
Website: www.tigerpress.com
Custom printing, digital prepress, packaging & bindery
services. (Woman/White, estab 1985, empl 70, sales
$8,800,000, cert: State)

7239   Spotlight Graphics, Inc.
9-B Whalley Way   Southwick, MA 01077
(413) 998-3232   Nancy Barmashi Sales
Fax: (413) 998-3232
Email: Nancy@SpotlightGraphicsInc.com
Website: www.SpotlightGraphicsInc.com
Large format printing. (Woman/White, estab 2013, empl 5,
sales $165,000, cert: State)

7240   Standard Modern Company, Inc.
186 Duchaine Blvd.   New Bedford, MA 02745
(508) 586-4300   Rodney Heger
Fax: (508) 584-4566
Email: rheger@standardmodern.com
Website: www.standardmodern.com
Commercial printing. (Woman/White, estab 1974, empl
44, sales $7,596,467, cert: State, WBENC)

7241   Starburst Printing & Graphics
300 Hopping Brook Rd   Holliston, MA 01764
(800) 244-8396   Jason Grondin VP
Fax: (508) 893-0955
Email: jgrondin@starburstprinting.com
Website: www.starburstprinting.com
Printing svcs: prepress, digital & offset & post press
services. (Hisp, estab 1988, empl 22, sales $2,600,000,
cert: State, NMSDC)

7242   Summit Press Inc.
63 Sixth St   Chelsea, MA 02150
(617) 889-3991   Lenore DelVecchio President
Fax: (617) 884-8096
Email: lenore@summitpress.com
Website: www.summitpress.com
Printing services: 2-6 color sheetfed. (Woman/White, estab
1961, empl 22, sales $2,910,000, cert: State)

7243   The Matlet Group
30 Industrial Way   Wilmington, MA 01887
(401) 834-3007   Sheldon Ross Director of Natl Accts
Fax: (401) 725-7896
Email: sross@thematletgroup.com
Website: www.thematletgroup.com
Printing & graphic services. (As-Pac, estab 2005, empl 408,
sales $99,498,000, cert: NMSDC)

Maryland

7244   Alpha Graphics, Inc.
3000 Chestnut Ave, Ste 101   Baltimore, MD
21211
(410) 727-1400   Christine Walsh President
Fax: (866) 568-7071
Email: cwalsh@alphagrap.com
Website: www.alpha-graphics.net
Large format printing: banners & signs, posters, mounting, laminating, framing, graphic design, menu boards,
point of purchase, adhesive vinyl, cut vinyl, trade show
display (Woman/White, estab 1973, empl 5, sales
$508,500, cert: State, City)

7245   Art & Negative Graphics, Inc.
4621 Boston Way Ste C   Lanham, MD 20706
(301) 459-8911   James Black Strategic Acct Exec
Fax: (301) 459-8819
Email: jblack@artneg.com
Website: www.artneg.com
Prepress, digital & offset printing; full bindery; mailing
services; storage and fulfillment. (Woman, estab 1981,
empl 42, sales $6,425,530, cert: State, WBENC)

7246   Black Classic Press
3921 Vero Rd Ste F   Halethorpe, MD 21227
(410) 242-6954   Kristance Coates Print Mgr
Fax: (410) 242-6959
Email: kristance@bcpdigital.com
Website: www.bcpdigital.com
Printing svcs: ultra short-run book & document printing,
digital. (AA, estab 1978, empl 9, sales $1,500,000, cert:
State)

7247   Britt's Industries Inc.
40 Hudson St Ste 112   Annapolis, MD 21401
(410) 266-8100   Elizabeth Britt President
Fax: (410) 224-3960
Email: contact@wosbprinting.com
Website: www.wosbprinting.com
Commercial printing, offset, digital, prepress, graphic
design, business cards, envelopes, letterhead, brochures,
pamphlets. (Woman/As-Pac, estab 1976, empl 17, sales
$784,035, cert: WBENC, 8(a))

7248   IVY Services, LLC
P.O. Box 20092   Baltimore, MD 21284
(410) 235-1489   Tammy Boccia VP
Fax: (410) 235-2489
Email: tboccia@ivy-services.com
Website: www.ivy-services.com
Offset printing: letterhead, envelopes, business cards,
brochures, flyers, string & button, metal clasp, latex,
peel & seal, tear strip & shrink wrapping. (Woman/
White, estab 2004, empl 2, sales $5,511,950, cert: State,
WBENC)

7249   The Strouse Corporation
1130 Business Pkwy S   Westminster, MD 21157
(410) 848-1611   Donald Pennington sales eng
Fax: (410) 848-9220
Email: dpennington@strouse.com
Website: www.strouse.com
Rotary die-cutting, slitting, 6 color printing, laminations.
(Woman/White, estab 1986, empl 70, sales $15,000,000,
cert: WBENC)

Michigan

7250 Graphic Resource Group
528 Robbins Dr   Troy, MI 48083
(248) 588-6100 Allen Pyc President
Fax: (248) 588-6101
Email: apyc@graphicresource.com
Website: www.graphicresource.com
Large format digital & screen printing, offset printing on plastics, promotional products. (Woman/White, estab 1990, empl 20, sales , cert: WBENC)

7251 Graywolf Printing
757 S Eton St   Birmingham, MI 48009
(248) 540-5930 Max Grayvold President
Fax: (248) 540-1748
Email: graywolf@ameritech.net
Website: www.graywolfprinting.com/
Printing services. (Nat Ame, estab , empl , sales $772,368, cert: NMSDC)

7252 Hatteras Printing, Inc.
12801 Prospect St   Dearborn, MI 48126
(313) 624-3300 Rebecca McFarlane VP
Fax:
Email: bmcfarlane@4hatteras.com
Website: www.4hatteras.com
Commercial printing. (Woman/White, estab 1977, empl 70, sales , cert: WBENC)

7253 Imax Company Inc.
22326 Woodward Ave   Ferndale, MI 48220
(248) 629-9680 Jay Williams President
Fax:
Email: jay@imaxprinting.com
Website: www.imaxprinting.com
Commercial printing, offset full color printing, multi page booklets, manuals, business cards, brochures, sales sheets, envelopes, posters, postcards, flyers, rack cards, special shapes (die cutting). (AA, estab 2009, empl 5, sales $879,852, cert: NMSDC)

7254 Impact Label Corp.
3434 S Burdick St   Kalamazoo, MI 49001
(269) 381-4280 Jill Jones Acct Mgr
Fax:
Email: jillj@impactlabel.com
Website: www.impactlabel.com
Labels, domed labels,tamper evident labels, nameplates, tags, polycarbonate overlays, control panel overlays, warning labels, product identification, serial numbers, security tags, inventory tags, asset labels, ingredient labels. (Woman, estab 1964, empl 50, sales , cert: WBENC)

7255 Kargilis Business Solutions, LLC
212 Shagbark Dr. Rochester Hills, MI 48309
(248) 477-1145 Marilyn Kargilis President
Fax:
Email: kargilisbiz@sbcglobal.net
Website:
Printing services: business forms, direct mail programs, commercial printing, labels, manuals, kit assembly, warehousing, document management & promotional products. (Woman, estab , empl 1, sales , cert: WBENC)

7256 Kimprint, Inc. dba Progressive Printing
1326 Goldsmith   Plymouth, MI 48170
(734) 459-2960 Bruce Price VP
Fax: (734) 453-6499
Email: sales@progressiveprint.com
Website: www.progressiveprint.com
Full color printing: flyers, brochures, postcards, directmail, stock & color consulting. (Woman/White, estab 1989, empl 20, sales $2,300,000, cert: WBENC)

7257 New Echelon
280 S Southbound Gratiot Ave Mt. Clemens, MI 48043
(586) 307-8001 Michael Arnold President
Fax: (586) 307-8002
Email: mcarnold@newechelon.com
Website: www.newechelon.com
Printing, bindery, big color output services. (AA, estab 1996, empl 8, sales , cert: NMSDC)

7258 Stylerite Label Corporation
2140 Avon Industrial Dr   Rochester Hills, MI 48309
(419) 367-3772 Danielle J. Kay Sales Exec/CSM
Fax: (800) 552-9441
Email: dkay@styleritelabel.com
Website: www.styleritelabel.com
Mfr Tags & Forms, short to long runs, 4 color process up to 8 colors, rolls, sheets, singles, fan-folded, continuous, printing on adhesive side of labels, lamination, UV varnish. (Woman/White, estab 1989, empl 25, sales $6,200,000, cert: WBENC)

7259 The MardonGroup LLC
701 Woodward Heights #128 Ferndale, MI 48220
(248) 336-3376 Shawn Torrence VP Bus Devel
Fax:
Email: s.torrence@mardongroup.com
Website: www.mardongroup.com
Sheet-Fed & Digital Printing, Design, Layout, Desktop Publishing, Binding, Envelopes, Mail list Processing, List Rental/Purchase, Offline Finishing, Digital/Mobile mktg. (AA, estab 2005, empl 15, sales , cert: NMSDC)

Minnesota

7260 Booth Publications Ink
1217 Seminole Ave   West St Paul, MN 55118
(651) 338-8140 Jason Booth CEO
Fax: (651) 209-3516
Email: jason@boothpublications.com
Website: www.boothpublications.com
Print services: off-set (web & sheet fed), digital, large format & plastic card printing. (Nat Ame, estab 1999, empl 6, sales $3,000,000, cert: NMSDC)

7261 Bywater Business Solutions LLC
800 Washington Ave SE Ste 203 Minneapolis, MN 55414
(763) 244-1090 Christopher Ferguson CEO
Fax: (612) 605-3304
Email: chris@bywater.co
Website: www.bywater.co
Printing: envelopes, labels, letterhead, notecards, folders, business forms, booklets, checks, business cards, direct mail, signs, annual reports, post-it notes. (Hisp, estab 2009, empl 3, sales $185,000, cert: State)

7262   Char-Dell Sign Co.
1017 109th Ave NE   Blaine, MN 55434
(763) 784-8252   Charlette Grandell VP
Fax: (763) 784-8210
Email: ken.grandell@fastsigns.com
Website: www.fastsigns.com/337
Wide Format Digital Printing, Banners, Banner Stands, Trade Show Booths, Trade Show Graphics,ADA & OSHA Compliant, Safety & Identification Materials, Presentation Materials, Posters, Name Tags, Large & Small Vehicle. (Woman/White, estab 1998, empl 4, sales $400,000, cert: City)

7263   Cimarron Graphics
15400 28th Ave N   Plymouth, MN 55447
(952) 697-3400   Barbara Schulz CEO
Fax: (952) 697-3399
Email: barb@cimgraphics.com
Website: www.cimgraphics.com
Commercial sheet fed & digital printing: brochures, postcards, catalogs, business forms, calendars, tabs, magnets, greeting cards, envelopes, letterhead, labels, annual reports, flyers, header cards, inserts, pocket folders. (Woman/White, estab 2004, empl 15, sales $1,598,609, cert: State)

7264   Clear Lake Press, Inc.
300 16th Ave SE   Waseca, MN 56093
(507) 835-4430   Phyllis Beschnett CEO
Fax: (507) 835-5673
Email: pbeschnett@clearlakepress.com
Website: www.clearlakepress.com
Marketing & printing solutions, sheet-fed, digital & variable, fulfillment, design services, collateral development & direct marketing, outdoor advertising & customized apparel services. (Woman/White, estab 1988, empl 34, sales $4,099,574, cert: WBENC)

7265   Dan Dolan Printing
2301 E Hennepin Ave   Minneapolis, MN 55413
(612) 379-2311   Jeanne Dolan CEO
Fax: (612) 379-0934
Email: jeannedolan@dolanprinting.com
Website: www.dolanprinting.com
Printing & marketing services: offset/lithographic printing, digital printing, large format printing, signage, banners, publications, business cards, textile printing, light boxes, trade show displays, pamphlet, letterhead, stationary, printed packaging. (Woman/White, estab 1985, empl 28, sales $6,434,227, cert: WBENC)

7266   Highlight Printing Inc.
3839 Washington Ave N   Minneapolis, MN 55412
(612) 522-7600   Lisa Bickford President
Fax: (612) 522-7584
Email: lisab@highlightprinting.com
Website: www.highlightprinting.com
Offset & digital 1-4 color printing, high-impact high-touch projects, thermography, design, direct mail, warehousing, kitting, niche fulfillment, distribution, work-flow system, saddle stitching, wire-o binding, binding. (Woman/White, estab 1900, empl 1, sales $1,205,000, cert: WBENC)

7267   Ideal Printers
645 Olive St   Saint Paul, MN 55130
(651) 855-1064   Emily Stevenson Acct Rep
Fax: (651) 855-1055
Email: Emily.stevenson@idealprint.com
Website: www.idealprint.com
Commercial sheetfed printing: 1-6 color & aqueous coating, brochures, newsletters, annual reports, posters, catalogs, packaging, stationary products. (Woman/White, estab 1979, empl 85, sales $12,625,028, cert: WBENC)

7268   IntegriPrint, Inc.
309 12th Ave S   Buffalo, MN 55313
(763) 682-3750   Jacqueline Wurm Owner
Fax: (763) 682-4791
Email: jackie@integriprint.com
Website: www.integriprint.com
Printing, graphic design & mailing services. (Woman/White, estab 1994, empl 5, sales $590,338, cert: WBENC)

7269   Lightning Printing dba Wallace Carlson Co.
10825 Greenbrier Rd   Minnetonka, MN 55305
(952) 277-1210   Ann Turbeville CEO
Fax: (952) 546-8755
Email: ann@wc-print.com
Website: www.wc-print.com
Printing svcs: 1-6color offset, sheetfed, aqueous coating, full color & B/W digital printing, mailing & fullfillment services. (Woman/White, estab 1984, empl 47, sales $9,128,000, cert: WBENC)

7270   Northstar Imaging Services, Inc.
1325 Eagandale Court Ste 130   Eagan, MN 55121
(651) 686-0477   Martha Smyre CEO
Fax:
Email: planroom@northstarimaging.com
Website: www.northstarimaging.com
Reprographic services, large & small format copying, plotting, scanning, color imagery & document management. (Woman/White, estab 1997, empl 5, sales $6,500,000, cert: State, City)

7271   SeaChange Print Innovations
14505 27th Avenue North   Plymouth, MN 55447
(763) 586-3700   Ann Marie Keene Business Dev
Fax:
Email: annmarie.keene@seachangemn.com
Website: www.seachangemn.com
Folding carton & marketing print production & Packaging, Marketing Printing, Commercial Printing, Direct Mail Printing, Digital Printing. (Woman/White, estab 2014, empl 90, sales $13,100,000, cert: WBENC)

7272   Team One Printing, Inc.
900 Sixth Ave SE Ste 180   Minneapolis, MN 55414
(612) 481-5907   Grace Wong
Fax:
Email: grace@teamoneprinting.com
Website: www.teamoneprinting.com
Commercial print & display graphics: brochures, newsletters, manuals, directories, catalogs, labels, direct mail pieces, portable trade show displays, banner stands, wall murals, vehicle graphics, sign & banner graphics, large format posters. (Woman/As-Pac, estab 2006, empl 3, sales , cert: NMSDC)

Missouri

7273 Brown Printing, Inc.
411 Madison St   Jefferson City, MO 65101
(573) 636-8012 Darla Porter President
Fax: (573) 635-3323
Email: dporter@brownprint.com
Website: www.modernlitho.com
Commercial printing, digital printing, mailing & fulfillment services, warehousing. (Woman/White, estab 1982, empl 36, sales $4,224,724, cert: State)

7274 Complete Solutions LLC
2233 N Village   St. Charles, MO 63303
(314) 640-6633 Donna Gastreich Owner
Fax: (314) 558-8320
Email: dgastreich@complete-solutionsllc.com
Website: www.complete-solutionsllc.com
Printing svcs: letterhead, business cards, envelopes, invoices, BOL, labels, tags, folders, binders, index tabs, brochures, catalogs & checks, direct mail services, promotional products & advertising specialty items. (Woman/White, estab 2008, empl 1, sales $28,000, cert: State, City)

7275 Isringhaus Printing LLC
11012 Lin Valle Dr, Ste D   Affton, MO 63123
(314) 416-9955 Patricia Isringhaus Owner
Fax: (314) 416-9956
Email: patti@isringhausprinting.com
Website: www.isringhausprinting.com
Commercial printing services. (Woman/White, estab 2002, empl 6, sales $600,000, cert: State)

7276 Modern Litho-Print Co.
6009 Stertzer Rd   Jefferson City, MO 65101
(573) 635-6119 Debra Patterson Cstmr consultant
Fax: (573) 636-2655
Email: debra@modernlitho.com
Website: www.modernlitho.com
Printing: annual reports, newsletters, books, magazines, promotional materials, labels, etc. (Woman/White, estab 1937, empl 88, sales $14,500,000, cert: State)

7277 PrintCOR Solutions
826 Heatherhaven Dr   Ballwin, MO 63011
(636) 891-9900 Kelly Kohn Owner
Fax: (636) 891-0204
Email: customerservice@printcorsolutions.com
Website: www.printcorsolutions.com
Labels/tags: blank stock labels, barcode pre-printed product labels, consecutively numbered barcode labels, thermal ribbons, integrated labels, piggy back labels, full color labels, die cut labels & custom labels. (Woman/White, estab 2006, empl 2, sales $1,500,000, cert: State)

7278 PrintFlex Graphics
2201 January Ave   St. Louis, MO 63110
(800) 406-7093 Elizabeth Pecha-Poelker CEO
Fax: (314) 781-8622
Email: eap@print-flex.com
Website: www.printflexgraphics.com
Promotional printing: instant redeemable coupons, dry release, folded & placed booklets, USDA & FDA direct food contact printing.
(Woman/White, estab 1995, empl 35, sales $6,128,000, cert: State, NWBOC)

7279 Watson Label Products
10616 Trenton Ave   St. Louis, MO 63132
(314) 493-9300 Robert Daugherty Reg sales Mgr
Fax: (314) 493-9399
Email: bob_daugherty@wlp.com
Website: www.wlp.com
Digital printing: harsh environment bar code labels for warehouses, assets, automotive, electronics, security, healthcare and library, proto-type packaging. (Woman/White, estab 1961, empl 25, sales $4,300,000, cert: WBENC)

Mississippi

7280 Ranger Distributing, Inc dba Ranger Label
286 Commerce Park Dr   Ridgeland, MS 39157
(601) 898-1380 Bob Anger VP
Fax: (601) 898-1387
Email: banger@rangerlabel.com
Website: www.rangerlabel.com
Prime 8 color pressure sensitive labels, blank thermal labels, complete color process controls. (Woman/White, estab 1979, empl 14, sales $3,000,000, cert: WBENC)

North Carolina

7281 DocuSource of North Carolina
2800 Slater Rd   Morrisville, NC 27560
(919) 459-5909 Michael Chorba President
Fax: (919) 459-5919
Email: mchorba@docusourceofnc.com
Website: www.docusourceofnc.com
Commercial digital printing, bindery, fulfillment & distribution services. (Woman/White, estab 2002, empl 46, sales $8,000,000, cert: State)

7282 Labels, Tags & Inserts, Inc.
2302 Air Park Dr   Burlington, NC 27215
(336) 227-8485 Rhonda Baker President
Fax: (336) 228-0861
Email: rhondab@lti-us.com
Website: www.labelstagsandinserts.com
Flexographic printing services: pressure sensitive labels, shrink film sleeves, vinyl labels, scratch off labels, tamper-evident labels, clear labels, hot foil labels, embossed labels, holographic labels. (Woman/White, estab 1995, empl 27, sales $7,000,000, cert: WBENC)

7283 PharmaPress, Inc.
3360 Old Lexington Rd   Winston-Salem, NC 27107
(973) 376-6625 Terri Roth President
Fax: (973) 376-3376
Email: pharmapress@gmail.com
Website: www.pharmapressinc.com
Mfr inserts, outserts, booklets, pamphlets, cards and pads. (Woman/White, estab 2004, empl 164, sales $2,400,000, cert: State)

7284 Progressive Business Solutions, Inc.
      508 New Hope Rd   Raleigh, NC 27610
      (919) 255-6500 Tim Catlett President
      Fax: (919) 255-6505
      Email: tcatlett@progform.com
      Website: www.progform.com
Commercial printing, business forms, promotional products, copy & computer paper, web ordering capabilities, office supplies, forms mgmt & warehouse dist. (AA, estab 1988, empl 27, sales $5,700,000, cert: NMSDC)

7285 Southern Print & Imaging, Inc.
      9311-D Monroe Rd   Charlotte, NC 28270
      (704) 708-5818 Barbara Jones President
      Fax: (704) 708-5878
      Email: barbara@allegracharlotte.com
      Website: www.allegracharlotte.com
Offset & digital printing, mail services, list sourcing, direct mail, brochures, flyers, newsletters, postcards, booklets & promotional products. (Woman/White, estab 2004, empl 4, sales $411,000, cert: City)

New Jersey

7286 4 Banner Inc. (DBA Alchemy Printing)
      125 5th Ave   Paterson, NJ 07524
      (973) 341-1311 Brett Haikins Production Coord
      Fax: (973) 977-8766
      Email: jobs@4banner.com
      Website: www.4banner.com
Large format printing: vinyl banners, mesh banners, dye sublimation fabric banners, trade show displays, banner stands, flatbed UV printing. Printing up to 10ft seamless. (As-Pac, estab 2010, empl 6, sales $550,000, cert: NMSDC)

7287 A+ Letter Service
      200 Syracuse Ct   Lakewood, NJ 08701
      (732) 905-2010 Elizabeth Fricke Sales Support
      Fax: (732) 905-4662
      Email: aplus@aplusletter.com
      Website: www.aplusletter.com
Print mailing inserts, postcards, brochures, marketing fulfillment, four-color digital printing, mailing services. (Woman/White, estab 1986, empl 75, sales $5,000,000, cert: State)

7288 American Plus Printers, Inc.
      2604 Atlantic Ave Ste 300 Wall, NJ 07719
      (732) 528-2170 Dianne Strohmenger President
      Fax: (732) 528-2174
      Email: diannes@amplusprint.com
      Website: www.americanplusprinters.com
Commercial printing, six color printing, digital page processing, photo retouching, color proofing & digital plate-making. (Woman/White, estab 2002, empl 10, sales $1,150,000, cert: State)

7289 Capital Printing Corporation
      420 South Ave   Middlesex, NJ 08846
      (732) 560-1515 Brett Russo
      Fax: (215) 560-8895
      Email: brettr@capitalprintingcorp.com
      Website: www.capitalprintingcorp.com
Printing services, die cutting & binding, automated in-line gluing & inserting, warehouse & mailing abilities. (Woman/White, estab 1983, empl 85, sales $15,100,000, cert: WBENC)

7290 CCG Marketing Services
      14 Henderson Dr   West Caldwell, NJ 07006
      (973) 808-0009 Steve Stern Sr Acct Exec
      Fax: (973) 808-9739
      Email: sstern@corpcomm.com
      Website: www.ccgms.com
Printing, offset, digital with variable data, web 1:1 Marketing with Variable Data, Digital Print Technology, Sales Collateral & Promotional Materials, Sales Force Support, Order Fulfillment. (Woman/White, estab 1900, empl 1, sales $20,000,000, cert: WBENC)

7291 CRW Graphics
      9100 Pennsauken Hwy   Pennsauken, NJ 08110
      (800) 820-3000 Kathleen Chinnici Acct Director
      Fax: (856) 665-1789
      Email: kchinnici@crwgraphics.com
      Website: www.crwgraphics.com
Digital & critical color prepress services & printing: 1 to 6 colors, bindery, fulfillment & mailing services. (Woman/White, estab 1993, empl 90, sales $15,500,000, cert: WBENC)

7292 Federal Direct
      150 Clove Road   Little Falls, NJ 07424
      (973) 272-7066 Angela Stubbs President
      Fax:
      Email: astubbs@feddirect.com
      Website: www.feddirect.com
Print, direct mail data & fulfillment services: data processing, sheet digital print, continuous form printing to 10 colors, continuous form laser (simplex, duplex, MICR) & inkjet personalization, bindery, fulfillment lettershop mailing services. (Woman/White, estab 1926, empl 125, sales $21,087,561, cert: WBENC)

7293 FrontEnd Graphics Inc.
      1951 Old Cuthbert Road, Ste 414   Cherry Hill, NJ 08034
      (856) 547-1600 Elizabeth Maul President
      Fax: (856) 547-3837
      Email: bettymaul@frontendgraphics.com
      Website: www.frontendgraphics.com
Layout, design, database mgmt, large project mgmt, digital photography, large output, direct to plate & press, finishing, distribution, kitting, mailing. Sheet fed, web, envelopes, label, manual, technical illustration, book publishing. (Woman/White, estab 1983, empl 13, sales $1,300,000, cert: WBENC)

7294 HighRoad Press, LLC
      220 Anderson Ave   Moonachie, NJ 07074
      (201) 708-6900 Hallie Satz CEO
      Fax: (201) 636-4088
      Email: hallie@highroadpress.com
      Website: www.highroadpress.com
Printing: web & sheet fed, offset sheet fed printing up to 8/C aqueous coating, offset half web didde press, coldset web & offset full web, packaging & DVD packaging. (Woman/White, estab 2004, empl 45, sales $10,000,000, cert: State, WBENC)

7295 Industrial Labeling Systems, Inc.
50 Kulick Rd   Fairfield, NJ 07004
(973) 882-9688   Keith Meyer Regional Sales Mgr
Fax: (973) 276-1882
Email: kmeyer@e-ilsi.com
Website: www.e-ilsi.com
Mfr & dist pressure-sensitive labels, prime labels, mailing labels, product ID labels, direct thermal labels, supermarket thermal scale labels, coupons, bar codes, tub labels, retail shelf marketing labels. (As-Pac, estab 1997, empl 23, sales $3,500,000, cert: State)

7296 Mahin Impressions, Inc. DBA Kirkwood Mahin
600 Meadowlands Parkway   Secaucus, NJ 07094
(201) 870-6300   Sharon Mahin President
Fax:
Email: smahin@kirkwood-mahin.com
Website: www.kirkwood-mahin.com
Offset & digital printing, digital & xerograhpy services, large format, finishing, binding, fullfillment & mailing. (Woman/White, estab 1983, empl 250, sales $20,000,000, cert: WBENC, SDB)

7297 Mountain Printing Company Inc.
P.O. Box 608   Berlin, NJ 08009
(856) 767-7600   Mark DiClementi Director of Ops
Fax: (856) 767-2698
Email: mark@mountainprinting.com
Website: www.mountainprinting.com
Commerical, packaging & digial printing services: bindery, pre-press, press, bindery, coatings, die cutting, foil stamping, embossing, box mfg & mailing capabilities. (Woman/White, estab 1962, empl 25, sales $2,499,116, cert: State)

7298 Nextwave Web LLC
229 Marshall St   Paterson, NJ 07503
(973) 742-4339   Alia Suqi Owner
Fax: (973) 742-5949
Email: alia@nextwaveweb.com
Website: www.nextwaveweb.com
Commercial offset & digital printing: print packaging/prototyping posters, banners, displays, customized shaped posters, books, booklets, magazines, catalogs, manuals, newsletters, flyers, brochures. (Woman/White, estab 2003, empl 8, sales $1,700,000, cert: State, WBENC)

7299 P/EK Press
7 Essex Rd   Scotch Plains, NJ 07076
(908) 305-1960   Ann Kahn Owner
Fax:
Email: annelizabethkahn@gmail.com
Website: www.pekpress.com
Commercial printing & graphic design: NCR forms, Brochures, Stationery, Posters, Direct Mail, Letterhead, Envelopes, Business Cards, Postcards, Note Cards, Presentation Folders, Pads. (Woman/White, estab 1989, empl 1, sales $126,000, cert: State)

7300 Positive Publications LLC
65 Madison Ave Ste 510   Morristown, NJ 07960
(973) 218-0310   Susan Poeton COO
Fax: (973) 455-0205
Email: spoeton@positivepublications.us
Website: www.positivepublications.us
Publishing, magazines, guides, pamphlets, periodicals, reprints, newsletters & e-newsletters. (Woman/White, estab 1998, empl 8, sales $827,880, cert: State)

7301 Primary Colors Graphics Inc.
629 Grove St 7th Fl   Jersey City, NJ 07310
(201) 526-9300   Cecilia Chin Controller
Fax: (201) 526-9298
Email: cecilia@primarycolorsgraphics.com
Website: www.primarycolorsgraphics.com
Commercial Offset Printing, Lithographic Printing, business cards, posters, finishing, trimming, die-cut, score, foil stamping, embossing. (As-Pac, estab 2012, empl 12, sales $1,303,673, cert: State)

7302 Regal Printing Company
One Graphics Dr   Ewing, NJ 08628
(609) 771-0555   Brian Haley Acct Exec
Fax: (609) 609-9609
Email: Brian.Haley@riegelcg.com
Website: www.riegelprintinginc.com
Digital pre-press services, conventional multi-color printing capabilities, digital print on demand, bindery & finishing, foil stamping, embossing, debossing & diecutting. (Woman/White, estab 1935, empl 75, sales $28,000,000, cert: WBENC)

7303 Riegel Printing Inc.
One Graphics Dr   Ewing, NJ 08628
(609) 771-0555   Brian Haley President
Fax: (609) 771-0947
Email: brian.haley@riegelprintinginc.com
Website: www.riegelprintinginc.com
Commercial printing svcs: pre-press, bindery, one to six color. (Woman/White, estab 1933, empl 70, sales $17,000,000, cert: WBENC)

7304 RJ Graphics, Inc.
206 Crown Point Rd   West Deptford, NJ 08086
(856) 848-1986   John Iannelli Director
Fax: (856) 848-5040
Email: jiannelli@rjgraphicsprinting.com
Website: www.rjgraphicsprinting.com
Commercial sheet-fed printing, digital printing, fulfillment, direct mail & web creative services. (Woman/White, estab 1979, empl 22, sales $3,300,000, cert: WBENC)

7305 Sheroy Printing
220 Entin Rd   Clifton, NJ 07014
(973) 242-4040   Robert Sternau Dir New Business Devel
Fax: (973) 242-8344
Email: roberts@onesourcenj.com
Website: www.onesourcenj.com
Graphic communications, marketing collateral, annual reports, catalogs, presentation kits, packaging, wide format point-of-purchase materials, direct mail & publications. (Woman, estab 1984, empl 65, sales $2,000,000, cert: State)

7306 Wheal-Grace Corporation
300 Ralph St   Belleville, NJ 07109
(973) 450-8100   Emil Salvini Director of Mktg
Fax:
Email: salvini@wheal-grace.com
Website: www.wheal-grace.com
Printing: corporate literature, product information, news magazines, business cards, letterheads, portfolios, posters. (Woman, estab 1946, empl 16, sales $11,301,000, cert: State)

New Mexico

7307   Captiva Group
3838 Bogan Ave NE   Albuquerque, NM 87109
(505) 872-2200   Jane Fernandez VP Business Dev
Fax: (505) 872-4200
Email: jfernandez@thecaptivagroup.com
Website: www.thecaptivagroup.com
Four color offset commercial printing; newsletters, business forms, envelopes, posters, books, etc. (Hisp, estab 1981, empl 100, sales , cert: NMSDC)

7308   R.W. Chavez, Inc.
1361 Flight Way SE   Albuquerque, NM 87106
(505) 264-2453   Nate Tapia Sales
Fax: (505) 883-0758
Email: Nate@stixon.com
Website: www.stixon.com
Commercial flexographic printing & mfr labels, pressure sensitive labels. (Woman/Hisp, estab 1985, empl 15, sales $2,800,000, cert: NWBOC)

New York

7309   Ampie Enterprises, Inc.
100 College Avenue Ste 130   Rochester, NY 14607
(585) 482-4400   Tina Paradiso President
Fax: (888) 629-9701
Email: tinap@imprintablesolutions.com
Website: www.imprintablesolutions.com
Envelopes, forms, carbonless sheets, reports, brochures & informational collateral. (Woman/White, estab 2013, empl 8, sales $1,500,000, cert: State)

7310   Classic Labels Inc.
217 River Ave   Patchogue, NY 11772
(718) 463-0256   Steven Ayala President
Fax: (718) 359-3262
Email: sayala@classiclabels.com
Website: www.classiclabels.com
Specialty pressure sensitive labels. (Hisp, estab 1979, empl 100, sales $3,000,000, cert: NMSDC)

7311   Dakota Print and Premiums LLC
150 Barton Road   White Plains, NY 10605
(914) 831-9101   Stuart Standard President
Fax: (914) 831-0668
Email: stuart@fuseprinting.com
Website: www.fuseprinting.com
Promotional products, commercial printing, wide format & transit advertising, vehicle wraps, directories, transit & marketing tools provider, screen printing, banners, posters, postcards, journals, award items, etc. (Woman/AA, estab 2004, empl 3, sales $606,000, cert: State, City, NMSDC)

7312   Duggal Visual Solutions, Inc.
10 W 24th St   New York, NY 10010
(212) 924-8100   Hillary Altman Design/Acct Mgr
Fax:
Email: hillary@duggal.com
Website: www.duggal.com
Printing, light box, digital display & fixtures. (As-Ind, estab 1963, empl 317, sales , cert: City, NMSDC)

7313   Fred Weidner & Daughter Printers
15 Maiden Ln, Ste 1601   New York, NY 10038
(212) 964-8676   Cynthia Weidner President
Fax: (212) 964-8677
Email: cynthia@fwdprinters.com
Website: www.fwdprinters.com
Printing services. (Woman/White, estab 1900, empl 6, sales , cert: State)

7314   Fulcrum Group
135 W 41st St   New York, NY 10036
(203) 909-6362   GIA VACCA Partner
Fax: (203) 909-6364
Email: gia@fulcrumpromos.com
Website: www.fulcrumgrp.com
Incentive Programs, Apparel, Promotional Merchandise, Printing & Creative Services, Large Format & Signage, Event Production, E-commerce& Fulfillment, Print Media. (Woman/White, estab 2010, empl 7, sales $1,200,000, cert: WBENC)

7315   Graphic Arts Inc.
11 Bertel Ave   Mount Vernon, NY 10550
(914) 663-8395   Wayne Purveille
Fax: (914) 663-0117
Email: wp@graphicartsinc.net
Website: www.graphicartsinc.net
Design & print brochures, newsletters, pamphlets, pocket folders, annual reports, sheets catalog mailing inserts, etc. (Woman/AA, estab 1994, empl 9, sales , cert: State, City, NMSDC)

7316   Minority Graphics Inc.
4202 Third Avenue   Brooklyn, NY 11232
(212) 255-4355   Tajuana Grant President
Fax: (212) 929-4237
Email: tg@minoritygraphics.com
Website: www.minoritygraphics.com
Offset & digital printing, fulfillment. (Woman/AA, estab 2004, empl 3, sales $190,000, cert: City, NMSDC)

7317   New York Image Studio LLC
68 Jay St Ste 810   Brooklyn, NY 11201
(212) 400-8889   Carole Fakler Owner
Fax:
Email: carole@nyimagestudio.com
Website: www.nyimagestudio.com
Post Production, PrePress, Image Editing, Photo Re-touching, Digital Printing, Large format printing, CGI, Design. (Woman/White, estab 2011, empl 5, sales $450,000, cert: State)

7318   No Other Impressions, Inc.
27 Tower Dr   Rochester, NY 14623
(585) 436-8500   Elaine McCarthy CEO
Fax: (585) 436-1606
Email: elaine@nootherimpressions.com
Website: www.nootherimpressions.com
Commercial color printing & fullfillment, digital & offset printing process. Complete in house bindery & fullfillment services. (Woman/White, estab 1990, empl 15, sales $1,800,000, cert: WBENC)

7319 North American D.F., Inc.
280 Watchogue Rd   Staten Island, NY 10314
(718) 698-2500 Debbie Ayala President
Fax: (718) 698-3600
Email: debbie@northamericandf.com
Website: www.northamericandf.com
Commercial printing: eight color, web & sheet fed, business forms, brochures, booklets, business stationary, folders, direct mailers, posters labels. (Woman/White, estab 1992, empl 10, sales $3,000,000, cert: State, City, WBENC)

7320 Panther Graphics Inc.
465 Central Ave   Rochester, NY 14605
(585) 546-7163 Henry Ehindero Sales Mgr
Fax: (585) 325-3943
Email: henry@panthergraphics.net
Website: www.panthergraphics.net
Commercial printing: brochures, coupons, marketing & promotional materials, large format printing, folding cartons, kit packing & distribution.
(AA, estab 1993, empl 25, sales , cert: State)

Ohio

7321 Associated Visual Communications, Inc.
200 Cherry Ave NE   Canton, OH 44702
(330) 452-4449 Raymond J Gonzalez President
Fax: (330) 452-1494
Email: rgonzalez@avcprint.com
Website: www.avcprint.com
Printing services: screen, digital & offset. (Hisp, estab 1979, empl 32, sales $2,814,501, cert: NMSDC)

7322 Bridge Media, LLC
1457 E 252nd St Ste 100 Euclid, OH 44117
(216) 526-3044 Craig Brooks, Sr. President
Fax:
Email: craig@bridge-ohio.com
Website: www.bridge-ohio.com
Printing: professional business cards, brochures & promotional materials, annual reports & glossy publications. (AA, estab 2008, empl 4, sales $65,000, cert: State)

7323 Cannell Graphics
5787 Linworth Rd   Worthington, OH 43085
(614) 330-9110 Nicole Dobson CEO
Fax: (614) 781-9759
Email: tjones@cannellgraphics.biz
Website: www.cannellgraphics.biz
Large & small digital, screen, offset format, mounting & laminating, scanning, document management, litigation support, copier services. (Woman/AA, estab 1964, empl 7, sales , cert: State, NMSDC)

7324 Commodity Management Services CMS
7233 Freedom Ave. NW   North Canton, OH 44720
(614) 207-2707 Curt Keels Business Dev Exec
Fax: (248) 208-1672
Email: ckeels@cmsprintsolutions.com
Website: www.cmsprintsolutions.com
Printing: business forms, print mgmt, print solutions, labels. (AA, estab 1999, empl 525, sales $72,893,797, cert: NMSDC)

7325 Copy King, Inc.
3333 Chester Avenue   Cleveland, OH 44114
(216) 861-3377 Peg Walsh President
Fax: (216) 861-6108
Email: peg@copy-king.com
Website: www.copy-king.com
Digital & offset press printing, binding, in house graphic design services, digital color printing, posters & large format printing, business cards. (Woman, estab 1995, empl 21, sales , cert: City)

7326 Corporate Document Solutions, Inc.
11120 Ashburn Rd   Cincinnati, OH 45240
(513) 595-8200 Mary Percy President
Fax: (513) 595-8205
Email: MPercy@cdsPRINT.com
Website: www.cdsPRINT.com
Design & pre-press services, layout compatibility, graphic file resolution, press imaging sizes & preferred file submission methods, black & white printing. (Woman/White, estab 1992, empl 18, sales $2,000,000, cert: WBENC)

7327 D Johnson Enterprises
912 Thayer Dr   Columbus, OH 43230
(614) 440-7559 Daniel Johnson President
Fax: (614) 269-7734
Email: LFBates00@aol.com
Website: www.djohnson-ent.com
Printing & imprinting services: digital 1-6 color & full color, news & media, scanning, digitizing, bulk mailing, books, charts, maps, brochures, menus, programs, wide angle custom formats, ad inserts, fliers, folders, envelopes. (AA, estab 1982, empl 8, sales $250,000, cert: NMSDC)

7328 Dana Graphics, Inc.
P.O. Box 42219   Cincinnati, OH 45242
(513) 351-4400 Debbie Coad Mgr, Cstmr service
Fax: (513) 351-4401
Email: debbie@danalink.com
Website: www.danalink.com
Graphic design, commercial & digital printing. (Woman/White, estab 1980, empl 8, sales $387,000, cert: WBENC)

7329 Dancor Inc.
2155 Dublin Rd   Columbus, OH 43228
(614) 737-3221 Michael Michalski Controller
Fax: (614) 340-2156
Email: mmichalski@dancorinc.com
Website:
Commercial printing. (Woman/White, estab , empl 1, sales $8,041,000, cert: WBENC)

7330 Hooven-Dayton Corporation
511 Byers Rd   Miamisburg, OH 45342
(937) 233-4473 Evan Arrindell VP Sales & Mktg
Fax: (937) 847-8011
Email: diversesupplier1@hoovendayton.com
Website: www.hoovendayton.com
print & convert pressure sensitive labels, coupons & custom specific solutions. (AA, estab 1935, empl 101, sales $24,899,000, cert: NMSDC)

7331   IC3D
     1697 Westbelt Dr   Columbus, OH 43228
     (614) 260-5631   Michael Cao CEO
     Fax:
     Email: michael@ic3dprinters.com
     Website: www.ic3dprinters.com/
3D printing services, prototyping & low volume manufacturing. (As-Pac, estab 2012, empl 10, sales $500,000, cert: NMSDC)

7332   Identity Systems, Inc.
     1324 Stimmel Road   Columbus, OH 43223
     (614) 448-1741   DeeDee Warden Acct Exec
     Fax: (614) 448-1749
     Email: dwarden@identitysystemsinc.com
     Website: www.identitysystemsinc.com
Commercial screen printing: vinyl, styrene, ABS & engraveable stock. Mfr name badges, signage, architectural signage, signage systems inserts, accordion/ spiral signs, engraved signs, nameplates, equipment tags, decals, plaques. (Woman/AA/As-Pac, estab 1986, empl 34, sales $3,626,392, cert: WBENC)

7333   JSCS Group, Inc. dba Market Direct
     3478 Hauck Road, Ste C   Cincinnati, OH 45241
     (513) 563-4900   Stephanie Harmon President
     Fax: (513) 733-8710
     Email: stephanie@marketdirectinc.com
     Website: www.marketdirectinc.com
Printing: offset & digital on-demand, direct marketing, direct mailing & fulfillment, mailing, target list development & management, graphic design. (AA, estab 2004, empl 5, sales $130,000, cert: NMSDC)

7334   RPI Color Service, Inc.
     1950 Radcliff Dr   Cincinnati, OH 45204
     (513) 471-4040   Karen Rellar EVP Mktg/Communications
     Fax: (513) 244-5387
     Email: karen.rellar@rpigraphic.com
     Website: www.rpigraphic.com
Off-set & digital printing, large & small format printing, die cutting, bindery & finishing, on demand printing, signage, packaging, sales samples, prototyping, displays, mailing services, point of sale materials, web-based tools. (Woman/AA/Hisp, estab 1969, empl 50, sales $9,200,000, cert: WBENC)

7335   SCANVenger Hunt LLC
     1275 Kinnear Road   Columbus, OH 43212
     (800) 975-5161   Sean Fields Director of Business Dev
     Fax: (612) 721-3370
     Email: sean@scanvengerhunt.biz
     Website: www.scanvengerhunt.biz
SCANVenger provides event services to corporations and organizations that drive engagement during conferences. Our services include event applications as well as registration badges for attendees. Our gamification platform can also be used for team buildi (AA, estab 2012, empl 3, sales $155,000, cert: NMSDC)

7336   Swimmer Printing dba Alphagraphics
     1701 E 12th St   Cleveland, OH 44114
     (216) 623-1005   Judith Swimmer President
     Fax: (216) 623-1185
     Email: us320@alphagraphics.com
     Website: www.us320.alphagraphics.com
One to four color offset printing, B&W & color copy services, Mailing services, Digital archiving, Poster & banner printing, Prepress & design services, Finishing & bindery services. (Woman/White, estab 1991, empl 9, sales $1,400,000, cert: City)

7337   Ten 10 Design LLC
     115 Wilson Mills Rd, Ste 6   Chardon, OH 44024
     (440) 286-4367   Joe Zulandt Sales Mgr
     Fax: (440) 286-5168
     Email: joe@ten10designllc.com
     Website: www.ten10designllc.com
Printing (offset and digital), promotional items, ad specialties, mailing services, labels & decals, graphic design, web design. (Woman/AA, estab 2008, empl 3, sales $250,000, cert: State, NMSDC, WBENC)

7338   Three Leaf Productions, Inc.
     261 West Johnstown Rd #200 Gahanna, OH 43230
     (614) 626-4941   Ron Stokes President
     Fax: (614) 626-8880
     Email: rstokes@three-leaf.com
     Website: www.three-leaf.com
Commercial & large digital format printing: retail packaging, point of purchase displays, banners & signs, fulfillment services, pick & pack, kitting, promotional premiums. (AA, estab 1995, empl 15, sales $10,271,000, cert: State, NMSDC)

Oklahoma

7339   Choctaw Nation of Oklahoma
     2712 Enterprise Blvd   Durant, OK 74701
     (580) 924-1120   Kolton Prince Sales
     Fax: (580) 924-1131
     Email: kolton@texprintone.com
     Website: www.texprintone.com
Commercial printing products. (Nat Ame, estab 1979, empl 11, sales $6,000,000, cert: NMSDC)

7340   OakTree Software, Inc.
     1437 S Boulder Ave, Ste 300   Tulsa, OK 74119
     (918) 584-7900   Tony Floyd Business Dev
     Fax: (918) 584-1396
     Email: tony.floyd@oaktreesoftware.com
     Website: www.oaktreesoftware.com
IT Consulting, training and services (Woman/White, estab 1995, empl 100, sales $10,000,000, cert: WBENC)

7341   Professional Image
     12437 E 60th St   Tulsa, OK 74146
     (918) 461-0609   Michelle Sparks President
     Fax: (918) 615-1837
     Email: msparks@calvertco.com
     Website: www.pi-pkg.com
Printing svcs: full color, digital prepress, custom graphic design, digital die templates, foil stamping, aqueous & UV coating, lamination, embossing, color mgmt. (Woman/White, estab 1984, empl 43, sales , cert: WBENC)

Oregon

7342　Industrial Safety Solutions Corporation
14791 SE 82nd Dr　Clackamas, OR 97015
(503) 303-5958　Rhonda Evans President
Fax: (503) 303-5968
Email: revans@industrialsafetysolution.com
Website: www.industrialsafetysolution.com
Industrial labeling systems, in-house pipe marking, 5S,
Kaizen & general directional labeling. (Woman/As-Pac,
estab 2004, empl 6, sales $854,257, cert: State)

7343　PrintSync, Inc.
6775 SW 111th Ave, Ste 10　Beaverton, OR 97008
(503) 520-2000　Angela Willis President
Fax: (503) 520-2001
Email: supplier.diversity@printsync.com
Website: www.printsync.com
Printing & copying, direct mail & fulfillment. (Woman/
White, estab 1991, empl 10, sales $2,048,000, cert:
WBENC)

Pennsylvania

7344　Brenneman Printing, Inc.
1909 Olde Homestead Lane　Lancaster, PA 17601
(717) 299-2847　David Carson Dir Sales & Mktg
Fax: (717) 299-4965
Email: dave.carson@brennemaninc.com
Website: www.brennemaninc.com
Commercial printing: offset printing 1-5 colors, thermography, digital printing, variable data printing, inkjet addressing, mailing services, inserting, database management,
online ordering storefronts, mail list acquisition, custom
distribution services. (Woman/White, estab 1969, empl
30, sales , cert: State, WBENC)

7345　Chaucer Press, Inc.
535 Stewart Rd　Wilkes-Barre, PA 18706
(570) 825-2005　Patricia Frances CEO
Fax: (570) 825-0535
Email: pfrances@chaucerpress.com
Website: www.chaucerpress.com
Printed packaging & on-pack promotional materials:
pressure-sensitive, cut & extended content labels, folding
cartons, inserts, on-serts, blister cards, sleeves,
foilstamping, embossing, screen printing, structural
design. (Woman/White, estab 1965, empl 52, sales
$15,000,000, cert: WBENC)

7346　Diamond Graphics Inc.
456 Acorn Lane　Downingtown, PA 19335
(610) 269-7010　Barbara Martin Owner
Fax: (610) 269-7335
Email: barb@diamondgraphicsprint.com
Website: www.diamondgraphicsprint.com
Commercial Printing, Direct Mail, Web Offset, Brochures,
Pharmaceutical inserts, Letters, Flyers, Circulars, Instruc-
tion Manuals, Note Pads, Inserts, Reply Cards, Order Cards.
(Woman, estab 1999, empl 40, sales $6,500,000, cert:
WBENC)

7347　Graphic Arts, Incorporated
2867 East Alleghany Ave　Philadelphia, PA 19134
(215) 382-5500　Fred Binder Acct Exec
Fax: (215) 425-9715
Email: fbinder@galitho.com
Website: www.galitho.com
Full color sheet fed printing: finish, fulfill & mail.
(Woman/White, estab 1928, empl 100, sales $6,135,881,
cert: City, WBENC)

7348　Imprints Unlimited Inc.
4950 Parkside Ave　Philadelphia, PA 19131
(215) 879-9484　Jimmy Sams CEO
Fax: (215) 879-8466
Email: jwsams@imprints-unlimited.com
Website: www.imprints-unlimited.com
Commercial printing. (AA, estab 1985, empl 6, sales ,
cert: City)

7349　Innovation Marketing Communications LLC
232 Conestoga Rd　Wayne, PA 19154
(215) 802-2885　George Slater Major Accts Mgr
Fax: (215) 464-7664
Email: gslater@Phoenixlitho.com
Website: www.innomc.com
Creative, offset & digital printing, wide format, physical
& virtual events, warehousing & web-to-print solutions.
(As-Pac, estab 1973, empl 92, sales $20,500,000, cert:
NMSDC)

7350　Migu Press Inc.
260 Ivyland Rd　Warminster, PA 18974
(215) 957-9763　Ken Bucker New Business Devel
Fax: (215) 957-3240
Email: kenb@migu4u.com
Website: www.migu4u.com
Commercial printing. (Woman/White, estab 1988, empl
28, sales , cert: State, WBENC)

7351　Movad
801 Bristol Pike　Bensalem, PA 19020
(215) 638-2679　Terri Gasbarra Business Dev
Fax: (215) 638-1720
Email: bhanf@gostrata.com
Website: www.movadcorp.com
Digital & offset printing, mailing services, bindery &
finishing, fulfillment, variable data printing, database
services, graphic design & pre-press, online ordering &
proofing. (Woman/White, estab 1986, empl 11, sales
$1,500,000, cert: WBENC)

7352　PAP Technologies, Inc.
1813 Colonial Village Ln　Lancaster, PA 17601
(717) 399-3333　Michael Robinson President
Fax: (717) 394-3333
Email: mrobinson@paptech.net
Website: www.paptech.net
Printing, warehousing, distribution, fulfillment &
machine automation, electrical control panels. (AA,
estab 1988, empl 54, sales , cert: State, NMSDC)

7353 Standard Offset Printing Co., Inc.
433 Pearl St PO Box 19603 Reading, PA 19603
(610) 375-6174 Hobart Clark Rep
Fax: (610) 375-6254
Email: hclark@standardgroup.com
Website: www.standardgroup.com
6 color offset printing, digital black & white, digital full color, aqueous coating, film lamination, UV coatings, online ordering, trim, fold, stitch, die cutting, coil binding, hand assembly, flexible laminated magnets. (Woman/White, estab 1900, empl 160, sales $25,000,000, cert: State)

7354 TMMPROMOS.COM dba The Artifactori
140 Christopher Ln, Ste 101 Harleysville, PA 19438
(215) 513-1693 Victoria Magagna President
Fax: (215) 513-1840
Email: tori@theartifactori.com
Website: www.theartifactori.com
Commercial Printing, Large-Format Printing, Direct mail, Fulfillment, Warehousing, and Custom Distribution, Branded Promotional Products, and Custom Apparel. (Woman/White, estab 2014, empl 3, sales $617,000, cert: WBENC)

7355 Triangle Press Inc.
6720 Allentown Blvd Harrisburg, PA 17112
(717) 541-9315 Tammy Shelley VP
Fax: (171) 703-1060
Email: tammy@trianglepress.net
Website: www.trianglepress.net
Graphic design, wide format printing, digital printing, variable data, 5-color offset printing, fulfillment & delivery. (Woman/White, estab 1970, empl 21, sales $3,175,100, cert: WBENC)

7356 Unity Printing Co., Inc.
5848 State Route 981 Latrobe, PA 15650
(724) 537-5800 Lisa Frederick President
Fax: (724) 539-1881
Email: wbenc@unityprinting.com
Website: www.unityprinting.com
Digital Printing, Offset Printing, Direct Mail, services, Variable Data Services, Warehousing. (Woman/White, estab 1979, empl 35, sales , cert: WBENC)

7357 Universal Printing Company LLC
1205 O'Neill Hwy Dunmore, PA 18512
(570) 342-1243 Margaret McGrath CEO
Fax: (570) 585-0962
Email: mah@universalprintingcompany.com
Website: www.universalprintingcompany.com
Commercial printing, fulfillment, 4, 8 & 10 color presses with roll-to-sheet capabilities. (Woman/White, estab 1995, empl 150, sales $32,396,000, cert: WBENC)

Puerto Rico

7358 3A Press
P.O. Box 47 Lajas, PR 00667
(787) 899-0110 Marie Rosado President
Fax: (787) 899-0155
Email: mrosado@3apress.com
Website: www.3apress.com
Mfr & print pharmaceutical, commercial & folding cartons, inserts, stitched & perfect bound booklets/magazines, printed literature. (Hisp, estab 1996, empl 126, sales $11,200,000, cert: NMSDC)

7359 Pardo and Company, LLC
P.O. Box 190639 San Juan, PR 00919
1 787-9277 Isabel Pardo President
Fax: 1 787-4550
Email: isabel.pardo@pardoandcompany.com
Website: www.pardoandcompany.com
Pardo and Company (ï¿½Pardoï¿½) is an enterprise that has a close relationship with Bio-Nuclear of Puerto Rico, Inc. We not only purchase and resell products from then, but we share facilities (given our lease agreement) (Woman/Hisp, estab 2013, empl 1, sales , cert: NMSDC)

South Carolina

7360 National Beverage Screen Printers, Inc
12000 Main St Williston, SC 29853
(803) 266-5272 Janet Roberson President
Fax: (803) 266-5301
Email: jroberson@nbsinc.net
Website: www.nbsinc.net
Screen printing, digital printing, plastic injection & metal fabrication. (Woman/White, estab 1984, empl 38, sales $7,000,000, cert: WBENC)

Tennessee

7361 A-1 Printing Services
810 E Brooks Rd Memphis, TN 38116
(901) 396-2023 Frazer Windless President
Fax: (901) 344-8734
Email: fwindless@a1printingsvc.com
Website: www.a1printingsvc.com
Commercial sheet-fed printing. (AA, estab 1988, empl 12, sales $1,179,800, cert: NMSDC)

7362 Advanced Label Worx
1006 Larsen Dr Oak Ridge, TN 37830
Jeanie Bone Mktg Dir
Fax: (865) 813-2718
Email: jbone@advancedlabelworx.com
Website: www.advancedlabelworx.com
Flexographic pressure-sensitive labels, specialty converting, die-cut components, digital imprinting. (Woman/White, estab 1968, empl 120, sales , cert: WBENC)

7363 Broadwater & Associates Group, Inc.
315 Tenth Ave N, Ste 93 Nashville, TN 37203
(615) 256-6707 Al Jenkins Solutions Consultant
Fax: (615) 256-6708
Email: al.jenkins@broadwaterprint.com
Website: www.broadwaterprint.com
Commercial printing, promotional products. (AA, estab 2001, empl 5, sales $353,000, cert: State)

7364 Graphic Label Solutions
2407 Pulaski Hwy   Columbia, TN 38401
(931) 490-0019 Allison Spader VP
Fax: (931) 490-0024
Email: allison@graphiclabelsolutions.com
Website: www.graphiclabelsolutions.com/
Labels, decals, overlays, nameplates, membrane switches, RFID, EAS. (Woman/White, estab 2002, empl 5, sales $5,000,000, cert: State, WBENC)

7365 Tec-Print, LLC
4600 Cromwell Ave, Ste 101   Memphis, TN 38118
(865) 471-1846 Lynn Higgs Business Develop
Fax: (865) 475-6973
Email: lhiggs@nashua.com
Website: www.tec-print.com
Printing: labels, tickets, cash register receipts, brochures, pamphlets, forms, digital off-set or roll fed web, etc. (AA, estab 2004, empl 23, sales $896,000, cert: NMSDC)

7366 Women in Printing, LLC
2285 Hwy 47 N   White Bluff, TN 37187
(615) 797-9811 Teri Doochin President
Fax: (615) 797-9042
Email: tdoochin@womeninprinting.com
Website: www.womeninprinting.com
Flexographic & offset printing, films & laminated structures, labels, coupons, blister-board, offset and rotary printing, finished pouches & bags. (Woman/White, estab 2004, empl 15, sales $2,500,000, cert: WBENC)

7367 Worldwide Business Group
158 Madison Ave, Ste 101   Memphis, TN 38103
(901) 454-9290 Kathryn Dewey Regional Sales
Fax: (901) 297-4125
Email: Kdewey@worldwidebg.com
Website: www.worldwidebg.com
Printed product labels: pressure sensitive, reseal & extended content, bill paper forms, jumbo roll forms & Information for Use inserts. (AA, estab 2000, empl 26, sales $5,000,000, cert: NMSDC)

Texas

7368 AC Printing LLC
3400-1 S Raider Dr   Euless, TX 76040
(817) 267-8990 Robert Bolt Sales
Fax: (817) 354-0880
Email: acpsales@acprinting.com
Website: www.acprinting.com
Commercial printing. (As-Ind, estab 1989, empl 40, sales $7,790,014, cert: State, NMSDC, SDB)

7369 Advanced Business Graphics, Inc.
680 S Royal Lane, Ste 200   Coppell, TX 75019
(972) 471-3740 Sales Sales
Fax: (972) 393-1680
Email: abgi@abgi.com
Website: www.abgi.com
Printed products-business forms, checks, labels, commercial printing, promotional items, packaging, printer supplies, stationery items, presentation materials, office supplies. (Woman/White, estab 1995, empl 8, sales $5,884,880, cert: State, WBENC)

7370 Alliance of Diversity Printers, LLC
15950 Dallas Parkway Ste 400   Dallas, TX 75248
(214) 856-8368 Terri Quinton CEO
Fax:
Email: terri@adp-llc.com
Website: www.adp-llc.com
Print management solution. (Woman/As-Pac/Hisp, estab 2008, empl 12, sales $12,700,000, cert: State, NMSDC, WBENC)

7371 Bayside Printing Co, Inc
160 Lockhaven Dr   Houston, TX 77073
(281) 209-9500 David Solis VP of Business Dev
Fax: (281) 209-9569
Email: david@baysideprinting.com
Website: www.baysideprinting.com
Commercial multi-color printing: prepress, multiple sheet fed presses, 6 color, coaters, in-house bindery, die cutting & assembly, mailing & fulfillment. (Woman/Hisp, estab 1973, empl 30, sales $7,000,000, cert: NMSDC, WBENC)

7372 Best Press Inc.
4201 Airborn Dr   Addison, TX 75001
(972) 930-1000 Brian Rozansky Mktg/Business Develop
Fax: (972) 930-1030
Email: admin@bestpress.com
Website: www.bestpress.com
Commercial printing. (Woman/White, estab 1993, empl 100, sales $13,200,000, cert: State, WBENC)

7373 Creative Menus & Folders, LLC dba Texas Covers
409 Old Hwy 80   Olden, TX 76466
(254) 653-2775 Renee Forguson Asst Production Mgr
Fax: (254) 653-2776
Email: reneeforguson@texascovers.com
Website: www.texascovers.com
Presentation/Executive Binders, folders, business cards, printing (screen, digital, offset, foil stamp, deboss, specialty color cast printing, plastic ID badge holders, ID badges, name tags, souvenir printing, banners, signage, laminating, caps. (As-Pac, estab 2015, empl 19, sales $135,353, cert: NMSDC)

7374 Digi-Color, LP
4414 Hollister   Houston, TX 77040
(713) 934-9800 Barkla Tully Managing Partner
Fax: 713*349810
Email: barkla@digi-color.com
Website: www.digi-color.com
Digital printing; climate-controlled warehousing & fulfillment, mailing, on-line inventory management - ordering & reporting, on-demand 4 color & black/white digital printing, document management services, binding & finishing, packaging, kitting. (Woman/White, estab 2004, empl 20, sales $4,525,142, cert: State, WBENC)

7375 Dragonfly Group
1015 Amesbury Dr Murphy, TX 75094
(972) 742-2215 Laura McClain President
Fax: (972) 881-0820
Email: laura@thedragonflygroup.net
Website: www.thedragonflygroup.net
Print production & creative design: litho, UV, web, silkscreen, digital & flexo printing, full bindery, finishing, diecutting, assembly, kitting & fulfillment. (Woman/Nat Ame, estab 2004, empl 1, sales $1,163,510, cert: WBENC)

7376 Dynamic Color Graphics
P.O. Box 161758 Fort Worth, TX 76161
(817) 520-6631 Kathy Bowers President
Fax: (817) 520-6638
Email: kathy@dynamiccolorgraphics.com
Website: www.dynamiccolorgraphics.com
Printing: large format digital printing, banners, posters, trade show graphics, booths, vehicle graphics, floor graphics, murals, fine art reproduction, digital photo lab. (Woman/White, estab 2000, empl 19, sales $9,403,342, cert: State)

7377 Exalt Printing Solutions
1875 Monetary Lane Carrollton, TX 75006
(972) 245-3858 Lisa Marta CEO
Fax:
Email: lisa@exaltprinting.com
Website: www.exaltprinting.com
Printing, promotional & office products, forms, labels, brochures, checks, direct mail. (Woman, estab 2004, empl 48, sales $8,150,000, cert: State, WBENC)

7378 FBC Enterprises, Inc.
5110 Rondo Dr Fort Worth, TX 76106
(817) 740-1951 Teresa McClain Sales Rep
Fax: (817) 740-1571
Email: tmcclain@customgs.com
Website: www.customgs.com
Commercial printing, web & sheetfed, bindery svcs: direct mail, booklets, catalogs, posters, pocket folders, door hangers & brochures, hand assembly, kitting, custom distribution & fulfillment. (Woman/White, estab 1990, empl 45, sales $4,500,000, cert: WBENC)

7379 Global Bridge Infotech Inc.
5525 N Macarthur Blvd, Ste 670 Irving, TX 75038
(972) 550-9400 Vishnu Sethuraman Swarna Dir
Business Dev
Fax: (972) 550-9490
Email: vishnu@gbitinc.com
Website: www.gbitinc.com
Commercial, full-color web offset printing, sheet-fed, digital design & print. (As-Ind, estab 2006, empl 97, sales $9,000,000, cert: State, NMSDC)

7380 ISSGR, Inc. dba ImageSet
6611 Portwest Dr Ste 190 Houston, TX 77024
(713) 869-7700 Debbi Briggs President
Fax: (713) 869-7707
Email: diversity@imageset.com
Website: www.imageset.com
Digital printing, large format graphics, premedia & graphic design. (Woman/White, estab 1985, empl 31, sales $4,325,248, cert: WBENC)

7381 Label Systems, Inc.
4111 Lindberg Dr Addison, TX 75001
(972) 387-4512 Amy Van Brunt President
Fax: (972) 387-4935
Email: amy@labelsystemsinc.com
Website: www.labelsystemsinc.com
Mfr custom labels, flexography, hot stamping & silkscreening, promotional products & incentive programs (Woman/White, estab 1994, empl 10, sales $350,000, cert: State, WBENC)

7382 Marfield Corporate Stationery
1225 E Crosby Rd Ste B-1 Carrollton, TX 75006
(877) 245-9122 Lee Ann Packard CEO
Fax: (800) 432-9404
Email: leeann_packard@marfield.com
Website: www.marfield.com
Printing, engraving, embossing, foil stamping: business cards, letterheads & envelopes. (Woman/White, estab 1968, empl 17, sales $2,000,000, cert: State)

7383 Nicholas Earth Printing, LLC
7021 Portwest Dr. Ste 100 Houston, TX 77024
(713) 880-0195 Arita C. Nicholas CEO
Fax: (713) 880-4095
Email: anicholas@nicholasearth.com
Website: www.nicholasearth.com
Sheetfed printing, UV & aqueous coating, web printing & inline, digital prepress & computer to plate, digital archiving, bindery, fulfillment, outdoor advertising. (Woman/AA, estab 2003, empl 18, sales $13,000,000, cert: State, CPUC)

7384 Nieman Printing
10615 Newkirk St Dallas, TX 75220
(214) 458-8011 James Quinonez Acct Rep
Fax: (972) 869-3632
Email: jq@niemanprinting.com
Website: www.niemanprinting.com
Digital pritning: short runs, small press, large press up to 12 colors with UV or AQ on paper or plastic. (Woman/White, estab 1984, empl 160, sales $22,000,000, cert: State, WBENC)

7385 Parker Business Forms, Inc.
7395 Frint Dr Beaumont, TX 77705
(409) 842-5251 Heather Camp VP
Fax: (409) 842-5528
Email: heather@parkerbf.com
Website: www.parkerbf.com
Commercial & industrial printing: letterheads, envelopes, thank you cards, note cards, Christmas Cards, carbonless forms - invoices, purchase orders, shipping manifest, etc., full color(shortand long run). (Woman/White, estab , empl 20, sales $6,000,000, cert: WBENC)

7386 Peacock Press LLC
538 Shepherd Garland, TX 75042
(972) 272-7764 Ru Patel COO
Fax: (201) 573-1275
Email: Ru@peacockpress.net
Website: www.peacockpress.net
Digital printing, offset printing, complete finishing capabilities. (As-Ind, estab 2003, empl 15, sales $2,500,000, cert: State, NMSDC)

7387 Technology Media Group
1262 Viceroy Dr   Dallas, TX 75247
(214) 267-0535 Amanda Clarke Business Dev
Fax: (214) 637-9320
Email: amandaclarke@tmguniverse.com
Website: www.tmguniverse.com
Offset print, digital print, high speed web printing, signage (retail, pop, interior, exterior, etc), wearables, screenprint, embroidery, promotional, warehousing, fulfillment, distribution, graphic design, envelope manufacturing, foil stamp, die cut. (Woman/White, estab 1986, empl 75, sales $9,000,000, cert: State)

Virginia

7388 BBR Print Inc.
807 Oliver Hill Way   Richmond, VA 23219
(804) 901-2535 Brooke Rhodes Cstmr svc
Fax: (804) 230-1244
Email: brooke@jamesriverpress.com
Website: www.jamesriverpress.com
Printing services: in-house art dept, offset press & copy svcs, bindery. (Woman/White, estab 1997, empl 15, sales $1,143,000, cert: State)

7389 Grubb Printing & Stamp Co.
3303 Airline Blvd, Ste 1G Portsmouth, VA 23701
(757) 465-7855 Darla Alexander Sales Rep
Fax: (757) 465-3737
Email: darla@grubbprint.com
Website: www.grubbprint.com
Commercial printing. (Woman, estab 1900, empl 16, sales $17,002,000, cert: State)

7390 JoMoCo Studio LLC
8416 Staples Mill Rd   Richmond, VA 23228
(804) 262-3555 Joe Coleman Mgr
Fax: (804) 262-1055
Email: engraving@jomocostudio.com
Website: www.jomocostudio.com
Engraving: stainless steel, brass, aluminum & plastic signs, nameplates, name badges, labels, legends, tags, awards & plaques, vinyl signs, braille signs, acrylic awards & laser engraved metals & glass. (Woman/White, estab 1985, empl 3, sales $523,155, cert: State)

7391 PCT Law Group, PLLC
330 John Carlyle St Ste 300 Alexandria, VA 22314
(703) 881-9141 Raymond Millien Owner
Fax: (201) 573-1275
Email: rmillien@pctlg.com
Website:
PCT Law Group, PLLC is a law firm with offices in Washington, D.C., Northern Virginia, and Jacksonville, FL that provides legal services and representation in the complementary core areas of corporate (AA, estab 2007, empl 3, sales $1,095,270, cert: State)

7392 Premier Reprographics, Inc.
4701-A Eisenhower Ave   Alexandria, VA 22304
(703) 370-6612 Vickie Banks CEO
Fax:
Email: vickie@premierrepro.com
Website: www.premierrepro.com
Digital printing, copying, binding, scanning, posters, manuals, newsletters, booklets, reports, proposals, marketing collateral, presentations, laminating, blueprinting, drymounting, large & small format color. (Woman/AA, estab 1993, empl 10, sales $1,000,000, cert: State)

Washington

7393 Angel Screen Printing, Inc.
8459 S 208th St, Bldg N   Kent, WA 98031
(206) 755-7737 Rex Korrell Mktg Mgr
Fax: (253) 872-4118
Email: rex@angelscreenprinting.net
Website: www.angelscreenprinting.net
Screen printing and Embroidery services. (Woman/As-Pac, estab 2004, empl 8, sales $672,896, cert: State, NMSDC)

7394 EE Printing. LLC
8258 S 192nd St   Kent, WA 98032
(425) 656-1250 Tory Nguyen
Fax: (425) 656-4421
Email: tory@eeprinting.com
Website: www.eeprinting.com
From one color to full color, offset to digital, business forms, business cards, stationary, bulk volume envelopes, signs, posters, manuals, books, NCR forms, flyer, brochures. (Woman/As-Pac, estab 2007, empl 3, sales $190,752, cert: State, NMSDC)

7395 Risque Inc.
1122 N State St Bellingham, WA 98225
(360) 738-1280 Nadeem Israr President
Fax: (360) 738-0864
Email: nadeem@copysource.com
Website: www.copysource.com
Printing services: digital printing, poster printing, offset printing, copying, publishing, etc. (Woman/As-Ind, estab 1990, empl 15, sales $1,200,000, cert: State)

Wisconsin

7396 Badgerland Products, Inc.
145 Industrial Dr   Twin Lakes, WI 53181
(262) 877-2158 Mike Siegler Acct Mgr
Fax: (262) 877-2150
Email: Mike@blplabels.com
Website:
Mfr pressure sensitive labels, wharehousing & order fulfillment. (Woman/White, estab 1981, empl 15, sales , cert: State)

7397   Crossmark Graphics, Inc.
       16100 W Overland Dr   New Berlin, WI 53151
       (262) 821-1343 Tammy Rechner President
       Fax: (262) 821-5354
       Email: trechner@crossmarkgraphicsinc.com
       Website: www.crossmarkgraphicsinc.com
Print communication, litho, UV printing, lenticular, POS,
digital, PURLs, fulfillment/kit packing & web-to-print.
(Woman/White, estab 1987, empl 48, sales $12,703,065,
cert: WBENC)

7398   Flex Pre-Press, Inc.
       6812 S 112th St   Franklin, WI 53132
       (414) 427-8833 Burt Tabora President
       Fax: (414) 427-8834
       Email: btabora@flexprepress.com
       Website: www.flexprepress.com
Photopolymer printing plates, DuPont WaterProofs, color
keys, film negatives, analog & digital proofing, high-end
color separations, photo retouching, package design, file
management & printing, digital plates. (Hisp, estab 1995,
empl 15, sales $1,100,000, cert: State, NMSDC)

7399   H.Derksen & Sons Co., Inc.
       250 Industrial Dr   Omro, WI 50310
       (920) 685-4000 Mike Willeford VP
       Fax:
       Email: mike@hderksen.com
       Website: www.hderksen.com
Pressure sensitive labels, wide format digital printing,
business forms, computer paper, paper & packaging
products, mobility solutions, bar code label printers, bar
coding software. (Nat Ame, estab 1900, empl 11, sales
$8,000,000, cert: NMSDC)

7400   Industrial Graphics Inc.
       304 Industrial Dr   Fredonia, WI 53021
       (262) 692-2424 Teri Swenson Acct Mgr
       Fax: (262) 692-2426
       Email: tswenson@igc-image.com
       Website: www.industrialgraphics.com
Digital Printing, Screen Printing, Creative Services, Cad Cut
Lettering, Fleet Wrapping, Advertising, Point of Purchase
Displays, Priting on Metals, Prototyping, High Volume
Sourcing, Architectural Decorating, Wall Paper Printing,
Ceiling Tile Printing. (Woman/White, estab 1969, empl 20,
sales $2,750,000, cert: State)

7401   Kubin-Nicholson Corporation
       8440 N 87th St   Milwaukee, WI 53224
       (414) 586-4300 Margaret Rees CEO
       Fax: (414) 586-6808
       Email: rees.p@kubin.com
       Website: www.kubin.com
Commerical printed products: billboards, banners, transit
posters, in store signs, floor graphics, wall scapes, vehicle
wraps, building wraps, POP displays. (Woman/White,
estab 1935, empl 63, sales $16,000,000, cert: State)

7402   Promo Print Solutions Inc.
       420 S Koeller St, Ste 208   Oshkosh, WI 54902
       (920) 233-7900 Paula Condor President
       Fax: (920) 233-7913
       Email: paula.condor@promoprintsolutions.com
       Website: www.promoprintsolutions.com
print collateral: in-store promotions, sales promotions,
commerical printing, giveaways & sampling. (Woman/
White, estab 2000, empl 4, sales $2,087,395, cert:
WBENC)

7403   Red Oak Label, LLC
       2923 S 160th St   New Berlin, WI 53151
       (262) 780-9797 Lori Schinker President
       Fax: (262) 780-9780
       Email: redoaklabl@aol.com
       Website: www.redoaklabel.com
Pressure sensitive flexographic labels & tags. (Woman/
White, estab 1997, empl 6, sales $510,900, cert:
WBENC)

PROFESSIONAL SERVICES: Financial
Provide various financial consulting services: auditing/tax, 401K, pension and employee benefits, risk and injury management insurance, asset management and investment advice, money management seminars, collection services, etc. NAICS Code 54

California

7404 Advertising Audit Services International, LLC
32663 Red Maple St, Ste 100   Union City, CA 94587
(415) 828-0779 Pankaj Sewal Chief Auditing Officer
Fax: (520) 844-1940
Email: psewal@adauditservintl.com
Website: www.adauditservintl.com
Contract compliance audits & analysis: vendor compliance, financial accounting accuracy & advertiser best practices. (As-Ind, estab 2000, empl 22, sales $2,000,000, cert: NMSDC)

7405 Amerivet Securities, Inc.
26550 Silverado Court   Moreno Valley, CA 92555
(888) 960-0644 Elton Johnson Jr. President
Fax: (951) 346-5533
Email: amerivet@yahoo.com
Website: www.amerivetsecurities.com
Securities business, commodities business & registered investment advisory business. (AA, estab 1993, empl 3, sales $17,000, cert: CPUC)

7406 Blaylock Robert Van
350 Frank H Ogawa Plaza, 10th Fl   Oakland, CA 94612
(510) 208-6100 Tarrell Gamble VP
Fax: (510) 625-1065
Email: tgamble@brv-llc.com
Website: www.brv-llc.com
Investment banking & financial services: corporate debt & equity underwriting, equity research, share repurchase, pension sales & trading & municipal finance. (AA, estab 1991, empl 48, sales $14,050,000, cert: NMSDC)

7407 Coast to Coast Financial Solutions Inc.
101 Hodencamp Rd Ste 120 Thousand Oaks, CA 91360
(888) 877-4700 John Mastro Director
Fax: (805) 777-9275
Email: jmastro@c2cfsi.com
Website: www.c2cfsi.com
Debt collection services. (AA, estab 2002, empl 14, sales $1,412,059, cert: NMSDC)

7408 Consumer Financial Service Corporation
1500 Park Ave, Ste 116   Emeryville, CA 94608
(510) 596-4100 Loy Sheflott President
Fax: (510) 596-4105
Email: lsheflott@consumerfinancial.com
Website: www.consumerfinancial.com
Financial services. (Woman/White, estab 1994, empl 30, sales $1,100,000, cert: WBENC)

7409 Garnier Group and Associates
10679 Westview Parkway, 2nd Fl.   San Diego, CA 92126
(858) 530-2468 Winslow Garnier President
Fax: (858) 726-6000
Email: winslow@garniergroup.com
Website: www.garniergroup.com
Equipment finance leasing, appraisal services, computer leasing, analytical lab instrumentation leasing. (AA, estab 2003, empl 19, sales $7,023,000, cert: NMSDC, CPUC, 8(a))

7410 Jules & Associates, Inc.
515 S Figeroa St, Ste 1950   Los Angeles, CA 90071
(213) 362-5600 Vincent Alexander Sr Acct Exec
Fax: (213) 362-5610
Email: vincea@julesandassociates.com
Website: www.julesandassociates.com
Equipment finance corporate acquisitions. (Hisp, estab 1989, empl 31, sales , cert: CPUC)

7411 LNL Solutions LLC
423 W Adams Ave   Alhambra, CA 91801
(424) 256-5894 Philip Li Dir of Finance
Fax:
Email: info@lnl-solutions.com
Website: www.lnl-solutions.com
Middle market & boutique accounting & financial services. (As-Pac/Hisp, estab 2013, empl 2, sales , cert: State, City, NMSDC)

7412 Merrimak Capital Company LLC
10 Pimentel Court   Novato, CA 94949
(415) 475-4100 Monica Fleury VP of Ops
Fax: (415) 884-5644
Email: mfleury@merrimak.com
Website: www.merrimak.com
Financing solutions: operating leases, capital leases, lease lines, sale leasebacks & technology refresh leases. (Woman/White, estab 1991, empl 36, sales $130,266,396, cert: CPUC, WBENC)

7413 Pacific Rim Capital, Inc.
15231 Laguna Canyon Rd Ste 250 Irvine, CA 92618
(949) 389-0800 Tom Budnick VP Sales
Fax: (949) 389-0900
Email: sales@pacrimcap.com
Website: www.pacificrimcapital.com
Lease financing: materials handling & IT equip, also dist new & reconditioned IT hardware. (AA, estab 1990, empl 60, sales , cert: NMSDC)

7414 Receivables Solutions, Inc.
2910 Inland Empire Blvd Ste 100 Ontario, CA 91764
(909) 360-8140 Regina Cameron
Fax: (909) 360-8368
Email: rcameron@rsinc.us
Website: www.rsinc.us
National accounts receivable management (ARM), 1st party collections (pre-charge off), 3rd party collections & billing. (Woman/AA, estab 2015, empl 2, sales , cert: CPUC)

7415 Sequoia Financial Services
28632 Roadside Dr Ste 110 Agoura Hills, CA 91301
(818) 409-6000 Roy C. duPlessis CEO
Fax: (818) 707-7070
Email: roy.c.duplessis@sequoiafinancial.com
Website: www.sequoiafinancial.com
Collection services. (Woman/AA, estab 1991, empl 73, sales $3,000,000, cert: CPUC)

7416 Southern California Leasing Inc.
180 E Main, Ste 204 Tustin, CA 92780
(714) 573-9804 Barbara Griffith President
Fax: (714) 573-9806
Email: bgriffith@socalleasing.com
Website: www.socalleasing.com
Equipment leasing & financing. (Woman/White, estab 1992, empl 7, sales $1,200,000, cert: WBENC)

7417 Strategic Partners Consultants
8889 W Olympic Blvd #1000 Beverly Hills, CA 90211
(310) 870-7055 Brenda West CEO
Fax:
Email:
brenda.west@strategicpartnersconsultants.com
Website: www.strategicpartnersconsultants.com/
page/168/1
Consulting & outsourcing, Bank Regulatory Compliance issues, Internal Audit functions & Risk Assessment activities. (Woman, estab 2014, empl 3, sales , cert: WBENC)

7418 The Gilson Group, LLC
2967 Michelson Dr Ste G102 Irvine, CA 92612
(949) 830-3499 Catherine Doll CEO
Fax:
Email: Catherine@TheGilsonGroup.com
Website: www.TheGilsonGroup.com
Accounting, mergers, financial analysis, due diligence, internal controls, general ledger, forecasting, cash flow, process improvement, Quickbooks, SOX, SEC, cost accounting, financial reporting, internal audit, risk management, GAAP. (Woman/White, estab 2006, empl 20, sales $502,000, cert: WBENC)

7419 Venpalia LLC
1331 N Cuyamaca St, Ste G El Cajon, CA 92020
(619) 788-3781 Liza Amog Principal
Fax:
Email: liza@venpalia.com
Website: www.venpalia.com
Finance, risk management. (Woman/As-Pac, estab 2010, empl 1, sales $150,000, cert: NMSDC, CPUC)

Colorado

7420 Aspen Capital Company, Inc.
4489 Roaring Fork Court Loveland, CO 80538
(303) 716-2898 Pegy Tomcheck
Fax:
Email: plapp@aspencapitalcompany.com
Website: www.aspencapitalcompany.com
Custom asset tracking & invoicing solutions, educational laptop program lease structures, unique iPad refresh programs, consignment solutions, electronic invoicing & billing processes, web based equipment stores. (Woman/White, estab 2001, empl 8, sales $10,385,908, cert: WBENC, NWBOC)

Connecticut

7421 Airlink Ground Transportation, LLC
39 Old Ridgebury Rd D1-243 Danbury, CT 06810
(203) 297-6060 Atif Jilani Member
Fax: (203) 297-6076
Email: atif@airlinklimo.com
Website: www.airlinklimo.com
Black Car Service to/from CT,NY,NJ airports (As-Ind, estab 2011, empl 3, sales $185,320, cert: NMSDC)

7422 Argus Investors' Counsel, Inc.
1281 E Main St Stamford, CT 06902
(203) 316-9000 Sharon Wagoner President
Fax: (203) 356-0533
Email: swagoner@argusinvest.com
Website: www.argusinvest.com
Manage portfolios: pensions, endowments & foundations. (Woman/White, estab 1960, empl 6, sales $595,953, cert: WBENC)

7423 Soundview Capital Solutions
116 Washington Ave North Haven, CT 06473
(203) 821-7830 John Abella CEO
Fax:
Email:
johnabella@soundviewcapitalsolutions.com
Website: www.soundviewcapitalsolutions.com
Third-party leasing specializing in technology financing. (Hisp, estab 2009, empl 3, sales $100,000, cert: NMSDC)

District of Columbia

7424 McKissack & McKissack of Washington, Inc.
901 K St, NW 6th Fl Washington, DC 20001
(202) 347-1446 Lisa Anders VP
Fax: (202) 347-1489
Email: registrations@mckinc.com
Website: www.mckinc.com
Budget & scope preparation, scheduling, programming, financial consulting. (Woman/AA, estab 1990, empl 100, sales $24,010,225, cert: State, City, NMSDC)

Florida

7425 AMI Risk Consultants
1336 SW 146th Court Miami, FL 33184
(305) 173-1589 Mario Madarang Actuary Analyst
Fax:
Email: MarioM@amirisk.com
Website: www.amirisk.com
Property/casualty actuarial & risk management consulting. (As-Pac, estab 1992, empl 7, sales , cert: NMSDC)

7426 Carter-Health LLC
4201 Vineland Road Ste I-13-14 Orlando, FL 32811
(407) 296-6689 Rodney Carter President
Fax: (407) 296-6693
Email: rodney@carterhealth.com
Website: www.carter-health.com
Carter-Health is a turn-key solutions provider for creating sterile environments for I.V. compounding facilities. Our expertise in this area assists healthcare facilities in meeting the stringent requirements of (AA, estab 2007, empl 5, sales $2,500,000, cert: NMSDC)

7427   Commonwealth Capital Corp
       17755 US Hwy 19 N Ste 400 Clearwater, FL 33764
       (877) 654-1500 Kimberly Springsteen-Abbott
       Business Dev
       Fax: (727) 450-5360
       Email: kspringsteen@ccclease.com
       Website: www.ccclease.com
Equipment leasing: IT, telecom & medical equipment.
(Woman/White, estab 1978, empl 45, sales $27,000,000,
cert: WBENC)

7428   Empower Benefits Inc. dba Corestream
       3606 Enterprise Ave, Ste 304   Naples, FL 34104
       (917) 686-5886 Zach Malone President
       Fax:
       Email: zmalone@corestream.com
       Website: www.corestream.com
Provides consolidated payroll deduction, voluntary
benefits portals, employee discount shopping portals,
group auto insurance real time comparative quoting,
online enrollment and voluntary benefits brokerage. (As-
Ind, estab 2006, empl 30, sales , cert: NMSDC)

7429   Enfusion, Inc.
       2429 Grand Teton Circle   Winter Park, FL 32792
       (407) 802-0006 Anita White CEO
       Fax:
       Email: anita@enfusionfinance.com
       Website: www.enfusionfinance.com
Financial intelligence consulting, expense & cost mgmt.
(Woman/AA, estab 2007, empl 1, sales , cert: WBENC)

7430   Hanks Hanks and Associates LLC
       213 S Dillard St Ste 120 B Winter Garden, FL 34787
       (301) 653-5134 Phadra Hanks CEO
       Fax:
       Email: phanks@hhallcmd.com
       Website: www.hhallcmd.com
Financial management & accounting, program manage-
ment, management consulting & smart business solutions.
(Woman/AA, estab 2002, empl 45, sales $4,000,000, cert:
State)

7431   Risk & Re-Insurance Solutions Corporation
       1500 San Remo Ave Ste 247B Coral Gables, FL
       33146
       (770) 437-8880 Steven Pacholick VP
       Fax: (770) 437-8883
       Email: spacholick@rrisc.com
       Website: www.rrisc.com
Risk management, advisory & risk financing needs to
corporate & governmental clients. (Hisp, estab 2001, empl
10, sales $2,550,000, cert: NMSDC)

Georgia

7432   Corporate Reports, Inc.
       3610 Piedmont Rd NE Ste 200 Atlanta, GA 30305
       (404) 233-2230 Brooke Graydon President
       Fax: (404) 856-4257
       Email: brooke.graydon@corporatereport.com
       Website: www.corporatereport.com
Annual & sustainability/corporate responsibility/citizen-
ship reporting. (Woman, estab 1984, empl 25, sales
$3,500,000, cert: WBENC)

7433   Infinite Financial Concepts, LLC
       P.O. Box 953   Stone Mountain, GA 30086
       (678) 933-5304 Amin Hassan President
       Fax:
       Email: amin@ifc326.com
       Website: www.ifc326.com
Accounting & financial reporting. (AA, estab 2011, empl
1, sales $67,000, cert: City)

7434   Long & Associates, LLC
       5755 N Point Pkwy Ste 29 Alpharetta, GA 30022
       (678) 905-5095 Martin Long
       Fax: (505) 333-4143
       Email: martin.long@lacpallc.com
       Website: www.lacpallc.com
Accounting & consulting services: employee benefit
plans audits (for both public and privately held companies), Sarbanes-Oxley (SOX) compliance testing &
internal controls assessment. (Woman/AA, estab 2002,
empl 3, sales $367,000, cert: NMSDC)

7435   Resurgens Risk Management, Inc.
       1201 Peachtree St NE 400 Colony Square Ste 1730
       Atlanta, GA 30361
       (678) 298-5119 Clifton McKnight, Sr. Asst VP
       Fax: (404) 873-1574
       Email: cmcknight@rrmgt.com
       Website: www.rrmgt.com
Human resources consulting services, financial products,
employee benefits, commercial property & liability
insurance & consultative services. (AA, estab 1987, empl
33, sales $3,000,000, cert: NMSDC)

7436   RiverStone Associates, LLC
       750 Olde Clubs Dr   Alpharetta, GA 30022
       (770) 656-7820 Monty Brinkley President
       Fax: (770) 840-8666
       Email: mbrinkley@riverstone-us.com
       Website: www.riverstone-us.com
Professional svcs: internal audit, accounting, IT security,
process improvement & risk management solutions.
(AA, estab 2007, empl 2, sales $91,000, cert: State)

7437   VAAS Professionals, LLC
       325 Edgewood Ave Ste 600 Atlanta, GA 30312
       (404) 223-1058 Steve Julal Owner
       Fax:
       Email: steve.julal@vaasprofessionals.com
       Website: www.vaasprofessionals.com
Accounting & finance services, audits, payroll solutions,
capital & treasury management, reviews, computer &
technology assessments, financial reporting, due
diligence & human capital management. (AA, estab
2005, empl 4, sales , cert: 8(a))

Illinois

7438   Adelfia LLC
       400 E Randolph Str Ste 705 Chicago, IL 60601
       (312) 240-9500 Stella Marie Santos
       Fax: (312) 240-0295
       Email: sbsantos@adelfiacpas.com
       Website: www.adelfiacpas.com
Assurance & advisory services: financial audit, compliance
examination, internal audit, agreed-upon procedures, tax
services, tax preparation, payroll tax returns, tax notices/
audit assistance, tax planning, accounting services.
(Woman/As-Pac/Hisp, estab 2011, empl 30, sales
$541,996, cert: State, City, NMSDC)

7439   Ariel Investments
       200 E Randolph St Ste 2900 Chicago, IL 60601
       (312) 726-0140 Gary L. Rozier Senior VP
       Fax: (312) 726-7473
       Email: grozier@arielinvestments.com
       Website: www.arielinvestments.com
Financial management services. (AA, estab 1983, empl 88,
sales $54,074,660, cert: NMSDC)

7440   B3 Consulting Inc.
       1025 N Riverwalk St   Chicago, IL 60610
       (312) 722-9420 Alexis LeFevour CEO
       Fax:
       Email: alexis.lefevour@b3consultinginc.com
       Website: www.b3consultinginc.com
Risk Advisory Svcs: Entity Wide, Risk Assessments, Internal
Audit, Sarbanes Oxley, Third Party Validation, Business
Process Architecture, Compliance Services, Contract
Compliance, Regulatory/Other Compliance. (Woman/
White, estab 2016, empl 1, sales , cert: City, WBENC)

7441   Cabrera Capital Markets, LLC
       10 S LaSalle St Ste 1050 Chicago, IL 60603
       (312) 236-8888 William Feeley Managing Dir
       Fax: (312) 236-8936
       Email: mfeeley@cabreracapital.com
       Website: www.cabreracapital.com
Investment banking services, domestic & international
equity brokerage, taxable fixed income brokerage, mergers
& acquisitions. (Hisp, estab 2001, empl 74, sales
$25,109,305, cert: State, NMSDC)

7442   Davenport Capital Management
       312 N Clark St Ste 500 Chicago, IL 60654
       (312) 445-6406 Thomas Davenport Managing
       Partner
       Fax: (773) 496-8972
       Email: thomas@davenportcap.com
       Website: www.davenportcap.com
Merchant banking, strategic advisory & investments. (AA,
estab 2014, empl 4, sales $800,000, cert: NMSDC)

7443   E.C. Ortiz & Co., LLP
       333 S Des Plaines St, Ste 2-N   Chicago, IL 60661
       (312) 876-1900 Edilberto C. Ortiz Managing Partner
       Fax: (312) 876-1911
       Email: ecortiz@ecortiz.com
       Website: www.ecortiz.com
Auditing, accounting, consulting, taxation, employee
benefit plan audits, management services & financial
advice. (As-Pac, estab 1974, empl 65, sales $3,968,725,
cert: State, City, NMSDC)

7444   Global Capital, Ltd.
       205 W. Wacker Dr. Ste 730 Chicago, IL 60606
       (312) 846-6918 Brian McNally VP Business Dev
       Fax:
       Email: Brian@globelease.com
       Website: www.globalcapitalltd.com
Equipment leasing & financing: aircraft, rails, trailers,
vehicles, computers, manufacturing & construction
equipment. (Woman/White, estab 1999, empl 4, sales
$31,119,345, cert: WBENC)

7445   Holland Capital Management LLC
       303 West Madison Ste 700 Chicago, IL 60606
       (312) 553-4830 Valerie King Director of Mktg
       Fax: (312) 553-4848
       Email: vking@hollandcap.com
       Website: www.hollandcap.com
Equity & fixed income institutional management.
(Woman/AA/As-Ind, estab 1991, empl 22, sales
$6,966,000, cert: State, NMSDC)

7446   Loop Capital Markets
       111 W Jackson Blvd Ste 1901 Chicago, IL 60604
       (312) 356-5008 Sidney Dillard Partner
       Fax: (312) 922-7137
       Email: nancy.ziagos@loopcapital.com
       Website: www.loopcapital.com
Corporate debt & issuances, sub notes, floating rate
notes, bonds, securities, credit cards, equity, common
stock, variable rate debt, etc. (AA, estab 1997, empl 150,
sales , cert: NMSDC)

7447   Sierra Forensic Group
       30 S Wacker Dr Ste 2200 Chicago, IL 60606
       (312) 674-7100 Adrian Sierra CEO
       Fax: (312) 674-7155
       Email: adrian.sierra@sfg-global.com
       Website: www.sfg-global.com
Forensic accounting & investigative services. (Hisp, estab
2005, empl 8, sales $327,688, cert: NMSDC)

Indiana

7448   Engaging Solutions, LLC
       3965 N Meridian St Ste 1B Indianapolis, IN 46208
       (317) 283-8300 Debbie Wilson Managing
       Principal
       Fax: (317) 283-8301
       Email: debbie@engagingsolutions.net
       Website: www.engagingsolutions.net
Fiscal Management & Accountability, Financial Compliance Audits, Program Audits, Financial Reviews, Compilations, Agreed Upon Procedures, Internal Controls
Reviews, Tax Preparation, Ta Audit Representation.
(Woman/AA, estab 2005, empl 26, sales $2,009,000,
cert: State)

7449 Putnam Industries Inc.
4582 NW Plaza W Dr# 100 Zionsville, IN 46077
(317) 275-3153 Dee Anne Delk President
Fax: (317) 275-3153
Email: jpickens@putnamindustriesinc.com
Website: www.putnamindustriesinc.com
Equipment leasing & finance: computers, software, hardware, copiers, office furniture, fleet vehlices, medical equipment, trucks, buses, lighting, HVAC systems, bulldozers, forklifts, heavy machinery, telephone systems, alarm systems. (AA, estab 2007, empl 5, sales $3,836,816, cert: State, NMSDC)

7450 Solace Risk Management
9247 N Meridian St Ste 221 Indianapolis, IN 46260
(317) 423-3947 Charles Moorer President
Fax: (317) 489-6122
Email: charles.moorer@srm-cs.com
Website: www.srm-cs.com
Designs comprehensive fully insured & self-insured risk financing & risk management programs. (AA, estab 2011, empl 3, sales , cert: State, NMSDC)

Massachusetts

7451 Spafford Leasing Associates, Inc.
1350 Main St Ste 318 Springfield, MA 01103
(413) 526-0975 Angela Flebotte CEO
Fax: (314) 526-0978
Email: angelaf@spafford.com
Website: www.spafford.com
Equipment leasing, computer systems, hospital equipment, copiers, telephone systems, computer software, manufacturing equipment, for lease terms ranging from 3-7 years. (Woman/White, estab 1989, empl 2, sales $500,000, cert: WBENC)

7452 The Locator Services Group Ltd.
280 Summer St Ste 400 Boston, MA 02210
(617) 859-0600 Kim Sawyer President & General Counsel
Fax: (617) 859-0640
Email: ksawyer@tlsgltd.com
Website: www.tlsgltd.com
Asset & unclaimed funds identification & recovery program. (Woman/White, estab 1994, empl 23, sales $34,948,343, cert: WBENC)

Maryland

7453 Beasley Financial Group LLC
4815 Coyle Rd, Ste 103 Owings Mills, MD 21117
(877) 265-1264 Marcus Beasley CEO
Fax: (410) 998-2098
Email: mbeasley@beasleyfinancialgroup.com
Website: www.beasleyfinancialgroup.com
Financial advisory, brokerage & consulting: 401(k) retirement plans, life, health, dental, disability & long term care insurance benefit plans. (Woman/AA, estab 2005, empl 3, sales $82,194, cert: State)

7454 Beyond The Bottom Line, Inc.
1300 Mercantile Lane Ste 139-MM Largo, MD 20774
(301) 322-4083 Corinda Davis President
Fax:
Email: bblinc@beyondbottomline.com
Website: www.beyondbottomline.com
Budget formulation, execution & monitoring processes, data mining to compile raw data to help clients recognize significant facts, relationships, trends, patterns, exceptions & anomalies. (Woman/AA, estab 2003, empl 16, sales $1,202,364, cert: State)

7455 DeAnder Associates LLC
7233 Hanover Pkwy, Ste D Greenbelt, MD 20770
(301) 262-0111 Edward Prater Bus Devel Spec
Fax: (301) 262-2966
Email: eprater@deander.com
Website: www.deander.com
Financial management consulting: finance & accounting, contract closeout & administration, grants management, compliance assistance & accounting system review and implementation. (Woman/AA, estab 1997, empl 35, sales $2,966,827, cert: State)

7456 EurekaFacts, LLC
51 Monroe St, PE-10 Rockville, MD 20850
(240) 403-1646 Jorge Restrepo DirBusiness Dev
Fax: (301) 610-0640
Email: certifications@eurekafacts.com
Website: www.eurekafacts.com
Research design, rigorous data collection, & advanced analytic & statistical services. (Hisp, estab 2003, empl 23, sales $4,281,146, cert: NMSDC)

7457 Gonzalez, Hawkins & Johnson LLC
P.O. Box 2705 Upper Marlboro, MD 20772
(240) 865-6052 Alejandro Gonzalez Partner
Fax: (240) 865-6052
Email: agonzalez@ghjaccounting.com
Website: www.ghjaccounting.com
Federal Financial Consulting. (Woman/AA/Hisp, estab 2008, empl 3, sales $50,788, cert: State, 8(a))

7458 New Century Advisors, LLC
2 Wisconsin Circle, Ste 940 Chevy Chase, MD 20815
(240) 395-0550 Ellen Safir President
Fax: (240) 395-0565
Email: esafir@ncallc.com
Website: www.newcenturyadvisors.com
Investment Management Services. (Woman/White, estab 2002, empl 13, sales $5,562,000, cert: WBENC)

Michigan

7459 Baron Wealth Management
3150 Livernois Rd, Ste 250 Troy, MI 48083
(248) 251-0161 Crystal Steinhour Ops Mgr
Fax: (248) 251-0162
Email: crystal@baron-wealth.com
Website: www.baron-wealth.com
Comprehensive wealth management services, income tax, retirement, cash flow, estate, investment, compensation, benefits & insurance planning. (Woman/White, estab 2010, empl 6, sales , cert: WBENC)

7460   Centennial Securities Advisory Services
       515 Ship St, Ste 211   Saint Joseph, MI 49085
       (269) 982-4188 Jim Roberts President
       Fax: (269) 982-4189
       Email: jim@jrcent.com
       Website: www.jrcent.com
Registered Investment Advisory firm, wealth management,
investments, investing, 401k, IRA, pension, foundation,
financial advisor. (Nat Ame/Hisp, estab 2014, empl 3, sales
$300,000, cert: NMSDC)

7461   Chippewa Capital LLC
       3190 Tri Park Dr   Grand Blanc, MI 48439
       (810) 579-0579 Thomas Barrett VP
       Fax: (810) 579-0628
       Email: thomas.barrett@macarthurcorp.com
       Website: www.chippewacapital.com
Equipment leasing, painting,trucking, warehousing &
distribution. (Nat Ame, estab 2000, empl 35, sales
$2,000,000, cert: NMSDC)

7462   EVO Accounting & Financial Services
       16200 W Seven Mile Rd   Detroit, MI 48235
       (313) 835-3900 Vencie Jackson President
       Fax: (313) 835-7982
       Email: vjackson@evoaccounting.com
       Website: www.evoaccounting.com
Accounting & financial services, tax & payroll. (AA, estab
1970, empl 15, sales $748,478, cert: State)

7463   First Independence Bank
       44 Michigan Ave   Detroit, MI 48226
       (313) 256-8400 Rhonda Pugh Branch Admin
       Fax: (313) 256-8811
       Email: rhondapugh@firstindependence.com
       Website: www.firstindependence.com
Banking services. (AA, estab 1970, empl 62, sales
$13,737,000, cert: NMSDC)

7464   Gonzales Financial Consulting, LLC
       4707 Charest   Waterford, MI 48327
       (810) 706-1687 Rogelio Gonzales Managing
       Member
       Fax: (248) 876-9657
       Email: roy@gonzalesfc.com
       Website: www.gonzalesfc.com
Retirement plan consulting services, insurance coverage
review, broker management & risk management support
services, commercial liability, property, general liability,
worker's compensation. (Hisp, estab 2015, empl 4, sales ,
cert: NMSDC)

7465   L J Ross Associates, Inc.
       4 Universal Way   Jackson, MI 49204
       (517) 544-9100 Kaylyn Todd Mktg & Contracts Mgr
       Fax: (517) 544-9101
       Email: kaylyn@ljross.com
       Website: www.ljross.com
Debt collection: consumer & commercial debts. (AA, estab
1992, empl 115, sales $8,621,679, cert: NMSDC)

7466   Lakefront Capital, LLC
       28175 Haggerty Rd   Novi, MI 48377
       (248) 994-9001 Sandy Fuchs Director Ops and
       Client Service
       Fax: (248) 465-2066
       Email: sandy.fuchs@lakefrontts.com
       Website: www.lakefrontts.com
Lease financing & portfolio management. (As-Pac, estab
2002, empl 8, sales $10,000,000, cert: NMSDC)

7467   Martin, Arrington, & Desai, & Meyers P.C., CPA
       30200 Telegraph Rd, Ste 444   Bingham Farms, MI
       48025
       (248) 645-5370 Bettye Arrington Managing Dir
       Fax: (248) 645-5020
       Email: bvam49@sbcglobal.net
       Website: www.madmcpa.com
Audit, accounting, agreed upon procedures, due
diligence, revenue recovery, tax consulting, information
technology, survey & evaluation research, professional
recruitment. (AA, estab 1975, empl 16, sales $1,300,000,
cert: State)

7468   Minority Alliance Capital, LLC
       6960 Orchard Lake Road Ste 306 West
       Bloomfield, MI 48322
       (248) 236-5182 Tim McCormick VP - Sales
       Fax: (248) 539-1397
       Email: mccormick.t@mac-leasing.com
       Website: www.mac-leasing.com
Equipment leasing: computer & software, office furniture & fixtures, production & process control. (AA, estab
1999, empl 14, sales $248,000,000, cert: NMSDC)

7469   Optimal Leasing LLC
       4301 Orchard Lake Rd, Ste 180-173   West
       Bloomfield, MI 48323
       (248) 738-2699 Larry Robinson CEO
       Fax: (248) 702-1495
       Email: larry@optimaleasingcompany.com
       Website: www.optimalleasingcompany.com
Third party lease financing of capital equipment. (AA,
estab 1996, empl 50, sales , cert: NMSDC)

7470   Renaissance Capital Alliance
       5440 Corporate Dr, Ste 275   Troy, MI 48098
       (248) 220-4113 Galen Kersten Natl Acct Mgr
       Fax: (248) 299-7810
       Email: gkersten@rcalliance.com
       Website: www.rcalliance.com
Equipment leasing: materials handling, lift trucks,
transportation & warehousing equipment; fleet mgmt
services. (AA, estab 2001, empl 13, sales $20,000,000,
cert: NMSDC, CPUC)

Minnesota

7471   Amare & Associates LLC dba ABA Tax Accounting
       10670 Hawthorn Trail   St. Paul, MN 55129
       (866) 936-0430 Amare Berhie CEO
       Fax: (866) 936-0430
       Email: amare@abataxaccounting.com
       Website: www.abataxaccounting.com
Finance & accounting outsourcing svcs: transaction
processing & staffing services. (AA, estab 1989, empl 2,
sales $24,375, cert: State, City, NMSDC)

7472 Certes Financial Pros, Inc.
5775 Wayzata Blvd #550   St. Louis Park, MN 55416
(952) 345-4141 Sally Mainquist President
Fax: (952) 417-9028
Email: getalife@certespros.com
Website: www.certespros.com
Provide high-end financial professionals on an interim & project basis. (Woman/White, estab 1994, empl 170, sales $12,000,000, cert: State)

7473 Diversified Adjustment Service, Inc.
600 Coon Rapids Blvd   Coon Rapids, MN 55433
(763) 783-2301 Tara LaFave Admin Asst
Fax: (763) 783-2390
Email: diversity@diversifiedadjustment.com
Website: www.diversifiedadjustment.com
Managed collection svcs: accounts recievable mgmt & credit reporting, debt collection, pre-collect & skip-tracing svcs. (Woman/White, estab 1981, empl 100, sales $14,400,000, cert: CPUC, WBENC)

7474 M & M Consultants, Inc.
7250 River Shore Ln   Champlin, MN 55316
(763) 422-9299 Nancy McLaughlin CEO
Fax: (763) 427-6631
Email: macnj9299@cs.com
Website:
Collection svcs: commercial receivables, consumer & commercial bad checks. (Woman/White, estab 1900, empl 24, sales , cert: State)

Missouri

7475 Colt Safety, Inc.
8300 Manchester Rd   St. Louis, MO 63144
(314) 961-4414 Christine Bierman CEO
Fax: (314) 961-9166
Email: christine@coltsafety.com
Website: www.coltsafety.com
Inventory management, electronic payment, EDI capable, histories & usages, tracking. (Woman/White, estab 1980, empl 11, sales $9,192,080, cert: State)

North Carolina

7476 Calloway & Associates, Inc.
5920 S Miami Blvd, Ste 202   Morrisville, NC 27560
(919) 433-0245 Cassandra Johnson VP Ops
Fax: (919) 433-0248
Email: cassandra@calloway-assoc.com
Website: www.calloway-assoc.com
Financial accounting, management & technical consulting. (Woman/AA, estab 1985, empl 12, sales $1,000,000, cert: State)

7477 Falcon Square Capital, LLC
4000 Westchase Blvd   Raleigh, NC 27607
(919) 825-1534 Melissa Pendergrass CEO
Fax: (919) 867-5734
Email: mpendergrass@falconsquarecapital.com
Website: www.falconsquarecapital.com
Trading, research, portfolio construction, transition management, client commission arrangements & other institutional brokerage services. (Woman/White, estab 2013, empl 16, sales $1,711,975, cert: WBENC)

7478 Innovation Partners LLC
5950 Fairview Road, Ste 806 Charlotte, NC 28210
(704) 708-5461 Anthony Lawrence Principal
Fax: (704) 708-5492
Email: alawrence@innovationpartnersllc.com
Website: www.innovationpartnersllc.com
Deferred compensation plans, retirement planning, actuarial, pension funds, investment banking, reinsurance, securities portfolio management, risk management, asset portfoilo management, underwriting services. (Woman/AA, estab 2007, empl 20, sales $1,500,000, cert: NMSDC, CPUC, WBENC)

7479 Main Street Mobile Billboards
2610 Tuckaseegee Rd   Charlotte, NC 28208
(888) 788-7492 Brendon Henderson CEO
Fax:
Email: brendon@mainstreetmobilebillboards.com
Website: www.mainstreetmobilebillboards.com
Mobile truck billboard & walking billboards advertising. (AA, estab 2013, empl 2, sales , cert: State, City, NMSDC)

7480 Registry Partners, Inc.
2966 S Church St, Ste 293   Burlington, NC 27215
(336) 226-3359 Dave Winstead Dir Business Dev
Fax: (336) 464-2710
Email: davewinstead@registrypartners.com
Website: www.RegistryPartners.com
Registry Partners was founded to provide operational, research, & educational support services to health care providers and their Tumor / Cancer Registries across the country. (Woman/White, estab 2002, empl 50, sales $2,000,000, cert: State)

New Jersey

7481 Allen, Maxwell & Silver, Inc.
17-17 Route 208 N Ste 340 Fair Lawn, NJ 07401
(201) 871-0044 Lisa Freidman CEO
Fax: (201) 871-1197
Email: Lisa@amscollections.com
Website: www.amscollections.com
Commercial collections. (Woman/White, estab 1992, empl 38, sales $2,650,000, cert: WBENC)

7482 Ateeca Inc.
107 B2 Corporate Blvd,   South Plainfield, NJ 07080
(908) 668-1250 George Davis Sr Business Mgr.
Fax: (908) 755-9567
Email: gdavis@ateeca.com
Website: www.ateeca.com
Payroll services. (Woman/As-Pac, estab 2005, empl 180, sales , cert: NMSDC, WBENC)

7483 Broad Street Capital Markets LLC
494 Broad St Ste 206 Newark, NJ 07102
(862) 367-9930 Andrew Adderly CEO
Fax: (862) 505-2059
Email: mdejesus@broadscm.com
Website: www.broadscm.com
Investment Banking & Securities Dealing, Investment Advice, Administrative Management & General Management Consulting. (AA/Hisp, estab 2000, empl 8, sales , cert: State, NMSDC)

7484　C & M Associates, Inc.
119 Dean St　Harrington Park, NJ 07640
(201) 637-6217　Daniel Greene President
Fax: (201) 767-6510
Email: dnlcminc@aol.com
Website:
General construction; Office Renovations; Interior Finishes; HVAC; Cogeneration; Fire Prevention; Engineering & Design (AA, estab 1989, empl 2, sales $31,438, cert: State, City, NMSDC)

7485　Enhanced Due Diligence Advisory, Inc.
910 Garden St　Hoboken, NJ 07030
(973) 727-7248　Wayne Chau
Fax: (425) 656-4421
Email: wchau@eddadvisory.com
Website: www.eddadvisory.com
Risk assessment of domestic/international assets, compliance, audit & logistics strategy. (As-Pac, estab 2015, empl 3, sales $15,050, cert: State, NMSDC)

7486　Runnymede Capital Management, Inc.
10 Wilrich Glen Rd　Morristown, NJ 07960
(973) 267-6886　Andrew Wang Sr VP
Fax: (979) 543-0072
Email: awang@runnymede.com
Website: www.runnymede.com
Manages investment portfolios of institutions (Taft-Hartley, captive insurance, public pension fund, corporate, non-profit) & high-net-worth individuals. (As-Pac, estab 1993, empl 8, sales $1,500,000, cert: NMSDC)

New York

7487　All Occasions Concierge, LLC
1333A North Ave, Ste 149　New Rochelle, NY 10804
(914) 481-8312　Sterling Jasper CEO
Fax: (914) 481-8315
Email: sterling.jasper@alloccasionsconcierge.com
Website: www.alloccasionsconcierge.com
With over fifteen years in the hospitality business, we provide professional concierge services for busy lifestyles.We specialize in catering to the needs of C-level professionals.Our corporate programs offer companies and luxury office buildings on-site (AA, estab 2006, empl 4, sales $20,000, cert: NMSDC)

7488　BCA Watson Rice LLP
5 Penn Plaza, 15th Fl　New York, NY 10001
(212) 447-7300　Bennie Hadnott Managing Partner
Fax: (212) 683-6031
Email: blhadnott@bcawatsonrice.com
Website: www.bcawatsonrice.com
Financial auditing services, retirement plan audits, forensic accounting services, internal control services & tax compliance services. (AA/As-Pac, estab 1982, empl 299, sales $4,597,538, cert: State)

7489　C.L. King & Associates, Inc.
410 Park Ave　New York, NY 10022
(212) 364-1834　Jason Freed
Fax: (212) 364-1835
Email: jcf@clking.com
Website: www.clking.com
Investment banking services, stock (equity) underwriting, bond (fixed income/debt) underwriting, mergers & acquisitions advisory, securities sales, trading & distribution, stock buybacks & pension fund asset mgmt. (Woman/White, estab 1972, empl 125, sales $45,242,635, cert: WBENC)

7490　CastleOak Securities, L.P.
110 E 59th St, 2nd Fl　New York, NY 10022
(646) 521-6700　Philip Ippolito CFO
Fax: (212) 308-7342
Email: ochukwu@castleoaklp.com
Website: www.castleoaklp.com
Primary & secondary sales & trading of fixed income, equity, municipal & money market securities. (AA, estab 2006, empl 70, sales $23,087,000, cert: NMSDC)

7491　CAVU Securities, LLC
800 Third Ave, Fl 10　New York, NY 10022
(212) 916-3855　Shanker Merchant Managing Dir
Fax:
Email: smerchant@cavusecurities.com
Website: www.cavusecurities.com
Model Validation (DFAST), Investment Banking, Financial Institutions Capital Raise, M&A Recapitalization Advisory, Capital Markets, and Investor Relations (AA, estab 2010, empl 1, sales , cert: NMSDC)

7492　CAVU Securities, LLC.
800 Third Avenue 10th Fl　New York, NY 10022
(212) 916-3840　Jose Reyes
Fax: (866) 525-5201
Email: jreyes@cavusecurities.com
Website: www.cavusecurities.com
Full service brokerage, investment banking & funds distribution. (AA, estab 2013, empl 12, sales $1,500,000, cert: NMSDC)

7493　Corporate Leasing Associates, Inc.
21 Morris Ave　Rockville Center, NY 11570
(212) 732-5571　Mitch Gelnick Diversity Sales
Fax: (212) 596-6777
Email: mitch@corplease.com
Website: www.corplease.com
Operating lease structures, lease purchase, sale & leaseback, step down & step up payments, balloon payments, single investor leases, etc. (Woman/White, estab 1982, empl 6, sales $4,654,218, cert: State, CPUC, WBENC)

7494　DACK Consulting Solutions
2 William St Ste 202　White Plains, NY 10601
(914) 686-7102　Aleksandra Chancy CEO
Fax: (914) 686-7103
Email: ggayle@dackconsulting.com
Website: www.dackconsulting.com
Cost consulting, estimating, scheduling & project management services. (Woman/AA, estab 1997, empl 24, sales $1,000,000, cert: State, City)

7495 Delta Risk Capital Group LLC
860 Fifth Ave (2L) New York, NY 10065
(212) 961-6825 Shanker Merchant Principal
Fax:
Email: shanker.merchant@DeltaRiskCapital.com
Website: www.DeltaRiskCapital.com
Model Validation Services pursuant to FHFA Requirements and Dodd-Frank Financial Regulations, Valuation on Securities, Valuation of Residential and Commercial Mortgages, Mortgage and Asset backed securities, Investment Banking, Capital Raising. (As-Pac, estab 1900, empl 1, sales $55,475, cert: NMSDC)

7496 Divine Capital Markets
39 Broadway, 36 Fl New York, NY 10006
(212) 344-5867 Patsy Senese Mgr inst sales
Fax: (212) 509-5867
Email: patsy@divinecapital.com
Website: www.divinecapital.com
Investment banking, underwriting & distributions, research, corporate share repurchase programs, proprietary VWAP trading, municipal & corporate bonds, international equities. (Woman/White, estab 1997, empl 12, sales $13,900,000, cert: WBENC)

7497 EXIGIS LLC
589 8th Ave Fl 8 New York, NY 10018
(800) 928-1963 Armand Alvarez CEO
Fax: (800) 928-1963
Email: sales@exigis.com
Website: www.exigis.com
Risk management services, risk, insurance & business process automation technology. (Hisp, estab 2002, empl 35, sales $1,550,000, cert: NMSDC)

7498 Flash Exterminating, Inc.
164 Maujer St Brooklyn, NY 11206
(347) 748-8023 James Swint President
Fax: (614) 455-8653
Email: flashexterminating@gmail.com
Website: www.flashexterminating.com
Flash stands for pest elimination. Sealing entry points and having Certified Food Safety handlers on staff to act as consultants to city and state department inspections ensures your facility is in top notch order avoiding the penalties and fines (AA, estab 2009, empl 3, sales $197,000, cert: City, NMSDC)

7499 IMB Development Corporation, LLC
55 Exchange Place Ste 401 New York, NY 10005
(646) 619-8757 Tarrus Richardson CEO
Fax: (646) 506-4055
Email: trichardson@imbdc.com
Website: www.imbdc.com
Enterprise risk management & insurance solutions, supplier diversity strategy & capacity building, M&A advisory & direct private equity investing. (AA, estab 2010, empl 5, sales $7,117,682, cert: State, NMSDC)

7500 Lebenthal Holdings, LLC
521 Fifth Ave Fl 15 New York, NY 10175
(877) 425-6006 Steven Willis Sr Managing Dir
Fax:
Email: swillis@lebenthal.com
Website: www.lebenthalcapitalmarkets.com
Underwrites securities, equity & corporate debt underwriting. (Woman/White, estab 2007, empl 38, sales $13,179,068, cert: WBENC)

7501 Rozario & Associates, P.C.
55 Broadway 20th Fl New York, NY 10006
(212) 301-2770 Rovin Rozario Managing Partner
Fax: (718) 859-2345
Email: rrozario@rozariolaw.com
Website: www.rozariolaw.com
Rozario & Associates, P.C., is a New York City-based law firm, certified by NMSDC as a Minority Business Enterprise. We have built our reputation on the quality of our attorneys and staff members, who provide superior client service, high-quality legal (AA, estab 2005, empl 9, sales $821,000, cert: NMSDC)

7502 Samuel A. Ramirez & Company, Inc.
61 Broadway 29th Fl NewYork, NY 10006
(212) 248-1214 Lawrence Goldman Managing Dir
Fax: (212) 248-3856
Email: larry.goldman@ramirezco.com
Website: www.ramirezco.com
Investment banking & capital markets, distribution, brokerage, corporate share repurchase & research services. (Hisp, estab 1971, empl 135, sales $51,908,098, cert: NMSDC)

7503 Tigress Financial Partners LLC
114 W 47th St New York, NY 10036
(212) 430-8700 George Orr
Fax: (646) 862-2908
Email: gorr@tigressfp.com
Website: www.tigressfp.com
Financial services: rtesearch, trade execution, asset management, corporate advisory & investment banking. (Woman, estab 2010, empl 9, sales $100,000, cert: State, City, WBENC)

7504 Topeka Capital Markets Inc.
40 Wall St, Ste 1702 New York, NY 10005
(212) 709-5706 Sylvester McClearn COO
Fax: (212) 709-1365
Email: sm@topekacapitalmarkets.com
Website: www.topekacapitalmarkets.com
Agency-only trading domestic & international equities, traders, sales traders & research analysts. (AA, estab 2010, empl 28, sales , cert: City, NMSDC)

7505 Williams Capital Management, LLC
650 Fifth Avenue, 9th Floor New York, NY 10019
(212) 461-6112 Jeffrey Paul Senior Portfolio Mgr
Fax: (212) 461-6034
Email: finance@willcapmanagement.com
Website: www.willcapmanagement.com
Investment svcs: cash management & short-term fixed income investment strategies. (AA, estab 2002, empl 5, sales , cert: State, City, NMSDC, CPUC)

Ohio

7506 Kaiser Consulting, LLC
818 Riverbend Ave   Powell, OH 43065
(614) 300-1088 Lori Kaiser CEO
Fax:
Email: lkaiser@kaiserconsulting.com
Website: www.kaiserconsulting.com
Financial & accounting consulting. (Woman, estab 1994, empl 63, sales $4,440,000, cert: WBENC)

7507 Kanu Asset Managment, LLC
4015 Executive Park Dr Ste 402 Cincinnati, OH 45241
(513) 769-2700 Enyi Kanu CEO
Fax: (513) 769-2703
Email: ktrent@kanuinvestments.com
Website: www.kanuasset.com
Registered Investment Advisory Firm (RIA) - Investments, Wealth Management, Financial Planning, Insurance, Portfolio Management, Institutional Consulting & Advisory Services. (AA, estab 1996, empl 5, sales , cert: NMSDC)

7508 McCarthy, Burgess & Wolff
26000 Cannon Rd   Cleveland, OH 44146
(440) 735-5100 Paul Joseph Director of Business Dev
Fax: (440) 735-5110
Email: paul.joseph@mbandw.com
Website: www.mbandw.com
Commercial collections & receivables. (Woman/White, estab 2000, empl 203, sales $17,200,000, cert: WBENC)

7509 The Pension & Retirement Group LLC
5900 Roche Dr Ste 435 Columbus, OH 43229
(800)3855304 Curtis Clark Managing Partner
Fax:
Email: cclark@thepensionandretirementgroup.com
Website: www.thepensionandretirementgroup.com
Financial Wellness, Retirement Planning, Insurance, Investments, 401(k) & 403(b) Plan Management, Retirement Income Planning, Supplement Benefits, Securities, Mutual Funds, IRA's. (AA, estab 2005, empl 3, sales $500,000, cert: NMSDC)

7510 Triton Services Inc.
8162 Duke Blvd Mason, OH 45040
(513) 679-6800 Daniel Hockersmith
Fax: (513) 679-6808
Email: DHockersmith@tritonservicesinc.com
Website: www.tritonservicesinc.com
Mechanical contracting, design, install & service HVAC, plumbing and site development of commercial & industrial facilities. Triton also specializes in trechhless technology. (As-Ind, estab 2003, empl 165, sales , cert: NMSDC)

Pennsylvania

7511 Caterpillar to Butterfly, LLC
12575 Chilton Rd   Philadelphia, PA 19154
(215) 632-2575 Davida Godett CEO
Fax: (866) 525-5201
Email: godett@caterpillartobutterfly.net
Website: www.caterpillartobutterfly.net
Financial services. (Woman/AA, estab 2013, empl 1, sales , cert: NMSDC)

7512 Exude, LLC
325 Chestnut St Ste 1000 Philadelphia, PA 19106
(215) 875-8730 Caesar Williams President
Fax:
Email: cwilliams@exudeinc.com
Website: www.exudeinc.com
Employee Benefits, Human Resources & Risk Management Consulting. (AA, estab 2013, empl 2, sales $293,231, cert: State, NMSDC)

Puerto Rico

7513 Alvarado Tax & Business Advisors LLC
P.O. Box 195598   San Juan, PR 00918
(787) 620-7744 Miguel Rodriguez Admin
Fax: (787) 999-4646
Email: mrodriguez@alvatax.com
Website: www.alvatax.com
Tax & business consulting, outsourcing, business operations, government compliance resolution issues, financial management, business, development, business continuation
& succession, business governance. (Hisp, estab 2002, empl 32, sales $5,506,828, cert: NMSDC)

Rhode Island

7514 Axiom Actuarial Consulting
26 Knapton St   Barrington, RI 02806
(860) 550-0740 Carlos Fuentes President
Fax:
Email: carlos-fuentes@axiom-actuarial.com
Website: www.axiom-actuarial.com
Actuarial consulting: dental & vision coverages, pension, life insurance, employee benefits, special risk insurance, reinsurance, investment, finance & strategy. (Hisp, estab 2008, empl 4, sales $75,000, cert: 8(a))

Texas

7515 Akisha Networks, Inc.
5868 A-1 Westheimer Rd, Ste 224   Houston, TX 77057
(713) 840-7424 Ronald Smith VP
Fax: (713) 877-8867
Email: info@akisha.net
Website: www.akisha.net
Akisha Networks Inc (ANI) is a full service Digital Systems Integrator that designs, builds and manages IP convergence solutions for today's intelligent commercial buildings. (AA, estab 2001, empl 8, sales $395,776, cert: NMSDC)

7516 Bley Investment Group
4200 S Hulen, Ste 519   Fort Worth, TX 76109
(817) 732-2442 Laura Bley President
Fax: (817) 732-5997
Email: laurab@bleyinvestments.com
Website: www.bleyinvestments.com
Financial services. (Woman/White, estab 1990, empl 7, sales $565,000, cert: State, WBENC)

7517 Capital Institutional Services, Inc.
1700 Pacific Ave, Ste 1100 Dallas, TX 75201
(214) 978-4767 Wendy Dailey Dir of Business Dev
Fax:
Email: wdailey@capis.com
Website: www.capis.com
Global execution services & commission management
solutions. (Woman/White, estab 1977, empl 74, sales
$49,957,374, cert: State, WBENC)

7518 Goldman, Imani & Goldberg, Inc.
9894 Bissonnet St Ste 900 Houston, TX 77036
(713) 395-5120 Karl Miller Director of Mktg & Client
Dev
Fax: (713) 395-5127
Email: kmiller@giginconline.com
Website: www.giginconline.com
Collection programs, accounts receivable management,
third party recovery. (AA, estab 2003, empl 26, sales
$2,800,000, cert: NMSDC, 8(a))

7519 Harris & Dickey, LLC.
4127 Wycliff Ave Dallas, TX 75219
(972) 672-7597 Kelly Harris Partner
Fax: (214) 219-0455
Email: Kelly.Harris@Harris-Dickey.com
Website: www.harris-dickey.com
Accounting, finance, tax, internal audit, technology risk &
special project assistance. (Woman/White, estab 2010,
empl 12, sales $1,662,658, cert: State, City, WBENC)

7520 JN3 Global Enterprises LLC
6034 W Courtyard Dr Ste 150 Austin, TX 78730
(512) 501-1155 James Nowlin CEO
Fax: (214) 446-8556
Email: jnowlin@excelglobalpartners.com
Website: www.ExcelGlobalPartners.com
Corporate financial strategy & implementation. (AA, estab
2007, empl 10, sales $1,500,000, cert: State, NMSDC)

7521 Kipling Jones & Co., Ltd.
1200 Smith St Ste 1600 Houston, TX 77002
(713) 353-4688 Robbi Jones President
Fax: (713) 353-8787
Email: rjones@kiplingjones.com
Website: www.kiplingjones.com
Investment banking, financial advisory, bond underwriting
& guidance. (Woman/AA, estab 2008, empl 7, sales
$500,000, cert: State, City)

7522 Pharos Financial Services L.P.
300 Crescent Ct, Ste 1380 Dallas, TX 75201
(214) 855-0194 Vincent Mullins Natl sales Mgr
Fax: (214) 855-1230
Email: vmullins@pharosfinancial.com
Website: www.pharosfunds.com
Financial loan & lease products. (AA, estab 2002, empl 12,
sales , cert: State)

7523 PMB Precision Medical Billing Inc.
8203 Willow Place Dr S Ste 230 Houston, TX 77070
(713) 672-7211 Petria McKelvey CEO
Fax: (713) 672-7624
Email: petria@precisionmedicalbilling.com
Website: www.precisionmedicalbilling.com
Revenue recovery & collections services. (Woman/AA,
estab 1995, empl 13, sales $1,611,635, cert: State, WBENC)

7524 PRO Consulting Services, Inc.
500 Lovett Blvd Ste 250 Houston, TX 77006
(713) 523-1800 Victor Juarez President
Fax: (713) 523-9699
Email: vjuarez@proconsrv.com
Website: www.proconsrv.com
Accounts receivables management services, commercial
collections. (Hisp, estab 1992, empl 90, sales
$4,500,000, cert: NMSDC)

7525 Real Time Resolutions, Inc.
1349 Empire Central Dr Ste 150 Dallas, TX 75247
(214) 599-6557 Mark Hutto SVP - Business Devel
Fax:
Email: client.services@rtresolutions.com
Website: www.realtimeresolutions.com
Financial services & asset recovery: auto, credit card,
mortgages, direct demand accounts, student loans,
installment loans & commercial loans. (Woman, estab
2000, empl 320, sales , cert: WBENC)

Virginia

7526 Gemini Financial Strategists LLC
10 Naples Rd Stafford, VA 22554
(202) 631-1430 Jeremy Williams Managing
Partner
Fax:
Email: jeremy_williams@gmfis.com
Website: www.gmfis.com
(Financial management & analysis, retirement plan
implementation/ administration, employee retirement
planning benefits. (AA, estab 2008, empl 6, sales
$230,000, cert: State)

7527 Kodiak Finance LLC
8000 Towers Crescent Dr Ste 1350 Vienna, VA
22182
(703) 266-9199 Marcy Dilworth President
Fax: (703) 991-7178
Email: mdilworth@kodiakfinance.com
Website: www.kodiakfinance.com
Computer leasing & sales, asset management. (Woman/
Nat Ame, estab 2004, empl 10, sales $560,357, cert:
NMSDC, WBENC)

7528 RER Solutions Inc.
950 Herndon Pkwy, Ste 200 Herndon, VA 20170
(703) 742-6789 Errin Green CEO
Fax: (703) 742-3336
Email: Errin.Green@rer-solutions.com
Website: www.rer-solutions.com
Comprehensive business, real estate & financial mgmt.
services, asset sale support, due diligence, portfolio
management systems, technical & admin support
personnel, financial modeling, document & records
management, risk management. (Woman/AA, estab
1989, empl 27, sales $2,633,597, cert: State, 8(a))

7529   Technology Ventures
       7930 Jones Branch Dr Ste 310 McLean, VA 22102
       (703) 917-1650 John Earl Dir Business Dev
       Fax: (703) 917-1690
       Email: jearl@tventures.net
       Website: www.tventures.net
IT & Financial Staffing, Government & Consulting Services,
Financial Services, Healthcare Communications, Consumer
& Retail. (As-Ind, estab 1998, empl 150, sales , cert: State)

Washington

7530   Adekoya Business Consulting LLC
       33021 Hoyt Rd SW   Federal Way, WA 98023
       (206) 817-9775 Andre Adekoya CEO
       Fax: (253) 517-9080
       Email: andrew@adekoyabc.com
       Website: www.adekoyabc.com
Business solutions, strategic financial planning & analysis,
audits, market (digital) competitive analytics & revenue
growth opportunities identification, resource planning,
process re-engineering & system implementation. (AA,
estab 2013, empl 5, sales $425,000, cert: State)

Wisconsin

7531   One Accord, LLC
       P.O. Box 241763   Milwaukee, WI 53224
       (414) 855-6342 Shanna Reid President
       Fax: (877) 345-6550
       Email: smreid@oneaccord.biz
       Website: www.oneaccord.biz
Risk management & reinsurance brokerage. (Woman/AA,
estab 2002, empl 3, sales $80,000, cert: State, City)

Alabama

7532 C. Edward Lewis & Associates
3415 Buckboard Rd   Montgomery, AL 36116
(334) 272-3365 Charles Lewis President
Fax: (800) 360-2430
Email: charleslewis@celewisohs.com
Website: www.celewisohs.com
EEO & human resources training & consulting. (AA, estab 2004, empl 2, sales $20,000, cert: NMSDC)

7533 EAP Lifestyle Management, LLC
1605 Main St   Daphne, AL 36526
(800) 788-2077 Patricia Vanderpool Owner
Fax: (251) 621-5361
Email: pvanderpool@eaplifestyle.com
Website: www.eaplifestyle.com
Employee assistance program & work/life svcs, substance abuse professional svcs, workplace training & presentation, continuing education, critical incident stress svcs. (Woman/White, estab 1998, empl 10, sales $210,924, cert: WBENC)

Arizona

7534 HR Wise, LLC
8399 E Indian School Rd Ste 101 Scottsdale, AZ 85251
(480) 626-2109 Gregory O'Keefe CEO
Fax: (480) 626-1451
Email: gokeefe@hrwisellc.com
Website: www.hrwisellc.com
Davis Bacon-Act Certified Payroll, Payroll Services, Human Resource Management, Talent Management, Benefits Administration, Time and Attendance, Human Capital Management, HR Business Process Outsourcing (HRBPO). (Hisp, estab 2008, empl 6, sales $290,000, cert: NMSDC, 8(a))

California

7535 ClearPath Management Group, Inc
1215 W Center St Ste 102 Manteca, CA 95337
(209) 239-8700 Natasha Giordano Corporate Services Mgr
Fax: (209) 239-8810
Email: wbe@clearpathwm.com
Website: www.clearpathwm.com
Contractor payroll, employer of record service, Contingent workforce management, business process outsourcing, Independent contractor compliance. (Woman/White, estab 2010, empl 16, sales $35,000,000, cert: WBENC)

7536 E. L. Goldberg & Associates
950 Siskiyou Dr   Menlo Park, CA 94025
(650) 854-0854 Edie Goldberg CEO
Fax: (650) 854-0844
Email: edie@elgoldberg.com
Website: www.elgoldberg.com
Human Resources Management Consulting, Talent Management, Performance Management, Career Management, Succession Planning, Selection, Leadership Development, Competency Modeling, Benchmarking, HR Strategic Planning. (Woman/White, estab 2001, empl 1, sales $300,000, cert: CPUC)

7537 Employers Choice Online Inc.
9845 Painter Ave. Ste B Whittier, CA 90605
(800) 424-7011 Jesus Ariel Lopez Procurement Contract Specialist
Fax: (562) 261-1404
Email: bids@ecoinc.us
Website: www.employerschoicescreening.com
Employment background checks, drug testing, physical exams & Form 1-9 services. (Hisp, estab 2011, empl 20, sales $1,637,316, cert: NMSDC, CPUC, 8(a), SDB)

7538 HR Allen Consulting Services
6065 Sundale Way Ste. 98 Fair Oaks, CA 95628
(916) 370-7849 Michael Allen President
Fax:
Email: mallen@hrallenconsulting.com
Website: www.hrallencs.com
Human resource consulting & outsourcing. (AA/Hisp, estab 2005, empl 10, sales $100,000, cert: State)

7539 Los Remedios
2377 S Sabre Ave   Fresno, CA 93727
(619) 813-6445 Patricia Alvarado Owner
Fax:
Email: pa@remedysupportservices.com
Website:
Management & human resources consulting. (Woman/Hisp, estab 1995, empl 1, sales , cert: State)

7540 Translating Services, Inc.
1516 S Bundy Dr Ste 311 Los Angeles, CA 90025
(310) 453-3302 Lisa Lazar President
Fax: (310) 453-6002
Email: languages@lazar.com
Website: www.lazar.com
Translation, interpreting. (Woman/White, estab 1999, empl 8, sales , cert: WBENC)

Colorado

7541 Champion Business Services
2121 S Blackhawk St, Ste 120 Aurora, CO 80014
(303) 873-9147 Carol McCallister President
Fax: (303) 873-9149
Email: carol@championbusiness.com
Website: www.championbusiness.com
Clerical support svcs, help supply svcs, Ccmputer pogramming, data entry processing & preparation, business svcs, clerical skills training, facilities mgmt support svcs. (Woman/AA, estab 1986, empl 5, sales $139,347, cert: State)

7542   Employee Development Systems, Inc.
        7300 S Alton Way Ste 5J Centennial, CO 80112
        (800) 282-3374 Sherman Updegraff Managing Dir
        Fax: (303) 221-0704
        Email: sherm@edsiusa.com
        Website: www.employeedevelopmentsystems.com
Personal training: self-confidence, understanding behavioral styles, communication skills, listening skills, self-
motivation & personal accountability. (Woman/White,
estab 1900, empl 1, sales , cert: NWBOC)

Florida

7543   HRSS Consulting Group
        1970 Michigan Ave, Bldg D   Cocoa, FL 32922
        (321) 576-1314 Karen Gregory President
        Fax:
        Email: kgregory@hrssconsultinggroup.com
        Website: www.hrssconsultinggroup.com
Organizational development and talent management.
(Woman/As-Pac/Hisp, estab 2012, empl 6, sales $230,000,
cert: State, WBENC)

7544   Midwest Background Inc.
        200 Central Ave, Ste 820   St Petersburg, FL 33701
        (727) 592-8275 Syan Kazi Dir of Business Devel
        Fax:
        Email: media@mbiworldwide.com
        Website: www.mbiworldwide.com
Background screening & hiring solutions. (Woman/White,
estab 1998, empl 27, sales $2,700,000, cert: NWBOC)

7545   Moten Tate, Inc.
        301 E. Pine St Ste 250 Orlando, FL 32801
        (407) 843-3277 Kenneth Moten CEO
        Fax: (407) 843-3814
        Email: kmoten@motentate.com
        Website: www.motentate.com
Human resource management: staffing, HR project mgmt,
reward strategies, employee development & HR
outsourcing. (AA, estab 1997, empl 100, sales $3,400,000,
cert: State, NMSDC)

7546   Sobriety On the Sea
        4302 Hollywood Blvd 125 Hollywood, FL 33021
        (954) 923-7333 Danette Arthur President
        Fax: (954) 923-7722
        Email: sos@doctorsos.org
        Website: www.DrArthur.org
Pre-employment & random drug testing services.
(Woman/AA, estab 2001, empl 4, sales , cert: State)

7547   Steven C. Fraser, P.A.
        221 W Hallandale Beach Blvd, Ste 201   Hallandale
        Beach, FL 33009
        (305) 809-6781 Steve Fraser Managing Dir
        Fax: (609) 385-4966
        Email: sfraser@fraserlawfl.com
        Website: www.fraserlawfl.com
We are civil trial lawyers. (AA, estab 2008, empl 2, sales ,
cert: State)

7548   Suncoast Compliance Services, LLC
        16765 Fishhawk Dr, Ste 325   Lithia, FL 33547
        (813) 653-4559 Vincent McGrew President
        Fax: (888) 217-9389
        Email: vroy.mcgrew@usamdt.com
        Website: www.usamdt.com/westcentralflorida
Pre-employment background screening, drug-free
workplace policy development & implementation, on-
site drug & alcohol testing, Employer Assistance Program referral, supervisor training for DOT & non-DOT
employees. (AA, estab 2012, empl 1, sales , cert: State,
NMSDC)

7549   The Management Edge, Inc.
        12360 66th St, Ste S Largo, FL 33773
        (727) 588-9481 Patty Dunn Dir Ops/Finance
        Fax: (727) 531-0895
        Email: patty.dunn@mgtedge.com
        Website: www.themanagementedge.com
Organization dev, team building & partnering, executive
& staff dev, training & coaching, conflict resolution,
consensus building. (Woman/White, estab 1986, empl
18, sales $908,000, cert: State, WBENC)

Georgia

7550   Assessment Plus, Inc.
        2180 Satellite Blvd Ste 400 Duluth, GA 30097
        (770) 925-3990 Brielle Fetrow Project Coord
        Fax:
        Email: brielle.fetrow@assessmentplus.com
        Website: www.assessmentplus.com
Employee opinion surveys, customers satisfaction
surveys, leadership development, 360-degree feedback
assessments, executive & leadership coaching, exit
interviews & team assessments. (Woman/White, estab
1984, empl 14, sales $650,000, cert: WBENC)

7551   Career Connection, Inc.
        1170 Peachtree St Ste 1200 Atlanta, GA 30309
        (404) 814-5282 Cody Stowers
        Fax:
        Email: cstowers@ccicareers.com
        Website: www.ccicareers.com
Staff augmentation, workforce solutions, permanent
placement, recruitment, personnel management, HR
services, administrative management, call center,
customer support, IT support, Information technology,
facilities management. (Woman/White, estab 1986,
empl 1000, sales $40,000,000, cert: WBENC)

7552   CyQuest Business Solutions, Inc.
        3645 Market Place Blvd Ste 130 East Point, GA
        30344
        (404) 761-6699 DeVan Brown CEO
        Fax: (404) 761-5984
        Email: devan@cyquesthr.com
        Website: www.cyquesthr.com
HR outsourcing solutions: compensation, employee
benefits, retirement plans, HRIS systems, payroll
processing, employee recruitment & retention. (AA,
estab 2004, empl 8, sales $107,500, cert: State, NMSDC)

7553   eVerifile.com Inc.
        900 Circle 75 Pkwy Ste 1550 Atlanta, GA 30339
        (404) 585-4487 Jennifer Brown VP Business Dev
        Fax:
        Email: jennifer.brown@everifile.com
        Website: www.everifile.com
Criminal background investigations, action notification
and/or information analytics & grading, US Government
watch searches, certificate & license verification, motor
vehicle reports, employment & reference verification. (AA,
estab 1900, empl 1, sales $12,000,000, cert: NMSDC)

7554   McPherson, Berry & Associates, Inc.
        4158 S River Ln Ste 110 Ellenwood, GA 30294
        (800) 325-5269 LaSonya Berry CEO
        Fax: (831) 306-5269
        Email: lasonya@mcphersonberryassoc.com
        Website: www.mcphersonberry.com
Human Rrsource training, consulting & team building
event planning. (Woman/AA, estab 2000, empl 3, sales
$250,000, cert: NMSDC, WBENC)

7555   Springboard Benefits, LLC
        695 Pylant St NE Ste 232 Atlanta, GA 30306
        (205) 790-1060 Amy Parkman CEO
        Fax:
        Email: aparkman@springboardbenefits.com
        Website: www.springboardbenefits.com
Project management & consulting, employee on-boarding
& off-boarding, hire to retire, new hires, open enrollment,
ACA, variable hour tracking, medicare exchange & early
termination exchanges. (Woman/White, estab 2014, empl
6, sales $250,000, cert: WBENC)

7556   Steelbridge Solutions, Inc
        2451 Cumberland Pkwy Ste 3228 Atlanta, GA 30339
        (404) 259-0865 Susan Richards President
        Fax: (404) 662-2433
        Email: susan.richards@steelbridgesolutions.com
        Website: www.SteelBridgeSolutions.com
Human Capital Consulting, Human Resource Consulting,
Business Transformation Consulting, Change Management
Consulting, Human resource Information System Consult-
ing, HR Transformation, HR Strategy, HR Technology.
(Woman/White, estab 2013, empl 1, sales $900,000, cert:
WBENC)

Illinois

7557   JRA Consulting Services, Inc.
        10225 W Higgins Rd Rosemont, IL 60018
        (847) 430-3682 Ross Wolfson Talent Acquisition
        Mgr
        Fax: (847) 720-4196
        Email: rwolfson@hrcontracting.com
        Website: www.hrcontracting.com
Human resources staffing, permanent & contract posi-
tions. (Woman, estab 1997, empl 4, sales $2,000,000, cert:
NWBOC)

7558   Ossanna Corporation
        2775 Algonquin Rd, Ste 260   Rolling Meadows, IL
        60008
        (847) 255-2800 Mariaelena Estrada Office Mgr
        Fax: (847) 255-5263
        Email: mestrada@ossanna.com
        Website: www.ossanna.com
Human resource professionals: consulting, option-to-
hire & permanent basis. (Woman/White, estab 1988,
empl 16, sales $4,439,000, cert: State, WBENC)

Indiana

7559   HR Alternative Consulting, Inc.
        10641 Medinah Dr   Indianapolis, IN 46234
        (317) 852-3590 Ann Fisher President
        Fax: (317) 852-3590
        Email: afisher@hralternativeconsulting.com
        Website: www.hralternativeconsulting.com
Customized human resources services. (Woman/White,
estab 2003, empl 2, sales , cert: State, City)

7560   Work-Comp Management Services
        760 Park East Blvd #5   Lafayette, IN 47905
        (765) 447-7473 Julie Ott, Owner/Nurse Mgr
        Fax: (765) 449-8504
        Email: jott@workcompms.com
        Website: www.workcompms.net
On-site occupational health services, work comp case
management, pre-employment random drug screening,
certified collections. (Woman/White, estab 1996, empl
55, sales $3,600,000, cert: WBENC)

Louisiana

7561   Debra Gould & Associates, Inc.
        P.O. Box 871211   New Orleans, LA 70187
        (504) 244-6576 Debra Gould President
        Fax: (504) 245-2488
        Email: djgould@gouldassoc.com
        Website: www.gouldassoc.com
Diversity, change management, team building, leader-
ship, project management, Six Sigma & communication.
(Woman/AA, estab 1996, empl 2, sales $578,642, cert:
WBENC)

7562   OutSolve, LLC
        3116 5th St Metairie, LA 70002
        (888) 414-2410 Tracy Leefe Principal
        Fax: (504) 486-2411
        Email: tleefe@outsolve-hr.com
        Website: www.outsolve-hr.com
Affirmative action planning & compliance consulting:
affirmative action plan preparation & implementation,
audit support, compensation analyses, EEO-1 & Vets 100
reports. (Woman, estab 1998, empl 12, sales
$4,100,000, cert: WBENC)

Maryland

7563 AEIO, LLC
1250 Connecticut Ave, NW Ste 200 Washington, MD 20036
(202) 251-3545 Dionne Word CEO
Fax: (866) 854-6619
Email: dword@aeioonline.com
Website: www.aeioonline.com
Human resource management, staff augmentation, conference management services. (Woman/AA, estab 2001, empl 20, sales $700,000, cert: State)

7564 Full Disclosure
2 Industrial Park Dr Ste B Waldorf, MD 20602
(877) 214-4717 Felicia Denman President
Fax: (877) 214-4707
Email: fdenman@full-disclosure.org
Website: www.full-disclosure.org
Preemployment screening, background checks, criminal records, employment verification, education verification, terrorist watch list, reference check, civil records, professional license verification. (Woman/AA, estab 2006, empl 1, sales , cert: State)

7565 HR Anew, Inc.
6350 Stevens Forest Rd Ste 250 Columbia, MD 21046
(410) 381-5220 Melanie Freeman President
Fax: (410) 381-5229
Email: mfreeman@hranew.com
Website: www.hranew.com
Human resource management & consulting, training & professional development, management & employee coaching, recruitment & hiring, executive search, staff augmentation, event & conference planning , employee relations. (Woman/AA, estab 1999, empl 17, sales $2,200,000, cert: State)

7566 The HR Source
8181 Professional Place Ste 120 Landover, MD 20785
(301) 459-3133 Patricia Hall Jaynes CEO
Fax:
Email: pathj@thehrsource.com
Website: www.thehrsource.com
Human resources staffing & consulting services, interim/temporary & permanent staffing services, outplacement & payroll services, administrative interim/temporary & permanent staffing services. (Woman/AA, estab 1994, empl 5, sales $2,894,265, cert: State, NMSDC, WBENC)

Michigan

7567 Aha! Leadership LLC
49425 Deer Run   Northville, MI 48167
(248) 882-2354 Robyn Marcotte President
Fax:
Email: robyn.marcotte@ahaleadership.com
Website: www.ahaleadership.com
Leadership Training & Development, Human Resources Consulting Services; Customer Service Training & Development. (Woman/White, estab , empl 1, sales , cert: WBENC)

7568 Ashlor Management Corporation
3710 Davison Rd   Flint, MI 48506
(810) 275-0690 Charles Kuta President
Fax: (810) 275-0706
Email: charles@ashlorstaffing.com
Website: www.ashlorstaffing.com
HR, staffing, payroll & complete benefit administration. (Hisp, estab 2015, empl 5, sales , cert: NMSDC)

7569 The Orsus Group, Inc.
3155 W Big Beaver Rd Ste 216 Troy, MI 48084
(248) 530-3685 Will Montgomery President
Fax:
Email: wmontgomery@theorsusgroup.com
Website: www.theorsusgroup.com
Employment screening: criminal checks, sex offender registry, employment & education verification, motor vehicle records, credit checks, sanctions checks, drug screening, prohibited parties. (AA, estab 2007, empl 8, sales $900,000, cert: NMSDC)

Minnesota

7570 Inclusion, Inc.
126 N 3rd St Ste 412 Minneapolis, MN 55401
(612) 339-2202 Shirley Engelmeier CEO
Fax: (612) 339-4350
Email: shirley@inclusion-inc.com
Website: www.inclusion-inc.com
Diversity & inclusion strategies: web based survey, diversity & inclusion assesment, customized skills based training, changing business behaviors, micro-inequities & on-the-job application. (Woman/White, estab 2001, empl 21, sales , cert: WBENC)

Missouri

7571 Quest Management Consultants
12125 Woodcrest Executive Dr Ste 205 St. Louis, MO 63141
(314) 453-9999 Joe Wiley President
Fax: (314) 548-6661
Email: jwiley@questmc.com
Website: www.questmc.com
Human resource consulting: outplacement & career transition, staffing & career management. (AA, estab 2003, empl 8, sales $928,111, cert: State)

New Jersey

7572 Diversified Consulting Consortium, LLC
5 Tenalfy Rd, Ste 404 Englewood, NJ 07631
(908) 669-4633 Antonette Alonso
Fax: (925) 932-1950
Email:
talonso@diversifiedconsultingconsortium.com
Website:
www.diversifiedconsultingconsortium.com
HR management consulting, training, investigations, diversity management, affirmative action, employee coaching & counseling, labor relations. (Woman/AA/Hisp, estab 2012, empl 6, sales , cert: NMSDC)

7573 Fintech Consulting LLC DBA ApTask
120 S. Wood Ave Ste 300 Iselin, NJ 08830
(732) 355-8000 Eddie Bright CEO
Fax:
Email: edbright@aptask.com
Website: www.aptask.com
Staffing, workforce solutions, strategic outsourcing. (As-Ind, estab 2010, empl 90, sales $25,644,109, cert: NMSDC)

7574 Strategic Benefit Solutions
106 Madison Ave Atlantic City, NJ 08401
(609) 957-5309 Le Phan CEO
Fax: (609) 385-4966
Email: lphan@sbscompanies.com
Website: www.sbscompanies.com
Strategic Benefit Solutions is a full service consulting firm for voluntary worksite benefit solutions with a proven track record of delivering successful benefit solutions that deliver the results you and your employees require. (Woman/As-Pac, estab 2011, empl 6, sales $500,000, cert: NMSDC)

New York

7575 Can-Am Consultants Inc.
208 Mill St Rochester, NY 14614
(585) 777-4040 Cathryn Bell CEO
Fax:
Email: carrie.bell@can-amconsultants.com
Website: www.can-amconsultants.com
Recruitment & Payroll, Recruitment, Staffing & Payroll of Engineering, Technical & IT Personnel. (Woman/White, estab 2003, empl 150, sales $19,494,834, cert: State)

7576 Corporate Screening Consulting, LLC
4201 N Buffalo Rd Ste 10 Orchard Park, NY 14127
(716) 583-4629 Maria DiPirro President
Fax:
Email: MDiPirro@CorpScreen.com
Website: www.corpscreen.com
Risk management advisory services, Risk Avoidance consulting, litigation support, corporate compliance, due diligence, fraud analysis, background investigations & loss prevention program design. (Woman/White, estab 2007, empl 3, sales $250,000, cert: State)

7577 Crown Consulting Services Company
P.O. Box 292 Buffalo, NY 14207
(800) 868-1323 Anthony Fitzgerald CEO
Fax: (800) 496-1167
Email: afitzgerald@cpmsllc.com
Website: www.cpmsllc.com
Human resource ,anagement consulting, training, programs & policy development, executive coaching, seminars & workshops. (AA, estab 2000, empl 2, sales $65,000, cert: State)

Ohio

7578 Global to Local Language Solutions, LLC
1776 Mentor Ave Ste 319 Cincinnati, OH 42512
(513) 526-5011 Grace Bosworth President
Fax: (513) 752-7907
Email: grace@g2local.com
Website: www.g2local.com
Interpreting/translation services, interpreter training & language training. (Woman/White, estab 2009, empl 3, sales , cert: State, WBENC)

7579 Pathfinder
6836 Ashfield Dr Cincinnati, OH 45242
(513) 721-6611 John Hawkins President
Fax: (513) 762-8588
Email: jhawkins@managementperformance.com
Website: www.managementperformance.com
Labor consulting, human resource & organizational development. (AA, estab 1974, empl 6, sales $1,200,000, cert: NMSDC)

7580 Strategic Performance Systems, LLC
2206 Highland Ave Cincinnati, OH 45219
(513) 602-6200 Deborah Heater CEO
Fax: (513) 723-0062
Email: debheater@strategicperformancesystems.com
Website: www.strategicperformancesystems.com
Employee Development: management, leadership, compliance & risk reduction strategies, Human Resources Best Practices: effective human resources functions, Diversity Climate Assessments. (Woman/AA, estab 2013, empl 1, sales $130,000, cert: State)

7581 Stryker Green, LLC
1240 Sharonbrook Dr Twinsburg, OH 44087
(330) 963-9985 Sandy Moore CEO
Fax: (727) 290-9852
Email: sjohnson@strykergreen.com
Website: www.strykergreen.com
Human Resource Solutions consulting & managed services. (Woman/AA, estab 2012, empl 2, sales $63,700, cert: NMSDC)

Pennsylvania

7582 Advance Sourcing Concepts, LLC
3000 McKnight East Dr Ste 201 Pittsburgh, PA 15237
(412) 415-5081 Judith Bernhard President
Fax: (412) 415-5085
Email: jbernhard@ascpeople.com
Website: www.ascpeople.com
Human Resources contract & sourcing. (Woman/White, estab 2005, empl 4, sales $1,200,000, cert: State, WBENC)

7583   Bradley Partnerships, Inc.
       207 Malbec Lane Ste 100 Wexford, PA 15090
       (724) 779-8170 Lois Bradley President
       Fax: (724) 799-8175
       Email: lois@bradleypartnerships.com
       Website: www.bradleypartnerships.com
Organizational & human resource consulting services.
(Woman/White, estab 2002, empl 7, sales $350,000, cert:
State, 8(a))

7584   BRODY Professional Development
       115 West Ave Ste 114 Jenkintown, PA 19046
       (215) 886-1688 Heather Shafter Client Partner
       Fax: (215) 886-1699
       Email: heather@BrodyPro.com
       Website: www.BrodyPro.com
Training & coaching. (Woman/White, estab 1983, empl 5,
sales $924,400, cert: WBENC)

7585   Career Concepts, Inc.
       Hillcrest II, 721 Arbor Way Ste 180 Blue Bell, PA
       19422
       (610) 941-4455 Sharon Imperiale President
       Fax: (610) 941-0267
       Email: simperiale@cciconsulting.com
       Website: www.cciconsulting.com
Management consulting, human resources,
outplacement/career transition, recruiting, managerial &
executive coaching, leadership development, training.
(Woman/White, estab 1988, empl 50, sales $15,835,800,
cert: State, WBENC)

Puerto Rico

7586   Smart Option Search
       P.O. Box 194088 San Juan, PR 00917
       (787) 767-2373 Melissa Concepcion Esterrich
       President
       Fax: (787) 772-9369
       Email: mconcepcion@smartoptionsearch.com
       Website: www.smartoptionsearch.com
Recruiting and Human Resources Consulting. (Woman/
Hisp, estab 2000, empl 10, sales $398,000, cert: NMSDC)

Texas

7587   24/7 Background Checks LLC
       11520 N Central Expressway Ste 230 Dallas, TX
       75243
       (214) 206-3565 Jones Ajatuaewo President
       Fax: (214) 503-3738
       Email: jones@criminal411.com
       Website: www.criminal411.com
Pre employment screening services: driving records,
education & employment verification. (Woman/AA, estab
2004, empl 25, sales $600,000, cert: State, NMSDC)

7588   AGResearch International, LLC
       P.O. Box 460 McKinney, TX 75070
       (214) 842-4540 Patti T. Mayer President
       Fax: (972) 692-8918
       Email: patti.mayer@agresearch.info
       Website: www.agresearch.info
Human capital services, benchmarking studies. (Woman/
White, estab 2002, empl 15, sales $1,450,278, cert:
State, WBENC)

7589   Aspire HR, Inc.
       5151 Belt Line Rd Ste 1125 Dallas, TX 75254
       (972) 372-2793 Randy Griffith President
       Fax: (214) 880-9914
       Email: rgriffith@aspirehr.com
       Website: www.aspirehr.com
HR services for SAP ERP HCM solutions, implementations, upgrades & support, payroll, HR renewal, data
conversions & migrations. (Woman/White, estab 1998,
empl 41, sales , cert: WBENC)

7590   Bashen Corporation
       2603 Augusta Dr, Ste 200 Houston, TX 77057
       (800) 994-1554 Janet Bashen CEO
       Fax: (713) 780-8056
       Email: sales@bashencorp.com
       Website: www.bashencorp.com
HR consulting services: EEO compliance administration,
EEO investigations/ position statements & investigative
reports, workplace training, affirmative action planning,
diversity strategies, risk management. (Woman/AA,
estab 2013, empl 20, sales $1,578,181, cert: NMSDC,
WBENC)

7591   Brook Consultants Inc.
       2500 N Dallas Pkwy Ste 180 Plano, TX 75093
       (972) 473-8918 Matt Jones VP of Sales
       Fax:
       Email: sales@brookvms.com
       Website: www.brookvms.com
Human Resource Management services, Contractor
onboarding, competence evaluation, E-Verify & background checks. (Woman/White, estab 2006, empl 125,
sales $60,000,000, cert: WBENC)

7592   G&A Partners
       4801 Woodway Ste 210 Houston, TX 77056
       (713) 784-1181 David Vasquez VP
       Fax: (866) 286-0436
       Email: dvasquez@gnapartners.com
       Website: www.gnapartners.com
Professional Employer Organization (PEO) & Human
Resources Outsourcing & Consulting. (Hisp, estab 1995,
empl 175, sales $131,230,000, cert: State)

7593 Human Capital International, LLC dba Integrated
      Human Capital
      7300 Viscount Blvd Ste 103 El Paso, TX 79925
      (915) 781-2665 Rosa Santana CEO
      Fax: (210) 978-0850
      Email: rosa.santana@ihcus.com
      Website: www.ihcus.com
HR consulting, temporary staffing, professional & executive placement, payroll svcs, skill testing, vendor mgmt,
on-site staff mgmt. (Woman/Hisp, estab 2002, empl 34,
sales $18,926,874, cert: State, NMSDC, WBENC)

7594 InGenesis, Inc.
      10231 Kotzebue St   San Antonio, TX 78217
      (210) 366-0033 Dr. Veronica Edwards CEO
      Fax: (210) 568-4582
      Email: commercial@ingenesis.com1
      Website: www.ingenesis.com
Workforce solutions: direct placement, direct hire,
executive search, temporary staffing, contingent staffing,
managed vendor, recruitment process outsourcing,
managed services programs & locum tenens. (Woman/
Hisp, estab 1900, empl 1, sales $139,000,000, cert:
NMSDC, WBENC)

7595 KAS Consulting Group
      3625 North Hall Ste 610 Dallas, TX 75219
      (214) 528-3326 Keith Scott CEO
      Fax: (214) 528-7023
      Email: keith@kasconsulting.com
      Website: www.kasconsulting.com
Human resources consulting, direct staffing & placement
svcs, outplacement svcs, performance mgmt & appraisals,
leadership & performance coaching. (AA, estab 2002,
empl 3, sales $1,000,000, cert: State)

Virginia

7596 Beacon Group, LLC
      1940 Duke St, Ste 200 Alexandria, VA 22314
      (703) 684-3144 Vicki Coward-Rosen CEO
      Fax: (202) 318-0652
      Email: vicki@beacongroupllc.com
      Website: www.beacongroupllc.com
Manage government medical facilities, EEO investigations,
counseling, EEO mediation, diversity training, staffing.
(Woman/AA, estab 2003, empl 32, sales $850,000, cert:
State)

7597 Helios HR LLC
      1925 Isaac Newton Sq E Ste 200 Reston, VA 20190
      (703) 860-3882 Ellyn Krause VP Finance
      Fax: (703) 852-7375
      Email: ekrause@helioshr.com
      Website: www.helioshr.com
HR Effectiveness & Compliance Analysis, Employee
Assimilation & Onboarding, Employee Regulation Require-
ments, Policy Maintenance, Employee Relations &
Retention, Maintain & Implement Employee Performance
Management. (Woman/White, estab 2001, empl 20, sales
$3,670,154, cert: State, WBENC)

7598 RKL Resources
      6933 Commons Plaza Ste 245 Chesterfield, VA
      23831
      (804) 638-5991 Tawanda Johnson Owner
      Fax:
      Email: tjohnson@rklresources.com
      Website: www.rklresources.com
Human resources solutions: recruitment, training,
organizational development, employee relations &
audits. (Woman/AA, estab 2013, empl 2, sales $552,167,
cert: State)

West Virginia

7599 Edwards Management Consultants, Inc.
      110 S. George St Ste 1 Charles Town, WV 25414
      (703) 349-1412 Christine Edwards President
      Fax:
      Email: christinec@edwardsemc.com
      Website: www.edwardsemc.com
HR Advisor/Consulting Services, HR Support Services,
Recruitment - Short/Long Term Entry Level/Mid to
Senior Level Candidates Managenment and Perfor-
mance Management. (Woman/AA, estab 2005, empl 5,
sales , cert: NMSDC)

PROFESSIONAL SERVICES: Management Consulting

Provide general management consulting services: survey research, economic forecasting, transportation studies, facilities and program management, strategic planning, training and development. NAICS Code 54

Alabama

7600　MJLM Engineering & Technical Services
4825 University Square Ste 14 Huntsville, AL 35816
(256) 890-1855 Allison M Rhen Dir Business Dev
Fax: (256) 270-1595
Email: arhen@mjlm.com
Website: www.mjlmengineering.com
Management consulting, auditing & assurance, tax & technology consulting, performance improvement, management performance reviews, human resources risk assessment, cost analysis of core processes. (AA, estab 2003, empl 100, sales $16,963,661, cert: State)

7601　Paragon Management Group
P.O. Box 687 Cotondale, AL 35453
(205) 409-2948 Ty Jones President
Fax: (205) 409-4662
Email: tjones@paragon-mgmt.com
Website: www.paragon-mgmt.com
Management consulting, supply chain management strategy, operations, technology & organization solutions. (Woman/AA, estab 2006, empl 5, sales $180,000, cert: NMSDC)

7602　PROJECTXYZ, Inc.
1500 Perimeter Pkwy Ste 126 Huntsville, AL 35806
(256) 721-9001 Larry Lewis
Fax: (256) 721-9960
Email: Larry.Lewis@projectxyz.com
Website: www.projectxyz.com
Healthcare consulting, project mgmt, IT, engineering & prototype/fabrication services. (Woman/AA, estab 2005, empl 30, sales $900,000, cert: State)

7603　Terrell & Associates, LLC
2210 S Tallassee Dr Tallassee, AL 36078
(334) 283-5156 Shandra Terrell President
Fax: (334) 283-5156
Email: sterrell@terrellassociates.net
Website: www.terrellassociates.net
Training: diversity, difficult people, teamwork, customer service, speaking engagements, research & evaluation, etc. (Woman/AA, estab 2001, empl 1, sales , cert: NWBOC)

Arizona

7604　Banda Group International, LLC
1799 E Queen Creek Rd Ste 1 Chandler, AZ 85286
(480) 636-8734 Elisonia Valle Business Dev Mgr
Fax: (480) 718-7890
Email: elisoniav@bandagroupintl.com
Website: www.bandagroupintl.com
Safety management, risk management, project management, training & associated engineering disciplines. (Hisp, estab 2003, empl 88, sales $9,049,000, cert: NMSDC, SDB)

7605　Tax Roof, LLC (DBA) JT Project Management Office
1 E Washington St Ste 500 Phoenix, AZ 85004
(623) 374-6455 Dionne Joseph Thomas President
Fax:
Email: admin@taxroof.com
Website: www.jtprojectmanagementoffice.com
Program/Project Management & Implementation, Initiation; Planning; Execution; Monitoring & Control; Closing. (Woman/AA, estab 2011, empl 2, sales , cert: State, City, WBENC)

California

7606　Alorica Inc.
5 Park Plaza Ste 1100 Irvine, CA 92614
(949) 527-4600 Kyle Baker VP sales
Fax: (949) 527-4708
Email: kyle.baker@alorica.com
Website: www.alorica.com
Business process outsourcing, customer management solutions. (As-Pac, estab , empl 22000, sales $570,000,000, cert: NMSDC, CPUC)

7607　Being Present Inc
8601 Sunland Blvd, Ste 53 Sun Valley, CA 91352
(818) 473-5323 Sonya Shelton CEO
Fax:
Email: sonya@executiveleader.com
Website: www.ExecutiveLeader.com
Management consulting & executive coaching services. (Woman/Hisp, estab 2006, empl 4, sales $970,003, cert: NMSDC, WBENC)

7608　Celerity Consulting Group, Inc.
2 Gough St, Ste 300 San Francisco, CA 94103
(415) 986-8850 Rachelle Yowell CEO
Fax: (415) 986-8851
Email: ryowell@consultcelerity.com
Website: www.consultcelerity.com
Litigation & business consulting: strategic planning, quality control processes. (Woman/White, estab 2001, empl 98, sales $16,604,529, cert: CPUC)

7609　Cervantes-Delgado, Inc.
471 W Lambert Rd, Ste 100 Brea, CA 92821
(714) 990-3940 Luis Cervantes President
Fax: (714) 990-4073
Email: ldc@cervantes-delgado.com
Website: www.cervantes-delgado.com
Management consulting. (Hisp, estab 2001, empl 3, sales , cert: CPUC)

7610　Dilan Consulting Group
55 New Montgomery, Ste 518 San Francisco, CA 94105
(415) 937-0621 Eugene Dilan CEO
Fax:
Email: office@dilanconsulting.com
Website: www.dilanconsulting.com
Organizational Development & Change. (Hisp, estab 2010, empl 1, sales , cert: NMSDC)

7611 Elia Erickson, LLC
11620 Wilshire Blvd. 9th Fl Los Angeles, CA 90025
(310) 479-0217 Lisa Erickson CEO
Fax: (888) 479-0593
Email: lisa@expertmediatraining.com
Website: www.expertmediatraining.com
Media training, presentation training, public speaking training, communication consulting, business coaching, publicity training. (Woman/White, estab 1999, empl 1, sales $128,741, cert: State, City, CPUC)

7612 Emerson Human Capital Consulting, Inc.
2199 Harbor Bay Pkwy Alameda, CA 94502
(510) 545-4435 Tricia Emerson CEO
Fax: (510) 545-4435
Email: temerson@emersonhc.com
Website: www.emersonhc.com
Training, diversity training & workshops, change mgmt, organizational design, communications, intercultural svcs, process design, IT implementation, user acceptance. (Woman/White, estab 2001, empl 35, sales $7,459,817, cert: WBENC)

7613 Excelerate, Inc.
5 Snowapple Irvine, CA 92614
(949) 679-9235 John Webster Dir Business Dev
Fax: (949) 679-6679
Email: info@exceleratecomm.com
Website: www.iexcelerate.com
Management consulting: strategy development, training & coaching. (Woman/White, estab 2002, empl 4, sales $250,000, cert: CPUC, WBENC)

7614 Fostering Executive Leadership, Inc.
4790 Irvine Blvd, Ste 105-432 Irvine, CA 92620
(949) 651-6250 Dr. Tammy Wong CEO
Fax: (949) 271-5665
Email: Tammy@fosteringexecutiveleadership.com
Website: www.FosteringExecutiveLeadership.com
Executive coaching, building leadership, team performance, communication, accountability & strategy. (Woman/White, estab 2006, empl 300, sales $1,500,000, cert: CPUC, WBENC)

7615 ICE Safety Solutions Inc.
47703 Fremont Blvd Fremont, CA 94538
(877) 743-8423 Pamela Isom CEO
Fax:
Email: pam@getice.com
Website: www.getice.com
Safety training: CPR, first aid, ERT, AED, forklift, Fire safety, fire extinguisher training, safety consulting & curriculum dev. (Woman/AA/Hisp, estab 1999, empl 12, sales $1,800,000, cert: NMSDC, CPUC, WBENC)

7616 Imani Lee, Inc.
11297 Senda Luna Llena Bldg. B San Diego, CA 92130
(858) 523-9733 Lee Martin CEO
Fax: (858) 523-9533
Email: translations@imanilee.com
Website: www.imanilee.com
Translation & Localization, Transcription, Transcreation, Interpreting, Intl Social Media Mgmt, Consulting Services, Language & Culture training, Subtitling & Voiceover, Educational Curriculum Development. (AA, estab 2002, empl 10, sales $1,526,000, cert: NMSDC, CPUC)

7617 Julianna Hynes & Associates
1638 Freed Circle Pittsburg, CA 94565
(925) 207-1578 Julianna Hynes Principal
Fax:
Email: julianna@juliannahynes.com
Website: www.juliannahynes.com
Executive coaching & leadership development services. (Woman/AA, estab 2003, empl 1, sales $139,599, cert: WBENC)

7618 K'ontinuous Technologies, Inc.
1304 W 2nd St, Ste 346 Los Angeles, CA 90026
(213) 334-3951 Steve Buchanan President
Fax:
Email: sbuchanan@kontinuoustech.com
Website: www.kontinuoustech.com
Program Management Oversight, Program/Project Definition & Direction, Program/Project Tracking & Documentation, Technical Resource Allocation, Client/ Vendor Relations, Change Management, Risk Management. (AA/Hisp, estab 2015, empl 1, sales , cert: State)

7619 LKG-CMC, Inc.
707 Wilshire Blvd, Ste 3600 Los Angeles, CA 90017
(213) 892-0789 Evelyn Jackson VP
Fax: (213) 892-1424
Email: lkgcmc@lkgcmc.com
Website: www.lkgcmc.com
Project controls & configuration mgmt consulting: document control, cost control & estimating, scheduling & business continuity planning. (Woman/White, estab 1987, empl 70, sales , cert: CPUC)

7620 Los Remedios
2377 S Sabre Ave Fresno, CA 93727
(619) 813-6445 Patricia Alvarado Owner
Fax:
Email: pa@remedysupportservices.com
Website:
Management & human resources consulting. (Woman/ Hisp, estab 1995, empl 1, sales , cert: State)

7621 Nesso Strategies
3435 Camino Del Rio S, Ste 314 San Diego, CA 92108
(619) 546-7885 Judy Hissong President
Fax:
Email: Judy@NessoStrategies.com
Website: www.NessoStrategies.com
Speaking, training, consulting & facilitation, communication & conflict management, leadership development, accountability, diversity & inclusion. (Woman/White, estab 2009, empl 3, sales $240,000, cert: City, CPUC)

7622 Osceola Consulting llc
One Blackfield Dr, Ste 410 Tiburon, CA 94920
(800) 986-1960 Neda Najibi VP Business Ops
Fax: (206) 339-1541
Email: nnajibi@osceolac.com
Website: www.osceolac.com
Management consulting, business process consulting, information technology procurement, & computer & data processing services. (Nat Ame, estab 2006, empl 27, sales $6,103,929, cert: NMSDC, CPUC)

7623   ROI Communication Inc.
5274 Scotts Valley Dr Ste 207   Scotts Valley, CA 95066
(831) 430-0170   JoAnn Webster CFO
Fax: (831) 430-0176
Email: accounting@roico.com
Website: www.roico.com/index.html
Strategy & planning, leader & manager communication, measurement, benchmarking & analysis, employee experience, change communication, creative & visual design, sales communication, communication architecture. (Woman/White, estab 2001, empl 73, sales , cert: CPUC, WBENC)

7624   SCMSP (dba) of Spotswood Consulting
92 Corporate Park Ste 812   Irvine, CA 92606
(800) 716-2360   Derek Spotswood President
Fax: (800) 716-2360
Email: derek@scmsp.com
Website: www.scmsp.com
Management consulting, business & technology solutions. (AA, estab 2006, empl 20, sales $2,200,000, cert: NMSDC, 8(a))

7625   Wentworth Consulting Group, LLC
4616 Dolores Ave   Oakland, CA 94602
(510) 482-6278   Audrey Waidelich Business Mgr
Fax:
Email: info@wentworthconsulting.com
Website: www.wentworthconsulting.com
Training, leadership development, organization development, executive coaching, instructional design, workplace mediation & meeting facilitation. (Woman/White, estab 2011, empl 1, sales $890,200, cert: CPUC, WBENC)

Colorado

7626   LFL International Inc.
4 W Dry Creek Circle Ste 100   Littleton, CO 80120
(303) 791-8405   Loretta Lovell CEO
Fax: (303) 791-8007
Email: LFLINC@aol.com
Website: www.LFLINC.com
Professional, administrative & anagement support services: program/, project & construction management services. (Woman/AA, estab 1990, empl 1300, sales $3,150,000, cert: City, NMSDC)

7627   Merrill Consulting Associates
10561 Wintersweet Ct   Parker, CO 80134
(303) 805-8245   Dr. Herbert Merrill II CEO
Fax: (303) 805-4451
Email: hmerrill@merrillca.com
Website: www.merrillca.com
Organizational change & transformation. (AA, estab 2004, empl 8, sales $46,505, cert: State)

7628   Sanchez, Tennis & Associates, LLC
470 Fountaintree Ln   Boulder, CO 80304
(303) 449-5921   Anita Sanchez Director
Fax:
Email: anita@sancheztennis.com
Website: www.SanchezTennis.com
Organizational development consulting. (Woman/Hisp, estab 1976, empl 2, sales $230,000, cert: NMSDC)

Connecticut

7629   Daniel Penn Associates, LLC
151 New Park Ave, Ste 106   Hartford, CT 06106
(860) 232-8577   Tony Rodriguez President
Fax: (860) 760-6060
Email: info@danielpenn.com
Website: www.danielpenn.com
Mgmt consulting firm, consulting svcs, productivity improvement, supply chain optimization, lean mfg, maintenance mgmt, supplier diversity, mfr systems improvement. (Hisp, estab 1978, empl 13, sales , cert: State, NMSDC)

7630   Framework LLC
1 Atlantic St, Ste 405   Stamford, CT 06901
(203) 563-0644   Cecile Girard COO
Fax: (203) 563-0634
Email: cgirard@framework-llc.com
Website: www.framework-llc.com
Develop & integrate sustainable business strategy & practices & communicate performance to stakeholders. (Woman/White, estab 2003, empl 6, sales , cert: WBENC)

7631   HOPET Engineering Services LLC
151 New Park Ave   Hartford, CT 06106
(860) 251-9587   Rosa Valenzuela President
Fax:
Email: rosa@HopetEngineeringServices.com
Website: www.hopetengineeringservices.com
Project management & engineering, government & commercial contracts project management, supply chain, value stream mapping, sourcing strategies, earned value management systems, risk mitigation plans & root cause analysis. (Woman/Hisp, estab 2013, empl 1, sales , cert: State)

7632   N-Touch Strategies, LLC
263 Tresser Blvd, 9 Fl   Stamford, CT 06901
(855) 686-8247   Natasha Williams Managing Partner
Fax: (203) 564-1402
Email: nwilliams@ntouchstrategies.com
Website: www.ntouchstrategies.com
Strategic management, Initiate & Accelerate growth, Improve organizational efficiency, Leadership Development. (Woman/AA, estab 2010, empl 17, sales $2,250,000, cert: NMSDC, WBENC, 8(a))

District of Columbia

7633   H Rizvi Consulting Inc.
1345 S Capitol St SW 807   Washington, DC 20003
(832) 640-7374   Hamid Rizvi President
Fax:
Email: hamid.rizvi@hrizviconsulting.com
Website: www.hrizviconsulting.com
Consulting, Administrative, and Training Services. (As-Ind, estab 2017, empl , sales , cert: NMSDC)

7634 MPF Federal
1050 17th St, NW Ste 600 Washington, DC 20036
(202) 776-0655 Anna Gilmore-Hall Director
Fax:
Email: info@mpffederal.com
Website: www.mpffederal.com
Program & Project Management, Innovative Technology
Services & Comprehensive Management Consulting.
(Woman/AA, estab 2012, empl 43, sales $2,955,000, cert:
8(a))

Delawar

7635 DecisivEdge LLC
131 Continental Dr Ste 409 Newark, DE 19713
(302) 299-1570 Michele Frayler
Fax: (302) 299-1578
Email: michele.frayler@decisivedge.com
Website: www.decisivedge.com
Business consulting & technology services, business
architecture & performance, business analytics, data
warehouse strategy, design, development & governance,
marketing analytics development. (As-Ind, estab 2007,
empl 41, sales $4,739,862, cert: NMSDC)

Florida

7636 Advaion LLC
1560 Sawgrass Corporate Pkwy 4th Fl Sunrise, FL
33323
(954) 331-7969 Bhuvan Satyaketu Ops Mgr
Fax: (954) 206-0997
Email: bsatyaketu@advaion.com
Website: www.advaion.com
Transaction & risk solutions, acquisition integration svcs,
risk assessment, Sarbanes-Oxley section svcs, process &
control documentation, entity level controls review,
corporate governance. (Woman/As-Pac, estab 2003, empl
10, sales $1,900,000, cert: NMSDC)

7637 American Sign Language Services Corporation
3700 Commerce Blvd Ste. 216 Kissimmee, FL 34741
(407) 518-7900 Julian Ignatowski CFO
Fax: (407) 518-7903
Email: gabrielle@aslservices.com
Website: www.aslservices.com
Interpretation services, sign language, onsite interpreting,
Video Relay Services (VRS) & Video Remote Interpreting
(VRI). (Woman/Hisp, estab 1997, empl 125, sales
$8,750,000, cert: State, NMSDC)

7638 Argos Global Partner Services, LLC
240 Crandon Blvd. Ste 201 Key Biscayne, FL 33149
(305) 365-1096 Luciana Ciuchini CEO
Fax: (305) 365-1097
Email: LCiuchini@argosus.com
Website: www.argosgps.com
Supply chain solutions, sourcing, consolidation, import,
export, purchasing, quality control, logistics and warehousing. (Woman/Hisp, estab 2005, empl 15, sales
$20,120,630, cert: NMSDC)

7639 Blue Isis LLC
525 Caribbean Dr E Summerland Key, FL 33042
(717) 412-1900 Dawn Mahan CEO
Fax:
Email: dmahan@blueisisllc.com
Website: www.blueisisllc.com
Project management consulting & talent development
services, management consulting services, program
management, portfolio management, governance,
budgeting, forecasting, strategic planning, resource
management. (Woman/Hisp, estab 2009, empl 10, sales
$1,000,000, cert: State)

7640 Caraballo Consulting & Associates, LLC
11312 NW 65 St Doral, FL 33178
(305) 204-2493 Lourdes Cordeiro Dir of New Bus
Fax: (305) 513-4086
Email: Lourdes@caraballoconsulting.com
Website: www.caraballoconsulting.com
Regulatory Compliance & Submissions, Clinical, Quality
Assurance, Manufacturing, Project Management, Black
Belt, Lean Manufacturing, Engineering & Specialized
Engineering. (Woman/Hisp, estab 2015, empl 10, sales
$91,000, cert: NMSDC)

7641 CMA Enterprise Incorporated
207 Laurel Oak Lane Ste B Davie, FL 33325
(954) 476-3525 Gail Birks Williams President
Fax: (954) 370-0803
Email: cma@cma-ent.com
Website: www.cma-ent.com
Management consulting, business process re-engineering, supplier/corporate diversity initiatives, employee
relations, training. (Woman/AA, estab 1990, empl 2,
sales , cert: State, WBENC)

7642 Corporate Fitness Works, Inc.
1200 16th St. N St. Petersburg, FL 33705
(727) 522-2900 Ken Viglio Sr Dir Business Dev
Fax:
Email: businessdevelopment@teamcfw.com
Website: www.corporatefitnessworks.com
Manage customized fitness centers & wellness programs, feasibility studies, facility layout & design,
equipment recommendations. (Woman/White, estab
1988, empl 669, sales $15,447,523, cert: WBENC)

7643 Government Business Solutions
12905 SW 132nd St, Ste 4 Miami, FL 33186
(786) 293-1601 Lourdes Martin-Rosa President
Fax: (786) 293-1602
Email: lourdes@govbizsolutions.com
Website: www.govbizsolutions.com
Educate small businesses on procuring federal, state &
local government contracts. (Woman/Hisp, estab 2002,
empl 6, sales $125,000, cert: State, WBENC, 8(a))

7644 GreenPath Energy Solutions
3218 E Colonial Dr Ste G Orlando, FL 32803
(321) 948-3623 Samuel Graham CEO
Fax: (321) 281-8380
Email: sgraham@greenpathes.com
Website: www.greenpathenergysolutions.com
Energy monitoring, energy auditing, retro-commission-
ing, web-based energy dashboard management soft-
ware. (AA, estab 2006, empl 3, sales $175,000, cert:
State, City, NMSDC)

7645 Leadership Dimensions International
19402 SW 68th St   Fort Lauderdale, FL 33332
(954) 294-8464 Anthony Griffiths Managing Dir
Fax:
Email: tg@leadershipdimensions.us.com
Website: www.eadershipdimensions.us.com
Leadership development • Coaching skills develoepemnt •
Personal empowerment/motivation • Teambuilding. (AA,
estab 2012, empl 1, sales , cert: State, City)

7646 Maria R Pearson Inc. dba Own Your World
3450 SE Kubin Ave   Stuart, FL 34997
(772) 287-5833 Maria Pearson President
Fax: (772) 287-4233
Email: mariapearson@OwnYourWorld.net
Website: www.OwnYourWorld.net
Training & management consulting: communication,
presentation skills, leadership effectiveness, time mgmt,
process & system improvement. (Woman/Hisp, estab
1993, empl 1, sales $151,000, cert: State)

7647 Premier Remodeling Services, Inc.
5703 Red Bug Lake Rd, Ste 328   Winter Springs, FL
32708
(407) 489-8510 Geoff Gilpin
Fax: (301) 576-5000
Email: ggilpin@premiergroupadvisors.com
Website: www.premiergroupadvisors.com
Policy, Planning & Program Support, Information Manage-
ment, Human Capital Optimization, Education & Training,
Infrastructure Management, Sustainability Planning,
Engineering & Technical Assistance, Supplier Management.
(AA, estab 2006, empl 8, sales $1,500,000, cert: NMSDC,
8(a))

7648 Program Evaluation Services Inc.
5521 Oak Hollow Dr   Titusville, FL 32780
(321) 243-4809 Gina Beckles CEO
Fax:
Email: ginabeckles@cfl.rr.com
Website: www.programevaluationservices.com
Program evaluation & performance measurement,
analytical & administrative services. (Woman/AA, estab
2006, empl 2, sales $40,000, cert: NMSDC)

7649 The Bench Team LLC
1200 Brickell Ave Ste 1950 Miami, FL 33131
(305) 777-3599 Marcus Fontaine Principal
Fax:
Email: marcus.fontaine@thebenchteam.com
Website: www.thebenchteam.com
Accreditation Readiness, Care Management, Program
Development, Regulatory Compliance Readiness, Clinical &
Non-Clinical Managed, Care Training, System Redesign,
Process & Workflow Improvement. (AA, estab 2015, empl
6, sales $430,000, cert: State)

7650 Wightman & Associates LLC
720 W Montrose St   Clermont, FL 34711
(757) 574-4386 Louis Dommer III CFO
Fax:
Email: ldommer@wightman-associates.com
Website: www.Wightman-Associates.com
Training & organizational development products &
services. (Woman/White, estab 2011, empl 12, sales
$836,000, cert: State)

Georgia

7651 Asil White Enterprises, Inc.
5530 Wheatfield Ln   Powder Springs, GA 30127
(404) 786-8931 Lisa White President
Fax: (866) 267-6269
Email: lw@thinkaweinc.com
Website: www.thinkaweinc.com
Instructional design, training materials, professional &
mgmt dev training, coaching, time mgmt , organizational
dev, performance improvement, project mgmt.
(Woman/AA, estab 2004, empl 1, sales $73,109, cert:
State)

7652 Bellwether Services
950 Eagles Landing Pkwy, Ste 123   Stockbrdige,
GA 30281
(404) 386-2437 John Wilkerson Exec Dir
Fax: (770) 506-0950
Email: sales@bellwether-services.com
Website: www.bellwether-services.com
Supplier audit, cost reduction, order fulfillment, process
mapping, Six Sigma projects, inventory mgmt, total
quality mgmt, business process engineering, supply
chain rate negotiations, logistics modeling & optimization. (AA, estab 2004, empl 4, sales $102,000, cert:
State)

7653 Full Circle Events
6070 Black Water Trail   Atlanta, GA 30328
(404) 236-0440 Sally Silverman Owner
Fax: (404) 252-2199
Email: sally.fullcircle@comcast.net
Website: www.fullcircleeventsinc.com
Event, meeting & conference planning. (Woman/White,
estab 2002, empl 5, sales $416,897, cert: WBENC)

7654 Horizon Leadership, Inc.
3295 River Exchange Dr Ste 560 Norcross, GA
30092
(770) 552-5511 Cindy Larkin President
Fax: (770) 552-5511
Email: clarkin@horizonleadership.com
Website: www.horizonleadership.com
Facilitation, presentation & influencing skills,
teambuilding, change management, coaching skills, etc.
(Woman/White, estab 2002, empl 4, sales $2,300,000,
cert: WBENC)

7655 J.O. Rodgers and Associates, Inc.
4 Hunt Valley Dr   Lithonia, GA 30058
(770) 482-9452 James Rodgers President
Fax: (770) 484-6428
Email: jora@thediversitycoach.com
Website: www.thediversitycoach.com
Management consulting, coaching, executive education,
culture scans, vision formulation, valuing differences
workshop, diversity council installation, & Six Sigma.
(AA, estab 1987, empl 3, sales $206,000, cert: State)

7656 LBJR Consulting LLC
2942 Darlington Run   Duluth, GA 30097
(678) 662-9159 Lavoska Barton President
Fax: (866) 841-9765
Email: lbarton@lbjrconsulting.com
Website: www.lbjrconsulting.com
Project Management & Planning, Cost management &
Control, Budget prioritization & Management, Vendor
Management & Control, Financial / Variance Analysis of
projects, Process Management, Six Sigma Black Belt. (AA,
estab 2005, empl 4, sales , cert: State)

7657 LEAP Leadership
1011 Carriage Lane SE   Smyrna, GA 30082
(404) 414-8624 Kim Radford Partner
Fax: (336) 545-4491
Email: kr@leaplead.com
Website: www.leaplead.com
Leadership education, executive coaching & organizational
development services. (Woman/AA, estab 2009, empl 3,
sales $590,405, cert: NMSDC)

7658 Renaissance Management Solutions, LLC
6555 Sugarloaf Pkwy Ste 307 Duluth, GA 30097
(404) 484-4116 Russell Julian CEO
Fax: (404) 521-4116
Email: russell@ren-mgt.com
Website: www.ren-mgt.com
Training services & systems: front-end training analysis,
training systems design & curriculum development to
delivery, logistics & evaluation. (AA, estab 2005, empl 3,
sales $420,000, cert: 8(a))

7659 The Cadence Group, Inc.
1095 Zonolite Rd Ste 105 Atlanta, GA 30306
(404) 874-0544 James Washburn
Fax: (404) 874-0541
Email: jwashburn@cadence-group.com
Website: www.cadence-group.com
Information management: acquire, organize & disseminate
information. (Woman/White, estab 1988, empl 46, sales
$2,890,048, cert: WBENC)

7660 Translation Station
3460 Chamblee Dunwoody Way   Chamblee, GA
30341
(770) 234-9387 Phyllis Stallman President
Fax: (770) 234-0641
Email: sales@translation-station.com
Website: www.translation-station.com
Foreign language translation: technical, legal,medical
documents, benefits, software localization, website
translation, interpretation for meetings, conferences,
courts, depositions, conflict resolution, etc. (Woman/
White, estab 1998, empl 5, sales $703,000, cert: WBENC)

7661 Tricia Browning Design Group
102 Westside Dr LaGrange, GA 30240
(706) 883-7741 Tim Donahue
Fax: (706) 882-2466
Email: tdonahue@nimlok-westgeorgia.com
Website: www.nimlok-westgeorgia.com
Trade Show booths, Exhibits, Graphic Design, Display
Advertising, Commercial Photography, Advertising Ser-
vices, Design Services (Woman/White, estab 1996, empl 8,
sales $2,180,000, cert: WBENC)

7662 VYD and Associates, LLC
3306 Blanton Dr   Scottdale, GA 30079
(404) 966-8411 Vonetta Daniels CEO
Fax: (404) 390-3673
Email: vonetta.daniels@gmail.com
Website: www.vydandassociates.com
Management consulting: business strategy, business
process engineering, supply chain management,
revenue cycle & cost optimization; program performance measurement & evaluation, strategic planning,
budget & performance. (Woman/AA, estab 2010, empl
1, sales $37,500, cert: NMSDC, WBENC, 8(a))

Illinois

7663 B2B Strategic Solutions, Inc.
150 N Michigan Ave Ste 2800 Chicago, IL 60601
(312) 368-1700 Donna Bryant President
Fax: (866) 213-8350
Email: info@b2bssi.com
Website: www.b2bssi.com
Management consulting, information technology,
technical training, strategic planning, professional
development, leadership, customer service, training,
business writing. (Woman/AA, estab 2003, empl 20,
sales $1,254,000, cert: State, NMSDC)

7664 CGN & Associates, Inc.
415 SW Washingotn   Peoria, IL 61602
(309) 495-2100 Patrick Dierker Associate Partner
Fax: (309) 495-2370
Email: patrick.dierker@cgnglobal.com
Website: www.cgnglobal.com
Business consulting: operations, execution & technology
mgmt, analysis, design & implementation of complex
operational transformations, strategy development,
solution design, implementation & optimization
techniques. (As-Pac, estab 1995, empl 125, sales , cert:
State, NMSDC)

7665 EMS Consulting
1157 N. St Marks Place   Palatine, IL 60067
(224) 465-1115 Liz Kistner President
Fax: -
Email:
lkistner@enrollmentmarketingsolutions.com
Website: www.emsconsultgroup.com
Project & program management consulting. (Woman/
White, estab 2006, empl 1, sales , cert: WBENC)

7666 Kairos Consulting Worldwide
935 West Chestnut Ste 455 Chicago, IL 60642
(312) 757-5197 Lynn Sutton Managing Principal
Fax: (312) 757-5492
Email: lynn.sutton@kairosworldwide.com
Website: www.kairosworldwide.com
Technology consulting: change management & process
reengineering, process management, strategic planning
& project management. (Woman/AA, estab 2004, empl
1, sales $36,000, cert: State, WBENC)

7667   MarketZing Inc.
       875 N Michigan Ave Ste 3100 Chicago, IL 60611
       (312) 794-7880 Aleen Bayard Principal
       Fax: (312) 794-7801
       Email: aleen@aleenbayard.com
       Website: www.marketzing.org
Change management project design & execution, culture
& values alignment work, strategic planning facilitation &
implementation support, employee engagement and team
effectiveness, organizational & leadership development.
(Woman/White, estab 1999, empl 1, sales $350,000, cert:
WBENC)

7668   Mary O'Connor and Co
       220 W River Dr   St. Charles, IL 60174
       (630) 443-4300 Mary O'Connor President
       Fax: (630) 443-7003
       Email: moconnor@mocandco.com
       Website: www.mocandco.com
Meeting & event mgmt, online event registration, program
dev, employee training & dev, speaker svcs, hotel mgmt,
transportation, food & beverage mgmt. (Woman/AA, estab
1995, empl 22, sales $5,000,000, cert: WBENC)

7669   MJ Learning Inc.
       605 S Maple Ave   Oak Park, IL 60304
       (708) 613-5401 Sarah Gee CEO
       Fax: (708) 613-5401
       Email: sarah@mjlearning.com
       Website: www.mjlearning.com
Professional & management development training.
(Woman/White, estab 2010, empl 5, sales $500,000, cert:
WBENC)

7670   Multilingual Connections, LLC
       847 Chicago Ave, Ste 250   Evanston, IL 60202
       (773) 292-5500 Jill Bishop CEO
       Fax: (312) 488-4116
       Email: jill@mlconnections.com
       Website: www.multilingualconnections.com
Translation/interpretation services (all languages), workplace language training (Spanish and ESL - English as a
Second Language), diversity training and workplace
harassment prevention training and leadership development. (Woman/White, estab 2005, empl 12, sales
$1,504,000, cert: WBENC)

7671   Nancy Conner Consulting, LLC
       1235 Berry Lane   Flossmoor, IL 60422
       (847) 456-5601 Nancy Conner CEO
       Fax:
       Email: nancy@nancyconner.com
       Website: www.nancyconner.com
Supply chain, supplier development, small business
partnerships, negotiation, community outreach & advocacy. (Woman/White, estab 2016, empl 1, sales , cert:
WBENC)

7672   Professional Dynamic Network, Inc.
       20280 Governors Hwy Ste 106 Olympia Fields, IL
       60461
       (708) 747-4361 Geraldine Smothers CEO
       Fax: (708) 747-7057
       Email: info@pdnseek.com
       Website: www.pdnseek.com
Temporary & permanent staffing, recruitment, management consulting, education & training. (Woman/AA, estab
1995, empl 167, sales $3,415,745, cert: City, NMSDC)

7673   Renee Francque Consulting
       505 N Lake Shore Dr Ste 613 Chicago, IL 60611
       (312) 953-9121 Renee Francque Owner
       Fax:
       Email: reneefrancqueconsulting@gmail.com
       Website:
Program, Project, Product & Process Management,
Organizational Change Mgmt, Communication Strategy,
Advisory Consulting for Senior Leadership, Corporate
Strategy, Business Plan Development. (Woman/White,
estab 2010, empl 1, sales $212,750, cert: City, WBENC)

7674   RGMA
       401 S LaSalle St Ste 1401 Chicago, IL 60605
       (312) 419-7250 Ralph Moore President
       Fax:
       Email: ralphmoore@rgma.com
       Website: www.rgma.com
Provides supplier diversity services to drive shareholder
value in an increasingly diverse, global economy. (AA,
estab 1979, empl 8, sales , cert: NMSDC)

7675   TrainSmart, Inc.
       1600 Golf Rd, Ste 1200   Rolling Meadows, IL
       60008
       (847) 991-8181 Leslie Ciborowski President
       Fax: (847) 991-8190
       Email: leslie.ciborowski@trainsmartinc.com
       Website: www.trainsmartinc.com
Computer training, performance solutions, team
building, customer service, leadership skills, manufacturing quality training, needs analysis, instructural design,
assessments, programming. (Woman/White, estab 1993,
empl 6, sales , cert: WBENC)

7676   Trilogy Consulting Group, Inc.
       2021 Midwest Rd, Ste 200   Oak Brook, IL 60523
       (630) 953-6278 Kathy Martin-Smith VP
       Fax: (847) 683-2919
       Email: kmartin-smith@trilogy-consulting.com
       Website: www.trilogy-consulting.com
Health plan admin reviews & audits. (Woman/White,
estab 1995, empl 3, sales $679,217, cert: State, WBENC)

7677   Trinal, Inc.
       329 W 18th St, Ste 401   Chicago, IL 60616
       (312) 738-0500 Gladys Rodriguez GM
       Fax: (312) 738-1840
       Email: info@trinalinc.com
       Website: www.trinalinc.com
Strategic business management consulting, procurement policy development & economic development
program monitoring. (Woman/AA/Hisp, estab 1997,
empl 14, sales , cert: State)

7678   Tristana R Harvey Career Planning & Consulting
       Series LLC
       5135 S Kenwood Ave, Box 504 Chicago, IL 60615
       (312) 351-0272 Tristana Harvey Owner
       Fax: (866) 305-1774
       Email:
       tristana_harvey@harveycareerplanning.com
       Website: www.harveycareerplanning.com
Counseling, coaching & consulting, training programs
that create awareness, increase education & produce
behavior change. (Woman/AA, estab 2010, empl 2, sales
$125,000, cert: State, City, 8(a))

7679 Universal. Innovative. Intelligent, Inc.
P.O. Box 1711   Bolingbrook, IL 60440
(630) 981-1931 Kimberly Johnson President
Fax: (630) 755-4180
Email: kjohnson@universal3i.com
Website: www.myfavoritethings-u3i.com
Management & marketing consulting. (Woman/AA, estab 2003, empl 1, sales $98,600, cert: State)

Indiana

7680 Advanced Systems
508 Sunshine Dr   Valparaiso, IN 46385
(317) 845-5017 Christy Poturkovic Reg sales Mgr
Fax: (317) 841-3321
Email: ChristyP@SuccessStrategiesLLC.com
Website: www.processspecialist.com
Business consulting services, education & training: process improvement, strategic planning, leadership development, management & supervision training, sales training, customer service training, quality improvement. (Woman/White, estab 1997, empl 1, sales $75,000, cert: City)

7681 Bulldog Consulting Services
P.O. Box 65   Leo, IN 46765
(517) 455-7016 Sharon Miller President
Fax: (517) 455-7016
Email: smiller@bulldogmeansbusiness.com
Website: www.BulldogMeansBusiness.com
Process Assessment, Process Improvements, Program/Project Management, Process Documentation, and Training. (Woman/White, estab 2007, empl 3, sales $200,000, cert: State)

7682 Growing Kids Pediatrics, LLC
3707 Charlestown Rd, Ste C1   New Albany, IN 47150
(812) 944-4575 Rosie Nolot Office Mgr
Fax: (812) 944-4886
Email: contact@growingkidspediatrics.com
Website: www.growingkidspediatrics.com/
Pediatric Office-we see children from 0 - 21 years of age. (Woman/White, estab 2010, empl 4, sales , cert: State)

7683 Intrinz Inc.
12175 Visionary Way, Ste 430   Fishers, IN 46037
(317) 288-2267 Patricia Musariri Gurnell President
Fax: (781) 486-9101
Email: patricia.musariri@intrinzincorp.com
Website: www.intrinzincorp.com
Project Management, Corporate Treasury, Corporate Tax, International Business, Global Sourcing, Language Translation, Business Strategy & Business Consulting Services. (Woman/AA, estab 2011, empl 5, sales $1,250,000, cert: NMSDC)

7684 Prairie Quest Consulting
4211 Hobson Court Ste A Fort Wayne, IN 46815
(260) 420-7374 Martha Martin Program Mgr
Fax: (260) 420-3536
Email: mmartin@pqcworks.com
Website: www.pqcworks.com
Project mgmt: application development, business case analysis, conceptual & functional process design, project plans, budgets, tracking assessment & metrics. (Woman/White, estab 2004, empl 150, sales $12,340,945, cert: WBENC)

7685 Raymond Young & Associates, LLC
10705 Club Chase   Fishers, IN 46037
(317) 459-0797 Raymond Young President
Fax: (317) 915-7533
Email: rayyoungjr@msn.com
Website: www.raymondyoungassociates.com
Business consulting, planning, business preformance, competitive analysis, service quality & retention, project management & six sigma principals. (AA, estab 2007, empl 1, sales $19,000, cert: State)

Kentucky

7686 Catalyst Learning Co.
310 W Liberty St, Ste 403   Louisville, KY 40202
(502) 584-7737 Elizabeth LaRue Accountant
Fax: (502) 584-7334
Email: elarue@catalystlearning.com
Website: www.catalystlearning.com
Provides proven learning & development tools. (Woman/White, estab 1994, empl 14, sales , cert: NWBOC)

Louisiana

7687 Henry Consulting LLC
1010 Common St Ste 2500 New Orleans, LA 70112
(504) 529-9890 Allen Square Dir
Fax: (504) 529-9899
Email: allen.square@henryconsulting.net
Website: www.henryconsulting.net
Management consulting services. (AA, estab 2001, empl 15, sales $1,941,921, cert: NMSDC)

7688 Scroggins Consulting, LLC
P.O. Box 6258   Shreveport, LA 71136
(800) 539-5831 Tiya Scroggins CEO
Fax: (888) 540-0783
Email: ty@scrogginsconsulting.com
Website: www.scrogginsconsulting.com
Management services: process assessment, conflict resolution, diversity, leadership development & motivation. (Woman/AA, estab 2002, empl 4, sales $75,000, cert: State)

7689 WCJ Consultants, LLC
16415 Crepemyrtle Dr   Baton Rouge, LA 70817
(225) 921-6314 Kimberly Bardell Co-Owner
Fax:
Email: kbardell@wcjconsultants.com
Website: www.wcjconsultants.com
Management consulting & professional services. (Woman/AA, estab 2008, empl 3, sales , cert: 8(a))

Massachusetts

7690 3D Leadership Group LLC
396 Washington St, Ste 207   Wellesley, MA 02481
(781) 453-9800 Sue Williamson Co-Founder
Fax:
Email: sue.Williamson@3dleadershipgroup.com
Website: www.3dleadershipgroup.com
Executive Coaching, Team Coaching, Transition Coaching, Leadership Workshops, Assessments. (Woman/White, estab 2008, empl 2, sales $1,528,044, cert: WBENC)

7691 Chrysalis Coaching & Consulting
595 E Fourth St Ste 1 Boston, MA 02127
(617) 283-8705 Karen Carmody President
Fax:
Email: kcarmody@chrysaliscoachingconsulting.com
Website: www.chrysaliscoachingconsulting.com/
Corporate coaching, organizational effectiveness, & corporate wellness services. (Woman/White, estab 2012, empl 1, sales $81,126, cert: WBENC)

7692 Communication Management, Inc.
5 Perkins Glen   Eastham, MA 02642
(508) 255-3789 Joseph Perkins President
Fax: (508) 255-0495
Email: jperkins@cmiglobal.com
Website: www.cmiglobal.com
Communications skills, training, onsite & online business writing & presentation skills training programs. (AA, estab 1991, empl 1, sales $85,950, cert: State, NMSDC)

7693 EnVision Performance Solutions
9 Pond View Cir   Sharon, MA 02067
(781) 793-0896 Irene Stern Frielich President
Fax:
Email: irene.frielich@envision-performance.com
Website: www.envision-performance.com
Custom instructional design & training development services; needs assessment, curriculum development, instructor-led classes, virtual classes, elearning, on-the-job training, performance support. (Woman/White, estab 1998, empl 1, sales $325,000, cert: State, WBENC)

7694 Imbue Partners, LLC
36 N Liberty St   Middleton, MA 01949
(978) 887-9215 Frank Hover Principal
Fax: (978) 777-5734
Email: fhover@imbuepartners.com
Website: www.imbuepartners.com
Strategic planning, organizational capability building & process improvement. (Woman/White, estab 2010, empl 6, sales $505,000, cert: WBENC)

7695 Incite, Inc.
14 St. Charles St   Boston, MA 02116
(617) 521-9050 Beth Rogers President
Fax: (617) 521-9051
Email: brogers@pointtaken.net
Website: www.pointtaken.net
Custom communication skills training workshops; Presentation Skills, Facilitation Skills, Negotiation Skills. (Woman/White, estab 1997, empl 4, sales $1,800,000, cert: WBENC)

7696 The Asaba Group
220 No Main St, Ste 102   Natick, MA 01760
(508) 655-8100 Katrice Rivers Business Mgr
Fax: (508) 655-1955
Email: krivers@asabagroup.com
Website: www.asabagroup.com
Strategic assessments, strategic support services, organizational improvement. (AA, estab 1999, empl 10, sales $1,000,000, cert: NMSDC)

Maryland

7697 Andean Consulting Solutions International, LLC
11140 Rockville Pike Ste 100-155 Rockville, MD 20852
(202) 618-1455 Andres Echeverri President
Fax:
Email: andres@acsitranslations.com
Website: www.acsitranslations.com
Language translation & interpretation services in over 60 languages. (Hisp, estab 2011, empl 2, sales $585,000, cert: State, 8(a))

7698 Applied Development LLC
7 S Front St Ste 200 Baltimore, MD 21202
(410) 571-4016 Kimberly Citizen
Fax: (360) 886-1350
Email: kcitizen@applied-dev.com
Website: www.applied-dev.com
Process improvement, automation, analytics & cyber security, project management, business process improvement, strategic communications, cybersecurity & administrative support. (Woman/AA, estab 2011, empl 12, sales $687,000, cert: State, City, NMSDC, 8(a))

7699 Cheseldine Management Consulting, LLC
P.O. Box 1307   Leonardtown, MD 20650
(301) 475-2272 Margaret Cheseldine CEO
Fax: (301) 560-6633
Email: margiec@md.metrocast.net
Website: www.cheseldine.org
Management consulting, asset, property & construction management. (Woman/White, estab 2008, empl 11, sales $512,000, cert: State)

7700 Contracting Resources Group, Inc.
1133 Light St   Baltimore, MD 21230
(443) 708-0908 Moira Rivera Senior Evaluation Assoc
Fax:
Email: mrivera@contractingrg.com
Website: www.contractingrg.com/
Management consulting, federal government contracting solutions, program & project management, training, acquisition support, financial management support, marketing & communications, IT professional services. (Woman/White, estab 2002, empl 51, sales $2,500,000, cert: 8(a))

7701 Destiny Management Services, LLC
8737 Colesville Rd Ste 710 Silver Spring, MD 20910
(301) 650-0047 Donna Mitchell President
Fax: (301) 650-5945
Email: donnam@destinymgmtsvcs.com
Website: www.destinymgmtsvcs.com
Management Consulting, Business Solutions, IT, Staff Augmentation, Compliance Reviews, Contacts Management, Human Capitol Development. (Woman/AA, estab 1996, empl 10, sales $1,300,000, cert: State, WBENC)

7702 DPN Group, LLC
516 N Charles St Ste 303 Baltimore, MD 21201
(410) 905-4036 Andrea Jackson Principal
Fax: (443) 869-2519
Email: ajackson@dpngroup.net
Website: www.dpngroup.net
Management consulting: public outreach, supplier diversity & inclusion consulting, strategic planning, workforce development, performance evaluation, policy development, & compliance monitoring. (Woman/AA, estab 2008, empl 4, sales $204,000, cert: State)

7703 Ivy Planning Group, LLC
15204 Omega Dr, Ste 110 Rockville, MD 20850
(301) 963-1669 Cynthia Featherson President
Fax: (301) 963-8068
Email: cfeatherson@ivygroupllc.com
Website: www.ivygroupllc.com
Diversity consulting & training, strategic planning, change mgmt, customer service, executive coaching, assessments & surveys, knowledge mgmt, performance measurement & mgmt, training & development. (Woman/AA, estab 1990, empl 30, sales , cert: WBENC)

7704 Lord and Tucker Management Consultants, LLC
4140 Holbrook Ln Huntingtown, MD 20639
(866) 517-0477 Dawn Tucker President
Fax: (866) 517-0477
Email: info@ltmctraining.com
Website: www.ltmctraining.com
Staff development & training: life skills, career development & entrepreneurship, customer service, time mgmt, organizational dev, financial mgmt, budgeting, resume writing & interview skills. (Woman/AA, estab 2004, empl 1, sales $20,395, cert: State)

7705 Mitaja Corporation
8115 Maple Lawn Blvd, Ste 350 Fulton, MD 20759
(301) 332-0649 Mihir Patel Dir of Sales
Fax: (301) 965-8714
Email: mpatel@mitajacorp.com
Website: www.mitajacorp.com
Staff Augmentation, RPO, Managed Services, Managed Projects, and Consulting Services. (As-Pac, estab 2014, empl 50, sales $3,000,000, cert: 8(a))

7706 Muse GME Enterprises LLC
2 Wisconsin Circle, #700 Chevy Chase, MD 20815
(301) 244-4947 Gwen Muse-Evans CEO
Fax:
Email: g.museevans@gmeenterprises.net
Website: www.gmeenterprises.net
Organizational governance, program review & dev, professional &mgmt development, quality management, strategic planning, committee establishment, regulatory compliance, risk governance. (Woman/AA, estab 2014, empl 3, sales $154,300, cert: State, WBENC, SDB)

7707 NAID (Native American Industrial Distributors,Inc)
9706 Pennsylvania Ave   Upper Marlboro, MD 20772
(912) 925-8674 Ann Marie Gardner Mktg Media Specialist
Fax: (912) 925-8674
Email: agardner@naid.com
Website: www.naid.com
Information & telecommunications systems life cycle support; security & anti-terrorism products & svcs, mgmt svcs, training svcs. (Nat Ame, estab 1983, empl 31, sales $8,800,000, cert: State)

7708 Performance Development Corporation
17308 Twin Ridge Court   Silver Spring, MD 20905
(301) 421-0118 Sharon Fountain President
Fax: (301) 421-0119
Email: Sharon@SharonFountain.com
Website: www.SharonFountain.com
Training: interpersonal competence, communication, feedback, assertiveness, conflict management, self-esteem/self confidence, leadership/management/supervisory skills, team building, organizational skills, time management/managing multiple priorities. (Woman/White, estab 1980, empl 1, sales $57,635, cert: NWBOC)

7709 Pivotal Practices Consulting
6301 Ivy Lane, Ste 800   Greenbelt, MD 20770
(301) 220-3179 Katheryn Kim Business Dev Assoc
Fax: (301) 220-1242
Email: info@pivotalpractices.com
Website: www.pivotalpractices.com
Organizational climate assessments & engagements: surveys & diagnostic tools, improve individual, team & organizational performance. (Woman/AA, estab 2011, empl 10, sales $2,307,552, cert: NMSDC, WBENC, 8(a))

7710 PositivePsyche.Biz Corp.
World Trade Center 401 E Pratt St, Ste 2432
Baltimore, MD 21202
(410) 844-5060 Enrique Ruiz President
Fax: (844) 490-8575
Email: enrique@positivepsyche.biz
Website: www.positivepsyche.biz
Program Management, design, planning, staffing, measurement, execution, management, QA and QC of large-scale operations. (Hisp, estab 2008, empl 16, sales $700,000, cert: 8(a))

7711 Sheila Lee & Associates, LLC - Learning Everywhere
1518 W Pratt St Baltimore, MD 21223
(410) 233-6922 Sheila S. Lee CEO
Fax: (443) 759-6526
Email: sheilalee@learningeverywhere.com
Website: www.learningeverywhere.com
Organizational development, curriculum design & training. (Woman/AA, estab 2005, empl 8, sales , cert: State, NMSDC, WBENC)

7712   TrailBlazer Consulting, LLC
199 E Montgomery Ave, Ste 100   Rockville, MD 20850
(240) 599-7983   Maura Dunn President
Fax: (800) 861-6755
Email: info@trailblazer.us.com
Website: www.trailblazer.us.com
Program design & development, Management & organizational support for enterprise-wide operations, Electronic content management (ECM) solution selection, design, development, & implementation, Records & Information Management. (Woman/White, estab 2013, empl 7, sales $2,000,000, cert: WBENC)

Michigan

7713   Allis Information Management
4300 W Sugnet Rd   Midland, MI 48640
(989) 835-5811   Sue LaBonville President
Fax:
Email: slabonville@allisinfo.com
Website: www.allisinfo.com
Business research, market research, business intelligence, marketing services, IT support. (Woman/As-Pac, estab 1979, empl 17, sales $1,884,979, cert: WBENC)

7714   ASG Renaissance
27655 Middlebelt Rd Ste 140   Farmington Hills, MI 48334
(248) 477-5432   Maureen Michaels Acct Mgr
Fax: (248) 477-2072
Email: mmichaels@asgren.com
Website: www.asgren.com
Consulting svcs: information technology, public relations, engineering, mktg, minority technical assistance programs, etc. (Woman/Hisp, estab 1987, empl 200, sales $206,586,000, cert: NMSDC, WBENC)

7715   BTS Consulting & Training LLC
211 N. First St #200   Brighton, MI 48116
(586) 322-3065   Mary Temple Managing Partner
Fax: (810) 208-0961
Email: mary.temple@btsmichigan.com
Website: www.btsmichigan.com/
Designs, develops & delivers customized training solutions, instructional design, course development, training delivery, project and curriculum management, conference and event coordination, travel administration. (Woman/White, estab 1991, empl 10, sales $2,600,000, cert: WBENC)

7716   Coach for Higher
2015 Geddes Ave   Ann Arbor, MI 48104
(734) 255-7833   Nan Reed Twiss Owner
Fax:
Email: nan@CoachForHigher.com
Website: www.CoachForHigher.com
Executive & Leadership Coaching Services for Individuals, Teams & Organizations. (Woman/White, estab 2010, empl 1, sales , cert: WBENC)

7717   Contract Source & Assembly Inc.
5230 33rd St SE   Grand Rapids, MI 49512
(616) 897-2185   Bryce Cooper
Fax: (913) 677-3358
Email: bryce@contractmi.com
Website: www.contractmi.com
Light Manufacturing & Contract Assembly, Contract Packaging & Inventory Management, Supply Chain Management, Inspection & Re-work. (As-Pac, estab 2001, empl 13, sales $18,000,000, cert: NMSDC)

7718   DSSI LLC
40 Oak Hollow St Ste 225   Southfield, MI 48033
(248) 208-8340   Kathy Young
Fax: (248) 208-9098
Email: kyoung@directsourcing.com
Website: www.directsourcing.com
Purchasing services. (As-Ind, estab 2000, empl 100, sales $110,000,000, cert: NMSDC)

7719   Focused Coaching LLC
1945 Pauline Blvd, Ste 10   Ann Arbor, MI 48103
(734) 663-0420   Lisa Pasbjerg CEO
Fax: (734) 663-0420
Email: lpasbjerg@focusedcoaching.net
Website: www.focusedcoaching.net
Leadership development, executive coaching, assessment & facilitation services. (Woman/White, estab 2006, empl 1, sales $104,000, cert: WBENC)

7720   Global LT, Inc.
1871 Woodslee Dr   Troy, MI 48083
(248) 763-9920   Karen Markatos Sr Business Devel Mgr
Fax: (248) 731-7551
Email: kmarkatos@global-lt.com
Website: www.Global-LT.com
English, foreign language, cross-cultural, diversity training; relocation translation, interpreting svcs; video/film narration. (AA, estab 1979, empl 120, sales $26,333,524, cert: NMSDC)

7721   Innovative Learning Group, Inc.
514 E Fourth St   Royal Oak, MI 48067
(248) 544-1568   Gayle Holsworth Performance Consultant
Fax: (248) 544-2159
Email: gayle.holsworth@innovativeLG.com
Website: www.innovativeLG.com
Human performance consulting, needs assessment, training design & development, evaluation. (Woman/White, estab 2004, empl 14, sales $3,000,000, cert: WBENC)

7722   Jim Roberts Enterprises LLC
515 Ship St Ste 211   Saint Joseph, MI 49085
(269) 982-4188   Jim Roberts President
Fax: (269) 982-4189
Email: jim@jimrobertsenterprises.com
Website: www.jimrobertsenterprises.com
Management consulting, financial, facility management, real estate & project management consulting services. (Nat Ame/Hisp, estab 2004, empl 1, sales $163,000, cert: NMSDC)

7723 Learning Designs, Inc.
2609 Crooks Rd Troy, MI 48084
(248) 269-0808 Julie Gieraltowski Ops Mgr
Fax: (248) 269-0809
Email: jgieral@learningdesigns.com
Website: www.learningdesigns.com
Training & consulting: performance consulting, instructional design, training delivery, technology solutions & evaluation. (Woman/White, estab 1984, empl 18, sales $2,029,000, cert: WBENC)

7724 Pyramid Quality Solutions & Innovations, Inc.
30680 Montpelier Dr Ste 350 Madison Heights, MI 48071
(248) 577-1356 Ossie Nunn CEO
Fax: (248) 577-1398
Email: onunn@pqsiinc.com
Website: www.pqsiinc.com
Quality & industrial engineering consulting: sequencing (JIT), rework & repair svcs, manuals & procedures, kitting & assembly, supplier representation, logistics, quality standards implementation, error & mistake proofing, etc. (AA, estab 2002, empl 150, sales $3,450,000, cert: NMSDC)

7725 Utility Reduction Analysts, Inc.
12935 S West Bayshore Dr Ste 240 Traverse City, MI 49684
(888) 586-2121 Jennifer Wynn Stoll President
Fax: (231) 929-7790
Email: jwstoll@utilityreduction.com
Website: www.utilityreduction.com
Full service utility cost reduction company. Our thorough analysis provides information on rates/tariffs, promotions, refund processing, market opportunities, consumption patterns, & available deregulation options. (Woman/White, estab 1991, empl 5, sales $410,000, cert: WBENC)

7726 Vani Quality Quest, Inc.
23600 Michigan Ave Dearborn, MI 48124
(248) 733-0000 Jagdish Vani President
Fax: (248) 733-0002
Email: jvani@vqqinc.com
Website: www.vqqinc.com
Containment inspection, rework svcs, SQI consulting & training, problem solving, customer liaison, QC employee staffing services. (As-Pac, estab 1992, empl 60, sales , cert: NMSDC)

7727 VAS Consulting Services
33228 W 12 Mile Rd Farmington Hills, MI 48334
(248) 553-6603 Glenn Stafford President
Fax: (248) 848-9367
Email: gstafford@vas4.com
Website: www.vas4.com
Consulting services: develop minority supplier programs, strategic alliances & joint ventures. (AA, estab 2001, empl 1, sales $250,000, cert: NMSDC)

Minnesota

7728 Alliant Consulting, Inc.
555 7th St W, Ste 101 Saint Paul, MN 55102
(651) 291-0607 Brennan Malanaphy CFO
Fax: (651) 291-1498
Email: proposal@alliantconsulting.com
Website: www.alliantconsulting.com
Management consulting: operational assessment, redesign & implementation to improve service, quality & productivity (Woman/White, estab 1997, empl 4, sales $505,200, cert: WBENC)

7729 Beehive PR Inc.
1021 Bandana Blvd E Ste 226 Saint Paul, MN 55108
(651) 789-2232 Rebecca Martin Exec Director, Talent & Ops
Fax: (651) 789-2230
Email: rmartin@beehivepr.biz
Website: www.beehivepr.biz
Strategic planning, competitive intelligence, brand positioning, crisis management, media coaching, communications. (Woman/White, estab 1998, empl 13, sales $2,219,403, cert: WBENC)

7730 CultureBrokers, LLC
1610 5th St NE Minneapolis, MN 55413
(651) 321-2167 Lisa Tabor President
Fax:
Email: lisa@culturebrokers.com
Website: www.culturebrokers.com
Diversity & inclusion services, diversity recruitment, cultural competence training, strategic planning, inclusion initiatives, employee engagement and retention, community relations, community engagement, equity initiatives. (Woman/AA, estab 2005, empl 1, sales $25,000, cert: City)

7731 ECM Instructional Systems
5816 11th Ave S Minneapolis, MN 55417
(888) 685-0877 Michael Mazyck President
Fax:
Email: mazyck@ecminstructionalsystems.com
Website: www.ecminstructionalsystems.com
Instructional design, training, professional development & evaluation services, Learning & Development. (AA, estab 2004, empl 4, sales , cert: State, City)

7732 Hollstadt & Associates, Inc.
1333 Northland Dr 220 Mendota Heights, MN 55120
(952) 898-6813 Molly Jungbauer CEO
Fax: (952) 513-4702
Email: mjungbauer@hollstadt.com
Website: www.hollstadt.com/
Management & technology consulting: portfolio, program & project management, business analysis, training programs. (Woman/White, estab 1990, empl 200, sales $32,713,064, cert: WBENC)

7733   JIT Energy Services
23505 Smithtown Rd Ste 280   Excelsior, MN 55331
(952) 474-3410   Jamie Aragon CEO
Fax: (952) 470-5761
Email: jamie.a@jitservicesinc.com
Website: www.jitservicesinc.com
Energy efficiency consulting & energy mgmt services.
(Woman/Hisp, estab 1991, empl 12, sales $173,840,860,
cert: NMSDC, WBENC)

7734   MDA Leadership Consulting
150 S 5th St, Ste 3300   Minneapolis, MN 55402
(612) 332-8182   Linda Barrett Dir Business Svcs
Fax:
Email: info@mdaleadership.com
Website: www.mdaleadership.com
Talent management, leadership development, organizational performance (Woman/White, estab 1981, empl 31,
sales $4,422,000, cert: State)

7735   Nelson Consulting LLC
1010 West Lake St Ste 100-113   Minneapolis, MN
55408
(612) 460-5250   Stacia Nelson Owner
Fax:
Email: Stacia@pivotstrategiesconsulting.com
Website: www.pivotstrategiesconsulting.com
Communications strategy, organizational change management, reputation management, sustainability, corporate
social responsibility, (Woman/White, estab 2015, empl 7,
sales $465,000, cert: WBENC)

7736   Risk Management Consulting Services, LLC.
35 Pineview Lane N   Plymouth, MN 55441
(952) 544-0354   Gwen McFadden Managing Partner
Fax: (952) 544-0357
Email: gwen@rmcsllc.com
Website: www.riskconsultingservices.net
Insurance placement, insurance & risk management
consulting services, RFP/RFQ consulting, insurance
placement, risk management consulting, due diligence
projects, claims consulting & management. (Woman/AA,
estab 1997, empl 2, sales $150,000, cert: NMSDC, 8(a))

7737   Talencio, LLC
708 N 1st St Ste 341   Minneapolis, MN 55401
(612) 703-4236   Paula Norbom President
Fax: (612) 703-4236
Email: pnorbom@talencio.com
Website: www.talencio.com
Accounting & Finance, Clinical Research, Data Analysis &
Statistics, Engineering, Health Care Policy & Reform,
Human Resource Management, Informatics, Information
Technology, Interim Leadership, Lean & Six Sigma, Market-
ing, Operations. (Woman/White, estab 2008, empl 6, sales
$1,037,000, cert: WBENC)

7738   Vuelta Management Group, LLC
1507 Chelmsford St   Saint Paul, MN 55108
(651) 329-8609   Scott Hamilton President
Fax: (651) 329-8609
Email: shamilton@vueltamanagement.com
Website: www.vueltamanagement.com
Project Management; Process Improvement; Lean Six
Sigma; Supply Chain Management; Inventory Manage-
ment; Purchasing; Production Management. (Hisp, estab
2009, empl 1, sales $162,117, cert: State, NMSDC)

Missouri

7739   Kwame Building Group, Inc.
1204 Washington Ave Ste 200   Saint Louis, MO
63103
(314) 862-5344   Joshua Randall VP
Fax: (314) 862-1855
Email: jrandall@kwamebuildinggroup.com
Website: www.kwamebuildinggroup.com
Program & construction mgmt services: project scheduling, estimating, cost controls, document controls, value
engineering, quality assurance & project inspection.
(Hisp, estab 1991, empl 75, sales $6,100,000, cert: City)

7740   Mustardseed Cultural & Environmental Svcs, LLC
222 W Gregory Blvd #211   Kansas City, MO 64114
(816) 333-2424   Timberlyn Smith, President
Fax: (816) 572-6328
Email: tsmith@m-c-e-services.net
Website: www.m-c-e-services.net
Environmental, safety & cultural resource management
consulting. (Woman/AA, estab 2003, empl 5, sales
$290,308, cert: State, City)

7741   P/Strada, LLC
406 W 34th st.   Kansas City, MO 64111
(816) 256-4577   Patrice Manuel CEO
Fax: (816) 753-0472
Email: pat@pstrada.com
Website: www.pstrada.com
Organizational development & homeland security
consulting. (Woman/AA, estab 2001, empl 42, sales
$3,370,000, cert: State, City, NMSDC)

7742   Project Controls Group, Inc.
2 Campbell Plaza, Bldg C   St. Louis, MO 63139
(314) 647-0707   Viola Pancratz Principal
Fax: (314) 647-0709
Email: vpancratz@projectcontrolsgroup.com
Website: www.projectcontrolsgroup.com
Cost engineering & estimating, CPM scheduling, claims
analysis, document control, claims analysis, construction
management, program management. (AA, estab 2003,
empl 22, sales $1,430,353, cert: State, NMSDC)

7743   PryCor Technologies, LLC
20 S Sarah St   St Louis, MO 63108
(302) 528-0965   Seqwana Pryor CEO
Fax:
Email: ceo.prycortechnologies@gmail.com
Website: www.prycortechnologies.com
Management consulting & training: Lean Six Sigma.
(Woman/AA, estab 2016, empl 1, sales , cert: WBENC)

Mississippi

7744   AGF Enterprise LLC
1060 E Countyline Rd Ste 3A-104   Ridgeland, MS
39157
(601) 500-2325   Anthony Fairley Managing
Partner
Fax: (877) 349-6085
Email: anthonygf@agfenterprise.com
Website: www.agfenterprise.com
Learning Management System (LMS), Tracking &
Reporting Easily track goal progress, knowledge gains,
ROI, Regulatory Compliance Train, assess.. (AA, estab
2013, empl 1, sales $376,000, cert: NMSDC)

North Carolina

7745 Aseptic Haven LLC
3330 Black Jack Simpson Rd   Greenville, NC 27858
(252) 258-5935 Felicia Richardson Owner
Fax:
Email: FeliciaRichardson@aseptichaven.com
Website: www.aseptichaven.com
Consulting & training services, Life Sciences, Workforce Development, Inclusion & Diversity. (Woman/AA, estab 2014, empl 1, sales , cert: State)

7746 Dynamic Consulting Solutions
163 Stratford Ct, Ste 165   Winston-Salem, NC 27103
(336) 724-0501 Kale Evans
Fax: (336) 724-0503
Email: kale_dcs@northstate.net
Website: www.dcs-corp.net
Motivational speaking, leadership training & development, change mgmt process consulting, strategic planning, business process consulting, call center operations & sales analysis. (AA, estab 2001, empl 2, sales $125,000, cert: State)

7747 Flash Domain
56 Contesky Dr   Cherokee, NC 28719
(828) 736-0234 Kimberly Peone CEO
Fax:
Email: kapeone67@gmail.com
Website:
Strategic consulting technology services & managed services. (Woman/Nat Ame, estab 2010, empl 2, sales $13,645, cert: State)

7748 LMK Clinical Research Consulting, LLC
9815 J Sam Furr Rd   Huntersville, NC 28078
(704) 464-3291 Isaiah Howard Director of Mktg
Fax:
Email: Isaiah.Howard@lmkclinicalresearch.com
Website: www.lmkclinicalresearch.com
Strategic development, project management & quality control of documents & content that support clinical development. (Woman/AA, estab 2013, empl 10, sales $285,000, cert: WBENC)

7749 Proficient Learning LLC
1508 Military Cutoff Rd Ste 304 Wilmington, NC 28403
(910) 795-1376 Pamela Marinko CEO
Fax: (910) 795-1376
Email: pam.marinko@proficientlearning.com
Website: www.proficientlearning.com
Instructor-led, virtual, eLearning & mobile learning solutions. (Woman/White, estab 2005, empl 23, sales $3,200,000, cert: WBENC)

7750 Tactegra
18 Cabarrus Ave W   Concord, NC 20825
(704) 793-0800 Leanne Kinsella Dir Business Devel
Fax: (980) 225-0129
Email: info@tactegra.com
Website: www.tactegra.com
Management consulting, program/project management, IT project support services, staff augmentation & process management. (AA/Hisp, estab 2007, empl 50, sales $3,700,000, cert: NMSDC)

7751 The Future Procurement Group, LLC
3513 McPherson St   Waxhaw, NC 28173
(203) 913-9598 Silas Carter
Fax: (612) 338-7399
Email: scarter@thefutureprocurementgroup.com
Website: www.thefutureprocurementgroup.com
Consulting Services, Strategic Sourcing, Procurement Management, Supplier Diversity, Program Devel, Training, Vendor Management, - Supplier Evaluation, Process Review & Analysis, Cost Management, Management Consulting. (AA, estab 2011, empl 1, sales , cert: NMSDC)

Nebraska

7752 Inspection Experts, Inc.
808 P St Ste 318 Lincoln, NE 68508
(410) 715-3939 Maureen Faulconer VP
Fax: (614) 386-1999
Email: mfaulconer@ieinc.net
Website: www.ieinc.net
Environmental services, health & safety consulting, industrial hygiene, facilities & asset management & development. (Woman/As-Ind, estab 2004, empl 16, sales $3,365,268, cert: State)

New Jersey

7753 Bardess Group Ltd.
15 Morey Ln, Ste 100   Randolph, NJ 07869
(973) 895-3500 Barbara Pound CEO
Fax: (973) 895-1900
Email: bspound@bardess.com
Website: www.bardess.com
Management consulting; data management, business performance management, IT, business planning & process improvement, reveune & asset management. (Woman/White, estab 1997, empl 25, sales , cert: State)

7754 Candid Services
80 Pine St   Bridgewater, NJ 08807
(732) 874-1345 Meghana Patel CEO
Fax:
Email: contact@candidcorp.com
Website: www.candidcorp.com
Pharmaceutical & medical device consulting services, computer system validation, non compartmental analysis (NCA), Clinical data analysis & handling, SAS programming & Regulatory Affairs consulting. (Woman/As-Pac, estab 2015, empl 2, sales , cert: WBENC)

7755 Davis & Company, Inc.
11 Harristown Rd   Glen Rock, NJ 07452
(201) 445-5100 David Pitre VP consulting svcs
Fax: (201) 445-5122
Email: david.pitre@davisandco.com
Website: www.davisandco.com
Communication consulting & implementation, strategic planning & research, implementation, writing & design. (Woman/White, estab 1984, empl 17, sales $3,350,000, cert: State, WBENC)

7756 Microexcel Inc.
One Harmon Plaza 10th Fl Secaucus, NJ 07094
(201) 787-4562 Ayub Qhadri President
Fax: (201) 221-7825
Email: ayub.qhadri@microexcel.com
Website: www.microexcel.com
Global management consulting, technology services &
outsourcing. (As-Ind, estab 2001, empl 75, sales
$28,000,000, cert: State)

7757 QualComp Consulting Services LLC
675 US Highway One Ste B203 North Brunswick, NJ
08902
(800) 511-8758 Victor Arriaran Principal
Fax: (855) 511-2724
Email: victor.arriaran@qualcomp.com
Website: www.qualcomp.com
Quality systems design & implementation, audit & inspection readiness, complaint remediation, process control &
process improvement, risk management , design control,
root cause analysis, Corrective & Preventive Action. (Hisp,
estab 2010, empl 4, sales $1,521,586, cert: NMSDC)

7758 The Forefront Group
26 Sunflower Circle Lumberton, NJ 08048
(609) 265-1825 Bonnie Keith Owner
Fax: (609) 265-9737
Email: bkeith@theforefrontgroup.com
Website: www.theforefrontgroup.com
Admin management consulting, education support svcs,
professional & management development training.
(Woman/White, estab 2002, empl 10, sales , cert: WBENC)

7759 Vitiello Communications Group
825 Georges Rd Ste 6 North Brunswick, NJ 08902
(732) 238-6622 Jill Vitiello President
Fax: (732) 238-4078
Email: nadine.green@vtlo.com
Website: www.vtlo.com
Communications, employee engagement, strategic change
& leadership communications. (Woman/White, estab
1990, empl 6, sales $3,500,000, cert: WBENC)

Nevada

7760 American Project Management LLC
11700 W Charleston Blvd, Ste 170-315 Las Vegas,
NV 89135
(702) 220-4562 Jane Lee Managing Partner
Fax: (702) 220-9784
Email: jlee@apmlasvegas.com
Website: www.apmlasvegas.com
Project Scheduling & Cost Control, Earned Value Manage-
ment System (EVMS) Implementation, Computer Program-
ming & Embedded Software Development Services & Staff
Augmentation. (Woman/As-Pac, estab 2003, empl 2, sales ,
cert: NMSDC, NWBOC)

7761 Operations Service Systems
9716 Terrace Green Ave   Las Vegas, NV 89117
(800) 878-6906 Susan Beyer President
Fax: (702) 233-4836
Email: sue@suebeyer.com
Website: www.suebeyer.com
Training & development: operations, dev, customer
service & results oriented training systems. (Woman/
White, estab 2000, empl 2, sales $255,000, cert:
WBENC)

7762 Purpose & Action, LLC
3225 McLeod Dr, Ste 100
miguel@coachmiguel.com Las Vegas, NV 89121
(760) 438-9907 Miguel de Jesus
Fax: (787) 633-0029
Email:
Website: www.coachmiguel.com
Business management, global sales/marketing. (Hisp,
estab 2011, empl 1, sales , cert: NMSDC)

7763 SVI. Inc.
440 Mark Leany Dr   Henderson, NV 89011
(702) 567-5256 Nancy Munoz Sales Mgr
Fax: (702) 567-3020
Email: nancy.munoz@specialtyvehicles.com
Website: www.specialtyvehicles.com
Sales & distributer of people mover products, ie Buses,
Trams, Trolleys, Golf Carts, Ground Maintence Vehicles
and vehicle parts. (Woman/Hisp, estab 2003, empl 13,
sales $14,036,900, cert: State)

New York

7764 AIOPX Management Consulting
1007 La Quinta Dr   Webster, NY 14580
(585) 627-1716 David Powe Partner & Lead
Consultant
Fax: (585) 627-1716
Email: dpowe@aiopx.com
Website: www.AIOPX.com
Operation Excellence (OpEx): lean, six sigma, total
quality, practical process improvement & the Toyota
production system. (AA, estab 2012, empl 1, sales
$125,000, cert: NMSDC)

7765 Axiom Consulting LLC
126 W Main St   Endicott, NY 13760
(800) 563-2758 Wayne McCray CEO
Fax: (919) 463-9062
Email: info@4axiomcorp.com
Website: www.4axiomcorp.com
MRO sales, business process outsourcing, staffing,
training. (AA, estab 2001, empl 150, sales $6,000,000,
cert: NMSDC)

7766 Carlin Solutions, LLC
      237 Flatbush Ave Ste 128 Brooklyn, NY 11217
      (917) 463-3592 Carla Franklin Managing Dir
      Fax: (646) 217-3159
      Email: carla@carlinsolutions.com
      Website: www.carlinsolutions.com
Requirements analysis, staff augmentation, program
management, project management, operational improve-
ment, management consulting, Strategic Planning,
Business Development, Strategic Market Analysis.
(Woman/AA, estab 2003, empl 3, sales $414,000, cert:
City, NMSDC, WBENC)

7767 Chapman Lean Enterprise
      81 Rock Hill Rd Rochester, NY 14618
      (585) 406-7804 Christopher Chapman President
      Fax: (951) 684-0738
      Email: cdchapman1@chapmanlean.com
      Website: www.chapmanlean.com
Lean process improvement training & consultation
services. (AA, estab 2010, empl 1, sales $40,000, cert:
NMSDC)

7768 Gillespie Associates, Ltd.
      1501 East Ave Ste 200 Rochester, NY 14610
      (585) 244-1331 Patricia Barry Business Dev Mgr
      Fax: (585) 244-3758
      Email: pbarry@gillespieassociates.com
      Website: www.gillespieassociates.com
Performance consulting, customized training & development, sales performance institute, e-learning solutions,
web-based learning, technical documentation, business
process documentation.
 (Woman/White, estab 1989, empl 9, sales $1,292,286,
cert: State, WBENC)

7769 Green Silk Associates, LLC
      10440 Queens Blvd., Ste 5J Forest Hills, NY 11375
      (917) 445-2443 Deb Seidman President
      Fax: (646) 224-3532
      Email: dseidman@greensilkassociates.com
      Website: www.greensilkassociates.com
Organizational effectiveness & leadership development
services, innovation, planning, problem-solving meeting/
offsite facilitation; team development; organization
design; executive coaching; & talent management consulting. (Woman/White, estab 2009, empl 1, sales , cert:
City)

7770 Hyun & Associates, Inc.
      222 Riverside Dr, #3B New York, NY 10025
      (917) 327-0992 Jane Hyun President
      Fax:
      Email: jhyun@hyunassociates.com
      Website: www.hyunassociates.com
Leadership, diversity training & coaching services.
(Woman/As-Pac, estab 1997, empl 3, sales $275,000, cert:
NMSDC)

7771 Impact Consulting, LLC
      1177 Ave of the Americas 5th Fl New York, NY
      10036
      (973) 727-1574 Lucy Sorrentini CEO
      Fax: (973) 595-6190
      Email: Lucy@impactconsultingus.com
      Website: www.impactconsultingus.com
Leadership & organizational development, consulting,
coaching & training services. (Woman/Hisp, estab 2015,
empl 3, sales , cert: State, City, WBENC)

7772 International Institute for Learning, Inc. (IIL)
      110 E 59th St, 31st Fl New York, NY 10022
      (212) 758-0177 Amy Gershen Cert Mgr
      Fax: (212) 755-0777
      Email: amy.gershen@iil.com
      Website: www.iil.com
Project management, six sigma & MSP training &
consulting services. (Woman/White, estab 1991, empl
87, sales $1,300,000,000, cert: WBENC)

7773 JDR Consulting, LLC
      4305 Broadway Ste 41 New York, NY 10033
      (917) 324-2443 John Rivers CEO
      Fax: (212) 923-8222
      Email: jrivers@jdrconsulting.net
      Website: www.jdrconsulting.net
Management consulting, program & project management, systems & and accounting services. (AA, estab
2004, empl 9, sales $6,000,000, cert: State, NMSDC)

7774 Jennifer Brown LLC
      20 E 9th St, Ste 4U New York, NY 10003
      (917) 769-1599 Jennifer Brown CEO
      Fax: (212) 253-5335
      Email: info@jenniferbrownconsulting.com
      Website: www.jenniferbrownconsulting.com
Leadership consulting, HR training, coaching, speaker,
communications, diversity, global, teams, facilitator,
facilitation, career planning, leaders, inclusive, inclusion,
innovative, innovation, empowered, empowerment.
(Woman/White, estab 2004, empl 15, sales $1,400,000,
cert: City, WBENC)

7775 JR Language Translation Services, Inc.
      2112 Empire Blvd Ste 1C Rochester, NY 14580
      (877) 771-0145 Douglas Dohr Language Solutions
      Specialist
      Fax: (585) 486-1033
      Email: douglas.dohr@jrlanguage.com
      Website: www.jrlanguage.com
Document Translation, Web site & software localization,
Scripts, Manuals, Brochures, Contracts. (Woman/Hisp,
estab 2006, empl 8, sales $2,414,201, cert: State,
WBENC)

7776 KGM Consulting Inc.
      30 Wall St New York, NY 10005
      (212) 791-1555 Maggie McGovern Admin/Finance
      Fax: (212) 791-1270
      Email: mmcgovern@kgmcon.com
      Website: www.kgmcon.com
Technology management solutions: echnology project
mgmt, circuit provisioning mgmt & voice systems admin,
carrier & telecom expense mgmt svcs, staff augmentation. (Woman/White, estab 1996, empl 30, sales
$3,952,677, cert: City, WBENC)

7777   KnowledgeSources Consulting Inc.
23 W 73rd St Ste 1103   New York, NY 10023
(212) 362-1606   Peggy Decker Principal
Fax: (212) 721-5877
Email: peggy@knowledgesources.com
Website: www.knowledgesources.com
Employee/Financial Advisor Learning & Development;
Customer Events.
Specifically: employee engagement, organizational
development, professional development, training, coach-
ing, facilitating. (Woman/White, estab 2009, empl 1, sales
$400,000, cert: WBENC)

7778   Shaheen & Associates, Inc.
37 Maple Ave   Armonk, NY 10504
(914) 273-9000   William Shaheen COO
Fax: (914) 273-5188
Email: w.shaheen@shaheeninc.com
Website: www.shaheeninc.com
Telecom auditing & cost-containment services. (Woman/
White, estab 1988, empl 8, sales $2,400,000, cert: WBENC)

7779   The Caswood Group, Inc.
811 Ayrault Rd, Ste 2   Fairport, NY 14450
(585) 425-0332   Isabel Casamayor President
Fax: (585) 223-2601
Email: icasamayor@caswood.com
Website: www.caswood.com
Specialty sales teams, analytics, data collection & management, sample management. (Woman/White, estab 1996,
empl 38, sales $6,258,447, cert: WBENC)

7780   The Madison Consulting Group, Inc.
41 Madison Ave 31st Fl   New York, NY 10010
(212) 532-0703   Diana Justice Consultant & Mktg
Mgr
Fax:
Email: d.justice@tmcginc.com
Website: www.themadisonconsultinggroup.com
Training & consulting: executive coaching, organizational
consulting & strategic resourcing. (Woman/White, estab
1993, empl 11, sales $1,103,130, cert: City, WBENC)

7781   The Real Advice Plus LLC
108 5th Ave, Ste 20-B   New York, NY 10011
(718) 812-8856   Tony Brown President
Fax: (718) 789-2985
Email: tbrown@t-rap.com
Website: www.t-rap.com
Management consulting, executive search consulting,
diversity consulting & career development coaching
services. (AA, estab 2006, empl 1, sales $60,000, cert:
State, City)

7782   Tribal Capital Markets, LLC
405 Lexington Ave 54th Fl   New York, NY 10174
(212) 850-2295   Sean Harte CEO
Fax: (212) 202-4927
Email: sharte@tribalcap.com
Website: www.tribalcap.com
With a strong capital structure, TCM offers client focused
services in both Fixed Income trading and origination as
well as Equity trading. Our Equity staff provides proficient
execution capabilities (Nat Ame, estab 1995, empl 14,
sales $4,000,000, cert: NMSDC)

Ohio

7783   Alegre, Inc.
3101 W Tech Rd   Miamisburg, OH 45342
(937) 885-6786   Don Phillips Business Dev Mgr
Fax: (937) 885-6787
Email: dphillips@alegreinc.com
Website: www.alegreinc.com
Supply chain mgmt, program mgmt, customer engineering & quality interface, warehousing & distribution
processes, sorting & containment, rework processes,
light assembly processes. (Woman/As-Pac, estab 1992,
empl 30, sales $20,000,000, cert: NMSDC)

7784   APB & Associates, Inc.
55 Erieview Plaza Ste 328   Cleveland, OH 44114
(216) 541-2900   Andre Bryan President
Fax: (216) 541-2901
Email: abryan@apbandassociates.com
Website: www.apbandassociates.com
Document management services, office technology,
organizational design, business process improvement,
telecommunications & office automation consulting.
(AA, estab 2004, empl 12, sales $2,200,000, cert: State,
NMSDC, SDB)

7785   Arnold Solutions, LLC
4228 E 178th St   Cleveland, OH 44128
(216) 533-2837   Reginald E. Arnold CEO
Fax: -
Email: arnoldsolutionsllc@gmail.com
Website: www.arnoldsolutionsllc.com
Consulting, administrative & innovative leadership,
Federal Law, HR, PMP, Fleet Management, IT, BPM,
Supply Chain Management, Strategic Analysis, Construc-
tion Management, Contract Procurement. (Woman/AA,
estab 2014, empl 2, sales , cert: State, City)

7786   ATS Training and Consulting Co
1991 Crocker Rd Ste 340   Westlake, OH 44145
(440) 249-0095   P. Rani Maddali President
Fax: (440) 348-1974
Email: pm@ats-tc.com
Website: www.ats-tc.com
Training & consulting services: lean, Six Sigma, supply
chain, organizational devel, change mgmt, team building
& executive coaching. (Woman/As-Ind, estab 2001, empl
20, sales $1,060,000, cert: NMSDC, WBENC, 8(a))

7787   Berkshire Group Inc.
2711 W Market St, Ste 5310   Akron, OH 44334
(800) 556-5549   Janet Kendall White CEO
Fax:
Email: janet@berkshire-leadership.com
Website: www.berkshire-leadership.com
Consulting & leadership development, strategic planning, process & profit improvement; training & development; executive coaching & facilitation. (Woman/White,
estab 1993, empl 4, sales $309,000, cert: WBENC)

7788 Compass Consulting Services, LLC
P.O. Box 221347 Beachwood, OH 44122
(216) 299-7335 Tameka Taylor President
Fax: (216) 595-0518
Email: tameka@compassconsultingservices.com
Website: www.compassconsultingservices.com
Organizational development, diversity & inclusion management, conflict management, communication, leadership development, team building. (Woman/AA, estab 2008, empl 2, sales $231,638, cert: State, NMSDC, WBENC)

7789 Diverse Supply Chain Partner, LLC
4132 E Village Dr Mason, OH 45040
(513) 274-8035 Cheryl El-Alfi President
Fax:
Email: cheryl@diversepartner.com
Website: www.diversepartner.com
Strategic business development consulting services to help diverse business enter & grow within the corporate supply chain. (Woman/White, estab 2014, empl 1, sales $22,000, cert: WBENC)

7790 Equilibrium Perceptum LLC
11839 Pearl Rd, Ste 101 Strongsville, OH 44136
(216) 278-1866 Ramana Gaddamanugu
Fax: (202) 265-1743
Email: ramana@epfocus.com
Website: www.epfocus.com
Management consulting services: systems & process reviews, strategy documentation, risk management / risk assessments / risk analysis assistance, data analysis, data review, data preparation. (As-Pac, estab 2014, empl 1, sales , cert: State, City)

7791 GPI Enterprises Inc.
3637 Medina Rd, Ste 60 Medina, OH 44256
(330) 321-2461 Christopher Murillo President
Fax: (330) 247-9911
Email: chris.murillo@e-gpi.com
Website: www.e-gpi.com
Management consulting services, process analysis/ development, data analysis, project management & IT support. (Hisp, estab 2001, empl 16, sales $1,050,000, cert: State, City, 8(a))

7792 Howse Solutions LLC
17325 Euclid Ste 2030 Cleveland, OH 44112
(1440) 318-4720 Christopher Howse President
Fax: (614) 573-7255
Email: chowse@howsesolutions.com
Website: www.howsesolutions.com
experience leading analysts, developers, and project teams; and defining, creating, and delivering business solutions.
Company Data DUNS number: 027010665 EIN number: 26-3326464 (AA, estab 1900, empl 1, sales $255,000, cert: State, City, SDB)

7793 Impact Instruction Group, LLC
P.O. Box 632 Hilliard, OH 43026
(614) 286-8265 Amy Franko CEO
Fax:
Email: amy@impactinstruction.com
Website: www.impactinstruction.com
Corporate training & development, leadership training programs & professional development strategies for emerging women leaders. (Woman/White, estab 2007, empl 8, sales , cert: WBENC)

7794 Improve Consulting & Training Group LLC
4600 Euclid Ave Ste 320 Cleveland, OH 44103
(216) 539-8737 Ellen Burts-Cooper Sr Managing Partner
Fax:
Email: ellen@improveconsulting.biz
Website: www.improveconsulting.biz
Leadership development & continuous improvement. (Woman/AA, estab 2005, empl 10, sales $700,000, cert: State)

7795 Integrity Development
8050 Beckett Center Dr Ste 317 West Chester, OH 45069
(513) 874-6836 Eric Ellis CEO
Fax: (513) 874-0356
Email: ericellis@integritydev.com
Website: www.integritydev.com
Diversity training, leadership development, conflict mgmt, strategic planning, cultural assessment, executive coaching & team building. (AA, estab 1991, empl 6, sales , cert: NMSDC)

7796 Monterey Consultants, Inc.
5335 Far Hills Ave, Ste 311 Dayton, OH 45429
(937) 436-4536 Gary Munoz President
Fax: (509) 479-9425
Email: gary.munoz@mcix.com
Website: www.mcix.com
Management consulting, organizational development & business process improvement, strategic planning, change management, process improvement, outreach & marketing & customer service. (Hisp, estab 1996, empl 16, sales $2,704,856, cert: NMSDC)

7797 Pep Promotions
151 W Fourth St Ste 700 Cincinnati, OH 45202
(513) 826-3871 Dave Kroeger President
Fax: (513) 826-3875
Email: kroegerd@peppromotions.com
Website: www.peppromotions.com
Project management, promotional programs. (AA, estab 2004, empl 125, sales $11,000,000, cert: NMSDC)

7798 PepperOak
9520 LeSaint Dr Fairfield, OH 45014
(513) 400-3484 Alisa Culyer President
Fax: (216) 397-6968
Email: alisa@pepoak.com
Website: www.pepoak.com
Landscape Management. (Woman/AA, estab 2016, empl 30, sales $1,300,000, cert: NMSDC, WBENC)

7799 SimpleQuE, Inc.
249 S Garber Dr   Tipp City, OH 45371
(740) 305-0868   Jim Lee President
Fax: (940) 305-0875
Email: jlee@simpleque.com
Website: www.simpleque.com
Management consulting services. (As-Pac, estab 2005, empl 26, sales $2,100,000, cert: NMSDC)

7800 Sritech Global Inc.
1900 Polaris Pkwy, Ste 450   Columbus, OH 43240
(614) 477-2944   Sheela Kunduru President
Fax: (614) 573-7255
Email: ksheela@sritechglobal.com
Website: www.sritechglobal.com
Business process consulting, Business process improvement, Enterprise process & product quality assurance, Independent verification & validation. (Woman/As-Pac, estab 2013, empl 1, sales $698,593, cert: State)

7801 SRM & Associates, LLC
1123 Firth Ave   Worthington, OH 43085
(614) 505-1209   Victoria Schneider President
Fax:
Email: vschneider@srm-consulting.net
Website: www.srm-consulting.net
Risk Management Consulting services, Safety & Environmental Consulting, Process Safety Management, Risk Management Planning, Safety & Environmental Program Development, Auditing & Training. (Woman/White, estab 2011, empl 4, sales $370,000, cert: WBENC)

7802 The CADD Department, Inc.
13916 Euclid Ave Ste 5   East Cleveland, OH 44112
(216) 269-5901   Wayne Grant CEO
Fax: (216) 397-6968
Email: wgrant@thecaddept.net
Website: www.thecaddept.net
Progressive civil / structural engineering, construction supervision & surveying, design, surveying & construction phase services. (AA, estab 2007, empl 4, sales , cert: State, City)

Oklahoma

7803 Gina Sofola & Associates, Inc.
5801 Broadway Extension Ste 310   Oklahoma City, OK 73118
(203) 613-9471   Gina Sofola President
Fax: (405) 272-0313
Email: gsofola@sofolaassociates.com
Website: www.sofolaassociates.com
Project mgmt: facility mgmt, transportation, strategic planning, engineering & feasibility studies, cost control, scheduling, building assessment, document mgmt, contract admin, interior design, transportation analysis, environmental assessment. (Woman/AA, estab 1999, empl 20, sales , cert: State)

Pennsylvania

7804 Clarity Concepts Inc.
240 Dechert Dr   Gulph Mills, PA 19406
(610) 825-3705   Jane Downey President
Fax:
Email: janedowney@clarityconceptsinc.com
Website: www.clarityconceptsinc.com
Customized training programs.Leadship training. Personal branding.Team development.Risk management services. (Woman/White, estab 1996, empl 2, sales $220,000, cert: WBENC)

7805 Deidre Anderson Enterprises
3959 Welsh Rd Ste 170   Willow Grove, PA 19090
(215) 618-2435   Valerie Brown-Baul COO
Fax: (888) 679-0760
Email: INFO@TRAILBLAZERS-INC.COM
Website: www.trailblazers-inc.com
Management solutions, leadership, continuous improvement, productivity, profit & performance, training & coaching programs, goal attainment, leadership development & mental performance. (Woman/AA, estab 2005, empl 17, sales $125,000, cert: State)

7806 Elevate USA Inc
1606 Jackson St   Philadelphia, PA 19145
(561) 445-3845   Michael Shalek Consultant
Fax: (215) 359-0595
Email: michael@elevate4success.com
Website: www.elevate4success.com
Training services: custom, interactive & practical workforce education, on-site training, e-learning, & coaching solutions. (Woman/White, estab 2007, empl 5, sales $600,500, cert: State, WBENC)

7807 Evolve Advisors I, LLC
85 Overhill Rd   Bala Cynwyd, PA 19004
(610) 420-5535   Peri Higgins President
Fax: (312) 421-4659
Email: phiggins@evolveadvisors.com
Website: www.evolveadvisors.com
Management consulting, assess, baseline, restructure & redesign business processes. (Woman/AA, estab 2012, empl 3, sales $108,000, cert: NMSDC, WBENC)

7808 Innovative Business Products & Services, LLC
P.O. Box 722   Monroeville, PA 15146
(412) 894-3132   Harvey Smith, Sr. VP Finance
Fax:
Email: ibpshssr@outlook.com
Website: www.artistecard.com/ibps
Diversity, inclusion & sensitivity training, recruiting diversity talent services; diversity website review; diversity mission/vision statement development; & re-entry of ex-offenders into job market services. (Woman/AA, estab 2015, empl 7, sales , cert: NMSDC)

7809 KnowledgeStart, Inc.
300 King St   Pottstown, PA 19464
(610) 650-0448   Bryan Yingst Internet Dir
Fax: (610) 650-0450
Email: byingst@knowledgestart.com
Website: www.knowledgestart.com
Diversity & Inclusion training. (As-Pac, estab 2001, empl 12, sales $850,000, cert: NMSDC)

7810 Lima Consulting Group, LLC
40 Lloyd Ave Ste 108B Malvern, PA 19335
(212) 671-0309 Paul Lima Managing Partner
Fax:
Email: plima@limaconsulting.com
Website: www.LimaConsulting.com
Administrative Management & General Management Consulting, Marketing Consulting, Process, Physical Distribution & Logistics Consulting. (Hisp, estab 2004, empl 26, sales $739,087, cert: NMSDC)

7811 Nexlevel Consulting Services, LLC
1122 Parkview Dr   New Kensington, PA 15068
(412) 436-9098 Tammy Davis CEO
Fax: (412) 774-2752
Email: tldavis@nexlevelconsultingllc.com
Website: www.nexlevelconsultingllc.com
Training, Organizational Change Management, Communications (Woman/AA, estab 2006, empl 4, sales $235,000, cert: State, WBENC)

7812 Quacoapit LLC
7121 Lynford St   Philadelphia, PA 19149
(267) 315-5147 Chea Kunwon CEO
Fax:
Email: Ckunwon@Quacoapit.com
Website: www.quacoapit.com
Quality & Compliance Consulting Services. (AA, estab 2017, empl 3, sales , cert: NMSDC)

7813 Quality Solutions Now, Inc.
3251 Olympic Dr   Emmaus, PA 18049
(610) 462-4090 Brette Travaglio President
Fax: (610) 928-7253
Email: brette@qualitysolutionsnow.com
Website: www.qualitysolutionsnow.com
Strategic, on-demand support & tactical project management svcs, product launch, regulatory compliance, large-scale change, process improvement. (Woman/White, estab 2004, empl 1, sales $2,064,000, cert: NWBOC)

7814 Sustainable Solutions Corporation
155 Railroad Plaza Ste 203 Royersford, PA 19468
(610) 569-1047 Tad Radzinski President
Fax: (610) 569-1040
Email: Tad@SustainableSolutionsCorporation.com
Website:
www.sustainablesolutionscorporation.com
Sustainable Buildings & Operations, Corporate Sustainability, Training & Education, Seminars. (Woman/White, estab 2001, empl 15, sales $1,387,831, cert: WBENC)

7815 TayganPoint Consulting Group
1118 General Washington Memorial Blvd. Ste 210
Washington Crossing, PA 08977
(215) 302-2500 R CEO
Fax: (267) 274-2515
Email: info@tayganpoint.com
Website: www.tayganpoint.com
Consulting services: business process improvement, strategy development & execution, change management & communications, program management. (Woman/White, estab 2009, empl 69, sales $18,700,000, cert: WBENC)

7816 Taylor Consulting and Contracting, LLC
625 Main St Avoca, PA 18641
(570) 414-0880 Karen Tomaine CEO
Fax: (570) 414-0884
Email: ktomaine@taylorcc.com
Website: www.taylorcc.com
Management & consulting services. (Woman/White, estab 2001, empl 15, sales $564,000, cert: State)

7817 The Claiborne Consulting Group, Inc.
1800 JFK Blvd, Ste 300   Philadelphia, PA 19103
(914) 388-4165 Julian Gray VP HR, Staffing GM
Fax: (215) 695-5544
Email: julian.gray@claibornecg.com
Website: www.claibornecg.com
Management Consulting : Business Process Re-engineering, Business Case Dev, Software Selection, Organization Change Management, Technical Content Writing, Startup Consultation, Digital Brand Management. (AA/As-Pac, estab 2015, empl 10, sales , cert: NMSDC)

7818 Veris Associates, Inc. dba VerisVisalign
P.O. Box 245   West Point, PA 19486
(11) 267-8007 Trisha Daly Office Mgr
Fax: (11) 267-8029
Email: trishadaly@verisvisalign.com
Website: www.verisvisalign.com
Consulting & training: process engineering, compliance consulting & corporate learning. (Woman/White, estab 2003, empl 38, sales $3,500,000, cert: State, WBENC)

7819 XCELLAS, LLC
275 Dilworth Lane   Langhorne, PA 19047
(267) 329-9051 Peniel Ortega Managing Dir
Fax: (844) 923-5527
Email: peniel.ortega@xcellas.com
Website: www.xcellas.com
Consulting assessment & requirements, project management solution strategies, implementation & optimization. (Woman/Hisp, estab 2013, empl 10, sales $584,437, cert: State, NMSDC, WBENC)

Puerto Rico

7820 Development Management & Consulting Group
P.O. Box 142343   Arecibo, PR 00614
(787) 897-0830 Miguel Ruiz Principal Engineer
Fax: (787) 897-0870
Email: eduardo.hernandez@dmcginc.com
Website: www.dmcginc.com
Validation Master Planning/Management, Commissioning & Qualification (C&Q), Decommissioning & Records Management, GMP Documentation Review / Generation, Cleaning & Process/Packaging Validation. (Hisp, estab 2000, empl 64, sales $3,000,000, cert: NMSDC)

7821 Impactivo LLC
PMB 140 1357 Ashford Ave   San Juan, PR 00907
(787) 993-1508 Maria Fernanda Levis-Peralta CEO
Fax:
Email: maria.levis@gmail.com
Website: www.impactivo.com
Systems Research, Policy Analysis, Strategic Planning & Financial Sustainability, Community Health Needs Assessment, Strategic Planning, Data Driven Decision Making, Project Planning, Tech Assistance, Performance Improvement. (Woman/Hisp, estab 2010, empl 5, sales , cert: NMSDC)

7822   Integrated Management & Controls, Inc.
P.O. Box 229   Manati, PR 00674
(787) 462-4739   Ismael Jaime President
Fax:
Email: ismael.jaime@imanagementcontrols.com
Website: www.imanagementcontrols.com
Program Management, Portfolio Management, Project Management, Construction Management, Project Controls, Cost Control, Planning, Scheduling, Document & Contract Management, Engineering, Design, Qualification Schedule, Design Schedules. (Hisp, estab 2014, empl 3, sales $390,000, cert: NMSDC)

Rhode Island

7823   Granger Warburton Consulting, LLC
79 West St   East Greenwich, RI 02818
(401) 965-1288   Bethany Warburton Principal Consultant
Fax:
Email: bethany@grangerwarburton.com
Website: www.grangerwarburton.com
Learning management system design & deployment, elearning creation, software application development, project management, business analysis, change management, documentation & process design. (Woman/White, estab 2013, empl 2, sales $127,000, cert: State)

South Carolina

7824   DESA, Inc
400 Percival Rd   Columbia, SC 29206
(803) 743-1124   Diane E Sumpter President
Fax: (803) 782-6741
Email: dianes@desainc.com
Website: www.desainc.com
Conference management, construction management, facilities management, business services. (Woman/AA, estab 1986, empl 30, sales $1,811,901, cert: State)

7825   GIME LLC
1544 Remount Rd Ste B   North Charleston, SC 29405
(843) 277-7552   Angela Gailliard President
Fax:
Email: gime.llc@gmail.com
Website: www.bbizsolutions.com
Workforce Solutions, Consulting Services, Administrative & Management Support, Professional Business Services. (Woman/AA, estab 2009, empl 1, sales , cert: State)

7826   Sharp Business Consulting Services LLC
1320 Main St Ste 300   Columbia, SC 29210
(803) 600-7941   Mitchell Wyatt CEO
Fax: (803) 724-1201
Email: mitchell.wyatt@gmail.com
Website: www.sharpbusinessconsulting.com
Growth & market penetration, profitability, repeat clients, customer service & strong community presence. (AA, estab 2006, empl 23, sales $1,642,774, cert: State, 8(a))

Tennessee

7827   Remnant Management Group Inc.
2550 Meridian Blvd Ste 200   Franklin, TN 37067
(615) 403-1567   Stephanie Beard CEO
Fax: (615) 567-8001
Email: info@remnantgroup.com
Website: www.theremnantgroup.com
Employee development training & construction management services, leadership training & development, workforce development, curriculum selection & customization, construction management workforce development. (Woman/AA, estab 2006, empl 5, sales $103,774, cert: State)

Texas

7828   2M Research Services, LLC
500 E Border St, Ste 680   Arlington,, TX 76010
(817) 707-6483   Marcus Martin CEO
Fax: (866) 250-2447
Email: mmartin@2mresearch.com
Website: www.2mresearch.com
Research, program evaluation & technical assistance, substantial research, program assessment, data collection, program assessments, evaluation design efforts, program evaluations, data collection, performance measurement. (AA, estab 2011, empl 30, sales $750,000, cert: 8(a))

7829   ABT International Corporation
2591 Dallas Pkwy, Ste 300   Frisco, TX 75034
(469) 879-2642   Mike Buckhaulter Owner
Fax: (972) 678-0955
Email: mbuckhaulter@abticorp.com
Website: www.abticorp.com/pages/3/index.htm
Project management agreements.
(AA, estab 2003, empl 5, sales $95,000, cert: State)

7830   Access Sciences Corporation
1900 West Loop South Ste 1450   Houston, TX 77027
(713) 664-4357   Todd Brown
Fax: (713) 664-4825
Email: tbrown@accesssciences.com
Website: www.accesssciences.com
Information & records mgmt, enterprise content mgmt & regulatory compliance, information management consulting & outsourcing. (Woman/White, estab 1985, empl 62, sales , cert: State, WBENC)

7831   AHRMDCO International LLC
14405 WaltersRdSte 1002   Houston, TX 77014
(713) 589-3688   Roderick Lemon President
Fax: (281) 764-1266
Email: rlemon@ahrmdcoint.com
Website: www.ahrmdcoint.com
Organizational development: customer service, time mgmt, partenering & team building, supervisor, executive coaching, project mgmt, web & graphic design, employee assessment surveys & interviewing techniques. (AA, estab 2002, empl 20, sales $115,000, cert: State, NMSDC)

7832 Alfa Management Solutions LLC
1228 Grant Ave   Lantana, TX 76226
(214) 642-5907 Frank Wilson Managing Dir
Fax: (940) 584-0393
Email: fwilson@aflams.com
Website: www.alfams.com/
Critical Path Method Scheduling & Control, Project &
Program Management Support, Develop, Implement &
Monitor Schedule, Report Progression of Program/
Projects, Customize Schedule for Client Specific Needs.
(AA, estab 2007, empl 2, sales $313,500, cert: 8(a))

7833 Austin Texas Mediators LLC
4500 Williams Dr. Ste 212-111 Georgetown, TX
78633
(512) 966-9222 Barbara Allen Owner
Fax: (512) 863-2267
Email: info@motexas.com
Website: www.mediatorsoftexas.com
Train the trainer; sensitivity training; sexual harassment in
the workplace training; non-confrontational communication skills training; conflict resolution in the work place.
(Woman/White, estab 2014, empl 15, sales , cert: State)

7834 Beacon Training Service, Inc.
1229 Mohawk Trail   Richardson, TX 75080
(972) 404-0069 Diana Stein Managing Principal
Fax: (972) 404-0059
Email: diana@beacontraining.com
Website: www.beacontraining.com
Computer/technical, management/supervisory, profes-
sional development & project management training.
(Woman/White, estab 1987, empl 4, sales $1,000,000,
cert: State, WBENC)

7835 CAET Project Management Consultants
1139 Keller Pkwy Ste B Keller, TX 76248
(817) 741-6546 Molly Sandlin President
Fax:
Email: molly@caetpmc.com
Website: www.caetpmc.com
Owner Representation & Financial Consulting, Development of project budget, cost estimation, Assist & develop
contract strategies, Conduct requests for proposals (RFPs)
& manage process for receipt & review. (Woman/White,
estab 2016, empl 5, sales $150,000, cert: State, WBENC)

7836 Caldwell Everson PLLC
2777 Allen Pkwy, Ste 950 Houston, TX 77019
(713) 654-3000 Faye Caldwell Managing Partner
Fax: (713) 654-3002
Email: fcaldwell@caldwelleverson.com
Website: www.caldwelleverson.com
Management employment, drug-testing, commercial,
product liability & general civil litigation. (Woman/White,
estab 1997, empl 6, sales $940,180, cert: State, WBENC)

7837 Career Management International, Inc.
4801 Woodway Dr Ste 300 East Houston, TX 77056
(713) 623-8780 Susan Silvano CEO
Fax: (713) 623-4569
Email: info@careermanagement.com
Website: www.careermanagement.com
Career transition & outplacement; training; team building
& organizational development. (Woman/White, estab
1975, empl 18, sales $3,000,000, cert: City, WBENC)

7838 Deirdre Sanborn & Associates
4321 Bretton Bay Lane   Dallas, TX 75287
(214) 308-1408 Deirdre Sanborn Owner
Fax: (214) 308-1408
Email: deirdre@deirdresanborn.com
Website: www.deirdresanborn.com
Executive Coaching, Leadership Coaching, Team Integra-
tion, Team Management & Strategic consulting.
(Woman/White, estab 2014, empl 3, sales $50,000,
cert: WBENC)

7839 DiversityInPromotions, Inc.
5057 Keller Springs Rd Ste 300 Addison, TX
75001
(469) 718-5589 Rodney Woods
Fax: (469) 718-5600
Email: rwoods@diversityinpromotions.com
Website: www.diversityinpromotions.com
Program Assessment, Strategic Planning, Policy Devel-
opment, Metrics Development, Communication Plan
(Internal & External), Mentor/Protege Development,
Government Reporting (Subcontract Plan). (AA, estab
1998, empl 18, sales $1,200,000, cert: State, NMSDC)

7840 D'Onofrio Consulting Partners
1700 Post Oak Blvd   Houston, TX 77056
(713) 963-3673 Margaret D'Onofrio Principal &
Exec Coach
Fax: (281) 286-1129
Email:
margaret@donofrioconsultingpartners.com
Website: www.donofrioconsultingpartners.com
Coaching for individuals, teams & organizations.
(Woman/White, estab 2007, empl 1, sales $1,168,885,
cert: WBENC, NWBOC)

7841 Dramatic Conclusions, LLC
3900 Vitruvian Way Ste 231 Addison, TX 75001
(469) 855-0543 Pam Boyd Owner
Fax:
Email: pam@dramaticconclusions.com
Website: www.dramaticconclusions.com
Management & employee training & consulting.
(Woman/White, estab 1999, empl 1, sales $53,296,
cert: State, WBENC)

7842 FFG Strategic Consulting LLC
363 N. Houston Pkwy E Ste 1100 Houston, TX
77060
(832) 412-2524 Colette Lewis
Fax: (281) 454-7513
Email: colette.lewis@ffgsconsulting.com
Website: www.ffgsconsulting.com
Program/project management, engineering consulting,
technical resources, project planning, construction
management, project scheduling, project controls,
system engineering, six sigma methodology analysis,
mechanical engineering. (Woman/AA, estab 2011, empl
5, sales $50,000, cert: State, NMSDC, WBENC)

7843   Hybrid Teams, Inc.
    3023 Cape Buffalo Trail   Frisco, TX 75034
    (847) 530-9034   Mac Choi President
    Fax: (847) 307-5429
    Email: info@hybridteams.com
    Website: www.hybridteams.com
Enterprise content management professional services,
document management, consulting services. (As-Pac,
estab 2006, empl 3, sales $306,000, cert: NMSDC)

7844   JFE International Consultants, Inc.
    18705 Stoneridge Dr   Dallas, TX 75252
    (214) 728-6903   J. Francisco Escobar President
    Fax: (214) 692-6056
    Email: francisco@jfeintl.com
    Website: www.jfeintl.com
Management consulting, contract diagnostics, compensation principles, negotiations, performance evaluations &
measurements, internal/external process audits. (Hisp,
estab 2003, empl 1, sales $214,595, cert: NMSDC)

7845   Jill Hickman Companies
    1721 Palomino Ln   Kingwood, TX 77339
    (281) 358-8580   Jill Hickman President
    Fax: (281) 358-8580
    Email: jill@jillhickman.com
    Website: www.jillhickman.com
Training & development services: leadership, supervision,
consultative sales, customer service & team building, pre-
employment assessment, executive advisement, strategic
planning. (Woman, estab 1998, empl 1, sales $141,956,
cert: WBENC)

7846   Languages Houston
    1001 S Dairy Ashford Ste 100   Houston, TX 77077
    (832) 359-4226   Elena Tsilina CEO
    Fax:
    Email: info@languageshouston.com
    Website: www.languageshouston.com
Foreign language classes & translation services. (Woman/
White, estab 2015, empl 20, sales , cert: State, WBENC)

7847   Lone Star Interpreters LLC
    2800 Post Oak Blvd, Ste 1400 Ste 4100   Houston, TX
    77056
    (832) 399-2100   Marie Mills CEO
    Fax: (832) 399-2101
    Email: Marie.Mills@lonestarinterpreters.com
    Website: www.lonestarinterpreters.com
Language services in over 200 languages: Translation &
Localization, Transcription, Interpretation: On Site,
Telephonic & Video, Voice Prompt Translating, Voice
Prompt Recording. (Woman/AA, estab 2007, empl 40, sales
$266,000, cert: State, NMSDC)

7848   Mind The Gap, LLC
    901 Parkwood Ct   McKinney, TX 75070
    (314) 378-6426   Beth Anagnos Principal
    Fax:
    Email: betha@mindthegapcoaching.com
    Website: www.mindthegapcoaching.com
Leadership coaching, customized coaching programs for all
levels of leadership. (Woman/White, estab 2007, empl 5,
sales $68,302, cert: WBENC)

7849   Niche Assurance LLC
    9894 Bissonnet St   Houston, TX 77036
    (281) 636-2749   Peter Kiilu
    Fax: (281) 809-7155
    Email: Peter.kiilu@nicheconsult.net
    Website: www.nicheconsult.net
Financial & IT risk management, business performance
improvement, Internal control design & implementation,
Sarbanes-Oxley Act compliance, FCPA compliance,
internal audits, I.T. audits, cyber security, SAP security.
(AA, estab 2007, empl 4, sales $150,000, cert: State,
NMSDC)

7850   Obsidian Technical Communications, Ltd.
    3522 White Oak Dr   Houston, TX 77007
    (281) 732-5940   Erik Pettine Director of Sales
    Fax: (281) 732-6569
    Email: erikp@obsidianlearning.com
    Website: www.obsidianlearning.com
Consulting: job performance, end-user performance
support, custom training strategy & development,
documentation, e-learning, knowledge mgmt & change
mgmt. (Woman/White, estab 1998, empl 26, sales
$3,700,000, cert: WBENC)

7851   PABULUM Consulting, LLC
    1002 Gemini St Ste 225D   Houston, TX 77058
    (713) 538-4719   Ferrel Bonner CEO
    Fax: (832) 224-9902
    Email: ferrelbonner@pabulumconsulting.com
    Website: www.pabulumconsulting.com
Military Intelligence, Security & Emergency Management,
Special Operations & Tactical Communications. (AA, estab
2007, empl 2, sales $58,000, cert: State, City, 8(a))

7852   Phoenix Translations
    2110 White Horse Trail   Austin, TX 78757
    (512) 343-8389   Deborah Wright CEO
    Fax: (512) 343-6721
    Email: service@phoenixtranslations.com
    Website: www.phoenixtranslations.com
Technical translation services. (Woman/AA/Hisp, estab
2000, empl 20, sales $2,500,000, cert: State, WBENC)

7853   Phronetik
    5851 Legacy Circle 6th Fl   Plano, TX 75024
    (877) 844-3575   Tania Martin-Mercado President
    Fax: (469) 453-3095
    Email: taniame@phronetik.com
    Website: www.phronetik.com
Research & Development, Technical Support,
Interoperability, Patient Portal Development, Privacy &
Security, Clinical Documentation, Mobile Health, Decision
Support Systems, Telemedicine, Custom Development.
(Woman/Hisp, estab 2013, empl 11, sales , cert: WBENC)

7854   Possible Missions, Inc.
    150 W Parker Rd., Ste 602   Houston, TX 77076
    (713) 271-3746   Paula Mendoza CEO
    Fax: (832) 575-3746
    Email: paula@possiblemissions.com
    Website: www.possiblemissions.com
Project management solutions, plan, execute & complete
projects within budget and on schedule. (Woman/Hisp,
estab 2001, empl 33, sales $2,100,000, cert: State, City,
NMSDC, 8(a))

7855   Proje Inc.
        6942 FM 1960 E, Ste 362   Humble, TX 77346
        (832) 293-5633 Kay Robinson COO
        Fax: (860) 321-7602
        Email: sales@projeinc.com
        Website: www.projeinc.com
Project Mgmt Leadership & analytical thinking, Crisis
Management, Integration & Consolidation, Risk Analysis &
Adjustment, Medicare Advantage. (Woman/White, estab
2004, empl 38, sales $8,800,119, cert: WBENC)

7856   Risk Mitigation Worldwide
        9800 Northwest Frwy Ste 600 Houston, TX 77092
        (713) 864-9997 Michele Ward VP Business Devel
        Fax: (713) 864-9981
        Email: michele@legalwatch.com
        Website: www.legalwatch.com
Training & consulting services: communications to
minimize & avoid potential lawsuits, claims & internal
disputes. (Woman/AA, estab 1997, empl 6, sales , cert:
State, NMSDC, WBENC)

7857   RWG Consulting, Inc.
        2560 King Arthur Blvd. Ste 124-34 Dallas, TX 75056
        (972) 386-7601 Anton Gates Managing Partner
        Fax:
        Email: agates@rwgconsulting.com
        Website: www.rwgconsulting.com
Training, Instructional Design, Project Management,
Organizational Change Management, SAP Training Development, Staff Augmentation, Business Process Optimization, Contract to Hire. (AA, estab 2013, empl 15, sales
$900,000, cert: State, NMSDC)

7858   Sales Trac Coaching & Mgmt Development
        10012 SIlvertree Dr   Dallas, TX 75243
        (214) 215-1108 David Tyson CEO
        Fax:
        Email: davidt@salestrac.net
        Website: www.salestrac.net
Leadership Development & Performance Management,
Management training, Sales Management training, sales
training, service focused training, customer service
training, Generational training. (AA, estab 2007, empl 1,
sales , cert: State, NMSDC)

7859   Seilevel Partners, LP
        3410 Far West Blvd Ste 265 Austin, TX 78731
        (512) 527-9952 Christine Wollmuth
        Fax: (623) 321-1327
        Email: cwollmuth@seilevel.com
        Website: www.seilevel.com
Business analysis consulting, business analyst staffing,
assessment, mentoring & training. (As-Ind, estab 2000,
empl 30, sales , cert: State, NMSDC)

7860   Shea Writing and Training Solutions, Inc.
        11602 Burdine St Houston, TX 77035
        (713) 723-9142 Evalyn Shea President
        Fax: (713) 723-9143
        Email: info@sheaws.com
        Website: www.sheaws.com
Technical writing & editing, risk assessment & meeting
scribing, web content, training materials, proposals,
presentations, reports, technical manuals, etc. (Woman/
White, estab 1997, empl 18, sales $2,481,699, cert: State,
City, WBENC)

7861   Sirius Solutions, LLLP
        1233 West Loop South Ste 1800 Houston, TX
        77027
        (713) 888-0488 Kathy Pattillo Director Business
        Devel
        Fax: (171) 388-8023
        Email: kpattillo@sirsol.com
        Website: www.sirsol.com
Management consulting: finance, internal audit, information technology, accounting, risk, operations, process
improvement, strategy & tax. (Woman, estab 1998, empl
230, sales , cert: WBENC, NWBOC)

7862   Stalwart Consulting, LLC
        23501 Cinco Ranch Blvd Ste H120 #129 Katy, TX
        77494
        (513) 722-6852 Benjamin Armenta CEO
        Fax:
        Email: barmenta@stalwartmc.com
        Website: www.stalwartmc.com
Management consulting & advisory service, technology
development & delivery, project management & business analysis & projections. (Hisp, estab 2016, empl 5,
sales , cert: City)

7863   The Conxsis Group, Inc.
        1910 McCartney Court   Arlington, TX 76012
        (817) 348-0060 Abdul Shakir President
        Fax: (817) 469-8311
        Email: ashakir@conxsis.com
        Website: www.conxsis.com
Environmental consulting, financial, economic, business
consulting, large & small business teaming, M/WBE
Programs, marketing & business development. (AA,
estab 2002, empl 16, sales $370,000, cert: State)

7864   The i4 Group
        100 N. Central Expy Ste 510 Richardson, TX 75080
        (612) 207-2751 Charles Maddox Business Director
        Fax: (651) 393-5435
        Email: charles.sr@thei4group.com
        Website: www.thei4group.com
Training & coaching for Scaled Agile, Agile, and IT
business process improvement, Lean Six Sigma, project
management training & certification. (AA, estab 2013,
empl 87, sales $6,852,000, cert: State, NMSDC)

7865   The Innis Company
        14643 Dallas Pkwy, Ste 635   Dallas, TX 75254
        (972) 702-9484 Karyl Innis CEO
        Fax: (972) 404-9004
        Email: kinnis@inniscompany.com
        Website: www.inniscompany.com
Executive coaching. (Woman/White, estab 1994, empl 5,
sales $1,500,000, cert: State, WBENC)

7866   The Tagos Group, LLC
        8 E Greenway Plaza Ste 1340 Houston, TX 77046
        (713) 850-7031 Maria Traver Office Mgr
        Fax: (713) 850-7071
        Email: mtraver@tagosgroup.com
        Website: www.tagosgroup.com
Business consulting, services & products: supply chain
mgmt, transportation & logistics mgmt, speciality
maintenance & call center operations. (AA, estab 2007,
empl 9, sales $500,000, cert: NMSDC)

7867 Tray-Tec, Inc.
2598 Wilson Rd   Humble, TX 77396
(281) 441-7314 Darell Fowler VP
Fax: (281) 441-7316
Email: traytec@traytec.com
Website: www.traytec.com
Installers of process equipment such as trays, packings, distributors in towers, reactors, and drums. We perform installation and repairs of nozzles, and we perform vessel shell repairs. (Hisp, estab 2005, empl 20, sales $10,000,000, cert: State)

7868 Tre Weekly Magazine
3202 N Shiloh Rd   Garland, TX 75044
(972) 675-4383 Shayne Hohman Mktg Coord.
Fax: (972) 675-3764
Email: marketing@trenews.com
Website: www.baotreonline.com/
Tre magazine circulates nearly 125,000 publications nationwide on a weekly basis: with a readership census of 112,000 people in Dallas alone. (As-Pac, estab 1997, empl 25, sales $1,600,000, cert: NMSDC)

7869 Valerie & Company
1412 Main Ste 1110 Dallas, TX 75202
(214) 290-0100 Valerie Sokolosky President
Fax: (214) 290-0102
Email: valerie@valerieandcompany.com
Website: www.valerieandcompany.com
Leadership development: management development, team building, executive coaching. (Woman/White, estab 1981, empl 2, sales $250,000, cert: State, WBENC)

Virginia

7870 A. Reddix & Associates Inc.
1215 N Military Hwy, Ste 754   Norfolk, VA 23502
(757) 410-7704 Charmian Lee Contracts Dir
Fax: (866) 742-2557
Email: finance@ardx.net
Website: www.ardx.net
Workforce training & technical assistance, innovative information technology & security solutions & support, collaborative conferencing & events management, quality, compliance & revenue audits, policy documentation & management. (Woman, estab 2006, empl 105, sales , cert: State)

7871 AEi International LLC
7686 Richmond Hwy, Ste 118   Alexandria, VA 22306
(410) 988-3966 Jenna Reese CEO
Fax:
Email: jenna.reese@aeiintl.com
Website: www.aeiintl.com
Management consulting & technology, strategic consulting, digital experience & enterprise technology related-services, staff augmentation. (Woman/AA, estab 2007, empl 12, sales $1,200,000, cert: 8(a))

7872 Aerobodies Fitness Company, Inc.
950 N Washington St Ste 311 Alexandria, VA 22314
(703) 402-8477 Fran Bishop CEO
Fax:
Email: franb@afmsco.com
Website: www.afmsco.com
Program management services, acquisition support, organizational development, and occupational health services to federal and private sector agencies. (AA, estab 1997, empl 25, sales $750,000, cert: WBENC, 8(a))

7873 Assura, Inc.
7814 Carousel Lane   Ashland, VA 23294
(804) 672-8714 Karen Cole CEO
Fax: (804) 672-6442
Email: karen.cole@assuraconsulting.com
Website: www.assurainc.com
Consulting: Governance, Risk & Compliance (GRC), Enterprise Risk Management (ERM), cyber-security, business continuity planning & Information Technology (IT) audit. (Woman/White, estab 2010, empl 1, sales , cert: State, WBENC)

7874 Burton-Fuller Managment
5516 Falmouth St, Ste 201 Ste 201 Richmond, VA 23230
(804) 217-6380 Vicki Funk Office Mgr
Fax: (804) 217-6380
Email: support@burtonfuller.com
Website: www.burtonfuller.com
Management consulting. (Woman/White, estab 1989, empl 5, sales , cert: State)

7875 C.W. Hines and Associates, Inc.
344 Churchill Cir, Sanctuary Bay   White Stone, VA 22578
(804) 435-8844 Cheryl Hudson President
Fax: (804) 435-8855
Email: turtlecwh@aol.com
Website: www.cwhinesassociates.org
Management training & consulting: performance excellence coaching, diversity, teambuilding, leadership development, communications, customer service, strategic thinking, strategic planning, supervisory effectiveness, executive coaching, mediation. (Woman/AA, estab 1998, empl 19, sales $850,000, cert: State, City, NMSDC)

7876 Capitol Management Consulting Services, Inc.
1600 Chain Bridge Rd   McLean, VA 22101
(571) 318-6404 Akshat Prasad President
Fax: (703) 854-1418
Email: corporate@capitolmcs.com
Website: www.capitolmcs.com
Management consulting, organizational governance, performance optimization, strategy, technology, and training services. (As-Ind, estab 2011, empl 1, sales $89,294, cert: State, 8(a))

7877 DP Distribution & Consulting, LLC
7305 Hancock Village Dr, Ste 109   Chesterfield, VA 23832
(804) 307-7706 Darren Reeves President
Fax:
Email: dreeves@dpdconline.com
Website: www.dpdconline.com
Quality Assurance & Regulatory for Manufacturing, Auditing, 510K, FDA regulation. (Woman/White, estab 2000, empl 1, sales $300,000, cert: State)

7878 EMY Consulting LLC
13406 Poplar Woods   Chantillly, VA 20151
(703) 943-8129 Elena Yearly President
Fax:
Email: eyearly@emyconsulting.biz
Website: www.emyconsulting.biz
Management consulting solutions. (Woman/White, estab 2013, empl 1, sales $201,000, cert: State, WBENC)

7879 Evans Inc.
2750 Properity Ave, Ste 425 Fairfax, VA 22031
(703) 663-2480 Ana Gross Office Mgr
Fax: (703) 663-0308
Email: sevans@evansincorporated.com
Website: www.evansincorporated.com
Business process consulting, change mgmt &
reengineering, enterprise IT investment analysis & integration, ethical leadership training, process & data modeling,
performance mgmt, competency framework changes &
development, user interface. (Woman/White, estab 1993,
empl 10, sales $1,500,000, cert: WBENC)

7880 FM Solutions, PLLC
901 E Byrd St Ste 1210 Richmond, VA 23219
(804) 288-3173 Wendy Henley Principal
Fax: (804) 288-3174
Email: wendyh@fmsolutions-us.com
Website: www.fmsolutions-us.com
Project & program mgmt, facilities mgmt, consulting &
supplemental staffing, space allocation analyses & programming, strategic space & facilities planning, relocation
mgmt. (Woman/White, estab 2003, empl 4, sales
$394,143, cert: State)

7881 ITMC Solutions
12841 Braemar Village Plaza Bristow, VA 20136
(571) 239-1653 Nicole Johnson Business Devel
Assoc
Fax: (703) 656-4934
Email: njohnson@itmcsolutions.com
Website: www.itmcsolutions.com
Strategic consulting: program mgmt, capital planning,
portfolio mgmt, performance mgmt, business process re-
engineering, IT strategic planning, Cloud Ccmputing
strategic planning, enterprise architecture, risk management, IV &V. (Woman/AA, estab 2010, empl 3, sales
$500,000, cert: State)

7882 KAPAX Solutions LLC
44308 Navajo Dr Ashburn, VA 20147
(571) 239-0653 Katrecia Nolen President
Fax:
Email: Katrecia.Nolen@kapaxsolutions.com
Website: www.kapaxsolutions.com
Professional services & management consulting, strategic
planning, system integration & project management
support services. (Woman/AA, estab 2011, empl 1, sales
$70,000, cert: State)

7883 KickStart Specialists, LLC
11809 Crown Prince Circle Henrico, VA 23238
(855) 454-2578 Robert Riley Principal
Fax: (855) 454-2578
Email: rriley@kickstartspecialists.com
Website: www.KickStartSpecialists.com
Leadership development & training; roles & responsibilities, business objectives, business case evaluation, teambuilding; project & program management consulting;
project board training; health checks. (Woman, estab
2011, empl 2, sales $68,640, cert: State)

7884 Lapine Group, Inc.
8200 Greensboro Dr Ste 900 McLean, VA 22102
(703) 940-6005 Jason Narkiewicz Sr strategist
Fax: (703) 940-6002
Email: lapineinfo@lapinegroup.com
Website: www.lapinegroup.com
Management consulting. (Woman/White, estab 2006,
empl 10, sales $3,730,000, cert: WBENC)

7885 Project Management and Consulting LLC
512 Lafayette Boulevard, Ste 2 Fredericksburg,
VA 22401
(800) 971-3194 Bryan Rock CEO
Fax: (800) 971-3024
Email: brock@pmcllcva.com
Website: www.pmcva.com
Business management & consulting, small business
consulting, minority-owned business consulting. (AA,
estab 2007, empl 1, sales $195,000, cert: State)

7886 SAK Management Consulting
2217 Princess Anne St Ste 204-1 Fredericksburg,
VA 22401
(570) 328-0405 Semy Kakoma Principal
Fax:
Email: semyk@sak-consultingcpas.com
Website: www.sak-consultingcpas.com
DOD audit readiness, IT audits for NIST 800 compliance,
Fed accounting, Fed financial statement support, Real
Property accounting & compliance, human resources &
information technology management & advisory
services. (AA, estab 2011, empl 6, sales $950,000, cert:
8(a))

7887 Savi Solutions, Inc.
8200 Greensboro Dr, Ste 900 McLean, VA 22102
(571) 258-7602 Smita Iyer CEO
Fax:
Email: siyer@savisolutions.biz
Website: www.savisolutions.biz
Strategic Planning, Program/Project Management,
Merger & Acquisition Support, Systems Implementation
(ERP/CRM/SCM), Cloud Based Implementation Solu-
tions, Business Requirement Analysis, System Design
and Development. (As-Ind, estab 2010, empl 3, sales
$552,551, cert: WBENC)

7888 The Boulevard Consulting Group, LLC
2001 Jefferson Davis Hwy Ste 412 Arlington, VA
22202
(703) 566-6895 James Bagg Managing Partner
Fax:
Email: james.bagg@boulevardcg.com
Website: www.boulevardcg.com
Operations Research/Analysis, Lean Six Sigma, Systems &
Process Improvement/Analysis, Modeling & Simulation,
Optimization, Strategic Planning, Risk Analysis, Risk
Management, Financial Modeling/Forecasting &
Analysis. (Nat Ame, estab 2013, empl 4, sales $600,000,
cert: 8(a))

7889 The MASY Group
6214 Old Franconia Rd Ste B Alexandria, VA 22310
(703) 888-8121 Mia Elsheikh Ops Support Mgr
Fax:
Email: mia.elsheikh@masygroup.com
Website: www.masygroup.com
Intelligence & risk management services, accountable &
innovative intelligence & security solutions. (As-Pac, estab
2006, empl 45, sales $7,000,000, cert: 8(a))

7890 The Perspectives Group
7620 Little River Turnpike Ste 205 Annandale, VA
22003
(703) 837-1197 James E Lawson Dir. Business Dev
Fax: (703) 837-9662
Email: jlawson@theperspectivesgroup.com
Website: www.theperspectivesgroup.com
Public participation & outreach, advisory boards &
governance, collaboration, facilitation, graphic design,
mediation & dispute resolution, message development,
policy development, process design, strategic planning,
training & education. (Woman, estab 1991, empl 6, sales
$990,000, cert: State)

7891 TMS Consulting LLC
2776 S Arlington Mill Dr Ste 114 Arlington, VA
22206
(703) 272-4719 Tafadzwa Matinenga President
Fax:
Email: info@tmsconsultingservices.us
Website: www.tmsconsult.us
Global management consulting. (Woman/AA, estab 2015,
empl 3, sales , cert: State)

7892 Visions2000 Inc.
312 Tides Run   Yorktown, VA 23692
(757) 898-5010 Che Henderson VP
Fax: (757) 898-5010
Email: che@visions2000inc.com
Website: www.visions2000inc.com
Consulting & training solutions: diversity, leadership,
teambuilding, change management, life work planning &
job search assistance. (Woman/AA, estab 1990, empl 2,
sales $59,169, cert: NMSDC)

Washington

7893 Cascade Management and Consulting
26211 178th St SE   Monroe, WA 98272
(206) 778-4322 Amy Hoyt Owner
Fax:
Email: info@cascademgtconsulting.com
Website: www.cascademgtconsulting.com
Project & program management, IT & global rollouts,
business continuity/disaster recovery, brand integrity,
change management & collaborative communications.
(Woman/White, estab 2015, empl 1, sales , cert: State)

7894 Groundwork Tech, LLC
P.O. Box 489   Bellevue, WA 98004
(425) 209-0588 Jeff Foster Principal
Fax: (425) 209-0588
Email: jeff@groundworktech.com
Website: www.groundworktech.com
Professional Management Services, consulting services
& resources to enhance, re-engineer & develop cus-
tomer business. (AA, estab 2014, empl 3, sales
$180,000, cert: State)

7895 Rafael A Colon Voices Internacional
5145 Illahee Ln NE   Olympia, WA 98516
(360) 459-7228 Rafael Colon President
Fax: (360) 459-8419
Email: rafael@voicesinternacional.com
Website: www.voicesinternacional.com
Consulting, training, organizational operations &
administration, leadership & management development,
program development & management, communication
effectiveness & meeting facilitation, peak performance
& team unity practices. (Hisp, estab 1994, empl 1, sales
$217,500, cert: State, NMSDC)

7896 Rivet Consulting LLC
2212 Queen Anne Ave N, Ste 127   Seattle, WA
98109
(888) 201-1422 Courtney Klein Managing Partner
Fax:
Email: courtney@rivetconsulting.com
Website: www.rivetconsulting.com
Project Managers, Program Managers, Marketing
Managers, Marketing Coordinators, Financial Analysts,
Business Analysts, Social Media Experts, Search Market-
ing Experts, Data Analysts,   Market Researchers,
Marketing Communications Managers. (Woman, estab
2013, empl 30, sales , cert: WBENC)

7897 Shee Atiká Technologies, LLC
218 Main St Ste 425 Kirkland, WA 98033
(858) 254-3312 Lauren Engle Ops/Mktg Assoc
Fax: (425) 284-2114
Email: lauren.engle@sheeatikatech.com
Website: www.sheeatikatech.com
Engineering, technical support services, resource
planning & management svcs, studies & analysis,
operations analysis, strategic planning, business process
improvement, system requirements, training & education requirements. (Nat Ame, estab 2005, empl 32, sales
$5,371,107, cert: 8(a))

Wisconsin

7898 Urban Strategies US LLC DBA SMCG
759 N Milwaukee St Ste 414 Milwaukee, WI
53202
(414) 221-9500 Jim Milner CEO
Fax: (414) 225-8996
Email: jmilner@sectormanagement.biz
Website: www.sectormcg.com
Leadership development, assessing/shaping organizational culture, stretching leadership capacity & acceler-
ating the development of those who follow through
effective coaching. (AA, estab 2002, empl 3, sales , cert:
State, NMSDC)

PROFESSIONAL SERVICES: Public Relations/ Marketing

Provide services including business research and marketing plans, data collection and analysis, meeting planning, needs assessments, corporate imaging enhancement, focus groups, fundraising, technical writing, media relations, etc. NAICS Code 54

Alabama

7899 Marketry Inc.
1630 29th Ct S Birmingham, AL 35209
(205) 802-7252 Gillian Waybright Business Mgr
Fax:
Email: gwaybright@marketryinc.com
Website: www.marketryinc.com
Qualitative marketing research: focus groups, ethnography, online discussions, online video focus groups, interviews, dyads, triads, observational research, ideation, shop-a-longs, online bulletin boards, video diaries. (Woman/White, estab 1995, empl 5, sales , cert: WBENC)

7900 Optimum Financial Corporation
1300 Meridian St Ste 12 Huntsville, AL 35801
(256) 539-3994 Thomas Parker Dir Business Dev
Fax: (256) 539-3922
Email: tparker@optimumcorp.com
Website: www.optimumcorp.com
At Optimum Financial Corporation we are experts in managing people, processes, and technology. Our primary purpose is working in partnership with our clients to provide effective solutions. (AA, estab 1995, empl 20, sales $1,000,000, cert: NMSDC)

7901 PM Group, Inc.
4324 Midmost Dr Ste 200 Mobile, AL 36609
(251) 445-7804 Juan Peasant
Fax: (559) 441-9001
Email: juan@pmgroupnow.com
Website:
Branding & Marketing, Social Media Marketing, creative & design dev, print, web development & video production. (AA, estab 2004, empl 3, sales $226,910, cert: NMSDC)

Arizona

7902 Class Act Designs
18239 N 40th St, Ste 109 Phoenix, AZ 85032
(602) 843-3109 Debbie Perkins CEO
Fax: (602) 788-0250
Email: classactdesigns@peoplepc.com
Website:
Advertising, public relations, media, graphic design & strategy marketing. (Woman/AA, estab 1992, empl 6, sales $26,100, cert: City)

7903 Denise Meridith Consultants Inc.
1201 E Palo Verde Dr Phoenix, AZ 85014
(602) 763-9900 Denise Meridith CEO
Fax: (602) 222-9072
Email: denisemeridithconsultants@cox.net
Website: www.denisemeridithconsultants.com
Public relations, marketing, lobbying, human resources management, training, organizational development. (Woman/AA, estab 2001, empl 1, sales , cert: City)

7904 EventPro Strategies, Inc.
7373 N. Scottsdale Road, Ste B-120 Scottsdale, AZ 85283
(480) 449-4100 Kelly Springs-Kelley Director of Mktg
Fax: (480) 283-1190
Email: kkelley@eventprostrategies.com
Website: www.eventprostrategies.com
Marketing, public relations & promotional events. (Woman/White, estab 1999, empl 32, sales $6,700,000, cert: WBENC)

7905 JVJ Can 22 Corp
3260 N Hayden, Ste 210 Scottsdale, AZ 85251
(480) 626-7919 Michelle Candelaria CEO
Fax: (480) 304-4848
Email: mc@cts10.com
Website: www.CTS10.com
SEO Search Engine Optimization Social Media Management   Reputation monitoring   Protect Your Reputation Video Upload to Social Media sites Social Shopping Carts   Social Contests   Social Deals FaceBook   LinkedIN   Twitter   Pi (Woman/Hisp, estab 2016, empl 7, sales , cert: NMSDC)

7906 Katherine Christensen & Associates, Inc.
107 S Southgate Dr Chandler, AZ 85226
(480) 893-6110 Katherine Christensen, CMP, DMCP President
Fax: (480) 893-7775
Email: kc@kc-a.com
Website: www.kc-a.com
Meeting management, trade association management & public relations. (Woman/White, estab 1992, empl 12, sales $731,957, cert: WBENC)

7907 MakPro Services, LLC
2036 N Gentry Mesa, AZ 85213
(480) 890-1927 Teresa Makinen Principal
Fax: (480) 964-7555
Email: teresa@makprosvc.com
Website: www.makprosvc.com
Public outreach, public involvement, meeting facilitation, construction partnering, organizational management & event planning services. (Woman/White, estab 1998, empl 5, sales $300,000, cert: State)

7908 Morrissey & Associates, LLC
P.O. Box 25967 Scottsdale, AZ 85255
(480) 515-2688 Neysa Morrissey CEO
Fax: (480) 393-1966
Email: admin@morrisseytravel.com
Website: www.MorrisseyTravel.com
Meeting, Event & Travel, Site Research & Selection, Analysis & Cost Containment Solutions, Contract Negotiations & Risk Mitigation, Strategic Meetings Management (SMM); Program Itinerary & Agenda Development, Housing & Registration, Trade Show Management. (Woman/As-Pac, estab 2007, empl 1, sales $151,168, cert: State, WBENC, 8(a))

7909 Phoenix Electronic Business Solutions, LLC
      1001 E Warner Rd, Ste 102   Tempe, AZ 85284
      (480) 897-8479 Peggy Darnell President
      Fax:
      Email: peg.darnell@systrends.com
      Website: www.systrends.com
Promotion & marketing collateral, brochures, trade shows,
website content, technical writing & specifications,
requirements, user documentation, projects & plans,
schedules, reports. (Woman/White, estab 1986, empl 5,
sales $1,968,978, cert: CPUC)

7910 Squala LLC
      2909 E Broadway   Phoenix, AZ 85040
      (602) 547-7020 Angela Lawrence Dir Natl sales
      Fax:
      Email: alawrence@sherrimayco.com
      Website: www.sherrimayco.com
Brand development, graphic design, copy writing, direct
marketing integrated campaigns, websites, mobile, data
analytics & public relations, web, sheetfed, digital variable,
large format, flexo, retail packaging & folding cartons.
(Woman/White, estab 2010, empl 10, sales $3,550,646,
cert: WBENC)

California

7911 Acento Advertising, Inc.
      2001 Wilshire Blvd Ste 600 Santa Monica, CA 90403
      (310) 843-8300 Donnie Broxson EVP
      Fax: (310) 829-2424
      Email: dbroxson@acento.com
      Website: www.acento.com
Integrated marketing programs for the U.S. Hispanic &
total market segments. (Hisp, estab 1983, empl 50, sales
$32,067,933, cert: NMSDC, CPUC)

7912 Acme Arts Inc.
      19709 Horseshoe Dr   Topanga, CA 90290
      (310) 455-1413 Scott Ferguson Partner
      Fax:
      Email: scott@sferguson.com
      Website: www.sferguson.com
Marketing communications services, copywriting, creative
direction, strategic brand consulting, original music,
complete production for educational & promotional
corporate videos. (Woman/Hisp, estab 1990, empl 2, sales
$234,000, cert: CPUC, WBENC)

7913 Afaf Translations, LLC
      15655 Liberty St   San Leandro, CA 94578
      (510) 684-4586 Afaf Steiert President
      Fax: (510) 740-0578
      Email: afaf@afaftranslations.com
      Website: www.afaftranslations.com
Translation, interpreting, voice-over, desktop publishing,
transcription, localization, language proficiency evaluations & cultural consultation. (Woman/AA, estab 2004,
empl 2, sales , cert: WBENC)

7914 AfterViolet Inc.
      1100 Glendon Ave #1715 Los Angeles, CA 90024
      (917) 331-5637 Christopher Bodmer Innovation
      Consultant
      Fax:
      Email: cab@afterviolet.com
      Website: www.afterviolet.com
Innovation & branding, Product, service & experience
design, Marketing & innovation strategy, Graphic design
services, Consumer research. (Hisp, estab 2013, empl 6,
sales $243,857, cert: NMSDC)

7915 Alter Agents
      617 S Olive St, Ste 1010   Los Angeles, CA 90014
      (213) 612-0356 Angela Woo Co-Founder
      Fax:
      Email: angela@alteragents.com
      Website: www.alteragents.com
Market research & brand strategy, brand building,
targeting, marketing strategy/dev, product development,
shopper insights & in-market performance. (Woman,
estab 2010, empl 10, sales , cert: NWBOC)

7916 AP42
      2303 Camino Ramon #280   San Ramon, CA 94583
      (925) 901-1100 Imelda Alejandrino CEO
      Fax: (925) 901-1104
      Email: imelda@ap42.com
      Website: www.ap42.com
Create ads, direct marketing programs, website content,
logo design, email blasts, collateral materials. (Woman/
As-Pac, estab 2001, empl 7, sales $720,000, cert:
WBENC)

7917 Artisan Creative Inc.
      1830 Stoner Ave Ste 6 Los Angeles, CA 90025
      (310) 312-2062 Katty Douraghy President
      Fax: (310) 312-0670
      Email: kattyd@artisancreative.com
      Website: www.artisancreative.com
Design & development solutions: marketing, advertising,
communications & production teams in the digital,
broadcast, mobile & print space. (Woman/White, estab
1996, empl 15, sales $3,000,000, cert: WBENC)

7918 AW Distributing, Inc.
      2024 Middlefield Rd   Redwood City, CA 94063
      (408) 835-4816 Joseph Lam Category Specialist
      Fax:
      Email: josephlam@awdus.com
      Website: www.awdus.com
Product development, market research, product sales &
marketing, product design, promotion, manufacture,
logistics, warehouse & IT management. (Woman/As-Pac,
estab 2007, empl 20, sales $15,000,000, cert: State)

7919 Bleu Marketing Solutions
      101 Lucas Valley Road Ste 300 San Rafael, CA
      94903
      (415) 345-3317 Jennifer Giordano Acct Director
      Fax:
      Email: jgiordano@bleusf.com
      Website: www.bleumarketing.com
Direct marketing, strategy & consulting, media planning,
design & creative implementation, marketing program
systems & IT support. (Woman/White, estab 2001, empl
25, sales $2,500,000, cert: WBENC)

7920 BrandGov
125 Humphrey Lane   Vallejo, CA 94591
(800) 215-0280 K Patrice Williams President
Fax: (800) 215-0280
Email: supplier@brandgov.com
Website: www.brandgov.com
Brand Strategy & Lobbying, Integrated Branding & Marketing Solutions, Supplier Diversity Outreach, Website & Mobile Application Development, Logo Development, Brochures, Graphic Designs, Technical Procurement. (Woman/AA, estab 2007, empl 4, sales $79,780, cert: NMSDC, CPUC)

7921 Briabe Media, Inc.
634A Venice Blvd   Venice, CA 90291
(310) 694-3283 James Briggs CEO
Fax: (310) 694-3284
Email: james.briggs@briabemedia.com
Website: www.briabemedia.com
Multicultural mobile marketing solutions, SMS & MMS campaigns, mobile advertising & mobile website development. (AA/Hisp, estab 2006, empl 15, sales $3,000,000, cert: NMSDC)

7922 CCS/PR, Inc.
2888 Loker Avenue East Ste 316 Carlsbad, CA 92010
(760) 929-7514 Gayle Mestel President
Fax: (760) 438-5230
Email: gaylem@ccspr.com
Website: www.ccspr.com/
Marketing communications/consulting products & services: case studies, magazine articles, press releases/kits, video scripts, website content, blogs, PPTs, newsletters, marketing collateral, testimonial quotes, brochures, pitches. (Woman/White, estab 1966, empl 6, sales $1,405,334, cert: WBENC)

7923 Chica Intelligente LLC
5757 Wilshire Blvd Penthouse 3 Los Angeles, CA 90036
(323) 360-4191 Katrina Jefferson Owner
Fax:
Email: katrina@chicaintelligente.com
Website: www.chicaintelligente.com
Digital marketing, enhance or develop digital marketing programs through integrated experiential Marketing, online branding & increase target audience. (Woman/AA/Hisp, estab 2013, empl 2, sales $98,000, cert: CPUC)

7924 CLC Publicidad
14431 Ventura Blvd, Ste 545 Sherman Oaks, CA 91423
(818) 635-7318 Carlos Cordoba President
Fax:
Email: carlos@visionstrategyandinsights.com
Website: www.visionstrategyandinsights.com
Consumer research & insights into the Hispanic population, qualitative & quantitative research services. (Hisp, estab 1996, empl 5, sales $1,500,000, cert: NMSDC, CPUC)

7925 Coast to Coast Conferences & Events
100 W Broadway Ste 250 Long Beach, CA 90802
(562) 980-7566 Michelle Manire President
Fax: (562) 980-7560
Email: michelle@ctcconferences.com
Website: www.ctcconferences.com
Meeting & event management: site selection, contract negotiations, housing, on line registration, transportation, on site services, on site registration, exhibit management, event planning & destination management. (Woman/White, estab 1994, empl 4, sales $700,000, cert: State, WBENC)

7926 Cook & Schmid, LLC
740 13th St, Ste 502   San Diego, CA 92101
(619) 814-2370 Jon Schmid President
Fax: (619) 814-2375
Email: jschmid@cookandschmid.com
Website: www.cookandschmid.com
Public relations, advertising and marketing agency. (As-Pac/Hisp, estab 2006, empl 10, sales $1,006,305, cert: NMSDC, CPUC)

7927 Corporate Translations, Inc.
1300 Aviation Blvd   Redondo Beach, CA 90278
(310) 376-1400 Richard Gronbach President
Fax: (310) 376-1394
Email: rwg@CorporateTranslations.com
Website: www.CorporateTranslations.com
Provides native-speaking, technical language translation, multilingual document publishing, audio/video production & certified interpreting. (Woman/White, estab 1995, empl 10, sales $1,205,000, cert: State, CPUC)

7928 Cuadra Associates, Inc.
11835 W Olympic Blvd, Ste 855   Los Angeles, CA 90064
(310) 478-0066 Carlos Cuadra President
Fax: (310) 477-1078
Email: carlos@cuadra.com
Website: www.cuadra.com
Develop software, manage information collections, in both paper and electronic form, in libraries, museums, archives, and records departments. (Hisp, estab 1978, empl 22, sales , cert: State)

7929 Culturati Research & Consulting, Inc.
12625 High Bluff Dr, Ste 218   San Diego, CA 92130
(858)70500 Lisa Raggio Acct Exec
Fax:
Email: Lisa.Raggio@CulturatiResearch.com
Website: www.CulturatiResearch.com
Market research, custom research solutions. (Woman/Hisp, estab 2004, empl 18, sales $1,000,000,000, cert: CPUC)

7930 DM Connect LLC
4223 Glencoe Ave, Ste A-130 Marina Del Rey, CA 90292
(800) 778-2990 Dawn Perdew Managing Partner
Fax:
Email: accounting@dumontproject.com
Website: www.thedumontproject.com
Marketing Consulting Services. (Woman/White, estab 2008, empl 23, sales $1,700,000, cert: WBENC)

7931 DoubleShot Creative, LLC
499 Seaport Court Ste 205 Redwood City, CA 94063
(415) 992-7468 Kathy Hutton VP Strategy
Fax:
Email: kathy@doubleshotcreative.com
Website: www.doubleshotcreative.com
Creative & strategic marketing services, executive communications, marketing strategy and implementation, presentations, videos, messaging, campaign strategy, event creative concepts, social media, blogs, professional bios. (Woman/White, estab 2007, empl 2, sales $1,000,000, cert: WBENC)

7932 Elevate Planning
13575 Zivi Ave Chino, CA 91710
(951) 217-1028 Viviana Salvia Owner
Fax:
Email: viviana@elevateplanning.com
Website: www.elevateplanning.com
Experiential marketing & event planning. (Woman/White, estab 2003, empl 1, sales $85,000, cert: WBENC)

7933 Everfield Consulting, LLC
2075 W 235th Pl Torrance, CA 90501
(310) 251-7165 Delbara Dorsey Partner/Mktg Dir
Fax:
Email: deldorsey@everfieldconsulting.com
Website: www.everfieldconsulting.com
Marketing Consulting Services, Administrative & Management, Display Advertising, Advertising, Public Relations, Media Buying, Direct Mail Advertising, Advertising Material Distribution Services. (Woman/AA/As-Pac, estab 2011, empl 2, sales , cert: State, City, CPUC, WBENC)

7934 ExpoMarketing Group LLC
2741 Dow Ave Tustin, CA 92780
(949) 777-1051 Laurie Pennacchi CEO
Fax:
Email: laurie@expomarketing.com
Website: www.expomarketing.com
Trade show exhibits: custom rental & custom-built exhibits, portable exhibits & peripherals, large format graphics, program management & logistics, & in-house design & creative services. (Woman/White, estab 1991, empl 13, sales $2,596,339, cert: CPUC, WBENC)

7935 Freddie Georges Production Group
5595 Fresca Dr La Palma, CA 90623
(714) 367-9260 Frederique Georges CEO
Fax: (714) 367-9261
Email: freddieg@freddiegeorges.com
Website: www.freddiegeorges.com
Trade show & special events: design, fabrication, project management, rental solutions & logistical support. (Woman/White, estab 2001, empl 25, sales $8,570,000, cert: WBENC)

7936 Hard Hat Communications
77386 Preston Trail Palm Desert, CA 92211
(760) 772-6035 Beverly Voran Owner
Fax:
Email: hardhatcomm@verizon.net
Website:
Public affairs, group process facilitation, strategic planning, board development, fund development planning & implementation & translation services. (Woman/White, estab 1997, empl 1, sales $70,000, cert: State, CPUC)

7937 HispaniSpace LLC
2100 W Magnolia Blvd Ste A/B Burbank, CA 91506
(818) 843-0220 Mario X. Carrasco Partner
Fax: (818) 351-8294
Email: mario@thinknowresearch.com
Website: www.thinknowresearch.com
Online market research solutions for the U.S. Hispanic consumer. (Hisp, estab 2010, empl 8, sales $1,583,661, cert: NMSDC, CPUC)

7938 Hunter-Blyden, Katherine
P.O. Box 94893 Pasadena, CA 91104
(626) 344-8730 Katherine Hunter-Blyden Managing Dir
Fax: (270) 294-8730
Email: khb@katherinehunterblyden.com
Website: www.khbmarketinggroup.com
Develop marketing strategies, evaluate marketing channels & tactics & define programs that align with growth profitable goals. (Woman/AA, estab 2012, empl 1, sales , cert: CPUC)

7939 Ilana Ashley Events
24226 Park Granada Calabasas, CA 91302
(818) 963-8670 Ilana Rosenberg CEO
Fax:
Email: ilana@ilanaashleyevents.com
Website: www.IlanaAshleyEvents.com
Full-service event production, plan and design corporate events, gala affairs, holiday parties, soirées, weddings, and other social events. (Woman/White, estab 2013, empl 2, sales $108,476, cert: WBENC)

7940 InnovaSafe Technology Escrow Services
28502 Constellation Rd Valencia, CA 91355
(800) 239-3989 John Stulman CEO
Fax: (661) 295-5515
Email: jstulman@innovasafe.com
Website: www.innovasafe.com
Source Code Escrow
Software Escrow
Technology Escrow
Software Verification
Hardware Verification (Woman/White, estab 2001, empl 6, sales $800,000, cert: State)

7941 Innovate Marketing Group
300 S Raymond Ave Pasadena, CA 91105
(626) 817-9588 Amanda Ma CEO
Fax: (626) 628-1806
Email: amanda@innovatemkg.com
Website: www.innovatemkg.com
Experiential event & production agency, product launch, conferences, meetings, sponsorship activations, award & galas. (Woman/As-Pac, estab 2014, empl 3, sales , cert: State, NMSDC, CPUC, WBENC)

7942 JR Resources
1130 Camino Del Mar Ste H Del Mar, CA 92014
(858) 481-1074 Waren Katz Acct Exec
Fax: (858) 481-1284
Email: warren@jrresources.com
Website: www.jrresources.com
Promotional products & marketing services. (Woman, estab 1991, empl 10, sales $4,151,500, cert: CPUC, WBENC)

7943 Language Select, LLC.
7590 N Glenoaks Blvd, Ste 100   Los Angeles, CA 91504
(818) 394-3407 Pola Aghakhanians Cstmr care team
Fax: (818) 768-1811
Email: pa@languageselect.com
Website: www.languageselect.com
Simultaneous & consecutive interpreting services. (As-Pac/Hisp, estab 2009, empl 100, sales $11,700,000, cert: NMSDC)

7944 Latin Nation Live LLC
3245 N San Fernando Rd   Los Angeles, CA 90065
(213) 924-5683 Ricardo Gieseken President
Fax: (212) 271-0665
Email: ricardo@lnlagency.com
Website: www.lnlagency.com
Experiential Marketing, Diversity Marketing, Taste-maker/influencer marketing, Event production, Government affairs/tradeshows, Asset design & procurement, Brand Strategy, Brand Development, Shopper Marketing. (Hisp, estab 2008, empl 10, sales $1,000,000, cert: NMSDC)

7945 Liehr Marketing & Communications, Inc.
1899 Western Way Ste 400A Torrance, CA 90501
(310) 781-3727 Elisa Liehr President
Fax:
Email: eliehr@lmconline.net
Website: www.lmconline.net
Marketing & research, copywriting, design, interactive, video, web development, design & programing. (Woman/White, estab 1987, empl 6, sales $780,000, cert: WBENC)

7946 Lightbox Libraries
320 Hedge Rd   Menlo Park, CA 94025
(650) 298-4759 Cindy Lee founder
Fax:
Email: cindy.lee@lightboxlibraries.com
Website: www.lightboxlibraries.com
Lightbox Libraries is a custom photography and video production company. We specialize in producing On-Brand image libraries for all your Marcom materials, shooting both domestic and internationally. (Woman/As-Pac, estab 2011, empl 2, sales $1,954,051, cert: NMSDC)

7947 Livings Life Science Solutions, LLC
3446 Glen Ave   Carlsbad, CA 92010
(747) 777-2226 Eneetra Livings Owner
Fax:
Email: Eneetra@livingslifescience.com
Website: www.livingslifesciencesolutions.com
Strategic marketing, strategic business consulting, scientific & commercial planning, marketing operations & tactical execution. (Woman/AA, estab 2015, empl 1, sales $600,000, cert: NMSDC, NWBOC)

7948 Luth Research
1365 4th Avenue   SAN DIEGO, CA 92101
(619) 234-5884 Candice Hinds Assoc Dir, Business Dev
Fax: (619) 234-5888
Email: chinds@luthresearch.com
Website: www.luthresearch.com
Market research, enhanced data & data collection solutions, qualitative & quantitative research methodologies. (Woman/White, estab 1977, empl 90, sales , cert: WBENC)

7949 Marketing Maven Public Relations, Inc.
2390 C Las Posas Rd, Ste 479   Camarillo, CA 93010
(310) 994-7380 John Carnett Director, Business Devel
Fax: (310) 868-0222
Email: john@marketingmavenpr.com
Website: www.marketingmavenpr.com
Public Relations, Hispanic Marketing, Social Media Management, Digital Advertising, Deep Dive Research, Brand Analysis, Graphic Design, Media Traning, Clip Tracking, Event Execution. (Woman/Nat Ame, estab 2009, empl 13, sales $1,259,534, cert: State, CPUC, WBENC, 8(a))

7950 Meeting Planners Plus
3069 Taylor Way   Costa Mesa, CA 92626
(714) 668-1126 Rosa McArthur President
Fax: (714) 662-3769
Email: rlmcarthur@meetingplannersplus.com
Website: www.meetingplannersplus.com
Meeting & special event management; tradeshow production, seminars, conferences, retreats, board meetings. (Woman/AA, estab 1993, empl 1, sales $50,000, cert: CPUC)

7951 Meijun LLC
9888 Carroll Centre Rd Ste#210   San Diego, CA 92126
(619) 333-8698 Huy Ly
Fax:
Email: hly@meijun.cc
Website: www.meijun.cc
Web development & marketing agency, custom software solutions, web & mobile development, design & strategy, digital marketing services, SEO, content marketing & marketing automation integration. (As-Pac, estab 2011, empl 5, sales , cert: NMSDC, CPUC)

7952 Model People Inc
709 Stratford Ct   Del Mar, CA 92014
(858) 755-7150 Claire Brooks President
Fax: (858) 755-5757
Email: cbrooks@modelpeopleinc.com
Website: www.modelpeopleinc.com
Qualitative research, ethnographic research, consumer research, deep insights research, consumer video production, consumer brand consulting. (Woman/White, estab 2000, empl 3, sales $1,400,000, cert: WBENC)

7953 Multi-Cultural Convention Services Network (MCCSN)
212 Sweetwood St   San Diego, CA 92114
(619) 265-2561 Clara Carter CEO
Fax:
Email: info@mccsn.com
Website: www.mccsn.com
Meeting & event management, hotel sourcing & contract negotiations & business consulting services. (Woman/AA, estab 2004, empl 1, sales $62,471, cert: CPUC)

7954　Outward Media, Inc.
9229 Sunset Blvd, Ste 410　Los Angeles, CA 90069
(310) 274-5312　Paula Chiocchi President
Fax: (310) 274-4284
Email: paula@outwardmedia.com
Website: www.outwardmedia.com
Email marketing; creative design, deployment, statistical reporting & campaign management. (Woman/White, estab 1998, empl 8, sales $5,000,000, cert: WBENC)

7955　Parle Enterprises, Inc.
800 Airport Blvd, Ste 21　Burlingame, CA 94010
(415) 467-3100　Sharon Flaxman CEO
Fax: (415) 467-7103
Email: sharon@parle.com
Website: www.parleinnovation.com
Media, marketing sponsorships, advertising, oppportunity programs, promotional marketing. (Woman/Hisp, estab 1997, empl 8, sales $1,400,000, cert: NMSDC, CPUC)

7956　PLAN C Agency
120 E 8th St Ste 912　Los Angeles, CA 90014
(310) 492-5298　Giancarlo Pacheco President
Fax: (213) 386-5698
Email: giancarlo@plancagency.com
Website: www.plancagency.com
Multicultural marketing & public relations agency with expertise reaching Asian American Market. (As-Pac, estab 2003, empl 15, sales $2,000,000, cert: CPUC)

7957　ProExhibits
48571 Milmont Dr　Fremont, CA 94538
(916) 364-9013　Cheryl Borsh Acct Exec
Fax: (408) 734-3698
Email: CBorsh@ProExhibits.com
Website: www.proexhibits.com
Trade show exhibit & events. (Woman/White, estab 1987, empl 40, sales $1,040,000, cert: CPUC)

7958　Purpose Generation LLC
535 Mission St 14th Fl　San Francisco, CA 94105
(917) 243-4777　Nellie Morris Co-Founder
Fax:
Email: nellie@purposegeneration.com
Website: www.purposegeneration.com/
Millennial marketing, market research, millennials, gen Y, project management, consulting, strategy, consumer insights, quantitative research, product sampling, product co-creation, quantitative research, influencer strategy. (Woman/White, estab 2013, empl 4, sales $758,280, cert: WBENC, NWBOC)

7959　Q & A Research, Inc.
64 Digital Dr　Novato, CA 94949
(415) 883-1188　Warren Pino
Fax: (415) 883-1344
Email: warren.pino@qar.com
Website: www.qar.com
Quantitative & qualitative market research, web surveys, telephone interviewing, mail surveys, focus groups & mystery shopping. (Hisp, estab 1993, empl 83, sales $7,127,000, cert: CPUC)

7960　RED Company
10323 Los Alamitos Blvd　Long Beach, CA 90720
(562) 498-1270　Carmela Roth President
Fax: (775) 743-7095
Email: carmela.roth@redcompany.com
Website: www.redcompany.com
Meeting & event planning: site review, contract negotiation, vendor relations, sponsorship cultivation to onsite management, ground transportation, registration services, staffing, hotel block/rooming lists, hospitality, activities. (Woman/White, estab 2007, empl 22, sales $10,600,000, cert: CPUC, WBENC)

7961　Red Kite Business Advisors LLC
3525 Del Mar Heights Rd, Ste 202　San Diego, CA 92130
(858) 232-4555　Evelyn Olson Lamden Principal
Fax: (858) 792-7331
Email: evelyn@redkitesite.com
Website: www.redkitesite.com
Marketing, advertising, public speaking, seminars, workshops, strategic planning, brand assessment & development, integrated campaign strategies, media plan development, online & traditional marketing. (Woman/As-Pac, estab 2007, empl 1, sales $60,473, cert: CPUC, WBENC)

7962　RevOne Design, Inc.
1649B Adrian Rd　Burlingame, CA 94010
(650) 468-2996　Sean Carlin Dir Business Dev
Fax: (650) 779-5892
Email: sean@revonedesign.com
Website: www.revonedesign.com
Graphic & Production Design, Photography & Photo Retouching, Digital/Web & Print Communications, Creative Concepting & Campaign Design & Copywriting. (Woman/Hisp, estab 2011, empl 7, sales $300,000, cert: NMSDC)

7963　RMD Group Inc.
2311 E South St　Long Beach, CA 90805
(562) 866-9288　Laura Milanes COO
Fax: (979) 543-0072
Email: laura@rmdgroupinc.com
Website: www.rmdgroupinc.com
Experiential Marketing, Digital & Social Media, Large Format Graphic Printing, Vehicle Fabrication, Trade Show Design, Trade Show Booth Builder, Millwork, Data Collection. (Hisp, estab 1993, empl 25, sales $6,000,000, cert: NMSDC)

7964　Ruiz Strategies
1900 Ave of the Stars Ste 1800　Los Angeles, CA 90067
(310) 853-3605　Michele Ruiz President
Fax: -
Email: inquiries@ruizstrategies.com
Website: www.RuizStrategies.com
Develop & execute transformational content messaging strategies, social media, new media, traditional media & virtual technologies. (Woman/Hisp, estab 2011, empl 12, sales $1,036,000, cert: NMSDC, CPUC, WBENC)

7965 Samantha Smith Productions LLC
2325 Third St Ste 407 San Francisco, CA 94107
(415) 626-7925 Samantha Smith Owner
Fax: (415) 626-4154
Email: samantha@samanthasmithproductions.com
Website: www.samanthasmithproductions.com
Meeting & event planning. (Woman, estab 2003, empl 5, sales $1,500,000, cert: WBENC)

7966 Sax Productions Inc.
1055 W 7th St 33rd Fl PH Los Angeles, CA 90017
(213) 232-1682 Tamara Keller COO
Fax: (602) 899-1698
Email: tamara@saxproductions.com
Website: www.saxproductions.com
Brand marketing & storytelling, digital strategy, innovation & public relation. (Woman/AA, estab 2012, empl 6, sales $83,602, cert: NMSDC, WBENC)

7967 Shiloh Event Management
P.O. Box 2772 Santa Clara, CA 95050
(408) 899-5464 Huong Burrow Director of Events
Fax: (866) 542-2071
Email: Huong@shiloh-events.com
Website: www.shiloh-events.com
Event strategies, event production, event marketing solutions & event management services. (As-Pac, estab 2013, empl 3, sales $28,000, cert: NMSDC)

7968 Specialized Marketing Services, Inc.
3421 W Segerstrom Ave Santa Ana, CA 92704
(714) 955-5450 John Snook Exec VP
Fax: (949) 553-0891
Email: jsnook@teamsms.com
Website: www.teamsms.com
Strategic marketing devel, copywriting, print mgmt, database mgmt/processing, mailing svcs, warehousing, fulfillment/hand assembly, internet application, telemarketing. (Woman/Hisp, estab 1988, empl 23, sales $8,161,000, cert: WBENC)

7969 Strategic Business Communications
12175 Dearborn Pl Poway, CA 92064
(858) 679-1805 Jim Hernandez President
Fax: (858) 668-3142
Email: jhernandez@sbcinc.com
Website: www.sbcinc.info
Sales & Marketing Training & Consulting, Meeting & Event Planning. (As-Pac, estab 1987, empl 10, sales $2,400,000, cert: NMSDC)

7970 Sundial Marketing Research, Inc.
30 Center St San Rafael, CA 94901
(415) 200-1461 Nancy Kelber President
Fax: (877) 295-3615
Email: nancy@sundialresearch.com
Website: www.sundialresearch.com
Market research to the medical device, pharmaceutical & biotechnology industries. (Woman/White, estab 2010, empl 6, sales $2,500,000, cert: WBENC)

7971 Undisclosed Location, Inc
5761 Sonoma Mountain Rd Santa Rosa, CA 95404
(415) 295-4920 Barbara Gorder President
Fax: (847) 556-6489
Email: barbara.gorder@unlo.com
Website: www.unlo.com
Marketing, advertising & communications solutions, strategic brand advertising, mobile marketing consulting & content development, website development, packaging design, presentation consulting & event promotions. (Woman/White, estab 2003, empl 10, sales $1,000,000, cert: WBENC)

7972 Valencia, Perez & Echeveste
1605 Hope St, Ste 250 S. Pasadena, CA 91030
(626) 403-3200 Patricia Perez President
Fax: (626) 403-1700
Email: patricia@vpepr.com
Website: www.vpepr.com
Public relations & marketing communications. (Hisp, estab 1987, empl 25, sales , cert: NMSDC)

7973 Vic Salazar Enterprises, LLC
2514 Jamacha Rd, Ste 502-21 El Cajon, CA 92019
(619) 517-4744 Vic Salazar President
Fax: (619) 334-4156
Email: vicsalazar@cox.net
Website: www.vicsalazar.com
Public Relations, Hispanic Marketing, Video Production, Media Training, Advertising, Crisis Communications, Hard Drive Storage, Printing, Labeling, Promotional Items, Event Production. (Hisp, estab 2008, empl 1, sales $12,000, cert: CPUC)

Colorado

7974 AC Mechanical & Engineering, Inc.
5160 Parfet St, Ste B2 Wheatridge, CO 80033
(303) 432-9700 Vince Carabelos VP
Fax: (303) 467-7795
Email: vince@hvacdenver.com
Website: www.hvacdenver.com
Heating, Air Conditioning, Ventilation Service & Installation Contractors (Woman/White, estab 1999, empl 6, sales $850,000, cert: State)

7975 Andavo Meetings & Incentives
6430 S. Fiddlers Green Circle Ste 220 Greenwood Village, CO 80111
(720) 398-5507 Brenda Rivers President
Fax: (303) 721-1762
Email: brivers@andavomeetings.com
Website: www.andavomeetings.com
Meetings, incentives & event planning & management. (Woman/White, estab 1982, empl 10, sales $10,200,000, cert: WBENC)

7976 Egg Strategy, Inc.
1360 Walnut St Ste 102 Boulder, CO 80302
(303) 546-9311 Matthew Sommers Dir of Ops
Fax:
Email: boulderinfo@eggstrategy.com
Website: www.eggstrategy.com
Marketing consulting, innovation, brand strategy, market research, consumer insight. (Woman/White, estab 2005, empl 50, sales $10,000,000, cert: WBENC)

7977 MorSports & Events, Inc. dba MorEvents
3333 S Bannock St Ste 790 Englewood, CO 80110
(720) 381-5000 Betsy Mordecai President
Fax: (720) 381-5005
Email: betsy@morevents.com
Website: www.morevents.com
Event planning, meeting coordination & hospitality mgmt.
(Woman/White, estab 1996, empl 12, sales $3,500,000,
cert: WBENC)

7978 Translation Excellence
2620 S Parker Rd Ste 210 Aurora, CO 80014
(720) 325-0459 Nisar Nikzad President
Fax: (720) 325-1563
Email: info@translationexcellence.com
Website: www.translationexcellence.com
Translation, interpretation, interpretation equipment &
language classes. (As-Ind, estab 2010, empl 5, sales
$422,000, cert: City, 8(a))

7979 Vladimir Jones
P.O. Box 387 Colorado Springs, CO 80901
(719) 473-0704 Trudy Rowe CFO
Fax: (719) 473-0754
Email: trowe@vladimirjones.com
Website: www.vladimirjones.com
Marketing services: strategic planning, research, advertising
& public relations, creative development & production,
television, print, radio, out of home, digital & on-line
communications, media planning & buying, account
planning. (Woman/White, estab 1970, empl 71, sales
$21,863,320, cert: NWBOC)

Connecticut

7980 Adams & Knight, Inc.
80 Avon Meadow Lane Avon, CT 06001
(860) 676-2300 Marc McFarland SVP Financial
Services
Fax: (860) 676-1940
Email: marc.mcfarland@adamsknight.com
Website: www.adamsknight.com
Integrated marketing: research, strategy, brand develop-
ment, advertising, design, collateral development, public
relations, social media, experiential, event marketing,
digital experiences including websites & interactive tools,
SEO/SEM. (Woman/White, estab 1987, empl 39, sales
$8,547,385, cert: State)

7981 BCM Media
30 Old Kings Highway S Darien, CT 06820
(203) 326-1477 Brenda McKenna Managing Dir
Fax:
Email: bmckenna@bcmmedia.biz
Website: www.bcmmedia.biz/
Advertising, Media Consulting, Media Planning, Negotia-
tions, B2B Advertising, B2C Advertising, Trade Advertising,
Multimedia Planning and Buying, Global Media Planning,
National Media Planning, Local Media Planning, Public
Relations. (Woman/White, estab 2013, empl 9, sales
$855,047, cert: WBENC)

7982 CYMA Systems Inc.
360 Tolland Turnpike #2D Manchester, CT 06042
(860) 791-6356 Nisha Sunil HR Mgr
Fax: (860) 791-6372
Email: hr@cymasys.com
Website: www.cymasys.com
CYMA Systems Inc. is a professional staffing and solutions firm headquartered in the Greater Hartford Area,
CT. We provide customers with leading edge technology
solutions and augment their IT staff needs. (As-Ind,
estab 2006, empl 179, sales $16,800,000, cert: NMSDC)

7983 domo domo IMG
435 Elm St Monroe, CT 06468
(203) 270-3515 Deb Adams CEO
Fax: (203) 270-3516
Email: judy@domomarketing.com
Website: www.domomarketing.com
Brand strategy & optimization, strategic positioning,
new product launches, line extensions, NPD innovation,
trend & market analyses. (Woman, estab 1996, empl 16,
sales $1,840,000, cert: WBENC)

7984 Peralta Illustration & Design LLC
431 Howe Ave Shelton, CT 06484
(203) 513-2222 Ramon Peralta
Fax: (303) 292-1934
Email: ramon@peraltadesign.com
Website: www.peraltadesign.com
Digital interactive design: web development, web
applications, corporate identity & marketing, branding.
(Hisp, estab 2003, empl 6, sales , cert: NMSDC)

7985 Touchpoint Integrated Communications, LLC
16 Thorndal Circle Darien, CT 06820
(203) 665-7705 Karen Kluger CEO
Fax:
Email: kkluger@tpointmedia.com
Website: www.tpointmedia.com
Communication: broadcast, print, digital, social, mobile,
email, direct mail. (Woman/White, estab 2010, empl 40,
sales $8,100,000, cert: WBENC)

7986 TruEvents LLC
111 Bradley Rd Madison, CT 06443
(800) 363-8122 James Cash President
Fax: (877) 363-8122
Email: james.cash@be-tru.com
Website: www.be-tru.com
Marketing, Graphic Design, Creative Design, Web, Retail
Packaging, Retail Strategy, Digital, Digital Store Displays,
Retail POS, Merchandising,
Tradeshows, Meeting Production, Event Production,
Ideation, Strategy. (Woman/White, estab 2000, empl 12,
sales $2,082,729, cert: WBENC)

District of Columbia

7987 Delucchi Plus
2101 L St. NW Washington, DC 20037
(202) 349-4000 Jay Vilar VP
Fax:
Email: jvilar@delucchiplus.com
Website: www.delucchiplus.com/
Global strategic communications, research & brand
strategy, digital marketing & PR. (Woman/White, estab
2007, empl 41, sales $11,200,000, cert: State)

7988 Jones Public Affairs
      1420 K St NW, Ste 1050 Washington, DC 20005
      (202) 591-4000 Carrie Jones Principal, Managing Dir
      Fax:
      Email: carrie@jpa.com
      Website: www.jpa.com
Public Relations, Health Communications, Influencer
Relations (Media relations, advocacy engagement, social &
digital media, policy & issues advocacy, stakeholder
engagement). (Woman/White, estab 2007, empl 21, sales
$7,700,000, cert: NWBOC)

7989 OmniStudio, Inc.
      1140 19th St NW, Ste 320 Washington, DC 20036
      (202) 785-9605 Eileen Kessler President
      Fax: (202) 785-9609
      Email: ekessler@omnistudio.com
      Website: www.omnistudio.com
Corporate & product identity, publications & periodicals,
annual reports, collateral material, advertisements &
direct mail, exhibits & trade show support, conference &
meeting packages, directories & data publishing. (Woman/
White, estab 1980, empl 14, sales $1,890,025, cert:
WBENC)

7990 P.A.L.S. LLC
      1808 I St NW Washington, DC 20006
      (202) 396-7257 Richette Haywood Managing
      Member
      Fax: (202) 396-7258
      Email: richettehaywood@palsllc.biz
      Website: www.palsllc.biz
Marketing & public relations, event management, administration support, concierge. (Woman/AA, estab 1995, empl
3, sales $350,000, cert: State)

7991 Premier Consultants International, Inc.
      1020 16th St NW Ste 201 Washington, DC 20036
      (202) 319-1211 Renard H. Marable
      Fax: (202) 265-1743
      Email: rmarable@premiercon.com
      Website: www.premiercon.com
Marketing & business development services. (AA, estab
2000, empl 1, sales , cert: State, City)

7992 Scott Circle Communications, Inc.
      1900 L St, NW Ste 705 Washington, DC 20036
      (202) 207-3645 Laura Gross Principal
      Fax:
      Email: info@scottcircle.com
      Website: www.scottcircle.com
Public relations & event-planning. (Woman/White, estab
2006, empl 3, sales , cert: WBENC)

7993 SEW, Inc.
      717 D St NW Ste 300 Washington, DC 20004
      (202) 403-4739 Thedis Miller CEO
      Fax: (202) 628-6618
      Email: tmiller@4sew.com
      Website: www.4sew.com
Human capital mgmt svcs, customer relationship mgmt
(CRM) & [roject mgmt (PMP), large team operations
support, business planning, executive coaching, administrative support. (Woman/AA, estab 2004, empl 1, sales
$104,000, cert: NMSDC)

7994 Swanson Communications
      1025 Vermont Ave NW Ste 1005 Washington, DC
      20005
      (202) 783-5500 Kelly Swanson President
      Fax: (202) 783-5516
      Email: kswanson@swansonpr.com
      Website: www.swansonpr.com
Marketing & public relations, business development,
communications outreach & relationship building.
(Woman/White, estab 2006, empl 3, sales $372,849,
cert: State)

7995 The Webster Group
      5185 MacArthur Blvd, NW Ste 250 Washington,
      DC 20016
      (202) 741-1271 Wendy Drake CEO
      Fax: (202) 237-0036
      Email: wendy@webstergroupinc.com
      Website: www.webstergroupinc.com
Event Planning & Management Services, Conferences,
Trade Shows, Workshops, Training, Meetings, Product
Launches, Annual Retreats, Galas. (Woman, estab 1995,
empl 17, sales $2,177,443, cert: WBENC)

7996 Washingtonian Custom Media
      1828 L St NW, Ste 200 Washington, DC 20036
      (202) 862-3500 James Byles President
      Fax: (202) 221-7318
      Email: jbyles@washingtonian.com
      Website: www.washingtoniancustommedia.com
Communications strategy, print & digital publications,
magazines, brochures, white papers, annual reports,
content development, content strategy, audience
development, writing, editing, website design, graphic
design, website development. (Woman/White, estab
1965, empl 80, sales $10,000,000, cert: WBENC)

Delware

7997 Barron Marketing Communications
      833 Washington St Wilmington, DE 19801
      (302) 658-1627 Patricia D. Barron President
      Fax: (302) 658-5798
      Email: pbarron@barronmarketing.com
      Website: www.barronmarketing.com
Mktg print communications: direct mail, catalogs,
displays, premiums, POS, broadcast, packaging, media,
outdoor. (Woman/White, estab 1976, empl 9, sales
$1,000,000, cert: State)

Florida

7998 A-Plus Meetings and Incentives
      901 Ponce de Leon Blvd. Ste 600 Coral Gables, FL
      33134
      (786) 888-3203 Jay Klein COO
      Fax: (305) 445-7545
      Email: jklein@aplusmeetings.com
      Website: www.aplusmeetings.com
Meeting planning, online registration, venue selection,
audio-visual management, production development,
airline travel, ground transportation & hospitality desk
staffing. (Woman/White, estab 1993, empl 21, sales
$10,382,504, cert: CPUC, WBENC)

7999   Avenue Event Group LLC
501 N Orlando Avenue Ste 313-312 Orlando, FL 32789 Orlando, FL 32801
(650) 784-0175 Sean Hughes Mktg
Fax:
Email: sean@avenueeventgroup.com
Website: www.avenueeventgroup.com
National event planning & logistics services: Venue Selection, Meeting Logistics, Hotel Coordination, Group Transportation, Vendor Procurement, Unique Entertainment. (Woman/White, estab 2013, empl 5, sales $1,300,000, cert: WBENC)

8000   Chasm Communications, Inc.
13045 W Linebaugh Ave Ste 101 Tampa, FL 33626
(813) 283-0908 Jennifer Williams President
Fax:
Email: jwilliams@chasmcommunications.com
Website: www.chasmcommunications.com
Marketing & web design, app design, digital marketing & traditional print marketing. (Woman, estab 2006, empl 7, sales $845,317, cert: WBENC)

8001   Clarocision Research & Marketing
2818 N University Dr   Coral Springs, FL 33065
(954) 741-2234 Karlene Facey CEO
Fax:
Email: kfacey@crmfirm.com
Website: www.crmmfrm.com
Focus Groups & Surveys, diverse consumer & healthcare panels, research tools & processes, fully-equipped facilities, Taste testing. (Woman/AA, estab 2007, empl 30, sales $1,000,000, cert: State)

8002   Cordova Marketing Group
2702 Wright Ave   Winter Park, FL 32789
(321) 972-8181 Tom Cordova President
Fax:
Email: tom@covacova.com
Website: www.covacova.com
Multi-culutral Marketing, Sponsorship, Broadcasting, Naming Rights, Events, Ticket Sales, Community Outreach, Executive Recruitment. (Hisp, estab 1998, empl 2, sales $375,000, cert: NMSDC)

8003   Creative Zing Promotion Group
189 S Orange Ave Ste 1130a Orlando, FL 32801
(407) 514-0044 Pamela D Aniello President
Fax: (800) 493-3977
Email: pamela@creativezing.com
Website: www.creativezing.com
Integrated marketing & promotions, complex contest & sweepstakes administration. (Woman/White, estab 2007, empl 9, sales $1,300,000, cert: WBENC)

8004   Detail Planners, LLC
1452 Distant Oaks Dr   Wesley Chapel, FL 33543
(813) 991-1348 Anita Jentzen, CMP, CMM President
Fax: (813) 464-2873
Email: anita@detailplanners.com
Website: www.detailplanners.com
Plan & manage corporate meetings & events. (Woman/White, estab 2004, empl 5, sales $1,900,000, cert: WBENC)

8005   EuroAmerican IP, LLC
2511 NW 16th Lane Bay#2 Pompano Beach, FL 33064
(866) 972-6467 Tami Dana Mgr of Ops
Fax: (954) 977-2949
Email: tami@euroamericanproducts.com
Website: www.EuroAmericanProducts.com
Manufacturers Reps/Distribution based business that provides various industries and government facilities with our unique line of products within the medical, outdoor and health & beauty arenas. (Woman/White, estab 2007, empl 15, sales $500,000, cert: State)

8006   Executive Meeting Management, Inc.
6996 Piazza Grande Ave #314 Orlando, FL 32835
(407) 399-7681 Heather Wilson President
Fax: (407) 641-9151
Email: hwilson@execmm.com
Website: www.execmm.com
Meeting management. (Woman/White, estab 2004, empl 1, sales $1,026,779, cert: WBENC)

8007   Fortes Laboratories
1005 W Busch Blvd Ste 101 Tampa, FL 33612
(813) 390-6536 Steven Seigel CFO
Fax: (813) 932-1107
Email: info@forteslabs.com
Website: www.forteslabs.com
Drug testing, national forensic, toxicology laboratory, drug & alcohol testing. (Woman/White, estab 1994, empl 15, sales , cert: State)

8008   HAS Art Solutions LLC
3139 Philips Hwy, Ste 100   Jacksonville, FL 32207
(904) 503-9800 Heather Sams President
Fax: (904) 503-9801
Email: HASams@HASartsolutions.com
Website: www.HASartsolutions.com
We are an art consulting, art design, and procurement firm with over 25 years of experience in providing clients with solutions to their aesthetic needs. We provide artwork and artwork programs to all types of businesses, from interior design (Woman/White, estab 2010, empl 7, sales $355,000, cert: State)

8009   HMB Enterprises LLC
5401 S Kirkman Rd, Ste 310   Orlando, FL 32819
(678) 887-7670 Harry Bailey President
Fax: (888) 233-6455
Email: hbailey@hmbenterprises.net
Website: www.hmbenterprises.net
Healthcare Risk Management System (HRMS) Airborne Pathogen Elimination system (KIlls MRCR, Staph and many other airborne pathogens under 3 microns) Purlalizer(KIlls MRCR, Staph (AA, estab 2005, empl 5, sales $425,000, cert: State, NMSDC)

8010   Imagine Enterprises International
8600 Commodity Circle #109   Orlando, FL 32819
(407) 409-7310 Heidi Brumbach CEO
Fax:
Email: heidi@technischcreative.com
Website: www.technischcreative.com
Event Planning & Production, Venue Research & Selection, Venue Negotiation & Contracting, Room Block Management, Speaker Selection, Event Marketing, Food & Beverage Management, Event Registration, Audio Visual. (Woman/White, estab 1999, empl 4, sales , cert: WBENC)

8011 Ingenium Research Boutique, Inc.
       8057 Solitaire Ct   Orlando, FL 32836
       (407) 309-2742 Maria Parra President
       Fax:
       Email: mlparra@ingeniumresearch.com
       Website: www.ingeniumresearch.com
Qualitative marketing research, focus groups, ethnographic interviews, in-depth interviews, shop-alongs,
qualitative techniques. (Woman/Hisp, estab 2011, empl 2,
sales $500,000, cert: WBENC)

8012 Inktel Direct
       13975 NW 58th Ct   Miami Lakes, FL 33014
       (305) 523-1129 Jason Schlenker VP Business Dev
       Fax: (305) 827-0341
       Email: jason.schlenker@inktel.com
       Website: www.inktel.com
Direct marketing: call center, fulfillment, direct mail,
database marketing. (Hisp, estab 1997, empl 580, sales ,
cert: NMSDC)

8013 ITC TRANSLATIONS USA INC
       900 East Indiantown Road, Ste 302   Jupiter, FL
       33477
       (561) 746-6242 Allison Paxton Business Dev Mgr
       Fax: (561) 746-6242
       Email: a.paxton@itcglobaltranslations.com
       Website: www.itcglobaltranslations.com
Technical, scientific & communication translation services
in over 25 languages. (Woman/White, estab 1999, empl
30, sales $5,500,000, cert: WBENC)

8014 JCQ Services, Inc
       7200 Lake Ellenor Dr, Ste 130   Orlando, FL 32809
       (407) 889-4944 Eliana Fuguet Project Coord
       Fax: (407) 889-9244
       Email: eliana@jcqservices.com
       Website: www.jcqservices.com
We are a complete renovation subcontractor, from flooring
to ceiling and moving, storage and transportation and
selective demolition (Hisp, estab 2000, empl 25, sales
$1,550,000, cert: State)

8015 Key Lime Interactive
       8750 NW 36th St, Ste 475   Doral, FL 33178
       (305) 809-0555 Ania Rodriguez President
       Fax:
       Email: accounting@keylimeinteractive.com
       Website: www.keylimeinteractive.com
Qualitative & quantitative research, usability testing,
mobile research, card sorting, remote intercept testing,
expert reviews, ethnography, competitive benchmarking,
eye tracking, shop along. (Woman/Hisp, estab 2009, empl
17, sales $3,686,319, cert: NMSDC, WBENC)

8016 Lingua Franca Translations, LLC
       1111 Brickell Ave Ste 1140 Miami, FL 33156
       (305) 913-7193 Marcela Arbelaez CEO
       Fax: (630) 985-7300
       Email: marcela.arbelaez@lftranslations.com
       Website: www.lftranslations.com
Translations, interpretations & transcriptions into and from
over 240 languages. (Woman/Hisp, estab 2011, empl 3,
sales $138,000, cert: NMSDC)

8017 M. Gill & Associates, Inc.
       4770 Biscayne Blvd, Ste 1050   Miami, FL 33137
       (305) 576-7888 Marie Gill President
       Fax: (305) 576-0089
       Email: info@mgillonline.com
       Website: www.mgillonline.com
Management & public relations consulting. (Woman/
AA, estab 1990, empl 10, sales , cert: State)

8018 Media Global Group, LLC
       2000 Ponce de Leon Blvd 102 Coral Gables, FL
       33134
       (786) 431-4555 Maria Gonzalez-Pacheco CEO
       Fax: (786) 431-4554
       Email: mgonzalez@mggmedia.com
       Website: www.mggmedia.com
Digital Media Outlets & Out-of-Home (OOH), TV, Radio
& Print Media. (Woman/Hisp, estab 2008, empl 10, sales
$3,600,000, cert: NMSDC)

8019 Nobles Research, Inc.
       8321 Golden Prairie Dr   Tampa, FL 33647
       (813) 977-7700 Kevin Nobles President
       Fax: (813) 971-0346
       Email: kevin@noblesresearch.com
       Website: www.noblesresearch.com
Qualitative research. (AA, estab 2001, empl 1, sales
$270,000, cert: NMSDC)

8020 Orlando Conference Management Group, Inc.
       13124 Sunkiss Loop   Windermere, FL 34786
       (407) 948-5706 Lori Lombardi Ryan President
       Fax: (484) 952-5706
       Email: llr@ocmg.net
       Website: www.ocmg.net
Meeting management, logistics & events planning.
(Woman, estab 1993, empl 2, sales , cert: State, WBENC)

8021 Paragon Events, Inc.
       352 NE 3rd Ave   Delray Beach, FL 33444
       (561) 243-3073 Renee Radabaugh CEO
       Fax: (561) 274-4849
       Email: info@paragon-events.com
       Website: www.paragon-events.com
Meeting & special events. (Woman/White, estab 1989,
empl 12, sales $5,514,280, cert: WBENC)

8022 Prestige Auto Specialists
       4250 St. Charles Way   Boca Raton, FL 33434
       (954) 428-6689 Marcello Serrato President
       Fax: (954) 428-6684
       Email: mserrato@prestigeautous.com
       Website: www.prestigeautous.com
Event production, media fleet management, marketing
& communication. (Hisp, estab 1985, empl 30, sales
$52,000,000, cert: NMSDC)

8023 Quest Corporation of America
       17220 Camelot Court   Land O'Lakes, FL 34638
       (813) 926-2942 Sharlene Francois President
       Fax: (813) 926-2962
       Email: corporate@usa.com.com
       Website: www.QCAusa.com
Public relations, partnering, marketing, creative services, media, publications, printing, aerial photography,
advertising, technology support, web design & data
storage, transportation support svcs. (Woman/White,
estab 1995, empl 14, sales $3,075,300, cert: State)

8024 RBB Public Relations LLC
      355 Alhambra Cir Ste 800 Coral Gables, FL 33134
      (305) 448-7450 Marsha Rhymer Controller
      Fax: (305) 448-5027
      Email: marsha.rhymer@rbbpr.com
      Website: www.rbbpr.com
Marketing, Public Relations. (Woman/White, estab 2001,
empl 41, sales $6,401,984, cert: WBENC)

8025 Republica, LLC
      2153 Coral Way 5th Fl Miami, FL 33145
      (786) 347-4700 Jorge A. Plasencia CEO
      Fax: (786) 346-7479
      Email: jp@republica.net
      Website: www.republica.net
Branding, advertising, promotions, digital and communications company. (Hisp, estab 2006, empl 100, sales
$14,500,000, cert: State, NMSDC)

8026 ROUGE 24, Inc.
      5279 Grande Palm Cir   Delray Beach, FL 33484
      (561) 213-0260 Todd Victor Dir of Accts
      Fax:
      Email: Todd.Victor@Rouge24.com
      Website: www.rouge24.com
Brand Strategy, Identity Design, Packaging, Style Guides,
Adaptation, Process Management, Marketing Materials,
In-Store Signage. (Woman/White, estab 2009, empl 1,
sales $2,500,000, cert: WBENC)

8027 SFM Services, Inc.
      9700 NW 79th Ave   Hialeah Gardens, FL 33016
      (305) 818-2424 Christian Infante VP
      Fax: (305) 818-3510
      Email: cinfante@sfmservices.com
      Website: www.sfmservices.com
Complete janitorial services, landscape services, and
security guard services. (Hisp, estab 1987, empl 480, sales
$12,000,000, cert: NMSDC)

8028 Trickey Jennus, Inc.
      5300 W Cypress St Ste 285 Tampa, FL 33607
      (813) 831-2325 Kathie Craft Comella COO
      Fax: (813) 831-2595
      Email: kathie@trickeyjennus.com
      Website: www.trickeyjennus.com
Strategy review & rational, collaborative account planning,
strategic media planning, specialized direct marketing,
campaign development, web services, social media
strategy, creative services. (Woman/White, estab 2005,
empl 7, sales $1,015,266, cert: State)

8029 Vistra Communications, LLC
      18315 N US Highway 41   Lutz, FL 33549
      (813) 961-4700 BRIAN A. BUTLER President
      Fax: (813) 961-4702
      Email: BRIAN@CONSULTVISTRA.COM
      Website: www.ConsultVistra.com
Public relations, strategic communications, homeland
security, information technology, management consulting,
training & curriculum development. (AA, estab 2007, empl
69, sales $9,900,000, cert: City, NMSDC, 8(a))

8030 Wragg & Casas Public Relations, Inc.
      1221 Brickell Ave Ste 730 Miami, FL 33131
      (305) 372-1234 Ramon Casas Accting Supervisor
      Fax: (305) 372-8565
      Email: rcasas@wraggcasas.com
      Website: www.wraggcasas.com
Strategic counseling, media relations, reputation & crisis
management, brand visibility & public affairs. (Hisp,
estab 1991, empl 10, sales $1,300,000, cert: State,
NMSDC)

Georgia

8031 Benchmarc360, Inc.
      6340 Sugarloaf Pkwy Ste 200 Atlanta, GA 30097
      (678) 291-0011 Ann Godi CEO
      Fax: (678) 291-9020
      Email: ann@benchmarc360.com
      Website: www.benchmarc360.com
Strategic solutions, strategic event marketing, conference, meeting & event mgmt, destination mgmt, trade
shows, incentive programs, site selection & contract
negotiations. (Woman/White, estab 1992, empl 23, sales
$32,800,000, cert: NWBOC)

8032 CMT Agency
      1417 Dutch Valley Place Ste A Atlanta, GA 30324
      (404) 233-4644 Shelly Justice CEO
      Fax: (404) 233-8863
      Email: sjustice@cmtagency.com
      Website: www.cmtagency.com
Spokesmodels, event staffing, brand ambassadors,
product demonstrators, celebrity look-a-likes & corporate presenters. (Woman/White, estab 2001, empl 11,
sales $2,119,677, cert: WBENC)

8033 Colour One O One, Inc.
      4995 Avalon Ridge Pkwy Ste 100 Norcross, GA
      30071
      (404) 350-1700 Taylor Lepera Sales Assoc
      Fax: (404) 350-1708
      Email: tlepera@studio101.com
      Website: www.colour101.com
Strategic marketing programs for the retail, food,
beverage, sports & entertainment industries. (Woman/
White, estab 1983, empl 9, sales $697,000, cert:
WBENC)

8034 Creative Juice LLC
      75 Marietta St, Ste 503   Atlanta, GA 30303
      (404) 947-8599 Octavia Gilmore Owner
      Fax: (215) 965-1513
      Email: octavia@itscreativejuice.com
      Website: www.itscreativejuice.com
Graphic design & web design services, logo, branding,
print design, infographics, brochures, tradeshow
graphics, marketing, web design & development,
Wordpress, email marketing, copy writing, blogging,
local SEO & motion graphics. (Woman/AA/Hisp, estab
2013, empl 4, sales $315,000, cert: City)

8035 Folio, Inc. Design & Illustration
1145 Zonolite Rd NE, Ste 2   Atlanta, GA 30306
(404) 888-6599 Margaret Lisi
Fax: (949) 830-5172
Email: margaret@stir-marketing.com
Website: www.stir-marketing.com
Marketing & communications services, create content & media, employee engagement/change management & event marketing. (Woman/White, estab 1993, empl 10, sales $1,200,000, cert: WBENC)

8036 Food Service Supply Inc.
5350 McEver Rd Ste A Flowery Branch, GA 30542
(800) 367-4421 Darren Hawkins Contract sales Mgr
Fax: (770) 965-6938
Email: dhawkins@fsrfoodservice.com
Website: www.fsrfoodservice.com
FSR provides all types of traytop food service supplies (retherm or conventional). Lids, disposable & reusable items, menus, room service items. (Woman/White, estab 1985, empl 11, sales $12,000,000, cert: State)

8037 Freeman Resources Group LLC.
730 Shorter Terr   Atlanta, GA 30318
(404) 696-7224 David Freeman COO
Fax: (404) 343-4591
Email: dafreeman4@gmail.com
Website:
Medical Supplies/Equipment -Bandadges ,First Aid Kits,Gloves,Mask Wheel Chairs,Defribillattors
Industrial Safety Supplies-Work Clothing ,Boots ,Ear ,Head and Eye Protection (AA, estab 2007, empl 15, sales $205,000, cert: State)

8038 Grow Now, LLC
1320 Ellsworth Industrial Blvd NW   Atlanta, GA 30318
(404) 254-3281 Bob McNeil CEO
Fax: (404) 254-5131
Email: b.mcneil@grownowllc.com
Website: www.grownowllc.com
Marketing communications, advertising, promotional marketing, public relations & activations. (AA, estab 2013, empl 24, sales $8,600,000, cert: State, NMSDC)

8039 Harris HR Services, Inc.
3340 Peachtree Rd, Ste 1800 Tower Place 100
Atlanta, GA 30326
(678) 264-8679 Derrick Harris President
Fax: (678) 534-8843
Email: dbharris@standbytalent.com
Website: www.standbytalent.com
(AA, estab , empl 1, sales , cert: NMSDC)

8040 Insights Marketing
3131 Piedmont Rd. Ste 205 Atlanta, GA 30305
(404) 872-9899 Keshia Walker President
Fax: (404) 872-9699
Email: kw@insights-mpc.com
Website: www.insights-mpc.com
Multi-cultural research development & analysis, marketing, promotion, special event program development & execution. (Woman/AA, estab 1998, empl 10, sales $390,000, cert: NMSDC, WBENC)

8041 LightPath OM LLC dba strut AGENCY
1235 Oriole Dr, SW   Atlanta, GA 30311
(404) 855-4568 Tashion Macon, PhD, MBA
President
Fax:
Email: tashion@strutagency.com
Website: www.strutagency.online
Creative design, cross-cultural communications, and consumer marketing strategy. (Woman/AA, estab 2008, empl 15, sales $325,000, cert: NMSDC, WBENC)

8042 Maveryck Marketing Group, LLC
3726 Upton Ct   Ellenwood, GA 30294
(770) 681-0731 Keith Philpot Managing Member
Fax: (678) 228-1834
Email: kphilpot@maveryckmarketing.com
Website: www.maveryckmarketing.com
Strategic market planning & implementation. (AA, estab 2005, empl 1, sales $60,000, cert: NMSDC)

8043 McDowell Information Group Public Relations LLC.
233 Mitchell St, Ste 500   Atlanta, GA 30303
(844) 462-3693 Nathan Banks Sr Managing
Partner
Fax:
Email: Nathan@mcdowellpr.com
Website: www.mcdowellpr.com
Public relations, Web Development, Voice Overs, Military/Corporate engagement, Minority Community Relations, Stage Productions, lighting & Event Planning. (AA, estab 2014, empl 10, sales $25,000, cert: NMSDC)

8044 Modo Modo Agency LLC
3175 Northside PkwyNW Bldg 300, Ste 700
Atlanta, GA 30327
(770) 436-3100 Moira Vetter CEO
Fax: (770) 436-3090
Email: moira@modomodoagency.com
Website: www.modomodoagency.com
Marketing, brand development, thought leadership, lead generation, internal communications, publications, web sites, integrated marketing campaigns, direct response. (Woman/White, estab 2007, empl 15, sales $1,535,000, cert: WBENC)

8045 National Business Advisory Group, Inc.
540 Powder Springs St, Ste C16   Marietta, GA 30064
(770) 974-8100 Silah Williams CEO
Fax: (404) 601-6119
Email: swilliams@mynbag.com
Website: www.mynbag.com
Market research & strategy consulting services. (AA, estab 2011, empl 5, sales $150,000, cert: NMSDC)

8046 Printing Systems, LLC
2759 Delk Rd, Ste 2300   Marietta, GA 30067
(404) 855-3021 Sherrica Davis New Bus Specialist
Fax: (909) 455-0188
Email: sdavis@printingsys.com
Website: www.printingsys.com
At Printing Systems we utilize innovation to maximize target marketing success, increase return on investments and impact CRM through increasing consumer databases and identifying consumer purchasing habits. (AA, estab 2002, empl 7, sales $2,300,000, cert: NMSDC)

8047   Q&A Entertainment Inc.
1514 E Cleveland Ave Ste 116   East Point, GA 30344
(404) 762-5665   Sheila Merritt Dir new Business Dev
Fax: (404) 762-5664
Email: smerritt@QandAEntertainment.com
Website: www.QandAEntertainment.com
Event production & marketing services: production &
management, marketing & promotion, ideation & creation
& sponsorships. (Woman, estab 1999, empl 3, sales
$830,788, cert: WBENC)

8048   Sojo, Inc.
4400 N Point Pkwy Ste 153   Alpharetta, GA 30022
(770) 360-6330   Sophie Gibson President
Fax: (770) 360-6370
Email: sophie.gibson@sojoinc.com
Website: www.sojoinc.com
Technology marketing, marketing communications.
(Woman/AA, estab 2001, empl 11, sales $2,300,000, cert:
NMSDC)

8049   Southeast Exhibits and Events
1000 Marietta St Ste 124   Atlanta, GA 30318
(470) 865-2007   Jamal Lewis President
Fax:
Email: Info@southeastexhibit.com
Website: www.Southeastexhibit.com
Trade show exhibits & design. (Woman/AA, estab 2014,
empl 5, sales , cert: NMSDC)

8050   SPAR Solutions, LLC
360 Interstate North Pkwy SE Ste 220   Atlanta, GA
30339
(855) 772-7765   Swami Ganapathy Dir, Solutions
Consulting
Fax: (248) 569-1501
Email: sganapathy@sparsolutions.com
Website: www.sparsolutions.com
CRM Solutions for Sales, Marketing, Customer Service,
Field Service, Contract Management
Contact Centers - Omni-channel customer interactions -
Telephony, Email, Chat, Social Media
Complex business process automation and management,
Systems Integratio (As-Ind, estab 2003, empl 60, sales
$3,670,000, cert: NMSDC)

8051   TDEFERIAMEDIA, Inc.
9795 Talisman Dr   Johns Creek, GA 30022
(404) 630-0639   Antenor Tony President
Fax: (770) 619-5982
Email: contact@tdeferiamedia.com
Website: www.tdeferiamedia.com
Marketing, branding consulting & creative production,
ethnic market study & plans, media buying, translation &
interpretation in Spanish, digital & social media expertise.
(Hisp, estab 2007, empl 1, sales $140,000, cert: NMSDC)

8052   The Capre Group
115 Perimeter Center Place Ste 1120   Atlanta, GA
30346
(678) 443-2280   Kim Gavlak Controller
Fax: (678) 443-2288
Email: kgavlak@capregroup.com
Website: www.capregroup.com
Strategic marketing consulting. (Woman/White, estab
2001, empl 14, sales $4,750,000, cert: WBENC)

8053   The Crafton Group, Inc.
1107 Lanier Blvd   Atlanta, GA 30306
(404) 873-3019   Crafton Langley President
Fax:
Email: crafton.langley@thecraftongroup.com
Website: www.thecraftongroup.com
Marketing & communications: research, strategy,
branding, design, advertising, promotion, product
development, media. (Woman/White, estab 1996, empl
15, sales $90,000, cert: City, WBENC)

8054   VonCreations, Inc.
2886 Branchwood Dr   East Point, GA 30344
(404) 347-1054   Yvonne J. Wiltz CEO
Fax: (404) 344-6115
Email: vonco3@bellsouth.net
Website: www.voncreations.com
Meeting planning & management, conferences, special
events & marketing campaigns. (Woman/AA, estab
1989, empl 2, sales $145,279, cert: NMSDC, WBENC,
8(a))

Idaho

8055   Milligan Events
4477 W Emerald St Ste C125   Boise, ID 83706
(208) 387-0770   Janell McGill Owner
Fax: (208) 344-5366
Email: info@milliganevents.com
Website: www.milliganevents.com
Event & meeting planning & logistics. (Woman/White,
estab 1994, empl 26, sales $2,913,929, cert: WBENC)

Illinois

8056   Bamboo Worldwide Inc.
30 N Racine Ave, Ste 300   Chicago, IL 60607
(773) 227-4848   Tracy Thirion President
Fax:
Email: tracyt@bambooinc.com
Website: www.bambooworldwide.com
Consulting services specializing in branding, innovation
& market research. (Woman/White, estab 2002, empl 5,
sales $1,700,545, cert: WBENC)

8057   Beaman Public Relations, Inc.
401 N Michigan Ave, Ste 1300   Chicago, IL 60611
(312) 751-9689   Robin Beaman President
Fax: (312) 751-9405
Email: rbeaman@beamaninc.com
Website: www.beamaninc.com
Public relations, marketing & advertising services.
(Woman/AA, estab 1996, empl 7, sales $1,084,431, cert:
State, City, NMSDC)

8058   Classical Marketing LLC
2300 Cabot Dr, Ste 390   Lisle, IL 60532
(847) 969-1696   Susan Mazanek Managing
Partner
Fax: (847) 969-1769
Email: smazanek@classicalmarketing.com
Website: www.classicalmarketing.com
Marketing programs for clients in retail, financial
services, automotive, health care. (Woman/White, estab
1999, empl 8, sales $3,400,000, cert: WBENC)

8059 Creative & Response Research Services, Inc.
500 N Michigan Ave, 12th Fl Chicago, IL 60611
(312) 828-9200 Robbin Jaklin CFO
Fax: (312) 527-3113
Email: robbinj@crresearch.com
Website: www.crresearch.com
Custom market research, internet surveys, phone surveys, focus groups, qualitative & quantitative research. (Woman/White, estab 1960, empl 120, sales $23,268,888, cert: State, WBENC)

8060 Data Research Inc.
2525 Cabot Dr Ste 107 Lisle, IL 60532
(630) 281-8307 Leslie Gunner Losh President
Fax: (630) 281-8339
Email: lgunnerlosh@mindseyeresearch.com
Website: www.mindseyeresearch.com
Market research services. (Woman/White, estab 1982, empl 46, sales $3,600,000, cert: WBENC)

8061 Elemento L2, LLC
401 S LaSalle St, Ste 1501 Chicago, IL 60605
(312) 465-2355 Ivan Lopez Managing Dir
Fax: (312) 465-2356
Email: chemistry@elementol2.com
Website: www.elementol2.com
Multicultural marketing, experiential, PR, shopper & digital marketing. (Hisp, estab 2011, empl 15, sales $1,048,333, cert: NMSDC)

8062 Epko Industries, Inc.
1200 Arthur Ave Elk Grove Village, IL 60007
(847) 437-4000 Gary Rothschild Treasurer
Fax: (847) 437-4017
Email: grothschild@epko.com
Website: www.mdcwall.com
MDC Wallcoverings is a national distributor of commrcial wallcoverings and wallcoatings, including but not limited to custom, digital, vinyl, textile, acoustical wallcoverings; Tabrasa (TM) Dry-Erase Paint, and specialty paint. (Woman/White, estab 1946, empl 150, sales $50,025,000, cert: State)

8063 Eved Services, Inc.
4811 Oakton St, Ste 250 Skokie, IL 60077
(773) 764-7000 Alexis Feczko Director of Sales Ops
Fax: (847) 982-9610
Email: sales@eved.com
Website: www.eved.com/
Event services, destination management, technology services. (Woman/White, estab 2004, empl 25, sales $8,100,000, cert: WBENC)

8064 Frontline Public Strategies, Inc.
100 E. Washington St Springfield, IL 62701
(217) 528-3434 Kim Robinson President
Fax: (217) 528-6545
Email: kimrobinson@frontline-online.net
Website: www.frontline-online.net
Public relations, marketing, event planning & public affairs. (Woman/White, estab 2001, empl 12, sales $1,200,000, cert: State, WBENC)

8065 Gladstone Painting Company
P.O. Box 871 Elmhurst, IL 60126
(630) 782-0973 Mary Hinchley President
Fax: (630) 782-0901
Email: gladstoneptg@aol.com
Website:
commercial painting contractor (Woman/White, estab 1975, empl 10, sales , cert: City, WBENC)

8066 Group O, Inc.
4905 77th Avenue Milan, IL 61264
(210) 213-2258 Mike De La Cruz Sr VP, Business Dev & Diversity
Fax: (309) 736-8301
Email: supplierdiversity@groupo.com
Website: www.groupo.com
Single source integrated marketing solutions, customer loyalty, rebate administration & fulfillment, gift cards, inbound & outbound call center services, 4-color printing, print personalization, direct mail & fulfillment. (Hisp, estab 1974, empl 1200, sales $765,000,000, cert: NMSDC)

8067 Ivan Carlson & Associates
2224 W Fulton Chicago, IL 60612
(312) 829-4616 Tina Carlson President
Fax: (312) 829-1308
Email: tina@ivancarlson.com
Website: www.ivancarlson.com
Event production & management, logistics, staging, sound & lighting. (Woman/White, estab 1974, empl 25, sales $3,370,000, cert: WBENC)

8068 JRS Consulting, Inc.
1316 Gregory Ave Wilmette, IL 60091
(847) 920-1701 Jennifer Schade President
Fax: (847) 920-1702
Email: jenny.schade@JRSconsulting.net
Website: www.JRSconsulting.net
Market research, management consulting, marketing & internal & external communications initiatives. (Woman/White, estab 2002, empl 1, sales $78,794, cert: WBENC)

8069 JumpGarden Consulting, LLC
1534 Washington Ave Wilmette, IL 60091
(312) 286-0119 Sheila Cahnman President
Fax: (847) 853-0735
Email: sheila@jumpgardenllc.com
Website: www.jumpgardenllc.com
Healthcare design, planning & marketing solutions. (Woman/White, estab 2014, empl 1, sales , cert: State, City, WBENC)

8070 K.O. Strategies
2903 N Wolcott, Ste B Chicago, IL 60640
(312) 307-4206 Catherine O'Malley President
Fax:
Email: kate@kostrategies.com
Website: www.kostrategies.com
Strategic communications, public affairs, stakeholder relations, crisis leadership & strategic planning/presentations. (Woman/White, estab 2006, empl 2, sales $268,000, cert: WBENC)

8071 Kathy Schaeffer and Associates, Inc.
17 N State St, Ste 1690 Chicago, IL 60602
(312) 251-5100 Kathy Schaeffer President
Fax: (312) 251-0081
Email: kschaeffer@ksapr.com
Website: www.ksapr.com
Public relations. (Woman/White, estab 1994, empl 5, sales
, cert: City)

8072 L3 Agency
1452 E 53rd 1452 E 53rd Chicago, IL 60615
(312) 268-5207 Larvetta Loftin CEO
Fax:
Email: larvetta.loftin@l3eventeurs.com
Website: www.thel3agency.com
Marketing and communications, digital content creation,
PR, advertising, brand experiences, corporate sponsorship,
community outreach, and social philanthropy. (Woman/
AA, estab 2000, empl 4, sales $30,000, cert: NMSDC)

8073 Liberty Lithographers, Inc.
18625 W Creek Dr Tinley Park, IL 60477
(708) 633-7450 Angela Hipelius CEO
Fax: (708) 633-7449
Email: ahipelius@libertycreativesolutions.com
Website: www.libertycreativesolutions.com
Marketing services: graphic design, direct mail campaigns,
research, promotions & loyalty campaigns, marketing
collateral, advertising, web design, brand development,
corporate identity. (Woman/White, estab 1964, empl 53,
sales $11,000,000, cert: State, WBENC)

8074 Marketing Innovators International Inc.
9701 W Higgins Rd Ste 400 Rosemont, IL 60018
(847) 696-1111 Merrie Marinovich Acct Exec
Fax: (847) 696-3194
Email: mmarinovich@marketinginnovators.com
Website: www.marketinginnovators.com
Employee recognition award programs. (Woman/White,
estab 1978, empl 70, sales , cert: WBENC)

8075 Matrex Exhibits
301 S Church St Addison, IL 60101
(630) 628-2233 Jeff Foulk VP Business Dev
Fax: (630) 628-2263
Email: info@matrexexhibits.com
Website: www.matrexexhibits.com
Tradeshow exhibits, design, construction & mgmt, graphic
design & production, tradeshow svcs. (Woman/White,
estab 1987, empl 66, sales $27,000,000, cert: WBENC)

8076 Media Link, Inc.
1902 17th St Rock Island, IL 61201
(309) 786-5142 Adrian Wille Mktg Consultant
Fax:
Email: adrian@medialinkinc.com
Website: www.medialinkinc.com
Media Buying, Advertising, Marketing, PR, Public Relations,
Media Campaign, Marketing Research. (Woman/White,
estab 2001, empl 4, sales $1,046,821, cert: State, WBENC)

8077 Metaphrasis Language and Cultural Solutions, LLC
1147 W Ohio, Ste 306 Chicago, IL 60714
(815) 464-1423 Elizabeth Colon President
Fax: (815) 464-1747
Email: ecolon@metaphrasislcs.com
Website: www.metaphrasislcs.com
Language services, interpretation, translation & corpo-
rate trainings. (Woman/Hisp, estab 2007, empl 6, sales
$2,100,000, cert: State, WBENC)

8078 MHJohnson & Associates, Inc.
1918 S Michigan Ave Ste 302 Chicago, IL 60616
(312) 949-9164 Marilyn Johnson Principal
Fax: (312) 873-3888
Email: marilyn@mhjohnson.com
Website: www.mhjohnson.com
Marketing management, program, product development
& mgmt, organizational development. (Woman/AA, estab
2001, empl 2, sales $225,000, cert: WBENC)

8079 PACO Communications, Inc. d/b/a PACO Collective
400 S. Green St Unit H Chicago, IL 60607
(312) 281-2040 Ozzie Godinez CEO
Fax: (312) 971-5911
Email: marketing@pacocollective.com
Website: www.pacocollective.com
Hispanic marketing, advertising, public relations &
community outreach, web design & development. (Hisp,
estab 2006, empl 40, sales $21,000,000, cert: NMSDC)

8080 PCH Communications
600 W Fluton Fl 4 Chicago, IL 60661
(312) 384-1906 Alice Pollard SVP Ops
Fax:
Email: alice@discovercg.com
Website: www.commongroundmgs.com
Advertising/Marketing, Strategic Planning/Development,
Creative, Public Relations, Event Marketing, Multicultural
Marketing, Digital Marketing , Shopper/Retail Marketing,
Content Development, Research
Promotions/Sponsorship's. (AA/Hisp, estab 2014, empl
256, sales $35,276,000, cert: NMSDC)

8081 Public Communications Inc.
1 E Wacker Dr Ste 2450 Chicago, IL 60601
(312) 558-1770 Pamela Oettel CFO
Fax:
Email: poettel@pcipr.com
Website: www.pcipr.com
Develop integrated communications strategies: Advocacy
Programs, Board Counsel, Branding & Positioning,
Competitive Analysis, Consumer Marketing, Conserva-
tion & Wildlife Issues, Crisis/Issues Management &
Monitoring. (Woman/White, estab 1962, empl 50, sales
$6,111,500, cert: State, WBENC)

8082 Quicksilver Associates, Inc.
18 W Ontario St Chicago, IL 60654
(312) 943-7622 Diane MacWilliams President
Fax: (312) 664-4213
Email: dianem@quicksilvernow.com
Website: www.quicksilvernow.com
Print, video, meeting planning, production, web &
interactive media. (Woman/White, estab 1976, empl 22,
sales $4,600,000, cert: WBENC)

8083 Reilly Connect
625 N Michigan Ave Ste 1705 Chicago, IL 60611
(312) 600-6780 Susan Reilly President
Fax:
Email: susan.reilly@reillyconnect.com
Website: www.reillyconnect.com/
Social media marketing, brand activation & events, video production, public relations. (Woman/White, estab 1996, empl 5, sales , cert: WBENC)

8084 Research Explorers, Inc
1111 New Trier Ct Wilmette, IL 60091
(847) 853-0237 Lisa Gaines McDonald President
Fax:
Email: lisa@researchexplorers.com
Website: www.reserachexplorers.com
Market research & consulting services: qualitative research, focus groups, in-depth interviews, ethnographies, brain storming & idea generation sessions. (Woman/AA, estab 1994, empl 1, sales $305,087, cert: City)

8085 Ritz Communications
1445 N State Pkwy, Ste 2305 Chicago, IL 60610
(312) 932-0992 Elisabeth Ritz President
Fax: (312) 932-9905
Email: elisabeth.ritz@ritzcommunications.com
Website: www.ritzcommunications.com
Public relations & marketing communications agency specializing in healthcare & health information technology. (Woman, estab 2003, empl 20, sales , cert: WBENC)

8086 Signature Media Group Talk
1327 W Washington Blvd Chicago, IL 60607
(312) 226-5552 Pam Redwood President
Fax: (312) 226-5557
Email: pam@smgspeakers.com
Website: www.smgspeakers.com
Public communications, speakers bureau, brand creation awareness, client advertising, ad management, creative services, custom publishing, event planning, media planning, media relations, corporate communications. (Woman/AA, estab 2009, empl 2, sales $400,000, cert: State, City)

8087 Strategic Marketing, Inc.
350 S Northwest Hwy Ste 304 Park Ridge, IL 60068
(847) 720-7500 Leslie Reinhardt Controller
Fax: (847) 720-7590
Email: lreinhardt@smialcott.com
Website: www.smialcott.com
Marketing research services. (Woman/White, estab 1980, empl 23, sales $7,636,812, cert: WBENC)

8088 Total Event Resources
1920 N Thoreau Dr Ste 105 Schaumburg, IL 60173
(847) 397-2200 Lynnea Walsh Director of Ops
Fax: (847) 397-2210
Email: lwalsh@total-event.com
Website: www.total-event.com
Corporate communications, event production, entertainment [roduction, meeting management, experiential learning & destination management. (Woman/White, estab 1995, empl 15, sales $3,320,000, cert: WBENC)

8089 Wedgeworth Business Communications
2215 Enterprise Dr Ste 1506 Westchester, IL 60154
(708) 223-0019 Pamela G. Wedgeworth President
Fax: (708) 223-0034
Email: pamela@wedgeworthbiz.com
Website: www.wedgeworthbiz.com
Visual communications: video production, multimedia creation, print & electronic collateral, event coordination. (Woman/AA, estab 1999, empl 2, sales $320,000, cert: City, WBENC)

Indiana

8090 Coles Marketing Communications
3950 Priority Way Ste 106 Indianapolis, IN 46240
(317) 571-0051 Barbara Coles President
Fax: (317) 571-0052
Email: bcoles@colesmarketing.com
Website: www.colesmarketing.com
Marketing communications services: graphic design, web design, e-communications, public relations, media relations, word of mouth marketing, videography, photography. (Woman/White, estab 1985, empl 10, sales $1,250,000, cert: State, City)

Kansas

8091 A.S.K. Associates, Inc.
1505 Kasold Dr Lawrence, KS 66047
(800) 315-4333 Kenneth Martinez President
Fax: (785) 841-2668
Email: kenm@askusa.com
Website: www.askusa.com
Conference, convention, trade show, meeting, seminar support services. (Woman/Hisp, estab 1979, empl 15, sales $6,600,000, cert: State)

8092 Exhibit Arts, LLC
326 N Athenian Wichita, KS 67203
(316) 264-2915 Beth Harshfield Managing Member
Fax: (316) 262-9176
Email: beth@exhibitarts.net
Website: www.exhibitarts.net
Exhibit design, fabrication & management, project management, conference support services, warehousing & fulfillment center services. (Woman/Nat Ame, estab 2000, empl 160, sales $18,843,000, cert: NMSDC, NWBOC)

8093 Meeting Excellence, Inc.
7300 West 110th St Ste 700 Overland Park, KS 66210
(913) 693-4675 Kory Oplinger Director of Sales
Fax: (913) 890-4796
Email: koplinger@meeting-excellence.com
Website: www.meeting-excellence.com
Corporate meetings, events & incentive travel services. (AA, estab 2003, empl 4, sales $1,113,929, cert: NMSDC)

8094   The Lexinet Corporation
       701 N Union   Council Grove, KS 66846
       (620) 767-7000 Lindsey Boyer President
       Fax: (620) 767-7100
       Email: indseyb@lexinetcorporation.com
       Website: www.lexinetcorporation.com
Marketing campaigns & programs, custom personalized
variable data printed direct mail, fully-integrated marketing centers, complete multi-channel solutions. (Woman,
estab 1991, empl 18, sales $3,100,000, cert: WBENC)

Kentucky

8095   ConvenePro
       1792 Alysheba Way Ste 160 Lexington, KY 40509
       (859) 276-0065 Delphine Hepp Acct Director
       Fax:
       Email: dhepp@convenepro.com
       Website: www.convenepro.com
Event management, marketing & communications, live
speaker programs, conferences & trade shows, promotional presentations, satellite broadcasts/webcasts, live &
virtual training workshops, product training. (Woman/
White, estab 1995, empl 50, sales , cert: NWBOC)

8096   Corporate World Public Relations
       4017 Whiteblossom Estates Ct   Louisville, KY 40241
       (678) 592-8516 Ray Callender, Jr. VP
       Fax: (502) 425-7653
       Email: ray.callender@corpworldpr.com
       Website: www.corpworldpr.com
Exhibits design & management services. (AA, estab 1984,
empl 10, sales $262,000, cert: NMSDC)

8097   Digital Business Solutions, Inc.
       517 S Fourth St   Louisville, KY 40202
       (502) 562-7895 Cynthia Masters CEO
       Fax: (502) 562-7896
       Email: cyndi@dbswebsite.com
       Website: www.dbswebsite.com
Web & digital dev, design, strategy & marketing, websites,
apps, mobile, hosting, interactive infographics, SEO, digital
business strategy, online marketing. (Woman/White, estab
2000, empl 20, sales $1,700,000, cert: WBENC)

8098   Intrinzic Marketing & Design
       One Levee Way, Ste 3121   Newport, KY 41071
       (859) 261-2200 Tami Beattie Office Mgr
       Fax: (859) 261-2102
       Email: info@intrinzicbrands.com
       Website: www.intrinzicinc.com
Marketing & design: creative concepting, campaign dev,
graphic design, copywriting, public relations, website
design, email marketing & media planning. (Woman/
White, estab 1989, empl 12, sales , cert: WBENC)

8099   Mackey Group LLC
       2250 Mackey Pike   Nicholasville, KY 40356
       (859) 887-0866 Nancy Wiser President
       Fax: (859) 887-0337
       Email: nancy@wiserstrategies.com
       Website: www.wiserstrategies.com
Public relations, marketing, market research, corporate
relations, crisis planning & response, media relations,
branding creative services, writing, graphic design,
photography, video production & editing, print production
management. (Woman, estab 2011, empl 1, sales
$300,000, cert: WBENC)

8100   New West LLC
       9630 Ormsby Station Rd   Louisville, KY 40223
       (888) 867-7811 Melvin Graham Managing Dir
       Fax: (502) 891-2514
       Email: mgraham@newwestagency.com
       Website: www.newwestagency.com
Advertising, Public Relations, Brand Strategy, Website &
Mobile App Development, Social Media, Multicultural
Marketing, SEO/SEM/PPC, Event Planning & Video
Production. (AA, estab 2002, empl 28, sales $5,500,000,
cert: NMSDC)

Massachusetts

8101   Causemedia, Inc.
       50 Hunt St Ste 140 Watertown, MA 02472
       (617) 558-6850 Donna Latson Gittens Principal
       Fax: (617) 558-6851
       Email: info@causemedia.com
       Website: www.moreadvertising.com
Communications, advertising & marketing agency.
(Woman/AA, estab 1997, empl 8, sales $4,636,330, cert:
State, NMSDC, WBENC)

8102   Color Media Group, LLC
       4 Copley Pl, Ste 120   Boston, MA 02116
       (617) 266-6961 Josefina Bonilla President
       Fax: (617) 663-6961
       Email: josefina@colorboston.com
       Website: www.colormagazineusa.com
Web advertising, signature events, event management,
strategic marketing initiatives, new markets, media
buying services, public relations. (Woman/Hisp, estab
2007, empl 3, sales $289,000, cert: State)

8103   Conover + Gould Strategic Communications, Inc.
       69 Milk St #101 Westborough, MA 01581
       (508) 789-9273 Heather Conover CEO
       Fax: (866) 533-9881
       Email: hconover@conovergould.com
       Website: www.conovergould.com
Public relations & marketing communications, environmental communications & event management.
(Woman/White, estab 1984, empl 9, sales $1,528,016,
cert: State)

8104   Consolidated Marketing Services, Inc.
       841 Woburn St   Wilmington, MA 01887
       (800) 474-5756 Andrew Bausman key Acct Mgr
       Fax: (978) 657-5210
       Email: abausman@cmsassociates.com
       Website: www.cmsassociates.com
Marketing svcs: fulfillment, printing, mailing, promotional products, graphics & catalogs. (Woman/White,
estab 1900, empl 1, sales $4,000,000, cert: WBENC)

8105   Early Bird Power LLC
       1 Adams St   Milton, MA 02186
       (888) 763-2759 Shaun Pandit CEO
       Fax: (864) 845-5507
       Email: shaunpandit@earlybirdpower.com
       Website: www.earlybirdpower.com
Facilitator of procurement services for electricity, natural
gas, and renewable energy credits. Energy Consulting
and risk management. (As-Ind, estab 2009, empl 1, sales
$500,000, cert: State)

8106 EMI Strategic Marketing Inc.
      15 Broad St   Boston, MA 02109
      (617) 224-1101 Paul OBrien VP controller
      Fax: (617) 224-1190
      Email: pobrien@emiboston.com
      Website: www.emiboston.com
Marketing services. (Woman/White, estab 1989, empl 40, sales $6,000,000, cert: State)

8107 Full Circle Design
      380 Main St Unit 301 Stoneham, MA 02180
      (781) 333-8878 Lisa Guilmet President
      Fax:
      Email: lisa@fullcircledesign.co
      Website: www.fullcircledesign.co
Branding, print and graphic design, web design and development, and varios digital marketing services. (Woman/White, estab 2011, empl 4, sales , cert: WBENC)

8108 Grand Design, Inc.
      42 Chestnut St 3rd Fl Salem, MA 01970
      (978) 741-0112 Debra Glabeau Principal
      Fax:
      Email: dglabeau@greatisland.com
      Website: www.greatisland.com
Graphic design & marketing communications solutions, brand development, logos & corporate identity systems, naming & taglines, collateral & brochures, websites, email & direct mail programs, print advertising, sales kits. (Woman/White, estab 1982, empl 2, sales , cert: State)

8109 Inspired Marketing
      20 Maple St 4th Fl, Ste 1 Springfield, MA 01103
      (413) 303-0101 Lauren Mendoza Office Mgr
      Fax:
      Email: lauren@inspiredmarketing.biz
      Website: www.inspiredmarketing.biz
Marketing, Event Planning, Social Media, Media Buying, Advertising, Graphic Design (Woman/White, estab 2009, empl 6, sales $632,920, cert: WBENC)

8110 Kelley Chunn & Associates
      184 Dudley St Ste 106 Boston, MA 02119
      (617) 427-0997 Kelley Chunn Principal
      Fax: (617) 427-3997
      Email: kc4info@aol.com
      Website: www.kelleychunn.com
Multicultural marketing & public relations services. (Woman/AA, estab 1991, empl 1, sales $160,000, cert: State)

8111 NXTevent, Inc.
      60K St, 4th Fl Boston, MA 02127
      (617) 904-9053 Joanne O'Connell GM
      Fax: (617) 307-6257
      Email: connect@nxtevent.com
      Website: www.nxtevent.com
Event & destination management. (Woman/White, estab 2001, empl 8, sales $2,447,766, cert: State, WBENC)

8112 The Castle Group
      38 Third Avenue Charlestown, MA 02129
      (617) 337-9535 Alexa DiMario Exec Asst
      Fax: (617) 337-9539
      Email: adimario@thecastlegrp.com
      Website: www.thecastlegrp.com/home
Public relations & events management. (Woman/White, estab 1996, empl 22, sales $5,300,000, cert: WBENC)

8113 Twirling Tiger Press Inc.
      7 Jeffrey Road   Franklin, MA 02038
      (508) 520-3258 Maureen Joyce President
      Fax:
      Email: mjoyce@twirlingtigermedia.com
      Website: www.twirlingtigermedia.com
Writing & graphic design, creation of design & imagery, development, scheduling & trafficking, & content generation, advertising, printing, promotions, publications, RFPs & proposals, social media, websites, white papers. (Woman/White, estab 2013, empl 2, sales $187,000, cert: WBENC)

Maryland

8114 BrightKey, Inc.
      60 West St, Ste 300   Annapolis, MD 21401
      (301) 604-3305 Krystal Dyer Business Solutions
      Fax: (240) 646-7040
      Email: kdyer@brightkey.net
      Website: www.brightkey.net/
Marketing research, strategy & creative services. (Woman/White, estab 1988, empl 526, sales $33,696,365, cert: WBENC)

8115 DESTIN Enterprises, LLC
      8630 Guilford Rd, Ste 114   Columbia, MD 21046
      (443) 538-1351 Edward Crenshaw President
      Fax: (410) 290-6900
      Email: ej_crenshaw@destinenterprises.com
      Website: www.destinenterprises.com
DESTIN Enterprise, LLC is a diversity consulting, training and solutions fir that specializes in raising awareness toward disabilities and veterans transition issues. Our signature diversity training program is "Preparing Employers to Reintegrate PROFESSIONAL SERVICES: Public Relations/Marketing (AA, estab 2008, empl 8, sales $61,000, cert: State)

8116 Hargrove Inc.
      One Hargrove Dr   Lanham, MD 20706
      (301) 306-3000 Meghan Muniz Natl Sales Exec
      Fax: (301) 306-9318
      Email: MeghanMuniz@hargroveinc.com
      Website: www.hargroveinc.com
Events, exhibits & trade shows: venue selection, staffing, design, menu development, security, building of stages, set design, AV & lighting services. (Woman/White, estab 1946, empl 225, sales $73,000,000, cert: WBENC)

8117 Humdinger Enterprises LLC
      P.O. Box 4542 Crofton, MD 21114
      (410) 279-0205 Alexis Jenkins Managing Member
      Fax: (410) 510-1031
      Email: alexis@humdingerenterprise.com
      Website: www.humdingerenterprises.com
Event planning: festivals, concerts, meetings, award shows & broadcast events. (Woman/White, estab 2008, empl 5, sales $230,681, cert: State)

8118   JDC Events, LLC
8720 Georgia Ave Ste 801   Silver Spring, MD 20910
(240) 512-4219   Jennifer Collins President
Fax:
Email: jennifer@jdc-events.com
Website: www.jdc-events.com
Meeting & event management: custom-designed logistical solutions, guidance & communications, meetings, conferences & special events. (Woman/AA, estab 1997, empl 4, sales $2,040,000, cert: NMSDC, WBENC, 8(a))

8119   McMillon Communications, Inc.
12902 Argyle Circle   Fort Washington, MD 20744
(301) 292-9141   Doris McMillon CEO
Fax: (301) 292-9142
Email: doris@mcmilloncommunications.com
Website: www.mcmilloncommunications.com
Marketing support solutions, public relations & strategic partnership development. (Woman/AA, estab 1986, empl 3, sales $4,528,979, cert: State, WBENC)

8120   Mjach Designs
5100 Buckeystown Pike #250   Frederick, MD 21704
(410) 366-0505   Rose Colvin Admin
Fax: (410) 366-5003
Email: rose@mjachdesigns.com
Website: www.mjachdesigns.com
Graphic design, marketing & communications, web design & implementation, print production, marketing & advertising, public relations, media planning & buying, research & copywriting. (Woman/White, estab 2003, empl 5, sales $336,640, cert: State, City)

8121   MultiLingual Solutions, Inc.
11 N Washington St Ste 300   Rockville, MD 20850
(301) 424-7444   Paul Keys VP Business Dev
Fax: (301) 424-7331
Email: pkeys@mlsolutions.com
Website: www.mlsolutions.com
Document Translation, On-site and Remote Interpretation, Website & Software Localization, Multicultural Marketing & Advertising, Language, Cultural and Executive Training & Curriculum Development, Desktop Publishing. (Woman/Hisp, estab 2002, empl 162, sales $9,729,040, cert: NMSDC, WBENC)

8122   Pensari, LLC
107 Theodora Court   Forest Hill, MD 21050
(410) 588-5465   Hans Plate
Fax: (410) 588-5466
Email: hans.plate@pensari.com
Website: www.pensari.com
Market research specializing in healthcare research, qualitative & quantitative research. (Hisp, estab 2013, empl 1, sales , cert: NMSDC)

8123   Program Management of America
1153 N Bentalou St   Baltimore, MD 21216
(410) 945-7489   Walter G Brooks Sr
Fax: (410) 945-5115
Email: wbrooks@pmamerica.com
Website: www.pmamerica.com
Support svcs for outreach programs, conferences, & exhibits (show site arr. & logistical support); warehousing/ distribution; database design/maintain(materials request process, mailing list mgmt, etc.). (AA, estab 1996, empl 2, sales , cert: State)

8124   Slice, Inc dba SliceWorks
20301 Highland Hall Dr   Montgomery Village, MD 20886
(301) 519-8101   Kathleen Rabil CEO
Fax: (301) 519-8104
Email: kathi@slice-works.com
Website: www.slice-works.com
Graphic design, marketing strategy consulting, marketing communications & campaign development, social media strategy consulting & execution, website design & development, brand consulting, publication layout & design. (Woman/White, estab 1997, empl 4, sales $445,690, cert: WBENC)

8125   Sutter Design, Inc. dba The Sutter Group
4640 Forbes Blvd. Ste 160A   Lanham, MD 20706
(301) 459-5445   Karen Sutter President
Fax: (301) 459-9129
Email: karen@sutter-group.com
Website: www.sutter-group.com
Marketing, advertising & public relations: brand, creating logos, corporate collateral, websites, direct mail & e-marketing campaigns, advertising & public relations. (Woman/White, estab 1987, empl 8, sales $1,000,000, cert: State, City, WBENC)

8126   TMNcorp
8720 Georgia Ave, Ste 206   Silver Spring, MD 20910
(301) 565-0770   Nhora Barrera Murphy President
Fax: (301) 565-0773
Email: nbarrera@tmncorp.com
Website: www.tmncorp.com
Communication & social marketing, advertising, media relations, research & evaluation & cultural adaptation services. (Woman/Hisp, estab 1999, empl 20, sales $4,850,000, cert: State)

Michigan

8127   Airfoil Public Relations, Inc.
336 North Main St   Royal Oak, MI 48067
(248) 304-1400   Sharon Neumann SVP, Finance & Admin
Fax: (248) 304-1401
Email: neumann@airfoilgroup.com
Website: www.airfoilgroup.com
Marketing communications. (Woman/White, estab 2000, empl 37, sales $7,200,000, cert: WBENC)

8128   Archer Corporate Services
6703 Haggerty Road, Ste B   Belleville, MI 48111
(734) 713-3166   Dawn Collins Director, Client Services
Fax: (734) 731-3191
Email: dcollins@theacsadvantage.com
Website: www.theacsadvantage.com
Marketing support svcs: B2B fulfillment, rebates, direct response, sweepstakes, customer service, merchandising. (AA, estab 2004, empl 25, sales $19,100,000, cert: NMSDC)

8129   BPI Communications, LLC
13700 Oakland Ave   Highland Park, MI 48203
(313) 957-5459   Jim Suddendorf EVP sales/mlktg
Fax: (313) 957-5457
Email: j.suddendorf@bpicommunications.com
Website: www.bpicommunications.com
Fulfillment & direct marketing solutions. (AA, estab 2005, empl 10, sales $107,000,000, cert: NMSDC)

8130   Bromberg & Associates, LLC
3320 Caniff St   Hamtramck, MI 48212
(313) 871-0080   Catherine Radloff Acct Mgr
Fax: (888) 225-1912
Email: services@BrombergTranslations.com
Website: www.brombergtranslations.com
Translations & interpretations: over 60 languages. (Woman/White, estab 1999, empl 25, sales $257,015, cert: WBENC)

8131   Collaborative Advantage Marketing
2987 Franklin St   Detroit, MI 48207
(248) 723-0793   Adam Lord Sales Rep
Fax: (866) 283-0379
Email: adam@camtrade.com
Website: www.camtrade.com
Category Management Quality Assurance Programs Total Product Design Business Analysis Brand Management Full Service Marketing Headquarter Selling. (Woman, estab 1999, empl 18, sales , cert: WBENC)

8132   Essential Events & Travel Planners
20001 Greenfield   Detroit, MI 48235
(313) 891-4612   Marion Allbritton Owner
Fax: (313) 369-9931
Email: essparty1@yahoo.com
Website: www.essentialpartyplanners.com
Event coordinating svcs, corporate events, charter bus svcs, catering & decorating, rental svcs. (Woman/AA, estab 1993, empl 6, sales $95,000, cert: State)

8133   Harris Marketing Group, Inc.
102 Pierce St   Birmingham, MI 48009
(248) 723-6300   Wendy Vadnais Finance Director
Fax: (248) 723-6301
Email: wvadnais@harris-hmg.com
Website: www.harris-hmg.com/
Integrated marketing campaigns, loyalty programs, brand advertising, targeted direct mail, fulfillment, media, public relations, training materials, website development, event marketing & viral marketing. (Woman/White, estab 1976, empl 10, sales $4,425,995, cert: WBENC)

8134   M3D Experiences, Inc.
16753 Black River Dr   Northville, MI 48168
(415)84633   Matthew Binkowski Principal, Chief Creative Officer
Fax:
Email: mattb@m3de.com
Website: www.m3dexperiences.com
Brand identities & multi-sensory experiences, successful marketing campaigns & develop memorable logos, marketing collateral & content. (Woman/White, estab 2011, empl 4, sales , cert: WBENC)

8135   Maestro LLC
7107 Elm Valley Dr   Kalamazoo, MI 49009
(800) 319-2122   Tagg Petersen Dir Business Dev
Fax: (269) 585-4019
Email: tagg@meetmaestro.com
Website: www.meetmaestro.com
Training, brand consulting, management consulting services, solution based contractors. (Woman/White, estab 2007, empl 31, sales $7,612,178, cert: State)

8136   RSVP Premier Group, LLC
900 Wilshire Dr Ste 202   Troy, MI 48084
(248) 663-4107   Tamika Brown CEO
Fax: (248) 519-2399
Email: tbrown@rsvppremier.com
Website: www.rsvppremier.com
Event planning & management, meeting planning, conference planning, incentive trips, trade shows/expos, event design & décor, event production, celebrity entertainment, talent & speaker booking. (Woman/AA, estab 2002, empl 4, sales $109,450, cert: WBENC)

8137   Skyline Exhibits West Michigan
4768 Danvers Dr. SE   Kentwood, MI 49512
(616) 301-8708   Eloy Cantu President
Fax: (616) 301-8705
Email: cantul@skylinewm.com
Website: www.skyline.com
Trade show marketing, seminars, workshops. (Hisp, estab 2004, empl 5, sales $900,000, cert: NMSDC)

8138   Smith-Dahmer Associates, LLC
116 State St   Saint Joseph, MI 49085
(269) 983-4748   Lori Stanwood Director Key Accts
Fax: (269) 983-4220
Email: loristanwood@smithdahmer.com
Website: www.smithdahmer.com
Marketing research & consulting, custom qualitative & quantitative methodologies, innovation & design research processes. (Woman/White, estab 1995, empl 30, sales $9,000,000, cert: WBENC)

8139   Special D Events, Inc.
535 Woodward Heights   Ferndale, MI 48220
(248) 336-8600   Carol Galle President
Fax: (248) 336-8610
Email: administrator@specialdevents.com
Website: www.specialdevents.com
Corporate event planning. (Woman/White, estab 1992, empl 17, sales $2,200,000, cert: WBENC)

8140   Strategic Market Research Group, Inc.
37129 Saint Martins St   Livonia, MI 48152
(734) 452-9104   Ami Nienus President
Fax: (734) 452-9104
Email: ami@smrginc.com
Website: www.smrginc.com
Market research. (Woman/As-Ind, estab 2007, empl 1, sales $20,000, cert: WBENC)

8141   Uproar Communications Ltd.
4667 Freedom Dr   Ann Arbor, MI 48108
(734) 975-8888   Heather Wendt President
Fax: (734) 975-9806
Email: wendthb@uproarcom.com
Website: www.uproarcom.com
Communications & marketing services. (Woman/White, estab 1998, empl 20, sales , cert: WBENC)

8142 Wilson-Taylor Associates, Inc.
      242 Lighthouse Circle   Manistee, MI 49660
      (231) 291-1275 Joanne Cleaver President
      Fax: (866) 543-0790
      Email: jycleaver@wilson-taylorassoc.com
      Website: www.wilson-taylorassoc.com
Content strategy & execution, writing, editing, research,
website content, digital publishing, strategic communication consulting, communication training, career training,
media training, communication coaching. (Woman/White,
estab 1998, empl 2, sales $110,000, cert: WBENC)

Minnesota

8143 AllOut Marketing, Inc.
      5775 Wayzata Blvd #700 St. Louis Park, MN 55416
      (952) 404-0800 Ruth Lane CEO
      Fax: (763) 244-8001
      Email: ruthlane@alloutsuccess.com
      Website: www.alloutsuccess.com
Medical marketing consulting, market research, web
development, graphic design, event management & public
relations. (Woman/Hisp, estab 1995, empl 8, sales
$722,000, cert: State)

8144 Azul 7, Inc.
      800 Hennepin Ave Ste 700 Minneapolis, MN 55403
      (612) 767-4335 Sara O'Brien Business Devel lead
      Fax: (612) 767-4335
      Email: hello@azul7.com
      Website: www.azul7.com
Build better brands, products & services, strategy &
innovation consulting, research, digital product & service
design along with innovation process training. (Woman,
estab 2007, empl 16, sales $1,868,437, cert: WBENC)

8145 Char Mason & Associates, LLC, dba Mason Creative
      695 Mount Curve Blvd   Saint Paul, MN 55116
      (651) 698-2678 Char Mason Owner
      Fax:
      Email: char@masoncreative.biz
      Website: www.masoncreative.biz
Event planning agency. (Woman/White, estab 2000, empl
1, sales $117,469, cert: State)

8146 Creative Connections
      4049 Blackhawk Rd   Eagan, MN 55122
      (651) 261-7886 Marianne Badar Ohman Owner
      Fax: (651) 261-7886
      Email: marianne@creativeconnections.net
      Website: www.creativeconnections.net
Communications consulting, marketing communications
project management, conference, meeting, tradeshow &
event planning & production, team leadership,
teambuilding training & services. (Woman/White, estab
1998, empl 1, sales $61,500, cert: City)

8147 D.Trio Marketing Group
      401 N Third St, Ste 480 Minneapolis, MN 55401
      (612) 436-0401 Fred Driver Business Dev Dir
      Fax: (612) 436-0324
      Email: fdriver@dtrio.com
      Website: www.dtrio.com
Direct marketing, strategy, creative, list, DP, print and
lettershop production, fulfillment & graphic design
services. (Woman/White, estab 2000, empl 12, sales
$3,500,000, cert: WBENC)

8148 deZinnia, Inc.
      1032 W 7th St St. Paul, MN 55102
      (651) 695-1041 Michele Boone CEO
      Fax: (651) 695-1048
      Email: sbboone@dezinnia.com
      Website: www.dezinnia.com
Program management, graphic design, marketing,
marketing communications, digital architecture.
(Woman/White, estab 1993, empl 14, sales $1,322,045,
cert: State, City, WBENC)

8149 Five Star Productions
      7400 Metro Blvd   Minneapolis, MN 55439
      (952) 831-7309 Cindy Black President
      Fax: (952) 835-3706
      Email: cjblack@fivestarproductions.net
      Website: www.fivestarproductions.net
Full-service production and event management, national
sales meetings and conventions; recognition, incentive,
and awards programs; entertainment and keynote
speakers; product launches; philanthropic and special
events. (Woman/White, estab 1989, empl 3, sales
$1,300,000, cert: WBENC)

8150 Futura Marketing, Inc.
      9531 W 78th St Ste 250 Eden Prairie, MN 55344
      (952) 843-5400 Kelly Wold Smith President
      Fax: (952) 843-4899
      Email: kelly@futuramarketing.com
      Website: www.futuramarketing.com
Marketing svcs: strategic planning, project management
& creative design. (Woman/White, estab 1999, empl 13,
sales $1,146,520, cert: WBENC)

8151 Group Ventures Inc.
      1770 James Ave S, Ste 2   Minneapolis, MN 55403
      (612) 821-0511 Ann Wellmuth President
      Fax: (612) 677-3337
      Email: ann@groupventuresinc.com
      Website: www.groupventuresinc.com
Event & meeting planning, coordination & execution of
incentive trips, sales & organizational meetings, board of
directors meetings, conventions & tradeshows.
(Woman/White, estab 1997, empl 1, sales $14,000,000,
cert: WBENC)

8152 Groups Meetings Incentives, Inc.
      1700 Niagara Lane N, Ste 100   Plymouth, MN
      55447
      (612) 349-5565 Sharon Anderson Accountant/
      Benefits Coord
      Fax: (612) 341-3223
      Email: sharon.anderson@gmitravelinc.com
      Website: www.gmitravelinc.com
Full travel, meeting & conference services, merchandise
& administrative services. (Woman/White, estab 1984,
empl 6, sales $6,950,399, cert: WBENC)

8153 KDG InterActive, Inc.
      8010 Demontreville Trail Lake Elmo, MN 55042
      (651) 748-8480 Lynette Kramer President
      Fax: (651) 748-5025
      Email: lynette@kdg.com
      Website: www.kdg.com
Design & develop interactive marketing, education &
training solutions. (Woman/White, estab 1991, empl 11,
sales $1,200,000, cert: WBENC)

8154 LEE Branding
945 Broadway St NE Ste 280 Minneapolis, MN 55413
(612) 843-8477 Terri Lee CEO
Fax: (612) 843-8479
Email: terri@leebranding.com
Website: www.leebranding.com
Consumer-minded, strategic brand development. (Woman/White, estab 2011, empl 15, sales $4,100,000, cert: WBENC)

8155 Neka Creative LLC
P.O. Box 211481 Saint Paul, MN 55121
(651) 207-9656 Rosemary Ugboajah President
Fax:
Email: rosemaryu@nekacreative.com
Website:
Brand development, Competitive Analysis, Brand Audits, Qualitative Research, Quantitative Research, Strategic Positioning, Brand Development, Culture Plans, Brand Workshops
Brand Blueprints, Marketing/Communication. (Woman/AA, estab 2009, empl 1, sales , cert: NMSDC)

8156 Nina Hale Inc.
100 S 5th St, Ste 2000 Minneapolis, MN 55402
(612) 392-2427 Sarah Petit Sales and Mktg Mgr
Fax:
Email: businessinquiry@ninahale.com
Website: www.ninahale.com
Digital direct marketing; search engine optimization (SEO), paid placement, social media consulting, analytics & reporting, local search. (Woman/Nat Ame/Hisp, estab 2005, empl 65, sales $9,185,283, cert: WBENC)

8157 One 2 One Marketing Inc.
12101 12th Avenue South Burnsville, MN 55337
(952) 567-2730 Elaine Grundhauser CEO
Fax: (952) 567-2755
Email: elaine.g@one2onemktg.com
Website: www.one2onemktg.com
Strategic promotional programs. (Woman/White, estab 1995, empl 9, sales $1,600,000, cert: WBENC)

8158 Perkins & Associates, LLC
400 Grovaland Ave, Ste 2309 Minneapolis, MN 55403
(612) 810-8361 Frank Perkins Owner
Fax:
Email: frank@perkinsbridge.com
Website: www.perkinsbridge.com
Marketing & business development. (AA, estab 2000, empl 1, sales $125,000, cert: City, NMSDC)

8159 Showcraft, Inc.
1357 Larc Industrial Blvd Burnsville, MN 55337
(952) 890-4200 Jeryl Beaulieu President
Fax: (952) 808-0558
Email: jeryl@showcraft.com
Website: www.showcraft.com
Trade show exhibits, events & environments. (Woman/White, estab 1996, empl 14, sales $500,000, cert: WBENC)

8160 SmartBase Solutions LLC
411 Washington Ave N Minneapolis, MN 55401
(612) 767-9940 Kris Lynch CEO
Fax: (612) 767-9748
Email: klynch@smartbasesolutions.com
Website: www.smartbasesolutions.com
Database marketing solutions, measure, analyze, & improve marketing & sales activities. (Woman/White, estab 2005, empl 20, sales , cert: WBENC)

8161 The Research Edge LLC
1821 University Ave W #N177 St. Paul, MN 55104
(651) 644-6006 Cheryl Powers President
Fax: (651) 644-6015
Email: cheryl@theresearchedge.com
Website: www.theresearchedge.com
Marketing research services, focus groups, in-depth interviews, qualitative research, quantitative research, phone surveys, online surveys, online focus groups, customized market research services full-service market research services. (Woman/White, estab 1995, empl 5, sales $350,000, cert: WBENC)

8162 Touch Of Magic Inc.
P.O. Box 9311 St. Paul, MN 55109
(651)7489442 Lori Hurley Chief Entertainment Officer
Fax:
Email: lori@atouchofmagicentertainment.com
Website: www.atouchofmagicentertainment.com
Event planning, Company Picnics, Corporate Events, Holiday Parties, Banquets, Trade Shows, Sales Meetings, Festivals, Fairs, Mitzvahs, Birthday Parties, Team Building, Schools, Churches, etc. (Woman/White, estab 1986, empl 2, sales $250,000, cert: WBENC)

8163 Tunheim Partners, Inc.
8009 34th Ave S, Ste 1100 Minneapolis, MN 55425
(1612) 210-4639 Ginny Melvie Sr Exec Asst
Fax: (952) 851-1610
Email: gmelvie@tunheim.com
Website: www.tunheim.com
Public Relations, Public Affairs, Strategic Communications, Crisis Communications, Branding - Marketing, Research & Opinion Polling. (Woman/White, estab 1990, empl 45, sales $5,750,000, cert: WBENC)

8164 Type A Events, LLC
10701 Red Circle Dr Minnetonka, MN 55343
(763) 682-4846 Jennifer Braun CEO
Fax: (763) 684-0061
Email: jennifer@typeaevents.com
Website: www.typeaevents.com
Strategic event management. (Woman/White, estab 2009, empl 40, sales $9,000,000, cert: WBENC)

8165 Visions, Inc.
8801 Wyoming Ave N Brooklyn Park, MN 55445
(763) 425-4251 Rick Hansen President
Fax: (763) 425-4616
Email: rick.hansen@visionsfirst.com
Website: www.visionsfirst.com
Web design, print design, advertising & promotion, corporate identification, logo branding, packaging, interactive media, flash animation, video & special effects, 3D animation, web-based applications. (Nat Ame, estab 1985, empl 87, sales $18,059,329, cert: NMSDC)

Missouri

8166　Brighton Agency, Inc.
7711 Bonhomme Ave Ste 100 Saint Louis, MO 63105
(314) 726-0700 Tina VonderHaar CEO
Fax: (314) 721-8517
Email: accounting@brightonagency.com
Website: www.brightonagency.com
Strategic planning, brand development, digital marketing & production, marketing consulting, public relations, advertising, promotions, media planning, audio & video production, event marketing, online, mobile & app development. (Woman/White, estab 1989, empl 71, sales $9,030,143, cert: State, WBENC)

8167　Credit Financial Group Inc.
141 Chesterfield Business Pkwy   Chesterfield, MO 63005
(636) 536-5344 Vincent Andaloro President
Fax: (636) 536-9456
Email: vince@latinpak.com
Website: www.latinpak.com
Direct marketing services. (Hisp, estab 1996, empl 11, sales $1,600,000, cert: State, NMSDC)

8168　Decision Insight Inc.
2940 Main St Kansas City, MO 64108
(816) 221-0445 Tami Kaegi Office Mgr
Fax: (816) 221-9955
Email: info@decisioninsight.com
Website: www.decisioninsight.com
Market research services. (Woman/White, estab 1983, empl 22, sales $3,440,000, cert: WBENC)

8169　Moxi Events, LLC
1904 Grassy Ridge Rd   Saint Louis, MO 63122
(615) 454-2008 Jaime Ratino Acct Mgr
Fax: (314) 329-3330
Email: jratino@moxievents.com
Website: www.moxievents.com
Corporate event planning, meetings, conferences, incentive programs & special events. (Woman, estab 2008, empl 7, sales $267,125, cert: WBENC)

8170　Mozaic Management, Inc.
5257 Shaw Ave Ste 204 St. Louis, MO 63110
(314) 446-6400 Mary Ann Gibson CEO
Fax: (314) 446-6411
Email: mgibson@mozaicltd.com
Website: www.mozaicltd.com
Marketing communications: strategic brand consulting, concept & design, creative execution, digital photography, illustration, photo retouching, interactive web services, art production, prepress, large format digital printing, sales promotion, etc. (Woman/White, estab 2003, empl 130, sales $30,000,000, cert: WBENC)

8171　MT & Associates, LLC
P.O. Box 11584 7461 Bland Saint Louis, MO 63105
(314) 724-2138 Shelly Tisius President
Fax: (314) 754-9241
Email: MT@mtapractice.com
Website: www.MTAPractice.com
Sign language interpreting services. (Woman, estab 2013, empl 5, sales $27,000, cert: State)

8172　Ole Tyme Produce Inc.
92 Produce Row   Saint Louis, MO 63102
(314) 436-5010 Jim Adams President
Fax: (314) 436-4288
Email: jadams@oletyme.com
Website: www.oletyme.com
Monday-Saturday fresh produce deliveries to Saint Louis and the surrounding area. (Woman/White, estab 1973, empl 48, sales $28,000,000, cert: State, City)

8173　Stakeholder Insights, LLC
319 N 4th St Ste 820 St. Louis, MO 63102
(314) 454-1923 Lisa Richter Managing Principal
Fax:
Email: lisa@stakeholderinsights.com
Website: www.stakeholderinsights.com
Market & employee research services, supports branding, change management, competitive intelligence, customer experience, employee engagement and retention, message testing, public opinion & website usability. (Woman/White, estab 2006, empl 3, sales $408,312, cert: WBENC)

8174　The Vandiver Group, Inc.
16052 Swingley Ridge Rd Ste 210 St. Louis, MO 63017
(314) 991-4641 Donna Vandiver CEO
Fax: (314) 991-4651
Email: tvg@vandivergroup.com
Website: www.vandivergroup.com
Strategic communications & public relations, corporate image & reputation management, branding, market research & training. (Woman/White, estab 1993, empl 10, sales $1,432,900, cert: State, WBENC)

North Carolina

8175　ABZ Design Group, Inc.
1300 S Mint St, Ste 100   Charlotte, NC 28203
(704) 374-1072 Libby (Elizabeth) Rose President
Fax: (704) 374-1075
Email: libby@abzdesign.com
Website: www.abzdesign.com
Marketing communications & graphic design. (Woman/White, estab 1982, empl 11, sales , cert: State)

8176　Avantgarde Translations
5960 Fairview Rd Ste 400 Charlotte, NC 28210
(704) 496-2735 Jael Williams Admin Asst
Fax: (800) 575-8262
Email: submissions@avantgardetranslations.com
Website: www.avantgardetranslations.com
Translating written material, interpretation services, revising, editing, proofreading & laying out translated documents, cultural consulting. (Woman/AA, estab 2004, empl 3, sales $200,789, cert: NMSDC, WBENC)

8177　Bellomy Research, Inc.
175 Sunnynoll Ct Winston-Salem, NC 27106
(336) 721-1140 Sandy Moore Senior Dir Admin
Fax: (336) 354-1556
Email: smoore@bellomyresearch.com
Website: www.bellomyresearch.com
Marketing research services: design, data collection, analysis, interpretation, reporting & delivering point-of-view. (Woman, estab 1977, empl 100, sales $14,600,000, cert: State)

8178   Confero, Inc.
       535 Keisler Dr Ste 204 Cary, NC 27518
       (919) 469-5200 Elaine Buxton President
       Fax: (919) 380-7136
       Email: ebuxton@conferoinc.com
       Website: www.conferoinc.com
Mystery shopping & customer satisfaction studies,
training, brand management. (Woman/White, estab 1987,
empl 23, sales , cert: WBENC)

8179   Content Spectrum
       1832 Folly Gate Ct   Charlotte, NC 28262
       (980) 309-1465 David Springston Owner
       Fax: (805) 466-4090
       Email: contentspectrum@gmail.com
       Website: www.contentspectrum.net
Copywriting, Editing, Graphic design (banners, fliers,
magazines, newsletters, posters, etc.), Translation services,
Website development & maintenance. (Woman/AA, estab
2015, empl 1, sales $58,000, cert: NMSDC)

8180   GNB Ventures, LLC DBA Sisco Safety
       1800F Associates Lane Ste F Charlotte, NC 28217
       (704) 488-4468 Naomi Reale CEO
       Fax: (704) 824-8884
       Email: Naomi@siscosafety.com
       Website: www.SiscoSafety.com
Event planning services. (Woman/White, estab 2011, empl
12, sales $1,100,000, cert: WBENC, NWBOC)

8181   It's My Affair, LLC
       P.O. Box 680202 8711 Walden Ridge Drive Char-
       lotte, NC 28216
       (704) 394-4928 Karen Lawrence President
       Fax: (980) 207-3675
       Email: karen@itsmyaffair.com
       Website: www.itsmyaffair.com
Special events & meeting management: meetings,
conferences, tradeshow management, grand openings,
corporate recognition, launch parties, incentives. (Woman/
AA, estab 2002, empl 2, sales $70,000, cert: WBENC, 8(a))

8182   Lockman-Brooks Marketing Services, LLC
       6135 Park Dr S Ste 510 Charlotte, NC 28210
       (704) 293-5666 Linda Lockman-Brooks President
       Fax:
       Email: linda@lockmanbrooks.com
       Website: www.lockmanbrooks.com
Strategic marketing consulting: commununity relations &
outreach, leadership consulting, communications planning
& project management. (Woman/AA, estab 1998, empl 1,
sales $68,000, cert: NMSDC)

8183   Marketing Resource Solutions, LLC
       720 W Main St Jamestown, NC 27282
       (336) 510-7523 Larry Fairley President
       Fax: (336) 510-7557
       Email: lfairley@marketingresourcesolutions.com
       Website: www.marketingresourcesolutions.com
Marketing strategies: print production management, direct
mail, commercial printing, creative concept & design &
database management services. (AA, estab 2000, empl 10,
sales $650,000, cert: NMSDC)

8184   TCG Events
       2923 S. Tryon St Ste 230 Charlotte, NC 28203
       (704) 376-1943 Cassie Brown President
       Fax: (704) 870-3873
       Email: cbrown@tcgevents.com
       Website: www.tcgevents.com
Event planning & production, video production, graphic
design and art direction, conference management,
entertainment production, incentive programs, corporate awards programs, destination management.
(Woman/White, estab 1985, empl 5, sales $2,400,000,
cert: WBENC)

8185   The Media Pro
       4613 Hunters Creek Lane   Raleigh, NC 27606
       (919) 805-1061 Jill Hammergren Owner
       Fax: (919) 516-0750
       Email: jill@themediapro.biz
       Website: www.themediapro.biz
Media, marketing & communications, visual storytelling,
creative writing, videos, animations & graphic, live TV,
network programming, PSAs, video, film, e-learning,
government, training & & multimedia purposes.
(Woman, estab 1987, empl , sales , cert: WBENC)

8186   The Special Event Company
       6112 Saint Giles St   Raleigh, NC 27612
       (919) 459-8785 Barbara Leedy Director of
       Business Dev
       Fax: (919) 459-8793
       Email: barbara@specialeventco.com
       Website: www.specialeventco.com/
Event & meeting management. (Woman/White, estab
2001, empl 15, sales $5,000,000, cert: WBENC)

8187   Wray Ward, LLC
       900 Baxter St Charlott, NC 28204
       (704) 332-9071 Kent Panther VP strategic
       planning
       Fax: (704) 375-5971
       Email: kpanther@wrayward.com
       Website: www.wrayward.com
Marketing communications, strategic planning, brand
development, account leadership, advertising, media
planning and buying, interactive & web marketing,
direct marketing, public relations & social media.
(Woman/White, estab 1977, empl 65, sales $23,345,000,
cert: State)

North Dakota

8188   Global Sales Advisors
       523 Belmont Rd Grand Forks, ND 58201
       (701) 792-3394 Andra Hargrave Owner
       Fax:
       Email: andralazar@earthlink.net
       Website:
Marketing, direct marketing, diversity outreach, sales
training. (AA, estab 2002, empl 2, sales $70,000, cert:
State)

Nebraska

8189 Bozell and Jacobs LLC
      1022 Leavenworth St   Omaha, NE 68102
      (402) 965-4300 Robin Donovan President
      Fax: (402) 965-4399
      Email: rdonovan@bozell.com
      Website: www.bozell.com
Marketing Communications, Branding, Digital Marketing,
Interactive Design & Development, Social Media, Media,
Public Relations, Market Research, Data Analytics.
(Woman/White, estab 1921, empl 38, sales $3,200,000,
cert: WBENC)

8190 J.P. Cooke Company
      1311 Howard St   Omaha, NE 68102
      (402) 342-7175 JOHN COOKE President
      Fax: (800) 342-1260
      Email: john@jpcooke.com
      Website: www.jpcooke.com
J.P. Cooke Company is a financially sound 125-year-old
leader in the Marking and Identification Industry.   Our
products include Stamps, Signs, Embossing Seals, Name
Badges, Daters, Inks and Numbering (Woman/White, estab
1900, empl 30, sales $4,000,000, cert: State)

New Jersey

8191 AG Marketing & Consulting Group
      554 W Broad St 1st Fl Rear Westfield, NJ 07090
      (908) 456-5700 April Gregory President
      Fax:
      Email: april@aprilgregoryinc.com
      Website: www.agmarketingconsulting.com
Brand development, event marketing & marketing plan-
ning, social media & web implementation services.
(Woman/AA, estab 2000, empl 3, sales $250,000, cert:
State)

8192 Baldwin & Obenauf, Inc.
      50 Division St Ste 401 Somerville, NJ 08876
      (908) 685-1510 Joanne Obenauf CEO
      Fax: (908) 707-9181
      Email: jmobenauf@baldwinandobenauf.com
      Website: www.bnoinc.com
Marketing & communications, strategic, creative &
production, brand strategy, identity packages, advertising,
print & digital collateral, web & mobile sites, corporate
intranets, mobile apps, social media campaigns, videos.
(Woman/White, estab 1981, empl 46, sales $7,267,000,
cert: State, WBENC)

8193 Breakthrough Marketing Technology
      110 E. Shearwater Court Ste 11 Jersey City, NJ
      07305
      (201) 604-3600 Elaine Harris President
      Fax: (201) 915-1994
      Email: elaine@breakthroughgroup.com
      Website: www.breakthroughgroup.com
Marketing, strategic planning, market research, learning,
coaching, implementation planning. (Woman/AA, estab
2002, empl 13, sales $432,000, cert: State, WBENC)

8194 Briechle-Fernandez Marketing Services
      625 Industrial Way West, Ste 7   Eatontown, NJ
      07724
      (732) 982-8222 Lorenzo Fernandez President
      Fax: (732) 982-8223
      Email: lorenzo.fernandez@bfmarketing.com
      Website: www.bfmarketing.com
Advertising, public relations, promotional items,
graphics design. (Hisp, estab 1984, empl 24, sales
$5,063,096, cert: State)

8195 BUZZRegistration
      3525 Quakerbridge Rd Ste 908 Hamilton, NJ
      08619
      (888) 202-2262 Megan Buzzetta CEO
      Fax: (609) 424-0230
      Email: info@buzzregistration.com
      Website: www.buzzregistration.com
Registration management services for meeting planners.
Focus on the core planning of your events and leave
attendee management to our registration team.
(Woman/White, estab 2011, empl 25, sales $4,647,794,
cert: WBENC)

8196 Cajam Marketing, Inc.
      8 Haviland Dr   Millstone Twp, NJ 08535
      (609) 371-1325 Kathy Gould President
      Fax:
      Email: kgould@cajammarketing.com
      Website: www.cajammarketing.com
Offline & online marketing initiatives through analytics.
(Woman/White, estab 2001, empl 5, sales $400,000,
cert: State)

8197 Digital Brand Expressions
      4499 Rt 27   Kingston, NJ 08528
      (609) 688-8558 Veronica Fielding President
      Fax: (609) 688-8556
      Email: vfielding@digitalbrandexpressions.com
      Website: www.digitalbrandexpressions.com
Search engine marketing consultancy & services firm.
Focus: search engine marketing/optimization/advertis-
ing and/or search engine image protection. (Woman,
estab 2002, empl 10, sales $860,000, cert: WBENC)

8198 Distinctive Marketing, Inc.
      516 Bloomfield Ave   Montclair, NJ 07042
      (973) 746-9114 Diane Spencer
      Fax: (973) 783-5555
      Email: dmiassociates@verizon.net
      Website: www.distinctivemktg.com
Marketing research, focus groups, telephone surveys,
event planning & mgmt, consulting, etc. (Woman/AA,
estab 1990, empl 12, sales , cert: State)

8199 Executive Meetings & Incentives, Inc.
      685 US Hwy 202/206 N 2nd Fl Bridgewater, NJ
      08876
      (908) 864-5800 Larry Hambro Business Devel
      Fax: (908) 864-5801
      Email: rgiaimo@eminj.com
      Website: www.eminj.com
Meeting planning, global, full service meeting, event &
incentive planning, logistic services. (Woman/White,
estab 1982, empl 18, sales $2,746,000, cert: State)

8200   FirstEye Media Works
       59 Lincoln Park Ste 375 Newark, NJ 07102
       (973) 494-9705 Kimberlee Williams CEO
       Fax:
       Email: kwilliams@femworksllc.com
       Website: www.femworksllc.com
Integrated campaigns, events & custom campaign photography. (Woman/AA, estab 2004, empl 5, sales $503,611, cert: NMSDC, WBENC)

8201   Focus USA, Inc
       95 North State Route 17 Ste 103 Paramus, NJ 07652
       (201) 489-2525 Meg Ugenti VP New Business Dev
       Fax: (201) 489-4499
       Email: meg@focus-usa-1.com
       Website: www.focus-usa-1.com
Direct & data marketing services, consumer & business database aggregator, buyer behavior profiling, data & email appending, email marketing, digital solutions, mobile marketing, social media marketing. (Woman/White, estab 1994, empl 25, sales $4,200,000, cert: WBENC)

8202   Global Organization and Planning Services, LLC
       302 Springfield Ave, Ste 411 Newark, NJ 07103
       (973) 374-6637 Vanessa Whitehead Owner
       Fax: (770) 745-5345
       Email: vanessa@globalorganizationplanning.com
       Website: www.globalorganizationplanning.com
Event planning & management services: business meetings, conferences, tours, trips, receptions, cruises, accommodations & travel, program & agenda development, logistics management, etc. (Woman/AA/Nat Ame, estab 2002, empl 10, sales , cert: City)

8203   Global Planners, Inc.
       3525 Quakerbridge Rd Ste 909 Hamilton, NJ 08619
       (609) 689-0001 Megan Buzzetta CEO
       Fax: (609) 689-0069
       Email: wbereg@globalplanners.com
       Website: www.globalplanners.com
Meeting & event coordination, contract negotiation, on line attendee registration, on site staff support, site selection, travel agency. (Woman/White, estab 2000, empl 14, sales $3,368,000, cert: WBENC)

8204   HEPCO Inc.
       160 Pehle Ave Ste 202 Saddle Brook, NJ 07663
       (201) 843-4400 Antonio Levato
       Fax: (201) 843-0025
       Email: antonio@hepcoinc.com
       Website: www.hepcoinc.com
HEPCO provides contract labor (job shoppers), temp-to-perm and permanent staffing solutions covering the entire disciplines of: Engineering, Information Systems, Telecommunications and Facility Management. HEPCO currently has 150 (Woman/White, estab 1973, empl 270, sales $14,695,426, cert: State)

8205   Impact Consulting Enterprises LLC
       172 S Clinton St   East Orange, NJ 07018
       (973) 337-2028 Cheryl McCants Principal
       Fax: (877) 337-2276
       Email: cmccants@eimpactconsulting.com
       Website: www.eimpactconsulting.com
Marketing, Communication, Special Campaigns & Media Relations. (Woman/AA, estab 1989, empl 12, sales $175,000, cert: State, NMSDC, WBENC, 8(a))

8206   InGroup, Inc.
       P.O. Box 206 Midland Park, NJ 07432
       (201) 612-1230 Marlene C. Bauer President
       Fax: (201) 612-1232
       Email: wbe@ingroupinc.com
       Website: www.ingroupinc.com
Strategy & customized support services for marketing programs, outreach communications & public relations. (Woman/White, estab 1995, empl 5, sales $461,884, cert: State, City, SDB)

8207   Magee Enterprises, LLC dba Event1Source
       68 Abbond Court   Plainfield, NJ 07063
       (888) 299-2250 Dion Magee Co-Owner
       Fax:
       Email: dion@event1source.com
       Website: www.event1source.com
Event management & meeting sourcing. (Woman/AA, estab 1994, empl 2, sales $195,000, cert: State)

8208   Marketsmith Inc.
       2 Wing Dr   Cedar Knolls, NJ 07927
       (973) 889-0006 Jill Draper President
       Fax:
       Email: jdraper@marketsmithinc.com
       Website: www.marketsmithinc.com
Media: strategic consulting; media planning, buying & optimization; traditional; programmatic display; mobile; paid social; social CRM. (Woman/White, estab 1999, empl 72, sales $9,417,082, cert: WBENC)

8209   MarketView Research Group, Inc.
       115 River Rd, Ste 105   Edgewater, NJ 07020
       (201) 840-5300 Deirdre Hart VP
       Fax: (201) 840-6502
       Email: deirdre.hart@mvrg.com
       Website: www.marketviewresearch.com
Quantitative marketing research. (Woman/White, estab 1989, empl 35, sales $8,021,000, cert: State)

8210   Meadowlands Consumer Center Global Marketing Resea
       301 Rt. 17N Ste 503 Rutherford, NJ 07070
       (201) 865-4900 Andrea C. Schrager CEO
       Fax: (201) 865-0408
       Email: info@consumercenters.com
       Website: www.consumercenters.com
Qualitative market research & strategic consulting: study design, strategy development, branding & new product R & D. (Woman/White, estab 1984, empl 50, sales $5,200,000, cert: State, WBENC)

8211   Meeting Logistics, LLC
       890 Mountain Ave   New Providence, NJ 07974
       (908) 771-0804 Catherine Mullen President
       Fax: (908) 771-0349
       Email: cmullen@mtglogistics.com
       Website: www.mtglogistics.com
Meeting, event, convention management, trade show support, incentive programs, special events, advisory boards, awards, educational programs, training programs. (Woman, estab 2000, empl 5, sales $1,933,790, cert: WBENC)

8212   MMI Inc.
       350 W Passaic St   Rochelle Park, NJ 07662
       (201) 556-1188 Michele McKenna President
       Fax: (201) 556-1189
       Email: mmckenna@MarketAnalytics.com
       Website: www.marketanalytics.com
International research: customer, competitive & market
intelligence solutions, qualitative & quantitative solutions.
(Woman/White, estab 2002, empl 10, sales $1,200,000,
cert: State, WBENC)

8213   Mona Terrell & Associates LLC
       1610 Division Ave   Piscataway, NJ 08854
       (732) 752-4690 Mona Terrell President
       Fax:
       Email: mona@monaterrell.com
       Website: www.monaterrell.com
Corporate communications, public relations, public affairs,
social responsibility & sustainability programs. (Woman/
AA, estab 2009, empl 1, sales $150,000, cert: State,
WBENC)

8214   Paragon Productions Inc.
       1900 Shadow Brook Dr   Wall Township, NJ 07719
       (732) 282-9088 Susanne Ardolino President
       Fax: (732) 282-9089
       Email: susanne@paragonproductionsinc.com
       Website: www.paragonproductionsinc.com
Marketing & communications, Design, Scheduling, Staging,
Audio Visual, Guest Speaker & Entertainment require-
ments. (Woman/White, estab 1995, empl 4, sales
$895,000, cert: State)

8215   Raare Solutions LLC
       4 Lorettacong Dr   Lake Hopatcong, NJ 07849
       (800) 693-2994 Rekha Gibbons Business Dev Dir
       Fax: (866) 378-2475
       Email: rekha.gibbons@raaresolutions.com
       Website: www.raaresolutions.com
CRM & customer data analysis, marketing campaign design
& management services, focusing on luxury brands.
(Woman/White, estab 2004, empl 17, sales $2,100,000,
cert: WBENC)

8216   Smith Design Associates Inc.
       8 Budd St   Morristown, NJ 07960
       (973) 429-2177 Jenna Smith CEO
       Fax:
       Email: Jenna@smithdesign.com
       Website: www.smithdesign.com
Brand Identity & Package Design, Seamless Account +
Project Management, Visual Strategy + Positioning, Verbal
Expression + Brand Package Design, Design Production +
Realization.
Visual (Woman/White, estab 1978, empl 25, sales
$7,000,000, cert: State, WBENC)

8217   Stokes Creative Group, LLC
       1666 Route 206   Southampton, NJ 08088
       (609) 859-8400 Jeanette Morenski Business Devel
       Fax:
       Email: info@stokescg.com
       Website: www.stokescg.com
Website design & branding; safety & training videos;
construction photography; public relations; advertising.
(Woman, estab 1989, empl 25, sales $1,700,000, cert:
WBENC)

8218   Strategic Research I
       101 Morgan Lane   Plainsboro, NJ 08536
       (609) 751-5231 Venky Jagannathan Principal
       Fax:
       Email: venky.jagan@srinsights.com
       Website: www.srinsights.com
Pharmaceutical Marketing Research, Marketing Consulting, Big Data Analysis. (As-Ind, estab 2006, empl 20,
sales , cert: State)

8219   Taurus Market Research
       1810 Englishtown Rd   Old Bridge, NJ 08857
       (732) 251-7772 Beth Kamenitz Dir client Dev
       Fax: (732) 251-9008
       Email: beth@taurusresearch.com
       Website: www.taurusresearch.com
Qualitative & quantitative market research: concept,
product, packaging & advertising testing, one-on-one in-
depth interviewing, intercept/exit interviewing, ethnographies & consumer panels, in-house recruiting.
(Woman/White, estab 1992, empl 53, sales $1,000,000,
cert: City)

8220   The Lane Group LLC
       14-25 Plaza Rd North Ste 3N Fair Lawn, NJ 07410
       (201) 398-9230 Tracey Lane President
       Fax: (844) 604-0134
       Email: tlane@tlgmeetings.com
       Website: www.tlgmeetings.com
Event & meeting planning, production & management
(Woman/White, estab 2000, empl 15, sales $2,226,800,
cert: State, WBENC)

8221   TMW Enterprises, Inc.
       76 Park Ave   Flemington, NJ 08822
       (908) 638-6070 Regina Foy President
       Fax: (908) 638-8202
       Email: regina@tmwenterprises.com
       Website: www.tmwenterprises.com
Audio visual equipment & staging services: sales
meetings, product launches & award ceremonies.
(Woman/White, estab 1992, empl 6, sales $2,650,000,
cert: WBENC)

8222   Websignia
       60 Park Place Ste 404 Newark, NJ 07102
       (973) 732-4750 Steve Jones CEO
       Fax: (973) 732-4749
       Email: diversity@websignia.net
       Website: www.websignia.net
Digital marketing, visual design for web & print, digital
marketing & custom web & mobile applications. (AA,
estab 2003, empl 13, sales $670,000, cert: NMSDC)

New Mexico

8223   Slow Life Games, LLC
       9 Piedras Negras   Santa Fe, NM 87505
       (505) 603-8930 Jason Zeaman President
       Fax: (216) 378-1450
       Email: jason@handcraftedlearning.com
       Website: www.HandcraftedLearning.com
Design & develop custom training: virtual webinars, in-
person classroom & stand alone eLearning, interactive
training, (Woman/As-Pac, estab 2011, empl 2, sales
$716,617, cert: NMSDC)

Nevada

8224 Ad Hoc Communication Resources, LLC
6 Benevolo Dr   Henderson, NV 89011
(702) 567-1115 Shelli Ryan President
Fax: (702) 567-1117
Email: shelli@adhocCR.com
Website: www.adhocCR.com
Business & corporate management consulting svcs:
editing, technical writing, public realtions, news & publicity, product launches, media outreach, industry analyst
outreach, whitepapers, press releases. (Woman/White,
estab 1996, empl 2, sales $304,129, cert: WBENC)

8225 MYS LLC
1000 N Green Valley Pkwy, Ste 440-592   Henderson,
NV 89074
(800) 933-9720 Laura Silva Project Director
Fax: (216) 378-1450
Email: info@mysfirm.com
Website: www.mysfirm.com
Project management & brand management services,
strategic marketing services, print & digital media.
(Woman/AA/Hisp, estab 2014, empl 2, sales $122,600,
cert: NMSDC, WBENC)

New York

8226 aLanguageBank
159 W 25th St, 6th Fl   New York, NY 10001
(212) 213-3336 Maxwell Davidson Mgr of New Bus
Fax: (212) 343-2940
Email: MaxwellD@alanguagebank.com
Website: www.alanguagebank.com
Translation & localization services. (As-Pac, estab 1999,
empl 10, sales $950,000, cert: NMSDC)

8227 Analytic Partners, Inc.
360 Lexington Ave   New York, NY 10017
(212) 599-7630 Nancy Smith President
Fax: (212) 599-7644
Email: alina.okun@analyticpartners.com
Website: www.analyticpartners.com
Marketing research, behavorial analysis, Marketing Mix
Modeling. (Woman, estab , empl 1, sales , cert: WBENC)

8228 BuzzBack Market Research dba Buzzback LLC
989 Sixth Ave   New York, NY 10036
(646) 315-7575 Andrea Levene SVP Finance/Admin
Fax: (646) 417-6479
Email: info@buzzback.com
Website: www.buzzback.com
Full service market research. (Woman, estab 2000, empl
37, sales , cert: WBENC)

8229 BuzzBack, LLC
989 Sixth Ave, 5th Fl   New York, NY 10018
(646) 519-8010 Carol Fitzgerald President
Fax:
Email: alevene@buzzback.com
Website: www.buzzback.com
Market research, concept screening & optimization,
attitude & usage studies, package testing, naming studies,
advertising evaluation, brand exploratory, segmentation
studies, online diaries, custom panels. (Woman/White,
estab 2000, empl 35, sales , cert: WBENC)

8230 CBA Research Corp.
59 Clubhouse Ln   Scarsdale, NY 10583
(914) 478-9355 Judy Bernstein VP Qual Insights
Fax: (914) 478-9358
Email: judy_bernstein@cba-link.com
Website: www.cba-link.com
Qualitative marketing research, focus groups, insights,
moderating, analysis, ethnographies, depth interviews,
shop-alongs, brand imagery, new product development,
concept/messaging. (Woman/White, estab 1967, empl
3, sales $1,063,279, cert: WBENC)

8231 Company 20, Inc.
555 Eighth Ave Ste 2201 New York, NY 10018
(212) 784-6453 Michele Lasky VP
Fax: (212) 967-2590
Email: michelelasky@company20.com
Website: www.company20.com
Event marketing; planning; management; consulting;
production; charity fundraisers; celebrity; athlete
foundations; cause-related; sports; special events;
corporate meetings; consumer promotions; incentives;
hospitality. (Woman/White, estab 2005, empl 5, sales
$2,085,000, cert: WBENC)

8232 Complemar Partners
500 Lee Rd Ste 200 Rochester, NY 14606
(585) 647-5890 Jason Aymerich President
Fax: (585) 647-5807
Email: JAymerich@complemar.com
Website: www.complemar.com
Marketing & sales communication programs. (Woman/
White, estab 2004, empl 65, sales $5,195,389, cert:
WBENC)

8233 Converge Marketing Services, LLC
33 E 33rd St 3rd Fl New York, NY 10016
(203) 536-9414 Maarten Terry President
Fax:
Email: maartent@convergedirect.com
Website: www.convergemarketingservices.com
Media buying, planning & strategy, print production
services & paper procurement. (AA, estab 2017, empl
17, sales , cert: NMSDC)

8234 Dayton T. Brown, Inc.
1175 Church St Bohemia, NY 11716
(631) 589-6300 Charles Gortakowski
Fax: (631) 567-8540
Email: cgortakowski@dtb.com
Website: www.dtb.com
Comprehensive Information Development, Manage-
ment, and Delivery Services, Engineering writing,
illustration, xml/sgml, technical publications, IETM,
Arbortext Epic, Framemaker, Interleaf, Autotrol, Isodraw,
Autocad, Full-service (Woman/White, estab 1950, empl
350, sales $36,000,000, cert: State)

8235 Design & Source Productions, Inc.
143 W 29th St 3rd Fl New York, NY 10001
(212) 265-8632 Laura Tufariello President
Fax:
Email: laura@dsnyc.com
Website: www.design-and-source.com
Design & develop branded & private label products,
custom creative packaging solutions. (Woman/White,
estab 1996, empl 7, sales $8,400,000, cert: City, WBENC)

8236 DEVLINHAIR Production Inc.
120 Wooster St 3rd Fl New York, NY 10012
(212) 941-9009 Dorothy Devlin Co-Founder
Fax: (212) 941-9008
Email: supplier-diversity@devlinhair.com
Website: www.devlinhair.com
Corporate event planning: meetings, conferences, internal sales/mktg campaigns, film, video training programs, interactive media. (Woman/White, estab 1991, empl 13, sales $14,938,324, cert: WBENC)

8237 Ebony Marketing Systems, Inc.
79 Alexander Ave, Ste 31-A Bronx, NY 10454
(718) 742-0006 Kai Fuentes Ops Dir
Fax: (718) 742-0067
Email: kfuentes@ebonysystems.com
Website: www.ebonysystems.com
Market research studies & services. (Woman/AA, estab 2011, empl 1, sales $650,000, cert: City, NMSDC)

8238 Eclipse Direct Marketing LLC
173 Mineola Blvd Ste 402 Mineola, NY 11501
(212) 931-8344 Kris Thelen CEO
Fax: (212) 931-8344
Email: kthelen@eclipsedm.com
Website: www.eclipsedm.com
Tracking & analytics, strategy planning with marketing departments. (Woman/White, estab 2003, empl 7, sales $7,700,000, cert: WBENC)

8239 Extrovertic Communications, LLC
30 W 21st St 3rd Fl New York, NY 10010
(646) 312-6001 Dorothy Wetzel Chief Extrovert
Fax: (646) 224-9646
Email: dorothy@extrovertic.com
Website: www.extrovertic.com
Creative (print, video and digital), relationship marketing, patient education, social media, & marketing consulting. (Woman/White, estab 2009, empl 27, sales $7,933,003, cert: WBENC)

8240 Foglamp Research Corp.
100 Greenwich Rd Bedford, NY 10506
(914) 682-4127 Kate Horn CEO
Fax: (855) 232-0016
Email: kate.horn@foglampresearch.com
Website: www.foglampresearch.com
Due diligence, reputational risk inquiries, surveys, interviews & local market intelligence research in emerging & frontier markets. (Woman/White, estab 2013, empl 3, sales $237,811, cert: WBENC)

8241 Greater Than One Inc.
395 Hudson St 10014 New York, NY 10014
(212) 252-9332 Elizabeth Apelles CEO
Fax: (212) 367-0813
Email: eapelles@gthegtogroup.com
Website: www.wwww.thegtogroup.com
marketing services: strategies, assessments, metrics analytics, consumer research, behavior analytics, communications planning, engagement. (Woman/White, estab 2000, empl 100, sales $50,000,000, cert: City, WBENC)

8242 Human Touch Translations Ltd.
1010 Northern Blvd Ste 208 Great Neck, NY 11021
(646) 358-4972 Erika Nagy President
Fax: (888) 679-7082
Email: info@humantouchtranslations.com
Website: www.humantouchtranslations.com
Translation servivces, 120 languages, interpreting documents, technical documents, legal documents, scientific papers, journal and magazine articles, educational materials, medical documents, market research surveys. (Woman/White, estab 2010, empl 5, sales , cert: State, WBENC)

8243 Imagine 360 Marketing
340 E 64th St Ste 17N New York, NY 10065
(212) 313-9616 Yael Penn President
Fax:
Email: ypenn@i360m.com
Website: www.i360m.com
Strategic marketing and innovative design to increase brand awareness, acquire new business and retain existing customers. (Woman/White, estab 2005, empl 7, sales , cert: WBENC)

8244 Intstrux LLC
15 W 39th St, 13th Fl New York, NY 10018
(646) 688-2782 Sanjiv Mody CEO
Fax:
Email: sanjiv.mody@pixacore.com
Website: www.pixacore.com
Digital communication, strategy & implementation services, marketing, training, corporate communication, live events initiatives. (As-Ind, estab 2007, empl 30, sales $7,577,436, cert: NMSDC)

8245 Ivy Cohen Corporate Communications, Inc.
2098 Frederick Douglass Blvd. Ste 10M New York, NY 10026
(212) 399-0026 Ivy Cohen CEO
Fax: (212) 504-8311
Email: ivy@ivycohen.com
Website: www.ivycohen.com
Branding, promotions, corporate communications & organizational issues. (Woman/White, estab 2001, empl 1, sales $326,063, cert: City, WBENC)

8246 Keeper of the Brand
894 Otsego Rd West Hempstead, NY 11552
(917) 697-1699 Donyshia Boston-Hill CEO
Fax: (347) 454-9432
Email: db@keeperofthebrand.com
Website: www.keeperofthebrand.com/
Marketing Plans & Strategies, Media Buying, TV, Radio, Print & Digital Solutions, Broadcast Media Distribution, Brand Dev, Consumer Insight, Copyright, Transactional Engagement, Programming & Campaign Mgmt, Graphic Design, Creative Services. (Woman/AA, estab 2013, empl 6, sales $125,000, cert: State, NMSDC, WBENC)

8247 Kipany Productions, Ltd.
32 E 39 St New York, NY 10016
(212) 883-8300 Salman Ali President
Fax: (212) 883-0409
Email: rfp@kipany.com
Website: www.kipany.com
Marketing communication svcs: direct response TV sales & outbound telemarketing; video, print, Internet direct mktg/web design & placement. (Woman/White, estab 1979, empl 30, sales , cert: WBENC)

8248 Kupcha Marketing Services
      2 Hayes Rd   Amity Harbor, NY 11701
      (917) 432-9481 Elizabeth Kupcha President
      Fax: (501) 631-2446
      Email: liz@kupchamkt.com
      Website: www.kupchamkt.com
Marketing consulting: proposal management, presentation preparation/coaching, publicity & event planning. (Woman/AA, estab 2010, empl 1, sales $50,000, cert: State, City)

8249 Lightbeam Communications Corp
      1787 Madison Ave, Ste 710   New York, NY 10035
      (917) 498-1738 Roben Allong CEO
      Fax:
      Email: robena@lightbeamnyc.com
      Website: www.lightbeamnyc.com
Qualitative research. (Woman/AA, estab 2009, empl 1, sales $284,000, cert: City)

8250 Mirror Show Management, Inc.
      855 Hard Rd   Webster, NY 14580
      (585) 232-4020 Wendy Marold Dir Sales & Mktg
      Fax: (585) 232-3148
      Email: supplierdiversity@mirrorshow.com
      Website: www.mirrorshow.com
Exhibit design & management firm. (Woman/White, estab 1993, empl 85, sales $45,416,388, cert: WBENC)

8251 Novatek Communications, Inc.
      500 HelendaleRdSte 280   Rochester, NY 14609
      (585) 482-4070 Amy Castronova CEO
      Fax: (585) 482-4070
      Email: Patty.Setchell@novatekcom.com
      Website: www.novatekcom.com
User & service writing, computer-based training, e-learning & multimedia. (Woman/White, estab 1989, empl 29, sales $1,504,910, cert: State, WBENC)

8252 Percepture
      104 W 40th St.   New York, NY 10018
      (800) 707-9190 Thor Harris CEO
      Fax:
      Email: supplierdiversity@percepture.com
      Website: www.percepture.com
Public relations & marketing. (AA, estab 2004, empl 4, sales $2,369,876, cert: NMSDC)

8253 Sage Advertising LLC
      71 Atkinson Rd   Rockville Centre, NY 11570
      (516) 320-9225 Jodi O'Sullivan Partner
      Fax:
      Email: jodi@sage-agency.com
      Website: www.sage-agency.com
Marketing strategies & materials, print, collateral, digital, trade show & video production. (Woman, estab 2008, empl 7, sales $101,089, cert: WBENC)

8254 Site Solutions Worldwide
      1023 Route 146   Clifton Park, NY 12065
      (518) 399-7181 Lisa Appiarius Bus Relations Spec
      Fax: (518) 399-3033
      Email: LisaA@sswmeetings.com
      Website: www.sitesolutionsworldwide.com
Meeting svcs: site selection, meeting management, contract negotiations, online registration, speaker coordination, exhibitor coordination & on-site meeting management. (Woman/White, estab 2001, empl 14, sales $8,764,783, cert: State, WBENC)

8255 Spiral Design Studio, LLC
      135 Mohawk St   Cohoes, NY 12047
      (518) 326-1135 Lauren Payne Managing Partner
      Fax: (518) 326-2342
      Email: lauren@spiraldesign.com
      Website: www.spiraldesign.com
Graphic design, advertising, marketing, website design, web page design, responsive design, mobile website design, internet marketing, digital marketing, email marketing, branding, logo design, corporate identity, print design, print marketing. (Woman/White, estab 1989, empl 10, sales $948,500, cert: State, WBENC)

8256 Strategic Marketing & Promotions, Inc.
      10 N Main St   Pearl River, NY 10965
      (845) 623-7777 Greg Caglione President
      Fax: (845) 623-7780
      Email: gcaglione@smpglobal.com
      Website: www.smpglobal.com
Mfr, design & produce point of purchase display fixtures, signage, retail consumer packaging. Assembly, fulfillment, inventory management, distribution center. (Woman/White, estab 2001, empl 85, sales $5,000,000, cert: State)

8257 StudioLabs LLC.
      298 5th Ave, 5th Fl   New York, NY 10001
      (646) 880-6892 Elizabeth Young President
      Fax:
      Email: liz@studiolabs.com
      Website: www.studiolabs.com
Websites, online software, mobile applications, digital ads, online tools & digital marketing products. (Woman/White, estab 2003, empl 25, sales $2,321,566, cert: City, WBENC)

8258 The CementBloc
      32 Old Slip 15th Fl New York, NY 10005
      (646) 829-2002 Art Chavez Partner
      Fax:
      Email: achavez@thebloc.com
      Website: www.thebloc.com
Global branding, full-service professional promotion, medical strategy, patient education, payer strategy, digital strategy & communications planning/execution. (Woman/White, estab 2000, empl 175, sales $41,900,000, cert: WBENC)

8259 The Mixx
      350 7th Ave Ste 1403 New York, NY 10001
      (212) 695-6663 Erin Geoghegan Business Liaison
      Fax: (212) 695-6664
      Email: hi@themixxnyc.com
      Website: www.themixxnyc.com
Strategic branding, messaging & marketing firm: corporate identity & brand platforms, brand collateral, annual reports & Bbochures, advertising campaigns, direct mail campaigns, web design & development, multi-media marketing plans. (Woman/White, estab 1996, empl 18, sales $4,618,130, cert: WBENC)

8260   The Mundial Group, Inc.
       28 E 28th St   New York, NY 10016
       (212) 213-1400 Felix Sencion
       Fax: (212) 213-1411
       Email: billing@mundialgroup.net
       Website: www.mundialsportsnetwork.com
Marketing; Print Sport Publication; Print Advertising; Digital
Advertdsing: display, flash, mobile, pre-roll, branded
content production (Hisp, estab 1999, empl 11, sales , cert:
NMSDC)

8261   The Thomas Collective LLC
       37 w 28th st 12th floor   new york, NY 10001
       (212) 229-2294 Erin Donley Special Projects Coord
       Fax:
       Email: edonley@thethomascollective.com
       Website: www.thethomascollective.com
Marketing communications, Brand Development, Public
Relations & Digital/Social Media. (Woman/White, estab
2004, empl 20, sales $5,000,000, cert: WBENC)

8262   TITANIUM Worldwide LLC
       350 7th Ave Ste 1403 New York, NY 10001
       (646) 952-8440 Erin Geoghegan Director of Client
       Relations
       Fax: (212) 695-6664
       Email: sd@titaniumww.com
       Website: www.titaniumww.com
Media, marketing, communications & consulting: Branding/
Creative/Strategy, Content/Messaging, Digital/Social/
Mobile, Film/Video Production, Event Marketing, Business
Intelligence, Data Warehousing, Development/Deployment.
(Woman/White, estab 2014, empl 4, sales , cert: WBENC)

8263   View Finders Market Research
       11 Sandra Ln   Pearl River, NY 10965
       (845) 735-7022 Janet Gaines Owner
       Fax: (845) 735-7256
       Email: jgaines@view-finders.com
       Website: www.view-finders.com
Focus group management, consumer & business research,
advertising testing, product definition, concept development, attitudinal research, usage testing, customer satisfaction & new product development. (Woman/White, estab
1983, empl 25, sales $700,000, cert: WBENC)

8264   Weinman Schnee Morais, Inc.
       250 W 57th St Ste 2212 New York, NY 10107
       (212) 906-1900 Cynthia Weinman Principal
       Fax: (212) 906-1909
       Email: cweinman@wsm-inc.com
       Website: www.wsm-inc.com
Marketing research, 50% qualitative & 50% quantitative.
(Woman/White, estab 1993, empl 12, sales , cert: WBENC)

8265   Yorkville Marketing Consulting LLC
       425 E 79 St Ste 11M New York, NY 10075
       (646) 284-2481 Dina Shapiro CEO
       Fax:
       Email: Dina.Shapiro@YorkvilleConsulting.com
       Website: www.YorkvilleConsulting.com
Corporate Brand Strategy, Marketing, Organization Planning, Marketing Capabilities, Training. (Woman, estab 2013,
empl 1, sales , cert: WBENC)

8266   Zebra Strategies
       421 7th Avenue Ste 1100 New York, NY 10001
       (212) 244-3960 Denene Jonielle Rodney CEO
       Fax: (917) 591-2934
       Email: denene@zstrategies.net
       Website: www.zstrategies.net
Qualitative market research services. (Woman/AA, estab
2001, empl 10, sales $1,541,000, cert: WBENC)

Ohio

8267   Acadia Lead Management Services Inc.
       4738 Gateway Circle Ste A100 Kettering, OH
       45440
       (888) 605-3194 Tami Randall Mgr
       Fax: (866) 435-8442
       Email: tlr@acadialms.com
       Website: www.acadialms.com
Customized industry data, marketing information & sales
leads, lead qualification, lead nurturing, marketing
dashboard & lead management. (Woman/White, estab
1999, empl 21, sales $768,000, cert: WBENC)

8268   Affordable Language Services
       8944 Blue Ash Rd   Cincinnati, OH 45242
       (513) 745-0888 Kristi Reynek Chief Mktg Officer
       Fax: (513) 793-4577
       Email: kreynek@affordablelanguages.com
       Website: www.affordablelanguages.com
Translation & interpreting services, voice-over &
transcription. (Woman/White, estab 2000, empl 14,
sales $2,209,000, cert: WBENC)

8269   Baker Creative Ltd.
       386 Main St   Groveport, OH 43125
       (614) 836-3845 Michele Cuthbert Principal
       Fax: (614) 836-1801
       Email: mbaker@baker-creative.com
       Website: www.baker-creative.com
Graphic Design, Marketing Consulting, Advertising,
Public Relations, Display Advertising. (Woman/Hisp,
estab 2003, empl 10, sales $150,000, cert: State,
WBENC, SDB)

8270   Bascom & Adams Business Solutions, LLC
       1209 Hill St North Ste 227 Pickerington, OH
       43147
       (614) 252-7880 Christine Adams President
       Fax: (614) 252-7838
       Email: chrisadams@bascomadams.com
       Website: www.bascomadams.com
Marketing communications, public relations, special
events, outreach & engagement. (Woman/AA, estab
2002, empl 1, sales $30,000, cert: State, City)

8271   Blue Star Design LLC
       4164 Lorain Ave   Cleveland, OH 44113
       (216) 334-1312 Julia Briggs CEO
       Fax: (216) 334-1312
       Email: julia@bluestar-design.com
       Website: www.bluestar-design.com
Graphic design, branding, marketing & web services.
(Woman/White, estab 1999, empl 6, sales $756,988,
cert: State, City)

8272 Charm Consulting
2957 Cranbrook Dr   Cincinnati, OH 45251
(513) 290-6357 Toyia Montgomery CEO
Fax:
Email: charmconsulting3@gmail.com
Website: www.charmconsulting3.com
Branding, public relations & event services. (Woman/AA, estab 2014, empl 3, sales $10,716, cert: State)

8273 Gong Gong Communications
746 Green Crest Dr   Westerville, OH 43081
(614) 388-8918 Amanda Sage CEO
Fax:
Email: amanda@gonggongcommunications.com
Website: www.gonggongcommunications.com
Corporate, non-profit event planning & marketing, Offline & online experiential marketing campaigns, Target social media & e-mail marketing campaigns, Podcast production & promotion. (Woman/White, estab 2009, empl 3, sales , cert: WBENC)

8274 Illumination Research, Inc.
5947 Deerfield Blvd Ste 203 Mason, OH 45040
(513) 774-9588 Karri Bass President
Fax: (513) 770-0296
Email: kbass@illumination-research.com
Website: www.illumination-research.com
Qualitative market research. (Woman/White, estab , empl 29, sales $6,593,000, cert: WBENC)

8275 Incite Visual Communications
P.O. Box 1017   Milford, OH 45150
(513) 575-5100 Michael Perry Business Dev Dir
Fax:
Email: mike@incitevisual.com
Website: www.incitevisual.com
Branding/marketing design, Branding, Package Design, Print & Digital Sales/Marketing Assets, Point of Sale materials, Product Sell Sheets, FSI, Event Promotional assets. (Woman/White, estab 2001, empl 2, sales $186,000, cert: WBENC)

8276 Market Inquiry, Inc.
5825 Creek Rd   Cincinnati, OH 45242
(513) 794-1088 Cathy Noyes Owner
Fax: (513) 794-1176
Email: cathy@marketinquiry.com
Website: www.marketinquiry.com
Qualitative & quantitative research. (Woman/White, estab 1995, empl 20, sales $1,164,000, cert: WBENC)

8277 MMP LLC
7588 Central Parke Blvd, Ste 321   Mason, OH 45040
(513) 234-0560 Linda Dektas Owner
Fax:
Email: linda@creativestorm.com
Website: www.creativestorm.com
Websites, ads-print & broadcast, brochures, logo design, digital marketing, direct mail, social media, promotions, displays, promotional items & apparel. (Woman/White, estab 1999, empl 5, sales $1,000,000, cert: WBENC)

8278 Partners In Planning One Inc.
7061 Larkspur Lane   Liberty Township, OH 45044
(513) 755-1091 Nancy Caine President
Fax: (513) 755-1852
Email: ncainepip@aol.com
Website: www.partnersinplanning.org
Meeting planning & event svcs: food & beverage negotiation, budget control, meeting set up & contract negotiations. (Woman/White, estab 1997, empl 1, sales $26,000, cert: WBENC)

8279 Penn and Associates, Inc.
3547 Fenley Rd   Cleveland Heights, OH 44121
(216) 932-4368 Catherine Penn President
Fax: (216) 932-4368
Email: catherine@pennandassociates.com
Website: www.pennandassociates.com
Marketing research & evaluation consulting. Quantitative research (primary research), Secondary research, Economic Analysis, Program evaluation, Online surveys, Data analysis, Report writing. (Woman/White, estab 1987, empl 1, sales , cert: State, City)

8280 Quez Media Marketing
1138 Prospect Ave E   Cleveland, OH 44115
(216) 910-0202 Jose Vasquez CEO
Fax: (216) 910-0202
Email: info@quezmedia.com
Website: www.quezmedia.com
Marketing communications, online storefronts, data services, creative services, print. (Hisp, estab 2009, empl 17, sales $1,646,098, cert: State, City, NMSDC)

8281 R/P Marketing Public Relations
1500 Timberwolf Dr   Holland, OH 43528
(614) 428-6056 Robin Walters VP Business Dev
Fax: (419) 241-2297
Email: rwalters@r-p.com
Website: www.r-p.com
Marketing, advertising & public relations services. (Woman/White, estab 1993, empl 25, sales $5,559,217, cert: WBENC)

8282 Rhonda Crowder & Associates LLC
1465 E 112th St Cleveland, OH 44106
(216) 352-3330 Wayne Dailey Creative Dir
Fax:
Email: wayne@rhondacrowderllc.com
Website: www.rhondacrowderllc.com
Communications, content creation, graphic design, fundraising & media relations services. (Woman/AA, estab 2011, empl 5, sales $12,000, cert: State)

8283 The Voice of Your Customer
2303 Gilbert Ave   Cincinnati, OH 45206
(513) 281-3228 Crystal Kendrick President
Fax: (513) 281-3030
Email: crystal@thevoiceofyourcustomer.com
Website: www.thevoiceofyourcustomer.com
Survey Research, non-exempt employee training, mystery observations, secret shopping, competitive analysis, market analysis & media campaigns. (Woman/AA, estab 2006, empl 4, sales $550,000, cert: State)

8284 Various Views Research, Inc.
11353 Reed Hartman Hwy, Ste 200 Cincinnati, OH 45241
(513) 387-2208 Doug van der Zee Dir Business Dev
Fax:
Email: dvanderzee@variousviews.com
Website: www.variousviews.com
Market research, qualitative research methodologies, focus groups, in-depth interviews & product tests. (Woman/White, estab 2007, empl 75, sales $3,500,000, cert: WBENC)

8285 Visibility Marketing, Inc.
24700 Chagrin Blvd Ste 306 Beachwood, OH 44122
(440) 684-9920 Montrie Rucker Adams Chief Visibility Officer
Fax: (216) 803-0111
Email: mra@visibilitymarketing.com
Website: www.visibilitymarketing.com
Marketing communications & public relations, public & media relations services & strategic marketing campaigns. (Woman/AA, estab 2000, empl 2, sales $41,494, cert: State, City, WBENC, 8(a))

Oklahoma

8286 Bullseye Database Marketing, LLC
5546 S 104th East Ave Tulsa, OK 74146
(918) 587-1731 Deborah Kobe Norris CEO
Fax:
Email: dnorris@bullseyedm.com
Website: www.bullseyedm.com
Direct marketing, direct mail, email, mobile & social media, strategic campaign direction, creative services, on-time, on-budget, error-free production, response tracking & analysis. (Woman/White, estab 1988, empl 8, sales $1,638,390, cert: WBENC)

Oregon

8287 Paulette Carter Design, Inc. (PCD Group)
5257 NE MLK Jr Blvd Ste #301 Portland, OR 97211
(503) 525-2989 Danielle Bastron Controller
Fax: (503) 226-7668
Email: danielle@pcdgroup.com
Website: www.pcdgroup.com
Marketing svcs: custom websites, intranets & online applications, content mgmt, customer relationship mgmt tools, custom work flow & productivity applications, e-commerce, systems & data integration. (Woman/White, estab 1996, empl 12, sales , cert: WBENC)

8288 Stewart Marketing Group, LLC
905 N Harbour Dr, Unit 3 Portland, OR 97217
(503) 270-7857 Michael Stewart President
Fax:
Email: michael@stewartmarketinggroup.com
Website: www.stewartmarketinggroup.com
Conference & event planning, training & seminar materials, travel & hospitality, point of purchase displays, media & CD/DVD disc storage, office supplies. (AA, estab 2006, empl 1, sales $130,000, cert: State, NMSDC)

8289 The Kingfisher Group, LLC
10260 SW Greenburg Rd Ste. 400 Portland, OR 97223
(503) 567-8730 Mary Lou Kayser CEO
Fax:
Email: mlk@maryloukayser.com
Website: www.maryloukayser.com
Content Marketing Strategies, Visual Strategic Planning, Creativity & Innovation, Training & Development, Presentation Skills Development. (Woman/White, estab 2012, empl 1, sales , cert: State)

Pennsylvania

8290 2nd Spark Consulting LLC
31 E Butler Ave 1st Fl Ambler, PA 19002
(215) 948-3055 Stefanie Freeling Finance Mgr
Fax: (267) 481-7004
Email: sfreeling@2ndspark.com
Website: www.2ndspark.com
Marketing consulting & creative advertising, customer insights, situation analysis, war games, portfolio architecture strategy, buying process, positioning, messaging, branding, campaign development, media planning, tactical planning. (Woman/As-Pac, estab 2009, empl 20, sales $1,726,022, cert: WBENC)

8291 Apex Impact Marketing LLC
1720 Kendarloren Dr Ste. 714 Jamison, PA 18929
(215) 489-5460 Howard Wilensky Partner
Fax:
Email: howard@focusmx.com
Website: www.focusmx.com
Marketing Strategy, Digital Strategy & Planning Websites, Microsites, Landing Pages, Creative & Design (Wordpress,Kentico, Sitecore, .NET), eCRM Programs, Social Media Campaigns, Mobile & Tablet Applications, Online Advertising. (Woman/White, estab 2009, empl 14, sales , cert: WBENC)

8292 Bosha Design Inc.
707 Burmont Rd Drexel Hill, PA 19026
(610) 622-4422 Barbara Bosha President
Fax: (610) 622-6344
Email: barb@boshadesign.com
Website: www.boshadesign.com
Print & web graphic design: corporate communications, business collateral, annual reports, web design & dev, identity systems, brochures, newsletters, advertising, exhibits & signage. (Woman/White, estab 1986, empl 4, sales $527,457, cert: WBENC)

8293 Brandwidth Solutions, LLC
108 Samantha Lane Lansdale, PA 19446
(215) 997-8575 Debra Harrsch CEO
Fax:
Email: dharrsch@brandwidthsolutions.com
Website: www.brandwidthsolutions.com
Marketing communications, digital, 3D interactive, video & social media. (Woman, estab 2005, empl 7, sales $718,392, cert: WBENC)

8294 Chelsea Partners Inc.
108 Arch St Ste 1202 Philadelphia, PA 19106
(215) 603-7300 Tempa Berish President
Fax: (215) 827-5800
Email: tempa@chelseapartners.com
Website: www.chelseapartners.com
Graphic design, printing (digital, flat sheet and web), presort mailing services & fulfillment. (Woman/White, estab 1998, empl 13, sales $2,120,795, cert: State, City, WBENC)

8295 Community Marketing Concepts, Inc.
7300 City Ave Ste 330 Philadelphia, PA 19151
(215) 871-0900 Daud Hadi Public Relations
Fax: (215) 871-5920
Email:
johnpaul@communitymarketingconcepts.com
Website: www.communitymarketingconcepts.com
Public relations & marketing, research, strategic development, social & issue management programs, brand messaging, publicity & media placement, event planning, corporate & community relations, sponsorships, graphic & web design. (Woman/AA, estab 1998, empl 10, sales $2,400,000, cert: State, City, NMSDC)

8296 DaBrian Marketing Group
500 Penn St, Ste 201 Reading, PA 19602
(610) 743-5602 Daniel Laws Owner
Fax: (888) 865-2104
Email: dlaws@dabrianmarketing.com
Website: www.dabrianmarketing.com
Digital marketing agency, original and strategic digital marketing solutions. (AA, estab 2008, empl 9, sales $949,000, cert: State, NMSDC)

8297 Eitzen Creative LLC
202 Dudley Avenue Narberth, PA 19072
(610) 660-0220 Pamela Eitzen President
Fax:
Email: pam@eobcreative.com
Website: www.eobcreative.com
Graphic design, strategic communications, branding, advertising, video, animation, corporate & employee communications, corporate identity, investor relations materials, websites, exhibit design & meeting support. (Woman, estab 2012, empl 3, sales $268,944, cert: WBENC)

8298 Fox Specialties, Inc. dba Encompass Elements
2750 Morris Road Lansdale, PA 19446
(215) 822-5775 Neil Paternoster Business Dev Exec
Fax: (215) 822-7977
Email: npaternoster@encompasselements.com
Website: www.encompasselements.com
Marketing communications. (Woman/White, estab 1995, empl 95, sales $15,000,000, cert: WBENC)

8299 GLOBO
145 Greenwood Ave Wyncote, PA 19095
(800) 555-3010 Alec Kissell Sales Ops Mgr
Fax:
Email: alec@helloglobo.com
Website: www.helloglobo.com
Translation, telephone interpreting & video remote interpreting services. (Hisp, estab 2010, empl 43, sales $6,900,000, cert: NMSDC)

8300 Gray Consulting, Inc.
190 N Independence Mall West Ste 201 Philadelphia, PA 19107
(215) 413-7880 Scott Gray CEO
Fax: (215) 825-1343
Email: scott.gray@clincierge.com
Website: www.clincierge.com
Meeting & event planning, logistical services, travel, attendee mgmt, web conferencing, audio/visual production, food & beverage coordination, on-site mgmt, incentive trips, sales meetings. (Woman/White, estab 1994, empl 35, sales $3,413,602, cert: State)

8301 Linguis-Techs, Inc.
408 Executive Dr Langhorne, PA 19047
(215) 860-8152 Lisa O'Rourke Dir of Finance
Fax: (215) 579-9548
Email: Lisa@SommerConsulting.com
Website: www.sommerconsulting.com
Qualitative marketing research, strategy & motivational profile of target audiences on conscious, unconscious & emotional levels. (Woman/Hisp, estab 1991, empl 11, sales $3,855,315, cert: State, NMSDC)

8302 Markitects, Inc.
107 W Lancaster Ave, Ste 203 Wayne, PA 19087
(610) 687-2200 Francine Carb CEO
Fax: (610) 687-2212
Email: fcarb@markitects.com
Website: www.markitects.com
Strategic marketing, branding, public relations & communications. (Woman, estab 1994, empl 12, sales $2,000,000, cert: WBENC)

8303 mdgroup
575 E Swedesford Rd Ste 101 Wayne, PA 19087
(610) 825-2660 LaQuinta Jernigan Senior Director, Business Dev
Fax:
Email: laquinta.jernigan@mdgroup.com
Website: www.mdgroup.com
Global strategic meeting management, incentive travel, sales meetings, corporate events, product launches, training, road shows, corporate retreats, and board of director meetings. (Woman, estab 2002, empl 61, sales $17,713,000, cert: State)

8304 MFR Consultants, Inc.
128 Chestnut St Atrium at Olde City Philadelphia, PA 19106
(215) 238-9270 Maria Roberts CEO
Fax: (215) 238-9733
Email: mfrizelle@mfrconsultants.com
Website: www.mfrconsultants.com
Strategic marketing, multimedia, graphic design, web & application development, management consulting. (Woman/AA, estab 1989, empl 15, sales $4,114,966, cert: State)

8305 MOD Worldwide
1429 Walnut St Fl 2 Philadelphia, PA 19102
(215) 732-7666 Nina Stanley President
Fax:
Email: nina@modworldwide.com
Website: www.modworldwide.com
Brand, marketing, digital, 3D visualization, graphic design, digital media, internet marketing, film, website development, production, visual effects, and print production. (Woman, estab 2002, empl 20, sales $3,000,000, cert: City, WBENC)

8306   Modern Graphics
118 Dickerson Rd Ste B   North Wales, PA 19454
(215) 619-4700   Diane Connor President
Fax: (215) 619-4711
Email: dconnor@modernsbc.com
Website: www.modernsbc.com
Branding, web design, collateral & digital literature, logo design, graphic design, internal & external corporate communications. (Woman/White, estab 1999, empl 8, sales $2,100,000, cert: WBENC)

8307   Naxion, Inc.
1835 Market St   Philadelphia, PA 19103
(215) 496-6870   Patricia Green Special Projects Coord
Fax:
Email: pgreen@naxionthinking.com
Website: www.naxionthinking.com
Provide trusted decision support in innovation, opportunity assessment & pricing, launch strategy, brand health & lifecycle management. (Woman/White, estab 1911, empl 86, sales $22,000,000, cert: WBENC)

8308   Rector Communications, Inc.
2300 Chestnut St, Ste. 360   Philadelphia, PA 19103
(215) 963-9661   Marion Rector President
Fax: (216) 963-9672
Email: marion@rector.com
Website: www.rector.com
Corporate Communications, Employee Communications, Branding, Business Development, Marketing Services, Management Consulting, Graphic Design & Annual Reports. (Woman/White, estab 1983, empl 5, sales $654,514, cert: City, WBENC)

8309   Slice Communications, LLC
234 Market St, Fl 4   Philadelphia, PA 19106
(215) 600-0050   Brian McDonnell Business Dev
Fax:
Email: bmcdonnell@slicecommunications.com
Website: www.slicecommunications.com/
Public relations & social media, stories, editorials, research, data, trends, case studies, events & digital assets. (Woman/White, estab 2008, empl 15, sales , cert: City, WBENC)

8310   SPRYTE Communications
200 S Broad St, Ste 1160   Philadelphia, PA 19102
(215) 545-4715   Lisa Simon CEO
Fax: (215) 545-4717
Email: lsimon@sprytecom.com
Website: www.sprytecom.com
Public relations & marketing consulting. (Woman/White, estab 1990, empl 6, sales $1,527,267, cert: State, WBENC)

8311   The Melior Group, Inc.
1528 Walnut St, Ste 1414   Philadelphia, PA 19102
(215) 545-0054   Linda McAleer President
Fax: (215) 545-0078
Email: lmcaleer@meliorgroup.com
Website: www.meliorgroup.com
Marketing research & consulting, analysis, implications & recommendations. (Woman/White, estab 1982, empl 10, sales $1,500,000, cert: State)

Puerto Rico

8312   DC Engineering Group, PSC
FIrst Federal Savings Bldg, Ste 820 Ponce de Leon Ave 1519   San Juan, PR 00693
1 787-2599   Daianyk Cordova CEO
Fax: (860) 791-6372
Email: dcordova@dc-eng.com
Website: www.dc-eng.com
DC Engineering is a Professional Services Corporation that offer Project Management and Inspection Services During Construction. We also provide permit procurement services and environmental services. (Woman/Hisp, estab 2011, empl 8, sales , cert: NMSDC)

8313   Desde Mi Huerto, Inc.
P.O. Box 61   Patillas, PR 00723
(787) 202-0392   Raul Rosado Admin
Fax: (860) 791-6372
Email: Desdemihuerto@gmail.com
Website: www.caribbeanecoseeds.com
We can deliver and merchandize in the island of Puerto Rico and ship to the southern USA (Woman/Hisp, estab 2012, empl 6, sales , cert: NMSDC)

8314   Maremar Design, Inc.
Urb Casa Linda Court 20 B St   Bayamon, PR 00959
(787) 731-8795   Marina Rivon President
Fax:
Email: marina@maremar.com
Website: www.maremar.com
Graphic design, corporate identity, logos, stationary, graphic standards manual, design consultancy, sales literature, collateral, point of purchase, annual peports, corporate profiles, brochures, newsletters. (Woman/Hisp, estab 1997, empl 2, sales $99,000, cert: NMSDC)

Rhode Island

8315   Advertising Ventures, Inc.   dba (add)ventures
117 Chapman St   Providence, RI 02905
(401) 453-4748   Joseph R. Miech COO
Fax: (401) 453-0095
Email: jmiech@addventures.com
Website: www.addventures.com
Marketing, branding, public relations, advertising, graphic & interactive design. (Hisp, estab 1989, empl 42, sales $9,891,991, cert: State)

8316   FAVOR Design + Communications
582 Great Rd Ste 201   North Smithfield, RI 02896
(508) 272-0522   Rene Payne Principal
Fax:
Email: rene@favordesignco.com
Website: www.favordesignco.com
Graphic & web design services, branding, creative direction, brand identity, content creation, copywriting, positioning, book design, packaging, interactive design, product design, typography, editorial, environmental retail. (Woman/AA, estab 2004, empl 1, sales $335,817, cert: WBENC)

8317 Katie Schibler & Associates LLC
      5875 Post Rd, Unit 1 East Greenwich, RI 02818
      (401) 398-0830 Katie Schibler Founder
      Fax:
      Email: partnerships@schiblerandassociates.com
      Website: www.katieschibler.com
Project Management, Event Planning, Marketing Consulting, Social Media Planning, Social Media Strategy, Copywriting, Sales Strategy, Strategic Planning, Partnership Consulting, PR/Media Relations. (Woman, estab 2011, empl 4, sales , cert: WBENC)

8318 North Star Marketing, Inc.
      1130 Ten Rod Rd Ste D-208 North Kingstown, RI 02852
      (401) 294-0133 April Williams President
      Fax: (401) 294-9282
      Email: april@fortheloveofmarketing.com
      Website: www.fortheloveofmarketing.com
Marketing & PR: direct mail, advertising, strategy, email marketing & public relations. (Woman/White, estab 1997, empl 10, sales $708,613, cert: State, WBENC)

South Carolina

8319 DP Technology LLC
      328 Shiloh Church Rd   Piedmont, SC 29673
      (864) 845-6006 Kim Donald Dir of Ops
      Fax: (864) 845-5507
      Email: kimberlydonald@att.net
      Website:
DP Technology LLC is a machine shop having and operating CNC Machinery for new products and repair/refurbished products. We provide speedy, accurate and up to date customer service and hands on service to our customers. (Woman/White, estab 2002, empl 10, sales $550,000, cert: State)

Tenessee

n
8320 Behind the Scenes
      7850 Stage Hills Blvd Ste 103 Bartlett, TN 38133
      (901) 937-3926 Kerri Blair Project Mgr
      Fax: (901) 383-4191
      Email: Kerri@btsmemphis.com
      Website: www.btsmemphis.com
Procurement, warehousing, mail merge & related activities, event & production management. (Woman/White, estab 2000, empl 17, sales $2,000,000, cert: WBENC)

8321 Bytes of Knowledge, Inc.
      1212 6th Ave N Nashville, TN 37208
      (615) 383-9005 Nancy Bass Lead Visual Artist, eLearning
      Fax:
      Email: sales@bytesofknowledge.com
      Website: www.bytesofknowledge.com
Website design, mobile & software development, brand support, social marketing, digital elearning, business strategy, network design & maintenance & entrepreneur consulting. (Woman/White, estab 1995, empl 22, sales $2,964,288, cert: WBENC)

8322 Genome Explorations
      711 Jefferson Ave, Ste 415 Memphis, TN 38163
      (800) 344-5708 Ed Henderson Dir, sales/Mktg
      Fax: (901) 578-5709
      Email: ehenderson@genome-explorations.com
      Website: www.genome-explorations.com
Genome Explorations provides researchers with a (As-Pac, estab 2002, empl 7, sales $1,000,000, cert: State)

8323 Miller Tanner Associates, LLC
      2070 Lebanon Rd   Lebanon, TN 37087
      (615) 466-2600 Dawn Barnes Dir, Global Sales
      Fax: (615) 466-5621
      Email: dawn@millertanner.com
      Website: www.millertanner.com
Global meeting & event planning. (Woman/White, estab 1997, empl 50, sales $26,000,000, cert: WBENC)

8324 Superior DataWorks, LLC
      340 Poplar View Ln E Ste 1 Collierville, TN 38017
      (901) 861-6301 Sharon Vega President
      Fax: (901) 861-6302
      Email: svega@superiordataworks.com
      Website: www.superiordataworks.com
Market research: ad testing, A&U studies, customer/employee satisfaction measurement, new product testing, web-based survey research, database management & fulfillment services. (Woman/White, estab 1992, empl 4, sales $167,400, cert: WBENC)

Texas

8325 70kft, LLC
      325 N. St. Paul St Ste 3000 Dallas, TX 75201
      (214) 653-1600 Tiffany Bryant
      Fax: (214) 653-1601
      Email: tiffany@70kft.com
      Website: www.70kft.com
Design, public relations & digital marketing disciplines. (AA, estab 2003, empl 25, sales $3,251,230, cert: State, NMSDC)

8326 All About Events
      7810 Chinon Circle   Houston, TX 77071
      (713) 723-1618 Elmer Rogers Owner
      Fax: (713) 391-8249
      Email: elmer@allaevents.com
      Website: www.allaevents.com
Event planning, ceremonies, conferences, conventions, exhibitions, fundraisers, meetings, receptions, seminars & trade shows. (Woman/AA, estab 2005, empl 2, sales , cert: State, City, NMSDC)

8327 Boone DeLeon Communications, Inc.
      3100 S Gessner, Ste 110   Houston, TX 77063
      (713) 952-9600 Leo De Leon Jr President
      Fax: (713) 952-9606
      Email: leo@boonedeleon.com
      Website: www.boonedeleon.com
Marketing, advertising, public relations, promotions, retail overlays, couponing & sampling, Spanish translations. (Hisp, estab 1979, empl 7, sales $1,656,911, cert: State, City)

8328 BrandEra, Inc.
219 S Main St Ste 301 Fort Worth, TX 76104
(817) 927-7750 Elizabeth Owens Principal
Fax: (817) 924-8603
Email: bo@branderamarketing.com
Website: www.branderamarketing.com
Strategic planning, sales/promotional initiatives, advertising, press materials, designing/maintaining websites, marketing materials, planning special events. (Woman/White, estab 2004, empl 4, sales $935,118, cert: State, WBENC)

8329 Consumer and Market Insights, LLC (CMI)
3010 Lyndon B Johnson Fwy Ste 1200 Dallas, TX 75234
(972) 939-9500 Royalyn Reid President
Fax: (972) 939-9544
Email: royalyn.reid@thecmiteam.com
Website: www.thecmiteam.com
Market research, training & strategic event planning. (Woman/AA, estab 1998, empl 16, sales $502,529, cert: State, NMSDC, WBENC, SDB)

8330 CS Creative
9108 Chancellor Row   Dallas, TX 75247
(214) 905-8008 Cindy Slayton President
Fax: (214) 905-9832
Email: cindy@cs-creative.com
Website: www.cs-creative.com
Graphic design svcs: corporate communications, identity devel & mgmt. (Woman/White, estab 1989, empl 20, sales , cert: WBENC)

8331 Cybersoft Technologies Inc.
4422 FM 1960 W, Ste 300   Houston, TX 77068
(281) 453-8504 Milind Sethi
Fax: (281) 895-9555
Email: milind.sethi@cybersoft.net
Website: www.cybersoft.net
Cybersoft Technologies was founded in Houston, Texas in 1996, providing "superior" IT Business solutions an services to clients nation-wide.
Solutions include ERP, WEB Technologies, EAI, Microsoft Technologies, Data Management, (As-Ind, estab 1996, empl 50, sales $7,000,000, cert: State, NMSDC)

8332 Dallas Fan Fares, Inc.
5485 Beltline Rd, Ste 270   Dallas, TX 75254
(972) 239-9969 Kaye Burkhardt President
Fax: (972) 458-8937
Email: kburkhardt@fanfares.com
Website: www.fanfares.com
Corporate meeting, incentive trips & sporting event planning. (Woman/White, estab 1980, empl 27, sales $26,443,000, cert: WBENC)

8333 DirecToHispanic, LLC
4909 N McColl Rd   McAllen, TX 78504
(562) 624-4680 Lauren Boyle
Fax: (203) 271-8051
Email: lauren.boyle@directohispanic.com
Website: www.directohispanic.com
Marketing promotions agency. (Hisp, estab 2004, empl 12, sales $2,700,000, cert: NMSDC)

8334 DiversityInPromotions, LLC
15851 Dallas Pkwy, Ste 404   Addison, TX 75001
(972) 789-5330 Rodney Woods CEO
Fax: (972) 789-5331
Email: rwoods@diversityinpromotions.com
Website: www.diversityinpromotions.com
Advertising, marketing, promotions, public relations, supplier diversity program management, event planning & sponsorships. (AA, estab 1998, empl 9, sales $1,500,000, cert: NMSDC)

8335 Elias Events, LLC
6214 Beverly Hill, Ste 24   Houston, TX 77057
(713) 334-1800 Deborah Elias President
Fax: (713) 334-9670
Email: deborah@eliasevents.com
Website: www.eliasevents.com
Meeting planning, production schedules, resource & staff management, marketing & communications strategy & delivery, graphic design, public relations, marketing/press collateral, website development & social media support. (Woman/White, estab 1998, empl 2, sales $10,111,567, cert: City)

8336 ETC Group, Inc.
1112 Copeland Rd Ste 400 Arlington, TX 76011
(817) 462-0103 Bill Nichols VP
Fax: (817) 795-5331
Email: bnichols@etconline.net
Website: www.etconline.net
Corporate travel management, groups, meeting & incentive, promotional marketing. (Woman/White, estab 1989, empl 25, sales $40,000,000, cert: State, WBENC)

8337 Event Source Professionals, inc.
4109 Gateway Court 300 Colleyville, TX 76034
(817) 267-6698 Dara Hall EVP
Fax: (817) 545-1926
Email: Dara@ESPinc-usa.com
Website: www.espinc-usa.com
Executive meeting, corporate conference & event planning services, travel, site selection, trade shows, exhibits, security, destination management, online and/or onsite registration. (Woman/White, estab 1988, empl 4, sales $2,489,000, cert: WBENC)

8338 Farrow-Gillespie & Heath LLP
1700 Pacific Ave Ste 3700 Dallas, TX 75201
(214) 361-5600 Liza Farrow-Gillespie Partner
Fax: (214) 203-0651
Email: liza@fghlaw.net
Website: www.fghlaw.com
Employment law; employment litigation and arbitration defense; internal employment investigations; internal audits; employee handbooks; contract preparation and review; personal injury defense; advertising (Woman/White, estab 2007, empl 22, sales $1,761,000, cert: CPUC, WBENC)

8339 Focus Latino
720 Barton Creek Blvd   Austin, TX 78746
(512) 306-7393 Guy Antonioli President
Fax: (512) 328-6844
Email: gcafocuslatino@austin.rr.com
Website: www.focuslatino.com
Qualitative Research & Strategic Planning, Focus Groups, Triads, Dyads, IDIs, Ethnographies (In-Homes & Shop-Alongs) & Quanti-Qualis. (Woman/Hisp, estab 1996, empl 5, sales $814,366, cert: State)

8340 Galloway Research Services
      4751 Hamilton Wolfe, Ste 100   San Antonio, TX
      78229
      (210) 734-4346 Linda Brazel GM
      Fax:
      Email: lbrazel@gallowayresearch.com
      Website: www.gallowayresearch.com
Design, conduct & analyze marketing research surveys.
(Woman/White, estab 1965, empl 150, sales , cert: State)

8341 Garcia Baldwin Inc.
      8647 Wurzbach Rd Ste J100 San Antonio, TX 78240
      (210) 222-1933 Yvonne Garcia CEO
      Fax: (210) 222-1935
      Email: ygarcia@mvculture.com
      Website: www.mvculture.com
Market & advertising, promotions/merchandising, event
marketing, market research creative services, media
strategies. (Woman/Hisp, estab 1998, empl 42, sales
$12,791,077, cert: State, NMSDC, NWBOC)

8342 Global Exhibit Management
      P.O. Box 331641   Fort Worth, TX 76163
      (817) 370-1400 Jeannine Swan President
      Fax: (817) 370-1500
      Email: jswan@globalexhibitmanagement.com
      Website: www.globalexhibitmanagement.com
Exhibit & event svcs: rental or purchase options, design &
project management. (Woman/White, estab 2002, empl
10, sales $737,681, cert: State, WBENC)

8343 Integrity International, Inc.
      11767 Katy Frwy, Ste 750   Houston, TX 77079
      (877) 955-0707 Susan Lake Project Mgr
      Fax: (281) 955-0540
      Email: info@tarrenpoint.com
      Website: www.tarrenpoint.com
Documentation consulting services, project management,
content development (technical documentation), graphic
design, technical illustration, desktop publishing, editing &
quality assurance, indexing, localization & translation.
(Woman/White, estab 1994, empl 63, sales $6,000,000,
cert: State, WBENC)

8344 Ivie & Associates, Inc.
      601 Silveron Blvd   Flower Mound, TX 75028
      (972) 899-4723 Jodi Marsh SVP Communications &
      Business Dev
      Fax:
      Email: jodi.marsh@ivieinc.com
      Website: www.ivieinc.com
Advertising & marketing support services: print procurement, print management, media, creative, digital, development, communication/PR services, shopper marketing,
kitting & fulfillment, staffing, publishing, CRM. (Woman/
White, estab 1993, empl 650, sales $1,065,000,000, cert:
WBENC)

8345 K. Fernandez and Associates LLC
      10601 RR 2222 Ste R13 Austin, TX 78730
      (210) 614-1052 Karla Fernandez Parker CEO
      Fax: (210) 614-1059
      Email: karla@kfernandez.com
      Website: www.kfernandez.com
Marketing services. (Woman/Hisp, estab 1996, empl 11,
sales $2,640,615, cert: State)

8346 Listo Translating Services & More LLC
      830 S Mason Rd, Ste B2-A Katy, TX 77450
      (832) 592-9264 Roxana Heredia CEO
      Fax: (832) 592-9264
      Email: roxana@listotranslating.com
      Website: www.houston-translation.com/
Translation & interpretation services. (Woman/Hisp,
estab 2012, empl 2, sales $150,000, cert: State, City,
NMSDC)

8347 LNT 3 Group
      545 E John Carpenter Frwy Ste 300 Irving, TX
      75062
      (214) 650-9966 Marqueax Price President
      Fax: (972) 719-9195
      Email: marqueax.price@lnt3group.com
      Website: www.lnt3group.com
Marketing, e-communications, business development &
new media services & support. (Woman/AA, estab 2010,
empl 1, sales , cert: State)

8348 Magic Moments Parties and Events
      4760 Preston Rd Ste 244-257 Frisco, TX 75034
      (214) 688-9900 Courtney Rai VP Sales and Mktg
      Fax: (214) 688-9908
      Email: courtney@magicmomentsevents.com
      Website: www.magicmomentsevents.com
Event planning, custom design & décor, floral design,
event lighing, drapery, theme decor, props, interactive
LED dance floor, custom artwork. (Woman/White, estab
2004, empl 12, sales $550,000, cert: WBENC)

8349 Malkoff Promotions
      4904 Stony Ford Dr   Dallas, TX 75287
      (972) 248-4354 Lynne Malkoff President
      Fax:
      Email: lynne@lmpspecialties.com
      Website: www.lmpspecialties.com
Marketing & promotional solutions. (Woman/White,
estab 1989, empl 5, sales , cert: State, WBENC)

8350 Mobius Partners Enterprise Solutions
      1711 Citadel Plaza   San Antonio, TX 78209
      (216) 621-9653 Arlene Watson Principal
      Fax: (216) 621-9654
      Email: arlene@mobiusgrey.com
      Website: www.mobiusgrey.com
Design & visual communications, marketing development & branding. (Woman/AA/Hisp, estab 2002, empl 4,
sales $33,600,000, cert: State, NMSDC)

8351 MSR Group, Inc.
      3060 Communications Pkwy, Ste 200   Plano, TX
      75093
      (214) 291-2920 Lauren Dunnaway Director, Sales
      & Mktg
      Fax: (214) 291-2930
      Email: lauren.dunnaway@infinxglobal.com
      Website: www.infinixglobal.com
Meeting management, Site selection, negotiation &
venue contracting. (Woman/White, estab 1994, empl
25, sales $14,787,000, cert: State, WBENC)

8352   OMS Strategic Advisors, LLC
2591 Dallas Pkwy, Ste 300   Frisco, TX 75034
(214) 207-7720 Lawrence Gardner President
Fax: (469) 533-7404
Email: lawrence.gardner@omsstrategicadvisors.com
Website: www.omsstrategicadvisors.com
commercial real estate services firm specializing in tenant
representation, project leasing, strategic marketing and
related consulting. We are a network of senior professionals with extensive relationships in the industry. (Woman/
AA, estab 2009, empl 2, sales $560,000, cert: State,
NMSDC)

8353   Onyx Power and Gas LLC
13155 Noel Rd Ste 900 Dallas, TX 75240
(214) 871-5574 Loraine Sutton Mgr
Fax: (469) 533-7404
Email: vinnies@onyxpg.com
Website: www.onyxpg.com
Energy management and procurement; power sales;
consultation concerning strategies to control and reduce
energy costs; consultation concerning market and bid
analysis and contract evaluation. (AA, estab 2009, empl 14,
sales $250,000, cert: State, NMSDC)

8354   Open Channels Group, LLC
1320 S. University Dr Ste 220 Fort Worth, TX 76107
(817) 332-0404 Tonya Veasey CEO
Fax: (817) 531-1520
Email: info@ocgpr.com
Website: www.ocgpr.com
Public Relations, Multicultural Strategy Development,
Integrated Communications, Digital Strategies, Public
Involvement, Advertising & Marketing. (Woman/AA, estab
2005, empl 20, sales $1,794,160, cert: NMSDC)

8355   Outreach Strategists LLC
2727 Allen Pkwy., Ste 1300   Houston, TX 77019
(713) 247-9600 Mustafa Tameez Managing Dir
Fax: (713) 247-9605
Email: marketing@outreachstrategists.com
Website: www.outreachstrategists.com
Corporate & strategic communications, messaging, government affairs, public relations & marketing, ethnic & media
relations, advocacy, constituent engagement, community
outreach, graphic design, crisis management. (As-Ind, estab
2003, empl 5, sales $500,000, cert: State)

8356   Planning Professionals, Ltd.
1210 W McDermott Ste 111 Allen, TX 75013
(469) 854-6991 Mollie Wallace CEO
Fax: (469) 854-6992
Email: mwallace@planningprofessionals.com
Website: www.planningprofessionals.com
Web dev, logistical support, hotel site selection, electronic
mktg, on-site staffing, food & beverage selection, contract
negotiation, transportation, airfare, event marketing, signs,
graphics, premiums & giveaways, mail fulfillment. (Woman/
White, estab 1994, empl 12, sales $6,265,000, cert:
WBENC)

8357   Production & Event Services, Inc.
9425 Sandy Ln   Manvel, TX 77578
(281) 585-0569 Cindy Kutch President
Fax: (281) 585-9945
Email: cindy@eventsplanning.com
Website: www.EventsPlanning.com
Special event services: sound, lighting, staging, theme
decor, drapery, entertainment, catering, event planning,
production & show management. (Woman/White, estab
2003, empl 10, sales $240,000, cert: WBENC)

8358   Regali Inc.
518 N Interurban St   Richardson, TX 75081
(972) 726-8830 Renee Dutia President
Fax: (972) 726-8860
Email: renee@regaliinc.com
Website: www.regaliinc.com
Diversified global marketing & technology services,
integrating promotional programs, creative development & technology. (Woman/As-Ind, estab 1989, empl
7, sales , cert: State, NMSDC)

8359   Rutherford Enterprises, Inc.
17304 Preston Rd Ste 1020 Dallas, TX 75252
(214) 438-1185 Al Rutherford President
Fax: (214) 439-1199
Email: alrutherford@teamrutherford.net
Website: www.teamrutherford.net
Convention, meeting & event planning, event management, communications, sourcing & site selection,
housing management, attrition mitigation
exhibit & logistics management, senior executive travel
support. (AA, estab 1998, empl 10, sales $1,032,594,
cert: NMSDC)

8360   Sanders Wingo Advertising, Inc.
2222 Rio Grande Bldg C, Fl 3 Austin, TX 78705
(512) 476-7949 Leslie Wingo President
Fax: (512) 476-7950
Email: lwingo@sanderswingo.com
Website: www.sanderswingo.com
Strategic planning, account planning, public relations,
research, brand creation, account services, media
planning, buying & creative services. (AA/Hisp, estab
1958, empl 76, sales $27,800,000, cert: NMSDC)

8361   Steel Digital Studios, Inc.
6414 Bee Cave Rd, Ste B   Austin, TX 78746
(800) 681-8809 Andrea Wallace Business Dev Dir
Fax: (800) 709-5104
Email: andrea.wallace@steelbranding.com
Website: www.steelbranding.com
Family targeted marketing. (Woman/White, estab 2000,
empl 25, sales $4,321,750, cert: State, WBENC)

8362   Strategar LLC
3100 Independence Pkwy, Ste 311-204   Plano, TX
75075
(972) 948-3781 Yareli Esteban CEO
Fax:
Email: yareli@strategar.com
Website: www.strategar.com
Marketing services: marketing, advertising, translations,
web development, creative services, SEM, traditional
media, content production & support of promotional
events. (Woman/Hisp, estab 2013, empl 3, sales , cert:
State)

8363 Studio B Dallas, LLC
      2719 Randal Lake lane   Spring, TX 77388
      (281) 528-7000 MJ Moreau President
      Fax:
      Email: mj@studiobdallas.com
      Website: www.studiobdallas.com
Strategic design, brand identity, packaging, retail store
design & restaurant store design & merchandising.
(Woman/White, estab 2009, empl 1, sales $165,000, cert:
City)

8364 Studio J Designworks LLC
      7750 N. Macarthur Blvd Ste 120-356 Irving, TX
      75063
      (972) 556-0511 Gina Jacobson Owner
      Fax:
      Email: gina.jacobson@studiojdesignworks.com
      Website: www.studiojdesignworks.com
Visual communication solutions, branding, tag line
development, trade show & event marketing, copywriting
& copy editing, flash animation & development. (Woman/
White, estab 2008, empl 2, sales , cert: State, WBENC)

8365 T3
      1801 N Lamar Blvd   Austin, TX 78701
      (512) 499-8811 Gay Gaddis CEO
      Fax: (512) 499-8811
      Email: gay.gaddis@t-3.com
      Website: www.t-3.com
Integrated marketing solutions. (Woman/White, estab
1989, empl 175, sales , cert: WBENC)

8366 Tandem Axle Inc. dba Mixed Media Creations
      2300 Rockbrook Dr Ste D Lewisville, TX 75067
      (972) 221-1600 Whitney Stockstill Business Ops
      Mgr
      Fax:
      Email: whitney@mailmmc.com
      Website: www.mixedmediacreations.com
Graphic Design, Large-Scale Design, Web Development,
Digital Media, Photography / Videography, Printing
Services, Creative Consultation, Copywriting / Editing,
Marketing Campaigns, Branded Merchandise. (Woman/
White, estab 2007, empl 27, sales $2,800,000, cert: State,
WBENC)

8367 Teneo Linguistics Company, LLC
      4700 Bryant Irvin Ct. Ste 301 Fort Worth, TX 76107
      (817) 441-9974 Hana Laurenzo CEO
      Fax: (817) 231-0052
      Email: hana@tlctranslation.com
      Website: www.tlctranslation.com
Foreign language translation & interpreting services.
(Woman/White, estab 2007, empl 8, sales $1,000,000,
cert: State, WBENC)

8368 The Backshop, Inc. DBA Mercury Mambo
      1107 S 8th St Austin, TX 78704
      (512) 447-4440 Liz Arreaga Partner
      Fax: (310) 496-3025
      Email: liz@mercurymambo.com
      Website: www.mercurymambo.com
Research & strategic planning, sales promotions, shopper
marketing, retail merchandising, online/social media, field
management, brand advertising experiential marketing,
bilingual local market staffing. (Woman/Hisp, estab 1999,
empl 3, sales $1,062,732, cert: NMSDC, WBENC)

8369 The ID Development Group
      8811 Teel Pkwy, Ste 100 - 5233 Frisco, TX 75035
      (214) 295-5414 Julian Dorise President
      Fax:
      Email: jdorise@iddevelop.com
      Website: www.iddevelop.com
Project designs, creative interior environments,
tradeshow events & marketing campaigns. (AA, estab
2010, empl 5, sales , cert: NMSDC)

8370 The Maxcel Company
      6600 LBJ Freeway Ste 109 Dallas, TX 75240
      (972) 644-0880 Gwenna Brush President
      Fax: (972) 680-2488
      Email: gwenna.brush@maxcel.net
      Website: www.maxcel.net
Plan & manage meetings, conventions & incentive travel
programs. (Woman/White, estab 1995, empl 6, sales ,
cert: State, WBENC)

8371 Trilogy LLC
      5601 Democracy Dr Ste 105 Plano, TX 75024
      (972) 473-8911 Jeff Hoedebeck VP Business Devel
      Fax: (972) 473-8907
      Email: jeffh@trilogymktg.com
      Website: www.trilogymktg.com
Experiential marketing: product sampling, product
demonstrations, product merchandising & sponsorship
activations. (AA/Hisp, estab 2002, empl 10, sales
$3,500,000, cert: State, NMSDC)

8372 Ultimate Ventures
      4400 Beltway Dr   Addison, TX 75001
      (972) 732-8433 Val Lenington VP
      Fax: (972) 732-8677
      Email: val@ultimateventures.com
      Website: www.ultimateventures.com
Special events, transportation, conference & convention
services, corporate meeting & team building, inbound
incentive programs & customized sightseeing tours.
(Woman/White, estab 1993, empl 12, sales , cert:
WBENC)

8373 Ward Creative Commuications, Inc.
      1235 N Loop West, Ste 1200   Houston, TX 77008
      (713) 869-0707 Deborah Buks President
      Fax: (713) 869-2947
      Email: dbuks@wardcc.com
      Website: www.wardcc.com
Media, community & employee relations; public affairs;
marketing communications, graphic design; special
events; crisis management. (Woman/White, estab 1990,
empl 1, sales , cert: State)

Utah

8374 Andinas dba/ Inlingua Utah
      602 E 300 S Salt Lake City, UT 84102
      (801) 355-3775 Don Durham Business Dev
      Fax:
      Email: don@inlinguautah.com
      Website: www.inlinguautah.com
Language classes, interpretation & translation services,
translate websites, technical & legal documents.
(Woman/Hisp, estab 1996, empl 15, sales $1,013,000,
cert: NMSDC)

Virginia

8375   360 Virtual Assistance, LLC
905 22nd St   Newport News, VA 23607
(757)2441045   Natalie Robertson CEO
Fax: (757) 244-1065
Email: sales@360virtualassistance.com
Website: www.360virtualassistance.com
Integrated document preparation, multimedia creation, content design, layout, printing, optical scanning, research, technical writing. (AA, estab 2013, empl 1, sales $56,000, cert: State, NMSDC)

8376   AetherQuest Solutions, Inc.
6400 Arlington Blvd Ste 850   Falls Church, VA 22042
(571) 297-4000   Andrea Bauerfeind dr, event svcs
Fax:
Email: abauerfeind@aetherquest.com
Website: www.aetherquest.com
Event management, conference planning, site selection venue contract negotiation; comprehensive registration services; exhibit hall management; sponsorship programs; speaker management; housing and travel. (As-Pac, estab 2002, empl 23, sales $3,124,665, cert: State)

8377   All About Presentation, LLC
707 E Main St Ste 1615   Richmond, VA 23219
(804) 381-4002   Andrea Lyons CEO
Fax:
Email: andrea@allaboutpresentation.com
Website: www.allaboutpresentation.com
Event management: plan, design, manage and produce corporate events. (Woman/AA, estab 2007, empl 5, sales , cert: State)

8378   Bare International Inc.
3702 Pender Dr, Ste 305   Fairfax, VA 22030
(703) 995-3132   Lynne Brighton Senior VP
Fax: (888) 313-6861
Email: lbrighton@bareinternational.com
Website: www.bareinternational.com
Mystery shopping, employee surveys, video mystery shopping. (Woman/White, estab 1987, empl 300, sales $16,000,000, cert: WBENC)

8379   Candice Bennett & Associates, Inc.
9621 Masey McQuire Ct   Lorton, VA 22079
(703) 919-6231   Candice Bennett President
Fax: (703) 924-0190
Email: clb@candicebennett.com
Website: www.candicebennett.com
Market research, communications, organizational assessment & development. (Woman/White, estab 2003, empl 7, sales $619,866, cert: State, WBENC)

8380   Customer Relationship Metrics
100 Glenn Dr, Ste A-11   Sterling, VA 20164
(410) 643-1136   Dr. Jodie Monger President
Fax: (703) 935-0517
Email: jmonger@metrics.net
Website: www.metrics.net
Automated, email & website customer surveys, metrics designs, customer satisfaction & loyalty programs, data collection, analysis, reporting & consulting. (Woman/White, estab 1993, empl 14, sales $3,500,000, cert: WBENC)

8381   DGS Create, Inc.
6400 Arligton Blvd   Falls Church, VA 22042
(703) 776-1919   Christine Francis Owner
Fax: (703) 533-9110
Email: christine@printdgs.com
Website: www.dgscreate.com
Graphic design, digital printing, mailing & e-mailing services & online communication channels. (As-Ind/Hisp, estab 2012, empl 21, sales $1,854,501, cert: NMSDC)

8382   Elizabeth Coffey Design
1616 Claremont Ave   Richmond, VA 23227
(804) 266-2193   Elizabeth Coffey Principal
Fax: (804) 266-2193
Email: ecoffey@elizabethcoffeydesign.com
Website: www.elizabethcoffeydesign.com
Graphic design solutions, brochures, publications, catalogs, advertisements, direct mail, websites, displays and banners, invitations, logos & identity packages. (Woman/White, estab 2000, empl 1, sales $85,000, cert: State)

8383   Exhibit Edge Inc.
4315-A Walney Road   Chantilly, VA 20151
(703) 230-0000   Bev Gray President
Fax: (703) 230-0023
Email: bev.gray@exhibitedge.com
Website: www.exhibitedge.com
Trade show exhibit services: design & fabricate custom exhibits, rent trade show displays & exhibits, large format graphics & banners. (Woman/White, estab 1992, empl 20, sales $3,450,000, cert: WBENC)

8384   Frontline Marketing LLC
2248 Dabney Rd, Ste J   Richmond, VA 23230
(804) 359-2422   Henry Howells President
Fax: (804) 358-1673
Email: h.howells@frontline-exhibits.com
Website: www.frontline-exhibits.com
Mfr, design & dist trade show & outdoor event exhibits & office environments. (Woman/White, estab 1992, empl 5, sales $635,000, cert: State)

8385   Johnson, Inc.
201 W Broad St Ste 600   Richmond, VA 23220
(804) 644-8515   Andre Dean Corp VP
Fax: (804) 644-0835
Email: adean@johnsonmarketing.com
Website: www.johnsonmarketing.com
Marketing & communications. (AA, estab 1993, empl 15, sales $2,750,000, cert: State)

8386   KTL Communications LLC
5055 Seminary Rd, 1220 Unit   Alexandria, VA 22311
(703) 662-0465   Amir Khan Owner
Fax:
Email: amir@ktl-communications.com
Website: www.ktl-communications.com
Language Service Provider (LSP), translation, in person interpretation, DTP, localization, language tutoring & language authentication services. (Woman/As-Ind, estab 2013, empl 2, sales $78,000, cert: State)

8387 LeapFrog Solutions, Inc.
3201 Jermantown Rd Ste 350 Fairfax, VA 22030
(703) 273-7900 Kathleen Jerabek Contracts Mgr
Fax: (703) 273-7902
Email: kjerabek@leapfrogit.com
Website: www.leapfrogit.com
Strategic marketing communications: web site design, graphic design, branding/marketing campaigns, multimedia, corporate collateral materials. (Woman/White, estab 1996, empl 11, sales $893,494, cert: State, WBENC)

8388 Montage Marketing Group, LLC
8000 Westpark Dr Ste 480 McLean, VA 22102
(703) 215-4201 Mercedita Roxas-Murray CEO
Fax: (301) 654-6781
Email: mroxasmurray@montagemarketinggroup.com
Website: www.montagemarketinggroup.com
Full cycle integrated experiential marketing: Audience intelligence/data & market analysis, Strategy development, campaign conceptualization, creative development, experiential design. (Woman/As-Pac, estab 2015, empl 3, sales $1,900,000, cert: State, NMSDC, WBENC, 8(a))

8389 Nexus Direct, LLC
101 W Main St Ste 400 Norfolk, VA 23510
(757) 340-5960 Suzanne Nowers CEO
Fax: (757) 340-5980
Email: suzanne@nexusdirect.com
Website: www.nexusdirect.com
Direct marketing, marketing spend, strategy, creative, messaging, production, media buying, data analytics, processing, modeling & overall analysis & attribution of the direct marketing program results. (Woman/White, estab 2004, empl 30, sales $6,243,833, cert: WBENC)

8390 Office Remedies, Inc. d.b.a. ORI
171 Elden St, Ste 160 Herndon, VA 20170
(703) 478-0910 Kathleen Benson President
Fax: (703) 478-0936
Email: KathyB@oriresults.com
Website: www.ORIresults.com
Strategic research planning, sample & questionnaire design, qualitative & quantitative research, data collection, technology-based online research, data coding & entry, database mgmt & integration, statistical analysis & interpretation. (Woman/White, estab 1988, empl 75, sales $22,971,050, cert: WBENC)

8391 Rhudy & Co. Communications and Marketing, Inc.
14342 Lander Rd Midlothian, VA 23113
(804) 897-0762 Michele Rhudy President
Fax: (866) 451-1894
Email: michele@rhudy.biz
Website: www.rhudy.biz
Public relations, communications & marketing consulting: strategic communications planning, media relations, writing services. (Woman/White, estab 2003, empl 16, sales $2,200,000, cert: State, WBENC)

8392 The Dominion Group Marketing Research & Consulting
1800 Alexander Bell Dr Ste 515 Reston, VA 20191
(703) 234-2360 Susan Wyant President
Fax: (703) 234-1281
Email: swyant@thedominiongrp.com
Website: www.thedominiongrp.com
Marketing research, competitive intelligence, & consulting, qualitiative methodologies. (Woman/White, estab 1993, empl 14, sales $2,934,757, cert: WBENC)

8393 The InnovateHers
713 Huntsman Rd Sandston, VA 23150
(804) 263-0491 Tasha Chambers Principal
Fax:
Email: info@theinnovatehers.com
Website: www.theinnovatehers.com
PR Communications Plans News Releases Crisis Communications Executive Speeches Media Monitoring Community Engagement Events Theme Conceptualization Venue Selection Celebrity/Talent Contract Negotiation Event Styling Volunteer Management Guest Management. (Woman/AA, estab 2017, empl 1, sales , cert: State)

Washington

8394 Blue Crest Creative, LLC
5108 S Myrtle St Seattle, WA 98118
(800) 476-0128 Troy Shelby Creative Director
Fax: (615) 649-0561
Email: shelbyt@bluecrestcreative.com
Website: www.bluecrestcreative.com
Corporate Identity Design, Branding, Logo, Letterhead, Business Cards, Print Design, Brochures, Invitations, Direct Mail, Newsletters, Internet Design, Architecture planning, Web Design, eNewsletters, Maintenance, SharePoint. (AA, estab 2011, empl 1, sales $105,600, cert: City, NMSDC)

8395 Green Cat Dzine, Inc.
5412 101st St SW Mukilteo, WA 98275
(206) 406-8329 Elisabeth Rumpelsberger President
Fax: (206) 508-9147
Email: liz@greencatdzine.com
Website: www.greencatdzine.com
Graphic design: print, online (web), environmental graphics, strategic branding, promotions, online development, logo work, posters, brochures, invitations, tradeshow exhibit designs. (Woman/White, estab 2001, empl 1, sales $148,000, cert: State)

8396 PRR, Inc.
1501 4th Ave, Ste 550 Seattle, WA 98101
(206) 623-0735 Rachel Novotny Business Dev Asst
Fax: (206) 623-0781
Email: bd@prrbiz.com
Website: www.prrbiz.com
Public relations, marketing, market research, social & digital media, graphic design, facilitation, public involvement & advertising services. (Woman/White, estab 1981, empl 86, sales , cert: State)

Wisconsin

8397 Market Probe, Inc.
      2655 N Mayfair Rd   Milwaukee, WI 53226
      (414) 778-6000 Bonnie Lockwood Senior VP
      Fax: (414) 778-3730
      Email: info@marketprobe.com
      Website: www.marketprobe.com
Market research & cstmr satisfaction research svcs. (As-
Ind, estab 1976, empl 250, sales $40,000,000, cert: State,
NMSDC)

8398 Mazur/Zachow, Inc.
      1025 S Moorland Rd Ste 300 Brookfield, WI 53005
      (262) 938-9244 Michele Conway President
      Fax: (262) 938-9255
      Email: michelec@mazurzachow.com
      Website: www.mazurzachow.com
data collection services, marketing research studies, focus
groups, IDI's, ethnographic studies, in-home product
placements & music tests. (Woman/White, estab 1983,
empl 16, sales $315,000, cert: WBENC)

8399 Meetings & Incentives Worldwide, Inc.
      10520 Seven Mile Road   Caledonia, WI 53108
      (773) 851-0908 Dan Tarpey VP Sales & Mktg
      Fax: (262) 835-0620
      Email: dtarpey@meetings-incentives.com
      Website: www.meetings-incentives.com
Global strategic meeting & event management, strategic
meeting management implementation, global strategic
sourcing & contracting, attendee management. (Woman/
White, estab 1967, empl 275, sales $109,000,000, cert:
WBENC)

8400 Revelation, LLC
      222 N Midvale Blvd Ste 18   Madison, WI 53705
      (608) 622-7767 Brian Lee President
      Fax:
      Email: brian@experiencerevelation.com
      Website: www.experiencerevelation.com
Public relations, media buying, ad buying, advertising,
social media consulting, internet marketing, web marketing & speaking engagements. (As-Pac, estab 2010, empl 3,
sales $170,000, cert: NMSDC)

8401 Rivera & Associates, Inc.
      1543 S 14th St   Milwaukee, WI 53204
      (414) 736-1255 Michael Rivera CEO
      Fax:
      Email: michael.rivera@riveraprfirm.com
      Website: www.riveraprfirm.com
Public Relations, Marketing, Strategic Communication,
Multicultural Marketing, Public Information & Outreach,
Media Relations, Language Translations, Management
Consulting, Brand Awareness, Environmental Marketing.
(Hisp, estab 1997, empl 1, sales , cert: State)

PROFESSIONAL SERVICES: Staffing Services
Firms provide temporary and permanent personnel placement, contract and direct hire, personnel consulting, training and employment services. NAICS Code 54

Alabama

8402 CD Covenant Distributors International LLC
1400 Commerce Blvd Ste 12 Anniston, AL 36207
(256) 832-4385 Rod Lemon CEO
Fax: (256) 832-4386
Email: rlemon@cdcovenant.com
Website: www.cdcovenant.com
CD Covenant Distributors International (CD) is a Minority Owned, Small/ Disadvantage, Service Disable Veteran Owned Small Business Business (MBE, SBE, DBE). CD was incorporated in 2001 in the State of Alabama. We are a reputable provider of MRO Products a (AA, estab 2001, empl 6, sales $254,000, cert: City, NMSDC, 8(a))

8403 EALI Logistics Solutions LLC
123 N 7th St Gadsden, AL 35901
(785) 213-5493 JT Johnson President
Fax: (256) 547-4824
Email: jt@EaliLogistics.com
Website: www.EaliLogistics.com
EcoChemPro product is 100% biodegradable cleaner/ degreaser, contains no VOC's, no acids, no alkalis, no butyl, and has a neutral pH, and it is safe for people to use and it is environmental friendly. This product can replace multiple (AA, estab 2014, empl 6, sales $60,000, cert: NMSDC)

8404 RecruitSource, Inc.
3532 Seventh Ct S Birmingham, AL 35222
(205) 322-6822 Jane Smith CEO
Fax: (205) 322-6805
Email: jsmith@recruitsource.org
Website: www.rsi-services.com
Contract management services: staff augmentation, advertising & marketing. (Woman/As-Pac, estab 2001, empl 4, sales , cert: WBENC)

8405 Sirius Technical Services, Inc.
6215 Rangeline Rd, Ste102 Theodore, AL 36582
(251) 443-1166 Susie Bush COO
Fax: (251) 443-1177
Email: susie.bush@siriustechnical.com
Website: www.siriustechnical.com
Temporary & permanent personnel. (Woman/White, estab 2005, empl 400, sales $28,000,000, cert: State, NWBOC)

8406 SK Services, LLC
45281 US Hwy 78 Lincoln, AL 35096
(205) 763-1818 Sonya Jacks President
Fax:
Email: sonya.jacks@skstaffing.com
Website: www.skstaffing.com
Staffing, temp to hire & contingent staffing. (Woman/ White, estab 2010, empl 9, sales , cert: WBENC)

8407 Tech Providers, Inc.
2117 Magnolia Ave S Birmingham, AL 35205
(205) 930-9664 Eleanor Estes CEO
Fax: (205) 313-5830
Email: eleanorestes@techproviders.com
Website: www.techproviders.com
Permanent IT staffing needs, IT software developers, IT systems or database administrators, financial staffing & engineering staffing. (Woman/White, estab 1998, empl 135, sales $10,701,387, cert: WBENC)

Arizona

8408 Temporaries Plus, Inc.
601 E Eighth Ave Pine Bluff, AR 71601
(870) 535-5507 Kayla Cheatwood Sales
Fax: (870) 535-5502
Email: kcheatwood@ateamtemp.com
Website: www.ateamtemp.com
Temporary staffing services. (Woman/AA, estab 1995, empl 7, sales $5,300,000, cert: WBENC)

8409 All About People, Inc.
2141 E Camelback Rd #105 Phoenix, AZ 85016
(949) 397-1226 Charles Mitchell Acct Exec
Fax: (602) 955-6646
Email: charles@allaboutpeople.net
Website: www.allaboutpeople.net
Temporary & executive level staffing. (AA, estab 2002, empl 87, sales , cert: NMSDC)

8410 Axis Employment Services
7000 N 16th St, Ste 120-501 Phoenix, AZ 85020
(602) 301-8115 Tran Tran CEO
Fax: (602) 242-2025
Email: tran@axisemployment.com
Website: www.axisemployment.com
Temporaries, temp-to-hire & direct hire searches, drug testing, Criminal/County searches, software testing, education & employment verification. (Woman/As-Pac, estab 2002, empl 6, sales $2,130,000, cert: State, City)

8411 AZ Construction Resources, Inc., dba AZCR Staffing
2601 W Dunlap Ave Ste #4 Phoenix, AZ 85021
(602) 870-3515 Kim Jones Director of Sourcing
Fax: (602) 870-3536
Email: kjones@azcrstaffing.com
Website: www.azcrstaffing.com
Temporary and Temp to Perm Employees to the Industrial, Oil & Construction Industries (Woman/Hisp, estab 2006, empl 100, sales $11,093,000, cert: NMSDC, WBENC)

8412 Bridgeport Resources, LLC
930 W Watson Dr P.O. Box 85283 Tempe, AZ 85283
(480) 456-6031 Diana Lemos-Marquez
Fax: (407) 270-9241
Email: diana@bridgeportresources.com
Website: www.bridgeportresources.com
Direct placement staffing service, Finance, Accounting, Administration, Customer Service, Education, Engineering, IT, Healthcare, Management, Manufacturing, Sales/Marketing, Human Resources. (Woman/Hisp, estab 2013, empl 2, sales , cert: NMSDC)

8413 Egnite LLC
     4747 E Elliot Rd Bldg 29, Ste 600 Phoenix, AZ 85044
     (602) 931-5000 Alex Luevano VP
     Fax: (480) 725-8882
     Email: alex.luevano@egniteinc.com
     Website: www.egniteinc.com
Direct placement, contract, contract to hire & project
solutions. (Woman/Hisp, estab 2007, empl 5, sales
$325,000, cert: State)

8414 Scott Business Group, LLC
     668 N 44th St Ste 300 Phoenix, AZ 85008
     (480) 694-2619 Milagros Gonzalez-Scott
     Fax: (623) 321-1327
     Email: millie@scottbiz.net
     Website: www.scottbiz.net
Contract & temporary staffing. (AA, estab 2003, empl 105,
sales $3,451,356, cert: State, City, NMSDC)

8415 Source Group Professionals
     4729 E Sunrise Dr Ste 244 Tucson, AZ 85718
     (520) 870-5114 Rodger P. Garner GM - BDM
     Fax: (888) 472-0881
     Email: rgarner@sourcegrouppros.com
     Website: www.sourcegrouppros.com
Staffing services. (Woman/White, estab 2003, empl 35,
sales $1,273,000, cert: WBENC)

California

8416 3 Bridge Networks LLC
     601 Montgomery St #715 San Francisco, CA 94111
     (415) 692-6944 Caleb Hill Managing Partner
     Fax:
     Email: caleb.hill@3bridgenetworks.com
     Website: www.3bridgenetworks.com
Recruiting services, direct hire & temporary consults
ranging from staff to VP levels within Accounting &
Finance. (As-Pac, estab 2011, empl 7, sales , cert: NMSDC,
CPUC)

8417 A.P.R., Inc. (Alpha Professional Resources)
     100 E Thousand Oaks Blvd Ste 240 Thousand Oaks,
     CA 91360
     (805) 371-5644 Rick C. Ramirez VP of Ops
     Fax: (805) 435-7472
     Email: rick@alphaprotemps.com
     Website: www.alphaprotemps.com
Technical IT personnel on contract or contract to hire or
permanent. (AA/Hisp, estab 1993, empl 155, sales
$15,605,246, cert: NMSDC, CPUC)

8418 Absolute Employment Solutions, Inc.
     P.O. Box 2446 Culver City, CA 90231
     (323) 931-6262 Penelope Sherman- Hunt President
     Fax: (323) 931-6211
     Email: phunt@absoluteemploymentsolutions.com
     Website: www.absoluteemploymentsolutions.com
Staffing services: direct-hire, temporary-to-hire & temporary. (Woman/AA, estab 2001, empl 3, sales $350,000,
cert: State, CPUC, SDB)

8419 AgileTalent, Inc.
     1900 S Norfolk Ave. San Mateo, CA 94403
     (650) 931-2572 Jay Singh
     Fax: (866) 929-6049
     Email: Jay.Singh@AgileTalentInc.com
     Website: www.agiletalentinc.com
IT contract staffing & recruiting. (As-Ind, estab 2011,
empl 48, sales $4,600,000, cert: NMSDC, CPUC)

8420 APR Consulting, Inc.
     1370 Valley Vista Dr #280 Diamond Bar, CA 91765
     (909) 396-5375 Daniel Benninghoff VP
     Fax: (909) 396-5377
     Email: dbenninghoff@aprconsulting.com
     Website: www.aprconsulting.com
Supporting Managed Staffing (MSP)/Vendor Manage-
ment, System (VMS) Programs, Direct Hire Search,
Contract Labor, Administrative & Clerical, Accounting &
Finance, Human Resources, Call Center & Customer
Care, Information Technology. (Woman/As-Pac, estab
1980, empl 750, sales $65,000,000, cert: NMSDC, CPUC,
WBENC)

8421 ATR International, Inc.
     1230 Oakmead Pkwy Ste 110 Sunnyvale, CA
     94085
     (408) 328-8085 Angelique Alvarez Chief Diversity
     Relations Officer
     Fax: (408) 328-8001
     Email: angeliques@atr1.com
     Website: www.atrinternational.com
Temporary employment svcs. (Woman/Hisp, estab 1988,
empl 100, sales $96,000,000, cert: NMSDC)

8422 Bratton & Co., Inc. DBA Hyperdrive Agile
     1547 Palos Verdes Mall, Ste 198 Walnut Creek,
     CA 94597
     (925) 330-6970 Mary Louie Owner
     Fax:
     Email: mary@brattoninc.com
     Website: www.hyperdriveagile.com
Temporary staffing: administration, project management, technology, marketing & public relations.
(Woman/As-Pac, estab 2009, empl 2, sales $3,000,000,
cert: WBENC)

8423 Canon Recruiting Group LLC
     26531 Summit Circle Santa Clarita, CA 91351
     (661) 252-7400 Ryan McAhren Recruiting Mgr
     Fax: (661) 252-7880
     Email: ryan@canonrecruiting.com
     Website: www.canonrecruiting.com/index.htm
Identification, evaluation & recruit Executives, Professionals, IT Technical, Accounting, Environmental &
Industrial staffing. (Woman/White, estab 1980, empl
300, sales $15,000,000, cert: WBENC)

8424 Crowdstaffing, a Zenith Talent Company
     6030 Hellyer Ave Ste 100 San Jose, CA 95138
     (844) 467-2300 Bret Bass Dir Content Strategy
     Fax:
     Email: bret@crowdstaffing.com
     Website: www.crowdstaffing.com
Staffing & recruiting: software and OS, hardware, QA &
automation, IT, mobile applications & platforms &
professional. (As-Ind, estab 2000, empl 25, sales
$14,000,000, cert: NMSDC)

8425 Dawson & Dawson Staffing Inc.
      26522 La Alameda Ste 110 Mission Viejo, CA 92691
      (949) 421-3966 Kathy Dawson President
      Fax: (949) 421-5155
      Email: kathy.dawson@dawsondawsoninc.com
      Website: www.dawsondawsoninc.com
National search & staffing employment services. (Woman/
White, estab 2008, empl 14, sales $3,544,239, cert:
WBENC)

8426 Delta Computer Consulting, Inc.
      25550 Hawthorne Blvd Ste 106-108 Torrance, CA
      90505
      (310) 541-9440 Claudia Marroquin Acct Exec
      Fax: (310) 541-9330
      Email: C.Marroquin@deltacci.com
      Website: www.deltacci.com
Human Capital Recruiting & Deployment, IT Staff Recruiting & Augmentation. (Woman/White, estab 1987, empl
165, sales $28,000,000, cert: NWBOC)

8427 Enterprise Resource Services, Inc.
      400 Continental Blvd #6170 El Segundo, CA 90245
      (424) 888-3771 Ladie Ella Daya Natl Acct Mgr
      Fax: (866) 791-3691
      Email: ella@ersstaffing.com
      Website: www.ersstaffing.com
Staffing, payroll & IT consulting services: temp, temp-to-
hire & direct hire. (As-Pac, estab 2001, empl 25, sales
$3,851,150, cert: State, CPUC)

8428 Genesis Professional Staffing, Inc.
      2600 West Olive Avenue 5th Fl Burbank, CA 91505
      (818) 333-5153 Marcus T. Moore CEO
      Fax: (888) 750-5553
      Email: marcus.moore@gpstaffing.com
      Website: www.gpstaffing.com
Staffing: permanent hires, temp-to-hire, temporary
placement, payrolling & consulting. (AA, estab 2003, empl
25, sales , cert: NMSDC)

8429 Government Staffing Associates
      101 Howard St, Ste 490 San Francisco, CA 94105
      (415) 692-6905 Steven Strawser Owner
      Fax: (888) 241-4606
      Email: sf@govstaff.org
      Website: www.govstaff.org
Temporary, contract & permanent staffing solutions. (As-
Pac, estab 2009, empl 11, sales $833,429, cert: City,
NMSDC, CPUC)

8430 Grove Technical Resources
      9035 Rosewood Ave West Hollywood, CA 90048
      (786) 390-7119 Neal Polister President
      Fax: (866) 285-9230
      Email: ncpolister@grovetr.com
      Website: www.grovetechnicalresources.com
Technical staffing & consulting services. (Woman/White,
estab 2005, empl 2, sales , cert: CPUC, WBENC)

8431 Hart Employment Services
      220 S Kenwood St #320 Glendale, CA 91205
      (626) 405-0778 Rhonda Minarcin President
      Fax: (626) 577-8514
      Email: gsa@hartjobs.com
      Website: www.hartjobs.com
Staffing services. (Woman/White, estab 1988, empl 6,
sales $1,833,485, cert: WBENC)

8432 Harvest Technical Services
      1839 Ygnacio Valley Rd #390 Walnut Creek, CA
      94598
      (925) 937-4874 Renee Bush Harvest Technical
      Services
      Fax: (925) 937-8090
      Email: renee@harvtech.com
      Website: www.harvtech.com
Temporary technical staffing personnel. (Woman/
White, estab 1997, empl 85, sales $12,018,213, cert:
WBENC)

8433 HBL Search
      118 Prospect Ave Ste 4 Long Beach, CA 90803
      (562) 754-6925 Halvern Logan President
      Fax:
      Email: halvern@hblsearch.com
      Website: www.hblsearch.com
Staffing: accountants, finance, banking, IT, engineering,
sales & HR. (AA, estab 2013, empl 1, sales , cert:
NMSDC)

8434 Healthcare Staffing Professionals, Inc.
      6914 Canby Ave Ste 109 Reseda, CA 91335
      (818) 921-3126 Cornelius Mamboleo
      Fax: (818) 936-0158
      Email: corneliusm@hsp-inc.com
      Website: www.hsp-inc.com
Staffing & recruiting: Healthcare, IT, Admin and
Finance. (AA, estab 2006, empl 120, sales $6,000,000,
cert: State, NMSDC)

8435 Human Potential Consultants, LLC
      454 E Carson Plaza Dr, Ste 102 Carson, CA
      90746
      (310) 756-1560 Garnett Newcombe CEO
      Fax: (310) 756-1562
      Email: drnewcombe@aol.com
      Website: www.hpcemployment.org
Staffing services: administrative, janitorial, warehouse
& production service workers. (Woman/AA, estab
1997, empl 7, sales $580,000, cert: City, NMSDC)

8436 IMS
      7755 Center Ave Ste 1100 Huntington Beach, CA
      92647
      (714) 840-3775 Kristi Newman Dir Client Svcs
      Fax:
      Email: knewman@imssvs.com
      Website: www.imssvs.com
IT Contract, Consulting, Contract-to-Hire & Full Time
placement services. (Woman/White, estab 1973, empl
35, sales $7,600,293, cert: State)

8437 Inconen Corporation
      6133 Bristol Pkwy Ste 232 Culver City, CA 90230
      (310) 410-1931 Gordon Ross CEO
      Fax: (310) 410-1751
      Email: register@inconen.com
      Website: www.inconen.com
Temporary employees & pay-rolled employees. (As-Ind,
estab 1978, empl 120, sales $13,351,317, cert: NMSDC,
CPUC)

8438   Inconen Temporary Services, Inc.
6133 Bristol Pkwy Ste 225 Culver City, CA 90230
(310) 216-6715 Gordon Ross CEO
Fax: (310) 216-7629
Email: gordon@e-its.com
Website: www.e-its.com
Staffing svcs: temporary, payroll svcs, engineers & IT professionals. (As-Ind, estab 1996, empl 25, sales $1,592,435, cert: NMSDC, CPUC)

8439   Integrated Talent Solutions, Inc. dba Vivo
7901 Stoneridge Dr Ste 440 Pleasanton, CA 94588
(925) 271-6800 Marilyn Weinstein CEO
Fax: (925) 271-6801
Email: info@vivoinc.com
Website: www.vivoinc.com
Staffing services: contract, contract-to-hire & full-time/ direct positions. (Woman/White, estab 2006, empl 15, sales $5,100,000, cert: WBENC)

8440   Integritas Resources, Inc.
12304 Santa Monica Blvd. Ste 300 Los Angeles, CA 90025
(310) 584-7295 Lindy Huang Werges CEO
Fax: (310) 775-9793
Email: lhwerges@integritasresources.com
Website: www.integritasresources.com
Executive search, recruitment & staffing, direct hire, contract, contract-to-hire, temporary, or project basis. (Woman/As-Pac, estab 2014, empl 3, sales $646,557, cert: City, NMSDC, CPUC, WBENC)

8441   Invero Group
8560 Vineyard Ave Ste 504 Rancho Cucamonga, CA 91730
(909) 373-8120 Daniel Phillips President
Fax: (909) 373-8123
Email: daniel@inverogroup.com
Website: www.inverogroup.com
Staffing & recruiting: temporary, direct hire & contingent staffing solutions. (Woman, estab 2001, empl 75, sales $1,988,644, cert: WBENC)

8442   Josephine's Professional Staffing, Inc.
2158 Ringwood Ave   San Jose, CA 95131
(408) 943-0111 Josephine Hughes CEO
Fax: (408) 943-9649
Email: josephine@jps-inc.com
Website: www.jps-inc.com
Staffing svcs: temp, contract, yemporary-to-hire, full-time placement, payroll svcs, vendor-on-site. (Woman/As-Pac, estab 1988, empl 10, sales $3,248,000, cert: State, City, NMSDC, WBENC)

8443   Kavaliro
5401 Old Redwood Hwy Ste 104 Petaluma, CA 94954
(704) 525-3457 Timothy M. Harrington Managing Dir
Fax: (626) 628-3666
Email: tharrington@kavaliro.com
Website: www.kavaliro.com
Staffing services: Information Technology (IT); Engineering; Finance & Accounting; Administrative & Professional; & Project Solutions & Delivery. (Woman/As-Pac, estab 2003, empl 200, sales $41,700,000, cert: NMSDC, CPUC)

8444   Lighthouse Management Group Inc.
1650 The Alameda San Jose, CA 95126
(408) 579-6200 Nirav Shah Managing Dir
Fax: (408) 579-6211
Email: nirav.shah@lighthousemg.com
Website: www.lighthousemg.com
Staffing, temporary & temp-to-hire, senior-level consulting & management professionals. (As-Ind, estab 2006, empl 20, sales $8,500,000, cert: NMSDC)

8445   Loan Administration Network Inc.
18952 MacArthur Blvd Ste 315 Irvine, CA 92612
(949) 752-5246 Charlene Nichols President
Fax: (949) 752-5329
Email: charlene_nichols@lani.com
Website: www.lani.com
Temporary, Temp-to-Hire, Direct Hire staffing services: Accounting, Finance, Healthcare, Banking, Credit Unions, Title, Escrow, Mortgage industries. Clerical, mid-level, Management, Executive positions. (Woman/White, estab 1992, empl 12, sales $5,600,000, cert: CPUC)

8446   MIDCOM
1275 N Manassero St Anaheim, CA 92807
(714) 507-3723 Anastacia Warunek VP
Fax: (714) 459-7055
Email: stacy@midcom.com
Website: www.midcom.com
Recruit & place technical & professional personnel. (Woman/White, estab 1979, empl 635, sales $92,000,000, cert: WBENC)

8447   NetSource, Inc.
P.O. Box 590665 San Francisco, CA 94159
(415) 831-3681 Lana Bondar VP Sales
Fax: (415) 831-3680
Email: lana@netsourceweb.com
Website: www.netsourceweb.com
pPacement, contracting & consulting services. (Woman/White, estab 1997, empl 50, sales $800,000, cert: State, CPUC, WBENC)

8448   Partners In Diversity, Inc.
690 E Green St Ste 101 Pasadena, CA 91101
(626) 793-0020 Arlene Apodaca VP
Fax: (626) 793-0022
Email: arlene.apodaca@p-i-d.biz
Website: www.partnersindiversity.com
Staffing support: clerical & non-clerical. (Woman/Hisp, estab 2002, empl 100, sales $3,584,272, cert: State, CPUC, WBENC)

8449   Peoples Choice Staffing, Inc.
1269 W Pomona Rd, Ste 107 Corona, CA 92882
(951) 735-0550 Denise Peoples CEO
Fax: (951) 735-0561
Email: dapeoples@peopleschoicestaffing.com
Website: www.peopleschoicestaffing.com
Staffing: temporary, temporary-Hire or full-time placement services. (Woman/AA, estab 2003, empl 200, sales $19,037,280, cert: NMSDC, CPUC)

8450   Pivotal Search Partners
       2531 Greenwich St   San Francisco, CA 94123
       (415) 323-6339 Yuvraj Singh President
       Fax:
       Email: yuvraj@pivotalsearchpartners.com
       Website: www.pivotalsearchpartners.com
Staffing Solutions: IT, Engineering & Accounting & Finance,
Direct Hire, Contract & Contract to Hire & VSP / MSP
Contingent Workforce staffing solutions. (As-Ind, estab
2012, empl 6, sales $538,000, cert: NMSDC, CPUC)

8451   Plan b Solutions, Inc.
       29222 Rancho Viejo Rd   San Juan Capistrano, CA
       92675
       (949) 221-9301 Doreen Wakefield CEO
       Fax: (949) 769-6199
       Email: info@planbsolutions.com
       Website: www.planbsolutions.com
IT staffing & professional svcs, contract, contract-to-hire &
permanent placement. (Woman/White, estab 2000, empl
20, sales $4,800,000, cert: WBENC)

8452   PM Business Holdings LLC
       733 Hindry Ave, Ste C205   Inglewood, CA 90301
       (310) 242-3171 Derrick Ferguson CEO
       Fax:
       Email: pmbh14@gmail.com
       Website: www.brilliantmindssolutions.com
Computer Systems Design Services, employment placement & executive search services (AA, estab 2012, empl 1,
sales , cert: NMSDC)

8453   POGO Inc.
       6265 Greenwich Dr Ste 103 San Diego, CA 92122
       (858) 587-4970 Fredrica McGraw Regional Director
       Fax: (858) 642-7504
       Email: fmcgraw@getpogo.com
       Website: www.getpogo.com
Temporary staffing services. (Woman/White, estab 2011,
empl 7, sales $2,500,000, cert: CPUC, WBENC)

8454   Proven Solutions Inc
       9444 Waples St Ste 440 San Diego, CA 92121
       (858) 412-1122 Louis Song Sr Partner
       Fax: (858) 412-1100
       Email: lsong@provenrecruiting.com
       Website: www.provenrecruiting.com
Consulting, staffing & solutions. (As-Pac, estab 2007, empl
49, sales $16,800,000, cert: NMSDC, CPUC)

8455   PTS Staffing Solutions
       9960 Research Dr, Ste 200   Irvine, CA 92618
       (949) 268-4021 June Stein President
       Fax: (949) 268-4040
       Email: jstein@ptsstaffing.com
       Website: www.ptsstaffing.com
Engineering & professional staffing: petrochemical, power,
transportation & infrastructure. (Woman/White, estab
1995, empl 200, sales $28,000,000, cert: WBENC)

8456   Quality Driver Solutions, Inc.
       320 S Milliken Ave, Ste A Ontario, CA 91761
       (510) 453-4655 Angelica Dazhan Regional Mgr
       Fax: (510) 785-9696
       Email: angelica@qualitydriversolutions.com
       Website: www.qualitydriversolutions.com
Full service staff: temps, temp to hire, long term dedicated
& direct hire placements. (Hisp, estab 2004, empl 23, sales
, cert: NMSDC)

8457   RennickBarrett Recruiting, Inc.
       82-408 Brewster Dr   Indio, CA 92203
       (760) 863-0076 Vinette Morris President
       Fax: (888) 564-1059
       Email: vinette@rennickbarrett.com
       Website:
Direct & temporary/contract labor, high level, hard to
fill positions at the senior and executive management
levels. (Woman/AA, estab 2008, empl 4, sales
$1,246,000, cert: City)

8458   SearchPros
       6363 Auburn Blvd   Citrus Heights, CA 95621
       (916) 721-6000 Myla Ramos CEO
       Fax: (916) 721-6006
       Email: myla@spstaffing.com
       Website: www.spstaffing.com
Human capital staffing & solutions: temporary staffing,
contract to hire, long-term contract, project staffing,
direct hire, payrolling services, retained searches,
outplacement services. (Woman/AA/As-Pac, estab 2005,
empl 100, sales $20,000,000, cert: NMSDC)

8459   SuperbTech, Inc.
       5800 Hannm Ave Ste 150 Culver City, CA 90230
       (310) 645-1199 Jan Davis President
       Fax: (310) 645-5401
       Email: jdavis@superbtechinc.com
       Website: www.superbtechinc.com
Staffing:contract, temporary & permanent placement.
(Woman/AA, estab 1998, empl 7, sales , cert: CPUC,
WBENC)

8460   The ACT 1 Group, Inc.
       1999 W 190th St   Torrance, CA 90504
       (800) 383-1965 Gary Randazzo Dir of Natl
       Communications
       Fax: (714) 842-3127
       Email: hrcg-rfxmanager@act-1.com
       Website: www.act1group.com
Staffing, payrolling & workforce mgmt svcs: financial,
energy, healthcare & high technology industries.
(Woman/AA, estab 1978, empl 1535, sales
$476,000,000, cert: NMSDC, CPUC)

8461   The Mice Groups, Inc.
       1730 S Amphlett Blvd Ste 100 San Mateo, CA
       94402
       (650) 655-7655 Sofia Gomez VP Recruiting
       Fax: (650) 571-6751
       Email: sofia@micegroups.com
       Website: www.micegroups.com
IT contract, contract-to-hire & full-time employment
positions. (Hisp, estab 2000, empl 100, sales
$100,000,000, cert: NMSDC, CPUC)

8462   TheraEx Rehab Services, Inc.
       1191 Central Blvd Ste E Brentwood, CA 94513
       (707) 342-5200 Rey Rivera President
       Fax: (415) 937-6882
       Email: Info@theraexstaffing.com
       Website: www.theraexstaffing.com
Healthcare staffing: Registered Nurses (RN), Licensed
Vocational Nurses (LVN), Certified Nurse Assistants
(CNA), Physical therapist (PT), Occupational Therapist
(OT). (As-Pac, estab 2009, empl 64, sales $668,000, cert:
NMSDC)

8463   Tiffany Stuart Solutions, Inc.
       390 Diablo Rd. Ste 220 Danville, CA 94526
       (925) 855-3600 Topher Hollinger Client Services
       Director
       Fax: (925) 855-3609
       Email: topherh@go2dynamic.com
       Website: www.go2dynamic.com
Temporary contractors, temp to hire & direct hire.
(Woman/White, estab 1997, empl 150, sales $5,200,000,
cert: CPUC, WBENC)

8464   Two Roads Professional Resources, Inc.
       5122 Bolsa Ave, Ste 112 Huntington Beach, CA
       92649
       (714) 901-3804 Tammy Gottschalk President
       Fax: (714) 901-3814
       Email: tgotts@2roads.com
       Website: www.2roads.com
Provide temporary staffing in the technical, engineering,
and information technology services. (Woman/White,
estab 1996, empl 125, sales $12,168,000, cert: CPUC)

8465   Vertisystem Inc.
       39300 Civic Center Dr, Ste 230 Fremont, CA 94538
       (702) 241-5131 Shaloo Jeswani Sr BDM
       Fax: (510) 474-1440
       Email: shaloo@vertisystem.com
       Website: www.vertisystem.com
Staff Augmentation, Full-Time Placements, contract to
Hire, IT Projects & Consulting. (Woman/As-Pac, estab
2008, empl 120, sales $20,000,000, cert: CPUC)

8466   Vidhwan Inc dba E-Solutions, Inc.
       2 N Market St Ste 400 San Jose, CA 95113
       (408) 239-4647 Eric Kumar Acct Mgr
       Fax: (408) 521-0167
       Email: eric.kumar@e-solutionsinc.com
       Website: www.e-solutionsinc.com
IT & ITES staffing, recruitment & deployment: permanent,
contract, contract to hire & project based staffing.
(Woman/As-Ind, estab 2003, empl 450, sales $22,800,000,
cert: NMSDC, CPUC)

8467   Vitesse Recruiting & Staffing, Inc.
       1432 Edinger Avenue, Ste 100 Tustin, CA 92780
       (714) 210-5959 Kim N. Zastrow President
       Fax: (714) 210-5950
       Email: KnZastrow@VitesseRecruiting.com
       Website: www.VitesseRecruiting.com
Temporary or permanent human resources employment
services. (Woman/As-Pac, estab 2000, empl 3, sales , cert:
State, CPUC)

8468   Workforce Solutions Group
       26090 Towne Centre Dr Foothill Ranch, CA 92679
       (949) 588-5812 Colleen Jones COO
       Fax: (949) 588-6737
       Email: cjones@wsgcorp.com
       Website: www.workforcesolutionsgroup.com
Staffing & direct hire: contract, temporary & direct hire
placement. (Woman/Hisp, estab 2002, empl 11, sales ,
cert: City, NWBOC)

8469   WorkSquare West
       4401 Crenshaw Blvd, Ste 220 Los Angeles, CA
       90043
       (323) 294-9675 Natasha White President
       Fax: (323) 294-9678
       Email: natasha@worksquare.com
       Website: www.worksquare.com
Recruiting,Temporary to Permanente Staffing Firm
(Woman/AA, estab 2008, empl 4, sales , cert: NMSDC)

8470   Xtra Pair of Hands
       4307 San Joaquin Plz Newport Beach, CA 92660
       (404) 825-4398 Kym Smith Managing Partner
       Fax: (404) 825-4398
       Email: info@xtrapairofhands.com
       Website: www.xtrapairofhands.com
Staffing & recruiting: temp, temp-to-hire & direct hire
placements. (Woman/AA, estab 2007, empl 4, sales
$250,000, cert: State, CPUC)

8471   Zempleo, Inc.
       4000 Executive Parkway Ste 240, Bishop Ranch 8
       San Ramon, CA 94583
       (925) 284-0377 SABRINA CHISHOLM VP
       Fax: (925) 284-0374
       Email: SCHISHOLM@ZEMPLEO.COM
       Website: www.zempleo.com
Temporary staffing, payrolling & direct hire services.
(Hisp, estab 2005, empl 1000, sales $62,860,000, cert:
NMSDC, CPUC)

Colorado

8472   Action Staffing Solutions
       1409 W 29th St Loveland, CO 80538
       (970) 667-4202 Robin Fischer CEO
       Fax: (970) 667-1036
       Email: robin@myactionstaffing.com
       Website:
Temporary to permanent employee placement, contract
personnel, long-term, executive placement, direct hire,
on-site management. (Woman/AA, estab 2008, empl 7,
sales $1,500,000, cert: State, City, 8(a))

8473   Colorado Network Staffing, Inc.
       8787 Turnpike Dr, Ste 220 Westminster, CO
       80031
       (303) 430-1441 Pam Fritzler President
       Fax: (303) 430-1441
       Email: pam@conetstaff.com
       Website: www.conetstaff.com
Non-technical & technical staff augmentation. (Woman/
White, estab 1996, empl 12, sales , cert: WBENC)

8474   Equity Staffing Group
       98 Inverness Dr E Ste 320 Englewood, CO 80112
       (612) 999-1112 Megan Huberty
       Fax: (303) 482-1729
       Email: EnterpriseSolutions@EquitySG.com
       Website: www.equitystaffing.com
Staffing, consulting, contingent, or direct-hire workforce
solutions. (Nat Ame, estab 2009, empl 60, sales
$85,617,000, cert: NMSDC)

8475 IntelliSource
1899 Wynkoop St Ste 900 Denver, CO 80202
(303) 692-1100 Matt Pollard SVP
Fax: (303) 692-1199
Email: mpollard@intellisource.com
Website: www.intellisource.com
Staffing solutions, temporary, temp to perm, project management, outsourcing, contract & direct hire. (Woman/White, estab 1999, empl 300, sales , cert: WBENC)

8476 Job Store, Inc.
7100 E Hampden Ave Ste A Denver, CO 80224
(303) 757-7686 Julie DeGolier President
Fax: (303) 757-5604
Email: Julie@jobstorestaffing.com
Website: www.jobstorestaffing.com
Tempoary office, clerical admin support, accounting & technical & light industrial personnel. (Woman/White, estab 1974, empl 14, sales $8,400,419, cert: WBENC)

8477 MHa Technical Staffing, Inc.
7475 Dakin St, Ste 350 Denver, CO 80221
(303) 428-1728 Thomas R. Leyba VP Ops
Fax: (303) 428-1769
Email: t.leyba@martinez-hromada.com
Website: www.mhatech.com/
Temporary eng support personnel: civil, electrical, structural, mechanical, HVAC, programmers, subcontract, construction mgmt, designers & drafters. (Hisp, estab 1992, empl 65, sales , cert: City, NMSDC)

8478 Nexus Staffing Solutions Corp.
4701 Marion St, Ste 307 Denver, CO 80216
(303) 736-2008 Barbara Butler Business Dev Mgr
Fax:
Email: bonnie@nexusstaffingllc.com
Website: www.nexusstaffingllc.com/
Staffing: Engineering, Construction & Call Centers. (Woman/White, estab 2010, empl 12, sales , cert: WBENC)

8479 Prestige Staffing, Inc.
1873 S Bellaire St, Ste 320 Denver, CO 80222
(303) 691-0111 Tina Leischner President
Fax: (303) 691-0980
Email: tina@prestigecareer.com
Website: www.prestigecareer.com
Permanent, contract & temp positions. (Woman/White, estab 2003, empl 2, sales $350,000, cert: WBENC)

8480 Primesource Staffing
400 S. Colorado Blvd, Ste 400 Denver, CO 80246
(303) 869-2990 Dennis Hatcher Controller
Fax: (303) 869-2997
Email: dhatcher@primesourcestaffing.com
Website: www.primesourcestaffing.com
Staffing services. (Woman, estab 1996, empl 27, sales $20,600,000, cert: WBENC)

Connecticut

8481 Corporate Aviators, Inc.
6 Berkshire Blvd Ste 392 Bethel, CT 06801
(203) 207-0077 Margaret Vernet President
Fax: (203) 207-0200
Email: cai@corporateaviators.com
Website: www.corporateaviators.com
Aviation staffing: temp, temp to perm, full-time placement & payrolling; corporate pilots & flight attendants. (Woman/White, estab 1987, empl 100, sales $1,175,640, cert: State, WBENC)

8482 JOBPRO Temporary Services, Inc.
36 Main St   East Hartford, CT 06118
(800) 404-7795 Catherine Beck President
Fax:
Email: cbeck@job-pro.com
Website: www.jobproworks.com
Staffing: temporary, temp-to-hire & direct placements: office, accounting, light industrial & technical niches. (Woman/White, estab 1981, empl 10, sales $8,700,000, cert: State)

8483 Key Alliance Staffing, LLC
406 Farmington Ave   Farmington, CT 06032
(860) 676-7733 Sandra Hathaway
Fax: (860) 676-7734
Email: shathaway@keyalliancestaff.com
Website: www.keyalliancestaffing.com
Staffing: contract, contract to hire, or direct hire personnel. (Woman/White, estab 2008, empl 32, sales $2,586,000, cert: State)

8484 MY HR Supplier
1266 E Main St Ste 700R Stamford, CT 06902
(203) 274-8595 Omer Mutaqi COO
Fax: (203) 557-6023
Email: omutaqi@myhrsupplier.cm
Website: www.myhrsupplier.com
Human capital talent: IT, administrative & office support, clerical & accounting. (Woman/As-Ind, estab 2011, empl 53, sales , cert: State, NMSDC)

8485 Skylightsys, LLC
175 Capital Blvd Ste 402 Rocky Hill, CT 06067
(860) 289-9096 Shalu Arora President
Fax: (860) 289-9172
Email: arora@skylightsys.com
Website: www.skylightsys.com
Staffing services. (Woman/As-Ind, estab 2005, empl 9, sales , cert: State)

8486 Stratoserve LLC
18 Colonial Ct Cheshire, CT 06410
(203) 768-5690 Subroto Roy President
Fax: (203) 271-8051
Email: subroto.roy@stratoserve.com
Website: www.stratoserve.com
Consulting, research and training. (As-Pac, estab 2005, empl 1, sales , cert: NMSDC)

8487 Talus Partners, LLC
321 Main St Farmington, CT 06032
(860) 678-4410 Steve Massucci Mgr
Fax:
Email: accounting@taluspartners.com
Website: www.taluspartners.com
IT, Engineering & Accounting contract & direct hire staffing. Certified Project Managers, Web Developers, Analysts. (Woman/White, estab 2011, empl 35, sales $5,500,000, cert: NWBOC)

8488 Technical Staffing Solutions Corp.
P.O. Box 102 Southport, CT 06890
(203) 259-7200 Robert Martinez President
Fax: (203) 256-1682
Email: tecstasol@aol.com
Website: www.technicalstaffingsolutions.com
Technical search & placement: permanent & contract. (Hisp, estab 1990, empl 50, sales , cert: State)

District of Columbia

8489 Adept Professional Staffing Inc.
1629 K St, NW Ste 300 Washington, DC 20006
(301) 883-4308 Elizabeth Joseph CEO
Fax: (301) 883-4308
Email: tavares@adeptprostaffing.com
Website: www.adeptprostaffing.com
Recruitment service for Accounting, Legal & Administrative Assistants, Permanent & Temporary placements. (Woman/AA, estab 2010, empl 1, sales $795,000, cert: State)

8490 JustinBradley, Inc.
1725 I St, NW Ste 300 Washington, DC 20006
(202) 457-8400 Andrew Chase EVP
Fax: (202) 457-8500
Email: asc@JustinBradley.com
Website: www.JustinBradley.com
Recruiting & staff augmentation. (Woman/White, estab 2002, empl 85, sales $6,016,267, cert: WBENC)

8491 Midtown Personnel, Inc.
1130 Connecticut Ave. NW Ste 1101 Washington, DC 20036
(202) 887-4747 Elijah Mendoza Proposal Mgr
Fax: (202) 887-4748
Email: elijah@themidtowngroup.com
Website: www.themidtowngroup.com
Staffing services: direct hire, temp to hire, temporary, executive search. (Woman/White, estab 1989, empl 35, sales $15,400,000, cert: WBENC)

8492 National Associates, Inc.
1130 Connecticut Ave, NW Ste 530 Washington, DC 20036
(202) 223-7606 Oscar Hannaway President
Fax: (202) 296-7558
Email: ohannaway@naipersonnel.com
Website: www.naipersonnel.com
Permanent & temporary staffing: administrative, clerical, professional, technical & light industrial. (AA, estab 1987, empl 18, sales $9,600,000, cert: NMSDC)

8493 Proxy Personnel, LLC
1100 H St, NW Ste 260 Washington, DC 20005
(202) 639-9300 Kim Siew
Fax: (202) 639-9630
Email: kim.siew@proxypersonnel.com
Website: www.proxypersonnel.com
Temporary staffing, recruiting & administrative services. (AA, estab 2004, empl 100, sales $5,000,000, cert: State)

Florida

8494 ABSP Staffing, LLC
2339 Vintage St Sarasota, FL 34240
(941) 587-4974 Ashley Black COO
Fax:
Email: amyersblack@abspstaffing.com
Website: www.abspstaffing.com
Staffing, contract, contract-to-perm & permanent hiring. (Woman/White, estab 2015, empl 2, sales , cert: State)

8495 Airetel Staffing, Inc.
P.O. Box 915864 Longwood, FL 32791
(407) 788-2015 Mike Tomaso Natl aquisitions Mgr
Fax: (407) 682-9705
Email: mt@airetel.com
Website: www.airetel.com
Full-time, contract & contract-to-hire staffing solutions. (Woman/White, estab 2000, empl 10, sales $3,570,000, cert: WBENC)

8496 Albion Healthcare Staffing
10162 W Sample Rd Coral Springs, FL 33065
(954) 796-3336 Francisco Arteaga Division Dir
Fax:
Email: francisco@albionbiomed.com
Website: www.albionstaffing.com
Staffing services for Pharmaceutical & Medical Device companies. (Woman, estab 2005, empl 5, sales , cert: State)

8497 Alpha1 Staffing/Search Firm, LLC.
3350 SW 148th Ave, Ste 220 Miramar, FL 33027
(954) 734-2744 Garrie Harris President
Fax: (954) 734-2828
Email: gharris@alpha1staffing.com
Website: www.alpha1staffing.com
Staffing solutions, recruitment, assessment, training, development, and career management, to outsourcing and workforce consulting. (Woman/AA, estab 2007, empl 500, sales $13,000,000, cert: NMSDC)

8498 BioStaff Solutions Inc.
4007 Blushing Rose Court Oviedo, FL 32766
(407) 542-6006 Jim Owens
Fax: (203) 271-8051
Email: jowens@biostaffsolutions.com
Website: www.biostaffsolutions.com
Provide clinical staffing services: contract, contract to hire & direct placements in SAS Programming, Clinical Programming, Biostatistics, Clinical Data Management, Pharmacovigilance, Clinical Monitoring. (Woman/Hisp, estab 2014, empl 3, sales , cert: NMSDC)

8499 Career Center, Inc.
      1236 NW 18th Ave   Gainesville, FL 32609
      (352) 378-2300 Carolynn Buchanan Owner
      Fax: (352) 371-2573
      Email: cbuchanan@tempforce.net
      Website: www.tempforcegainesville.com
Staffing: temporary, temp to perm & direct hire. (Woman/
White, estab 1979, empl 11, sales $934,261, cert: State,
City)

8500 CareersUSA, Inc.
      6501 Congress Ave Ste 200 Boca Raton, FL 33487
      (561) 995-7000 Jennifer Johnson Exec VP & General
      Counsel
      Fax: (561) 995-7001
      Email: jjohnson@careersusa.com
      Website: www.careersusa.com
Temporary, temp-to-hire, direct hire placements &
payrolling services. (Woman/White, estab 1981, empl
10000, sales $32,000,000, cert: State, WBENC)

8501 CAREERXCHANGE
      10689 N Kendall Dr Ste 209 Miami, FL 33176
      (305) 595-3800 Sue Romanos CEO
      Fax: (305) 279-8903
      Email: sue@cxcinc.com
      Website: www.careerxchange.com
Staffing solutions, full-time direct hire placement, executive search, temporary & temp to hire placement.
(Woman/Hisp, estab 1988, empl 25, sales $10,930,000,
cert: State)

8502 Future Force Personnel
      15800 NW 57th Ave   Miami Lakes, FL 33014
      (407) 851-0039 Adela Gonzalez CEO
      Fax: (407) 240-1419
      Email: adela@futureforcepersonnel.com
      Website: www.futureforcepersonnel.com
Temporary, temp to hire & direct hire placements.
(Woman/Hisp, estab 1992, empl 15, sales $17,500,000,
cert: NMSDC)

8503 Garcia & Ortiz Staffing, LLC
      888 Executive Center Dr W, Ste 101   St. Petersburg,
      FL 33702
      (727) 342-1007 Jeremy Lavin operation Mgr
      Fax:
      Email: jlavin@garciaortiz.com
      Website:
Staffing: accounting, finance & banking professionals on a
temporary, project & permanent basis. (Hisp, estab 2005,
empl 5, sales $900,000, cert: State)

8504 GDKN Corporation
      1779 North University Dr Ste 102 Pembroke Pines,
      FL 33024
      (954) 985-6650 Dave Das Staffing Project Coord
      Fax: (954) 985-6652
      Email: ddas@gdkn.com
      Website: www.gdkn.com
Staffing: information technology, engineering, professional, administrative & clerical, IT consulting, custom
application development. (As-Ind, estab 1993, empl 400,
sales $18,000,000, cert: State, NMSDC)

8505 Genesis Global Recruiting
      3000 SW 148 Ave, Ste 116   Miramar, FL 33027
      (800) 780-2232 Jim Cochran Dir of Recruiting
      Fax:
      Email: jcochran@genesis-global.com
      Website: www.genesis-global.com
Staffing & workforce solutions: direct hire, temporary
workforce & contract consulting. (Woman/Hisp, estab
1999, empl 167, sales $16,500,000, cert: WBENC)

8506 Genoa Employment Solutions, Inc.
      1560 Sawgrass Corporate Pkwy FL 4 Sunrise, FL
      33323
      (954) 604-6056 Walter Ruf CEO
      Fax: (800) 360-5589
      Email: wruf@genoausa.com
      Website: www.genoausa.com
Staffing services: engineering, IT, office support, human
resources & purchasing. (Hisp, estab 2009, empl 162,
sales $19,878,000, cert: NMSDC)

8507 GlobalVise Inc.
      10335 Cross Creek Blvd Ste 8 Tampa, FL 33647
      (813) 333-0400 Sanjay Mehta President
      Fax: (813) 200-1188
      Email: sanjay@globalvise.com
      Website: www.globalvise.com
Permanent, temporary & contract staffing solutions. (As-
Ind, estab 2008, empl 8, sales $2,758,764, cert: State,
NMSDC, 8(a))

8508 Hamilton-Malone Corp
      31958 US 19 N   Palm Harbor, FL 34684
      (727) 781-7747 Eileen McQuown President
      Fax: (727) 781-7547
      Email: eileen@accordstaff.com
      Website:
Temporary & temp to hire staffing, executive search.
(Woman/White, estab 1993, empl 4, sales $80,000,000,
cert: State)

8509 Innovative Systems Group of Florida, Inc. dba ISGF
      100 E Pine St Ste 605 Orlando, FL 32801
      (407) 481-9580 Thomas Bryan Managing Partner
      Fax: (407) 481-9588
      Email: tbryan@isgf.com
      Website: www.isgf.com
Temporary, contract, contract to hire, direct hire staffing
& recruitment in information technology, accounting &
finance, sales & marketing. (As-Pac, estab 1996, empl
30, sales $3,210,000, cert: State, City, NMSDC, CPUC)

8510 I-Tech Personnel Services, Inc.
      5627 Atlantic Blvd, Ste 1 Jacksonville, FL 32207
      (904) 381-1911 Marco Tran President
      Fax: (904) 727-9400
      Email: mtran@itechpersonnel.com
      Website: www.itechpersonnel.net
Staffing svcs: clerical, technical professionals & light
industrial, temporary to permanent, direct hire placement & on-site management. (As-Pac, estab 1998, empl
125, sales $3,580,000, cert: State, NMSDC)

8511   Key Technical Resources, Inc.
       5733 N Andrews Way   Fort Lauderdale, FL 33309
       (954) 771-1554 Kathy Gallagher President
       Fax: (954) 771-7553
       Email: kathy@keytechnical.com
       Website: www.keytechnical.com
Full time, contract & temporary placement: information
technology, accounting & finance. (Woman/White, estab
1999, empl 5, sales $1,828,000, cert: WBENC)

8512   KeyStaff, Inc.
       3540 Forest Hill Blvd #203 West Palm Beach, FL
       33406
       (561) 688-9184 Jessica Irons Business Devel
       Fax: (561) 688-0759
       Email: jirons@mykeystaff.com
       Website: www.mykeystaff.com/
IT/technical staffing solutions. (Woman, estab 1990, empl
60, sales $50,000,000, cert: State, WBENC)

8513   Premier Advisors Staffing and Sales, LLC
       7138 Spikerush Ct   Lakewood Ranch, FL 34202
       (313) 869-8868 Richard Burns President
       Fax: (941) 388-8113
       Email: rburns@premierhealthcareadvisors.com
       Website: www.premierhealthcareadvisors.com
Staffing and Recruiting. (AA, estab 2015, empl 1, sales
$1,000,000, cert: State, NMSDC)

8514   Pro-Staffing Agency
       981 W Commercial Blvd   Fort Lauderdale, FL 33309
       (954) 530-2894 Marie Morency Owner
       Fax: (954) 539-2826
       Email: marie@pro-staffinggroup.com
       Website: www.pro-staffinggroup.com
Recruiting, staffing & business management. (Woman/AA,
estab 2016, empl 2, sales , cert: NMSDC)

8515   Qualese, LLC
       3035 Honeysuckle Rd   Largo, FL 33770
       (727) 488-6373 Roberto Filippelli President
       Fax: (727) 683-9508
       Email: Roberto.Filippelli@qualese.com
       Website: www.qualese.com
Recruiting & staffing agency. (Hisp, estab 2015, empl 1,
sales , cert: NMSDC)

8516   Rapid Staffing, Inc.
       P.O. Box 602   Valrico, FL 33595
       (813) 651-1242 Lani Harless President
       Fax: (813) 654-6822
       Email: lani@rapidstaffing.com
       Website: www.rapidstaffing.com
Staffing services: temporary & temporary to permanent
employees. (Woman/Hisp, estab 2002, empl 5, sales
$2,227,174, cert: State, NMSDC)

8517   Resource Employment Solutions
       5900 Lake Ellenor Dr, Ste 100   Orlando, FL 32809
       (321) 234-9363 Eddy Dominguez VP Business Devel
       Fax: (321) 800-3550
       Email: eddy_d@resourceemployment.com
       Website: www.resourceemployment.com
Employment agency, staffing services & recruitment
company. (Hisp, estab 1995, empl 35000, sales
$111,000,000, cert: NMSDC)

8518   Spherion Corporation
       8130 Baymeadows Way W Ste 103 Jacksonville,
       FL 32256
       (904) 448-9102 Shelley Sherman Sr Mgr, Qualifi-
       cation
       Fax: (954) 375-9529
       Email: info@spherion.com
       Website: www.spherion.com
National staffing: temp, temp to perm & direct placement staffing. (Woman/White, estab 1946, empl 1500,
sales $14,089,000, cert: WBENC)

8519   Staffing By Choice LLC
       7975 NW 154th St #380   Miami Lakes, FL 33016
       (954) 417-5627 Matthew Marsh VP Bus Acquisi-
       tion
       Fax: (800) 948-8054
       Email: mmarsh@cpabychoice.com
       Website: www.staffingbychoice.com
Staffing, recruiting & executive search services: accounting, finance, sales & operations professionals, permanent, temp to perm & contract roles. (As-Pac, estab
2002, empl 7, sales $360,000, cert: NMSDC)

8520   StaffWorks, Inc.
       2935 First Ave N Ste 4 Saint Petersburg, FL 33713
       (727) 322-1320 Toni Baroncelli President
       Fax: (727) 323-3512
       Email: toni@staffworks.net
       Website: www.staffworks.net
Staffing: permanent or temporary placement of execu-
tive level, consulting, support & clerical positions.
(Woman, estab 1998, empl 9, sales $550,000, cert:
State)

8521   Techno-Transfers of Florida, Inc.
       4609 NW 26th Ave   Boca Raton, FL 33434
       (561) 212-2383 Virginia Mendiola Director
       Fax:
       Email: vmendiola@techno-transfers.com
       Website: www.techno-transfers.com
IT personnel for temporary contract, temp-to-perm roles
& full-time positions. (Woman/Hisp, estab 1992, empl 6,
sales $350,000, cert: State)

8522   TransHire
       3601 W Commercial Blvd #12 Fort Lauderdale, FL
       33309
       (954) 484-5401 Yvonne Rasbach President
       Fax: (954) 484-5905
       Email: yvonne@TransHiregroup.com
       Website: www.TransHiregroup.com
Staffing svcs: office, clerical, admin support, word
processing, light industrial, on-site mgmt programs &
payrolling svcs, temp, contract & permanent placement.
(Woman/Hisp, estab 1984, empl 9, sales $21,575,122,
cert: State, NMSDC)

8523   Vinali LLC
       2860 Delaney Ave   Orlando, FL 32806
       (407) 574-2000 Gianni Petruccelli Acct Mgr
       Fax:
       Email: gianni@vinalistaffing.com
       Website: www.vinalistaffing.com/
Permanent and temporary staffing services across
technology, accounting, logistics and healthcare.
(Woman/Hisp, estab 2016, empl 15, sales $5,000,000,
cert: State)

Georgia

8524 Apollos Partners LLC
PO Box 49755   Atlanta, GA 30359
(404) 437-7500 Bryan Payne Managing Partner
Fax:
Email: bryan@apollospartners.com
Website: www.apollospartners.com
Direct-hire placements, accounting & finance positions.
(AA, estab 2009, empl 1, sales $225,000, cert: NMSDC)

8525 Ashton Staffing, Inc
3590 Cherokee St Ste Kennesaw, GA 30144
(770) 419-1776 Jennifer Coon-Leeper Major Accts
Mgr
Fax: (770) 419-0069
Email: jleeper@ashtonstaffing.com
Website: www.ashtonstaffing.com
Direct hire & contract recruiting: technology, financial,
management. (Woman/White, estab 1995, empl 35, sales
$16,100,000, cert: WBENC)

8526 ASK Staffing, Inc.
3805 Crestwood Parkway Ste 260 Duluth, GA 30096
(770) 813-8947 Manish Karani President
Fax: (770) 813-8376
Email: mkarani@askstaffing.com
Website: www.askstaffing.com
Permanent placement & information technology staff
augmentation. (Woman/As-Pac, estab 1995, empl 300,
sales $22,000,000, cert: NMSDC, WBENC)

8527 Bison Data Systems, Inc.
5425 Peachtree Pkwy   Peachtree Corners, GA 30092
(888) 242-5737 Wesley Owens CEO
Fax: (678) 894-4676
Email: sscott@bisonstaffing.com
Website: www.bisonstaffing.com
Staffing, Technology, Light, Industrial & Health Care
industries. (AA, estab 2014, empl 37, sales $12,000,000,
cert: NMSDC)

8528 Blue Ocean Ventures LLC
2814 Spring Rd Ste 116 Atlanta, GA 30339
(404) 279-2777 Robert Jordan
Fax: (732) 656-0019
Email: robert.jordan@blue-oceanventures.com
Website: www.blue-oceanventures.com
Recruting, permanent hire & staffing. (AA/As-Ind, estab
2012, empl 10, sales $109,690, cert: NMSDC)

8529 Boomers Consulting, LLC
P.O. Box 246 Lithonia, GA 30058
(678) 476-8243 Pamela Garr Managing Dir
Fax: (770) 879-9217
Email: pgarr@boomersconsultingllc.com
Website: www.boomersconsultingllc.com
Talent acquisition & consulting, staffing/recruiting ser-
vices. (Woman/AA, estab 2011, empl 1, sales , cert: State,
City, CPUC)

8530 COMFORCE
2400 Meadowbrook Pkwy Duluth, GA 30096
(678) 648-7422 Shivani Sardana Recruiter
Fax:
Email: shivani.sardana@comforce.com
Website: www.comforce.com
Contingent staffing, information technology consulting
& human resource outsourcing solutions. (As-Ind, estab
1962, empl 500, sales $438,000,000, cert: NMSDC)

8531 Corporate Temps, Inc.
5950 Live Oak Parkway Ste 230 Norcross, GA
30093
(770) 934-1710 Shawn Menefee President
Fax: (770) 449-1944
Email: shawn@corporatetemps.com
Website: www.corporatetemps.com
Temporary & permanent staffing. (AA, estab 1991, empl
250, sales $11,125,149, cert: State, City, NMSDC)

8532 DoverStaffing
2451 Cumberland Pkwy Ste 3418 Atlanta, GA
30339
(770) 434-3040 Sanquinetta Dover CEO
Fax: (770) 434-3345
Email: sdover@doverstaffing.com
Website: www.doverstaffing.com
Staffing, training, call center svcs. (Woman/AA, estab
1996, empl 200, sales , cert: NMSDC, WBENC)

8533 EC London & Associates
101 Marietta St NW, Ste 3310 Atlanta, GA 30303
(404) 688-6607 Edward C. London CEO
Fax: (404) 688-6250
Email: elondon@bellsouth.net
Website: www.eclondon.com
Facilities support & staffing services. (AA, estab 1981,
empl 50, sales $1,821,984, cert: City)

8534 Enterprise Project Solutions Group Corporation
204 Kobuk Court   Canton, GA 30114
(470) 466-2627 Christi Stewart President
Fax: (678) 302-6919
Email: mstewart@thrupoint.io
Website: www.thrupoint.io
Staff Augmentation (Woman/White, estab 2005, empl 5,
sales $1,500,000, cert: WBENC)

8535 Excel Staffing Inc.
1174 Grimes Bridge Rd Ste 100 Roswell, GA
30075
(678) 461-8701 Khushnood Elahi Sales/ Mktg
Mgr
Fax: (678) 722-0355
Email: k.elahi@4esi.com
Website: www.4esi.com
Staffing svcs: sales & marketing, executive, accounting &
finance, engineering & manufacturing, industrial, office
professionals, IT managed svcs & e-business svcs. (As-
Ind, estab 2001, empl 10, sales $9,000,000, cert:
NMSDC)

8536　Excelsior Staffing LLC
526 Forest Pkwy Ste E Forest Park, GA 30297
(404) 366-8611 Sundra Kinman Business Dev Mgr
Fax: (404) 366-8684
Email: skinman@excelsiorstaffing.com
Website: www.excelsiorstaffing.com
Staffing services: temporary, temporary to permanent, direct placement & VNP. (AA, estab 2007, empl 4, sales $450,000, cert: NMSDC)

8537　FirstPro Inc.
P.O. Box 420559 Atlanta, GA 30342
(404) 250-7179 Michelle Kennedy Dir of Mktg
Fax: (404) 257-7343
Email: m.kennedy@firstproinc.com
Website: www.firstproinc.com
Executive search, professional placement & staffing: accounting, administrative, call center, clerical, collections, finance, healthcare, human resources, information technology, legal, light industrial, life sciences, management consulting. (Woman/White, estab 1986, empl 125, sales $31,900,000, cert: WBENC)

8538　Global Personnel Solutions, Inc.
1143 Laney Walker Blvd Augusta, GA 30901
(706) 722-4222 Giselle Brown Acct Mgr
Fax: (706) 724-6969
Email: gbrown@gapersonnel.com
Website: www.globalpersonnelsol.com
Full service staffing services. (Woman/AA, estab 1987, empl 10, sales $4,475,681, cert: NMSDC)

8539　Heagney Logan Group, LLC
2002 Summit Blvd Ste 300 Atlanta, GA 30319
(404) 267-1351 Jeannette Weigelt Principal
Fax: (404) 267-1351
Email: info@heagneylogan.com
Website: www.heagneylogangroup.com
Management Consulting, IT Consultant Staffing, Project Management, ERP Consulting, Remote Development, Contract Technical Staffing. (AA, estab 2009, empl 3, sales $924,954, cert: State, City, NMSDC)

8540　Infinite Resouce Solutions
2400 Herodian Way SE Ste 205 Smyrna, GA 30080
(404) 645-7065 Leigh Sicina COO
Fax: (866) 952-8633
Email: lsicina@infiniters.com
Website: www.infiniters.com
Resource management & professional staffing. (Woman/White, estab 2013, empl 50, sales $2,464,410, cert: WBENC)

8541　Kinetix LLC
50 Glenlake Parkway Ste 625 Atlanta, GA 30328
(770) 390-8360 Shannon Russo CEO
Fax: (770) 390-8389
Email: srusso@kinetixhr.com
Website: www.kinetixhr.com
Recruiting & placement services. (Woman/White, estab 1990, empl 120, sales $100,000, cert: WBENC)

8542　Lorentine Green & Associates, Inc.
12104 Jefferson Creek Dr Alpharetta, GA 30005
(770) 616-6326 Lorentine F. Green President
Fax: (630) 985-7300
Email: lorentine@lorentinegreen.com
Website: www.lorentinegreen.com
Recruiting & project management, Permanent Placement, Contract & Contract to Permanent. (AA, estab 2013, empl 7, sales $300,000, cert: NMSDC)

8543　Management, Analysis & Utilization, Inc. DB 3Ci
501 Greene St Augusta, GA 30901
(706) 823-2337 Brenda Johnson Mktg Admin Specialist
Fax: (706) 823-2388
Email: mausupplier@mau.com
Website: www.mau.com
Temporary services & direct placement: office, industrial, medical, professional IT personnel. (Nat Ame, estab 1973, empl 7500, sales $336,097,903, cert: NMSDC)

8544　MarketPro Inc.
53 Perimeter Center E Ste 200 Atlanta, GA 30346
(404) 978-1005 Cindy Underwood VP
Fax: (855) 873-0920
Email: cindy@marketproinc.com
Website: www.marketproinc.com
Contract, contract to hire or direct hire: marketing, advertising & communications. (Woman/White, estab 1996, empl 20, sales $15,650,000, cert: WBENC)

8545　Olivine LLC
970 Peachtree Industrial Blvd. Ste 100 Suwanee, GA 30024
(770) 596-5155 Rajeev Maddur Sr Acct Mgr
Fax:
Email: rajeevm@olivinellc.com
Website: www.olivinellc.com
IT Consulting Services, Contract, Contract to Hire and Direct hire placements. (As-Ind, estab 2006, empl 20, sales $235,000, cert: NMSDC)

8546　Pareto Solutions Group, Inc.
8 Piedmont Center Ste 210 Atlanta, GA 30305
(770) 804-8020 Shaun Harvill CEO
Fax: (404) 574-2283
Email: sharvill@paretosg.com
Website: www.paretosg.com
Staffing: temporary, temp-to-hire & direct hire placement of accounting, finance & IT professionals. (Woman/Hisp, estab 2006, empl 55, sales $570,000, cert: WBENC)

8547　PharmaCare Solutions, Inc.
5555 Glenridge Connector Ste 200 Atlanta, GA 30342
(404) 459-2847 Cassandra Tancil CEO
Fax:
Email: ctancil@pharmacaresolutions.com
Website: www.pharmacaresolutions.com
Contract & temporary health professional staffing, analytical data reporting, health management initiatives & clinical support services. (Woman/AA, estab 2003, empl 1, sales $65,580, cert: NMSDC)

8548 Preferred Personnel Solutions, Inc.
425 Barrett Pkwy Ste 4045 Kennesaw, GA 30144
(678) 662-6471 Marci Barthelmeus Business Dev
Specialist
Fax: (770) 795-7956
Email: marci@preferredpersonnel.com
Website: www.preferredpersonnel.com
Staffing svcs: light industrial, manufacturing, logistics &
distribution, office & admin, call center, accounting &
finance, executive search. (Woman/White, estab 2002,
empl 500, sales $11,900,000, cert: WBENC)

8549 ProKatchers LLC
1766 Baxley Pine Trace Suwanee, GA 30024
(706) 254-7008 Samay Shah CEO
Fax:
Email: samay@prokatchers.com
Website: www.prokatchers.com/
Traditional staffing & recruiting, direct placement & payroll
services, workforce solution programs. (As-Pac, estab
2015, empl 200, sales $8,500,000, cert: NMSDC, CPUC)

8550 Quality Staffing of America, Inc.
3525 Piedmont Rd NE 6 Piedmont Center, Ste 401
Atlanta, GA 30305
(404) 477-0020 Ken Richards President
Fax:
Email: ken@qualitystaffingamerica.com
Website: www.QualityStaffingAmerica.com
Temporary/contingent staffing services. (Woman/White,
estab 2013, empl 200, sales $7,400,000, cert: WBENC)

8551 Search Wizards, Inc.
1427 Cartecay Dr NE Atlanta, GA 30319
(404) 846-9500 Leslie O'Connor President
Fax: (404) 935-0979
Email: leslie@searchwizards.com
Website: www.searchwizards.net
Staffing: IT, finance & human resources, contract, contract-
to-hire & full time. (Woman/White, estab 2000, empl 71,
sales $10,840,732, cert: WBENC)

8552 Soft Source, Inc.
3883 Rogers Bridge Rd Ste 404B Duluth, GA 30097
(678) 957-1049 Mohammad Malik
Fax: (678) 957-1061
Email: malik@softsourceinc.com
Website: www.softsourceinc.com
Staffing, recruiting, staff augmentation, placement,
engineering, environmental remediation, design build. (As-
Ind, estab 1999, empl 10, sales $4,200,000, cert: State)

8553 Southern Crescent Personnel, Inc.
7179 Jonesboro Rd Ste 101 Morrow, GA 30260
(770) 968-4602 Krystal Pate President
Fax: (770) 968-4606
Email: kpate@scp-jobs.com
Website: www.scp-jobs.com
Temporary, temp-to-hire & perm placement: administrative, medical & dental positions. (Woman/White, estab
1993, empl 4, sales , cert: WBENC)

8554 The Experts Bench, Inc.
1325 Satellite Blvd 615 Suwanee, GA 30024
(770) 757-5831 Ramsey A'Ve Market Practice
Lead
Fax: (678) 935-4371
Email: ramseya@tebww.com
Website: www.tebww.com/
Professional services. staff marketing & accounting
contractors. (Woman/White, estab 2002, empl 20, sales
$1,819,000, cert: WBENC)

8555 The Mom Corps, Inc.
1205 Johnson Ferry Rd Ste 136-507 Marietta, GA
30068
(888) 438-8122 Allison OKelly CEO
Fax: (866) 760-6076
Email: allison@momcorps.com
Website: www.momcorps.com
Temporary staffing. (Woman/White, estab 2005, empl
15, sales $11,240,405, cert: WBENC)

8556 VersoGenics Inc, dba Comforce
990 Hammond Dr Ste 700 Atlanta, GA 30328
(813) 349-1779 Julie Weissman Sr Bus Dev. Mgr
Fax: (770) 255-7901
Email: julie.weissman@comforce.com
Website: www.comforce.com
Temporary staffing services, permanent placement
services & Statement of Work projects. (As-Ind, estab
1974, empl 12000, sales , cert: NMSDC)

Iowa

8557 CareerPros, LLC dba Sedona Staffing Services
2065 Holliday Dr Dubuque, IA 52002
(563) 556-3040 Nikki Kiefer President
Fax: (563) 556-3041
Email: nikki@careerpros.com
Website: www.careerpros.com
Staffing services: temporary, temp-to-hire, smart-hire,
contract & staff leasing. (Woman/White, estab 1993,
empl 18, sales $11,700,000, cert: WBENC)

8558 Chenhall's Staffing, Inc
2119 E 12th St Davenport, IA 52803
(563) 386-3800 Bob Hickman President
Fax:
Email: bhickman@chenhallstaffing.com
Website: www.chenhallstaffing.com
Staffing augmentation, recruiting & HR, contingent
staffing augmentation; temp to perm & transitional
probationary staffing recruitment, screening, testing &
placement; corporate recruitment, career counseling &
outplacement. (Nat Ame, estab 1955, empl 7, sales ,
cert: NMSDC, 8(a))

8559 SelectOne Staffing Services LLC
222 Third Ave SE Ste 240-B Cedar Rapids, IA
52401
(319) 373-2325 Vincent Clayton President
Fax: (866) 337-4415
Email: vclayton@genatek.net
Website: www.genatek.net
Recruiting & staffing: engineering, IT development,
telecommunications, technical support. (AA, estab 2003,
empl 10, sales $75,000, cert: NMSDC)

Illinois

8560   AltaStaff LLC
        19 S La Salle Ste 800 Chicago, IL 60603
        (312) 269-9990 Taz Wilson President
        Fax: (312) 296-9990
        Email: kkossack@altastaff.com
        Website: www.altastaff.com
Staffing services: temporary, temp-to-hire & direct-hire
placements for administrative, creative, financial & sales
support. (Woman/White, estab 2007, empl 5, sales
$40,000, cert: State)

8561   Amazing Edibles Gourmet Catering, Inc.
        2419 W 14th St Unit C Chicago, IL 60608
        (312) 563-1600 Andrea Herrera President
        Fax: (312) 563-1601
        Email: amazingedibles@aol.com
        Website: www.amazingediblescatering.com
Amazing Edibles is a custom, full service caterer. We
provide breakfast, brunch, lunch, dinner, snacks, and party
options. We deliver to the Chicago Metropolitan Area. We
specialize in Professional Development and Training
Catering. (Woman/Hisp, estab 1994, empl 10, sales
$963,488, cert: State)

8562   Anchor Staffing Inc.
        9901 S Western Ave, Ste 206   Chicago, IL 60643
        (773) 881-0530 Joyce Johnson CEO
        Fax: (773) 881-4139
        Email: jjohnson@anchorstaffing.com
        Website: www.anchorstaffing.com
Temporary & direct hire staffing & employment services.
(Nat Ame/As-Ind, estab 2002, empl 350, sales
$2,600,000,000, cert: State, NMSDC)

8563   A-PRO EXECS, LLC
        208 S Lasalle St Ste 1450 Chicago, IL 60604
        (312) 855-1515 Gladys Jossell Owner
        Fax: (312) 855-0866
        Email: gjossell@aol.com
        Website: www.aprotemps.com
Temporary & permanent placement
services:administrative/legal office support, accounting,
customer service & information technology. (Woman/AA,
estab 2004, empl 4, sales $2,700,000, cert: WBENC)

8564   Arlington Resources, Inc.
        4902 Tollview Dr   Rolling Meadows, IL 60008
        (224) 232-5900 Patricia Casey President
        Fax: (847) 590-9498
        Email: pcasey@arlingtonresources.com
        Website: www.arlingtonresources.com
Temporary staffing services, temp to hire & direct hire
placement of Human Resources Professionals. (Woman/
White, estab 1997, empl 25, sales $6,000,000, cert: City)

8565   Assured Healthcare Staffing, LLC
        495 N Riverside Dr Ste 203 Gurnee, IL 60031
        (847) 775-7445 Christine Hammerlund President
        Fax: (847) 775-7446
        Email: chris@assuredhealthcare.com
        Website: www.assuredhealthcare.com
Healthcare staffing: Registered Nurses, Licensed Practical
Nurses, Certified Nurses Aids, Pharmacists, Pharmacy
Techs, Medical Assistants, Medical Billers. (Woman/White,
estab 2007, empl 70, sales $2,257,000, cert: WBENC)

8566   Cube Hub Inc.
        600 N Commons Dr Ste 109 Aurora, IL 60504
        (630) 746-1239 Sunil Bakhshi Business Dev Mgr
        Fax:
        Email: sunil@cube-hub.com
        Website: www.cube-hub.com
Technology, Training, Staffing & Professional Services,
Staffing/Recruiting services, Software Development, IT,
Engineering, Professional, Marketing, Healthcare,
Clinical, Scientific, Finance/Audit, Telecommunication,
etc. (Woman/AA/As-Ind, estab 2014, empl 28, sales
$3,580,640, cert: NMSDC)

8567   Deegit, Inc.
        1900 E Golf Rd. Ste 925 Schaumburg, IL 60173
        (847) 330-1985 Jim Dimitriou CEO
        Fax: (847) 330-1987
        Email: jdimitriou@deegit.com
        Website: www.deegit.com
Temp and Perm, project-based services(SOW) & Recruitment process outsourcing(RPO). (As-Ind, estab 1993,
empl 150, sales $30,000,000, cert: State, NMSDC)

8568   DMD Consulting, LLC
        230 S Clark St Ste 113 Chicago, IL 60604
        (312) 809-6987 Darlene Drab CEO
        Fax: (815) 524-5330
        Email: darlene@dmdconsulting.net
        Website: www.dmdconsulting.net
Permanent placement, interim resourcing, and co-
sourcing, Audit & Compliance, Accounting and Finance,
Tax and Information Technology. (Woman/AA, estab
2008, empl 20, sales $408,865, cert: State, City, WBENC)

8569   Global Staffing Services, Inc.
        925 S Main St Rockford, IL 61101
        (815) 968-5797 Michele Caldwell CEO
        Fax: (815) 968-5798
        Email: mec611@earthlink.net
        Website: www.global-staffing.com
Staffing: flexible, contract & permanent placement,
employment & background assessment. (Woman/AA,
estab 2000, empl 4, sales , cert: NMSDC)

8570   IlinkResources Staffing
        24402 W Lockport Rd Ste 226 Plainfield, IL 60544
        (815) 230-5256 Manal Baya VP of Sales
        Fax: (815) 230-5326
        Email: connect@ilinkresources.com
        Website: www.ilinkresources.com
Recruiting & staffing. (Woman/White, estab 2011, empl
6, sales $93,400, cert: State)

8571   JRA Consulting Services, Inc.
        10225 W Higgins Rd   Rosemont, IL 60018
        (847) 430-3682 Ross Wolfson Talent Acquisition
        Mgr
        Fax: (847) 720-4196
        Email: rwolfson@hrcontracting.com
        Website: www.hrcontracting.com
Human resources staffing, permanent & contract
positions. (Woman, estab 1997, empl 4, sales
$2,000,000, cert: NWBOC)

8572   Loftus & O'Meara Staffing Inc.
        211 E Ontario Ste 1050 Chicago, IL 60611
        (312) 944-2102 Cindy Loftus Co-Owner
        Fax: (312) 944-7009
        Email: cloftus@loftusomeara.com
        Website: www.loftusomeara.com
Staffing: temporary, temp-to-hire & direct hire. (Woman, estab 1978, empl 7, sales $1,804,597, cert: WBENC)

8573   Mullins & Associates, Inc.
        522 S Northwest Hwy   Barrington, IL 60010
        (847) 382-1800 Terri Mullins President
        Fax: (847) 382-1329
        Email: tmullins@thebigcom.com
        Website:
Contract, contract for hire & permanent placement services: engineering & IT fields. (Woman/White, estab 1964, empl 41, sales $5,000,000, cert: WBENC)

8574   Mutual Target Associates, Inc.
        7002 Hamilton Dr Gurnee, IL 60031
        (847) 855-0059 Chandra Govind CEO
        Fax: (847) 850-2701
        Email: cgovind@mtaincorporated.com
        Website: www.mtaincorporated.com
Permanent placements, contract & contract to hire services. (As-Pac, estab 2005, empl 6, sales $750,000, cert: NMSDC)

8575   Myriad Technical Services
        40 Shuman Blvd Ste 210 Naperville, IL 60563
        (630) 369-6369 Mihir Dash President
        Fax: (630) 369-6569
        Email: jobs@myriadcorp.com
        Website: www.myriadcorp.com
Staffing recruiting. (As-Pac, estab 1997, empl 40, sales $4,000,000, cert: State)

8576   Premier Systems, Inc
        14489 John Humphrey Ste 202 Ste 202 Orland Park, IL 60462
        (708) 349-9200 Tariq Khan Acct Mgr
        Fax: (708) 349-2194
        Email: tkhan@premiersystemsinc.com
        Website: www.premiersystemsinc.com
IT consulting & staffing, project mgmt, systems programming & admin: IBM mainframe midrange, client server, PeopleSoft, SAP & Microsoft based systems; e-commerce devel. (As-Pac, estab 1993, empl 30, sales $2,713,000, cert: City, NMSDC)

8577   Professional Dynamic Network, Inc.
        20280 Governors Hwy Ste 106 Olympia Fields, IL 60461
        (708) 747-4361 Geraldine Smothers CEO
        Fax: (708) 747-7057
        Email: info@pdnseek.com
        Website: www.pndseek.com
Temporary & permanent staffing, recruitment, management consulting, education & training. (Woman/AA, estab 1995, empl 167, sales $3,415,745, cert: City, NMSDC)

8578   PSI Resources, LLC
        2001 Butterfield Rd, Ste 1040 Downers Grove, IL 60515
        (630) 968-0061 Tina Thomas President
        Fax:
        Email: tthomas@psiresources.net
        Website: www.psiresources.net
Staffing & recruiting services. (Woman/White, estab 1993, empl 45, sales $1,411,062, cert: State, City, WBENC)

8579   Resource Technology Associates, LLC
        10225 W Higgins Rd   Rosemont, IL 60018
        (847) 430-3667 Andrew Konik VP
        Fax:
        Email: akonik@rta-inc.com
        Website: www.rta-inc.com
Staffing support, outbound recruitment. (Woman/White, estab 1984, empl 22, sales $2,000,000, cert: NWBOC)

8580   RJSL Group
        1956 W Erie St Unit 1E Chicago, IL 60622
        (312) 282-4654 Richard Lee CEO
        Fax: (267) 508-4365
        Email: richard@rjslgroup.com
        Website: www.rjslgroup.com
Staffing and recruiting agency, IT & business resources. (As-Pac, estab 2006, empl 10, sales $201,804, cert: State, City, NMSDC)

8581   Seville Staffing LLC
        180 N Michigan Ave Ste 1510 Chicago, IL 60601
        (312) 368-1144 Janet Sloan President
        Fax: (312) 368-0207
        Email: jsloan@sevillestaffing.com
        Website: www.sevillestaffing.com
Temporary staffing: clerical, office, administrative, light industrial. (Woman/White, estab 1979, empl 7, sales $5,000,000, cert: State)

8582   Shar Enterprises Inc dba HKA Staffing Services
        800 Waukegan Rd Ste 200 Glenview, IL 60025
        (847) 998-9300 Kristin Haffner President
        Fax: (847) 729-6941
        Email: khaffner@hkastaffing.com
        Website: www.hkastaffing.com
Staffing services. (Woman/White, estab 1989, empl 45, sales $1,200,000, cert: WBENC)

8583   Sterling Engineering, Inc.
        Two Westbrook Corporate Center Ste 300
        Westchester, IL 60154
        (630) 993-3433 Rama Kavaliauskas President
        Fax: (630) 516-1192
        Email: rama@sterling-engineering.com
        Website: www.sterling-engineering.com
Engineering & technical staff augmentation solutions. (Woman/White, estab 1969, empl 75, sales $2,691,294, cert: WBENC)

8584 Superior Staffing
  P.O. Box 1551 Melrose Park, IL 60161
  (630) 516-3505 Heriberto Vale CEO
  Fax: (630) 516-3501
  Email: hvale@superior-staffing.com
  Website:
Staffing: temp light industrial & clerical. (Hisp, estab 2001, empl 600, sales $15,000,000, cert: NMSDC)

8585 Synergy Global Systems
  1580, South Milwaukee Ave Ste 425 Libertyville, IL 60048
  (847) 367-7730 Eric Johnson Director Business Dev
  Fax: (847) 483-1467
  Email: diversity@synergygbl.com
  Website: www.synergygbl.com/
Staffing solutions & services, temporary staffing, permanent placement, career transition, talent development, outsourcing. (Woman/As-Ind, estab 2006, empl 1113, sales $89,040,000, cert: NMSDC, WBENC)

8586 Workforce Management Inc.
  525 W Wise Rd, Ste C Schaumburg, IL 60193
  (847) 466-5335 Tina Ross President
  Fax: (847) 466-5759
  Email: tina@workforcemgmtinc.com
  Website: www.workforcemgmtinc.com
Staffing solutions, recruitment, placement & management. (Woman/White, estab 2014, empl 3, sales , cert: WBENC)

Indiana

8587 Alpha Rae Personnel, Inc.
  347 W Berry St, Ste 700 Fort Wayne, IN 46802
  (260) 426-8227 Rae Pearson President
  Fax: (260) 426-1152
  Email: businessoffice@alpha-rae.com
  Website: www.alpha-rae.com
Contract & temporary staffing, executive search, HR management & HR department outsourcing, employee training, electronics & embedded software contract engineering & manufacturing development. (Woman/AA, estab 1980, empl 400, sales , cert: State, WBENC)

8588 DaMar Staffing Solutions
  8900 Keystone Crossing, Ste 1060 Indianapolis, IN 46240
  (317) 566-8320 Tiffany Thompson President
  Fax: (317) 566-8576
  Email: tiffany.thompson@damarstaffing.com
  Website: www.damarstaffing.com
Staffing: direct hire, temp-to-hire, temporary. (Woman/AA, estab 2003, empl 7, sales $622,423, cert: State, City, 8(a))

8589 Diverse Staffing Services
  6325 Digital Way, Ste #100 Indianapolis, IN 46278
  (1317) 813-8000 Amber Slaughter Business Dev Mgr
  Fax:
  Email: aslaughter@diversestaffing.com
  Website: www.diversestaffing.com
Recruiting & staffing solutions: information technology, engineering, life sciences, sales & business operations. (AA, estab 1999, empl 3000, sales , cert: State, NMSDC)

8590 First Call Temporary Services Inc.
  6960 Hillsdale Ct Indianapolis, IN 46250
  (317) 596-3280 John Kulish Sales Mgr
  Fax: (317) 596-3284
  Email: jkulish@fcqs.com
  Website: www.firstcallinc.com
Staffing services: temp and temp-hire. (Woman/White, estab 1991, empl 31, sales $18,000,000, cert: WBENC)

8591 Smart IT Staffing, Inc.
  6500 Technology Center Dr Ste 300 Indianapolis, IN 46278
  (513) 530-0600 Bill Ryle Director of Sales
  Fax: (513) 530-0066
  Email: bryle@getsmarterit.com
  Website: www.getsmarterit.com
Information Technology Workforce Solutions. (Woman/AA, estab 2005, empl 480, sales $47,900,000, cert: NMSDC, WBENC)

8592 Specialized Staffing Solutions, LLC
  1001 E Jefferson South Bend, IN 46617
  (574) 234-9944 Jacqueline Barton President
  Fax: (463) 234-9949
  Email: jbarton@specializedstaffing.biz
  Website: www.specializedstaffing.biz
Temporary, permanant, technical & professional staffing, employment services, human resource mgmt, managed services. (Woman/As-Pac, estab 2002, empl 27, sales $17,000,000, cert: State)

Kansas

8593 Choson Resource LLC
  1999 N Amidon, Ste 100B Wichita, KS 67203
  (316) 729-0312 Kim Silcott President
  Fax: (316) 729-0709
  Email: kim@chosonresource.com
  Website: www.Chosonresource.com
Aerospace engineering & staffing services for the air, defense & space industries. (Woman/As-Pac, estab 2010, empl 4, sales $4,254,100, cert: NMSDC)

8594 Kansas Personnel Services, Inc
  2815 SW Wanamaker Rd Topeka, KS 66614
  (785) 272-9999 Patricia Bossert President
  Fax: (785) 273-7799
  Email: patti@keystaffing.com
  Website: www.keystaffing.com
Temporary staffing services, long-term & short-term: clerical, office, light industrial, warehouse, & environmental personnel. (Woman/White, estab 1989, empl 126, sales $3,000,000, cert: WBENC)

8595 Staffing Kansas City Inc.
  9930 College Blvd Overland Park, KS 66210
  (913) 663-5627 Michelle Hays Sales Exec
  Fax: (913) 663-3141
  Email: michelle@staffingkc.com
  Website: www.staffingkc.com
Temporary & permanent employment placement. (Woman, estab 1998, empl 5, sales $2,283,865, cert: State)

Kentucky

8596   Anew Technology Solutions, Inc.
       3310-C Gilmore Industrial Blvd   Louisville, KY 40213
       (502) 472-7461 Nina Carter President
       Fax: (502) 964-1123
       Email: anewtechnology@aol.com
       Website:
products and services that help to increase the safety,
health and sustainability of our environment. Our services
range from environmental cleanup, testing and an innovative focus on sustainability. (Woman/AA, estab 2009, empl
1, sales , cert: State)

8597   J.Y. Legner Associates, Inc.
       800 W Market St, Ste 102   Louisville, KY 40202
       (502) 585-9000 Josephine Legner CEO
       Fax: (502) 585-9011
       Email: jlegner@jyla.com
       Website: www.jyla.com
Staffing & HR mgmt, temporary staffing, long-term
employee leasing. (Woman/AA, estab 1999, empl 70, sales
, cert: NMSDC)

8598   TKT-nectir Global Staffing LLC
       9200 Shelbyville Rd Ste 600 Louisville, KY 40222
       (502) 499-9440 Tierra Kavanaugh Wayne CEO
       Fax: (502) 499-9404
       Email: info@tktandassociates.com
       Website: www.tktnectir.com
Staffing services: telecommunications, healthcare, government, financial services, utilities, manufacturing and
supply/chain logistics, contingent staffing, direct hire,
permanent staffing, rapid deployment. (Woman/AA, estab
2012, empl 85, sales $2,767,250, cert: NMSDC, WBENC)

Louisiana

8599   Delta Personnel, Inc.
       2709 L & A Rd 2709 L & A Rd Metairie, LA 70001
       (504) 833-5200 Ingrid Delahoussaye Owner
       Fax: (504) 833-5296
       Email: tlawrence@deltapersonnel.com
       Website: www.deltapersonnel.com
Staffing & payroll payroll services. (Woman/Hisp, estab
1968, empl 6, sales $2,900,000, cert: NMSDC, WBENC)

8600   Frazee Recruiting Consultants, Inc.
       2351 Energy Dr, Ste 1100   Baton Rouge, LA 70808
       (225) 231-7880 Chris Bien Business Dev consultant
       Fax: (225) 231-7887
       Email: sales@frazeerecruit.com
       Website: www.frazeerecruit.com
Professional staffing, direct hire search, contract/tempo-
rary. (Woman/White, estab 1998, empl 150, sales
$6,000,000, cert: WBENC)

8601   Infinitive Solutions
       1615 Poydras St Ste 900 New Orleans, LA 70112
       (504) 648-6810 Robin McCall President
       Fax:
       Email: rmccall@infinitive-solutions.com
       Website: www.infinitive-solutions.com
Staffing services including temporary and contract.
Professional, Healthcare, Educational support personnel.
(AA, estab 2013, empl 125, sales $1,185,950, cert: WBENC)

8602   Jean Simpson Personnel Services, Inc.
       1318 Shreveport-Barksdale Hwy   Shreveport, LA
       71105
       (318) 869-3494 Angel Scott Admin Asst
       Fax: (318) 868-0790
       Email: ascott@jeansimpson.com
       Website: www.jeansimpson.com
Temporary & full-time staffing: clerical, industrial &
professional. (Woman/White, estab 1974, empl 33, sales
, cert: WBENC)

8603   Preferred Standards, LLC
       654 Lobdell Ave   Baton Rouge, LA, LA 70806
       (225) 924-9552 Derrick Toussaint CEO
       Fax: (225) 924-9661
       Email: dtoussaint@pstandards.net
       Website: www.pstandards.org
Professional staffing, recruiting & payroll services. (AA,
estab 2013, empl 5, sales $1,312,529, cert: NMSDC)

8604   SureTemps LLC
       1631 Elysian Fields Ave   New Orleans, LA 70117
       (504) 947-3353 Maurice Robichaux President
       Fax: (504) 373-5788
       Email: suretemps@ymail.com
       Website: www.suretemps.biz
Personnel staffing: labors, data entry clerks, custodial
services, full food services & supervisors/managers for
long or short term basis. (AA, estab 2011, empl 500,
sales $1,550,000, cert: City)

8605   Topp Knotch Personnel, Inc.
       401 Whitney Ave Ste 312 Gretna, LA 70056
       (866) 744-2974 Diedria Joseph CEO
       Fax: (504) 376-8708
       Email: diedria@tkpsi.com
       Website: www.tkpsi.com
Staffing svcs: admin, clerical, customer service, accounting, marketing, computer technology. (Woman/AA,
estab 1900, empl 1, sales $4,055,182, cert: City)

8606   Universal Personnel, LLC
       1100 Poydras St Ste 1300 New Orleans, LA 70163
       (504) 561-5627 Michele Vignes President
       Fax: (504) 561-1595
       Email: michelev@universal-personnel.com
       Website: www.universal-personnel.com
Technical staffing, career & contract job placement:
engineering, drafting, architecture & information
technology, professional, administrative & clerical.
(Woman/White, estab 1980, empl 650, sales
$57,118,011, cert: WBENC)

Massachusetts

8607   Aries Group, Inc.
       500 Cummings Center Ste 1750 Beverly, MA
       01915
       (877) 806-7977 Frances Dichner President
       Fax: (978) 998-6841
       Email: fran@ariesgroupinc.com
       Website: www.ariesgroupinc.com
Contract & permanent placement staffing services.
(Woman/White, estab 2000, empl 10, sales $7,732,415,
cert: WBENC)

8608   East Coast Staffing Solutions
651 Orchard St Ste 307   New Bedford, MA 02744
(508) 990-7670   Randy Silva Business Devel
Fax:
Email: Randy@EastCoastStaffingSolutions.com
Website: www.EastCoastStaffingSolutions.com
Staffing, direct hires, temporary placements & contractual assignments. (AA, estab 2009, empl 5, sales $105,650,836, cert: State)

8609   Griffin Staffing Network, LLC
1145 Main St Ste 508   Springfield, MA 01103
(413) 788-0751   Michelle O'Meara
Fax: (804) 343-0014
Email: momeara@griffinstaffingnetwork.com
Website: www.griffinstaffingnetwork.com
Staffing services. (Woman/AA, estab 2013, empl 2, sales , cert: State)

8610   Hollister Staffing, Inc.
75 State St, 9th Fl   Boston, MA 02109
(617) 654-0200   Kip Hollister CEO
Fax: (617) 830-0023
Email: kip@hollisterstaff.com
Website: www.hollisterstaff.com
Recruiting services: direct hire, contract & contract-to-hire. (Woman, estab 1988, empl 70, sales $21,500,000, cert: WBENC)

8611   John Leonard Employment Services, Inc.
75 Federal St, Ste 1120   Boston, MA 02110
(617) 348-2607   Derek McKinley President
Fax:
Email: dmills@johnleonard.com
Website: www.johnleonard.com
Temporary employment: office support personnel. (Woman/White, estab 1969, empl 18, sales $7,009,497, cert: State, City, WBENC)

8612   KNF&T Staffing Resources
3 Post Office Square   Boston, MA 02109
(617) 574-8200   Joanna DiTrapano Director of Mktg
Fax: (508) 836-5463
Email: jditrapano@KNFT.com
Website: www.knft.com
Staffing services: administrative, accounting, finance & healthcare personnel. (Woman/White, estab 1983, empl 35, sales $14,000,000, cert: State, WBENC)

8613   S & S Staffing, LLC
50 Lake Ave   Worcester, MA 01604
(508) 799-7171   Karen DeMichele President
Fax: (508) 799-7272
Email: karen@savvystaffing.com
Website: www.savvystaffing.com
Staffing solutions: long or short term, temporary & permanent. (Woman/White, estab 2006, empl 15, sales $12,000,000, cert: State)

8614   Snelling Staffing Services
3 Courthouse Lane Ste 2   Chelmsford, MA 01824
(978) 970-3434   Bernice Kaiser Owner/General Mgr
Fax: (978) 970-3637
Email: bernice@snelling-ma.com
Website: www.snelling.com/chelmsford
Staffing: engineering, administrative, finance & accounting, sales & marketing, manufacturing direct hire/temp-to-hire/contract labor. (Woman/White, estab 1988, empl 6, sales $2,000,000, cert: WBENC)

8615   The Panther Group Inc.
5 Mill & Main Place Ste 430   Maynard, MA 01754
(617) 248-0780   Allison Parker VP Business Dev
Fax:
Email: aparker@thepanthergrp.com
Website: www.thepanthergrp.com
Temporary, Temp to Hire & Direct Hire staffing solutions & Managed Service Programs (MSP) for contingent labor. (AA, estab 1992, empl 65, sales , cert: NMSDC)

8616   The Resource Connection, Inc.
161 S Main St Ste 300   Middleton, MA 01949
(978) 777-9333   Janet Santa Anna President
Fax: (978) 777-3360
Email: janet@resource-connection.com
Website: www.resource-connection.com
Staffing services: temporary, temp-to-hire, & direct placement of administrative, clerical & light industrial personnel. (Woman, estab 1987, empl 9, sales $8,300,000, cert: State, City, WBENC)

8617   The Vesume Group, LLC
21 High St Ste 210A   North Andover, MA 01845
(978) 687-6000   Jori Blumsack COO
Fax: (978) 687-6006
Email: jori@thevesumegroup.com
Website: www.thevesumegroup.com
Staffing, contract, contract-to-hire & permanent placement of IT, Engineering, Manufacturing, Accounting/ Finance & Call Center professionals. (Woman/White, estab 2009, empl 9, sales $3,663,666, cert: WBENC)

8618   Total Technical Services, Inc.
225 Wyman St   Waltham, MA 02451
(800) 776-0562   Tim Hovey VP
Fax: (781) 642-1091
Email: thovey@total-tech.com
Website: www.total-tech.com
Temporary, contract & permanent staffing svcs, on-site managed vendor program & payroll svcs. (AA/Hisp, estab 1992, empl 300, sales , cert: NMSDC)

8619   United Personnel Services
1331 Main St   Springfield, MA 01103
(413) 314-6057   Christine Phillips VP Ops
Fax: (413) 747-9021
Email: cphillips@unitedpersonnel.com
Website: www.unitedpersonnel.com
Staffing: temporary, temp-to-hire & full-time placements. (Woman/White, estab 1987, empl 28, sales $11,608,395, cert: State, WBENC)

Maryland

8620   All-Pro Placement Service, Inc.
116 Old Padonia Rd, Ste D   Cockeysville, MD 21030
(410) 308-9050   Jennifer Quinn VP
Fax: (410) 308-9055
Email: jennifer@allproplacement.com
Website: www.allproplacement.com
Staffing: temp, temp-to-perm & direct hire permanent placements, clerical, executive level, warehousing. (Woman/White, estab 2002, empl 6, sales $3,895,000, cert: State, City, 8(a))

8621 Beacon Staffing Alternatives
16-2 S Philadelphia Blvd   Aberdeen, MD 21001
(410) 297-6600 Sheryl Kohl President
Fax: (410) 297-6601
Email: sheryl@beaconstaffing.com
Website: www.Beaconstaffing.com
Staffing services. (Woman/White, estab 1999, empl 300, sales $4,441,779, cert: State, WBENC)

8622 BizyBee Professional Staffing & Biz'Ness Solutions
8181 Professional Pl #205 Hyattsville, MD 20785
(301) 459-1233 Danae Hubbard President
Fax: (301) 459-1234
Email: bzbpro@yahoo.com
Website: www.bzbpro.com
Temporary staffing, employment, recruitment, staff augmentation & HR that services. (Woman/AA, estab 2011, empl 5, sales $500,000, cert: State, 8(a))

8623 Crews Control Inc
8161 Maple Lawn Blvd Ste 120   Fulton, MD 20759
(301) 604-1200 Andrea Keating CEO
Fax: (301) 604-1215
Email: info@crewscontrol.com
Website: www.crewscontrol.com
Recruitment, staffing & payroll services. (Woman/White, estab 1988, empl 13, sales $15,000,000, cert: WBENC)

8624 Crosby Corporation
14405 Laurel Place, Ste 201   Laurel, MD 20707
(301) 585-3105 Howard Petty President
Fax: (301) 576-8015
Email: hpetty@crosbycorp.com
Website: www.crosbycorp.com
Human capital solutions: technical staff augmentation, direct placement services, outsourced projects, educational services & workforce mgmt solutions. (AA, estab 2001, empl 100, sales $4,000,000, cert: State, City, 8(a))

8625 Federal Staffing Resources LLC
2200 Somerville Rd Ste 300 Annapolis, MD 21401
(410) 990-0795 Tracy Balazs CEO
Fax: (410) 990-0797
Email: tbalazs@fsrpeople.com
Website: www.fsrpeople.com
Workforce solutions & integrative business solutions, recruitment & staffing. (Woman/As-Pac, estab 2004, empl 266, sales $31,325,000, cert: State, NMSDC, WBENC)

8626 Infojini Inc.
10015, Old Columbia Rd, Ste B 215   Columbia, MD 21046
(443) 257-0086 Sandeep Harjani Director
Fax: (443) 283-4249
Email: commercialrfi@infojiniconsulting.com
Website: www.infojiniconsulting.com
Recruitment, training, assessment, outsourcing & consulting services, temporary & permanent positions. (As-Ind, estab 2006, empl 256, sales $15,800,000, cert: State)

8627 PMC Group Inc dba Piper Staffing
8117 Harford Rd, Ste D   Baltimore, MD 21234
(410) 286-1874 Kimberley West President
Fax: (866) 714-9442
Email: kimberley@pmcgrpinc.com
Website: www.piperstaffing.com
Multiple & diverse staffing solutions. (Woman/AA, estab 2010, empl 104, sales $1,669,345, cert: State)

8628 The All-Star Group Companies, Inc.
3710 Commerce Dr, Bldg 1005   Baltimore, MD 21227
(443) 543-7801 Tyrone Cypress VP sales/Mktg
Fax: (410) 242-7166
Email: sales@allstarcompanies.net
Website: www.allstarcompanies.net
Human capital assets; recruiting & staffing. (AA, estab 1995, empl 800, sales $19,200,000, cert: State)

8629 The BOSS Group
4350 East West Hwy, Ste 307   Bethesda, MD 20814
(301) 802-3672 Truelove, Charisse Owner
Fax: (240) 238-9886
Email: linda@thebossgroup.com
Website: www.thebossgroup.com
Human capital solutions, source, evaluate & place exclusive creative, marketing, communications & interactive talent. (Woman/White, estab , empl 1, sales , cert: WBENC)

8630 The HR Source
8181 Professional Pl #120 Landover, MD 20785
(301) 459-3133 Patricia Hall Jaynes CEO
Fax:
Email: pathj@thehrsource.com
Website: www.thehrsource.com
Human resources staffing & consulting services, interim/temporary & permanent staffing services, outplacement & payroll services, administrative interim/temporary & permanent staffing services. (Woman/AA, estab 1994, empl 5, sales $2,894,265, cert: State, NMSDC, WBENC)

Michigan

8631 Abacus Service Corporation
35055 W Twelve Mile, Ste 215   Farmington Hills, MI 48331
(503) 542-7409 Chris Mills Business Devel Mgr
Fax: (248) 479-0811
Email: chris@abacusservice.com
Website: www.abacusservice.com
Staff augmentation, contract, temporary & permanent placement services. (Woman/As-Ind, estab 2004, empl 325, sales $22,200,000, cert: NMSDC, WBENC, 8(a))

8632 Accura Services, LLC
51470 Oro Dr   Shelby Township, MI 48315
(586) 884-4417 Jenifer Cugliari Member
Fax: (586) 884-4417
Email: jen@accuraservicesllc.com
Website: www.accuraservicesllc.com
Direct & contract staffing services specializing in Engineering, Technical & Professional areas. (Woman, estab 2015, empl 3, sales , cert: WBENC)

8633 Acro Service Corp.
39209 Six Mile Rd, Ste 250   Livonia, MI 48152
(734) 591-1100 Edward Troost VP Bus Devel
Fax:
Email: etroost@acrocorp.com
Website: www.acrocorp.com
Staffing & related human capital management services. (AA, estab 1983, empl 250, sales $300,000,000, cert: NMSDC)

8634   Blake Group LLC
30986 Stone Ridge Dr Ste 14205   Wixom, MI 48393
(248) 238-5776   Jim Blake Sr Exec VP
Fax: (248) 779-1783
Email: james@blakegroupllc.com
Website: www.blakegroupllc.com
Information Technology professional executive staffing.
(Woman/AA, estab 2010, empl 7, sales $1,500,000, cert:
NMSDC)

8635   Community Based Staffing
4369 Seebaldt   Detroit, MI 48204
(313) 744-5771   David Cross President
Fax:
Email: david.cross@cb-staffing.com
Website: www.cb-staffing.com
Direct hire & staffing: machine operators, production
associates, welders, quality inspectors, press operators.
(AA, estab 2016, empl 50, sales $150,000, cert: NMSDC)

8636   CrossFire Group LLC
691 N Squirrel Rd Ste 118   Auburn Hills, MI 48326
(866) 839-2600   Deborah Schneider CEO
Fax: (248) 856-4001
Email: dschneider@xfiregroup.com
Website: www.xfiregroup.com
Recruiting, Staffing, Business Process Outsourcnig, professional temporary & contract staffing, permanent placement, vendor management &payroll services to large and
medium size firms. (Woman/White, estab 2002, empl
1500, sales $10,000,000, cert: WBENC)

8637   Crystal Employment Services, LLC
32355 Howard St   Madison Heights, MI 48071
(248) 588-9540   Michael Stanley Partner
Fax:
Email: mstanley@crystaleng.com
Website: www.crystaleng.com
Staffing services. (Hisp, estab 2004, empl 300, sales , cert:
NMSDC)

8638   Entech Staffing Solutions
1800 Crooks Road   Troy, MI 48084
(248) 528-1444   Colleen Myers Director of Sales and
Recruiting
Fax: (248) 528-6982
Email: cmyers@teamentech.com
Website: www.teamentech.com
Temporary staffing: administrative,
technical, medical & light industrial positions, short term,
long term & permanent employment. (Woman/White,
estab 1900, empl 1, sales $11,500,000, cert: WBENC)

8639   Galaxy Software Solutions, Inc.
5820 N Lilley Rd, Ste 8   Canton, MI 48187
(734) 717-7969   Dileep Tiwari VP
Fax: (734) 629-4287
Email: dileep@galaxy-soft.com
Website: www.galaxy-soft.com
Staffing highly skilled candidates/consultants on contract
and on a full-time basis. (Woman/As-Pac, estab 2004, empl
251, sales $24,000,000, cert: WBENC)

8640   Gonzalez Production Systems
1670 Highwood East   Pontiac, MI 48340
(248) 884-0315   Bill Kelly New Business Devel
Fax: (248) 209-4723
Email: bkelly@gonzales-group.com
Website: www.gonzalez-group.com
Contract Placement, Contract to Direct, Direct Placement, Managed Services. (Hisp, estab 1975, empl 800,
sales $50,000,000, cert: NMSDC)

8641   G-TECH Services, Inc.
17101 Michigan Avenue   Dearborn, MI 48126
(313) 425-3666   Shelby Medina Dir of Business
Devel
Fax: (313) 436-8044
Email: smedina@gogtech.com
Website: www.gogtech.com
Contract & direct hire staffing solutions,   engineering/
technical support; information technology; finance/
accounting; scientific; administration/clerical; co-
employment training & payroll services. (Woman/White,
estab 1986, empl 650, sales $56,000,000, cert: WBENC)

8642   Harvard Resource Group
210 W Big Beaver Rd Ste 310   Troy, MI 48084
(248) 528-1110   Mark Hicks VP
Fax: (248) 528-1119
Email: mhicks@hrgus.com
Website: www.harvardresourcegroup.com
Staffing: permanent, contract, temp to perm, professional & organizational dev, mgmt & leadership dev,
wireless dev & deployment svcs. (Nat Ame, estab 2001,
empl 6, sales $3,000,000, cert: NMSDC)

8643   Hattrick Professional Staffing
3228 Norton Lawn   Rochester Hills, MI 48307
(248) 289-6241   Julie Campbell Owner
Fax:
Email: julie.campbell@hattrick-staffing.com
Website: www.hattrick-staffing.com
Staffing, Direct Hire, Contract or Temp to hire place-
ments within areas of Engineering, Design, Finance/
Accounting, IT, Professional, Technical placements &
Executive positions. (Woman/White, estab 2015, empl 1,
sales , cert: WBENC)

8644   Human Capital Staffing LLC
6001 N Adams Rd, Ste 208   Bloomfield Hills, MI
48304
(248) 593-1950   Mary Adams President
Fax: (248) 593-1951
Email: madams@hcsteam.com
Website: www.hcsteam.com
Staffing services. (Woman/Nat Ame, estab , empl 10,
sales , cert: NMSDC)

8645   Inteligente Solutions, Inc.
17199 N Laurel Park Dr Ste 321   Livonia, MI 48152
(734) 338-8970   Kathy DeCaires VP
Fax: (734) 338-8946
Email: kdecaires@igsstaff.com
Website: www.igsstaff.com
Staffing svcs; general labor & light industrial; long term
to permanent, clerical & admin support staffing. (Hisp,
estab 1993, empl 500, sales , cert: NMSDC)

8646 K&A Staffing, LLC
38700 Van Dyke Rd. Ste 150 Sterling Heights, MI 48312
(586) 806-6614 Justin Tappero COO
Fax: (586) 619-9900
Email: jtappero@knaresourcegroup.com
Website: www.knaresourcegroup.com
Staffing services. (As-Ind, estab 2011, empl 16, sales , cert: NMSDC)

8647 Linked, LLC
6633 18 Mile Rd   Sterling Heights, MI 48314
(586) 231-1234 Marie Khoury President
Fax:
Email: Marie.Khoury@linkedps.com
Website: www.linkedps.com
Staffing, candidate search, recruitment, contract & direct placement services. (Woman/White, estab 2012, empl 4, sales , cert: WBENC)

8648 MCM Staffing, LLC
415 W 11 Mile Rd   Madison Heights, MI 48076
(248) 436-2616 Courtney Morales Hofmann President
Fax:
Email: courtney@mcmstaffing.com
Website: www.mcmstaffing.com
Staffing services. (Woman/Hisp, estab 2011, empl 950, sales , cert: NMSDC, WBENC)

8649 Michigan Staffing
29400 Van Dyke Ste 308 Warren, MI 48093
(586) 574-3572 Frances Lucido VP
Fax: (586) 751-8772
Email: fllucido@michiganstaffing.com
Website: www.michiganstaffing.com
Temporary, contract & direct staffing services: administrative, customer service, light industrial, technical, professional & skilled trades. (Woman/White, estab 2002, empl 75, sales , cert: WBENC)

8650 National Career Group
1745 Hamilton Rd   Okemos, MI 48864
(517) 706-0111 Nadia Sellers CEO
Fax:
Email: barbara@nationalcareergroup.com
Website: www.nationalcareergroup.com
Permanent staffing & Human Relations Training. (Woman/AA, estab 1997, empl 10, sales $700,000, cert: WBENC)

8651 National Career Group Training & Development
4021 W Michigan Ave, Ste 3   Lansing, MI 48917
(517) 327-1830 Ahmed Mortis VP Mktg
Fax: (517) 327-1836
Email: ahmed@nationalcareergroup.com
Website: www.nationalcareergroup.com
Executive staffing & training svcs, sales & mktg, IT, finance, engineering, HR permanent & contract staffing; diversity, team building, workplace violence & leadership training. (Woman/AA, estab 1997, empl 40, sales , cert: WBENC)

8652 NexTech Professional Services
25200 Telegraph Rd. Ste 110   Southfield, MI 48033
(248) 416-1718 Rosanne Davis President
Fax: (248) 416-1190
Email: rosanne.davis@nextechps.com
Website: www.nextechps.com
Contract & permanent placement: engineering, technology, finance & executive recruiting. (As-Pac, estab 1994, empl 10, sales $2,600,000, cert: NMSDC)

8653 PDS Services, LLC
37633 Pembroke   Livonia, MI 48152
(734) 953-3300 Derek Dyer President
Fax: (734) 953-9701
Email: derek@pdsstaffing.com
Website: www.pdsstaffing.com
Staffing services: contract, contract to hire & permanent placements. (AA, estab 2005, empl 260, sales $9,000,000, cert: NMSDC)

8654 Personnel Unlimited Inc.
29400 Van Dyke Ave   Warren, MI 48093
(586) 751-5608 Frances Lucido President
Fax: (586) 751-8772
Email: fllucido@personnel-unlimited.com
Website: www.personnel-unlimited.com
Temporary & Contract Staffing for Admin, Clerical, Tech/Professional. (Woman, estab 2008, empl 7, sales $2,462,679, cert: WBENC)

8655 Populus Group
3001 W Big Beaver Rd Ste 400 Troy, MI 48084
(425) 372-1249 Matthew King Business Dev Support
Fax: (248) 712-8099
Email: making@populusgroup.com
Website: www.populusgroup.com
Temporary staffing services. (Hisp, estab 2002, empl 160, sales $369,000,000, cert: NMSDC, CPUC)

8656 Premier Automation Contractors
9015 Davison Rd   Davison, MI 48423
(248) 421-7360 Lisa VanWyk engineering Accts Dir
Fax: (810) 412-0664
Email: lisa@premierac.com
Website: www.premierac.com
Direct & contract hire staffing for skilled trades. (Woman/White, estab 2008, empl 200, sales $12,000,000, cert: WBENC)

8657 Premier Staff Services
16250 Northland Dr Ste 224 Southfield, MI 48075
(248) 809-9675 Michael Garcia Acct Mgr
Fax: (248) 809-6752
Email: michael.garcia.rep@gmail.com
Website: www.premierstaffservices.net
Contract staffing, temporary help & direct placement of clerical, administrative, financial, janitorial, maintenance, engineering & IT human resources. (AA, estab 2011, empl 24, sales $11,000,000, cert: NMSDC, 8(a))

8658   Reliance One, Inc.
1700 Harmon Road Ste One   Auburn Hills, MI 48326
(248) 922-4500   Chad Toms VP of Sales
Fax: (248) 922-5660
Email: ctoms@reliance-one.com
Website: www.reliance-one.com
Staffing, direct & contract, employment, payroll. (Hisp, estab 1998, empl 700, sales , cert: NMSDC)

8659   Scope Services, Inc.
2095 Niles Rd   St. Joseph, MI 49085
(269) 982-2888   TRISH MELCHER President
Fax: (269) 983-8040
Email: TMMELCHER@SCOPE-SERVICES.COM
Website: www.scope-services.com
Human capital management, contract &project staffing & managed staffing/consulting, executive search, contingency direct hire placement, career consulting & outplacement services. (Woman, estab 1965, empl 569, sales , cert: WBENC)

8660   Snelling Personnel Services
2265 Livernois   Troy, MI 48083
(248) 362-5090   Larry Wright CEO
Fax: (248) 362-4540
Email: ldwright@snellingmetrodetroit.com
Website: www.snellingmetrodetroit.com
Temporary, temporary-to-hire & permanent placement: clerical, medical, technical, professional, engineering & information technology. (Woman/AA, estab 1987, empl 25, sales , cert: WBENC)

8661   Staffing Source Personnel dba DriverSource
15340 Michigan Ave   Dearborn, MI 48126
(313) 624-9500   David J. Olshansky Co-Founder
Fax: (313) 624-9533
Email: dolshansky@driversource.net
Website: www.driversource.net
Commercial driver leasing & recruiting services. (Woman/Hisp, estab 1998, empl 350, sales , cert: WBENC)

8662   The Bartech Group, Inc.
27777 Franklin Rd, Ste 600   Southfield, MI 48034
(248) 208-4515   Michelle Hyland Dir Sales & Mktg
Fax:
Email: bartechinfo@bartechgroup.com
Website: www.bartechgroup.com
Contract & temporary staffing svcs: technical, office, computer & utility support svcs, facilities mgmt, IT solutions & support. (AA, estab 1977, empl 2972, sales , cert: NMSDC)

8663   The Targa Group
33228 W 12 Mile Rd #108   Farmington Hills, MI 48334
(248) 514-2295   Rob Ganesan President
Fax:
Email: rganesan@thetargagroup.com
Website: www.thetargagroup.clom
Staffing, Process Improvement & Information Technology. (As-Pac, estab 2009, empl 6, sales $250,000, cert: NMSDC)

8664   Trialon Corporation
1477 Walli Strasse Blvd   Burton, MI 48509
(810) 742-8500   Robert Feys sales engineer
Fax: (810) 742-8512
Email: rfeys@trialon.com
Website: www.trialon.com
Technical Staffing and Engineering & Test Services to the Automotive, Aerospace, Military, Consumer Electronics, Medical, and Telecommunications Industries. (Woman/White, estab 1982, empl 750, sales $25,050,000, cert: WBENC)

8665   Venator Staffing
888 W Big Beaver Rd, Ste 450   Troy, MI 48084
(248) 269-0000   Michael Teats Sales Mgr
Fax: (248) 269-9506
Email: michael@venatornet.com
Website: www.venatornet.com
Accounting, finance & administrative staffing: temp & permanent placement. (As-Pac, estab 2001, empl 25, sales $2,500,000, cert: NMSDC)

8666   VETBUILT Services, Inc.
1927 Rosa Parks Blvd Ste 125   Detroit, MI 48216
(989) 493-1240   Hector Malacara CEO
Fax: (313) 964-2682
Email: hmalacara@vetbuilt.com
Website: www.vetbuiltservices.com
Staffing services. (Hisp, estab 2013, empl 300, sales $6,853,851, cert: NMSDC)

8667   Wrightway Enterprises, Inc.
744 Lothrop   Detroit, MI 48202
(248) 362-5090   Larry Wright President
Fax: (248) 362-4540
Email: ldwright@snellingmetrodetroit.com
Website: www.snellingmetrodetroit.com
Staffing services: permanent & temporary. (AA, estab 1987, empl 13, sales $2,550,000, cert: NMSDC)

Minnesota

8668   Advent Creative Group
7101 York Ave S, Ste 240   Edina, MN 55435
(952) 746-5668   Mary Younggren Owner
Fax: (952) 920-9405
Email: maryy@adventcreativegroup.com
Website: www.adventcreativegroup.com
Advertising, communications, creative, marketing & interactive hiring resources, contract & full-time basis. (Woman/White, estab 2007, empl 4, sales $606,822, cert: WBENC)

8669   Avenue Staffing Inc.
7000-57th Ave N Ste 120   Minneapolis, MN 55428
(763) 537-6104   Chuck Okitikpi President
Fax: (763) 537-7514
Email: chuck@avenuestaffing.com
Website: www.Avenuestaffing.com
Temporary & permanent employment. (AA, estab 2006, empl 48, sales $1,200,000, cert: NMSDC)

8670 Billinda Group LLC
4651 Nicols Rd, Ste 106-108 Eagan, MN 55122
(651) 379-5082 Bill Fitch CEO
Fax: (651) 379-2297
Email: bill@techpowerES.com
Website: www.Techpoweres.com
Contract, contract to permanent & direct placement.
(Woman/White, estab 2005, empl 28, sales $3,700,000,
cert: WBENC)

8671 Celarity
8120 Penn Ave Ste 220 Minneapolis, MN 55431
(952) 941-0022 Marlene Phipps President
Fax: (952) 941-0709
Email: marlene@celarity.com
Website: www.celarity.com
Contract, temporary recruiting, staffing, full-time direct
hires. (Woman, estab 1992, empl 110, sales $7,092,546,
cert: WBENC)

8672 Dahl Consulting, Inc.
418 County Rd D East St. Paul, MN 55117
(651) 772-9225 Corey Johnson CEO
Fax: (651) 772-9250
Email: corey@dahlconsulting.com
Website: www.dahlconsulting.com
Vendor management services, staff augmentation,
permanent search. (Woman/White, estab 1993, empl 808,
sales $87,902,216, cert: WBENC)

8673 Doherty Staffing Solutions, Inc.
7645 Metro Blvd Edina, MN 55439
(952) 818-3251 David Tuenge Program Mgr
Fax: (952) 832-1962
Email: dtuenge@dohertystaffing.com
Website: www.dohertystaffing.com
Contract & temporary staffing. (Woman/White, estab
1980, empl 151, sales $400,337,900, cert: WBENC)

8674 HighCloud Solutions, Inc.
15212 60th Ave N Minneapolis, MN 55446
(612) 605-0694 Raghu Chejarla President
Fax:
Email: raghu@highcloudsolutions.com
Website: www.highcloudsolutions.com
Staffing, contracting/temp job positions. (Woman/As-Ind,
estab 2015, empl 3, sales , cert: State, City)

8675 IG, Inc. dba Indrotec
17 Washington Ave N Minneapolis, MN 55401
(612) 371-7402 Kathleen Dolphin CEO
Fax: (612) 977-1402
Email: kathydolphin@mydolphingroup.com
Website: www.myindrotec.com
We supply companies with light industrial and assembly
staff. (Woman/White, estab 1968, empl 16, sales
$20,000,100, cert: WBENC)

8676 Just In Case, Inc.
6900 Shady Oak Rd, #250 Eden Praire, MN 55344
(952) 925-3789 Diane Blomberg CEO
Fax: (952) 925-9009
Email: Diane.Blomberg@Justincasestaffing.com
Website: www.casestaffingsolutions.com/
Staffing, consulting & integration: packaging, shipping &
receiving, taping & assembly, clerical positions, administrative jobs, inbound call center positions, customer support.
(Woman/White, estab 1981, empl 9, sales $5,900,000,
cert: WBENC)

8677 Latitude Technology Group, Inc.
6800 France Avenue South Ste 500 Edina, MN
55435
(952) 767-6802 Dorreen Schmidt CEO
Fax: (952) 767-6801
Email: dschmidt@latitude-group.com
Website: www.latitude-group.com
Staffing svcs: contract, contract to hire & permanent
placement services. (Woman/White, estab 2002, empl
45, sales $6,000,000, cert: WBENC)

8678 Nexpro Personnel Services, Inc.
5353 Gamble Dr, Ste 112 Minneapolis, MN 55416
(952) 224-9855 Julia Zimmer Owner
Fax: (952) 224-9859
Email: jzimmer@nexprojobs.com
Website: www.nexprojobs.com
Staffing services: administrative, clerical, temporary,
contract, word processors, data entry, customer service
reps, accounting & payroll, light industrial, receptionist,
executive assistants (Woman/White, estab 2000, empl
40, sales $5,000,000, cert: WBENC)

8679 Pelican Staffing Solutions
401 N 3rd St Ste 425 Minneapolis, MN 55401
(612) 545-5330 Ebi Itie President
Fax: (612) 545-5326
Email: ebi@pelicanstaffing.com
Website: www.pelicanstaffing.com
Contract & temporary staffing, staff & vendor manage-
ment. (Woman/AA, estab 2011, empl 11, sales , cert:
City, NMSDC)

8680 Select Source International
13911 Ridgedale Dr, Ste 230 Minnetonka, MN
55305
(952) 546-3300 Mandeep Sodhi CEO
Fax: (952) 546-3500
Email: sales@selectsourceintl.com
Website: www.SelectSourceIntl.com
Temporary Staffing, Information Technology Staffing,
Information Technology Services, Engineering Services,
Financial Services, Government Services, Retail Services,
Energy & Utility Services, Application Development,
Mobile Development. (As-Ind, estab 2000, empl 773,
sales $74,018,880, cert: NMSDC)

8681 Serenity Staffing LLC
6180 W 143rd St Savage, MN 55378
(612) 834-6444 Jennifer Sabby President
Fax: (952) 216-0251
Email: jsabby@serenity-staffing.com
Website: www.serenity-staffing.com
Place Human Resource professionals. (Woman/White,
estab 2005, empl 5, sales $281,316, cert: WBENC)

8682 Synico Staffing
3033 Excelsior Blvd Ste 495 Minneapolis, MN
55416
(612) 926-6000 Jerry Marsh VP
Fax: (612) 926-6005
Email: jmarsh@synico.com
Website: www.synico.com
Staffing services. (AA, estab 1996, empl 450, sales
$13,000,000, cert: NMSDC)

8683 The Advent Group
7101 York Ave S, Ste 240 Edina, MN 55435
(952) 920-9119 Mary Younggren Owner
Fax: (952) 920-9405
Email: mary@adventgroupco.com
Website: www.adventgroupofcompanies.com
Staffing office support positions, administrative & account-ing support, call center/customer service, human re-sources, mortgage/financial areas, manufacturing & logistics. (Woman/White, estab 2002, empl 12, sales , cert: WBENC)

8684 United Staffing, Inc.
5501 Lakeland Ave Ste 212 Minneapolis, MN 55429
(763) 535-2989 Tony Nagberi President
Fax: (763) 535-2756
Email: tony@unitedstaffingusa.com
Website: www.unitedstaffingusa.com
Staffing: office, industrial, legal, IT, financial, administra-tive. (AA, estab 1997, empl 450, sales $3,000,000, cert: NMSDC)

Missouri

8685 Above All Personnel dba S.M. Huber Ent., Inc.
2228 S Big Bend Blvd St. Louis, MO 63117
(314) 781-6008 Susan Huber President
Fax: (314) 781-0432
Email: team@aboveallpersonnel.com
Website: www.aboveallpersonnel.com
Temporary, temp-to-hire, direct hire employment svcs: clerical, accounting, customer service, data processing. (Woman/White, estab 1995, empl 750, sales $3,400,000, cert: State)

8686 American Staffing LLC
11424A Dorsett Rd Maryland Heights, MO 63043
(314) 872-7070 Diane Fennel President
Fax: (314) 870-7077
Email: dfennel@americanstaffingstl.com
Website: www.americanstaffingstl.com
Staffing: temp, temp to hire & permanent. (Woman/White, estab 2002, empl 12000, sales $6,777,000, cert: State)

8687 Application Engineering Group
12300 Old Tesson Rd, Ste 100-G St. Louis, MO 63128
(314) 842-9110 Chris Rakel Sr Acct Mgr
Fax:
Email: chris.rakel@aeg-inc.com
Website: www.aeg-inc.com
Provide contract, contract to hire & direct hire IT employ-ment services. (Hisp, estab 1992, empl 35, sales , cert: State)

8688 C & S Business Services, Inc.
1731 Southridge Dr Jefferson City, MO 65109
(573) 635-9295 Paula Benne President
Fax: (573) 635-4145
Email: paula@cs-business.com
Website: www.cs-business.com
Staffing, temporary, direct hire, contract, employment verification, criminal background checks. (Woman/White, estab 1977, empl 12, sales $4,000,000, cert: State)

8689 Chief of Staff LLC
601 E 63rd St Kansas City, MO 64110
(816) 581-2776 Marny Burke Govt Accts Mgr
Fax:
Email: government@chiefofstaffkc.com
Website: www.chiefofstaffkc.com
Temporary administrative staffing services, office management, receptionist, accounting & finance, HR, customer service/call room & data entry/records management positions. (Woman/White, estab 2011, empl 8, sales $1,190,023, cert: State)

8690 Creative On Call Inc.
101 S Hanley Road Ste 1210 St. Louis, MO 63105
(866) 316-8919 Stuart Koenig EVP Client Services
Fax:
Email: stuart@creativesoncall.com
Website: www.creativesoncall.com
Placement agency, recruit professionals with creative, marketing, communications and/or interactive expertise for permanent, contract & freelance positions. (Woman/White, estab 1995, empl 47, sales $4,000,000, cert: State, WBENC)

8691 Critique Personnel Service, Inc.
1100 S Jefferson Ave St. Louis, MO 63104
(314) 772-5445 Monique Jeans Dir client svcs
Fax: (314) 772-5450
Email: mjeans@critiquepersonnel.com
Website: www.critiquepersonnel.com
Temporary & permanent staffing services. (AA, estab 1997, empl 50, sales , cert: State)

8692 EH, Inc.
415 S 18th St Ste 205 63103 St. Louis, MO 63103
(618) 314-0132 Breck Newman St Louis Regional Mgr
Fax:
Email: bnewman@hirelevel.com
Website: www.hirelevel.com
Staffing services, temporary employment, temporary-to-hire & direct hire. (Woman/White, estab 1995, empl 90, sales $32,577,783, cert: WBENC)

8693 NextGen Information Services Inc.
906 Olive St Ste 600 Saint Louis, MO 63101
(314) 588-1212 Christy Herschbach Admin Asst
Fax: (314) 588-1211
Email: supplierdiversity@nextgen-is.com
Website: www.nextgen-is.com
IT consulting services: project mgmt, custom application dev, legacy transition svcs & staff augmentation, staff augmentaion. (Woman/Hisp, estab 1997, empl 300, sales , cert: State, City, WBENC)

8694 Pangaea, Inc.
1403 Hwy F Defiance, MO 63341
(314) 925-1783 Heather Everett President
Fax:
Email: HEverett@Pangaea-inc.com
Website: www.Pangaea-inc.com
Supplemental staffing services, contract, direct place-ment, and contract to hire resources. (Woman/White, estab 2008, empl 10, sales $750,000, cert: State)

8695 Shelgin Partners
9211 Phoenix Village Pkwy   O'Fallon, MO 63368
(636) 625-2333 Gerri Lynn Zschetzsche Partner
Fax: (636) 625-2356
Email: glz@shelgin.com
Website: www.shelgin.com
Recruiting agency: direct recruitment, advertising, job boards, candidate referrals & partner referrals. (Woman/White, estab 2005, empl 5, sales $553,000, cert: State)

8696 Supplemental Medical Services, Inc.
10916 Schuetz Road   St. Louis, MO 63146
(314) 997-8833 Gretchen Curry President
Fax: (314) 997-3115
Email: gcurry@stafflinkusa.com
Website: www.stafflinkusa.com
Temporary, contract, travel & direct hire healthcare personnel. (Woman/AA, estab 1987, empl 125, sales $2,643,128, cert: State, NMSDC)

8697 The Herring IMPACT Group
12977 N Outer 40 Dr Ste 300 St. Louis, MO 63141
(314) 392-0658 Lauren Herring CEO
Fax: (314) 453-0531
Email: diversity1@ighr.com
Website: www.ighr.com
Career transitions, relocation support, talent development, and outplacement services. (Woman/White, estab 1988, empl 117, sales $15,000,000, cert: State, WBENC, NWBOC)

Mississippi

8698 HRD Results, LLC
P.O. Box 13333 Jackson, MS 39236
(601) 213-6358 Richard L Conerly Owner
Fax: (601) 899-9972
Email: richard@hrdresults.com
Website: www.hrdresults.com
Provide excellent products and services to buyers in a timely manner. (AA, estab 2006, empl 10, sales , cert: State)

8699 RAKS Fire Sprinkler LLC
215 Mobile St   Hattiesburg, MS 39401
(601) 261-0820 Romero Ali CEO
Fax: (601) 899-9972
Email: rali75@yahoo.com
Website: www.raks.co/
Fire Protection Services and Products: Fire Sprinkler System, (Wet, Dry, and Special Hazards) Design, New Installation, Inspection and Maintainance. Fire Alarm system, Design New Installation (AA, estab 2010, empl 8, sales $291,046, cert: State)

8700 TempStaff Inc.
962 North St   Jackson, MS 39202
(601) 353-4200 Carolyn Boteler President
Fax: (601) 714-4679
Email: carolyn@tempstaff.net
Website: www.tempstaff.net
Temporary & permanent employment. (Woman/White, estab 1979, empl 24, sales , cert: WBENC)

Montana

8701 Brady Co., Inc. dba A2Z Staffing Solutions
50 West 14th St Ste 300   Helena, MT 59601
(406) 443-7664 Anna Kazmierowski CEO
Fax: (406) 443-7842
Email: anna@a2zmontana.com
Website: www.a2zmontana.com
Workforce solutions, temporary staffing, temporary to permanent placement & direct hire services, employee payroll, scientific & technical staffing, technical & professional recruitment & construction labor. (Woman/White, estab 2003, empl 7, sales $4,517,215, cert: State, WBENC, SDB)

North Carolina

8702 Ascendo Resources, LLC
4201 Congress St, Ste 460   Charlotte, NC 28209
(704) 626-7486 Rick Ferretti Partner
Fax: (888) 758-5936
Email: rferretti@ascendo.com
Website: www.ascendo.com
Executive recruiting & temporary staffing, temporary & project opportunities. (Hisp, estab 2008, empl 100, sales $27,000,000, cert: NMSDC)

8703 Associate Staffing, LLC
303C Atkinson St   Laurinburg, NC 28352
(980) 224-8754 Michael Norton Director
Fax:
Email: mnorton@associatestaffingllc.com
Website: www.associatestaffingllc.com
Recruiting & staffing, contract, contract to permanent & direct placement basis. (Woman/White, estab 2008, empl 450, sales $13,400,000, cert: WBENC)

8704 Aten Solutions, Inc.
2000 Regency Pkwy, Ste 295   Cary, NC 27518
(919) 465-3366 Leah Brown CEO
Fax: (919) 465-3884
Email: lbrown@a10clinical.com
Website: www.a10clinical.com
Staffing solutions: clinical research, clinical data management, statistical programming & biostatistics space, clinical trial svcs & staffing support. (Woman/AA, estab 2004, empl 64, sales $8,000,000, cert: NMSDC, WBENC, 8(a))

8705 Automated Results Computer Consulting, LLC
242 S Caldwell St   Brevard, NC 28712
(888) 326-8404 Brian Finkbone VP
Fax: (832) 201-7780
Email: BrianFinkbone@AutomatedResults.com
Website: www.automatedresults.com
Automated Results delivers integrated information solutions designed to link people with resources. Our goal; to enable continuous improvement of production and business processes while creating a return on investment for our clients. (Woman/White, estab 2000, empl 8, sales $452,000, cert: State)

8706 BPN Concepts
      8305 University Executive Park Dr Ste 330 Charlotte, NC 28262
      (980) 335-0656 Brenda Harris Owner
      Fax: (866) 214-5299
      Email: info@bpnconcepts.com
      Website: www.bpnconcepts.com
Executive search & staffing services. (Woman/AA, estab 2011, empl 6, sales , cert: State, City)

8707 CEO Inc.
      412 Louise Ave   Charlotte, NC 28204
      (704) 372-4701 Deborah Millhouse President
      Fax: (704) 372-4707
      Email: debby@ceohr.com
      Website: www.ceohr.com
Temporary staffing, payrolling, HR consulting, executive search & placement. (Woman/White, estab 1994, empl 15, sales $2,995,605, cert: State)

8708 Concierge Staffing LLC
      160 S Main St   Graham, NC 27253
      (336) 270-3035 Denise Brown Owner
      Fax: (877) 247-5231
      Email: denise.brown@concierge-staffing.com
      Website: www.concierge-staffing.com
Staffing services and solutions. (Woman/AA, estab 2014, empl 50, sales $100,000, cert: State)

8709 Cyber Shield Consulting Inc.
      8300 Boone Blvd, Ste 500   Vienna, NC 22182
      (571) 358-5602 Doug Marland Business Devel Mgr
      Fax: (866) 262-7565
      Email: operations@cybershieldincorporated.com
      Website: www.cybershieldincorporated.com
Human capital services, temporary & permanent. (AA, estab 2013, empl 25, sales $25,000, cert: NMSDC)

8710 Greer Group
      3109 Charles B. Root Wynd   Raleigh, NC 27612
      (919) 571-0051 Mark Blume Client Devel Mgr
      Fax:
      Email: sales@thegreergroup.com
      Website: www.thegreergroup.com
Staffing services: temporary staffing, temporary to direct hire staffing, direct hire recruitment, payrolling services & onsite staffing management. (Woman/White, estab 1986, empl 16, sales $15,802,034, cert: WBENC)

8711 Greytree Partners
      121 Greenwich Rd Ste 211 Charlotte, NC 28211
      (704) 899-4082 Clarence Fisher Chief Solutions Architect
      Fax: (704) 973-0767
      Email: clarence.fisher@GreytreePartners.com
      Website: www.GreytreePartners.com
Identification, recruitment & placement of information technology and engineering services professionals on a contract or permanent basis. (AA, estab 2004, empl 30, sales $2,400,000, cert: State, NMSDC)

8712 Jennifer Temps, Inc.
      1973 JN Pease Pl Ste 201 Charlotte, NC 28262
      (212) 964-8367 Jennifer Singleton President
      Fax: (212) 349-8433
      Email: jsingleton@jennifertemps.com
      Website: www.jennifertemps.com
Temporary staffing. (Woman/AA, estab 1992, empl 8, sales $4,500,000, cert: NMSDC)

8713 nDemand Consulting LLC
      2923 S Tryon St, Ste 220   Charlotte, NC 28203
      (704) 965-0781 Oscar Frazier Owner
      Fax: (704) 288-1782
      Email: ofrazier@ndemandconsulting.com
      Website: www.ndemandconsultingllc.com
Recruiting & staffing services. (Woman/AA, estab 2004, empl 10, sales $20,000, cert: State)

8714 Quality Staffing Solutions, Inc.
      120 Towerview Ct   Cary, NC 27513
      (919) 481-4114 Phyllis Moffett CEO
      Fax: (919) 481-1092
      Email: pmoffett@quality-staffing.com
      Website: www.quality-staffing.com
Staffing solutions. (Woman/White, estab 1995, empl 400, sales $6,526,751, cert: WBENC)

8715 Reblee, Inc. dba Allegiance Staffing
      7701-O Sharon Lakes Rd   Charlotte, NC 28210
      (704) 556-1770 Lisa Gaddy Acct Mgr
      Fax: (704) 556-0633
      Email: lgaddy@allegiancestaffing.com
      Website: www.allegiancestaffing.com
Contract staffing. (Woman/White, estab 1993, empl 8, sales $4,500,000, cert: State)

8716 Right Choice Solutions, Inc.
      316 W Millbrook Rd Ste. 213 Raleigh, NC 27609
      (919) 324-3557 Layce Adams Ops Mgr
      Fax:
      Email: layce@thercsolutions.com
      Website: www.thercsolutions.com
Staffing: temporary staffing, temp to hire & direct hire quality candidates. (Woman/AA, estab 2005, empl 7, sales $101,369, cert: NMSDC)

8717 Sappenfield Staffing, Inc.
      1014 S Tryon St Ste 101 Charlotte, NC 28203
      (704) 332-4710 Rob Sappenfield Jr VP
      Fax: (704) 332-4227
      Email: rsappenfield@sappenfieldstaffing.com
      Website: www.sappenfieldstaffing.com
Staffing: temporary, temp/hire, direct hire & payroll services. (Woman/White, estab 1995, empl 3, sales $1,800,000, cert: State)

8718 Two Hawk Employment Services, Inc.
      3021 N Roberts Ave   Lumberton, NC 28360
      (910) 738-3014 Harvey Godwin, Jr. Owner
      Fax: (910) 738-2819
      Email: harvey.godwin@twohawk.net
      Website: www.twohawk.net
Temporary & permanent employment services: general labor, supervisory & administration positions. (Nat Ame, estab 1999, empl 50, sales $24,000,000, cert: NMSDC)

8719 Xcentri, Inc.
412 Louise Ave   Charlotte, NC 28204
(704) 369-3211 Debby Millhouse President
Fax: (704) 372-4707
Email: Deborah.millhouse@xcentri.com
Website: www.xcentri.com
Staffing & recruiting (temp, contract to hire and direct hire); HR Consulting; Background Checks; Drug Screening (Woman/White, estab 2014, empl 200, sales $9,586,491, cert: WBENC)

New Hampshire

8720 CCSI Inc.
62 Portsmouth Ave   Stratham, NH 03885
(800) 598-0255 Sarah Latiolais Acct Mgr
Fax: (603) 778-8941
Email: sarah@ccsiinc.com
Website: www.ccsiinc.com
Temp & permanent staffing: IT, accounting, finance, HR, sales, admin, marketing & clinical staff. (Woman/White, estab 1998, empl 256, sales $16,000,000, cert: WBENC)

8721 The Spencer Thomas Group LLC
One Falkland Place   Portsmouth, NH 03801
(603) 835-3707 Lori Perkins Acct Mgr
Fax: (800) 380-6970
Email: lori.perkins@spencer-thomas.com
Website: www.spencer-thomas.com
Recruiting, staffing, consulting, PeopleSoft, SAP, Oracle, web deveoplers, project mgmt, program mgrs, outsourced payroll svcs, employee leasing. (Woman/White, estab 1998, empl 3, sales $20,000,000, cert: WBENC)

New Jersey

8722 Accountants For You Inc.
1175 Marlkress Rd, #1040   Cherry Hill, NJ 08034
(215) 988-7200 Marcia Libes President
Fax: (215) 988-9475
Email: marcia.libes@accountantsforyou.com
Website: www.accountantsforyou.com
Staffing & recruiting: temporary, temporary to permanent & permanent placement of accounting, finance, human resource & office professionals. (Woman/White, estab 2006, empl 10, sales $1,376,195, cert: WBENC)

8723 ACCU Staffing Services
911 Kings Hwy N   Cherry Hill, NJ 08034
(856) 482-2222 Debra Fordyce Operation Mgr
Fax: (856) 779-8808
Email: cherryhill@accustaffing.com
Website: www.accustaffing.com
Staffing svcs: human resources, planned staffing, direct placement, corporate outplacement svcs & on-site consulting/mgmt funcations. (Woman/White, estab 1979, empl 100, sales , cert: WBENC)

8724 APN Consulting Inc.
1100 Cornwall Rd   Monmouth Junction, NJ 08852
(609) 924-3400 Francis Moser Business Dev Mgr
Fax:
Email: francis@apnconsultinginc.com
Website: www.www,apnconsultinginc.com
Contract, contract-to-hire & full time staffing services. (As-Ind, estab 2002, empl 250, sales $20,300,000, cert: NMSDC)

8725 Bear Staffing Services, Corp.
47 S. Broad St.   Woodbury, NJ 08096
(856) 848-0082 Sherri Johnson President
Fax: (866) 597-0307
Email: sjohnson@bearstaff.com
Website: www.bearstaff.com
Temporary, temp to hire & direct hire staffing services. (Woman/White, estab 2005, empl 500, sales $7,200,000, cert: WBENC)

8726 CNC Consulting
50 E Palisades Ave Ste 422 Englewood, NJ 07631
(201) 541-9122 Wade Mcmurray Business Dev Mgr
Fax: (201) 541-9128
Email: wmcmurray@cncconsulting.com
Website: www.cncconsulting.com
IT professionals for consulting contracts. (AA, estab 1996, empl 25, sales $3,000,000, cert: State)

8727 Datanomics, Inc.
991 US Hwy 22 West Ste 301 Bridgewater, NJ 08807
(908) 707-8200 Lori Vail CEO
Fax: (908) 707-9600
Email: vail@datanomics.com
Website: www.datanomics.com
IT staffing, helpdesk, desktop support, administration, technical writers, validation specialists, business/systems
analysts, programmers, mainframe, client/server, & web. (Woman/White, estab 1982, empl 100, sales , cert: State)

8728 Elite Personnel Group, LLC
220 Davidson Ave. Ste 102   Somerset, NJ 08873
(908) 722-1111 Lourdes Salazar Junior Recruiter
Fax: (732) 595-5340
Email: msalazar@eliteitpersonnel.com
Website: www.eliteitpersonnel.com
National recruiting and talent acquisition. (As-Pac, estab 2007, empl 40, sales $45,000,000, cert: State)

8729 Fabergent, Inc.
63 Ramapo Valley Rd, Ste 214   Mahwah, NJ 07430
(201) 378-0036 Ratna Silpa Gorantla President
Fax: (201) 328-3179
Email: Ratna@fabergent.com
Website: www.fabergent.com
Contract & full-time positions IT staffing in Java, .Net, SharePoint, SAP, Oracle, BI, Analytics, networking & IT security. (Woman/As-Pac, estab 2005, empl 125, sales , cert: State)

8730   Frink-Hamlett Legal Solutions
P.O. Box 2022   Teaneck, NJ 07666
(201) 357-8975   Katherine Frink-Hamlett President
Fax: (201) 624-7600
Email: katherine@frinkhamlett.com
Website: www.frinkhamlett.com
Provide legal professionals: attorneys, compliance &
paralegals on a temporary and permanent basis. (Woman/
AA, estab 2004, empl 3, sales $1,383,371, cert: NMSDC,
WBENC)

8731   Glenmont Group Inc.
39 S Fullerton Ave Ste 9   Montclair, NJ 07042
(973) 746-0600   Kate Potters President
Fax: (973) 273-4853
Email: kate.potters@glenmontgroup.com
Website: www.glenmontgroup.com
Recruiting & staffing. (Woman/White, estab 2001, empl
22, sales $2,404,882, cert: State, WBENC)

8732   Harita Infotech
601 Crest Stone Circle   Princeton, NJ 08540
(609) 216-1844   Kaushal Sampat President
Fax:
Email: kaushalsampat@haritainfotechinc.com
Website: www.haritainfotechinc.com
Consulting & Permanent resources in the Business, IT &
general fields. (As-Pac, estab 2014, empl 10, sales
$130,000, cert: State)

8733   Industrial Staffing Services
25 Kennedy Blvd Ste 200   East Brunswick, NJ 08816
(732) 390-7100   Marilyn Heiberger President
Fax: (732) 390-7118
Email: marilyn@industrial-staffing.com
Website: www.industrial-staffing.com
Place contract & permanent workers for all types of
staffing needs: staff augmentation, payroll-servicing,
&project staffing with qualified & certified pre-screened
personnel in all industrial, technical and administrative
positions. (Woman/White, estab 2003, empl 25, sales ,
cert: State, City, WBENC)

8734   IT Staffing, Inc.
5 Bliss Court Ste 200   Woodcliff Lake, NJ 07677
(201) 505-0493   Jerry G. Myers Director, Business
Dev
Fax: (201) 586-0389
Email: jerry.myers@itstaffinc.com
Website: www.itstaffinc.com
Strategic contract sourcing, consulting, staff augmentation,
managed teams & outsourcing. (Woman, estab 1998, empl
78, sales $11,500,000, cert: State)

8735   Jersey Staffing Solutions, LLC
400 Valley Rd Ste 106   Mt. Arlington, NJ 07856
(973) 810-4495   Kristi Telschow CEO
Fax: (973) 306-3346
Email: ktelschow@jerseystaffing.com
Website: www.jerseystaffing.com
Staffing, temporary, temp-to-perm & permanent staffing.
(Woman/White, estab 2010, empl 35, sales $2,160,000,
cert: WBENC)

8736   Jomsom Staffing Services
4390 US Highway One, Ste 203   Princeton, NJ
08540
(973) 446-5627   Ross Lazio Business Dev Exec
Fax:
Email: rlazio@jomsomjobs.com
Website: www.jomsomstaffing.com
Staffing solutions, full-time & part-time resources,
temporary, temporary to permanent & permanent
placement basis. (Woman/As-Ind, estab 2008, empl 55,
sales $3,500,000, cert: NMSDC)

8737   MetaSense Inc.
100 Technology Way, Ste 320   Mt. Laurel, NJ
08054
(856) 873-9950   Jatin V Mehta CEO
Fax: (856) 475-0555
Email: jmehta@metasenseusa.com
Website: www.metasenseusa.com
Information system staffing, software development, web
design, outsourcing, business process outsourcing,
knowledge pocess outsourcing. (Woman/As-Pac, estab
1999, empl 5, sales $767,000, cert: State)

8738   Next Step Staffing
725 River Road   Edgewater, NJ 07020
(646) 829-1800   Joy Pratcher CEO
Fax: (212) 901-6983
Email: joy@nsstaff.com
Website: www.nsstaff.com
IT solutions, full-time, permanent placement or temporary contract basis. (Woman/AA/Hisp, estab 2012, empl
5, sales $1,804,633, cert: NMSDC, WBENC)

8739   Perry Temps, Inc.
525 Route 73, South Ste 201   Marlton, NJ 08053
(856) 596-9400   Wendy Brooks Dir Business Dev
Fax: (856) 596-9124
Email: wbrooks@perryresources.com
Website: www.perryresources.com
Temporary staffing: administrative, accounting, clerical,
customer service call center personnel. (Woman, estab
1986, empl 8, sales $2,174,927, cert: WBENC)

8740   Professional Resource Partners
14 Rickland Dr   Randolph, NJ 07869
(201) 259-4739   Stefanie Wichansky CEO
Fax:
Email: swichansky@prp-us.com
Website: www.professionalresourcepartners.com
Life Science Consulting & Staffing: contract, contract-to-
perm, permanent basis across functional areas.
(Woman/White, estab 2012, empl 20, sales $454,478,
cert: WBENC)

8741   RHO, Inc.
507 Omni Dr   Hillsborough, NJ 08844
(908) 359-0808   Deborah Johnson President
Fax: (908) 359-3152
Email: deborah.johnson@rho-inc.com
Website: www.rho-inc.com
Staffing, consulting & training services. (Woman/Hisp,
estab 1981, empl 120, sales , cert: WBENC)

8742　Sharpened Image, Inc.
2004 Morris Ave. Ste 1　Union, NJ 07083
(908) 349-8403　Tamara Mangum President
Fax: (908) 349-8405
Email: tthomas@sharpenedimage.com
Website: www.sharpenedimage.com
Staffing & employment services: temporary, temp-to-perm, permanent employee searches. (Woman/AA, estab 2004, empl 35, sales $1,540,000, cert: State)

8743　Software Folks, Inc. dba Saviance Technologies
16 Bridge St　Metuchen, NJ 08840
(732) 593-8015　Anuj Sakhuja Client Relationsip Mgr
Fax: (732) 626-6022
Email: anuj.sakhuja@saviance.com
Website: www.saviance.com
Information technology staffing: contract, contract-to-hire & permanent. (As-Pac, estab 1999, empl 60, sales $7,725,180, cert: NMSDC)

8744　TNT Staffing
70 Kinderkamack Rd, Ste 202　Emerson, NJ 07630
(201) 497-6305　Jacqueline Tarnowski Dir Recruiting
Fax: (201) 754-9755
Email: jackie@tntstaffing.com
Website: www.tntstaffing.com
Staff Augmentation & Direct Full Time Placement Services. (Woman/AA, estab 2005, empl 25, sales $4,328,500, cert: State)

8745　UserEdge Technical Personnel
1812 Front St.　Scotch Plains, NJ 07076
(908) 387-7601　Jay Madlangbayan President
Fax: (908) 442-7654
Email: jay@useredge.com
Website: www.useredge.com
Direct hire recruitment, short & long-term contract assignments, outsourced staffing. (As-Pac, estab 1995, empl 30, sales $1,750,000, cert: State, NMSDC)

New Mexico

8746　Sabio Systems, LLC
4520 Montgomery NE Ste 2　Albuquerquqe, NM 87109
(505) 792-8604　Frank D Quintana Federal Solutions Mgr
Fax: (505) 232-6967
Email: frank@sabiosystems.com
Website: www.sabiosystems.com
Staffing services: information technology, MIS, accounting & finance. (Hisp, estab 2006, empl 10, sales $1,480,000, cert: 8(a))

Nevada

8747　My Next Career Path Staffing, LLC
400 S. Fourth St, Ste 500　Las Vegas, NV 89101
(844) 579-6627　Renee Boyce President
Fax: (702) 727-1944
Email: rboyce@mncpstaffing.com
Website: www.mncpstaffing.com
Consulting & staffing: analysts, system/network administrators, project managers, developers, bookkeepers, designers, customer service experts & marketing specialists. (AA, estab 2014, empl 40, sales $1,000,000, cert: State, NMSDC, CPUC, 8(a))

New York

8748　24 Seven Inc.
120 Wooster St　New York, NY 10012
(212) 966-4426　Meghan Dewey President
Fax: (212) 966-2313
Email: mdewey@24seveninc.com
Website: www.24seveninc.com
Staffing svcs: freelance, freelance to fulltime, fulltime & executive search services. (Woman/White, estab 2000, empl 93, sales $125,326,911, cert: WBENC)

8749　Admiral Staffing Inc.
18 W 30th St　New York, NY 10001
(212) 714-3543　Ray Rafeek
Fax: (312) 240-0295
Email: irshaad@admiralstaffinginc.com
Website: www.admiralstaffinginc.com/index.html
Temporary to permanent staffing services. (As-Pac, estab 2010, empl 25, sales $492,000, cert: City, NMSDC)

8750　Associate Resource Management, Inc.
2527 Merrick Rd　Bellmore, NY 11710
(516) 785-6211　Kim Robertson Exec Director
Fax:
Email: kim@armi.bz
Website: www.armi.bz
Staffing solutions: Front Desk Staff, Receptionist, Centralized Scheduling, Clerical Staff, Human Resources, Customer Service, Office Support Staff, Office Manager, Data Entry Clerks, Accounting, Bookkeepers, Administrative. (Woman/White, estab 2006, empl 6, sales $1,700,000, cert: WBENC)

8751　Atrium Staffing
387 Park Ave S, 3rd Fl　New York, NY 10016
(732) 902-5917　Kelly Couto Associate VP
Fax: (888) 731-0121
Email: supplierdiversity@atriumstaff.com
Website: www.atriumstaff.com
Temporary & direct-hire staffing: administration, finance, professional services & science. (Woman/White, estab 1995, empl 201, sales $283,949,389, cert: WBENC)

8752   CompliStaff, Inc.
       381 Lewis St   West Hempstead, NY 11552
       (646) 595-0040 April Bernstein VP
       Fax:
       Email: april.bernstein@complistaff.com
       Website: www.complistaff.com
Staffing & recruitment solutions in legal, compliance,
accounting, audit & risk management. (Woman/White,
estab 2010, empl 8, sales $1,270,000, cert: City, WBENC)

8753   Dale Workforce Solutions, LLC
       1751 2nd Ave, Ste 103   New York, NY 10128
       (212) 860-2000 Lois Dale Holtzman President
       Fax: (646) 349-3379
       Email: LDale@Daleworkforce.com
       Website: www.daleworkforce.com/
Staff Augmentation, Independent Contractor Compliance,
Payroll Services. (Woman/White, estab 2012, empl 10, sales
$1,200,000, cert: WBENC)

8754   Distinctive Personnel
       424 west 33rd St   new york, NY 10001
       (917) 952-2766 Gonzalo Vergara Founder/Chairman
       Fax:
       Email: gus@distinctivepersonnel.com
       Website: www.distinctivepersonnel.com
Staffing services: temporary, permenant, executive search,
managed service providers, vendor managed services/,
payroll outsourcing. (Hisp, estab 1983, empl 16, sales
$710,000,000, cert: City)

8755   Elmark Group, Inc.
       499 7th Ave 22 N Tower New York, NY 10018
       (212) 856-9888 Ellen Marcus President
       Fax: (212) 856-0826
       Email: ellen@marcusjobs.com
       Website: www.marcusjobs.com
Contingency & retained accounting & finance search
services in the areas of financial reporting, general accounting, accounting policy, internal audit, SOX compliance, risk
management, financial & strategic analysis. (Woman/
White, estab 1991, empl 5, sales $1,243,000, cert: WBENC)

8756   Geneva Consulting Group, Inc.
       14 Vanderventer Ave Ste 250 Port Washington, NY
       11050
       (516) 767-6695 Gina Santorio Dir Business Dev
       Fax: (516) 944-2356
       Email: gsantorio@genevaconsulting.com
       Website: www.genevaconsulting.com
IT consulting & full-time placement services, payrolling
services. (Woman/White, estab 1997, empl 50, sales
$8,021,175, cert: WBENC)

8757   iT Resource Solutions.net, Inc.
       10 Technology Dr, Ste 1   East Setauket, NY 11733
       (631) 941-2622 Andrea Dunkle Dir Diversity Mgmt
       Fax: (631) 941-4877
       Email: adunkle@it-rs.net
       Website: www.it-rs.net
Staffing: information technology consultants. (Woman/
White, estab 1995, empl 45, sales , cert: City, WBENC)

8758   Journee Technology Staffing Inc..
       2117Buffalo Rd Ste 275 Rochester, NY 14624
       (585) 210-5314 Orville Dixon President
       Fax: (585) 627-1022
       Email: orville@journeetechnologystaffing.com
       Website: www.journeetechnologystaffing.com
Staffing solutions. (Woman/AA, estab 2007, empl 2,
sales $310,000, cert: State)

8759   Lee Anav Chung White Kim Ruger & Richter LLP
       156 Fifth Ave Ste 303 New York, NY 10010
       (212) 271-0664 Annie Chen Legal Asst
       Fax: (212) 271-0665
       Email: anniechen@lacwkrr.com
       Website: www.leeanavchung.com
LEE ANAV CHUNG LLP is a law firm committed to
providing its clients with sophisticated legal advice and
representation on complex legal matters. (As-Pac, estab
2003, empl 30, sales $3,100,000, cert: NMSDC)

8760   Noor Associates, Inc.
       622 Third Avenue, 7th Floor New York, NY 10017
       (212) 812-3390 Maruf Ali Project Mgr
       Fax:
       Email: maruf@noorinc.com
       Website: www.noorinc.com
Professional services: staffing, consulting & project
based solutions. (As-Ind, estab 2005, empl 10, sales ,
cert: City, NMSDC)

8761   Noor Staffing Group, LLC
       295 Madison Ave 15th Fl New York, NY 10017
       (212) 878-2000 Frank Cumbo Sr VP
       Fax: (212) 949-3928
       Email: fcumbo@seguesearch.com
       Website: www.seguesearch.com
Staffing, skills evaluation, reference, background checks
& market intelligence. (As-Ind, estab 2005, empl 200,
sales $55,000,000, cert: City, NMSDC)

8762   Nueva Solutions Inc
       1410 Broadway Ste # 1904 New York, NY 10018
       (212) 937-0056 Punit Shetty Business Devel
       Fax: (212) 273-3798
       Email: punit@nuevainc.com
       Website: www.nuevainc.com
IT Staffing - contingent & permanent. (Woman/As-Ind,
estab 2008, empl 17, sales $3,200,000, cert: State)

8763   Penda Aiken, Inc.
       330 Livingston St, 2 Fl Brooklyn, NY 11217
       (718) 643-4880 Susie Fryer Business Dev Mgr
       Fax: (718) 643-9573
       Email: sfryer@pendaaiken.com
       Website: www.pendaaiken.com
Staffing & HR solutions: testing & evaluating, recruiting
& retention, quality control, insurance protection,
prompt service & guarantee. (Woman/AA, estab 1990,
empl 225, sales $6,815,855, cert: State, City, NMSDC)

8764   Pride Technologies LLC
       420 Lexington Ave Ste 2220 New York, NY 10170
       (614) 991-5895 David Hellard Major Accts Mgr
       Fax: (212) 235-5358
       Email: joshua.kaplan@pridetech.com
       Website: www.pridetech.com
Project management & staffing services. (Hisp, estab
1983, empl 800, sales $97,000,000, cert: NMSDC)

8765 QED National
350 Seventh Ave, 10 Fl New York, NY 10001
(212) 481-6868 Colleen Molter President
Fax: (212) 481-0414
Email: cmolter@qednational.com
Website: www.qednational.com
IT temporary & permanent staffing. (Woman/White, estab 1993, empl 40, sales $14,281,567, cert: State)

8766 SRI - Steam Recruiters International
916 Bedford Avenue Brooklyn, NY 11205
(929) 333-4593 Stevenson Dunn Jr, VP
Fax: (888) 530-7971
Email: Stevenson@STEAMRecruiters.com
Website: www.STEAMrecruiters.com
Technology staffing, executive search & professional recruiting services. (AA/Nat Ame/As-Ind/Hisp, estab 2007, empl 65, sales $2,000,000, cert: State, SDB)

8767 Temporary Staffing by Suzanne, Ltd.
370 Lexington Ave, Ste 902 New York, NY 10017
(212) 856-9500 Suzanne G. Davis President
Fax: (212) 856-4426
Email: sdavis@suzannenyc.com
Website: www.suzannenyc.com
Temporary staffing: administrative, secretarial, computer, reception, research, clerical, editorial, project coordinator, events registration & data entry positions. (Woman/White, estab 1999, empl 6, sales $3,085,963, cert: State, City)

8768 Tower Legal Solutions
65 Broadway 17th Fl. New York, NY 10006
(212) 430-6300 Leslie Firtell CEO
Fax:
Email: ckalogiannis@towerls.com
Website: www.towerls.com
Staffing: temporary attorneys, paralegals & project space. (Woman/White, estab 2007, empl 74, sales $60,245,864, cert: WBENC)

Ohio

8769 Acloche Staffing
1800 Watermark Dr Ste 430 Columbus, OH 43215
(614) 824-3700 Kimberly Shoemaker CEO
Fax: (614) 824-3770
Email: kshoemaker@acloche.com
Website: www.acloche.com
Human capital strategies & workforce resources, recruiting, customized search program. (Woman/White, estab 1968, empl 100, sales $36,494,135, cert: WBENC, NWBOC)

8770 Career Connections Staffing Services Inc.
26260 Center Ridge Road Westlake, OH 44145
(866) 424-1233 Brian DeChant President
Fax: (888) 274-5357
Email: bdechant@go2itgroup.com
Website: www.go2itgroup.com
Temporary & permanent information technology & medical support staffing. (Woman/White, estab 1996, empl 45, sales $3,776,350, cert: WBENC)

8771 Crown Services, Inc.
2800 Corporate Exchange Dr Ste 120 Columbus, OH 43231
(614) 844-5429 Karen Siravo Business Dev Mgr
Fax: (614) 899-2918
Email: ksiravo@crownservices.com
Website: www.crownservices.com
Staffing services. (Woman/White, estab 1968, empl 192, sales , cert: WBENC)

8772 Eastern Personnel Services, Inc.
619 Central Ave. Cincinnati, OH 45202
(513) 421-4666 Angelita Jones VP Employment Svcs
Fax: (513) 421-0531
Email: ajones@easternpersonnelservices.com
Website: www.easternpersonnelservices.com
Staffing: professional, contract, temporary, temp to hire, contract management & on-site supervision. (Woman/AA, estab 1987, empl 7, sales $3,625,356, cert: State, NMSDC)

8773 Great Work Employment Services, Inc.
2034 E Market St Akron, OH 44312
(330) 535-3800 Bob Frankish Dir Business Dev
Fax: (330) 535-3872
Email: bfrankish@greatwork.jobs
Website: www.greatwork.cc
Temporary staffing services. (Woman/White, estab 1992, empl 16, sales $7,600,000, cert: WBENC)

8774 Hunter International, Inc.
38100 Colorado Ave Avon, OH 44011
(440) 389-0023 Gabrielle Christman President
Fax: (440) 389-2682
Email: gchristman@hirecruiting.com
Website: www.hirecruiting.com
Project based staffing solutions, contract or temporary, contract to permanent. (Woman/White, estab 2006, empl 100, sales $10,000,120, cert: WBENC)

8775 JLS Staffing & Management dba Total Staffing Solutions
11562 Chester Rd Cincinnati, OH 45246
(513) 771-9675 Amy Mullett Owner
Fax: (513) 824-8900
Email: amullett@totalstaffsolutions.com
Website: www.totalstaffsolutions.com
Staffing Solutions: temporary positions, temp to hire, as well as direct hire placements. (Woman/White, estab 2012, empl 10, sales $10,200,000, cert: WBENC)

8776 KNK Recruiting, LLC
6562 Pleasant Valley Court Loveland, OH 45140
(513) 265-5741 Matt Baker CEO
Fax:
Email: mbaker@knkrecruiting.com
Website: www.knkrecruiting.com
Recruitment Process Outsourcing (RPO), recruiting & placement solutions. (AA, estab 2009, empl 1, sales $230,871, cert: State)

8777 Maverick Direct, Inc.
P.O. Box 1247 Bath, OH 44210
(330) 668-1800 Cindy Janos President
Fax: (330) 668-1886
Email: cjanos@callmaverick.com
Website: www.callmaverick.com
Staffing & search firm capabilities in the IT and IS arena.
(Woman/White, estab 1999, empl 43, sales $5,200,000,
cert: NWBOC)

8778 OneSource Services
6700 Beta Dr Ste 110 Mayfield Village, OH 44143
(440) 565-4434 Tom Puletti Ops
Fax: (440) 460-3979
Email: tpuletti@1-sourceservices.com
Website: www.1-sourceservices.com
Temporary, temporary to hire, direct hire & payroll services
for technical, professional, and light industrial skill sets.
(Woman/White, estab 2014, empl 25, sales $500,000, cert:
NWBOC)

8779 Portfolio Creative, LLC
777 Goodale Blvd Ste 300 Columbus, OH 43212
(614) 839-4897 Shelli Welch Director, Ops
Fax: (614) 839-6808
Email: shelli@portfoliocreative.com
Website: www.portfoliocreative.com
Staffing services: marketing, advertising, design, project
management. (Woman/White, estab 2005, empl 140, sales
$6,500,000, cert: WBENC)

8780 Proteam Solutions, Inc.
2750 Airport, Ste 120 Columbus, OH 43219
(614) 454-6488 Tracy Stearns Dir Client Relations
Fax: (614) 536-0019
Email: tstearns@psi92.com
Website: www.psi92.com
Supplemental staffing, direct hire, temp-to-hire, light
industrial, administrative & career placement. (AA, estab
1992, empl 16, sales $10,817,800, cert: NMSDC)

8781 Quick Employment LLC
2800 Euclid Ave, Ste 310 Cleveland, OH 44101
(216) 361-3030 Sherall Hardy President
Fax: (216) 361-3970
Email: quickemp@cs.com
Website: www.quickemp.com
Employment services: office services, data
entry, receptionist, accounting clerks, file clerks, office
administrative, IT, General Labor, shipping & receiving,
porters, maintenance, drivers, CDL A, CDL B, dental assistants & medical assistants. (Woman/AA, estab 2001, empl
30, sales $524,549, cert: State, City, NMSDC)

8782 Reesential Inc.
15804 Terrace Dr Cleveland, OH 44112
(216) 451-1820 Charee Fountain President
Fax: (216) 451-1871
Email: cfountain@reesential.com
Website: www.reesential.com
Information Technology Staffing: contract, contract to hire
& direct hire placement services. (Woman/AA, estab 2014,
empl 2, sales , cert: WBENC)

8783 Spherion of Lima Inc.
216 N Elizabeth St Lima, OH 45801
(419) 224-8367 Judith Cowan VP
Fax: (419) 224-6938
Email: JudithC@Spherion-Schulte.com
Website: www.spherion.com/nwohio
Recruiting and staffing. (Woman/White, estab 1982,
empl 38, sales $26,000,000, cert: WBENC)

8784 Staffing Solutions Enterprises
5915 Landerbrook Dr Ste 100 Cleveland, OH
44124
(440) 684-7218 Amy Elder Sales Team Mgr
Fax: (440) 684-7218
Email: aelder@staffsol.com
Website: www.staffsol.com
Staffing & workforce management: temporary, temp-to-
hire, direct placement, recruiting, managed staffing
services, payrolling. (Woman/White, estab 1974, empl
20, sales $10,434,625, cert: City, WBENC)

8785 Supplemental Staffing
5333 Southwyck Blvd. Toledo, OH 43614
(419) 866-8367 Mary Stoneking President
Fax: (419) 865-9701
Email: mstoneking@supplemental.com
Website: www.supplemental.com
Employment services. (Woman/White, estab 1978, empl
3000, sales , cert: WBENC)

Oregon

8786 BeginRight Employment Services
3708 NE 122nd Ave. Portland, OR 97220
(503) 254-5959 Cindy Wilkerson VP Sales and
Service
Fax: (503) 254-5999
Email: cwilkerson@beginright.com
Website: www.beginright.com/
Temporary, seasonal, contract to hire & direct hire
staffing services: clerical, administrative, accounting,
technical, engineering & professional placements,
payrolling services. (Woman/White, estab 1985, empl
15, sales $7,200,000, cert: State)

8787 Collaborative Vision LLC
7883 SW Barnard Dr Beaverton, OR 97007
(503) 941-9444 Lisa Matar Founder
Fax: (503) 941-9449
Email: Lisa@CVhires.com
Website: www.cvhires.com
Staffing, Direct Hire, Permanent, Contract, Temp,
Contingent Staffing Support. (Woman/As-Ind, estab
2008, empl 19, sales $579,845, cert: State)

8788 OLSA Resources, Inc
3485 NW John Olsen Place Hillsboro, OR 97124
(503) 608-7895 Olsa Martini President
Fax: (503) 608-7896
Email: olsamartini@olsaresources.com
Website: www.olsaresources.com
Staffing & recruiting svcs: IT & engineering. (Woman/
White, estab 1996, empl 75, sales $12,000,000, cert:
WBENC, SDB)

8789 S. Brooks and Associates Inc.
      1130 NE Alberta St   Portland, OR 97211
      (503) 284-7930 Lynn Sanders
      Fax: (503) 284-7977
      Email: lsanders@sbrooks.com
      Website: www.sbrooks.com
Staffing: permanent & temporary. (Woman/AA, estab
1981, empl 5, sales $3,000,000, cert: State)

Pennsylvania

8790 Advantage Resource Group
      1600 Valley View Blvd   Altoona, PA 16602
      (814) 944-3571 Bonnie Williams VP Admin
      Fax: (814) 944-1308
      Email: bonnie.williams@theadvantages.com
      Website: www.theadvantages.com
Temporary Staffing, Temporary to hire/contract staffing,
Direct Hire, Executive Placement, HR audits, Employee
handbooks & Job Descriptions, HR Consulting & training,
Resume writing & exit interviews. (Woman/White, estab
1953, empl 12, sales $3,000,000, cert: State, WBENC)

8791 America's Staffing Partner, Inc.
      35 E Elizabeth Ave, Ste 41   Bethlehem, PA 18018
      (610) 625-2511 Jorge Cruz CEO
      Fax:
      Email: jcruz@americasstaffingpartner.com
      Website: www.americasstaffingpartner.com
Contracted support personnel: administrative, logistics,
healthcare, technical & trades. (Hisp, estab 2006, empl
250, sales $7,040,000, cert: 8(a))

8792 Assurance Staffing, Inc.
      4660 Trindle Rd Ste 100 Camp Hill, PA 17011
      (717) 920-9190 Cinde Holste Mgr
      Fax: (717) 920-9192
      Email: jobs@assurancestaf.com
      Website: www.assurancestaf.com
Professional Staffing Services, Temporary, Temp to Hire &
Direct Hire placements. (Woman/White, estab 2003, empl
35, sales $879,179, cert: State, WBENC)

8793 Becker Technical Staffing, Inc.
      312 Old Lancaster Rd   Merion Station, PA 19066
      (610) 667-9155 Renee Becker President
      Fax: (610) 934-0221
      Email: renee@beckertek.com
      Website: www.beckertek.com
Staffing: technical, pharmaceutical/healthcare, marketing
sciences & financial/accounting talent acquisition.
(Woman/White, estab 2008, empl 30, sales $2,000,000,
cert: State, WBENC)

8794 Blue Plate Minds, Inc.
      PO Box 1428   Paoli, PA 19301
      (610) 240-9001 Karen Carroll Owner
      Fax: (610) 240-9003
      Email: karen@blueplateminds.com
      Website: www.blueplateminds.com
Full time & freelance staffing: advertising & marketing,
graphic & web designers/directors, editors, writers &
proofreaders. (Woman/White, estab 1999, empl 25, sales
$1,376,000, cert: WBENC)

8795 Bradley Temporaries, Inc. dba Bradley Staffing
      Gro
      1400 Liberty Ridge Dr Ste 103 Wayne, PA 19087
      (610) 254-9999 Brad Burns VP
      Fax: (610) 644-1038
      Email: Brad@Bradleystaffinggroup.com
      Website: www.BradleyStaffingGroup.com
Temporary & direct hire placement services. (Woman/
White, estab 1984, empl 6, sales $2,030,000, cert:
WBENC)

8796 Chartwell Staffing Services, Inc.
      245 Centerville Rd Ste 2 Lancaster, PA 17603
      (717) 370-7003 Matt Henderson
      Fax: (717) 370-7004
      Email: matt@chartwellstaff.com
      Website: www.chartwellstaff.com
Temporary staffing & permanent placement. (Woman/
White, estab 2011, empl 8000, sales $300,000,000, cert:
WBENC)

8797 Choice Counsel, Inc.
      535 Smithfield St, Ste 614 Oliver Buildling
      Pittsburgh, PA 15222
      (412) 355-0900 Cynthia Scott President
      Fax: (412) 355-0901
      Email: cynthiascott@choicecounsel.com
      Website: www.choicecounsel.com
Legal staffing, attorneys & paralegals in temporary and
temporary-to-hire positions. (Woman, estab 1998, empl
50, sales $2,400,000, cert: WBENC)

8798 Choice One Staffing Group, Inc.
      2009 MacKenzie Way Ste 250 Cranberry Town-
      ship, PA 16066
      (724) 452-5800 Julie Sacriponte President
      Fax:
      Email: julie@choice1staffing.com
      Website: www.choice1staffing.com
Temporary, temp to hire & direct hire capacities, custom
employee testing, background screens, drug screens,
payroll services & skill marketing. (Woman/White, estab
2003, empl 525, sales $3,300,000, cert: WBENC)

8799 Hobbie Professional Staff Management
      3426 Hamilton Blvd Allentown, PA 18103
      (610) 433-3677 Denise Hobbie President
      Fax: (610) 433-7227
      Email: dhobbie@hobbieprofessional.com
      Website: www.hobbieprofessional.com
Light industrial, administrative & clerical staffing:
temporary & direct hire. (Woman/White, estab 1997,
empl 20, sales , cert: State, WBENC)

8800 HTSS, Inc.
      860 Broad St Ste 111 Emmaus, PA 18049
      (610) 432-4161 Pat Howells President
      Fax: (610) 432-5409
      Email: phowells@htss-inc.com
      Website: www.htss-inc.com
Staffing & recruiting services. (Woman/White, estab
1993, empl 7, sales $4,900,000, cert: State, WBENC)

8801   JH Technical Services, Inc.
       200 Hightower Blvd, Ste 403   Pittsburgh, PA 15205
       (412) 788-1174 Cynthia Harrison President
       Fax:
       Email: charrison@jhtechnical.com
       Website: www.jhtechnical.com
Staffing services. (Woman/White, estab 1996, empl 11,
sales $3,443,126, cert: State, WBENC)

8802   JURISolutions dba JuriStaff, CYLA, JXP Search
       1600 Market St, 38th Fl   Philadelphia, PA 19103
       (215) 383-3514 Shannon Homa Mktg Communica-
       tions Specialist
       Fax: (877) 751-9388
       Email: shoma@jsl-hq.com
       Website: www.jurisolutions.com
Temporary & permanent legal staffing. (Woman/White,
estab 1997, empl 117, sales $9,422,175, cert: State, CPUC,
WBENC)

8803   Krown Employment Services, LLC
       801 Vinial St, Ste 102   Pittsburgh, PA 15212
       (412) 567-7136 Pamela Weigand President
       Fax: (412) 567-0113
       Email: pweigand@krownempsvc.com
       Website: www.krownempsvc.com
Staffing: Administrative, Accounts Payable/Receivable Call
Center, Clerical, General Labor, Hospitality, Light Industrial,
Janitorial, Maintenance & Warehouse. (Woman/White,
estab 2013, empl 250, sales $1,250,000, cert: WBENC)

8804   McCallion Temps, Inc.
       601 N Bethlehem Pike   Montgomeryville, PA 18936
       (215) 855-8000 Lisa McCallion President
       Fax: (215) 855-8820
       Email: lmccallion@mccalliongroup.com
       Website: www.mccallionstaffing.com
Staffing, temporary, temp to hire & direct hire personnel.
(Woman/White, estab 1979, empl 12, sales $7,001,821,
cert: NWBOC)

8805   Partner's Consulting, Inc.
       2004 Sproul Road, Ste 206   Broomall, PA 19008
       (215) 939-6294 Matthew Robbins Delivery Mgr
       Fax:
       Email: mrobbins@partners-consulting.com
       Website: www.partners-consulting.com
Information technology recruiting for full-time, temp-to-
perm & contract positions. (Woman/White, estab 2006,
empl 40, sales $6,000,000, cert: State, WBENC)

8806   RomAnalytics, LLC
       1228 Erin Court   Collegeville, PA 19426
       (610) 420-7526 Kathy Roman President
       Fax:
       Email: Kathy.Roman@RomAnalytics.com
       Website: www.romanalytics.com/
Recruiting & staffing, contract staffing or permanent staff
recruiting. (Woman/White, estab 2013, empl 1, sales
$728,000, cert: State, WBENC)

8807   Solomon International, LLC
       635 Coles Ct   Harleysville, PA 19438
       (609) 510-9705 Paul Solomon President
       Fax: (215) 565-2509
       Email: paul.solomon@solomonsint.com
       Website: www.solomonsint.com
Employment services, temporary & direct hire employment & IT consulting services. (Woman/As-Pac, estab
2004, empl 20, sales $1,018,354, cert: State)

8808   Staffing Pharm, LLC
       P.O. Box 23   Cresco, PA 18326
       (610) 272-4993 Dora Pereda President
       Fax:
       Email: dora.pereda@staffingpharm.com
       Website: www.staffingpharm.com/
Professional staffing services: pharmaceutical,
healthcare, biotechnology & research industries.
(Woman/Hisp, estab 2012, empl 1, sales $85,000, cert:
NMSDC)

8809   STAFFusion
       210 W. Pike St. Ste #3   Canonsburg, PA 15317
       (724) 916-4772 Paula Davey President
       Fax: (724) 916-4777
       Email: paula@staffusion.us
       Website: www.staffusion.com
Staffing, recruiting professionals, personnel, office,
administrative, (Woman/White, estab 2003, empl 60,
sales $1,750,000, cert: WBENC)

8810   The Carney Group
       1777 Sentry PkwyWest, Ste 301   Blue Bell, PA
       19422
       (215) 646-6200 Daniel Lamken Sales
       Fax:
       Email: dlamken@carneyjobs.com
       Website: www.carneyjobs.com
Staff augmentation or permanent hire. (Woman/White,
estab 1992, empl 250, sales $10,000,000, cert: State,
WBENC)

8811   The Drexel Group, Inc
       1832 Market St   Camp Hill, PA 17011
       (717) 730-9841 Romayne Johnson President
       Fax: (717) 730-9845
       Email: romayne@thedrexelgroup.com
       Website: www.thedrexelgroup.com
Staffing: temporary, permanent, temp to hire, direct hire
& contingency. (Woman/White, estab 1994, empl 200,
sales $3,430,086, cert: State, WBENC)

Puerto Rico

8812   Caribbean Temprorary Services, Inc.
       P.O. Box 11873   San Juan, PR 00690
       (787) 620-5500 Xiomara Villamil VP Corporate
       Affairs
       Fax: (787) 620-0698
       Email: xiomara.villamil@ctspr.com
       Website: www.ctspr.com
Staffing services. (Woman/Hisp, estab 1983, empl 5000,
sales , cert: NMSDC)

8813   Job Hunters LLC
       P.O. Box 56012   Bayamon, PR 00960
       (787) 998-7210 John Bruno
       Fax: (303) 292-1934
       Email: bruno@jobhunters-pr.com
       Website: www.clasificadosonline.com/
       PartnersListingJ
Temporary & permanent staffing. (Woman/Hisp, estab
2013, empl 50, sales $1,200,000, cert: NMSDC)

8814   PSS Pathfinders Inc.
       CIM II 90 carr 165 Ste 310 Guaynabo, PR 00958
       (787) 622-6868 Georyanne Rios Alvarez President
       Fax: (787) 622-6870
       Email: grios@psspathfinders.com
       Website: www.psspathfinders.com
Staffing solutions: temporary, temporary to hire & executive search. (Woman/Hisp, estab 1985, empl 425, sales
$8,448,618, cert: WBENC, SDB)

8815   The Cervantes Group
       PO Box 16409   San Juan, PR 00908
       (787) 729-7597 Joanna Bauza President
       Fax: (787) 724-7948
       Email: joanna@thecervantesgroup.com
       Website: www.thecervantesgroup.com
Staffing solutions, short or long-term requirements.
(Woman/Hisp, estab 2004, empl 22, sales $2,800,000,
cert: WBENC)

8816   Weil Group, Inc.
       Urb. Villa Blanca Calle Aquamarina #78 Ste 1
       Caguas, PR 00725
       (787) 633-0025 Milagros del R Gonzalez GM
       Fax: (787) 286-1833
       Email: mgonzalez@weilgroup.com
       Website: www.weilgroup.com
Temporary employment agency, outsourcing IT & automation services: management and/or admin, help desk,
servers, WAN, email system, desktop, maintenance,
backup & restore. (Hisp, estab 1994, empl 50, sales
$11,000,000, cert: NMSDC)

8817   Wisdom Resources, Inc.
       350 Chardon Ave. Ste 119 San Juan, PR 00918
       (787) 963-1048 Aissa Betancourt President
       Fax: (787) 963-1049
       Email: aissa@snellingpr.com
       Website: www.snellingpr.com
Staffing services: executive, career, temporary, temp-to-
hire & contractors, background check & drug testing
services. (Woman/Hisp, estab 2008, empl 137, sales
$5,200,000, cert: NMSDC, WBENC)

Rhode Island

8818   Silverman McGovern Staffing
       284 W Exchange St   Providence, RI 02903
       (401) 632-0580 Faye Silverman Managing Partner
       Fax: (401) 632-0584
       Email: faye@silvermanmcgovern.com
       Website: www.silvermanmcgovern.com
Staffing: Legal, Marketing/Creative, Accounting/Finance,
Administrative, Technical. (Woman/White, estab 2003,
empl 7, sales , cert: WBENC)

South Carolina

8819   Augusta Temporaries, Inc. dba Manpower
       101 Broadus Ave   Greenville, SC 29601
       (864) 233-4162 Pamela Davis Financial Mgr
       Fax: (864) 233-0037
       Email: pamelia.davis@manpowersc.com
       Website: www.manpowersc.com
Temporary staffing & customer service. (Woman/White,
estab 1978, empl 550, sales $12,500,000, cert: WBENC)

8820   DP Professionals, Inc.
       3741 Landmark Dr Ste 200 Columbia, SC 29204
       (803) 738-0066 Barbara Blau President
       Fax: (803) 738-0074
       Email: barbara@dppit.com
       Website: www.dppit.com
Staffing & recruiting: information technology professionals for contract employment & direct placement.
(Woman/White, estab 1996, empl 100, sales , cert:
NWBOC)

8821   Eastern Design Services
       25 Woods Lake Rd, Ste 301   Greenville, SC 29607
       (864) 271-1228 John Crain Office Mgr
       Fax: (864) 232-3970
       Email: jcrain@easterndesign.com
       Website: www.easterndesign.com
Technical & professonal staffing: engineers, designers,
drafters, office professionals, information technology &
administrative personnel. (Woman/White, estab 1979,
empl 5, sales $2,714,000, cert: State)

8822   Express Employment Professionals
       9557 Two Notch Rd Ste N Columbia, SC 29223
       (803) 788-8721 Northan Golden CEO
       Fax: (803) 788-7631
       Email: northan.golden@expresspros.com
       Website: www.expresspros.com
Temporary & permanent staffing. (AA, estab 2007, empl
4, sales $450,000, cert: NMSDC)

8823   Marketplace Staffing Services Inc.
       200 Adley Way   Greenville, SC 29606
       (864) 286-3900 Jason Mitchell Dir of Sales
       Fax:
       Email: jmitchell@marketplacestaffing.com
       Website: www.marketplacestaffing.com
Comprehensive staffing & onsite managed contract
labor services: manufacturing, warehouse & light
industrial staffing solutions. (AA, estab 1996, empl 25,
sales $9,000,000, cert: NMSDC)

Tennessee

8824   A-One, LLC
       3639 New Getwell Rd., Ste 1 & 2   Memphis, TN
       38118
       (901) 367-5757 Sterlyn Howell Owner
       Fax: (901) 367-7593
       Email: astaffing2@yahoo.com
       Website: www.aonestaffing.com
Temp, temp-to-perm & permanent placement. (Woman/
AA, estab 2001, empl 32, sales $2,200,000, cert: City,
WBENC)

8825 Atlas Management Corporation
750 Old Hickory Blvd Bldg Two, Ste 265 Brentwood, TN 37027
(615) 620-0977 Warren Sawyers President
Fax: (615) 620-0989
Email: wsawyers@atlasmanagement.us
Website: www.atlasmanagement.us
Recruiting, staffing, call center services, business unit outsourcing. (AA, estab 2003, empl 10, sales $2,600,000, cert: State, SDB)

8826 Comprehensive Medical Staffing, Inc.
3173 Kirby Whitten Pkwy #103 Bartlett, TN 38134
(901) 779-4168 Charlotte Boyce COO
Fax:
Email: charlotte.boyce@compmedstaffing.com
Website: www.compmedstaffing.com
Contingent staffing, temporary medical employees (RN, Registered Nurse, LPN, Licensed Practical Nurse, CNA Certified Nursing Assistants). (Woman/AA, estab 2015, empl 75, sales $390,942, cert: State, City)

8827 Gem Quality
2033 Castaic Lane Knoxville, TN 37932
(865) 560-9891 Jason Campbell President
Fax: (865) 560-3219
Email: jcampbell@gem-quality.com
Website: www.gemcareinc.com
HR services, temporary to hire, direct placement, commercial & professional staffing. (Woman/AA, estab 2005, empl 200, sales $6,428,737, cert: NMSDC, WBENC)

8828 MasterStaff, Inc.
611 Potomac Pl, Ste 103 Smyrna, TN 37167
(615) 223-5627 Jennifer Sheets CEO
Fax: (615) 223-8797
Email: jennifer@masterstaffemployment.com
Website: www.masterstaffemployment.com
Professional recruitment & placement, temporary & temp to hire employees, human resource consulting & contract staffing. (Woman/White, estab 1999, empl 450, sales $7,500,000, cert: WBENC)

8829 neMarc Professional Services, Inc.
2500 Mt. Moriah Rd, Ste H231 Memphis, TN 38115
(901) 360-1804 Carmen Bassett President
Fax: (901) 360-1813
Email: carmenbassett@bellsouth.net
Website: www.nemarcstaffing.com
Temporary, permanent placement, temp-to-perm staffing svcs: clerical, administrative, distribution, warehouse, IT, accounting & professional placement. (Woman/AA, estab 2002, empl 5, sales $742,000, cert: State, NMSDC)

8830 Omni Staffing Plus, Inc.
80 N Tillman, Ste 201 P.O. Box 11421 Memphis, TN 38111
(901) 843-8433 Dinah Terry
Fax: (901) 452-8868
Email: dterry@omnistaffingplus.com
Website: www.omnistaffingplus.com
Temporary/permanent staffing. (Woman/AA, estab 1999, empl 6, sales $1,874,214, cert: NMSDC)

8831 Presidio Service Solutions, Inc.
701 Scarboro Rd Ste 222 Oak Ridge, TN 37830
(865) 481-8007 Alfredo F. Rodriguez President
Fax: (865) 481-8009
Email: alrod@presidio-ssi.com
Website: www.presidio-ssi.com
(PSSI) is a progressive, Veteran and Minority-owned Technology and Engineering Staffing and Services Firm that provides innovative project related staffing solutions and professional services to our Government related clients and (Hisp, estab 2007, empl 14, sales $900,000, cert: State)

8832 Provide Staffing Services LLC
6765 E Shelby Dr   Memphis, TN 38141
(901) 505-0005 Pat Morris Mgr
Fax: (901) 505-0110
Email: pat@provide-staffing.com
Website: www.pscstaffing.net
Temporary Employees, Clerical positions. (Woman/White, estab 2013, empl 170, sales , cert: City)

8833 Reliable Building Solutions, Inc.
6232 Airpark Dr Chattanooga, TN 37421
(423) 954-9834 Kathy Sok President
Fax: (423) 894-0152
Email: KSOK6322@AOL.COM
Website: www.rbsi-online.com
We provide Complete facility management service to include: Janitorial, Floor maintenance, Emergency services, and provide wholesale of Janitorial supplies, equipment and chemicals. (Woman/As-Pac, estab 1992, empl 45, sales $2,800,000, cert: State)

8834 Strata-G, LLC
2027 Castaic Ln Knoxville, TN 37932
(865) 934-3400 Leah Berry Division Mgr, Business Services
Fax: (865) 934-3439
Email: lberry@stratag.org
Website: www.stratag.org
Environmental Consulting Services; Process, Physical Distribution and Logistics Consulting Services; Environmental Redmediation; Waste Management Services (Woman/White, estab 2002, empl 65, sales $7,050,000, cert: State)

Texas

8835 Adventus Technologies, Inc.
6001 Savoy Ste 511 Houston, TX 77036
(713) 995-4446 Vicki Semander
Fax: (312) 240-0295
Email: vsemander@adventus-tech.com
Website: www.adventus-tech.com
Professional, para professional & administrative personnel: Project Mgt, Finance & Accounting Support, General Consulting Services, Acquisition and Procurement Mgt, Publication, & Logistic Support Services. (Woman/AA, estab 2005, empl 8, sales $376,000, cert: State, City, NMSDC, 8(a))

8836   Akorbi (Elahi Enterprises dba Akorbi)
       6504 International Pkwy Ste 1500 Plano, TX 75093
       (214) 256-9222 Cheryl Parker Natl Director of Client
       Partnerships
       Fax: (214) 256-9222
       Email: cparker@akorbi.com
       Website: www.akorbi.com
IT consulting & recruitment: information technology,
telecommunications, professional services & language
solutions, technical staffing, professional placements,
custom application development & business communications. (Woman/AA, estab 2003, empl 964, sales
$34,000,000, cert: NMSDC)

8837   All Temps 1 Personnel
       2606 Martin Luther King Jr. Ste 222 Dallas, TX
       75215
       (214) 426-0091 Ronald Hay II President
       Fax: (214) 426-2861
       Email: rlhay2@alltemps1.com
       Website: www.alltemps1.com
Staffing services. (AA, estab 1990, empl 10, sales
$11,800,000, cert: NMSDC)

8838   Alleare Consulting, LLC
       3625 N. Hall St Ste 685 Dallas, TX 75219
       (214) 559-9878 Thomas Arnold CFO
       Fax:
       Email: thomas.arnold@alleareconsulting.com
       Website: www.alleareconsulting.com
Recruiting, staffing & consulting services: permanent
placement, contract & contract-to-hire. (Woman, estab
2010, empl 32, sales $816,030, cert: State, WBENC)

8839   AllTex Staffing & Consulting LLC dba Abba Staffing
       2350 Airport Fwy Ste 130 Bedford, TX 76022
       (817) 354-2800 Darla Beggs CEO
       Fax: (817) 354-2801
       Email: darla@abbastaffing.com
       Website: www.abbastaffing.com
Direct Placement, Contingent-to-hire-Personnel, Contract
personnel, Temporary personnel. (Woman/White, estab
2001, empl 5, sales $390,000,000, cert: State, WBENC)

8840   AMP Personnel Services, LLC
       3700 N 10th St, Ste 302 McAllen, TX 78501
       (956) 627-0477 Marisa Sonnier Admin
       Fax: (956) 627-0801
       Email: amppersonnelservices@gmail.com
       Website: www.amppersonnel.com
Staffing services: professional, administrative & commercial job placement. (Woman/Hisp, estab 2012, empl 2,
sales $100,000, cert: State, 8(a))

8841   ASAP Personnel Inc.
       17311 Dallas Pkwy Dallas, TX 75248
       (972) 432-6667 Evelyn Touchette President
       Fax: (866) 528-2023
       Email: evelyn@asapdo.com
       Website: www.asapdo.net
Staffing & Personnel Services. (Woman/White, estab 2010,
empl 22, sales $500,000, cert: State, City)

8842   AXIS Staffing
       1111 W Mockingbird Ln   Dallas, TX 75247
       (214) 638-4000 Jacob Joseph President
       Fax: (214) 636-4333
       Email: Jacob_Joseph@axisstaff.com
       Website: www.axisstaff.com
Staffing services. (As-Pac, estab 1993, empl 10, sales
$4,500,000, cert: State)

8843   BBM Staffing
       4242 Medical Dr, Bldg 2200   San Antonio, TX
       78229
       (210) 822-0717 Liz Moreno Ops Mgr
       Fax:
       Email: lmoreno@bbmstaffing.com
       Website: www.bbmstaffing.com
Recruiting, temporary, temp to hire & direct hire
solutions. (Woman/Hisp, estab 2009, empl 300, sales
$11,000,000, cert: State, NMSDC)

8844   Bestica, Inc.
       3463 Magic Dr Ste 303 San Antonio, TX 78229
       (210) 614-4198 Harvinder Singh CEO
       Fax: (210) 399-0694
       Email: harvinder@bestica.com
       Website: www.bestica.com
IT consulting & staffing firm. (As-Ind, estab 2005, empl
185, sales $7,500,000, cert: NMSDC, 8(a))

8845   Brooke Staffing Companies, Inc.
       3900 Essex, Ste 555   Houston, TX 77027
       (713) 337-2222 Joe Stephens Treasurer
       Fax: (713) 337-2239
       Email: joes@brookecompanies.com
       Website: www.brookecompanies.com
Temporary & full-time placement services. (Woman,
estab 1989, empl 213, sales $8,718,523, cert: City,
WBENC)

8846   Burnett Specialists
       9800 Richmond Avenue Ste 800 Houston, TX
       77042
       (713) 358-1437 Rick Burnett VP Regional Mgr
       Fax: (713) 977-5974
       Email: rick@burnettspecialists.com
       Website: www.burnettspecialists.com
Temporary, contract & direct-hire placement: clerical &
administrative, accounting & financial, legal, human
resources, information technology, sales, medical,
customer service, light industrial & electronics personnel. (Woman/White, estab 1974, empl 115, sales
$66,200,000, cert: WBENC)

8847   Burns Search LLC
       1415 Legacy Dr, Ste 310   Frisco, TX 75034
       (214) 213-4053 Ann Burns CEO
       Fax: (214) 618-1988
       Email: aburns@burnssearch.com
       Website: www.burnssearch.com
Staffing, recruiting, consulting: technical, accounting,
finance, executive search. (Woman/White, estab 1999,
empl 8, sales $1,394,555, cert: WBENC)

8848   C&T Information Technology Consulting, Inc.
201 S Lakeline Ste 803   Cedar Park, TX 78613
(512) 610-0040   Jennifer Conway Dir Sales/Mktg
Fax: (512) 231-8044
Email: sales@candttech.com
Website: www.candttech.com
Entry level, High End & Mid-Level Technical Staffing &
Consulting. Project Management, Enterprise Architecture &
Technical Solutions Provider Perm Placement, Technical
Recruiting. (Woman/White, estab 2003, empl 34, sales
$5,115,202, cert: State)

8849   Choice Hire Staffing LLC
3106 Highway 377 S   Brownwood, TX 76801
(325) 643-1416   Melissa Mauricio Owner
Fax: (325) 643-1513
Email: melissa@choicehirestaffing.com
Website: www.choicehirestaffing.com
Temporary, seasonal, temp to hire & direct placement.
(Woman, estab 2013, empl 3, sales , cert: State)

8850   Confidential Search Solutions, LLC.
7330 San Pedro Ave, Ste 610   San Antonio, TX 78216
(210) 802-4771   Iris Dalfrey CEO
Fax: (800) 709-1127
Email: idalfrey@confidentialss.com
Website: www.confidentialsearchsolutions.com
Staffing/recruiting: direct hire, temp-to-hire, temporary,
contract & payroll recruiting services in accounting &
finance, human resources, sales & marketing, supply chain
management, project management, IT helpdesk. (Woman/
AA, estab 2009, empl 3, sales $34,000, cert: State, City,
NMSDC, WBENC)

8851   Employee Risk Management Co. Inc.
4639 Corona, Ste 99   Corpus Christi, TX 78411
(361) 808-8367   Laura Escobar President
Fax: (361) 808-8369
Email: laura@atrecruiters.com
Website: www.atpersonnelservices.com
Recruiting, direct hire & temporary placement, Background
checks, Drug screens, Safety Assured. (Woman/Hisp, estab
1994, empl 10, sales $6,000,000, cert: State)

8852   Evins Personnel Consltants
6430 Richmond Ave Ste 415   Houston, TX 77057
(713) 977-8555   Helen Royston Acct Rep
Fax: (713) 787-5078
Email: staffing@hrnetconnection.com
Website: www.HRnetConnection.com
Temporary staffing, direct hire, temp to hire staffing.
(Woman/White, estab 1967, empl 5000, sales $15,000,000,
cert: State)

8853   Execusane Inc
2306 Stillwater Dr   Mesquite, TX 75181
(972) 277-1176   Shiree Alexander President
Fax:
Email: shayes@execusane.com
Website: www.execusane.com
Direct Placement, Executive Recruiting, HR Consulting,
Staffing/Contract Recruiting. (Woman/AA, estab 2012, empl
1, sales $20,845, cert: State)

8854   Foremost Staffing, Inc.
3991 West Vickery   Fort Worth, TX 76107
(817) 346-4738   Vicki Jordan President
Fax: (817) 346-7040
Email: vjordan@foremoststaffing.com
Website: www.foremoststaffing.com
Staffing: temporary, temp to hire, direct placements &
payroll services. (Woman/White, estab 2007, empl 100,
sales $2,261,595, cert: State, WBENC)

8855   Fulgent Solutions Inc.
5700 Granite Pkwy Ste 200   Plano, TX 75024
(972) 506-7335   Shan Adaikalam President
Fax:
Email: Shan.adaikalam@fulgentsol.com
Website: www.fulgentsol.com
Enterprise business consulting & staffing, technology,
temporary, temporary-to-hire & permanent placement
services. (As-Ind, estab 2013, empl 15, sales $1,500,000,
cert: State)

8856   GS Infovision LLC   dba Global Systems LLC
1200 Walnut Hill Lane, Ste 2220   Irving, TX 75038
(214) 717-4344   Shekhar Gupta VP
Fax: (240) 554-2470
Email: account@globalsyst.com
Website: www.globalsyst.com
IT Consulting, Staffing, BPO, IT Consulting, temporary,
contract, temp to perm & permanent staffing solutions.
(Woman/As-Pac, estab 2005, empl 110, sales
$11,000,000, cert: NMSDC)

8857   Hawkins, Associates, Inc.
909 NE Loop 410, Ste 104   San Antonio, TX 78209
(210) 349-9911   Elizabeth Hawkins VP
Fax: (210) 349-3393
Email: liz@hawkinspersonnel.com
Website: www.hawkinspersonnel.com
Temporary, temp-to-hire, direct hire professional
services, payrolling services & on-site management
services. (Woman/White, estab 1977, empl 35, sales
$18,000,000, cert: State)

8858   HirePower Personnel, Inc.
14100 SW Freeway, Ste 320   Sugar Land, TX
77478
(281) 295-5701   Celeste Glass President
Fax:
Email: celeste.glass@hppstaffing.com
Website: www.hppstaffing.com
Temp, Temp to Hire & Direct Hire Placements. (Woman/
White, estab , empl 1, sales , cert: State, WBENC)

8859   Imprimis Group
4835 LBJ Frwy, Ste 1000   Dallas, TX 75244
(972) 419-1635   Valerie Freeman CEO
Fax: (972) 419-1798
Email: vfreeman@imprimis.com
Website: www.imprimis.com
Staffing; temp, temp to hire, direct hire: admin/office,
accounting, bilingual, cstnmr svc, legal, mktg, medical,
mortgage, etc. (Woman/White, estab 1982, empl 60,
sales $21,000,000, cert: State, WBENC)

8860 InGenesis, Inc.
        10231 Kotzebue St   San Antonio, TX 78217
        (210) 366-0033 Dr. Veronica Edwards CEO
        Fax: (210) 568-4582
        Email: commercial@ingenesis.com1
        Website: www.ingenesis.com
Workforce solutions: direct placement, direct hire,
executive search, temporary staffing, contingent staffing,
managed vendor, recruitment process outsourcing,
managed services programs & locum tenens. (Woman/
Hisp, estab 1900, empl 1, sales $139,000,000, cert:
NMSDC, WBENC)

8861 Inreach IT Solutions, LLC
        P.O. Box 1311   Wylie, TX 75098
        (972) 442-5332 Torshia Watson CEO
        Fax: (214) 550-8810
        Email: Torshia@InreachITSolutions.com
        Website: www.InreachITSolutions.com
Staffing, payroll services & project management, direct
hire, contract-to-hire, temporary. (Woman/AA, estab 2012,
empl 1, sales , cert: State, WBENC)

8862 International Genesis Professional Solutions, Inc.
        P.O. Box 692205   San Antonio, TX 78269
        (210) 867-4182 Shelah Simmons CEO
        Fax: (210) 525-1557
        Email: simmons@genesisprofsol.com
        Website: www.genesisprofsol.com
Human Capital, Business Process Optimization & Project
Management, Strategic Executive
Recruitment, Human Resources Staffing (Temporary Help
Service). (Woman/AA, estab 2006, empl 5, sales $149,100,
cert: State)

8863 KeyStaff Inc.
        2909 Hillcroft St, Ste 620 Ste 620 Houston (HARRIS),
        TX 77057
        (713) 422-2710 Tammie Jeffers Branch Mgr
        Fax: (512) 697-2845
        Email: tammie.jeffers@keystaffinc.com
        Website: www.keystaffinc.com
Staffing: temporary, temp-to-perm & direct-hire placements. (Woman, estab 2004, empl 20, sales $18,989,644,
cert: State, City)

8864 Labor On Demand Inc., Dba, LOD Resource Group
        851 Culebra Road 4241 East Piedras Drive, Ste 150
        San Antonio, TX 78201
        (210) 865-0445 Richard Tovar Business Dev
        Fax: (210) 736-1440
        Email: Rtovar@laborondemand247.com
        Website: www.lodstaffing.com/
Temporary & permanent employment services. (Woman/
Hisp, estab 2003, empl 31, sales $6,127,317, cert: State,
8(a), SDB)

8865 LiveWell Insurance Products, Inc.
        2425 Holly Hall, Ste H 106   Houston, TX 77054
        (281) 827-7909 Glen Reaux President
        Fax: (630) 985-7300
        Email: g.reaux@thenewfaceofhealthcare.com
        Website: www.thenewfaceofhealthcare.com
Marketing & advertising services. (AA, estab 2013, empl 4,
sales , cert: State, NMSDC)

8866 LK Jordan & Associates
        7550 IH 10 West Ste 105 San Antonio, TX 78229
        (210) 488-9360 Stefanie Chavez Business Dev
        Fax: (210) 488-9364
        Email: stefanie.chavez@lkjordan.com
        Website: www.lkjordan.com
Staffing services: temporary, temporary to hire & direct
hire employees. (Woman/White, estab 1990, empl 52,
sales $25,000,000, cert: State)

8867 Lotus Staffing Group, LLC
        1925 E Beltline Rd Ste 419 Carrollton, TX 75006
        (972) 410-3685 Tyra Roberts Managing Dir
        Fax: (972) 418-6666
        Email: tyra@lotusstaffingagency.com
        Website: www.lotusstaffingagency.com
Contingent staffing solutions. (Woman/AA/Hisp, estab
2008, empl 23, sales $3,450,000, cert: State, City)

8868 Magnum Staffing Services, Inc.
        2900 Smith St, Ste 250   Houston, TX 77006
        (713) 658-0068 Caroline Brown President
        Fax: (713) 523-3621
        Email: caroline.brown@magnumstaffing.com
        Website: www.magnumstaffing.com
Background, drug-screening, SS verification, temporary
placement, temp-to-hire, direct hire, industrial, clerical
& managerial arenas. (Woman/White, estab 1996, empl
43, sales $38,000,000, cert: WBENC)

8869 MIT Professionals, Inc.
        523 Lovett Blvd   Houston, TX 77006
        (713) 934-9700 Rebecca Morgan President
        Fax: (713) 513-5610
        Email: rebecca@mitprof.com
        Website: www.mitprof.com
Staffing services: information technology, supply chain
resources, engineering & professional services.
(Woman/White, estab 1995, empl 6, sales , cert: State)

8870 Mobile Temporary Services
        9110 Jones Rd Ste 131 Houston, TX 77065
        (713) 344-4148 Allison Holmes President
        Fax: (713) 456-2329
        Email: allison@mobiletempstaff.com
        Website: www.mobiletempstaff.com
Temporary employees, direct hire, temp-to-perm &
contract employees, on-site applications, backgrounds
checks, drug-screen & on-boarding. (Woman/AA, estab
2016, empl 4, sales , cert: WBENC, SDB)

8871 Primary Services LP
        520 Post Oak Blvd Ste 550 Houston, TX 77027
        (713) 850-7010 MaryKay Foy-Hinton Strategic
        Accts Mgr
        Fax:
        Email: marykay@primaryservices.com
        Website: www.primaryservices.com
Staffing solutions, contract, contract-to-hire & direct hire
placement. (Woman/White, estab 1988, empl 39, sales
$44,928,501, cert: WBENC)

8872   QSTAFF Incorporated
P.O. Box 580622   Houston, TX 77258
(281) 218-6574   Richard Green
Fax: (281) 286-2657
Email: r.green@qualified-staff.com
Website: www.qualified-staff.com
Staffing svcs: accounting, admin, clerical, chemical plant operators, data entry, engineering, IT, light industrial. (Woman/Hisp, estab 1999, empl 75, sales $3,000,000, cert: State, WBENC)

8873   RD Data Solutions
2340 E Trinity Mills Ste 349   Carrollton, TX 75006
(972) 899-2334   Reuben D'Souza CEO
Fax:
Email: reuben.dsouza@rddatasolutions.com
Website: www.rddatasolutions.com
Technology staffing: SAP & ERP. (Woman/As-Pac, estab 2002, empl 26, sales $25,000,000, cert: State, NMSDC)

8874   Recruiting Force, LLC
1464 E. Whitestone Blvd. Ste 1903   Cedar Park, TX 78613
(512) 996-0999   Rudy Uribe President
Fax: (866) 406-3517
Email: rudy.uribe@recruitveterans.com
Website: www.recruitveterans.com
Direct hire professional executive search, permanent placement, information technology, engineering, project management, logisitics, finance, accounting. (Hisp, estab 2003, empl 60, sales $4,437,363, cert: NMSDC, 8(a))

8875   Remedy Intelligent Staffing
8610 N Capitol of Texas Hwy, Ste 195   Austin, TX 78731
(512) 502-9000   Kathy Stanley Director of Sales
Fax: (512) 502-9305
Email: kathys@remedystaff.com
Website: www.remedystaff.com
Staffing services: administrative, finance, accounting, customer service, IT, logistics & light industrial. (Woman/White, estab 1963, empl 8, sales $6,000,000,000, cert: State)

8876   Resource Personnel Consultants, LLC
14070 Proton Rd   Farmers Branch, TX 75244
(972) 371-2934   Peter Christensen Acct Mgr
Fax: (972) 371-2922
Email: pchristensen@rpccompany.com
Website:
Staffing: clerical, administrative & customer service employees, temporary, temporary to permanent or direct hire. (Woman/Hisp, estab 2001, empl 8, sales $1,827,499, cert: State)

8877   Right Staff Inc.
4919 McKinney Ave   Dallas, TX 75205
(214) 953-0900   Al Cotton diversity Mgr
Fax: (214) 615-6030
Email: acotton@rightstaffinc.com
Website: www.rightstaffinc.com
Staffing services: permanent, temporary, project staff augmentation, computer software & hardware, computer programing, systems design, technology infrastructure. (Woman/White, estab 1998, empl 15, sales $3,000,000, cert: State, City, WBENC)

8878   Riverway Business Services
5213 Spruce St Ste 100   Bellaire, TX 77401
(713) 664-5900   Margo Costello President
Fax: (713) 664-9710
Email: margo.costello@riverway.jobs
Website: www.riverway.jobs
Staffing services: administrative/clerical, accounting, human resource, professional & information technology. (Woman/White, estab 1990, empl 22, sales $2,000,000, cert: WBENC)

8879   RMPersonnel, Inc.
4707 Montana Avenue   El Paso, TX 79903
(915) 565-7674   Debra Underwood Branch Mgr-San Antonio
Fax: (915) 565-7687
Email: debras@rmpersonnel.com
Website: www.rmpersonnel.com
Staffing services: employee leasing, temporaries, temp to hire, executive recruiting & HR consulting services. (Woman/Hisp, estab 1990, empl 33, sales $34,000,000, cert: WBENC)

8880   Saba Quaility System
1456 FM 1960 W   Houston, TX 77090
(281) 537-7676   Patricia Carter Mgr/HR Business Devel
Fax: (281) 537-7676
Email: qualitysystem.qs@gmail.com
Website: www.qualitysystemssite.com
IT staffing, sourcing, prescreening, interviewing & placement. (Woman/As-Ind, estab 2010, empl 14, sales $1,700,000, cert: State)

8881   Smith & Dean, Inc.
11511 Katy Frwy Ste 430   Houston, TX 77079
(713) 785-7483   Gary Urena CEO
Fax: (713) 785-7601
Email: gurena@dpsinc-texas.com
Website: www.deansprofessionalservices.com
Staffing solutions, recruiting, workshops & seminars, IT consulting. (Woman/AA, estab 1993, empl 2180, sales $10,681,149, cert: State, City, NMSDC, WBENC)

8882   SNS Global Corporation
1000 Heritage Center Circle   Round Rock, TX 78664
(512) 250-2959   Misty Carr HR
Fax:
Email: m.carr@snsglobalstaffing.com
Website: www.snsglobalstaffing.com
Staffing services. (As-Ind, estab 2003, empl 20, sales , cert: State, NMSDC)

8883   SOLRAC Corporation
6 Founders Blvd Ste A   El Paso, TX 79906
(915) 772-3073   Masazumi Aso Exec VP & COO
Fax: (915) 772-8975
Email: maso@solraccorp.com
Website: www.solraccorp.com
Assembly, sorting & rework operation, staffing services, warehouse & logistic operation. (Hisp, estab 1989, empl 300, sales $1,000,000, cert: State, NMSDC)

8884 Solution Tech Staffing Inc.
2825 Wilcrest, Ste 678   Houston, TX 77042
(713) 988-5325 Emon Carroll President
Fax: (713) 988-8679
Email: emon@ststaff.com
Website: www.ststaff.com
Staffing: short term temporary, long term temporary, temp-to-hire & direct hire. (Woman/AA, estab 2001, empl 7, sales , cert: State, City)

8885 Southwest Staffing
12025 Rojas, Ste L El Paso, TX 79936
(915) 857-9719 James Tidwell Director
Fax: (877) 266-9222
Email: info@southweststaffing.com
Website: www.southweststaffing.com
Temporary employee placement & management, staffing & recruiting solutions in technical & professional placement. (Woman/Hisp, estab 1994, empl 23, sales $15,298,011, cert: State)

8886 SV Meditrans, Inc.
100 S 8th St Richmond, TX 77469
(832) 520-8742 Rohini Dinesh CEO
Fax: (800) 579-0219
Email: rohinid@svmtinc.com
Website: www.svmtinc.com
Staffing services, interviews, screening & training. (Woman/As-Pac, estab 2002, empl 20, sales $1,650,000, cert: WBENC)

8887 The Burchell Group
11200 W Broadway #2348   Pearland, TX 77584
(281) 607-5990 Jamie Burchell President
Fax:
Email: jamie@theburchellgroup.com
Website: www.theburchellgroup.com
Staffing solutions: engineering, information technology & GIS. (Hisp, estab 2001, empl 45, sales , cert: NMSDC)

8888 The Omega Staff, LLC
14756 Dallas Pkwy, Ste 805   Dallas, TX 75254
(972) 948-7754 Michelle Deriggs Owner
Fax: (469) 546-4748
Email: mderiggs@omegastaff.com
Website: www.omegastaff.com
Professional recruiting & staffing services to automotive, engineering, defense, and manufacturing companies. (Woman/AA, estab 2007, empl 6, sales $130,000, cert: State, City)

8889 The Unbeatable Connection LLC
111 Brand Lane, Ste 3   Stafford, TX 77477
(832) 363-2566 La Teasha Smith Owner
Fax: (832) 518-1615
Email: tuctruckingsales@gmail.com
Website: www.tuctrucking.com/
Staffing services: temp, temp to perm & direct hire positions. (Woman/AA, estab 2010, empl 5, sales $308,826, cert: City, NMSDC)

8890 TriQuest Business Services, LLC
13526 George Rd, Ste 201   San Antonio, TX 78230
(210) 598-1539 Stephanie Balditt President
Fax: (210) 775-5940
Email: stephanie@triquestbusiness.com
Website: www.triquestbusiness.com
Temporary & permanent placement services: IT, Accounting, Finance, Administrative & Human Resource placement. (Woman/Hisp, estab 2010, empl 6, sales $931,239, cert: State)

8891 Walker Elliott, LP
11200 Westheimer   Houston, TX 77042
(713) 482-3750 Victor M. Taveras Contract Mgr
Fax:
Email: belliott@walker-elliott.com
Website: www.walker-elliott.com
Information technology & healthcare direct hire, contract & contract to hire placement firm. (Woman/White, estab 2006, empl 17, sales , cert: WBENC)

Utah

8892 Premier Employee Solutions LLC
346 South Mountain Way Dr Orem, UT 84058
(800) 385-0855 Amanda Foster Risk Analyst and Claims Mgr
Fax:
Email: amcbride@thepremierpride.com
Website:
Staffing & payroll services. (Woman/White, estab 2005, empl 250, sales $271,194,101, cert: WBENC)

Virginia

8893 ABBTECH Professional Resources
45635 Willow Pond Plaza   Sterling, VA 20164
(703) 450-5252 Jenny Seek Natl Acct Mgr
Fax: (703) 450-2286
Email: jennys@abbtech.com
Website: www.abbtech.com
Staffing: temporary/contract, temporary/contract to direct hire or direct placement services. (Woman, estab 1992, empl 350, sales , cert: State)

8894 Action Technology Inc.
3121 E Boundary Ct Midlothian, VA 23112
(804) 464-1271 Thomas Hammerstone Reg Mgr
Fax: (804) 893-3982
Email: thammerstone@action-tech.com
Website: www.action-tech.com
Staff augmentation: direct hire, contract & temporary. (Woman/White, estab 1982, empl 200, sales $8,000,000, cert: State, CPUC, WBENC)

8895 ARK Solutions Inc.
1939 Roland Clarke Pll Ste 300 Reston, VA 20191
(703) 502-6999 Anuj Khurana Managing Dir
Fax: (703) 657-0670
Email: Anuj@ARKSolutionsInc.com
Website: www.arksolutionsinc.com
Staffing & consulting, staffing support, Enterprise IT Solutions, Information Assurance Solutions, Business Process Management & Integration Competency. (Woman/As-Ind, estab 2003, empl 43, sales , cert: State)

8896 BEST Employment SoluTions, LLC
110 Coliseum Crossing   Hampton, VA 23666
(757) 589-2675 Kipland Albright Owner
Fax: (813) 533-9087
Email: kalbright@thebestllc.com
Website: www.thebestllc.com
Staffing: Light Industrial, Warehousing, Manufacturing,
Admin Clerical, Customer Support, & Transportation
positions. (AA, estab 2016, empl 20, sales , cert: State,
NMSDC)

8897 Cammas & Associates
5870 Trinity Pkwy Ste 170 Centreville, VA 20120
(703) 579-1100 Diane Cammas Owner/Mgr
Fax: (703) 997-5384
Email: Diane.Cammas@Snelling.com
Website: www.Snelling.com/NoVa
Staffing & recruiting services: Administrative & Support,
Information Technology, Accounting & Finance, Human
Resources, Engineering, Manufacturing & Production,
Construction, Pharmaceutical, Sales & Marketing. (Woman/
White, estab 2008, empl 3, sales , cert: WBENC)

8898 Cynet Systems Inc.
21000 Atlantic Blvd #740   Sterling, VA 20166
(571) 645-5910 Arpit Paul Talent Management
Fax: (866) 838-0907
Email: arpitp@cynetsystems.com
Website: www.cynetsystems.com
IT & engineering staffing consulting, direct/full time hiring,
contract (temp hiring) or contract to hire services. (As-Ind,
estab 2010, empl 798, sales $52,500,000, cert: NMSDC,
CPUC)

8899 Gillman Services, Inc.
3300 Tyre Neck Rd Ste E Portsmouth, VA 23703
(757) 439-0800 Jeremy Andrews Exec Acct Mgr
Fax: (757) 686-2085
Email: jandrews@gillmanservices.com
Website: www.gillmanservices.com
Staffing services. (Woman/White, estab 2008, empl 300,
sales $8,850,000, cert: State)

8900 Hire 1 Staffing
P.O. Box 34337 Richmond, VA 23234
(804) 223-2110 Sandra Smith Owner
Fax:
Email: ssmith@hire1staffing.net
Website: www.hire1staffing.net
Temporary staffing: administrative, clerical, call center/
customer service representatives & light industrial posi-
tions. (Woman/AA, estab 2005, empl 1, sales , cert: State)

8901 Key Personnel, Inc.
5540 Falmouth St, Ste 100   Richmond, VA 23230
(804) 716-9450 Thomas Bowles President
Fax: (804) 716-9427
Email: thomasbowles@keypersonnel.net
Website: www.keypersonnel.net
Staffing: temporary, temporary to hire & direct hire
employment services. (AA, estab 1998, empl 40, sales
$2,000,000, cert: State)

8902 Leading Edge Systems Richmond
3711-A Westerre Pkwy   Richmond, VA 23233
(804) 673-5100 Adish Jain Mgr
Fax: (804) 673-5680
Email: adishj@leadingedgesys.com
Website: www.leadingedgesys.com
Staffing svcs; information tech, clerical support &
professional svcs. (As-Ind, estab 1997, empl 42, sales
$4,500,000, cert: State)

8903 McKinley Marketing Partners, Inc.
111 Franklin St Alexandria, VA 22314
(703) 836-4445 Michelle Boggs President
Fax: (703) 836-4554
Email: marketing@mckinleyinc.com
Website: www.mckinleymarketingpartners.com/
Staffing: short-term marketing mgrs. (Woman/White,
estab 1995, empl 15, sales $9,395,256, cert: WBENC)

8904 MillenniumSoft, Inc
8301 Arlington Blvd, Ste 504,   Fairfax, VA 22031
(703) 698-9232 Swathi Billa
Fax: (703) 991-4551
Email: time@millenniumsoft.com
Website: www.millenniumsoft.com
Permanent, long term or short term staffing. (Woman/
As-Ind, estab 2000, empl 45, sales $293,466,000, cert:
State, NMSDC)

8905 Outcomes Inc.
4215 Lafayette center Dr Ste 6 Chantilly, VA
20151
(703) 996-8833 Sonali Kakatkar CEO
Fax: (703) 852-7327
Email: sonali@out-comes.com
Website: www.out-comes.com
Staffing, recruiting, payroll services & vendor managed
services. (Woman/As-Ind, estab 2002, empl 8, sales
$700,000, cert: State, NMSDC, WBENC, SDB)

8906 Preferred Staffing Group/Preferred Temporary
Services, Inc.
2001 Jefferson Davis Highway Ste 303 Arlington,
VA 22202
(703) 415-0182 Barbara Posner President
Fax: (703) 415-0187
Email: ejackson@ourpsg.com
Website: www.ourpsg.com
Staffing svcs: administrative, telecommunications fiber
optic, IT, legal, light construction, housekeeping.
(Woman/White, estab 1987, empl 150, sales $1,500,000,
cert: WBENC)

8907 ProTask Inc.
542 Springvale Road   Great Falls, VA 22066
(703) 231-4275 Jessie Covington Senior Acct Mgr
Fax:
Email: jcovington@protaskinc.com
Website: www.protaskinc.com/
Staffing solutions, IT contractors, IT consultants, IT Staff
Augmentation, Traditional direct hire talent search (full
life cycle), Executive recruitment. (Woman/White, estab
2010, empl 22, sales $3,300,000, cert: State, WBENC)

8908 Seaborn Health Care Inc.
16600 Jefferson St Amelia Court House, VA 23002
(727) 398-1710 Jacqueline Amadio President
Fax: (727) 392-0321
Email: Jacky@seabornhc.com
Website: www.seabornhc.com
Staffing svcs: medical, clerks & administration, IT Tech, legal & accounting. (Woman/White, estab 1995, empl 50, sales $1,000,000, cert: 8(a))

8909 Skill Path Talent, Inc.
8300 Boone Blvd, Ste 500 Vienna, VA 22182
(571) 358-5602 Sharon Campbell Business Devel Mgr
Fax: (866) 262-7565
Email: operatons@skillstalent.com
Website: www.skillstalent.com
Human capital services, temporary & permanent placement. (AA, estab 2013, empl 25, sales $50,000, cert: NMSDC)

8910 TeamPeople LLC
180 S Washington St Ste 200 Falls Church, VA 22046
(917) 751-6088 Kathy Roma Dev Consultant
Fax: (202) 454-0664
Email: kroma@teampeople.tv
Website: www.teampeople.tv
Media Staffing & Support Services. (Woman/White, estab 2004, empl 600, sales $51,714,354, cert: WBENC)

8911 Temporary Solutions, Inc.
10550 Linden Lake Plaza, Ste 200 Manassas, VA 20109
(703) 361-2220 Gala Johnson VP of Mktg and Contract Services
Fax: (703) 368-2640
Email: gjohnson@eeihr.com
Website: www.eeihr.com
Staffing services: temporary staffing, temp-to-hire staffing, direct placement, on-site services & single source mgmt solutions. (Woman/White, estab 1980, empl 921, sales $7,245,894, cert: State, WBENC)

Washington

8912 2rbConsulting, Inc.
19515 North Creek Parkway Ste 310 Bothell, WA 98011
(425) 406-7644 Betta Beasley CEO
Fax: (866) 227-6586
Email: betta@2rbconsulting.com
Website: www.2rbconsulting.com
Provide contract consultants, permanent staff & managed services at all levels of expertise. (Woman, estab 2007, empl 25, sales $3,200,000, cert: WBENC)

8913 All StarZ Staffing and Consulting LLC
841 Central Ave N Ste C-208 Kent, WA 98032
(253) 277-4000 Debra Kerner Mgr
Fax: (866) 563-9229
Email: debra@allstarzstaffing.com
Website: www.allstarzstaffing.com
Staffing solutions: candidate sourcing, screening, selection, retention & labor cost management. (Woman/White, estab 2005, empl 150, sales $3,043,715, cert: WBENC)

8914 Allegiance Staffing
400 Industry Dr, Ste 180 Tukwila, WA 98188
(253) 854-7000 Luis Perez Acct Mgr
Fax: (844) 273-0952
Email: lperez@allegiancestaffing.com
Website: www.allegiancestaffing.com
Staffing solutions: temporary, contract employees, executive search & permanent placement. (Woman/White, estab 1994, empl 10, sales $6,500,000, cert: State)

8915 Allovus Design, Inc.
15822 Peacock Hill Ave NW Gig Harbor, WA 98332
(253) 222-0274 Hayley Nichols Client Services Director
Fax: (425) 902-4850
Email: hayley@allovus.com
Website: www.allovus.com
Staffing services, direct hire, staff augmentation & studios project teams. (Woman/White, estab 2009, empl 75, sales $9,000,000, cert: WBENC)

8916 Ci2i Services, Inc.
410 Bellevue Way SE Ste 205 Bellevue, WA 98004
(425) 279-7992 Raul Ramos CEO
Fax: (425) 749-7138
Email: raul@ci2iservices.com
Website: www.Ci2iServices.com
IT Consulting & Staffing services: Program & Project Management, Software development, Business strategy & Marketing resource needs. (As-Ind, estab 1998, empl 40, sales $3,600,000, cert: State, NMSDC)

8917 MB Diversity
6523 California Ave SW, Ste B-255 Seattle, WA 98136
(206) 941-2834 Anthony Burnett Owner
Fax:
Email: anthony@mbdiversity.com
Website: www.MBDiversity.com
Staffing recruiting & managed resources. (AA, estab 2014, empl 10, sales $573,315, cert: State, City, NMSDC)

Wisconsin

8918 Division 10 Personnel Services of Milwaukee, Inc.
4425 N Port Washington Rd, Ste 401 Milwaukee, WI 53212
(414) 963-8700 Wendy Koppel, CPC President
Fax: (414) 963-8787
Email: wendy@division10personnel.com
Website: www.division10personnel.com
Recruiting & staffing: Administrative & Professional level candidates. (Woman/White, estab 1980, empl 30, sales $1,563,690, cert: State, WBENC)

8919 Elite Human Capital Group
155 S Executive Dr Ste 200 Brookfield, WI 53005
(262) 785-0900 Aaron Sramek Mgr of Professional Services
Fax: (262) 785-0901
Email: aarons@elitehumancapital.com
Website: www.elitehumancapital.com
Human resource outsourcing, temporary & permanant placement. (Woman/White, estab 2003, empl 35, sales $6,953,826, cert: State)

8920   Hatch Staffing Services
       700 W Virginia St, Ste 400   Milwaukee, WI 53204
       (414) 272-4544 Lucas Harvey Branch Mgr
       Fax: (414) 272-7901
       Email: lucas@hatch.com
       Website: www.hatch.com
Staffing services: temp, temp to hire & direct hire candidates. (Woman/White, estab 1983, empl 23, sales
$12,269,000, cert: WBENC)

8921   SEEK Careers/Staffing, Inc.
       P.O. Box 148   Grafton, WI 53024
       (262) 377-8888 Debbie Fedel VP Business Devel
       Fax: (262) 377-2760
       Email: dfedel@seekcareers.com
       Website: www.seekcareers.com
Staffing services, office/accounting, light industrial &
skilled manufacturing positions. (Woman/White, estab
1971, empl 96, sales $53,824,639, cert: State)

PROFESSIONAL SERVICES: Technical
Provide consulting services on a variety of technically oriented topics: technical writing and editing, information systems, record management, educational research, scientific research, program evaluation, nuclear energy consulting, technical manuals. NAICS Code 54

California

8922   KDJA Services LLC
223 Cynthia Ave   Vallejo, CA 94589
(888) 551-0227 Karen Adams Owner
Fax: (888) 551-0686
Email: karenadams2289@att.net
Website:
Statistical report writing, qualitative & quantitative research, data collection & data analysis of laws & policies, demographic & geographic impact, strategic planning & recommendations. (Woman/AA, estab 2012, empl 1, sales , cert: State)

Connecticut

8923   Access Consulting
31 Island Heights Circle   Stamford, CT 06902
(203) 975-2950 Arun Sinha President
Fax: (702) 549-3287
Email: contact@accessc.com
Website: www.accessc.com/
Corporate communications, marketing communications & technical writing services. (As-Ind, estab 2003, empl 2, sales $95,000, cert: NMSDC)

Florida

8924   The Med Writers LLC
9314 Forest Hill Blvd, Ste 6   Wellington, FL 33411
(561) 247-2190 Karen Vieira President
Fax:
Email: karen@themedwriters.com
Website: www.themedwriters.com
Medical & scientific writing, offsite writing services. (Woman/AA, estab 2007, empl 8, sales $174,704, cert: CPUC)

Georgia

8925   A-Z Sophisticated Solutions
12850 Hwy 9 N, Ste 600-205   Alpharetta, GA 30004
(404) 996-1358 Ana Maria Marin Managing Dir
Fax: (404) 996-1187
Email: ap@a-zssolutions.com
Website: www.a-zssolutions.com
Engineering, Technical Writing, Technical Instruction & written Translation services. Technical Writing: brochures, user manuals, creation, proofread & editorial. Technical Instruction: plastics seminars & CAE plastics. (Woman/Hisp, estab 2010, empl 1, sales $87,275, cert: WBENC)

8926   Continental Technical Services
260 Peachtree St, Ste 2200   Atlanta, GA 30303
(404) 527-6297 Willie Dunlap CEO
Fax: (404) 527-6201
Email: henri@ctsnationally.com
Website: www.ctsnationally.com
Staff augmentation, temporary personnel, technical publications, integrated logistics support, validations & verifications, ECPs, technical writing, quality assurance & control, quality inspection. (AA, estab 1992, empl 54, sales $7,400,000, cert: NMSDC)

8927   Eubio, LLC
P.O. Box 16555   Atlanta, GA 30321
(404) 632-2435 Alita Anderson Principal
Fax:
Email: alita@eubiomed.com
Website: www.eubiomed.com
Medical communications, medical writing. (Woman/AA, estab 2012, empl 2, sales $885,503, cert: City, NMSDC, WBENC)

8928   Research Analysis Group
303 Perimeter Center N Ste 300 Atlanta, GA 30346
(770) 558-6302 Tara Dixon Dir, Business Devel
Fax: (770) 558-6302
Email: Info@evaluation-group.com
Website: www.evaluation-group.com
Consulting, evaluation, scientific writing, technical assistance, strategic planning, metric development program design & data analysis & management services. (Woman/AA/Hisp, estab 2009, empl 7, sales $125,000, cert: 8(a))

Indiana

8929　Techcom, Inc.
P.O. Box 39206　Indianapolis, IN 46239
(317) 865-2530　Ilene Adams President
Fax:
Email: inadams@techcom.com
Website: www.techcom.com
Technical publications producer including: engineering, research, writing, data management, photography, illustration, CAD drawing, video production, animation, interactive multimedia creation. (Woman, estab 1976, empl 38, sales , cert: WBENC)

Michigan

8930　Good Fortune Trading Co. dba GFT Services
3959 Nash Dr　Troy, MI 48083
(248) 884-4635　Janice Girling President
Fax:
Email: janice.girling@gftservices.com
Website: www.gftservices.com
Procurement services, project planning, technical writing. (Woman/White, estab 2016, empl 1, sales , cert: WBENC)

North Carolina

8931　Whitsell Innovations Inc.
18 Kendall Dr　Chapel Hill, NC 27517
(919) 321-9017　Robin Whitsell President
Fax:
Email: robin.whitsell@whitsellinnovations.com
Website: www.whitsellinnovations.com
Medical, scientific & technical writing, GCP, GMP & GLP, clinical regulatory writing, clinical study reports, protocols, investigator brochures, narratives & full submissions of investigational new drug, applications & new drug applications. (Woman/White, estab 2006, empl 32, sales $5,262,000, cert: WBENC)

Pennsylvania

8932　KB COMM LLC
985 State Rd　West Grove, PA 19390
(610) 357-8625　Kathy Breuninger Owner
Fax: (610) 869-3579
Email: kathy@kbcommllc.com
Website: www.kbcommllc.com
Scientific & technical writing services, business & marketing communications; instructions & procedures; installation, operation & maintenance manuals; computer documentation; training materials & document templates. (Woman, estab 2006, empl 8, sales $610,154, cert: WBENC)

Texas

8933　A. Miller Consulting Services, Inc.
2540 King Arthur Blvd, Ste 219　Lewisville, TX 75210
(972) 580-0812　Amy Miller President
Fax: (972) 580-0872
Email: amiller@mcs.biz
Website: www.mcs.biz
Technical documentation: technical writing, project mgmt, technical illustration & graphics creation, web design, web-based training dev, manual dev & consolidation, proposal writing & consulting, process dev & documentation, engineering guides. (Woman/White, estab 2000, empl 26, sales $2,449,127, cert: WBENC)

8934　Integrity International, Inc.
11767 Katy Frwy, Ste 750　Houston, TX 77079
(877) 955-0707　Susan Lake Project Mgr
Fax: (281) 955-0540
Email: info@tarrenpoint.com
Website: www.tarrenpoint.com
Documentation consulting services, project management, content development (technical documentation), graphic design, technical illustration, desktop publishing, editing & quality assurance, indexing, localization & translation. (Woman/White, estab 1994, empl 63, sales $6,000,000, cert: State, WBENC)

8935　TECHNIKOS Information Development, LLC
P.O. Box 2693　Stafford, TX 77497
(281) 568-7955　Ora Gibson CEO
Fax: (281) 568-7955
Email: ora@technicallyclear.com
Website: www.technicallyclear.com
Technical writing, editing, formatting, reviewing, proofreading, documentation, manuals, guides, web content, user guides, operations manuals, procedure manuals, processes, procedures, training guides. (Woman/AA, estab 2007, empl 2, sales $98,374, cert: State, NMSDC)

RECORDING & VIDEO PRODUCTION
Produce videos (in studio or remote), TV shows, records, sound recordings, pre and post production services, talent arrangers, video distribution. NAICS Code 51

Arizona

8936 Blade Inc
3033 N Central Ave Ste 440 Phoenix, AZ 85012
(602) 307-5577 Louise Parker President
Fax: (602) 307-5885
Email: Louise@BladeInc.com
Website: www.bladeinc.com
Production, Editing, Video Production, Video Editing, Post Production, 3D Animation, Animation, Motion Graphics, VFX, Visual Effects, Visual Design, Motion Design, Illustration. TV Commercials, Web, Training, Corporate. (Woman/White, estab 2002, empl 65, sales $704,000, cert: WBENC)

California

8937 Aahs Entertainment, Inc.
10707 Camarillo St, Ste 312 Toluca Lake, CA 91602
(818) 279-2416 Gwenn Smith President
Fax:
Email: gwenn@aahsentertainment.com
Website: www.aahsentertainment.com
Video Production Services, Media Production, Media Services, Advertising, Marketing, Content Creation, Branded Content, Brand Marketing, DVD Extras, DVD Special Features, Marketing, Advertising, EPKs. (Woman/AA, estab 2011, empl 1, sales , cert: WBENC)

8938 Agnew Multilingual
741 Lakefield Rd, Ste C Westlake Village, CA 91361
(805) 494-3999 Julia Leonhardt Acct Exec - Translation Svcs
Fax: (805) 494-1749
Email: j.leonhardt@agnew.com
Website: www.agnew.com
Translation, interpretation & audiovisual production. (Woman/White, estab 1986, empl 9, sales $1,135,153, cert: CPUC, WBENC, SDB)

8939 Hybrid Edit, LLC
5782 W. Jefferson blvd. Los Angeles, CA 90016
(310) 586-9799 Susan Munro President
Fax: (310) 264-8497
Email: diversity@hybridcollective.tv
Website: www.hybridcollective.tv
Commercial, television & motion picture post production & production services: creative editorial offline, online/compositing, color correction, graphic design, motion graphic design, sound design & mixing. (Woman/White, estab 2009, empl 8, sales $1,400,000, cert: WBENC)

8940 International Communication Network
901 Lane Ave, Ste 200 Chula Vista, CA 91914
(619) 421-0426 Michelle Diaz COO
Fax:
Email: MDiaz@Inctv50.com
Website: www.Inctv50.com
Television broadcasting, video production, marketing, Hispanic market. (AA, estab 1997, empl 5, sales , cert: NMSDC)

8941 Kaboom Productions
2169 Folsom St Ste 201M San Francisco, CA 94110
(415) 434-2666 Lauren Schwartz Exec Producer, Owner
Fax:
Email: lauren@kaboomproductions.com
Website: www.kaboomproductions.com
TV commercials, corporate videos, branded content, TV shows, feature films. (Woman/White, estab 1997, empl 3, sales $3,051,256, cert: WBENC)

8942 Little Minx
1758 Berkeley St Santa Monica, CA 90404
(310) 566-0536 Kimberly Rosenthal Controller
Fax:
Email: kim@littleminx.tv
Website: www.littleminx.tv
Commercials, independent films, branded content & high-profile music videos. (Woman/White, estab 2001, empl 4, sales $2,440,338, cert: CPUC)

8943 Panaloma Productions, LLC
2015 Half South Sherbourne Dr Los Angeles, CA 90034
(424) 298-0966 Rashaan Dozier-Escalante President
Fax: (310) 876-0260
Email: Rashaan@PanalomaProductions.com
Website: www.PanalomaProductions.com
Develop & produce media, event production, films (training, PSA's, security, informational for employees & the public, documentaries) & written (training classes, SOPs, curriculums). (Woman/AA, estab 2012, empl 1, sales $150,000, cert: 8(a))

8944 Pellinore Productions, Inc.
5215 Sepulveda Blvd, Unit 11D Culver City, CA 90230
(310) 391-9021 Joan Zierler Exec Producer
Fax: (310) 391-1884
Email: joan@pellinore.net
Website: www.pellinore.net
Digital/video/film production & post-production, commercials, promos, videos for corporate communications, integrated marketing & branded marketing for broadcast, internet & social media. (Woman/As-Pac, estab 2009, empl 1, sales $823,637, cert: CPUC, WBENC)

8945   Showreel International Inc.
639 S. Glenwood Place, Ste. 200   Burbank, CA 90038
(323) 464-5111   Jessica Ristic CEO
Fax: (323) 464-4216
Email: jessica@weareshotglass.com
Website: www.weareshotglass.com
Film & video production. (Woman, estab 1985, empl 7, sales , cert: State)

8946   The Traveling Picture Show Company
1531 N. Cahuenga Blvd   Los Angeles, CA 90028
(323) 769-1115   Kate Bacon Partner
Fax:
Email: kate@thetpsc.com
Website: www.thetpsc.com
Commercial video production services, television commercials, online branded content &visual media. (Woman/White, estab 2011, empl 9, sales $5,500,000, cert: WBENC)

8947   Total Media Group
432 N Canal St   South San Francisco, CA 94080
(650) 583-8236   Megan McKenna Acct Exec
Fax: (650) 534-4708
Email: megan@totalmediagroup.com
Website: www.totalmediagroup.com
Video production, motion graphics, 3D animation, editorial, event production, web design & mobile apps. (Woman/White, estab 1971, empl 10, sales $4,900,000, cert: WBENC)

Connecticut

8948   Anderson Productions Inc.
71 Dolphin Rd   Bristol, CT 06010
(503) 287-3004   Tom Stanwicks Sales/Mktg
Fax: (503) 287-3004
Email: TStanwicks@anderson3.com
Website: www.andersonprod.com
Video production, post production, graphics, animations, sound design, audio editing, product models, digital signage. (Woman, estab 1994, empl 24, sales $4,500,000, cert: WBENC)

8949   Creative Video Corporation
9 Mott Ave, Ste 108   Norwalk, CT 06850
(203) 866-8700   Francisca Bogdan Production Specialist
Fax: (203) 854-9946
Email: francisca.bogdan@creativevideocorp.com
Website: www.creativevideocorp.com
Corporate communication videos & multi-media products, internal communications, sales & markeitng, event opening video, promotional video, event coverage. (Woman/Hisp, estab 1997, empl 4, sales $380,000, cert: NMSDC)

Delaware

8950   DelVideo Productions
583 Barley Court   Smyrna, DE 19977
(302) 223-4049   Milton Melendez VP
Fax:
Email: info@delvideo.com
Website: www.delvideo.com
Bilingual video production, Pre-Production, Pre-Planning & vision writing, Location & set assessment, Research, Script writing, Talent arrangement, Recording Services, Video recording, Audio capture & recording, Project management, Directing. (Woman/AA/Hisp, estab 2013, empl 2, sales , cert: State, 8(a))

Florida

8951   Campbell Advertising and Design, LLC
103 NE 4th St   Delray Beach, FL 33444
(561) 562-6119   Courtney Campbell Principal
Fax:
Email: courtney@campbellcreative.com
Website: www.campbellcreative.com
Photography, art direction, web videos, social content, broadcast commercials, testimonial videos, training videos, animated videos. (Woman/White, estab 2010, empl 6, sales $1,600,000, cert: WBENC)

8952   Coda Sound Inc.
4819 N Hale Ave   Tampa, FL 33614
(813) 353-8151   Maritza Astorquiza Owner
Fax:
Email: maritza@codasoundusa.com
Website: www.codasoundusa.com
Event production: sound, lights, stages & audio visual. (Woman/Hisp, estab 1998, empl 2, sales $471,000, cert: State, City, NMSDC)

8953   Graphix 360, LLC
7777 N Wickham Rd Ste 12710   Melbourne, FL 32940
(321) 693-9293   Bobbi Gerardot CEO
Fax:
Email: Bobbi@Graphix360.com
Website: www.Graphix360.com
Multimedia design, photo, video, graphic/web design & printing services, multimedia equipment. (Woman/White, estab 2013, empl 4, sales $70,000, cert: City)

8954   Kreative Kontent Co.
4044 NE 7th Ave Ste 100   Fort Lauderdale, FL 33334
(954) 312-3660   Deborah Margolis Horwitz President/Exec Producer
Fax: (954) 312-3661
Email: debbie@kreativekontent.com
Website: www.kreativekontent.com
Production specializing in content creation, broadcast, web based, theatrical & marketing fulfillment programs, broadcast commercials, corporate video communications, product placement, branded content, promotional products. (Woman/White, estab 2010, empl 4, sales $2,000,000, cert: WBENC)

Georgia

8955   A-1 Audio Visual, LLC
       863 Flat Shoals Rd SE Ste C359 Conyers, GA 30094
       (800) 805-7210 Keith McNeil CEO
       Fax: (800) 341-4988
       Email: kmcneil@a1audiovisual.com
       Website: www.a1audiovisual.com
Audio visual, video & lighting. (AA, estab 2003, empl 6,
sales $190,000, cert: State, NMSDC)

8956   Onyx Media Services, Inc.
       57 Forsyth St NW Ste 250-G Atlanta, GA 30303
       (404) 420-0030 Jennifer Rocke VP of Finance
       Fax: (866) 736-4812
       Email: info@onyxmsgroup.com
       Website: www.onyxmsgroup.com
Production services: audio visual, facility, technical
production design, presentation video, graphic design,
sound reinforcement, theatrical lighting. (AA, estab 2006,
empl 15, sales $300,000, cert: NMSDC)

8957   Popoff Enterprises Inc.
       3035 Wallace Circle SE   Atlanta, GA 30339
       (404) 307-1979 Dana Popoff President
       Fax:
       Email: popoffdana@gmail.com
       Website: www.popoffenterprises.com
Video production & still photography services, commercial
distribution, web sites, point of purchase, social media,
internal corporate communications - training, company
meetings & conferences, President's address, legacy
knowledge, etc. (Woman, estab 1997, empl 1, sales
$138,750, cert: WBENC)

8958   Positive Promotions Ltd. TV
       2118 Sableshire Way   Conyers, GA 30013
       (404) 296-7880 Josetta Shropshire Howard Presi-
       dent
       Fax: (404) 296-7914
       Email: service@positivepromotionsltd.com
       Website: www.positivepromotionsltd.com
Televison & video production services. (Woman/AA, estab
1992, empl 3, sales $111,000, cert: SDB)

8959   Works of Bawbee Films
       704 Brambling Way   Stockbridge, GA 30281
       (478) 390-7375 Brian Ezeike Video Producer
       Fax:
       Email: info@wobfilms.com
       Website: www.wobfilms.com
Video production/digital content creation, write, shoot &
edit a wide variety of video content. (AA, estab 2010, empl
1, sales $44,400, cert: NMSDC)

Illinois

8960   Hootenanny LLC
       230 E Ohio St Ste 700 Chicago, IL 60611
       (312) 266-0777 Elizabeth Tate President
       Fax: (312) 266-0776
       Email: liz@hootenanny.tv
       Website: www.hootenanny.tv
Post-production, creative editorial, finishing, graphic
design & visual effects, television, print, web, corporate
video & interactive media. (Woman/White, estab 2008,
empl 11, sales $2,500,000, cert: State, WBENC)

8961   Rocket Productions Inc.
       1100 W Cermak Rd Ste 301-B Chicago, IL 60607
       (312) 431-1040 Hector Perez
       Fax: (312) 431-1042
       Email: hector@rocketchicago.com
       Website: www.rocketchicago.com
Video production, TV commercials, infomercials &
training videos, media buying, documentaries, public
service announcements (PSAs) & educational videos.
(Hisp, estab 2002, empl 6, sales $258,419, cert: State)

Indiana

8962   Holloway House Productions
       501 San Ricardo Court   Greenwood, IN 46142
       (310) 963-0409 Lisa Holloway Creative Visionary
       Fax: (310) 963-0409
       Email: Lisa-Holloway@att.net
       Website:
Full service video production. (Woman, estab 2010,
empl 1, sales , cert: State)

8963   Multitek Corporate Communications
       6531 Greencove Ave   Evansville, IN 47715
       (812) 760-7488 Earl Milligan President
       Fax:
       Email: earl.milligan@gmail.com
       Website: www.multitekcorporate.com
Corporate safety & training video production services,
construction archival videos, 3 d survey mapping, drone
aerial photography & videography. (AA, estab 1984,
empl 1, sales , cert: State)

Massachusetts

8964   Real Cool Productions, Inc.
       800 S Main St, Ste 203   Mansfield, MA 02048
       (508) 878-8907 Pia Proal President & COO
       Fax:
       Email: pia@realcoolprod.com
       Website: www.realcoolproductions.com
Integrated communications, technology & production
services, internal & external facing content (mixed
media, animations and videos), corporate overviews,
business documentaries, executive interviews & announcements, testimonials, product videos, training
(Woman/White, estab 2010, empl 11, sales $1,400,000,
cert: WBENC)

Michigan

8965   Freshwater Film, Inc.
3061 Myddleton Court   Troy, MI 48084
(248) 840-5400   Sue Witham CEO
Fax: (248) 645-9934
Email: sue@mediumfilm.com
Website: www.mediumfilm.com
Film & digital production, influential storytelling, relevant creative content & serious production expertise. (Woman/White, estab 1991, empl 1, sales $656,756, cert: WBENC)

8966   Seventy 7 Productions
620 Cherry Ave   Royal Oak, MI 48073
(313) 610-0109   Nora Urbanski Producer
Fax:
Email: Nora@seventy7productions.com
Website: www.seventy7productions.com
We are a full service video production company. We provide video production, post production and creative services for broadcast commercials, social media videos, 360 and VR videos, etc. (Hisp, estab 2011, empl 5, sales , cert: NMSDC)

8967   ShawneTV Inc
29558 English Way   Novi, MI 48377
(248) 669-1868   Shawne Duperon CEO
Fax: (248) 438-1661
Email: shawne@shawnetv.com
Website: www.shawnetvpromotions.com
Promotional & sponsorships, media & networking training, TV production. (Woman/White, estab 1999, empl 1, sales $300,000, cert: WBENC)

8968   VideoWorks Production Services, Inc.
4851 Fernlee Ste 100   Royal Oak, MI 48073
(248) 563-0371   Ruben Rodriguez President
Fax: (248) 548-6834
Email: ruben@videoworksonline.com
Website: www.videoworksonline.com
Video production: instructional & training videos, corporate, communications, news-style event coverage, multi-camera events & live media tours. (Hisp, estab 1995, empl 2, sales $150,000, cert: NMSDC)

Minnesota

8969   Orange Filmworks Inc.
3912 Harriet Ave   Minneapolis, MN 55409
(612) 868-7875   Marco Baca Owner
Fax: (612) 825-2039
Email: marco@orangefilmworks.com
Website: www.orangefilmworks.com
Broadcast television commercials, videos or commercials for web, long format instructional video, internal & in-store content. (Hisp, estab 2005, empl 1, sales $674,623, cert: NMSDC)

8970   Peterson Productions LLC
1501 Spring Valley Rd   Golden Valley, MN 55422
(763) 521-4746   Janie Peterson President
Fax:
Email: janie@PetersonProductionsLive.com
Website: www.PetersonProductionsLive.com
Video production house for corporate communications. (Woman/White, estab 2007, empl 2, sales $195,000, cert: State)

8971   Slang Productions, LLC
3207 E 51st St   Minneapolis, MN 55417
(612) 310-4622   Sue Lang Principal
Fax: (612) 724-5357
Email: sue@slangproductions.net
Website: www.slangproductions.net
Production: live events, video, audio & interactive media. (Woman/White, estab 2003, empl 2, sales $200,560, cert: WBENC)

Missouri

8972   CAC REPS, LLC
5965 jamieson ave   St. Louis, MO 63109
(314) 752-0994   Charlene Colombini Owner
Fax:
Email: charlenecolo@hotmail.com
Website: www.cacreps.com
Design, illustration, photography, computer imaging, computer 3D Rendering, video production & post, videography & on set styling. (Woman/White, estab 2008, empl 1, sales $65,000, cert: State, CPUC)

8973   Haller Concepts, Inc.
4501 Mattis Rd   St Louis, MO 63128
(314) 913-5626   Mike Haller President
Fax:
Email: mikeh@hallerconcepts.com
Website: www.hallerconcepts.com
Corporate, event, training, web & TV video production filming. (Woman/White, estab 1982, empl 2, sales $174,400, cert: State)

New Jersey

8974   Harlan Media LLC
494 Broad St, Ste 104   Newark, NJ 07102
(973) 623-6200   Harlan Brandon CEO
Fax: (973) 623-6222
Email: hb@harlanmedia.com
Website: www.harlanmedia.com
Film & Video Production, Marketing, Advertising, Public Relations, Graphic Design, Independent Artist and Writers, Direct Mail Advertising, Commercial Photography (AA, estab 2008, empl 8, sales , cert: NMSDC)

8975 KVibe Productions, LLC
591 Summit Ave Ste 101 Jersey City, NJ 07306
(201) 936-8033 Khoa Le CEO
Fax:
Email: khoa.le@kvibe.com
Website: www.kvibe.com
Video production, product video, corporate video, commercial production, feature films. (As-Pac, estab 2005, empl 2, sales , cert: State)

New York

8976 Adrienne Nicole Productions, LLC
14 Dekalb Ave 3rd Fl Brooklyn, NY 11201
(646)5994911 Adrienne Nicole Exec Producer
Fax:
Email: info@producedbyanp.com
Website: www.producedbyanp.com
Videography, aerial video, drone video photography, progress photos, story development, pre-production, post-production, motion graphics and animation, casting, photography, progress photos. (Woman/AA, estab 2011, empl 1, sales $986,000, cert: State, City, NMSDC)

8977 Amber Heavenly USA, Ltd.
250 Lafayette St 4th Fl New York, NY 10012
(212) 352-1888 Michelle Curran President
Fax: (212) 352-1208
Email: michelle@ambermusic.com
Website: www.ambermusic.com
Commercial music production, composition, music licensing & publishing. (Woman/White, estab 1997, empl 7, sales $1,400,000, cert: State, WBENC)

8978 Bardin Palomo Ltd.
432 W 19th St Ste 3 New York, NY 10011
(212) 989-6113 Robert Palomo President
Fax: (212) 989-6314
Email: rrpalomo@bardinpalomo.com
Website: www.bardinpalomo.com
Special Events design and production company specializing in floral design, lighting design, stage design, prop and furniture rental. We sdesign and supply all visuals for any type of event. (Hisp, estab 1992, empl 5, sales $3,200,000, cert: NMSDC)

8979 Cutter Productions
236 W 27th St Ste 1001 New York, NY 10001
(646) 588-1133 Hillary Cutter Exec Producer
Fax:
Email: hillary@cutterproductions.com
Website: www.cutterproductions.com
Full-service production. (Woman, estab 2005, empl 4, sales , cert: WBENC)

8980 Loftin Productions
104 Belmont Pkwy Hempstead, NY 11550
(917) 825-5412 Dushka Petkovich Co-Owner
Fax: (212) 727-3939
Email: vze26rdi@verizon.net
Website: www.loftinpro.com/
Produce product demonstration & employee training videos. (Woman/AA, estab 1991, empl 2, sales $16,000, cert: State)

8981 Mary Nittolo Inc. dba The Studio
12 W 27th St 11th FL New York, NY 10001
(212) 661-1363 Mary Nittolo CEO
Fax: (212) 661-1607
Email: mary@studionyc.com
Website: www.studionyc.com
Art & animation studio, 3d/2d animation, motion capture, animatics, pre-vis, storyboards, presentation art, digital art, comps & character design. (Woman/As-Pac/Hisp, estab 1988, empl 30, sales $3,500,000, cert: State, City)

8982 Media2, Inc. dba M2
72 Madison Ave, Fl 2 New York, NY 10016
(212) 213-4004 Cathy Humphrey Producer
Fax: (212) 213-4024
Email: cathy@m2nyc.tv
Website: www.m2nyc.tv
Creative offline editorial, 2D/3D design & animation, television & live event production, install digital & high definition production studios, monitors, cameras & lighting. (AA/Hisp, estab 1997, empl 10, sales $25,000,000, cert: NMSDC)

8983 Resilient Media
10 E 39th St, 4th Fl New York, NY 10016
(646) 580-9391 Emilio Mahomar CEO
Fax: (212) 725-3743
Email: emilio@resilient.tv
Website: www.resilient.tv
Production, post production, duplication & language localization (translation, closed captions, subtitles, language dubbing). (Hisp, estab 2010, empl 2, sales $200,000, cert: NMSDC)

8984 TimeLine Video
One Bridge St Irvington, NY 10533
(914) 591-7360 Timothy Englert VP Dev
Fax: (914) 591-7461
Email: tim@timelinevideo.com
Website: www.timelinevideo.com
Video, production & post-production, graphic design. (Woman/White, estab 1994, empl 7, sales $1,700,000, cert: WBENC)

8985 Transcendent Enterprise
37 W 26th St, Ste 408 New York, NY 10010
(718) 304-6384 Chris Alvarez CEO
Fax:
Email: chris@t-enter.com
Website: www.transcendententerprise.com
Video production, live stream services, post production, editing & filming, photography. (AA/As-Pac/Hisp, estab 2004, empl 4, sales $230,000, cert: City, NMSDC)

8986   VMIX, LLC.
163 William St, 3 Fl   New York, NY 10038
(800) 436-8618   Wening Cintron Relationship Mgr
Fax: (646) 475-4368
Email: wening@vmix.tv
Website: www.vmix.tv
Digital media, audio/visual (A/V) content, music, television & urban entertainment. (AA, estab 2004, empl 2, sales , cert: State)

8987   Wild Child Editorial, Inc.
44 W 28th St, 15 Fl   New York, NY 10001
(212) 725-5333   Scott Spanjich Managing Dir
Fax: (212) 725-2932
Email: scott@wildchildpost.com
Website: www.wildchildpost.com
TV commercials, music videos, feature films & emerging media. (Woman/Hisp, estab 1995, empl 15, sales $4,500,000, cert: WBENC)

Pennsylvania

8988   Crossover Ent. LLC
728 Copeland St   Pittsburgh, PA 15232
(651) 347-3831   Freya Saxon Producer
Fax:
Email: fs@deepcea.com
Website: www.deepcea.com
Script to screen production, Corporate Videos, Training Videos, Commercials, Film & Documentaries. (AA, estab 2014, empl 14, sales , cert: State)

8989   Karasch & Associates
1646 W Chester Pike Ste 4   West Chester, PA 19382
(800) 621-5689   Edward Sarkissian Sales Mgr
Fax: (610) 696-2008
Email: esarkissian@karasch.com
Website: www.karasch.com
Video production, duplications & captioning services. (Woman, estab 1980, empl 25, sales $4,000,000, cert: State, WBENC)

South Carolina

8990   Mad Monkey, Inc.
1631 Main St   Columbia, SC 29201
(803) 252-2211   Lorie Gardner CEO
Fax:
Email: lorie@gomadmonkey.com
Website: www.gomadmonkey.com
Creates video stories for television, laptops, mobile devices & social platforms. (Woman/White, estab 2000, empl 15, sales $1,650,351, cert: State, WBENC)

8991   Red Heritage Media, LLC
1974 Carolina Place, Ste 200C   Fort Mill, SC 29708
(803) 792-7331   Gerry Martin Exec Producer
Fax:
Email: gerry@redheritagemedia.com
Website: www.redheritagemedia.com
Content creation, film, documentary, commercial & episodic television production industry. (Nat Ame, estab 2015, empl 3, sales , cert: 8(a))

Texas

8992   1820 Productions, LLC
6301 N Riverside Dr Bldg One, Ste 2C   Irving, TX 75039
(972) 869-7777   Sara Madsen Miller COO
Fax: (972) 869-7793
Email: Sara@1820productions.com
Website: www.1820productions.com
Television & film production, creative concept development, producing, directing, editing, graphics and animation, marketing, script writing, industrial or marketing videos from script to screen. (AA, estab 2001, empl 5, sales $1,012,000, cert: State, NMSDC)

8993   CM Productions, Inc.
4228 North Central Expressway Ste 340   Dallas, TX 75206
(214) 528-2700   Carrie Martinez President
Fax:
Email: carrie@cmproductions.tv
Website: www.cmproductions.tv
Video production, employee & marketing communications, documentaries, commercials, scriptwriting, stunning photography & sharp editing, still photography. (Woman/White, estab 1900, empl 1, sales $194,628, cert: WBENC)

8994   IS Productions, Inc.
1957 E Irving Blvd   Irving, TX 75060
(214) 924-6481   Margie Aguilar President
Fax:
Email: margie@i-s-p.net
Website: www.i-s-p.net
Teleproduction, graphic design services, motion picture & video production. (Woman/Hisp, estab 1998, empl 3, sales $700,000, cert: State, WBENC)

8995   Julye Newlin Productions, Inc.
129 E 13th St   Houston, TX 77008
(713) 869-3609   Julye Newlin Owner
Fax: (713) 862-6505
Email: julye@julyenewlin.com
Website: www.julyenewlin.com
Video, film & photography services: digital video, digital editing, web, broadcast, print advertising, CD business cards, DVD presentations, etc. (Woman/White, estab 1993, empl 3, sales , cert: City, WBENC)

8996 Small Pond Video Productions, Inc.
2217 Clarebrooke Dr.   Grand Prairie, TX 75050
(214) 686-1092 Silvana Rosero President
Fax: (972) 985-5554
Email: silvana@smallpondvideo.com
Website: www.smallpondvideo.com
Video production & meeting support, marketing, motivational, product introductions, testimonials, training videos
& broadcast commercials. (Woman/Hisp, estab 2002, empl
2, sales $178,412, cert: State, NMSDC, WBENC)

8997 Sue Abrams Productions, LLC
2709 Prestonwood Dr   Plano, TX 75093
(972) 418-2034 Sue Abrams Owner
Fax: (972) 307-8137
Email: sue@saproductions.net
Website: www.saproductions.net
Video production: sales pieces, public education videos,
corporate overviews, recruiting videos, commercials,
training pieces, product launches, event videos & video
news releases. (Woman/White, estab 1999, empl 1, sales
$152,620, cert: WBENC)

Virginia

8998 Chitra Productions, LLC
4873 S Oliver Dr Ste 100 Virginia Beach, VA 23455
(757) 495-0234 Vibhaa Vermani CEO
Fax:
Email: vibhaa@chitraproductions.com
Website: www.chitraproductions.com
Education & training support, research & development,
administration & management support, logistics &
scheduling, information technology, professional support
services, engineering support services, graphics & multimedia support. (Woman/As-Ind, estab 2008, empl 80,
sales $8,921,613, cert: 8(a))

Washington

8999 Native Ways LLC - Apachewolf Productions
15313 NE 13th Place PO Box 6292 Bellevue, WA
98008
(360) 930-9615 Freddie Begay CEO
Fax:
Email: chipbegay@gmail.com
Website: www.apachewolf.com
Video productions, video shooting & editing services,
develop & create television & radio commercials, video
streaming, DVD & CD duplication, Radio/TV broadcast
development & marketing. (Nat Ame, estab 2015, empl 1,
sales $17,000, cert: State, SDB)

9000 Visual Media Group, dba VMG/studio520
13228 NE 20th St, Ste 400   Bellevue, WA 98005
(425) 457-7100 Kelly Sparks CEO
Fax: (425) 457-7104
Email: supplierdiversity@vmgstudio520.com
Website: www.vmgstudio520.com
Visual & Image Generation, Graphic Support, Motion
Graphics, Animation, Visual Effects, Audio Recording,
Website Design, Time Lapse Video, Flash, Powerpoint
Presentations, Interactive Media, Training Video.
(Woman/White, estab 2004, empl 13, sales $1,300,000,
cert: WBENC)

SPORTS & RECREATION
Manufacturers of boats, travel trailers, athletic equipment and supplies, bicycle accessories, luggage, fishing rods and tackle, physical activity and wellness classes. NAICS Code 42

California

9001 Strive Well-Being, Inc.
5920 FriarsRd, Ste 103　San Diego, CA 92108
(619) 684-5700　Amit Sangani President
Fax:
Email: reg@strive2bfit.com
Website: www.strive2bfit.com
Onsite Physical Activity Classes, Onsite Stress Management Classes, Musculoskeletal Strengthening Classes, Fitness Center Staffing & Management, Fitness & Wellness Program Management, Fitness Facility Design & Development. (As-Ind, estab 2008, empl 15, sales , cert: NMSDC, 8(a))

Florida

9002 Tavarez Sporting Goods
1840 22nd St　Miami, FL 33145
(347) 441-9690　Manuel Tavarez Managing Partner
Fax:
Email: tavarezsports@gmail.com
Website: www.tavarezsports.com
Sporting goods & fitness apparel, baseballs, softballs, baseball bats, gloves, batting gloves, catcher's equipment, helmets, volleyballs, soccer balls, basketballs, boxing equipment, martial arts equipment, sports bags to sports apparel. (Hisp, estab 2014, empl 5, sales , cert: NMSDC)

Missouri

9003 Cherry
1712 Main St, Ste 232　Kansas City, MO 64108
(816) 377-1832　Thalia Cherry President
Fax:
Email: info@cherrysportsgear.com
Website: www.cherrysportsgear.com
Sporting goods, corporate apparel, tee shirts, athletic equipment & uniforms. (AA, estab 2011, empl 3, sales $87,000, cert: NMSDC)

Texas

9004 HLF Distributing, Inc.
1213-B N Post Oak Rd　Houston, TX 77055
(713) 932-9320　update
Fax: (713) 932-9320
Email: info@huskybicycles.com
Website: www.huskybicycles.com
Dist industrial & commercial bicycles & tricycles: wheels, tires, tubes, chains, tools & lubricants. (Woman/White, estab 1993, empl 7, sales $2,600,000, cert: WBENC)

TELECOMMUNICATIONS
Manufacture and distribute telecommunications systems and products: CATV, telephones, intercoms, test and control equipment, etc. Includes firms which provide cellular and internet services, phone line installation, service and consulting. NAICS Code 51

Alabama

9005   Palco Telecom Service Inc.
2914 Green Cove Rd   Huntsville, AL 35803
(256) 527-0213 Brian Piechocki President
Fax: (256) 883-3484
Email: bpiechocki@palcotelecom.com
Website: www.gotopalco.com
Telecommunications: logistics, forward & reverse, technical product repair upgrade & remanufacture, warranty fulfillment. (Woman/White, estab 1986, empl 250, sales $17,193,208, cert: WBENC)

Arizona

9006   Denali Telecom Solutions, Inc.
6524 S McAllister Ave   Tempe, AZ 85283
(855) 239-7776 Karen Tynan CEO
Fax:
Email: karen.tynan@denalicorp.com
Website: www.denalicorp.com
Mfr telecommunications products & value added service solutions for Broadband & Network Projects. (Woman/As-Pac, estab 2013, empl 4, sales $1,000,000, cert: WBENC)

9007   Native Technology Solutions Inc.
7065 W Allison Rd   Chandler, AZ 85226
(480) 639-1234 Mabel Tsosie
Fax: (480) 639-1235
Email: mtsosie@gilarivertel.com
Website: www.native-tech.net
Cabling & computing services, structured cabling, phone, security systems, video conferencing, & technology solutions. (Nat Ame, estab 2007, empl 14, sales $4,000,000, cert: State)

9008   Tower Safety and Instruction
3620 S 40th St   Phoenix, AZ 85040
(480) 313-0678 Kathy Brand CEO
Fax:
Email: Kathy@towersafety.com
Website: www.towersafety.com
Safety School for the Wireless/Crane Industry, Wireless & Microwave, Construction & Telecommunications-Fiber Optics/Copper Installation & Testing, Project Management, Installation, Telecommunications Maintenance & Testing. (Woman/White, estab 2013, empl 8, sales $50,000, cert: WBENC)

California

9009   Aponi Products and Services
3805 Florin Rd Ste 1228 Sacramento, CA 95823
(916) 392-6571 Lisa M Davis lacy Owner
Fax: (916) 392-6577
Email: lisad@aponitelecommunication.com
Website: www.aponitelecom.com
Telecommunication Equipment, Installation, Voice, Data, Cabling, Maintenance, Repair, Security System, DVR, Security Cameras. (Woman/Nat Ame, estab 2007, empl 7, sales $360,000, cert: State, 8(a))

9010   Business Communications Solutions
9910 Irvine Center Dr   Irvine, CA 92618
(949) 333-1000 Afsaneh Rajab CEO
Fax: (949) 333-1001
Email: srajab@bcsconsultants.com
Website: www.bcsconsultants.com
Telecommunication & networking: phone systems, internet & telephone services, cabling, networking, & server room design & installation. (Woman/White, estab 2001, empl 15, sales $3,700,000, cert: State)

9011   Cico Electrical Contractors Inc.
365 Whipporwill Dr   Riverside, CA 92507
(951) 213-2229 Ron Veloz Office Mgr
Fax: (951) 684-0738
Email: ron.veloz@cicoele.com
Website: www.cicoele.com
Electrical, Electrical Subcontractor, New Construction, Remodeling, Renovations, Improvements-Relocations, Maintenance, Switchgear Change out, Critical Power-UPS, Generators, Predictive Maintenance (circuit (Hisp, estab 2004, empl 25, sales $4,464,384, cert: NMSDC)

9012   Clean Sweep Group Inc
8306 Wilshire Blvd #7009 Beverly Hills, CA 90211
(310) 985-0504 Leo Williams, II CEO
Fax: (323) 686-5351
Email: leo.williams@csgiusa.com
Website: www.csgiusa.com
We are a veteran minority business enterprise. We provide an ultraviolet light disinfection and education service which greatly reduces the threat of hospital acquired infections and their increased costs and safety risks. (AA, estab 2011, empl 16, sales , cert: NMSDC)

9013   Coast to Coast Communications
34145 Pacific Coast Hwy 635   Dana Point, CA 92629
(949) 481-6550 Nikki Clark Natl Acct Exec
Fax: (949) 481-6550
Email: nikki@c2ccomm.com
Website: www.c2ccomm.com
Voice, data cabling & phone systems. (Woman/White, estab 2000, empl 10, sales $3,500,000, cert: WBENC)

9014   DataOptek Corp.
573 E Fairview Blvd, Ste 2   Inglewood, CA 90302
(800) 878-9857 Roderick Byrd Business Dev
Fax: (310) 412-2330
Email: rbyrd@dataoptek.com
Website: www.dataoptek.com
Structured cabling, LAN, WAN, VoIP, wireline, wireless network infrastructure installations & maintenance. (AA, estab 1999, empl 2, sales $200,000, cert: NMSDC, CPUC)

9015 E-3 Systems
      1220 Whipple Rd   Union City, CA 94587
      (510) 487-7393 Kofi Tawiah President
      Fax: (510) 487-7794
      Email: kofi@e3systems.com
      Website: www.e3systems.com
Low voltage voice & data structured cabling, electronic
security systems & telecom. (AA, estab 1989, empl 58,
sales $3,900,000, cert: NMSDC, CPUC)

9016 GovMobile, LLC
      120 Vantis, Ste 300   Aliso Viejo, CA 92656
      (949) 505-9600 Lambert Matias President
      Fax:
      Email: lmatias@govmobile.com
      Website: www.govmobile.com
Mobility, Wireless & Internet of Things (IoT)solutions. (As-
Pac, estab 2013, empl 2, sales $1,200,000, cert: 8(a))

9017 Herca Telecomm Services Inc
      18610 Beck St   Perris, CA 92570
      (951) 940-5941 Hector Castellon CEO
      Fax: (951) 940-5458
      Email: hector.castellon@hercatelecomm.com
      Website: www.hercatelecomm.com
Tower erection, lines & antennas, microwave, general
construction, excavation, trenching, electrical, concrete,
demolition. (Hisp, estab 2005, empl 29, sales $4,035,556,
cert: State)

9018 JM Fiber Optics, Inc.
      13941 Ramona Ave Ste A Chino, CA 91710
      (909) 628-3445 Marlene Vidana Business Dev Mgr
      Fax: (909) 628-1990
      Email: mvidana@jmfiberoptics.com
      Website: www.jmfiberoptics.com
Fiber optic & copper voice, video & data communication
systems, transit system passenger information systems &
intrusion dectection systems. (Hisp, estab 1992, empl 8,
sales $5,701,490, cert: State, City, NMSDC, CPUC, SDB)

9019 Pinnacle Telecommunications, Inc. (PTI Solutions)
      4242 Forcum Ave, Ste 200   McClellan, CA 95652
      (916) 426-1046 Heather Sula Mktg Program Mgr
      Fax: (916) 426-1085
      Email: itb@pti-s.com
      Website: www.pti-s.com
Install communications cabling & equipment, cell tower
upgrades, structured wire, WiFi & laser communications.
(Woman/White, estab 1984, empl 140, sales $17,000,000,
cert: CPUC, WBENC)

9020 Serene Innovations
      14731 Carmenita Rd   Norwalk, CA 90650
      (562) 407-5400 James McGehee Sales Coord
      Fax:
      Email: j.mcgehee@sereneinnovations.com
      Website: www.sereneinnovations.com/
Amplified Phones, TV Listening Devices, Ringer/Flasher,
Alerting Notification System, Telephone Amplifier. (As-Pac,
estab 2004, empl 15, sales $3,000,000, cert: NMSDC)

9021 Tempest Telecom Solutions, LLC
      136 W Canon Perdido Ste 100 Santa Barbara, CA
      93101
      (805) 879-4800 Elda Rudd VP Mktg
      Fax: (805) 690-3345
      Email: tempestsupplier@tempesttelecom.com
      Website: www.tempesttelecom.com/
New & refurbished networking equipment. (Woman/
White, estab 2005, empl 160, sales , cert: CPUC, WBENC)

9022 Unified TelData Inc.
      425 2nd St San Francisco, CA 94107
      (415) 977-7031 Eric Clauss GSS
      Fax: (415) 977-7231
      Email: eclauss@utdi.com
      Website: www.utdi.com
Communications solutionsL Avaya, Cisco & Nortel
hardware & services. (Woman/White, estab 1981, empl
50, sales $10,000,000, cert: CPUC, 8(a))

9023 Universal Network Development Corp.
      2555 Third St Ste 112 Sacramento, CA 95818
      (916) 475-1200 Cinthia Larkin Kazee President
      Fax: (916) 475-1202
      Email: undc@undc.com
      Website: www.undc.com
Telecommunication eng, fiber optic & copper splicing,
installation & repair, project mgmt, CAD drafting.
(Woman/As-Pac, estab 1980, empl 75, sales $4,234,625,
cert: CPUC)

9024 WP Electric & Communications, Inc.
      14198 Albers Way   Chino, CA 91710
      (909) 606-3510 Debra Rooney President
      Fax: (909) 606-3515
      Email: debi@wpelectric.com
      Website: www.wpelectric.com
Electrical & network cabling services. (Woman/White,
estab 1975, empl 45, sales $7,800,000, cert: CPUC,
WBENC)

Colorado

9025 M.R. Research
      8003 S Corona Way   Centennial, CO 80122
      (303) 795-4353 Madeline K. Reilly President
      Fax: (303) 794-2639
      Email: rkreilly@aol.com
      Website: www.m-r-research.com
Applied research, electronic design & telecommunications components for satellites, base stations & mobile
wireless systems. (Woman/Hisp, estab 2010, empl 4,
sales $334,900, cert: NMSDC)

9026 Sage Telecommunications Corp.
      6700 Race St   Denver, CO 80229
      (303) 227-0986 Betsy Hoaglund President
      Fax: (303) 227-0991
      Email: betsy.hoaglund@sagecom.net
      Website: www.sagecom.net
Engineers, build & maintain fiber optic, cable & other
networks. (Woman/White, estab 1992, empl 90, sales
$10,000,000, cert: State)

9027 Tripwireless, Inc.
14401 E 33rd Place Ste A Aurora, CO 80011
(720) 361-4998 Kimberly Koch CEO
Fax: (484) 971-0110
Email: kym@tripwireless.com
Website: www.tripwireless.com
Network infrastructure equipment & services, cell sites, microwave, outside power plant, transmission, routers, data centers, de-commissioning, trenching, fiber, installation & preventative maintenance. (Woman/White, estab 2005, empl 6, sales $11,200,000, cert: WBENC)

Connecticut

9028 IQ Telcom, LLC dba IQ Telecom
78 Beaver Road Wethersfield, CT 06109
(860) 882-0500 Carol Guerra Director of Business Dev
Fax: (860) 882-0505
Email: carol.guerra@iqt360.com
Website: www.iqt360.com
Telecommunications expense: voice, data & wireless, audit, optimization, spend base lining, invoice processing, monthly reporting for cost allocation, vendor/carrier mgmt; contract negotiation, network design & optimization. (Woman/White, estab 2001, empl 35, sales $3,000,000, cert: State, WBENC)

9029 VisionPoint LLC
152 Rockwell Rd Newington, CT 06111
(860) 436-9673 Louise Mastroianni Acct Mgr
Fax: (860) 436-9790
Email: visionpointct@gmail.com
Website: www.visionpointllc.com
Technology acquisition, integration, design, installation, technical meeting support & service. (Woman/White, estab 2003, empl 24, sales $7,002,015, cert: WBENC)

District of Columbia

9030 MJS Communications LLC
1343 First St NW Washington, DC 20001
(888) 829-1658 Marlon Boykin President
Fax: (888) 829-1658
Email: mboykin@mjscommunications.biz
Website: www.mjscommunications.biz
Information technology, telecommunications services, structure cabling system, voice/data cabling, CCTV cabling, POS & wireless, CCTV, digital video recorders, Interior/exterior cameras, monitors, perimeter security. (AA, estab 2009, empl 2, sales $110,000, cert: State, City)

9031 National Fiber and Copper, Inc.
1701 Pennsylvania Avenue NW Ste 300 Washington, DC 20006
(202) 729-6339 Kimberly Valentine President
Fax: (301) 829-4978
Email: KimValentine@NationalFiberandCopper.com
Website: www.nationalfiberandcopper.com
Low-voltage communication installation & services, communications, structured cabling, fiber optics, network installation & management, VOIP, phone systems, security solutions, on-site & support services. (Woman/White, estab 1999, empl 10, sales $1,350,000, cert: City, WBENC, SDB)

9032 Tecknomic LLC
2322 First St NW Washington, DC 20001
(202) 829-2953 Dexter Spencer President
Fax: (202) 318-8996
Email: dspencer@tecknomic.com
Website: www.tecknomic.com
Emergency management & services training, information technology, wireless/wireline communications. (AA, estab 2003, empl 12, sales $391,000, cert: State, 8(a))

Florida

9033 Advanced IT Concepts, Inc.
1351 Sundial Point Winter Springs, FL 32708
(407) 914-2484 Gabriel Ruiz President
Fax: (321) 323-1376
Email: eve.maldonado@aitcinc.com
Website: www.aitcinc.com
Telecommunications & Information Technology services. (Hisp, estab 2006, empl 51, sales $24,860,693, cert: City, 8(a))

9034 Call One Inc
400 Imperial Blvd Cape Canaveral, FL 32920
(800) 749-3160 Jamie Henderson Acct Mgr
Fax: (321) 799-9222
Email: jhenderson@calloneonline.com
Website: www.calloneonline.com
Dist telecommunications equipment: audio video teleconferencing & headsets. (Woman/White, estab 1987, empl 80, sales $46,224,057, cert: WBENC)

9035 Clean Clean, Inc.
3580 NW 56th St, Ste 106C Fort Lauderdale, FL 33309
(954) 777-9555 Gary Plancher Sales Mgr
Fax: (954) 636-3883
Email: gplancher@cleancleaninc.com
Website: www.cleancleaninc.com
Telecommunications. (Woman/AA, estab 2004, empl 6, sales , cert: NMSDC)

9036 ClearTone Communications Inc.
840 Edgewood Ave S, Ste 209 Jacksonville, FL 32205
(904) 240-0490 Jerry Irizarry President
Fax: (904) 240-0984
Email: jerry@cleartonejax.com
Website: www.cleartonejax.com
Telecommunications, voice, data & structured cabling. (Hisp, estab 2007, empl 1, sales $35,000, cert: State)

9037 Data Stream Mobile Technologies Inc.
11521 Interchange Circle S Miramar, FL 33025
(954) 271-1240 Richardson Barnes New Business Devel
Fax:
Email: Rbarnes@dswltech.net
Website: www.dswltech.net/
Wireless communications, cable, twisted pair, & fiber optics. (AA, estab 1998, empl 42, sales , cert: State, NMSDC)

9038 Data Voice, Inc.
1900 S Harbor City Blvd, Ste 124   Melbourne, FL 32901
(321) 724-1231 Amanda Mktg Coord
Fax: (321) 409-5772
Email: amanda@data-voice.net
Website: www.data-voice.net
Telecommunications, electronic communications system, structured cabling, hardware, software, peripherals, electronic mfg. (AA, estab 1989, empl 40, sales $4,290,000, cert: State)

9039 FermiTron, Inc.
8129 Tumeric Ct   Orlando, FL 32817
(407) 513-2716 Guilford Cantave President
Fax: (877) 781-2345
Email: gcantave@fermitron.com
Website: www.fermitron.com
Commercial, industrial, medical & military/aerospace development; R&D, Analog & Digital Circuit Design, Firmware Development & Implementation, Schematic Capture, PCB Layout, RF, Wireless, Circuit Prototyping & Assembly. (AA, estab 2012, empl 1, sales $25,766, cert: State, NMSDC)

9040 Satya Acquisition Management, Inc. dba SAM, Inc.
3300 South OBT Ste 106 Orlando, FL 32839
(267) 973-4228 Bob Chopra President
Fax: (407) 656-0313
Email: bchopra@sam-inc.com
Website: www.sam-inc.com
Telecommunications, new site builds, antenna modifications, generator installations, microwave installations, temporary cell site installations, small cells & Distributed Antenna Systems. (As-Pac, estab 2006, empl 2, sales $350,000, cert: NMSDC)

9041 Sencommunications, Inc.
912 Chad Lane   Tampa, FL 33619
(813) 626-4404 Stacie Miller VP
Fax: (813) 621-2280
Email: gdumicich@sencomm.com
Website: www.sencomm.com
Provides telephone headsets, desksets, teleconferencing units, and other products. (Woman/White, estab 1989, empl 31, sales $15,728,924, cert: WBENC)

9042 Smith Corona/Comfort Telecommunications
1407 SE 47th Terr   Cape Coral, FL 33904
(800) 399-3224 Louise Bergen Sales
Fax: (239) 768-1218
Email: louise@comfortel.com
Website: www.comfortel.com
Mfr & dist telephone headsets & accessories. (Woman/White, estab 1985, empl 15, sales $5,000,000, cert: State)

9043 TSG Enterprises, LLC dba RadiusPoint
1211 StateRd436, Ste 295 Casselberry, FL 32707
(407) 661-6840 Sharon Watkins CEO
Fax:
Email: sales@radiuspoint.com
Website: www.radiuspoint.com
Telecommunications & utility invoices auditing, expense management & bill processing. (Woman/White, estab 1992, empl 42, sales , cert: WBENC)

9044 USA Telecom Solutions
2700 W Cypress Creek Rd Ste D100 Fort Lauderdale, FL 33309
(954) 970-0098 Charles Murphy President
Fax:
Email: Charles@usatelecomsolutions.com
Website: www.usatelecomsolutions.com
Telecommunications svcs & business technology. (AA, estab 2003, empl 5, sales $75,000, cert: NMSDC)

Georgia

9045 Agile Perspective
27 Edwin Pl   Atlanta, GA 30318
(917) 648-7544 Rae-Anne Alves
Fax: (415) 762-8390
Email: rae-anne.alves@anagileperspective.com
Website: www.anagileperspective.com
Telecommunication sourcing, cost reduction initiatives, strategic management, best practice benchmarking, technology integration. (Woman/AA/Hisp, estab 2012, empl 1, sales , cert: NMSDC, WBENC)

9046 Atlanta Communications Co.
1510 Huber St   Atlanta, GA 30318
(404) 875-9316 Carrie Davis Exec Asst
Fax: (404) 875-1691
Email: cdavis@atlantacomm.com
Website: www.atlantacomm.com
Dist, service, install, rent, site preparation & project management of two-way communications equipment. (Woman/AA, estab 1947, empl 43, sales , cert: WBENC)

9047 Concise, Inc.
191 Peachtree St, Ste 3300   Alanta, GA 30303
(404) 736-3669 David Johnson CEO
Fax: (678) 868-1802
Email: info@conciseinc.com
Website: www.conciseinc.com
Telecommunications svcs: network & telephone cabling, wireless networks, surveillance & security systems. (AA, estab 2003, empl 2, sales $560,000, cert: NMSDC, 8(a))

9048 Digicomm Systems, Inc.
3221 Hill St, Ste 103-B Duluth, GA 30096
(770) 497-8080 Undra Patrick VP Ops
Fax: (770) 497-0651
Email: management@digicommsystems.com
Website: www.digicommsystems.com
Telecommunication services: data center design & consulting, data network design & consulting, systems integration & installation, internal communications, low-voltage cabling, equipment relocation. (Woman/AA, estab 1988, empl 7, sales , cert: City, NMSDC)

9049 FamTeck, LLC
4484 Covington Hwy, Ste 105   Decatur, GA 30038
(404) 822-1117 Conrad Meertins CEO
Fax: (770) 593-8430
Email: cmeertins@famteck.com
Website: www.famteck.com
Develop solutions that provide optimal performance allowing you to do more with less.Core Competencies•Streamline IT Operations with Pre (AA, estab 2006, empl 7, sales , cert: NMSDC)

9050 HYPEFAN
3560 Morning Ivy Way   Suwanee, GA 30024
(404) 217-7933 Derrick Brown CEO
Fax: (888) 558-5742
Email: DS@HYPEFAN.COM
Website: www.hypefan.com
No Cheerstix! No Thunderstix! No foam hands! Bring the HYPE with HypeSticks . There is nothing quite like the HypeStick, with 6 distinct areas of real estate for cross-marketing opportunities, two faces on the main, two on the handle, a lanyard can be at (AA, estab 2004, empl 3, sales , cert: NMSDC)

9051 Litra Manufacturing Inc.
6733-A Jones Mill Ct   Norcross, GA 30092
(800) 445-4617 Skip York Sales Mgr
Fax: (770) 446-7032
Email: skipyork@litramfg.com
Website: www.litramfg.com
Mfr copper & pre-terminated fiber optic cable assemblies: coax, multipair copper cable assemblies, high strand fiber assemblies, single-mode, multi-mode, fiber jumpers, components & accessories. (Woman/White, estab 1986, empl 25, sales , cert: CPUC)

9052 Management Data Systems International, Inc. dba MDSI
6225 Shiloh Rd   Alpharetta, GA 30005
(1678) 455-2963 Krista Thompson CEO
Fax: (678) 947-1568
Email: krista.thompson@mdsiinc.com
Website: www.mdsiinc.com
Telecommunication & data communications products: data CPE & voice related (PBX) equipment, optical technologies, core routing, switching, OSP, transmission & transport devices. (Woman/White, estab 1900, empl 1, sales $75,000,000, cert: NMSDC, WBENC)

9053 Norris Sapp, Inc.
2469 Winshire Dr   Decatur, GA 30035
(770) 593-3762 Norris Sapp President
Fax: (770) 593-8430
Email: norrissapp@hotmail.com
Website: www.norrissappinc.com
Freight transportation : general supplies, construction, heavy equipment, building materials, hazardous materials, less than truckload, and courrier services. (AA, estab 1996, empl 3, sales $5,005,000, cert: State)

9054 North Georgia Telecom, Inc.
1755 Enterprise Dr Ste D Buford, GA 30518
(678) 482-0015 Tom McClure President
Fax: (678) 482-1973
Email: k.potts@ngtinc.com
Website: www.ngtinc.com
Install, deinstall, switching sales, asset mgmt. (Woman/White, estab 1994, empl 20, sales , cert: WBENC)

9055 ProComm Telecommunications, Inc.
1377 Business Center Dr   Conyers, GA 30094
(770) 760-8660 Keith Reardon VP of Ops
Fax: (770) 760-7470
Email: kreardon@procommtelecom.com
Website: www.procommtelecom.com
Installation, engineering & design telecommunications networks: wireless, fiber optics, digital cross connects, switch, multiplexer & channel bank, calibrate & repair test equipment. (Woman/White, estab 1989, empl 55, sales $7,000,000, cert: WBENC)

9056 Washington Communications Group LLC
6465 Hwy 85   Riverdale, GA 30274
(770) 991-3000 Stacy Washington President
Fax:
Email: washingtoncommunication@yahoo.com
Website: www.washingtoncommunication.com
Structured Network Cabling, Fiber Optic Installation, Single mode, Multimode, Fiber Optic Testing & Termina-tions, Voice/Data Network Installation, Business & VoIP Phone Systems, Patch panel installation & termination. (AA, estab 2013, empl 10, sales $190,000, cert: State)

Illinois

9057 Chicago Communications, LLC
200 W Spangler Ave   Elmhurst, IL 60126
(630) 832-3311 Lisa MacGillivray Mktg Dir
Fax: (630) 832-7599
Email: sales@chicomm.com
Website: www.chicomm.com
Dist, install & maintain communication equipment. (Woman/White, estab 2004, empl 68, sales $10,000,000, cert: State, WBENC)

9058 ClearSounds Communication
1743 Quincy Ave, Ste 155   Naperville, IL 60540
(866) 657-2855 Michelle Maher Dir of sales/Ops
Fax: (630) 654-9219
Email: michelle.maher@clearsounds.com
Website: www.clearsounds.com
Amplified phones, Bluetooth headsets, amplified neckloops, mobile accessories & listening systems for people with hearing loss and those looking for a remark-able listening experience. (Woman/White, estab 2004, empl 15, sales , cert: WBENC)

9059 CollinsEngineers, Inc.
123 N Wacker Dr, Ste 900   Chicago, IL 60606
(312) 704-9300 Janet Wackrow
Fax: (312) 704-9320
Email: jwackrow@collinsengr.com
Website: www.collinsengr.com
Collins Engineers, Inc. is a consulting engineering firm specializing in the planning, inspection, evaluation, design, and construction management of transportation facilities such as ports, airports, rail, roads, and bridges; and commercial facilities (Woman/White, estab 1979, empl 201, sales $37,600,000, cert: State)

9060   Integrated Installations, inc.
514 Pratt Ave N   Schaumburg, IL 60193
(847) 985-1170 Kate Novelle Contracts/Sales Dir
Fax: (847) 985-1177
Email: kate@i3install.com
Website: www.i3install.com
Telecom installation services, Wireless & Wireline Industries. (Woman/White, estab 2000, empl 25, sales $2,330,161, cert: State, CPUC, WBENC, NWBOC)

9061   Level-(1) Global Solutions, LLC
22 W Washington Ste 1500 Chicago, IL 60602
(312) 202-3300 Thomas McElroy CEO
Fax: (312) 202-3310
Email: tdm@level-1.com
Website: www.level-1.com
Infrastructure solutions: office technology & data ctr facilities, IDF/telecom infrastructure, UPS power protection, emergency generator power, HVAC enviromental systems, fire protection, security & access control, CATV & LAN/WAN video surveillance. (AA, estab 2001, empl 12, sales $1,800,000, cert: City)

9062   Phoenix Business Solutions LLC
12543 S Laramie Ave   Alsip, IL 60803
(708) 388-1330 Peggy Hrindak CEO
Fax: (708) 388-1446
Email: phrindak@getpbsnow.com
Website: www.getpbsnow.com
Design, install & maintain telecom & data systems. (Woman/White, estab 2000, empl 35, sales $5,853,538, cert: WBENC)

9063   Raptor Industries, Inc.
1602 N Park Dr   Mount Prospect, IL 60056
(708) 417-9190 Anthony Kalama
Fax: (847) 768-1701
Email: gkalama@raptorindustriesinc.com
Website: www.raptorindustriesinc.com
Voice, Data, Fiber Optic & CATV Cable Installation and Certification, Copper and Fiber Optic Splicing, Audio/Visual, CCTV, Riser Management, Intercom. (As-Pac, estab 2013, empl 5, sales $162,554, cert: State, City, NMSDC)

9064   SI Tech Inc.
1101 N Raddant Rd   Batavia, IL 60510
(630) 761-3640 Ramesh Sheth (ramesh@sitech-bitdriver.com) President
Fax: (630) 761-3644
Email: admin@sitech-bitdriver.com
Website: www.sitech-bitdriver.com
Mfr & develop fiber optic communications products. (As-Ind, estab 1984, empl 20, sales , cert: NMSDC)

9065   TelePlus, Inc.
724 Racquet Club Dr   Addison, IL 60101
(630) 543-3066 Mike Warda Sales Mgr
Fax: (630) 543-3075
Email: mwarda@telepluscom.com
Website: www.telepluscom.com
Voice/data low voltage cabling systems, electrical, paging systems, CCTV, Nortel BCM and Norstar telephone systems. (Woman/White, estab 1986, empl 56, sales $6,250,000, cert: City, WBENC)

9066   The Northridge Group, Inc.
9700 W Higgins Rd Ste 600 Rosemont, IL 60018
(847) 692-7053 Katie Francis Director of Mktg
Fax: (847) 518-2263
Email: katie.francis@northridgegroup.com
Website: www.northridgegroup.com
Telecommunications. (Woman/AA/Hisp, estab 1999, empl 82, sales $10,000,000, cert: City, WBENC)

9067   Viadata1 Communications Inc.
3118 Elder Ln   Franklin Park, IL 60131
(773) 593-1346 Eddie Villariny President
Fax: (773) 496-8151
Email: edvilla@viadata1.net
Website: www.viadata1.net
Low Voltage Cabling, Fiber Optic, CCTV, Card Access, Wireless Access Points, Network Data Center design & Installation, Data & Voice Cabling. Computer equipment installation. (Hisp, estab 2008, empl 4, sales $800,000, cert: NMSDC)

Indiana

9068   C-CAT, Inc.
1726 W. 15th St   Indianapolis, IN 46202
(317) 568-2899 Kristi Johnson President
Fax: (317) 568-3718
Email: kjohnson@c-cat.com
Website: www.c-cat.com
Infrastructure & low-voltage cabling services: video, voice & data, security/safety cabling & Cat 5E, Cat-6 & fiber-optic wiring systems. (Woman/White, estab 2001, empl 15, sales $4,000,000, cert: WBENC)

9069   Dixon Phone Place, Inc.
5335 N Tacoma Ave, Ste 3   Indianapolis, IN 46220
(317) 251-3504 Juli Fritsch
Fax: (317) 251-8240
Email: dixonphoneplace1@att.net
Website: www.dixonphone.com
Telephone equipment, plantronics telephone & computer headsets, cell phone corded & bluetooth headsets, corded & wireless headsets, telephone parts, line & handset cords, polycom conference equipment, cordless phones, business phones. (Woman/White, estab 1983, empl 2, sales , cert: State, City)

9070   Summitline Industries, Inc.
7822 Opportunity Dr   Fort Wayne, IN 46825
(260) 490-2213 Stan Richard President
Fax: (260) 490-2313
Email: stan.richard@summitline.com
Website: www.Summitline.com
Telecommunications, supply chain solutions, material mgmt, warehousing & kit fulfillment. (AA, estab 1983, empl 20, sales $15,000,000, cert: NMSDC, CPUC)

9071 Telamon Corporation
1000 E 116th St   Carmel, IN 46032
(317) 818-6757 John L. Weeks Director of Sales
Fax: (317) 818-6666
Email: john.weeks@telamon.com
Website: www.telamon.com
Mfr & dist voice & data communications products: cables
& connectors to cstmrs specs, modular voice & data
accessories; engineering & install telecommunication
equip. (As-Pac, estab 1984, empl 1100, sales
$782,000,000, cert: NMSDC)

Kentucky

9072 Strategic Communications, LLC
310 Evergreen Rd, Ste 100   Louisville, KY 40243
(502) 493-7234 Kathy Mills CEO
Fax: (502) 657-6512
Email: info@yourstrategic.com
Website: www.yourstrategic.com
Voice, data & communications solutions: structured
cabling, telecommunications systems, carrier services,
security/alarm, data communications products & services.
(Woman/Nat Ame/As-Pac, estab 1993, empl 40, sales
$4,200,000, cert: NMSDC, WBENC)

Louisiana

9073 New Orleans Teleport, Inc.
201 B Travis St   Lafayette, LA 70503
(337) 704-0550 Barbara Lamont President
Fax: (337) 704-0552
Email: customercare@callsplus.net
Website:
Telecommunications, audio & video productions, SAT
trucks, call center, satellite transmission, voice, video,
data, internet, broadcast services. (Woman/AA, estab
1987, empl 33, sales , cert: State)

9074 TCN
1016 Harimaw Court E   Metairie, LA 70001
(504) 838-9600 Victor Hess Sales Mgr
Fax:
Email: vhess@executonesystems.com
Website: www.executonesystems.com
Furnish & install wiring, digital & Voice over IP telephone
systems, Overhead Paging, Music, Sound, Masking, School
Intercom & Mass Notification Systems. (Woman/White,
estab 1947, empl 28, sales $357,531,124, cert: WBENC)

Massachusetts

9075 C.E. Communication Services, Inc.
25 Grove St   Franklin, MA 02038
(866) 966-1555 Bruce Baltz
Fax: (508) 528-2570
Email: bruceb@cecommunication.com
Website: www.cecommunication.com/
Dist telecommuncations & networking products. (Woman/
White, estab 1998, empl 10, sales , cert: State)

9076 C4Cable, LLC
257 Scadding St   Taunton, MA 02780
(508) 944-5573 Carole Derringer Principal
Fax:
Email: caroled@c4cable.com
Website: www.c4cable.com
Dist Telecommunications & Data Networking Products:
Bulk Copper & Fiber Optic Cables, Patch Panels, Enclo-
sures, Copper & Fiber Patch Cords, Pre-Terminated MTP/
MPO Backplane Fiber Cables & Cassettes, Free Standing
Racks. (Woman/White, estab 2014, empl 2, sales
$10,000, cert: State, WBENC)

9077 Coastal Telecommunications Inc.
35 Main St Ste 116C   Topsfield, MA 01983
(978) 744-4900 Angela Gill President
Fax: (978) 744-9802
Email: angela@gocti.us
Website: www.gocti.us
Low Voltage Cabling, Voice & Data Structured Cabling,
Communication System Design, Installation & Mainte-
nance, Voice & Network Equipment & Service Solutions.
(Woman/AA, estab 1990, empl 5, sales $250,000, cert:
State, WBENC)

Maryland

9078 Crest Telecom, Inc.
P.O. Box 410   Bel Air, MD 21014
(410) 420-1044 Tammy Halley Principal
Fax:
Email: tammy.halley@cresttelecom.com
Website: www.cresttelecom.com
Wireless & wireline telecommunication products:
routers, microwave radios, central service units, cross
connect panels, fuse alarm panels, racks, fiber manage-
ment systems, filters, duplexers, cable, channel element
cards, etc. (Woman, estab 2007, empl 10, sales , cert:
WBENC)

9079 G TECH Contracting, LLC
8008 Dorado Terr   Brandywine, MD 20613
(240) 793-8908 Agustin Nunez CEO
Fax: (301) 627-6037
Email: anunez@gtechcontracting.com
Website: www.gtechcontracting.com
Integrated security, voice/data communications,
residential & small commercial A/V systems. (Hisp, estab
2013, empl 5, sales $1,200,000, cert: 8(a))

9080 KSC Consultant Services LLC
18216 Darnell Dr   Olney, MD 20832
(240) 389-1882 Kimberlie Manns Owner
Fax: (240) 389-1957
Email: kmanns@kscconsultants.net
Website: www.kscconsultants.net
Telecommunication consulting & infrastructure wiring,
designing & installing voice & data infrastructure/
cabling, troubleshoot, repair, testing & installing voice &
data lines, rewiring, installing & replacing jacks.
(Woman/AA, estab 2004, empl 2, sales $60,000, cert:
State, SDB)

9081 SRL TotalSource LLC
      83 High St Ste B Waldorf, MD 20602
      (301) 885-0097 John Johnson COO
      Fax:
      Email: jjohnson@srltotalsource.com
      Website: www.srltotalsource.com/
Wireless Telecommunications Carriers, Data Processing,
Hosting, and Related Services. (AA, estab 2011, empl 6,
sales $589,253, cert: State, 8(a))

Michigan

9082 Cellular Solutions Signal Enhancing Specialists
      2737 N Meridian Rd   Sanford, MI 48657
      (989) 687-4023 Devin O'Neil Acct Exec
      Fax: (989) 687-4029
      Email: aimeek@cellularsolutions.com
      Website: www.cellularsolutions.com
Cellular signal enhancement throughout homes, vehicles,
small commercial buildings & large facilities. (Woman/
White, estab 2004, empl 13, sales $8,000,000, cert:
WBENC)

9083 Communication Brokers, Inc.
      437 44th St SW   Grand Rapid, MI 49548
      (616) 301-3733 Denise Booms-Pepin CEO
      Fax: (616) 301-3773
      Email: jemelander@cbitelecom.com
      Website: www.cbitelecom.com
Telecommunications consulting services, data, local &
wireless communications analysis. (Woman/White, estab
1991, empl 30, sales $3,250,000, cert: WBENC)

9084 Prima Communications, Inc.
      P.O. Box 338   Schoolcraft, MI 49087
      (269) 679-3800 Charlotte Hubbard Owner
      Fax: (269) 679-3804
      Email: primaadmin@voyager.net
      Website: www.primacommunications.com
Technical communications. (Woman/White, estab 1991,
empl 25, sales , cert: WBENC)

Minnesota

9085 Building Systems Solutions, Inc.
      1250 E Moore Lake Dr Ste 230 Fridley, MN 55432
      (763) 502-1515 Megan Beaver CEO
      Fax:
      Email: Meganb@bssmn.com
      Website: www.buildingsystemssolutions.com
Design commercial audio & communications systems:
paging, sound masking, music & emergency notification
systems. (Woman/White, estab 2003, empl 2, sales
$200,145, cert: State)

9086 Seacom
      2150 Third St Ste 6&14 White Bear Lake, MN 55110
      (651) 653-3200 Sandee Ebbott President
      Fax: (651) 653-4453
      Email: sandee_ebbott@seacomllc.com
      Website: www.seacomllc.com
Telecommunication solutions: legacy equipment, VoIP,
video conferencing, voice & data cabling, electrical cabling,
data networking & security systems. (Woman/White, estab
2010, empl 7, sales $1,600,000, cert: WBENC)

9087 Technology Management Corporation
      4790 Lakeway Terr   Shorewood, MN 55331
      (952) 470-0217 Brendon O'Brien Dir Business Dev
      Fax: (952) 470-0153
      Email: bobrien@tmc-1.com
      Website: www.tmc-1.com
Telecommunications consulting: cable design; phone
system design; phone, data, & internet network design,
data/server room design. telecommunications audit &
contract negotiation. (Woman/White, estab 1988, empl
12, sales $788,715, cert: State, City, WBENC, NWBOC)

9088 TRiCOM Communications
      1301 Corporate Center Dr., Ste 160   Eagan, MN
      55121
      (651) 686-9000 Diane Evans President
      Fax: (651) 686-9999
      Email: diane.evans@tricom1.com
      Website: www.tricom1.com
Design & install structured cabling: copper & fiber
optics, Data Centers, Telecom Rooms, Equipment
Rooms, Outside Plant Construction, Security Cameras,
Card Access Systems, In-Building Wireless Distributed
Antenna Systems (DAS). (Woman/White, estab 1989,
empl 20, sales $2,250,000, cert: State, City, WBENC)

Missouri

9089 American Cable Products LLC
      4 Forest Park Circle Dr   Lake St. Louis, MO 63367
      (636) 265-6602 Richard Politte Managing Partner
      Fax: (636) 265-2166
      Email: rmpolitte@amercp.net
      Website: www.americancableproducts.com
Install voice & data cable, routers, switches, modems,
racks, wireless equipment, fiber optic cable & hardware,
PA & video systems, arial cable & single mode fiber &
buried drop service, trenching, boring, etc. (As-Pac,
estab 2002, empl 25, sales $12,000,000, cert: State, City,
CPUC, SDB)

9090 Capital International Communications, LLC
      8762 St. Charles Rock Rd Ste 101 St. Louis, MO
      63021
      (314) 707-7717 Dr. Don Cook, Sr. CEO
      Fax: (636) 227-2114
      Email: dr_doncook@capintlcomm.com
      Website: www.capintlcomm.com
Dist telecommunications, electrical & industrial supplies,
public payphone services provider. (AA, estab 2002,
empl 3, sales $2,700,000, cert: State)

9091 eTech Solutons, LLC
      1813 Zumbehl Rd   Saint Charles, MO 63303
      (314) 282-8318 Sara Hagemeyer Owner
      Fax: (866) 899-7206
      Email: brad@etechstl.com
      Website: www.etechstl.com
Cellphone supplier, Cellphone repair, Tablet repair,
Tablet supplier, small electronic repair - ie micro solder-
ing, laptop repair, Cellphone & tablet data recovery,
Chipoff data recovery, jtag data recovery, cellphone
forensics. (Woman/White, estab 2012, empl 2, sales
$530,000, cert: WBENC)

North Carolina

9092 Atlantic Communication Products, Inc.
4324 Barringer Dr Ste. 112 Charlotte, NC 28217
(704) 676-5880 Winn Pray President
Fax: (704) 676-5885
Email: w.pray@goacp.com
Website: www.goacp.com
Resell voice & data products, installation & maintenance services of wire & cabling. (Hisp, estab 1997, empl 10, sales $900,000, cert: NMSDC)

9093 Carolina Liquid Chemistries
313 Gallimore Dairy Rd Greensboro, NC 27409
(336) 722-8910 Patricia Shugart
Fax: (336) 722-8915
Email: pgshugart@carolinachemistries.com
Website: www.carolinachemistries.com
Clinical chemistry analyzers and reagents. Also available-reagents for use on Olympus, Beckman Synchron analyzers. General chemistry and urine drug testing. nationwide network of factory trained service engineers and applications specialists. (Woman/White, estab 1994, empl 65, sales $21,000,000, cert: State)

9094 Lexair Electronics Sales Corp.
4807-B Koger Blvd Greensboro, NC 27407
(336) 294-5300 Jackie McCaw Acct Exec
Fax: (336) 294-5305
Email: jackiemccaw@lexairsales.com
Website: www.lexairsales.com
Dist communications equipment: headsets, telephones, audio conferencing equipment & peripherals. (Woman/White, estab 1998, empl 15, sales $6,550,000, cert: WBENC)

9095 Quantum Technology Group, LLC
P.O. Box 762 Cornelius, NC 28031
(800) 918-3510 Adam Jones President
Fax: (800) 928-5430
Email: amjones@qtg-llc.com
Website: www.qtg-llc.com
Information technology, cabling infrastructure, IP converged telephony systems, voice mail solutions, access control, paging systems, mass notification systems, video teleconferencing, CATV. (AA, estab 2007, empl 16, sales $338,454, cert: 8(a))

9096 Team Telecom, LLC
220 N. Main St Lexington, NC 27292
(888) 305-4772 Jennifer Sturgell
Fax: (336) 236-9960
Email: jsturgell@teamtelecom.net
Website: www.teamtelecom.net
Dist new, surplus & refurbished telecommunications equipment. (Woman/AA, estab 2005, empl 8, sales $3,050,000, cert: State, NMSDC, WBENC)

9097 TelExpress
406 Interstate Dr Archdale, NC 27263
(434) 990-2644 Tabitha Brock Sr scct Mgr
Fax: (434) 990-2643
Email: tabitha@telexpressinc.com
Website: www.telexpressinc.com
Mfr central office, wireless,cable, fiber & DC power equipment. (Woman/White, estab 1992, empl 35, sales $5,785,800, cert: WBENC)

9098 Walker and Associates, Inc.
7129 Old Hwy 52 P.O. Box 1029 Welcome, NC 27374
(336) 731-5236 Jane Brightwell VP Business Dev
Fax: (336) 731-3089
Email: governcon@walkerfirst.com
Website: www.walkerfirst.com
Dist data & telecommunication equip, material mgmt & installation. (Woman/White, estab 1970, empl 120, sales , cert: CPUC)

Nebraska

9099 Mills Marketing & TeleServices, LLC
P.O. Box 8500 Omaha, NE 68108
(402) 707-5654 Lee Mills CEO
Fax: (402) 561-6481
Email: teleservices.leemills@usa.net
Website:
Outsourcing, local & long distance telephone service, bilingual VoIP customer contact center, 50 seats. (AA, estab 1990, empl 57, sales , cert: State)

New Jersey

9100 D.M. Radio Service Corp.
45 Perry St Chester, NJ 07930
(908) 879-2525 Sandy Drysdale President
Fax: (908) 879-2322
Email: sdrysdale@csiradio.com
Website: www.csiradio.com
Dist two-way radio communications equipment, design/ build service, supply & support for radio systems, Emergency Call Boxes, BDA & DAS systems. (Woman/ White, estab 1968, empl 6, sales $700,000, cert: State)

9101 e.comm Technologies
11 Melanie Ln East Hanover, NJ 07936
(973) 503-5814 Chuck Tarantino global Acct Mgr
Fax: (973) 739-0083
Email: ctarantino@ecommt.com
Website: www.ecommtechnologies.com
Avaya's Radvision video conferencing, contact center, call recording, speech access, predictive dialers, wireless solutions, video conferencing both room to room & desktop to desktop. (Woman, estab 1999, empl 20, sales $6,622,113, cert: State)

9102 Kane Communications LLC
572 Whitehead Rd Ste 201 Trenton, NJ 08619
(609) 586-8800 Bob Coyle Dir Business Dev
Fax: (609) 586-8855
Email: bcoyle@kanecomm.com
Website: www.kanecomm.com
Voice & data, sound & secuirty, audio & video, building automation, inside & outside plant copper & fiber systems. (Woman/White, estab 2003, empl 46, sales $4,600,000, cert: State)

9103   Spectrotel, Inc.
       3535 Route 66, Building 7   Neptune, NJ 07753
       (732) 345-7936 Rob Adams Premier Acct Specialist
       Fax:
       Email: radams@spectrotel.com
       Website: www.spectrotel.com
Dedicated Voice Services, Business Calling Services (POTs),
VoIP Services, Conferencing Services, Managed Services,
Network Monitoring, Managed Security, Cyber Security,
SD-WAN, Dedicated Network Services, Dedicated Internet
Access, Virtual Network Svcs. (Hisp, estab 1997, empl 130,
sales $78,000,000, cert: NMSDC)

9104   The Seideman Company
       4 Canterbury Ct   Marlton, NJ 08053
       (856) 988-0117 Patricia Seideman Owner
       Fax: (856) 983-6690
       Email: pseideman@aol.com
       Website: www.seidemancompany.com
Telecommunications & data networking services. (Woman/
White, estab 1991, empl 2, sales $156,382, cert: WBENC)

9105   TRAK Communications, Inc.
       710 Tennant Rd Ste 101   Manalapan, NJ 07726
       (732) 786-1355 Randi Smaldone President
       Fax:
       Email: rsmaldone@trakcommunications.com
       Website: www.trakcommunications.com
Telecommunications Billing Audit & Consulting Services,
Contract Negotations, contract compliance audits, wireless
audits & optimizations, Bid Management Services, Vendor
Management, Telecom Expense Management. (Woman/
White, estab 1999, empl 2, sales $338,371, cert: WBENC)

New York

9106   Annese & Associates, Inc.
       4781 Route 5 W   Herkimer, NY 13350
       (315) 849-9194 Yvonne Annese LoRe VP Corp
       projects
       Fax: (315) 453-4575
       Email: yannese@annese.com
       Website: www.annese.com
Design, install & maintain IP telephony, wireless, voice &
data networks, remote monitoring, 24 x 7 maintenance,
security. (Woman/White, estab 1970, empl 94, sales
$53,000,010, cert: State)

9107   Coranet Corp.
       2 Washington St Ste 701   New York, NY 10004
       (212) 635-2770 Michael Madigan Acct Exec
       Fax: (212) 635-2775
       Email: mmadigan@coranet.com
       Website: www.coranet.com
VoIP convergence solutions, data networking, project
mgmt, video networking, structured cabling systems,
mobility & wireless solutions, installation & maintenance,
IP audits, call center applications, billing audits, e-collabo-
ration. (Woman/White, estab 1987, empl 85, sales
$63,000,000, cert: State, WBENC)

9108   HAVE, Inc.
       309 Power Ave   Hudson, NY 12534
       (518) 828-2000 Lowell Stringer Sales
       Fax: (518) 828-2008
       Email: lstringer@haveinc.com
       Website: www.haveinc.com
Custom audio/video/data cable assemblies, dist bulk
cable, connectors, tools & accessories. (Woman/White,
estab 1977, empl 18, sales $3,120,541, cert: City)

9109   Information Transport Solutions Inc.
       3204 Route 22   Patterson, NY 12563
       (855) 472-7701 Laura Donelan President
       Fax: (917) 423-0417
       Email: ladonelan@4yourits.com
       Website: www.4yourITS.com
Wireless & structured cabling: wifi, DAS, AV, Access
Control & Sound Masking. (Woman/White, estab 2001,
empl 5, sales $796,000, cert: WBENC)

9110   Pivotel LLC
       6066 State Hwy 12   Norwich, NY 13815
       (607) 334-7400 Ronald Martin Jr Tech Sales Eng
       Fax: (607) 336-2904
       Email: ron.martin@pivotelonline.com
       Website: www.pivotelonline.com
Communications & network wiring: AC/DC & fiber optic
cabling & terminations. (Woman/White, estab 2001,
empl 30, sales $200,000, cert: WBENC)

9111   Reliance Communications, LLC
       555 Wireless Blvd   Hauppauge, NY 11788
       (631) 952-4800 Jeanne Healey VP Mktg
       Fax: (631) 240-8339
       Email: jeanne.healey@reliance.us
       Website: www.reliance.us
Dist wireless communications handsets & accessories.
(As-Ind, estab 2005, empl 290, sales $715,079,538, cert:
NMSDC)

9112   Saia Communications, Inc.
       100 Stradtman St   Buffalo, NY 14206
       (716) 892-2900 Cheryl Kirchmeyer Sales
       Fax: (716) 892-2983
       Email: cheryl.kirchmeyer@saiacomm.com
       Website: www.saiacomm.com
Motorola two-way radio products. (Woman/White,
estab 1980, empl 25, sales $5,000,000, cert: State)

9113   Sintel Satellite Services
       373 Nesconset Hwy # 133 Hauppauge, NY 11788
       (212) 202-0678 Sanjay Singhal COO
       Fax: (212) 504-8297
       Email: sanjay@sintelsat.com
       Website: www.sintelsat.com
Satellite communication & terrestrial telecom solutions,
infrastructure rebuilding, IP connectivity, fiber, microwave & satellite, Vsat, broadcasting & IT solutions.
(Woman/As-Ind, estab 1997, empl 30, sales $1,132,000,
cert: State, City)

Ohio

9114　Cincinnati Cable Technology
1177 W 8th St, Ste A　Cincinnati, OH 45203
(513) 579-1888　Sheryl Yeager President
Fax: (513) 579-9888
Email: sherylyeager@ccablet.com
Website: www.ccablet.com
Structured cabling, fiber optics, coax network infrastructure, wireless networks, security solutions, IP based door entrance, IP security cameras, audio/visual system design. (Woman, estab 2010, empl 7, sales $1,500,000, cert: WBENC)

9115　ClarkTel Communications Corp.
1661 Copley Rd　Akron, OH 44320
(330) 869-8657　Terence Clark CEO
Fax: (330) 869-8515
Email: tclark@clarktel.net
Website: www.clarktelcommunications.com
Design, installation, warranty & service business telephone systems: NEC, Nortel, Mitel, Toshiba, Panasonic, Comdial, Vodavi Sprint, voice/data cable. (AA, estab 1996, empl 10, sales $885,445, cert: State)

9116　Fine Line Communications Inc.
P.O. Box 91　Aurora, OH 44202
(330) 562-0731　Barbara Hoover President
Fax: (330) 562-0821
Email: bhoover@finelinecomm.com
Website: www.finelinecomm.com
Design, intall & maintain voice & data network systems. (Woman/White, estab 1981, empl 25, sales $4,421,242, cert: State, WBENC)

9117　Net Activity
9535 Midwest Ave #114　Garfield Heights, OH 44125
(216) 503-5150　John Marion CFO
Fax: (216) 503-5148
Email: info@netactivity.us
Website: www.netactivity.us
Hardware & Software reseller, VoIP Phone Systems; hosted & on-site, Connectivity; dedicated data & voice communication, Cloud Back-up; proprietary infrastructure & Microsoft Azure, Remote network & hardware managed services. (As-Ind, estab 2002, empl 11, sales $1,377,695, cert: 8(a), SDB)

9118　Ohio Cables, LLC
5288 Dietrich Ave　Orient, OH 43146
(614) 991-0404　Amanda (Mindy) Dimel Owner
Fax: (614) 319-6446
Email: mindy@ohiocables.com
Website: www.ohiocables.com
Mfr & dist cables. (Woman/White, estab 2008, empl 2, sales $950,000, cert: City)

9119　One Source Mobile
1066 Reading Rd　Mason, OH 45040
(513) 870-9300　Amy Baumhower President
Fax: (513) 870-0695
Email: abaumhower@onesourcemobile.com
Website: www.onesourcemobile.com
Telecommunication services: wireless cell phone accessories, bluetooth items, car chargers & holsters etc. (Woman/White, estab 2005, empl 10, sales $925,000, cert: WBENC)

9120　SpeakSpace, LLC
600 Superior Ave., Ste 1300 P.O. Box 451280
Westlake 44145 Cleveland, OH 44114
(440) 263-1919　Becky Behan Managing Partner
Fax: (440) 899-1263
Email: beckybehan@speakspace.com
Website: www.speakspace.com
Teleconferencing services/conference calling, audio, web & video conferencing services. (Woman/White, estab 1999, empl 5, sales $850,000, cert: WBENC)

9121　The Fishel Company
1810 Arlingate Ln　Columbus, OH 43228
(614) 274-8100　Dinah Dennen Mktg Coord
Fax: (614) 274-6794
Email: DLDennen@teamfishel.com
Website: www.teamfishel.com
Underground & aerial utility construction; inside & outside installation of fiber optic, copper, coaxial cabling; right of way services; structured cabling; network electronic installation; conduit construction & maintenance (Woman/White, estab 1936, empl 1525, sales $189,316,151, cert: WBENC)

9122　US Communications and Electric
4933 Neo Pkwy　Garfield Heights, OH 44128
(216) 478-0810　Jim Connole COO
Fax: (216) 478-0829
Email: jconnole@uscande.com
Website: www.uscande.com
Technology-based communications cabling systems, design & install outdoor copper systems, horizontal copper cabling solutions. (Woman/White, estab 1996, empl 78, sales $17,000,000, cert: State, City, WBENC)

Oklahoma

9123　Ford Audio-Video Systems, Inc.
4800 W Interstate 40　Oklahoma City, OK 73128
(214) 600-5433　Uriel Carrasco Acct Mgr
Fax:
Email: carru@fordav.com
Website: www.fordav.com
Design, mfr & install audio video communication equip: conference & board rooms, network operation ctrs, war rooms, command & control rooms, emergency response ctrs, video conferencing, media streaming, educational & training facilities. (Woman/As-Pac/Hisp, estab 1973, empl 450, sales $200,000,000, cert: WBENC)

9124　Leader Communications Inc.
4600 S.E. 29th St. Ste 300　Del City, OK 73115
(405) 670-9000　Thomas L. Long Ops Mgr
Fax: (405) 670-8561
Email: tom.long@lcibest.com
Website: www.lcibest.com
System engineering, program mgmt, telecommunications & logistics mgmt, antenna installs, telephone installations, coummincations facilities operations & maintenance. (AA, estab 1999, empl 259, sales , cert: State)

Oregon

9125   Tribal One Broadband Technologies, LLC
3201 Tremont   North Bend, OR 97459
(541) 756-3899   Karl Kennedy Mgr
Fax: (541) 266-0377
Email: kkennedy@orcacomm.com
Website:
Metro ethernet & TDM transport, internet access, LAN support, colocation. (Nat Ame, estab 2002, empl 5, sales , cert: State)

Pennsylvania

9126   Clark Resources, Inc.
321 N Front St   Harrisburg, PA 17101
(717) 230-8861   Christa Anderson
Fax: (717) 230-8870
Email: ChristaAnderson@fclarkresources.com
Website: www.fclarkresources.com
Inbound and outbound telephone services. Call Center/ Customer Support Center. (AA, estab 2002, empl 180, sales $6,000,000, cert: State, NMSDC)

9127   Enterprise Cable Group, Inc.
805 W Fifth St   Lansdale, PA 19446
(215) 361-4114   Susan Walters WBE Dir
Fax: (215) 361-4118
Email: susan.walters@enterprisecablegroup.com
Website: www.enterprisecablegroup.com
Communication & computer cable systems design & installation. (Woman/White, estab 2001, empl 20, sales $2,420,839, cert: State)

9128   Fiber Business Solutions Inc.
P.O. Box 103   Fairview Village, PA 19409
(484) 576-0876   Cindy Gallo President
Fax: (610) 539-2295
Email: cgallo@fbsginc.com
Website:
Fiber Optic Cable Placement & Splicing, Copper Cable Placement & Splicing, Right of Way & Permit Acquisition Services, Engineering & Design Services, CAD & As-Built Services, Project Management Services. (Woman/White, estab 2004, empl 8, sales $1,300,000, cert: WBENC, 8(a))

9129   MobileStrat, Inc.
642 Cowpath Rd, Ste 390   Lansdale, PA 19446
(215) 237-3874   Larry Blackshear CEO
Fax: (215) 261-6031
Email: lblackshear@mobilestrat.com
Website: www.mobilestrat.com
Wireless, cellular, voice & data, gap analysis, billing management, WiFi site surveys
wire line, WAN design, WiFi security. (AA, estab 2004, empl 18, sales , cert: NMSDC)

Puerto Rico

9130   B&B Communications Group
220 Plaza Western Auto PMB-370 Ste 101   Trujillo Alto, PR 00976
(787) 760-2698   Benjamin Bravo Sales
Fax: (787) 755-8778
Email: bbravo@bbcorp.net
Website: www.bbcorp.net
Communications, Fiber Optics, UPS, Cabling, Network, Cat-5e, cat-6, cat-6a, telecomm, telecommunications, voice, data, IP phones, power supply, design, site survey, training, service (Woman/Hisp, estab 2014, empl 5, sales , cert: State, NMSDC)

South Carolina

9131   Globenet Telecommunications, LLC
210 Titus Ln   Pineville, SC 29468
(828) 320-3291   Cavid Middleton President
Fax: (888) 558-5742
Email: dlmiddleton@charter.net
Website: www.globenetusa.net
Low voltage system integration, install security devices & fiber optic cable. (AA, estab 2007, empl 32, sales $14,500,000, cert: CPUC)

Tennessee

9132   Ashaun
5100 Poplar Ave Ste 726   Memphis, TN 38137
(901) 312-7025   Anthony Tate CEO
Fax: (901) 312-7039
Email: atate@ashaun.com
Website: www.ashaun.com
Call center services. (AA, estab 2000, empl 35, sales $1,300,000, cert: State, NMSDC)

9133   Madison Group Inc.
6551 Stage Oaks Dr. Ste 1   Bartlett, TN 38134
(901) 791-4116   martha pitts VP
Fax: (901) 791-4129
Email: martha.pitts@madisong.com
Website: www.madisong.com
Dist telecommunication products; central office integra- tion, switching, transport, carrier, access, data, power; kitting, cable assemblies, material mgmt. (Woman/ White, estab 1991, empl 9, sales $3,500,000, cert: State, CPUC, WBENC)

9134   Power & Telephone Supply Co,
2673 Yale Ave   Memphis, TN 38112
(800) 238-7514   Annmarie Templeton Natl Acct Mgr
Fax: (901) 320-3084
Email: annmarie.templeton@ptsupply.com
Website: www.ptsupply.com
Communications products. (Woman/White, estab 1963, empl 350, sales , cert: State, City, CPUC, WBENC)

9135 Tel-XL
5462 McGill Memphis, TN 38120
(866) 848-3595 Linda Hawkins President
Fax: (901) 767-6564
Email: lhawkins@tel-xl.com
Website: www.tel-xl.com
Dist new & refurb telecom equip, systems, accessories. (Woman/White, estab 2002, empl 1, sales , cert: WBENC)

9136 Walker Warren Communications
155 S Mendenhall Rd Memphis, TN 38117
(901) 337-6326 Carol Walker Principal
Fax: (901) 624-7997
Email: carol@ww911.net
Website: www.ww911.net
Radio Systems /Infrastructure, 2-way radios, mobile (vehicles), Telephone Systems, GPS, Logger Recorders, Computer Aided Dispatch Systems, Redundancy analysis for critical applications. (Woman/AA, estab 2016, empl 2, sales $33,000, cert: City, WBENC)

Texas

9137 Aerowave Technologies
875A N Mill St Lewisville, TX 75057
(214) 222-2376 Gina Gardenhire President
Fax: (214) 222-2010
Email: ginag@aerowavetech.com
Website: www.aerowavetech.com
Two-way radio communications, batteries, chargers & belt-clips. (Woman/White, estab 2000, empl 17, sales $3,000,000, cert: State, WBENC)

9138 Austin Tele-Services Partners, LP dba Genesis ATS
4209 S Industrial Dr Ste 300 Austin, TX 78744
(512) 437-3041 Patrick Manning VP Business Dev
Fax: (512) 329-8091
Email: pmanning@genesis-ats.com
Website: www.genesis-ats.com
IT, Networking, Telecommunications & Computer related equipment & services. (Hisp, estab 2003, empl 45, sales $25,000,000, cert: State, NMSDC)

9139 Clearvue Networks, LLC
100 E Main St Ste 201 Round Rock, TX 78664
(512) 861-5319 Shanna Schmidt Admin Asst
Fax: (512) 300-0207
Email: shanna.schmidt@clearvuenetworks.com
Website: www.clearvuenetworks.com
Business networking solutions, work station installs/configs, server installs/configs, network assessments, wireless installs, telecom services, voice/data/fiber cabling, alarm/surveillance systems, card access security systems. (Hisp, estab 2011, empl 9, sales , cert: State)

9140 Continental Wireless, Inc.
10455 Vista Park Rd Dallas, TX 75238
(972) 926-7443 Rita Weber President
Fax: (972) 707-0145
Email: sales@cntlwire.com
Website: www.cntlwire.com
Wireless communication, dist & rent two way radios. (Woman/White, estab 2000, empl 30, sales $8,018,559, cert: State, WBENC)

9141 Crystal Application Software Services, LLC
3201 Cherry Ridge Dr Ste B-218 San Antonio, TX 78230
(210) 698-2410 Veronica Vela Acct Mgr
Fax: (210) 698-2410
Email: veronica.vela@cnetcable.com
Website: www.cnetcable.com
Design-build telecommunications, low voltage cabling, wireless & access points, voice & data networks, security cameras, audio & visual, fiber optics, phone systems & microwave. (Hisp, estab 2014, empl 10, sales , cert: State)

9142 Diamond P Enterprises, Inc.
P.O. Box 483 Brownwood, TX 76804
(325) 643-5629 Domingo Perez President
Fax: (325) 646-5653
Email: info@diamondpenterprises.com
Website: www.diamondpenterprises.com
Cable Placing Materials, Closures/Splicing Materials, Copper Cable, Cutting & Distribution, Corrugated Products, Fiber Optic Cable, Cutting & Distribution. (Hisp, estab 1995, empl 87, sales $60,309,360, cert: NMSDC, CPUC)

9143 Dynamic Voice Data
4403 Greenbriar Dr Stafford, TX 77477
(800) 838-5070 Tina Greenfield Business Dev Mgr
Fax: (800) 852-5338
Email: tgreenfield@dvd-inc.com
Website: www.dvd-inc.com
Mfr custom OEM products using injection mould technology, interconnect products & telephone parts, harnesses & power supplies. (Woman/As-Pac, estab 1993, empl 15, sales $11,300,000, cert: State, NMSDC)

9144 Genesis Networks Integration Services, LLC
600 N. Loop 1604 East San Antonio, TX 78232
(210) 489-6600 Nicole Nash supplier diversity asst
Fax: (210) 489-6612
Email: nicole.nash@genesisnet.com
Website: www.genesisnet.com
Provides engineering, furnish & installation services for data & phone networks, network management architecture, implementation & support, information systems security management, server & virtualization management. (Hisp, estab 2010, empl 77, sales $16,526,811, cert: State, NMSDC)

9145 JG Haney & Associates LLC
9711 Haven Crossing Court Houston, TX 77065
(281) 653-2441 Joyce Haney CEO
Fax: (281) 653-2134
Email: haney@jghaneyassociates.com
Website: www.jghaneyassociates.com
Telecommunications Services, IT products & services, data acquisition systems, telemetry products, circuit card assemblies, shipping containers, test set cases, special nonmetallic, preformed packing material & acquisition program management. (Woman/AA, estab 2011, empl 2, sales $300,000, cert: 8(a))

9146   KMM Telecommunications
       4051 N Hwy 121 Ste 400 Grapevine, TX 76051
       (844) 566-8488 Sarah McNab Director, HR & Mktg
       Fax:
       Email: s.mcnab@kmmcorp.net
       Website: www.kmmcorp.net
Sourcing products & services; contract management;
inventory planning & procurement; material management
& deployment; material warehousing; material fulfillment,
3PL services; last-mile staging services; reverse logistics.
(Woman/White, estab 1991, empl 130, sales
$892,823,959, cert: CPUC, WBENC)

9147   Matrix Telecommunication Services, Inc.
       11127 Shady Trail, Ste 103 Ste 515 Dallas, TX 75229
       (972) 438-7161 Steve Mitchell President
       Fax: (972) 438-7495
       Email: Connectsys@aol.com
       Website: www.Cableinstalling.com
Install & maintain voice, data & fiber structured cabling
systems. (Woman/AA, estab 1984, empl 13, sales
$1,000,000, cert: State)

9148   Micro-Design, Inc.
       10210 Monroe Dr   Dallas, TX 75229
       (972) 488-8725 Douglas Ramsey VP of Ops
       Fax: (972) 488-8724
       Email: dramsey@levelcon.com
       Website: www.micro-design.com
Remote telemetry solutions: wireless, WiFi, cellular &
satellite, engineering & solutions for CNG pump stations &
infrastructure. (Woman, estab 1984, empl 15, sales
$2,000,000, cert: State)

9149   On Air Solutions, Inc.
       5415 Chevy Chase Houston, TX 77056
       (713) 961-3990 Becky Martin Dir
       Fax: (832) 615-3062
       Email: bmartin@onairsol.com
       Website: www.onairsol.com
Wireless infrastructure projects & telecommunications
svcs: in-building wireless system engineering & installation, tower erection/construction; site maintenance, site
acquisition, project management. (Woman/White, estab
2003, empl 6, sales $56,000, cert: State)

9150   Operational Technologies Corporation
       4100 NW Loop 410, Ste 23 San Antonio, TX 78229
       (210) 731-0000 Louisa Alaniz Sr Mgr. Client Services
       Fax: (210) 785-3458
       Email: louisa.alaniz@otcorp.com
       Website: www.otcorp.com
Fulfillment center kitting, warehousing & distribution,
telecommunications & communications engineering &
installation, environmental svcs. (Hisp, estab 1986, empl
70, sales $15,192,216, cert: State, NMSDC, CPUC)

9151   Premier Paging, Inc.
       12220 Murphy Rd Ste F Stafford, TX 77477
       (281) 575-8500 Lea Bogle President
       Fax: (281) 575-8577
       Email: lea.bogle@premierwirelesstx.com
       Website: www.premierwirelesstx.com
Wireless equipment, accessories & service, GPS tracking
for fleets & assets, electronic forms. (Woman/White, estab
1993, empl 17, sales $2,500,000, cert: State, WBENC)

9152   Ransor, Inc.
       7055 Pipestone   Schertz, TX 78154
       (210) 651-6451 Randy Sorrell VP
       Fax: (210) 651-6214
       Email: randy@ransor.com
       Website: www.ransor.com
Install communication equipment & maintains mono-
poles, guyed & self supporting towers, tower construction, tower modifications & tower maintenance.
(Woman/White, estab 1987, empl 7, sales $984,000,
cert: State)

9153   Sky Communications, Inc.
       6101 Long Prairie Rd, Ste 744-162   Flower
       Mound, TX 75028
       (214) 789-5090 Tom Kincannon Exec VP
       Fax: (972) 539-6928
       Email: Tom.Kincannon@skycomglobal.com
       Website: www.skycomglobal.com
Telecommunications services, engineering, design,
implementation & managed services, unified communications, VOIP, call center & project management. (AA,
estab 1995, empl 13, sales $1,735,567, cert: State,
NMSDC)

9154   Superior Fiber & Data Services Inc.
       10907 Shady Trail, Ste 103   Dallas, TX 75220
       (214) 357-5679 Jerri Strong Acct Mgr
       Fax: (214) 357-0705
       Email: jstrong@sfdcabling.com
       Website: www.sfdcabling.com
Communications cabling: voice, data, fiber. (Woman/
White, estab 1998, empl 26, sales $5,200,000, cert:
State)

9155   Telecom Electric Supply Company
       1304 Capital Ave   Plano, TX 75074
       (972) 422-0012 Bill Hargraves Sales Exec
       Fax: (972) 422-0467
       Email: bill@tes.com
       Website: www.tes85.com
Dist electric, utility, construction & telecommunication
supplies. (AA, estab 1985, empl 16, sales $22,900,000,
cert: State, NMSDC)

9156   Teltech Communications, LLC
       1621 W. Crosby Road Ste 112 Carrollton, TX
       75006
       (972) 466-0480 Lisa Hanlon Managing Partner
       Fax: (972) 466-0484
       Email: lisa@ttcsales.com
       Website: www.teltech.com
Network infrastructure equipment, wireless, wireline,
asset & inventory management services. (Woman/
White, estab 1999, empl 17, sales $35,300,000, cert:
State, NMSDC, WBENC)

9157   The Wilkins Group, Inc.
       1710 Firman Dr, Ste 200 Richardson, TX 75081
       (972) 479-1090 ConTrenia McKinzie Cameron VP
       Administration
       Fax: (972) 479-1099
       Email: trenia@wilkins.com
       Website: www.wilkins.com
Telecommunications services, equipment installation,
voice, video & data systems. (Woman/AA, estab 1986,
empl 30, sales $10,990,000, cert: State, NMSDC)

Virginia

9158 Opterna-AM Inc.
44901 Falcon Pl Ste 116 Sterling, VA 20166
(571) 294-7652 Matt Onojafe Dir Govt Contracting
Fax: (703) 803-8313
Email: matt.onojafe@opterna.com
Website: www.opterna.com
Fiber optic products & solutions, fiber optic communication solutions. (As-Ind, estab 1994, empl 17, sales $10,000,000, cert: NMSDC)

9159 Secured Network Solutions, Inc.
929 Ventures Way Ste 113 Chesapeake, VA 23320
(757) 819-7647 Alphonzo Barney President
Fax: (888) 785-8447
Email: team@teamsns.com
Website: www.eamsns.com
Telecommunications & information technology: cabling, design, install, fiber optics single/multi-strand, fiber fusion & splicing, LAN/WAN/wireless network engineering, drafting & information systems security. (AA, estab 2006, empl 11, sales , cert: State)

9160 Shore Communications, Inc.
600 N Witchduck Rd, Ste 106   Virginia Beach, VA 23462
(757) 468-0855 Laura Castner President
Fax:
Email: Lcastner@shorecomusa.com
Website: www.shorecomusa.com
Engineering, design, installation & testing structured cabling systems, telephone & paging systems, including adds, moves or changes to existing systems. (Woman/White, estab 1995, empl 28, sales , cert: State)

9161 Simba Enterprises LLC
21 Fort Evans Rd, Ste F Leesburg, VA 20176
(703) 782-4042 Ali Sajjad CEO
Fax:
Email: asajjad@simbacom.net
Website: www.simbacom.net
Satellite-based telecommunications & information technology solutions worldwide. (As-Ind, estab 2005, empl 10, sales $3,500,000, cert: State)

9162 TEKCONNX
608 Westwood Office Park   Fredericksburg, VA 22401
(703) 635-4439 Kevin Wlliams CEO
Fax:
Email: KEVINW@TEKCONNX.COM
Website: www.tekconnx.com
Interactive Audio Visual (IAVT) Solutions & Integration, A/V Telepresence Conferencing (HW & SW), Design/Build Interactive Audio Visual Solutions, Command & Control Centers, Wireless Video/Audio Solutions. (AA, estab 2013, empl 3, sales $850,000, cert: State, NMSDC)

9163 Roadswest Construction Inc.
307 N Olympic Ave, Ste 209 P.O. Box 263 Arlington, WA 98223
(360) 403-8782 Kirby Lundberg VP
Fax: (360) 474-1749
Email: RoadsWestInc@verizon.net
Website: www.RoadsWestInc.com
Dist, service & install voice & data wiring & audio/vidio systems. (Nat Ame, estab 1987, empl 30, sales $873,949, cert: State)

Washington

9164 SurgiMark, Inc.
1703 Creekside Loop Ste 110 Yakima, WA 98902
(509) 965-1911 Barbara Yarger President
Fax: (509) 965-4852
Email: custserv@surgimark.com
Website: www.surgimark.com
SurgiMark's VIA-GUARD® line of disposable surgical suction tips features a unique blend of industry-leading performance, inventory consolidation, and infection control for every hospital operating room and outpatient surgery center, land or sea. With qua (Woman/White, estab 1987, empl 5, sales , cert: State)

Wisconsin

9165 1Prospect Technologies, LLC
P.O. Box 1045   Rhinelander, WI 54501
(715) 369-1119 Brad Kowieski Dir of Business Develop
Fax: (715) 369-4719
Email: info@1prospect.com
Website: www.oneprospect.com
Design & build flexible cabling infrastructure supporting multiple voice, data, video & multimedia systems. (Nat Ame, estab 2000, empl 33, sales $10,400,000, cert: State)

9166 Onyx Communication
11016 N Mequon Square Dr   Milwaukee, WI 53092
(262) 236-0648 Jess Ferguson Owner
Fax: (262) 236-4181
Email: regferg@aol.com
Website:
Voice & data cable installation, ethernet hubs switches & routers, phone systems, wireless bridges & service furniture. (AA, estab 1999, empl 5, sales , cert: State)

```
┌─────────────────────────────────────────────┐
│                   TEXTILES                    │
│   Includes thread, trimmings, woven and nonwoven │
│   material manfucaturers. NAICS Code 31       │
└─────────────────────────────────────────────┘
```

California

9167 A & R Tarpaulins Inc.
16246 Valley Blvd   Fontana, CA 92335
(909) 829-4444 Didi Truong Aerospace Project Mgr
Fax:
Email: didi@artech2000.com
Website: www.artech2000.com
We specialize in MLI (Multilayer insulation), Acoustic blankets, payload fairing, sound barriers, high temperture insulation & protection, thermal radiational heat control, EMI & RFI shielding, antistatic & security enclosures. (Woman/As-Pac, estab 1976, empl 49, sales $4,500,000, cert: CPUC)

9168 H & A Enterprise
530 N Baldwin Park Blvd   City Of Industry, CA 91746
(909) 714-3960 Huma Latif Owner
Fax: (213) 291-3041
Email: ahuma@hotmail.com
Website: www.hnaenterprise.com
Dist textile goods, socks, towels, bar mops . (Woman/As-Ind, estab 2012, empl 1, sales , cert: NMSDC)

9169 International Textile and Apparel, Inc.
1875 Century Park E Ste 1040 Los Angeles, CA 90067
(310) 556-8088 Shoaib Kothawala CEO
Fax: (310) 556-3671
Email: nbaresabidia@intlinen.com
Website: www.donothaveone.com
Mfr towels, bar mop towels & shop towels, weaving dye & finish, cut & sew. (As-Pac, estab 1983, empl 15, sales , cert: NMSDC)

Georgia

9170 PBR Inc.
335 Athena Dr   Athens, GA 30601
(706) 354-3700 Palak Patel Exec Business Devel
Fax: (706) 354-3737
Email: palak@skaps.com
Website: www.skaps.com
Fabricate Geosynthetic & nonwoven drainage products, produce polypropylene & polyester needle-punched nonwoven geotextiles from 2 to 32 ounces per square yard. (As-Pac, estab 1995, empl 250, sales $390,000,000, cert: NMSDC)

9171 Unitex International Inc.
680 Satellite Blvd, NW Ste 200 Suwanee, GA 30024
(770) 232-0060 Anwer Shakoor Director
Fax: (770) 232-0038
Email: a.shakoor@unitexonline.com
Website: www.unitexonline.com
Textile & fabric finishing. (As-Ind, estab 1990, empl 27, sales $44,000,000, cert: NMSDC)

Illinois

9172 R&R Textile Mills Inc.
1101 N Lombard Rd   Lombard, IL 60148
(630) 424-8000 Rajan Barad COO
Fax:
Email: rbarad@rrtextilemills.com
Website: www.rrtextilemills.com
Mfr & dist textile products. (As-Ind, estab 1988, empl 40, sales $9,800,000, cert: NMSDC)

Maine

9173 Auburn Manufacturing, Inc.
P.O. Box 220   Mechanic Falls, ME 04256
(207) 345-8771 Kathie M Leonard CEO
Fax: (207) 345-3380
Email: kleonard@auburnmfg.com
Website: www.auburnmfg.com
Design & mfr heat-resistant textiles for MRO applications. (Woman/Hisp, estab 1979, empl 49, sales $10,300,000, cert: WBENC)

Michigan

9174 National Manufacturing, Inc.
25426 Ryan Rd   Warren, MI 48091
(586) 755-8983 Paul Cano Sales
Fax:
Email: Paul.cano@nationalmanufacturinginc.com
Website: www.nationalmanufacturinginc.com
Leather & vinyl wrapping of steering wheels, pull handles, shift knobs, arm rests, bolsters. We as well can sew by hand or machine. Which we have done emergency kits, jack bags, utility bags, tools bags for the automotive industry. (Hisp, estab 1964, empl 32, sales , cert: NMSDC)

Missouri

9175 Phoenix Textile Corporation
21 Commerce Dr   OFallon, MO 63366
(314) 291-2151 Scott Rodgers VP of Sales
Fax: (314) 291-7169
Email: srodgers@phoenixtextile.com
Website: www.phoenixtextile.com
Reusable institutional textiles & interior products. (Woman, estab 1983, empl 100, sales , cert: WBENC)

North Carolina

9176 Kilop USA, Inc.
4100 Mendenhall Oaks Pkwy   High Point, NC 27265
(336) 402-5979 Christine Chen President
Fax: (336) 885-4110
Email: cchen@kilopusa.com
Website: www.kilopusa.com
Global nonwoven and textile raw material supply chain services. (Woman/As-Pac, estab , empl 1, sales , cert: NMSDC, WBENC)

New Jersey

9177   Centryco Inc.
       300 W Broad St   Burlington, NJ 08016
       (609) 386-6448 Mary Gordon President
       Fax: (609) 386-6739
       Email: mtg@centryco.com
       Website: www.centryco.com
Mfr point of operation barriers for machinery & equipment: bellows, way covers, telescoping covers, flat bellows
& screens, spring guards/covers. (Woman/White, estab
1949, empl 32, sales $3,910,958, cert: WBENC)

9178   Offray Specialty Narrow Fabrics, Inc.
       4 Essex Ave Ste 403 Bernardsville, NJ 07924
       (908) 879-3636 Denise A. Offray CEO
       Fax:
       Email: doffray@osnf.com
       Website: www.osnf.com
Engineer & mfr quality, high performance, innovative
narrow fabric textiles, weave specialty branded yarns.
(Woman/White, estab 1921, empl 45, sales $8,674,420,
cert: State)

New York

9179   Sigmatex, Inc
       551 Fifth Ave, Ste 1110   New York, NY 10176
       (212) 593-0934 Marcia Rodriguez GM
       Fax: (212) 888-3859
       Email: Mrodriguez@sigmatexlanier.com
       Website: www.sigmatexlanier.com
Mfr institutional textile products: terry towels, sheets &
pillowcases, table linens, kitchen linen, aprons, blankets.
(Woman/As-Ind, estab 1976, empl 25, sales $18,155,425,
cert: State)

Ohio

9180   Casco Manufacturing Solutions, Inc.
       3107 Spring Grove Ave   Cincinnati, OH 45225
       (513) 681-0003 David Stewart Business Dev Mgr
       Fax: (513) 853-3605
       Email: dstewart@cascosolutions.com
       Website: www.cascosolutions.com
Design & mfr fabric or textiles products. (Woman/White,
estab 1959, empl 52, sales $5,300,000, cert: WBENC)

South Carolina

9181   Calitex International
       106 Thousand Oaks Ct   Summerville, SC 29485
       (864) 278-2621 John Sylvester President
       Fax: (864) 278-2619
       Email: john@calitexintl.com
       Website: www.calitex.us
Dist Industrial Fabrics, Cotton Canvas, Single fill duck,
Numbered Ducks, Army Duck, Twill, cotton & Polycotton
Blends, Treated fabric for Tarps, Tents, Tipis, Boat covers.
(Woman/As-Ind, estab 2005, empl 2, sales $1,500,000,
cert: NMSDC)

9182   MVP Textiles and Apparel, Inc.
       1031 Le Grand Blvd   Charleston, SC 29492
       (843) 216-8380 Mary Propes CEO
       Fax: (843) 216-8386
       Email: marypropes@mvpgroupint.com
       Website: www.mvptextiles.com
Mfr textiles. (Woman/White, estab 2005, empl 15, sales
$16,800,000, cert: WBENC)

Texas

9183   Orr Textile Co., Inc.
       4777 Blalock   Houston, TX 77041
       (713) 939-7788 Hilary Orr VP sales
       Fax: (713) 939-7714
       Email: hilary@orrtextile.com
       Website: www.orrtextile.com
Dist sheets, towels, blankets, pillows, bath mats, robes,
slippers, kitchen towels, bar mops, table linen, napkins,
janitorial supplies, mops, buckets and wringers, mattress
pads, pillow slips, pool towels, spa linen, chef wear, etc.
(Woman/White, estab 1967, empl 11, sales , cert:
WBENC)

Washington

9184   Lancs Industries Holdings, LLC
       12704 NE 124th St, Bldg 36   Kirkland, WA 98034
       (425) 823-6634 Raymond Suarez
       Fax: (425) 820-6784
       Email: rsuarez@lancsindustries.com
       Website: www.lancsindustries.com
Mfr custom lead wool blankets, glovebags, tents,
protective clothing, related shielding & containment
products & supplies for nuclear naval shipyards &
maintenance facilities; nuclear remediation, decontamination, decommissioning & laboratory sites. (AA, estab
2010, empl 65, sales $6,000,000, cert: State)

Arizona

9185   El Sol Travel, Inc.
4500 S. Lakeshore Dr Ste 450 Tempe, AZ 85282
(480) 693-0218 Christine Davidson VP Business
Travel Solutions Strategist
Fax: (480) 894-9418
Email: cdavidson@elsoltravel.net
Website: www.elsoltravel.net
Full service travel agency. (Woman/White, estab 1986, empl 27, sales $213,395,700, cert: WBENC)

California

9186   Azzurro Travel, Inc.
4712 Admiralty Way #138 Marina Del Rey, CA 90292
(800) 835-8234 Chris Chappell Dir. of Business Dev
Fax: (888) 834-7114
Email: cchappell@azzurrotravel.com
Website: www.azzurrotravel.com
Full service travel agency. (Woman, estab 2008, empl 10, sales $1,476,418, cert: WBENC)

9187   Incentive Travel Inc.
311 Fourth Ave, Ste 617   San Diego, CA 92101
(619) 515-0880 Penny Wing President
Fax: (619) 231-1402
Email: penny@incentiveinc.com
Website: www.incentiveinc.com
Incentive & meeting planning, consulting, creating, promoting. (Woman/White, estab 1988, empl 14, sales $5,000,000, cert: WBENC)

9188   Pinnacle Travel Services, LLC
390 N Sepulveda Blvd #3100 El Segundo, CA 90245
(310) 343-4284 Bob Singh President
Fax: (310) 343-4234
Email: ptsbsingh@earthlink.net
Website: www.pinnaclecallsolutions.com
Full service travel agency. (Hisp, estab 1999, empl 150, sales $10,600,000, cert: NMSDC)

Florida

9189   Cruise.Com
255 E Dania Beach Blvd   Dania Be3ach, FL 33004
(954) 805-7810 Jessica Speirs Reg sales Director
Fax: (954) 266-6641
Email: jspeirs@cruise.com
Website: www.cruise.com
Leisure products: cruise, affinity revenue share program. (Woman/White, estab 2002, empl 200, sales , cert: WBENC)

9190   Landry & Kling, Inc.
1390 S Dixie Hwy   Coral Gables, FL 33146
(305) 661-1880 Cyndi Murphy VP Corporate
Planning
Fax: (305) 661-0977
Email: cmurphy@landrykling.com
Website: www.landrykling.com
Full service travel agency. (Woman/White, estab 1982, empl 24, sales $11,739,216, cert: WBENC)

Georgia

9191   Georgia International Travel, Inc.
6285 Barfield Rd Ste 150 Atlanta, GA 30328
(404) 851-9166 Vela McClam Mitchell CEO
Fax: (404) 851-9460
Email: corporatetravel@dt.com
Website: www.gitravel.com
Corporate travel management. (Woman/AA, estab 1984, empl 24, sales $21,000,000, cert: NMSDC)

Illinois

9192   Corporate Travel Consultants dba CorpTrav
450 E. 22nd St #100 Lombard, IL 60148
(630) 691-9100 Diversity Registrations
Fax: (630) 691-1088
Email: diversityregistrations@corptrav.com
Website: www.corptrav.com
Full service travel agency. (Woman/As-Pac/Hisp, estab 1976, empl 100, sales , cert: WBENC)

9193   Travelex International, Inc.
2500 W. Higgins Road   Hoffman Estates, IL 60169
(847) 882-0400 Ursula Pearson President
Fax: (847) 882-1212
Email: ursulap@travelexonline.com
Website: www.travelexonline.com
Full service travel agency, travel management. (Woman/White, estab 1992, empl 12, sales $725,435, cert: State, WBENC)

Kansas

9194   WingGate Travel, Inc.
8645 College Blvd, Ste 100 Overland Park, KS 66210
(913) 451-9200 Young Sexton CEO
Fax: (913) 451-9680
Email: young.sexton@winggatetravel.com
Website: www.winggatetravel.com
Full service travel management, online fulfillment, VIP executive travel & leisure travel services. (Woman/As-Pac, estab 1991, empl 38, sales $4,000,000, cert: NMSDC)

Massachusetts

9195 E&P Enterprise
One Maple St   Milford, MA 01757
(508) 488-1160 Kerin McKinnon SVP global
Fax: (508) 488-1560
Email: kerin.mckinnon@atlastravel.com
Website: www.atlastravel.com
Full service travel agency. (Woman, estab 1986, empl 138, sales $179,000,000, cert: WBENC)

Michigan

9196 American Center Travel
2451 W Stadium Blvd   Ann Arbor, MI 48103
(734) 827-1030 Sue Konarska Owner
Fax:
Email: sue.act@travelleaders.com
Website: www.travelleaders.com
Full service travel agency. (Woman/As-Ind, estab 1986, empl 4, sales , cert: NMSDC)

9197 Arcade Travel, Inc.
7879 Jackson Rd, Ste A   Ann Arbor, MI 48103
(734) 424-3996 Jim Kimble President
Fax: (734) 424-3999
Email: JKimble@BoersmaTravel.com
Website: www.boersmatravel.com
Full service travel agency. (AA, estab 1945, empl 23, sales $24,000,000, cert: NMSDC)

9198 Boersma Travel Services
3368 Washtenaw Ave   Ann Arbor, MI 48104
(734) 971-3148 James Kimble President
Fax: (734) 971-7294
Email: jkimble@boersmatravel.com
Website: www.boersmatravel.com
Full svc travel agency. (AA, estab 1945, empl 17, sales , cert: NMSDC)

9199 Departure Travel Management
344 N Old Woodward, Ste 100   Birmingham, MI 48011
(210) 913-8016 Maria Garcia Reg Acct Exec
Fax: (210) 366-0198
Email: maria@dtmdeparture.com
Website: www.dtmdeparture.com
Full service travel agency. (AA, estab 1999, empl 21, sales $29,000,000, cert: NMSDC, WBENC)

9200 Michigan East West Travel
400 Galleria Officentre, Ste 124   Southfield, MI 48034
(248) 352-2525 Joanne Rhee Owner
Fax:
Email: lime1225@gmail.com
Website:
Travel services. (Woman/As-Pac, estab 1999, empl 4, sales , cert: NMSDC)

9201 Motor City Travel
29566 Northwestern Hwy Ste 400 Southfield, MI 48034
(248) 799-0752 Tracey Campbell VP of Business Dev
Fax: (248) 799-0767
Email: tcampbell@MOTORCITYTRAVEL.COM
Website: www.MOTORCITYTRAVEL.COM
Full service travel agency. (Woman/AA, estab , empl 1, sales $12,095,618, cert: NMSDC)

9202 Sky Bird Travel & Tours Inc.
26500 Northwestern Hwy Ste 260 Southfield, MI 48076
(248) 727-1697 Arvin Shah President
Fax: (248) 372-4810
Email: info@skybirdtravel.com
Website: www.skybirdtravel.com
Full svc travel agency. (As-Ind, estab 1976, empl 52, sales , cert: NMSDC)

9203 The Travel Exchange
755 W Big Beaver Ste 100   Troy, MI 48084
(248) 269-9721 Pamela Edwartoski President
Fax: (248) 269-9769
Email: pam@travelexchangemi.com
Website: www.travelexchangemi.com
Full service travel agency. (Woman/White, estab 1976, empl 15, sales , cert: WBENC)

Minnesota

9204 Metro Travel
9298 Central Ave NE, Ste 222   Minneapolis, MN 55434
(763) 784-0560 Diane Cyrus CEO
Fax: (763) 784-0560
Email: dianecyrus@metrotravel.biz
Website: www.metrotravel.biz
Full service travel management. (As-Ind, estab 1982, empl 14, sales $890,000, cert: NMSDC)

North Carolina

9205 Aquila Travel & Events
2 Mill Creek Ct Greensboro, NC 27407
(336) 580-9796 Yolande Wainwright President
Fax: (336) 852-7431
Email: aquila@triad.rr.com
Website: www.eventsbyaquila.com
Corporate event & travel services. (Woman/AA, estab 2008, empl 1, sales , cert: State)

New York

9206 Town & Country Travel, Inc. DBA Travel Support Center
732 Pittsford Victor Rd   Pittsford, NY 14534
(585) 381-2850 Teresa Johnson CEO
Fax: (585) 381-1987
Email: teresa@towncountrytravel.com
Website: www.towncountrytravel.com
Full service travel agency. (Woman/White, estab 1984, empl 10, sales $7,499,798, cert: WBENC)

9207 Van Zile Travel
3540 Winton Place   Rochester, NY 14623
(585) 244-1100 Rebecca Mineo VP
Fax: (585) 244-3410
Email: katie@vanzile.com
Website: www.vanzile.com
Full service travel agency. (Woman/White, estab 1911, empl 45, sales $35,000,000, cert: WBENC)

Ohio

9208 ATG
7775 Walton Pkwy Ste 100 New Albany, OH 43054
(614) 901-4100 Paula Aquizap Sr Proposal Admin
Fax: (614) 901-3131
Email: paquizap@atg.travel
Website: www.atgtravel.com
Full service travel agency. (Woman/White, estab 1995, empl 3000, sales $593,580,200, cert: WBENC)

9209 Uniglobe Travel Designers
480 S Third St   Columbus, OH 43215
(614) 237-4488 Elizabeth Blount McCormick President
Fax: (614) 237-4516
Email: elizabethb@uniglobetd.com
Website: www.uniglobetraveldesigners.com
Full service travel agency. (Woman/AA, estab 1981, empl 36, sales $22,500,000, cert: City, NMSDC, WBENC)

Texas

9210 The Alamo Travel Group LP
8930 Wurzbach Rd   San Antonio, TX 78240
(210) 593-0084 Patricia Pliego Stout President
Fax: (210) 614-2448
Email: pstout@alamotravel.com
Website: www.alamotravel.com
Full service travel agency. (Woman/Hisp, estab 1990, empl 61, sales $111,000,000, cert: State, NMSDC, WBENC)

9211 The Travel Group LLC
5930 Royal Lane Ste E277 Dallas, TX 75230
(800) 514-9132 Greg Corley COO/CFO
Fax:
Email: info@thetravelgroup.travel
Website: www.thetravelgroup.travel
Full service travel agency. (Woman/As-Pac, estab 1986, empl 55, sales $15,000,000, cert: WBENC)

9212 Travel Acquisition Group, Ltd.
5700 W Plano Pkwy Ste 1400 Plano, TX 75093
(972) 422-4000 Steve McSwain Exec VP
Fax: (972) 422-2331
Email: steve@artatravel.com
Website: www.artatravel.com
Corporate travel, management & consulting. (Woman/White, estab 1980, empl 21, sales $30,500,000, cert: State, WBENC)

Virginia

9213 Omega World Travel
3102 Omega Office Park   Fairfax, VA 22031
(703) 359-0200 Jackie Olt Mktg and PR Specialist
Fax: (703) 359-8889
Email: jolt@owt.net
Website: www.OmegaTravel.com
Full service travel agency. (Woman/White, estab 1972, empl 475, sales $1,400,000,000, cert: WBENC)

Wisconsin

9214 JCCOB Smith Gardner Smith/Keystone AMEX Tvl Svs
16735 W Greenfield Ave   New Berlin, WI 53151
(262) 782-8750 Art Smith President
Fax: (262) 796-9914
Email: artkeystone@yahoo.com
Website: www.travelbykeystone.com
Full service travel agency. (AA, estab 1990, empl 12, sales $705,000, cert: NMSDC)

WOOD PRODUCTS
Produce videos (in studio or remote), TV shows, records, sound recordings, pre and post production services, talent arrangers, video distribution. NAICS Code 51

Alabama

9215   Containers Plus, Inc.
       3068 Alabama Hwy 53   Huntsville, AL 35806
       (256) 746-8002 Ajesh Khanijow Business Devel
       Fax:
       Email: akhanijow@containersplususa.com
       Website: www.containerplususa.com
Wooden crates, pallets, cardboard boxes, heat shrink, milspec packaging, packaging, RFID, UID, Mil-std-129, mil-std-2073, warehousing, logistics, hazmat packaging. (As-Pac, estab 2014, empl 5, sales $180,000, cert: NMSDC)

California

9216   Commercial Lumber & Pallet Company, Inc.
       135 Long Ln   City of Industry, CA 91746
       (626) 968-0631 Kathleen Dietrich VP
       Fax: (626) 330-9363
       Email: kathy@clcpallets.com
       Website:
Mfr & dist wooden pallets, skids & boxes. (Hisp, estab 1941, empl 100, sales $35,000,000, cert: CPUC)

9217   Cutter Lumber Products
       10 Rickenbacker Cir   Livermore, CA 94550
       (925) 443-5959 Todd Samuels GM
       Fax: (925) 443-0648
       Email: todd@cutterlumber.com
       Website: www.cutterlumber.com/
Mfr wooden pallets, wooden boxes. (As-Pac, estab 1965, empl 85, sales , cert: NMSDC, CPUC)

9218   Pallet Recovery Service Inc.
       P.O. Box 35   Westley, CA 95387
       (209) 839-1224 Lisa Kilcoyne President
       Fax: (209) 839-1164
       Email: lisa@palletrecoveryservice.com
       Website: www.palletrecoveryservice.com
Mfr new pallets, dist repairable pallets, remove unwanted scrap pallets. (Woman/White, estab 2007, empl 14, sales $596,456, cert: WBENC)

9219   TransPak
       2111 Abalone Ave   Torrance, CA 90501
       (424) 731-2301 Amber Griggs Business Dev Mgr
       Fax: (424) 731-2301
       Email: amber.griggs@transpak.com
       Website: www.transpak.com
Mfr wood crates & crating systems, custom packaging solutions, logistics, transportation & rigging services. (Woman/White, estab 1952, empl 800, sales $120,000,000, cert: WBENC)

9220   Winship Stake and Lath
       P.O. Box 909   Riverside, CA 92502
       (951) 682-8761 Lisa Winship Hankin President
       Fax: (951) 683-7442
       Email: lisa@winshipstakeandlath.com
       Website: www.winshipstakeandlath.com
Mfr & dist wood stakes & lath used in building, surveying & landscaping. (Woman/White, estab 1972, empl 8, sales $400,000, cert: CPUC)

Colorado

9221   Pro Pallet, Inc.
       920 E Collins   Eaton, CO 80615
       (970) 353-5311 Jean Kyne President
       Fax: (970) 454-3286
       Email: propallet@qwestoffice.net
       Website: www.propallet.net
New, recycled & new/recycled pallets, crates & boxes. (Woman/White, estab 1988, empl 45, sales $8,258,291, cert: WBENC)

Florida

9222   Pallet Consultants Corporation
       951 SW 12th Ave   Pompano Beach, FL 33069
       (954) 946-2212 Brian Groene President
       Fax: (954) 946-3661
       Email: brian.groene@palletconsultants.com
       Website: www.palletconsultants.com
Recycle wood pallets, mfr new & used pallets. (Hisp, estab 1996, empl 178, sales , cert: NMSDC)

Georgia

9223   A & B Pallets, Inc.
       6323 Riverview Rd   Mableton, GA 30126
       (404) 691-0567 Alberto Dominguez President
       Fax: (404) 691-1267
       Email: aandbpalletsinc@yahoo.com
       Website: www.aandbpalletsinc.com
Recycled, new & remanufactured pallets. (Hisp, estab 1997, empl 15, sales , cert: NMSDC)

9224   Pallet Central Enterprises, Inc.
       2B Lenox Pointe   Atlanta, GA 30324
       (404) 671-3494 Jameson Humber Asst Sales Mgr
       Fax: (404) 564-9715
       Email: Jhumber@palletcentralent.com
       Website: www.palletcentralent.com
Pallets. (Woman/As-Pac, estab 2005, empl 25, sales $26,000,000, cert: WBENC)

Illinois

9225 Harvey Pallets Inc.
      2200 W 139th St   Blue Island, IL 60406
      (708) 293-1831 Manuel Tavarez President
      Fax: (708) 293-1835
      Email: manuel@harveypallets.com
      Website: www.harveypallet.com
Mfr wood pallets, skids, crates & lumber. (Hisp, estab
1997, empl 50, sales $24,000,000, cert: NMSDC)

9226 Perma Treat of Illinois
      P.O. Box 99   Marion, IL 62959
      (618) 694-2898 Sara Bond CEO
      Fax: (618) 993-8680
      Email: sara@permatreatlumber.com
      Website: www.permatreatlumber.com
Wood Treated products: Utility Poles, Railroad Ties, Pallets,
Wood Quality Control Inspection, Rail Spur on site can ship
via rail or truck. (Woman/White, estab 1982, empl 7, sales
$330,866, cert: State, WBENC)

9227 Phoenix Woodworking Corporation
      P.O. Box 459   Woodstock, IL 60098
      (815) 338-9338 Sandra Pierce President
      Fax: (815) 338-9383
      Email: spierce@phoenixwoodworking.com
      Website: www.phoenixwoodworking.com
Custom & commercial cabinetry & casework, reception
centers, filing cabinets, wooden lockers & millwork,
custom desks & wooden store fixtures. (Woman/White,
estab 1996, empl 10, sales , cert: State, WBENC)

Maryland

9228 Timber Industries, LLC
      P.O. Box 6879   Towson, MD 21285
      (410) 823-8300 Danielle Sutphen Sales & Mktg
      Coord
      Fax: (410) 828-7892
      Email: danielle.sutphen@timberindustries.com
      Website: www.timberindustries.com
Custom & standard pallets, skids & crates. (Woman/White,
estab 2013, empl 6, sales $2,500,000, cert: State, WBENC)

Michigan

9229 J&G Pallets and Trucking, Inc.
      2971 Bellevue   Detroit, MI 48207
      (313) 921-0222 Les Lance Business Mgr
      Fax: (313) 921-0220
      Email: llance@jgpalletsandtrucking.com
      Website: www.jgpalletsandtrucking.com
Wood pallets, design custom pallets, recycle/reuse wood
pallets & wood pallet materials. (Woman/AA, estab 1992,
empl 22, sales $1,625,000, cert: NMSDC)

Minnesota

9230 R and L Woodcraft, Inc
      823 Industrial Park Dr SE   Lonsdale, MN 55046
      (507) 744-2318 Randall Rivers Business Devel
      Fax: (507) 744-2382
      Email: Randall@randlwoodcraft.com
      Website: www.randlwoodcraft.com
Mfr commercial millwork & casework: cabinets,
countertops, workstations, service counters, point of
service counters, tables, booths, upholstered seating,
running trim, trash recepticles, lockers & toilet partitions. (Woman/White, estab 1986, empl 22, sales
$3,600,000, cert: WBENC)

New Jersey

9231 Bett-A-Way Pallet Systems
      110 Sylvania Pl   South Plainfield, NJ 07080
      (800) 795-7255 Laura Vaccaro VP Business Dev
      Fax: (908) 222-2544
      Email: laura.vaccaro@bettaway.com
      Website: www.bettaway.com
Pallet management: sales, repairs, retrievals & inventory
management. (Woman/White, estab 1996, empl 15,
sales $20,986,000, cert: WBENC)

9232 US Lumber Inc.
      668 S Evergreen Ave   Woodbury Heights, NJ
      08097
      (856) 853-1770 Lita Abele CEO
      Fax: (856) 384-8351
      Email: lita@uslumberinc.com
      Website: www.uslumberinc.com
Mill & cut lumber & plywood. (Woman/As-Pac, estab
1974, empl 10, sales $5,093,000, cert: 8(a))

New York

9233 Ongweoweh Corp
      5 Barr Road   Ithaca, NY 14850
      (607) 266-7070 Alison Meyer Supplier Diversity
      Mgr
      Fax: (607) 266-7085
      Email: ameyer@ongweoweh.com
      Website: www.ongweoweh.com
Mfr & dist wooden pallets & specialty containers. (Nat
Ame, estab 1978, empl 96, sales $162,289,435, cert:
NMSDC)

Ohio

9234 LEFCO Worthington, LLC
18451 Euclid Ave   Cleveland, OH 44112
(216) 432-4422 Larry Fulton President
Fax: (216) 432-4424
Email: Larry.Fulton@LEFCOWorthington.com
Website: www.LEFCOWorthington.com
Dist wooden crates, OSB Boxes, custom pallets, sub-assembly & packaging services. (AA, estab 2003, empl 30, sales $3,600,000, cert: State, NMSDC)

9235 Prime WoodCraft
5755 Granger Rd Ste 900 Independence, OH 44131
(216) 588-9053 Michelle Morere Admin
Fax: (216) 588-9094
Email: michelle@primewoodcraft.com
Website: www.primewoodcraft.com
Warehousing, pallets, third party logistics. (As-Ind, estab 1997, empl 300, sales , cert: NMSDC)

9236 The Lima Pallet Company, Inc.
1470 Neubrecht Rd   Lima, OH 45801
(419) 229-5736 Tracie Sanchez President
Fax: (419) 229-6038
Email: tsanchez@limapallet.com
Website: www.limapallet.com
Mfr wood pallets & crates. ISP certified. (Woman/White, estab 1977, empl 49, sales $3,000,000, cert: WBENC)

9237 Wood Concepts
2401 Train Ave   Cleveland, OH 44113
(216) 579-0500 Jacquline Even President
Fax: (216) 579-0503
Email: jackieeven@att.net
Website: www.woodconceptsinc.com
Mfr & fabricate casework, millwork & cabinetry. (Woman/White, estab 1983, empl 8, sales $1,025,215, cert: City)

Puerto Rico

9238 Caribe Pallets and Packaging Corp.
P.O. Box 1886   Trujillo Alto, PR 00977
(787) 755-3622 Jose Bolivar VP
Fax: (787) 755-3636
Email: caribepallets@gmail.com
Website:
Mfr wood pallets. (Hisp, estab 1988, empl 18, sales , cert: NMSDC)

9239 Paleteras Unidas, Inc.
P M B 461 HC01 Box 29030 HC 1 Box 29030 PMB 461 CAGUAS, PR 00725
(787) 789-0110 Jorgelina González VP
Fax: (787) 789-0143
Email: jgonzalez@paleteras.net
Website:
Wooden pallets, skids & crates; pre-cut lumber, pallet Heat Treatment for ISPM15 Compliance, transportation, pallet recycling. (Hisp, estab 1967, empl 40, sales , cert: NMSDC)

Texas

9240 Austin Lumber Company, Inc.
630 S Washington St   La Grange, TX 78945
(512) 476-5534 Laura Culin President
Fax: (512) 476-8337
Email: info@austinlumbercompany.com
Website: www.austinlumbercompany.com
Construction mill. (Woman/White, estab 1929, empl 5, sales , cert: State, City)

Virginia

9241 Scott Pallets Inc
8660 Crowder St P.O. Box 657 Amelia Courthouse, VA 23002
(804) 561-2514 Jo Anne Webb President
Fax: (804) 561-2664
Email: joannew@tds.net
Website:
Mfr wooden pallets: standard warehouse & custom designed, cut stock, dunnage & double shredded bark mulch. (Woman/White, estab 1966, empl 16, sales $986,868, cert: WBENC)

A INDEX#

A INDEX#

A

Company	INDEX#
AMEX Investments, LLC	2177
AMG Engineering & Machining, Inc.	6523
AMI Risk Consultants	7425
Amick Brown LLC	4312
Amity Industries	6616
AMKO Trading	4169
Ammex Plastics	7072
Amneal Pharmaceuticals	6200
Amodu Engineering Solutions, LLC	2301
AMP Personnel Services, LLC	8840
AmPac Chemical Company Inc.	1987
Ampak Co., Inc.	1953
Ampcus Inc.	5637
Ampie Enterprises, Inc.	7309
AmpliTech Inc.	2846
Amreli Technology Solutions, LLC	5771
AMSYSCO, Inc.	4115
Amtec Molded Products, Inc.	7046
Amtech Electrocircuits, Inc.	2826
Amtek Consulting LLC	5490
Amzur Technologies, Inc.	4514
Ana M Fisher dba A & A Glove & Safety Co.	4249
Anacapa Technologies, Inc.	2188
Anahau Energy, LLC	1869
Analysts International Corporation (AIC)	4981
Analytic Partners, Inc.	8227
Analytiks International, Inc.	4982
Anchor Point Technology Resources, Inc	4757
Anchor Staffing Inc.	8562
Ancira	1803
Andavo Meetings & Incentives	7975
Andean Consulting Solutions International, LLC	7697
Anderson & Egan, Co.	3173
Anderson Advertising dba The Anderson Group	1242
Anderson Burton Construction	2189
Anderson Express, Inc.	4004, 6346
Anderson Productions Inc.	8948
Anderson Seal Inc.	4066
Andinas dba/ Inlingua Utah	8374
Andrew Associates, Inc.	1070
Andrew Vazquez Inc.	3561
Anesthesia Equipment Supply, Inc.	6264
Anew Technology Solutions, Inc.	8596
Anexa Biomedical, Inc.	6137
Angel Flight Marketing Services, Inc.	1115
Angel Screen Printing, Inc.	7393
AnITConsultant, LLC	4780
Annese & Associates, Inc.	9106
Anthony's Janitorial/Maintenance Service Ltd.	2132
Antina Promotions, LLC	1434
A-One, LLC	8824
Aonsoft International, Inc	4683
AP42	7916
Apac Chemical Corp.	1870
APB & Associates, Inc.	7784
APCO Worldwide Inc.	1075
Apex Beverage Equipment Distribution Group, LLC.	4239
Apex Computer Systems, Inc.	4313
Apex CoVantage	5638
Apex Impact Marketing LLC	8291
Apex Investigative Services Inc.	2462
Apex IT Services	4833
Apex Office Products, Inc.	6714
Apex Spring & Stamping	6433
APG Office Furnishings	3875
API Consultants	1698
APImaging, Inc.	7011, 7178
APISource, Inc.	1427
A-Plus Meetings and Incentives	7998
APN Consulting Inc.	8724
Apollo Energy Components Inc. t/a Apollo Supply	3989
Apollo Professional Solutions, Inc.	5092
Apollos Partners LLC	8524
Aponi Products and Services	1586, 9009
Application Engineering Group	5031, 8687
Applications Alternatives, Inc.	4834
Applied Computer Solutions	4314
Applied Controls & Contracting Services, Inc.	1604
Applied Development LLC	4835, 7698
Applied Geo Technologies, Inc.	5059
Applied Integrity Consulting, LLC	5639
Applied Training Resources Inc.	5491
Applied Wireless LAN, Inc.	4836
AppliedInfo Partners, Inc.	5109
APR Consulting, Inc.	8420
A-PRO Execs, LLC	8563
Apropos Promotions	1309
AptoTek Inc.	5406
Aptude, Inc.	4684
AquaCast Liner LLC	6132
Aqual Corp.	2190
Aquatech International Corporation	3079, 4193
Aquent LLC	4793
Aquila Travel & Events	9205
Aquinas Consulting, LLC	4469
ArachnidWorks, Inc.	1140
Aranda Tooling, Inc.	6478
ARBA Technology, Inc.	4685
Arbee Associates	3864
Arbill Industries, Inc.	4187
Arborsys Group	5110
Arcade Travel, Inc.	9197
Archaeological Consulting Services, Ltd.	3109
Archer & Associates I, Inc.	3345
Archer Corporate Services	8128
Architechnical, Inc.	1708
Architect for Life - A Professional Corporation	1778, 3263
Architectural Design Collaborative	1709
Architectural Flooring Resources, Inc.	3871
Archura, LLC	5640
Arco Caribe Architects, PSC	1774
Arcons Design Studio Professional Corporation	1740
Arcturis, Inc.	1735
ARD Logistics, LLC	3581

C

C

D

E

E

M

	INDEX#
Mustardseed Cultural & Environmental Services, LLC	7740
Mutex Systems Inc.	5193
Mutual Target Associates, Inc.	8574
MVC Consulting Inc.	4729
MVP Plastics, Inc.	7115
MVP Textiles and Apparel, Inc.	1674, 9182
MW Logistics, LLC	3784
MWIDM Inc.	4507
MX4 Electronics, Inc.	2699
My Brother's Salsa LLC	3436
My Future Consulting, Inc	3313
MY HR Supplier	8484
My Next Career Path Staffing, LLC	8747
MYCA Material Handling Solutions, Inc.	6062
Myca Multimedia and Training Solutions, LLC	5373
Myers Power Products, Inc.	2782
Myers Stevens Group, Inc.	7029
Myriad Technical Services	8575
Myron Zucker, Inc.	2837
MYS LLC	8225
MyThreeSons Gourmet, LLC	3370, 3459
MyWay Logistics LLC	3664
MZI Group Inc.	4730
MZN Construction, Inc.	2207

N

	INDEX#
N.C. & Sons	2321
N2 Services Inc	4542
Nadicent Technologies LLC	4476
NAECO, LLC	2676
NAID (Native American Industrial Distributors,Inc)	7707
NAIWBE Natural As I Wanna Be	2439
Nakitare Builders LLC	2234
Nak-Man Corporation	6666
Nance Carpet & Rug Inc.	3837
Nancy Conner Consulting, LLC	7671
Nanland LLC	3385
Nation Waste Inc.	3268
National Alliance Security Agency, Inc.	2534
National Associates, Inc.	8492
National Beverage Screen Printers, Inc	7360
National Business Advisory Group, Inc.	8045
National Career Group	8650
National Career Group Training & Development	8651
National Eagle Security, Inc.	2470
National Fiber and Copper, Inc.	9031
National Freight Logistics Inc.	3606
National Gifts Ltd.	1500
National Industrial Supply Co.	3955
National Integrated Systems	4148
National Manufacturing, Inc.	9174
National Material Co.	6677
National Material Company, L.L.C.	6667
National Material Supply Co, LLC	4158
National Material Trading, LLC	6668
National Office Works, Inc.	6724
National Packaging, LLC	6829

N

	INDEX#
National Relocation Services, Inc. dba NRS, Inc.	2893
Nationwide Auto Transport, Inc.	3727
Nationwide Envelope Specialists, Inc.	6739
Nationwide Investigations & Security, Inc.	1636, 2550
Nationwide Transportation & Logistics Services Inc	3667
Native American Natural Foods LLC	3431
Native Technology Solutions Inc.	4288, 9007
Native Trax Logistics LLC	3737
Native Ways LLC - Apachewolf Productions	8999
NatSoft Corporation	5194
Natural Enrichment Industries	1897
Naughton Energy Corp.	1977
NavasDRSTi, LLC	6193
Navatar Consulting Group Inc.	5311
Navigator Express	3785
Navisource Holdings LLC dba Golden Hill Foods LLC	3450
Naxion, Inc.	8307
nbj Architecture	1784
NC Moving & Storage Solutions	3476
NCRI-National Catastrophe Restoration, Inc.	2267
NCS Technologies, Inc.	5195
nDemand Consulting LLC	8713
NDR Energy Group, LLC	1938
Need a Part Now, LLC	1831
Neighboring Concepts, PLLC	1743
Neka Creative LLC	8155
Nelson Consulting LLC	7735
Nelson Search Group	3341
neMarc Professional Services, Inc.	8829
Neo Tech Solutions, Inc.	5196
Neo Technologies, Inc.	4867
NES Incorporated	3177
Nesso Strategies	7621
Nest Builders	2914
Nestor Reyes, Inc.	3571
Net Activity	5374, 9117
Net Anchor, Inc.	5005
Neta Scientific, Inc.	6012
NetCablesPlus Inc.	5903
Netfast Technology Solutions Inc.	5312
NETHOST, Inc.	5718
NetPlus Marketing, Inc.	1251
Netrion Global Solutions, Inc	4731
NetSource, Inc.	8447
NetTarius Technology Solutions, LLC	5197
NetVision Resources, Inc.	5719
Network Embroidery Inc.	1560
Neutral Posture, Inc.	3900
Never Ending Technology, Inc.	4277
New Age Transportation, Distribution & Warehousing	3651
New Century Advisors, LLC	7458
New Century Packaging Systems, LLC	6969
New Century Technologies Inc.	5821, 6709
New Computech, Inc.	5895
New Concepts, Inc.	6686
New Eagle, LLC	3956
New Echelon	7257